Hoover's Handbook of Private Companies 2015

HOOVERS™

A D&B COMPANY

Austin, Texas

Hoover's Handbook of American Business 2015 is intended to provide readers with accurate and authoritative information about the enterprises covered in it. Hoover's researched all companies and organizations profiled, and in many cases contacted them directly so that companies represented could provide information. The information contained herein is as accurate as we could reasonably make it. In many cases we have relied on third-party material that we believe to be trustworthy, but were unable to independently verify. We do not warrant that the book is absolutely accurate or without error. Readers should not rely on any information contained herein in instances where such reliance might cause financial loss. The publisher, the editors, and their data suppliers specifically disclaim all warranties, including the implied warranties of merchantability and fitness for a specific purpose. This book is sold with the understanding that neither the publisher, the editors, nor any content contributors are engaged in providing investment, financial, accounting, legal, or other professional advice.

The financial data (Historical Financials sections) in this book are from a variety of sources. Mergent Inc., provided selected data for the Historical Financials sections of publicly traded companies. For private companies and for historical information on public companies prior to their becoming public, we obtained information directly from the companies or from trade sources deemed to be reliable. Hoover's, Inc., is solely responsible for the presentation of all data.

Many of the names of products and services mentioned in this book are the trademarks or service marks of the companies manufacturing or selling them and are subject to protection under US law. Space has not permitted us to indicate which names are subject to such protection, and readers are advised to consult with the owners of such marks regarding their use. Hoover's is a trademark of Hoover's, Inc.

HOOVERS™
A D&B COMPANY

10 9 8 7 6 5 4 3 2 1

Publishers Cataloging-in-Publication Data

Hoover's Handbook of American Business 2015

Includes indexes.

ISBN: 978-1-63053-407-3

ISSN 1073-6433

1. Business enterprises — Directories. 2. Corporations — Directories.

HF3010 338.7

U.S. AND WORLD BOOK SALES

Mergent Inc.
580 Kingsley Park Drive
Fort Mill, SC
29715
Phone: 800-342-5647
e-mail: orders@mergent.com
Web: www.mergentbusinesspress.com

Mergent Inc.

CEO: Jonathan Worrall

Executive Managing Director: John Pedernalis

Executive Vice President of Sales: Fred Jenkins

Managing Director of Relationship Management: Chris Henry

Managing Director of Print Products: Thomas Wecera

Production Research Assistant: Erin Keane

MERGENT CUSTOMER SERVICE

Support and Fulfillment Manager: Melanie Horvat

ABOUT MERGENT INC.

Mergent, Inc. is a leading provider of business and financial data on global publicly listed companies. Based in the U.S, the company maintains a strong global presence, with offices in New York, Charlotte, San Diego, London, Tokyo and Melbourne.

Founded in 1900, Mergent operates one of the longest continuously collected databases of: descriptive and fundamental information on domestic and international companies; pricing and terms and conditions data on fixed income and equity securities; and corporate action data. In addition, Mergent's Indxis subsidiary develops and licenses equity and fixed income investment products based on its proprietary investment methodologies. Our licensed products have over $9 billion in assets under management and are offered by major investment management firms. The Indxis calculation platform is the chosen technology for some of the world's largest index companies. Its index calculation and pricing distribution protocols are used to administer index rules and distribute real-time pricing data.

Abbreviations

AFL-CIO – American Federation of Labor and Congress of Industrial Organizations
AMA – American Medical Association
AMEX – American Stock Exchange
ARM – adjustable-rate mortgage
ASP – application services provider
ATM – asynchronous transfer mode
ATM – automated teller machine
CAD/CAM – computer-aided design/computer-aided manufacturing
CD-ROM – compact disc – read-only memory
CD-R – CD-recordable
CEO – chief executive officer
CFO – chief financial officer
CMOS – complementary metal oxide silicon
COO – chief operating officer
DAT – digital audiotape
DOD – Department of Defense
DOE – Department of Energy
DOS – disk operating system
DOT – Department of Transportation
DRAM – dynamic random-access memory
DSL – digital subscriber line
DVD – digital versatile disc/digital video disc
DVD-R – DVD-recordable
EPA – Environmental Protection Agency
EPS – earnings per share
ESOP – employee stock ownership plan
EU – European Union
EVP – executive vice president
FCC – Federal Communications Commission
FDA – Food and Drug Administration
FDIC – Federal Deposit Insurance Corporation
FTC – Federal Trade Commission
GATT – General Agreement on Tariffs and Trade
GDP – gross domestic product
HMO – health maintenance organization
HR – human resources
HTML – hypertext markup language
ICC – Interstate Commerce Commission
IPO – initial public offering
IRS – Internal Revenue Service
ISP – Internet service provider
kWh – kilowatt-hour
LAN – local-area network
LBO – leveraged buyout
LCD – liquid crystal display
LNG – liquefied natural gas
LP – limited partnership
Ltd. – limited
mips – millions of instructions per second
MW – megawatt
NAFTA – North American Free Trade Agreement
NASA – National Aeronautics and Space Administration
NASDAQ – National Association of Securities Dealers Automated Quotations
NATO – North Atlantic Treaty Organization
NYSE – New York Stock Exchange
OCR – optical character recognition
OECD – Organization for Economic Cooperation and Development
OEM – original equipment manufacturer
OPEC – Organization of Petroleum Exporting Countries
OS – operating system
OSHA – Occupational Safety and Health Administration
OTC – over-the-counter
PBX – private branch exchange
PCMCIA – Personal Computer Memory Card International Association
P/E – price to earnings ratio
RAID – redundant array of independent disks
RAM – random-access memory
R&D – research and development
RBOC – regional Bell operating company
RISC – reduced instruction set computer
REIT – real estate investment trust
ROA – return on assets
ROE – return on equity
ROI – return on investment
ROM – read-only memory
S&L – savings and loan
SEC – Securities and Exchange Commission
SEVP – senior executive vice president
SIC – Standard Industrial Classification
SOC – system on a chip
SVP – senior vice president
USB – universal serial bus
VAR – value-added reseller
VAT – value-added tax
VC – venture capitalist
VoIP – Voice over Internet Protocol
VP – vice president
WAN – wide-area network

Contents

Companies Profiled

Companies Profiled (continued)

Companies Profiled (continued)

Companies Profiled (continued)

Companies Profiled (continued)

Companies Profiled (continued)

Companies Profiled (continued)

Companies Profiled (continued)

About Hoover's Handbook of Private Companies 2015

Finding current relevant information about non-public companies can be a challenge, as many of these organizations see secrecy as a competitive strategy. In this edition of *Hoover's Handbook of Private Companies,* we have done for you the tough work of compiling these hard-to-find facts.

We consider this volume to be one of the premier sources of business information on privately held enterprises in the US. It features the facts on 900 of the largest and most influencial of those enterprises. Entries feature overviews of company operations, up to five years of financial information, product information, and lists of company executives as found in Hoover's huge database of company information. Some larger and more visable companies will feature an additional History section.

HOOVER'S ONLINE FOR BUSINESS NEEDS

In addition to Hoover's widely used MasterList and Handbooks series, comprehensive coverage of more than 40,000 business enterprises is available in electronic format on our website at www.hoovers.com. Our goal is to provide our customers with the fastest path to business with insight and actionable information about companies, industries, and key decision makers, along with the powerful tools to find and connect to the right people to get business done. Hoover's has partnered with other presigious business information and service providers to bring you all the right business information, services, and links in one place.

We welcome the recognition we have received as a provider of high-quality company information — online, electronically, and in print — and continue to look for ways to make our products more available and more useful to you.

Hoover's Handbook of Private Companies is one of our four-title series of handbooks that covers, literally, the world of business. The series is available as an indexed set, and also includes *Hoover's Handbook of American Business, Hoover's Handbook of World Business,* and *Hoover's Handbook of Emerging Companies.* This series brings you information on the biggest, fast-growing, and most influential enterprises in the world.

We believe that anyone who buys from, sells to, invests in, lends to, competes with, interviews with, or works for a company should know all there is to know about that enterprise. Taken together, this book and the other Hoover's products and resources represent the most complete source of basic corporate information readily available to the general public.

HOW TO USE THIS BOOK

This book has four sections:

1. "Using Hoover's Handbooks" describes the contents of our profiles and explains the ways in which we gather and compile our data.
2. "A List-Lover's Compendium" contains lists of the largest and fastest-growing private companies. The lists are based on the information in our profiles, or compiled from well-known sources.
3. The company profiles section makes up the largest and most important part of the book — 900 profiles of major private enterprises, arranged alphabetically.
4. Three indexes complete the book. The first sorts companies by industry groups, the second by headquarters location. The third index is a list of all the executives found in the Executives section of each company profile.

Using Hoover's Handbooks

SELECTION OF THE COMPANIES PROFILED

The 900 enterprises profiled in this book include the largest and most influential companies in America. Among them are:

- private companies, from the giants (Cargill and Koch) to the colorful and prominent (Bad Boy Entertainment and L.L. Bean)
- mutuals and cooperative organizations owned by their customers (State Farm Insurance, Ace Hardware, Ocean Spray Cranberries)
- not-for-profits (Red Cross, Kaiser Permanente, Smithsonian Institution)
- joint ventures (Motiva Enterprises, Dow Corning)
- partnerships (PricewaterhouseCoopers, Baker & McKenzie)
- universities (Columbia, Harvard, University of California)
- government-owned corporations (US Postal Service and New York City's Metropolitan Transportation Authority)
- and a selection of other enterprises (National Basketball Association, AFL-CIO, Texas Lottery Commission).

ORGANIZATION

The profiles are presented in alphabetical order. You will find the commonly used name of the enterprise at the beginning of the profile; the full, legal name is found in the Locations section. If a company name is also a person's name, such as Henry Ford Health System or Mary Kay, it will be alphabetized under the first name; if the company name starts with initials, for example, L.L. Bean or S.C. Johnson, look for it under the combined initials (in the above examples, LL and SC, respectively).

Basic financial data are listed under the heading Historical Financials. The annual financial information contained in the profiles is current through fiscal year-ends occuring as late as October 2014. We have included certain nonfinancial developments , such as officer changes, through December 2014.

OVERVIEW

In the first section of the profile, we have tried to give a thumbnail description of the company and what it does. The description will usually include information on the company's strategy, reputation, and ownership. We recommend that you read this section first.

HISTORY

This extended section, which is available for some of the larger and more well-known companies, reflects our belief that every enterprise is the sum of its history and that you have to know where you came from in order to know where you are going. While some companies have limited historical awareness, we think the vast majority of the enterprises in this book have colorful backgrounds. We have tried to focus on the people who made the enterprises what they are today. We have found these histories to be full of twists and ironies; they make fascinating reading.

EXECUTIVES

Here we list the names of the people who run the company, insofar as space allows. In the few cases where available, we have shown the ages and pay of key officers. In some instances the published data is for the previous year, although the company has announced promotions or retirements since year-end. The pay represents cash compensation, including bonuses, but excludes stock option programs.

Although companies are free to structure their management titles any way they please, most modern corporations follow standard practices. The ultimate power in any corporation lies with the shareholders, who elect a board of directors, usually including officers or "insiders" as well as individuals from outside the company. The chief officer, the person on whose desk the buck stops, is usually called the chief executive officer (CEO). Often, he or she is also the chairman of the board.

As corporate management has become more complex, it is common for the CEO to have a "right-hand person" who oversees the day-to-day operations of the company, allowing the CEO plenty of time to focus on strategy and long-term issues. This right-hand person is usually designated the chief operating officer (COO) and is often the president of the company. In other cases one person is both chairman and president.

A multitude of other titles exists, including chief financial officer (CFO), chief administrative officer, and vice chairman. We have always tried to include the CFO, the chief legal officer, and the chief human resources or personnel officer.

The people named in the Executives section are indexed at the back of the book.

The Executives section also includes the name of the company's auditing (accounting) firm, where available.

LOCATIONS

Here we include the company's full legal name and its headquarters, street address, telephone and fax numbers, and Web site, as available. The back of the book includes an index of companies by headquarters locations.

In some cases we have also included information on the geographic distribution of the company's business, including sales and profit data. Note that these profit numbers, like those in the Products/Operations section below, are usually operating or pretax profits rather than net profits. Operating profits are generally those before financing costs (interest income and payments) and before taxes, which are considered costs attributable to the whole company rather than to one division or part of the world. For this reason the net income figures (in the Historical Financials section) are usually much lower, since they are after interest and taxes. Pretax profits are after interest but before taxes.

Headquarters for companies that are incorporated in Bermuda, but whose operational headquarters are in the US, are listed under their US address.

PRODUCTS/OPERATIONS

This section contains selected lists of products, services, brand names, divisions, subsidiaries, and joint ventures. We have tried to include a company's major lines and most familiar brand names.

The nature of this section varies by company and the amount of information contained in Hoover's storehouse of business information. If the company publishes sales and profit information by type of business, we have included it.

COMPETITORS

In this section we have listed companies that compete with the profiled company. This feature is included as a quick way to locate similar companies and compare them. The universe of competitors includes all public companies and all private companies with sales in excess of $500 million. In a few instances we have identified smaller private companies as key competitors.

HISTORICAL FINANCIALS

Here we have tried to present as much data about each enterprise's financial performance as we could compile in the allocated space. The information varies somewhat from industry to industry and is less complete in the case of private companies that do not release data. (We have always tried to provide annual sales and employment, although in some instances those numbers are simply not available). There are a few industries, venture capital and investment banking, for example, for which revenue numbers are not reported as a rule. In the case of private companies that do not publicly disclose financial information, we have statistics when reliable sources are available.

The following information is generally present.

A five-year table, with relevant annualized compound growth rates, covers:

- Sales — fiscal year sales (year-end assets for most financial companies)
- Net income — fiscal year net income (before accounting changes)
- Net profit margin — fiscal year net income as a percent of sales (as a percent of assets for most financial firms)
- Employees — fiscal year-end or average number of employees

The information on the number of employees is intended to aid the reader interested in knowing whether a company has a long-term trend of increasing or decreasing employment. As far as we know, we are the only company that publishes this information in print format.

The numbers on the left in each row of the Historical Financials section give the month and the year in which the company's fiscal year actually ends. Thus, a company with a March 31, 2010, year-end is shown as 3/10. The last item in the Financials section is a graph, which for private companies shows net income, or, if that is unavailable, sales.

Key year-end statistics are included in this section for insurance companies and companies required to file reports with the SEC. They generally show the financial strength of the enterprise, including:

- Debt ratio (long-term debt as a percent of shareholders' equity)
- Return on equity (net income divided by the average of beginning and ending common shareholders' equity)
- Cash and cash equivalents
- Current ratio (ratio of current assets to current liabilities)
- Total long-term debt (including capital lease obligations)
- Fiscal year sales for financial institutions

Hoover's Handbook of

Private Companies

A List-Lover's Compendium

The 200 Largest Companies by Sales in Hoover's Handbook of Private Companies 2015

Rank	Company	Sales ($ bil.)
1	CANDID COLOR SYSTEMS INC.	$21,742
2	VENTURE ELEC CNTRCTRS INC.	$16,704
3	KAISER FNDTN HOSPITALS INC	$14,795
4I	NNOVATIVE MFG SOL CORP.	$13,076
5	CLOSING USA LLC	$12,556
6	TRAMMO INC.	$12,153
7	WAKEFERN FOOD CORP.	$11,010
8	TENASKA MARKETING VENTURES	$10,310
9	GROWMARK INC.	$10,171
10	HOVENSA LLC	$10,048
11	ALLEGIS GROUP INC.	$9,544
12	HY-VEE INC.	$8,014
13	ASSOC WHLSL GROCERS INC.	$7,852
14	ZEN-NOH GRAIN CORPORATION	$7,704
15	CFJ PROPERTIES LLC	$7,672
16	U.S. VENTURE INC.	$7,346
17	STANFORD UNIVERSITY	$6,815
18	MORTGAGE INVESTORS CORP	$6,746
19	CGB ENTERPRISES INC.	$6,213
20	CONSOLIDAT GRAIN & BARGE CO	$5,997
21	CH2M HILL COMPANIES LTD.	$5,932
22	HILL/AHERN FIRE PROTECT LLC	$5,669
23	CHALMETTE REFINING L.L.C.	$5,648
24	AEROTEK INC.	$5,119
25T	AUBER OIL COMPANY	$5,088
26	NORTHERN TIER ENERGY LP	$4,979
27	BANNER HEALTH	$4,878
28	BATTELLE MEM INSTITUTE INC	$4,796
29	LUKOIL PAN AMERICAS LLC	$4,746
30	EBY-BROWN COMPANY LLC	$4,730
31	INTERMOUNTAIN HLTH CARE INC	$4,700
32	PLACID REFINING COMPANY LLC	$4,700
33	UNIVERSITY OF WASHINGTON INC	$4,563
34	OCHSNER CLINIC FOUNDATION	$4,514
35	AK PERMANENT FUND CORP	$4,441
36	SHI INTERNATIONAL CORP.	$4,390
37	ST. JOSEPH HEALTH SYSTEM	$4,223
38	MEDSTAR HEALTH INC.	$4,176
39	WINCO HOLDINGS INC.	$4,104
40	SENTARA HEALTHCARE	$4,068
41	CATHOLIC HEALTH EAST	$4,058
42	LEXA INTERNATL CORPORATION	$3,954
43	THE WHITING-TURNER CNTRCTNG	$3,782
44	CHRISTUS HEALTH	$3,654
45	KWIK TRIP INC.	$3,640
46	THE WALSH GROUP LTD	$3,618
47	UNIVERSITY OF WI SYSTEM	$3,539
48	THE GOLUB CORPORATION	$3,485
49	TEKSYSTEMS INC.	$3,319
50	BLACK & VEATCH HLDNG COMP	$3,279
51	FAIRVIEW HEALTH SERVICES	$3,218
52	MEMORIAL HERMANN HLTH SYST	$3,195
53	SANFORD HEALTH	$3,106
54	BON SECOURS HLTH SYSTEM INC	$3,085
55	LA DEP OF WATER AND POWER	$3,082
56	PETROLEUM TRADERS CORP	$3,067
57	RALEY"S	$3,054
58	MCCARTHY HOLDINGS INC.	$3,008
59	BIOURJA TRADING LLC	$2,992
60	AXEL JOHNSON INC.	$2,982
61	RICH PRODUCTS CORPORATION	$2,859
62	MEM HERMANN HLTHCRE SYS	$2,841
63	MCCARTHY BLDG COMPANIES INC.	$2,816
64	WILBUR-ELLIS COMPANY	$2,812
65	CEDARS-SINAI MEDICAL CENTER	$2,798
66	OTSUKA AMERICA INC	$2,755
67	ALLINA HEALTH SYSTEM	$2,743
68	NEW YORK POWER AUTHORITY	$2,673
69	TEMP U CMNWLTH SYS HGHR ED	$2,635
70	SPECTRUM HEALTH HOSPITALS	$2,595
71	UNIVERSITY OF MD MED SYS COR	$2,571
72	IMMACULATE MARY HOME	$2,569
73	STANFORD HEALTH SERVICES	$2,511
74	CAREGROUP INC.	$2,462
75	JOHNS HOPKINS HLTH SYS CORP	$2,439
76	INDIANA UNIV HEALTH INC.	$2,425
77	NY ST CATHOLIC HLTH PLAN INC	$2,413
78	THE WASHINGTON UNIVERSITY	$2,393
79	ERP OPERATING LTD PRTNRSHP	$2,388
80	IOWA HEALTH SYSTEM	$2,380
81	J M SMITH CORPORATION	$2,363
82	THE METHODIST HOSPITAL	$2,331
83	ARCTIC SLOPE REGIONAL CORP	$2,297
84	ST JOSEPH OF THE PINES INC	$2,286
85	UNIV HOSPITALS HLTH SYST INC.	$2,266
86	RIDDLE VILLAGE	$2,243
87	A-1 SPCLZD SVCS & SUPP INC.	$2,215
88	CITY PUBLIC SVCS OF SAN ANTO	$2,213
89	NORTHWEST DAIRY ASSOCIATION	$2,207
90	SCHAUMBOND GROUP INC.	$2,200
91	UMASS MEMORIAL HLTH CRE INC	$2,186
92	TRUMAN ARNOLD COMPANIES	$2,173
93	OR HLTH & SCI UNIV MDCL GRP	$2,170
94	KNIGHTS OF COLUMBUS	$2,148
95	INOVA HEALTH SYSTEM	$2,141
96	HENRY FORD HEALTH SYSTEM	$2,118
97	DPR CONSTRUCTION INC.	$2,112
98	MEMORIAL HLTH SVCS CORP	$2,094
99	FRANCISCAN ALLIANCE INC.	$2,066
100	VIZIO INC.	$2,006
101	OHIOHEALTH CORPORATION	$2,000
102	ASSOCIATED FOOD STORES INC.	$1,957
103	SCRIPPS HEALTH	$1,954
104	SW CATH HLTH NTWRK COR	$1,940
105	ST. VIN HOS & HLTHCRE CTR INC	$1,889
106	SCHOOL BRD OF ORANGE CTY FL	$1,877
107	FIDELITY INV CHAR GFT FND	$1,875
108	ESTES EXPRESS LINES INC.	$1,865
109	UNITED SPACE ALLIANCE LLC	$1,860
110	PRIN GEORGE'S CNTY PUB SCHLS	$1,855
111	SD WHEAT GROWERS ASSOC	$1,848
112	PRO PETROLEUM INC.	$1,831
113	SUFFOLK CONSTR CO INC.	$1,825
114	COUNTY OF MARICOPA	$1,820
115	INVACARE CORPORATION (TW)	$1,801
116	JOHNS HOPKINS HOSPITAL	$1,792
117	NYSARC INC.	$1,789
118	WHEATON FRANCISCAN SVC INC	$1,763
119	H.D.R. INC.	$1,761
120	SUTTER HLTH SACRA SIERR REG	$1,752
121	API GROUP INC.	$1,731
122	PRAIRIE FARMS DAIRY INC.	$1,721
123	NORTHWESTERN MEM HLTHCRE	$1,702
124	OREGON UNIVERSITY SYSTEM	$1,701
125	WALSH CONSTRUCTION COMP	$1,698
126	CHILDREN"S HOSPITAL MED CTR	$1,693
127	THE CARLE FOUNDATION	$1,691
128	INOVA HEALTH CARE SERVICES	$1,664
129	ORLANDO HEALTH INC.	$1,652
130	RDO EQUIPMENT CO	$1,650
131	CARY OIL CO. INC.	$1,647
132	COC PROPERTIES INC.	$1,647
133	LEHIGH VAL HLTH NTWRK INC	$1,621
134	NORDIC PCL CONSTRUCT INC.	$1,617
135	PCL CONSTRUCT ETRPRS INC	$1,617
136	SUTTER WEST BAY HOSPITALS	$1,616
137	ARYZTA LLC	$1,608
138	GENPACT LIMITED	$1,600
139	PACIFIC RETIREMENT SVCS INC.	$1,598
140	D/L COOPERATIVE INC.	$1,585
141	C.R. ENGLAND INC.	$1,579
142	ATLANTIC HEALTH SYSTEM INC.	$1,564
143	MULTICARE HEALTH SYSTEM	$1,564
144	CONTINUUM ENERGY SVCS L.L.C.	$1,558
145	ALRO STEEL CORPORATION	$1,554
146	MWH GLOBAL INC.	$1,545
147	ESSENTIA HEALTH	$1,545
148	HUGHES SATELLITE SYST CORP	$1,543
149	FCTG HOLDINGS INC.	$1,535
150	STEWART"S SHOPS CORP.	$1,528
151	MFA INCORPORATED	$1,511
152	FERROUS PROCESS & TRDNG CO	$1,506
153	SWINERTON INCORPORATED	$1,506
154	AUGUST HLTHCR CTR APPL VALL	$1,505
155	AHS HOSPITAL CORP.	$1,498
156	FIESTA MART INC.	$1,484
157	SAPP BROS. INC.	$1,483
158	BRD OF ED OF BALTIMORE CTY	$1,481
159	BALTIMORE CTY PUBL SCHL SYS	$1,480
160	OSF HEALTHCARE SYSTEM	$1,477
161	MAIN LINE HEALTH INC.	$1,475
162	BL CRSS BL SHLD OF AZ INC	$1,472
163	SHAMROCK TRADING CORP	$1,469
164	RUSH UNIVERSITY MEDICAL CTR	$1,450
165	SPECTRUM HEALTH SYSTEM	$1,446
166	EPIC AVIATION LLC	$1,439
167	PALO ALTO MED FNDTN HLTHCR	$1,434
168	EDUCATIONAL TESTING SVC INC	$1,432
169	SWINERTON BUILDERS	$1,429
170	SEACOAST NRSNG AND REH CTR	$1,422
171	ROCKHILL MENNONITE HOME	$1,417
172	ATLANTIC DIVING SUPPLY INC.	$1,410
173	NORTHWESTERN MEM HOSPITAL	$1,401
174	TRUE VALUE COMPANY	$1,399
175	NATL ASSOC OF LTR CARRIERS	$1,393
176	AFF FOODS MW COOP INC	$1,392
177	THE MITRE CORPORATION	$1,389
178	KGBO HOLDINGS INC	$1,387
179	PEACEHEALTH	$1,372
180	TEMPLE U HEALTH SYSTEM INC.	$1,356

SOURCE: HOOVER'S, INC., DATABASE, DECEMBER 2014

The 200 Largest Companies by Sales in Hoover's Handbook of Private Companies 2015 (continued)

Rank	Company	Sales ($ bil.)
181	THE CHILDREN"S HOSPITAL COR	$1,349
182	BARRY-WEHMILLER GROUP INC.	$1,333
183	LEGACY HEALTH	$1,326
184	CTRYMRK COOP HLDNG COR	$1,326
185	STEWART & STEVENSON LLC	$1,324
186	RICELAND FOODS INC.	$1,315
187	MFA OIL COMPANY	$1,301
188	MD VA MLK PRO COOP ASSO INC	$1,296
189	THE UNI OF CHICAGO MDCL CTR	$1,295
190	MILWAUKEE PUBLIC SCHOOLS	$1,293
191	BAPTIST HEALTHCARE SYST INC.	$1,290
192	BEALL'S INC.	$1,289
193	BAYST HLTH SYS HLTH SVC INC.	$1,286
194	MAVERIK INC.	$1,274
195	GRANDVIEW HEALTH HOME	$1,262
196	NANA REGIONAL CORP INC.	$1,258
197	HDR ENGINEERING INC.	$1,258
198	BETH ISRAEL MEDICAL CENTER	$1,257
199	WESTERN OREGON UNIVERSITY	$1,252
200	THOMAS JEFF UNIV HSPTLS INC.	$1,250

The 200 Largest Employers in Hoover's Handbook of Private Companies 2015

Rank	Company	Employees
1	KAISER FNDATION HOSPITALS INC	175668
2	DAKOTA ELECTRIC ASSOCIATION	100000
3	ALLEGIS GROUP INC.	85000
4	HY-VEE INC.	62000
5	CATHOLIC HEALTH EAST	50000
6	BANNER HEALTH	35000
7	MAXIM HEALTHCARE SERVICES INC.	35000
8	HEARTLAND HEALTH	32000
9	UNIV OF WISCONSIN SYSTEM	31992
10	UNIV HOSPITALS HLTH SYST INC.	30000
11	NORTH SHORE UNIV HOSPITAL	30000
12	LIFE CARE CENTERS OF AMER INC.	29000
13	NYSARC INC.	28000
14	UNIVERSITY OF WASHINGTON INC	27228
15	ALLINA HEALTH SYSTEM	26400
16	CH2M HILL COMPANIES LTD.	26000
17	OREGON UNIVERSITY SYSTEM	26000
18	CHRISTUS HEALTH	25000
19	SCHOOL BRD OF ORANGE CTY FL	25000
20	MEDSTAR HEALTH INC.	24100
21	INTERMOUNTAIN HLTH CARE INC	23000
22	HENRY FORD HEALTH SYSTEM	23000
23	SENTARA HEALTHCARE	22000
24	THE GOLUB CORPORATION	21741
25	ST. JOSEPH HEALTH SYSTEM	21500
26	STAFF FORCE INC.	20000
27	BON SECOURS HLTH SYSTEM INC	19000
28	IOWA HEALTH SYSTEM	18923
29	ESSENTIA HEALTH	18177
30	FAIRVIEW HEALTH SERVICES	18000
31	PRINCE GEORGE"S CTY PUB SCHLS	18000
32	WHEATON FRANCISCAN SVCS INC.	18000
33	OCEAN BEAUTY SEAFOODS LLC	18000
34	UNIVERSITY OF GEORGIA	17800
35	INDIANA UNIVERSITY HEALTH INC.	17242
36	BRD OF ED OF BALTIMORE CTY	17000
37	WAKE COUNTY PUBLIC SCHL SYS	17000
38	SPECTRUM HEALTH SYSTEM	16996
39	MEM HERMANN HLTHCRE SYS	16505
40	THE SALVATION ARMY	16168
41	UNIVERSITY OF SOUTH FLORIDA	16165
42	INOVA HEALTH SYSTEM	16000
43	NYPRO INC.	16000
44	DEKALB COUNTY BOARD OF ED	16000
45	OHIO HEALTH CORPORATION	15000
46	AKAL SECURITY INC.	15000
47	ADVANCE SERVICES INC.	14200
48	MILWAUKEE PUBLIC SCHOOLS	14154
49	WINCO HOLDINGS INC.	14000
50	MEMORIAL HERMANN HLTH SYS	14000
51	RALEY"S	14000
52	THE METHODIST HOSPITAL	14000
53	OR HLTH & SCI UNIV MED GRP	14000
54	ESTES EXPRESS LINES INC.	14000
55	HOSPITAL SISTERS HEALTH SYST	14000
56	ALSCO INC.	13585
57	SCRIPPS HEALTH	13445
58	JOHNS HOPKINS HLTH SYS CORP	13000
59	INOVA HEALTH CARE SERVICES	13000
60	DUVAL COUNTY PUBLIC SCHOOLS	13000
61	BODDIE-NOELL ENTERPRISES INC.	13000
62	BAPTIST HEALTHCARE SYST INC.	12601
63	ST. VINCE HOSP AND HLTHCR CTR	12185
64	BD OF ED-MEMPHIS CTY SCHLS	12015
65	UNIV OF MD MED SYST CORP	12000
66	CAREGROUP INC.	12000
67	JOHNS HOPKINS HOSPITAL	12000
68	LEHIGH VALLEY HLTH NTWRK INC.	12000
69	BALTIMORE CTY PUB SCHL SYST	12000
70	STEWARD HLTHCRE SYSTEM LLC	12000
71	UNIVERSITY OF TENNESSEE	12000
72	PAN-O-GOLD BAKING CO.	12000
73	THE ROMAN CATH ARCHBISH LA	12000
74	METHODIST LE BONHEUR HLTHCR	11459
75	SAN DIEGO DATA PROC CORP INC.	11130
76	SPECTRUM HEALTH HOSPITALS	11000
77	WELLSTAR HEALTH SYSTEM INC.	11000
78	LANDRUM PROF EMPLYR SVCS INC.	11000
79	ST. MARYS DEAN VENTURES INC	11000
80	WAKE FOREST U BAPT MED CTR	11000
81	UNDERWRITERS LABS INC.	10846
82	OCHSNER CLINIC FOUNDATION	10500
83	KWIK TRIP INC.	10500
84	UNITED SPACE ALLIANCE LLC	10500
85	PALMETTO HEALTH	10200
86	BEALL'S INC.	10100
87	MCLAREN HLTHCRE CORPORATION	10003
88	UMASS MEMORIAL HLTHCRE INC	10000
89	ORLANDO HEALTH INC.	10000
90	MERCY HOSP EAST COMMUNITIES	10000
91	LOUDOUN CTY PUB SCHL DIST	10000
92	THOMAS JEFFERSON UNIVERSITY	10000
93	BELCAN CORPORATION	10000
94	COOP FOR ASSIST/REL EVRYWHR	10000
95	PDS TECH INC.	10000
96	UMASS MEMORIAL HOSPITALS INC.	10000
97	UC HEALTH	10000
98	THE CHLDRN'S HOSP OF PHIL FDN	10000
99	ON TIME STAFFING LLC	10000
100	BAPTIST MEM HLTHCRE CORP	9877
101	CATHOLIC BISHOP OF CHICAGO	9604
102	THE WASHINGTON UNIVERSITY	9600
103	MANAGEMENT AND TRNG CORP	9500
104	BAPTIST HEALTH SOUTH FL INC.	9374
105	OAKWOOD HEALTHCARE INC.	9200
106	LESTER E. COX MEDICAL CENTERS	9100
107	TEMP U-CMNWLTH SYS OF HGR ED	9061
108	SCHOOL BOARD OF BREVARD CTY	9031
109	FRANCISCAN ALLIANCE INC.	9000
110	KALEIDA HEALTH	9000
111	NORTHSHORE UNIV HLTHSYS	9000
112	CHRISTIANA CARE HLTH SVCS INC.	8800
113	UNIVERSITY OF MISSISSIPPI	8700
114	CREIGHTON ALEGENT HEALTH	8600
115	NCH CORPORATION	8500
116	RICH PRODUCTS CORPORATION	8400
117	UNIV HLTH SYST OF EAST CAR INC	8373
118	PITT COUNTY MEMOR HSPTL INC	8373
119	AVERITT INCORPORATED	8210
120	AVERITT EXPRESS INC.	8208
121	FIESTA MART INC.	8200
122	OREGON STATE UNIVERSITY	8188
123	BETH ISRAEL MEDICAL CENTER	8100
124	ACCENTCARE INC.	8060
125	LA DEP OF WATER AND POWER	8000
126	CEDARS-SINAI MEDICAL CENTER	8000
127	THE CHLDRN'S HSPTL CORP	8000
128	LEGACY HEALTH	8000
129	THE RES FNDN OF ST UNIV OF NY	8000
130	PRINCE WILLIAM CTY PUB SCHLS	8000
131	RIVERSIDE HLTHCRE ASSOC INC.	8000
132	SCOTT & WHITE MEMORIAL HSPTL	8000
133	NORTHSIDE HOSPITAL INC.	8000
134	GUILFORD COUNTY SCHL SYSTM	8000
135	GRANITE SCHOOL DISTRICT	8000
136	RIVERSIDE HOSPITAL INC.	8000
137	INTL RESCUE COMMITTEE INC.	8000
138	MOUNT CARMEL HEALTH SYSTEM	8000
139	WAKEMED	7933
140	H.D.R. INC.	7800
141	CHILDREN"S HSPTL MED CENTER	7700
142	UNIV OF IA HSPTLS AND CLINICS	7638
143	WAKE FOREST BAPT MED CENTER	7612
144	E TX MED CNTR REG HLTHAR SYST	7600
145	TEMPLE UNIV HLTH SYSTEM INC.	7573
146	MAXIFACIAL DENTAL SURGERY	7500
147	HARTFORD HOSPITAL	7500
148	SAINT LOUIS UNIVERSITY	7500
149	GEORGIA REGENTS UNIVERSITY	7500
150	DIVERS MAINTENANCE SYST LLC	7500
151	BATTELLE MEMORIAL INST INC	7457
152	SUMMA HEALTH SYSTEM	7406
153	AHS HOSPITAL CORP.	7300
154	ANNE ARUNDEL COUNTY BD OF ED	7200
155	SANFORD NORTH	7200
156	HACKENSACK UNIV MDCL CENTER	7175
157	HERSHEY ENT & RESORTS CO	7100
158	BLACK & VEATCH HOLDING CO	7017
159	MWH GLOBAL INC.	7000
160	THE MITRE CORPORATION	7000
161	COBORN"S INCORPORATED	7000
162	THE MOSES H CONE MEM HOSP	7000
163	BAPTIST HEALTH	7000
164	HILLCO LTD.	7000
165	SANFORD CLINIC NORTH	7000
166	PARKVIEW HEALTH SYSTEM INC.	7000
167	UNIVERSITY OF WYOMING	7000
168	YNG MN'S CHRIST ASSO-GRTR TW	7000
169	LINCOLN PUBLIC SCHOOLS INC	6950
170	SWEDISH HEALTH SERVICES	6916
171	HEALTH FIRST INC.	6900
172	WINSTON-SALEM/FORSYTH CTY SC	6841
173	E BATON ROUGE PAR SCHL DIST	6800
174	JFK HEALTH SYSTEM INC.	6735
175	PEACEHEALTH	6690
176	MULTICARE HEALTH SYSTEM	6510
177	C.R. ENGLAND INC.	6500
178	CARE NEW ENG HLTH SYSTEM INC	6500
179	SCOTTSDALE HEALTHCARE CORP.	6500
180	NHS HUMAN SERVICES INC.	6500

SOURCE: HOOVER'S, INC., DATABASE, DECEMBER 2014

The 200 Largest Employers in Hoover's Handbook of Private Companies 2015 (continued)

Rank	Company	Employees
181	CSAA INSURANCE GROUP	6500
182	EDWARD-ELMHURST HEALTHCARE	6500
183	TALLAHASSEE MEM HLTHCR INC.	6430
184	BALL STATE UNIVERSITY	6426
185	MAIMONIDES MED CENTER INC	6382
186	MERCY HLTH SPRINGFIELD COMM	6300
187	CFJ PROPERTIES LLC	6250
188	SAINT ELIZABETH MED CTR INC.	6227
189	CUMBERLAND COUNTY SCHOOLS	6210
190	RHODE ISLAND HOSPITAL	6200
191	YORK HOSPITAL	6200
192	CONTRACK INTERNATIONAL INC.	6200
193	INDEP SCHL DIST 1 OF TULSA CTY	6115
194	WELLMONT HEALTH SYSTEM	6114
195	HDR ENGINEERING INC.	6111
196	CHI-IOWA CORP.	6100
197	SHRINERS HSPTLS FOR CHLDRN	6100
198	DEACONESS HEALTH SYSTEM INC.	6086
199	SIMPLIFIED BUS SOLUTIONS INC.	6008
200	ARCTIC SLOPE REGIONAL CORP	6000

The Top 100 Companies by Net Income in Hoover's Handbook of Private Companies 2015

Rank Company	Headquarters	Net Income ($bil)
1 ALASKA PERMANENT FUND CORP	AK	4,520
2 CANDID COLOR SYSTEMS INC.	OK	2,535
3 CLOSING USA LLC	NY	1,945
4 ERP OPERATING LTD PARTNERSHIP	IL	1,905
5 STANFORD UNIVERSITY	CA	1,559
6 ST. LUKE"S HEALTH SYSTEM FNDN	TX	1,156
7 INDIANA UNIVERSITY HEALTH INC.	IN	763
8 SADDLE BUTTE PIPELINE LLC	CO	656
9 LUDWIG INST FOR CANCER RES	NY	648
10 BANNER HEALTH	AZ	615
11 FIDELITY INV CHAR GIFT FUND	MA	599
12 THE WASHINGTON UNIVERSITY	MO	558
13 INTERMOUNTAIN HLTH CARE INC	UT	547
14 SECURITIES INV PROT CORP	DC	512
15 UNIVERSITY OF WI SYSTEM	WI	503
16 WILLIAM MARSH RICE UNIV INC	TX	460
17 THE UCLA FOUNDATION	CA	447
18 KAISER FOUNDATION HSPTLS INC	CA	429
19 VANGUARD CHAR ENDOW PRGRM	PA	425
20 UNIVERSITY OF WA INC	WA	425
21 STANFORD HEALTH SERVICES	CA	416
22 THE DAVID & LUCILE PACKARD FO	CA	413
23 THE METHODIST HOSPITAL	TX	387
24 OPEN SOCIETY INSTITUTE	NY	376
25 PREMIER PURCHAS PRTNRS L.P.	NC	371
26 WALTON FAMILY FOUNDATION INC	AR	369
27 INNOVATIVE MFG SOLU CORP.	IL	369
28 PRODUCERS RICE MILL INC.	AR	368
29 PILOT CORPORATION	TN	366
30 CHALMETTE REFINING L.L.C.	LA	364
31 ST. JOSEPH HEALTH SYSTEM	CA	349
32 TEKSYSTEMS INC.	MD	328
33 PREMIER HLTHCR SOLUTIONS INC.	NC	327
34 THE MOSES H CONE MEM HSPTL	NC	324
35 WELLS FARGO FNDN MINNESOTA	MN	322
36 SENTARA HEALTHCARE	VA	308
37 AEROTEK INC.	MD	307
38 OHIO HEALTH CORPORATION	OH	304
39 THE NATL PHILANTHROPIC TRUST	PA	303
40 THE PEW CHARITABLE TRUSTS	PA	300
41 INOVA DIAGNOSTICS INC.	CA	293
42 THE MET MUSEUM OF ART	NY	290
43 MEMORIAL HLTH SERVICES CORP	CA	285
44 ST. VIN HSPTL AND HLTHCR CTR	IN	280
45 S MN BEET SUGAR COOPERATIVE	MN	275
46 NW MEMORIAL HOSPITAL	IL	270
47 VARIETY CHILDREN"S HOSPITAL	FL	269
48 JOHN TEMPLETON FOUNDATION	PA	261
49 UMASS MEMORIAL HLTH CARE INC	MA	253
50 CAREGROUP INC.	MA	252
51 MULTICARE HEALTH SYSTEM	WA	245
52 NY CMTY TRST & CMTY FNDS INC	NY	239
53 AMER TRANSMISSION CO LLC	WI	237
54 NORTHERN TIER ENERGY LP	CT	231
55 TX SCOTT RITE HSPTL CHLDRN FO	TX	227
56 ALLINA HEALTH SYSTEM	MN	226
57 WINCO HOLDINGS INC.	ID	226
58 CITATION OIL & GAS CORP.	TX	225
59 OR HLTH & SCI UNIV MED GROUP	OR	221
60 OUR LDY OF THE LAKE HSPTL INC.	LA	215
61 THE SALVATION ARMY	NY	207
62 WI ALUM RESEARCH FOUNDATION	WI	206
63 BAYLOR UNIVERSITY	TX	205
64 FRANCISCAN ALLIANCE INC.	IN	205
65 THE HOWARD UNIVERSITY	DC	202
66 INOVA HEALTH CARE SERVICES	VA	200
67 WAKE FOREST BAPT MED CENTER	NC	196
68 SHARP MEMORIAL HOSPITAL	CA	195
69 MAIN LINE HEALTH INC.	PA	194
70 LAHEY CLINIC INC.	MA	192
71 TEMPLE U CMNWLTH SY HGHR ED	PA	192
72 THE SALVATION ARMY	GA	192
73 GENPACT LIMITED	NY	191
74 GROWMARK INC.	IL	190
75 TUDOR INVESTMENT CORP	CT	187
76 TX A & M UNI SYS HLTH SCI CNTR	TX	186
77 HILL/AHERN FIRE PROTECT LLC	IL	186
78 UNIVERSITY OF RICHMOND	VA	185
79 IMMACULATE MARY HOME	PA	185
80 UNIVERSITY OF WI FOUNDATION	WI	184
81 UNIVERSITY OF NC HOSPITALS	NC	183
82 VENTURE ELEC CONTRAC INC.	WI	182
83 MILTON HERSHEY SCHL & TRST	PA	180
84 WHEATON FRANCISCAN SVCS INC.	IL	177
85 ASSOC WHOLESALE GROCERS INC.	KS	176
86 CYSTIC FIBROSIS FOUNDATION	MD	175
87 NEW YORK POWER AUTHORITY	NY	175
88 VAN ANDEL INSTITUTE	MI	173
89 SCHWAB CHARITABLE FUND	CA	173
90 FAIRVIEW HEALTH SERVICES	MN	169
91 DRUCKENMILLER FOUNDATION	NY	169
92 CEDARS-SINAI MEDICAL CENTER	CA	168
93 UNITED SPACE ALLIANCE LLC	TX	168
94 METHODIST HSPTLS DALLAS INC	TX	165
95 NEWTON-WELLESLEY HLTHCR SYS.	MA	165
96 JOHNS HOPKINS HLTH SYS CORP	MD	163
97 TRSTS EST OF BERN PAUAHI BISH	HI	160
98 IOWA HEALTH SYSTEM	IA	159
99 NWEST FARM CRDT SVCS ACA	WA	159
100 RCKFLLR UNIV FCLTY STDNTS CL	NY	159

SOURCE: HOOVER'S INC., DATABASE, DECEMBER 2014

The Top 100 Companies by Total Assets in Hoover's Handbook of Private Companies 2015

Rank	Company	Sales ($ bil.)
1	AK PERMANENT FND CORP	$49,797
2	STANFORD UNIVERSITY	$34,785
3	ERP OPERATING LTD PRTNRSHP	$22,835
4	KAISER FNDN HOSPITALS INC	$22,753
5	KNIGHTS OF COLUMBUS	$19,402
6	TX CTY AND DIST RTRMNT SYST	$17,829
7	SHIRES HOUSING INC.	$15,191
8	LA DEP OF WATER AND POWER	$12,628
9	INNOVATIVE MFG SOL CORP.	$10,085
10	CITY PUB SVCS OF SAN ANTON	$10,084
11	UNIV OF WASHINGTON INC	$10,040
12	MILTON HERSHEY SCHL TRST	$9,942
13	THE WASHINGTON UNIVERSITY	$9,807
14	NEW YORK POWER AUTHORITY	$9,121
15	NRTHWST FARM CRDT SVCS ACA	$8,697
16	UNIV OF WISCONSIN SYSTEM	$8,556
17	MODERN WOODMEN OF AMER	$8,318
18	SHRINERS HOSP FOR CHLDRN	$8,052
19	BANNER HEALTH	$7,597
20	INTERMOUNTAIN HLTH CRE INC	$7,553
21	TRSTEES EST BERNICE PAUAHI	$7,277
22	WILLIAM MARSH RICE UNIV INC	$6,687
23	FARM CREDIT WEST	$6,669
24	UNIVERSAL SVC ADMIN CO	$6,655
25	CATHOLIC HEALTH EAST	$6,236
26	DAVID & LUCILE PACKARD FNDN	$6,194
27	ADV HLTH AND HSPTLS CORP	$6,053
28	THE METHODIST HOSPITAL	$5,895
29	FID INV CHARITABLE GIFT FUND	$5,615
30	THE PEW CHARITABLE TRUSTS	$5,612
31	SENTARA HEALTHCARE	$5,307
32	LIBERTY PROP LTD PRTNRSHP	$5,178
33	COUNTY OF MARICOPA	$5,154
34	ST. JOSEPH HEALTH SYSTEM	$5,027
35	SCHOOL BD OF ORANGE CTY FL	$4,989
36	NORTHWESTERN MEM HLTHCR	$4,702
37	SOUTHERN NV WATER AUTH	$4,677
38	MACK-CALI REALTY L. P.	$4,526
39	TRANSUNION HOLDING CO INC.	$4,492
40	TRANSUNION CORP.	$4,472
41	CHRISTUS HEALTH	$4,465
42	VENTURE ELEC CNTRCTRS INC.	$4,409
43	GREENSTONE FRM CRDT SVCS	$4,317
44	TEMPLE UNIV CMMNWLTH SYST	$4,129
45	OREGON UNIVERSITY SYSTEM	$4,047
46	HUGHES SATELLITE SYST CORP	$4,042
47	PSECU SERVICES INC.	$4,005
48	MEMORIAL HERMANN HLTH SYS	$3,977
49	THE SALVATION ARMY	$3,919
50	UNIVERSITY OF TENNESSEE	$3,885
51	CEDARS-SINAI MEDICAL CNTR	$3,855
52	MEM HERMANN HLTHCR SYSTEM	$3,826
53	UNIV OF MD MED SYS CORP	$3,814
54	UNIVERSITY OF RICHMOND	$3,807
55	LODGING RLJ TRUST L P	$3,718
56	INOVA HEALTH SYSTEM	$3,621
57	NORTHWESTERN MEM HOSPITAL	$3,570
58	MEDSTAR HEALTH INC.	$3,545
59	THE SALVATION ARMY	$3,514
60	THE MET MUSEUM OF ART	$3,472
61	CITIZENS ENERGY GROUP	$3,457
62	ALLINA HEALTH SYSTEM	$3,441
63	TENNESSEE ENRGY ACQ CORP	$3,426
64	TRUSTEES OF BOSTON COLLEGE	$3,395
65	OR HLTH & SCI UNIV MDCL GRP	$3,358
66	AMER TRANSMISSION CO LLC	$3,338
67	ORLANDO-ORANGE CTY XPRSWY	$3,330
68	MA PORT AUTHORITY	$3,322
69	FARM CREDIT SERVICES IL ACA	$3,304
70	IOWA HEALTH SYSTEM	$3,298
71	DEKALB CNTY PUBLIC LIBRARY	$3,297
72	FRANCISCAN ALLIANCE INC.	$3,222
73	WESTERN OREGON UNIVERSITY	$3,186
74	UNIV HOSPITALS HLTH SYS INC.	$3,177
75	SCHWAB CHARITABLE FUND	$3,176
76	SANFORD HEALTH	$3,151
77	OHIO HEALTH CORPORATION	$3,121
78	CH2M HILL COMPANIES LTD.	$3,056
79	TEXAS CHILDREN"S	$3,033
80	RCKFELLER UNIV FCLTY STU CLB	$3,006
81	TRI-CNTY MET TRANS DIST OR	$2,978
82	ASSOC ELEC COOPERATIVE INC.	$2,972
83	ST. JUDE CHLDRN'S RES HOSP	$2,930
84	THE SALV ARMY CNTRL TERR	$2,909
85	TRUSTEES OF TUFTS COLL INC.	$2,901
86	IN UNIVERSITY HEALTH INC.	$2,869
87	CLOSING USA LLC	$2,817
88	MEMORIAL HLTH SRVCS CORP	$2,805
89	BON SECOURS HLTH SYST INC	$2,799
90	HOVENSA LLC	$2,770
91	FAIRVIEW HEALTH SERVICES	$2,770
92	JOHNS HOPKINS HOSPITAL	$2,770
93	VANGRD CHAR ENDWMNT PRGM	$2,765
94	UNIVERSITY OF SOUTH FL	$2,764
95	CASE WESTERN RES UNIV	$2,762
96	CAREGROUP INC.	$2,758
97	WAKE CNTY PUBLIC SCHL SYST	$2,758
98	UNIVERSITY OF WI FNDATION	$2,754
99	KY HIGHER ED ASSIST AUTH	$2,744
100	MULTICARE HEALTH SYSTEM	$2,722

SOURCE: FORBES, NOVEMBER 2014

Hoover's Handbook of

Private Companies

The Companies

A C & T CO INC

LOCATIONS

HQ: A C & T CO INC
11535 HOPEWELL RD, HAGERSTOWN, MD 217402178
Phone: 8004583835
Web: WWW.ACANDT.COM

HISTORICAL FINANCIALS

Company Type: Private

Income Statement FYE: June 30

	REVENUE ($ mil.)	NET INCOME ($ mil.)	NET PROFIT MARGIN	EMPLOYEES
06/11	310	2	0.9%	300
06/10	244	6	2.5%	—
Annual Growth	26.8%	(54.8%)	—	—

2011 Year-End Financials

Debt ratio: —
Return on equity: 0.90%
Cash ($ mil.): 2
Current ratio: 1.10
Long-term debt ($ mil.): —
Dividends
Yield: —
Payout: —
Market value ($ mil.): —

AAA COOPER TRANSPORTATION

They might not give you a map like that other AAA but AAA Cooper Transportation can freight your cargo from point A to point B. A non-union regional less-than-truckload (LTL) freight hauler AAA Cooper (ACT) operates in a dozen southeastern US states as well as Puerto Rico; it also maintains facilities in Chicago and a few other industrial crossroads. (LTL carriers combine freight from multiple shippers into a single truckload.) ACT operates about 80 terminals and a fleet of approximately 2100 tractors and 6700 trailers. ACT also offers freight brokerage services and dedicated contract carriage. The company was founded in 1955.

Geographic Reach

ACT operates facilities in the Southeast Southwest Midwest and Puerto Rico. It has nearly 40 manufacturing facilities nationwide and partners with carriers to extend its coverage into Canada and Mexico.

Operations

The company's four primary service offerings include; LTL Services dedicated services international Services (including port services) and fleet maintenance services.Its port services provide services to the port the shipper and the customer. It transloads the goods from the container to its trailer or dock and returns the container to the port. Its fleet maintenance services provide maintenance services for all types of diesel engines including the CAT VOLVO International Detroit and Cummins brands. The company's distribution operations offer assembly operations manufacturing plant transfers warehouse transfers wholesale distribution and retail distribution.

Sales and Marketing

ACT customers include Schneider Logistics Volvo Logistics Mastio & Company GlobalTranz Technicolor John Deere and Nissan.

Strategy

When it comes to growth strategies for truckers service geography rules the road. In 2013 ACT opened a service center at Corpus Christi Texas. In 2012 it opened a service center in the major metropolitan area of Indianapolis.

EXECUTIVES

President CEO, Reid Dove
Director Dedicated Services, Charles (Charlie) Prickett
VP Operations, Lee McMillan
National Account Manager, Michael Haggerty
Account Manager, Brad Williams

LOCATIONS

HQ: AAA COOPER TRANSPORTATION
1751 KINSEY RD, DOTHAN, AL 36303-5877
Phone: 334-793-2284
Web: WWW.AAACOOPER.COM

PRODUCTS/OPERATIONS

Selected Services

Dedicated
- Company branding
- Specialized equipment

International LTL
LTL
Port
- Consolidation
- Drayage
- Transloading

COMPETITORS

Arkansas Best
Averitt Express
Con-way Freight
Estes Express
FedEx Freight
Old Dominion Freight
R+L Carriers
Saia
Southeastern Freight Lines
UPS Freight
YRC Worldwide

HISTORICAL FINANCIALS

Company Type: Private

Income Statement FYE: January 1

	REVENUE ($ mil.)	NET INCOME ($ mil.)	NET PROFIT MARGIN	EMPLOYEES
01/12	520	7	1.5%	4,193
01/11	468	(6)	—	—
01/10*	418	(28)	—	—
12/08	519	4	0.9%	—
Annual Growth	0.1%	16.3%	—	—

*Fiscal year change

2012 Year-End Financials

Debt ratio: —
Return on equity: 1.50%
Cash ($ mil.): 0
Current ratio: 1.10
Long-term debt ($ mil.): —
Dividends
Yield: —
Payout: —
Market value ($ mil.): —

ABINGTON MEMORIAL HOSPITAL INC

Abington Memorial Hospital brings health care to residents of southeastern Pennsylvania. The not-for-profit community hospital has some 670 beds. In addition to general medical and surgical care the hospital offers specialized care centers for cancer and cardiovascular conditions operates high-tech orthopedic and neurological surgery units and serves as a regional trauma care facility. It also runs an inpatient pediatric unit in affiliation with The Children's Hospital of Philadelphia. Abington Memorial also known as Abington Health operates the neighboring 125-bed Lansdale Hospital and several area outpatient facilities.

Geographic Reach

Abington Memorial provides care to residents of southeastern Pennsylvania. The hospital serves Montgomery Bucks and Philadelphia counties.

Operations

The not-for-profit community hospital has some 670 beds and employs about 1100 physicians. Its specialty units include the Pilla Heart Center the Rosenfeld Cancer Center the Diamond Stroke Center as well as a level II trauma center and institutes for senior health and bariatric surgeries. Abington Memorial is affiliated with several medical schools including the Temple University School of Medicine and offers residency programs and postgraduate medical education.

In addition to its hospitals Abington Memorial operates an extensive outpatient care facility named Abington Health Center-Warminster. The Warminster facility is located in Bucks County and features an inpatient hospice center (added in 2009). Other outpatient facilities include Abington Health Center-Schilling (in Willow Grove) Abington Health Center-Blue Bell and Abington Physicians at Montgomeryville.

Altogether the organization's facilities handle 650000 outpatient visits and 39000 inpatient admissions each year; Abington Memorial also provides some $55 million in annual community benefits including charity care.

Additionally Abington Memorial operates a nursing school and a clinical research center.

Strategy

Abington Memorial began using the Abington Health moniker to reflect its larger network of facilities after it acquired Lansdale Hospital which was previously known as Central Montgomery Medical Center from Universal Health Services in 2008. Abington Memorial has since invested in a number of improvements at the acquired hospital. The main Abington Memorial facility has also been enhanced including a new hybrid operating room for cardiac procedures in 2013. The system further expanded by constructing a new outpatient health center in Blue Bell in 2012.

Also in 2012 the organization entered an affiliation agreement with the nearby Holy Redeemer Health System to improve care in the region.

Mergers and Acquisitions

In 2013 Abington Memorial acquired a home health agency the North Penn Visiting Nurse Association (NPVNA). The purchase expanded the geographic reach of Abington Memorial's home health operations.

Company Background

Abington Memorial first opened its doors in 1914.

EXECUTIVES

executive Vice President, Margaret M. (Meg) McGoldrick
CIO, Alison L. Ferren
Chief of Internal Medicine and Medical Director Physician Network, Keith Sweigard
Chief Patient Safety Officer, John J. Kelly
SVP Professional Services and Quality Assurance, Gary R. Candia
Chief Financial Officer at Abington, Michael Walsh
SVP Patient Services and Chief Nursing Officer, Barbara Wadsworth
VP Personnel, Meghan Patton
Chairman, John Durham
President and CEO Abington Health and Abington Memorial Hospital, Laurence M. Merlis
Director of Financial Services, Raymond Leichner
Auditors: PricewaterhouseCoopersLLP

LOCATIONS

HQ: ABINGTON MEMORIAL HOSPITAL INC
1200 OLD YORK RD, ABINGTON, PA 19001-3788
Phone: 215-481-2000
Web: WWW.AMH.ORG

PRODUCTS/OPERATIONS

Selected Facilities

Abington Health Center Blue Bell Campus (Blue Bell PA)
Abington Health Center Schilling Campus (Willow Grove PA)
Abington Health Center Warminster Campus (Warminster PA)
Abington Memorial Hospital (Abington PA)
Abington Physicians at Montgomeryville (North Wales PA)
Lansdale Hospital (Lansdale PA)

COMPETITORS

Albert Einstein Healthcare Network
Aria Health
Crozer-Keystone Health System
Doylestown Hospital
Grand View
Jefferson Health System
Memorial Hospital (PA)
Mercy Health System
Moses Taylor Hospital
North Philadelphia Health System
TUHS
Tenet Healthcare
University of Pennsylvania Health System
Virtua Memorial

HISTORICAL FINANCIALS

Company Type: Private

Income Statement FYE: June 30

	REVENUE ($ mil.)	NET INCOME ($ mil.)	NET PROFIT MARGIN	EMPLOYEES
06/11	702	21	3.1%	4,018
06/10	783	16	2.1%	—
06/09	704	(36)	—	—
06/08	28	25	87.1%	—
Annual Growth	189.7%	(4.7%)	—	—

2011 Year-End Financials

Debt ratio: —
Return on equity: 3.10%
Cash ($ mil.): 48
Current ratio: 1.80
Long-term debt ($ mil.): —
Dividends
Yield: —
Payout: —
Market value ($ mil.): —

ACADEMY SCHOOL DISTRICT 20

LOCATIONS

HQ: ACADEMY SCHOOL DISTRICT 20
1110 CHAPEL HILLS DR, COLORADO SPRINGS, CO 809203923
Phone: 7192341200
Web: WWW.ASD20.ORG

HISTORICAL FINANCIALS

Company Type: Private

Income Statement FYE: June 30

	REVENUE ($ mil.)	NET INCOME ($ mil.)	NET PROFIT MARGIN	EMPLOYEES
06/13	209	3	1.8%	3,000
06/12	203	3	1.8%	—
06/11	208	4	2.2%	—
06/10	212	0	—	—
Annual Growth	(0.5%)	—	—	—

ACADIAN AMBULANCE SERVICE INC.

From ground to air and back again Acadian Ambulance Service is all about getting Southerners to the hospital safe and sound. The company provides ground and air medical transportation service to millions of residents in Louisiana Mississippi and Texas. Along with its ground ambulances the company operates a handful of helicopter ambulances through affiliate Metro Aviation. Its many subsidiaries provide a broad array of additional services including telemedicine (remote patient monitoring) paramedic training services chartered transportation and emergency medical services to offshore oil projects. Established in 1971 Acadian Ambulance Service is owned by its employees through a private stock option plan.

Operations

Acadian's fleet includes more than 400 ground ambulances helicopters and fixed-wing aircraft.

Strategy

The company has expanded its operations through the years through occasional acquisitions. Building its business in Texas in late 2012 Acadian acquired StarPlus EMS in McKinney. The purchase expanded the firm's presence in North Texas and added 50 employees eight ambulances and three wheelchair vans to Acadian's Texas fleet. In 2011 it purchased Central Texas EMS an emergency and non-emergency transport services provider in three counties as well as Humble-based NorthStar EMS which extended operations in Harris and Montgomery counties.

EXECUTIVES

Chairman and CEO, Richard Zuschlag
President and COO, David A. Pierce
EVP and CFO, David L. Kelly
EVP and Chief Medical Officer, Ross D. Judice
VP Public Relations and Marketing, W. Keith Simon
VP-Insurance, Diane Groh
Vice President of Finance, Eddy Dupuis
VP Air Services, Erroll Babineaux
Vice President of Operations, Courtney Juneau
EVP and Chief Administrative Officer, John Zuschlag
VP Marketing and Public Relations, C. Randall Mann
VP Fleet Maintenance and Materials Management, Bill Vidacovich
President of Acadian Ambulance Service, Jerry Romero
President of Safety Management Systems LLC, Scott Domingue
President of Acadian Monitoring Services, Blane Comeaux
Director of National EMS Academy, Kirk LaCour
Senior Vice President of Legal and Governmental Affairs, Allyson Pharr
Vice President Controller, Gregory Hill

LOCATIONS

HQ: ACADIAN AMBULANCE SERVICE INC.
130 E KALISTE SALOOM RD, LAFAYETTE, LA 70508-8308
Phone: 337-291-3333
Web: WWW.ACADIAN.COM

PRODUCTS/OPERATIONS

Selected Subsidiaries

Acadian Ambulance Service
Acadian Monitoring Services
Air Med Services LLC
Executive Aircraft Charter Service
National EMS Academy
Safety Management Systems LLC

COMPETITORS

Air Methods
CHC Group
Envision Healthcare
LogistiCare
Rural/Metro
Safe Ride Services
Wackenhut Services

HISTORICAL FINANCIALS

Company Type: Private

Income Statement FYE: December 31

	REVENUE ($ mil.)	NET INCOME ($ mil.)	NET PROFIT MARGIN	EMPLOYEES
12/12	357	2	0.6%	2,385
12/11	380	9	2.4%	—
12/10	358	7	2.0%	—
12/09	290	4	1.6%	—
Annual Growth	7.1%	(23.1%)	—	—

2012 Year-End Financials

Debt ratio: —
Return on equity: 0.60%
Cash ($ mil.): 8
Current ratio: 0.80
Long-term debt ($ mil.): —
Dividends
Yield: —
Payout: —
Market value ($ mil.): —

ACTION FOR BOSTON COMMUNITY DEVELOPMENT REAL ESTATE CORP.

Action For Boston Community Development (ABCD) strives to make helping others as easy as 1-2-3. The not-for-profit serves more than 100000 low-income people in New England in areas such as advocacy child care consumer services education health and housing. The group operates through a decentralized model that utilizes a city-wide network of Area Planning Action Councils Neighborhood Service Centers and Family Service Centers. It partners with more than a dozen programs like SUMMERWORKS (work experience for low-income teens) Foster Grandparents Urban College of Boston and another 10 or so government agencies. ABCD was established in 1962 as one of several national programs to combat poverty.

Geographic Reach

From its headquarters in Boston ABCD and its affiliates maintain a presence in every Boston neighborhood.

Operations

The organization offers a series of core services and unique programs to Boston neighborhoods and communities. It boasts a network of 14 neighborhood service sites consisting of Neighborhood Service Centers Family Service Centers and Area Planning Action Councils.

Strategy

As it works to cater to the specific needs of these neighborhoods and communities ABCD partners with a pair of affiliate organizations to extend the reach of its services. The John F. Kennedy Family Service Center provides services to the Charlestown area. Catering to the heart of Chinatown the Asian American Civic Association also assists ABCD to boost its capacity.

One initiative of the ABCD group is ensuring that people have heating assistance during the cold winter months. It supplements the funds provided by the federal fuel assistance funds.

EXECUTIVES

Vice Chairman, Thelma D. Burns
Vice Chairman, Kathleen Flynn
VP Administration and Human Resources, Harold Mezoff
President and CEO, John J. Drew
General Counsel, Anita Lichtblau
VP Workforce Development and Technology Services, Mark Isenburg
Vice Chairman, James A. Owens Jr.
Treasurer, Jean Babcock
Chairperson, Juliette Mayers
Executive Vice President, Sharon Scott-Chandler
VP Field Operations, Michael Vance
VP Real Estate and Energy Serives, John Wells
Finance, Marjorie Lombard
Public Information, Susan Kooperstein
Vice President Institutional Advancement, Christina Sieber
Vice Chairman, Thelma D. Burns
Vice Chairman, Kathleen Flynn
Vice Chairman, James A. Owens Jr.
Auditors: KPMGLLP

LOCATIONS

HQ: ACTION FOR BOSTON COMMUNITY DEVELOPMENT REAL ESTATE CORP.
178 TREMONT ST, BOSTON, MA 02111-1006
Phone: 617-357-6000
Web: WWW.BOSTONABCD.ORG

PRODUCTS/OPERATIONS

Selected Services

Adult Education
Child care choices of Boston
Elder education
Energy and fuel services
Family services
Head start and early childhood education
Health
Housing
Immigration Services
Jobs and Job training
Money management
Nutrition and food
Youth programs

HISTORICAL FINANCIALS

Company Type: Private

Income Statement FYE: August 31

	REVENUE ($ mil.)	NET INCOME ($ mil.)	NET PROFIT MARGIN	EMPLOYEES
08/10	151	(0)	—	1,000
08/09	143	0	0.2%	—
08/09	0	0	—	—
Annual Growth	—	—	—	—

2010 Year-End Financials

Debt ratio: —
Return on equity: —
Cash ($ mil.): 8
Current ratio: 1.70
Long-term debt ($ mil.): —
Dividends
Yield: —
Payout: —
Market value ($ mil.): —

ACTIONET INC.

LOCATIONS

HQ: ACTIONET INC.
2600 PARK TWR DR STE 1000, VIENNA, VA 22180
Phone: 7032040090
Web: WWW.ACTIONET.COM

HISTORICAL FINANCIALS

Company Type: Private

Income Statement FYE: December 31

	REVENUE ($ mil.)	NET INCOME ($ mil.)	NET PROFIT MARGIN	EMPLOYEES
12/13	298	23	8.0%	1,352
12/08	23	3	13.4%	—
12/07	15	1	11.9%	—
12/06	1,392	0	—	—
Annual Growth	(19.7%)	—	—	—

2013 Year-End Financials

Debt ratio: —
Return on equity: 8.00%
Cash ($ mil.): 22
Current ratio: 2.30
Long-term debt ($ mil.): —
Dividends
Yield: —
Payout: —
Market value ($ mil.): —

ACTIONTEC ELECTRONICS INC.

Actiontec Electronics aims to broaden your approach to networking. The company makes gateways routers modems and other broadband connection equipment used to create wireless home networks. Its fiber optic routers allow broadband television and other content to be distributed to multiple devices throughout the home over coaxial cables. Actiontec sells its equipment through partnerships with broadband service providers and equipment makers such as Qwest Verizon Cisco and Entropic. It also sells directly through retailers including Amazon.com Best Buy and Wal-Mart.

Geographic Reach

The company's US offices are located in Sunnyvale California and Colorado Springs Colorado. Actiontec also has international offices in Shanghai China and Taipei Taiwan.

Sales and Marketing

Major customers include Micronics Apple Sasktel BellAliant Century Link and Telus.

Strategy

The company has strategically positioned itself to capitalize on the proliferation of wireless home networks and entertainment devices offering a product portfolio that encompasses IP-based video services DSL modems wireless networking devices and network adapters. Actiontec's zControl home automation controller lets the user manage electronics such as lights thermostats and garage door openers from an Internet-enabled computer mobile phone or TV.

In 2012 Actiontec rolled out its Multi-band MoCA (Multimedia over Coax) Network Adapter that supports all three pay TV segments in the same device. The adapter leverages MoCA technology to deliver robust and reliable Pay-TV services to every corner of the home.

EXECUTIVES

Chief Business Development Officer, Brian Henrichs
President CEO, Dean Chang
Director Marketing, Lesley Kirchman
Chief Financial Officer, Brian Paul
VP Operations & Hardware Engineering, Minsiu Huang
VP Engineering, Chuang Li
Chief Software Technology Officer, Bo Xiong
VP Channel Sales, Mike Ehlenberger

LOCATIONS

HQ: ACTIONTEC ELECTRONICS INC.
760 N MARY AVE, SUNNYVALE, CA 94085-2908
Phone: 408-752-7700
Web: WWW.ACTIONTEC.COM

COMPETITORS

Belkin
Buffalo Technology
D-Link
NETGEAR
SMC Networks
ZyXEL Communications

HISTORICAL FINANCIALS

Company Type: Private

Income Statement FYE: December 31

	REVENUE ($ mil.)	NET INCOME ($ mil.)	NET PROFIT MARGIN	EMPLOYEES
12/11	201	5	2.8%	350
12/10	162	1	1.1%	—
12/07	183	0	—	—
12/06	145	0	—	—
Annual Growth	6.7%	—	—	—

2011 Year-End Financials

Debt ratio: —
Return on equity: 2.80%
Cash ($ mil.): 34
Current ratio: 0.50
Long-term debt ($ mil.): —
Dividends
Yield: —
Payout: —
Market value ($ mil.): —

ADAC PLASTICS INC.

EXECUTIVES

Chairman, Ken Hungerford
President and CEO, Jim Teets
Global Director Sales and Marketing, Jeff Ackerman
COO, Doug Evans
General Counsel, John Shape

Director Human Resources and Communications, Cindy Vermetti
Auditors: CroweHorwathLLP

LOCATIONS

HQ: ADAC PLASTICS INC.
5920 TAHOE DR SE, GRAND RAPIDS, MI 495467123
Phone: 6169570311
Web: WWW.ADACPLASTICS.COM

PRODUCTS/OPERATIONS

Selected Products

Access Systems
- Door handles (interior and exterior)
- Liftgate handles
- Tailgate handles
- Trunk release handles

Lighting
- Fog lights
- Interior lighting
- License lamps
- Reflectors
- Side markers
- Turn signals

Trim
- Antenna modules
- Cowl vent grilles
- Fuel filler doors
- License modules

COMPETITORS

Cascade Engineering
Engineering Solid Solutions
Grote Industries
Hella
Johnson Controls
Lear Corp
Magna International
North American Lighting
Peterson Manufacturing
SportPaint
Truck-Lite

HISTORICAL FINANCIALS

Company Type: Private

Income Statement FYE: December 31

	REVENUE ($ mil.)	NET INCOME ($ mil.)	NET PROFIT MARGIN	EMPLOYEES
12/12	226	7	3.2%	800
12/07	177	25	14.6%	—
12/06	177	3	2.2%	—
12/05	1,820	0	—	—
Annual Growth	—	—	—	—

2012 Year-End Financials

Debt ratio: ——
Return on equity: 3.20%
Cash ($ mil.): 0
Current ratio: 1.00
Long-term debt ($ mil.): —
Dividends
Yield: —
Payout: —
Market value ($ mil.): —

ADAMS FAIRACRE FARMS INC.

EXECUTIVES

VP and Owner, Donald Adams
President and Owner, Ralph Adams
Center Operations Director Owner, Steve Adams
General Manager Kingston Garden Center, Phil Burley
General Manager Adams Power Equipment, Joseph (Joe) Conte
General Manager Poughkeepsie Garden Center, Greg Draiss
Newburgh Store Manager, Barbara Johnson
Director Marketing, William (Bill) Lessner
Controller, Joseph N. Proto
General Manager Newburgh Garden Center, Eric Foose
Adams Cafe Manager and Executive Chef, Joseph (Joe) DeMichiel
General Manager Adams Fences, Ken Fredericks
Manager Poughkeepsie Seafood, Frank LaManna
General Manager and Owner, Patrick Adams
Manager Newburgh Meat Department, Bob DeWitt

LOCATIONS

HQ: ADAMS FAIRACRE FARMS INC.
765 DUTCHESS TPKE, POUGHKEEPSIE, NY 126032000
Phone: 8454544330
Web: WWW.ADAMSFARMS.COM

COMPETITORS

Cumberland Farms
Golub
Harry and David
Home Depot
Lowe' s
Sears
Stop & Shop
TOPS Markets
Target Corporation
Wal-Mart
Wegmans

HISTORICAL FINANCIALS

Company Type: Private

Income Statement FYE: January 31

	REVENUE ($ mil.)	NET INCOME ($ mil.)	NET PROFIT MARGIN	EMPLOYEES
01/12	122	0	0.7%	550
01/11	115	1	1.3%	—
01/09	1,039	0	—	—
Annual Growth	—	1968.7%	—	—

2012 Year-End Financials

Debt ratio: ——
Return on equity: 0.70%
Cash ($ mil.): 3
Current ratio: 0.60
Long-term debt ($ mil.): —
Dividends
Yield: —
Payout: —
Market value ($ mil.): —

ADENA HEALTH SYSTEM

Adena Health System hopes to be an Eden for those seeking health care. The system serves the residents of 12 counties in southern and central Ohio centered on the city of Chillicothe. Its main facility is the 225-bed Adena Regional Medical Center which provides general medical and surgical care as well as specialty care in a number of areas including cardiology women's health oncology and rehabilitation. The health system also features outpatient clinics surgery centers medical office buildings and a counseling center among other facilities. The history of the Adena Health System goes back to 1895 when a group of local women established an emergency hospital in the wake of a fatal train wreck.

Geographic Reach

Adena Health caters to the Ohio counties of Athens Fayette Gallia Highland Hocking Jackson Pickaway Pike Ross Scioto and Vinton.

Strategy

Adena Health completed a $45 million expansion project at its main hospital complex in 2010 that added about 70 new patient beds to expand capacity for cardiology orthopedic pediatric and women's health services. It also added on the PAC-CAR Medical Education Center in 2008 to provide nurse training in partnership with Ohio University and Wright State University.

The health network has also established itself as a regional referral center by collaborating with other area hospitals and physicians. Adena Health formed the Southern Ohio Health Care Network consortium with O'Bleness Health and Holzer Health in 2007 to improve care in the region.

EXECUTIVES

President and CEO, Mark H. Shuter, age 54
Chairman, David Strickland
Vice Chairman, Chad Harris
Interim CFO, Dawn Bennett Johnson
Chief Medical Officer, John Fortney
Chief Nursing Officer, Judith Henson
Chief Revenue Cycle and Information Technology Officer, Linn Weimer
Chief Medical Information Technology, Sathish Jetty

LOCATIONS

HQ: ADENA HEALTH SYSTEM
272 HOSPITAL RD, CHILLICOTHE, OH 45601-9031
Phone: 740-779-7500
Web: WWW.ADENA.ORG

PRODUCTS/OPERATIONS

Selected Services

Behavioral Health
Colon and Rectal Services
Endocrinology and Diabetes
Endoscopy Home Care
Hospitalist Laboratory
Occupational Health
Pain Management
Radiology
Rehabilitation Services
Sleep Urology
Surgery and Procedures
Wound Care

Selected Facilities

Adena Counseling Center (Chillicothe)
Adena Health Center Jackson
Adena Health Center Oak Hill
Adena Health Center Waverly
Adena Health Center Western Avenue (Chillicothe)
Adena Health Pavilion (Chillicothe)
Adena Home Care Services (Chillicothe)
Adena Medical Office Building (Chillicothe)
Adena Regional Medical Center (Chillicothe)
Adena Rehabilitation & Wellness Center (Chillicothe)
Adena Urgent Care Centers (Chillicothe and Waverly)
Greenfield Area Medical Center

COMPETITORS

Catholic Health Initiatives
Catholic Health Partners
Fairfield Medical Center
Licking Memorial Health Systems
Mount Carmel Health
Nationwide Children' s Hospital
OhioHealth

HISTORICAL FINANCIALS

Company Type: Private

Income Statement FYE: December 31

	REVENUE ($ mil.)	NET INCOME ($ mil.)	NET PROFIT MARGIN	EMPLOYEES
12/09	315	15	5.0%	2,200
12/07	252	9	3.8%	—
12/06	231	16	7.2%	—
12/05	207	10	5.0%	—
Annual Growth	11.1%	11.1%	—	—

Year-End Financials

Debt ratio: ——
Return on equity: 5.00%
Cash ($ mil.): 70
Current ratio: 0.50
Long-term debt ($ mil.): —
Dividends
Yield: —
Payout: —
Market value ($ mil.): —

ADVANCED TECHNOLOGY INTERNATIONAL

LOCATIONS

HQ: ADVANCED TECHNOLOGY INTERNATIONAL
5300 INTERNATIONAL BLVD, NORTH CHARLESTON, SC 294186937
Phone: 8437603200
Web: WWW.CMTC.SCRA.ORG

HISTORICAL FINANCIALS

Company Type: Private

Income Statement FYE: June 30

	REVENUE ($ mil.)	NET INCOME ($ mil.)	NET PROFIT MARGIN	EMPLOYEES
06/14	273	2	1.0%	117
06/13	224	1	0.9%	—
06/12	160	1	1.1%	—
06/11	149	0	—	—
Annual Growth	22.3%	—	—	—

2014 Year-End Financials

Debt ratio: —
Return on equity: 1.00%
Cash ($ mil.): 98
Current ratio: 1.10
Long-term debt ($ mil.): —

Dividends
Yield: —
Payout: —
Market value ($ mil.): —

ADVENTIST HEALTHCARE INC.

From the newest newborn to the most senior senior Adventist HealthCare takes care of residents living throughout Maryland the metropolitan Washington DC-area and northwestern New Jersey. The not-for-profit network with its more than 2000 physicians is home to three acute care hospitals two specialty care hospitals that offer inpatient and outpatient behavioral health care and more than a dozen home health and rehabilitation operations. Its acute care hospitals include Hackettstown Regional Medical Center Shady Grove Adventist Hospital and Washington Adventist Hospital which combined have 1045 beds. Founded in 1907 Adventist HealthCare is affiliated with the Seventh-Day Adventist Church.

The network's behavioral health care facilities include the Reginald S. Lourie Center for Infants and Young Children which promotes the emotional health of parent-child relations through education training research and evaluation as well as early prevention and intervention. Its offerings include an early head start program to benefit low-income families parent-child programs a therapeutic nursery and the state-approved Lourie Center School a private non-public school for children (from age 4 through the fifth grade) with emotional and multiple disabilities. Another system school The Ridge School of the Eastern Shore provides general and special education to adolescents with emotional or behavioral health problems.

Additionally Adventist HealthCare provides employee assistance programs and behavioral health and wellness services through its LifeWork Strategies Inc. subsidiary.

Adventist HealthCare operates facilities in Rockville Germantown Cambridge Takoma Park and Silver Spring Maryland and in Hackettstown New Jersey. Its home health agencies operate throughout much of Maryland and parts of Washington D.C.

Adventist HealthCare has a five-year strategic plan that focuses on physician integration and providing greater access to health care based on needs at the community level. Collaboration is part of a larger consolidation trend among the industry in order to strengthen all health care organizations financially and geographically.

Toward that end Adventist HealthCare entered into a joint venture with The GW Medical Faculty Associates (MFA) the largest independent physician group in metropolitan Washington D.C. in 2011. The venture is designed to increase access to care and allow the organizations to increase the number of Adventist-employed physicians. Under the agreement all current and future Adventist Medical Group physicians and their staffs will be employees of the new venture. The agreement also strengthens the financial positions of both entities as they follow the federal mandate to implement electronic patient health records at all hospitals.

Adventist HealthCare's strategic vision calls for physical expansion through both new construction and the possible relocation of its Washington Adventist Hospital to the White Oak area of Montgomery County. In 2012 the organization broke ground on the Aquilino Cancer Center a new free-standing comprehensive cancer center on its Shady Grove Adventist Hospital campus in Rockville. The facility funded through donation will include medical oncologist radiation oncologist and other physician offices and is expected to open in 2013.

Another plan is to build a fourth acute care hospital with roughly 85 beds in Clarksburg Maryland. The Clarksburg Community Hospital campus would include a skilled nursing care center physician offices and outpatient treatment facilities. Adventist HealthCare has filed a certificate of need (CON) application with the state and is awaiting approval. Upon approval the site could be operational within three years.

The network is also taking measures to operate more efficiently and effectively by eliminating processes that are unnecessary and adopting green practices to lower energy costs.

EXECUTIVES

President Adventist Behavioral Health, Kevin Young
President and CEO, William G. (Bill) Robertson, age 54
EVP and COO, Terry Forde
Vice President General Counsel, Kenneth B. DeStefano
Vice President System Strategy & Chief Development Officer, Paula S. Widerlite
Sr. Vice President & Chief Quality Integrity Officer, Susan L. Glover
Vice President Financial Management, Thomas Chan
President Adventist Senior Living Services, George L. Child
VP Adventist Home Health and Specialty Services, Keith Ballenger
President Shady Grove Adventist Hospital, John Sackett
EVP and CFO, James G. Lee
SVP and Chairman Next Century Health, Jere D. Stocks
VP Expanded Access Washington Adventist Hospital, Geoffrey Morgan
Chief Development Officer Shady Grove Adventist Hospital, William H. Smith
President Hackettstown Regional Medical Center, Jason C. Coe
Chair, David E. Weigley
VP and Chief Medical Officer Washington Adventist Hospital, Chris Magee
President Shady Grove Adventist Hospital, Dennis Hansen
President Washington Adventist Hospital, Joyce Portela
Vice President Marriott International, Mark E. Griffin
Vice President of patient care services for Shady Grove Adventist Hospital, Skip Margot
VP and Administrator Adventist Rehabilitation Hospital of Maryland, Doris Reinhart
Chief Medical Officer Adventist Rehabilitation Hospital of Maryland, Terrence Sheehan
Executive Medical Director Adventist HealthCare Behavioral Health Services and Medical Director The Behavioral Health Services of Washington Adventist Hospital, Peter M. Levine
Director Strategic Communications Adventist HealthCare Behavioral Health Services, Clarencia J. Stephen
Associate Vice President Mission Integration and Spiritual Care, Ismael Gama
Director Communications Washington Adventist Hospital, Lydia Parris
Director Medical Staff Services and Physician Development Washington Adventist Hospital, Dan Tucker
Vice President Business Development, Robert Jepson
VP and CIO, Kathleen Dyer
Associate Executive Director The Reginald S. Lourie Center for Infants and Young Children, James Venza
Medical Director The Reginald S. Lourie Center for Infants and Young Children, James Herrera
Director of Development The Reginald S. Lourie Center for Infants and Young Children, Elizabeth Franzino
Associate VP Quality and Patient Safety/Interim Chief Nursing Officer Washington Adventist Hospital, Aisha Bivens
Vice Chairman, Robert T. Vandeman
Owner, Andrea Bray
President Washington Adventist Hospital, Joyce Newmyer
Senior Vice President Booz Allen Hamilton, Nancy E. Hardwick
Sr. Vice President Chief Human Resources Officer, Marta Perez
Vice President Financial Operations, Maureen Dymond
Vice President Physician Integration Innovation and Population-Based Care and President, Patrick Garrett
Vice President Public Relations and Marketing, Thomas Grant
Vice President Revenue Cycle, Mel Eisele
Vice President & Administrator, Brent Reitz
Trustee, David C. Stump, age 64
Trustee, Elaine L. Arthur
Trustee, Jeffrey J. Pargament
Trustee, Seth T. Bardu
Trustee, Ruth E. Bulger
Trustee, William K. Miller
Trustee, Charles L. Cheatham
Trustee, Peter H. Plamondon Jr.
Trustee, Norton A. Elson
Trustee, Mark E. Griffin
Trustee, Robin Thomashauer
Trustee, Steven L. Tuck
Vice Chairman, Robert T. Vandeman

LOCATIONS

HQ: ADVENTIST HEALTHCARE INC.
1801 RES BLVD STE 400, ROCKVILLE, MD 20850
Phone: 301-315-3030
Web: WWW.ADVENTISTHEALTHCARE.COM

PRODUCTS/OPERATIONS

Selected Facilities

Acute Care
- Clarksburg Community Hospital (planned; Clarksburg MD)
- Hackettstown Regional Medical Center (Hackettstown NJ)
- Shady Grove Adventist Emergency Center (Germantown MD)
- Shady Grove Adventist Hospital (Rockville MD)
- Washington Adventist Hospital (Takoma Park MD)

Specialty Care
- Adventist Behavioral Health
  - Adventist Behavioral Health Eastern Shore (Cambridge MD)
  - Adventist Behavioral Health Rockville (Rockville MD)
- Adventist Rehabilitation Hospital of Maryland (Rockville and Takoma Park MD)
- Reginald S. Lourie Center for Infants and Young Children (Rockville MD)

Selected Home Health Services

Nursing and Home Health
- Adult nursing
- Diabetes management
- Maternal/child care
- Nutrition management
- Pediatric nursing
- Personal care
- Pre- and post-op care
- Rehabilitation
- Wound care

Home Assistance
- Laundry and linens
- Light housekeeping
- Meal preparation
- Medication reminders
- Personal care

COMPETITORS

Anne Arundel Medical Center
Bon Secours Health
Calvert Memorial Hospital
Christiana Care
Dimensions Healthcare
Franklin Square Hospital Center
Frederick Memorial
GBMC
Georgetown University Hospital
Inova
Johns Hopkins Health System
Johns Hopkins Medicine
MedStar Health
Providence Hospital (Washington DC)
Suburban Hospital
Trinity Health (Novi)
University of Maryland Medical System

HISTORICAL FINANCIALS

Company Type: Private

Income Statement FYE: December 31

	REVENUE ($ mil.)	NET INCOME ($ mil.)	NET PROFIT MARGIN	EMPLOYEES
12/11	760	15	2.1%	5,236
12/10	785	62	8.0%	—
12/09	852	35	4.1%	—
12/02	521	0	—	—
Annual Growth	4.3%	—	—	—

2011 Year-End Financials

Debt ratio: ——
Return on equity: 2.10%
Cash ($ mil.): 15
Current ratio: 0.90
Long-term debt ($ mil.): —
Dividends
Yield: —
Payout: —
Market value ($ mil.): —

ADVOCATE HEALTH AND HOSPITALS CORPORATION

LOCATIONS

HQ: ADVOCATE HEALTH AND HOSPITALS CORPORATION
3975 HIGHLAND AVE, DOWNERS GROVE, IL 605151515
Phone: 6305729393
Web: WWW.ADVOCATEHEALTH.COM

HISTORICAL FINANCIALS

Company Type: Private

Income Statement FYE: December 31

	REVENUE ($ mil.)	NET INCOME ($ mil.)	NET PROFIT MARGIN	EMPLOYEES
12/12	3,645	419	11.5%	4,110
12/01	2,014	114	5.7%	—
Annual Growth	5.5%	12.5%	—	—

2012 Year-End Financials

Debt ratio: ——
Return on equity: 11.50%
Cash ($ mil.): 271
Current ratio: 0.40
Long-term debt ($ mil.): —
Dividends
Yield: —
Payout: —
Market value ($ mil.): —

ADVOCATE HEALTH AND HOSPITALS CORPORATION

Advocate Lutheran General Hospital also known simply as Lutheran General provides acute and long-term medical and surgical care to the residents of Park Ridge Illinois and the surrounding northern suburban Chicago area. As one of the largest hospitals in the region Lutheran General boasts nearly 640 beds and a Level I trauma center. Its operations also include a complete children's hospital and pediatric critical care center. Lutheran General serves as a teaching hospital and its specialized programs include oncology cardiology women's health emergency medicine and hospice care. Lutheran General is part of the Advocate Health Care network.

Geographic Reach

The hospital system is the primary academic referral hospital for northwest Chicago and north Greater Chicago.

Operations

Lutheran General the sixth largest hospital in the Chicago area is a not-for-profit faith-based organization related to the Evangelical Lutheran Church in America and the United Church of Christ. With some 1150 physicians representing more than 50 specialties and subspecialties Advocate Lutheran General saw 62500 patients in its emergency department in 2012.

That year the company reported more than 29000 admissions 19000 surgeries and more than 4000 births.

Strategy

Increase its services to meet specific demographics in 2012 Lutheran General opened a new South Asian Cardiovascular Center in the Midwest; it also launched Expressions a program aimed at helping seniors in the early stages of Alzheimer's disease.

That year thee hospital introduced a new Pet Therapy program to the Adult Oncology unit. It also launched of its neuroendovascular program to expand Lutheran General's acute stroke care to provide advanced acute stroke care to patients throughout the northern Chicago area.

Company Background

Lutheran General serves those who live in the northern suburban Chicago area specifically Park Ridge Illinois.

The hospital was founded in 1897.

EXECUTIVES

Director Public Relations, Marcia Opal
Manager Media Relations, Colette Urban
VP Finance, James Kelley
President, David A. Stark
VP Operations Professional Services, Steven Sundberg
President LGH Medical Staff, John Sage
VP Mission and Spiritual Care, Kathie Bender Schwich
Chairman Pediatrics, David Sheftel

LOCATIONS

HQ: ADVOCATE HEALTH AND HOSPITALS CORPORATION
1775 DEMPSTER ST, PARK RIDGE, IL 60068-1143
Phone: 847-723-6105
Web: WWW.ADVOCATEHEALTH.COM

Selected Hospitals

Advocate BroMenn Medical Center
Advocate Children's Hospital - Oak Lawn
Advocate Children's Hospital - Park Ridge
Advocate Christ Center for Breast Care
Advocate Christ Medical Center
Advocate Christ Medical Center - Physical Rehabilitation Center Center for Hearing and Sleep Center
Advocate Christ Outpatient Center
Advocate Christ Outpatient Center - Lockport
Advocate Condell Medical Center
Advocate Eureka Hospital
Advocate Good Samaritan Hospital
Advocate Good Shepherd Hospital
Advocate Illinois Masonic Medical Center
Advocate Lutheran General Hospital
Advocate South Suburban Hospital
Advocate Trinity Hospital

PRODUCTS/OPERATIONS

Selected Services

Adult Day Hospital
Adult Down Syndrome Center
Anticoagulation Center
Behavioral Health
Caldwell Breast Center
Cancer Care
Center for Fetal Care
Children's Services
The Comprehensive Continence Center
Emergency Services
Heart and Vascular
Hyperbaric Treatment
Interventional Radiology
Joint Reconstruction & Replacement
Nutrition Services Opthamology
Outpatient Testing Prep Instructions
Pain Management Center
Rehabilitation
Senior Services
Sleep Disorders
Surgical Services
The Center for Robotic Surgery
Women's Services
Wound Care

COMPETITORS

Children' s Hopsital of Chicago
Gottleib Memorial Hospital
NorthShore University HealthSystem
Northwest Community Healthcare
Northwestern Lake Forest Hospital
Northwestern Memorial HealthCare
Provena Health
Resurrection Health Care
Rush System for Health
University of Chicago Medical Center

HISTORICAL FINANCIALS

Company Type: Private

Income Statement FYE: December 31

	REVENUE ($ mil.)	NET INCOME ($ mil.)	NET PROFIT MARGIN	EMPLOYEES
12/12	692	102	14.8%	4,818
12/02	2,603	(6)	—	—
Annual Growth	(12.4%)	—	—	—

2012 Year-End Financials

Debt ratio: ——
Return on equity: 14.80%
Cash ($ mil.): 271
Current ratio: 0.70
Long-term debt ($ mil.): —
Dividends
Yield: —
Payout: —
Market value ($ mil.): —

AEROTEK INC.

Aerotek a unit of staffing powerhouse Allegis Group offers commercial and technical staffing services throughout North America. Through several divisions Aerotek staffs workers such as engineers mechanics scientists and technical professionals as well as administrative staff members general laborers and tradespeople. It also provides training and support services. Along with aerospace auto and engineering companies Aerotek's clients include companies from the construction energy manufacturing health care and finance industries. Established as a small staffing firm in 1983 Aerotek now operates from more than 200 non-franchised offices in the US and Canada as well as parts of Europe.

Operations

Aerotek has expanded its operations over the years through organic growth and acquisitions especially in niche markets such as the biotechnology health care clinical research chemical and plastics sectors. Despite the economic downturn demand within these industries has been consistent along with engineering giving Aerotek some continuity during the recession. Aerotek has also widened its client focus to include the niche market of minority and woman-owned companies.

EXECUTIVES

Vice President Technical & Professional Services, Mark Cooper
President, Todd M. Mohr
CFO, Thomas B. (Tom) Kelly
Senior Vice President Strategic Sales & Operations, Chad Koele
Senior Vice President Recruiting Operations & Delivery, John Flanigan
Vice President of Human Resources, Rodney H. Scaife
Vice President Government Services, John King
Regional Vice President Mid-Atlantic, Burt Baptiste
Regional Vice President Northeast, John Rudy
Vice President Divisional Operations, Kim Caldwell
Regional Vice President Midwest, Marty Schager
Regional Vice President Central, Mike Hansen
Regional Vice President Southeast, Tim Clements
Regional Vice President West, Tony Bartolucci
Vice President Strategic Sales, Vinay Nayak
Vice President Account Strategy, Dave Veres
Regional Vice President Northwest, Brooks Wells
Vice President Canada, Bryan Toffey
Vice President of Human Resources, Tanya Axenson
Vice President Human Capital Solutions, Brad Kennedy
Regional Vice President Mid-Atlantic, Jeff Colvin

LOCATIONS

HQ: AEROTEK INC.
7301 PARKWAY DR, HANOVER, MD 21076-1159
Phone: 410-694-5100
Web: WWW.AEROTEK.COM

PRODUCTS/OPERATIONS

Selected Industries

Accounting and Finance
Administrative
Aerospace & Defense
Architecture
Automotive
Aviation
Call Center
Clinical Research
Construction
Energy
Engineering
Environmental
Labor
Manufacturing
Mortgage
Scientific

COMPETITORS

AMN Healthcare
Adecco
Bryant Bureau
CDI
COMFORCE
Kelly Services
Kforce
MSX International
ManpowerGroup
Medical Staffing Network
On Assignment
Pinnacle Staffing
Randstad Holding
Robert Half

HISTORICAL FINANCIALS

Company Type: Private

Income Statement FYE: December 31

	REVENUE ($ mil.)	NET INCOME ($ mil.)	NET PROFIT MARGIN	EMPLOYEES
12/12	5,119	307	6.0%	4,200
12/11	4,481	226	5.0%	—
12/09	3,446	193	5.6%	—
12/09	2,372	87	3.7%	—
Annual Growth	29.2%	51.8%	—	—

2012 Year-End Financials

Debt ratio: ——
Return on equity: 6.00%
Cash ($ mil.): 10
Current ratio: 3.30
Long-term debt ($ mil.): —
Dividends
Yield: —
Payout: —
Market value ($ mil.): —

AFFILIATED FOODS MIDWEST COOPERATIVE INC.

Affiliated Foods Midwest Cooperative is a wholesale food distribution cooperative that supplies more than 800 independent grocers in some 15 Midwestern states. From its handful of distribution centers in Kansas Nebraska and Wisconsin the co-op distributes fresh produce meats deli items baked goods dairy products and frozen foods as well as general merchandise and equipment. It distributes goods under the Shurfine brand (from Topco Associates) and IGA labels. Additionally Affiliated Foods Midwest provides marketing merchandising and warehousing support services for its members. The cooperative was formed in 1931 to make wholesale purchases for a group of retailers in Nebraska.

Geographic Reach

Norfolk Nebraska-based Affiliated Foods Midwest Cooperative Elwood Kansas and Kenosha Wisconsin. It serves customers in 16 states across the Midwest.

EXECUTIVES

Exec V Pres, Tim Goetsch, age 64
Vice President Of State Government Relations, Paul Korbel
Vp Of Business Development, Wayne Hall
V Pres, Tim Myers
Vice President Of Information Technology, Linda Mattson
Vice President Of Sales And Marketing, Angie McLean
Cpo And Vice President Procurement, Robert Rothove
Senior Vice President Financial Projects, Tim Gage
Vice President Information Technology, Mattson Linda

LOCATIONS

HQ: AFFILIATED FOODS MIDWEST COOPERATIVE INC.
1301 W OMAHA AVE, NORFOLK, NE 68701-5872
Phone: 402-371-0555
Web: WWW.AFMIDWEST.COM

PRODUCTS/OPERATIONS

Selected Private-Label Brands

Clear Value
Cow Belle Creamery (ice cream)
Full Circle (organic natural products)
PAWS Premium (pet products)
Shurfine
TopCare
Valu Time
Wide Awake Coffee Co. (coffee)
World Classics Trading Company

COMPETITORS

Associated Wholesale Grocers
C&S Wholesale
Central Grocers
Certco
Dearborn Wholesale Grocers
Kroger
McLane
Nash-Finch
SUPERVALU
Wal-Mart

HISTORICAL FINANCIALS

Company Type: Private

Income Statement FYE: June 29

	REVENUE ($ mil.)	NET INCOME ($ mil.)	NET PROFIT MARGIN	EMPLOYEES
06/13	1,391	2	0.2%	850
06/12	1,486	2	0.2%	—
06/10	1,356	2	0.2%	—
06/10	1,241	4	0.4%	—
Annual Growth	3.9%	(14.6%)	—	—

2013 Year-End Financials

Debt ratio: —
Return on equity: 0.20%
Cash ($ mil.): 25
Current ratio: 0.20
Long-term debt ($ mil.): —
Dividends
Yield: —
Payout: —
Market value ($ mil.): —

AGFINITY INC.

LOCATIONS

HQ: AGFINITY INC.
260 FACTORY RD, EATON, CO 806153481
Phone: 9704544000
Web: WWW.AGFINITYINC.COM

HISTORICAL FINANCIALS

Company Type: Private

Income Statement FYE: June 30

	REVENUE ($ mil.)	NET INCOME ($ mil.)	NET PROFIT MARGIN	EMPLOYEES
06/09	202	3	1.6%	190
06/08	186	10	5.6%	—
06/07	1,541	0	—	—
Annual Growth	(63.8%)24588.6%		—	—

2009 Year-End Financials

Debt ratio: —
Return on equity: 1.60%
Cash ($ mil.): 1
Current ratio: 0.70
Long-term debt ($ mil.): —
Dividends
Yield: —
Payout: —
Market value ($ mil.): —

AKAL SECURITY INC.

EXECUTIVES

CEO, Sat Nirmal K. Khalsa
President, Daya S. Khalsa, $90,000 total compensation
Judicial Security Division Director, Mike Francis
SVP, Gurutej S. Khalsa
VP Human Resources, Janet Gunn
Chief Compliance Officer, Dev Suroop K. Khalsa

LOCATIONS

HQ: AKAL SECURITY INC.
7 INFINITY LOOP, ESPANOLA, NM 875326737
Phone: 5057537832
Web: WWW.AKALSECURITY.COM

PRODUCTS/OPERATIONS

Selected Services

Aviation security services (airport programs)
Investigations (US and international corporate clients)
Personal protection (US corporate executives)
Security officer services (guarding programs)
Security systems integration (design installation and integration of electronic security surveillance and access control systems)
Security training programs (Akal Training Academy)
Third country national personnel (trained former military personnel from Asia and Africa)

COMPETITORS

AlliedBarton Security
Command Security
D&D Security Training
Guardsmark
Securitas Security Services North America
Tyco Fire & Security
Walden Security

HISTORICAL FINANCIALS

Company Type: Private

Income Statement FYE: December 31

	REVENUE ($ mil.)	NET INCOME ($ mil.)	NET PROFIT MARGIN	EMPLOYEES
12/11	461	3	0.8%	15,000
12/10	466	2	0.5%	—
12/09	698	0	0.0%	—
Annual Growth	(18.7%)29351.6%		—	—

2011 Year-End Financials

Debt ratio: —
Return on equity: 0.80%
Cash ($ mil.): 0
Current ratio: 0.90
Long-term debt ($ mil.): —
Dividends
Yield: —
Payout: —
Market value ($ mil.): —

AKRON PUBLIC SCHOOLS

LOCATIONS

HQ: AKRON PUBLIC SCHOOLS
70 N BROADWAY ST, AKRON, OH 443081911
Phone: 3307611661
Web: WWW.AKRONSCHOOLS.COM

HISTORICAL FINANCIALS

Company Type: Private

Income Statement FYE: June 30

	REVENUE ($ mil.)	NET INCOME ($ mil.)	NET PROFIT MARGIN	EMPLOYEES
06/08*	283	17	6.1%	3,937
12/05	200	0	—	—
06/04	1	0	12.2%	—
06/03	0	0	—	—
Annual Growth	—	—	—	—

*Fiscal year change

2008 Year-End Financials

Debt ratio: —
Return on equity: 6.10%
Cash ($ mil.): 95
Current ratio: —
Long-term debt ($ mil.): —
Dividends
Yield: —
Payout: —
Market value ($ mil.): —

ALABAMA FARM CREDIT ACA

LOCATIONS

HQ: ALABAMA FARM CREDIT ACA
1740 EVA RD NE, CULLMAN, AL 350556006
Phone: 2567377128
Web: WWW.ALABAMAFARMCREDIT.COM

HISTORICAL FINANCIALS

Company Type: Private

Income Statement FYE: December 31

	ASSETS ($ mil.)	NET INCOME ($ mil.)	INCOME AS % OF ASSETS	EMPLOYEES
12/12	462	9	2.0%	46
12/11	431	7	1.8%	—
Annual Growth	7.2%	17.1%	—	—

2012 Year-End Financials

Debt ratio: —
Return on equity: 35.70%
Cash ($ mil.): 0
Current ratio: —
Long-term debt ($ mil.): —
Dividends
Yield: —
Payout: —
Market value ($ mil.): —

ALABAMA FARMERS COOPERATIVE INC.

Alabama Farmers Cooperative (AFC) provides farmers in the Yellowhammer state with a range of agricultural supplies and services. The co-op offers animal feed crop fertilizer and home-gardening items such as seed and hand tools as well as grain storage and hardware. AFC comprises 37 member associations including about 90 retail locations. Expanding through joint ventures it boasts one of the largest farmer-owned agriculture businesses in the southeastern US. Its Bonnie Plants is one of the biggest suppliers of vegetable and herb plants for home gardeners. BioLogic makes forage products for wild game. AFC supplies the foodservice industry with fresh fish through its SouthFresh Farms catfish farm.

Geographic Reach

AFC based in Alabama serves the southeastern US.

Operations

The cooperative operates through more than half a dozen divisions including Feed Farm & Home; Universal Seed & Supply/ECS; Bonnie Plants; BioLogic/Mossy Oak; Agri-AFC LLC; and SouthFresh Farms.

It has about 90 retail outlets located in Florida Georgia Alabama and Mississippi. Among them more than 60 are co-op stores and the balance operates under the Agri-AFC banner name.

Sales and Marketing

AFC serves customers through a network of sales representatives.

Financial Performance

AFC has been ranked as one of Alabama's top 25 privately owned companies boasting sales totaling more than $450 million.

Company Background

Founded in 1936 the co-op was originally known as the Tennessee Valley Fertilizer Cooperative. It changed its name in 1960 to reflect its statewide reach.

EXECUTIVES

Hr Director & Vp, Marie B Cook
Vice President, John Gamble
Vp-feed Farm & Home, Steve Moore
Vice President, Robert Slate
Vice President And General Manager Andersons Peanut, Dennis Finch

LOCATIONS

HQ: ALABAMA FARMERS COOPERATIVE INC.
121 SOMERVILLE RD NE, DECATUR, AL 356012659
Phone: 2563536843
Web: WWW.ALAFARM.COM

PRODUCTS/OPERATIONS

Selected Divisions

Agri-AFC LLC
BioLogic/Mossy Oak
Bonnie Plants
Feed Farm & Home
SouthFresh Farms
Universal Seed & Supply/ECS

COMPETITORS

Ag Processing Inc.
Andersons
CHS
Color Spot Nurseries
DeBruce Grain
Farmers Cooperative Company
GROWMARK
Heartland Co-op
Monrovia Nursery
Orscheln Farm and Home
Scoular
Southern States
Tennessee Farmers Co-op
Watonwan Farm Service
West Central Co-op

HISTORICAL FINANCIALS

Company Type: Private

Income Statement FYE: July 31

	REVENUE ($ mil.)	NET INCOME ($ mil.)	NET PROFIT MARGIN	EMPLOYEES
07/13	592	17	2.9%	3,000
07/11	450	9	2.0%	—
07/10	400	8	2.0%	—
07/09	393	0	—	—
Annual Growth	10.8%	—	—	—

2013 Year-End Financials

Debt ratio: —
Return on equity: 2.90%
Cash ($ mil.): 4
Current ratio: 0.70
Long-term debt ($ mil.): —
Dividends
Yield: —
Payout: —
Market value ($ mil.): —

ALAMANCE REGIONAL MEDICAL CENTER INC.

Alamance Regional Medical Center is a not-for-profit hospital serving the residents of North Carolina. the medical center has some 240 beds. Services include cancer care behavioral health cardiology radiology women's services and home health care. It also provides a sleep lab pain center and birthing center. Its satellite Mebane Medical Park includes general practice surgery and cancer centers and the West End Medical Park provides primary care. Other facilities include a pediatric rehabilitation clinic sports rehabilitation center a nursing home and a retirement community. Alamance Regional Medical Center is a part of not-for-profit Cone Health's regional network of healthcare providers.

Change in Company Type

Cone Health acquired Alamance Regional Medical Center in 2013.

Geographic Reach

Cone Health's network is serves people in Alamance Caswell Forsyth Guilford Randolph Rockingham and surrounding counties in North Carolina.

Operations

Alamance Regional Medical Center's physicians serve more than 200000 people in the Alamance-Caswell area each year.

Strategy

The Center is investing in infrastructure expansion to keep up with patient demand. In 2013 Alamance Regional Medical Center began a $62 million construction project to double the size of the Emergency Department create a new Cancer Center and increase the size of operating rooms and outpatient surgical care areas. The Emergency Department expansion will add 27500 sq. ft. and the Cancer Center expansion will add 40000 sq. ft.

In 2012 Alamance Regional Medical Center expanded clinical capabilities for stroke and neurological patients with a new high-tech telemedicine service.

To provide convenient access to cancer care for residents of Caswell County and the surrounding area in 2011 Alamance Regional Medical Center opened a cancer clinic in Yanceyville through a partnership with Caswell Family Medical Center.

Company Background

In late-2011 the boards of Alamance Regional Medical Center and Cone Health approved a partnership to make Alamance a part of Greensboro North Carolina-based Cone Health.

Alamance Regional Medical Center was formed in 1995.

EXECUTIVES

VP Strategic Management, Robert (Bob) Byrd
Chairman, F. D. Hornaday III, age 63
President and CEO, John G. Currin Jr.
Public Relations, Tracey Grayzer
Senior Vice President CFO, Rex A. Street
Chief Information Officer, Jesse Long
Chief Operating Officer and Senior Vice President, Preston Hammock
Chief Nursing Officer and Senior Vice President, Lea Gillis

LOCATIONS

HQ: ALAMANCE REGIONAL MEDICAL CENTER INC.
1240 HUFFMAN MILL RD, BURLINGTON, NC 27215-8700
Phone: 336-538-7000
Web: WWW.ARMC.COM

COMPETITORS

Carolinas HealthCare System
Cumberland County Hospital System
Duke University Health System
FirstHealth of the Carolinas
High Point Regional Health System
Morehead Memorial Hospital
Novant Health
UNC Hospitals
Vidant Health
Wake Forest University Baptist Medical Center

HISTORICAL FINANCIALS

Company Type: Private

Income Statement FYE: December 31

	REVENUE ($ mil.)	NET INCOME ($ mil.)	NET PROFIT MARGIN	EMPLOYEES
12/08*	208	(10)	—	1,500
09/07	87	0	0.8%	—
12/06	1,637	0	—	—
Annual Growth	(64.3%)	—	—	—

*Fiscal year change

2008 Year-End Financials

Debt ratio: —
Return on equity: (-5.00%)
Cash ($ mil.): 16
Current ratio: 1.60
Long-term debt ($ mil.): —
Dividends
Yield: —
Payout: —
Market value ($ mil.): —

ALASKA NATIVE TRIBAL HEALTH CONSORTIUM

The Alaska Native Tribal Health Consortium (ANTHC) brings good health to Alaska Natives. The company is a not-for-profit statewide health care organization managed by regional tribal governments and their respective regional health organizations (also known as RHIOs). The organization connects disparate medical providers by providing a range of health programs and services including community health care public health advocacy and education initiatives health research (including water and sanitation) and medical supply distribution. The 150-bed Alaska Native Medical Center (ANMC) a native-owned hospital is jointly managed by ANTHC and Southcentral Foundation a regional health corporation based in the Cook Inlet region.

Geographic Reach

ANTHC and ANMC are located in Anchorage Alaska. The organization provides services throughout the state.

Operations

ANMC's services are reserved primarily for Alaska Native Tribal groups with the exception of its Urgent Care centers and Emergency Room. (Emergency rooms are compelled to take patients of all types under US fair care guidelines.) The hospital handles about 8000 patient admissions each year as well as 290000 outpatient and 57000 emergency room visits. It also conducts some 10000 surgeries and 500 births.

The organization's primary mission is to improve the health of Alaska natives through health sanitation technology and advocacy services. It conducts a number of community outreach programs and it works to create a continuum of care for its members so they can move smoothly through the health care process (including initial specialist and follow-up care visits). The hospital is the regional hub of that health care continuum offering general and specialist care in a range of fields. ANTHC also operates outpatient care centers and it operates an extensive telemedicine network (allow providers to care for and consult with patients in outlying areas).

ANTHC provides administrative support to Alaska's Tribal health groups and it supports state legislative efforts such as the reauthorization of the Indian Health Care Improvement Act. The consortium formed in 1997 also works to improve the Alaskan health system by participating in strategic summit meetings and sponsoring electronic health record initiatives.

Financial Performance

Earnings for ANTHC came in at about $475 million in fiscal 2012 about 35% of which came from patient service revenue. Other major operating segments include compact revenue (31% of sales) and grant and project income (25%).

Strategy

Infrastructure and service expansions are a key means of growth for ANTHC. In 2012 the organization announced plans to add a housing facility on the ANMC campus to aid patients who have to travel for care. Also that year ANMC expanded its maternal child health and neurosurgery departments due to increasing patient populations in the Anchorage area. In 2010 the medical center opened the only Level II trauma center in Alaska making it a referral hospital for major trauma cases.

The organization has also improved its health care technology resources; it expanded the use of electronic health records (EHRs) at ANMC in 2012 and it is expanding its telemedicine operations (as telemedicine is becoming an increasingly popular way for specialists to see patients without the expense of a personal visit). It has increased other community outreach efforts as well such as smoking cessation and behavioral health programs.

EXECUTIVES

CEO and Director, Don Kashevaroff
Vice Chair, Lincoln A. Bean Sr.
Chairman and President, Ray Alstrom
COO, Susan Childers
Chief Financial Officer, Garvin Federenko
Chief Executive Officer, Roald Helgesen
Chief Information Officer, Stewart Ferguson
CEO and Director, Don Kashevaroff
Director, Robert J. Henrichs
Director, Andrew (Andy) Jimmie, age 78
Director, Evelyn Beeter
Director, Mike Zacharof
Director, H. Sally Smith
Director, Linda Clement
Director, Emily Hughes
Director, Katherine Gottlieb
Vice Chair, Lincoln A. Bean Sr.
Director, Bernice Kaigelak
Director, Charlene Nollner
Director, Andrew (Andy) Teuber

LOCATIONS

HQ: ALASKA NATIVE TRIBAL HEALTH CONSORTIUM
4000 AMBASSADOR DR, ANCHORAGE, AK 99508-5909
Phone: 907-729-1900
Web: WWW.ANTHC.ORG

PRODUCTS/OPERATIONS

2012 Sales

	$ mil.	% of total
Patient revenue	166	35
Compact revenue	148	31
Grant & project revenue	116	25
Warehouse revenue	22	5
Investment income	6	1
Other	15	3
Total	**475**	**100**

Selected Services

Ear Nose Throat
Emergency and Trauma
Family Medicine
Imaging and Laboratory Services
Internal Medicine Clinic
Maternal Fetal Medicine
OB/GYN Services
Oncology
Orthopedics Clinic
Pediatric ICU
Pediatrics
Pharmacy Services
Pregnancy and Childbirth
Primary Care Services
Respiratory Care

COMPETITORS

HCA
Immediate Care
PeaceHealth
Providence Health & Services
South Peninsula Hospital
Tenet Healthcare

HISTORICAL FINANCIALS

Company Type: Private

Income Statement FYE: September 30

	REVENUE ($ mil.)	NET INCOME ($ mil.)	NET PROFIT MARGIN	EMPLOYEES
09/12	447	21	4.9%	1,850
09/11	427	24	5.8%	—
09/09	414	28	6.8%	—
09/09	348	14	4.2%	—
Annual Growth	8.6%	13.7%	—	—

2012 Year-End Financials

Debt ratio: —
Return on equity: 4.90%
Cash ($ mil.): 155
Current ratio: 2.50
Long-term debt ($ mil.): —
Dividends
Yield: —
Payout: —
Market value ($ mil.): —

ALBERICI CONSTRUCTORS INC.

LOCATIONS

HQ: ALBERICI CONSTRUCTORS INC.
8800 PAGE AVE, SAINT LOUIS, MO 631146106
Phone: 3147332000
Web: WWW.ALBERICI.COM

HISTORICAL FINANCIALS

Company Type: Private

Income Statement FYE: December 31

	REVENUE ($ mil.)	NET INCOME ($ mil.)	NET PROFIT MARGIN	EMPLOYEES
12/13	578	0	—	2,000
12/12	489	0	—	—
12/11	543	0	—	—
12/10	551	0	—	—
Annual Growth	1.6%	—	—	—

2013 Year-End Financials

Debt ratio: —
Return on equity: —
Cash ($ mil.): 77
Current ratio: 0.90
Long-term debt ($ mil.): —
Dividends
Yield: —
Payout: —
Market value ($ mil.): —

ALBERICI CORPORATION

Alberici helped shape the St. Louis skyline; it now sets its sights —or its construction sites — across North America. Alberici Corporation parent of Alberici Constructors encompasses a group of enterprises with a presence in North America Central America South America and Europe. Operations include construction services building materials and steel fabrication and erection units. Alberici offers general contracting design/build construction management demolition and specialty contracting services. It also offers facilities management. The Alberici family still holds the largest share of the employee-owned firm.

Geographic Reach

Alberici is active throughout North America and has offices in St. Louis Missouri; Detroit Michigan; Atlanta Georgia; Topeka Kansas; Burlington Ontario; Saskatoon Saskatchewan; and Leon Mexico.

Operations

The company boasts more than a dozen operating companies in the US Canada and Mexico that serve the automotive energy health care industrial manufacturing and wastewater treatment markets. Its Gunther-Nash subsidiary provides construction services to the mining industry. Another division Vertegy specializes in construction consulting for green and sustainable projects.

Financial Performance

Alberici's annual revenues exceeds $1 billion. Nearly 80% of its revenue comes from repeat clients. The company reported more than $530 million in industrial revenues in 2012 thanks to a recovering economy supporting demand for major industrial projects in the US and Canada.

Strategy

The heavy construction firm is working to diversify its business both geographically and by entering new specialty markets. Alberici also partners with other firms on large projects. Indeed the company joined forces with URS Corporation to build a $900 million cement plant for Holcim (US). The plant about an hour north of St. Louis is one of the largest in the world. Alberici also built the Seabrook Gate Complex a concrete and steel floodgate system in New Orleans. Some of Alberici's completed projects include casinosfor Ameristar modernization and new facilities for Anheuser-Busch and factories for Boeing.

In 2013 the Associated General Contractors of St. Louis awarded Alberici with top prizes at its 16th Annual Keystone Awards for the company's work on the Seabrook Gates Complex and the Knights of Columbus Child Development Center. Alberici has won 14 Keystone Awards more than any other general contractor.

Mergers and Acquisitions

Expanding it range of capabilities in January 2012 Alberici acquired water treatment facility specialist CAS Construction. The addition of CAS which has built facilities throughout the central and western US strengthens Alberici's capabilities in the water market. The company was renamed CAS Constructors.

In early 2013 Alberici closed on its acquisition of Flintco LLC a century-old Native American-owned contractor based in Tulsa Oklahoma. With offices in Oklahoma New Mexico Texas Arkansas and California Flintco presented an attractive geographic diversification opportunity for Alberici.

Company Background

The company founded in 1918 by John S. Alberici.

EXECUTIVES

Svp Administration And Contract Review Officer Alberici Group, James E Frey
Vp And Project Director Alberici Constructors, David Calcaterra
Vp And General Counsel, Trevor Ladner
President and CFO Alberici Group Inc, Gregory T. (Greg) Hesser
COO, LeRoy J. Stromberg
VP Support Services and CIO, Frank C. Kropiunik
President and CEO, Gregory J. (Greg) Kozicz

EVP, Michael W. (Mike) Burke
EVP, Craig M. Fesler
VP and General Manager Kienlen Constructors, Matthew L. (Matt) Grieshaber
EVP, Chris Hermann
President Alberici Constructors Ltd., David Gough
Vp Estimating Alberici Group, Ronald W Wiese
Vice President Automotive, Steven Moffattcv
Chairman, John S. Alberici

LOCATIONS

HQ: ALBERICI CORPORATION
8800 PAGE AVE, SAINT LOUIS, MO 63114-6106
Phone: 314-733-2000
Web: WWW.ALBERICI.COM

PRODUCTS/OPERATIONS

Selected Markets

Automotive
Building
Energy
Green building
Health care
Industrial
Manufacturing/Food and Beverage
Mining infrastructure
Steel fabrication
Water and Wastewater Treatment

Selected Subsidiaries and Brands

Alberici Global Group GmbH
- Alberici Constructors Ltd. (Canada)
- Alberici Construcciones S.A. de C.V. (Mexico)

Alberici Group Inc.
- Alberici Constructors Inc.
- Alberici Global Automotive Constructors (automotive construction)
- Alberici Healthcare Constructors
- Alberici Industrial LLC
- CAS Construction LLC (water wastewater)
- Flintco LLC (Native American-owned contractor)
- Gunther-Nash Inc. (shaft slope and tunnel construction for mining industry)
- Hillsdale Fabricators (steel fabrication)
- Kienlen Constructors (structural concrete structural steel)
- Vertegy (green building consulting)

COMPETITORS

Barton Malow	Jacobs Engineering
Bechtel	McCarthy Building
Black & Veatch	Parsons Corporation
DPR Construction	Peter Kiewit Sons'
Fluor	TIC Holdings
Hensel Phelps Construction	Tutor Perini
	Walbridge Aldinger
Hoffman Corporation	Walsh Group
Hunt Construction	Zachry Inc.

HISTORICAL FINANCIALS

Company Type: Private

Income Statement FYE: December 31

	REVENUE ($ mil.)	NET INCOME ($ mil.)	NET PROFIT MARGIN	EMPLOYEES
12/12	772	0	—	2,080
12/11	713	0	—	—
Annual Growth	8.2%	—	—	—

2012 Year-End Financials

Debt ratio: —
Return on equity: —
Cash ($ mil.): 155
Current ratio: 1.10
Long-term debt ($ mil.): —
Dividends
Yield: —
Payout: —
Market value ($ mil.): —

ALDRIDGE ELECTRIC INC

Aldridge Electric powers up the Windy City and other parts of the Midwest. The electrical contractor divides its business into six main areas: airport industrial power drilling highway and transit. It works on projects ranging from Chicago's subway system to its airport runways. Additional activities include services for street lighting traffic signals high-voltage cabling and splicing and foundation drilling. Aldridge Electric has worked for clients such as Commonwealth Edison Company and Exelon Corporation. It sister companies in the family-owned AldridgeGroup include Aldridge Construction GFS Construction and Woodward Brothering.

Operations

Aldridge Electric has more than 1200 pieces of equipment.

It is the general contractor and subcontractor of choice for the multi-million dollar O'Hare Modernization Program (OMP) intended to reduce delays and improve efficiency at the Chicago international airport. Aldridge completed several OMP contracts involving the construction extension and relocation of several runways in addition to the installation of taxiway lights and navigational equipment.

The company is also participating in a $130 million project the Oak Glen Substation a two-circuit 34.5-kV to 69-kV collection substation on the site of Oak Glen Wind Farm near Blooming Prairie Minnesota. It was selected to provide electrical service and maintenance lighting DelDOT Intelligent Traffic Management Systems (ITMS) bridge monitoring instrumentation and the design and installation of a sand-bypass system over the main span of on a new cable stay bridge.

Aldridge Electric's drilling division has enjoyed a robust backlog due to the growing demand in the wind energy market. The division has worked to drill foundations for wind turbines and transmission lines that criss-cross the US.

Ownership

Aldridge Electric is owned by CEO Ken Aldridge the grandson of company's founder.

Company Background

Leonard "Len" Aldridge started the business in 1932 and incorporated it in 1952.

EXECUTIVES

CEO, Kenneth W. (Ken) Aldridge
President, Stephen E. (Steve) Rivi
Executive Vice President, Tom McLinden
EVP Transit, Warren Aldridge
EVP and Division Manager Drilling Highway and Telecom, Ed Kutschke
Division Manager National Power, Wayne Gearig
Executive Vice President Chief Financial Officer, Alan Handley
Vice President Drilling Division, Brian Mazzei
Vice President Transit, Tim Bradley
Vice President National Transit Division, Keith George

LOCATIONS

HQ: ALDRIDGE ELECTRIC INC
844 E ROCKLAND RD, LIBERTYVILLE, IL 60048-3358
Phone: 847-680-5200
Web: WWW.ALDRIDGE-ELECTRIC.COM

PRODUCTS/OPERATIONS

Selected Divisions and Services

Airport
- Approach lighting systems
- Control system
- Electrical vaults
- Hangar facility electrical
- High-voltage cable pulling splicing and terminating
- Hold pad perimeter lighting and limit lighting
- Parking lot lighting
- Parking structure rehabilitation
- Runway and taxiway lighting
- Site utility work
- Terminal rehabilitation work
- Traffic management and control

Drilling
- Bridge foundations
- Building structure foundations
- Communication tower foundations
- Drilled shafts for sewer lift stations
- Drilling for earth-retention systems
- High-mast lighting tower foundations
- Sign foundations
- Transmission line foundations

Highway
- Closed-loop detection
- High-mast lighting
- Highway lighting
- Intelligent transportation systems
- Lighting systems design/build
- Municipal street lighting
- RTMS detection systems
- Subdivision street lighting
- Surveillance camera systems
- Surveillance systems
- Traffic interconnect systems
- Traffic signal systems
- Variable message signs

Industrial
- Design/build capabilities
- Electrical maintenance and renovations
- Electrical power distribution and lighting for new construction and existing facilities
- Energy conservation upgrades and retrofits
- Fire alarm and security
- Movable bridge power lighting and control systems
- Process control systems
- Supervisory control and data acquisition systems
- Tenant build-out
- Voice data communication systems and CCTV

Power
- Design/build
- Fiber optic cabling
- Interconnect yard construction
- Project management
- Overhead elecrical construction
- Substation construction
- Solar panal installation
- Turbine wiring
- Underground electrical construction

Transit
- Catenary systems
- Communications systems
- Traction power 3rd rail systems
- Train control

Affiliates in the AldridgeGroup
Aldridge Canada
GFS Construction LLC
Woodward Brothering

COMPETITORS

Bayview Electric Company	Integrated Electrical Services
EEI	Kelso-Burnett
EMCOR	Mass Electric
Faith Technologies	Motor City Electric

HISTORICAL FINANCIALS

Company Type: Private

Income Statement FYE: March 31

	REVENUE ($ mil.)	NET INCOME ($ mil.)	NET PROFIT MARGIN	EMPLOYEES
03/12	248	1	0.5%	500
03/11	208	2	1.0%	—
03/10	272	10	3.8%	—
Annual Growth	(4.5%)	(65.8%)	—	—

2012 Year-End Financials

Debt ratio: —
Return on equity: 0.50%
Cash ($ mil.): 18
Current ratio: 1.30
Long-term debt ($ mil.): —
Dividends
Yield: —
Payout: —
Market value ($ mil.): —

ALEXANDRIA EXTRUSION COMPANY

EXECUTIVES

President and CEO, Tom Schabel
COO, Al Sholts
VP Sales, Brian Bloedorn
Director of Operations, Brad Hoven
Director of Organizational Development, Lynette Kluver
Marketing Manager, Steve Schabel
President Alexandria Plastics, Joe Schabel

LOCATIONS

HQ: ALEXANDRIA EXTRUSION COMPANY
401 COUNTY ROAD 22 NW, ALEXANDRIA, MN 563084974
Phone: 3207627657
Web: WWW.ALEXANDRIAINDUSTRIES.COM

COMPETITORS

Alcoa
Hydro Aluminium
Rio Tinto Alcan

HISTORICAL FINANCIALS

Company Type: Private

Income Statement FYE: December 31

	REVENUE ($ mil.)	NET INCOME ($ mil.)	NET PROFIT MARGIN	EMPLOYEES
12/13	104	0		350
12/12	85	0	—	—
12/11	72	0	—	—
12/10	62	0	—	—
Annual Growth	18.5%	—	—	—

2013 Year-End Financials

Debt ratio: —
Return on equity: —
Cash ($ mil.): 0
Current ratio: 0.90
Long-term debt ($ mil.): —
Dividends
Yield: —
Payout: —
Market value ($ mil.): —

ALEXANDRIA INOVA HOSPITAL

Inova Alexandria Hospital provides medical surgical and therapeutic services in northeastern Virginia. The hospital was founded in 1872 and became part of the not-for-profit Inova Health System in 1997. Inova Alexandria Hospital has about 320 beds. The hospital offers specialty services such as heart and cancer treatment women's and children's health care emergency medicine vascular procedures interventional radiology and sleep disorder and heartburn treatment services. The Inova Health System provides health care services in northern Virginia through a network of hospitals clinics assisted living centers and other provider facilities.

EXECUTIVES

CEO, Christine Candio
COO, Daniel Jackson
President Medical Staff, Stephen Rosenfeld

LOCATIONS

HQ: ALEXANDRIA INOVA HOSPITAL
4320 SEMINARY RD, ALEXANDRIA, VA 22304-1535
Phone: 703-504-3000
Web: WWW.INOVA.ORG

COMPETITORS

Ascension Health
Bon Secours Health
HCA
Johns Hopkins Health System
MedStar Health

HISTORICAL FINANCIALS

Company Type: Private

Income Statement FYE: December 31

	REVENUE ($ mil.)	NET INCOME ($ mil.)	NET PROFIT MARGIN	EMPLOYEES
12/08	276	24	9.0%	1,750
12/06	247	22	9.2%	—
12/05	233	22	9.8%	—
12/01	180	10	5.7%	—
Annual Growth	6.2%	13.4%	—	—

2008 Year-End Financials

Debt ratio: —
Return on equity: 9.00%
Cash ($ mil.): 2
Current ratio: 1.90
Long-term debt ($ mil.): —
Dividends
Yield: —
Payout: —
Market value ($ mil.): —

ALL POINTS COOPERATIVE

All Points Cooperative provides agricultural support services to farmers and ranchers in central Nebraska. The cooperative offers seed energy fuel agronomy storage and purchasing services along with financial credit marketing and purchasing assistance for its member/farmers. Its agronomy services include fertilizer application soil sampling and crop planning and management. Its energy division offers bulk fuel bulk oil heating oil and propane delivery. It also operates retail outlets including two Ampride Convenience Stores and the Trustworthy Feed and Hardware Store. In addition to its headquarters in Gothenburg Nebraska All Points has cooperative operations in 12 other communities.

EXECUTIVES

Director, Ed Oberg
Vice Chairman, Jeff Beattie
Director, Tim Easterday
Director, Seth Gruber
Director, Jeffrey Huffman
Director, Fred Nisley
Director, Bruce Rickertson

LOCATIONS

HQ: ALL POINTS COOPERATIVE
120 8TH ST, GOTHENBURG, NE 69138-1006
Phone: 308-537-7141
Web: WWW.ALLPOINTSCOOP.COM

COMPETITORS

ADM
AGRI Industries
Ag Processing Inc.
Andersons
Bartlett and Company
CHS
Cargill
DeBruce Grain
GROWMARK
Land O' Lakes Purina Feed
NC Hybrids
Scoular

HISTORICAL FINANCIALS

Company Type: Private

Income Statement FYE: September 30

	REVENUE ($ mil.)	NET INCOME ($ mil.)	NET PROFIT MARGIN	EMPLOYEES
09/12	236	7	3.2%	150
09/08	192	10	5.6%	—
09/06	91	0	—	—
09/05	0	0	—	—
Annual Growth	—	—	—	—

2012 Year-End Financials

Debt ratio: —
Return on equity: 3.20%
Cash ($ mil.): 3
Current ratio: 0.30
Long-term debt ($ mil.): —
Dividends
Yield: —
Payout: —
Market value ($ mil.): —

ALLEGIS GROUP INC.

Clients in need of highly skilled technical and other personnel might want to take the pledge of Allegis. The group is one of the world's largest staffing and recruitment firms. Among its companies are Aerotek (engineering automotive and scientific professionals) Stephen James Associates (recruitment for accounting financial and cash management positions) and TEKsystems (information technology staffing and consulting). Other Allegis units include sales support outsourcer MarketSource. Chairman Jim Davis helped found the company (originally known as Aerotek) in 1983 to provide contract engineering personnel to two clients in the aerospace industry.

Geographic Reach

The company operates through more than 300 offices worldwide including its corporate headquarters in Hanover Maryland. Outside of the US the company has operations in Canada Europe the Middle East the Pacific Rim Puerto Rico and the UK.

Operations

Allegis Group has more than 9000 internal employees including 3000 dedicated recruiters and 100000 contract employees working with customers around the world.

Strategy

The company has expanded its geographical footprint and improved its position in specialist staffing markets through the use of acquisitions.

Mergers and Acquisitions

In 2011 Allegis obtained Aston Carter a London-based information technology recruitment firm with expertise in serving the banking and financial services sectors. The deal extended Allegis' international presence as Aston has more than half a dozen offices sprinkled throughout Europe and Asia.

Back in 2009 the company's Stephen James Associates beefed up its presence on the East Coast with the acquisition of professional recruiting firm Stafford Paige.

EXECUTIVES

CEO, Michael (Mike) Salandra
Chairman, James C. (Jim) Davis
CFO, Paul J. Bowie
CIO, Mercedes Kelch
President - International Operations, Chris Hartman

LOCATIONS

HQ: ALLEGIS GROUP INC.
7301 PARKWAY DR, HANOVER, MD 21076-1159
Phone: 410-579-3000
Web: WWW.ALLEGISGROUP.COM

PRODUCTS/OPERATIONS

Selected Subsidiaries

Aerotek
- Aerotek Automotive
- Aerotek Aviation LLC
- Aerotek Canada
- Aerotek CE
- Aerotek Commercial Staffing
- Aerotek E&E
- Aerotek Energy Services
- Aerotek Germany
- Aerotek Netherlands
- Aerotek Professional Services
- Aerotek Scientific LLC
- Aerotek United Kingdom

Allegis Group Canada
Allegis Group Europe
Allegis Group India
Allegis Group Services
InSearch Worldwide
Major Lindsey & Africa
MarketSource Inc
Stephen James Associates
TEKsystems
- TEKsystems Canada
- TEKsystems Germany
- TEKsystems Netherlands
- TEKsystems United Kingdom

COMPETITORS

ASG Renaissance
Adecco
CDI
Curran Partners
ExecuNet
Heidrick & Struggles
Horton International
Innovative Management Solutions Group
Kelly Services
Korn/Ferry
ManpowerGroup
RDL Corporation
Randstad Holding
Robert Half
Snelling Staffing
Volt Information

HISTORICAL FINANCIALS

Company Type: Private

Income Statement FYE: December 31

	REVENUE ($ mil.)	NET INCOME ($ mil.)	NET PROFIT MARGIN	EMPLOYEES
12/12	9,544	0	—	85,000
12/11	8,275	438	5.3%	—
12/09	6,405	406	6.3%	—
12/09	4,880	316	6.5%	—
Annual Growth	25.0%	—	—	—

2012 Year-End Financials

Debt ratio: —
Return on equity: —
Cash ($ mil.): 347
Current ratio: 2.60
Long-term debt ($ mil.): —
Dividends
Yield: —
Payout: —
Market value ($ mil.): —

ALLEN LUND COMPANY INC.

The Allen Lund Company (ALC) knows loads; it matches shippers' loads with a network of truckload and less-than-truckload (LTL) carriers. (LTL carriers collect consolidate and haul freight from multiple shippers.) The brokerage firm arranges the transport of dry refrigerated (predominantly produce) and flatbed cargo. It operates from 30 offices throughout more than 20 US states. ALC Logistics ALC Perishable Logistics and ALC International (an international division) assist shippers in managing transportation costs tracking and tracing shipments managing appointments and executing freight forward management services overseas. The company was founded in 1976 by Allen Lund and his wife Kathie Lund.

Geographic Reach

The company's international division provides transportation services worldwide along with transportation to and from the US including Puerto Rico Hawaii Alaska and ground transportation for Canada and Mexico.

Operations

ALC has a Logistics & Software division ALC Logistics.

Strategy

In an effort to expand its operation in 2012 the company opened a new office in Joplin Missouri and another in McAllen Texas which mainly focuses on handling heavy haul flatbed particularly in and out of Mexico. In addition the company opened four additional offices in 2012.

Mergers and Acquisitions

In an effort to grow its business in early 2014 ALC acquired Wisconsin based Northern Freight Service Inc. a company provides truckload LTL and intermodal services to the customers ranging from small shippers to FORTUNE 500 shippers.

EXECUTIVES

President, Allen Lund
VP Human Resources, Terry Walker
VP Support Services, Kenny Lund
Director MarCom, Nora Trueblood
VP Sales and Operations, David Lund
CFO, Steve Doerfler
VP Sales and Operations, Eddie Lund
Director Recruiting, Glenda Aiello
Manager Accounting, Kristi J. Anderson
Director ALC Perishable Logistics, Craig Cahill

LOCATIONS

HQ: ALLEN LUND COMPANY INC.
4529 ANGELES CREST HWY # 300, LA CANADA FLINTRIDGE, CA 91011-3259
Phone: 818-790-1110
Web: WWW.ALLENLUND.COM

PRODUCTS/OPERATIONS

Selected Services

Software and Logistics
- LTL Freight
- Scheduling
- Spot Pricing and Bid Management
- Truck Load

Transportation Services
- Dry Van
- Flatbed Trucking
- International Freight Shipping
- LTL Freight
- Refrigerated Transportation

COMPETITORS

C.H. Robinson Worldwide
CEVA Logistics
Con-way Inc.
Menlo Worldwide
Pacer Transportation Solutions
Ryder System
UTi Worldwide
Universal Truckload Services

HISTORICAL FINANCIALS

Company Type: Private

Income Statement FYE: October 31

	REVENUE ($ mil.)	NET INCOME ($ mil.)	NET PROFIT MARGIN	EMPLOYEES
10/12	313	3	1.0%	310
10/11	313	3	1.0%	—
10/10	322	2	0.8%	—
10/09	287	4	1.7%	—
Annual Growth	2.9%	(13.2%)	—	—

2012 Year-End Financials

Debt ratio: —
Return on equity: 1.00%
Cash ($ mil.): 10
Current ratio: 2.00
Long-term debt ($ mil.): —
Dividends
Yield: —
Payout: —
Market value ($ mil.): —

ALLINA HEALTH SYSTEM

Allina Health System (aka Allina Hospitals and Clinics) is a not-for-profit health care system that goes all in to protect people's #1 asset –their good health. The health system owns and operates about a dozen hospitals a network of nearly one hundred clinics and specialty centers and a whole bunch of pharmacies. Its vast system of provider locations serve residents throughout Minnesota and western Wisconsin providing disease prevention programs along with specialized inpatient and outpatient services. Allina's Aspen Medical Group division also operates a range of outpatient clinics providing primary and specialty care. Allina is led by CEO Ken Paulus who previously served as the system's COO.

Operations

Allina has 12 hospitals (about 1800 beds) more than 90 clinics and 14 pharmacies. The largest hospital in the group is Abbott Northwestern Hospital with about 600 beds followed by United Hospital which has about 450 beds. Five of Allina's hospitals are in the Minneapolis/St. Paul metropolitan area (where the system has more than a 30% share of the health care market) five are scattered throughout the rest of Minnesota and one is in western Wisconsin. The health system reported more than 113000 inpatient admissions in 2011 1.2 million outpatient admissions and more than 3.3 million clinic visits.

Financial Performance

In 2013 Allina reported a 4% increase in revenue due to increased payments for patient services. Net income spiked more than 100% as investment returns rose and financing losses dropped.

Strategy

The system's wide-ranging locations combined with its huge number of facilities have prompted Allina to embark on a multi-year initiative to install electronic medical records (EMR) at all of its hospitals and clinics. The installation gives medical providers the ability to track a patient's progress through any of the myriad health care settings operated by Allina. The EMR also gives patients access to coordinated care between the different providers as well as the ability to see portions of their medical records and lab results online. Patients can also schedule appointments and make use of a number of health and wellness tools all via the Internet.

Allina is the first Minnesota health care organization to earn the Davies Award the industry's preeminent award for health information technology.

Despite Allina's already hefty size the system has a partnership with retail clinic provider MinuteClinic which offers basic health care at CVS Caremark stores. The hospital also has a multi-year collaboration with HealthPartners designed to reduce total medical costs at both hospitals.

In 2013 Courage Center and Allina merged Sister Kenny Rehabilitation Institute and Courage Center. The merger of the two entities (which focus on the health and well-being of people with disabilities) served Allina's goal of expanding its network.

EXECUTIVES

VP; President Mercy Hospital, Sara Criger
EVP Hospital Division; Interim President Mercy Hospital, Jeffrey D. (Jeff) Peterson
VP; President United Hospital, Tomi S. Ryba
VP; President Unity Hospital, Lori Wightman, age 54
EVP Clinic and Community Division, Robert A. Wieland
Media Manager, David Kanihan
Chairwoman, Christine A. Morrison
Chief Clinical Officer, Penny Ann Wheeler
President and CEO, Kenneth (Ken) Paulus, age 55
Media Relations, Gloria O'Connell
General Counsel, Elizabeth Truesdell Smith
VP; President Abbott Northwestern Hospital, Ben Bache-Wiig
VP; President United Hospital, Thomas (Tom) O'Connor
EVP Administration and CFO, Duncan P. Gallagher
Media Contact, Tim Burke
President St. Francis Regional Medical Center, Michael Baumgartner
VP Penny George Institute for Health and Healing, Courtney J. Baechler
SVP and CIO, Susan Heichert
Vice President Patient Care, Terry Graner
Vice President Operations, Daryl Schroeder
Vice President Operations Cardiovascular Service Line, Tom Talley
Director, Rodney A. (Rod) Young, age 59
Director, Mark W. Sheffert, age 66
Director, Mark S. Jordahl
Director, Gary C. Bhojwani
Director, Jean Delaney Nelson
Director, Nathan K. (Nate) Garvis
Director, ReBecca (Becky) Koenig Roloff, age 59
President CEO and Director, Kenneth (Ken) Paulus, age 54
Director, Sabbarao Inampudi
Director, William L. Beer
Director, Hugh Nierengarten
Director, Joan Thompson
Director, Joseph Goswitz
Director, Gloria Perez
Auditors: Deloitte&ToucheLLP

LOCATIONS

HQ: ALLINA HEALTH SYSTEM
2925 CHICAGO AVE, MINNEAPOLIS, MN 55407-1321
Phone: 612-262-5000
Web: WWW.ALLINAHEALTH.ORG

PRODUCTS/OPERATIONS

Selected Hospitals

Abbott Northwestern Hospital (Minneapolis MN)
Buffalo Hospital (Buffalo MN)
Cambridge Medical Center (Cambridge MN)
Mercy Hospital (Coon Rapids MN)
New Ulm Medical Center (New Ulm MN)
Owatonna Hospital (Owatonna MN)
Phillips Eye Institute (Minneapolis MN)
River Falls Area Hospital (River Falls WI)
St. Francis Regional Medical Center (Shakopee MN)
United Hospital (St. Paul MN)
Unity Hospital (Fridley MN)

COMPETITORS

Bethesda Hospital
Catholic Health Initiatives
CentraCare Health
Children' s Hospitals and Clinics of Minnesota
Fairview Health
Hazelden
HealthEast Care System
Mayo Clinic
Methodist Hospital (MN)
North Memorial Health Care
Park Nicollet Health Services
Regions Hospital
St. John' s Hospital (Minnesota)
University of Minnesota Medical Center

HISTORICAL FINANCIALS

Company Type: Private

Income Statement

FYE: December 31

	REVENUE ($ mil.)	NET INCOME ($ mil.)	NET PROFIT MARGIN	EMPLOYEES
12/11	2,743	225	8.2%	22,347
12/09	2,978	281	9.4%	—
12/07	2,533	97	3.9%	—
Annual Growth	2.0%	23.3%	—	—

2011 Year-End Financials

Debt ratio: ——
Return on equity: 8.20%
Cash ($ mil.): 16
Current ratio: 1.60
Long-term debt ($ mil.): —
Dividends
Yield: —
Payout: —
Market value ($ mil.): —

ALRO STEEL CORPORATION

EXECUTIVES

Purchasing Industrial Supply, Shane Clark
Chairman and CEO, Alvin Glick
President and COO, Mark Alyea
VP Assistant Secretary and Treasurer, Randy Glick
Vice Chairman; President Alro Metals, Barry Glick
VP and Secretary, Carl Glick
Director Customer Account Services, John Rumler

LOCATIONS

HQ: ALRO STEEL CORPORATION
3100 E HIGH ST, JACKSON, MI 492036413
Phone: 5177875500
Web: WWW.ALRO.COM

COMPETITORS

Carlisle Companies
Central Steel & Wire
Contractors Steel
Flame Metals Processing
Mill Steel
Peerless Steel
Tyco

HISTORICAL FINANCIALS

Company Type: Private

Income Statement

FYE: May 31

	REVENUE ($ mil.)	NET INCOME ($ mil.)	NET PROFIT MARGIN	EMPLOYEES
05/14	1,613	0	—	2,000
05/13	1,553	0	—	—
05/12	1,605	0	—	—
05/11	1,348	0	—	—
Annual Growth	6.2%	—	—	—

2014 Year-End Financials

Debt ratio: ——
Return on equity: —
Cash ($ mil.): 88
Current ratio: 2.80
Long-term debt ($ mil.): —
Dividends
Yield: —
Payout: —
Market value ($ mil.): —

ALSCO INC.

Alsco has built a big business outfitting its customers in uniforms linens and related products. Operating from some 150 branches in about 10 countries worldwide the company (whose name stands for American linen supply company) rents and sells uniforms linens towels and clean room garments to more than 140000 customers in North America. It also manages janitorial services provides washroom supplies and launders and sterilizes garments. Alsco serves the automotive food processing restaurant medical and IT industries as well as the federal government. Founded in 1889 by George Steiner the company is owned and operated by the Steiner family.

Geographic Reach

Utah-based Alsco has locations in Australia Brazil Canada China Germany Italy New Zealand Singapore Switzerland Thailand and the US.

Strategy

Alsco heavily promotes its green cleaning solutions and the company has focused on international expansion in recent years. In 2014 the company expanded its uniform and linen services in Texas with a branch in San Antonio and service centers in Austin Houston and Waco.

In addition to uniforms and linens Alsco supplies promotional products for trade shows conventions golf outings sales meetings and other special events and occasions. 800x600

Company Ownership

Alsco is owned and operated by the family of its founder George Steiner. It was formerly known at Steiner Corp.

EXECUTIVES

Co-ceo, Kevin K Steiner, age 63

LOCATIONS

HQ: ALSCO INC.
505 E SOUTH TEMPLE, SALT LAKE CITY, UT 841021004
Phone: 8013288831
Web: WWW.ALSCO.COM

PRODUCTS/OPERATIONS

Selected Products and Services

Clean room garments
Gown room management
Hospitality/restaurant apparel
Laundry services
Linens
Mats
Mops
Napkins
Restroom service
Towels
Uniform rental and sales
Vacuum filters
Washroom supplies

COMPETITORS

ARAMARK
Angelica Corporation
Berendsen
Cintas
Crothall Healthcare
Diversey
ISS A/S
Rentokil Initial
ServiceMaster
Sodexo USA
Superior Uniform Group
Swisher Hygiene

Ecolab	Tranzonic
G&K Services	UniFirst
Healthcare Services	

HISTORICAL FINANCIALS

Company Type: Private

Income Statement FYE: December 31

	REVENUE ($ mil.)	NET INCOME ($ mil.)	NET PROFIT MARGIN	EMPLOYEES
12/13	633	33	5.2%	13,585
12/12	614	35	5.8%	—
12/11	556	43	7.8%	—
12/10	544	0	—	—
Annual Growth	5.1%	—	—	—

2013 Year-End Financials

Debt ratio: —
Return on equity: 5.20%
Cash ($ mil.): 32
Current ratio: 1.40
Long-term debt ($ mil.): —
Dividends
Yield: —
Payout: —
Market value ($ mil.): —

AMERICA CHUNG NAM (GROUP) HOLDINGS INC.

Ever wondered where all that paper and plastic to be recycled goes? If this company is any indication a lot of it goes to China. America Chung Nam is the largest exporter of recovered paper in the US and a leading exporter in Europe and Asia. The company exports recovered fiber sources to Chinese paper mills where they can be converted into fiberboard cardboard and packaging. It also collects and exports a number of grades of post-consumer plastics. The company sources its materials through exclusive relationships with recycling facilities waste management companies and distribution centers.

Geographic Reach

The company has operations in North America Asia and Europe. It has offices in the US (Jersey City Los Angeles and Wilmington North Carolina) Europe (the Netherlands and the UK) and Asia (China and Japan).

Strategy

America Chung Nam supplies fiber materials to Nine Dragons Paper China's largest packaging manufacturer. Nine Dragons converts into the packaging material that is used to ship various Chinese products to consumers across the world. Once delivered the packaging is ready for recycling and export back to China. In 2013 Nine Dragons operated 35 production lines and had an annual capacity of 14 million metric tons.

In 2011 America Chung Nam shipped about 355000 20-ft. equivalent units of recyclable materials from the US and was ranked #1 in US containerized exports for the 11th consecutive year according to The Journal of Commerce.

Ownership

Founder Yan Cheung owns the company.

Company Background

America Chung Nam was founded in 1990 by Yan Cheung and Ming Chung Liu. Recognizing the demand for packaging materials driven by China's product exports and having a ready source for fiber materials through America Chung Nam Ms. Cheung established Nine Dragons Paper in 1996.

EXECUTIVES

Chief Executive Officer Worldwide Marketing, Peter Wang
Deputy CEO Asia Pacific Region, Teresa Cheung
President and CEO, Yan Cheung

LOCATIONS

HQ: AMERICA CHUNG NAM (GROUP) HOLDINGS INC.
1163 FAIRWAY DR, CITY OF INDUSTRY, CA 91789-2846
Phone: 909-839-8383
Web: WWW.ACNI.NET

COMPETITORS

Caraustar Recovered Fiber Group	International Paper
Guanwei Recycling	RockTenn CP
	Weyerhaeuser

HISTORICAL FINANCIALS

Company Type: Private

Income Statement FYE: December 31

	REVENUE ($ mil.)	NET INCOME ($ mil.)	NET PROFIT MARGIN	EMPLOYEES
12/09	1,125	16	1.5%	250
12/08	1,363	7	0.6%	—
12/08	0	0	—	—
Annual Growth	—	—	—	—

2009 Year-End Financials

Debt ratio: —
Return on equity: 1.50%
Cash ($ mil.): 18
Current ratio: 1.20
Long-term debt ($ mil.): —
Dividends
Yield: —
Payout: —
Market value ($ mil.): —

AMERICA'S HOME PLACE INC.

America's Home Place builds custom homes on its customers' land. The company builds single-family detached houses with more than 100 custom floor plans and designs. Its two- to five-bedroom cabin chalet ranch two-story and split-level houses range in price from about $80000 to more than $300000. Sizes start at about 900 sq. ft. and go up to to 4000 sq. ft. America's Home Place operates nearly 40 home building and model centers in the southeastern US. Buyers typically already own their land from a single lot to many acres. The company also assists buyers who are not landowners in locating available property. President Barry Conner owns the company he founded in 1972.

Customizable home options include choice of flooring lighting roofing siding cabinets and countertops. The company uses products with such brand names as Armstrong (flooring) CertainTeed (roofing and siding) Sherwin-Williams (paint) and Whirlpool (appliances).

America's Home Place traditionally services its customers at retail outlets where buyers select their design carpet paint tile and window options. However the company added to its marketing strategy to begin providing model centers which feature full-sized model homes plus product and sales centers. The company builds its homes in Florida Georgia Louisiana Mississippi North Carolina South Carolina and Tennessee.

America's Home Place does not offer financing. However it does have relationships with several preferred lenders that are recommended to homebuyers.

EXECUTIVES

Vice President Technology, Alan Cooper
District Vice President, Phil Lelievre

LOCATIONS

HQ: AMERICA' S HOME PLACE INC.
2144 HILTON DR, GAINESVILLE, GA 30501-6172
Phone: 770-532-1128
Web: WWW.AMERICASHOMEPLACE.COM

COMPETITORS

Beazer Homes	M.D.C.
D.R. Horton	NVR
David Weekley Homes	PulteGroup
KB Home	Standard Pacific
Lennar	The Ryland Group

HISTORICAL FINANCIALS

Company Type: Private

Income Statement FYE: December 31

	REVENUE ($ mil.)	NET INCOME ($ mil.)	NET PROFIT MARGIN	EMPLOYEES
12/12	155	7	4.6%	275
12/11	125	4	3.7%	—
12/07	173	8	4.9%	—
12/06	184	11	6.3%	—
Annual Growth	(2.9%)	(7.8%)	—	—

2012 Year-End Financials

Debt ratio: —
Return on equity: 4.60%
Cash ($ mil.): 3
Current ratio: 0.20
Long-term debt ($ mil.): —
Dividends
Yield: —
Payout: —
Market value ($ mil.): —

AMERICAN BUREAU OF SHIPPING INC

One of the world's largest ship classification societies American Bureau of Shipping (ABS) offers inspection and analysis services to verify that vessels are mechanically and structurally fit. The not-for-profit company's surveyors examine ships in major ports throughout the world assessing whether the vessels comply with ABS rules for design construction and maintenance. Additionally its engineers consult with shipbuilders on proposed designs and repairs. The not-for-profit company operates from more than 150 offices in about 70 countries. For-profit subsidiaries ABS Group offers risk management consulting services while ABS Nautical Systems provides fleet management software. ABS was founded in 1862.

Geographic Reach ABS operates through a network of 150 offices in 70 countries. Its main divisional offices reside in China Singapore the UK and the US.

Strategy

ABS's strategy for growth includes building upon its core capabilities in inspection integrity management and project quality management services. These services have also been the foundation for growth in the fast-growing regions of the Middle East and the Asia-Pacific. In 2011 it established operations in Western Australia and West Africa with new offices in Perth Australia and Lagos Nigeria.

Additionally ABS Group invested in building its presence in Europe with added business development resources in London and the acquisition of Safetec Nordic AS in Trondheim Norway. The investment positioned ABS Group to capitalize on projects in the North Sea from both Norway and Aberdeen.

In 2012 the company opened a new energy technology center in Korea and extended its services in Singapore an important region for catering to the deepwater sector.

EXECUTIVES

SVP and CTO, Todd W. Grove
VP and Division President Americas, Robert W. Gilman
SVP and Chief Surveyor, Lenny Pendexter
SVP, Robert A. Giuffra
Vice President Global Marketing, Antonio Costa
Vice President External Affairs, Jean Gould
VP-Engrg, Robert Spencer
Vice President Occupational, John McDonald

LOCATIONS

HQ: AMERICAN BUREAU OF SHIPPING INC
16855 NORTHCHASE DR, HOUSTON, TX 77060-6010
Phone: 281-877-5800
Web: WWW.EAGLE.ORG

PRODUCTS/OPERATIONS

Selected Services

Casualty Response
Certification (Marine and Container)
Classification
Environmental
Statutory
Training
Type Approval

COMPETITORS

Accenture
BSI Group
Booz Allen
Bureau Veritas
ClassNK
Cotecna Inspection
Lloyd' s Register
Norske Veritas
SGS

HISTORICAL FINANCIALS

Company Type: Private

Income Statement

FYE: December 31

	REVENUE ($ mil.)	NET INCOME ($ mil.)	NET PROFIT MARGIN	EMPLOYEES
12/11	726	143	19.8%	3,000
12/09	648	180	27.9%	—
12/02	159	(9)	—	—
12/02	434	0	—	—
Annual Growth	5.9%	—	—	—

2011 Year-End Financials

Debt ratio: —
Return on equity: 19.80%
Cash ($ mil.): 85
Current ratio: 1.10
Long-term debt ($ mil.): —
Dividends
Yield: —
Payout: —
Market value ($ mil.): —

AMERICAN CHEMET CORPORATION

LOCATIONS

HQ: AMERICAN CHEMET CORPORATION
740 WAUKEGAN RD STE 202, DEERFIELD, IL 600154400
Phone: 8479480800
Web: WWW.CHEMET.COM

HISTORICAL FINANCIALS

Company Type: Private

Income Statement

FYE: June 30

	REVENUE ($ mil.)	NET INCOME ($ mil.)	NET PROFIT MARGIN	EMPLOYEES
06/14	218	5	2.5%	140
06/13	210	4	2.0%	—
06/12	246	6	2.6%	—
06/11	254	0	—	—
Annual Growth	(5.0%)	—	—	—

2014 Year-End Financials

Debt ratio: —
Return on equity: 2.50%
Cash ($ mil.): 1
Current ratio: 0.80
Long-term debt ($ mil.): —
Dividends
Yield: —
Payout: —
Market value ($ mil.): —

AMERICAN CHEMICAL SOCIETY

This group has a lot of chemistry. With more than 163000 members the American Chemical Society (ACS) is the world's largest scientific society. It provides information career development and educational resources to member chemists chemical engineers and technicians. ACS also publishes dozens of magazines journals and books and its Chemical Abstracts Service provides access to an online database o more than 70 million literature and research summaries from around the world. ACS also serves as an advocate for its members on public policy issues. The ACS Member Insurance Program provides insurance plans to members. The not-for-profit organization was founded in 1876 and chartered by Congress in 1937.

Geographic Reach

Based in Washington D.C. the ACS's international membership exceeds 24000 and represents more than 100 countries. More than 60% of the content and articles published in ACS journals and abstracts originates from outside the US. The society hosts an annual International Chemistry Olympiad.

Financial Performance

The ACS's revenue increased 2% in 2012 versus 2011 to just shy of $500 million. The increase was driven by a 3% rise in proceeds from electronic services the organization's largest source of income.

EXECUTIVES

Treasurer Chief Financial Officer, Brian A. Bernstein
Director District II, Diane Grob Schmidt
Director District III, Madeleine M. Joullie
Executive Director and CEO, Madeleine Jacobs
Chairman, Judith Benham
Secretary, Flint H. Lewis
Director District VI, Bonnie Charpentier
Immediate Past-President, Catherine T. Hunt
President, Bruce E. Bursten
President Chemical Abstracts Service CAS, Bob Massie
President ACS Publications Division, Brian Crawford
President spoke of the need for such a national organization, Charles F. Chandler
President for, Thomas J. Barton
Auditors: PricewaterhouseCoopersLLP

LOCATIONS

HQ: AMERICAN CHEMICAL SOCIETY
1155 16TH ST NW, WASHINGTON, DC 20036-4892
Phone: 202-872-4600
Web: WWW.PORTAL.ACS.ORG

PRODUCTS/OPERATIONS

2012 Revenue

	$ mil.	% of total
Electronic services	403	81
Dues	12	2
Membership insurance premiums refunds & fees	11	2
Printed services	10	2
Registration fees & booth sales	10	2
Investment income	10	2
Advertising	8	2
Net assets released from restriction	26	5
Other	6	1
Total	**499**	**100**

HISTORICAL FINANCIALS

Company Type: Private

Income Statement

FYE: December 31

	REVENUE ($ mil.)	NET INCOME ($ mil.)	NET PROFIT MARGIN	EMPLOYEES
12/08	451	(38)	—	2,000
12/05	411	26	6.4%	—
12/04	408	56	13.9%	—
12/03	421	29	7.0%	—
Annual Growth	1.4%	—	—	—

2008 Year-End Financials

Debt ratio: —
Return on equity: (-8.50%)
Cash ($ mil.): 29
Current ratio: 1.20
Long-term debt ($ mil.): —
Dividends
Yield: —
Payout: —
Market value ($ mil.): —

AMERICAN FEDERATION OF LABOR & CONGRESS OF INDUSTRIAL ORGANZATIO

Talk about spending a long time in labor: The AFL-CIO (American Federation of Labor and Congress of Industrial Organizations) has been focused on the task for more than a century. The AFL-CIO is an umbrella organization for more than 55 autonomous national and international unions. Altogether the AFL-CIO represents more than 12 million workers –from actors and airline pilots to marine engineers and machinists. It fights to improve wages and working conditions. The organization charters 50-plus state federations and about 500 central labor councils. Union members generally receive about 30% higher pay and more benefits than non-members. The AFL-CIO was created in 1955 by the merger of the AFL and the CIO.

Geographic Reach

Headquartered in Washington DC the AFL-CIO maintains regional offices and field staff nationwide. Through affiliations the group enjoys a global reach.

Operations

The AFL-CIO's executive council comprises about 55 executives. It monitors executive pay through its Executive PayWatch reports and case studies.

As part of the organization's emphasis on corporate responsibility it devotes blogs reports videos and other mediums to discuss the retail environment such as the dominance of Wal-Mart.

Strategy

The organization's membership has been decreasing due in part to the decline in manufacturing jobs and the increased use of temporary workers and automation. The AFL-CIO's 12.2 million members include 3.2 million members of Working America its community affiliate.

To strengthen and unify unions the AFL-CIO and the National Education Association (NEA) partnered to allow local NEA affiliates to join the federation at the local and state levels through affiliation with the national AFL-CIO. These local affiliates are called Directly Affiliated NEA locals (DANLs). In fiscal 2013 there were 39 DANLs across half a dozen states as well as the District of Columbia that altogether had a total of 38475 members.

To extend its reach further the AFL-CIO is affiliated with the Belgium-based International Trade Union Confederation (ITUC) which is a global union network. ITUC represents some 175 million workers across 150-plus countries and territories with about 310 national affiliates.

Company Background

Despite aggressive plans to increase recruiting the Teamsters and the Service Employees International Union (SEIU) left the AFL-CIO in 2005 over the issues of plummeting membership and the future course of the labor movement. They took 3.3 million members with them.

HISTORY

The American Federation of Labor (AFL) was formed in 1886 in Columbus Ohio by the merger of six craft unions and a renegade craft section of the Marxist-oriented Knights of Labor. Samuel Gompers a New York cigar factory worker who headed the AFL until his death in 1924 initiated the AFL's pragmatic focus: to work within the economic system to increase wages improve working conditions and abolish child labor.

Gompers' successes incensed employers whose arsenal supported by the US courts and public opinion included injunctions government-backed police forces to crush strikes and the Sherman Anti-Trust Act (used to assail union monopoly powers).

WWI's production needs boosted AFL membership to 4 million by 1919. Labor clashes with management were widespread in the 1920s amid the fear of Bolsheviks. As part of open-shop drives employers replaced strikers with southern African-Americans and Mexican workers.

The Great Depression brought more supportive public and pro-labor laws including the National Industrial Recovery Act (NIRA 1933) which allowed union organizing and collective bargaining. After NIRA was declared unconstitutional the Wagner Act (1936) restated many of NIRA's provisions and established the legal basis for unions.

Union power split in 1935 when AFL coal miner John L. Lewis began organizing unskilled workers. Lewis and his allies expelled from the AFL formed the Congress of Industrial Organizations (CIO 1938) and enjoyed success in unionizing the auto steel textile and other industries. By 1946 the AFL and CIO had 9 million and 5 million members respectively.

Amid postwar concern over rising prices communist infiltration and union corruption Congress passed the Taft-Hartley Act in 1947 (which outlawed closed shops). The new climate of hostility led the AFL (headed by plumber George Meany) and the CIO (headed by autoworker Walter Reuther) to merge in 1955. The AFL-CIO soon expelled the Teamsters and other unions on charges of corruption. (The Teamsters reaffiliated in 1987.)

AFL-CIO membership jumped after President Kennedy gave federal employees the right to unionize (1962); state county and municipal workers soon followed.

Union membership which peaked in the mid-1940s with more than a third of the US labor force was particularly hurt by a jump in imported goods in the 1970s and automation's triumph over manual labor in the 1980s. Legislation supported by the AFL-CIO included a law requiring 60 days' notice for plant closings (1988) and the Family Medical Leave Act (1993). But labor lost its battle against NAFTA (North American Free Trade Agreement) which it feared would export jobs to Mexico.

In 1995 John Sweeney former head of the Service Employees International Union (SEIU) became president of the AFL-CIO in its first contested election. Under Sweeney the union spent $35 million in advertising in 1996 to draw attention to issues. After years with little focus on organizing in 1997 the AFL-CIO launched a massive campaign to organize construction hospital and hotel workers in Las Vegas and committed a third of its budget to recruiting and reorganizing. It supported the Teamsters' successful strike against UPS in 1997 and in 1998 threw its weight behind the Air Line Pilots Association's walkout on Northwest Airlines. It approved a restructuring plan in 1999 and the next year spent significant time and money rallying members all across the US in support of losing presidential candidate Al Gore. In 2002 AFL-CIO announced its pledge of $750 million to create affordable housing in New York City.

At the group's 2005 convention the Teamsters and the SEIU broke ranks over Sweeney's inability to stem the tide of falling membership. They joined a rival group Change to Win Coalition led by SEIU's Andrew Stern.

In September 2009 Richard Trumka was elected president of the AFL-CIO.

EXECUTIVES

General Counsel, Jonathan (Jon) Hiatt
International President International Association of Machinists and Aerospace Workers, R. Thomas (Tom) Buffenbarger, age 63
President of AFSCME, Gerald W. McEntee
President, Richard L. Trumka, age 64
President of the AFL-CIO, John J. Sweeney, age 80
General President Sheet Metal Workers International Association, Michael J. (Mike) Sullivan
President ;, Ron Gettelfinger, age 68
Secretary and Treasurer The International Union United Automobile Aerospace and Agricultural Implement Workers of America, Elizabeth Bunn
International President International Brotherhood of Electrical Workers, Edwin D. (Ed) Hill
President American Postal Works Union, William Burrus
Secretary and Treasurer Emeritus American Federation of Teachers, Nat LaCour
President United Mine Workers of America, Cecil E. Roberts Jr.
Secretary and Treasurer American Federation of State County and Municipal Employees, William Lucy
International President Association of Flight Attendants-CWA, Patricia A. (Pat) Friend
VP American Federation of Teachers, Laura K. Rico
President of AFT, Randi Weingarten
President Screen Actors Guild, Alan Rosenberg
National President American Federation of Government Employees, John Gage, age 68
President Communications Workers of America, Larry Cohen, age 62
President International Union of Bricklayers and Allied Craftworkers, John J. Flynn
International President United Steelworkers, Leo W. Gerard
President U.S. Navy, Warren S. George
President of the International Union of Operating Engineers, Vincent J. Giblin
President Office and Professional Employees International Union, Michael Goodwin, age 72
President UA, William P. Hite
President Ironworkers, Joseph J. Hunt
International President Bakery Confectionery Tobacco Workers and Grain Millers International Union, Frank Hurt
International President International Federation of Professional and Technical Engineers, Gregory J. Junemann
International President Transport Workers Union, James C. Little
Vice President Laura Rico, John Prater
Past President California School Employees Association, Clyde Rivers
President Seafarers International Union of North America, Michael Sacco, age 77
President, Robert A. (Bob) Scardelletti
President of the International Association of Fire Fighters IAFF, Harold A. Schaitberger
International Brotherhood of Electrical Workers, Robbie Sparks
Past International President United Transportation Union, Paul C. Thompson, age 70
General President International Union of Painters and Allied Trades, James A. Williams
Secretary and Treasurer Office and Professional Employees International Union, Nancy Wohlforth
National President National Association of Letter Carriers, William H. (Bill) Young
President Building and Construction Trades Department, Mark H. Ayers
EVP, Arlene Holt Baker
President United American Nurses (UAN), Ann Converso
Executive Director California Nurses Association and National Nurses Organizing Committee, Rose Ann Demoro
President International Longshoremen's Association, Richard P. Hughes Jr.
International VP Human Affairs United Steelworkers, Fred Redmond
Secretary and Treasurer, Elizabeth (Liz) Shuler

LOCATIONS

HQ: AMERICAN FEDERATION OF LABOR & CONGRESS OF INDUSTRIAL ORGANZATIO
815 16TH ST NW, WASHINGTON, DC 20006-4101
Phone: 202-637-5000
Web: WWW.AFLCIO.ORG

PRODUCTS/OPERATIONS

Selected Departments

Accounting
Campaigns
Civil Human and Women' s Rights
Digital Strategies
Facilities Management
Government Affairs
Human Resources
Information Technology
International
Meetings and Travel
Office of General Counsel
Office of Investment
Organizing
Policy
Political
Public Affairs
Support Services

HISTORICAL FINANCIALS

Company Type: Private

Income Statement

FYE: June 30

	REVENUE ($ mil.)	NET INCOME ($ mil.)	NET PROFIT MARGIN	EMPLOYEES
06/11*	168	6	3.8%	380
08/09	0	0	—	—
06/08	150	(2)	—	—
Annual Growth	3.7%	—	—	—

*Fiscal year change

2011 Year-End Financials

Debt ratio: —
Return on equity: 3.80%
Cash ($ mil.): 18
Current ratio: 0.30
Long-term debt ($ mil.): —
Dividends
Yield: —
Payout: —
Market value ($ mil.): —

AMERICAN INFRASTRUCTURE INC.

American Infrastructure provides heavy civil construction services for projects in the Mid-Atlantic. Operating as Allan A. Myers in Pennsylvania and Delaware and as American Infrastructure in Maryland and Virginia the company builds and reconstructs highways water treatment plants medical facilities and shopping centers and offers site development for homebuilders. Its quarries and asphalt plants operate under the Independence Construction Materials (ICM) subsidiary which supplies aggregates asphalt and ready-mixed concrete to its construction companies. The family-run business was established in 1939 as Allan A. Myers and Son a local hauling company in the suburbs of Philadelphia.

Geographic Reach

The company and its subsidiaries operate in the Mid-Atlantic region through about 20 locations (including quarries and plants) in Pennsylvania Maryland Virginia and Delaware.

Operations

As a land developer interested in conservation American Infrastructure offers a unique all-terrain tree spade vehicle that is designed to carry large mature trees harvested from heavily wooded sites intended to be replanted on developed sites. The process allows mature trees to be saved and relocated on a developed site.

Sales and Marketing

American Infrastructure counts several companies and organizations among its current and former clients such as Hunt Building Company the City of Wilmington and Maryland State Highway Administration. Some past projects include Eagle Heights at Dover Air Force Base ($13.3 million) Cool Springs Reservoir ($18.6 million) and MD 43 ($46.7 million) located in Baltimore County Maryland.

EXECUTIVES

Senior Vice President, Robert A Herbein
Chairman and CEO, A. Ross Myers, age 64
Vice President Construction Management Services, Gordon Bryan
Vice President Equipment Services, Dave Markey
Vice President Of Safety And Claims, Mark Smith
Vice President, Del Zentgraf
Chairman and CEO, A. Ross Myers, age 64

LOCATIONS

HQ: AMERICAN INFRASTRUCTURE INC.
1805 BERKS RD, WORCESTER, PA 19490
Phone: 610-222-8800
Web: WWW.AMERICANINFRASTRUCTURE.COM

PRODUCTS/OPERATIONS

Selected Services

Site Development
- Concrete flatwork
- Excavation and grading
- Hauling
- Large-diameter tree relocation
- Milling and paving
- Rock drilling and blasting
- Soft dig capabilities
- Stone and curb
- Stormwater management
- Survey and stakeout
- Underground utilities

Transportation
- Asphalt paving
- Box culverts
- Bridges and structures
- Concrete paving
- Maintenance of traffic

Water Resources
- New water/wastewater treatment plants
- Reservoirs and dams
- Underground reservoirs
- Water and sewer transmission lines
- Wetland mitigation and reconstruction

Selected Subsidiaries

Allan A. Myers Inc.
American Infrastructure-Maryland
American Infrastructure-Virginia
Independence Construction Materials

COMPETITORS

Angelo Iafrate
Balfour Beatty Infrastructure
Barnhill Contracting
Branch Group
Cherry Hill Construction
English Construction Company
Lane Construction
Peter Kiewit Sons'
Skanska USA Civil
Traylor Bros.
Vecellio & Grogan

HISTORICAL FINANCIALS

Company Type: Private

Income Statement

FYE: December 31

	REVENUE ($ mil.)	NET INCOME ($ mil.)	NET PROFIT MARGIN	EMPLOYEES
12/11	545	1	0.3%	1,700
12/10	476	20	4.2%	
12/10	1,362	0	—	—
Annual Growth		—523392.7%	—	—

2011 Year-End Financials

Debt ratio: —
Return on equity: 0.30%
Cash ($ mil.): 4
Current ratio: 0.90
Long-term debt ($ mil.): —
Dividends
Yield: —
Payout: —
Market value ($ mil.): —

AMERICAN INSTITUTE OF CERTIFIED PUBLIC ACCOUNTANTS

It doesn't get any more exciting than the American Institute of Certified Public Accountants (AICPA). One of the nation's leading nonprofit professional associations AICPA has more than 385000 members from more than 125 countries who are involved in public accounting business education law and government. The group which generates just more than half of its revenue from membership dues promotes awareness of the accounting profession; identifies financial trends; sets certification licensing and professional standards; and provides information and advice to CPAs. AICPA distributes its information through websites conferences and forums and publications. The AICPA was founded in 1887.

Geographic Reach

The American Institute of Certified Public Accountants has offices in New Jersey New York North Carolina and Washington DC.

Financial Performance

The AICPA's 2012 revenue increased 2% vs. 2011 while net income was negative over the same period due to higher operating expenses related to the first year of operations of the institute's CGMA initiative. Higher membership and dues and an increase in professional development and member service conferences contributed to the revenue gain which was partially offset by a decrease in revenue from publications.

Strategy

The institute's Chartered Global Management Accountant (CGMA) designation is designed to reverse a shortage of PhD accounting faculty at US colleges and universities. Other recent initiatives have included private business financial reporting rebuilding investor confidence and implementation of the Sarbanes-Oxley Act.

Also in 2012 the institute launched the CPA Examination internationally in six countries and administered more than 7000 sections in Bahrain Brazil Japan Kuwait Lebanon and the United Arab Emirates.

EXECUTIVES

Senior Vice President Management Accounting, Arleen R. Thomas
President CEO, Barry C. Melancon
Senior Vice President Chief Operating Officer, Anthony J. Pugliese
VP Publishing Professional Education and Product Development, Robert Bouchard
Senior Vice President Public Practice & Global Alliances, Susan S. Coffey
Vice President Professional Standards and Services, Charles E. (Chuck) Landes
Senior Vice President Governmental & Public Affairs, Mark G. Peterson
Senior Vice President Communications Media, Janice M. Maiman
Director Academic and Career Development, Dennis Reigle
VP Practice Mobility and State Regulatory and Legislative Affairs, Sheri Bango
Chief Financial Officer, Scott H. Spiegel
VP Member Service and Operations, Victor Velazquez
Vice President State Societies, Cynthia S. Lund
Vice President Small Firm Interests, James Metzler
VP Office of CEO, Jay Rothberg
VP Business Industry and Government, Carol S. Scott, age 55
senior Manager of media relations, Shirley Twillman
Senior Manager Communications, Melora C. Heavey
Vice President Ethics and Practice Quality, James Brackens
Vice President Information Technology, Hem Nerkar
Chairman, Gregory J. Anton
Vice President Examinations, Craig N. Mills
General Counsel Secretary, Michael Buddendeck

Senior Vice President Strategy People & Innovation, Lawson Carmichael
Technical Manager, Andy Mrakovcic
Technical Manager, Irina Portnoy
Vice President Taxation, Edward Karl
Vice President Academics Professional Pathways & Inclusion, Jeannie Patton
Vice President Professional Publications, Linda Cohen
Vice President Firm Services & Global Alliances, Mark Koziel
Vice President State Regulatory and Legislative Affairs, Mat Young
Vice President Member Service, Peg McIntyre
Vice President Member Learning & Competency, Clar Rosso
Auditors: J.H.CohnLLP

LOCATIONS

HQ: AMERICAN INSTITUTE OF CERTIFIED PUBLIC ACCOUNTANTS
220 LEIGH FARM RD, DURHAM, NC 27707-8110
Phone: 919-402-4500
Web: WWW.TOTALTAXINSIGHTS.ORG

PRODUCTS/OPERATIONS

2012 Revenue

	$ mil.	% of total
Dues	113	51
Professional development & membership service conference	41	19
Professional examinations	25	11
Publications	21	10
Investment & other income	18	8
Contributions	2	1
Total	**223**	**100**

HISTORICAL FINANCIALS

Company Type: Private

Income Statement

FYE: July 31

	REVENUE ($ mil.)	NET INCOME ($ mil.)	NET PROFIT MARGIN	EMPLOYEES
07/09	199	(13)	—	400
07/08	209	9	4.7%	—
Annual Growth	(4.6%)	—	—	—

2009 Year-End Financials

Debt ratio: ——
Return on equity: (-6.80%)
Cash ($ mil.): 34
Current ratio: —
Long-term debt ($ mil.): —
Dividends
Yield: —
Payout: —
Market value ($ mil.): —

AMERICAN INSTITUTES FOR RESEARCH IN THE BEHAVIORAL SCIENCES

The American Institutes for Research (AIR) lives and breathes to enhance human performance. The not-for-profit organization conducts behavioral and social science research on topics related to education and educational assessment health international development and work and training. Clients including several federal agencies use AIR's research in developing policies. As a major ongoing initiative the organization provides tools to improve education both in the US and internationally particularly in disadvantaged areas. John C. Flanagan who developed the Critical Incident Technique personnel-selection tool to identify human success indicators in the workplace founded the organization in 1946.

Geographic Reach

Begun as a small research group affiliated with the University of Pittsburgh AIR's corporate headquarters and business offices are located in Washington DC. The group maintains about a dozen offices in the US. Domestic offices are located in San Mateo and Sacramento California; Atlanta Georgia; Honolulu Hawaii; Chicago and Naperville Illinois; Indianapolis Indiana; Baltimore Frederick and Silver Spring Maryland; Portland Oregon; Columbus Ohio; Chapel Hill North Carolina; New York New York; and Waltham Massachusetts. AIR also operates nearly 10 international offices located in Egypt Honduras Kenya Malawi Liberia Pakistan South Africa Cote d'Ivoire and Zambia.

Operations

AIR has organized its group into seven program areas: Analysis of Longitudinal Data in Education Research Assessment Education Health Human and Social Development Workforce and International Development Education and Research (IDER).

AIR's assessment program focuses on score reports and online reporting tools to translate large-scale testing data on student achievement into a benchmark for school performance. International human and social development programs aim to improve the quality of life and education in developing areas. It works to achieve this through teacher and school administrator training curriculum development and teaching materials coupled with mobilizing health communications HIV/AIDS education and raising awareness about such issues as child labor exploitation. Working with governments private health care providers and the general public AIR's health programs design implement and evaluate the impact of health care policies.

Strategy

The National Center for Education Statistics a key source for statistical data about education and AIR team up to develop large-scale databases for policymaking. Among various efforts AIR designs surveys and assessments develops questionnaires and tests items as well as informational materials. It also helps in producing The Condition of Education the agency's chief report. The organization's successes include campaigns that address public health emergencies such as the flu and H1N1 and the prevention of HIV/AIDS heart disease and birth defects.

Adding to its educational research capabilities AIR has pursued a number of strategic alliances and acquisitions. In 2011 the National Center for Analysis of Longitudinal Data in Educational Research (CALDER) began operating as a joint project of AIR. CALDER examines how public policies and community conditions impact teacher-student results. A year earlier AIR acquired Learning Point Associates a Chicago-based firm that delivers research in the educational sector. Its clients include state education agencies single-school districts private foundations and for-profit organizations.

Financial Performance

Reflecting its growth AIR has posted year-over-year increases in revenue since 2001. More than 95% of the organization's revenues go toward its projects.

EXECUTIVES

SVP and CFO, Marijo L. Ahlgrimm, age 53
General Counsel Ethics Officer and Secretary, Dona Kilpatrick
EVP and Chief Strategy Officer, Michael B. Kane
SVP Human Resources and Administration, Mark S. Fanning
SVP and Deputy Director Education Human Development and the Workforce, Mark Kutner
SVP and Director Health, Marilyn Moon
Executive Vice President Director, Jon Cohen
SVP and Director Federal Statistics, Laura Salganik
Managing Director Education Group, Larry Condelli
VP Human and Social Development, David Osher
VP Education Human Development and the Workforce, Deborah Parrish
Director of SEEP, Jay G. Chambers
Director of CSEF, Thomas (Tom) Parrish
Deputy Director of CSEF/SEEP, Jenifer J. Harr
VP Education Human Development and the Workforce, Michael S. (Mike) Garet
Managing Research Scientist, Jennifer O'Day
Co-Director Communication & Social Marketing Group, Julia Hunter Galdo
Managing Director Health Financing and Cost Containment, Steven A. Garfinkel
Vice President Assessment, Gary Phillips
VP and Director International Development, Jane Benbow
Principal Research Scientist, Nancy Matheson
VP Education Human Development and the Workforce, Dwayne Norris
Director Communications, Larry McQuillan
President CEO and Director, David Myers
Co-Director Communication & Social Marketing Group, Don L. Mullins Jr.
Chairman, Patricia B. Gurin
Vice Chairman, Lawrence D. Bobo
Chairman Chief Executive Officer, Greg Baroni
President Syracuse University, Nancy E. Cantor
VP Education Human Development and the Workforce, Mark S. Schneider
Executive Vice President Director, Gina Burkhardt
VP and Executive Director, Steve Kromer
Vice President Research and Evaluation, Hans Bos
VP Education Human Development and the Workforce, Sabrina Laine
SVP and Director Human and Social Development, Cheryl Vince Whitman
Executive Director Communications and Public Affairs, Patrick R. Riccards
VP Information Technology, Robert Holstein
President United Tribes Technical College, David Gipp
Chief Executive Officer, Cathy Provine
Director, Edward L. Hamburg, age 63
Director, Delano E. Lewis, age 75
Director, Sol H. Pelavin
President CEO and Director, David Myers
Vice Chairman, Lawrence D. Bobo
Director, Greg Baroni
Director, Robert F. Boruch
Director, Nancy E. Cantor
Director, Sara Kiesler
Director, Kathy McKinless
Director, Richard A. Smith
Director, Andrew Liakopoulos

LOCATIONS

HQ: AMERICAN INSTITUTES FOR RESEARCH IN THE BEHAVIORAL SCIENCES
1000 THMAS JFFERSON ST NW, WASHINGTON, DC 20007-3835
Phone: 202-403-5000
Web: WWW.AIR.ORG

PRODUCTS/OPERATIONS

Selected Program Areas

Education
Education assessment
Health
Human development
International development
Work & training

HISTORICAL FINANCIALS

Company Type: Private

Income Statement FYE: December 31

	REVENUE ($ mil.)	NET INCOME ($ mil.)	NET PROFIT MARGIN	EMPLOYEES
12/12	326	22	6.9%	1,175
12/11	300	13	4.3%	—
12/09	285	21	7.5%	—
12/09	299	18	6.0%	—
Annual Growth	3.0%	7.6%	—	—

2012 Year-End Financials

Debt ratio: —
Return on equity: 6.90%
Cash ($ mil.): 20
Current ratio: 1.20
Long-term debt ($ mil.): —
Dividends
Yield: —
Payout: —
Market value ($ mil.): —

AMERICAN INTERNET MORTGAGE INC.

LOCATIONS

HQ: AMERICAN INTERNET MORTGAGE INC.
4121 CAMINO DEL RIO S, SAN DIEGO, CA 921084103
Phone: 6196109900
Web: WWW.AIMLOAN.COM

HISTORICAL FINANCIALS

Company Type: Private

Income Statement FYE: December 31

	ASSETS ($ mil.)	NET INCOME ($ mil.)	INCOME AS % OF ASSETS	EMPLOYEES
12/12	228	38	16.9%	106
12/11	131	11	8.8%	—
12/10	132	26	20.2%	—
Annual Growth	31.0%	19.9%	—	—

2012 Year-End Financials

Debt ratio: —
Return on equity: 60.70%
Cash ($ mil.): 12
Current ratio: 0.10
Long-term debt ($ mil.): —
Dividends
Yield: —
Payout: —
Market value ($ mil.): —

AMERICAN LEBANESE SYRIAN ASSOCIATED CHARITIES INC.

LOCATIONS

HQ: AMERICAN LEBANESE SYRIAN ASSOCIATED CHARITIES INC.
501 SAINT JUDE PL, MEMPHIS, TN 381051905
Phone: 9015782150
Web: WWW.STJUDE.ORG

HISTORICAL FINANCIALS

Company Type: Private

Income Statement FYE: June 30

	REVENUE ($ mil.)	NET INCOME ($ mil.)	NET PROFIT MARGIN	EMPLOYEES
06/13	976	210	21.5%	1,200
06/12	780	72	9.3%	—
06/11	1,066	444	41.7%	—
06/10	869	0	—	—
Annual Growth	3.9%	—	—	—

2013 Year-End Financials

Debt ratio: —
Return on equity: 21.50%
Cash ($ mil.): 35
Current ratio: —
Long-term debt ($ mil.): —
Dividends
Yield: —
Payout: —
Market value ($ mil.): —

AMERICAN MEDICAL ASSOCIATION INC

LOCATIONS

HQ: AMERICAN MEDICAL ASSOCIATION INC
330 N WABASH AVE # 39300, CHICAGO, IL 606113586
Phone: 3124645000
Web: WWW.AMA-ASSN.ORG

PRODUCTS/OPERATIONS

2012 Sales

	$ mil.	% of total
Royalties &credentialing products	83	30
Books newsletters &online products	39	14
Membership dues	38	14
Insurance commissions	36	13
Advertising	19	7
Periodical online	17	6
Grants & other	10	4
Investment income	9	4
Periodical printsubscriptions	9	4
Other publishing	9	3
Other	0	1
Total	**273**	**100**

HISTORICAL FINANCIALS

Company Type: Private

Income Statement FYE: December 31

	REVENUE ($ mil.)	NET INCOME ($ mil.)	NET PROFIT MARGIN	EMPLOYEES
12/13	258	(6)	—	1,150
12/08*	3	(0)	—	—
06/06	1	(0)	—	—
12/05	0	0	—	—
Annual Growth	—	—	—	—

*Fiscal year change

2013 Year-End Financials

Debt ratio: —
Return on equity: (-2.70%)
Cash ($ mil.): 7
Current ratio: 0.30
Long-term debt ($ mil.): —
Dividends
Yield: —
Payout: —
Market value ($ mil.): —

AMERICAN PETROLEUM INSTITUTE INC

The American Petroleum Institute (API) is a trade association for the oil and natural gas industry. The group represents more than 580 corporate members including giants such as BP and Exxon Mobil as well as small independent companies with offices in more than 20 state capitals and overseas. Besides serving as an advocate in legislative regulatory and media arenas the API compiles data on industry operations. The organization's members come from several segments of the petroleum industry including upstream (exploration and production) downstream (refining and marketing) pipeline operations marine transportation and oil field service. The API was founded in 1919.

Geographic Reach

While the organization's focus in primarily domestic Washington D.C.-based API has offices in Beijing Singapore Dubai and now Brazil (Rio de Janeiro) as well as an office in Houston.

Operations

Recent hot issues for the API and its members include the Keystone XL Pipeline and hydraulic fracturing (aka fracking).

EXECUTIVES

Treasurer, Clarence P. Cazalot Jr., age 63
Chief Economist, John Felmy
Chairman, J. Larry Nichols
President CEO of the American Petroleum Institute, Jack N. Gerard
EVP Government Affairs, Marty Durbin
Group Director Upstream and Industry Operations, Erik Milito
Director Human Resources, Elizabeth Perry
News Media Contact, Cathy Landry
Vice President General Counsel, Harry Ng
Vice President Chief Financial Officer, John Robertson
Vice President Regulatory and Economic Policy, Kyle Isakower

LOCATIONS

HQ: AMERICAN PETROLEUM INSTITUTE INC
1220 L ST NW STE 900, WASHINGTON, DC 20005-4070
Phone: 202-682-8000
Web: WWW.RECYCLEOIL.ORG

HISTORICAL FINANCIALS

Company Type: Private

Income Statement FYE: December 31

	REVENUE ($ mil.)	NET INCOME ($ mil.)	NET PROFIT MARGIN	EMPLOYEES
12/09	197	19	9.6%	250
12/08	204	(10)	—	—
12/07	1,529	0	0.0%	—
Annual Growth	(64.1%)	31194.4%	—	—

2009 Year-End Financials

Debt ratio: —
Return on equity: 9.60%
Cash ($ mil.): 42
Current ratio: 0.80
Long-term debt ($ mil.): —
Dividends
Yield: —
Payout: —
Market value ($ mil.): —

AMERICAN PLANT FOOD CORPORATION

LOCATIONS

HQ: AMERICAN PLANT FOOD CORPORATION
903 MAYO SHELL RD, GALENA PARK, TX 775473291
Phone: 7136752231
Web: WWW.APFCORP.NET

HISTORICAL FINANCIALS

Company Type: Private

Income Statement FYE: October 31

	REVENUE ($ mil.)	NET INCOME ($ mil.)	NET PROFIT MARGIN	EMPLOYEES
10/14	224	9	4.1%	110
10/13	230	11	5.0%	—
10/12	247	15	6.3%	—
10/11	225	0	—	—
Annual Growth	(0.2%)	—	—	—

2014 Year-End Financials

Debt ratio: —
Return on equity: 4.10%
Cash ($ mil.): 12
Current ratio: 1.10
Long-term debt ($ mil.): —

Dividends
Yield: —
Payout: —
Market value ($ mil.): —

AMERICAN SYSTEMS CORPORATION

American Systems provides government and commercial clients with IT management and consulting services including custom engineering and application development. Its consulting division advises clients on such issues as network access and identity management data security and process optimization. The company also provides managed technical support and staffing. American Systems works with government customers to develop systems related to command and control logistics and national security functions. Its commercial-focused operations serve the energy financial services retail and telecom industries among others.

Geographic Reach

The company has 16 offices along the Eastern Seaboard and in Arizona and California.

Operations

American Systems' government unit serves every branch of the US military as well as government agencies ranging from the Federal Aviation Administration to the Department of Agriculture. Its commercial unit on the other hand has served such companies as AT&T The Coca-Cola Company and The Home Depot.

Mergers and Acquisitions

In 2012 company completed the acquisition of Science Applications International Corporation's (SAIC's) Test & Evaluation (T&E) business unit. The acquisition strengthened American Systems' T&E capabilities and expanded the company's offerings to include testing scientific engineering logistic administrative and ancillary support.

Company Background

The employee-owned company was established in 1975 as American Communications Corporation.

EXECUTIVES

EVP and COO, Peter Smith
President and CEO, William C. Hoover
EVP and CFO, Mark Danisewicz
CIO and CTO, Brian Neely
EVP Contracts and Administration, Joe Kopfman
Chairman, Donald R. Burklew
Auditors: Deloitte&ToucheLLP

LOCATIONS

HQ: AMERICAN SYSTEMS CORPORATION
14151 PK MADOW DR STE 500, CHANTILLY, VA 20151
Phone: 703-968-6300
Web: WWW.AMERICANSYSTEMS.COM

PRODUCTS/OPERATIONS

Selected Mergers and Acquisitions

FY2012
Science Applications International Corporation' s (SAIC' s) Test & Evaluation (T&E) business unit (undisclosed price; Raleigh NC; testing and evaluation services)

COMPETITORS

Affiliated Computer Services
Alion
Allen Corporation of America
Booz Allen
CACI International
Computer Sciences Corp.
General Dynamics Information Technology
HP Enterprise Services
IBM Global Services
Jacobs Engineering
Kratos Defense & Security Solutions
Lockheed Martin Information Systems
ManTech
Northrop Grumman Info Systems
Raytheon IIS
SAIC
SRA International
Unisys
Ventera

HISTORICAL FINANCIALS

Company Type: Private

Income Statement FYE: December 31

	REVENUE ($ mil.)	NET INCOME ($ mil.)	NET PROFIT MARGIN	EMPLOYEES
12/12	242	10	4.3%	1,150
12/11	250	16	6.7%	—
12/09	273	10	3.7%	—
12/09	230	6	3.0%	—
Annual Growth	1.6%	15.4%	—	—

2012 Year-End Financials

Debt ratio: —
Return on equity: 4.30%
Cash ($ mil.): 0
Current ratio: 1.50
Long-term debt ($ mil.): —

Dividends
Yield: —
Payout: —
Market value ($ mil.): —

AMERICAN TRANSMISSION COMPANY LLC

American Transmission Company is an entrepreneur in the US power grid business –a for-profit multi-state transmission-only utility. Connecting electricity producers to distributors American Transmission owns operates monitors and maintains 9440 miles of high-voltage electric transmission lines and 525 substations in portions of Illinois Michigan Minnesota and Wisconsin. The company a member of the Midwest Independent Transmission System Operator regional transmission organization operates the former transmission assets of some of its shareholders. About 30 utilities municipalities electric companies and cooperatives in its service area have an ownership stake in American Transmission.

Geographic Reach

American Transmission meets the power needs of about 5 million people in 72 counties in Illinois Michigan Minnesota and Wisconsin. It operates North central Wisconsin Michigan's Upper Peninsula and Northern Wisconsin South Central/Southwest Wisconsin and North Central Illinois Northeast Wisconsin and Southeast Wisconsin.

Operations

Unlike most other power utilities American Transmission is not engaged in the generation distribution or marketing of electricity. Its duties include reliable operation of the transmission system growing the system to meet current and future needs and upgrading and maintain the transmission equipment as needed.

Strategy

The company is trying to use its single focus on power transmission to win more customers. American Transmission has invested more than $2.2 billion on infrastructure upgrades (since 2001) including 1750 miles of power line. It has also built more 560 miles of new lines during this time period. By 2021 the company plans to spend a further $3.9-$4.8 billion on infrastructure improvement with a focus on adding new renewable sources to its expanded grid.

In 2012 it teamed up with ALLETE to study transmission options for transporting Midwestern wind energy as well as Canadian hydroelectric power into Minnesota Wisconsin and Michigan to help local utilities enhance reliability and meet renewable energy goals. To further enable movement of renewable energy that year the company and Minnesota Power agreed to develop a 50-mile double-circuit 345-kilovolt transmission line from the Mesabi Iron Range to the companies' jointly owned Arrowhead Substation in Duluth. The project is due to come into service in 2020.In 2011 it announced a plan to build seven new transmission line projects (1800 miles of new line) aimed at filling gaps in the existing transmission grid improving grid reliability and enabling increased delivery of renewable power in Iowa Wisconsin Illinois Indiana and Ohio. The projects in total will cost about $4 billion. It also agreed to purchase of the Zephyr Power Transmission Project (950 miles of transmission line between Wyoming and southern Nevada) in another $4 billion deal.

Boosting its transmission assets in 2011 American Transmission formed a transmission utility joint venture with Duke Energy. Duke-American Transmission Co. builds owns and operates new power transmission infrastructure across North America.

Ownership

The company is 88% owned by investor-owned utilities and 12% owned by municipalities municipal electric companies and electric cooperatives.

Company Background

American Transmission is one of the first forprofit transmission companies formed (in 2001) when the US market deregulated in the early 2000s.

In 2010 it signed two agreements with the Department of Energy to access $12.7 million in investment grants for incorporating smart grid technologies into its transmission system.

EXECUTIVES

Chairman President and CEO, John C. Procario
EVP and COO, Michael (Mike) Rowe
EVP Strategic Planning and Project Development, Randy Satterfield
EVP CFO and Treasurer, Michael (Mike) Hofbauer
VP System Planning, Ronald Snead
VP Compliance and Risk Management, Juanita Banks
EVP General Counsel and Corporate Secretary, Bill Marsan
Vice President Business Development, John Flynn
Vice President Human Capital, Lori Lorenz
Vice President Operations, Adam Manty
Executive Vice President General, William Marsan
Vice President, Dale Landgren
Chairman President and CEO, John C. Procario

LOCATIONS

HQ: AMERICAN TRANSMISSION COMPANY LLC
W234N2000 RDGVIEW PKY CT, WAUKESHA, WI 53188-1022
Phone: 262-506-6700
Web: WWW.ATCLLC.COM

PRODUCTS/OPERATIONS

Contributing Owners
Adams-Columbia Electric Cooperativ
Alger Delta Cooperative Electric Associatio
Badger Power Marketing Authority
Central Wisconsin Electric Cooperativ
City of Algoma
City of Columbus
City of Kaukauna
City of Menasha
City of Oconto Falls
City of Plymouth
City of Reedsburg
City of Sheboygan Falls
City of Sturgeon Bay
City of Sun Prairie
City of Wisconsin Rapids
Cloverland Electric Cooperativ
Edison Sault Electric Company
Madison Gas & Electric Company
Manitowoc Public Utilities
Marshfield Electric and Water Department
Ontonagon County Rural Electrification Associatio
Rainy River Energy
Rock Energy Cooperativ
Stoughton Utilities
Upper Peninsula Public Power Agency
Wisconsin Electric Power Company
Wisconsin Power & Light Company
Wisconsin Public Service Corporatio
WPPI Energy

COMPETITORS

AES
Ameren
Duke Energy
Exelon
FirstEnergy

HISTORICAL FINANCIALS

Company Type: Private

Income Statement FYE: December 31

	REVENUE ($ mil.)	NET INCOME ($ mil.)	NET PROFIT MARGIN	EMPLOYEES
12/12	603	237	39.4%	547
12/11	567	223	39.5%	—
12/10	556	219	39.5%	—
12/09	521	213	40.9%	—
Annual Growth	5.0%	3.6%	—	—

2012 Year-End Financials

Debt ratio: —
Return on equity: 39.40%
Cash ($ mil.): 0
Current ratio: 0.20
Long-term debt ($ mil.): —
Dividends
Yield: —
Payout: —
Market value ($ mil.): —

AMERICAN UNIVERSITY

Fulfilling the vision of George Washington for a national university in the country's capital American University was chartered by an Act of Congress in 1893 as a private independent co-educational institution under the auspices of the United Methodist Church. Today the school offers a broad range of undergraduate and graduate degree programs to more than 12000 students from 140 countries. Its student-teacher ratio is 12:1. American University has schools devoted to arts and sciences business communications international service public affairs and law. It is one of the top producers of Peace Corps volunteers serving overseas. Nine US presidents have served on American University's Board of Trustees.

Operations

American University is known for what else political activism (it has been named most politically active university in the nation by Princeton Review). But you don't have to be pursuing a degree in political science to attend American University; the school offers about 60 undergraduate degrees 50 master's and 10 doctoral degrees.

The school's research centers and institutes include projects focused on chemistry social sciences art design and business behavior. Its academic centers explore research areas that range from social media to war crimes and global peace.

Financial Performance

American University recognized total revenue growth of 4% in 2012 due to increases in revenue from net tuition and fees and federal grants and contracts. About 48% of net tuition and fees revenue in 2012 was funded by federal student financial aid programs (including loan grant and work-study programs). However the bad news for American University was that it suffered a net loss of $7.8 million due to higher operating expenses and a decrease in net capital gains.

Strategy

In 2010 American University ended a seven year fund-raising campaign that raised $211 million to support a number of campus initiatives. The money will be used to strengthen the school's academic programs develop new facilities and help secure American University's financial future.

The school has begun a $34 million construction plan on its North Hall located on the northwest corner of its main campus. The construction is scheduled for competition in the summer of 2013 and will provide 360 beds with shared living rooms for upperclassmen plus an 8000-sq. ft. fitness center. A three-story addition to Nebraska Hall also scheduled to be finished in the summer of 2013 will add 150 new beds in apartment-style units.

HISTORY

In 2005 the president of American University Benjamin Ladner was placed on administrative leave while the university investigated his "personal and travel expenses". He was subsequently dismissed from the university. The US Senate Finance Committee later found that the university's board of trustees had ignored damaging audit findings on Ladner's alleged lavish spending disregarded possible IRS sanctions and proposed retribution against a whistle-blower. Long-time administrator and alumnus Cornelius Kerwin filled the position of president in 2007.

EXECUTIVES

VP Finance and Treasurer, Donald L. (Don) Myers
President, Cornelius M. (Neil) Kerwin
VP Campus Life, Gail Short Hanson
CIO, David G. Swartz
Provost, Scott A. Bass
Executive Director University Communications and Marketing, Teresa (Terry) Flannery
Chief of Staff, David E. Taylor
Chairman, Jeffrey A. Sine
Vice Chairman, Patrick Butler
President CEO, Bob Lynch
President Strathmore, Monica Hazangeles
Auditors: PricewaterhouseCoopersLLP

LOCATIONS

HQ: AMERICAN UNIVERSITY
4400 MASSACHUSETTS AVE NW, WASHINGTON, DC 20016-8200
Phone: 202-885-1000
Web: WWW.AMERICAN.EDU

PRODUCTS/OPERATIONS

Selected Schools and Colleges

College of Arts and Sciences (CAS)
Kogod School of Business (Kogod)
School of Communication (SOC)
School of International Service (SIS)
School of Professional and Extended Studies (SPExS)
School of Public Affairs (SPA)
Washington College of Law (WCL)

HISTORICAL FINANCIALS

Company Type: Private

Income Statement FYE: April 30

	REVENUE ($ mil.)	NET INCOME ($ mil.)	NET PROFIT MARGIN	EMPLOYEES
04/13	507	90	17.9%	2,000
04/12	605	55	9.1%	—
04/09	54	(108)	—	—
04/08	398	23	6.0%	—
Annual Growth	5.0%	30.6%	—	—

2013 Year-End Financials

Debt ratio: —
Return on equity: 17.90%
Cash ($ mil.): 57
Current ratio: —
Long-term debt ($ mil.): —
Dividends
Yield: —
Payout: —
Market value ($ mil.): —

AMERICARES FOUNDATION INC.

AmeriCares Foundation provides emergency medical aid around the world. The not-for-profit charitable organization helps victims of natural disasters and supports long-term humanitarian programs by collecting medical supplies in the US and overseas and delivering them to places where they are needed. AmeriCares has provided aid in more than 135 countries worldwide. In the US the organization offers medical assistance runs a camp for kids with HIV/AIDS and conducts HomeFront a program that renovates housing for the needy in parts of Connecticut and New York. Robert C. Macauley founded AmeriCares in 1982.

In 2007 more than 98% of AmeriCare's expenses were allocated toward program services. About 1% was spent on fundraising with the balance of its funding going toward management and general expenses.

EXECUTIVES

President and CEO, Curtis R. (Curt) Welling, age 64
SVP Communications & Marketing, Carol Shattuck

SVP Development and Communications, Carolyn O'Brien
SVP Global Program Operations, Chrisoph Gorder
Director Corporate Relations, Geoff Kneisel
Director Logistics, Peter Tokarczyk
SVP Human Resources, Kevin R. Gilrain
Medical Director, Frank Bia
VP; Managing Director AmeriCares India, Purvish M. Parikh
Director Communications, Peggy Atherlay
SVP Finance and Technology, Katherine A. Sears

LOCATIONS

HQ: AMERICARES FOUNDATION INC.
88 HAMILTON AVE, STAMFORD, CT 06902-3100
Phone: 203-658-9500
Web: WWW.AMERICARESFREECLINICS.ORG

HISTORICAL FINANCIALS

Company Type: Private

Income Statement FYE: June 30

	REVENUE ($ mil.)	NET INCOME ($ mil.)	NET PROFIT MARGIN	EMPLOYEES
06/12	526	5	1.1%	125
06/11	671	(0)	—	—
06/10	795	(59)	—	—
06/09	1,197	35	3.0%	—
Annual Growth	(24.0%)	(44.8%)	—	—

2012 Year-End Financials

Debt ratio: —
Return on equity: 1.10%
Cash ($ mil.): 5
Current ratio: 0.60
Long-term debt ($ mil.): —
Dividends
Yield: —
Payout: —
Market value ($ mil.): —

AMERIGREEN ENERGY INC.

LOCATIONS

HQ: AMERIGREEN ENERGY INC.
1862 CHARTER LN STE 101, LANCASTER, PA 176016764
Phone: 7176651402
Web: WWW.AMERIGREEN.COM

HISTORICAL FINANCIALS

Company Type: Private

Income Statement FYE: September 30

	REVENUE ($ mil.)	NET INCOME ($ mil.)	NET PROFIT MARGIN	EMPLOYEES
09/14	257	0	0.0%	22
09/13	181	1	0.7%	—
09/12	93	0	0.0%	—
09/11	95	0	—	—
Annual Growth	39.1%	—	—	—

2014 Year-End Financials

Debt ratio: —
Return on equity: —
Cash ($ mil.): 0
Current ratio: 0.60
Long-term debt ($ mil.): —
Dividends
Yield: —
Payout: —
Market value ($ mil.): —

AMES CONSTRUCTION INC.

Ames Construction aims right for the heart of heavy construction. The company is a general contractor providing heavy civil and industrial construction services to the transportation mining and power industries mainly in the West and Midwest. The family-owned company works on highways airports bridges rail lines mining facilities power plants and other infrastructure projects. Ames also performs flood control environmental remediation reclamation and landfill work. Additionally the firm builds golf courses and undertakes commercial and residential site development projects. Ames typically partners with other companies to perform the engineering and design portion of construction jobs.

Geographic Reach

Ames Construction has offices in Minneapolis Denver Phoenix Salt Lake City and Corona California.

Strategy

Ames Construction is also known to take on subcontracting work. It contributed to the construction of the new Minnesota Twins ballpark. Ames also is serving as subcontractor and partner in a joint venture with Fluor and Balfour Beatty Rail that is undertaking the $1 billion design/build portion of a rail line project for the Denver Regional Transit District. The contract involves designing and constructing electrified commuter rail lines stations and a vehicle maintenance facility. The joint venture will also operate and maintain the system for a period of 40 years. All lines are expected to be in service by 2016.

Ownership

Ames Construction is family owned.

LOCATIONS

HQ: AMES CONSTRUCTION INC.
14420 COUNTY ROAD 5, BURNSVILLE, MN 55306-6997
Phone: 952-435-7106
Web: WWW.AMESCONSTRUCTION.COM

PRODUCTS/OPERATIONS

Selected Markets

Commercial
- Commercial site development
- Environmental remediation/ landfills
- Residential site development

Mining
- Contract mining
- Leach pad construction
- Mine development
- Mine infrastructure
- Mine reclamation/remediation
- Mine tailings dam

Power
- Coal fired
- Combined-cycle/natural gas
- Nuclear
- Transmission
- Wind

Transportation
- Airports
- Bridges
- Highways
- Railroads

Water resources
- Dams reservoirs and flood control
- Wastewater/water treatment
- Water delivery
- Water retention structures

COMPETITORS

American Civil Constructors Holdings
Balfour Construction
Clyde Companies
Granite Construction
Meadow Valley
Peter Kiewit Sons'
SEMA Construction
Skanska USA Civil
Sterling Construction
Tutor-Saliba

HISTORICAL FINANCIALS

Company Type: Private

Income Statement FYE: December 31

	REVENUE ($ mil.)	NET INCOME ($ mil.)	NET PROFIT MARGIN	EMPLOYEES
12/12*	582	5	1.0%	2,200
11/10	685	18	2.7%	—
11/08	707	53	7.5%	—
11/08	1,835	0	—	—
Annual Growth	—	1369.7%	—	—

*Fiscal year change

2012 Year-End Financials

Debt ratio: —
Return on equity: 1.00%
Cash ($ mil.): 9
Current ratio: 0.80
Long-term debt ($ mil.): —
Dividends
Yield: —
Payout: —
Market value ($ mil.): —

AMG NATIONAL TRUST BANK

LOCATIONS

HQ: AMG NATIONAL TRUST BANK
1155 CANYON BLVD STE 310, BOULDER, CO 803025195
Phone: 3034478877
Web: WWW.AMGNATIONAL.COM

HISTORICAL FINANCIALS

Company Type: Private

Income Statement FYE: December 31

	ASSETS ($ mil.)	NET INCOME ($ mil.)	INCOME AS % OF ASSETS	EMPLOYEES
12/13	273	4	1.5%	14
12/09	214	0	0.4%	—
Annual Growth	6.2%	50.9%	—	—

2013 Year-End Financials

Debt ratio: —
Return on equity: 14.50%
Cash ($ mil.): 23
Current ratio: —
Long-term debt ($ mil.): —
Dividends
Yield: —
Payout: —
Market value ($ mil.): —

ANDERSEN CONSTRUCTION COMPANY

Andersen Construction Company focuses on commercial and industrial construction projects in the Western US. The group which introduced concrete tilt-up construction to the Pacific Northwest builds everything from parking structures to medical facilities manufacturing plants and industrial complexes. It also works on institutional projects for the government and education markets. Other projects include tenant improvements seismic upgrades and remediation construction. The company provides construction management and general contracting and design/build delivery. It also offers startup and commissioning services. Chairman Andy Andersen founded the company in 1950.

EXECUTIVES

Vp It, Bob Durgan
Vice President, Richard Nicoll

LOCATIONS

HQ: ANDERSEN CONSTRUCTION COMPANY
6712 N CUTTER CIR, PORTLAND, OR 97217-3933
Phone: 503-283-6712
Web: WWW.ANDERSEN-CONST.COM

Andersen Construction operates from offices in Oregon and Idaho.

COMPETITORS

Absher
GLY Construction
Hoffman Corporation
Howard S. Wright Construction
M. A. Mortenson
PCL Construction Enterprises
Skanska USA Building
Swinerton Builders
Turner Corporation

HISTORICAL FINANCIALS

Company Type: Private

Income Statement FYE: January 31

	REVENUE ($ mil.)	NET INCOME ($ mil.)	NET PROFIT MARGIN	EMPLOYEES
01/12	284	0	0.1%	150
01/11	278	1	0.4%	—
01/06	198	0	0.5%	—
01/05	188	1	0.6%	—
Annual Growth	6.1%	(21.4%)	—	—

2012 Year-End Financials

Debt ratio: —
Return on equity: 0.10%
Cash ($ mil.): 20
Current ratio: 0.40
Long-term debt ($ mil.): —
Dividends
Yield: —
Payout: —
Market value ($ mil.): —

ANDERSON AND DUBOSE INC.

You might say this company keeps the Big Mac big and the Happy Meals happy. Anderson-DuBose Pittsburgh is a leading wholesale distributor that supplies food and non-food items to McDonald's and Chipotle fast-food restaurants in Ohio Pennsylvania New York and West Virginia. It serves about 500 Golden Arches locations with frozen meat and fish dairy products and paper goods and packaging as well as toys for Happy Meals. One of the largest black-owned companies in the US Anderson-DuBose was started in 1991 by Warren Anderson and Stephen DuBose who purchased control of a McDonald's distributorship from Martin-Brower. Anderson became sole owner in 1993 when he bought out his partner's stake in the business.

LOCATIONS

HQ: ANDERSON AND DUBOSE INC.
5300 TOD AVE SW, WARREN, OH 44481-9767
Phone: 440-248-8800
Web: WWW.ANDERSON-DUBOSE.COM

COMPETITORS

Golden State Foods
Gordon Food Service
Keystone Foods
MAINES
Martin-Brower
Meadowbrook Meat Company
Performance Food
Reinhart FoodService
Sysco
US Foods

HISTORICAL FINANCIALS

Company Type: Private

Income Statement FYE: December 28

	REVENUE ($ mil.)	NET INCOME ($ mil.)	NET PROFIT MARGIN	EMPLOYEES
12/12	394	1	0.4%	100
12/11	372	1	0.3%	—
12/10	341	1	0.5%	—
12/09	329	1	0.5%	—
Annual Growth	6.2%	(3.2%)	—	—

2012 Year-End Financials

Debt ratio: —
Return on equity: 0.40%
Cash ($ mil.): 5
Current ratio: 0.40
Long-term debt ($ mil.): —
Dividends
Yield: —
Payout: —
Market value ($ mil.): —

ANN & ROBERT H. LURIE CHILDREN'S HOSPITAL OF CHICAGO

When it comes to caring for kids Ann & Robert H. Lurie Children's Hospital of Chicago has the Windy City covered. Founded in 1882 the hospital provides a full range of pediatric services with acute and specialty care. Children's Hospital of Chicago provides services through its main hospital campus with about 300 beds and outpatient centers in Chicago's Lincoln Park neighborhood and through more than a dozen suburban outpatient centers and outreach partner locations in the greater Chicago area. A leader in pediatric research the hospital operates the Children's Hospital of Chicago Research Center and is the pediatric teaching facility of Northwestern University's Feinberg School of Medicine.

Geographic Reach

Based in Chicago Lurie Children's has cared for patients from throughout the US and about 35 countries around the globe.

Operations

Lurie Children's serves roughly 150000 patients each year and employs some 1250 pediatric specialists with expertise in 70 different specialties. The hospital is one of only about a dozen children's hospitals nationwide to perform more than 1000 liver transplants. The center performs on average 50 solid organ and 50 stem cell transplants annually.

A major research center Lurie Children's is one of nearly 30 interdisciplinary research centers and institutes belonging to the hospital's academic partner —Feinberg School of Medicine. The research center employs some 200 physician-scientists and research investigators who in 2010 were awarded about $40 million in extramural funding.

Strategy

In 2012 the hospital moved to the campus of the Feinberg School of Medicine in downtown Chicago. The move enhances opportunities for clinical research and academic engagement with its teaching partner. The hospital has all-private rooms even in the neonatal intensive care unit; private rooms are said to speed healing by reducing hospital-acquired infection and minimize noise. Due to Ann Lurie's $100 million donation towards the new hospital's construction the hospital changed its name from Children's Memorial Hospital to Ann and Robert H. Lurie Children's Hospital of Chicago that year.

The hospital is also working to enhance its specialist services and upgraded its information technology systems. In 2013 Lurie Children's implemented a Voalte system that allows nurses to communicate through rapid-response systems including text messages and high-definition voice calls. Also that year it opened the first pediatric gender identity clinic.

Financial Performance

Lurie Children's Hospital of Chicago saw revenues increase by 9% in 2012 following a 2% rise in 2011. The hospital points to growth in surgeries and outpatient visits as well as an improved patient mix and increased patient acuity. Net income dropped 46% on higher operating expenses (related to salaries benefits services supplies interest expense and other items) following a decline of 7% in 2011.

EXECUTIVES

President and CEO, Patrick M. Magoon
Chief Human Resource Officer, Robert Powell
Chief Marketing and Managed Care Officer, Maureen Murphy
CFO, Paula Noble
Communications and Media Strategist, Kathleen Keenan
President Children's Memorial Foundation, Thomas J. Sullivan
Head Division Hematology Oncology and Stem Cell Transplant, Morris Kletzel
Head Kidney Diseases (Nephrology), Craig B. Langman
Division Head Neurology, Leon G. Epstein
Head Division Rheumatology, Marisa S. Klein-Gitelman

LOCATIONS

HQ: ANN & ROBERT H. LURIE CHILDREN' S HOSPITAL OF CHICAGO
225 E CHICAGO AVE, CHICAGO, IL 60611-2991
Phone: 312-227-4000
Web: WWW.LURIECHILDRENS.ORG

Selected Illinois Locations

Lurie Children' s at Cadence Health (Winfield)
Main Hospital (Chicago)
Outpatient Center in Arlington Heights (Arlington Heights)
Outpatient Center in Glenview (Glenview)
Outpatient Center in Lake Forest (Lake Forest)
Outpatient Center in Lincoln Park (Chicago)

Outpatient Center in New Lenox (New Lenox)
Outpatient Center in Westchester (Westchester)
Outpatient Services in Grayslake (Grayslake)
Outpatient Services in Gurnee (Gurnee)
Outpatient Services in Lincoln Square (Chicago)
Pediatrics Uptown (Chicago)
Rehabilitation Services at Westbrook (Westchester)

PRODUCTS/OPERATIONS

Selected Services

Adolescent Medicine
Allergy and Immunology
Anesthesiology
Audiology
Autonomic Medicine
Brain Tumor
Cancer and Blood Disorders
Cardiology (Heart Center)
Child Abuse Pediatrics
Child and Adolescent Psychiatry
Clinical Nutrition
Convenient Care
Critical Care
Cystic Fibrosis
Dentistry and Oral Surgery
Dermatology
Emergency Medicine
Endocrinology
Epilepsy
Fetal Health
Gastroenterology Hepatology and Nutrition (Digestive Disorders)
Gender and Sex Development
General Pediatric Surgery
General Pediatrics
Genetics Birth Defects and Metabolism
Heart Failure and Transplants
HIV/AIDS Prevention
Infectious Diseases
Intestinal Transplants
Kidney Diseases
Kidney Transplants
Liver Transplants
Medical Imaging (Radiology)
Neonatology
Neurology
Neurosurgery
Occupational Therapy
Ophthalmology
Orthopaedic Surgery
Orthotics/Prosthetics
Otolaryngology (ENT)
Palliative Care
Pathology and Laboratory Medicine
Physical Therapy
Plastic and Reconstructive Surgery
Pulmonary Medicine
Rehabilitative Services
Rheumatology
Speech-Language Pathology
Spina Bifida Center
Sports Medicine
Stem Cell Transplants
Transitioning to Adult Care
Transplantation
Urology

COMPETITORS

Advocate Health Care
Advocate Lutheran General Hospital
Alexian Brothers Health System
Covenant Ministries
HCA
Loyola University Health System
Mercy Hospital and Medical Center
NorthShore University HealthSystem
Northwestern Lake Forest Hospital
Northwestern Memorial HealthCare
Provena Health
Rush System for Health
SSM Health Care
Sinai Health System
University of Chicago Medical Center

HISTORICAL FINANCIALS

Company Type: Private

Income Statement FYE: August 31

	REVENUE ($ mil.)	NET INCOME ($ mil.)	NET PROFIT MARGIN	EMPLOYEES
08/10	599	52	8.8%	2,800
08/09	533	(5)	—	—
08/08	410	(17)	—	—
08/05	403	43	10.9%	—
Annual Growth	8.3%	3.8%	—	—

2010 Year-End Financials

Debt ratio: —
Return on equity: 8.80%
Cash ($ mil.): 356
Current ratio: 0.60
Long-term debt ($ mil.): —
Dividends
Yield: —
Payout: —
Market value ($ mil.): —

ANNE ARUNDEL MEDICAL CENTER INC.

The ill and infirm get the royal treatment at Anne Arundel Medical Center. The full-service acute-care hospital serves the residents of Anne Arundel Calvert Prince George's and Queen Anne counties in Maryland. With about 380 beds the hospital administers care for women's health oncology pediatrics neurology orthopedics and cardiovascular care. The medical center also has weight loss sleep disorder and rehabilitation centers. Anne Arundel which opened its doors in 1902 and is part of the Anne Arundel Health System has expanded its service offerings through various affiliations with regional specialty and primary care clinics. It also has a partnership with Johns Hopkins Medicine.

Operations

With more than 900 staff members Anne Arundel handles some 28000 inpatient visits per year. It also manages more than 5000 births and 91000 emergency room visits.

Johns Hopkins and the not-for-profit Anne Arundel share some services faculty and patients through their collaboration. They also operate a joint outpatient urgent-care facility. Additionally the two organizations work together to perform clinical research projects and conduct physician graduate medical education programs. The companies first formed their alliance in 2007 with the goal of strengthening health care services in the region; the organizations renewed their strategic agreement in 2012.

Financial Performance

In 2012 Anne Arundel reported operating revenues of about $515 million. It also brought in some $33.5 million in profits.

Strategy

In 2011 Anne Arundel completed the last phase of a $424 million construction project that doubled the size of the medical center. The project added a new 50-bed patient tower and expanded emergency operating pediatric and outpatient facilities. The project is meant to help Anne Arundel keep up with a continued growth in demand for health care services throughout its service area.

In 2013 Anne Arundel opened a training center –the James and Sylvia Earl Simulation to Advance Innovation and Learning (SAIL) Center –to enhance its medical education programs and improve the quality and safety of care in the region. It also opened the Hackerman-Patz House that year to provide an affordable and convenient housing option for families of patients.

Also in 2013 the organization was designated as a Medicare accountable care organization (ACO) by the US government. ACOs work to coordinate care for Medicare patients to improve quality and reduce expenses.

EXECUTIVES

President and CEO, Martin L. Doordan
Sr. VP President AAMC Foundation, Lisa Hillman
SVP Medical Affairs, Joseph D. (Joe) Moser
President and CEO, Victoria W. Bayless
SVP Corporate Services; President Diagnostics Imaging, Carolyn W. Core
VP Quality and Patient Safety; President Pathways, Shirley J. Knelly
Media Relations, Justin D. Paquette
Director Geaton and JoAnn DeCesaris Cancer Institute, Barry R. Meisenberg
VP Human Resources, Nancy Luttrell
Interim Director Marketing and Public Relations, Annamarie DeCarlo
Chief Medical Officer and President Physician Enterprise LLC, Mitchell (Mitch) Schwartz
Chief Information Officer, Barbara Baldwin
CFO, Bob Reilly
Chairman, Biana Arentz
Vice Chairman, Edward Gosselin
COO and Chief Nursing Officer, Sherry B. Perkins
President AAMC Foundation and Chief Development Officer, Jan Wood
Vice President Clinical and Support Services, Jennifer Harrington
Vice President Physician Services, Stephen L. Clarke
Auditors: Ernst&YoungLLP

LOCATIONS

HQ: ANNE ARUNDEL MEDICAL CENTER INC.
2001 MEDICAL PKWY, ANNAPOLIS, MD 21401-3280
Phone: 443-481-1000
Web: WWW.AAHS.ORG

PRODUCTS/OPERATIONS

Selected Centers and Services

Blood Donor Center
Breast Center
Cardiac Cath Lab
Chest Pain Center
DeCesaris Cancer Institute
Diabetes Wound and Hyperbaric Center
Diagnostic Imaging
Heart and Vascular Institute
Joint Center
Laboratory
Pediatrics
Rehabilitation
Research Institute
Sleep Disorder Center
Spine Center
Stroke Center
Surgery
Women' s and Children' s Center

COMPETITORS

Ascension Health
Bon Secours Health
Catholic Health East
Dimensions Healthcare
Franklin Square Hospital Center
GBMC
Harbor Hospital
Johns Hopkins Health System
Johns Hopkins Medicine
LifeBridge Health
MedStar Health
Sinai Hospital of Baltimore
St. Agnes HealthCare
Sun Healthcare
University of Maryland Medical System

HISTORICAL FINANCIALS

Company Type: Private

Income Statement FYE: June 30

	REVENUE ($ mil.)	NET INCOME ($ mil.)	NET PROFIT MARGIN	EMPLOYEES
06/12	514	(33)	—	1,890
06/11	445	24	5.4%	—
06/10	413	20	4.9%	—
06/09	398	0	—	—
Annual Growth	8.9%	—	—	—

2012 Year-End Financials

Debt ratio: —
Return on equity: (-6.50%)
Cash ($ mil.): 16
Current ratio: 0.80
Long-term debt ($ mil.): —
Dividends
Yield: —
Payout: —
Market value ($ mil.): —

APi GROUP INC.

Holding company APi Group has a piece of the action in two main sectors: fire protection systems and industrial and specialty construction services. APi boasts about 40 subsidiaries which operate as independent companies across the US (nearly half of them in Minnesota) the UK and Canada. Services provided by the company's construction subsidiaries include HVAC and plumbing system installation; electrical industrial and mechanical contracting; industrial insulation; and garage door installation. Safety-focused units install a host of fire sprinkler detection security and alarm systems. The family-owned company was founded in 1926 by Reuben Anderson father of chairman Lee Anderson.

Geographic Reach

Minnesota-based APi Group operates companies throughout North America and the UK.

Sales and Marketing

APi Group serves several sectors such as security and defense education commercial industrial medical oil and gas and residential.

Operations

Through its various companies APi Group is involved in engineering designing constructing and installing LEED green-building certification program projects. Its divisions include Architectural Roofing and Mechanical Classic Industrial Services APi Construction APi Distribution and Industrial Fabricators among others.

Strategy Although APi Group companies are independent they often pool resources and work together to service clients.

Mergers and Acquisitions The highly acquisitive APi Group regularly acquires new companies to strengthen its growing group.

In 2013 the company's Western States Fire Protection (WSFP) acquired Advanced Fire an Oklahoma City-based fire-suppression company that specializes in military work. Buying Advanced Fire extends the company's reach in the fire protection industry and boosts its market share within Oklahoma City and the surrounding area. APi Group's Delta Fire Systems acquired Idaho's 3-D Fire which provides full-fire-system design fabrication installation testing and certification capabilities for commercial and private projects.APi Group previous purchases include Dynamic Fire Protection LLC (DFP) Omlid & Swinney Fire Protection and Security Canada-based Fire Stop Enterprises Ohio-based 3S and Kansas-based mainline pipeline contractor Jomax Construction.

EXECUTIVES

CFO and Treasurer, Gregory J. (Greg) Keup, age 55
President Metropolitan Mechanical Contractors Inc., Mark Anderson, age 53
Chairman, Lee R. Anderson Sr.
President and CEO, Russell (Russ) Becker
CIO, Julius J. Chepey
President and CEO Jamar, Michael P. (Mike) McParlan
COO, Gene Postma
VP APi Construction Company, Jerald P. (Jerry) Pederson
VP Acquisitions, Scott Hatfield
President Viking Automatic Sprinkler Company, Andy McCleery
President LeJeune Steel Company, Jim Torborg
VP APi Construction Company, Mark Udager
President APi Electric, Brad Boos
VP APi Distribution Inc., Shane Shipman
CEO Classic Industrial Services, Bernie Vining
President Classic Industrial Services, Mark Beuerle
President Grunau Company Inc, Lawrence (Larry) Loomis
President Industrial Contractors Inc, E. Lloyd Bushong
Plant Manager Industrial Fabricators, Peter Kaz
President NYCO, Rick Hansen
President Tessier's Inc., Rashid Kadir
President Garage Door Store and Twin City Garage Door Company, Lisa Donabauer
Executive Vice President, Fred L. Kroll
President APi National Service Group, Rock Marcone
President and CEO Davis-Ulmer Sprinkler and Rich Fire Protection Company Inc., R. Steve Ulmer
President Delta Fire Systems, Danny Schindler
President International Fire Protection, Kamran Malek
VP International Fire Protection, Ronnie Davidson
President and CEO Security Fire Protection, David Dixon
President Services, Frank Rich Jr.
CEO United States Fire Protection, Gregg Huennekens
President United States Fire Protection, Chad Huennekens
President and CEO VFP Fire Systems and Viking Automatic Sprinkler, Ryan Johnston
VP Vipond Fire Protection, Grant R. Neal
Vice President of Operations, Bernie M. Beliveau
Managing Director Vipond Fire Protection, John McCann
Branch Manager APi Systems Group Inc., Roddy J. Bieber
VP Vipond Systems Group, Michael (Mike) Godara
President APi Systems Integrators, Tim Pletrzak
President APi CAD Services, Brad Moore
CEO President United Piping Inc, R. J. (Bob) Schoneberger
President Island Fire Sprinkler Inc., Brian McMahon
President Reliance Fire Protection, Liam Knott
VP Vipond Systems, Bruce Tait
Vice President Controller, Mark Polovitz
President 3S Incorporated, Matt Euson
President American Fire Protection Group Inc., Mike Gengler
President Anco Products Inc., Mike Landes
VP APi Distribution Inc., Shane Shlpman
President APi National Service Group, Del Oliver
President Delta Fire Systems Inc., Bill Ball
President J Koski Company, John Koski
President Jomax Construction Company Inc., Max Nichols
President NEX US Alarm and Suppression LLC, Jon Bishop
President W & M Sprinkler Company Inc., Emile H. (Hank) Munier III

LOCATIONS

HQ: API GROUP INC.
1100 OLD HIGHWAY 8 NW, SAINT PAUL, MN 55112-6447
Phone: 651-636-4320
Web: WWW.APISYSTEMSGROUP.COM

PRODUCTS/OPERATIONS

Selected Subsidiaries

Fire Protection Systems
- Alliance Fire Protection Inc.
- APi National Service Group
- Davis-Ulmer Sprinkler Company
- Delta Fire Systems Inc.
- Grunau Company
- Halon Banking Systems
- International Fire Protection Inc.
- Island Fire Sprinkler Inc.
- Reliance Fire Protection
- Rich Fire Protection Co Inc.
- Security Fire Protection Company
- United States Fire Protection Company
- VFP Fire Systems Inc.
- Viking Automatic Sprinkler Company
- Vipond Fire Protection Inc. (Canada)
- Vipond Fire Protection Ltd. (UK)
- Western States Fire Protection Inc.

Industrial and Specialty Construction Services
- 3S Incorporated
- Anco Products Inc.
- APi CAD Services
- APi Construction Company
- APi Distribution Inc.
- APi Electric
- APi Supply Inc.
- Classic Industrial Services Inc.
- Doody Mechanical Inc.
- Garage Door Store
- Grunau Company Inc.
- Industrial Contractors Inc.
- Industrial Fabricators Inc.
- Jamar Company
- Jomax Construction Co.
- LeJeune Steel Company
- NYCO Inc.
- Tessier' s Inc.
- Twin City Garage Door Company

Low Voltage
- APi Systems Group Inc.
- APi Systems Integrators
- Vipond Systems Group

COMPETITORS

Comfort Systems USA	TDIndustries
EMCOR	Team
Integrated Electrical Services	Turner Industries
Irex	Tyco Fire & Security
John E. Green	

HISTORICAL FINANCIALS

Company Type: Private

Income Statement FYE: December 31

	REVENUE ($ mil.)	NET INCOME ($ mil.)	NET PROFIT MARGIN	EMPLOYEES
12/12	1,731	62	3.6%	4,237
12/11	1,484	52	3.6%	—
12/10	1,238	63	5.1%	—
12/09	1,358	63	4.7%	—
Annual Growth	8.4%	(0.6%)	—	—

2012 Year-End Financials

Debt ratio: —
Return on equity: 3.60%
Cash ($ mil.): 55
Current ratio: 1.10
Long-term debt ($ mil.): —
Dividends
Yield: —
Payout: —
Market value ($ mil.): —

APPLE AMERICAN GROUP LLC

This company must really enjoy casual dining in its neighborhood. Apple American Group is the largest franchisee of Applebee's with more than 440 Applebee's Neighborhood Grill & Bar locations in about two dozen states. The #1 casual dining chain in the US Applebee's restaurants offer a full-service menu of beef chicken and seafood entrees along with a wide selection of appetizers. Apple American's restaurants are found from coast to coast with large concentrations in the Midwest (Ohio Indiana Pennsylvania) and on the West Coast (California Washington). Founded in 1998 by CEO Greg Flynn Apple American is controlled by private equity firm Weston Presidio Service.

Strategy

As a franchise operator the company benefits from the fact that its eateries carry a well-known brand backed by by the national marketing muscle of Applebee's parent DineEquity. It pays for the privilege of operating Applebee's restaurants in the form of royalties and franchise fees. The company also agrees to abide by operating agreements designed to ensure consistency in food and service quality. Locally Apple American's restaurants compete for business against a wide range of independent operators as well as such national chains as Chili's (owned by Brinker International) and Outback Steakhouse (OSI Restaurant Partners).

Apple American has been rapidly building its base of casual dining eateries; it has more than doubled its locations since 2010. It operates via a decentralized business model where each geographic region is managed by a market president who has wide latitude in decision-making.

EXECUTIVES

EVP and CFO, Lorin M. Cortina
Chairman and CEO, Gregory G. (Greg) Flynn, age 50
Market President New Jersey and Delaware, Gary Koch
COO, Brad Pettinger
Market President Indiana, Monty Davis
Market President Pennsylvania and West Virginia, Keith Morrow
Market President Washington and Northern California, Dan Krebsbach
Market President Southern California and Southern Nevada, Mike Hebert

LOCATIONS

HQ: APPLE AMERICAN GROUP LLC
6200 OAK TREE BLVD # 250, CLEVELAND, OH 44131-6933
Phone: 216-525-2775
Web: WWW.APPLEAMERICAN.COM

Selected Locations

Alabama
California
Colorado
Delaware
Georgia
Idaho
Indiana
Maine
Massachusetts
Minnesota
Nevada
New Hampshire
New Jersey
New Mexico
New York
Ohio
Oregon
Pennsylvania
Rhode Island
Vermont
Washington
West Virginia
Wisconsin

COMPETITORS

Acapulco/El Torito Restaurants
Black Angus Steakhouse
Brinker
Carlson Restaurants
Cheesecake Factory
Cracker Barrel
Darden
Denny' s
Eat' n Park
Lone Star Steakhouse
Marie Callender
OSI Restaurant Partners
Red Robin
Ruby Tuesday
Texas Roadhouse

HISTORICAL FINANCIALS

Company Type: Private

Income Statement FYE: December 27

	REVENUE ($ mil.)	NET INCOME ($ mil.)	NET PROFIT MARGIN	EMPLOYEES
12/09	479	19	4.0%	5,500
12/08	431	9	2.3%	—
12/08	339	0	0.0%	—
Annual Growth	41.5%	3735526.7%	—	—

2009 Year-End Financials

Debt ratio: —
Return on equity: 4.00%
Cash ($ mil.): 6
Current ratio: 0.20
Long-term debt ($ mil.): —
Dividends
Yield: —
Payout: —
Market value ($ mil.): —

APPLIED CARD SYSTEMS INC.

Applied Card Systems is the servicing arm for Applied Bank a subprime consumer lender that issues secured and unsecured credit cards to customers with little or no credit history. Applied Card Systems processes payments from and provides customer service to more than 500000 holders of subprime Visa and MasterCard accounts. Applied Card Systems also services credit card accounts for third-party issuers primarily small and midsized financial institutions. Chairman Rocco Abessinio is the founder of both Applied Card Bank and Applied Card Systems which was formed in 1987. The company has offices in Florida and Pennsylvania.

Applied Card Systems owns and occupies the former headquarters of American Media publishers of the National Enquirer. Acquired in 2007 the Boca Raton Florida site had been closed since 2001 when anthrax sent to the publishing company killed an employee. The building underwent decontamination before being reopened.

Parenrt company Applied Bank whose main business is providing credit cards nationwide has two traditional bank branches in Delaware.

LOCATIONS

HQ: APPLIED CARD SYSTEMS INC.
5401 BROKEN SOUND BLVD NW, BOCA RATON, FL 33487-3512
Phone: 561-995-8820
Web: WWW.APPLIEDCARD.COM

COMPETITORS

Asset Acceptance Capital
Asta Funding
Encore Capital Group
Portfolio Recovery

HISTORICAL FINANCIALS

Company Type: Private

Income Statement FYE: December 31

	REVENUE ($ mil.)	NET INCOME ($ mil.)	NET PROFIT MARGIN	EMPLOYEES
12/09	162	21	13.5%	126
12/08	251	145	57.9%	—
12/07	1,520	0	0.0%	—
Annual Growth	(67.4%)	23844.9%	—	—

2009 Year-End Financials

Debt ratio: —
Return on equity: 13.50%
Cash ($ mil.): 169
Current ratio: 20.50
Long-term debt ($ mil.): —
Dividends
Yield: —
Payout: —
Market value ($ mil.): —

APPLIED RESEARCH ASSOCIATES INC.

Applied Research Associates (ARA) has defense down to a science. The research and engineering contractor develops tests and manages software and equipment for the aerospace and defense civil and commercial sectors. From more than 70 offices laboratories and testing and manufacturing facilities primarily in the US ARA provides expertise in system analysis blast testing environmental site characterization pavement evaluation robotic vehicles and other technologies and technical fields. The federal government including various US Department of Defense agencies is ARA's primary client. Founded in 1979 the company is owned by its employees.

Operations

Through its Vermont-based Vertek division ARA has undertaken such projects as the development of a remotely controlled robotic system useful for addressing such emergency needs as neutralizing bombs cleaning hazardous waste and fire fighting. The company had also developed a patented technology that creates fuel for turbine and diesel engines from plants and algae.

EXECUTIVES

President Chief Executive Officer, Robert H. (Rob) Sues
Chief Development Officer Secretary Vice President, Frank Maestas
Vice President and Software, Allen York
Senior Vice President and Automation & Geosciences Sector Manager, David Timian
Senior Vice President and Transportation, Curt Beckemeyer
Director of Operations, Terri Wirth-Koepenick
Senior Vice President, Scott E. Blouin
Executive Vice President, Lawrence A. Twisdale
Vice President Corporate Operations, Larry Ghormley
Senior Vice President, Joseph Smith
Chairman of the Board, John Healey
Director Vice President and oversees ARAs Southern, Rocky Mountain
Senior Vice President and Gulf Coast Sector Manager, Glen McDonald

Senior Vice President of Strategy Development, George Ullrich

LOCATIONS

HQ: APPLIED RESEARCH ASSOCIATES INC.
4300 SAN MATEO BLVD NE A220, ALBUQUERQUE, NM 87110-1295
Phone: 505-883-3636
Web: WWW.ARA.COM

COMPETITORS

CACI International
ComGlobal Systems
Epsilon Systems
General Dynamics Information Technology
Honeywell Technology Solutions
Innovative Technology Application
Leidos
Lockheed Martin Information Systems
Northrop Grumman Info Systems
ORION International Technologies
Photon Research Associates
Quantum Research
Raytheon IIS
Symvionics
Technology Service Corporation

HISTORICAL FINANCIALS

Company Type: Private

Income Statement FYE: September 30

	REVENUE ($ mil.)	NET INCOME ($ mil.)	NET PROFIT MARGIN	EMPLOYEES
09/12	226	2	1.2%	1,235
09/11	232	5	2.6%	—
09/08	196	8	4.2%	—
09/06	169	7	4.2%	—
Annual Growth	5.0%	(14.5%)	—	—

2012 Year-End Financials

Debt ratio: —
Return on equity: 1.20%
Cash ($ mil.): 26
Current ratio: 0.50
Long-term debt ($ mil.): —
Dividends
Yield: —
Payout: —
Market value ($ mil.): —

ARBITECH LLC

There's nothing arbitrary about Arbitech's business model. Arbitech sells a variety of new and used computer equipment made by such companies as Avaya Cisco Systems Hewlett-Packard IBM Microsoft Nortel and VMware. The company's wide range of products include PCs networking equipment servers storage systems components memories and software. In addition to new equipment the company deals in open-box discontinued and refurbished inventory a niche typically not served by other large distributors and resellers of computer products. Arbitech was co-founded in 2000 by CEO Torin Pavia and one of the company's partners William Poovey.

Arbitech has added services such as full configuration and online ordering and tracking to encourage more business from its partners. Rather than selling directly to the end user the company sells through partnerships with other resellers and distributors. By focusing on products that are most in demand and using a worldwide network of suppliers Arbitech is able to offer products at a price that provides higher profit margins for the company as well as its customers.

The company has jumped onto the virtualization bandwagon by expanding its sales of products for data centers primarily to the small and midsized business (SMB) market. In order to round out its server and storage center offerings Arbitech has inked a deal with Eaton to distribute its line of backup power enclosures and power distribution products.

EXECUTIVES

Chairman and CEO, Torin Pavia
EVP and General Counsel, Doug Kari
VP Business Relations and General Counsel, Frank G. Llaca Jr.
VP Business Initiatives, Jimmy Whalen
Account Manager, Evelyn Kent
Account Executive, Dan Reilly
Assistant Controller, Jamie Mudd
President and COO, Jim Binford
Inside Sales Representative, Mirna Escobar
Buyer:HP/Dell/Kingston/Microsoft, Houston Durand
Inside Sales Representative, Andrew Stewart
Operations Manager, John Wagner
Auditors: SVHPricewaterhouseCoopersLtd.

LOCATIONS

HQ: ARBITECH LLC
15330 BARRANCA PKWY, IRVINE, CA 92618-2215
Phone: 949-376-6650
Web: WWW.ARBITECH.COM

COMPETITORS

Arrow Electronics
Avnet
Ingram Micro
SYNNEX
Tech Data
Westcon

HISTORICAL FINANCIALS

Company Type: Private

Income Statement FYE: December 31

	REVENUE ($ mil.)	NET INCOME ($ mil.)	NET PROFIT MARGIN	EMPLOYEES
12/09	191	0	—	74
12/08	180	0	—	—
12/05	153	8	5.5%	—
Annual Growth	5.7%	—	—	—

2009 Year-End Financials

Debt ratio: —
Return on equity: —
Cash ($ mil.): 0
Current ratio: 0.70
Long-term debt ($ mil.): —
Dividends
Yield: —
Payout: —
Market value ($ mil.): —

ARCTIC SLOPE REGIONAL CORPORATION

The Inupiat people have survived the rigors of the Arctic for centuries and now they're surviving in the business world. The Inupiat-owned Arctic Slope Regional Corporation (ASRC) is the largest locally owned and operated business in Alaska. It gets the bulk of its of sales from energy services (ASRC Energy Services) and petroleum refining and marketing unit (Petro Star). Other operations include construction (ASRC Construction Holding) governmental services (ASRC Federal Holding) economic development (Alaska Growth Capital BIDCO) local services (Eskimos Inc.) and tourism (Tundra Tours).

Geographic Reach

ASRC represents 11000 members/shareholders in eight villages on the North Slope of Alaska: Anaktuvuk Pass Atqasuk Barrow Kaktovik Nuiqsut Point Hope Point Lay and Wainwright. ASRC has its head office in Barrow with a major administrative office in Anchorage. It has other subsidiary offices in the Lower 48 states.

Operations

The company seeks to adhere to traditional Inupiat values of protecting the land the environment and the native culture while developing economic programs.

It operates in four diverse major business segments: petroleum refining and marketing government services energy services and construction industries. Petro Star Inc. has two refineries (strategically positioned along the Trans-Alaska Pipeline) and serves Interior Alaska South Central Alaska Kodiak and Dutch Harbor.

ASRC Federal Holding Company provides professional and technical services to the federal government (aviation space and missile defense base operations resource and development engineering IT financial management and other).

ASRC Energy Services offers oilfield engineering operations maintenance construction fabrication regulation and permitting and other services to oil and gas companies.

ASRC Construction Holding Company provides construction services to commercial and government clients in Alaska the lower-48 the Gulf of Mexico and in other countries.

Alaska Growth Capital BIDCO offers economic development finance including small business loans and investments in economically challenged areas of Alaska.

Financial Performance

ARSC has distributed more than $543 million in dividends to shareholders since 1972. Since 2005 ARSC has distributed $16 million each year in benefits to its shareholders in the form of educational scholarships and community support funding as well as for training and development activities.

Strategy

In 2012 ASRC Construction Holding expanded into southeast Alaska with the acquisition of native-Alaskan owned McGraw's Custom Construction.

Ownership

ASRC is owned by Inupiat Eskimo shareholders.

Company Background

ASRC was set up to own and manage 5 million acres on Alaska's North Slope after the Alaska Native Claims Settlement Act in 1971 cleared the way for oil development in the area.

In 2010 ASRC protested the US Fish and Wildlife Service's designation of Alaskan North Slope oil-producing areas as a critical habitat for endangered polar bears claiming it would cost ASRC millions of dollars in lost oil revenues. In 2011 it led a coalition of Native groups to sue the Department of the Interior over this issue.

EXECUTIVES

Sevp And Coo, Mark W Kroloff, age 58
Vp And General Counsel, Alma McClellan Upicksoun
Vp Corporate Development, Craig Floerchinger
Senior Vice President General Manager, Bernard Nidowicz
Executive Vice President Operations And Maintenanc, John Sudderth
EVP Lands and Natural Resources, Richard K. Glenn
President and CEO, Rex A. Rock
Chairman and EVP Shareholder Community Programs, Crawford Patkotak
EVP and General Counsel, Denali Kemppel
EVP and COO, Butch Lincoln
EVP and CFO, Charlie Kozak

Vice President And General Manager, Frank Weiss
Vice President Operations, Brent Renfrew
Vice President, Pat Egger
Vice President, Graydon Lahmers
Senior Vice President Of External, Tara K Sweeney
Executive Vp, Donald Braden
Vice President Of Business Development, Chuck McGraw
Vice President Information Technology, Bob Anderson
Vice President, David Klein
Vice President Of Operations, Jim Stotts
Vice President Shareholder Development, James Patkotak
Executive Vice President Strategic, Jack Laasch
Senior Executive Vice President, Joe Panessiti
Senior Vice President Chief Operating, Larry Johnson
Vice President, Tara Maclean
Senior Executive Vice President, Kevin Kroloff
Senior Vice President Chief Operating, Bruce Clemens
Vice President, Colleen Nicholson
Vice President Marketing, Eben Hopson
Vice President Business Development, Bill Hassler
Vice President External Affairs, Tara Sweeny
Treasurer, Patsy Aamodt
Vice Chairman, George Sielak
Chairman and EVP Shareholder Community Programs, Crawford Patkotak
Treasurer, John Dittrich
Auditors: KPMGLLP

LOCATIONS

HQ: ARCTIC SLOPE REGIONAL CORPORATION
3900 C ST STE 801, ANCHORAGE, AK 99503-5963
Phone: 907-339-6000
Web:
WWW.ASRC.COM/CONTACT/PAGES/CONTACT%20ASRC.ASPX

COMPETITORS

Alaska Communications Systems
Baker Hughes
Halliburton
Nabors Industries
Noble
Schlumberger
T-Mobile USA
Tesoro

HISTORICAL FINANCIALS

Company Type: Private

Income Statement FYE: December 31

	REVENUE ($ mil.)	NET INCOME ($ mil.)	NET PROFIT MARGIN	EMPLOYEES
12/08	2,297	151	6.6%	6,000
12/07	1,777	207	11.7%	—
12/06	1,700	206	12.1%	—
12/05	1,566	127	8.1%	—
Annual Growth	13.6%	5.8%	—	—

2008 Year-End Financials

Debt ratio: —
Return on equity: 6.60%
Cash ($ mil.): 302
Current ratio: 0.80
Long-term debt ($ mil.): —
Dividends
Yield: —
Payout: —
Market value ($ mil.): —

ARKANSAS CHILDREN'S HOSPITAL

As the only pediatric medical center in the state Arkansas Children's Hospital (ACH) serves the youngest Razorbacks from birth to age 21. The not-for-profit hospital with its 370 beds specializes in childhood cancer pediatric orthopedics and neonatology. Besides acute care services it operates more than 80 specialty clinics and outpatient centers. One of the US's largest pediatric hospitals ACH is also engaged in teaching and medical research through its affiliation with the University of Arkansas for Medical Sciences. Its Arkansas Children's Hospital Research Institute focuses on biological mechanisms underlying birth defects diabetes-related complications and childhood diseases.

Geographic Reach

Based in Little Rock Arkansas on a campus that extends nearly 30 city blocks ACH serves children nationwide as one of the largest pediatric hospitals in the US. It has several locations across Arkansas in Little Rock Jonesboro and Lowell.

Operations

ACH each year performs more than 14000 operations and boasts 52000-plus emergency department visits nearly 324000 outpatient visits and about 14500 inpatient admissions.

ACH's Circle of Friends clinic treats more than 20000 patients annually. The clinic which opened in 2008 provides primary care as well as a broad range of specialty care services related to endocrinology dermatological conditions hemophilia and tuberculosis.

The hospital also offers community outreach services that include help for children of domestic abuse and wellness programs as well as a number of clinics to support those with eating disorders and diabetes.

Financial Performance

The hospital's 2012 budget was $519 million 82% of which came from net patient service revenue.

Strategy

The hospital opened a new $121 million south wing in mid-2012 that added more than 50 inpatient beds to the hospital's capacity. The nearly 260000-sq.-ft. four-story building features telemedicine technology (for remote patient care) new trauma rooms a dedicated orthopedics suite and a decontamination unit.

To its benefit ACH became the state's only pediatric Level I trauma center in 2010 after receiving a four-year designation from the Arkansas Department of Health. The designation means that the hospital is equipped for and capable of taking care of children with the most severe of traumas. Level I trauma centers serve as referral locations for hospitals that are unable to provide the same level of care.

As a prime destination for treatment ACH also runs Angel One Transport an intensive care medical transportation system that brings critically ill and injured infants children and adolescents as well as adult burn patients from throughout Arkansas and the surrounding states to ACH. It also boasts a high risk obstetric (HROB) transport program in partnership with the University of Arkansas for Medical Sciences. In 2013 ACH inked a contract with Aetna health insurance under which patients with Aetna health insurance will be able to seek in-network care at Arkansas Children's Hospital (ACH). The contract will allow the company to reach more families throughout the region.

EXECUTIVES

Vp Of Human Resources, Andree Trosclair
Senior Vice President Medical Director, Bonnie Taylor
President CEO and Director, Jonathan R. (Jon) Bates
COO, Scott R. Gordon
President Arkansas Childrens Hospital Research Institute, Richard F. Jacobs
SVP and CIO, Darrell T. Leonhardt
SVP and CFO, Gena G. Wingfield
SVP and COO, David T. Berry
President ACH Foundation, Fred Scarborough
Senior Vice President Chief Quality Officer, Jayant K. Deshpande
Senior Vice President Medical Director, W. Robert Morrow
Medical Director, James Aronso
Medical Director, Jose R Romero
Director Of Infection Control, Craig Gilliam
Vice President Of Family Support, Jeanette Purdue
Do Vice President Of Patient Care, Mary M Daniel
Vp Of Business Office, Carol Hudgens
Nursing Director, Terri Songer
Director Of Pharmacy, Marita Nazarian
Medical Director, John Fowlkes
Vp Of Ambulatory Care, Mark Winslow
Pharmacy Manager, Gary Perdue
Medical Director, Pam Howard
Medical Director, Christopher Smith
Ambulatory Services Director, Carol Graham
Vp General Cnsl, Rhonda Thorton
Medical Director, Steve Schexnayder
Vice President Of Clinical Svs, Cindy Holland
Vp Of Quality & Patient Safety, Pamela Brown
Nursing Director, Tami Graves
Vice President Clinical Excellence And Innovation, Tammy Webb
Vice Presidentpatient Care Services, Sandy Taylor
Nursing Director, Rebecca Kersten
Vice President Patient Care Services, Katie Lea
Director Of Admissions, Stephanie Jackson
Nursing Director, Gail Wilson
Nursing Director, Carrie Lee
Nursing Director, Leslie Bradley
Vice President Of Information, Michael Hart
Nursing Director, Jennifer Gernat
Nursing Director, Patty Mahoney
Vice President Patient Care Services, Mary Salassi
Senior Vice President, Katherine Friend
Senior Vice President Chief Nursing Officer, Leeanne Eddy
Vice President Patient Care Services, Katie Brandon
Vice President Of Business Office, Carol Hutchins
Nursing Director, Sharon Johnson
Medical Director, A N Ach
Vice President Finance, Cheryl Edwards
Nursing Director, Tamara Graves
Vice President Human Resources, Andre Trosclair
President CEO and Director, Jonathan R. (Jon) Bates
Secretary, Donnell Williams
Secretary, Michelle Leatherwood
Secretary, Kristy Davis
Secretary Home Visiting Network, Diane Chaney
Secretary, Tarina Goodwin
Secretary, Beth Bloodworth
Secretary, Shashi Dyamenahalli
Treasurer And Director, Paul Hart
Treasurer, Dorsey Jackson
Secretary, Ernest Banks
Secretary, Andrea Doss
Secretary And Director, J Hill
Secretary, Catherine Lee
Auditors: DeloitteTaxLLP

LOCATIONS

HQ: ARKANSAS CHILDREN' S HOSPITAL
1 CHILDRENS WAY, LITTLE ROCK, AR 72202-3500
Phone: 501-364-1100
Web: WWW.ACHRI.ARCHILDRENS.ORG

PRODUCTS/OPERATIONS

Selected Services

Ambulatory Surgery
Audiology
Center for Good Mourning
Cleft Clinic

Dennis Developmental Center
Dental Clinic
ECMO
Gastroenterology Clinic
Genetic and Metabolic Clinic
Infectious Diseases
Neuroscience Unit
Physical Medicine & Rehab Outreach Clinics
Sleep Disorders Center
Volunteer Services
WHAM (Wellness Health Action & Motivation) Clinic

COMPETITORS

Arkansas Heart Hospital
Baptist Health (Arkansas)
Children' s Healthcare of Atlanta
Children' s Medical Center of Dallas
Children' s Mercy Hospital
Children' s National Medical Center
Cook Children' s Health Care System
Dell Children' s Medical Center
East Tennessee Children' s Hospital
Jefferson Regional Medical Center of Arkansas
Methodist Healthcare
Shriners Hospitals For Children
St. Joseph' s Mercy Health Center
St. Jude Children' s Research Hospital
St. Vincent Health System
Texas Children' s Hospital
Universal Health Services
White County Medical Center

HISTORICAL FINANCIALS

Company Type: Private

Income Statement FYE: June 30

	REVENUE ($ mil.)	NET INCOME ($ mil.)	NET PROFIT MARGIN	EMPLOYEES
06/11	509	48	9.5%	3,700
06/10	513	42	8.4%	—
06/08	1	(0)	—	—
06/06	0	0	—	—
Annual Growth	—	—	—	—

2011 Year-End Financials

Debt ratio: —
Return on equity: 9.50%
Cash ($ mil.): 66
Current ratio: 2.30
Long-term debt ($ mil.): —
Dividends
Yield: —
Payout: —
Market value ($ mil.): —

ARLINGTON INDUSTRIES INC.

Thank goodness for zinc's abundance; the element has enabled Arlington Industry's dominance in manufacturing individual zinc die-cast line items. Arlington manufactures and distributes a slew of metallic and non-metallic fittings and connectors. Its lineup includes bushings cable connectors concrete pipe sleeves conduit bodies gaskets and screw couplings used in the electrical and construction markets. The company operates a sole plant in Scranton Pennsylvania. Since 2003 the privately-held manufacturing company has introduced more than 400 new products.

Sales and Marketing

Arlington products are sold throughout the US and Canada through stocking sales representatives who support the distributors' inventory.

Strategy

Arlington attributes its ability to ride the economic downturn to product development. Such developments focus on labor-saving devices offering competitive prices for electrical contractors. The company reports that more than 50% of its revenues are from its new patent-pending offerings enabling it to resist pricing pressures as well as motivate sales representatives with better commissions. Moreover Arlington has begun catering to audio/visual applications with a line of TV boxes and scoops and low-voltage mounting brackets.

In 2013 the company received additional payments of $1 million from Bridgeport Fittings in supplemental damages for sales of Whipper-Snap products from 2010 through 2012. Bridgeport was previously ordered to pay Arlington $3.62 million after a court ruling that 30 types of Bridgeport's Whipper-Snap products infringed Arlington's patent covering its SNAP-TITE products.

Company Background

Arlington was established in 1949 as a regional supplier of zinc fittings to the electrical industry. It was acquired by its present owners in 1956.

EXECUTIVES

Vice President Marketing, Raymond Kennedy

LOCATIONS

HQ: ARLINGTON INDUSTRIES INC.
1 STAUFFER INDUSTRIAL PAR, SCRANTON, PA 185179620
Phone: 5705620270
Web: WWW.AIFITTINGS.COM

PRODUCTS/OPERATIONS

Selected Products

Cord grip fittings
EMT (electrical metallic tubing) fittings
Fan/specialty boxes
Flex/AC/MC fittings
Grounding
Home theater security communications
NM (non-metallic) cable fittings and supports
Liquid-tight fittings
Mast parts
Rigid/IMC (intermediate metal conduit) fittings
Siding mounting blocks
Weatherproof products

COMPETITORS

Belden
Chicago Rivet
Encore Wire
Federal Screw Works
Freeport-McMoRan
General Cable
International Wire
Koch Enterprises
Leviton
Thomas & Betts
Woodhead Industries

HISTORICAL FINANCIALS

Company Type: Private

Income Statement FYE: December 31

	REVENUE ($ mil.)	NET INCOME ($ mil.)	NET PROFIT MARGIN	EMPLOYEES
12/13	126	0	—	320
12/12	109	0	—	—
12/11	99	0	—	—
12/09	89	0	—	—
Annual Growth	9.0%	—	—	—

2013 Year-End Financials

Debt ratio: —
Return on equity: —
Cash ($ mil.): 10
Current ratio: 1.40
Long-term debt ($ mil.): —
Dividends
Yield: —
Payout: —
Market value ($ mil.): —

ARNOLD MACHINERY COMPANY

Arnold Machinery helps keep construction on the move. Through its four divisions the company distributes construction mining ,Âindustrial and material handling equipment as well as farm machinery ,Âthroughout the US. ,ÂArnold Machinery ,Âalso offers used equipment and provides repair and maintenance rebuild exchange and rental services. OEM equipment suppliers include ,ÂVolvo ,Âand Hitachi (construction and m i i n g equipment); ,ÂHyster ,Â(a ,ÂNACCO ,Âbrand) ,Âand Unarco ,Â(forklifts warehouse equipment and other material handling equipment); and ,ÂBuhler ,Âand McFarlane ,Â(farm equipment). Chairman Alvin Richer has the controlling interest in the company.

The company's divisions include General Implement Distributors Mining Equipment ,ÂConstruction Equipment and Material Handling. ,ÂArnold Machinery ,Â operates about 20 branch facilities ,Âcovering some 15 states in the Western US.

Since its founding the company has expanded geographically and built its product offerings by acquiring complementary businesses. Arnold Machinery continues to acquire other distributors in its territory and to expand its ,Âfacilities in many markets.

L. E. "Doc" Arnold and Floyd Stannard founded predecessor company Stannard ,ÂArnold Machinery Company in 1929. The company's name was changed to Arnold Machinery Company upon the resignation of Stannard later that year.

EXECUTIVES

Vp And Operations Manager General Implement Distributors, Frank Loeffler
Corporate Vp; President Mining Division, John Ragsdale
Vice-president Sales, Darrell Buttars
Vice President Of Technical Marketing, Billy Greenlee

LOCATIONS

HQ: ARNOLD MACHINERY COMPANY
2955 W 2100 S, SALT LAKE CITY, UT 841191207
Phone: 8019724000
Web: WWW.ARNOLDMACHINERY.COM

COMPETITORS

Cashman Equipment
Empire Southwest
NES Rentals
Sunbelt Rentals
United Rentals

HISTORICAL FINANCIALS

Company Type: Private

Income Statement FYE: September 30

	REVENUE ($ mil.)	NET INCOME ($ mil.)	NET PROFIT MARGIN	EMPLOYEES
09/13	294	12	4.3%	450
09/12	306	13	4.3%	—
09/11	235	11	4.8%	—
09/10	191	0	—	—
Annual Growth	15.4%	—	—	—

2013 Year-End Financials

Debt ratio: —
Return on equity: 4.30%
Cash ($ mil.): 5
Current ratio: 0.10
Long-term debt ($ mil.): —
Dividends
Yield: —
Payout: —
Market value ($ mil.): —

ARROW HEAD REGIONAL MEDICAL CENTER

Find yourself dehydrated after searching the Inland Empire deserts for arrowheads? Arrowhead Regional Medical Center (ARMC) can fix you up. The San Bernardino County owned and operated hospital provides a range of health services from general medical and surgical care to emergency services rehabilitation inpatient psychiatric care pediatric and women's health services. It also serves as a Level II trauma center a regional burn center and medical training facility. ARMC with some 460 beds opened in 1999 to replace the aging San Bernardino County Hospital. The hospital also offers outpatient services on its main campus and at area clinics.

Geographic Reach

ARMC's main facility campus in Colton California includes an outpatient services complex. ARMC also runs three primary care Family Health Centers in the nearby towns of Fontana Rialto and San Bernadino as well as wound care and elder care clinics.

Operations

Along with a full range of health care services ARMC offers a about 10 residency programs including emergency and family medicine general surgery geriatrics orthopedics neurosurgery and gynecology. The hospital trains about 100 residents each year.

The ARMC emergency room handles about 130000 visits each year. The hospital's inpatient capacity handles about 25000 patients annually while its outpatient centers see some 250000 patients.

Strategy

To better serve the needs of patients in its service territory ARMC looks to expand services in high-demand areas. For instance an increase in cases of asthma (particularly among children) in the Central Valley led ARMC to expand its Breathmobile program an asthma clinic on wheels that travels to schools throughout San Bernadino County in 2010.

The hospital is also enhancing stationary outpatient care clinics. It added the ARMC Medical Office Building to its main campus in 2011; the center includes physician practices and an internal medicine clinic.

LOCATIONS

HQ: ARROW HEAD REGIONAL MEDICAL CENTER
400 N PEPPER AVE, COLTON, CA 92324-1801
Phone: 909-580-1000
Web: WWW.ARMC.SBCOUNTY.GOV

COMPETITORS

Anaheim Regional Medical Center
Cedars-Sinai Medical Center
Children' s Hospital of Orange County
City of Hope
Community Hospital of San Bernardino
Dignity Health
HCA
Kaiser Permanente
Loma Linda University Medical Center
Memorial Health Services
St. Jude Medical Center
Tenet Healthcare
Trinity Health (Novi)

HISTORICAL FINANCIALS

Company Type: Private

Income Statement FYE: June 30

	REVENUE ($ mil.)	NET INCOME ($ mil.)	NET PROFIT MARGIN	EMPLOYEES
06/09	225	25	11.3%	2,500
06/04	439	3	0.8%	—
06/03	313	(1)	—	—
06/02	313	(1)	—	—
Annual Growth	(4.6%)	—	—	—

2009 Year-End Financials

Debt ratio: —
Return on equity: 11.30%
Cash ($ mil.): 33
Current ratio: 1.10
Long-term debt ($ mil.): —
Dividends
Yield: —
Payout: —
Market value ($ mil.): —

ASPIRUS INC.

Aspirus provides a comprehensive range of health and medical services to residents in a 14-county region of central and northern Wisconsin as well as Michigan's Upper Peninsula. The health system operates the Aspirus Wausau Hospital a 320-bed multi-specialty regional health center and five smaller community hospitals. It also owns and operates the Aspirus Wausau Family Medicine residency program sponsored by the University of Wisconsin School of Medicine and Public Health. Its hospitals and network of community clinics provide specialized primary and emergency care. Aspirus also operates imaging centers hospice services home health care long-term care facilities and an outpatient dialysis center.

Operations

In 2012 Aspirus acquired the Wausau Family Medicine Residency Clinic from the University of Wisconsin School of Medicine and Publich Health and renamed it Aspirus Wausau Family Medicine the assumed operational accountability for the clinical practice. The residency program is accredited to train both osteopathic and allopathic (DO and MD) physicians and is sponsored by UW SMPH which also provides educational oversight.

EXECUTIVES

President and CEO, Duane L. Erwin, age 63
Senior Vice President of Finance and CFO Aspirus Wausau Hospital Aspirus Inc., Sidney Sczygelski
Executive Director Aspirus Network Inc., Joel Rueber
Interim President/COO Aspirus Wausau Hospital, Marita Hattem
President of Aspirus Clinics and Chief Clinical Integration Officer for Aspirus, Bud Chumbley
Vice President of Patient Care/Chief Nursing Officer, Kathy Drengler
CEO of Aspirus Grand View, Carol Goffnett
Vice President Marketing and Planning, Rick L. Nevers
Executive Director of Aspirus Health Foundation, Kalynn Pempek
Vice President of Information Technology/Chief Information Officer, Todd Richardson
Vice President of Extended Services, Jean Burgener
Senior Vice President of Legal Services and General Counsel for Aspirus, Cari Logemann
Vice President of Clinical Services, Jake Kempen
Vice President of Corporate Quality Services for Aspirus Inc, Jeanne Scinto

LOCATIONS

HQ: ASPIRUS INC.
333 PINE RIDGE BLVD, WAUSAU, WI 54401-4187
Phone: 715-847-2121
Web: WWW.ASPIRUS.ORG

PRODUCTS/OPERATIONS

Selected Facilities

Aspirus Grand View (Ironwood MI)
Aspirus Keweenaw (Laurium MI)
Aspirus Ontonagon (Ontonagon MI)
Aspirus Wausau Hospital (Wausau WI)
Langlade Hospital (Antigo WI)
Memorial Health Center (Medford WI)

COMPETITORS

Dean Health Systems Inc.
Howard Young Health Care
Luther Midelfort
ThedaCare Inc.
University of Wisconsin Hospital and Clinics

HISTORICAL FINANCIALS

Company Type: Private

Income Statement FYE: June 30

	REVENUE ($ mil.)	NET INCOME ($ mil.)	NET PROFIT MARGIN	EMPLOYEES
06/13	536	47	8.9%	3,900
06/12	529	26	4.9%	—
06/10	503	86	17.2%	—
06/10	0	0	—	—
Annual Growth	—	—	—	—

2013 Year-End Financials

Debt ratio: —
Return on equity: 8.90%
Cash ($ mil.): 85
Current ratio: 1.40
Long-term debt ($ mil.): —
Dividends
Yield: —
Payout: —
Market value ($ mil.): —

ASSOCIATED ELECTRIC COOPERATIVE INC.

Associated Electric Cooperative makes the connection between power and cooperatives. The utility provides transmission and generation services to its six member/owner companies which in turn provide power supply services to 51 distribution cooperatives in three Midwest states. (The distribution cooperatives have a combined customer count of about 875000 people.) Associated Electric operates 9645 miles of power transmission lines and has about 5895 MW of generating capacity from interests in primarily coal- and gas-fired power plants and from wholesale energy transactions with other regional utilities.

Geographic Reach

The cooperative is engaged in the wholesale transmission business with more than 70 investor-owned and municipal utilities electric cooperatives power marketing firms and regional transmission organizations. Associated Electric supplies wholesale power to 39 distribution cooperatives in Missouri three in southeast Iowa and nine in northeast Oklahoma.

Financial Performance

In 2012 Associated Electric's revenues dropped by 0.2% due to lower sales volume was the result of mild winter temperatures in 2012 that tamped down demand.

Despite the decrease in net sales the company's net income grew by 8% in 2012 thanks to lower operating expenses.

Strategy

The company is also looking to increase power generated from renewable sources in order to meet tightening emission regulations. It has contracted hydropower sources and it also gets wind energy from Missouri's first utility-scale wind farms the fourth of which the 150 MW Lost Creek Wind Farm. In 2012 Associated Electric signed a long-term power purchase agreement for 314 MW of power from BP Wind Energy's proposed Flat Ridge 2 Wind farm in Kansas boosting the cooperative's total wind power capacity to 600MW.

To meet growing demand the company is also growing its fossil-fueled power assets. In 2013 the city of New Madrid approved an option for Associated Electric to buy New Madrid Unit 1 power plant before their existing agreement ends in 2022.

In 2011 Associated Electric completed a 540 MW combined-cycle natural gas plant adjacent to its existing Chouteau Power Plant in Pryor Oklahoma boosting that location's overall capacity to 1062 MW.

Company Background

Six generation and transmission cooperatives/owners formed Associated Electric in 1961 to provide them with a wholesale power supply.

EXECUTIVES

Special Assistant to the CEO and General Manager, Michael M. (Mike) Miller
CEO and General Manager, James J. Jura
President Board of Directors, O. B. Clark
Director Power Production, Duane D. Highley
Secretary, R. Layne Morrill
Chairman, Emery O. Geisendorfer Jr.
CIO, Ronald H. Murphy
Manager Internal Audit, Michael E. (Mike) King
General Counsel, Patrick A. Baumhoer
CFO, David W. McNabb
Director Engineering and Operations, Roger S. Clark
Director Member Services and Corporate Communications, Joseph E. Wilkinson
Director Human Resources, Shawn P. Calhoun
Vice Chairman, John B. Killgore
Director Power Production, Kenneth S. Wilmot
Director, Harold E. Jordan
Director, Donald W. Shaw
Director, J. Chris Cariker
Director, John C. Farris
Director, Douglas H. Aeilts
President Northeast Missouri Electric Power Cooperative, Emery O. Geisendorfer Jr.
Director, Don R. McQuitty
Director, Jerry W. Divin
Auditors: KPMGLLP

LOCATIONS

HQ: ASSOCIATED ELECTRIC COOPERATIVE INC.
2814 S GOLDEN AVE, SPRINGFIELD, MO 65807-3213
Phone: 417-881-1204
Web: WWW.AECI.ORG

PRODUCTS/OPERATIONS

		2012 Sales
Members		82
Total	0	100

Member Transmission and Distribution Cooperativ
Central Electric Power Cooperativ
KAMO Power
M&A Electric Power Cooperativ
Northeast Missouri Electric Power Cooperativ
NW Electric Power Cooperative Inc.
Sho-Me Power Electric Cooperativ

COMPETITORS

Ameren	Great Plains Energy
Empire District Electric	Southern Union
	Westar Energy
GenOnEnergy	Xcel Energy

HISTORICAL FINANCIALS

Company Type: Private

Income Statement FYE: December 31

	REVENUE ($ mil.)	NET INCOME ($ mil.)	NET PROFIT MARGIN	EMPLOYEES
12/12	1,081	50	4.7%	600
12/11	1,083	46	4.3%	—
12/10	1,055	45	4.3%	—
12/09	988	37	3.8%	—
Annual Growth	3.1%	10.1%	—	—

2012 Year-End Financials

Debt ratio: —	
Return on equity: 4.70%	Dividends
Cash ($ mil.): 89	Yield: —
Current ratio: 0.70	Payout: —
Long-term debt ($ mil.): —	Market value ($ mil.): —

ASSOCIATED FOOD STORES INC.

EXECUTIVES

SVP Montana Region, Kelly Atkins
President Market Development Inc., Steve Miner
CEO, Neal Berube
SVP Supply Chain, Brian Duff
SVP Team Services, Tim Conner
SVP Retail Coordination, David Rice
VP Retail Services, Bob King
VP Store Brands, Roger White
SVP Logistics, Bryan Goins
SVP and CIO, Wade Judd
VP Perishables, Bill Price
VP Government Relations, Jerry Dewey
VP Center Store, Kevin Fitz

LOCATIONS

HQ: ASSOCIATED FOOD STORES INC.
1850 W 2100 S, SALT LAKE CITY, UT 841191304
Phone: 8019734400
Web: WWW.AFSTORES.COM

COMPETITORS

AMCON Distributing	SUPERVALU
C&S Wholesale	Safeway
GSC Enterprises	URM Stores
McLane	Unified Grocers
Nash-Finch	Wal-Mart

HISTORICAL FINANCIALS

Company Type: Private

Income Statement FYE: March 31

	REVENUE ($ mil.)	NET INCOME ($ mil.)	NET PROFIT MARGIN	EMPLOYEES
03/13	1,957	2	0.1%	300
03/12	2,011	5	0.3%	—
03/11	1,953	(6)	—	—
03/10	1,785	0	—	—
Annual Growth	3.1%	—	—	—

2013 Year-End Financials

Debt ratio: —	
Return on equity: 0.10%	Dividends
Cash ($ mil.): 105	Yield: —
Current ratio: 0.40	Payout: —
Long-term debt ($ mil.): —	Market value ($ mil.): —

ASSOCIATED GROCERS OF NEW ENGLAND INC.

AGNE gets the products you want on to grocers' shelves. Associated Grocers of New England (AGNE) is a leading wholesale grocery distributor. The retailer-owned organization supplies more than 650 independent grocers and convenience stores in six New England states and the Upstate New York and Albany area. AGNE supplies customers with baked goods fresh produce and meat as well as general grocery items and other merchandise. The grocery distributor also offers such retail support services as advertising marketing and merchandising. AGNE's retail arm operates about a half a dozen supermarkets under the Harvest Market Sully's Superette and Vista Foods banners. The cooperative was formed in 1946.

Geographic Reach

The New Hampshire-based company serves stores in Connecticut Maine Massachusetts New Hampshire Rhode Island and Vermont and the Upstate New York/Albany area.

Financial Peformance

AGNE rings up more than $475 million in annual sales.

Strategy

The 2011 liquidation of rival Associated Grocers of Maine which distributed products to hundreds of small independent grocery stores in Maine boosted AGNE's business in the state. To meet increasing demand AGNE is expanding its distribution facility in Pembroke New Hampshire. The 105000-square-foot addition to the existing 380000-square-foot facility is slated for completion by the end of 2014. It features an automated product movement system to reduce the "number of touches" and increase efficiency. The wholesaler has been gradually increasing its retail store operation in recent years with the purchase of individual member stores in its market area.

Mergers and Acquisitions

In a move to expand its retail coverage AGNE acquired Bi-Wise Market of Allentown New Hampshire in January 2014. In 2012 AGNE acquired Sully's Superette also in New Hampshire.

AGNE's acquisition of New Hampshire-based Manchester Wholesale Distributors (in 2009) helped boost sales during the economic downturn as did improved performance at its Associated Convenience Grocers division. Manchester Wholesale Distributors supplied convenience stores and food service operators throughout New Hampshire.

EXECUTIVES

President CEO of Associated Grocers of New England, Michael C. (Mike) Bourgoine
Manager Warehousing, James (Jim) Johnson
Manager Center Store Purchasing, Karen St. Louis
General Manager Convenience Store Division, Stephen Felton
SVP Sales and Retail Development, Michael J. (Mike) Violette
Director Retail Programs, Curt O'Hara

Director Information Technology, Kenneth (Ken) Peperissa
Manager Sales and Purchasing Bakery and Deli, William Carter
Vice President Wholesale Merchandising and Procurement, Allan Hulse
Manager Sales and Purchasing Produce, Lenny Miner
Director, Terry P. Appleby
Director, James G. (Jim) Crosby

LOCATIONS

HQ: ASSOCIATED GROCERS OF NEW ENGLAND INC.
11 COOPERATIVE WAY, PEMBROKE, NH 032753251
Phone: 6032236710
Web: WWW.AGNE.COM

COMPETITORS

Associated Wholesalers	McLane
Bozzuto' s	Pine State Trading
C&S Wholesale	SUPERVALU
Dole & Bailey Inc.	Shaw' s
Hannaford Bros.	

HISTORICAL FINANCIALS

Company Type: Private

Income Statement FYE: March 30

	REVENUE ($ mil.)	NET INCOME ($ mil.)	NET PROFIT MARGIN	EMPLOYEES
03/13	480	0	0.1%	625
03/09	340	0	0.2%	—
03/08	315	0	0.1%	—
03/07	1,996	0	—	—
Annual Growth	—	—	—	—

2013 Year-End Financials

Debt ratio: —
Return on equity: 0.10%
Cash ($ mil.): 8
Current ratio: 0.60
Long-term debt ($ mil.): —
Dividends
Yield: —
Payout: —
Market value ($ mil.): —

ASSOCIATED WHOLESALE GROCERS INC.

Associated Wholesale Grocers (AWG) knows its customers can't live on bread and milk alone. The second-largest retailer-owned cooperative in the US (behind Wakefern Food Corporation) AWG supplies more than 2800 retail outlets in some two dozen states from eight distribution centers. In addition to its wholesale grocery operation AWG offers a variety of business services to its members including marketing and merchandising programs shelf management insurance and store design. The firm sold its company-owned retail stores which operated under the Homeland and other banners in 2011 to focus on its wholesale business. AWG was founded by a group of independent grocers in 1924.

HISTORY

About 20 Kansas City Kansas-area grocers met in a local grocery in 1924 and organized the Associated Grocers Company to get better deals on purchases and advertising. They elected J. C. Harline president and each chipped in a few hundred dollars to make their first purchases. It took a while to find a manufacturer who would sell directly to them; a local soap maker was finally convinced and others gradually followed.

In 1926 the group was incorporated as Associated Wholesale Grocers (AWG). It outgrew two warehouses in four years finally moving to a 16000-sq.-ft. facility big enough to add new lines and more products. Membership doubled between 1930 and 1932 as grocers moved from ordering products a year ahead to the new wholesale concept and members took seriously the slogan: "Buy Sell Buy Some More." They met every week to plan how to sell their products and buyer and advertising manager Harry Small gave sales presentations and advertising ideas (his trade-in plan for old brooms sold more than two train-carloads of brooms in two weeks). Heavy newspaper advertising also paid off; AWG topped $1 million in sales in 1933.

The cooperative made its first acquisition in 1936 buying Progressive Grocers a warehouse in Joplin Missouri; a second warehouse named Associated Grocers was acquired the next year in Springfield Missouri. AWG continued building and expanding warehouses and annual sales were at $11 million by 1951.

Louis Fox became CEO in 1956. Fox maximized year-end rebates for members led several acquisitions and formed a new subsidiary for financing stores and small shopping centers where AWG members had a presence (Supermarket Developers). Sales increased nearly 15-fold to over $200 million in his first 15 years.

James Basha who succeeded Fox when he retired in 1984 saw sales reach $2.4 billion by the time of his own retirement in 1992.

Basha was followed by former COO Mike DeFabis once a deputy mayor of Indianapolis. DeFabis orchestrated several acquisitions including 41 Kansas City-area stores –most of which were quickly bought by members –from bankrupt Food Barn Stores in 1994 and 29 Oklahoma stores and a warehouse from Safeway spinoff Homeland Stores in 1995 (members bought all the stores).

AWG's non-food subsidiary Valu Merchandisers was established in 1995; its new Kansas warehouse began shipping health and beauty aids and housewares the following year to help members battle big discounters. Members narrowly defeated a proposal in late 1996 to convert the cooperative into a public company. Proponents promptly petitioned for a second vote which was defeated early the next year.

AWG veteran Doug Carolan succeeded DeFabis in 1998 becoming only the fifth CEO in the cooperative's history. The company bought five Falley's and 33 Food 4 Less stores in Kansas and Missouri from Fred Meyer in 1998 for $300 million. In a break with tradition AWG began operating the stores rather than selling them to members.

In 2000 after a months-long labor dispute with the Teamsters was resolved Carolan left AWG. The company's CFO Gary Phillips was named president and CEO later that year. In 2001 the company debuted a new format ALPS (Always Low Price Stores) –small stores that carry a limited selection of grocery top-sellers. Also that year AWG's Kansas City division began distributing to more than 10 new stores that had formerly been served by Fleming at the time the #1 US wholesale food distributor.

In 2002 supermarket operator Homeland Stores which operates stores in Oklahoma emerged from bankruptcy as a fully owned subsidiary of AWG. AWG formed a new subsidiary Associated Retail Grocers to oversee Homeland and its Falley's chain.

As a result of the 2003 sale of Fleming Companies' wholesale distribution business AWG picked up food distribution centers in Nebraska (two) Oklahoma (one) and Tennessee (two) and general-merchandise distribution centers in Tennessee and Kansas.

Introducing a "dollar" section in its stores in 2004 proved successful leading AWG to expand the category to more than 1000 food and non-food items. The following year it merged the corporate offices of its Homeland and Food 4 Less chains.

AWG took steps to expand its capacity and its territory in 2007 when it acquired a distribution center in Fort Worth from Albertsons. The cooperative also took on supply operations for Albertsons locations in Arkansas Louisiana and Texas.

In 2009 AWG acquired the assets of Little Rock Arkansas-based Affiliated Foods Southwest in 2009 adding about a dozen new stores.

During 2010 the firm introduced a paperless coupon program.

In December 2011 AWG sold its corporate supermarkets to a group of employees. The corporate stores included 76 retail locations operating under the Homeland United of Oklahoma and Country mart banners in Oklahoma and the Super Saver banner in northern Texas.

In late 2012 AWG completed a 35000-square-foot addition to its corporate headquarters in Kansas City. The location is also home to AWG's Kansas City distribution centers and its Valu Merchandisers division.

EXECUTIVES

President CEO, Jerry Garland, age 62
VP Corporate Sales Development, Stephen G. (Steve) Dillard
VP-Distr, John F. Lane
VP Sales Valu Merchandisers, Joe Busch
Auditors: GrantThorntonLLP

LOCATIONS

HQ: ASSOCIATED WHOLESALE GROCERS INC.
5000 KANSAS AVE, KANSAS CITY, KS 661061135
Phone: 9132881000
Web: WWW.AWGINC.COM

Selected States Served

Alabama
Arkansas
Florida
Georgia
Illinois
Indiana
Iowa
Kansas
Kentucky
Louisiana
Michigan
Mississippi
Missouri
Nebraska
New Mexico
North Carolina
Oklahoma
Ohio
South Carolina
Tennessee
Texas
Virginia
West Virginia
Wisconsin

COMPETITORS

Affiliated Foods	GSC Enterprises
Affiliated Foods Midwest	H. T. Hackney
Alex Lee	Kroger
Associated Grocers Inc.	McLane
C&S Wholesale	Nash-Finch
Central Grocers	SUPERVALU
Dearborn Wholesale Grocers	Spartan Stores
	Wakefern Food
	Wal-Mart

HISTORICAL FINANCIALS

Company Type: Private

Income Statement FYE: December 28

	REVENUE ($ mil.)	NET INCOME ($ mil.)	NET PROFIT MARGIN	EMPLOYEES
12/13	8,380	192	2.3%	5,500
12/12	7,852	175	2.2%	—
12/11	7,766	169	2.2%	—
12/10	7,251	0	—	—
Annual Growth	4.9%	—	—	—

2013 Year-End Financials

Debt ratio: —
Return on equity: 2.30%
Cash ($ mil.): 59
Current ratio: 0.40
Long-term debt ($ mil.): —
Dividends
Yield: —
Payout: —
Market value ($ mil.): —

ASSOCIATION OF UNIVERSITIES FOR RESEARCH IN ASTRONOMY INC.

There is nothing quasi-scientific about this aura. The Association of Universities for Research in Astronomy (AURA) is a consortium of universities and not-for-profit organizations devoted to the study of space. The organization was founded to create astronomical observing facilities for use by qualified researchers and to serve the community by offering public outreach education and dissemination of information. AURA was founded in 1957 and operates astronomical observatories at 34 US institutions and six international affiliates including Harvard University Ohio State University and the University of Toronto.

EXECUTIVES

President and Director, William S. (Bill) Smith
VP Science, Jay A. Frogel
VP Administration, Deborah Narcisso
Head of Mission Chilean Operations, Chris Smith
Manager Site Administration and Facilities Chilean Operations, Hernan Bustos
Manager Santiago Office Chilean Operations, Edilia Cerda
Chair, Bruce Carney
Vice Chair, Caty Pilachowski
Human Resources Manager Space Telescope Science Institute, Sheryl Bruff
Human Resources Manager Gemini Observatory, Neil Barker
Vice President Washington Operations, Carol Lane
Director, Elizabeth (Betsy) Hoffman
President and Director, William S. (Bill) Smith
Director, Frederic Chaffee
Director, Peter Gilman
Director, Daniel Larson
Vice Chair, Caty Pilachowski
Director, John Peoples Jr.
Director, Mark Phillips
Director, Maria Teresa Ruiz
Director, Michael Shull
Director, Paula Szkody

LOCATIONS

HQ: ASSOCIATION OF UNIVERSITIES FOR RESEARCH IN ASTRONOMY INC.
1212 NEW YORK AVE NW # 450, WASHINGTON, DC 20005-3987
Phone: 202-483-2101
Web: WWW.AURA-ASTRONOMY.ORG

PRODUCTS/OPERATIONS

Member Institutio	
Boston University /	1,993
California Institute of Technology /	1,972
Carnegie Institution of Washington /	1,997
Georgia State University /	2,008
Harvard University /	1,957
Indiana University /	1,957
Instituto de Astrofisica de Canarias /	2,005
Iowa State University /	1,992
Johns Hopkins University /	1,982
Kiepenheuer-Institut fur Sonnenphysik /	2,005
Massachusetts Institute of Technology /	1,981
Michigan State University /	1,997
Montana State University /	2,005
New Mexico State University /	1,999
Ohio State University /	1,957
Pennsylvania State University /	1,990
Pontificia Universidad Catolica de Chile /	1,997
Princeton University /	1,959
Rutgers University /	1,999
SUNY - Stony Brook /	1,986
Swinburne University /	2,008
Universidad de Chile /	1,992
University of Arizona /	1,972
University of California at Berkeley /	2,007
University of California at Santa Cruz /	1,957
University of Chicago /	1,957
University of Colorado /	1,977
University of Florida /	2,002
University of Hawaii /	1,978
University of Illinois at Urbana-Champaign /	1,980
University of Maryland /	1,986
University of Michigan /	1,957
University of Minnesota /	1,995
University of North Carolina at Chapel Hill /	1,995
University of Texas at Austin /	1,972
University of Toronto /	2,004
University of Virginia /	2,003
University of Washington /	1,986
University of Wisconsin /	1,957
Yale University /	1,958

HISTORICAL FINANCIALS

Company Type: Private

Income Statement FYE: September 30

	REVENUE ($ mil.)	NET INCOME ($ mil.)	NET PROFIT MARGIN	EMPLOYEES
09/11	211	(0)	—	1,000
09/10	197	(2)	—	—
09/09	180	(0)	—	—
09/08	186	(0)	—	—
Annual Growth	4.3%	—	—	—

2011 Year-End Financials

Debt ratio: —
Return on equity: —
Cash ($ mil.): 25
Current ratio: —
Long-term debt ($ mil.): —
Dividends
Yield: —
Payout: —
Market value ($ mil.): —

ASTRONAUTICS CORPORATION OF AMERICA

EXECUTIVES

Chief Executive Officer, Ronald E. Zelazo
Chairman Emeritus, Nathaniel K. Zelazo
President, Michael Russek
VP-Ops, Joseph Potts

LOCATIONS

HQ: ASTRONAUTICS CORPORATION OF AMERICA
4115 N TEUTONIA AVE, MILWAUKEE, WI 532096731
Phone: 4144494000
Web: WWW.ASTRONAUTICS.COM

PRODUCTS/OPERATIONS

Selected Products

Air
- Computers
  - Airborne file server
  - Air data computers
  - Digital air data computers
  - Mission and display processor
- Displays
  - Electronic flight bag/pilot information displays
  - Electronic warfare displays
  - Engine instrument and caution advisory system displays
  - Engine performance indicator
  - Integrated flight deck displays
  - Multi-function color displays
- Flight controls
  - Unmanned aerial vehicle (UAV) servo actuators
- Flight instruments
  - Attitude director indicators
  - Electronic flight instruments
  - Horizontal situation indicator
- Integrated avionics
  - Mission and display systems
- Navigation systems
  - Attitude heading reference systems
  - Digital attitude heading reference systems
  - High accuracy inertial navigation system

Land
- Components
  - Accelerometer triad assembly
  - Inertial single axis accelerometer
- Displays
  - Dash boards for tanks
- Fire
  - Fire control computer
  - Fire control systems
  - Line-of-sight stabilization and data link subsystem
  - Line-of-sight stabilization system
- Navigation
  - Land navigation systems
  - Miniature land navigation system
  - Modular azimuth positioning system

Sea
- Displays
  - Operating and control console
- Navigation
  - Seaborne navigation system
  - Ship integrated navigation system

Space
- High accuracy inertial navigation systems for the Space Shuttle
- Inertial single axis accelerometer
- Inertial measurement unit for tactical applications
- Space qualified inertial reference unit
- Two-axis rate assembly

COMPETITORS

BAE SYSTEMS
CIC International
Elbit Systems
L-3/IS
Moog
Raven Industries
Raytheon
Rockwell Collins

HISTORICAL FINANCIALS

Company Type: Private

Income Statement

FYE: May 31

	REVENUE ($ mil.)	NET INCOME ($ mil.)	NET PROFIT MARGIN	EMPLOYEES
05/08	235	19	8.3%	1,550
05/07	233	20	8.9%	—
05/06	353	0	—	—
Annual Growth	—23275.9%	—	—	—

2008 Year-End Financials

Debt ratio: ——
Return on equity: 8.30%
Cash ($ mil.): 2
Current ratio: 0.90
Long-term debt ($ mil.): —
Dividends
Yield: —
Payout: —
Market value ($ mil.): —

ATALANTA CORPORATION

EXECUTIVES

Chairman and CEO, George C. Gellert
CFO, Charles Stough
Manager Marketing and Public Relations, Jacque Folts
General Counsel, Robert Levy

LOCATIONS

HQ: ATALANTA CORPORATION
1 ATLANTA PLZ STE 3, ELIZABETH, NJ 072062120
Phone: 9083518000
Web: WWW.ATALANTA1.COM

PRODUCTS/OPERATIONS

Selected Brands

Atalanta
Casa Diva
Celebrity
Chimay Trappist Cheeses (North American imports only)
Del Destino
Martel
Zerto

Selected Products

Cheeses and accompaniments
Coffee
Desserts and baked goods
Frozen seafood
Fish
Fruit juice concentrate
Groceries
Meat
Pasta rice and grains
Specialty cheeses

COMPETITORS

Allied International Corporation of VA
American Milk Products
Boar' s Head
Cento
DPI Specialty Foods
European Imports
KeHE Distributors
Millbrook Distribution Services
World Finer Foods

HISTORICAL FINANCIALS

Company Type: Private

Income Statement

FYE: December 31

	REVENUE ($ mil.)	NET INCOME ($ mil.)	NET PROFIT MARGIN	EMPLOYEES
12/09	384	8	2.3%	150
12/07	348	10	3.1%	—
12/06	0	0	—	—
Annual Growth	—	—	—	—

2009 Year-End Financials

Debt ratio: ——
Return on equity: 2.30%
Cash ($ mil.): 7
Current ratio: 0.40
Long-term debt ($ mil.): —
Dividends
Yield: —
Payout: —
Market value ($ mil.): —

ATLANTIC DIVING SUPPLY INC.

Atlantic Diving Supply (doing business as ADS Tactical) is geared toward gearing up the military. Serving agencies in the Department of Defense the company specializes in helping customers procure tactical and operational military equipment. Like a retailer it sells 160000 products manufactured by some 1500 vendors including Camelbak FLIR L-3 Communications and Oakley but its niche offering is its supply management services. These services which are tailored to military customers include kitting (packaging related products in groups) assembly training custom sourcing product research and development and quality assurance. ADS Tactical filed an IPO in early 2011 but withdrew it six months later.

IPO

ADS Tactical in July 2011 called off its IPO just days before the company was to begin selling stock. (In August it formally withdrew its IPO filing.) The company cited "adverse market conditions" for the withdrawal. ADS sought up to $200 million in its IPO but wouldn't have received any of the proceeds which were earmarked to go to company owners and selling stockholders.

Sales and Marketing

While most of ADS Tactical's customers are within the Department of Defense and the Department of Homeland Security other customers include federal agencies defense contractors law enforcement and public safety organizations including fire departments and EMS. The company claims to employ many retired US military and law enforcement personnel.

Strategy

ADS Tactical's sales soared during the 2000s when it became a kind of middle-man for the Pentagon as the wars in Iraq and Afghanistan unfolded following the 9/11 attacks. Indeed the company enjoyed a steady rise in profits due in large part to year-over-year increases in its sales revenue and relatively low selling and administrative costs and other expenses. ADS intends to continue driving growth through a handful of long-term strategic efforts including continuing the expansion of its sales force broadening its product offerings to keep pace with the evolving technological needs of the military and attracting new customers from other defense-oriented government agencies and private security services organizations. However with the DOD and Homeland Security making up most of its business the company is vulnerable to cuts in the defense budget.

Ownership

CEO Luke Hillier owns a 58% stake in ADS while R. Scott LaRose holds a 25% stake and Daniel Clarkson a 17% stake.

EXECUTIVES

Vp Product Management, Kevin Hickey
Vp Marketing, Joe Kohl
Vice President Marketing, Christopher Philbrick
Chief Finc Officer Executive Vp, Karan Rai

LOCATIONS

HQ: ATLANTIC DIVING SUPPLY INC.
621 LYNNHVEN PKWY STE 400, VIRGINIA BEACH, VA 23452
Phone: 757-481-7758
Web: WWW.ADSINC.COM

PRODUCTS/OPERATIONS

Selected Products

Apparel
Bags packs and cases
Eyewear
Footwear
Hydration systems
Knives
Lighting
Medical
Tools
Training aids

COMPETITORS

Army and Air Force Exchange
Navy Exchange
Target Corporation
Wal-Mart

HISTORICAL FINANCIALS

Company Type: Private

Income Statement

FYE: December 31

	REVENUE ($ mil.)	NET INCOME ($ mil.)	NET PROFIT MARGIN	EMPLOYEES
12/11	1,409	50	3.6%	380
12/10	1,327	77	5.8%	—
12/09	938	54	5.8%	—
12/08	650	40	6.2%	—
Annual Growth	29.4%	7.8%	—	—

2011 Year-End Financials

Debt ratio: ——
Return on equity: 3.60%
Cash ($ mil.): 1
Current ratio: 1.00
Long-term debt ($ mil.): —
Dividends
Yield: —
Payout: —
Market value ($ mil.): —

ATLANTIC HEALTH SYSTEM INC.

Got a gash or gout in the Garden State? Atlantic Health System has more than 1600 beds for you to get better in. The not-for-profit Atlantic Health System (AHS) operates five acute care hospital providing general medical and surgical services to residents of northern New Jersey. Its flagship Morristown Medical Center serves as a regional trauma center and provides specialty care in a number of areas including oncology pediatrics and cardiac care. The system's Overlook Medical Center houses the Atlantic Neuroscience Institute; home to the Comprehensive Stroke Center. Its smaller Newton Medical Center serves patients in two New

Jersey counties as well as counties in Pennsylvania and New York.

Operations

The system's corporate health division provides employee assistance programs as well as a full range of corporate-related medical services including physicals smoking cessation work injury and travel medicine services. Its corporate clients include pharmaceutical companies manufacturing operations and municipal governments.

In addition to its hospitals AHS operates home care and hospice units that serve Essex Morris Somerset and Union counties. It also serves as the official health care provider for the New York Jets football team which has named its corporate headquarters and training facility the Atlantic Health Jets Training Center.

AHS provides educational that includes continuing medical education classes and residency programs in pharmacy and nursing to keep its medical staff current on medical technologies and techniques. Annually the hospital system teaches more than 250 medical residents through about a dozen residency programs in emergency and family medicine surgery and pediatrics among others. It is affiliated with Mount Sinai School of Medicine and the Mount Sinai Hospital giving AHS access to the major university hospital's resources.

Strategy

AHS is growing by acquiring other hospitals in northern New Jersey. In 2014 it acquired Pompton Plains-based Chilton Memorial Hospital (now Chilton Medical Center) and affiliated Chilton Health Network sites. The purchase added 260 beds plus related outpatient clinics. AHS became a three-hospital system in early 2011 when Newton Medical Center then known as Newton Memorial Hospital moved under the AHS umbrella. The deal expanded access to outpatient and preventative care throughout the region increased specialty care options and allowed for the improvement of facilities at the Newton campus.

EXECUTIVES

Vp; President Chilton Medical Center, Deborah K Zastocki, age 58
Vp; President Overlook Medical Center, Alan Lieber
Vp Behavioral And Integrative Medicine; Cio, Linda A Reed
President and CEO, Joseph A. Trunfio
Vp; President Morristown Medical Center, David J Shulkin
Vp System Development And Chief Strategy Officer, William D Neigher
Vice President Human Resources, Andrew Kovach
Medical Director, Theodor Feigelman
Vice Chairman, Robert A Toohey
Secretary, Anne Delaney

LOCATIONS

HQ: ATLANTIC HEALTH SYSTEM INC.
475 SOUTH ST, MORRISTOWN, NJ 07960-6459
Phone: 973-660-3100
Web: WWW.ATLANTICHEALTH.ORG

PRODUCTS/OPERATIONS

Selected Operations

Atlantic Home Care
Atlantic Hospice
Atlantic Neuroscience Institute (Overlook Hospital)
Carol G. Simon Cancer Center (Morristown and Overlook hospitals)
Chilton Medical Center
Gagnon Cardiovascular Institute (Morristown Hospital)
Goryeb Children' s Hospital
Morristown Medical Center
Newton Medical Center
Overlook Medical Center

COMPETITORS

Barnabas Health
Children' s Specialized Hospital
Chilton Medical Center
Community Health Systems
East Orange General Hospital
JFK Health System
JFK Medical Center
Newark Beth Israel Medical Center
Raritan Bay Medical Center
Robert Wood Johnson University Hospital at Rahway
Saint Barnabas Medical
St. Joseph' s Healthcare System
The Valley Hospital
Trinitas Regional Medical Center

HISTORICAL FINANCIALS

Company Type: Private

Income Statement FYE: December 31

	REVENUE ($ mil.)	NET INCOME ($ mil.)	NET PROFIT MARGIN	EMPLOYEES
12/12	1,564	144	9.2%	221
12/09	0	0	—	—
12/03	883	6	0.8%	—
12/01	857	9	1.1%	—
Annual Growth	5.6%	27.9%	—	—

2012 Year-End Financials

Debt ratio: ——
Return on equity: 9.20%
Cash ($ mil.): 175
Current ratio: 1.30
Long-term debt ($ mil.): —
Dividends
Yield: —
Payout: —
Market value ($ mil.): —

ATLANTIC METHANOL PRODUCTION COMPANY LLC

Atlantic Methanol Production Company (AMPCO) must have adopted "Waste not want not" as its motto. It tries not to waste the natural gas that is a by-product of its parent companies' production processes. A joint venture between Noble Energy (45% ownership) Marathon Oil (45%) and SONAGAS the National Gas Company of Equatorial Guinea (10%) the company operates one of the largest methanol plants in the world. The plant off the coast of Equatorial Guinea produces about 1 million tons of methanol annually—2% of the global market. AMPCO also distributes using three vessels and five terminals in Europe and US where it sells most of its production.

Geographic Reach

AMPCO's plant located on Bioko Island in Equatorial Guinea has the capacity to produce 3000 metric tons per day of methanol. It maintains storage at its production site at Punta Europa in Equatorial Guinea as well as in the US (Louisiana and Texas) the Netherlands and the UK.

Operations

The global demand for methanol is about 60 million metric tons per year of which Equitorial Guinea supplies 2% from its single plant. Methanol is used as an intermediate in the manufacture of several everyday products including adhesive resins for plywood and pressboard polyester fibers and packaging paints and coatings plastics and fuels and fuel additives. Some of methanol's fastest growth areas are in the acetic acid and fuels areas including biodiesel. Other applications include using methanol for fuel cells.

Feedstock for AMPCO's plant is supplied from natural gas production from the Alba field in Equatorial Guinea (operated by Marathon Oil and Noble Energy) under a contract that runs through 2026.

Sales and Marketing

The company manages its marketing and sales from its US-based headquarters in Houston. It markets in Europe through an agent solvadis methanol in Frankfurt Germany.

Financial Performance

While no separate financials are available Noble Energy reported that 2013 net income derived by Noble Energy and AMPCO increased primarily due to a 19% jump in the average realized sales price of methanol.

Strategy

AMPCO is reporting an increase in demand from Asia the US and Western Europe for methanol. There is also an expanding demand for methanol in the oilfield services sector along the coast of West Africa.To keep up with demand in 2013 AMPCO contracted with Mitsui O.S.K. Lines for two new methanol carriers.

Company Background

Noble Energy Marathon Oil and SONAGAS formed the JV in 1997.

Normal 0 false false false EN-US X-NONE X-NONE

/* Style Definitions */ table.MsoNormalTable {mso-style-name:"Table Normal"; mso-tstyle-rowband-size:0; mso-tstyle-colband-size:0; mso-style-noshow:yes; mso-style-priority:99; mso-style-qformat:yes; mso-style-parent:""; mso-padding-alt:0in 5.4pt 0in 5.4pt; mso-para-margin-top:0in; mso-para-margin-right:0in; mso-para-margin-bottom:10.0pt; mso-para-margin-left:0in; line-height:115%; mso-pagination:widow-orphan; font-size:11.0pt; font-family:"Calibri""sans-serif"; mso-ascii-font-family:Calibri; mso-ascii-theme-font:minor-latin; mso-hansi-font-family:Calibri; mso-hansi-theme-font:minor-latin;}

EXECUTIVES

President and General Manager, Paul Moschell
Manager Human Resources and Administration, Arthur (Budd) Buschmann
Chairman, W. Ken Keag
Vice Chairman, Juan A. Ndong
Vice President Marketing, Edson Jones
Manager Finance and Administration, Jim O'Casek
Vice President Operations and Resident Manager, Pedro Arasa
Vice Chairman, Juan Antonio
Vice Chairman President and General Manager, Paul Moschell
Vice Chairman, Juan A. Ndong
Vice Chairman, Juan Antonio

LOCATIONS

HQ: ATLANTIC METHANOL PRODUCTION COMPANY LLC
12600 NORTHBOROUGH DR # 150, HOUSTON, TX 770673200
Phone: 2818728324
Web: WWW.ATLANTICMETHANOL.COM

COMPETITORS

Celanese
Eastman Chemical
LyondellBasell
Methanex
OCI Partners LP

HISTORICAL FINANCIALS

Company Type: Private

Income Statement FYE: December 31

	REVENUE ($ mil.)	NET INCOME ($ mil.)	NET PROFIT MARGIN	EMPLOYEES
12/10	254	65	25.8%	342
12/08	341	122	35.8%	—
12/07	1,405	0		
Annual Growth	(43.4%)	10372.8%	—	—

2010 Year-End Financials

Debt ratio: —
Return on equity: 25.80%
Cash ($ mil.): 22
Current ratio: 0.90
Long-term debt ($ mil.): —
Dividends
Yield: —
Payout: —
Market value ($ mil.): —

ATTEBURY GRAIN LLC

LOCATIONS

HQ: ATTEBURY GRAIN LLC
3905 BELL ST STE A, AMARILLO, TX 791094281
Phone: 8063351639
Web: WWW.ATTEBURY.COM

HISTORICAL FINANCIALS

Company Type: Private

Income Statement FYE: December 31

	REVENUE ($ mil.)	NET INCOME ($ mil.)	NET PROFIT MARGIN	EMPLOYEES
12/07	215	2	1.1%	124
12/05	127	(0)	—	—
12/04	114	0	0.2%	—
12/03	108	0	—	—
Annual Growth	18.7%	—	—	—

2007 Year-End Financials

Debt ratio: —
Return on equity: 1.10%
Cash ($ mil.): 0
Current ratio: 0.10
Long-term debt ($ mil.): —
Dividends
Yield: —
Payout: —
Market value ($ mil.): —

AVERITT EXPRESS INC.

Small loads add up at Averitt Express. The company provides less-than-truckload (LTL) freight transportation service. (LTL carriers combine freight from multiple shippers into a single trailer.) It operates a fleet of about 3900 tractors and 11700 trailers from a network of some 80 terminals. Averitt Express directly serves the southern US and Mexico and it provides service elsewhere in North America through partnerships with other carriers such as Lakeville Motor Express and DATS. The company also offers truckload and expedited freight transportation along with logistics warehousing and international freight forwarding. Customers have included Home Depot Shoe Carnival and V.F. Corporation.

Geographic Reach

Averitt Express has 140 facilities in Alabama Arkansas California Florida Georgia Illinois Kentucky Louisiana Mississippi Missouri North Carolina Ohio Oklahoma South Carolina Tennessee Texas Virginia and Wisconsin. It also provides international transportation services to 100 different countries and more than 300 international destinations.

Strategy

The company aims to grow from solely a LTL carrier based in the Southeast to an international transportation and logistics company. To this end it continues to strategically broaden its geographic reach and range of services. Averitt Express in 2012 launched a new business unit zeroing in on retailers in need of distribution services. The new unit Averitt Retail Distribution Services offers customized delivery services catering to the unique requirements of retailers and is targeting retailers needing delivery in large Southern markets.

During 2010 Averitt Express responded to customer demand by expanding its flatbed operation launched early in the year. The move built upon the company's decision to bundle its full-load transportation offerings with national intermodal service. It has partnered with railroads in several key regions Union Pacific and BNSF in the West Norfolk Southern and CSX in the East and Midwest and Florida East Coast in Florida and Georgia.

Ownership

CEO Gary Sasser owns Averitt Express which was founded by Thurman Averitt as Livingston Merchants Co-op in 1958. Sasser bought the company from Averitt in 1971.

EXECUTIVES

President and CEO, Gary D. Sasser
EVP and COO, Wayne Spain
EVP Sales and Marketing, Phil Pierce
EVP and CFO, George Johnson
VP-Intl Dev, Charlie McGee

LOCATIONS

HQ: AVERITT EXPRESS INC.
1415 NEAL ST, COOKEVILLE, TN 38501-4328
Phone: 931-526-3306
Web: WWW.AVERITTEXPRESS.COM

PRODUCTS/OPERATIONS

Selected Services

Cross-border/domestic offshore (Canada Mexico Puerto Rico/Virgin Islands)
Dedicated
Expedited
Intermodal
International ocean/air (ocean/air Asia-Memphis Express)
LTL (regional nationwide distribution/consolidation)
Portside
Retail specialized services
Transportation management
Truckload (dry van flatbed brokerage)
Warehousing

COMPETITORS

AAA Cooper Transportation
Arkansas Best
C.H. Robinson Worldwide
Con-way Freight
Estes Express
FedEx Freight
J.B. Hunt
Old Dominion Freight
R+L Carriers
Schneider National
Southeastern Freight Lines
Swift Transportation
UPS Freight
YRC Worldwide

HISTORICAL FINANCIALS

Company Type: Private

Income Statement FYE: December 31

	REVENUE ($ mil.)	NET INCOME ($ mil.)	NET PROFIT MARGIN	EMPLOYEES
12/12	957	39	4.2%	8,208
12/11	917	30	3.3%	—
12/10	819	18	2.2%	—
12/09	766	5	0.7%	—
Annual Growth	7.7%	97.6%	—	—

2012 Year-End Financials

Debt ratio: —
Return on equity: 4.20%
Cash ($ mil.): 161
Current ratio: 4.00
Long-term debt ($ mil.): —
Dividends
Yield: —
Payout: —
Market value ($ mil.): —

AVI SYSTEMS INC.

EXECUTIVES

Chairman, Joe Stoebner
COO, Michael (Mike) Vergauwen
President and CEO, Jeff Stoebner
Chief Financial Officer, Randi Borth

LOCATIONS

HQ: AVI SYSTEMS INC.
9675 W 76TH ST STE 200, EDEN PRAIRIE, MN 553443707
Phone: 9529493700
Web: WWW.AVISYSTEMS.COM

Selected Locations

California
Colorado
Illinois
Iowa
Michigan
Minnesota
Missouri
Nebraska
North Dakota
Ohio
South Dakota
Texas
Wisconsin

COMPETITORS

ACT Teleconferencing
AT Conference
AVI-SPL
IVCi
PSAV Presentation Services

HISTORICAL FINANCIALS

Company Type: Private

Income Statement FYE: March 31

	REVENUE ($ mil.)	NET INCOME ($ mil.)	NET PROFIT MARGIN	EMPLOYEES
03/14	172	9	5.7%	233
03/13	143	7	5.0%	—
03/12	111	6	5.6%	—
03/11	89	0	—	—
Annual Growth	24.4%	—	—	—

2014 Year-End Financials

Debt ratio: —
Return on equity: 5.70%
Cash ($ mil.): 15
Current ratio: 1.90
Long-term debt ($ mil.): —
Dividends
Yield: —
Payout: —
Market value ($ mil.): —

AXEL JOHNSON INC.

The Johnson family of Stockholm Sweden has an investment arm that stretches across the ocean. Axel Johnson owns and operates North American businesses on behalf of the Johnson dynasty. The investment firm focuses on several industries such as energy medical device manufacturing and water treatment. Its portfolio includes Sprague Energy Parkson Corp. and Kinetico Incorporated. Axel Johnson's companies boast about $4 billion in annual revenues. Axel Johnson along with Axel Johnson AB and AXFast are all affiliated with Sweden-based Axel Johnson Group but are independent. Established in 1873 the Johnson family of companies is in its fourth generation of family ownership.

Operations

Axel Johnson which was formed in 1920 is a long-term investor that typically holds on to its companies for about 20 years. Some companies have been a part of Axel Johnson's portfolio for more than 40 years. Two of its holdings Parkson and Kinetico are part of Axel Johnson's AxWater Group which was formed in 2000.

Strategy

Through NewtrAX Axel Johnson makes minority investments in smaller businesses. NewtrAX has stakes in Cadence a manufacturer of cutting and piercing instruments used for the medical and industrial applications. It also owns portions of wood reclamation company Mountain Lumber Co. and Walk2Campus a real estate management and acquisition company. The company in late 2011 invested some $15 million in ConforMIS which develops and markets customized medical devices for the treatment of osteoarthritis and joint damage.

Financial Performance

Following the economic downturn the company has seen sales increase for several years. Axel Johnson's revenue rose by 6% in 2012 to $4.2 billion as compared to 2011. Energy product sales generated the largest portion of the company's revenue. The results were powered by higher commodity prices and growth at Kinetico Cadence and Mountain Lumber; the first two along with ConforMis and Walk2Campus reported record sales in 2012.

EXECUTIVES

President and CEO, Michael D. (Mike) Milligan, age 50
EVP, Ben J. Hennelly, age 43
Vice President Investor Relations & Marketing, Grant A.H. Brown
Manager Corporate Development, Erika M. Cafarella
EVP Tax, John C Pascale
VP of Sales, Tom Flaherty
CFO, Sally Sarsfield

LOCATIONS

HQ: AXEL JOHNSON INC.
155 SPRING ST FL 6, NEW YORK, NY 10012-5254
Phone: 646-291-2445
Web: WWW.AXELJOHNSON.COM

PRODUCTS/OPERATIONS

Selected Portfolio Companies

Cadence Incorporated
ConforMIS Inc.
Decisyon Inc.
Kinetico Incorporated
Mountain Lumber Company
Parkson Corporation
Sprague Energy Corp.
Walk2Campus Holdings LLC

COMPETITORS

CCMP Capital
Court Square Capital Partners
Enterprise Partners
KKR
Menlo Ventures
Sevin Rosen

HISTORICAL FINANCIALS

Company Type: Private

Income Statement FYE: December 31

	REVENUE ($ mil.)	NET INCOME ($ mil.)	NET PROFIT MARGIN	EMPLOYEES
12/11	3,954	22	0.6%	1,200
12/10	2,982	15	0.5%	—
12/09	2,598	11	0.5%	—
12/08	4,312	8	0.2%	—
Annual Growth	(2.9%)	39.9%	—	—

2011 Year-End Financials

Debt ratio: —
Return on equity: 0.60%
Cash ($ mil.): 41
Current ratio: 0.60
Long-term debt ($ mil.): —
Dividends
Yield: —
Payout: —
Market value ($ mil.): —

AZUSA PACIFIC UNIVERSITY

An evangelical Christian institution Azusa Pacific University (APU) has an enrollment of about 10000 undergraduate graduate and doctoral students. It offers approximately 60 fields of undergraduate study and about 50 graduate degree programs as well as a number of certificate and credentialing programs. Undergraduate students are required to complete ministry and service credits every semester; options include participating in ministries international service experience and doing volunteer work. APU traces its roots to 1899 and the Training School for Christian Workers the West Coast's first bible college.

Geographic Reach

In addition to its two main campuses (known as the East Campus and the West Campus) in Azusa a community located in the San Gabriel Valley northeast of Los Angeles the university has seven regional centers in Southern California.

Operations

APU has a student-to-faculty ratio of 12:1 and employs more than 1200 full-time part-time and adjunct faculty members. Full-time undergraduate tuition runs at some $30000 each year. In addition to theology the university's major programs include business sciences liberal arts music nursing education and visual and performing arts. It offers online programs to supplement classes held at its main campus and regional branch locations.

Financial Performance

Revenue was flat at about $220 million in 2012 as an increase in net tuition and fees –which account for more than 85% of earnings –was offset by declines in government grants and contracts private gifts and investment income. Net income fell 180% (to a loss of $12.5 million) as expenses related to student services and instruction increased; the university also reported an absence of gain on early swap terminations (which were present the previous year).

APU's annual budget runs at some $205 million. It has an endowment of more than $50 million.

Strategy

Five-year strategic plans (reaching through 2016) include improving resources for internal communication; enhancing support infrastructure for grants research and teaching; and increasing student and faculty diversity. APU is also working to restructure its curriculum.

EXECUTIVES

President on, Jon R. Wallace
Executive Vice President, David E. Bixby
VP Legal Affairs and Community Relations and General Counsel, Mark S. Dickerson
SVP Student Life and Dean of Students, Terry A. Franson
SVP People and Organizational Development, Deana L. Porterfield
EVP, John C. Reynolds
Provost, Mark E. Stanton
Senior Vice President Chief Financial Officer, Bob Johansen
Head Coach Defensive Coordinator, Brian Willmer
Vice President Emeritus, Hank Bode
President CEO and Trustee, Jon R. Wallace
Trustee, Michael Lizarraga
Trustee, David Le Shana
Trustee, Sheryl Patton
Trustee, Paul Szeto
Trustee, Raleigh Washington
Trustee, Robyn Dillon
Trustee, Ray Johnston

LOCATIONS

HQ: AZUSA PACIFIC UNIVERSITY
901 E ALOSTA AVE, AZUSA, CA 91702-2701
Phone: 626-969-3434
Web: WWW.APU.EDU

Selected Locations

Azusa CA
Los Angeles CA
Murrieta CA
Orange CA
Oxnard CA
San Bernardino CA
San Diego CA
Victorville CA

PRODUCTS/OPERATIONS

Selected Schools

American Language and Culture Institute
Azusa Pacific Online University
Center for Global Learning and Engagement
College of Liberal Arts and Sciences
School of Adult and Professional Studies
School of Behavioral and Applied Sciences
School of Business and Management
School of Education
School of Music
School of Nursing
School of Theology
School of Visual and Performing Arts
University Libraries

Selected Academic Programs

Adult and Professional Studies
Behavioral and Applied Sciences
Business and Management
Education
Liberal Arts and Sciences
Music and the Arts
Nursing
Theology

HISTORICAL FINANCIALS

Company Type: Private

Income Statement FYE: June 30

	REVENUE ($ mil.)	NET INCOME ($ mil.)	NET PROFIT MARGIN	EMPLOYEES
06/12	261	(0)	—	1,344
06/11	270	26	9.7%	—
06/09	227	8	3.8%	—
06/09	203	0	—	—
Annual Growth	8.7%	—	—	—

2012 Year-End Financials

Debt ratio: —
Return on equity: (-0.20%)
Cash ($ mil.): 31
Current ratio: —
Long-term debt ($ mil.): —
Dividends
Yield: —
Payout: —
Market value ($ mil.): —

BABSON COLLEGE

Babson students could babble on and on about business management. With an enrollment of more than 3000 students Babson College is lauded as one of the nation's leading business schools. The school's undergraduate programs combine liberal arts with business curriculum; it also grants master's degrees in business administration entrepreneurship and other fields. Babson students in their first year receive the practical experience of creating for-profit ventures. Babson's entrepreneurship program has been ranked at the top of such programs in publications including Entrepreneur and U.S. News & World Report.

Geographic Reach

Babson College's main campus is located in Babson Park near Wellesley Massachusetts. Its students come from across the US and 70 international countries.

Operations

While the F.W. Olin Graduate School of Business grants Master of Business Administration (MBA) degrees and customized Master of Science degrees the Arthur M. Blank Center for Entrepreneurship offers graduate and undergraduate courses in entrepreneurial leadership.

In addition to undergraduate and graduate degree programs Babson conducts collaborative research programs that connect students with scholars and area business leaders.

Financial Performance

Operating revenue rose 4% to about $178 million in fiscal 2013 from higher student tuition and fee earnings as well as income from auxiliary activities room and board services and other educational and non-educational programs. The increase was offset somewhat by a dip in contributions and grants and investment income.

Undergraduate tuition runs at some $43500 per year.

Strategy

Babson College is expanding and improving its undergraduate curriculum with the goal of integrating management and liberal arts focuses. In 2013 it began rolling out new guidelines that aim to increase the undergraduate programs' focus on social environmental and economic concerns as well as on creativity and entrepreneurship.

To increase entrepreneurship opportunities for students in 2012 Babson extended its Butler Venture Accelerator program to its San Francisco campus. Also that year the college widened international entrepreneurship opportunities by partnering with Shiv Nadar University to provide programs in India. In 2013 Babson launched a new Master's Degree in Entrepreneurial Leadership; it also opened a new innovation lab focused on supporting female entrepreneurs.

Company Background

Babson was founded in 1919 (as Babson Institute) by philanthropist educator and businessman Roger Babson.

EXECUTIVES

Chairman, Thomas T. (Tom) Stallkamp, age 68
Vice Chairman, Robert E. Weissman, age 73
President and Trustee, Leonard A. (Len) Schlesinger, age 61
Director Public Relations, Michael J. Chmura
Vice Provost Academic Affairs, Henry N. Deneault
Associate VP Financial Services and Controller, Richard Bowman
Chief of Staff and Associate VP Planning, Carol Hacker
VP Administration and CIO, Mary Rose
Vice Provost Entrepreneurship and Global Management, Stephen Spinelli Jr., age 60
VP College Marketing, Scott Timmins
VP Advancement, Richard Voos
Provost, Patricia Greene
College Registrar, Linda E. Kean
Vice Chairman, N. Lyle Howland
Vice President Institutional Investment Management, Kathryn D. Karlic
Chairman, Ronald G. Weiner
Vice Chairman, Anthony C. Woodruff
VP Finance and CFO, Philip N. (Phil) Shapiro
Manager Collection Management Library, Martha Burk
Web Services Librarian, Anna Burke
Murata Dean F.W. Olin Graduate School of Business, Mark Rice
Director Public Safety, John Jackson
Chief Investment Officer, Bruce T. Herring
Associate Director Public Relations, Barbara Spies Blair
Director Budget, Jeffrey Dubois
Dean Babson Executive Education, Elaine Eisenman
Dean Undergraduate School, Dennis Hanno
VP Development, Eric Graage
Director Student Financial Services and Associate Dean Undergraduate School, Melissa Shaak
Associate VP and Director Human Resources, Charles J. Anderson
Chief Executive Officer, Shahid Ansari
EVP and Executive Dean, Robert Fogel
Director Strategic Communications, Diane Fulman
Vice President General Counsel, Jonathan Moll
Dean Student Affairs, Betsy Newman
Chief Diversity Officer, Elizabeth Thornton
Vice President Babson Alumni, Kate Bellaud
Vice President of Development, Diana Zais
Vice President of Enrollment and Dean of Admissions, Grant M. Gosselin
Vice President for Governance, Jane Edmonds
President Elect | Babson College, Kerry Healey
Chief Operating Officer, Ranch Kimball
President Oxfam America and Drew Gilpin Faust, Raymond Offenheiser
Chief Marketing Officer, Sarah Sykora
Trustee, Andronico A. Luksic
Vice Chairman, Robert E. Weissman, age 73
Trustee, Joseph L. Winn
Trustee, Francis P. Jenkins Jr., age 71
President and Trustee, Leonard A. (Len) Schlesinger, age 61
Trustee, Edsel B. Ford II, age 65
Trustee, Joseph P. (Joe) Campanelli, age 58
Trustee, David F. (Dave) Lamere, age 53
Trustee, Delia H. (Bina) Thompson, age 64
Trustee, Myra M. Hart, age 73
Trustee, Thomas F. (Tom) Gilbane Jr., age 66
Trustee, William G. Burrill
Trustee, Karen K. Chandor
Trustee, Stephen Cutler
Trustee, Gloria M. Gutierrez
Trustee, Muhammad H. Habib
Vice Chairman, N. Lyle Howland
Trustee, Estefano E. Isaias Sr.
Trustee, Eric G. Johnson
Trustee, Kathryn D. Karlic
Trustee, Richard K. Miller
Trustee, Jeremiah J. Noonan
Trustee, Richard A. Renwick
Trustee, Thomas N. (Tom) Riley
Trustee, James W. Taylor
Trustee, Aaron M. Walton
Trustee, Lawrence Weber
Chairman, Ronald G. Weiner
Vice Chairman, Anthony C. Woodruff
Trustee, Craig R. Benson
Trustee, William D. Bygrave
Trustee, Theodore A. Clark
Trustee, Patrick McGonagle
Trustee, Bruce T. Herring
Trustee, Ann B. Hutchins
Trustee, Gary Zwerling
Auditors: PricewaterhouseCoopersLLP

LOCATIONS

HQ: BABSON COLLEGE
231 FOREST ST, BABSON PARK, MA 02457
Phone: 781-235-1200
Web: WWW.BABSONATHLETICS.COM

PRODUCTS/OPERATIONS

2012 Sales

	$ mil.	% of total
Program service fees	160	90
Net released assets	7	4
Endowment spending	6	4
Contributions & grants	2	2
Investment income	0	-
Total	**177**	**100**

Selected Academic Divisions

Accounting And Law
Arts And Humanities
Economics
Entrepreneurship
Finance
History And Society
Management
Marketing
Math And Science
Technology Operations And Information Management

HISTORICAL FINANCIALS

Company Type: Private

Income Statement FYE: June 30

	REVENUE ($ mil.)	NET INCOME ($ mil.)	NET PROFIT MARGIN	EMPLOYEES
06/12	170	4	2.5%	750
06/11	202	14	7.1%	—
06/10	176	0	0.4%	—
06/09	174	0	—	—
Annual Growth	(0.8%)	—	—	—

2012 Year-End Financials

Debt ratio: —
Return on equity: 2.50%
Cash ($ mil.): 37
Current ratio: —
Long-term debt ($ mil.): —
Dividends
Yield: —
Payout: —
Market value ($ mil.): —

BAKER MICHAEL JR INC

Michael Baker Jr. is the first-born subsidiary of engineering and construction consulting group Michael Baker. Michael Baker Jr. focuses on engineering design for civil infrastructure and transportation projects which include highways bridges airports busways corporate headquarters data centers correctional facilities and educational facilities. The unit also provides planning geotechnical and environmental services in the water/wastewater pipeline emergency and consequence management resource management and telecommunications markets. Recent projects include facilities for the US government.

Recently Michael Baker Jr. and its parent have benefited from increased government spending in the Department of Defense and Department of Homeland Security. The unit also is awarded work from state departments of transportation.

Michael Baker Jr. which was founded by its namesake brings a life-cycle approach to its projects and its long-term business strategy. It incorporates all phases of development from planning design and construction to operations maintenance and renewal.

EXECUTIVES

Vice President, Mike Sidani
Vp-const Serv Business Dev, Tom Donatelli
Vp-pipeline Eng Practice, Cory A Wilder
Vp-texas Transpo Operations, Juan Contreras
Asst Vp-connecticut Office, David Tudryn
Asst Vp Int'l-moon Township, Lois M Muller
Vp, Sam S Darghous
Vp-architecture Group, Ronald W Kretz
Vp-transportaion Business Indi, Kenton Zinn
Avp-architecture Practice, Kurt Fritz
Vp National Rail & Transit, David C Wilcock
Assist Vp Trans Planning Grp, Lorna Parkins
Assist Vp For Defense Market, Ronald M Schirato
Svp & Southeast Region Transpo, Scott Armstrong
Vp-philadelphia Pa Office, Mark Alisesky
Asst Vp-phoenix Transpo Market, Marta Gerber
Asst Vp-new Jersey Transpo, Magdy Hagag
Asst Vp-civil Structures & Con, Joseph Danyo
Asst Vp-transpo Design Operati, Kenneth J Collins
Vp, Jeffrey Sparrow
Avp-federal Programs, Mary A Buvens
Avp-pipeline Practice, Paul Carson
Avp-alternative Delivery Unit, Paul McIlree
Avp-federal Programs, Alfonso Riera
Avp-civil & Environmental Engi, Mark Osler
Vp-anchorage Al, Jeff Baker
Avp-anchorage Al, Shawn Snisarenko
Avp-civil & Environmental Eng, Dave Jula
Avp-defense Market, David Schaarsmith
Avp-mid Atlantic Region, Dwain Hathaway
Vice President, Michael Conaboy
Vice President, Walter G Lyons
Vice President, Keith Meyer
Asst Vp-transpo Operations Mgr, Jeffrey D May

LOCATIONS

HQ: BAKER MICHAEL JR INC
4301 DUTCH RIDGE RD, BEAVER, PA 15009-9600
Phone: 724-495-7711
Web: WWW.MBAKERCORP.COM

COMPETITORS

CH2M HILL
Camp Dresser McKee
Halliburton
KBR
Parsons Brinckerhoff

HISTORICAL FINANCIALS

Company Type: Private

Income Statement FYE: December 31

	REVENUE ($ mil.)	NET INCOME ($ mil.)	NET PROFIT MARGIN	EMPLOYEES
12/09	418	15	3.7%	1,798
12/07	351	10	2.9%	—
12/06	144	0	0.0%	—
Annual Growth	42.4%	5327.2%	—	—

BALL STATE UNIVERSITY

Students at this university are on the ball. Ball State University (BSU) has an enrollment of about 21000 undergraduate and graduate students. It offers about 180 undergraduate majors more than 100 master's degree programs and 17 doctoral six associate and two specialist degrees in seven academic colleges. It has a Teachers College as well as colleges of applied sciences and technology; architecture and planning; business; communication information and media; fine arts; and sciences and humanities. Notable alumni include late night talk show host David Letterman and Garfield comic strip creator Jim Davis.

Geographic Reach

BSU has students from 48 states two US territories about 43 countries and every Indiana county.

Operations

The university's 731-acre campus in Muncie Indiana includes 106 academic administrative auxiliary and residential buildings valued at more than $1 billion.

The institution enrolls more than 675 international students. Out-of-state students make up 13% of on-campus enrollment. BSU has a student-to-faculty ratio of 16:1.

Modern initiatives include harnessing geothermal energy to power the campus and raising scholarship money to attract more students from outside of Indiana. Renovation and new construction of buildings were part of a multi-year effort to upgrade the campus infrastructure that concluded in 2012.

In 2013 BSU launched three free online classes.

Financial Performance

The university generates more than 30% of its revenues from tuition and fees net of scholarship allowances. BSU's 6% increase in revenues in 2012 was due to increase in student tuition and fees and increased enrollment. Auxiliary enterprises revenues including housing and dining net revenues increased by $3.7 million as the result of rate increases and increased occupancy in apartments and residence halls partially offset by a decline in scholarship allowances from government and private sources.Net income increased by 13% in 2012 due to higher investment returns and capital appropriations partially offset by rise in operating expenses.

Company Background

The institution traces its origins to a private teacher's college in 1899. Officially founded in 1918 BSU became a university in 1965.

Glass jars filled with pickles apple butter and stewed tomatoes were part of the university's foundation. The family that gave us Ball canning jars and other glass containers donated the land for the original campus.

EXECUTIVES

President, Jo Ann M. Gora, age 68, $260,000 total compensation
VP University Advancement, Ben E. Hancock Jr.
VP Enrollment Marketing and Communications, Thomas R (Tom) Taylor Jr.
Provost and VP Academic Affairs, Terry S. King
VP Student Affairs and Dean of Students, Kay Bales
Associate VP Human Resources and State Relations, Thomas Morrison
Director Admissions and Orientation, Chris Munchel
Registrar and Director Registration and Academic Progress, Nancy Cronk
Director Alumni Services and Executive Assistant to the Alumni Council, Debbie Linegar
Executive Director University Development, Charles Jaggers
Dean University Libraries, Arthur Hafner
Head of Digital Libraries and Web Services, Phang Wibowo
Director Purchasing and Central Stores, Matt Stephenson
Associate VP Student Affairs and Director Housing and Residence Life, Alan Hargrave
Director Scholarships and Financial Aid, Robert Zellers
Dean College of Applied Sciences and Technology, Prof Mitchell (Mitch) Whaley
Dean College of Architecture and Planning, Prof Guillermo Vasquez de Velasco
Dean College of Communication Information and Media, Roger Lavery
Dean College of Fine Arts, Prof Robert Kvam
Dean College of Sciences and Humanities, Michael Maggiotto
Interim Dean Miller College of Business, Rodney Davis
VP Information Technology, Philip Repp
President Board of Trustees, Hollis E. Hughes Jr.
Vice President Board of Trustees, Frank Hancock
VP Business Affairs and Treasurer, Randy Howard
Dean Miller College of Business, Rajib Sanyal
Interim President Ball State Innovation Corporation, Wil Davis

LOCATIONS

HQ: BALL STATE UNIVERSITY
2000 W UNIVERSITY AVE, MUNCIE, IN 47306-0002
Phone: 765-289-1241
Web: WWW.CMS.BSU.EDU

PRODUCTS/OPERATIONS

Colleges
College of Applied Sciences and Technology
College of Architecture and Planning
College of Communication Information and Media
College of Fine Arts
College of Sciences and Humanities
Honors College
Miller College of Business
Teachers College
University College

HISTORICAL FINANCIALS

Company Type: Private

Income Statement FYE: June 30

	REVENUE ($ mil.)	NET INCOME ($ mil.)	NET PROFIT MARGIN	EMPLOYEES
06/11	240	32	13.4%	6,426
06/07	224	43	19.4%	—
06/06	219	24	11.1%	—
06/05	209	23	11.3%	—
Annual Growth	2.3%	5.4%	—	—

2011 Year-End Financials

Debt ratio: —
Return on equity: 13.40%
Cash ($ mil.): 120
Current ratio: 3.10
Long-term debt ($ mil.): —
Dividends
Yield: —
Payout: —
Market value ($ mil.): —

BALTIMORE CITY PUBLIC SCHOOL SYSTEMS (INC)

LOCATIONS

HQ: BALTIMORE CITY PUBLIC SCHOOL SYSTEMS (INC)
200 E NORTH AVE, BALTIMORE, MD 212025910
Phone: 4103968700
Web: WWW.BSFA.ORG

HISTORICAL FINANCIALS

Company Type: Private

Income Statement FYE: June 30

	REVENUE ($ mil.)	NET INCOME ($ mil.)	NET PROFIT MARGIN	EMPLOYEES
06/13	1,432	(4)	—	12,000
06/12	1,480	(18)	—	—
06/02	988	(23)	—	—
Annual Growth	3.4%	—	—	—

2013 Year-End Financials

Debt ratio: —
Return on equity: (-0.30%)
Cash ($ mil.): 147
Current ratio: —
Long-term debt ($ mil.): —
Dividends
Yield: —
Payout: —
Market value ($ mil.): —

BANK OF ST AUGUSTINE

LOCATIONS

HQ: BANK OF ST AUGUSTINE
120 STATE ROAD 312 W, SAINT AUGUSTINE, FL 320864282
Phone: 9048245600
Web: WWW.BANKSTAUG.COM

HISTORICAL FINANCIALS

Company Type: Private

Income Statement FYE: December 31

	ASSETS ($ mil.)	NET INCOME ($ mil.)	INCOME AS % OF ASSETS	EMPLOYEES
12/09	170	(1)	—	30
12/08	159	0	0.5%	—
12/07	153	1	1.2%	—
12/06	147	0	—	—
Annual Growth	4.9%	—	—	—

2009 Year-End Financials

Debt ratio: —
Return on equity: (-13.10%)
Cash ($ mil.): 6
Current ratio: —
Long-term debt ($ mil.): —
Dividends
Yield: —
Payout: —
Market value ($ mil.): —

BANNER HEALTH

Hoist this Banner high! Banner Health is one of the largest secular not-for-profit health systems in the US. The organization operates nearly two dozen hospitals (with roughly 4000 beds). It also operates clinics nursing homes clinical laboratories ambulatory surgery centers home health agencies and other healthcare-related organizations including physician practices and a captive insurance company. Banner Health participates in medical research in areas such as Alzheimer's disease and spinal cord injuries through its Banner Sun Health Research division. The company provides services in seven states in the western US; its largest concentration of facilities is in Arizona.

Operations

Banner Health is one of the first not-for-profit hospital operators to reinsure its employees through its captive insurance company Samaritan Insurance Funding. By offering this service Banner Health is able to diversify its risk improve cash flow and lower life insurance costs by about half a million dollars a year.

The multi-specialty system also operates a health plan in Arizona for Medicare-eligible patients. Its MediSunONE plan includes Medicare and Medicare Part D. In late 2011 the company joined forces with Aetna in what is called an accountable care collaboration (ACO). An ACO uses technology and a team-based approach to care for the hospital's patients. Doctors and hospitals assume accountability for patient outcomes and are rewarded financially for achieving higher quality greater efficiency and overall better patient outcomes. The partnership also includes a new product called Aetna Whole Health that allows Banner's patients access to a line of Aetna services including their own electronic patient record. In 2012 Banner collaborated with Blue Cross Blue Shield of Arizona to create a joint venture called The Blue Cross Blue Shield of Arizona Advantage. Pending regulatory approval the joint venture will provide enhanced Medicare plans and services to an estimated 25000 Medicare Advantage enrollees in Arizona.

Financial Analysis

Banner Health's income is generally derived through three channels: third-party payers such as commercial insurance managed care agreements Medicare and Medicaid and a small portion of self-pay patients as well as by borrowing funds and receiving philanthropic donations.

Its revenues grew by 3% in 2011. However its net loss increased by 105%.

Strategy

The health system tends to grow through construction. Banner Health is nearly always engaged in some sort of construction renovation or upgrade at its numerous facilities. The organization has more than $1 billion in construction projects in progress or completed in recent years. The system has expanded its facilities at Banner Baywood Medical Center Banner Del E. Webb Medical Center Banner Desert Medical Center Banner Thunderbird Medical Center Cardon Children's Medical Center and McKee Medical Center. It does occasionally pick up a new hospital through acquisition as with Arizona's Casa Grande Regional Medical Center the plans for which it announced in late 2012.

Banner Health also partners with M.D. Anderson Cancer Center to operate a comprehensive cancer center in Phoenix. Services include medical oncology radiation oncology surgical oncology pathology laboratory diagnostic imaging as well as other supportive clinical services. M.D. Anderson has clinical oversight for all aspects of care delivery. In 2012 the Center announced a $62.6 million expansion program to increase capacity.

Education looms large on Banner Health's list of priorities –the hospital operates one of the country's largest simulation education centers at its Banner Corporate Center-Mesa. Simulation education is an expanding field in which medical students use computerized mannequins to improve their surgical and medical skills. The school's research has paid off and with Scottsdale Healthcare Osborn Medical Center Banner Health invented the Sapien Transcatheter Heart Valve an artificial heart valve that can replace a diseased aortic heart valve without the open heart surgery that previously was required.

Company Background

Banner Good Samaritan Medical Center opened its doors as a 20-bed hospital in 1911. The medical center which is four months older than the state of Arizona marked its 100th anniversary in October 2011.

EXECUTIVES

EVP and Chief Administrative Officer, Ronald R. (Ron) Bunnell
VP-HR, Gerri Twomey
CEO Banner Baywood Medical Center, Don Evans
President CEO and Director, Peter S. Fine, age 62
EVP and Chief Medical Officer, John Hensing
CEO Fairbanks Memorial Hospital and Denali Center, Mike Powers
President Arizona West Region, Kathy Bollinger
CEO North Colorado Medical Center, Richard O. (Rick) Sutton
President Arizona East Region, Rebecca (Becky) Kuhn
CEO Banner Behavioral Health Hospital Scottsdale, Pat Little-Upah
VP-Comm, Dan Green
CEO Banner Good Samaritan Medical Center, Larry E. Volkmar
SVP General Counsel and Secretary, David M. Bixby
CEO Banner Lassen Medical Center, Bob Edwards
CEO Sterling Regional MedCenter, Julie Klein
CEO Banner Thunderbird Medical Center, Tom Dickson
CEO Washakie Medical Center, Margie R. Molitor
CEO Page Hospital, Sandy Haryasz
Senior Director Public Relations, Bill Byron
SVP Information Technology and CIO, Michael S. (Mike) Warden
CEO Banner Ironwood Medical Center, Julie Nunley
CEO Banner Del E. Webb Medical Center, John Harrington
President and CEO Banner Health Foundation, Andy Kramer
President Western Region, Jim Ferando
CEO Banner Home Care and Hospice, David Baker
CEO East Morgan County Hospital, Linda Thorpe
VP Design and Construction, Kip Edwards
CEO Banner Gateway Medical Center and Banner MD Anderson Cancer Center, Todd S. Werner, age 46
SVP and CFO, Dennis Dahlen
SVP and Chief Talent Officer, Ed Oxford
Chairman, Quentin P. Smith Jr.
CEO Banner Lassen Medical Center, Elizabeth (Liz) Woodyard
CEO Banner Boswell Medical Center, Dave Cheney
CEO Banner Desert Medical Center, Rob Gould
CEO Banner Gateway Medical Center, Pam Nenaber
CEO Banner Baywood Medical Center and Banner Heart Hospital, Laura Robertson
CEO Banner Medical Group, Jim Brannon
CEO Platte County Memorial Hospital, Shelby Nelson
Director Risk Management Western Region, Lynn Runyan

VP Strategy and Planning, Dan Weinman
VP Physician Resources Arizona, Don Maloney
VP Human Resources Arizona, Tom Koelbl
CFO Arizona East Region, Jeff Buehrle
CFO Arizona West Region, Greg Wojtal
CEO Cardon Children's Medical Center, Rhonda Anderson
CEO Banner Estrella Medical Center, Deb Krmpotic
CEO Banner Research, Eric (Bill) Reiman
CEO McKee Medical Center, Marilyn Schock
CEO Banner Churchill Community Hospital, John D'Angelo
CEO Community Hospital, Vincent B. DiFranco
Director Public Relations, Nancy Neff
VP Human Resources Western Region, Jimmy Duncan
VP Human Resources Banner Medical Group, Diane Ekstrand
Regional VP Clinical Services Western Region, Kathy Harris
CEO Banner Health Network, Chuck Lehn
CEO Banner Behavioral Health Hospital, Cherie Martin
CEO Banner Del E. Webb Medical Center, Debbie Flores
CEO Banner Good Samaritan Medical Center, Steve Narang
CEO Ogallala Community Hospital, Sharon Lind
Executive Vice President General Counsel, Jerome D. Jabbour
Vice President of Development, Kim Behrens
Vice President Digital Content, Stephanie Manning
Director, Christopher H. (Chris) Volk
President CEO and Director, Peter S. Fine, age 61
Director, Wilford A. Cardon
Director, Gilbert Davila
Director, William M. Dwyer
Director, Cheryl A. Wenzinger, age 65
Director, Martin L. Shultz, age 66
Director, Mark N. Sklar
Director, Ronald J. Creasman
Director, Michael J. Frick
Director, Susan Bartlett Foote
Director, Larry S. Lazarus
Director, Laren Bates
Auditors: Ernst&YoungLLP

LOCATIONS

HQ: BANNER HEALTH
1441 N 12TH ST, PHOENIX, AZ 85006-2887
Phone: 602-747-4000
Web: WWW.BANNERHEALTH.COM

Selected Facilities

Alaska
Fairbanks Memorial Hospital
Arizona
Banner Baywood
Banner Boswell
Banner Del E. Webb
Banner Desert
Banner Estrella
Banner Gateway
Banner Good Samaritan
Banner Heart
Banner Ironwood
Banner MD Anderson Cancer Center
Banner Thunderbird
Cardon Children's
Page Hospital
California
Banner Lassen Community Hospital
Colorado
East Morgan County Hospital
North Colorado Medical Center
McKee Medical Center
Sterling Regional MedCenter
Nebraska
Ogallala Community Hospital
Nevada
Banner Churchill Community Hospital
Wyoming
Community Hospital
Platte County Memorial Hospital
Washakie Medical Center

PRODUCTS/OPERATIONS

2011 Sales

	$ mil.	% of total
Patient service revenues	4,355	92
Other	385	8
Total	**4,741**	**100**

COMPETITORS

Community Health Systems
Dignity Health
HCA
Iasis Healthcare
Inova
John C. Lincoln Health Network
MedCath
Memorial Health System of East Texas
Northern Arizona Healthcare
Phoenix Children' s Hospital
Poudre Valley Health System
Providence Health & Services
Scottsdale Healthcare
St. Joseph Health System
Tenet Healthcare
Texas Health Resources
University of Arizona Health Network
Vanguard Health Systems
Wyoming Medical Center
Yuma Regional Medical Center

HISTORICAL FINANCIALS

Company Type: Private

Income Statement

FYE: December 31

	REVENUE ($ mil.)	NET INCOME ($ mil.)	NET PROFIT MARGIN	EMPLOYEES
12/12	4,878	614	12.6%	35,000
12/11	4,741	0	0.0%	—
12/10	4,863	382	7.9%	—
12/09	4,676	837	17.9%	—
Annual Growth	1.4%	(9.8%)	—	—

2012 Year-End Financials

Debt ratio: —
Return on equity: 12.60%
Cash ($ mil.): 52
Current ratio: 0.70
Long-term debt ($ mil.): —
Dividends
Yield: —
Payout: —
Market value ($ mil.): —

BAPTIST HEALTH

For those seeking medical salvation Baptist Health may be the answer to their prayers. The organization provides health services through about 175 points of care scattered throughout in Arkansas. Its facilities include eight hospitals and a number of rehabilitation facilities family clinics and therapy and wellness centers. Arkansas Health Group a division of Baptist Health runs more than 20 physician clinics across the state. Specialized services include cardiology women's health orthopedics rehabilitation and home and hospice care. Baptist Health's Parkway Village is a 90-acre retirement community for active seniors located close to Baptist Health Medical Center - Little Rock.

Operations

Along with the standard roster of health care services Baptist Health also offers Little Rock residents nine programs of health care study through its Baptist Health Schools Little Rock division. The school coordinates with Arkansas Tech University to offer Baptist Health RN graduates an online option to complete their Bachelor of Science in Nursing degree. Its average enrollment is about 1000 students each semester.

Strategy

The hospital system has been growing to meet the needs of its customers. In 2013 it began leasing Hot Spring County Medical Center in Malvern. The 72-bed acute care hospital was renamed Baptist Health Medical Center Hot Spring County. Baptist Health also bought nearly 40 acres in Conway and began construction on a medical center to serve Faulkner county.

EXECUTIVES

President CEO, Russell D. Harrington Jr.
SVP Financial Services, Bob Roberts
Chief Medical Officer, Guy Gardner
SVP Administrative Services, Troy Wells
SVP Diversified Services, Larry Lazenby
SVP Hospital Operations, Doug Weeks
Vice President Patient Care, Heber Springs
Vice President Clinical Services, Jerry Baugh

LOCATIONS

HQ: BAPTIST HEALTH
9601 INTRSTATE 630 EXIT 7, LITTLE ROCK, AR 72205-7299
Phone: 501-202-2000
Web: WWW.AHG.ORG

Selected locations – Arkansas

Arkansas Health Group (statewide)
BH Extended Care (Little Rock)
BHMC Arkadelphia
BHMC Heber Springs
BHMC Hot Spring County
BHMC Little Rock
BHMC North Little Rock
BHMC Stuttgart
Baptist Health Rehabilitation Institute (Little Rock)
Parkway Village (Little Rock)

COMPETITORS

Arkansas Children' s Hospital
Arkansas Heart Hospital
Baxter Regional Medical Center
Conway Regional Health System
Jefferson Regional Medical Center of Arkansas
Saline Memorial
Sparks Health System
St. Joseph' s Mercy Health Center
St. Vincent Health System
White County Medical Center

HISTORICAL FINANCIALS

Company Type: Private

Income Statement

FYE: December 31

	REVENUE ($ mil.)	NET INCOME ($ mil.)	NET PROFIT MARGIN	EMPLOYEES
12/09	924	64	7.0%	7,000
12/08	860	(204)	—	—
12/08	0	—	—	—
Annual Growth	—	—	—	—

2009 Year-End Financials

Debt ratio: —
Return on equity: 7.00%
Cash ($ mil.): 66
Current ratio: 1.40
Long-term debt ($ mil.): —
Dividends
Yield: —
Payout: —
Market value ($ mil.): —

BAPTIST HEALTH SOUTH FLORIDA INC.

Baptist Health South Florida (BHSF) has a good grip on Miami's health. The faith-based not-for-profit enterprise operates six acute-care hospitals a children's hospital and a vascular institute in the Miami area. Its flagship facility Baptist Hospital with more than 680 beds provides a comprehensive range of medical and surgical services. The system also includes South Miami Hospital with 460 beds as well as several smaller inpatient facilities in surrounding communities. In all BHSF hospitals contain about 1500 beds. In addition to inpatient services the organization provides ambulatory surgery primary and urgent care diagnostic imaging rehabilitation and home health services.

Operations

BHSF includes two diagnostic imaging centers 13 satellite diagnostic imaging centers and 16 urgent care centers.

Financial Performance

BHSF saw a slight increase in revenue net income and cash flow for 2013 based on increased patient revenues.

Strategy

Baptist Health South Florida's strategic goals focus on organic expansion through new construction and additions but also by acquisitions and through select partnerships when they meet its purposes. Additionally the health system works to improve patient care through medical equipment and information technology upgrades. For example it plans to spend $96 million to install an electronic health records (EHR) system by 2013.

EXECUTIVES

CFO, Ralph E. Lawson
President and CEO, Brian E. Keeley
Corporate VP and Chief Diversity Officer, Ricardo Forbes
CEO Mariners Hospital, Rick Freeburg
CEO Baptist Health Enterprises, Ana Lopez-Blazquez
CEO South Miami Hospital, Lincoln Mendez
VP Marketing and Public Relations, Jo Baxter
CEO West Kendall Baptist Hospital, Javier Hernandez-Lichtl
Chairman, Robert L. Dube
Chief Administrative Officer, George W. Foyo
CEO Homestead Hospital, William Duquette
CEO Doctors Hospital, Nelson Lazo
Assistant VP Marketing and Public Relations, Christine Kotler
CEO Baptist Health South Florida Foundation, Stephen Parsons
Medical Staff President, Eugene M. Eisner
Trustee, Wendell R. Beard, age 88
Trustee, Joyce J. Elam
Trustee, George E. Cadman III
Trustee, James Carr
Trustee, Rev William L. Chambers III
Trustee, Rev David W. Cleeland
Trustee, George M. Corrigan
Trustee, William H. Dickinson
Chairman, Robert L. Dube
Trustee, Herbert H. Greene
Trustee, George P. Harth
Trustee, Jay A. Hershoff
Trustee, Charles M. Hood III
Trustee, Norman M. Kenyon
Trustee, Rev Richard Ledgister
Trustee, Rev Wilner Maxy
Trustee, Paul D. May
Trustee, Rev Marcos A. Ramos
Trustee, Roberta Stokes
Trustee, W. Peter Temling
Trustee, Rev Tom Thompson
Trustee, J. Scott Weston
Trustee, Rev William W. White
Trustee, Tony Alonso
Trustee, Calvin H. Babcock
Trustee, Rev Gary Johnson
Trustee, Aida Shafer
Trustee, Ronald A. Shuffield
Trustee, Bill R. Tillett
Trustee, James W. Harris

LOCATIONS

HQ: BAPTIST HEALTH SOUTH FLORIDA INC.
6855 S RED RD STE 600, SOUTH MIAMI, FL 33143-3518
Phone: 305-596-1960
Web: WWW.BAPTISTHEALTH.NET

PRODUCTS/OPERATIONS

2013 Sales

	$ mil.	% of total
Managed Care	1,655	69
Medicare	278	12
Medicaid	122	5
Other	331	14
Total	**0**	**100**

Selected Florida Facilities

Baptist Hospital of Miami (Kendall)
Baptist Cardiac & Vascular Institute
Baptist Children' s Hospital
Doctors Hospital (Coral Gables)
Homestead Hospital (Homestead)
Mariners Hospital (Tavernier)
South Miami Hospital (South Miami)
West Kendall Baptist Hospital (Kendall)

Selected Services

Addiction treatment
Behavorial medicine
Blood conservation program
Cancer services
Cardiovascular services
Care and counseling services
Children' s health
Community wellness
Critical care center
Diabetes
eICU LifeGuard
Emergency
Endoscopy
Executive health
Gamma knife center
Heart surgery
Home care
Hyperbaric services
Imaging
Intensive care unit
International services
Interventional/surgical Services
Laboratory
Maritime medical services
Neonatal
Neuroscience
Nutrition counseling services
Occupational health
Online appointments
Orthopedics
Outpatient/diagnostic services
Pain center
Pastoral care
Pediatric
Pelvic health
Physical and speech therapy
Pregnancy and childbirth
Progressive care unit
Prostate cancer
Pulmonary services
Radiation oncology
Rehabilitation services
Robotic surgery
Senior services
Sleep diagnostic center
Sports medicine and orthopedic programs
Stroke services
Surgery
Weight-loss surgery
Wellness Center
Women' s health
Wound care

COMPETITORS

Adventist Health System Sunbelt Healthcare
Boca Raton Regional Hospital
Broward Health
Catholic Health East
HCA
Holy Cross Hospital Fort Lauderdale
Jackson Health System
Lakeland Regional Medical Center
Miami Children' s Hospital
Mount Sinai Medical Center of Florida
South Broward Hospital District
Tenet Healthcare
The Cleveland Clinic
University of Miami Hospital

HISTORICAL FINANCIALS

Company Type: Private

Income Statement

FYE: September 30

	REVENUE ($ mil.)	NET INCOME ($ mil.)	NET PROFIT MARGIN	EMPLOYEES
09/09*	616	121	19.7%	9,374
12/08	2	(1)	—	—
09/06	1,517	136	9.0%	—
09/05	1,459	193	13.2%	—
Annual Growth	(19.4%)	(11.0%)	—	—

*Fiscal year change

2009 Year-End Financials

Debt ratio: ——
Return on equity: 19.70%
Cash ($ mil.): 18
Current ratio: —
Long-term debt ($ mil.): —
Dividends
Yield: —
Payout: —
Market value ($ mil.): —

BAPTIST HEALTHCARE SYSTEM INC.

Baptist Health (formerly Baptist Healthcare System) owns eight acute -care hospitals in Kentucky with a total capacity of more than 2000 beds. The not-for-profit health system's largest facility is Baptist Hospital East a 520-bed hospital in Louisville that provides a wide range of health services with special expertise in cardiology rehabilitation and women's health. In addition to its owned facilities Baptist Healthcare manages Hardin Memorial a 300-bed hospital located in Elizabethtown and Pattie A. Clay Regional in Richmond with 100 beds. Founded as a single hospital in Louisville in 1924 the growing hospital system rebranded as Baptist Health in 2012.

Strategy

Baptist Health is expanding its network with the aim of covering more of rural western Kentucky. In November 2012 it acquired Trover Health System based in Madisonville which operates a 410-bed medical center and eight outpatient clinics in western Kentucky. In September Baptist Health acquired the Pattie A. Clay Regional Medical Center in Richmond. Both hospitals were renamed following their acquisition becoming Baptist Health Madisonville and Baptist Health Richmond respectively.

Along with inpatient acute care services Baptist Healthcare offers home health care services runs two outpatient surgery centers provides urgent care through a handful of clinics and operates a regional physicians' practice group. It also runs a community-based not-for-profit health care plan Bluegrass Family Health operating across the state and into parts of Indiana and Tennessee.

EXECUTIVES

President Chief Executive Officer at Baptist, Tommy J. Smith
President and CEO Bluegrass Family Health, James S. Fritz
President Western Baptist Hospital, Larry O. Barton
President Baptist Hospital East, David L. Gray
President Central Baptist Hospital, William G. Sisson
President Baptist Hospital Northeast, Chris Roty
President Baptist Regional Medical Center, Larry Gray
President Hardin Memorial Hopsital, Dennis Johnson
VP Reimbursement and Integrated Delivery Network, Elizabeth Monroe
Network Operations Manager, Scott Walkiewicz

LOCATIONS

HQ: BAPTIST HEALTHCARE SYSTEM INC.
4007 KRESGE WAY, LOUISVILLE, KY 40207-4677
Phone: 502-896-5000
Web: WWW.BHSI.COM

PRODUCTS/OPERATIONS

Selected Facilities and Operations (Kentucky)

Hospitals
- Baptist Hospital East (Louisville)
- Baptist Hospital Northeast (La Grange)
- Baptist Health Madisonville
- Baptist Regional Medical Center (Corbin)
- Central Baptist Hospital (Lexington)
- Hardin Memorial Hospital (Elizabethtown)
- Pattie A. Clay Regional Medical Center (Richmond)
- Western Baptist Hospital (Paducah)

Other operations
- Baptist East Milestone Wellness Center (Louisville)
- Baptist Express Care (various Walmarts in state)
- Baptist Medical Associates (medical practice group Louisville area)
- Baptist Urgent Care (Louisville)
- Bluegrass Family Health (provider-sponsored insurance)

COMPETITORS

Appalachian Regional Healthcare
Catholic Health Initiatives
Jewish Hospital & St. Mary' s HealthCare
Kindred Healthcare
Norton Healthcare
Pikeville Medical Center
University Health Care
University of Kentucky Chandler Hospital

HISTORICAL FINANCIALS

Company Type: Private

Income Statement FYE: August 31

	REVENUE ($ mil.)	NET INCOME ($ mil.)	NET PROFIT MARGIN	EMPLOYEES
08/12	1,290	90	7.0%	12,601
08/11	1,317	96	7.3%	—
08/09	1,231	75	6.2%	—
08/09	1,448	(14)	—	—
Annual Growth	(3.8%)	—	—	—

2012 Year-End Financials

Debt ratio: —
Return on equity: 7.00%
Cash ($ mil.): 152
Current ratio: 0.40
Long-term debt ($ mil.): —
Dividends
Yield: —
Payout: —
Market value ($ mil.): —

BAPTIST HOSPITAL OF MIAMI INC.

Baptist Hospital of Miami can treat many vices for Miami residents. The flagship facility of the Baptist Health South Florida health system provides residents of the city with a full range of health care services including pediatric cancer home health rehabilitation neurology and cardiovascular care. The hospital has more than 680 beds and includes the Baptist Children's Hospital which offers a pediatric emergency room and a neonatal intensive care unit. Baptist Hospital of Miami also includes the Baptist Cardiac & Vascular Institute a regional cancer program and a diabetes care center. Baptist Hospital of Miami was founded in 1960.

Operations

Baptist Children's Hospital offers 24-hour emergency care as well as two intensive care units and specialist services including pediatric cancer care. Baptist Hospital of Miami also contains the Baptist Cardiac and Vascular Institute which conducts treatment and research programs. The hospital's international care unit provides services to patients from the Caribbean Latin America and other regions. Other specialist divisions include a sleep diagnostic center and a spine care facility as well as a maternity ward. Baptist Hospital of Miami also operates several wellness centers.

As part of Baptist Health South Florida the Baptist Hospital of Miami is part of a network of six hospitals including South Miami Hospital Doctors Hospital and the West Kendall Baptist Hospital. In addition the health system includes outpatient care clinics including emergency surgery imaging and primary care centers.

Strategy

Controlling expenses through data management quality and wellness initiatives and other measures becomes increasingly important for the hospital and its affiliates as the cost of medical care in the US market continues to skyrocket. Maintaining an efficient organization is also imperative as the level of charity care provided by the system's facilities continues to rise in the face of economic difficulties.

As the largest hospital in the Baptist Health system Baptist Hospital of Miami takes a leading role in technology programs such as medical equipment and data management system upgrades. The Baptist Health network is in the process of installing an electronic health record (EHR) system to connect patient records across its facilities.

In 2012 Baptist Hospital of Miami launched a $90 million construction effort to expand the Cardiac and Vascular Institute. The new expanded institute facility will open in 2016 and will include centers for aneurysm treatment structural heart therapy and endovascular therapy. The project also includes expansion efforts on the hospital's surgery center which will have enhanced capabilities for neurological cardiac and robotic surgery procedures.

EXECUTIVES

CFO Baptist Health South Florida, Ralf Lawson
Controller, Maria Yanez

LOCATIONS

HQ: BAPTIST HOSPITAL OF MIAMI INC.
8900 N KENDALL DR, MIAMI, FL 33176-2197
Phone: 786-596-1960
Web: WWW.BAPTISTHEALTH.NET

PRODUCTS/OPERATIONS

Selected Centers and Services

Baptist Cardiac & Vascular Institute (Heart Care)
Baptist Children' s Hospital (Pediatrics)
Breast Care
Cancer Services
Center for Spine Care
Children' s Cancer Services
Children' s Emergency Center
Clinical Research Trials
Community Wellness
Critical Care/eICU LifeGuard
Diabetes Care
Diagnostic Imaging
Emergency Services
Endoscopy
Gynecology
Home Care
Intensive Care
International Services
Interventional
Maternity
Neonatal Intensive Care Unit
Neuroscience Center
Neurosurgery
Orthopedic Services
Pain Management
Physical & Speech Therapy
Pulmonary Services
Rehabilitation Services
Robotic Surgery
Senior Services
Sleep Diagnostic Center
Spine Care
Stroke Services
Surgery
Women' s Services

COMPETITORS

Broward Health
Catholic Health East
H. Lee Moffitt Cancer Center & Research Institute
HCA
Jackson Health System
Larkin Community Hospital
Miami Children' s Hospital
Mount Sinai Medical Center of Florida
South Broward Hospital District
University of Miami Hospital

HISTORICAL FINANCIALS

Company Type: Private

Income Statement FYE: September 30

	REVENUE ($ mil.)	NET INCOME ($ mil.)	NET PROFIT MARGIN	EMPLOYEES
09/08	908	81	9.0%	4,200
09/04	674	58	8.7%	—
09/03	569	57	10.1%	—
09/02	485	62	12.9%	—
Annual Growth	11.0%	4.5%		

2008 Year-End Financials

Debt ratio: —
Return on equity: 9.00%
Cash ($ mil.): 0
Current ratio: 0.20
Long-term debt ($ mil.): —
Dividends
Yield: —
Payout: —
Market value ($ mil.): —

BAPTIST HOSPITALS OF SOUTHEAST TEXAS

LOCATIONS

HQ: BAPTIST HOSPITALS OF SOUTHEAST TEXAS
3080 COLLEGE ST, BEAUMONT, TX 777014686
Phone: 4092125000
Web: WWW.BHSET.NET

HISTORICAL FINANCIALS

Company Type: Private

Income Statement FYE: June 30

	REVENUE ($ mil.)	NET INCOME ($ mil.)	NET PROFIT MARGIN	EMPLOYEES
06/14	234	(6)	—	1,759
06/13	234	6	2.6%	—
06/11	277	1	0.4%	—
06/08	246	0	—	—
Annual Growth	(0.8%)	—	—	—

2014 Year-End Financials

Debt ratio: —
Return on equity: (-2.90%)
Cash ($ mil.): 13
Current ratio: 1.00
Long-term debt ($ mil.): —
Dividends
Yield: —
Payout: —
Market value ($ mil.): —

BAPTIST MEMORIAL HOSPITAL

EXECUTIVES

President Chief Executive Officer, Stephen C. Reynolds
Executive Vice President Chief Operating Officer, Jason Little
Director Marketing, Juli Story
Executive Vice President Chief Administrative Officer, Robert S. (Bob) Gordon
Senior Vice President and Corporate Counsel, Gregory M. (Greg) Duckett
Chief Nursing Officer, Dana Dye
Chief Financial Officer, Cyndi Pittman
Assistant Administrator, Johnny Stanford
Chief Medical Officer, Christian C. (Chris) Patrick
Manager Patient Financial Services, Michelle Allen
Vice President Chief Medical Officer, Richard Drewry

LOCATIONS

HQ: BAPTIST MEMORIAL HOSPITAL
6019 WALNUT GROVE RD, MEMPHIS, TN 381202113
Phone: 9012265000
Web: WWW.BAPTISTONLINE.ORG

COMPETITORS

Methodist Healthcare
Parkwest Medical Center
Shelby County Health Care
St. Jude Children' s Research Hospital
Tenet Healthcare

HISTORICAL FINANCIALS

Company Type: Private

Income Statement FYE: September 30

	REVENUE ($ mil.)	NET INCOME ($ mil.)	NET PROFIT MARGIN	EMPLOYEES
09/13	504	17	3.4%	6,000
09/12	697	15	2.2%	—
09/03	429	26	6.1%	—
09/02	377	0	—	—
Annual Growth	2.7%	—	—	—

2013 Year-End Financials

Debt ratio: —
Return on equity: 3.40%
Cash ($ mil.): 13
Current ratio: 1.30
Long-term debt ($ mil.): —
Dividends
Yield: —
Payout: —
Market value ($ mil.): —

BARD COLLEGE

Although Shakespeare might appreciate the curriculum Bard College is not named for the Bard of Avon. Founded in 1860 by John Bard the school grants liberal arts degrees and provides a classical education. Bard's total enrollment of 1600 includes some 200 graduate students. First-year students are required to take a three-week Workshop in Language and Thinking that emphasizes the connection between expression and thought. Students must also complete a year-long senior project that is reviewed by faculty members. Donald Fagen and Walter Becker of the band Steely Dan both attended Bard (Fagen is an alum; Becker did not graduate) and penned the song "My Old School" as a sardonic tribute to their alma mater.

EXECUTIVES

President, Leon Botstein
VP Student Affairs, Mary Backlund
VP Administration, James (Jim) Brudvig
VP Academic Affairs and Director Bard Conservatory of Music, Robert L. Martin
Director Communications, Mark Primoff
Executive Vice President, Dimitri B. Papadimitriou
Dean Information Services and Director Libraries, Jeffrey (Jeff) Katz
Director Career Development, April Kinser
VP Development and Alumni Affairs, Debra R. Pemstein
Director Safety and Security, Ken Cooper
Director Financial Aid, Denise Ackerman
Vice President, Jonathan Becker

LOCATIONS

HQ: BARD COLLEGE
30 CAMPUS RD, ANNANDALE ON HUDSON, NY 12504-9800
Phone: 845-758-6822
Web: WWW.BARD.EDU

HISTORICAL FINANCIALS

Company Type: Private

Income Statement FYE: June 30

	REVENUE ($ mil.)	NET INCOME ($ mil.)	NET PROFIT MARGIN	EMPLOYEES
06/11	278	76	27.4%	525
06/10	181	(5)	—	—
06/09	164	0	—	—
06/08	126	17	13.7%	—
Annual Growth	29.9%	63.5%	—	—

2011 Year-End Financials

Debt ratio: —
Return on equity: 27.40%
Cash ($ mil.): 1
Current ratio: —
Long-term debt ($ mil.): —
Dividends
Yield: —
Payout: —
Market value ($ mil.): —

BARRY UNIVERSITY INC.

Barry University is a Catholic institution of Dominican heritage based in South Florida. With a student-faculty ratio of about 14:1 the liberal arts university annually enrolls about 3000 undergraduate students and some 4000 graduate students. The university's academic division includes two colleges (the College of Arts and Sciences and the College of Health Sciences) and seven schools. It offers more than 100 specializations and programs for undergraduate graduate and doctoral studies. Barry University also offers about 35 non-degree and certificate programs. Barry University was founded by the Adrian Dominican Sisters in 1940.

Geographic Reach

Barry University enrolls students from throughout the US and some 75 international countries. Its main campus consists of 120 acres in Miami Shores Florida. Its School of Adult and Continuing Education has satellite offices in 16 Florida counties. Other Barry University Schools have between two and five campus/satellite locations while the Andreas School of Law is located solely in Orlando.

Operations

The university's programs cover a range of subjects including art business communication education human studies law medicine nursing psychology social work and theology. Its professional study programs combined with graduate and undergraduate majors bring Barry University's total enrollment to some 9000 students.

Strategy

Barry University is focused on several key initiatives including creating excellence in its academic programs through evaluation and enhancement efforts; forming student-centered learning communities to increase retention and engagement; and ensuring financial growth through measures including building community relationships increasing fundraising efforts and implementing right-sizing and best practice strategies. Other improvement efforts relate to diversity community service and governance.

EXECUTIVES

President and Trustee, Sister Linda Bevilacqua, age 73
Assistant VP Administrative Information Systems, Traci A. Simpson
Chairperson, William J. Heffernan
Associate VP and University Budget Officer, Nicole Diez
Director Accounts Payable, Nancy Perez
Assistant Director Cashier and Business Office, Ronald LaBarrie
Director Alumni Programs, Renee Glover-Hodge
Assistant VP Communications and Marketing, Michael S. Laderman
Director Campus Ministry, Sister Arlene Scott
Director University Sponsorships, Caridad MacNamara
VP Institutional Advancement, Ann Paton
Assistant Vice Provost Enrollment, Angela M. Scott
Senior Director Graduate Admissions, Dave C. Fletcher

Trustee; President Barry University Alumni Association, Maura O'Shea-Owens
SVP Business and Finance, Bruce Edwards
Associate VP Finance and Chief Accounting Officer, Susan Kirkland
Controller, Judith Penate
Director Purchasing, Sandra Madison
VP Human Resources and General Counsel, John A. Walker
Assistant VP Alumni Relations, Sean Kramer
VP Student Affairs, Michael J. Griffin
Associate VP Student Affairs and Dean Students, Maria Luisa Alvarez
Director Career Services, Amy Diepenbrock
Executive Director Public Safety, Stanley A. Young
Provost, Linda M. Peterson
Vice President for Mission and Institutional Effectiveness, Christopher Starratt
Director Institutional Research, Shaunette Grant
Interim CTO, Yvette A-M Brown
Administrative Assistant, Andy Havens
Assistant Director of Athletics Operations, Maritza Ryder
Vice President for Institutional Advancement and External Affairs, Sara B. Herald
Vice President for Student Affairs, Scott F. Smith
Trustee, Joseph P. Klock Jr., age 65
Trustee, Nelson L. Adams III
Trustee, Gregory F. Greene
President and Trustee, Sister Linda Bevilacqua, age 73
Trustee, Alejandro Aguirre
Trustee, John M. Bussel
Trustee, Sister Mary Ann Caulfield
Trustee, Sister Rosemary T. Finnegan
Trustee, Robert B. Galt III
Trustee, Christopher J. Gruchacz
Trustee, Keith B. Kashuk
Trustee, Neta Kolasa
Trustee, Olga Melin
Trustee, Charles R. Modica, age 67
Trustee, Gerald W. Moore
Trustee, Michael O. O'Neil Jr.
Trustee, Sister Rosa Monique Pe?a
Trustee, Patricia M. Rosello
Trustee, Donald S. Rosenberg
Trustee, Rev Kenneth Schwanger
Trustee, Joel H. Sharp Jr.
Trustee, Sister Sharon Weber
Trustee, Patricia L. Clements
Trustee, Jorge A. Gross
Trustee, John P. Horan
Trustee; President Barry University Alumni Association, Maura O'Shea-Owens
Trustee, Eduardo A. Otero
Trustee, Susan A. Rosenthal
Trustee, Luigi Salvaneschi
Trustee, Sister Corinne Sanders
Trustee, Shirley Wiseman
Auditors: Deloitte&ToucheLLP

LOCATIONS

HQ: BARRY UNIVERSITY INC.
11300 NE 2ND AVE, MIAMI SHORES, FL 33161-6695
Phone: 305-899-3050
Web: WWW.BARRY.EDU

PRODUCTS/OPERATIONS

Selected Colleges and Schools

Adrian Dominican School of Education
College of Arts and Sciences
College of Health Sciences
D. Inez Andreas School of Business
Dwayne O. Andreas School of Law
Ellen Whiteside McDonnell School of Social Work
Frank J. Rooney School of Adult and Continuing Education
School of Human Performance and Leisure Sciences
School of Podiatric Medicine

HISTORICAL FINANCIALS

Company Type: Private

Income Statement

FYE: June 30

	REVENUE ($ mil.)	NET INCOME ($ mil.)	NET PROFIT MARGIN	EMPLOYEES
06/10	151	12	8.1%	1,407
06/09	147	8	5.7%	—
06/09	0	0	*%	—
Annual Growth	—3365457.7%	—	—	—

2010 Year-End Financials

Debt ratio: ——
Return on equity: 8.10%
Cash ($ mil.): 36
Current ratio: —
Long-term debt ($ mil.): —
Dividends
Yield: —
Payout: —
Market value ($ mil.): —

BARRY-WEHMILLER GROUP INC.

With Barry-Wehmiller you get the whole package. The company manufactures and supplies packaging corrugating paper converting filling and labeling automation equipment for a broad range of industries. It conducts business around the world through a group of 50 companies including Accraply (labeling machinery) Barry-Wehmiller Company (bottle washers and pasteurizers); HayssenSandiacre and Thiele Technologies (packaging systems); PneumaticScaleAngelus (bottle fillers and cappers); and FleetwoodGoldcoWyard (conveyor systems). Other divisions manufacture paper converting machinery and offer engineering/design consulting services. Chairman and CEO Bob Chapman and his family hold majority control the company.

Geographic Reach

Barry Wehmiller has operations in more than 50 locations spanning Asia Australia and the Americas.

Strategy

Barry Wehmiller's mantra is expansion through organic growth and acquisitions. The company has purchased more than 40 companies over approximately 20 years creating a mosaic of time and money-saving products and services in locations around the globe. In the same vein its businesses' operations are built upon lean manufacturing practices whereby employees are empowered and resources optimized to contribute to the end product's value.

Mergers and Acquisitions

In 2012 the company expanded its engineering IT consulting platform by buying Kansas-based Customer Driven Technology (CDT) a reseller of advanced IT and enterprise products for engineering and manufacturing companies. CDT provides products and services to address the rapidly changing landscape of product development product lifecycle management and global project collaboration. In 2013 this unit acquired the PTC software business of ENSER Corporation allowing it to more effectively service ENSER's existing PTC customers.

Company Background

Originally a provider of conveying equipment to St. Louis malt houses Barry-Wehmiller Companies was founded by Thomas Barry and Alfred Wehmiller in 1885. Ownership passed from the Wehmiller family to the Chapman family in 1963 and the Chapmans continue as the majority owners.

EXECUTIVES

Chairman and CEO, Robert H. (Bob) Chapman, age 69
VP CFO and Director, James W. (Jim) Lawson
CIO, Craig Hergenroether
CTO, Robert Richards

LOCATIONS

HQ: BARRY-WEHMILLER GROUP INC.
8020 FORSYTH BLVD, SAINT LOUIS, MO 63105-1707
Phone: 314-862-8000
Web: WWW.BWDESIGNGROUP.COM

PRODUCTS/OPERATIONS

Selected Operations

Engineering/Consulting
- Barry-Wehmiller Design Group Inc. (high-speed complex automated manufacturing and packaging system design)
- Barry-Wehmiller International Resources (IT consulting and engineering services)

Converting equipment
- Paper Converting Machine Company (PCMC)
  - Coaters
  - Narrow web in-line printing systems
  - Nonwovens converting equipment
  - Tissue converting equipment
  - Wide web flexo printing coating and laminating

Corrugating equipment
- MarquipWardUnited Inc. (corrugating sheeting and finishing equipment)

Packaging equipment
- Accraply Inc. (packaging label machinery)
- FleetwoodGoldcoWyard (conveyer systems)
- HayssenSandiacre (form/fill/seal packaging machinery)
- PneumaticScaleAngelus (fillers cappers seamers and labelers)
- Thiele Technologies Inc. (packaging systems)

Selected Markets

Corrugated paperboard and folded carton
Dairy
Food and beverage
Household
Medical and biotech
Packaging
Personal care
Pharmaceutical
Tissue and nonwovens

COMPETITORS

Bradman Lake
Gilbreth
Industria Macchine Automatiche
Klockner-Werke
STT Enviro
Sencorp Inc
Tetra Laval
Traco Manufacturing

HISTORICAL FINANCIALS

Company Type: Private

Income Statement

FYE: September 30

	REVENUE ($ mil.)	NET INCOME ($ mil.)	NET PROFIT MARGIN	EMPLOYEES
09/12	1,332	69	5.2%	4,500
09/11	1,240	0		
09/10	1,097	0		
09/09	976	0		
Annual Growth	10.9%	—	—	—

2012 Year-End Financials

Debt ratio: ——
Return on equity: 5.20%
Cash ($ mil.): 109
Current ratio: 0.90
Long-term debt ($ mil.): —
Dividends
Yield: —
Payout: —
Market value ($ mil.): —

BARTON MALOW COMPANY

Barton Malow scores by building end zones and home plates. The construction management and general contracting firm which has built its share of sporting facilities also focuses on projects such as schools hospitals offices and plants. Across the US and Mexico the company offers design/build and program management services ranging from the pre-planning stage to completion. Projects have included the Detroit Institute of Arts and Cultural Center and the Baltimore Orioles stadium. Affiliate Barton Malow Design provides architecture and engineering services while Barton Malow Rigging installs process equipment and machinery. Carl Osborn Barton founded the employee-owned firm as C.O. Barton Company in 1924.

Geographic Reach

Michigan-based Barton Malow operates about a dozen offices mostly in the East Coast. The firm also has an office in San Luis Potosi Mexico.

Financial Performance

Barton Malow's annual revenue exceeds $1 billion.

Strategy

Headquartered in a Detroit suburb Barton Malow has historically maintained a healthy relationship with the steel and auto industries. The company has expanded into new sectors and geographic markets however. It serves the federal market through its Florida-based L.C. Gaskins Construction Company.

In 2014 the firm was selected as the construction manager for a new Major League Soccer (MLS) stadium in Orlando Florida. Other recent projects include a new events center in Detroit and a Facility for Rare Isotope Breams at Michigan State University.

Company Ownership

The family of CEO Ben Maibach III a third-generation Barton Malow executive owns a controlling interest in the company.

EXECUTIVES

Senior Vice President And Chief, Lori Howlett
V Pres-mkt, Sheryl Maibach
Vp Human Resources, Jim Nahrgang
Vice President Energy And Environmental, Geoff Murken
Vice President And General Counsel, Ronald J Torbert
EVP and Corporate Secretary, Doug Maibach
Chairman and CEO, Ben C. Maibach
VP Central Region, Michael (Mike) Stobak
VP Central Region, Todd Ketola
SVP Eastern Region, Phil Kirby
VP Eastern Region, Carrie Shaeffer
VP Southeast Region, David Price
VP National Sports, Len Moser
President, Ryan Maibach
VP Central Region, Chuck Binkowski
SVP and CFO, Michael Dishaw
SVP Southeast Region, Rod Creach
VP Central Region, Dan Kovoch
Vp Preconstruction, Jeff Baxa
Vice President, John Wieland
Vice President, Joe Benvenuto
Vice President, Harvey Oliva
Vice President, Blair Engle
Vice President, Don Davis
EVP and Corporate Secretary, Doug Maibach
Chairman and CEO, Ben C. Maibach

LOCATIONS

HQ: BARTON MALOW COMPANY
26500 AMERICAN DR, SOUTHFIELD, MI 480342252
Phone: 2484365000
Web: WWW.BARTONMALOW.COM

Selected Locations

Atlanta
Baltimore
Charlottesville
Chicago
Columbus
Fairfax
Jacksonville
Oak Park
Orlando
Richmond
Southfield

PRODUCTS/OPERATIONS

Selcted Services
Architecture and planning
Building Information Management (BIM)
Concrete trade services
Construction management
Design/build
Facility audits
Facility services
Administration
Engineering
Maintenance repair and operations
General contractin
Interior design
Interior trade services
Preconstruction
Program management
Rigging
Special projects
Technology consulting

COMPETITORS

Alberici
Clark Enterprises
Fluor
Gilbane
H.J. Russell
Hensel Phelps Construction
Hunt Construction
KBR Building Group
M. A. Mortenson
McCarthy Building
Skanska USA Building
Turner Corporation
Walbridge Aldinger
Walsh Group
Whiting-Turner

HISTORICAL FINANCIALS

Company Type: Private

Income Statement FYE: March 31

	REVENUE ($ mil.)	NET INCOME ($ mil.)	NET PROFIT MARGIN	EMPLOYEES
03/14	1,078	2	0.3%	1,200
03/13	1,005	3	0.3%	—
Annual Growth	7.3%	(20.9%)	—	—

2014 Year-End Financials

Debt ratio: —
Return on equity: 0.30%
Cash ($ mil.): 61
Current ratio: 0.60
Long-term debt ($ mil.): —
Dividends
Yield: —
Payout: —
Market value ($ mil.): —

BATELLE MEMORIAL INSTITUTE

LOCATIONS

HQ: BATELLE MEMORIAL INSTITUTE
2555 INTERNATIONAL ST, COLUMBUS, OH 432284604
Phone: 8002012011
Web: WWW.BATTELLE.ORG

HISTORICAL FINANCIALS

Company Type: Private

Income Statement FYE: September 30

	REVENUE ($ mil.)	NET INCOME ($ mil.)	NET PROFIT MARGIN	EMPLOYEES
09/13	4,795	(7)	—	3
09/12	5,228	(20)	—	—
Annual Growth	(8.3%)	—	—	—

2013 Year-End Financials

Debt ratio: —
Return on equity: (-0.20%)
Cash ($ mil.): 112
Current ratio: 2.00
Long-term debt ($ mil.): —
Dividends
Yield: —
Payout: —
Market value ($ mil.): —

BATON ROUGE GENERAL MEDICAL CENTER

The first hospital founded in Louisiana's capital Baton Rouge General Medical Center is a not-for-profit full-service community hospital offering patients general medical and surgical care. Through the hospital's two locations Bluebonnet and Mid City Baton Rouge General also provides specialty services for cancer heart and neonatal care. In addition the nearly 450-bed health care facility provides services in areas such as burn treatment diabetes sleep disorders and behavioral health. Baton Rouge General Medical Center is the flagship facility of General Health System.

EXECUTIVES

EVP and Chief Business Development Officer, Dionne E. Viator
Chief Medical Officer, Floyd J. (Flip) Roberts Jr.
Interim President and CEO, Evelyn K. Hayes
Vice President Quality & Performance Improvement, Erin Zeringue
EVP and COO, Edgardo Tenreiro
VP Facilities Management, Peyton Grant
CFO, Kendall Johnson
Vice President Revenue Cycle, Don Shaw
President Baton Rouge General Foundation, Beth Veazey
Vice President Patient Relations, Anna Cazes
Vice President Information Technology, Bennett Cheramie
Vice President Marketing & Communications, Nicole Kleinpeter

LOCATIONS

HQ: BATON ROUGE GENERAL MEDICAL CENTER
3600 FLORIDA BLVD, BATON ROUGE, LA 70806-3842
Phone: 225-387-7000
Web: WWW.BRGENERAL.ORG

COMPETITORS

Lane Regional Medical Center
Our Lady of the Lake RMC
River Parishes Hospital
Woman' s Hospital

HISTORICAL FINANCIALS

Company Type: Private

Income Statement FYE: September 30

	REVENUE ($ mil.)	NET INCOME ($ mil.)	NET PROFIT MARGIN	EMPLOYEES
09/09	304	0	0.2%	394
09/08*	281	2	0.9%	—
12/05	0	0	—	—
09/00	431	(0)	—	—
Annual Growth	(3.8%)	—	—	—

*Fiscal year change

2009 Year-End Financials

Debt ratio: —
Return on equity: 0.20%
Cash ($ mil.): 71
Current ratio: 0.40
Long-term debt ($ mil.): —
Dividends
Yield: —
Payout: —
Market value ($ mil.): —

BATTELLE MEMORIAL INSTITUTE INC

HISTORY

Battelle Memorial Institute was founded with a $1.5 million trust willed by Gordon Battelle who died in 1923. Battelle was a champion of research for the advancement of humankind and before taking his father's place as president of several Ohio steel mills he had funded a former university professor's successful work to extract useful chemicals from mine waste. Battelle's mother upon her death in 1925 left the institute an additional $2.1 million. The institute opened in 1929.

The institute took on perhaps the most important project in its history in 1944 when it helped an electronics company's patent lawyer Chester Carlson find practical uses for his invention called xerography. Eventually Battelle developed the first photocopy machine and in 1955 it sold the patent rights for the machine to Haloid (now Xerox) in exchange for royalties.

During WWII Battelle worked on uranium refining for the Manhattan Project and in the early 1950s it established the world's first private nuclear research facility. The company also set up operations in Germany and Switzerland.

The tax man came knocking in 1961 questioning the tax-free status of some of Battelle's activities. The organization eventually had to pay $47 million. In 1965 Battelle developed a coin with a copper core and a copper-and-nickel-alloy cladding for the US Treasury.

As the result of a ruling that reinterpreted a clause in Gordon Battelle's will in 1975 the institute gave $80 million to philanthropic enterprises. This ruling coupled with the taxes that the organization was still unaccustomed to paying forced Battelle to re-examine its strategy.

Battelle co-developed the Universal Product Code (the bar code symbol found today on nearly all consumer goods packaging) in the 1970s. The institute also landed a lucrative contract from the US Department of Energy (DOE) to manage its commercial nuclear waste isolation program.

In 1987 Battelle chose Douglas Olesen –a 20-year veteran of the institute –to replace retiring CEO Ronald Paul. The company signed an extension with the DOE in 1992 to run its Pacific Northwest Laboratory (which it has operated since 1965).

An Ohio court in 1997 approved a seven-page agreement with the institute outlining the key principles that must be followed according to Gordon Battelle's will. This agreement replaced the 1975 decree and ended more than 20 years of scrutiny by the state attorney general's office.

In 1998 the DOE contracted Brookhaven Science Associates –a partnership between the State University of New York and Battelle –to operate Brookhaven National Laboratory. That year a Battelle contract to dispose of Vietnam War-era napalm drew national attention when subcontractor Pollution Control Industries backed out of the project citing safety concerns. Under Battelle's direction Houston-based GNI Group took the 3.4 million gallons of napalm off the US Navy's hands.

Battelle and the University of Tennessee in 1999 won a five-year contract to operate the US government's Oak Ridge National Laboratory. That year the institute made several breakthroughs in cancer research including FDA approval to test an inhalation delivery system for treating lung cancer.

In 2000 the company spun off OmniViz (data mining software) and Battelle Pulmonary Therapeutics (pulmonary and drug delivery technology) as wholly owned subsidiaries. In 2001 Battelle chose former Kodak EVP and CTO Carl Kohrt to replace Olesen. (Kohrt retired in January 2009 and was replaced by Jeffrey Wadsworth who has worked for the company since 2002.)

Battelle and several partners including BWX Technologies Washington Group International and Electric Power Research Institute won a 10-year contract in 2004 to operate Idaho National Laboratory a research facility established to focus on nuclear energy research and related technologies.

With offices in Japan and South Korea Battelle expanded its international reach to include India in 2008. The company formed a partnership in 2007 with oil and gas company PETRONAS to operate a renewable energy lab in Kuala Lumpur Malaysia.

Battelle underwent a leadership change in 2009 when Jeffrey Wadsworth took over as CEO replacing Carl Kohrt who retired.

EXECUTIVES

SVP International Partnerships, Richard C. Adams
Chairman, John B. McCoy Jr.
SVP National Security Global Business, Stephen E. Kelly
President and CEO, Jeffrey (Jeff) Wadsworth, age 64
Manager National Media Relations, Katy Delaney, age 48
EVP and CFO, I. Martin Inglis
SVP; Director Global Laboratory Operations Pacific Northwest National Laboratory, Michael Kluse
SVP; Director Global Laboratory Operations Idaho National Laboratory, Vice Adm. John J. Grossenbacher
SVP General Counsel and Secretary, Russell P. (Russ) Austin
corporate Senior Vice President President of Battelle ?s, Barbara L. Kunz
EVP Global Laboratory Operations, Ronald D. (Ron) Townsend
VP Energy Infrastructure, Mani Vadari
VP Strategy Development, Michael A. Aimone
VP and Manager Industrial and International Markets., Spencer Pugh
VP Education and STEM Learning, Eric D. Fingerhut
VP Navy and Special Operations Market Sector, Adm. Fred Byus
SVP, Thomas D. Snowberger
Senior Vice President of Human Resources, Tom Snowberger
corporate President of Battelle&rsquo, Marty Toomajian
Director, John K. Welch, age 64
Director, Michael G. (Mike) Morris, age 67
Director, Robert D. (Bob) Walter, age 67
Director, Bernadine P. Healy, age 68
Director, Gen. Lester L. Lyles, age 67
Director, Vicky A. Bailey, age 61
Director, Sean O'Keefe
Director, Russell A. Hulse
Auditors: Deloitte&ToucheLLP

LOCATIONS

HQ: BATTELLE MEMORIAL INSTITUTE INC
505 KING AVE, COLUMBUS, OH 432012681
Phone: 6144246424
Web: WWW.BATTELLE.ORG

PRODUCTS/OPERATIONS

Selected Laboratories and Research Facilities

Battelle Biomedical Research Center (West Jefferson OH)
Battelle Eastern Science and Technology Center (Aberdeen MD)
Battelle Frederick Operations (Maryland)
Battelle Geneva Operations (Switzerland)
Brookhaven National Laboratory (Upton NY)
Human Factors Transportation Center (Seattle)
Idaho National Laboratory (Idaho Falls)
Lawrence Livermore National Laboratory (Livermore CA)
Marine Science Laboratory (Sequim WA)
National Renewable Energy Laboratory (Golden CO)
Oak Ridge National Laboratory (Tennessee)
Battelle Duxbury Operations (Massachusetts)
Pacific Northwest National Laboratory (Richland WA)

Selected Inventions

Exploded-tip paintbrush (nylon brush for Wooster Brush Co. 1950)
Golf ball coatings (1965)
Heat Seat (microwaveable stadium cushion 1990s)
Holograms (work began in the 1970s)
Insulin injection pen (for Eli Lilly 1990s)
Oil spill outline monitor (1992)
PCB-cleaning chemical process (1992)
Photocopy machine (with Haloid 1940s)
Plastic breakdown process (1990s)
Sandwich coins (copper/copper-and-nickel-alloy cladding design for US Treasury 1965)
SenSonic toothbrush (with Teledyne/WaterPik 1990s)
Smart cards (cards embedded with tiny computer chips that store information 1980s)
Universal Product Code (co-creator; bar code 1970s)

COMPETITORS

Argonne National Laboratory
Berkeley Lab
Charles Stark Draper Laboratory
Institute for Defense Analyses
SwRI

HISTORICAL FINANCIALS

Company Type: Private

Income Statement FYE: September 30

	REVENUE ($ mil.)	NET INCOME ($ mil.)	NET PROFIT MARGIN	EMPLOYEES
09/14	4,769	(111)	—	7,457
09/13	4,795	(7)	—	—
09/12	5,228	(24)	—	—
09/11	5,499	0	—	—
Annual Growth	(4.6%)	—	—	—

2014 Year-End Financials

Debt ratio: —
Return on equity: (-2.30%)
Cash ($ mil.): 105
Current ratio: 1.50
Long-term debt ($ mil.): —
Dividends
Yield: —
Payout: —
Market value ($ mil.): —

BATTLE CREEK FARMERS COOPERATIVE NON-STOCK

EXECUTIVES

Board President and Manager Middle District (Tilden), Jerrell Dolesh
Manager Battle Creek, Dave Tomka
Manager Battle Creek South, Jim Porter Jr.
Manager Pierce, Marv Ernesti
Manager Plainview, Larry Petersen
Manager Osmond, Ron Woslager
Manager Bloomfield, Meril Friedrich
Manager D&S Oil, Dean Schueth
General Manager, Terry O. Samuelson
Director Human Resources and Safety, Dawn Pochop
Manager Agronomy Sales, Bryan Hoffman
Manager Energy/Transportation, Bryan Daum
Manager Grain Department, Matt Heimann
President White Grain Inc., Keith White
CEO Progressive Nutrition, Merlin Schlote
Controller, Dennis Erickson
General Manager, Dean Thernes
Marketing Director, Dave Spencer
Office Manager, Linda Berg
Sales Manager, Jerome Irlemeier
Manager South District (Madison), Dennis Kuchar
Manager South District (Battle Creek), Tom Osborn
Manager South District (Battle Creek), Craig Unkel
Manager Middle District (Pierce), Gerry Krueger
Manager Middle District (Pierce), Tim Spatz
Manager North District (Plainview), Dave Friedrich
Manager North District (Bloomfield), Phil Nielsen
Manager North District (Osmond), Dean Stueckrath

LOCATIONS

HQ: BATTLE CREEK FARMERS COOPERATIVE NON-STOCK
400 W FRONT ST, BATTLE CREEK, NE 687154402
Phone: 4026752375
Web: WWW.BCCOOP.COM

COMPETITORS

ADM	GROWMARK
Ag Processing	Pro-Fac
All Points Cooperative	Southern States
Cargill	

HISTORICAL FINANCIALS

Company Type: Private

Income Statement FYE: November 30

	REVENUE ($ mil.)	NET INCOME ($ mil.)	NET PROFIT MARGIN	EMPLOYEES
11/13	146	6	4.2%	90
11/12	200	6	3.3%	—
11/11	188	7	4.0%	—
11/10	120	0	—	—
Annual Growth	6.6%	—	—	—

2013 Year-End Financials

Debt ratio: —
Return on equity: 4.20%
Cash ($ mil.): 0
Current ratio: 0.10
Long-term debt ($ mil.): —
Dividends
Yield: —
Payout: —
Market value ($ mil.): —

BAUER BUILT INC.

LOCATIONS

HQ: BAUER BUILT INC.
1111 W PROSPECT ST, DURAND, WI 547361061
Phone: 7156728300
Web: WWW.BAUERBUILT.COM

COMPETITORS

American Tire Distributors	TBC
Discount Tire	TCI Tire Centers
Pep Boys	Wal-Mart
Pomp' s Tire Service	Wingfoot Commercial Tire Systems
Sears	

HISTORICAL FINANCIALS

Company Type: Private

Income Statement FYE: December 31

	REVENUE ($ mil.)	NET INCOME ($ mil.)	NET PROFIT MARGIN	EMPLOYEES
12/08	191	3	1.8%	450
12/06	171	2	1.5%	—
12/05	182	2	1.6%	—
12/04	161	0	—	—
Annual Growth	4.3%	—	—	—

2008 Year-End Financials

Debt ratio: —
Return on equity: 1.80%
Cash ($ mil.): 0
Current ratio: 0.40
Long-term debt ($ mil.): —
Dividends
Yield: —
Payout: —
Market value ($ mil.): —

BAY CITIES PAVING & GRADING INC.

Up among the tall trees or down by the bay Bay Cities Paving & Grading is on the job. The company provides highway and street construction services for private and public projects primarily in Northern California. Bay Cities Paving also performs road improvements renovations and extensions ,Äon existing roads. The company has provided work for such clients as the cities of Elk Grove Brentwood and Pleasant Hill and the school district of West Contra Costa. Bay Cities Paving & Grading is one of the largest Hispanic-owned firms in the US.

California ,ÄGovernor Arnold Schwarzenegger declared a fiscal emergency in December 2008 and the state's infrastructure construction industry has been among the most seriously impacted. To alleviate a budget shortfall of more than $11 billion the state has implemented measures including canceling planned projects and delaying payments to contractors including Bay Cities Paving.

EXECUTIVES

V Pres, Marlo Manqueros, age 56

LOCATIONS

HQ: BAY CITIES PAVING & GRADING INC.
1450 CIVIC CT BLDG B, CONCORD, CA 945205295
Phone: 9256876666
Web: WWW.BAYCITIES.US

COMPETITORS

AECOM	Parsons Brinckerhoff
Granite Construction	Reyes Construction
Ortiz Enterprises	

HISTORICAL FINANCIALS

Company Type: Private

Income Statement FYE: September 30

	REVENUE ($ mil.)	NET INCOME ($ mil.)	NET PROFIT MARGIN	EMPLOYEES
09/09	119	4	4.1%	250
09/08	96	9	9.8%	—
09/07	100	7	7.7%	—
09/06	73	0	—	—
Annual Growth	17.3%	—	—	—

2009 Year-End Financials

Debt ratio: —
Return on equity: 4.10%
Cash ($ mil.): 12
Current ratio: 0.60
Long-term debt ($ mil.): —
Dividends
Yield: —
Payout: —
Market value ($ mil.): —

BAY MEDICAL CENTER

Bay Medical Center is a 320-bed regional hospital located in the Florida panhandle. Formed in 1949 the center provides general medical and surgical services. The hospital's specialized services and programs include an open-heart surgery program a cancer center women's and children's health and emergency care. It also operates centers for sleep disorder and childhood communication disorders. Bay Medical Center has a staff of more than 300 physicians. The hospital also operates outpatient facilities for primary care and diagnostics. Bay Medical Center is operated by a joint venture between Sacred Heart Health System and LHP Hospital Group.

Change in Company Type

In 2012 Sacred Heart Health System and LHP Hospital Group formed a joint venture that will lease and operate the Bay Medical Center for 40 years. The transaction allows Bay Medical Center to retire all of its debt obligations; it also gives the hospital access to broader purchasing power and clinical resources. Its governing board will consist of representatives from LHP and Sacred Heart; the hospital will also have an independent board of trustees to oversee day-to-day operations.

Geographic Reach

From its main location in Panama City the hospital serves residents of seven counties in northwestern Florida.

Operations

Bay Medical Center features a level II trauma center. The hospital's cardiovascular surgery center features 16 suites and conducts some 10000 procedures annually including about 400 open-heart surgeries.

Most of Bay Medical Center's revenue comes from commercial and government insurance plan reimbursements. It also provides care to some self-pay customers. For low-income and uninsured patients the hospital typically provides some $30 million in charity and uncompensated care each year.

Strategy

Facility expansion measures at Bay Medical Center have included a new chest pain observation unit opened in 2013. Previously he hospital constructed a new patient tower to expand capacity and provide more private (single-patient) rooms for customers. The $60 million expansion project added

144 new patient rooms as well as lobby and cafeteria spaces and was completed in 2010. The tower also included new ICU surgery neurological nursing and orthopedic specialty units. The company divested some outpatient facilities to help offset construction expenses as well as to pay down debt.

EXECUTIVES

President and CEO, Stephen (Steve) Johnson

LOCATIONS

HQ: BAY MEDICAL CENTER
615 N BONITA AVE, PANAMA CITY, FL 32401-3623
Phone: 850-769-1511
Web: WWW.BAYMEDICAL.ORG

PRODUCTS/OPERATIONS

Selected Centers and Services

Blood Donor Center
Cancer Center
Diabetes Services
Diagnostic Services
Emergency Medicine
Family Birthing Center
HealthPlex Fitness
Heart and Vascular Institute
Hyperbaric Medicine
Infusion Therapy
Interventional Radiology
Pediatrics
Rehabilitation
Sleep Lab
Stroke Care
Surgical Services
Women' s Services
Wound Healing

COMPETITORS

Adventist Health System Sunbelt Healthcare
Baptist Health System
H. Lee Moffitt Cancer Center & Research Institute
HCA
Jackson County Hospital of Florida
Munroe Regional Health System
Sacred Heart Health System
Tallahassee Memorial HealthCare
UF&Shands

HISTORICAL FINANCIALS

Company Type: Private

Income Statement FYE: September 30

	REVENUE ($ mil.)	NET INCOME ($ mil.)	NET PROFIT MARGIN	EMPLOYEES
09/11	225	(0)	—	2,000
09/10	219	(5)	—	—
09/09	231	4	1.9%	—
09/08	221	2	1.3%	—
Annual Growth	0.6%	—	—	—

2011 Year-End Financials

Debt ratio: —
Return on equity: (-0.10%)
Cash ($ mil.): 20
Current ratio: 1.50
Long-term debt ($ mil.): —
Dividends
Yield: —
Payout: —
Market value ($ mil.): —

BAY REGIONAL MEDICAL CENTER

McLaren Bay Region provides a full range of medical services for the residents at the tip of Saginaw Bay in eastern Michigan. A part of McLaren Health Care the hospital's main campus has more than 400 beds and provides general medical and surgical care as well as specialty care in areas such as cardiovascular disease neuroscience oncology rehabilitation orthopedics and women's health. It also features an emergency room and Level II trauma center and provides home health and hospice care. A second campus McLaren Bay Special Care Hospital is a long-term acute care hospital serving patients requiring hospital stays of longer than 25 days. The regional provider also provides outpatient and home health services.

Geographic Reach

McLaren Bay Region has about 45 offices in Michigan counties including Auburn Bay Davison Essexville Lake Orion and Pinconning.

Operations

In addition to its two acute care centers McLaren Bay Region operates outpatient centers including the Nickless Volunteer Clinic which provides primary care for uninsured and underinsured residents of Bay County.

The hospital system has one of the largest multidisciplinary research programs in the state. It works with international pharmaceutical and device companies –as well as universities foundations and agencies –to create new and improved treatments for illnesses including cancers and infectious diseases.

Going hand-in-hand with clinical trials is teaching and McLaren Bay Region offers a roster of residency programs for up-and-coming medical professionals. The hospital works with Michigan State University's colleges of Human Medicine and Osteopathic Medicine.

Strategy

McLaren Bay Region is looking to expand its geographic reach in eastern Michigan. It is also widening its range of specialist services in areas such as oncology cardiovascular care and orthopedic rehabilitation. The organization launched a new cancer rehabilitation program in 2012; it also opened a new outpatient heart center featuring cardiac diagnostic capabilities in Mt. Pleasant.

Company Background

McLaren Bay Region was formed after the merging of four hospitals during the 1970s and 1980s with the idea of developing a full continuum of health services for Northeast Michigan. It changed its name to McLaren Bay Region from Bay Regional Medical Center in 2012.

EXECUTIVES

President CEO, Philip A. Incarnati
President and CEO, Alice Gerard
VP Finance and CFO, Brian Kay
Administrative Assistant, Jodi Reetz

LOCATIONS

HQ: BAY REGIONAL MEDICAL CENTER
1900 COLUMBUS AVE, BAY CITY, MI 48708-6831
Phone: 989-894-3000
Web: WWW.BAYREGIONAL.ORG

PRODUCTS/OPERATIONS

Selected Centers and Services

Bariatrics
Behavioral Health
Blood Conservation
Cancer Services
Cardiac
Diabetes
Diagnostic Imaging
Dialysis Services
Emergency Care
EMS
Family BirthPlace
Fitness Centers
Free Clinics
Health Insurance
Home Care
Implantable Hearing Solutions
Infectious Disease
Infusion Center
Intensive Care
Internal Medicine
Laboratory and Pathology
Lifeline
Medical Library
Medical Supplies & Equipment
Neurosciences
Nutritional Counseling
Ophthalmology
Orthopedics
Pain Management
Pediatrics
Primary Care
Proton Therapy
Pulmonary and Respiratory
Rehabilitation and Therapy
Robotic Surgery
Sleep Medicine
Stroke Center
Surgical and Endoscopy Services
Trauma
Urology
Walk-in Clinics
Women' s Services
Wound Care

COMPETITORS

Ascension Health
Covenant HealthCare
Crittenton Hospital
Detroit Medical Center
Genesys Health System
Genesys Regional Medical Center
Henry Ford Health System
Hurley Medical Center
Munson Healthcare
Select Medical
Sparrow Health System
St. John Health
University of Michigan Health System

HISTORICAL FINANCIALS

Company Type: Private

Income Statement FYE: September 30

	REVENUE ($ mil.)	NET INCOME ($ mil.)	NET PROFIT MARGIN	EMPLOYEES
09/12	278	22	8.1%	2,000
09/11	271	(6)	—	—
09/10	272	19	7.3%	—
09/09	263	2	0.9%	—
Annual Growth	1.8%	110.7%	—	—

2012 Year-End Financials

Debt ratio: —
Return on equity: 8.10%
Cash ($ mil.): 9
Current ratio: 1.40
Long-term debt ($ mil.): —
Dividends
Yield: —
Payout: —
Market value ($ mil.): —

BAYLOR UNIVERSITY

Don't mess with Texas and don't mess around at Baylor University. The world's largest Baptist institution of higher learning requires its more than 15000 students to follow a strict code of conduct. The university has approximately 150 undergraduate degree programs as well as about 75 masters and more than 30 doctoral programs. With a student-to-faculty ratio of 15:1 the private co-educational university also offers degrees from its law school (juris doctor) and theological seminary (master of divinity and doctor of ministry) as well as extensive research programs. Founded in 1845 the college is affiliated with the Baptist General Convention of Texas.

Geographic Reach

Baylor University has a 1000-acre campus on the banks of the Brazos River in Waco Texas. Its students hail from across the US and some 90 international countries.

Financial Analysis

Baylor University reported an 18% increase in revenues to $561 million in 2012 due to higher tuition fees and gifts. Net income fell by 101% (to a loss of some $2 million) due to higher program and support expenses.

The university's market endowment value was some $960 million as of mid-2012.

EXECUTIVES

Vice President for Marketing and Communications and Chief Marketing Officer, John M. Barry
VP Information Technology and Dean University Libraries, Pattie Orr
VP University Development, Dennis A. Prescott
Director Procurement Services, Tom Hoffmeyer
Senior Vice President for Operations & Chief Financial Officer, Reagan M. Ramsower
Assistant VP Enrollment Management, Diana M. Ramey
General Counsel, Charles D. Beckenhauer
Associate VP Student Life, Martha Lou Scott
Director Career Services, John Boyd
Dean Student Learning and Engagement, Frank Shushok Jr.
Vice President for Student Life, Kevin Jackson
Dean College of Arts and Sciences, Lee C. Nordt
Vice Provost Academic Affairs and Research and Director CASPER, Truell W. Hyde II
Dean School of Social Work, Diana R. Garland
Dean Hankamer School of Business, Terry S. Maness
Executive Vice President and Provost, Elizabeth Davis
Dean School of Engineering and Computer Science, Benjamin S. Kelley
Dean Honors College, Thomas S. Hibbs
Dean School of Law, Bradley J. B. Toben
Dean School of Music, William V. May Jr.
Dean Louise Herrington School of Nursing, Judith Wright Lott
Vice Provost Academic Affairs and Policy, Prof James Bennighof
VP and General Manager KWBU-TV, Kliff Kuehl
Associate VP Operational Planning and Director Budget, Wilson E. (Bud) McGregor
Vice Provost Institutional Effectiveness and Dean Graduate School, J. Larry Lyon
Associate VP Information Systems and Services, Rebecca L. (Becky) King
Assistant VP Client Services, Vicky Gerik
Assistant VP Information Technology Servers and Networks, Bob Hartland
President, Kenneth W. Starr, age 68
Chief of Staff, Karla Leeper
Chief of Police, James Doak
Dean Student Development, Elizabeth D. Palacios
Director Admission Services, Jennifer Carron
Dean School of Education, Jon M. Engelhardt
SVP Strategic Initiatives and Partnerships, Kathy Wills Wright
Director of Game Operations, Paula Young
Administrative Assistant, Suzy Daniel
Technical Director, Doyle Shirley
Director for Facilities, Drew Pittman
Dean School of Engineering & Computer Science, Dennis L. O'Neal
Professor and Dean Louise Herrington School of Nursing, Shelley F. Conroy
Dean George W. Truett Theological Seminary, David E. Garland
Regent, Harold R. Cunningham
Regent, R. Dary Stone, age 60
Regent, Ronald D. (Ron) Murff
Regent, Stan Allcorn
Regent, Joseph B. Armes
Regent, Wes Bailey
Regent, Robert E. (Bob) Beauchamp
Regent, Albert C. Black Jr.
Regent, Tommy L. Bowman
Regent, Linda Jean Brian
Regent, Duane Brooks
Regent, Steve Carmack
Regent, Bobby Dagnel
Regent, Gary Elliston
Regent, Sue Holt Getterman
Regent, David H. Harper
Regent, Neal T. (Buddy) Jones
Regent, Ramiro Pena Jr.
Regent, John Reimers

LOCATIONS

HQ: BAYLOR UNIVERSITY
700 S UNIVERSITY PARKS DR, WACO, TX 76706-1003
Phone: 254-710-3731
Web: WWW.BAYLOR.EDU

PRODUCTS/OPERATIONS

Selected Colleges and Schools

College of Arts and Sciences
George W. Truett Theological Seminary
Graduate School
Hankamer School of Business
Honors College
Law School
Louise Herrington School of Nursing
School of Education
School of Engineering and Computer Science
School of Music
School of Social Work

Selected Institutes

Allbritton Art Institute
Institute for Air Science
Institute for Faith and Learning
Institute for Oral History
Institute of Biblical and Related Languages
Institute of Biomedical Studies
J. M. Dawson Institute of Church-State Studies

HISTORICAL FINANCIALS

Company Type: Private

Income Statement FYE: May 31

	REVENUE ($ mil.)	NET INCOME ($ mil.)	NET PROFIT MARGIN	EMPLOYEES
05/12	560	(1)	—	1,550
05/11	474	139	29.3%	—
05/09	577	0	—	—
05/06	376	170	45.2%	—
Annual Growth	6.9%	—	—	—

2012 Year-End Financials

Debt ratio: —
Return on equity: (-0.30%)
Cash ($ mil.): 49
Current ratio: —
Long-term debt ($ mil.): —
Dividends
Yield: —
Payout: —
Market value ($ mil.): —

BAYLOR UNIVERSITY MEDICAL CENTER

Baylor University Medical Center at Dallas is the flagship institution of the Baylor Health Care System. The medical center (known as Baylor Dallas) serves 5 million Dallas area residents with more than 1000 inpatient beds and some 1200 physicians. It offers general medical and surgical services to specialty care in a wide range of fields including oncology cardiovascular disease and neuroscience. The hospital also features a Level I trauma center neonatal ICU and organ transplantation center. Founded in 1903 the Baylor Dallas campus includes the Charles A. Sammons Cancer Center and the Baylor Research Institute which conducts basic and clinical research across numerous medical specialties.

Operations

The Baylor University Medical Center campus consists of 20 specialty centers for treating a range of medical conditions. Primary facilities include the Charles A. Sammons Cancer Center Neuroscience Center Annette C. and Harold C. Simmons Transplant Institute James M. and Dorothy D. Collins Womens and Children's Center and the George Truett James Orthopaedic Institute as well as a top trauma center digestive care program and heart and vascular unit.

Strategy

The hospital received a boost in 2011 when Texas A&M's Health Science Center struck an affiliation with Baylor Health Care System. The two parties agreed to make Baylor Dallas a primary teaching hospital for A&M's third and fourth-year medical students. No hospital in the Baylor Health Care System held such a designation after it became independent from Baylor University in 1997.

As one of only two adult Level 1 trauma centers in the region Baylor Dallas has worked to bolster its emergency services to keep up with increasing demand. To this end it has broadened its Level 1 trauma capabilities increased the size of its minor emergency care area and added more patient care areas. The Riggs Emergency Department treats some 67000 patients each year.

Baylor Dallas' transplant program is considered a national leader in solid organ transplantation and in partnership with the program at Baylor All Saints Medical Center is one of only three programs worldwide to have performed more than 3000 adult liver transplants. The program is also known for its kidney pancreas heart and lung small bowel and blood and marrow transplants.

EXECUTIVES

President, John B. McWhorter III
Controller, James Poole
Director Human Resources, Wendie Carlson
Medical Director Baylor Heart and Vascular Institute, Clyde W. Yancy
Chief of Gastroenterology, C. Richard Boland
VP Medical Staff Affairs and Chief Medical Officer, Irving D. Prengler
Chief Nursing Officer, Claudia Wilder
COO, Doug Lawson
President Chief Executive Officer CEO of Baylor, Joel Allison

LOCATIONS

HQ: BAYLOR UNIVERSITY MEDICAL CENTER
2001 BRYAN ST STE 2200, DALLAS, TX 75201-3024
Phone: 214-820-0111
Web: WWW.BAYLORHEALTH.EDU

Selected Locations

A. Webb Roberts Hospital
Baylor Charles A. Sammons Cancer Center
Baylor Jack and Jane Hamilton Heart and Vascular Hospital
Carr P. Collins Hospital
Erik and Margaret Jonsson Medical and Surgical Hospital
George W. Truett Memorial Hospital
Karl and Esther Hoblitzelle Memorial Hospital
Baylor Specialty Hospital
Our Children's House at Baylor

COMPETITORS

CHRISTUS Health
Children' s Medical Center of Dallas
Dynacq Healthcare
Harris Methodist Fort Worth Hospital
Presbyterian Hospital of Dallas
Southwestern Medical Center
Texas Health Denton
Texas Health Resources

Parkland Health & Hospital System	The Methodist Health System

HISTORICAL FINANCIALS

Company Type: Private

Income Statement FYE: June 30

	REVENUE ($ mil.)	NET INCOME ($ mil.)	NET PROFIT MARGIN	EMPLOYEES
06/09	1,072	0	—	5,003
06/08	155	16	10.3%	—
06/06	937	114	12.2%	—
06/05	906	93	10.3%	—
Annual Growth	4.3%	—	—	—

2009 Year-End Financials

Debt ratio: —
Return on equity: —
Cash ($ mil.): 0
Current ratio: —
Long-term debt ($ mil.): —
Dividends
Yield: —
Payout: —
Market value ($ mil.): —

BAYSIDE FUEL OIL CORP

LOCATIONS

HQ: BAYSIDE FUEL OIL CORP
1776 SHORE PKWY, BROOKLYN, NY 112146546
Phone: 7186222900

HISTORICAL FINANCIALS

Company Type: Private

Income Statement FYE: December 31

	REVENUE ($ mil.)	NET INCOME ($ mil.)	NET PROFIT MARGIN	EMPLOYEES
12/13	252	1	0.6%	37
12/12	276	(3)	—	—
12/11	311	(0)	—	—
12/10	250	0	—	—
Annual Growth	0.3%	—	—	—

2013 Year-End Financials

Debt ratio: —
Return on equity: 0.60%
Cash ($ mil.): 2
Current ratio: 1.20
Long-term debt ($ mil.): —
Dividends
Yield: —
Payout: —
Market value ($ mil.): —

BAYSIDE FUEL OIL DEPOT CORP

EXECUTIVES

SVP and Secretary, Vincent Allegretti
Controller, Robert Selevan
President, Sergio Allegretti
SVP and Treasurer, Bartolo (Bart) Allegretti

LOCATIONS

HQ: BAYSIDE FUEL OIL DEPOT CORP
1776 SHORE PKWY, BROOKLYN, NY 112146546
Phone: 7183729800

COMPETITORS

Benit Fuel	Leffler Energy
Farm & Home Oil	Mirabito Fuel

HISTORICAL FINANCIALS

Company Type: Private

Income Statement FYE: December 31

	REVENUE ($ mil.)	NET INCOME ($ mil.)	NET PROFIT MARGIN	EMPLOYEES
12/12	276	(3)	—	36
12/05	195	1	0.6%	—
12/04	152	1	0.7%	—
12/03	146	0	—	—
Annual Growth	7.4%	—	—	—

2012 Year-End Financials

Debt ratio: —
Return on equity: (-1.20%)
Cash ($ mil.): 4
Current ratio: 1.10
Long-term debt ($ mil.): —
Dividends
Yield: —
Payout: —
Market value ($ mil.): —

BAYSTATE HEALTH SYSTEM HEALTH SERVICES INC.

Patients in need of medical care can dock at this bay. Not-for-profit Baystate Health is the largest health care services provider in western Massachusetts. The system operates four acute-care and specialty hospitals with a total of more than 830 beds including the flagship Baystate Medical Center which operates a Level 1 Trauma Center and a specialized children's hospital. Baystate Health also offers ancillary medical services such as cancer care respiratory care infusion therapy visiting nurse and hospice services through its regional clinics and agencies. The system controls for-profit health plan provider Health New England as well as clinical pathology firm Baystate Reference Laboratories.

Operations

Baystate Medical Center accounts for about 660 of the system's beds. Its other two acute care hospitals are the Baystate Franklin Medical Center and the Baystate Mary Lane Hospital. The system also runs a physicians group Baystate Medical Practices which operates more than two dozen physician practices in several surrounding counties and towns. Other outpatient centers include surgery centers imaging and radiology clinics and neighborhood health centers. Altogether its facilities serve a population of 750000 western New England residents and admit more than 43000 inpatients perform 34000 surgeries handle some 5000 births and conduct 1.3 million outpatient visits each year.

Baystate Health provides academic and community educational programs as well as conducts basic clinical and biomedical research. For instance the Baystate Medical Center is a teaching hospital that serves as the western campus of the Tufts University School of Medicine. Baystate Health also partners with a number of regional colleges to offer nursing programs.

In the research realm Tufts and Baystate Health work on biomedical studies through the Tufts Clinical and Translational Science Institute. Baystate Medical Center also has a partnership with the University of Massachusetts that forms the Pioneer Valley Life Sciences Institute. Areas of research include clinical care quality of care and diabetes and metabolism. The Baystate Health system receives about $10 million per year in research funding from the National Institutes of Health and other agencies.

Sales and Marketing

Patient service revenue accounts for a majority (65%) of the hospital system's sales and Medicare and Medicaid reimbursements make up 36% of patient service payments. Other sources include commercial insurers and private pay customers.

Financial Performance

Baystate Health reported $1.65 billion in revenues in 2012 up 7% from 2011 results. The organization has reported a steady increase in sales over the past five years. Net income also increased 14% to $46.7 million.

Strategy

Baystate Health has been conducting expansion and renovation efforts at its facilities in recent years including medical technology and information system upgrades. The system's largest effort was the construction of a $300 million clinical building on the Baystate Medical Center Campus. The addition was completed in 2012 and includes a heart and vascular center patient care rooms a new children's hospital emergency department endovascular center and surgical facility.

Other facilities and divisions are undergoing expansion as well and Baystate Medical Practices continues to grow by adding new practices on a regular basis. Baystate Health is also upgrading its medical equipment and its information technology systems.

EXECUTIVES

President and CEO, Mark R. Tolosky
Interim President Baystate Medical Practices, Gordon W. Josephson
President and CEO Health New England Inc., Peter F. Straley
SVP Human Resources, Paula C. Squires
President Baystate Visiting Nurse Association and Hospice, Ruth E. Odgren
Chief Strategy Officer Vice President Strategy & External Relations, Donna J. Ross
Senior Vice President, Evan M. Benjamin
SVP CFO and Treasurer, Dennis W. Chalke
VP Human Resources Operations and Total Compensation, Lawrence G. Emerson
VP Marketing and Communications, Suzanne B. Hendery
Vice President Finance Support Services, Peter A. Lyons
VP Government Community Relations and Public Affairs, Steven F. Bradley
VP Information Services and CIO, Mark B. Gorrell
Vice-President Clinical Facilities & Guest Services, Michael F. Moran
Vice President Surgery Anesthesia & Emergency Services, Deborah A. Provost
VP Workforce Planning, Jean Jackson
Deputy Chair Psychiatry, Benjamin Liptzin
Vice President of Development, Jane Albert
VP Development; Executive Director Baystate Health Foundation, Susan Toner
CEO Baycare Health Partners, Stephen J. Sweet
Chair, Richard B. Steele Jr.
Chair Department of Emergency Medicine, Niels K. Rathlev
Vice President Human Resources, Paul Judd
VP and Chief Information Officer, Joel L. Vengco
EVP and COO, Mark A. Keroack
VP and Chief Medical Information Officer, Neil R. Kudler
SVP; COO and Chief Nursing Office Baystate Medical Center, Nancy Shendell-Falik
COO and Chief Medical Officer Baystate Mary Lane Hospital and Baystate Health Eastern Region, Mohammed Shafeeq Ahmed
President Baystate Regional Markets, Chuck Gijanto

Chief Medical Officer Baystate Franklin Medical Center and the Baystate Health Northern Region, Gerda Maissel
President Baystate Visiting Nurse Association and Hospice Executive for Post Acute Care, Maura McQueeney
Vice President Diagnostic Services, Jason Newmark
Vice President Strategic Planning & Business Development, Jean Ahn
SVP Chief Academic Officer, Kevin T. Hinchey
Auditors: Ernst&YoungLLP

LOCATIONS

HQ: BAYSTATE HEALTH SYSTEM HEALTH SERVICES INC.
759 CHESTNUT ST, SPRINGFIELD, MA 01199-1001
Phone: 413-794-9939
Web: WWW.BAYSTATEHEALTH.COM

Selected Locations

Baystate Medical Center (Springfield)
Baystate Children's Hospital (Springfield)
Baystate Franklin Medical Center (Greenfield)
Baystate Mary Lane Hospital (Ware)
Outpatient Centers
Baystate Home Infusion & Respiratory Services
Baystate Medical Practices
Baystate Radiology and Imaging (BRI)
Baystate Reference Laboratories (BRL)
Baystate Visiting Nurse Association & Hospice
Brightwood Health Center
Chestnut Surgery Center
D'Amour Center for Cancer Care
High Street Center (adult and pediatrics)
Mason Square Neighborhood Health Center
Neurodiagnostics & Sleep Center
Orthopedic Surgery Center
Wesson Women & Infants Health Center

PRODUCTS/OPERATIONS

Sales

	% of total
Net patient service	65
Insurance	30
Other	5
Total	**100**

Selected Services

Ambulance
Anesthesiology
Behavioral health services
Birthing services
Cancer
Cardiovascular
Emergency medicine
Endoscopy
Home care and home medical supplies
Hospital medicine
Neurosciences
Obstetrics and gynecology
Pain management center
Pathology
Pediatrics
Radiology
Rehabilitation care
Reproductive medicine
Sleep program
Surgery
Weight management
Women' s health

COMPETITORS

Berkshire Health Systems
Cambridge Health Alliance
Cape Cod Healthcare
CareGroup
Catholic Health East
Harrington Memorial Hospital
Partners HealthCare
Shriners Hospitals For Children
Southcoast Hospitals Group
Steward Health Care
Universal Health Services
Vanguard Health Systems

HISTORICAL FINANCIALS

Company Type: Private

Income Statement FYE: September 30

	REVENUE ($ mil.)	NET INCOME ($ mil.)	NET PROFIT MARGIN	EMPLOYEES
09/07	1,286	125	9.7%	5,000
09/06	1,209	83	6.9%	—
09/05	0	0	—	—
09/04	0	0	—	—
Annual Growth	—	—	—	—

2007 Year-End Financials

Debt ratio: —
Return on equity: 9.70%
Cash ($ mil.): 61
Current ratio: 0.70
Long-term debt ($ mil.): —
Dividends
Yield: —
Payout: —
Market value ($ mil.): —

BAYSTATE MEDICAL CENTER INC.

Baystate Medical Center is the flagship facility of the Baystate Health System. It is a tertiary care facility and Level 1 trauma center that provides comprehensive acute care services to residents of Springfield Massachusetts and the surrounding region. The more than 650-bed medical center is also a teaching hospital serving as a secondary campus for Tufts University School of Medicine. The Baystate Medical Center campus includes Baystate Children's Hospital a 110-bed unit that boasts neonatal and pediatric ICUs. Other Baystate Medical Center operations include specialty programs in radiology cardiac care cancer and behavioral health.

Operations

As the only Level 1 trauma center in western Massachusetts the hospital is responsible for treating the most critical and urgent cases in the region. Baystate Medical Center is also home to the second-busiest emergency department in the state. Along with performing its own research activities Baystate Medical Center collaborates with the University of Massachusetts Amherst on biomedical technology research projects through the Pioneer Valley Life Sciences Institute. The center is home to one of only about 40 American College of Surgeons-accredited Level 1 Comprehensive Education Institutes in the world.

Strategy

To ensure that it is able to maintain its emergency care volumes and provide area communities with the latest technologies Baystate Medical Center opened a 640000-sq.-ft. facility in 2012 under the name Davis Family Heart and Vascular Center. The center features 32 cardiovascular critical care rooms separate pediatric triage and treatment areas and a new urgent care center as well as designated space for visiting family and friends.

EXECUTIVES

EVP and COO Baystate Health, Greg Harb
VP Human Resources, Paul D. Judd
SVP CFO and Treasurer Baystate Health, Dennis W. Chalke
Chief Physician Executive and President Baystate Medical Practices, Mark A. Keroack
Senior Vice President, Evan M. Benjamin
Vice President Marketing and Communications, Suzanne B. Hendery
Senior Vice President Human Resources, Paula C. Squires

LOCATIONS

HQ: BAYSTATE MEDICAL CENTER INC.
759 CHESTNUT ST, SPRINGFIELD, MA 01199-0001
Phone: 413-784-0000
Web: WWW.BAYSTATEHEALTH.ORG

PRODUCTS/OPERATIONS

Selected Programs & Services

Baystate Children's Hospital
Baystate Heart & Vascular Program
Baystate Regional Cancer Program
Department of Surgery
Regional Sleep Program
Women's Health

COMPETITORS

Berkshire Health Systems
Boston Medical Center
CareGroup
Catholic Health East
Children' s Hospital Boston
Connecticut Children' s Medical Center
Harrington Memorial Hospital
Hartford Health Care
Hospital of Central Connecticut
Partners HealthCare
Saint Francis Hospital and Medical Center
St. Elizabeth' s Medical Center
University of Connecticut Health Center
Yale New Haven Health System

HISTORICAL FINANCIALS

Company Type: Private

Income Statement FYE: September 30

	REVENUE ($ mil.)	NET INCOME ($ mil.)	NET PROFIT MARGIN	EMPLOYEES
09/10	884	64	7.3%	4,691
09/07	797	79	10.0%	
09/06	699	0	—	—
09/05	699	8	1.2%	—
Annual Growth	4.8%	49.4%	—	—

2010 Year-End Financials

Debt ratio: —
Return on equity: 7.30%
Cash ($ mil.): 51
Current ratio: 0.30
Long-term debt ($ mil.): —
Dividends
Yield: —
Payout: —
Market value ($ mil.): —

BEALL'S INC.

Residents of the Sun Belt have been known to leave their homes with Beall's on. The retail holding company operates through subsidiaries Beall's Department Stores Beall's Outlet and Burke's Outlet Stores in a dozen states. The multi-brand retailer has more than 535 department and outlet stores (about 200 are in Florida) located throughout states in the southern and western US including Arizona California Georgia Louisiana and Texas. Products range from off-price clothing and footwear for men and women to cosmetics gifts and housewares. Each chain has its own online shopping destination. The family-owned company was founded in 1915 by the grandfather of Chairman Robert Beall (pronounced "bell").

Geographic Reach

Beall's trio of chain's operate stores in Alabama Arkansas Arizona California Florida Georgia Kentucky Louisiana Mississippi Nevada New Mexico North Carolina South Carolina Tennessee Texas Virginia and West Virginia.

Operations

Beall's Inc. oversees operations of its three operating companies. Beall's Florida operates some 65 stores in the Sunshine State. Beall's Outlet operates about 300 stores in Arizona Florida and Georgia while Burke's Outlet operates more than 160 stores in about a dozen states.

Financial Performance

Privately-owned Beall's rings ups more than $1 billion in sales annually.

Strategy

The company's new president recruited in 2012 to run Beall's Outlet and Burke's Outlet stores has aspirations to transform the company into a major discount retailer much like its larger rivals TJX and Ross Stores. To that end the company plans to add new stores outside its traditional markets with an eye on establishing a national retail presence. Targets include adding 30 to 50 stores a year for the next several years and raising brand awareness beyond Florida.

With many of its stores in Arizona Florida and California (three of the states hit hardest by the housing crisis and deep recession) Beall's Inc. should have been in a heap of retail trouble. However its largest chain –Beall's Outlet –proved to be quite popular during this recession. Indeed the budget-priced outlet chain outperformed its two sister chains as well as more moderately priced department stores. The retailer has also benefited from the demise of other retailers including Goody's Linens 'n Things and Mervyn's.

The three operating companies share resources provided by Beall's Inc. such as distribution finance loss prevention and information systems. Conversely each chain is responsible for its purchasing product development real estate and advertising activities.

Company Background

Stores operating under the Bealls name in Alabama New Mexico and Texas are owned by Stage Stores and are not affiliated with Beall's Inc.

EXECUTIVES

Chairman, Robert M. (Bob) Beall II
Director Public and Goverment Affairs, William (Bill) Webster

LOCATIONS

HQ: BEALL' S INC.
1806 38TH AVE E, BRADENTON, FL 34208-4700
Phone: 941-747-2355
Web: WWW.BEALLSOUTLET.COM

PRODUCTS/OPERATIONS

Selected Retail Operations

Bealls Department Stores (Florida)
Bealls Outlet (deep-discount outlet stores in Arizona Florida Georgia)
Burke's Outlet (11 southern states)

COMPETITORS

Bed Bath & Beyond
Costco Wholesale
Dillard' s
J. C. Penney Company
Kohl' s
Macy' s
Nordstrom
Ross Stores
Sears
Stage Stores
TJX Companies
Target Corporation
The Gap
Wal-Mart

HISTORICAL FINANCIALS

Company Type: Private

Income Statement FYE: July 28

	REVENUE ($ mil.)	NET INCOME ($ mil.)	NET PROFIT MARGIN	EMPLOYEES
07/12	1,232	14	1.1%	9,100
07/11	1,166	15	1.3%	—
07/10*	1,123	11	1.0%	—
08/08	1,170	(8)	—	—
Annual Growth	1.3%	—	—	—

*Fiscal year change

2012 Year-End Financials

Debt ratio: —
Return on equity: 1.10%
Cash ($ mil.): 51
Current ratio: 0.30
Long-term debt ($ mil.): —
Dividends
Yield: —
Payout: —
Market value ($ mil.): —

BEARING DISTRIBUTORS INC.

Bearing Distributors Inc. (BDI) began as a regional Midwestern distributor of replacement parts to OEMs. Among the world's largest industrial suppliers today the company also provides maintenance and repair services as well as training and inventory management. Its offerings include bearings electrical power products material handling systems and motion control products hydraulic and pneumatic systems and fluid power components. BDI serves customers in automotive to power generation industries and from mining to food and beverage paper processing and package handling operations. Founded in 1935 the company a unit of Forge Industries has locations dotting North America Europe and Asia.

Geographic Reach

BDI operates more than 200 global branches spanning 12 countries including the US Canada Mexico Europe and Asia. Its distribution centers reside in Cleveland Ohio; Montreal and Mississauga Canada; Budapest Hungary; Tianjin China; Suzhou China; and Bangalore India.

Strategy

BDI grows its business through acquisitions and organic growth. As part of this strategy in early 2015 it purchased Munnell & Sherrill an industrial distribution company based in the Pacific Northwest with locations in Oregon Washington and Northern California.

In 2013 BDI opened a new branch in Flint Michigan to serve customers in central and southeastern Michigan. That year it also relocated a branch in Maine and a branch in Detroit to better serve its expanding customer base.

EXECUTIVES

V Pres, Steve Kieffer
V Pres, Bud Thayer
President and COO, John Ruth
Manager Product Group Specialist, David Strovers
Manager Conveying Equipment, Dan Paustian
Vice President Manufacturing, Clifton Estes
Vice President Src, Rick Copfer

LOCATIONS

HQ: BEARING DISTRIBUTORS INC.
8000 HUB PKWY, CLEVELAND, OH 441255788
Phone: 2166429100
Web: WWW.BDI-USA.COM

PRODUCTS/OPERATIONS

Selected Products

Adhesive sealant and lubricant products
- Adhesives
- Cleaners
- Epoxies
- Hand cleaners
- Lube systems
- Lubricants
- Micro poly
- Paints
- Sealants
- Silicones
- Solvents
- Thread lockers
- Thread repair

Bearings
- Ball and roller bearings
- Lubricated bearings
- Mounted bearing units
- Specialty bearings

Bulk chemicals
- Adhesives
- Metalworking fluids
- Surface treatment

Electrical Products
- Clutches and brakes
- DC SCR drives
- Electric motors
- Tachometers

Fluid power components
- Components
- Hydraulic cylinders and actuators
- Hydraulic and pumps
- Pressure gauges
- PVC fittings
- Temperature gauges
- Valves (ball butterfly hydraulic and pneumatic)

Industrial hose and fittings
- High pressure hose
- Hydraulic fittings
- PVC fittings
- Quick disconnect fittings
- Tube fittings

Linear motion control
- Electromechanical actuators
- Linear accelerators
- Linear actuators

Material handling products and systems
- Belt fasteners idlers and lacers
- Conveyors
- Conveyor components
- Drive components

Mechanical power transmission
- Belts
- Chain attachments
- Couplings
- Drive systems
- Gears
- Speed reducers

COMPETITORS

Applied Industrial Technologies
DXP Enterprises
HD Supply
Industrial Distribution Group
Lewis-Goetz
MRC Global
Milk Specialties Company
THG Corporation
W.W. Grainger
WESCO International

HISTORICAL FINANCIALS

Company Type: Private

Income Statement FYE: December 31

	REVENUE ($ mil.)	NET INCOME ($ mil.)	NET PROFIT MARGIN	EMPLOYEES
12/08	528	5	1.1%	850
12/07	502	13	2.6%	—
12/06	2,099	0	—	—
Annual Growth	—44021.8%		—	—

2008 Year-End Financials

Debt ratio: —
Return on equity: 1.10%
Cash ($ mil.): 5
Current ratio: 0.80
Long-term debt ($ mil.): —
Dividends
Yield: —
Payout: —
Market value ($ mil.): —

BEAVER STREET FISHERIES INC.

After more than 60 years of fishing Beaver Street Fisheries can tell a tale or two of the one that got away. It's a top supplier of fish and other seafood products to wholesalers retailers and food service operators. Sourcing its products from more than 50 countries family-owned Beaver Street Fisheries offers one of the largest selections of seafood in the US. It boasts a variety of fresh and frozen seafood –including octopus shrimp and turtle –sold under its flagship Sea Best brand as well as the HF's and Island Queen names. Beaver Street Fisheries also imports lamb from New Zealand and sells Silver Fern-brand pork and beef via its Florida-New Zealand Lamb & Meat unit.

Operations

Beaver Street Fisheries has expanded its products portfolio in recent years through the efforts of its sister companies Bahamas Food Service and Tropic Seafood. Based in Nassau Bahamas the company's food service operation specializes in food distribution as one of the largest full-line food service distributors in the Bahamas. The company's Tropic Seafood business concentrates on lobster tail and seafood processing in the Bahamas. Specifically it processes lobster tails conch and other seafood items under the Island Queen and Island Prince brand names for sale worldwide.

The company maintains 8 million cubic feet of freezer space in Jacksonville Florida and offers 27 loading bays to facilitate a speedy dock turnaround process. It also has a network of cold storage facilities works with carriers to ensure national and international delivery within 48 hours.

Strategy

The food service operation specializes in food distribution as one of the largest full-line food service distributors in the Bahamas. In 2012 it working to double the size of its warehouse in Nassau while also fine-tuning the company's automation labor and transportation processes. Beaver Street Fisheries hopes to automate the workforce management processes in Nassau so that it can boost order volume without greatly expanding its employee count there.

Company Background

Alfred and Hans Frisch started the business as a retail fish shop in 1950. It established the Sea Best brand in 1979.

EXECUTIVES

Chairman, Harry Frisch
President, Benjamin P. (Ben) Frisch
EVP, Hans Frisch
Executive Vice President of Beaver Street Fisheries, Mark Frisch

LOCATIONS

HQ: BEAVER STREET FISHERIES INC.
1741 W ST BEAVER, JACKSONVILLE, FL 32209
Phone: 9043545661
Web: WWW.BEAVERSTREETFISHERIES.COM

PRODUCTS/OPERATIONS

Selected Products

Fish and other seafood
- Albacore tuna
- Black cod
- Bluefish
- Calamari
- Catfish
- Clams
- Cod
- Conch
- Crab
- Crawfish
- Flounder
- Grouper
- Haddock
- Halibut
- Lake perch
- Langostinos
- Lobster
- Mackerel
- Mahi mahi
- Marlin
- Mullet
- Mussels
- Ocean catfish
- Ocean perch
- Orange roughy
- Oysters
- Pollock
- Salmon
- Scallops
- Sea bass
- Sea trout
- Shark
- Shrimp
- Snails/escargot
- Snapper
- Sole
- Squid
- Surimi
- Swordfish
- Tilapia
- Whiting
- Yellowfin tuna

Value-added
- Breaded seafood
- Crab cakes
- Crab patties
- Crabmeat stuffing
- Deviled crab
- Lobster tails
- Paella mix
- Salted fish
- Smoked fish

Other
- Alligator
- Beef
- Frog legs
- Lamb
- Octopus
- Pork
- Turtle

COMPETITORS

American Seafoods
Brown Packing Company
Colorado Boxed Beef
Del Monte Capitol Meat
Fishhawk Fisheries
Florida Fresh Seafood Corp.
Fossil Farms
Freedman Meats
Gorton' s
Harvest Meat Company
High Liner Foods
Icelandic Group
JBS USA
Jim Pattison Group
Maid-Rite Steak Company
Mims Meat
Niman Ranch
North Pacific Seafoods
Ocean Beauty Seafoods
Pacific Seafood Group
Pioneer Wholesale Meat
Red Chamber Co.
Ronald A. Chisholm Limited
SYSCO Newport Meat Company
Smithfield Foods
Trident Seafoods
Wolverine Packing

HISTORICAL FINANCIALS

Company Type: Private

Income Statement FYE: May 28

	REVENUE ($ mil.)	NET INCOME ($ mil.)	NET PROFIT MARGIN	EMPLOYEES
05/11	450	13	3.0%	200
05/10	442	19	4.4%	—
05/09	741	0	0.0%	—
Annual Growth	(22.0%)	41071.0%	—	—

2011 Year-End Financials

Debt ratio: —
Return on equity: 3.00%
Cash ($ mil.): 19
Current ratio: 1.80
Long-term debt ($ mil.): —
Dividends
Yield: —
Payout: —
Market value ($ mil.): —

BECK SUPPLIERS INC.

EXECUTIVES

President, Doug Beck
VP Friendship Food Stores, Brian Beck
Treasurer, Dean Beck
VP Operations, Ed Willman
Accounting, Bill Taylor
Project Engineer, Lee Beckman
Ace Check Cashing, Aaron Taylor
Webmaster, Adam Miller

LOCATIONS

HQ: BECK SUPPLIERS INC.
1000 N FRONT ST, FREMONT, OH 434201921
Phone: 4193325527
Web: WWW.FRIENDSHIPFOODSTORES.COM

COMPETITORS

Benit Fuel
Lykins
Sapp Bros

HISTORICAL FINANCIALS

Company Type: Private

Income Statement FYE: December 31

	REVENUE ($ mil.)	NET INCOME ($ mil.)	NET PROFIT MARGIN	EMPLOYEES
12/09	252	1	0.5%	250
12/08	316	0	0.2%	
12/07	1,300	0	—	—
Annual Growth	—	7165.1%	—	—

2009 Year-End Financials

Debt ratio: —
Return on equity: 0.50%
Cash ($ mil.): 1
Current ratio: 0.50
Long-term debt ($ mil.): —
Dividends
Yield: —
Payout: —
Market value ($ mil.): —

BECKMAN RESEARCH INSTITUTE OF THE CITY OF HOPE

LOCATIONS

HQ: BECKMAN RESEARCH INSTITUTE OF THE CITY OF HOPE
1500 DUARTE RD, DUARTE, CA 910103012
Phone: 6263598111

HISTORICAL FINANCIALS

Company Type: Private

Income Statement FYE: September 30

	REVENUE ($ mil.)	NET INCOME ($ mil.)	NET PROFIT MARGIN	EMPLOYEES
09/13	300	39	13.0%	250
09/09	239	30	12.9%	—
09/08	253	33	13.2%	—
09/07	70	0	—	—
Annual Growth	27.5%	—	—	—

2013 Year-End Financials

Debt ratio: ——
Return on equity: 13.00%
Cash ($ mil.): 70
Current ratio: 0.90
Long-term debt ($ mil.): —
Dividends
Yield: —
Payout: —
Market value ($ mil.): —

BEEBE MEDICAL CENTER INC.

Sea shells on the sea shore can be found near Beebe Medical Center. The health care provider offers emergency inpatient long-term care women's health and other medical services to residents of Sussex County Delaware. The hospital is located in the town of Lewes near Rehoboth Beach. It has approximately 210 beds and offers specialized services including cardiology orthopedic rehabilitation and oncology treatments. Beebe Medical Center offers outpatient services including wound care diabetes management surgery radiology and sleep disorder diagnosis. It also operates senior care centers home health agencies medical laboratories and a nursing school.

Operations

Beebe Medical Center has a staff of some 1400 health professionals including about 300 doctors. It handles some 50000 emergency room visits per year. In addition to the primary hospital facilities the health care provider operates the Beebe Health Campus (outpatient services) and the nearby Millville Emergency Center (a summertime clinic near Bethany Beach).

Strategy

Beebe Medical Center has expanded its facilities over the years to better serve area residents. It began an expansion aiming to double enrollment of the nursing school in 2012. Construction efforts at the main hospital facility include a new emergency and critical care wing added in 2008.

Company Background

Beebe Medical Center was founded in 1916 by two brothers Dr. James Beebe and Dr. Richard Beebe. The Beebe School of Nursing opened in 1921 and the outpatient Beebe Health Campus was completed in 2003.

EXECUTIVES

President and CEO, Jeffrey M. Fried
VP Corporate Affairs, Wallace E. Hudson
Treasurer, James Bartle
VP Human Resources, Catherine C. Halen
Director Physician Services, Marilyn Hill
Chair, Janet B. McCarty
Treasurer, Paul H. Mylander
Chairman, William S. Lee
President Operations, Donna A Streletzky
VP and CIO, Barbara P. Vugrinec
Vice Chairman, Jacquelyn O. Wilson
EVP and COO, Thomas K. Steiner
VP Patient Care Services, Vendla A. Esler
Interim VP Medical Affairs, Andrejs Strauss
President and CEO Beebe Medical Foundation, Alex A. Sydnor
VP Finance and CFO, Paul J. Pernice
Vice President Medical Operations and Informatics, Jeffrey E. Hawtof
President and CEO Beebe Physician Network, Debbie Craft
VP and CIO, Michael J. Maksymow
EVP and COO, Paul Minnick
Vice President Patient Care Services, Steve Rhone
Trustee, James D. Barr
Trustee, James Beebe Jr.
Trustee, Steven D. Berlin
Trustee, William L. Berry
Trustee, Eugene D. Bookhammer
Trustee, Joseph W. Booth
Trustee, Stephen M. Fanto
Trustee, Thomas L. King
Trustee, Halsey G. Knapp
Vice Chair, William S. Lee
Trustee, Robert H. Moore
Trustee, Esthelda R. Parker-Selby
Trustee, Anis K. Saliba
Trustee, Patricia D. Shreeve
Trustee, Robert J. White
Trustee, Jacquelyn O. Wilson
Trustee, Habib Bolourchi
Trustee, Michael L. Wilgus

LOCATIONS

HQ: BEEBE MEDICAL CENTER INC.
424 SAVANNAH RD, LEWES, DE 19958-1462
Phone: 302-645-3300
Web: WWW.BEEBEMED.ORG

Selected Delaware Locations

Beebe Health Campus (Rehoboth Beach)
Beebe Lab Express (Milton)
Beebe School of Nursing (Lewes)
Diabetes Management and Wound Care Center (Long Neck)
Georgetown Professional Park (Georgetown)
Gull House Adult Activities Center (Lewes)
Home Health Agency (Lewes)
Millville Walk-in Health Center (Millville)
Sleep Disorders Center (Rehoboth Beach)
Tunnell Cancer Center (Rehoboth Beach)

PRODUCTS/OPERATIONS

Selected Services

Bariatric
Cancer care
Cardiac & vascular
Community health
Diabetes management
Emergency
Home health
Hospitalist program
Imaging
Integrative health
Orthopedics
Rehabilitation
Senior care
Sleep Disorder
Surgical
Walk-in Healthcare
Wellness
Women's Health
Wound Care

COMPETITORS

Anne Arundel Medical Center
AtlantiCare
Catholic Health East
Christiana Care
Crozer-Keystone Health System
Inspira Health Network
Shore Memorial Hospital

HISTORICAL FINANCIALS

Company Type: Private

Income Statement FYE: June 30

	REVENUE ($ mil.)	NET INCOME ($ mil.)	NET PROFIT MARGIN	EMPLOYEES
06/10	259	15	5.9%	1,600
06/09	234	0	—	—
06/09	0	0	—	—
Annual Growth	—93081.6%	—	—	—

2010 Year-End Financials

Debt ratio: ——
Return on equity: 5.90%
Cash ($ mil.): 12
Current ratio: 0.30
Long-term debt ($ mil.): —
Dividends
Yield: —
Payout: —
Market value ($ mil.): —

BELCAN CORPORATION

Belcan provides engineering technical recruiting and staffing services to clients in the aviation consumer products and manufacturing industries among others. Its Belcan Engineering division offers design engineering engineering analysis and computer modeling to customers such as Lockheed Martin and UTC. The company also offers recruiting services –including interviewing screening and workforce management –to fill openings for highly skilled technical personnel through Belcan TechServices. BelFlex Staffing Network supplies light industrial and clerical employees to clients. Family-owned Belcan founded in 1958 by Ralph Anderson operates some 70 offices primarily in the US.

Geographic Reach

Ohio-based Belcan primarily serves clients nationwide as well as abroad. It operates about 70 locations worldwide.

Sales and Marketing

Belcan which serves several sectors counts customers such as aerospace giant UTC and defense leader Lockheed Martin among its list of clients.

Operations

The company operates through three divisions: Belcan Engineering Belcan TechServices and BelFlex Staffing Network.

Belcan Engineering provides design engineering engineering analysis and computer modeling as well as advanced manufacturing techniques. It offers engineering and automation design/build services to industry leaders in the Aviation Energy Marine Propulsion Heavy Equipment and Consumer Products sectors handling all projects in a secure environment.Belcan TechServices provides recruitment support and staffing for highly skilled technical employees. It sources interviews screens and assigns technical professionals across most industries. This division offers contract personnel direct-hire recruiting onsite workforce management and payroll services.BelFlex Staffing Network specializes in offering customized options to the light-industrial market such as temporary and contract staffing peak season/high volume staffing and contingent workforce management.

Strategy

Looking to give the unit its own identity Belcan in 2014 separated its $115 million staffing division to operate as a sister company under the newly rebranded name BelFlex Staffing Network. The network offers light-industrial flexible staffing —with 5000 employees and 25 offices —to companies in the Midwest and Southeast. The staffing company was initially built from Belcan's 2009 purchase of four staffing companies in Ohio Indiana Kentucky and Tennessee.

Mergers and Acquisitions

Belcan in 2013 focused on extending its reach into the UK through its purchase of Energy Resources Management Ltd. (ERM). As a result Belcan provides high-voltage electrical engineering personnel to major Distribution Network Operators across the UK.

Financial Performance

While Belcan is privately owned the company reports that its annual sales come in at more than $676 million.

EXECUTIVES

COO, Cleve L. Campbell
CFO, Michael J. Wirth
SVP, Lance H. Kwasniewski
President Staffing Solutions, Todd Cross
Chairman, Candace D. McCaw
CEO, Michael E. (Mike) McCaw
President TechServices Division, Arnie Johnson
Auditors: ClarkSchaeferHackett&Co.

LOCATIONS

HQ: BELCAN CORPORATION
10200 ANDERSON WAY, BLUE ASH, OH 45242-4718
Phone: 513-891-0972
Web: WWW.BELCAN.COM

PRODUCTS/OPERATIONS

Selected Services

Engineering
- Automation Design & Build
- Design Drafting
- Electrical Engineering
- Engineering Analysis
- Maintenance Repair & Overhaul
- Manufacturing Engineering
- Mechanical Engineering
- Project Management
- Software Engineering
- Systems Engineering

Technical
- Talent Acquisition
- Sourcing Screening and Onboarding
- Contingent Workforce Management
- Payrolling
- Subvendor Management
- Recruitment Process Outsourcing

Staffing Network
- Temporary/Contract Personnel
- Contingent Workforce Management
- Peak Season Staffing
- Direct Hire Placements
- Recruitment Process Outsourcing

COMPETITORS

AECOM
Accenture
Adecco
Allegis Group
Bartech
CDI
HP Enterprise Services
IBM Global Services
ManpowerGroup

HISTORICAL FINANCIALS

Company Type: Private

Income Statement

FYE: December 31

	REVENUE ($ mil.)	NET INCOME ($ mil.)	NET PROFIT MARGIN	EMPLOYEES
12/12	688	19	2.8%	10,000
12/11	623	22	3.7%	—
12/10	538	13	2.5%	—
12/09	452	1	0.4%	—
Annual Growth	15.0%	117.6%	—	—

2012 Year-End Financials

Debt ratio: —
Return on equity: 2.80%
Cash ($ mil.): 0
Current ratio: 1.40
Long-term debt ($ mil.): —

Dividends
Yield: —
Payout: —
Market value ($ mil.): —

BELCREST CAPITAL FUND LLC

LOCATIONS

HQ: BELCREST CAPITAL FUND LLC
2 INTERNATIONAL PL, BOSTON, MA 021104104
Phone: 6174828260

HISTORICAL FINANCIALS

Company Type: Private

Income Statement

FYE: December 31

	ASSETS ($ mil.)	NET INCOME ($ mil.)	INCOME AS % OF ASSETS	EMPLOYEES
12/10	795	119	15.0%	2
12/09	852	43	5.1%	—
Annual Growth	(6.7%)	173.2%	—	—

2010 Year-End Financials

Debt ratio: —
Return on equity: 381.80%
Cash ($ mil.): 1
Current ratio: —
Long-term debt ($ mil.): —

Dividends
Yield: —
Payout: —
Market value ($ mil.): —

BELLWETHER HOUSING

LOCATIONS

HQ: BELLWETHER HOUSING
1651 BELLEVUE AVE, SEATTLE, WA 981222014
Phone: 2066230506
Web: WWW.BELLWETHERHOUSING.ORG

HISTORICAL FINANCIALS

Company Type: Private

Income Statement

FYE: December 31

	ASSETS ($ mil.)	NET INCOME ($ mil.)	INCOME AS % OF ASSETS	EMPLOYEES
12/13	96	0	0.4%	84
12/10	78	(0)	—	—
12/09	75	(1)	—	—
12/06	110	0	—	—
Annual Growth	(1.9%)	—	—	—

2013 Year-End Financials

Debt ratio: —
Return on equity: 2.70%
Cash ($ mil.): 18
Current ratio: 14.80
Long-term debt ($ mil.): —

Dividends
Yield: —
Payout: —
Market value ($ mil.): —

BENCO DENTAL SUPPLY CO.

EXECUTIVES

President, Charles Cohen
Managing Director of Benco Dental, Richard Cohen
Chairman, Larry Cohen
VP Culture and People, George Rable
VP Operations, Lou Mangino
Founder Director, John Kois

LOCATIONS

HQ: BENCO DENTAL SUPPLY CO.
295 CENTERPOINT BLVD, PITTSTON, PA 186406136
Phone: 8004623626
Web: WWW.BENCO.COM

Selected Distribution Center Locations

Dallas Texas
Fort Wayne Indiana
Jacksonville Florida
Pittston Pennsylvania
Reno Nevada

PRODUCTS/OPERATIONS

Selected Brands

Large Equipment
- A-dec
- Belmont
- BIOLASE
- Cadent
- Gendex
- Instrumentarium
- Marus
- Midmark
- Pelton & Crane
- Sirona
- Soredex
- Vatech

Small Equipment
- Accutron
- Aceton
- Air Techniques
- Cadent
- KaVo
- Midmark
- Midwest
- Tuttnauer
- W&H

Supplies and technology (Benco brands)
- BencoNET
- BluChip rewards
- BluPrint (dental impression material)
- fas-TRACT
- HD
- Iris (dental pit and fissure sealant)
- Natural Extensions (nitrile gloves)
- Painless
- ValuGrip (latex gloves)
- Vision XR (oral x-ray film)
- XLR8 (dental equipment)
- Z3

COMPETITORS

Burkhart Dental
Cardinal Health
DENTSPLY
Darby Dental
Discus Dental
Henry Schein
McKesson
Owens & Minor
Patterson Companies
Sybron Dental

HISTORICAL FINANCIALS

Company Type: Private

Income Statement FYE: January 4

	REVENUE ($ mil.)	NET INCOME ($ mil.)	NET PROFIT MARGIN	EMPLOYEES
01/14*	620	8	1.4%	1,120
12/12	600	7	1.2%	—
12/07	389	5	1.3%	—
12/06	344	0	—	—
Annual Growth	8.8%	—	—	—

*Fiscal year change

2014 Year-End Financials

Debt ratio: —
Return on equity: 1.40%
Cash ($ mil.): 0
Current ratio: 0.70
Long-term debt ($ mil.): —
Dividends
Yield: —
Payout: —
Market value ($ mil.): —

BENDERSON PROPERTIES INC.

LOCATIONS

HQ: BENDERSON PROPERTIES INC.
7978 COOPER CREEK BLVD # 100, UNIVERSITY PARK, FL 342012141
Phone: 9413598303
Web: WWW.BENDERSON.COM

HISTORICAL FINANCIALS

Company Type: Private

Income Statement FYE: March 31

	ASSETS ($ mil.)	NET INCOME ($ mil.)	INCOME AS % OF ASSETS	EMPLOYEES
03/13	402	29	7.2%	280
03/12	374	19	5.3%	—
03/11	349	26	7.7%	—
03/10	355	0	—	—
Annual Growth	4.2%	—	—	—

2013 Year-End Financials

Debt ratio: —
Return on equity: 53.60%
Cash ($ mil.): 9
Current ratio: 0.30
Long-term debt ($ mil.): —
Dividends
Yield: —
Payout: —
Market value ($ mil.): —

BENTLEY UNIVERSITY

Bentley University formerly known as Bentley College offers undergraduate graduate and doctoral degree programs to its nearly 5600 enrolled students from around the world. It also offers professional development and certificate programs for executives and corporations. The focus at Bentley is on business; the school was a pioneer in integrating information technology into the business curriculum. In the belief that businesspeople need a broad education Bentley requires a liberal arts core of classes in behavioral and social sciences English and other subjects in the humanities math and natural sciences. Harry Bentley founded the institution as a school of accounting and finance in 1917.

Bentley University is situated on about 165 acres in Waltham west of Boston. The university supports a student-faculty ratio of 12:1 with more than 80% of its faculty holding doctoral degrees.

Bentley offers numerous on-campus activities outside its academic and research functions. These include cultural events athletics the arts volunteering and more than 100 student organizations.

In partnership with Bahrain Institute of Banking and Finance Bentley launched its "Bentley in Bahrain" degree program in 2002 expanding its campus to students in Bahrain and surrounding Gulf States in the Middle East.

Bentley's university designation and name change occurred in 2008.

EXECUTIVES

President, Gloria Cordes Larson
VP Academic Affairs and Provost, Michael J. Page
VP Administration and Finance, Kenneth B. Cody
Dean Arts and Sciences, Daniel L. Everett
VP Student Affairs and Dean of Students, J. Andrew Shepardson
Dean Business and Graduate School, Roy A. (Chip) Wiggins
CIO, Phillip G. Knutel
Vice Chairman, Robert P. (Bob) Badavas, age 61
Chairman, Steven P. Manfredi

LOCATIONS

HQ: BENTLEY UNIVERSITY
175 FOREST ST, WALTHAM, MA 02452-4713
Phone: 781-891-2000
Web: WWW.CYBER.BENTLEY.EDU

HISTORICAL FINANCIALS

Company Type: Private

Income Statement FYE: June 30

	REVENUE ($ mil.)	NET INCOME ($ mil.)	NET PROFIT MARGIN	EMPLOYEES
06/13	192	40	21.0%	911
06/12	185	(21)	—	—
06/10	183	34	18.9%	—
06/10	227	(2)	—	—
Annual Growth	(5.4%)	—	—	—

2013 Year-End Financials

Debt ratio: —
Return on equity: 21.00%
Cash ($ mil.): 20
Current ratio: —
Long-term debt ($ mil.): —
Dividends
Yield: —
Payout: —
Market value ($ mil.): —

BERGELECTRIC CORP.

EXECUTIVES

Executive Vice President of Bergelectric, Tom Anderson

LOCATIONS

HQ: BERGELECTRIC CORP.
5650 W CENTINELA AVE, LOS ANGELES, CA 900451501
Phone: 3103371377
Web: WWW.BERGELECTRIC.COM

Selected Locations

Agoura Hills CA
Austin TX
Costa Mesa CA
Denver
Durham NC
Escondido CA
Los Angeles
North Las Vegas NV
Orlando FL
Portland OR
Rancho Cordova CA
Tempe AZ

COMPETITORS

Cupertino Electric
EMCOR
Fisk Electric
Henkels & McCoy
Integrated Electrical Services
MYR Group
Morrow-Meadows
Rex Moore
Rosendin Electric
Sachs Electric

HISTORICAL FINANCIALS

Company Type: Private

Income Statement FYE: January 31

	REVENUE ($ mil.)	NET INCOME ($ mil.)	NET PROFIT MARGIN	EMPLOYEES
01/14	525	4	0.9%	2,100
01/13	478	3	0.6%	—
01/12	394	23	6.0%	—
01/11	403	0	—	—
Annual Growth	9.2%	—	—	—

2014 Year-End Financials

Debt ratio: —
Return on equity: 0.90%
Cash ($ mil.): 7
Current ratio: 1.40
Long-term debt ($ mil.): —
Dividends
Yield: —
Payout: —
Market value ($ mil.): —

BERKELEY ELECTRIC COOPERATIVE INC.

LOCATIONS

HQ: BERKELEY ELECTRIC COOPERATIVE INC.
551 RMBERT C. DNNIS BLVD, MONCKS CORNER, SC 29461
Phone: 8437618200
Web: WWW.BECSC.COM

HISTORICAL FINANCIALS

Company Type: Private

Income Statement FYE: December 31

	REVENUE ($ mil.)	NET INCOME ($ mil.)	NET PROFIT MARGIN	EMPLOYEES
12/13	217	0	0.1%	237
12/12	204	(0)	—	—
12/10	196	9	4.9%	—
12/09	176	0	—	—
Annual Growth	5.3%	—	—	—

2013 Year-End Financials

Debt ratio: —
Return on equity: 0.10%
Cash ($ mil.): 4
Current ratio: 0.60
Long-term debt ($ mil.): —
Dividends
Yield: —
Payout: —
Market value ($ mil.): —

BERKLEE COLLEGE OF MUSIC INC.

If you get accepted to this school you've no doubt hit a high note in your musical career. Berklee College of Music the largest independent music college in the world offers bachelor's degrees in a dozen majors including film scoring jazz composition music education music production and engineering performance and songwriting. Located in Boston the school has some 4000 students and 522 faculty members. Notable alumni include Branford Marsalis Quincy Jones Melissa Etheridge and Steely Dan vocalist Donald Fagen. Pianist Lawrence Berk founded the college in 1945. The school was named after his son Lee Berk who served as Berklee president from 1979 to 2004.

More than a quarter of Berklee's undergraduate students are from outside the US representing some 70 countries. This gives Berklee the distinction of having the highest percentage of international undergraduates of any college in the nation.

The school's Berkleeshares.com is a file-sharing Web site offering free online music lessons developed by school faculty and alumni. Berklee also has five internet music channels produced by its students.

EXECUTIVES

President, Roger H. Brown, age 58
VP Technology and Education Outreach, David S. Mash
VP International Programs, Larry A. Monroe
VP Berklee Media, David Kusek
VP External Affairs and Communications, Thomas P. Riley
senior Vice President for academic affairs, Lawrence J. Simpson
Vice President for Administration, John Eldert
Vice President for Special Programs, Rob Rose
Assistant VP International Programs, Greg Badolato
Associate Vice President for Information Technology, Scott V. Street
Vice President for Finance, Amelia Koch
Outreach Librarian Stan Getz Library, Rebecca Hunt
Vice President for Real Estate, William Whitney
Vice President for Human Resources, Christine Connors
Dean Professional Writing Division, Kari Juusela
Dean Professional Performance Division, Matt Marvuglio
Assistant VP Academic Affairs Curriculum, Jeanine Cowen
Assistant VP Academic Technology, Anthony Marvuglio
Director Communications, Matt Skelly
Director of Marketing, Mike King
Associate Vice President for Education Outreach Executive Director for Berklee City Music, Curtis Warner
Chief Financial Officer Vice President for Finance and Administration, Richard M. Hisey

LOCATIONS

HQ: BERKLEE COLLEGE OF MUSIC INC.
1140 BOYLSTON ST, BOSTON, MA 02215-3693
Phone: 617-266-1400
Web: WWW.BERKLEE.EDU

PRODUCTS/OPERATIONS

Selected Majors

Composition
Contemporary Writing and Production
Film Scoring
Jazz Composition
Music Business/Management
Music Education
Music Production and Engineering
Music Synthesis
Music Therapy
Performance
Professional Music
Songwriting

Selected Academic Departments

Music Technology
- Music Production and Engineering
- Music Synthesis

Professional Education
- Liberal Arts
- Music Business/Management
- Music Education
- Music Therapy
- Professional Music

Professional Performance
- Bass
- Brass
- Ear Training
- Ensembles
- Guitar
- Percussion
- Piano
- Strings
- Voice
- Woodwinds

Professional Writing
- Composition
- Contemporary Writing and Production
- Film Scoring
- Harmony
- Jazz Composition
- Songwriting

HISTORICAL FINANCIALS

Company Type: Private

Income Statement FYE: May 31

	REVENUE ($ mil.)	NET INCOME ($ mil.)	NET PROFIT MARGIN	EMPLOYEES
05/11	220	21	9.6%	—
05/09	171	0	—	—
05/07	127	37	29.5%	—
05/06	0	0	—	—
Annual Growth	—	1779.3%	—	—

2011 Year-End Financials

Debt ratio: —
Return on equity: 9.60%
Cash ($ mil.): 21
Current ratio: —
Long-term debt ($ mil.): —
Dividends
Yield: —
Payout: —
Market value ($ mil.): —

BERKSHIRE MEDICAL CENTER INC.

LOCATIONS

HQ: BERKSHIRE MEDICAL CENTER INC.
725 NORTH ST, PITTSFIELD, MA 012014124
Phone: 4134472000
Web: WWW.BERKSHIREMEDICALCENTER.NET

HISTORICAL FINANCIALS

Company Type: Private

Income Statement FYE: September 30

	REVENUE ($ mil.)	NET INCOME ($ mil.)	NET PROFIT MARGIN	EMPLOYEES
09/13	342	31	9.2%	1,375
09/12	339	43	12.8%	—
09/09	326	(1)	—	—
09/06	210	0	—	—
Annual Growth	7.2%	—	—	—

2013 Year-End Financials

Debt ratio: —
Return on equity: 9.20%
Cash ($ mil.): 31
Current ratio: 1.00
Long-term debt ($ mil.): —
Dividends
Yield: —
Payout: —
Market value ($ mil.): —

BERNER FOOD & BEVERAGE INC.

HISTORY

Berner Foods agreed in 2006 to implement safeguards after charges of environmental contamination were levied against the company in 2004. It also agreed to pay a $15000 penalty.

EXECUTIVES

President and CEO, Stephen A. (Steve) Kneubuehl
EVP and COO, Edward (Ed) Kneubuehl
EVP Berner Food and Beverage, Steven L. (Steve) Fay
CIO, Troy Grove
VP Quality Assurance, Gary Gold
EVP and CFO, William F. (Bill) Marchido
Legal Council, David Fischer

LOCATIONS

HQ: BERNER FOOD & BEVERAGE INC.
2034 E FACTORY RD, DAKOTA, IL 610189736
Phone: 8155634222
Web: WWW.BERNERFOODS.COM

PRODUCTS/OPERATIONS

Selected Products

Aerosol cheese
Canned beverages
- Avena con canela
- Coffee energy
- Horchata sabor de morro
- Iced latte
- Italian roast coffee
- Mexican horchata
- Meal replacement
- Nutritional
- Orange jubilee morir sonada
- Weight control

Jar cheese
Salsa conqueso
Shelf-stable dips

COMPETITORS

Associated Milk Producers
Atkins Nutritionals
BelGioioso Cheese
Crystal Farms Refrigerated Distribution Company
Dairy Farmers of America
Dean Foods
Energy Brands
Entner-Stuart
Goya

H. J. Heinz Limited
Land O' Lakes
Marathon Cheese
Medifast
Mondelez International
Nutrisystem
PepsiCo
Saputo Cheese USA Inc.
Sargento
Sartori Foods
Slim-Fast
Starbucks
Swiss-American
Tillamook County Creamery Association
Weight Watchers International

HISTORICAL FINANCIALS

Company Type: Private

Income Statement FYE: September 30

	REVENUE ($ mil.)	NET INCOME ($ mil.)	NET PROFIT MARGIN	EMPLOYEES
09/14	135	5	4.4%	300
09/12*	74	3	4.2%	—
12/08	65	(1)	—	—
Annual Growth	12.9%	—	—	—

*Fiscal year change

2014 Year-End Financials

Debt ratio: —
Return on equity: 4.40%
Cash ($ mil.): 0
Current ratio: 0.40
Long-term debt ($ mil.): —
Dividends
Yield: —
Payout: —
Market value ($ mil.): —

BERRY COMPANIES INC.

Savoring the fruit of its labor Berry Companies makes a living bulldozing big jobs. The employee-owned business runs eight divisions; each independently sells and rents new and used construction and material handling equipment. Berry Cos. specialize in graders tractors loaders excavators cranes rollers construction and woodworking supplies concrete equipment and small tools. The company's five distribution dealerships include White Star Machinery (Kansas); Bobcat of Dallas and Houston (Texas); K.C. Bobcat (Missouri); and Bobcat of the Rockies (Colorado). Berry Cos. also operates Berry Tractor and Equipment Berry Material Handling and Superior Broom (makes self-propelled road construction brooms).

The company has more than 20 locations in five states: Colorado Kansas Missouri Oklahoma and Texas. Each operating division runs autonomously and handles a lineup including equipment by Bobcat Komatsu Terex Yale by NACCO Bomag and Superior Broom.

Berry Co.'s strategy for expansion has captured a significant share of the heavy machinery market that supplies contractors governmental agencies and commercial builders. In early 2011 the company absorbed the operations of Colorado Machinery a Bobcat distributor into its Bobcat of the Rockies division which further expands the company's distribution network in that region. In 2009 it purchased Bobcat Operations of Conley Lott Nichols which gives it an even greater share in the north Texas market.

The construction equipment distribution business is fueled by the residential and non-residential construction industry which took a major beating during the Great Recession. As the industry recovers and Berry Cos. expands it has the advantage of being able to buy equipment to stock multiple outlets. Its regional locations grow by building a strong customer loyalty for repeat business based on reputation and service.

Weathering half a century of business is something to respect. Berry Cos. got its start when Fred Berry Jr. and his brother Paul bought the Sam H. Denney Road Machinery Co. in 1957 and renamed it Berry Tractor & Equipment Co. Seeing the wide open market for repairing Kansas' unpaved roads the material men (Fred and Paul) moved into dealing in motor graders.

EXECUTIVES

Chairman, Fred F. Berry Jr.
President Chairman Vice-President Secretary-Treasurer, Walter Berry
VP Administration and Treasurer, Judy Worrell
Controller, Rod Opliger
VP Bobcat Operations, John Engels
IT Director, Wayne Becker
General Manager Bobcat Houston Texas, Jonathan Tarpey
Accounting Manager, Denise Hightower
Assistant Controller, Cindi Montgomery

LOCATIONS

HQ: BERRY COMPANIES INC.
3223 N HYDRAULIC ST, WICHITA, KS 67219-3893
Phone: 316-838-3321
Web: WWW.BERRYCOMPANIESINC.COM

PRODUCTS/OPERATIONS

Selected Subsidiaries

Berry Material Handling
Berry Tractor and Equipment Co.
Bobcat Dallas/Fort Worth/ Longview
Bobcat of Houston
Bobcat of the Rockies
K.C. Bobcat
Superior Broom
White Star

COMPETITORS

Briggs Equipment
H&E Equipment
HOLT Texas
Hertz
IBT Inc.
Mustang CAT
NES Rentals
Sunbelt Rentals
United Rentals
Van Keppel
Victor L. Phillips

HISTORICAL FINANCIALS

Company Type: Private

Income Statement FYE: March 31

	REVENUE ($ mil.)	NET INCOME ($ mil.)	NET PROFIT MARGIN	EMPLOYEES
03/13	229	3	1.5%	520
03/09	178	0	0.3%	—
03/07	203	2	1.3%	—
03/07	1,240	0	—	—
Annual Growth	—	510.2%	—	—

2013 Year-End Financials

Debt ratio: —
Return on equity: 1.50%
Cash ($ mil.): 4
Current ratio: 0.30
Long-term debt ($ mil.): —
Dividends
Yield: —
Payout: —
Market value ($ mil.): —

BEST CHAIRS INCORPORATED

LOCATIONS

HQ: BEST CHAIRS INCORPORATED
1 BEST DR, FERDINAND, IN 475329233
Phone: 8123671761
Web: WWW.BESTHF.COM

HISTORICAL FINANCIALS

Company Type: Private

Income Statement FYE: December 31

	REVENUE ($ mil.)	NET INCOME ($ mil.)	NET PROFIT MARGIN	EMPLOYEES
12/13	233	0	—	875
12/12	217	0	—	—
12/11	209	0	—	—
12/10	195	0	—	—
Annual Growth	6.2%	—	—	—

2013 Year-End Financials

Debt ratio: —
Return on equity: —
Cash ($ mil.): 38
Current ratio: 2.60
Long-term debt ($ mil.): —
Dividends
Yield: —
Payout: —
Market value ($ mil.): —

BEST WESTERN INTERNATIONAL INC.

Western hospitality has really spread. Begun in 1946 by hotelier M. K. Guertin and named for its California origins Best Western has more than 4000 independently owned and operated hotels throughout the globe (including nearly 2200 in North America) making it the world's largest hotel brand (by number of rooms). Hotels sport its flag in about 90 countries and territories; Australia and the UK have the most outside the US. The company has more than 80 Best Western Premier luxury branded hotels which offer upscale amenities and services in North America Asia and Europe. Best Western is organized as a not-for-profit membership association with most of its sales coming from monthly fees and annual dues.

Geographic Reach

The company has hotel properties all over the world. Part of the company's strategic plan is ongoing global expansion. In addition to Asia the Middle East and Eastern Europe the company is targeting emerging markets such as Africa New Zealand Russia and South America for growth.

Sales and Marketing

Best Western attracts travelers through its marketing efforts. In 2010 it launched a program to reward members of its global Best Western Rewards loyalty program by matching the elite status of other hotel loyalty programs free of charge.

In 2011 the company introduced its latest brand –Best Western Plus. Included in the launch are approximately 800 Best Western Plus locations in North America which feature upper midscale hotels offering a more premium experience than regular Best Western hotels including updated furnishings bedding and bath amenities. Best Western Plus joins the company's Best Western (midscale) and Best Western Premier (luxury) brands giving the company a three-pronged approach to target travelers in different market segments.

Strategy

While the travel industry has been facing hard times as a result of the economic downturn Best Western claims that its hotels benefited from companies looking to cut costs by moving their hotel business to the mid-market sector. For example Best Western requires its hoteliers to provide complimentary Internet and local phone calls.

EXECUTIVES

President and CEO, David T. Kong
VP North American Development, Mark E. Williams
VP Brand Management and Member Services, Ron Pohl
Secretary Treasurer and Director, Devang (Dave) Amin
Vice President International Operations Asia, Glenn Souza
Director, Dave Francis
Director, Bonnie McPeake
Director, Beth Campbell
Vice Chairwoman, Julie Montmaneix
Secretary Treasurer and Director, Devang (Dave) Amin
Director, Jay Patel
Auditors: MukaiGreenlee&CompanyP.C.

LOCATIONS

HQ: BEST WESTERN INTERNATIONAL INC.
6201 N 24TH PKWY, PHOENIX, AZ 85016-2023
Phone: 602-957-4200
Web: WWW.BESTWESTERN.COM

Sales Office Locations
Atlanta
Bangkok
Beijing
Bogota
Buenos Aires
Chicago
Dallas
Dubai
Hong Kong
London
Los Angeles
Mexico City
Miami
Milan
New York City
Orlando
Rio de Janeiro
Sao Paolo
San Diego
Santiago
Seattle
Seoul
Singapore
St. Louis
Sydney
Tel-Aviv
Tokyo
Toronto
Washington DC.

PRODUCTS/OPERATIONS

Selected Hotels

Best Western
Brighton Inn (Brighton CO)
City Center Hotel (Philadelphia)
Courtesy Inn (Anaheim CA)
Kirkwood Inn (Saint Louis MO)
Mardi Gras Hotel & Casino (Las Vegas)
Plaza Hotel & Stuites at Medical Center (Houston)
Roehampton Hotel & Suites (Toronto MO)
West Deptford Inn (Thorofare NJ)
Victoria Place (London)
Best Western Plus
Hawthorne Terrace Hotel (Chicago)
Pioneer Square Hotel (Seattle)
Rio Grand Inn (Albuquerque NM)
Best Western Premier
Royal Saint Michel (Paris)

COMPETITORS

Accor
Carlson Hotels
Choice Hotels
Extended Stay America Inc.
Hilton Worldwide
InterContinental Hotels
La Quinta
Marriott
Red Lion Hotels
Scandic Hotels
ShoLodge
Sunburst Hospitality
USFS
Wyndham Worldwide

HISTORICAL FINANCIALS

Company Type: Private

Income Statement

FYE: November 30

	REVENUE ($ mil.)	NET INCOME ($ mil.)	NET PROFIT MARGIN	EMPLOYEES
11/07	220	(2)		1,015
11/06	205	2	1.2%	
11/05	1,260	0	—	—
Annual Growth	—	—	—	—

2007 Year-End Financials

Debt ratio: —
Return on equity: (-1.40%)
Cash ($ mil.): 22
Current ratio: 0.90
Long-term debt ($ mil.): —
Dividends
Yield: —
Payout: —
Market value ($ mil.): —

BETH ISRAEL MEDICAL CENTER

Residents of New York City's Lower East Side look to Beth Israel Medical Center to keep them healthy. A member of Continuum Health Partners the tertiary care medical facility has more than 1100 inpatient beds at two facilities in the New York area –its main location in Manhattan and another in Brooklyn. It also operates outpatient care centers and physician offices. Along with its patient care operations Beth Israel Medical Center maintains medical residency programs through its affiliation with Yeshiva University's Albert Einstein College of Medicine. The hospital also conducts institutional medical research with Rockefeller University and offers a nursing degree through its Phillips Beth Israel School of Nursing.

Geographic Reach

The hospital's main campus in Manhattan is known as the Beth Israel Medical Center-Petrie Campus. The Brooklyn location is known as Beth Israel Brooklyn; prior to 2012 the campus was known as the Beth Israel Medical Center-Kings Highway Division.

Operations

The main campus in Petrie has about 900 beds and hosts several major specialist units while the Brooklyn location has more than 210 beds and provides general medicine surgery radiology and intensive care services. Outpatient centers include the Phillips Ambulatory Care Center in Manhattan and the Beth Israel Ambulatory Surgi-Center in Brooklyn which provide diagnostic and ambulatory surgery services. Another affiliated clinic the Continuum Center for Health and Healing provides primary and specialty care as well as alternative services including acupuncture. The Beth Israel Medical Group operates several primary and specialty care physician clinics in Manhattan.

Altogether the Beth Israel Medical Center facilities handle about 59000 inpatient encounters annually. It also manages about 107000 emergency room visits 3500 births 11000 inpatient surgeries and 21000 outpatient surgeries. The center employs about 2300 medical and dental staff members.

Strategy

Continuum Health is investing in upgrades to Beth Israel Medical Center's facilities. For instance it added a new endoscopy suite at the Brooklyn campus in 2012. The main Petrie campus is renovating its emergency room and various inpatient units are increasing quality programs.

In 2012 a major expansion project was launched at the Continuum Center for Health and Healing to expand access to outpatient care for area residents; the program will add services including dermatology cardiology and podiatry. In addition the hospital opened a new cancer center in Manhattan in 2010 and a deluxe unit for high-income patients having orthopedic and other surgeries in 2008. Continuum Health is also upgrading some of Beth Israel Medical Center's IT functions including its radiology data management systems.

EXECUTIVES

SVP Medical Affairs and Medical Director, David B. Bernard
President, Harris M. Nagler
Chairman, Steven Hochberg, age 52
The Alfred and Gail Engelberg Department of Family Medicine, Robert M. Schiller
Chairman Medicine, Henry C. Bodenheimer
Clinical Director Continuum Heart Institute, Steven R. Bergmann
Co-Director Institue for Head and Neck Cancer, Roy B. Sessions
Vice Chairman, Sorrell Mathes
Trustee, Alan Batkin
Trustee, Michael Zimmerman
Vice Chairman, Sorrell Mathes

LOCATIONS

HQ: BETH ISRAEL MEDICAL CENTER
10 NATHAN D PERLMAN PL, NEW YORK, NY 10003-3881
Phone: 212-420-2000
Web: WWW.BIDMC.HARVARD.EDU

PRODUCTS/OPERATIONS

Selected Centers and Services

AIDS Services
Allergy and Immunology
Anesthesiology
Appel-Venet Comprehensive Breast Service
Asian Services
Beth Israel ALS Center
Beth Israel Hernia Center
Beth Israel Medical Group
Betty & Morton Yarmon Stroke Center
Brief Psychotherapy Research Program
Cancer Center (Oncology)
Center for Blood Management and Bloodless Medicine and Surgery
Center for Endovascular Surgery
Center for Health and Healing
Craniofacial and Cleft Palate Center
Cystic Fibrosis Center
Dermatology
Endocrinology and Metabolism
Epilepsy
Friedman Diabetes Institute
Genetics
Geriatrics
Heart Institute (Cardiology)
Hematology
Hospice
Hyman Newman Institute for Neurology and Neurosugery (INN)
The Chris and Morton P. Hyman Patient Care Unit
Hyperhidrosis Program
Incontinence
Integrative Medicine
Interventional Neuroradiology
Israeli Health Program
Karpas Health Information Center

Latino Health Institute
Live Well New York
Louis Armstrong Center for Music and Medicine: Lung Nodule Center
Maternity Services
Methadone Maintenance Treatment Program
Midwifery
Nephrology
Neurology
Orthopedics
Ostomy Program
Pain Medicine and Palliative Care
Pediatrics
Phillips Beth Israel School of Nursing
Primary Care
Psychiatry
Pulmonary and Critical Care Medicine
Radiation Oncology
Radiology
Rheumatology
Senior Health
Sleep Health
Speech-Language and Learning Center
Spine Institute
Sports Medicine
Stroke Centers
Styuvesant Square Chemical Dependency Services
Surgery
Urology
Vascular and Birthmarks Institute of New York
Women' s Health
Women' s Heart NY
Wound Healing Center

COMPETITORS

Bronx-Lebanon Hospital
Catholic Healthcare System
Kingsbrook Jewish Medical Center
Lutheran HealthCare
Maimonides Medical Center
MediSys Health Network
Memorial Sloan-Kettering
Montefiore Medical
NYU Hospital for Joint Diseases
New York City Health and Hospitals
NewYork-Presbyterian Healthcare
North Shore-Long Island Jewish Health System
SUNY Downstate

HISTORICAL FINANCIALS

Company Type: Private

Income Statement FYE: December 31

	REVENUE ($ mil.)	NET INCOME ($ mil.)	NET PROFIT MARGIN	EMPLOYEES
12/09	1,256	15	1.2%	8,100
12/08	932	(59)	—	—
Annual Growth	34.8%	—	—	—

2009 Year-End Financials

Debt ratio: —
Return on equity: 1.20%
Cash ($ mil.): 98
Current ratio: 0.40
Long-term debt ($ mil.): —
Dividends
Yield: —
Payout: —
Market value ($ mil.): —

BI-RITE RESTAURANT SUPPLY CO. INC.

Bi-Rite Restaurant Supply which does business as BiRite Foodservice Distributors is a leading foodservice supplier serving the San Francisco area and Northern California. The company distributes a full line of food equipment and supplies including meat and dairy items frozen foods dry groceries cleaning supplies china kitchen equipment and disposables. Its customers include restaurant operators hotels schools and healthcare facilities. A member of the UniPro Foodservice cooperative the family-owned company was founded in 1966 by cousins Victor and John Barulich.

Mergers and Acquisitions

In late 2012 the company acquired family-owned A&B Produce which supplies food to restaurants throughout the San Francisco Bay area.

EXECUTIVES

Vp Sales, Michael Pendergast
President, Steve Barulich
CEO, William (Bill) Barulich
General Manager, Aaron Barulich
CFO, Zack Barulich
VP Operations, Nathan Barulich
VP Purchasing, Tom Whiteside

LOCATIONS

HQ: BI-RITE RESTAURANT SUPPLY CO. INC.
123 S HILL DR, BRISBANE, CA 94005-1203
Phone: 415-656-0187
Web: WWW.BIRITE.COM

PRODUCTS/OPERATIONS

Selected Product Categories

Disposables
Equipment & supply
Food
Fresh cut produce
Fresh next-day protein
Fresh seafood
Janitorial

COMPETITORS

Dot Foods
Golden State Foods
Jacmar
MAINES
McLane Foodservice
Sysco
US Foods

HISTORICAL FINANCIALS

Company Type: Private

Income Statement FYE: December 31

	REVENUE ($ mil.)	NET INCOME ($ mil.)	NET PROFIT MARGIN	EMPLOYEES
12/12	258	4	1.8%	230
12/11	255	4	1.8%	—
12/10	271	4	1.8%	—
12/09	285	5	1.9%	—
Annual Growth	(3.2%)	(4.9%)	—	—

2012 Year-End Financials

Debt ratio: —
Return on equity: 1.80%
Cash ($ mil.): 12
Current ratio: 2.70
Long-term debt ($ mil.): —
Dividends
Yield: —
Payout: —
Market value ($ mil.): —

BIG 12 CONFERENCE INC

LOCATIONS

HQ: BIG 12 CONFERENCE INC
400 E JOHN CARPENTER FWY, IRVING, TX 750623955
Phone: 4695241000
Web: WWW.BIG12SPORTS.COM

HISTORICAL FINANCIALS

Company Type: Private

Income Statement FYE: June 30

	REVENUE ($ mil.)	NET INCOME ($ mil.)	NET PROFIT MARGIN	EMPLOYEES
06/13	217	2	1.1%	2
06/12	159	9	5.6%	—
06/09	144	(3)	—	—
Annual Growth	10.8%	—	—	—

2013 Year-End Financials

Debt ratio: —
Return on equity: 1.10%
Cash ($ mil.): 9
Current ratio: 0.30
Long-term debt ($ mil.): —
Dividends
Yield: —
Payout: —
Market value ($ mil.): —

BIG RIVERS ELECTRIC CORPORATION

LOCATIONS

HQ: BIG RIVERS ELECTRIC CORPORATION
201 3RD ST, HENDERSON, KY 424202979
Phone: 2708272561
Web: WWW.BIGRIVERS.COM

HISTORICAL FINANCIALS

Company Type: Private

Income Statement FYE: December 31

	REVENUE ($ mil.)	NET INCOME ($ mil.)	NET PROFIT MARGIN	EMPLOYEES
12/13	562	8	1.5%	599
12/12	568	11	2.0%	—
12/11	561	5	1.0%	—
12/10	527	0	—	—
Annual Growth	2.2%	—	—	—

2013 Year-End Financials

Debt ratio: —
Return on equity: 1.50%
Cash ($ mil.): 95
Current ratio: 1.80
Long-term debt ($ mil.): —
Dividends
Yield: —
Payout: —
Market value ($ mil.): —

BIG-D CONSTRUCTION CORP.

Big-D builds big things. With offices in Utah Arizona California and Wyoming the construction firm offers design/build services to customers in about 20 states. Big-D focuses on projects for clients in such industries as manufacturing health care hospitality food processing and distribution manufacturing and retail. The company's Signature Group builds high-end luxury homes as well as and condominiums spas and other special projects in resort communities. Clients have included SYSCO and Marriott. The company also operates a concrete division devoted to architectural structural and parking garage projects. Big-D was founded in 1967 by Dee Livingood. His family continues to lead the company.

Big-D has been courting more government projects as a way to weather the economic downturn which has put a halt on many commercial jobs. Among those public projects is the Utah Museum of Natural History at The University of Utah and the Wallace F. Bennett Federal Building in Salt Lake City. Big-D also is focusing on developing its eco-friendly construction business.

EXECUTIVES

Chairman and CEO, Jack Livingood
SVP and CFO, Larry Worrell
SVP, Dale Satterthwait
SVP Operations, Forrest McNabb
President Big-D Construction, Rob Moore
VP and Project Executive, Jim Allison
President Big-D Pacific, Ken Mitchell
Chief Estimator, Brandon Briggs
Subcontractor Manager, Jana Cochell
VP, Greg Dean
VP, Oscar Yousefi
VP, Cory Moore
Vice President Big-D Southwest, Louie Sarracino
Senior Vice President, Dale Satterthwaite
President Big-D Signature, Scott Dansie

LOCATIONS

HQ: BIG-D CONSTRUCTION CORP.
404 W 400 S, SALT LAKE CITY, UT 84101-1108
Phone: 801-415-6000
Web: WWW.BIG-D.COM

Selected Markets

Arizona
Arkansas
California
Colorado
Georgia
Hawaii
Idaho
Montana
Nevada
New Mexico
North Carolina
North Dakota
Oklahoma
Oregon
South Dakota
Tennessee
Texas
Utah
Washington

PRODUCTS/OPERATIONS

Selected Services

Construction management
Design/build
Field services
- Architectural concrete
- Finish carpentry
- Rough framing
- Structural concrete

General contracting
Green and Leadership in Energy and Environmental Design

Selected Industry Specializations

Commercial/public spaces (governmental educational and office complexes; mixed-use projects)
Food processing and distribution
Health care
Hospitality and resort
Manufacturing
Retail

COMPETITORS

Bechtel
Hensel Phelps Construction
J.F. Shea
Jacobsen Construction
Jaynes Companies
Layton
Okland Construction
Swinerton

HISTORICAL FINANCIALS

Company Type: Private

Income Statement FYE: December 31

	REVENUE ($ mil.)	NET INCOME ($ mil.)	NET PROFIT MARGIN	EMPLOYEES
12/12	541	0	—	433
12/11	554	0	—	—
12/10	259	0	—	—
12/09	0	0	—	—
Annual Growth	—	—	—	—

2012 Year-End Financials

Debt ratio: ——
Return on equity: —
Cash ($ mil.): 38
Current ratio: 1.20
Long-term debt ($ mil.): —
Dividends
Yield: —
Payout: —
Market value ($ mil.): —

BILLINGS CLINIC

Billings Clinic is an integrated health care system that serves the residents of Big Sky Country. Through a group of more than 320 doctors and other providers the clinic caters to some 570000 people in Billings Montana and in surrounding communities. It offers 45-plus specialties such as emergency and trauma cancer orthopedics birthing cardiovascular neurosciences dialysis and pediatrics. Its operations include a more than 270-bed hospital and the organization's main clinic. Additionally Billings Clinic operates the 90-bed Aspen Meadows Retirement Community and provides support services to several regional community hospitals. The not-for-profit health care system is owned by the community.

Geographic Reach

As the largest health care organization in the area Billings Clinic's service area comprises 40 counties and extends more than 120000 miles in Montana Wyoming and the western Dakotas.

Operations

With its vast service area the health care system provides a MedFlight advanced life support fixed-wing aircraft service that transports critically ill or injured patients from rural communities. The service averages 700 flights per year.

As part of its operations Billings Clinic runs a Level II emergency and trauma center 14-suite family birthing center Level III neonatal intensive care unit inpatient cancer care unit and a 15-bed transitional care unit. The health care system's cancer center provides both inpatient and outpatient care in Billings and the surrounding four-state region.

Billings Clinic is governed by a 12-member board consisting of mostly community members but also a pair of doctors and a physician CEO.

Strategy

Billings Clinic works with pharmaceutical sponsors on a variety of clinical research trials in various phases and indications. To this end it operates a research center with more than 20 years of experience in the areas of basic and clinical research. The center has participated in more than 200 clinical research studies with the help of some 5000 volunteer subjects since 1988.

The health care system has been growing. It expanded its capacity for infusions in 2012 when its Billings Clinic Cody location opened an infusion center. In late 2012 the organization also opened a new Stillwater Billings Clinic medical facility which combines Stillwater Community Hospital and Billings Clinic Columbus and integrates the billing process for the two health care facilities.

EXECUTIVES

Vp People Resources, Kellee J Fisk
CEO, Nicholas J. Wolter
VP and CIO, Chris Stevens
Physician in Chief, Mark C. Rumans
President Billings Clinic Foundation, Jim Duncan
VP Hospital Operations, Lu Byrd
CFO, Connie F. Prewitt
Vp Strategic Development And Corporate Compliance Officer, Kristianne Wilson
Director Of Radiology Services, Michael Wright
Director Of Patient Relations, Kathleen Girard
Medical Records Director, Julie Lovell
Vice President Corporate Operations, Karen McComish
CEO, Nicholas J. Wolter
Treasurer and Director, J. Scott Millikan
Director, David Brown
Secretary, Starla Harrington
Secretary And Director, Linda Overstreet
Board Member, J Shepard-lovell

LOCATIONS

HQ: BILLINGS CLINIC
2800 10TH AVE N, BILLINGS, MT 59101-0703
Phone: 406-657-4000
Web: WWW.BILLINGSCLINIC.COM

PRODUCTS/OPERATIONS

Selected Services

Advance Medical Directives
Allergy Asthma Immunology
Aspen Meadows - Skilled Nursing and Assisted Living
Anticoagulation Clinic
Breast Center
Cancer Center
Cardiovascular Services
Cardiovascular Surgery
Children' s Services
Continence Center
Community Training Center
Cosmetic Surgery
da Vinci Surgical System
Dermatology Center
Diabetes Management Center
Diagnostic Imaging
Diabetes
Dialysis Center
Eldercare Solutions
Emergency & Trauma Center
Emmi Educational Videos
Employer Services - Occupational Health
Endocrinology
Eye Center
Facial Plastic Surgery
Family Medicine
Family Birth Center
Gastroenterology
General Surgery
Genetic Counseling
Geriatric Assessment Program
Gynecologic Cancer
Heart Services
Heart Surgery
Home Oxygen & Medical Equipment
Hospitalist Program
Infectious Diseases
Insurance Finder
Internal Medicine
Laboratory Services
LifeFit
Maternal-Fetal Medicine
MedFlight Air Ambulance
Mental Health Services
Metabolism Center
Mohs Surgery
Nutrition Services
Neurosciences
Obstetrics & Gynecology
Occupational Health - Employer Services
Ophthalmology
Orthopedics & Sports Medicine

Palliative Care
Pediatrics
- Pediatric Center
- Pediatric Cancer
- Pediatric Diabetes
- Pediatric Gastroenterology
- Pediatric Pulmonology
- Rehabilitation (Therapy)

Pharmacy
Physical Medicine & Rehabilitation
Plastic Surgery
Primary Care for Adults
Pulmonary Rehabilitation Program
Radiology Services
Reproductive Medicine and Fertility Care
Robotic Surgery
SameDay Care
Senior Services
Sleep Disorders Center
Sports Medicine
Sports Specific Camps
Stroke Care
Surgery Center
Transitional Care Unit
Urology Services
Vascular Surgery
Vein Clinic
Women's Free Screenings
Women' s and Children' s Services

Selected Affiliate Hospitals and Clinics

Beartooth Billings Clinic - Red Lodge
Colstrip Medical Center - Colstrip
Daniels Memorial Healthcare - Scobey
Livingston HealthCare - Livingston
North Big Horn Hospital - Lovell
Pioneer Medical Center - Big Timber
Roundup Memorial Healthcare - Roundup
Sheridan Memorial Hospital Association
Stillwater Billings Clinic

COMPETITORS

Glendive Medical Center
St. Alexius Medical Center
St. James Healthcare
St. Patrick Hospital
Wyoming Medical Center

HISTORICAL FINANCIALS

Company Type: Private

Income Statement

FYE: June 30

	REVENUE ($ mil.)	NET INCOME ($ mil.)	NET PROFIT MARGIN	EMPLOYEES
06/12	506	21	4.2%	3,300
06/11	533	28	5.4%	—
06/10	494	25	5.2%	—
06/09	461	(11)	—	—
Annual Growth	3.2%	—	—	—

2012 Year-End Financials

Debt ratio: —
Return on equity: 4.20%
Cash ($ mil.): 13
Current ratio: 1.60
Long-term debt ($ mil.): —
Dividends
Yield: —
Payout: —
Market value ($ mil.): —

BIRKEY"S FARM STORE INC.

LOCATIONS

HQ: BIRKEY' ' S FARM STORE INC.
2102 W PARK CT, CHAMPAIGN, IL 618212986
Phone: 2178928255
Web: WWW.BIRKEYS.COM

HISTORICAL FINANCIALS

Company Type: Private

Income Statement

FYE: December 31

	REVENUE ($ mil.)	NET INCOME ($ mil.)	NET PROFIT MARGIN	EMPLOYEES
12/13	394	16	4.1%	350
12/12	355	15	4.3%	—
12/11	280	13	4.7%	—
12/10	245	0	—	—
Annual Growth	17.1%	—	—	—

2013 Year-End Financials

Debt ratio: —
Return on equity: 4.10%
Cash ($ mil.): 0
Current ratio: —
Long-term debt ($ mil.): —
Dividends
Yield: —
Payout: —
Market value ($ mil.): —

BJT INC.

A wholesaler of Southern comfort Mutual Distributing distributes alcoholic and nonalcoholic beverages in North Carolina. The company started in 1946 operates from seven locations across the state. Alcoholic beverage brands handled by Mutual Distributing include domestic and imported wine labels by Wyndham Estate Robert Mondavi Moet & Chandon and Folie a Deux and beers by Anchor Tecate Heineken and Sapporo. The company distributes bottled waters too such as Evian Perrier San Pellegrino and Fiji. Mutual Distributing caters to retail customers (supermarkets convenience stores and specialty package outlets restaurants and hotels) in every county in North Carolina.

The company's growth is spurred in part by increasing consumer interest in new alcoholic beverage categories such as moscatos (a sweet low-in-alcohol wine) and ready-to-drink wine-based cocktails coupled with the availability of lower-priced wines at many retail grocery chains. To maintain sales momentum Mutual Distributing has extended its already vast lineup in such categories as well as added labels from local and regional wine and beer producers.

Simultaneously the company has managed the upswing in demand by expanding its warehouse in Charlotte and upgrading its IT infrastructure. Its improved offerings and operations are intended to both strengthen relationships with regional and national chains and build market share.

EXECUTIVES

VP Sales, William Riley

LOCATIONS

HQ: BJT INC.
2233 CAPITAL BLVD, RALEIGH, NC 27604-1421
Phone: 919-828-3842
Web: WWW.MUTUALDISTRIBUTING.COM

PRODUCTS/OPERATIONS

List of Brands
Beer
Amstel
Anchor
Asahi
Ayinger
Bavaria
Bitburger
Bohemia
Caguama
Carolina
Carta Blanca
Charleston
Cottonwood
Del Mar
Dos Equis
Export 33
Grady's Grog
Harpoon
Heineken
Hoegaarden
Kingfisher
Lindemans
Mackeson
Maisels
Mendocino
Moosehead
Moretti
Murphy's
Orion
Peroni
Pinkus
Samuel Smith
Sapporo
Saranac
Sol
St Pauli Girl
Tecate
Tsingtao
Utica Club
Warsteiner
Weihenstephan
Non-alcoholic brands
Acqua Panna
Evian
Perrier
San Pellegrino
Zing Zang
Wine
Acacia
Alice White
Allegrini
Almaden
Andes Peak
Anselmi
Arbor Mist
Artesa
Avia
Avalon
Banrock Station
Barossa
Bertani
Benton-Lane
Biltmore
Black Box
Blackstone
Blue Nun
Bolla
Boutinot
Brancaia
Brolio
Burgess
Candoni
Canei
Carneros Creek
CH LaMothe
Chateau Morrisette
Childress Vineyards
Chocovine
Citra
CK Mondavi
Claude Jourdon
Cline
Clos du Bois
Coastal Vintners Pinecroft
Colombo
Concha y Toro
Condesa de LeGanza
Cooks
Covey Run
Cribari
Cypress Bend Vineyards
Deloach
Di Majo
Dry Sack
Dubonnet
Dyed In The Wool
Dynamite Vineyards
Edna Valley
Estancia
Estrella
Fabre Montmayou
Faustino
Ferrari Carano
Firesteed
Fisheye

Florio
Folie a Deux
Fonterutoli
Four Graces
Francis F. Copola
Franciscan
Freixenet
Frescobaldi
Gato
Gelisi Antonio
Girard
Glen Ellen
Goats do Roam
Gotham
Grahams
Grant Burge
Grgich
Groth Hakutsuru
Hardy's
Hess
Hogue
Hinnant Family Vineyards
Inglenook
J Lohr
J Roget
Jacobs Creek
Jewel
Joel Gott
Kenwood
Kijafa
Kim Crawford
Korbel
Kressmann
Kris
L Felipe Edwards
La Terre
La Vieille Ferme
Le Faux Frog
LeJon
Liberty School
Lillet
Little Boomey
Los Cardos
Los Vascos
Lost Vineyards
Louis Latour
Lucente
Lucky Duck
Manischewitz
Mahoney Vineyards
Marco Negri
Marcus James
Mark West
Marques de Caceres
Martini & Rossi
Matchbook
Mateus
Melini
Merryvale
Mezzacorona
Moet & Chandon
Mogen David
Mondoro
Monkey Bay
Montevina
Motovino
Mumm
Napa Cellars
Nathanson Creek
Nobilo
Noilly Prat
Oak Creek
Oak Leaf
Oak Vineyard
Old North State
Opus One
Palladio
Papio
Patient-Cottat
Patton Valley Vineyards
Paul Masson
Pedroncelli
Penfolds
Perrin
Picket Fence
Placido
Rabbit Ridge
Ramon Bilbao
Ravenswood
Raymond
Real
Renee Barbier
Reynold's
Rex Goliath
RH Phillips
Riunite
Robert Mondavi
Rocca delle Macie
Rodney Strong
Rosemount
Rosenblum
Ruffino
Rutherford Hill
Saintsbury
Salmon Harbor
Sandeman
Santa Margherita
Santa Rita
Santi
Sartori
Schmitt Sohne
Sebastiani
Sebastopol
Sho Chiku Bai
Silver Oak
Sonoma Cutrer
St Jacobs
Simi
St Supery
Stags Leap
Stephen Vincent
Stock
Straccali
Sutter Home
Sycamore Lane
SXS (Step by Step)
Takara
Talus
Taylor
Tiefenbrunner
Tiziano
Toad Hollow
Toasted Head
Tommasi
Tosti
Trackers Crossing
Trapiche
Tribuno
Trinchero
Trinity Oaks
Twin Fin
Valley Of The Moon
Vendange
Veramonte
Veuve du Vernay
Villa Maria
Volpaia
Walnut Crest
Warres
Woodbridge
Wyndham Estate
Yellowtail
Zaca Mesa
Zonin

COMPETITORS

Constellation Brands
Gambrinus
Glazer' s Wholesale Drug
National Distributing
National Wine & Spirits
Southern Wine & Spirits
The Charmer Sunbelt Group

HISTORICAL FINANCIALS

Company Type: Private

Income Statement FYE: December 31

	REVENUE ($ mil.)	NET INCOME ($ mil.)	NET PROFIT MARGIN	EMPLOYEES
12/09	200	6	3.1%	550
12/08	191	7	4.1%	—
12/06	172	4	2.4%	—
12/05	158	3	2.0%	—
Annual Growth	6.1%	17.8%	—	—

2009 Year-End Financials

Debt ratio: —
Return on equity: 3.10%
Cash ($ mil.): 0
Current ratio: 0.20
Long-term debt ($ mil.): —
Dividends
Yield: —
Payout: —
Market value ($ mil.): —

BLACK & VEATCH CORPORATION

One of the US's largest private companies Black & Veatch (BV) is a leading global engineering consulting and construction firm specializing in infrastructure development for the energy water environmental federal and telecommunications markets. BV offers environmental consulting operations and maintenance security design and consulting management consulting and IT services. With offices worldwide it has worked on coal nuclear and combustion turbine plants; drinking water and coastal water operations; and wireless and broadband installation. Clients include Sumitomo Corp. and Southern Water. The company was founded in 1915 in Kansas City Missouri by engineers E. B. Black and Tom Veatch.

Geographic Reach

Kansas-based Black & Veatch has more than 100 offices worldwide and has completed projects in more than 100 countries. The firm primarily operates in the US Europe and Asia.

Operations

BV is organized around key markets which include energy telecommunications water management consulting and projects for the federal government.

The group's operations in the global water markets impact water quality and quantity throughout the water cycle: from source to treatment to delivery to wastewater collection and treatment. A key player in water treatment and wastewater treatment design BV's water division works with utilities governments and industries worldwide. The company is seeing an increase in water projects following the economic recession which stifled the flow of capital.

Financial Performance

Black & Veatch posted $3.3 billion in revenue in 2012. The firm managed more than $1.8 billion in general contracting projects during the year.

Strategy

BV's telecommunications operations are growing quickly as communications infrastructure is being improved around the world. Clients include wireless and wireline operators satellite networks public safety agencies municipalities utilities and various government agencies including the departments of energy defense and Homeland Security and the EPA and FAA. The business will continue to grow thanks to the Sprint/Samsung mobile network upgrade project. BV is working to provide wireless site development services to support the infrastructure project.

The company's energy division which accounts for about 40% of revenues is another growing segment. Clients are busy with new projects to meet the growing demand for energy. BV is involved in major US transmission line work as well as power plant projects in places such as China India and the Middle East. Indeed in 2012 BV expanded its operations in India to meet the country's growing infrastructure requirements.

EXECUTIVES

Chairman President and CEO, Leonard C. (Len) Rodman
CEO Energy Business, O. H. (Dean) Oskvig
CFO, Karen L. Daniel, age 54
President Federal Services Division, William R. (Bill) Van Dyke
President Telecommunications, Martin G. Travers
Associate Vice President of Global Marketing & Communications for Black & Veatch, Carl Petz
EVP Expanded Scope Projects B&V Water, Bruce Ainsworth
President Water Business, Cindy Wallis-Lage
Chief Administrative Officer; President Administrative Division, James R. (Jim) Lewis
SVP B&V Energy Asia Middle East India Europe and B&V Water Asia Pacific, Hoe Wai Cheong
President Management Consulting, John Chevrette
President Construction and Procurement, Hal E. Smith
Chairman President & CEO, Steven L. Edwards
Associate Vice President for Black & Veatch&rsquo, Dan Rueckert
President Ronald Reagan&rsquo, Merrie Spaeth
Senior Vice President in Black &amp, Kurt Westermann
President Construction & Procurement, John E. Murphy
Director, Martha W. Gilliland
Director, Anthony G. (Tony) Fernandes, age 68
Director, Steven H. Wunning, age 62
Director, Joseph Nemec Jr., age 71
Director, T. M. (Don) Buck
Director, W. P. (Pat) Campbell
Director; President and CEO Black & Veatch Energy, O. H. (Dean) Oskvig
CFO and Director, Karen L. Daniel, age 55
Director; President and CEO Black & Veatch Water, Daniel W. (Dan) McCarthy
Director, H. P. Goldfield
SVP and Director Power Delivery Services, James Lusby
Auditors: KPMGLLP

LOCATIONS

HQ: BLACK & VEATCH CORPORATION
11401 LAMAR AVE, OVERLAND PARK, KS 66211-1598
Phone: 913-458-2000
Web: WWW.BV.COM

PRODUCTS/OPERATIONS

Market Sectors
Energy
Air quality control
Coal
Combustion turbine
Gas oil and chemicals
Hydropower
IGCC
Nuclear
Power delivery
Renewables
Environmental
Air quality
Compliance management
Due diligence
Field studies/in
Permitting
Prevention plans
Remediation
Watershed analysis and restoratio
Water/wastewater
Federal
Civil works
Disaster support
Facilities
Federal design-bui
Management programs
Security
Management consulting
Integrated strategy developmen
Process improvemen
Technology application services
Services
Asset management
Climate change solutions
Construction
Design/build
Engineering and design
Engineering consulting
Infrastructure planning
Management consulting
Procurement
Program management
SAP services
Smart utility
Water spares
Telecommunications
Broadband wireline
Cyber and physical security
Site acquisition services
Telecom for smart utilities
Utility automation
Utility telecommun
Wireless
Water
Conveyance systems and tunneling services
Drinking water
Hydropower
River and coastal management
Wastewater
Water resources

COMPETITORS

AECOM
AMEC
ARCADIS
Balfour Beatty Infrastructure
Bechtel
Burns & McDonnell
Burns and Roe
CH2M HILL
Costain
EA Engineering
Fluor
Foster Wheeler
HNTB Companies
Halcrow Group
Louis Berger
MWH Global
McDermott
Michael Baker
Mott MacDonald
Parsons Brinckerhoff
Parsons Corporation
SNC-Lavalin
Shaw Group
TIC Holdings
Tetra Tech
Zachry Inc.

HISTORICAL FINANCIALS

Company Type: Private

Income Statement FYE: December 31

	REVENUE ($ mil.)	NET INCOME ($ mil.)	NET PROFIT MARGIN	EMPLOYEES
12/09	1,163	58	5.0%	4,065
12/08	1,267	16	1.3%	—
12/07	1,287	33	2.6%	—
12/06	1,075	60	5.6%	—
Annual Growth	2.6%	(1.1%)	—	—

2009 Year-End Financials

Debt ratio: —
Return on equity: 5.00%
Cash ($ mil.): 16
Current ratio: —
Long-term debt ($ mil.): —
Dividends
Yield: —
Payout: —
Market value ($ mil.): —

BLANCHARD VALLEY FARMERS COOPERATIVE INC.

EXECUTIVES

General Manager, Jerry Silveus
Assistant Manager; Manager Agronomy, Michael (Mike) Tobe
Manager Petroleum Division, Steve Rodman
Grain Manager, Mitch Welty
Office Manager, Jean Drerup
Treasurer Board of Directors, Steven Cramer
Vice President Board of Directors, William Tong
Risk Coordinator, Joe Hochstettler
Stock Coordinator, Coleen Wright
Grain Accounting, Melissa Curtis
Chemical Sales Manager, Don Boehm
Accounts Payable and Accounts Receivable, Sam Clark
Operations Manager, David Koch
Operations Manager, Joel Althouse
Operations Manager, Bruce Frank
Operations Manager, John Bormuth
Vice President, Andy Jones
Treasurer Board of Directors, Steven Cramer
Director, Marvin Tuttle
Director, Mark Brian
Director, Shawn Beucler
Director, David Roberts
Director, Mike Stacy

LOCATIONS

HQ: BLANCHARD VALLEY FARMERS COOPERATIVE INC.
6566 COUNTY ROAD 236, FINDLAY, OH 458409769
Phone: 4194232611
Web: WWW.BVFCOOP.COM

PRODUCTS/OPERATIONS

Selected Services

Customer accounting
Feed
Grain
Petroleum
Seasonal grain

COMPETITORS

ADM
Ag Processing Inc.
CHS
Cargill
GROWMARK
Luckey Farmers

HISTORICAL FINANCIALS

Company Type: Private

Income Statement FYE: December 31

	REVENUE ($ mil.)	NET INCOME ($ mil.)	NET PROFIT MARGIN	EMPLOYEES
12/13	321	8	2.5%	122
12/12	335	5	1.6%	—
12/11	292	7	2.5%	—
12/10	196	0	—	—
Annual Growth	17.9%	—	—	—

2013 Year-End Financials

Debt ratio: —
Return on equity: 2.50%
Cash ($ mil.): 5
Current ratio: 0.10
Long-term debt ($ mil.): —
Dividends
Yield: —
Payout: —
Market value ($ mil.): —

BLARNEY CASTLE OIL CO.

EXECUTIVES

EVP, William J. (Bill) McCarthy
Petroleum Operations Director, Dennis P. McCarthy

Purchasing Manager, Brian C. McCarthy

LOCATIONS

HQ: BLARNEY CASTLE OIL CO.
12218 WEST ST, BEAR LAKE, MI 496149432
Phone: 2318643111
Web: WWW.BLARNEYCASTLEOIL.COM

COMPETITORS

Crystal Flash Energy
PetroLiance
Vesco Oil

HISTORICAL FINANCIALS

Company Type: Private

Income Statement FYE: March 31

	REVENUE ($ mil.)	NET INCOME ($ mil.)	NET PROFIT MARGIN	EMPLOYEES
03/14	525	5	1.1%	700
03/13	513	6	1.2%	—
03/12	501	4	0.8%	—
03/11	415	0	—	—
Annual Growth	8.2%	—	—	—

2014 Year-End Financials

Debt ratio: —
Return on equity: 1.10%
Cash ($ mil.): 7
Current ratio: 1.50
Long-term debt ($ mil.): —
Dividends
Yield: —
Payout: —
Market value ($ mil.): —

BLESSING HOSPITAL

Blessing Hospital is a not-for-profit acute care medical center that provides a wide range of health services to residents in areas of western Illinois northeast Missouri and southeast Iowa. Through its main campus location it provides primary and emergency care as well as specialty services including diagnostics and surgery. The hospital is home to centers of excellence in the treatment of cancer heart and cardiovascular ailments wound care and women's health issues. Blessing Hospital provides outpatient and behavioral health services at a nearby campus. It also operates family practice centers and provides home and hospice care services. It is part of the Blessing Health System.

Company Ownership

The larger Blessing Health System is managed by parent company Blessing Corporate Services. Besides Blessing Hospital the health system includes Illini Community Hospital Blessing Physician Services and Blessing-Rieman College of Nursing among other health care facilities. The system's for-profit Denman Services division markets and distributes medical equipment.

Geographic Reach

Blessing Hospital serves those who reside in western Illinois southeast Iowa and northeast Missouri.

Operations

As part of its operations Blessing Hospital boasts a medical staff of more than 240 physicians with an additional 2000 health care personnel. Its operations consist of a behavioral center body motion center breast center cancer center heart and vascular center sleep center and wound center as well as family practice centers.

Strategy

In 2012 Blessing Hospital merged its outpatient physical and occupational therapy services with ADVANCE Physical Therapy. The move has allowed the hospital's nationally accredited rehabilitation services department to focus on inpatients while ADVANCE concentrates on delivering physical and occupational therapy on an outpatient basis.

Blessing Hospital is working to boost its range of tertiary (acute specialty care) services to keep residents in the area from heading to larger towns more than 150 miles away. To this end it has built up its cardiac services and brought in a robotic surgical system.

EXECUTIVES

Medical Director Quality Management, Robert Merrick
CFO Blessing Health System, Patrick (Pat) Gerveler
VP Business Development Blessing Corporate Services, Rick Kempe
President CEO and Trustee, Maureen A. Kahn
Chief Nursing Officer, Jill Mason
Chief Medical Officer, George Liesmann
Chairman, Thomas H. Miller
President and CEO Blessing Affiliates and Blessing Corporate Services, Jerry R. Jackson
VP Corporate Compliance Blessing Corporate Services, Betty Kasparie
Chief Accounting Officer, Tim Moore
Chairman, Michael D. Klingner
Vice Chairman, Timothy D. Koontz
Vice Chairman, David Boster
Director Blessing Hospital Laboratory, Michael D. Johnston
Administrative Director Information Systems, Lee Ann Eickelschulte
Trustee, B. Bradford Billings, age 64
President CEO and Trustee, Maureen A. Kahn
Trustee, Thomas H. Miller
Vice Chairman, Timothy D. Koontz
Trustee, Nancy A. Bluhm
Vice Chairman, David Boster
Trustee, Jean A. Disseler
Trustee, Michael J. Foster
Trustee, Prince Lynn P. House
Trustee, Michael R. Hulsen
Trustee, Joseph A. Kuhlman

LOCATIONS

HQ: BLESSING HOSPITAL
BROADWAY AT 11TH ST, QUINCY, IL 62301
Phone: 217-223-1200
Web: WWW.BLESSINGHOSPITAL.ORG

PRODUCTS/OPERATIONS

Selected Services

Bariatric Services
Behavioral Center
Blessing FastCare Clinic
Body Motion Center
Breast Center
Cancer Center
Emergency Center
Heart & Vascular Center
Home Care
Hospice & Palliative Care
Hospital Medicine Program
Maternity Care
Nutrition Services
Orthopedic Surgical Services
Pain Management Service
Radiology
Rehabilitation Services
Renal Dialysis Services
Sleep Center
Surgical Services
Wound Center

COMPETITORS

Advocate BroMenn
Hospital Sisters Health System
Memorial Health System
St. John's Hospital (Illinois)

HISTORICAL FINANCIALS

Company Type: Private

Income Statement FYE: September 30

	REVENUE ($ mil.)	NET INCOME ($ mil.)	NET PROFIT MARGIN	EMPLOYEES
09/12	289	14	5.1%	2,500
09/08	238	(2)	—	—
09/07	230	16	7.1%	—
09/06	1,900	0	—	—
Annual Growth	—	483.6%	—	—

2012 Year-End Financials

Debt ratio: —
Return on equity: 5.10%
Cash ($ mil.): 68
Current ratio: 2.10
Long-term debt ($ mil.): —
Dividends
Yield: —
Payout: —
Market value ($ mil.): —

BLOOD SYSTEMS INC.

As one might assume from its name Blood Systems collects and provides blood to hospitals. The not-for-profit Blood Systems collects blood and provides blood products and services to more than 500 hospitals in about 20 states. Its network of blood bank facilities are operated through its United Blood Services and Blood Centers of the Pacific subsidiaries. Blood Systems also provides blood donor testing services through its Creative Testing Solutions (CTS) facilities. Its BioCARE division distributes plasma derivative products used in medical procedures.

Geographic Reach

Blood Systems has about 50 donor centers in Arizona California Colorado Idaho Louisiana Mississippi Montana Nevada New Mexico North Dakota South Dakota Texas Washington and Wyoming (through the United Blood Services and Blood Centers of the Pacific units). The company also has about 20 BioCARE locations and a handful of CTS and research labs scattered across the US.

Operations

Blood Systems gets more than half of revenues from blood component service fees made by the blood centers. Laboratory testing services (CTS) and sales of pharmaceutical products (BioCARE) make up most of the rest of sales.

The Blood Systems Research Institute conducts transfusion medicine research including investigational work on transfusion-transmitted diseases (such as HIV and HCV) and infectious diseases such as the West Nile Virus. It also prepares stem cells for research and therapeutic purposes.

Financial Performance

Blood Systems reported revenues of $735 million in 2012 a 2% increase over the previous year due to higher sales of laboratory testing services and pharmaceutical products. Net income fell 27% to $22.7 million in 2012 on higher expenses related to the costs of blood collection pharmaceutical supplies and testing products.

Strategy

Blood Systems primarily operates in the western and midwestern US and tends to grow by entering new hospital service contracts in strategic markets. In addition the company is working to improve its IT systems to give customers better access to its blood supplies. It rolled out a new online ordering system to its centers in 2012 and opened a fourth lab in Chicago. It also invests in facility and equipment upgrades as well as product research and development efforts to improve quality.

Company Background

The company which was founded in 1943 as the Salt River Valley Blood Bank is governed by a voluntary board of directors consisting of community and medical industry leaders.

EXECUTIVES

EVP and General Counsel, Scott M. Nelson
EVP and Chief Quality Officer, Mary Beth Bassett
EVP Business Services, Patrick Holt
Vice President Quality Management, Henri Bassett
Vice President Information Technology, Bob Boatright
Vice President Regional Operations, Beth Stensgaard
Vice President Regional Operations, Ken Newburg
Vice President Air Force Tx Program, Melissa Moreno
Medical Director, Holley Paul
Executive Vice President General, Bhavi Shah
Vice President Regional Operations, Michael Hayward
Auditors: GrantThorntonLLP

LOCATIONS

HQ: BLOOD SYSTEMS INC.
6210 E OAK ST, SCOTTSDALE, AZ 852571101
Phone: 4809464201
Web: WWW.BLOODSYSTEMS.ORG

PRODUCTS/OPERATIONS

2011 Sales

	$ mil.	% of total
Blood component service fees	369	51
Laboratory testing services	179	25
Sales of pharmaceutical products	152	21
Other services & income	21	3
Total	**722**	**100**

Selected Services

Blood Centers
- Blood Components
- Component Therapy
- Commonly Ordered Derivatives
- Modified Blood Components

Laboratory Services
- Donor Counseling
- Histocompatibility Laboratory (HLA)
- Immunohematology Reference Laboratory (IRL)

Special Collections
- Directed Donation
- Perioperative Blood Salvage
- Pre-operative Autologous Donation (PAD)
- Stem Cell Processing
- Therapeutic (Clinical) Apheresis

Transfusion Medicine
- Blood Management Services
- Compatibility Services

COMPETITORS

CSL
Daxor
FFF Enterprises
Grifols Inc.
HemaCare
New York Blood Center
Puget Sound Blood Center
Red Cross
SeraCare Life Sciences

HISTORICAL FINANCIALS

Company Type: Private

Income Statement FYE: December 31

	REVENUE ($ mil.)	NET INCOME ($ mil.)	NET PROFIT MARGIN	EMPLOYEES
12/13	743	65	8.8%	3,900
12/12	488	21	4.4%	—
12/11	67	0	1.2%	—
12/10	476	0		
Annual Growth	15.9%	—	—	—

2013 Year-End Financials

Debt ratio: —	Dividends
Return on equity: 8.80%	Yield: —
Cash ($ mil.): 19	Payout: —
Current ratio: 1.30	Market value ($ mil.): —
Long-term debt ($ mil.): —	

BLUE CROSS & BLUE SHIELD ASSOCIATION

Blue insurers prefer to sing a happy healthy tune. Health plan providers affiliated with the Blue Cross and Blue Shield Association (BCBSA) — known as "the Blues" —serve some 100 million members nationwide. The association is a federation of about 40 independent health insurance companies who license the Blue Cross and Blue Shield brand names. Member companies own the rights to sell Blue-branded health plans within defined regions. BCBSA coordinates some national programs such as BlueCard which allows members of one franchisee to have coverage in other service areas and the Federal Employee Program (FEP) which covers more than half of federal government employees retirees and their families.

HISTORY

Blue Cross was born in 1929 when Baylor University official Justin Kimball offered schoolteachers 21 days of hospital care for $6 a year. A major plan feature was a community rating system that based premiums on the community claims experience rather than members' conditions.

The Blue Cross symbol was devised in 1933 by Minnesota plan executive E. A. van Steenwyck. By 1935 many of the 15 plans in 11 states used the symbol. Many states gave the plans not-for-profit status and in 1936 the American Hospital Association formed the Committee on Hospital Service (renamed the Blue Cross Association in 1948) to coordinate them.

As Blue Cross grew state medical societies sponsored prepaid plans to cover doctors' fees. In 1946 they united under the aegis of the American Medical Association (AMA) as the Associated Medical Care Plans (later the Association of Blue Shield Plans).

In 1948 the AMA thwarted a Blue Cross attempt to merge with Blue Shield. But the Blues increasingly cooperated on public policy matters while competing for members and each Blue formed a not-for-profit corporation to coordinate its plan's activities.

Blue Cross insured about a third of the US by 1960. Over the next decade the Blues started administering Medicare and other government health plans and by 1970 half of Blue Cross' premiums came from government entities.

In the 1970s the Blues adopted such cost-control measures as review of hospital admissions; many plans even abandoned the community rating system. Most began emphasizing preventive care in HMOs or PPOs. The two Blues finally merged in 1982 to form the Blue Cross and Blue Shield Association (BCBSA) but this had little effect on the associations' bottom lines as losses grew.

By the 1990s the Blues were big business. Some of the state associations offered officers high salaries and perks but still insisted on special regulatory treatment.

But as lower-cost plans attracted the hale and hearty the Blues' customers became older sicker and more expensive. With their quasi-charitable status and outdated rate structures many Blues plans lost market share.

The Blues fought back by updating their technology and rate structures merging among themselves creating for-profit subsidiaries forming alliances with for-profit enterprises or (in some cases) dropping their not-for-profit status and going public –while still using the Blue Cross Blue Shield name.

Blue Cross of California became the first chapter to give up its tax-free status when it was bought by WellPoint Health Networks a managed care subsidiary it had founded in 1992. In a 1996 deal WellPoint became the chapter's parent and converted it to for-profit status assigning all of the stock to a public charitable foundation which received the proceeds of its subsequent IPO. WellPoint also bought the group life and health division of Massachusetts Mutual Life Insurance.

The for-profit switches picked up in 1997. Blue Cross of Connecticut merged with insurance provider Anthem and other mergers followed. Half the nation's Blues formed an alliance called BluesCONNECT (now BlueCard) competing with national health plans by offering employers one nationwide benefits organization. BCBSA also pursued overseas licensing agreements in Europe South America and Asia assembling a network of Blue Cross-friendly caregivers aiming for worldwide coverage.

In 1998 Blues in more than 35 states sued the nation's big cigarette companies to recoup costs of treating smoking-related illnesses. In a separate lawsuit Blue Cross and Blue Shield of Minnesota received nearly $300 million from the tobacco industry. In 1999 Anthem moved to acquire or affiliate with Blues in Colorado Maine Nevada and New Hampshire.

After years of discussions in 2000 the New York attorney general permitted Empire Blue Cross and Blue Shield to convert to for-profit status. The pace of for-profit conversions slowed down in following years however as state regulators became increasingly wary of signing off on the procedure. The improved financial situation of most of the not-for-profit Blues also took away a key incentive for for-profit conversion –access to capital markets.

In 2004 Anthem and WellPoint Health Networks merged and Anthem's name changed to WellPoint (though it continued to use the Anthem brand name in certain markets) becoming the largest for-profit health insurer in the nation. WellPoint acquired Empire Blue Cross and its parent WellChoice as well as non-Blue consumer-driven plan provider Lumenos in 2005. In addition to snapping up Blues providers the for-profit WellPoint acquired a number of non-Blue subsidiaries such as American Imaging Management while meeting the requirement that it get two-thirds of its insurance revenue from Blue products to keep its BCBSA license.

Consolidation among Blues plans continued when Health Care Service Corporation added its fourth not-for-profit Blues plan (Blue Cross and Blue Shield of Oklahoma) in 2005.

In 2007 BCBSA was approved under a Federal Savings Bank charter to provide health-related banking services through its Blue Healthcare Bank.

Two licensees Highmark and Independence Blue Cross had agreed to merge in 2008 but the deal was terminated in early 2009 after long delays and heavy regulatory concern that the merger would create an unfair advantage in the Pennsylvania market. Some consolidation continued however as Triple-S which operates under the Blue Shield brand in Puerto Rico acquired and absorbed Blue Cross licensee La Cruz Azul from Independence Blue Cross in 2009.

Highmark reached a formal affiliation agreement (including shared administrative and IT resources) with Blue Cross Blue Shield of Delaware in 2011.

Another regional Blues provider Cambia Health Solutions (formerly Regence Group) changed its name in 2011 to signify its diversification efforts though its BCBS subsidiaries continue to operate under the Regence name.

Three Blues companies –WellPoint Health Care Service Corp.(HCSC) and BCBS of Michigan – joined together in 2011 to invest in a commercial insurance exchange (Bloom Health) designed to allow businesses to contribute to employees' selected health coverage. The venture was part of the Blues' efforts to meet the changing US insurance needs under health reform laws.

EXECUTIVES

Svp Strategic Services And Chief Strategy Officer, Maureen E Sullivan
Vice President Operations, David R Gentile
President and CEO, Scott P. Serota, $1,307,804 total compensation
SVP Financial Services and Government Programs and CFO, Robert J. (Bob) Kolodgy
SVP Operations and CIO, Doug Porter
VP Government Programs, William A. Breskin
Chief Medical Officer, Trent Haywood
VP Enterprise Information Technology, Bhaskar Bulusu
VP National Programs, Kari Hedges
VP Health Policy and Analysis, Kris Haltmeyer
Vp Finance, David Murdoch, age 79
Vice President Consumer Brand Strategy, Cynthia Rolfe
Vice President Policy, Justine Handelman
Vice President Strategic Communications, Paul Gerrard
Vice President Deputy General Counsel, Scott Nehs
Medical Director, Mohammad Butt
Vice President Marketing, Vicki McDonald
Medical Director, Eden Branon
Vice President Human Resources, Ralph Volpe
Vice President Operations, Jack Werzinzyskwitz
Vice President Operations, Wayne Roberts
Vice President Communications, Stephanie Davis
Vice President Communications, Elizabeth Martin
Vice President, Catherine Peper
Vice President And Chief Technology, Cecilia Scalia
Vice President And Chief Technology, William Wright
Ex Vice President And Chief Operating, Stephen Granfield
Board Of Directors, Kerry Barnett
Treasurer, Alaine Zachary
Vice Chairman, Casper Sedgwick
Board Member, Leon Furlong
Auditors: BDOSeidmanLLP

LOCATIONS

HQ: BLUE CROSS & BLUE SHIELD ASSOCIATION
225 N MICHIGAN AVE FL 5, CHICAGO, IL 60601-7658
Phone: 312-297-6000
Web: WWW.BCBS.COM

PRODUCTS/OPERATIONS

Selected Blue Cross and Blue Shield Licensees

Arkansas Blue Cross and Blue Shield
Blue Cross and Blue Shield of Alabama
Blue Cross and Blue Shield of Arizona
Blue Cross and Blue Shield of Delaware
Blue Cross and Blue Shield of Florida
Blue Cross and Blue Shield of Kansas
Blue Cross and Blue Shield of Kansas City
Blue Cross and Blue Shield of Louisiana
Blue Cross and Blue Shield of Massachusetts
Blue Cross and Blue Shield of Michigan
Blue Cross and Blue Shield of Minnesota
Blue Cross and Blue Shield of Mississippi
Blue Cross and Blue Shield of Montana
Blue Cross and Blue Shield of Nebraska
Blue Cross and Blue Shield of North Carolina
Blue Cross and Blue Shield of North Dakota
Blue Cross and Blue Shield of Rhode Island
Blue Cross and Blue Shield of South Carolina
Blue Cross and Blue Shield of Tennessee
Blue Cross and Blue Shield of Vermont
Blue Cross and Blue Shield of Wyoming
Blue Cross of Idaho Health Service
Blue Cross of Northeastern Pennsylvania
California Physicians' Service (dba Blue Shield of California)
Cambia Health Solutions Inc. (formerly The Regence Group)
- Regence BlueCross and BlueShield of Oregon
- Regence BlueCross BlueShield of Utah
- Regence BlueShield of Idaho
- Regence BlueShield (Washington)

Capital BlueCross (Pennsylvania)
CareFirst
- CareFirst Blue Cross and Blue Shield (District of Columbia)
- CareFirst Blue Cross and Blue Shield of Maryland

Excellus BlueCross BlueShield of New York
Hawaii Medical Service Association
Health Care Service Corporation
- Blue Cross and Blue Shield of Illinois
- Blue Cross and Blue Shield of New Mexico
- Blue Cross and Blue Shield of Oklahoma
- Blue Cross and Blue Shield of Texas

HealthNow New York
- BlueCross and BlueShield of Western New York
- BlueShield of Northeastern New York

Highmark Blue Cross Blue Shield (Pennsylvania)
- Mountain State Blue Cross and Blue Shield (West Virginia)

Horizon Healthcare Services (dba Horizon Blue Cross and Blue Shield of New Jersey)
Independence Blue Cross (Pennsylvania)
Premera Blue Cross (Alaska and Washington)
Triple-S (Puerto Rico)
Wellmark
- Wellmark Blue Cross and Blue Shield of Iowa
- Wellmark Blue Cross and Blue Shield of South Dakota

WellPoint
- Anthem Blue Cross and Blue Shield of Colorado
- Anthem Blue Cross and Blue Shield of Connecticut
- Anthem Blue Cross and Blue Shield of Indiana
- Anthem Blue Cross and Blue Shield of Kentucky
- Anthem Blue Cross and Blue Shield of Maine
- Anthem Blue Cross and Blue Shield of Nevada
- Anthem Blue Cross and Blue Shield of New Hampshire
- Anthem Blue Cross and Blue Shield of Ohio
- Anthem Blue Cross and Blue Shield of Virginia
- Blue Cross and Blue Shield of Georgia
- Blue Cross and Blue Shield of Missouri (dba Anthem Blue Cross and Blue Shield)
- BlueCross BlueShield of Wisconsin (dba Anthem Blue Cross and Blue Shield)
- California Blue Cross (Anthem Blue Cross)
- Empire Blue Cross and Blue Shield of New York

International plans
- Blue Cross & Blue Shield de Uruguay
- BlueCross BlueShield of Panama

COMPETITORS

AMERIGROUP
Aetna
CIGNA
Centene
Coventry Health Care
Health Net
Humana
Kaiser Foundation Health Plan
Molina Healthcare
Principal Financial
UnitedHealth Group
WellCare Health Plans

HISTORICAL FINANCIALS

Company Type: Private

Income Statement FYE: December 31

	REVENUE ($ mil.)	NET INCOME ($ mil.)	NET PROFIT MARGIN	EMPLOYEES
12/11	392	(13)	—	1,880
12/06	320	14	4.5%	—
12/05	275	8	3.0%	—
12/04	270	11	4.3%	—
Annual Growth	5.4%	—	—	—

2011 Year-End Financials

Debt ratio: —
Return on equity: (-3.40%)
Cash ($ mil.): 270
Current ratio: 0.80
Long-term debt ($ mil.): —
Dividends
Yield: —
Payout: —
Market value ($ mil.): —

BLUE CROSS AND BLUE SHIELD OF ARIZONA INC.

Blue Cross Blue Shield of Arizona (BCBSAZ) provides health insurance products and services to some 1.3 million Arizonans. The not-for-profit company offers a variety of managed care plans to small and large employer groups individuals and families including PPO HMO and high-deductible health plans. It also provides dental vision and prescription drug coverage as well as supplemental health plans for Medicare beneficiaries. Additionally BCBSAZ's HealthyBlue wellness and disease management programs give members information and services that encourage healthy lifestyles. Founded in 1939 the company is an independent licensee of the Blue Cross and Blue Shield Association.

Geographic Reach

BCBSAZ serves customers throughout the state of Arizona from its offices in Chandler Flagstaff Phoenix and Tucson. It has a contracted network of some 21000 physicians and dentists located across the state as well.

Strategy

The company has been revamping many of its health plan offerings revising coverage terms and lowering premiums in an effort to attract more customers. Working with state and federal tax incentive programs BCBSAZ increased promotional efforts for its low-premium small business insurance plans in 2010 and 2011. In addition BCBSAZ has launched marketing campaigns targeting Arizona's Hispanic community which makes up 30% of the state's population.

To increase offerings for seniors BCBSAZ introduced a Medicare part D prescription drug plan in 2011. Then in 2012 the company formed a joint venture with Banner Health called Blue Cross Blue Shield of Arizona Advantage to jointly offer expanded Medicare plans and services to an estimated 25000 Medicare Advantage enrollees in Arizona.

To help reduce skyrocketing costs plaguing the health care industry the company has also been enhancing its HealthyBlue wellness program offering which promotes preventative care and fitness and allows for personalized online health assessment and coaching services. In 2010 BCBSAZ launched a web-based cost comparison tool.

Financial Performance

BCBSAZ processed some 15 million claims in 2011 paying out some $2.8 billion.

Mergers and Acquisitions

Occasional acquisitions also play a role in BCBSAZ's expansion efforts. In 2009 the firm bought up the 16000 customer accounts of LifeWise Health Plan of Arizona a unit of Premera Blue Cross that had decided to exit the Arizona market.

EXECUTIVES

President CEO and Director, Richard L. (Rich) Boals
SVP and Chief Service Officer, H. Jody Chandler

EVP External Operations, Susan H. Navran
Senior Vice President General Counsel, Deanna Salazar
EVP Internal Operations, Sandra Lee Gibson
SVP and CIO, Elizabeth A. Messina
SVP and CFO, Karen Abraham
SVP Health Services and Chief Medical Officer, Vishu Jhaveri
SVP Strategy Sales and Marketing, Jeff Stelnik
Vice President Pharmacy Management, Chris Hogan

LOCATIONS

HQ: BLUE CROSS AND BLUE SHIELD OF ARIZONA INC.
2444 W LAS PALMARITAS DR, PHOENIX, AZ 85021-4860
Phone: 602-864-4100
Web: WWW.BLUECROSSBLUESHIELDOFARIZONA.ETHICALAZ.COM

PRODUCTS/OPERATIONS

Selected Plans

Family and Individual Medical Plans
- BlueBasic Plus PPO
- BlueEssential Plus PPO
- BlueOptimum Plus PPO
- BluePortfolio Plus (high deductible PPO with HSA)
- BlueValue Plus PPO
- Medicare Part D
- Medicare Supplement

Group Medical Plans
- BlueAlliance benefit
- BluePreferred PPO
- BluePreferred HSA Plus (high deductable PPO with HSA)
- BlueSelect HMO
- Dental plans
- Eyewear plans
- GeoBlue Expat

COMPETITORS

Aetna
Banner Health
CIGNA HealthCare of Arizona
First Dental Health
Health Net
Humana
Southwest Catholic Health Network
UnitedHealth Group
Vanguard Health Systems
Western Dental Services

HISTORICAL FINANCIALS

Company Type: Private

Income Statement FYE: December 31

	ASSETS ($ mil.)	NET INCOME ($ mil.)	INCOME AS % OF ASSETS	EMPLOYEES
12/09	1,059	64	6.1%	1,278
12/08	975	71	7.4%	—
Annual Growth	8.6%	(9.9%)	—	—

BLUE TEE CORP.

EXECUTIVES

President Chief Executive Officer, William M. Kelly, age 64
Executive Vice President - Finance and Secretary, David P. Alldian
Group VP Metals Operations, Richard A. Secrist Jr.
Controller and Assistant Secretary, Thomas Caruso
Executive Director Benefit Plans, Annette Marino D'Arienzo
President, Mike Calvert
EVP, Ryan Secrist
VP; President Azcon, Ronnie Hirsch

LOCATIONS

HQ: BLUE TEE CORP.
250 PARK AVE S RM 203, NEW YORK, NY 100031495
Phone: 2125980880
Web: WWW.BLUETEE.COM

PRODUCTS/OPERATIONS

Selected Subsidiaries

Azcon Corporation (ferrous and nonferrous scrap; rail cars locomotives and parts; relay and reroll rail)
Brown-Strauss Steel (steel distribution including angles beams channels pipe and tubing)

Selected Azcon Services

Barge Services
Brokerage Services
Demolition Services
Foundries - Scrap Management
Industrial Plants - Scrap Management
Mill Service
Mine Services
Railroad Industry Services
Steel Mills - Scrap Management

Selected Brown-Strauss Steel Products and Services

Products:
Structural Angle
Structural Channels
Structural Pipe
Structural Tubing
Wide Flange Beams
Services:
Cambering
Inventory Stocking program
Length/cutting optimization program
Mill Brokerage
Saw Cutting
Track Torch Cutting

COMPETITORS

A. M. Castle
APi Group
Dover Corp.
Metals USA
OmniSource
Pacesetter Steel
RTI International Metals
Reliance Steel
Russel Metals
Ryerson
TTX
Trinity Industries
Wescast Industries

HISTORICAL FINANCIALS

Company Type: Private

Income Statement FYE: December 31

	REVENUE ($ mil.)	NET INCOME ($ mil.)	NET PROFIT MARGIN	EMPLOYEES
12/10	809	14	1.8%	900
12/09	564	(10)	—	—
Annual Growth	43.4%	—	—	—

2010 Year-End Financials

Debt ratio: —
Return on equity: 1.80%
Cash ($ mil.): 8
Current ratio: 0.10
Long-term debt ($ mil.): —
Dividends
Yield: —
Payout: —
Market value ($ mil.): —

BLUEBONNET ELECTRIC COOPERATIVE INC.

Bluebonnet Electric Cooperative's mission has echoes of the late Lady Bird Johnson's quest to spread bluebonnets and other wildflower seeds along Texas' highways. In this case the cooperative spreads power to homes and businesses in rural central and southeast Texas. One of the largest power distribution cooperatives in the state Bluebonnet Electric serves more than 81000 customers in 14 counties (a service area of more than 3800 square miles). The member-owned company which was formed in 1939 operates approximately 11000 miles of transmission and distribution lines and 19 substations. It purchases its wholesale power supply at 21 Lower Colorado River Authority-owned substations.

A long Texas drought caused a dust buildup on several of the co-op's insulators prompting a number of pole-top fires in late 2008 and early 2009. The utility is retrofitting the insulators to avoid a recurrence of the problem and ensure uninterrupted service.

Higher-than-normal summer heat drove up power demand in 2010. This resulted in Bluebonnet Electric reporting higher revenues and an improved net profit.

The heat and drought continued in 2011 and helped fuel a major wildfire in Bastrop over the Labor Day weekend. Bluebonnet Electric was subsequently confronted with a lawsuit which blamed it for the wildfire that destroyed almost 1600 homes (high winds brought down tree limbs on the coop's power lines sparking the blaze). The coop's executives ponted out that the trees which triggered the fire were on private property outside of the utility's easement and that Bluebonnet Electric could not be reasonably blamed for the conflagration.

In late 2011 the company lowered its electric rates to reflect lower natural gas commodity prices (natural gas accounts for 90% of the fuel Bluebonnet Electric uses to generate power).

In 1964 in order to avoid confusion with the Lower Colorado River Authority the utility originally known as the Lower Colorado River Electric Cooperative changed its name to Bluebonnet Electric Cooperative.

EXECUTIVES

Chairman, Richard Schmidt
CEO and General Manager, Mark Rose
General Manager, Elizabeth Kana
Secretary Treasurer and Director, James B. Kershaw
Assistant Secretary Assistant Treasurer and Director, Byron Balke
Vice Chairman, Ben Flencher
Chief Operating Officer, Johnny Sanders
Chief Engineer, Will Holford
Secretary Treasurer and Director, James B. Kershaw
Assistant Secretary Assistant Treasurer and Director, Byron Balke
Vice Chairman, Ben Flencher
Director, Kenneth (Ken) Mutscher
Director, Lyle L. Wolz
Director, Robert Mikeska
Director, Milton Shaw

LOCATIONS

HQ: BLUEBONNET ELECTRIC COOPERATIVE INC.
155 ELECTRIC AVE, BASTROP, TX 78602
Phone: 800-842-7708
Web: WWW.BLUEBONNETELECTRIC.COOP/HOME.ASPX

PRODUCTS/OPERATIONS

Sales

	$ mil.	% of total
Electric service	186	96
Capital credits	1	1
Other	5	3
Total	**193**	**100**

HISTORICAL FINANCIALS

Company Type: Private

Income Statement FYE: December 31

	REVENUE ($ mil.)	NET INCOME ($ mil.)	NET PROFIT MARGIN	EMPLOYEES
12/12	188	5	2.9%	265
12/11	199	5	2.9%	—
12/10	191	8	4.6%	—
12/09	186	4	2.5%	—
Annual Growth	0.4%	6.3%	—	—

2012 Year-End Financials

Debt ratio: —
Return on equity: 2.90%
Cash ($ mil.): 8
Current ratio: 0.80
Long-term debt ($ mil.): —

Dividends
Yield: —
Payout: —
Market value ($ mil.): —

BOARD OF EDUCATION OF FREDERICK COUNTY MD (INC)

LOCATIONS

HQ: BOARD OF EDUCATION OF FREDERICK COUNTY MD (INC)
191 S EAST ST, FREDERICK, MD 217015918
Phone: 3016445000
Web: WWW.FCPS.ORG

HISTORICAL FINANCIALS

Company Type: Private

Income Statement FYE: June 30

	REVENUE ($ mil.)	NET INCOME ($ mil.)	NET PROFIT MARGIN	EMPLOYEES
06/13	550	3	0.7%	3,500
06/12	543	(5)	—	—
06/05	0	0	—	—
06/03	0	0	—	—
Annual Growth	—	—	—	—

BOCA RATON REGIONAL HOSPITAL INC.

Serving the residents of Florida's southern Palm Beach County Boca Raton Regional Hospital provides a full range of medical services. The hospital with some 400 beds specializes in such services as oncology cardiology surgery orthopedics women's health and emergency medicine. As part of its operations the Boca Raton Regional Hospital campus includes centers for cancer and cardiovascular care wound healing and pain management rehabilitation pediatrics and clinical research. It also operates satellite clinics and provides services including outpatient surgeries home care and diagnostic imaging. The not-for-profit hospital was founded in 1967 and is governed by a voluntary board of directors.

Geographic Reach

Boca Raton Community Hospital serves the residents of Florida's southern Palm Beach County.

Operations

As part of its operations the hospital runs institutes dedicated to heart women's health orthopedics and cancer care. It also boasts technologically advanced diagnostic and imaging capabilities which it provides through an imaging services unit. Boca Raton Community Hospital serves as a Comprehensive Stroke Center designated by the Florida Agency for Health Care Administration. It employs more than 800 primary and specialty physicians.

Company Background

The hospital changed its name in 2010 from Boca Raton Community Hospital to Boca Raton Regional Hospital to reflect its broader services.

EXECUTIVES

VP and COO, Karen S. Poole
President CEO and Trustee, Jerry J. Fedele
VP Marketing and Communications, Thomas G. (Tom) Chakurda
Chairman, Christine E. Lynn
VP and CFO, Dawn P. Javersack
VP Operations, Mindy Sloane Shikiar
VP Human Resources, Mindy Raymond
Vice Chairman, Warren S. Orlando, age 71
Chief Nursing Officer, Eddy L. (Ed) Hannah
Chief Medical Officer, Charles Posternack
VP and Chief Nursing Officer, Melissa Durbin
President BocaCare, Frantz Python
CIO, Robin Hildwein
Vice President General Counsel Corporate Secretary, Alexander D. Eremia
Vice President for Strategic Affairs and Payer Relations, Daniel Sacco
President CEO and Trustee, Jerry J. Fedele
Vice Chairman, Warren S. Orlando, age 71

LOCATIONS

HQ: BOCA RATON REGIONAL HOSPITAL INC.
800 MEADOWS RD, BOCA RATON, FL 33486-2304
Phone: 561-395-7100
Web: WWW.BRRH.COM

PRODUCTS/OPERATIONS

Selected Services

Diagnostic Testing Services
- Cardiac Catheterization Echocardiography
- Electrocardiogram
- Electrophysiology Studies
- Exercise Stress Tests
- Holter Monitor
- Myocardial Biopsy
- Tilt Table Test
- Transesophageal Echocardiography

Surgical Services
- Angioplasty
- Coronary Bypass Surgery
- Endoscopic Vein Harvesting
- Minimally Invasive Heart Surgery
- Valve Replacement/Repair
- Surgical Ablations
- Treatment for Atrial Fibrillation including mini-maze surgery
- Aortic Surgery/Complex Aortic Aneurysms
- Endovascular Aortic Stent Graft Repair
- Hybrid Operating Room

Women' s Institute Service
- Full digital mammography
- Digital breast ultrasound
- Breast MRI
- Breast PEM scanning
- Bone mineral densitometry
- High risk screening
- Mobile mammography
- Needle localization
- Minimally-invasive breast biopsy by mammogram ultrasound and MRI
- Physical breast exam by a nurse practitioner
- Sentinel node mapping
- Galactography
- Genetic counseling/testing available
- Nurse navigation
- Clinical research studies
- Second opinion service
- Funding for underserved women
- Osteoporosis screenings
- Cardiac risk screenings
- Breast Cancer Risk Assessment Program

COMPETITORS

Baptist Health Care
Baptist Health South Florida
Broward Health
H. Lee Moffitt Cancer Center & Research Institute
HCA
Jackson Health System
Jupiter Medical Center
Larkin Community Hospital
Miami Children' s Hospital
Mount Sinai Medical Center of Florida
South Broward Hospital District
Tenet Healthcare
University of Miami Hospital

HISTORICAL FINANCIALS

Company Type: Private

Income Statement FYE: June 30

	REVENUE ($ mil.)	NET INCOME ($ mil.)	NET PROFIT MARGIN	EMPLOYEES
06/09	348	(17)	—	1,400
06/08	317	(53)	—	—
06/05	0	0		—
Annual Growth	—	—	—	—

2009 Year-End Financials

Debt ratio: —
Return on equity: (-4.90%)
Cash ($ mil.): 93
Current ratio: 1.50
Long-term debt ($ mil.): —

Dividends
Yield: —
Payout: —
Market value ($ mil.): —

BODDIE-NOELL ENTERPRISES INC.

Boddie-Noell Enterprises (BNE) is a hearty competitor in the fast-food business. The company is one of the largest franchise operators of Hardee's a fast-food chain owned by CKE Restaurants with about 330 locations the four southeastern states of Kentucky North Carolina South Carolina and Virginia. In addition the company owns The Highway Diner restaurant concept. BNE is also involved in real estate development through BNE Land & Development. The family owned company was started in 1962 by Carleton Noell and his nephews Nick and Mayo Boddie.

Geographic Reach

BNE owns 334 Hardee's locations throughout Kentucky North Carolina South Carolina and Virgina.

Strategy

The company previously owned the Texas Steakhouse & Saloon concept but it sold that operation in late 2012 to CB Holding owner of Charlie Brown's Steakhouse. BNE made the divestiture to focus solely on its Hardee's franchises.

EXECUTIVES

Senior Chairman, Mayo Boddie Sr., age 84
President and CEO, William L. (Bill) Boddie, age 60
President of Restaurant Operations, Mike Boddie, age 57
SVP and Chief Marketing Officer, Jerry Allsbrook

Vice Chairman, Nick B. Boddie
EVP Restaurant Development, Michael (Mike) Hancock
President BNE Land and Development, Doug Anderson
Director of Operations, Don Mack
vice Chairman Chief Administrative Officer of Boddie-Noell, James H. Waters
Auditors: Ernst&YoungLLP

LOCATIONS

HQ: BODDIE-NOELL ENTERPRISES INC.
1021 NOELL LN, ROCKY MOUNT, NC 27804-1761
Phone: 252-937-2000
Web: WWW.BNEINC.COM

PRODUCTS/OPERATIONS

Selected Operations

Restaurants
- Hardee' s
- The Highway Diner

Other
- BNE Land & Development (commercial and resort real estate development)
- Rose Hill Conference Center (Rocky Mount NC)

COMPETITORS

Biglari Holdings
Bojangles'
Burger King
Carolina Restaurant Group
Carrols
Chick-fil-A
DavCo Restaurants
McDonald' s
Sonic Corp.
Wendy' s
YUM!

HISTORICAL FINANCIALS

Company Type: Private

Income Statement FYE: December 31

	REVENUE ($ mil.)	NET INCOME ($ mil.)	NET PROFIT MARGIN	EMPLOYEES
12/12	395	13	3.5%	13,000
12/11	395	(9)	—	—
12/10	389	(49)	—	—
12/09	388	(6)	—	—
Annual Growth	0.5%	—	—	—

2012 Year-End Financials

Debt ratio: —
Return on equity: 3.50%
Cash ($ mil.): 24
Current ratio: 0.70
Long-term debt ($ mil.): —
Dividends
Yield: —
Payout: —
Market value ($ mil.): —

BON SECOURS HEALTH SYSTEM INC

Bon Secours Health System provides succor to the sick and injured. The Roman Catholic health care organization sponsored by the Bon Secours Ministries is home to about 20 hospitals with some 4400 licensed acute care beds. First founded in 1919 the organization's facilities are in six states in the eastern US from New York to Florida. In addition to its acute care hospitals the not-for-profit health care system operates numerous nursing homes and assisted-living facilities as well as outpatient centers hospices and home health care agencies. Its Global Ministry Initiative provides outreach for health care and social services in developing countries particularly Haiti Peru and South Africa.

Strategy

Bon Secours plans to continue to grow its operations in existing and new communities targeting expansion in ambulatory care elderly services and home health and hospice. The health system has opened several new ambulatory care centers in existing service territories and it is conducting renovation and expansion efforts at some of its hospital facilities.

Bon Secours has also initiated information technology restructuring efforts; it has developed a new clinical information management system (electronic medical records) ConnectCare which is being implemented at its facilities in gradual stages.

EXECUTIVES

Chairperson Bon Secours Ministries, Patricia A. (Pat) Eck
President CEO and Director, Richard J. (Rich) Statuto, age 57
CEO Bon Secours Baltimore Health System, Samuel L. Ross
CEO Bon Secours Charity Health System, Philip A. Patterson, age 45
Director, A. David Jimenez
President CEO and Director, Richard J. (Rich) Statuto, age 54
Director, Michael Carey
Director, Lucretia M. McClenney
Director, Richard M. Serafini
Director, Sister Mary Shimo
Director, Sister Alice M. Talone
Director, Laurie M. LaFontaine
Director, Chris Allen
Director, Richard Blair
Director, Sister Elaine Davia
Director, Roger Huang
Director, Myles N. Sheehan
Director, Marcia Dush
Director, Susan Sandlund

LOCATIONS

HQ: BON SECOURS HEALTH SYSTEM INC
1505 MARRIOTTSVILLE RD, MARRIOTTSVILLE, MD 21104-1301
Phone: 410-442-5511
Web: WWW.BSHSI.COM

Selected Facilities

Florida
- Bon Secours St. Petersburg Health System
  - Bon Secours - Maria Manor Nursing Care and Rehabilitation Center
  - Bon Secours Place at St. Petersburg
  - Bon Secours St. Petersburg Home Care Services

Kentucky
- Bon Secours Kentucky Health System
  - Our Lady of Bellefonte Hospital (Ashland)

Maryland
- Bon Secours Baltimore Health System
  - Bon Secours Hospital
  - Bon Secours Washington Village
  - Community Institute of Behavioral Sciences
  - Hollins Terrace/Benet House

New York
- Bon Secours Charity Health System
  - Bon Secours Community Hospital (Port Jervis)
  - Good Samaritan Hospital (Suffern)
  - St. Anthony Community Hospital (Warwick)
- Bon Secours New York Health System
  - Schervier Nursing Care Center (Riverdale)

Pennsylvania
- Altoona Regional Health System (joint venture)

South Carolina
- Bon Secours St. Francis Health System Inc.
  - St. Francis Hospital (Downtown and Eastside Campuses Greenville)
- Roper St. Francis Healthcare (Charleston joint venture)

Virginia
- Bon Secours Hampton Roads Health System
  - Bon Secours Maryview Nursing Care Center (Suffolk)
  - DePaul Medical Center (Norfolk)
  - Mary Immaculate Hospital (Newport News)
  - Maryview Medical Center (Portsmouth)
  - Province Place (Norfolk and Portsmouth)
  - St. Francis Nursing Care Center (Newport News)
- Bon Secours Richmond Health System (joint venture)
  - Memorial Regional Medical Center (Mechanicsville)
  - Richmond Community Hospital
  - St. Francis Medical Center (Midlothian)
  - St. Mary's Hospital (Richmond)

Selected Affiliations

Cosponsoring Congregational Relationships
- Bernardine Sisters of the Third Order of St. Francis (Newport News Virginia)
- Sisters of Charity of Saint Elizabeth of Convent Station (New Jersey and New York)

Affiliated Organizations
- Health Corporation of Virginia (Richmond)
- Medical Society of South Carolina and Carolinas Health Care System (Charleston)
- Life Care Services (Florida and Virginia)

COMPETITORS

Adventist HealthCare
Albany Medical Center
Albert Einstein Healthcare Network
Appalachian Regional Healthcare
Carilion Clinic
Catholic Health East
Catholic Health Initiatives
Centra Health Inc.
Christiana Care
Community Health Systems
Conemaugh Health System
Franklin Square Hospital Center
GBMC
Greenville Hospital System
HCA
Health Management Associates
Highlands Health
Inova
Johns Hopkins Medicine
MedStar Health
MediSys Health Network
New York City Health and Hospitals
Novant Health
Riverside Health System (Virginia)
Sentara Healthcare
St. Agnes HealthCare
University of Maryland Medical System
University of Miami Hospital
Virginia Hospital Center

HISTORICAL FINANCIALS

Company Type: Private

Income Statement FYE: August 31

	REVENUE ($ mil.)	NET INCOME ($ mil.)	NET PROFIT MARGIN	EMPLOYEES
08/11	3,308	158	4.8%	19,000
08/10	3,084	(41)	—	—
08/09	2,895	(291)	—	—
08/08	187	51	27.6%	—
Annual Growth	160.2%	45.1%	—	—

2011 Year-End Financials

Debt ratio: —
Return on equity: 4.80%
Cash ($ mil.): 159
Current ratio: 1.10
Long-term debt ($ mil.): —
Dividends
Yield: —
Payout: —
Market value ($ mil.): —

BOND BROS. INC.

LOCATIONS

HQ: BOND BROS. INC.
145 SPRING ST, EVERETT, MA 021494517
Phone: 6173873400
Web: WWW.BONDBROTHERS.COM

HISTORICAL FINANCIALS

Company Type: Private

Income Statement FYE: October 31

	REVENUE ($ mil.)	NET INCOME ($ mil.)	NET PROFIT MARGIN	EMPLOYEES
10/08	407	8	2.2%	350
10/07	348	0	—	—
10/06	336	0	—	—
Annual Growth	10.2%	147994.5%	—	—

2008 Year-End Financials

Debt ratio: —
Return on equity: 2.20%
Cash ($ mil.): 31
Current ratio: 1.20
Long-term debt ($ mil.): —
Dividends
Yield: —
Payout: —
Market value ($ mil.): —

BONGARDS'' CREAMERIES

LOCATIONS

HQ: BONGARDS' ' CREAMERIES
13200 COUNTY ROAD 51, NORWOOD, MN 553689743
Phone: 9524665521
Web: WWW.BONGARDS.COM

HISTORICAL FINANCIALS

Company Type: Private

Income Statement FYE: December 31

	REVENUE ($ mil.)	NET INCOME ($ mil.)	NET PROFIT MARGIN	EMPLOYEES
12/07	355	7	2.1%	350
12/06	252	(2)	—	—
12/05	249	(7)	—	—
12/04	252	0	—	—
Annual Growth	12.1%	—	—	—

2007 Year-End Financials

Debt ratio: —
Return on equity: 2.10%
Cash ($ mil.): 2
Current ratio: 0.30
Long-term debt ($ mil.): —
Dividends
Yield: —
Payout: —
Market value ($ mil.): —

BORGESS MEDICAL CENTER

Borgess Medical Center is part of the Borgess Health Alliance which is a member of the Ascension Health network. The general acute care facility which serves residents of southwestern Michigan houses more than 420 beds. It has a comprehensive offering of medical and surgical services including specialty care in areas such as cancer heart disease neuroscience and orthopedics. Borgess Medical Center also serves as a Level II trauma center and features a research institute a sleep disorders clinic a weight loss surgery center no-wait emergency room and outpatient facilities. The hospital was founded in 1889 by a local priest.

Operations

Borgess Medical Center sees more than 60000 visitors at its emergency and trauma facilities each year. Its specialist surgical facilities include operating rooms with comprehensive monitoring services for brain surgery spinal surgery and other complex procedures. The facility also serves as a regional behavioral health center. Its Stryker Center features extensive cardiovascular and neurological diagnosis and treatment resources as well as radiology pharmacy and same-day surgery units.

EXECUTIVES

Medical Director, Terry Baxter
CFO, Richard Felbinger
Director Of Physical Therapy, Joel Pennington
Medical Director, Michael Valitutto
Director Physician Recruitment, Jill Little
Pharmacy Manager, Irene Skylis
Medical Director, Rashmikant U Kothari
Vice President Of Sales, Gerald Robbins
Director Of Medical Records, Emmanuel Akosa
Medical Director, Mark Kanzawa
Medical Director Thoracic Surgery, Jerry Pratt
Vice President Operations, Linda Lawtonfache

LOCATIONS

HQ: BORGESS MEDICAL CENTER
1521 GULL RD, KALAMAZOO, MI 49048-1666
Phone: 269-226-7000
Web: WWW.BORGESS.COM

PRODUCTS/OPERATIONS

Selected Centers and Services

Behavioral Health
Birthing Center
Brain & Spine
Breast Care Centers
Cancer & Oncology
Cardiology Group
Critical Care
Dietary Services
Emergency & Trauma
Fibroid Center
Henry Ford
Inpatient Services
Laboratory Services
Osteoporosis Centers
Palliative Care
Radiology
Rehabilitation Services
Sleep Disorders
Vascular
Women' s Services

COMPETITORS

Bronson Health Care
Covenant HealthCare
Gerber Memorial
McLaren Health Care
Memorial Hospital & Health System
Sheridan Community Hospital
Sparrow Health System
Spectrum Health
Trinity Health (Novi)

HISTORICAL FINANCIALS

Company Type: Private

Income Statement FYE: June 30

	REVENUE ($ mil.)	NET INCOME ($ mil.)	NET PROFIT MARGIN	EMPLOYEES
06/11	474	7	1.5%	2,200
06/10	455	(6)	—	—
06/09	414	(5)	—	—
06/08	439	6	1.5%	—
Annual Growth	2.6%	3.3%	—	—

2011 Year-End Financials

Debt ratio: —
Return on equity: 1.50%
Cash ($ mil.): 32
Current ratio: 0.30
Long-term debt ($ mil.): —
Dividends
Yield: —
Payout: —
Market value ($ mil.): —

BOSTON MEDICAL CENTER CORPORATION

EXECUTIVES

CFO, Richard Silveria
Chief Endocrinology Diabetes and Nutrition, Shalender Bhasin
VP Professional Services, Peter Healy
President and CEO, Kate E. Walsh
Chief and Chair Medicine, David Coleman
SVP and Chief Medical Officer, Ravin Davidoff
Chief Infectious Diseases Division, Jerrold J. Ellner
Chief Orthopaedic Surgery, Thomas Einhorn
Senior Operations Manager Ambulatory Pediatrics, Ann Johnson
Director of Research, Rebecca Silliman
VP-Fin, Ronald Bartlett

LOCATIONS

HQ: BOSTON MEDICAL CENTER CORPORATION
1 BOSTON MEDICAL CTR PL # 1, BOSTON, MA 021182908
Phone: 6174145000
Web: WWW.BMC.ORG

COMPETITORS

Beth Israel Deaconess Medical Center
Brigham and Women' s Hospital
Cambridge Health Alliance
Care New England
CareGroup
Children' s Hospital Boston
Dana-Farber
Massachusetts General Hospital
Newton-Wellesley Hospital
Northeast Health System
Partners HealthCare
Shriners Hospitals For Children
Spaulding Rehabilitation Hospital
St. Elizabeth' s Medical Center
Steward Health Care

HISTORICAL FINANCIALS

Company Type: Private

Income Statement FYE: September 30

	REVENUE ($ mil.)	NET INCOME ($ mil.)	NET PROFIT MARGIN	EMPLOYEES
09/13	893	6	0.8%	4,200
09/12	886	2	0.3%	—
09/09	1,004	(12)	—	—
09/08	1,103	0	—	—
Annual Growth	(4.1%)	—	—	—

2013 Year-End Financials

Debt ratio: —
Return on equity: 0.80%
Cash ($ mil.): 139
Current ratio: 0.80
Long-term debt ($ mil.): —
Dividends
Yield: —
Payout: —
Market value ($ mil.): —

BOWEN ENGINEERING CORPORATION

Bowen Engineering understands the elements of earth wind and water. The company provides engineering and construction services for water wastewater earthwork concrete industrial power and underground utility projects. It operates through three divisions: Power and industrial; private water; and public works. The company which has offices in Indiana Tennessee and Ohio offers design/build general contracting and construction management services to public and private clients. Bowen Engineering was founded in 1967 by Robert Bowen. The Bowen family continues to lead the company.

Bowen is expanding. In 2009 the company moved its headquarters to Indianapolis –a move that positioned Bowen for growth.

The company has worked an many projects including the Indiana University central power plant and the Tennessee Valley Authority Kingston Fossil plant. Most recently Bowen has recently been awarded contracts to work on wind power projects in Indiana.

EXECUTIVES

Chairman, Robert L. Bowen
SVP Human Resources, Linda G. Hunter
SVP Work Procurement and Business Development, Todd A. Lemen
SVP Southern Division and Division Manager, Jeff Purdue
Business Development Leader Research and Development, Kris L. Bowen
Sr. Vice President Chief Financial Officer, Scot Evans
Operations Manager Central Public Works, Alan R. Holding
Contract Manager, Brian J. Stater

LOCATIONS

HQ: BOWEN ENGINEERING CORPORATION
8802 N MERIDIAN ST, INDIANAPOLIS, IN 46260-5380
Phone: 317-842-2616
Web: WWW.BOWENENGINEERING.COM

PRODUCTS/OPERATIONS

Selected Services

Mechanical
- Process mechanical equipment
- Process piping
- Process boilermaker ductwork
- Process instrumentation

Site-Civil
- Excavation
- Concrete

Structural
- Structural steel
- Engineered structures

COMPETITORS

Black & Veatch
CH2M HILL
F.A. Wilhelm
Garney Holding
Hagerman Construction
Hunt Construction

HISTORICAL FINANCIALS

Company Type: Private

Income Statement

FYE: September 30

	REVENUE ($ mil.)	NET INCOME ($ mil.)	NET PROFIT MARGIN	EMPLOYEES
09/09	365	16	4.4%	700
09/08	288	17	6.0%	—
09/07	60	0	—	—
Annual Growth	—42515.9%	—	—	—

2009 Year-End Financials

Debt ratio: —
Return on equity: 4.40%
Cash ($ mil.): 19
Current ratio: 0.30
Long-term debt ($ mil.): —
Dividends
Yield: —
Payout: —
Market value ($ mil.): —

BOY SCOUTS OF AMERICA

Scouts enter dens as Tigers and eventually take flight as Eagles. Boy Scouts of America (BSA) one of the nation's largest youth organizations has about 2.6 million youth members and more than 1 million adult leaders in its ranks. BSA offers educational and character-building programs emphasizing leadership citizenship personal development and physical fitness. In addition to traditional scouting programs (Tiger Cub Webelos and Boy Scouts ranging up to Eagle rank) it offers the Venturing program for boys and girls ages 14-21. BSA generates revenue through membership and council fees food and magazine sales and contributions. The organization was founded by Chicago publisher William Boyce in 1910.

Operations

BSA's group membership is supported through about 300 local Boy Scout councils. Additionally it hosts a National Scout Jamboree each year to bring all scouts together. The organization also operates a high-adventure base in West Virginia. The bases offer scouts a range of outdoor activities including backpacking camping canoeing and diving. The West Virginia location serves as the organization's permanent location for its annual Jamboree. BSA operates also bases in Florida Minnesota and New Mexico.

BSA also publishes Boys' Life monthly magazine which boasts more than 1 million subscribers and Scouting magazine for adults registered in Cub Scouting Boy Scouting Varsity Scouting and Venturing.

Financial Analysis

BSA's revenue increased 24% in 2013 to $283 over 2012's $229 million. The uptick was due to a bump in fees (44% of total revenue) primarily from the 2013 National Scout Jamboree as well as from contributions and bequests.

Strategy

BSA boasts programs that remain popular but in recent years membership growth has slowed with the recession and other societal forces including video games social media and other entertainment.

In 2013 Cub Scout membership (which accounts for more than 50% of total youth membership) dipped by about 7% while the ranks of the Boy Scouts decreased by 3%. Overall total youth membership declined by about 6% for the year continuing its downward trend. To boost membership and grow its organization BSA developed a strategic plan that involves reaching out to new groups of parents and students. To this end it has developed and maintained relationships with civic religious and fraternal organizations across the US including those that serve African-American Asian and Latino families. It has also analyzed Generation X and Millennial parents to determine how to best bring scouting to their families.

EXECUTIVES

V Pres, Terrence Dunn
Council Vice President Operations, Christopher M McKinney
Chief Scout Executive, Wayne Brock
Deputy Chief Scout Executive and COO, Gary P. Butler
National President, Robert M. Gates
CFO, Michael Ashline
Vice President Sales, Ed Caldwell
Vice President Human Resources, Jay Grossman
Executive Vice President For Operations, William Guglielmi
Vp Religious Emblems Great Salt Lake, Tim Strickland
Vice President Of Marketing, Bob Baumann
Vp Properties, Michael Semeraro
Vice President Of Development With, Mike Liddle
Vp Or Senior Vp, Ray Melcher
Vice President Marketing, Kurt Johnson
Hr Director & Vp, Jerry Jennings
Board Of Directors And Past Vp, Jim Whitlock
Vice President Of Finance, Pat Russell
Vice President, David Kulman
Council Vice President Of Program, John Coffee
Vice President, Terry Miller
Vp Or Senior Vp, Sandy Rogers
Membership Vice President, Tom Updegraff
Vice President For District Operations, Tom Russell
Vice President For Marketing, Mark Shadle
Vp Property Committee, John Pope
Executive Board And Vice President Boy, Thomas Yantis
Vice President And National Religious, Linda Hodges
Vp Operations Executive Board Suwannee, Richard Doran
Sales Vice President, Craig Ploeg
V Pres, Tony Jones
Varsity Scout Vice President, Bry Davis
Vice President Of Membership For, Jenny Cody
Vice President, Bill McGlothlin
Vice President Programs, Bobbi Jean
Vp Or Senior Vp, Paul Spellman
Vice President, Henry Rosenberg
Vice President Of Information Systems, Richard Havens
Vice President Fin For Cst Carolina, Larry Tarleton
Council Vp Program, Matt Flanagan
Vice President Of Program For, Doug King
Vice President Marketing Communication, Jeffrey Halik
Vp Support Services, Pete Marsh
District Advancement Committee Vp, Dave Nuttall
Vice President, Milton Ward
Area Vice President, G Lewis
Council Vice President, Bob Levin
Vp Program Vhc, Louis Schwing
Southern Region Venturing Vp, Emily Copeland
Vice President, Donald Belcher
Vice President Of Operations, Andrew Ratermann
Vice President For Program, Christine Crowell
Vice President, Jeanette Prenger
Vice President Of Properties W D Boyce, Wade Berry
Vice President, Richard Burdick
Vice President Vp, Kim Yeatman
Hr Director & Vp, Dan Cooke
Vice President Operations, Chad Lewis
Vice President Operations, Edward Stevens
Executive Vice President, William Cronk
Vice President Sales, Bill Mischke
Vice President Of Outdoor Adventures, Lonnie Herrington
Vice President Of Innovation Western, Chris John
Health Director, Susan Shurtz
Vice President Membership, Ken May
Vice President Chartering Organization, Carol Gersema
Executive Vp, Bill Albrecht
Treasurer, Randall Kopsa
Treasurer, Kathy Kolcaba
Director Board Of Directors, George Sparks
Board Member, Dale Gilliam
Executive Board Member, Melba Carlton
Board Member, Jackie David
Vice Chair Of Membership For Headwaters, Adrienne Boehm
Treasurer, Linda Spangler
Secretary, Leah Overson

Executive Committee Treasurer, Ray Chipman
Secretary, Roseann Conti Yezzi
Board Of Directors, Carl Enslen
Board Member, James Dean
Board Member, Kelley Maier
Treasurer, Sarah Weaver
Board Member, Geoffrey Parker
Board Member, Ronald Justus
Board Member, Billy Graham
Board Member, J Dotson
Board Member, Don Kellogg
Board Member, Russ Ketron
Board Member, John Ghiradelli
Board Member, Michael George
Secretary, Lisa Reverman
Treasurer, Joni Quick
Executive Board Member, Toby Capps
Board Of Directors, Kent McElhattan
Board Of Directors, Brian Hom
Board Of Directors, Joel Schmidt
Board Member, Judith McMahon
Board Member, Matt Elam
Exec Sect, Cathy Rohloff
Board Of Directors, Max Clark
Executive Board Member, Rex Brandstatter
Executive Board Member, Victor Coppola
Board Member, Dawn Dinsdale
Troop Treasurer, Dawnise Keller
Member Board Of Directors, Roger Blake
Secretary, Cynthia Workman
Executive Board Member, Wayne Briesemeister
Board Of Directors, John Clarey
Member Board Of Directors, Mark Rosenauer
Assistant Treasurer, R Buffenbarger
Troop Treasurer And Committee, Lisa McReady
Treasurer Committee Person, Ginger Creech
Board Of Directors, Margaret Turner
Secretary, Terri Comber
Board Member, Jim McIntosh
Auditors: PricewaterhouseCoopersLLP

LOCATIONS

HQ: BOY SCOUTS OF AMERICA
1325 W WALNUT HILL LN, IRVING, TX 750383096
Phone: 9725802000
Web: WWW.SCOUTING.ORG

PRODUCTS/OPERATIONS

2011 Youth Membership

	No.
Cub	1,583,166
Boy	848,291
Venturers	231,127
Explorers	112,783
Varsity	61,285
Total	**2,836,652**

2011 Revenue

	$ mil.	% of total
Fees	96	48
Supply operations	24	12
Magazines	1	1
Contributions & bequests	61	30
Net investment gain	8	4
Other (includes trading post sales)	9	5
Total	**201**	**100**

HISTORICAL FINANCIALS

Company Type: Private

Income Statement FYE: December 31

	REVENUE ($ mil.)	NET INCOME ($ mil.)	NET PROFIT MARGIN	EMPLOYEES
12/10	310	90	29.0%	2,800
12/09	287	145	50.5%	—
Annual Growth	8.0%	(37.9%)	—	—

2010 Year-End Financials

Debt ratio: —
Return on equity: 29.00%
Cash ($ mil.): 42
Current ratio: —
Long-term debt ($ mil.): —
Dividends
Yield: —
Payout: —
Market value ($ mil.): —

BRADLEY UNIVERSITY

Bradley University is a private university offering a wide breadth of higher education opportunities. The school provides 100 undergraduate programs in fields ranging from art science and education to business media and health. Bradley also confers graduate degrees in more than 30 academic fields including a Doctorate of Physical Therapy. With a student-to-teacher ratio of 12:1 the university has an enrollment of approximately 6000 students –more than 5000 of whom are undergraduates - that receive instruction from some 350 full-time faculty members.

Operations

Bradley offers courses through five colleges: Foster College of Business Administration Slane College of Communications and Fine Arts College of Education and Health Sciences Caterpillar College of Engineering and Technology and College of Liberal Arts and Sciences. The university has a 90% success rate for students who start careers or pursue additional degrees within six months of graduation.

Financial Performance

Bradley University increased revenues by 7% to $152 million in fiscal 2011 from increased tuition and fees as well as higher levels of government grants and appropriations. Tuition runs at about $28000 per year. Net income also increased 17% to $36 million in 2011 due to higher investment income.

Bradley has an endowment of some $237 million (as of mid-2012).

Company Background

The university was founded in 1897 as Bradley Polytechnic Institute by Lydia Moss Bradley as a memorial to her children and husband.

EXECUTIVES

Chairman Board of Trustees, Gerald L. (Gerry) Shaheen, age 69
President, Joanne K. Glasser
Controller, Pratima N. Gandhi
VP Business Affairs, Gary M. Anna
Secretary Board of Trustees, Kay W. McCurdy, age 63
Dean College of Liberal Arts and Sciences, Claire Etaugh
Manager Bookstore, Paul Kroenke
Dean Foster College of Business Administration, Robert (Rob) Baer
Associate Dean Foster College of Business Administration and Economics, Edward L. Sattler
Executive Director Smith Career Center, Jane C. Linnenburger
Director Career Development, Rick R. Smith
Executive Director Cullom-Davis Library, Barbara A. Galik
Director Human Resources, Nena M. Peplow
Senior Director Public Relations, M. Kathleen (Kath) Conver
Director Pre-Law Center, Maria L. Vertuno
Interim Provost and VP Academic Affairs, Robert (Bob) Bolla
VP Student Affairs, Alan G. Galsky
VP Advancement, Pat Vickerman
Assistant VP Communications, Shelley Epstein
Interim Athletic Director, Virnette House-Browning
Director Admissions, Rodney San Jose
Director Residential Living, Ryan Bair
Chief University Police, David A. Baer
Director Facilities Management, Ronald Doerzaph
Director Food Services, Ron Gibson
Registrar, Katherine M. Beaty
Director Employer Relations, Kelly Harris
Purchasing Accounts Administrator, Diane Smith
Vice Chairman Board of Trustees, Michael A. McCord
Assistant Athletic Director/Communications, Bobby Parker
Benefit Administrator, Dayna Fico
Director Conference Facilities, Charmin Hibberd
Director Student Center Operations, Pegi Meyer
Executive Director Alumni Relations, Lori W. Fan
Associate Provost Information Resources and Technology, Chuck Ruch
Executive Director Computing Services, Sandra H. Bury
Executive Director Instructional Technology and Media Services, Nial L. Johnson
Trustee, Robert J. (Bob) Clanin, age 70
Trustee, Rajesh K. (Raj) Soin, age 67
Trustee, Judson C. Mitchell
President and Trustee, Joanne K. Glasser
Trustee, David P. (Dave) Ransburg
Secretary Board of Trustees, Kay W. McCurdy, age 63
Trustee, Rex K. Linder
Trustee, Robert E. Turner
Vice Chairman Board of Trustees, Michael A. McCord
Trustee, Keith L. Alm
Trustee, Wayne E. Baum
Trustee, Carl M. Birkelbach
Trustee, Cheryl D. Corley
Trustee, Michael N. Cullinan
Trustee, Georgina E. Heard-Labonne
Trustee, William P. Heidrich
Trustee, Joan L. Janssen
Trustee, Wayne G. Klasing
Trustee, Michael A. Landwirth
Trustee, Harry L. Puterbaugh
Trustee, Michele J. Richey
Trustee, Mel J. Smith
Trustee, Thomas E. Spurgeon
Trustee, Douglas S. Stewart
Trustee, Donald L. Ullman
Trustee, W. Philip Wilmington
Auditors: PricewaterhouseCoopersLLP

LOCATIONS

HQ: BRADLEY UNIVERSITY
1501 W BRADLEY AVE, PEORIA, IL 61625-0003
Phone: 309-677-3150
Web: WWW.BRADLEY.EDU

PRODUCTS/OPERATIONS

Selected Colleges

Caterpillar College of Engineering and Technology
College of Education and Health Sciences
College of Liberal Arts and Sciences
Foster College of Business Administration
Slane College of Communications and Fine Arts

HISTORICAL FINANCIALS

Company Type: Private

Income Statement FYE: May 31

	REVENUE ($ mil.)	NET INCOME ($ mil.)	NET PROFIT MARGIN	EMPLOYEES
05/12	155	(18)	—	1,000
05/11	151	36	23.8%	—
05/10	141	30	21.8%	—
05/09	139	(63)	—	—
Annual Growth	3.6%	—	—	—

2012 Year-End Financials

Debt ratio: —
Return on equity: (-11.90%)
Cash ($ mil.): 1
Current ratio: —
Long-term debt ($ mil.): —
Dividends
Yield: —
Payout: —
Market value ($ mil.): —

BRANDEIS UNIVERSITY

Brandeis University offers more than 40 undergraduate majors and more than 30 master's and doctoral degree programs. Located just west of Boston it comprises the College of Arts and Sciences the Graduate School of Arts and Sciences the International Business School the Heller School for Social Policy and Management the Lown School for Near Eastern and Judaic Studies and the Rabb School of Continuing Studies. The university has an enrollment of more than 5000 students; the student/faculty ratio is 9-to-1. A nonsectarian Jewish community-sponsored institution Brandeis University was founded in 1948 and is named after the late Justice Louis Brandeis of the US Supreme Court.

EXECUTIVES

Chair, Malcolm L. Sherman
Dean Heller School for Social Policy and Management, Lisa M. Lynch
SVP and COO, Steven S. Manos
President and Trustee, Frederick M. Lawrence
Provost and Chief Academic Officer, Steve A. N. Goldstein
CIO and Vice Provost for Library and Technology Services, John Unsworth
Dean International Business School, Bruce Magrid
SVP Finance and CFO, Marianne Cwalina
SVP and Chief of Staff, David A. Bunis
Dean College of Arts and Sciences, Susan J. Birren
Chief Technology Officer at Brandeis University, Anna Tomecka
Trustee, Barton J. (Bart) Winokur, age 74
Trustee, Thomas P. Glynn, age 67
Trustee, Stephen B. Kay
Trustee, Perry M. Traquina
Trustee, Ronald A. Ratner
Trustee, Henry J. Aboodi
Trustee, Jonathan G. Davis
Trustee, Daniel J. Elkaim
Trustee, Daniel J. Jick
Trustee, Jeanette Lerman
Trustee, Barbara A. Mandel
Trustee, Louis Perlmutter
Trustee, Stephen R. Reiner
Trustee, Carol R. Saivatz
Trustee, Rhonda S. Zinner
Trustee, Paul M. Zlotoff
Trustee, Meyer G. Koplow
President and Trustee, Frederick M. Lawrence
Director, Jonathon S. Jacobson, age 52
Trustee, Stuart Lewtan
Trustee, Allen B. Alter

LOCATIONS

HQ: BRANDEIS UNIVERSITY
415 SOUTH ST MS110, WALTHAM, MA 02453-2700
Phone: 781-736-8317
Web: WWW.CYC.BRANDEIS.EDU

HISTORICAL FINANCIALS

Company Type: Private

Income Statement FYE: June 30

	REVENUE ($ mil.)	NET INCOME ($ mil.)	NET PROFIT MARGIN	EMPLOYEES
06/11	348	(19)	—	1,200
06/10	323	(24)	—	—
06/09	248	(173)	—	—
06/08	410	86	21.0%	—
Annual Growth	(5.4%)	—	—	—

2011 Year-End Financials

Debt ratio: —
Return on equity: (-5.70%)
Cash ($ mil.): 37
Current ratio: —
Long-term debt ($ mil.): —
Dividends
Yield: —
Payout: —
Market value ($ mil.): —

BRAZOS ELECTRIC POWER COOPERATIVE INC.

Brazos means "arms" in Spanish and the generation and transmission arms of Brazos Electric Power Cooperative reach across 68 Texas counties. It serves 16 member/owner distribution cooperatives and ‚Äone ‚Âmunicipality in Northern and Central Texas. Brazos Electric Power annually generates (through ‚Â its four power stations) ‚Âand/or accesses from other power marketers some 3655 MW of electric power. The cooperative's members include Comanche Electric Cooperative Association Heart of Texas Electric Co-op (McGregor) Mid-South Synergy (Navasota) United Coop Services (Cleburne) and Wise Electric (Decatur).

Brazos Electric Power is the largest generation and transmission cooperative in Texas. Its service region stretches from the Greater Houston area to Lubbock in the Texas Panhandle.

The cooperative is managed by a board of directors on which each of its member cooperatives has a representative. The board's ongoing strategy is to ‚Âfind ways ‚Âto generate buy and transmit power ‚Âat low costs and with high reliability.

Benefitting from federal government support in 2010 the co-op ‚Âwas selected by ‚ÂUSDA Rural Development's Rural Utilities Service to ‚Âget a $438.9 million loan guarantee to allow it to build 237 miles of new transmission lines and improve 52 miles of existing transmission lines.

Founded in 1941 Brazos Electric Power was the state's first electricity generation and transmission cooperative.

EXECUTIVES

V Pres, Hugh Lenox
V Pres, Johnny York
Executive Vice President & General, Richard M Caskill
Managing Director, Bill Parker
Vice President Of Acctng Auditing, J Copland
Vp Generation, David Murphy
Executive Vice Presi, Clifton Kamei
Treasurer, James Driver
Board Member, Monty Carlisle
Board Member, Jorden Wood
Auditors: PricewaterhouseCoopersLLP

LOCATIONS

HQ: BRAZOS ELECTRIC POWER COOPERATIVE INC.
2404 LA SALLE AVE, WACO, TX 767063928
Phone: 2547506500
Web: WWW.BRAZOSELECTRIC.COM

PRODUCTS/OPERATIONS

Member/Owners
Barlett Electric Cooperativ
BEPC
Comanche Electric Cooperativ
Cooke County Electric Cooperativ
CoServ Electric
Fort Belknap Electric Cooperativ
Hamilton County Electric Cooperativ
Heart of Texas Electric Cooperativ
HILCO Electric Cooperativ
J-A-C Electric Cooperativ
Mid-South Synergy
Navarro County Electric Cooperativ
Navasota Valley Electric Cooperativ
South Plains Electric Cooperativ
Tri-County Electric Cooperativ
United Cooperative Services
Wise Electric Cooperativ

COMPETITORS

AEP
CenterPoint Energy
El Paso Electric
Energy Future
Entergy
LCRA

HISTORICAL FINANCIALS

Company Type: Private

Income Statement FYE: December 31

	REVENUE ($ mil.)	NET INCOME ($ mil.)	NET PROFIT MARGIN	EMPLOYEES
12/09	963	56	5.9%	366
12/99	307	6	2.3%	—
12/98	286	0	0.3%	—
12/97	278	0	—	—
Annual Growth	10.9%	—	—	—

2009 Year-End Financials

Debt ratio: —
Return on equity: 5.90%
Cash ($ mil.): 1
Current ratio: 0.10
Long-term debt ($ mil.): —
Dividends
Yield: —
Payout: —
Market value ($ mil.): —

BRIDGEPORT HOSPITAL & HEALTHCARE SERVICES INC

Serving as a bridge to wellness and a port in the stormy waters of health care is the 425-bed Bridgeport Hospital. Part of the Yale New Haven Health System the facility offers acute care and specialized services to residents of Bridgeport Connecticut and surrounding counties. The hospital operates a cancer center a burn treatment center a heart center and a rehabilitation therapy center. Its medical staff includes nearly 600 physicians representing more than 60 specialties. Founded in 1878 as Fairfield County's first hospital Bridgeport Hospital has grown into a nearly $350 million regional health care organization.

Geographic Reach

Bridgeport Hospital is located in Bridgeport Connecticut. The facility gets about 260000 patient care visits each year including 20000 inpatient visits and nearly 240000 total outpatient visits to the hospital. It is the site of the only specialized burn care facility between New York and Boston.

Operations

Bridgeport Hospital is a teaching affiliate of Yale School of Medicine. Along with the main hospital Bridgeport is affiliated with several urgent care clinics throughout the region that offer routine and walk-in care.

Financial Analysis

More than 60% of Bridgeport Hospital's outpatient visits at any given time are from uninsured or underinsured patients.

Like most other health care providers the collapse of the economy and resulting loss of jobs caused Bridgeport Hospital to experience a surge in uninsured patients or patients with inadequate insurance coverage. As uninsured patient visits climbed so did the company's amount of bad debt expense related to patients who can't afford to pay their bills especially in the emergency room.

The hospital's annual operating expenses were about $337 million in 2011.

Strategy

Bridgeport Hospital has tried to alleviate some of the burden from uninsured or underinsured patients by diverting patients without emergent problems to more appropriate care settings such as one of its many satellite clinics.

The hospital is also awaiting the outcome of the nation's health care reform efforts to see how new laws would affect its bad debt load. Part of the health care reform package would require most of the country be covered by health insurance a requirement that would greatly reduce costs related to treating uninsured patients. Of course yet to been seen is how that requirement will affect hospitals' managed care contracts.

EXECUTIVES

SVP Medical Affairs and Chief Section of Nephrology, Bruce M. McDonald
Director Marketing, Audrey Wise
EVP and COO, Hope Juckel-Regan
SVP, Joseph E. Janell
Coordinator Media Relations, John Cappiello
SVP Patient Care Operations, MaryEllen Kosturko
VP, Michael Ivy
President CEO, William M. (Bill) Jennings, age 47
Senior Partner and President Oncology Associates, Robert Folman

LOCATIONS

HQ: BRIDGEPORT HOSPITAL & HEALTHCARE SERVICES INC
267 GRANT ST, BRIDGEPORT, CT 06610-2805
Phone: 203-384-3000
Web: WWW.BRIDGEPORTHOSPITAL.ORG

Selected satellite facilities

Fairfield Urgent Care Center (Fairfield Connecticut)
Fairfield Family Medical Care (Fairfield Connecticut)
Immediate Medical Care of Monroe (Monroe Connecticut)
First Aid Immediate Care Medical Center of Trumbull (Trumbull Connecticut)
Med-Now (Stratford Connecticut)
The Huntington Walk-In Medical Center (Shelton Connecticut)

COMPETITORS

Connecticut Children' s Medical Center
Essent Healthcare
Griffin Health
Griffin Hospital
Hospital of Central Connecticut
Mather Memorial Hospital
St. Vincent' s Health Services
Stamford Health
Waterbury Hospital
Western Connecticut Health Network
Yale-New Haven Hospital Saint Raphael Campus

HISTORICAL FINANCIALS

Company Type: Private

Income Statement

FYE: September 30

	REVENUE ($ mil.)	NET INCOME ($ mil.)	NET PROFIT MARGIN	EMPLOYEES
09/10	380	13	3.7%	150
09/09	0	0	72.1%	—
Annual Growth	151445.7%	7585.1%	—	—

2010 Year-End Financials

Debt ratio: —
Return on equity: 3.70%
Cash ($ mil.): 45
Current ratio: 1.40
Long-term debt ($ mil.): —
Dividends
Yield: —
Payout: —
Market value ($ mil.): —

BROCKTON HOSPITAL INC.

Signature Healthcare Brockton Hospital is a not-for-profit acute medical facility that serves southeastern Massachusetts. The hospital has 245 beds including about 30 beds in its skilled nursing unit. Its emergency department sees more than 62000 patients per year. Specialized services include radiation oncology cardiac care pediatrics orthopedics and joint replacement and inpatient and outpatient psychiatry. It is a community-based teaching hospital and part of the Signature Healthcare network. Brockton Hospital also formed a clinical affiliation with Beth Israel Deaconess Medical Center in 2013.

Geographic Reach

Signature Healthcare Brockton serves about 460000 people residing in more than 20 communities in southeastern Massachusetts.

Operations

Through the affiliation with Beth Israel Deaconess Brockton Hospital has access to Harvard-affiliated specialists as well as resources that will help to improve its residency and teaching programs. Brockton Hospital has also provided certain services in affiliation with Tufts Medical Center such as pediatric care.

The Signature Healthcare organization also includes affiliated primary care physician practices specialty outpatient clinics and a nursing school. Its Signature Medical Group operates practices in fields including primary diagnostic and urgent care as well as women's health.

Strategy

Signature Healthcare forms collaborative agreements with other providers to enhance medical services in the region. It also works to enhance its offerings by developing new services and programs in high-demand fields such as diabetes care and obesity treatment as well as diagnostic and orthopedic capabilities. In addition Signature Healthcare is working to reduce medical errors enhance employee productivity and increase consumer health awareness through the implementation of electronic health record (EHR) systems.

Company Background

Signature Healthcare Brockton Hospital was founded in 1896 as Brockton Hospital. It changed its name from Brockton Health to Signature Healthcare in 2008.

EXECUTIVES

President, Norman B. Goodman
Chief of Medicine and Cardiology, Burton J. Polansky
Vice President of HR, Jeff Miller
Auditors: Ernst&YoungLLP

LOCATIONS

HQ: BROCKTON HOSPITAL INC.
680 CENTRE ST, BROCKTON, MA 02302-3395
Phone: 508-941-7000
Web: WWW.SIGNATURE-HEALTHCARE.ORG

PRODUCTS/OPERATIONS

Selected Services

Acupuncture
Anesthesiology
Behavioral health
Cancer care
Cardiac care
Cardiac rehab
Concussion/Traumatic brain injury program
Critical care
CT scan
Diabetes information
Endoscopy
Emergency care
Eye services
Family practice
Gastroenterology
Hospitalists
Imaging
Infection control
Internal medicine
Laboratory
Maternal-Newborn Pavilion
MRI
Neurology
Nuclear medicine
Nurse midwifery services
Nutrition
Obstetrics/gynecology
Occupational therapy
Orthopedics
Otoplasty
Outpatient care
Pain management
Pediatrics
Perinatology
Physical therapy
Plastic surgery
Primary care
Radiology and medical imaging
Radiation therapy center/Vantage oncology
Respiratory therapy
Speech therapy
Stress test
Stroke center
Surgery
Transitional care
Ultrasound
Urgent care
Vascular lab
Weight and wellness center
Wound care

COMPETITORS

Boston Medical Center
CareGroup
Lahey Health System
McLean Hospital
Northeast Health System
Partners HealthCare
Steward Health Care

HISTORICAL FINANCIALS

Company Type: Private

Income Statement

FYE: September 30

	REVENUE ($ mil.)	NET INCOME ($ mil.)	NET PROFIT MARGIN	EMPLOYEES
09/12	222	19	8.9%	1,500
09/09	200	2	1.1%	—
09/06	168	8	4.8%	—
09/05	150	0	—	—
Annual Growth	5.8%	—	—	—

2012 Year-End Financials

Debt ratio: —
Return on equity: 8.90%
Cash ($ mil.): 5
Current ratio: 0.60
Long-term debt ($ mil.): —
Dividends
Yield: —
Payout: —
Market value ($ mil.): —

BRONSON METHODIST HOSPITAL INC

From your leg bone to your knee bone; your neck bone to your head bone Bronson Methodist Hospital has the specialists to cure what ails you. The 435-bed hospital is the flagship facility of the Bronson Healthcare Group a not-for-profit health care system. Bronson Methodist provides care in just about every specialty including orthopedics surgery and oncology. The hospital also contains specialist units for critical care (level I trauma center) neurology (primary stroke center) cardiology (Chest pain emergency center) women's health (BirthPlace) and pediatrics (children's hospital).

Geographic Reach

Bronson Methodist serves patients throughout southwestern Michigan from its main facility in Kalamazoo.

Operations

In addition to providing general emergency and specialty inpatient care to privately insured or self-paying customers the hospital serves a large percentage of Medicaid patients and provides charity care to uninsured patients. Altogether Bronson Methodist's charity and community outreach program contributions total more than $55 million annually.

The hospital contains the Bronson Children's Hospital which offers burn and wound neonatal development and newborn pulmonary services among others.

Strategy

All of the hospital's inpatient rooms are private; this transition was made to reduce infection rates and increase privacy for Bronson Methodist patients.

Bronson Methodist began participation in the bundled payment program of the Centers for Medicare and Medicaid Services in 2013. The program is designed to improve the quality of care delivery for Medicare patients by changing the way that providers are reimbursed for services.

EXECUTIVES

President and CEO, Frank Sardone
SVP Legal and Legislative Affairs and Corporate Compliance Officer, James B. (Chip) Falahee Jr.
SVP Clinical Operations, Katie Harrelson
SVP Medical Affairs and Chief Medical Officer, Scott D. Larson
VP and CFO, Mary Meitz
VP and Chief Human Resource Officer, John T. Hayden
Vice President System Quality Standards & Accreditation Chief Quality Officer for Bronson Battle Creek Hospital, Cheryl L. Knapp
Vice President Chief Medical Informatics Officer & Community, William J. Mayer
VP Bronson LakeView Operations, Sally Berglin
VP Public Affairs and Development, Robert Doud
VP Information Technology and CIO, Donna M. Roach
VP and Chief Nursing Officer, Denise J. Neely
Senior Vice President of Strategy and Communication, Sue Reinoehl

LOCATIONS

HQ: BRONSON METHODIST HOSPITAL INC
601 JOHN ST STE E-012, KALAMAZOO, MI 49007-5346
Phone: 269-341-7654
Web: WWW.BRONSONHEALTH.COM

PRODUCTS/OPERATIONS

Selected Services

Anticoagulation
Bereavement
Breast Health
Burn
Cancer Care
Critical Care
Diabetes
Flu
Heart and Vascular
Home Health
Hyperbaric Oxygen Therapy
Infusion
Laboratory
Medical and Surgical Weight Management
Neurosciences
Nutrition
Occupational Health
Orthopedics
Palliative Care
Pediatrics
Pharmacy
Pregnancy and Childbirth
Rehabilitation
Respiratory Care
Sleep
Surgery
Stomal Therapy
Testing and Imaging
Trauma and Emergency
Women' s Health
Wound

COMPETITORS

Ascension Health
Borgess Health
Bronson Battle Creek Community Hospital
Elkhart General Healthcare System
Hayes Green Beach Memorial Hospital
Holland Community Hospital
Spectrum Health
Trinity Health (Novi)
Zeeland Community Hospital

HISTORICAL FINANCIALS

Company Type: Private

Income Statement FYE: December 31

	REVENUE ($ mil.)	NET INCOME ($ mil.)	NET PROFIT MARGIN	EMPLOYEES
12/12	422	39	9.4%	2,861
12/09	524	41	7.9%	—
12/07	491	(1)	—	—
12/07	487	29	6.1%	—
Annual Growth	(2.8%)	5.9%	—	—

2012 Year-End Financials

Debt ratio: —
Return on equity: 9.40%
Cash ($ mil.): 0
Current ratio: 2.20
Long-term debt ($ mil.): —
Dividends
Yield: —
Payout: —
Market value ($ mil.): —

BRONX LEBANON HOSPITAL CENTER (INC)

Bronx-Lebanon Hospital Center cares for patients in the central and south Bronx no doubt while rooting for the Yankees a few blocks away. The health care provider maintains more than 970 beds across its two campuses as well as psychiatric and nursing home facilities. Hospital specialty units include chest pain orthopedic cancer and women's health centers. Bronx-Lebanon also manages a network of about 70 owned and affiliated medical practices (under the BronxCare brand). This network includes primary care doctors and specialty clinics as well as rehabilitation facilities. The hospital is also a primary teaching hospital for the Albert Einstein College of Medicine.

Geographic Reach

The hospital system serves residents of central and south Bronx in New York.

Operations

Aside from its two major hospitals Bronx-Lebanon Hospital operates a psychiatric facility a pair of specialized long-term care facilities and the BronxCare network of medical practices that include Dr. Martin Luther King Jr. Health Center and a 51-unit facility to house seniors and low-income residents. Bronx-Lebanon cares for those with mental or substance abuse problems through the Family Wellness Center. It also operates a 240-bed Special Care Center and the 90-bed Highbridge Woodycrest Center to provide long term health care to geriatric AIDS and disabled residents.

Strategy

Bronx-Lebanon emphasizes its role as a community health care provider not only through its BronxCare network but through a number of community outreach and service efforts including school-based programs mobile health units free health screening and even a weekly live television show that discusses health issues.

To accommodate the growing population in and around the Bronx the hospital system has expanded in recent years with a new children's wing for inpatient and outpatient services; a nine-story ambulatory care facility; and an extensive emergency room modernization. Bronx-Lebanon also maintains a short stay observation unit in the emergency room area to monitor and evaluate patients in cardiac distress prior to admission or discharge.

Bronx-Lebanon is one of many hospital organizations to have joined a regional health information organization (RHIO) to allow medical professionals to access a patient's medical records at any number of health care locations. Other members of the Bronx RHIO include Montefiore Medical Center Jacobi Medical Center St. Barnabas Hospital and Hebrew Home at Riverdale.

Bronx-Lebanon is also one of the few hospitals in New York that is fully computerized with a complete inpatient and outpatient electronic medical record.

The hospital center's expansion plans include a $42 million 60000 sq. ft ambulatory care facility and a $34 million 56000 sq. ft. life recovery center for chemical dependency services (both scheduled to be completed in 2014).

EXECUTIVES

President and CEO, Miguel A. Fuentes Jr.
VP Finance, Victor DeMarco
VP Patient Care Services and Chief Nursing Officer, Janine M Frumenti
CIO, Ivan Durbak

LOCATIONS

HQ: BRONX LEBANON HOSPITAL CENTER (INC)
1276 FULTON AVE, BRONX, NY 10456-3499
Phone: 718-590-1800
Web: WWW.BRONXLEBANONHOSPITAL.ORG

PRODUCTS/OPERATIONS

Selected Services

Anesthesiology
Asthma
- Adult
- Pediatric

Cardiology
Dentistry
Diabetes
- Adult
- Pediatric

Ear Nose & Throat
Gastroenterology
Hematology & Oncology
Neonatology
Neurology
Ophthalmology
Orthopaedics
Pediatrics
Physical Medicine
Psychiatry
Radiology
Special Care Center
Urology & Men's Health

Selected Academic Affiliations

Albert Einstein College of Medicine
Bronx Community College
Hostos Community College
Lehman College City University of New York
State University of New York at Stony Brook

COMPETITORS

Beth Israel Medical Center
Catholic Healthcare System
Continuum Health Partners
Lenox Hill Hospital
Maimonides Medical Center
Memorial Sloan-Kettering
Montefiore Medical
New York City Health and Hospitals
NewYork-Presbyterian Healthcare
North Shore-Long Island Jewish Health System
St. Luke' s-Roosevelt Hospital
Winthrop-University Hospital

HISTORICAL FINANCIALS

Company Type: Private

Income Statement FYE: December 31

	REVENUE ($ mil.)	NET INCOME ($ mil.)	NET PROFIT MARGIN	EMPLOYEES
12/09	709	22	3.1%	4,000
12/08	489	(45)	—	—
12/07	634	21	3.4%	—
12/06	513	11	2.2%	—
Annual Growth	11.4%	24.6%	—	—

2009 Year-End Financials

Debt ratio: —
Return on equity: 3.10%
Cash ($ mil.): 67
Current ratio: 0.60
Long-term debt ($ mil.): —
Dividends
Yield: —
Payout: —
Market value ($ mil.): —

BROOKHAVEN MEMORIAL HOSPITAL MEDICAL CENTER INC

Brookhaven Memorial Hospital Medical Center is an acute-care facility with more than 300 beds that serves patients primarily in Suffolk County on Long Island New York. The not-for-profit community hospital's Emergency Trauma and Chest Pain Pavilion is one of the largest emergency rooms on Long Island. Founded in 1956 Brookhaven Memorial also offers behavioral health services including inpatient and outpatient mental health and alcohol treatment services. In addition to hospital services the medical center operates two community health clinics and a specialty center that provides hemodialysis women's imaging and home health and hospice services.

Geographic Reach

The medical center serves those who reside in the Suffolk County area of Long Island New York which consists of 28 communities.

Operations

Brookhaven Memorial Hospital Medical Center comprises a main campus Level II Trauma Center/Emergency Room a pair of community multidisciplinary health centers and a downtown Patchogue facility for its hemodialysis program home health and hospice services and ambulatory women's imaging center. Its emergency department treats more than 70000 patients.

It operates the South Brookhaven Family Health Center in Patchogue and Shirley on a contractual basis along with Suffolk County Department of Health. Brookhaven Memorial logs the largest number of visits in the town of Patchogue.

Strategy

Brookhaven Memorial has been expanding and entering new markets. Brookhaven Memorial in 2014 embarked on a $60-million expansion project for its new Knapp Cardiac Center which spans some 60000 sq. ft. It also opened a Bellport Primary Care Center in 2014 to provide primary medicine to an underserved community.

EXECUTIVES

Chairman, Robert W. Schwarz
President and CEO, Thomas Ockers
President and CEO, Richard T. Margulis
VP Development and External Relations, Christopher (Chris) Banks
President Medical Staff, Dean Babich
CIO, Kevin Conroy
Trustee, Gary Brown
Trustee, William Lehmann

LOCATIONS

HQ: BROOKHAVEN MEMORIAL HOSPITAL MEDICAL CENTER INC
101 HOSPITAL RD, EAST PATCHOGUE, NY 11772-4870
Phone: 631-654-7100
Web: WWW.BROOKHAVENHOSPITAL.ORG

Selected Locations

Brookhaven Center for Wound Care and Hyperbaric Medicine - Patchogue New York
Brookhaven Family Medicine - Patchogue New York
Brookhaven Hemodialysis Center - Patchogue New York
Brookhaven Home Care - Patchogue New York
Brookhaven Hospice - Patchogue New York
Brookhaven Memorial Hospital Medical Center - Patchogue New York
Brookhaven Outpatient Imaging - Patchogue New York
Cardiac Rehabilitation - Patchogue New York
Diabetes Wellness Center - Patchogue New York
South Brookhaven Health Center East - Shirley New York
South Brookhaven Health Center West - Patchogue New York

PRODUCTS/OPERATIONS

Selected Services

Medical Services
- Behavioral Health
- Cancer Care
- Cardiology Department
- Family Medicine
- Long Island Orthopaedic and Spine Specialists
- Laboratory
- Neuroscience Center
- Pain Management
- Radiology Imaging
- Respiratory Care
- Surgery / Perioperative
- Women's Imaging / Health

Specialized Services
- Bariatric and Wellness Program
- Case Management
- Community Health Centers
- Coumadin Management Center
- Diabetes Wellness Center
- Hemodialysis Center
- Home Health Agency
- Hospice
- Nutrition
- Physical Rehabilitation
- Sleep Center
- Speech-Language Pathology
- Support Groups
- Wound Care / Hyperbaric Medicine

COMPETITORS

Catholic Health Services of Long Island
Catholic Healthcare System
Continuum Health Partners
Memorial Sloan-Kettering
New York City Health and Hospitals
North Shore-Long Island Jewish Health System
Peconic Bay Medical Center

HISTORICAL FINANCIALS

Company Type: Private

Income Statement FYE: December 31

	REVENUE ($ mil.)	NET INCOME ($ mil.)	NET PROFIT MARGIN	EMPLOYEES
12/09	298	(2)	—	1,900
12/06	269	6	2.6%	—
12/05	230	1	0.6%	—
12/04	230	1	0.6%	—
Annual Growth	5.3%	—	—	—

2009 Year-End Financials

Debt ratio: —
Return on equity: (-0.80%)
Cash ($ mil.): 18
Current ratio: —
Long-term debt ($ mil.): —
Dividends
Yield: —
Payout: —
Market value ($ mil.): —

BROOKLYN HOSPITAL CENTER

The Brooklyn Hospital Center has been taking care of ailing Kings County residents since before Brooklyn was a borough. Established in 1845 (before Brooklyn became part of New York City) the hospital houses some 460 beds and is a member of the NewYork-Presbyterian Healthcare System. It provides general medical and surgical care as well as a wide variety of specialty medical services including dialysis pediatrics obstetrics and cardiovascular care. The Brooklyn Hospital Center is affiliated with Weill Medical College of Cornell University. The hospital also operates a network of outpatient clinics providing primary and specialty care throughout the borough.

Operations

Each year the Brooklyn Hospital Center handles about 65000 ER visits 19000 inpatient stays and 150000 outpatient care visits. It has a medical staff of about 600 doctors. The hospital also conducts nursing and medical education programs.

Financial Performance

The Brooklyn Hospital Center has an annual operating budget of about $380 million.

Strategy

The Brooklyn Hospital Center is striving to increase the quality of its clinical programs and upgrade its infrastructure. It also aims to retain a quality medical staff and increase the hospitals educational and research activities.

Company Background

The Brooklyn Hospital Center filed for bankruptcy protection in 2005 when expensive expansion projects that didn't pay off as well as malpractice litigation left the company in more debt than it could manage. The hospital emerged from bankruptcy in 2007.

EXECUTIVES

Chairman, Carlos P. Naudon, age 63
SVP Nursing and Chief Nursing Officer, Opal Sinclair-Chung
President & Chief Executive Officer, Richard B. Becker
EVP, Paul A. Albertson
Chairman, Jonathan M. Weld
Director Nurse Recruitment, Cheryl Weekes
CIO, Irene Farrelly
Senior Vice President & Chief Financial Officer, Joseph J. Guarracino
Chairman Emergency Medicine, Lisando Irizarry
Senior Vice President General Counsel, Stacy A. Friedman
Chief Medical Officer, J. Richard Ludgin
Community Liaison, Helen Wong
Director Cancer Communications Department, Marva Shelton-DeLapp
Assistant VP Case Management and Utilization Review, Elizabeth Bonetti
Acting Director Patient Relations, Agatha George
Director Pastoral Care and Chaplain, Rev John O'Leary
Chairperson Surgery, Stephen Carryl
Chairman Radiology, Douglas Kiviat
Chairman and Chief Maternal-Fetal Medicine, Michael Cabbad
Administrator Obstetrics and Gynecology, Edith Olmeda
Vice President and Chief Quality Officer, Vasantha Kondamudi
Chairman Internal Medicine, M. Scott Reminick
Chairman Pediatrics, Kenneth Bromberg
Senior Vice President & Chief Nursing Officer, Patricia Winston
Vice President Internal Audit & Corporate Compliance, Lora Myers
Vice President External Affairs, Leroy R. Charles
Senior Vice President & Chief Medical Officer, Gary A. Stephens
Senior Vice President Chief Information Officer, Bill Moran
Senior Vice President Human Resources, John Lasky
Executive Vice President & Chief Operating Officer, Trent Crable
Vice President Chief Development Officer, Debbie Niederhoffer
Senior Vice President Strategic Planning, Joan Clark
Vice Chair, Anne Elizabeth Fontaine
Vice Chair, Calvin J. Simons
Senior Vice President Chief Information Officer & HIPPA Security Officer, Bill Moran
Vice President Nursing Operations, Mary Ann Healy-Rodriguez
Vice Chair, Anne Elizabeth Fontaine
Vice Chair, Calvin J. Simons
Auditors: Ernst&YoungLLP

LOCATIONS

HQ: BROOKLYN HOSPITAL CENTER
121 DEKALB AVE, BROOKLYN, NY 11201-5493
Phone: 718-250-8000
Web: WWW.TBH.ORG

PRODUCTS/OPERATIONS

Selected Services

Bariatric Surgery
Cancer Care
Dental Care and Oral Surgery
Dialysis Services
Emergency Medicine
Family Medicine
The Family Medicine Residency
Geriatric Care
Home Health Services
Imaging and Radiology
Inpatient Hospitalist Care
Obstetrics and Gynecology
Orthopaedic Surgery
Pediatrics
Pediatric Cancer Care
Pediatric Emergency Services
Pediatric and Neonatal Critical Care
Sleep Center
Spine and Neurosurgery
Stroke Center
TeleHealth
Vascular Surgery
Wound Care

COMPETITORS

Brookdale University Hospital
Catholic Healthcare System
Continuum Health Partners
Kingsbrook Jewish Medical Center
Maimonides Medical Center
Montefiore Medical
New York City Health and Hospitals
North Shore-Long Island Jewish Health System
SUNY Downstate
Winthrop-University Hospital

HISTORICAL FINANCIALS

Company Type: Private

Income Statement

FYE: December 31

	REVENUE ($ mil.)	NET INCOME ($ mil.)	NET PROFIT MARGIN	EMPLOYEES
12/12	384	5	1.4%	3,300
12/11	379	10	2.6%	—
12/10	388	5	1.5%	—
12/09	0	(0)	—	—
Annual Growth	7201.2%	—	—	—

2012 Year-End Financials

Debt ratio: —
Return on equity: 1.40%
Cash ($ mil.): 17
Current ratio: 0.80
Long-term debt ($ mil.): —
Dividends
Yield: —
Payout: —
Market value ($ mil.): —

BRUCE OAKLEY INC.

From little acorns mighty Oakleys grow. Bruce Oakley provides road and river (barge) transportation of dry bulk commodities as well as grain storage and bulk fertilizer sales. The company's trucking division which uses both end-dump and pneumatic tank trailers serves the continental US and Canada. Overall Bruce Oakley operates some 450 trailers. It maintains about half a dozen ports in Arkansas Louisiana and Missouri on the Arkansas Mississippi and Red rivers and the company's river barge transportation unit operates on those and other inland and intracoastal waterways. Grain storage services are available in five ports in Arkansas. Bruce Oakley was founded in 1968.

Additionally the company offers farm supplies including feed vet supplies fencing hay salt and lime. Its Oakley Beebe facility which can warehouse 2000 tons of bagged product provides bagging and spreading services for its wholesale fertilizer.

Bruce Oakley is in the thick of it when it comes to what Louisiana farmers decide to grow —corn or soy beans. Because corn is more marketable and easier to harvest farmers have traditionally chosen it over soybeans even though it draws a lower price per bushel. Soy beans which are not as hearty as corn require more immediate transport after harvest over much longer distances (250 miles to market compared to corn's 65 miles).

EXECUTIVES

VP Oakley Trucking, Benny Weatherford
Manager Oakley Pendleton Warehouse, Raymond Mannis
Manager Oakley Fertilizer, James Rainey
Operations Manager, J.O. Norman
Vice President, David Choate
Chief Financial Officer, Tim Cummins
Owner, Oakley Trucking

LOCATIONS

HQ: BRUCE OAKLEY INC.
3700 LINCOLN AVE, NORTH LITTLE ROCK, AR 72114-6448
Phone: 501-945-0875
Web: WWW.BRUCEOAKLEY.COM

PRODUCTS/OPERATIONS

Selected Products and Services

Bagging
Barges
Bulk fertilizer
Grain and grain storage
Oakley vessel freight
River ports and stevedoring
Trucking

COMPETITORS

American Commercial Lines
Bulkmatic
Comcar
GrainCorp
Groendyke Transport
Kansas City Southern
Superior Bulk Logistics

HISTORICAL FINANCIALS

Company Type: Private

Income Statement

FYE: September 25

	REVENUE ($ mil.)	NET INCOME ($ mil.)	NET PROFIT MARGIN	EMPLOYEES
09/08	1,160	31	2.8%	201
09/07	526	11	2.2%	—
Annual Growth	120.2%	170.9%	—	—

2008 Year-End Financials

Debt ratio: —
Return on equity: 2.80%
Cash ($ mil.): 3
Current ratio: 0.80
Long-term debt ($ mil.): —
Dividends
Yield: —
Payout: —
Market value ($ mil.): —

BRUCKNER TRUCK SALES INC.

LOCATIONS

HQ: BRUCKNER TRUCK SALES INC.
9471 E INTERSTATE 40, AMARILLO, TX 791186960
Phone: 8063766273
Web: WWW.BRUCKNERTRUCK.COM

HISTORICAL FINANCIALS

Company Type: Private

Income Statement FYE: June 30

	REVENUE ($ mil.)	NET INCOME ($ mil.)	NET PROFIT MARGIN	EMPLOYEES
06/14	490	10	2.1%	550
06/10	200	2	1.1%	—
06/09	229	4	1.9%	—
06/08	1,193	0	—	—
Annual Growth	(13.8%)	—	—	—

2014 Year-End Financials

Debt ratio: —
Return on equity: 2.10%
Cash ($ mil.): 33
Current ratio: 0.50
Long-term debt ($ mil.): —
Dividends
Yield: —
Payout: —
Market value ($ mil.): —

BRYAN MEDICAL CENTER

Bryan Medical Center (formerly BryanLGH Medical Center) is the centerpiece of a not-for-profit health care system serving residents of Lincoln Nebraska and surrounding communities. The medical center which operates as part of Bryan Health features two acute-care hospitals (Bryan East and Bryan West) housing a combined 670 beds. In addition to providing general medical and surgical care it serves as a regional trauma center and provides specialty care in areas such as cancer orthopedics and cardiology. The Bryan Health organization also includes a rural hospital and several outpatient clinics and it provides medical training home health care services and wellness programs.

Geographic ReachBryan Medical Center serves patients throughout Nebraska as well as portions of neighboring states including Kansas Iowa and South Dakota.OperationsIn addition to Bryan Medical Center the Bryan Health organization operates the Crete Area Medical Center a 25-bed community hospital. Outpatient facilities include the Bryan Heart Institute (cardiology and cardiothoracic surgery) the Bryan Physician Network (family practice urgent care and specialist locations) and Bryan LifePointe (wellness and fitness programs). In addition the network includes the Bryan College of Health Sciences which provides bachelor's and master's degrees in nursing and health professional fields and the Bryan Foundation. It also conducts community education activities.StrategyIn 2012 the health organization rebranded itself to reflect its expanded position in the region's health care market. BryanLGH Medical Center was renamed Bryan Medical Center and the broader health organization changed its name from the BryanLGH Health System to simply Bryan Health.Company BackgroundThe BryanLGH system was formed through the 1997 combination of Bryan Memorial Hospital (named after populist firebrand William Jennings Bryan) and Lincoln General Hospital. Bryan Health is part of the Heartland Health Alliance a group of about 40 Nebraska hospitals that work together to improve rural health care services through shared services and best practices.

EXECUTIVES

Director Trauma Center, Reginald Burton
President COO, John T. Woodrich
Public Relations, Edgar Bumanis
President CEO, Kimberly A. Russel

LOCATIONS

HQ: BRYAN MEDICAL CENTER
1600 S 48TH ST, LINCOLN, NE 68506-1283
Phone: 402-481-3190
Web: WWW.BRYANHEALTH.COM

PRODUCTS/OPERATIONS

Selected Services

Bariatrics
Cardiac Services
Cancer
Cardiothoracic Surgery
Childbirth/Family Birthplace
Corporate & Community Wellness
Diabetes Center
Early Detection
Emergency Department
Heart Valve Center of Excellence
Hospitalists
Independence Center
Inpatient Rehabilitation
Neuroscience
Mental Health
Orthopedics
Outpatient Specialty Clinic
Radiation Oncology
Radiology
Rehabilitation/Therapy
Robotic Surgery
Sleep Medicine
StarCare Air Ambulance
Substance Abuse
Trauma Center
Urgent Care
Vascular Services
Women' s & Children' s

COMPETITORS

Alegent Creighton Health
Catholic Health Initiatives
Children' s Hospital & Medical Center
Madonna Rehabilitation Hospital
Methodist Health System
Nebraska Medical Center
Saint Elizabeth Regional Medical Center

HISTORICAL FINANCIALS

Company Type: Private

Income Statement FYE: May 31

	REVENUE ($ mil.)	NET INCOME ($ mil.)	NET PROFIT MARGIN	EMPLOYEES
05/12	481	(4)	—	3,970
05/11	478	42	9.0%	—
05/10	457	23	5.2%	—
05/09	418	2	0.5%	—
Annual Growth	4.8%	—	—	—

2012 Year-End Financials

Debt ratio: —
Return on equity: (-0.90%)
Cash ($ mil.): 105
Current ratio: 2.90
Long-term debt ($ mil.): —
Dividends
Yield: —
Payout: —
Market value ($ mil.): —

BTC WHOLESALE DISTRIBUTORS INC.

LOCATIONS

HQ: BTC WHOLESALE DISTRIBUTORS INC.
100 AIRVIEW LN, ALABASTER, AL 350074834
Phone: 2053242581

HISTORICAL FINANCIALS

Company Type: Private

Income Statement FYE: December 31

	REVENUE ($ mil.)	NET INCOME ($ mil.)	NET PROFIT MARGIN	EMPLOYEES
12/13	216	2	1.0%	95
12/12	201	1	1.0%	—
12/11	201	1	0.8%	—
12/10	196	0	—	—
Annual Growth	3.2%	—	—	—

BUCKEYE POWER INC.

It has cost a few bucks to generate power but the effort has been well worth it for Buckeye Power an electricity generation and transmission cooperative that provides electricity to 24 distribution companies in Ohio and one in Michigan. Together they serve about 400000 homes and businesses in 77 of Ohio's 88 counties. The company was established by Ohio's rural electric co-ops to produce and transmit electric power for member systems throughout the state. Buckeye Power contracts with other Ohio electric companies to use their transmission systems to transmit power to its member electric distribution cooperatives.

Buckeye Power owns two of the three generating units at the Cardinal Generating Station on the Ohio River and contracts with other Ohio electric companies to use their transmission systems to transmit power to its member electric distribution cooperatives.

Buckeye Power is owned by 25 electric distribution cooperatives in Ohio (24 of the cooperatives are based in the state). A 25th Midwest Energy Cooperative based in Cassopolis Michigan serves about 1000 members in parts of Fulton and Williams counties in northwestern Ohio. Their coops' combined service areas cover 40% of the Michigan primarily its rural regions.

A super derecho storm in June 2012 with its very strong winds caused at least $12 million of damage to electric infrastructure in 21 counties across Ohio.

In addition to transmitting energy from traditional power plants Buckeye Power is looking to access a range of renewable sources and conservation measures to help the state meet its green energy goals. Its green portfolio includes contracts with a 150 MW wind energy farm biogas/landfill generation projects and a hydropower deal with the New York Power Authority. It also offers 100 kW-hour blocks of renewable power to members who wish to support environmental and energy goals by buying green power as well as a range of efficiency options (smart bulbs energy audits etc.) to individual customers.

Buckeye Power was formed by Ohio's electric cooperatives in 1959 as a statewide generation and transmission co-op. In the 1960s Buckeye Power and American Electric Power's Ohio Power unit teamed up to build the Cardinal Generating Station 1200 MW coal-fired power plant.

EXECUTIVES

President, Anthony J. (Tony) Ahern
VP Finance, Bob Daniel
Director Communications, Steve Oden
Auditors: KPMGPeatMarwickLLP

LOCATIONS

HQ: BUCKEYE POWER INC.
6677 BUSCH BLVD, COLUMBUS, OH 43229-1101
Phone: 614-846-5757
Web: WWW.OHIORURALELECTRIC.COOP

COMPETITORS

AEP
FirstEnergy
GenOnEnergy
Ohio Valley Electric

HISTORICAL FINANCIALS

Company Type: Private

Income Statement FYE: June 30

	REVENUE ($ mil.)	NET INCOME ($ mil.)	NET PROFIT MARGIN	EMPLOYEES
06/13	639	26	4.1%	300
06/12	626	31	5.0%	—
06/10	580	32	5.7%	—
06/10	538	15	2.8%	—
Annual Growth	5.9%	20.3%	—	—

2013 Year-End Financials

Debt ratio: —
Return on equity: 4.10%
Cash ($ mil.): 25
Current ratio: 0.40
Long-term debt ($ mil.): —
Dividends
Yield: —
Payout: —
Market value ($ mil.): —

BUCKNELL UNIVERSITY

Just getting into Bucknell University is an accomplishment. The highly selective private liberal arts school accepts only about 10% of applicants each year. Students who do get in some 3600 of them from around the world have the option to specialize in more than 50 majors and 60 minors. Bucknell confers both undergraduate and master's degrees in the liberal arts sciences engineering and music. It also offers programs in pre-law and pre-med. Bucknell tuition and fees total more than $58000; more than half of the student body typically receives financial aid. The school's student-to-faculty ratio is 10-to-1.

Geographic Background

In fiscal year 2013 Bucknell enrolled students from 46 states and 63 countries. The minority student enrollment is more than 500 with more than 175 foreign students.

Operations

Some 86% of undergraduates live on campus.

Bucknell has more than 350 full-time faculty members of which about 97% hold PhD or equivalent terminal degrees. Some 62% of faculty are tenured.

The university's Bertrand Library houses more than 800000 books.

Financial Performance

Bucknell's revenue increased by 4% in fiscal year 2013 thanks to higher net tuition and fees and an increase in net investment income from endowments.The university reported $74 million of net income in fiscal year 2013 (compared to a loss in 2012) due to stronger non-operating net investment income and post retiree credits and an increase in income from grants and capital gifts.

Company Background

Bucknell was founded in 1846 as the University at Lewisburg.

EXECUTIVES

Vice President Of Campus Environment, Lynn Pierson
Vice President, Lee Shand
Assoc Vp Finance, Dennis W Swank
Assoc Vp Facilities, Dennis Hawley
Controller/treasurer, Michael Cover
Board Member, Michael Milstein
Board Member, Christine Perry
Vice Chairwoman, Juli Cooper
Board Member, Kyle Miller
Board Member, Carol Graybeal
Board Member, Sue Ellen Henry
Board Member, Tom Rich
Auditors: KPMGLLP

LOCATIONS

HQ: BUCKNELL UNIVERSITY
1 DENT DR, LEWISBURG, PA 178372029
Phone: 5705772000
Web: WWW.BUCKNELL.EDU

HISTORICAL FINANCIALS

Company Type: Private

Income Statement FYE: June 30

	REVENUE ($ mil.)	NET INCOME ($ mil.)	NET PROFIT MARGIN	EMPLOYEES
06/14	206	92	45.0%	1,500
06/13	196	74	37.8%	—
06/12	189	(28)	—	—
06/11	184	0	—	—
Annual Growth	3.8%	—	—	—

2014 Year-End Financials

Debt ratio: —
Return on equity: 45.00%
Cash ($ mil.): 9
Current ratio: —
Long-term debt ($ mil.): —
Dividends
Yield: —
Payout: —
Market value ($ mil.): —

BUNKERS INTERNATIONAL CORP.

LOCATIONS

HQ: BUNKERS INTERNATIONAL CORP.
1071 S SUN DR STE 3, LAKE MARY, FL 327462405
Phone: 4073287757
Web: WWW.BUNKERSINTERNATIONAL.COM

HISTORICAL FINANCIALS

Company Type: Private

Income Statement FYE: December 31

	REVENUE ($ mil.)	NET INCOME ($ mil.)	NET PROFIT MARGIN	EMPLOYEES
12/08	436	1	0.4%	100
12/07	319	1	0.4%	—
12/01	436	0	0.0%	—
Annual Growth	0.0%	92.3%	—	—

2008 Year-End Financials

Debt ratio: —
Return on equity: 0.40%
Cash ($ mil.): 2
Current ratio: 1.10
Long-term debt ($ mil.): —
Dividends
Yield: —
Payout: —
Market value ($ mil.): —

BURKHART DENTAL SUPPLY CO.

EXECUTIVES

VP Sales and Branch Operations, Kathy Inman
Director Corporate Equipment Sales, Michael Norton
VP Corporate Operations, Greg Biersack
Director Corporate Technical Services, Shannon Bruil
Purchasing Manager, Robb Marshall
Branch Manager Anchorage and Tacoma, Jerry Ritsema
Branch Manager Austin Texas, Jim Lout
VP Sales, Jeff Reece
Branch Manager San Diego California, Jim Panigall
Branch Manager Spokane, David Wolkenhauer
Branch Manager Tulsa and Oklahoma City, George Reed
President, Lori Burkhart Isbell
Account Manager, Kristi Graham
Controller, Anneene French
Branch Manager Bay Area California, Lisa Wells
Branch Manager Boise Idaho, Derek Johnson
Branch Manager Phoenix Arizona, Steven Lappin
Branch Manager Denver Colorado, Mary Kehoe
Branch Manager Eugene Oregon, Andy Hutson
Branch Manager Houston Texas, Mark Oliver
Chief Financial Officer, Cary Campen
Marketing Manager, Holly Kean
Director Information Technology, Ron DeLaura
Director Merchandise, Bill Sundheimer
Director Logistics, Judi Griffin

LOCATIONS

HQ: BURKHART DENTAL SUPPLY CO.
2502 S 78TH ST, TACOMA, WA 984099053
Phone: 2534747761
Web: WWW.BURKHARTDENTAL.COM

PRODUCTS/OPERATIONS

Selected Services

Consulting
Equipment
Financing
Office planning and design
Practice management
Service
Supplies and inventory management
Technology

Selected Products

Equipment
- Amalgamators
- Cabinets
- Curing lights
- Delivery units
- Emergency equipment
- Hand pieces
- Instrument washers and cleaners
- Intraoral x-ray
- Lab equipment
- Mechanical room equipment
- Patient chairs
- Sterliizers
- Stools

Technology tools
- 3D cone beam CT and glasses
- CAD/CAM
- Intraoral cameras
- Lasers
- Microscopes
- Panoramic X-ray
- Phosphor plate systems
- Sensors

Supply Partners
3M/ESPE
A-dec
Air Techniques
Ammex
Axis
Belmont
Carestream
Coltene Whaledent
Crest
Crosstex
Dentsply
Dentsply Caulk
DMG America
Forest Dental
GC America
Gendex
Heraeus
Hu-Friedy
Ivoclar Vivadent
Kavo America
Kerr
Kimberly Clark
Kuraray America
Metrex
Midmark
Miltex
Oral-B
Pelton & Crane
Planmeca
Premier
SciCan
Septodont
Sirona
Soredex
StarDental
Sultan Heathcare
Sunstar
Supermax
Total Care
TPC
Young Dental

COMPETITORS

Benco Dental	McKesson Medical-Surgical
Cardinal Health	Owens & Minor
DENTSPLY	Patterson Companies
Darby Dental	Sybron Dental
Henry Schein	
McKesson	

HISTORICAL FINANCIALS

Company Type: Private

Income Statement FYE: December 31

	REVENUE ($ mil.)	NET INCOME ($ mil.)	NET PROFIT MARGIN	EMPLOYEES
12/09	142	1	1.2%	360
12/08	157	2	1.4%	—
12/07	471	0	—	—
Annual Growth	(45.0%)	36328.3%	—	—

2009 Year-End Financials

Debt ratio: ——
Return on equity: 1.20%
Cash ($ mil.): 6
Current ratio: 1.40
Long-term debt ($ mil.): —

Dividends
Yield: —
Payout: —
Market value ($ mil.): —

C & K MARKET INC.

EXECUTIVES

Chairman of the Board, Doug Nidiffer
President Chief Executive Officer, Greg Sandeno
Executive Vice President Chief Financial & Administrative Officer, Elizabeth Bauer
Executive Vice President Chief Information Officer, Alan Nidiffer
Vice President Merchandising & Marketing, Terry Spencer
Vice President Finance, Becky Olsen
Vice President Operations, Rocky Campbell ?????? Vice President
Vice President Controller, Jimmy Martini
Vice President Operations Taking over the operational reigns from Greg Sandeno, Rocky Campbell
Vice President Human Resources & General Counsel, Kate Wilkinson

LOCATIONS

HQ: C & K MARKET INC.
615 5TH ST, BROOKINGS, OR 974159199
Phone: 5414693113
Web: WWW.CKMARKET.COM

PRODUCTS/OPERATIONS

2012 Stores

	No.
Ray's Food	45
Pharmacy	15
Shop Smart Food	11
C&K	2
Chetco Pharmacy &	2
Total	**74**

COMPETITORS

7-Eleven	Safeway
CVS Caremark	Target Corporation
Costco Wholesale	Wal-Mart
Fred Meyer Stores	Walgreen
SUPERVALU	

HISTORICAL FINANCIALS

Company Type: Private

Income Statement FYE: December 31

	REVENUE ($ mil.)	NET INCOME ($ mil.)	NET PROFIT MARGIN	EMPLOYEES
12/10	457	3	0.8%	2,322
12/09	467	5	1.1%	—
12/07	1,513	0	0.0%	—
Annual Growth	(32.9%)	1737.3%	—	—

2010 Year-End Financials

Debt ratio: ——
Return on equity: 0.80%
Cash ($ mil.): 6
Current ratio: 0.10
Long-term debt ($ mil.): —

Dividends
Yield: —
Payout: —
Market value ($ mil.): —

C. B. FLEET COMPANY INCORPORATED

Some of C.B. Fleet's products are tucked away in medicine cabinets worldwide for those times of need. Established as a small family-run pharmacy in 1869 by Dr. Charles Browne Fleet today the company makes about 100 personal health and beauty care products that are distributed to more than 100 countries globally. C.B. Fleet's products include feminine care laxatives oral care skin care and oral rehydration product lines sold under brand names Summer's Eve Vera by CCS Norforms Clinomyn Oliva by CCS BioralSuero and Casen-Fleet among others. It also operates several subsidiaries such as CSS (Europe) DeWitt Personal Care (the UK) and Fleet Laboratories (Asia and Latin America).

Geographic Reach

Based in Virginia C.B. Fleet sells its productions worldwide in 100-plus countries supported by subsidiaries in Europe the UK Asia and Latin America.

Strategy

Despite previous acquisitions and licensing efforts C.B. Fleet has moved to prune its portfolio of holdings that no longer fit its long-term goals. Divesting its Italian unit Bergamon S.r.l. (purchased in 1994) to Omega Pharma N.V. a Belgium-based consumer healthcare firm was part of this strategy. Omega Pharma continues to distribute Fleet enema items through its Chefaro Pharma Italia S.r.l. as part of the agreement.

Sales and Marketing

C.B. Fleet markets its products through distributors.

C.B. Fleet's gastrointestinal and feminine care products typically don't lend themselves to conversation. Yet the firm in 2010 enlisted the help of New York public relations agency Robin Leedy & Associates to encourage moms to use social media such as Twitter or Facebook to discuss the benefits of the company's Pedia-Lax Fiber Gummies dietary fiber supplement for children. C.B. Fleet's banking on the brand as being viewed as a dietary supplement rather than a laxative to boost children's typically fiber-poor diets.

Company Background

The company is under the U.S. Food and Drug Administration's watchful eye and has responded to the group's safety alerts in year's past. Following a late 2008 FDA alert to consumers C.B. Fleet voluntarily recalled its Fleet Phospho-soda and Fleet Phospho-soda EZ-Prep Bowel Cleansing System. The FDA had determined that oral sodium phosphate solutions used to prepare patients for medical procedures such as colonoscopies should only be available by prescription.

EXECUTIVES

Vice President Of Sales, Cheryl Vernon
Vice President Domestic Marketing, Bruce Montgomery
National Accounts Manager, Mike Purvis
Vice President, Kathryn Sibande
National Sales Manager, Cliff Farlow

Vp Of Operations, Jeff Thompson
Treasurer, Joseph Carroll

LOCATIONS

HQ: C. B. FLEET COMPANY INCORPORATED
4615 MURRAY PL, LYNCHBURG, VA 24502-2235
Phone: 434-528-4000
Web: WWW.FLEETLABS.COM

PRODUCTS/OPERATIONS

Selected Products & Brands

Feminine care
- Summer' s Eve
- Norforms

Gastrointestinal care
- Fleet
- Casen Fleet

Oral rehydration
- OralSuero
- BioralSuero
- Sueroral

Oral care
- Clinomyn

COMPETITORS

CCA Industries
Colgate-Palmolive
GNC
Purdue Pharma
ReNew Life
Salix Pharmaceuticals
Schiff Nutrition International

HISTORICAL FINANCIALS

Company Type: Private

Income Statement FYE: December 31

	REVENUE ($ mil.)	NET INCOME ($ mil.)	NET PROFIT MARGIN	EMPLOYEES
12/08	232	(2)	—	696
12/07	235	13	5.8%	—
12/06	223	21	9.5%	—
12/05	213	9	4.6%	—
Annual Growth	2.9%	—	—	—

2008 Year-End Financials

Debt ratio: —
Return on equity: (-0.90%)
Cash ($ mil.): 38
Current ratio: 1.80
Long-term debt ($ mil.): —
Dividends
Yield: —
Payout: —
Market value ($ mil.): —

C.D. SMITH CONSTRUCTION INC.

One of the Midwest's top contractors C.D. Smith Construction works on commercial institutional and industrial projects. It builds manufacturing retail correctional health care and education facilities as well as water treatment plants. The company offers general contracting and design/build services and also provides specialty contracting services such as steel erection masonry and concrete work carpentry and demolition. Charles D. Smith grandfather of president Gary Smith founded the company in 1936.

C.D. Smith Construction has added Leadership in Energy and Environmental Design (LEED) Green Building services to its offerings. The company is a U.S. Green Building Council member and has LEED Accredited Project Managers to assist throughout the entire certification process. LEED promotes a whole-building approach to sustainability by recognizing performance in five key areas of human and environmental health

EXECUTIVES

Vp Field Operations, Steve Schmitz, age 58
Vice President, Michael Krolczyk
Secretary & Safety Director, Patrick Smith

LOCATIONS

HQ: C.D. SMITH CONSTRUCTION INC.
889 E JOHNSON ST, FOND DU LAC, WI 549352933
Phone: 9209242900
Web: WWW.CDSMITH.COM

COMPETITORS

Boldt
C. G. Schmidt
C. R. Meyer
Edward Kraemer & Sons
Hagerman Construction
Hunzinger Construction
J.H. Findorff & Son
Market & Johnson
R.A. Smith National
Sonag Company
Walsh Group

HISTORICAL FINANCIALS

Company Type: Private

Income Statement FYE: September 30

	REVENUE ($ mil.)	NET INCOME ($ mil.)	NET PROFIT MARGIN	EMPLOYEES
09/13	252	0	—	440
09/12	252	0	—	—
09/11	0	0	—	—
09/10	0	0	—	—
Annual Growth	—	—	—	—

2013 Year-End Financials

Debt ratio: —
Return on equity: —
Cash ($ mil.): 44
Current ratio: 1.20
Long-term debt ($ mil.): —
Dividends
Yield: —
Payout: —
Market value ($ mil.): —

C.R. ENGLAND INC.

The world's top refrigerated trucking company and one of North America's largest transportation firms C.R. England hauls refrigerated and dry cargo throughout the US. The family-owned company also serves parts of Canada and through alliances points in Mexico. C.R. England's fleet includes more than 3500 Freightliner Peterbilt Volvo and International tractors and 5500 trailers. Besides for-hire freight hauling C.R. England offers dedicated contract carriage in which drivers and equipment are assigned to a customer long-term; logistics services including freight brokerage; and intermodal railroad service.

Operations

The company's operations include national US US regional and Mexican truckload service as well as dedicated (customized) truck contracts and intermodal service.

In addition to freight brokerage C.R. England's England Logistics unit offers intermodal service for refrigerated cargo in which customers' containerized freight is shuttled between truck and railroad facility. The logistics unit also arranges the transportation of less-than-truckload quantities of freight and provides ground transportation of ocean containers for shipping lines.

This unit also provides global logistics – international shipping and freight forwarding solutions); supply chain management (freight management) and carrier services (factoring solutions fuel discounts tire discounts and other services).

C.R. England's business also benefits from operating five truck driving schools in the US and a course on becoming a freight broker. The school helps improve driver safety as well as provides a pool of qualified truck drivers for hire.

Strategy

Greening its fleet in 2014 C. R. England announced a multi-year liquefied natural gas (LNG) bulk fueling agreement with Shell. C.R. England will replace existing diesel trucks with LNG-powered trucks servicing southern California the most mature US market for fueling LNG-powered trucks.

The company is focusing on innovation in its intermodal and dedicated operations. The intermodal division has more than 1000 TempStack 53 ft. temperature-controlled containers which can be double-stacked on the flatcars of its partner railroad reducing customer costs increasing shipping capacity and efficiency and lowering fuel costs.

C.R. England is also beefing up its trucking operations working to deliver faster more secure shipments for its customers in its National and Regional divisions.

Its Mexico operations offer multiple border crossings and full-service connection yards to move shipments across the U.S. and Mexico border. In 2012 it boosted its regional division by introducing a new Texas regional service to meet the demands of larger volumes that move into and out of Mexico and across Texas.

Company Background

C.R. England was founded in 1920 by Chester Rodney England and is run by his descendants.

EXECUTIVES

President Mexico Division, David (Dave) Akers
EVP Maintenance, Todd D. England
EVP Operations Support, Corey D. England
CEO, Chad England
President, Josh England
COO, Brandon Harrison
EVP Corporate Sales and Marketing, David A. Kramer
COO, Zach England
Corporate VP Compliance and Safety, Dustin England
President National and Regional, Sam Scott
President Intermodal, Coby Bullard
President Dedicated, Tracy Brown
CFO, TJ McGeean
Vice President Of National Fleet Management, Ryan Holm
Vice President Intermodal, Daren Wingard
Vp Of Finance, Jim Colby
Vice President National Operations And Inside Sales, Dusty Jacobs
Corporate Vice President N America Equipment Leasing Sales And Contractor S, Mike Fife
Vice President Finance, T J McGeean
Co-Chairman, Daniel E. (Dan) England, age 67
Co-Chairman, Dean D. England

LOCATIONS

HQ: C.R. ENGLAND INC.
4701 W 2100 S, SALT LAKE CITY, UT 841201223
Phone: 8019742712
Web: WWW.CRENGLAND.COM

PRODUCTS/OPERATIONS

Selected Services

Dedicated service
Expedited priority rail service
Long haul truckload service
Mexico service
Short haul regional service

COMPETITORS

C.H. Robinson Worldwide
Central Refrigerated Service
Covenant
Landstar System
Marten Transport
Menlo Worldwide
Navajo Shippers
Prime Inc.

Transportation
Crete Carrier
Frozen Food Express
J.B. Hunt
KLLM Transport Services
Stevens Transport
Swift Transportation
Willis Shaw Express

HISTORICAL FINANCIALS

Company Type: Private

Income Statement FYE: December 31

	REVENUE ($ mil.)	NET INCOME ($ mil.)	NET PROFIT MARGIN	EMPLOYEES
12/13	1,628	37	2.3%	6,500
12/12	1,579	56	3.6%	—
12/11	1,315	55	4.3%	—
12/07	829	0	—	—
Annual Growth	11.9%	—	—	—

2013 Year-End Financials

Debt ratio: —
Return on equity: 2.30%
Cash ($ mil.): 24
Current ratio: 1.00
Long-term debt ($ mil.): —
Dividends
Yield: —
Payout: —
Market value ($ mil.): —

CADENCE MCSHANE CONSTRUCTION COMPANY LLC

With a certain cadence Cadence McShane Construction ‚Âhas been right in step with the top contractors in the US. A part of development and construction group The McShane Companies it provides general construction construction management and design/build services for commercial institutional and industrial projects in Texas and the central US. The ‚Âfirm is known for its school and ‚Âcommunity projects throughout Texas. ‚ÂIt also provides services to the manufacturing office multi-family residential government hospitality and retail markets. Recent projects include a 730000 sq. ft ‚ÂPort of Houston ‚Âdistribution center for ‚ÂFirst Industrial Realty. Cadence McShane was founded in 1995.

EXECUTIVES

Vp Estimating, William L Brady, age 62
Vp And Division Manager, Charles H White
Vice President, Roger Pavlovich
Vice President For The Houston Office Of Cadence McShane Construction, Rodney E Bowers
Vice President Multi Family And Senior Housing, David Tague
Vice President; Finance Vice President; Finance, Ellen Hilgendorf

LOCATIONS

HQ: CADENCE MCSHANE CONSTRUCTION COMPANY LLC
14860 MONTFORT DR STE 270, DALLAS, TX 752546719
Phone: 9722392336
Web: WWW.CADENCEMCSHANE.COM

Cadence McShane has offices Austin Houston and Dallas Texas.

PRODUCTS/OPERATIONS

Selected Project Areas

Community/Religious (churches)
Cultural (museums libraries)
Educational (K-12 schools and higher education)
Health care (medical centers labs medical suites and offices)
Hospitality (hotels)
Industrial (distribution assembly manufacturing)
Institutional (federal state county and municipal)
Offices (single-story to mid-rise)
Parking structures
Residential (multi-residence condominium complexes townhomes senior living)
Retail (shopping centers parking structures)

COMPETITORS

Austin Industries
Beck Group
FaulknerUSA
Gilbane Building Company
Harvey Builders
Hensel Phelps Construction
Hunt Construction
Manhattan Construction
Spawglass Holding
Structure Tone Southwest
Turner Corporation

HISTORICAL FINANCIALS

Company Type: Private

Income Statement FYE: September 30

	REVENUE ($ mil.)	NET INCOME ($ mil.)	NET PROFIT MARGIN	EMPLOYEES
09/10	158	1	0.8%	120
09/09	259	4	1.9%	—
09/07	724	0	—	—
Annual Growth	—	322.0%	—	—

2010 Year-End Financials

Debt ratio: —
Return on equity: 0.80%
Cash ($ mil.): 7
Current ratio: 1.00
Long-term debt ($ mil.): —
Dividends
Yield: —
Payout: —
Market value ($ mil.): —

CAHILL CONTRACTORS INC.

LOCATIONS

HQ: CAHILL CONTRACTORS INC.
425 CALIFORNIA ST # 2200, SAN FRANCISCO, CA 941042102
Phone: 4159860600
Web: WWW.CAHILL-SF.COM

HISTORICAL FINANCIALS

Company Type: Private

Income Statement FYE: December 31

	REVENUE ($ mil.)	NET INCOME ($ mil.)	NET PROFIT MARGIN	EMPLOYEES
12/13	233	(0)	—	162
12/12	195	1	0.8%	—
12/11	109	0	0.1%	—
12/10	146	0	—	—
Annual Growth	16.7%	—	—	—

2013 Year-End Financials

Debt ratio: —
Return on equity: (-0.30%)
Cash ($ mil.): 9
Current ratio: 0.20
Long-term debt ($ mil.): —
Dividends
Yield: —
Payout: —
Market value ($ mil.): —

CAJUN INDUSTRIES LLC

Offering a mixed gumbo of services Cajun Industries builds oil refineries power plants process plants water-treatment plants and other industrial and infrastructure projects primarily in Louisiana and Texas. Subsidiary Cajun Constructors provides a full range of services from design/build to maintenance; Cajun Deep Foundations offers drilling piles installation and related services. Cajun Maritime focuses on marine coastal and oilfield services including construction repair and power distribution. Cajun Equipment Services manages a fleet of trucks and trailers that transport heavy and specialized loads. Chairman and owner Lane Grigsby founded the company as Cajun Contractors and Engineers in 1973.

The group is typically engaged in a variety of public and private projects including the expansion of the Port Arthur Refinery in Texas to become the largest refinery in the US. Cajun won several cleanup and reconstruction projects in New Orleans following Hurricane Katrina; these included helping to pump floodwater out of the city and rebuilding the Industrial Canal levee. It was also awarded several projects to construct floodwalls in the area.

Cajun is licensed to perform construction in more than 20 states.

EXECUTIVES

Chairman, Lane Grigsby
President and CEO, Ken Jacob
EVP, Milton Graugnard
SVP Public Works Projects Constructors, Euclid Michel
VP Construction Services, Jan Lass
SVP Industrial Projects Constructors, Mike Barber
VP Estimating, Mike Lavespere
President Deep Foundations and Chairman Maritime, Mike Moran
President Constructors, Todd Grigsby
CFO, Shane Recile
Director Industrial Business Development Cajun Constructors, William Clouatre
Manager Business Development Deep Foundations, Kenny Wolf
SVP, Michael Calabrese
President Maritime, Jim Quackenbos
President Cajun Equipment Services, Mike Bates
VP Dallas Operations, Mark Reinhardt
VP Houston Operations, Tim Ricketts
Manager Business Development Cajun Maritime, Mark Broussard Jr.

LOCATIONS

HQ: CAJUN INDUSTRIES LLC
15635 AIRLINE HWY, BATON ROUGE, LA 70817-7318
Phone: 225-753-5857
Web: WWW.CAJUNUSA.COM

PRODUCTS/OPERATIONS

Selected Divisions

Cajun Constructors Inc.
Cajun Deep Foundations LLC
Cajun Equipment Services LLC
Cajun Maritime LLC

Selected Services

ASME code work
Bridge construction and repair
Building construction
Coastal restoration
Dock facility construction and repair
Deep foundation work
- Drill shafts
- Driven piles
- Earth retention
- Marine piles

Design/build
Emergency response
Hauling
Maintenance
Marsh and marine power transmission and distribution
Oilfield construction
Paving
Pipeline installation and repair
Plant dismantling and relocation
Procurement
Project management
Retrofits
Stevedoring
Structural steel erection
Turnarounds
Water quality

COMPETITORS

Bechtel
Boh Bros Construction
Eby
Fluor
Foster Wheeler
Jacobs Engineering
KBR
Lummus Technology
Performance Contractors
Shaw Group

HISTORICAL FINANCIALS

Company Type: Private

Income Statement FYE: September 30

	REVENUE ($ mil.)	NET INCOME ($ mil.)	NET PROFIT MARGIN	EMPLOYEES
09/12	246	18	7.4%	1,500
09/11	497	30	6.1%	—
09/10*	248	6	2.7%	—
06/09	374	18	5.0%	—
Annual Growth	(13.0%)	(0.3%)	—	—

*Fiscal year change

2012 Year-End Financials

Debt ratio: —
Return on equity: 7.40%
Cash ($ mil.): 62
Current ratio: 0.90
Long-term debt ($ mil.): —
Dividends
Yield: —
Payout: —
Market value ($ mil.): —

CALCOT LTD.

EXECUTIVES

Director Sales Administration, Ron Nickell
Assistant VP Futures, Cindy Walters
President and CEO, Jarral Neeper
Director Communications and Corporate Secretary, Mark Bagby
Manager Information Technology, Dan Lucas
VP Arizona Southern California and South Texas Operations, Paul Bush, age 43
VP Sales, John A. Burch
Field Representative Northern San Joaquin Valley & Sacramento Valley, Kevin M. Long
Chairman, Charles A. (Charlie) Fanucchi
CFO, Roxanne F. Wang
Field Representative Southern San Joaquin Valley and Sacramento Valley, Kevin Madding
Assistant VP Grower Services, Marci Cunningham
Treasurer and General Accountant, Miguel Mory
Export Sales Manager, Carlo Bocardo
President Chief Executive Officer, Bob Norris
Auditors: Eadie&PayneLLP

LOCATIONS

HQ: CALCOT LTD.
1900 E BRUNDAGE LN, BAKERSFIELD, CA 933072789
Phone: 6613275961
Web: WWW.CALCOT.COM

COMPETITORS

Cargill
Cotton Inc.
Dunavant Enterprises
International Cotton Marketing
J.G. Boswell Co.
JB Cotton
King Ranch
Plains Cotton
Plexus Cotton
Staplcotn
Weil Brothers Cotton

HISTORICAL FINANCIALS

Company Type: Private

Income Statement FYE: August 31

	REVENUE ($ mil.)	NET INCOME ($ mil.)	NET PROFIT MARGIN	EMPLOYEES
08/14	172	3	1.9%	150
08/13	195	1	0.8%	—
08/12	306	5	1.7%	—
08/11	399	0	—	—
Annual Growth	(24.4%)	—	—	—

2014 Year-End Financials

Debt ratio: —
Return on equity: 1.90%
Cash ($ mil.): 4
Current ratio: 0.40
Long-term debt ($ mil.): —
Dividends
Yield: —
Payout: —
Market value ($ mil.): —

CALIBRE SYSTEMS INC.

When it comes to information technology CALIBRE aims to please. Founded in 1989 the employee-owned company provides information technology and management services to government and commercial clients in the US. It specializes in data analytics modeling and simulation financial and cost management land management logistics and strategic planning among other areas. To expand its capabilities the company partners with a host of technology firms consulting firms educational institutions and other enterprises including AT&T IBM KPMG and George Mason University. The company operates from a handful of US offices as well as on-site at customer facilities.

Geographic Reach CALIBRE has offices in Virginia as well as Alabama California Texas and Washington. Its consultants however work on-site at customer locations across the US and in Afghanistan Kuwait and Qatar.

Sales and Marketing The company's primary client base is agencies of the federal government such as the Department of Defense the Department of Transportation the Army and the Air Force; it also serves associations and not-for-profits (Disabled American Veterans American Institute of Architects) and commercial entities (Boeing ManTech).

EXECUTIVES

President and CEO, Joseph A. Martore
SVP Business Development, Jeffrey E. Giangiuli
Chairman, Lt. Gen. Thomas P. (Tom) Carney
EVP and COO, John C. Mutarelli
EVP and Corporate Development Officer, W. Michael Polster
SVP Operations, Roland W. Carter
Vice President Contracts Administration, Mindy L. Scott
VP Human Resources, Michelle Voisinet Caylor
EVP and CFO, William O. Maxwell
EVP and CFO, Pamela A. Little
Director Communications and Creative Media, Jeanette McTegart
VP Sustainability and Environmental Management Domain, Ted S. Richan
VP Installation Operations Support, Charles J. Fowler
VP Performance and& Cost Management, Brian Rogers
Vice President Logistics & Management Services, David S. Singer
Vice President Performance & Cost Management, Michael J. Streff
VP Logistics Management Information and Technology, Hugh D. (Don) Taylor
VP Business Development, Daniel C. Myung
VP and CTO, Tarak G. Modi
Director Corporate Security, Katherine M. Hein
VP Information Technology, Timothy P. O'Connor
Vice President, Hugh Don
Vice President Installation Management & Transformation, Peter F. Tuebner
Executive Vice President and Chief Administrative Officer, Robert W. Larrick Jr.
Vice President Business Development, Thomas Wilson
Vice President Information Technology, Timothy P. OConnor
Vice President Business Development, Don Taylor
Vice President Business Development, Jeffrey Doerr
Vice President Human Resources, Michelle Caylor
Vice President Veterans, Scott A. Ehrmantraut
President CEO and Director, Joseph A. (Joe) Martore
Director, Charles A. P. Corcoran
Director Contracts Administration and Director, Mindy L. Scott
Director, James T. Scott
Director, Joseph H. Reynolds

LOCATIONS

HQ: CALIBRE SYSTEMS INC.
6354 WALKER LN STE 300, ALEXANDRIA, VA 22310-3252
Phone: 703-797-8500
Web: WWW.CALIBRESYS.COM

PRODUCTS/OPERATIONS

Selected Services
Data Analytics
Energy Environment and Safety Management
Financial and Cost Management
Installation and Land Management
Logistics and Acquisition Management
Program Management and Decision Support
Strategic Planning
Technology Solutions
Training Modeling and Simulation Services

COMPETITORS

Affiliated Computer Services
Alion
Booz Allen
CACI International
Computer Sciences Corp.
Computer Technology Associates
HP Enterprise Services
Lockheed Martin Information Systems
ManTech
Unisys

HISTORICAL FINANCIALS

Company Type: Private

Income Statement FYE: February 29

	REVENUE ($ mil.)	NET INCOME ($ mil.)	NET PROFIT MARGIN	EMPLOYEES
02/12	166	15	9.4%	682
02/11	157	10	6.5%	—
02/09	108	6	5.7%	—
02/08	99	5	5.3%	—
Annual Growth	13.9%	31.5%	—	—

2012 Year-End Financials

Debt ratio: —
Return on equity: 9.40%
Cash ($ mil.): 4
Current ratio: 2.00
Long-term debt ($ mil.): —
Dividends
Yield: —
Payout: —
Market value ($ mil.): —

CALIFORNIA COMMUNITY FOUNDATION

California Community Foundation supports not-for-profit organizations and public institutions in the Los Angeles area. The organization performs its function by offering funding for health and human services affordable housing early childhood education and community arts and culture. The 24th Street Theatre Antelope Valley Hospital and Community Arts Partnership are among the organizations to have received the foundation's grant funding. In times of emergency it has also pitched in to help groups in other areas. California Community Foundation was founded in 1915.

By 2015 the foundation hopes to have helped others find affordable housing and quality education access health care and discover the arts and culture.

EXECUTIVES

President and CEO, Antonia Hernandez
VP and CFO, Steve Cobb
Director Human Resources, Silvana Miller
SVP Programs, Alvertha Bratton Penny
Chair, Reveta Bowers
Chair Emeritus, Jane B. Eisner
EVP and COO, John E. Kobara
Director Communications, Namju Cho
Deputy Field Director Preschool Advocacy Initiative, Sandy Escobedo
Project Coordinator Community Foundation Land Trust, Rosie Diaz
President Community Foundation Land Trust, Ann Sewill
Director Project Management, Lynn Hansen
VP External and Donor Relations, Carol Bradford
Manager Donor and Prospect Research, Patrice Cablayan
Manager Scholarships, Kerry L. Franco
Charitable Business Development Officer, Mia Gorman
Director Donor Relations, Terri Mosqueda
Estate and Gift Planning Officer, Edward Mullen
Director Charitable Business Development, Barry Peterson
Controller, Carolyn Steffen
Network Coordinator, Teresita Vega
Director, David C. Bohnett
Director, James M. Rosser, age 72
Director, Sheldon M. Stone, age 59
Director, Quan Phung
Director, Tom Unterman
Director, Dennis Gertmenian
Director, Cynthia A. Telles, age 59
Chair, Reveta Bowers
Chair Emeritus, Jane B. Eisner
Director, Carolina Reyes
Director, Joanne Corday Kozberg
Director, David W. Fleming
Director, Preston Johnson
Director, Melanie Staggs
Director, Paul Schulz
Director, Jean Bixby Smith
Director, Catherine L. Unger
Director, Sonia Marie De Leon de Vega
Director, Ronald T. Vera
Auditors: KPMGLLP

LOCATIONS

HQ: CALIFORNIA COMMUNITY FOUNDATION
221 S FIGUEROA ST STE 400, LOS ANGELES, CA 90012-3760
Phone: 213-413-4130
Web: WWW.CALFUND.ORG

HISTORICAL FINANCIALS

Company Type: Private

Income Statement

FYE: June 30

	ASSETS ($ mil.)	NET INCOME ($ mil.)	INCOME AS % OF ASSETS	EMPLOYEES
06/11	1,242	139	11.2%	47
06/10	1,120	85	7.6%	—
06/09	1,066	(182)	—	—
06/08	1,257	(87)	—	—
Annual Growth	(0.4%)	—	—	—

2011 Year-End Financials

Debt ratio: —
Return on equity: 54.60%
Cash ($ mil.): 15
Current ratio: —
Long-term debt ($ mil.): —
Dividends
Yield: —
Payout: —
Market value ($ mil.): —

CALIFORNIA HOUSING FOUNDATION

LOCATIONS

HQ: CALIFORNIA HOUSING FOUNDATION
1200 CALIFORNIA ST # 104, REDLANDS, CA 923742945
Phone: 9097939800
Web: WWW.CHFCARES.COM

HISTORICAL FINANCIALS

Company Type: Private

Income Statement

FYE: June 30

	ASSETS ($ mil.)	NET INCOME ($ mil.)	INCOME AS % OF ASSETS	EMPLOYEES
06/13	98	2	2.7%	2
06/12	95	3	3.3%	—
06/10	86	(0)	—	—
Annual Growth	4.4%	—	—	—

2013 Year-End Financials

Debt ratio: —
Return on equity: 23.90%
Cash ($ mil.): 5
Current ratio: 0.20
Long-term debt ($ mil.): —
Dividends
Yield: —
Payout: —
Market value ($ mil.): —

CALIFORNIA INDEPENDENT SYSTEM OPERATOR CORPORATION

The California Independent System Operator (California ISO) manages a 25627-mile power transmission system (about 80% of California's power grid) balancing wholesale supply to meet retail demand. The enterprise directs the flow of electricity along long-distance high-voltage power lines that connect California with neighboring states as well as with Mexico and Canada. It manages the transmission lines and supervises maintenance but the transmission systems are owned and maintained by individual utilities. The not-for-profit public benefit corporation also acts as a transmission planner.

Operations

California ISO also keeps its eye on about 1400 powers plants with 59000 MW of capacity which serve some 30 million California customers. As the control center for the California power grid the company matches buyers and sellers of electricity facilitating nearly 30000 market transactions every day to ensure enough power is on hand to meet demand.

Strategy

The ISO identifies and approves improvements to be made to the grid by individual transmission owners in order to meet state and federal standards for reliability.

To diversify California's power base the corporation has opened up its system to integrate the storage of electricity from alternative sources such as solar wind hydro batteries and flywheels. By 2020 in order to meet stringent carbon emission regulations it is aiming to have 33% of the power on its grid generated by renewable sources (mainly wind solar hydro and biomass).

The ISO is also looking replace the power delivered to about 1.4 million consumers by Southern California Edison's permanent shut-down in 2013 of the San Onofre Nuclear Generating Station.

Company Background

The organization was formed by the state government in 1996. The Independent System Operator assumed computerized command of California's wholesale power grid in 1998.

EXECUTIVES

Vice President General Counsel Chief Administrative Officer, Nancy Saracino
VP Corporate Services, Steve Berberich
VP External Affairs, Karen Edson
VP Human Resources, Brenda Thomas
Vice President Operations, Eric Schmitt
Vice President Market and Infrastructure Development, Keith Casey
Vice President Technology, Petar Ristanovic
Auditors: PricewaterhouseCoopersLLP

LOCATIONS

HQ: CALIFORNIA INDEPENDENT SYSTEM OPERATOR CORPORATION
250 OUTCROPPING WAY, FOLSOM, CA 95630-8773
Phone: 916-351-4400
Web: WWW.CAISO.COM

HISTORICAL FINANCIALS

Company Type: Private

Income Statement FYE: December 31

	REVENUE ($ mil.)	NET INCOME ($ mil.)	NET PROFIT MARGIN	EMPLOYEES
12/07	200	46	23.0%	530
12/06	189	41	21.7%	—
12/05	131	0	0.0%	—
Annual Growth	23.5%	34621.9%	—	—

2007 Year-End Financials

Debt ratio: —
Return on equity: 23.00%
Cash ($ mil.): 220
Current ratio: 1.00
Long-term debt ($ mil.): —

Dividends
Yield: —
Payout: —
Market value ($ mil.): —

CALIFORNIA STATE UNIVERSITY LONG BEACH RESEARCH FOUNDATION

LOCATIONS

HQ: CALIFORNIA STATE UNIVERSITY LONG BEACH RESEARCH FOUNDATION
6300 E STATE UNIV DR 33, LONG BEACH, CA 908154669
Phone: 5629855537
Web: WWW.FOUNDATION.CSULB.EDU

HISTORICAL FINANCIALS

Company Type: Private

Income Statement FYE: June 30

	ASSETS ($ mil.)	NET INCOME ($ mil.)	INCOME AS % OF ASSETS	EMPLOYEES
06/12	169	1	1.1%	625
06/11	166	12	7.6%	—
06/10	155	4	2.7%	—
06/09	148	0	—	—
Annual Growth	4.4%	—	—	—

2012 Year-End Financials

Debt ratio: —
Return on equity: 3.70%
Cash ($ mil.): 0
Current ratio: 1.20
Long-term debt ($ mil.): —

Dividends
Yield: —
Payout: —
Market value ($ mil.): —

CANDID COLOR SYSTEMS INC.

LOCATIONS

HQ: CANDID COLOR SYSTEMS INC.
1300 METROPOLITAN AVE, OKLAHOMA CITY, OK 731082042
Phone: 4059478747
Web: WWW.OKLAHOMAPARTYPICS.COM

HISTORICAL FINANCIALS

Company Type: Private

Income Statement FYE: July 31

	REVENUE ($ mil.)	NET INCOME ($ mil.)	NET PROFIT MARGIN	EMPLOYEES
07/07	21,742	2,534	11.7%	300
07/05	22	1	8.3%	—
07/04	21	2	10.9%	—
07/03	21	0	—	—
Annual Growth	467.2%	—	—	—

2007 Year-End Financials

Debt ratio: —
Return on equity: 11.70%
Cash ($ mil.): 2
Current ratio: 1.70
Long-term debt ($ mil.): —

Dividends
Yield: —
Payout: —
Market value ($ mil.): —

CAPE COD HEALTHCARE INC.

There once was a man from Nantucket who broke his leg when he stepped in a bucket. Falmouth Hospital took care of the man and helped him devise a get-well plan and in the end he was hooked on Cape Cod Healthcare. Cape Cod Healthcare is a not-for-profit healthcare organization that includes two acute-care hospitals (Cape Cod Hospital and Falmouth Hospital) with a total of some 350 beds. It also operates a home health services agency (Visiting Nurse Association) primary and specialized care clinics medical labs a 130-bed skilled nursing and rehabilitation facility and a 60-unit assisted living facility. The health care system has a staff of more than 450 physicians.

Strategy

Cape Cod Healthcare has improved its finances in recent years through a number of cost-cutting measures including employee layoffs and process improvements.

While Cape Cod Healthcare enjoys a strong market share in the Cape Cod region it also struggles with seasonal fluctuations and high Medicare and Medicaid numbers within its patient load. As such the company could be impacted by health reform measures that would decrease Medicare reimbursement levels in future years. Cape Cod Healthcare plans to continue its efforts to control costs and increase efficiencies to keep its operations nimble and keep pace with the changing health care environment.

EXECUTIVES

President and CEO, Michael K. (Mike) Lauf, age 43
SVP Managed Care, Jack D. Lipomi
SVP and Chief Legal Officer, Michael G. Jones
SVP Marketing Communications and Business Development, Patrick Kane
COO, Arthur J. Mombourquette
Senior Vice President of Finance and Chief Financial Officer, Michael L. Connors
Chairman, Thomas Wroe Jr.
VP Human Resources, David Ryan
Chief Medical Officer, Donald A. Guadagnoli
Senior Vice President and Chief Information Officer, Jeanne Fallon
Vice President Human Resources, Dave Ryan
Vice President Patient Financial Services, Victor Oliveira
President Employed Physician Practices, Robert Kleinbauer
Chief Operating Officer at Falmouth Hospital, Jeffrey S. Dykens
Vice Chairman, William Zammer

LOCATIONS

HQ: CAPE COD HEALTHCARE INC.
88 LEWIS BAY RD, HYANNIS, MA 02601-5210
Phone: 508-957-8554
Web: WWW.CAPECODHEALTHCARE.COM

PRODUCTS/OPERATIONS

Selected Massachusetts Facilities

Bourne Health Center
Cape Cod Hospital (Hyannis)
Davenport Mugar Cancer Center (Hyannis)
Falmouth Hospital
Clark Cancer Center
Fontaine Medical Center (Harwich)
Heritage at Falmouth
JLM Care Center (Falmouth)
Mashpee Health Center
Sandwich Health Center
Wilkins Outpatient Medical Complex (Hyannis)

COMPETITORS

Baystate Health
Boston Medical Center
Cambridge Health Alliance
Care New England
CareGroup
Milford Regional Medical Center
Northeast Health System
Partners HealthCare
Southcoast Hospitals Group
Steward Health Care
Universal Health Services
Vanguard Health Systems
Winchester Healthcare

HISTORICAL FINANCIALS

Company Type: Private

Income Statement FYE: September 30

	REVENUE ($ mil.)	NET INCOME ($ mil.)	NET PROFIT MARGIN	EMPLOYEES
09/12	680	80	11.9%	1,850
09/11	648	37	5.7%	—
09/09	587	19	3.2%	—
09/08	27	(2)	—	—
Annual Growth	124.0%	—	—	—

2012 Year-End Financials

Debt ratio: —
Return on equity: 11.90%
Cash ($ mil.): 44
Current ratio: 0.90
Long-term debt ($ mil.): —

Dividends
Yield: —
Payout: —
Market value ($ mil.): —

CAPE COD HOSPITAL

Get too much sun or eat too much lobster while visiting Cape Cod? Never fear Cape Cod Hospital can treat whatever ails you. Cape Cod Hospital a subsidiary of Cape Cod Healthcare is a 260-bed acute care hospital that serves the Cape Cod Massachusetts area. Its specialty services include pediatrics maternity care cancer treatment and infectious disease therapeutics. The not-for-profit Cape Cod Hospital also includes a specialty cardiovascular center a psychiatry unit a surgical pavilion and a diagnostic imaging facility as well as outpatient medical offices.

Geographic Reach

Cape Cod Hospital is located on a 40-acre campus on the shoreline of Hyannis Massachusetts.

Operations

Cape Cod Hospital's emergency department treats about 84000 patients each year. The medical center also performs about 12500 surgeries and 1000 birth procedures each year as well as about 2 million laboratory tests. Its 20-bed Cape Psych Center provides inpatient and outpatient mental and behavioral services. The campus also includes more than a dozen medical offices buildings and a community health center. Cape Cod Hospital's staff includes about 300 physicians.

Strategy

To keep its facilities modern and efficient Cape Cod Healthcare renovated the lobby and entrance areas of the Cape Cod Hospital in 2010. It is also renovating the ER facilities and is upgrading the hospital's technology and information management systems. In addition the hospital expanded its inpatient capacity by adding a new wing with 120 beds in 2007.

To control the cost of providing hospital care parent Cape Cod Healthcare has also been expanding its outpatient and ambulatory care services. It is adding new urgent care centers and surgery centers both near the hospital and in surrounding communities.

Company Background

Cape Cod Hospital was established in Hyannis in 1920.

EXECUTIVES

Vice President Of Clinical Services, Susan Wing
President Employed Physician Practices, Robert Kleinbauer
Chief Operating Officer, Arthur Mombourquette
Exec Vice President Of Nursing, Debb Robinson
Director Of Radiology Services, Cheryl Crupi
Director Of Physical Therapy, Julie Drake
Vp Human Resources Cape Cod Healthcare, David Ryan
Director Of Infection Control, Gigi Dash
Vice President Patient Financial Services, Victor Oliveira
Vp Of Marketing Services, Patrick Kane
Director Of Radiology, John Panicek
Respiratory Therapy Director, Marcellus Johnson
Vp Finance, Richard D Puckett

LOCATIONS

HQ: CAPE COD HOSPITAL
27 PARK ST, HYANNIS, MA 02601-5203
Phone: 508-862-7575
Web: WWW.CAPECODORTHO.COM

COMPETITORS

Baystate Health
Boston Medical Center
Cambridge Health Alliance
Care New England
CareGroup
Children' s Hospital Boston
Milford Regional Medical Center
Northeast Health System
Partners HealthCare
Southcoast Hospitals Group
Steward Health Care
Sturdy Memorial
Universal Health Services
Winchester Healthcare

HISTORICAL FINANCIALS

Company Type: Private

Income Statement FYE: September 30

	REVENUE ($ mil.)	NET INCOME ($ mil.)	NET PROFIT MARGIN	EMPLOYEES
09/12	427	52	12.3%	1,700
09/11	409	29	7.1%	—
09/08*	352	(23)	—	—
12/07	83	(8)	—	—
Annual Growth	38.6%	—	—	—

*Fiscal year change

2012 Year-End Financials

Debt ratio: —
Return on equity: 12.30%
Cash ($ mil.): 21
Current ratio: 1.10
Long-term debt ($ mil.): —
Dividends
Yield: —
Payout: —
Market value ($ mil.): —

CAPITAL DISTRICT PHYSICIANS' HEALTH PLAN INC.

Capital District Physicians' Health Plan (CDPHP) is an independent not-for-profit health plan serving some 385000 members in two dozen New York counties. It offers employer-sponsored and individual managed care plans (including HMO PPO and consumer-directed plans) as well as a Medicare Advantage plan for seniors. The company's coverage include full coverage for some preventative medical services as well as options for covering prescription drugs dental work and vision services. CDPHP also provides wellness programs that help members with weight loss smoking cessation and chronic disease management.

Geographic Reach

CDPHP serves customers in 24 New York counties: Albany Broome Chenango Columbia Delaware Dutchess Essex Fulton Greene Hamilton Herkimer Madison Montgomery Oneida Orange Otsego Rensselaer Saratoga Schenectady Schoharie Tioga Ulster Warren and Washington.

Operations

In addition to its commercial and Medicare offerings CDPHP provides health plans under several state-subsidized insurance programs including Family Health Plus and Child Health Plus (intended for residents who don't qualify for Medicaid) and Healthy NY (intended for small businesses and sole proprietors). Altogether the CDPHP provider network includes more than 10000 physicians and facilities.

Financial Performance

CDPHP reported an 11% increase in revenues in 2011 to some $1.5 billion. Coupled with a rise in net investment income higher earnings resulted in an 11% increase in net income (to some $53 million) as well.

Strategy

CDPHP's self-proclaimed strategy is to use the majority of its premium income to pay out medical claims while maintaining necessary reserve levels to keep its solid financial performance and to comply with federal medical loss-ratio guidelines. It earmarks a small amount of income for operational expenses as well as to fund growth and wellness initiatives.

CDPHP also works to lower medical expenses by partnering with other regional care and plan providers. For instance it partnered with Trendshift in 2011 to provide a new group funding management system for employers.

Company Background

An association of local Albany physicians founded CDPHP in 1984.

EXECUTIVES

President Chief Executive Officer CEO, John D. Bennett
Senior Vice President Sales, Carole Montepare
Senior Vice President Chief Operating Officer, Barbara A. (Barb) Downs
SVP Strategy and Communications and Chief Strategy Officer, Robert R. Hinckley
Vice Chairman, Gennaro A. Daniels
Senior Vice President General Counsel, Frederick Galt
SVP Medical Affairs and Chief Medical Officer, Bruce D. Nash
Senior Vice President Chief Marketing Officer, Brian Morrissey
Senior Vice President Human Capital Management, Scott Klenk
Senior Vice President Information Technology and Chief Information Officer, Neil Brandmaier
Senior Vice President of Finance and Chief Financial Officer CFO, Bethany R. Smith

LOCATIONS

HQ: CAPITAL DISTRICT PHYSICIANS' HEALTH PLAN INC.
500 PATROON CREEK BLVD, ALBANY, NY 12206-5006
Phone: 518-641-3700
Web: WWW.CDPHP.COM

PRODUCTS/OPERATIONS

Selected Products

Dental and Vision Health Plans
- CVS ExtraCare Health Card
- Delta Dental

Government Plans
- Child Health Plus
- Family Health Plus
- Medicaid Select Plan
- Medicare Choices (HMO)

Group Health Plans
- Embrace Health
- Exclusive Provider Organization (EPO)
- Group Medicare
- High Deductible Health Plans (HDHP)
- Health Maintenance Organization (HMO)
- Healthy Direction
- Lifestyle Riders
- Preferred Provider Organization (PPO)
- Transitional Health Plans
- Health Funding Arrangements
- Flexible Spending Accounts
- Health Reimbursement Arrangement
- Health Savings Account

Individual Health Plans
- Healthy New York
- Non-Group Health Plans

COMPETITORS

Aetna
CIGNA
EmblemHealth
Fidelis Care New York
Humana
Independent Health
MVP Health Plan
UnitedHealth Group
WellPoint
excellus bluecross blueshield rochester region
healthnow new york inc

HISTORICAL FINANCIALS

Company Type: Private

Income Statement FYE: December 31

	REVENUE ($ mil.)	NET INCOME ($ mil.)	NET PROFIT MARGIN	EMPLOYEES
12/09	1,037	33	3.2%	700
12/03	818	(1)	—	—
12/02	719	9	1.3%	—
12/01	636	32	5.1%	—
Annual Growth	6.3%	0.4%	—	—

2009 Year-End Financials

Debt ratio: —
Return on equity: 3.20%
Cash ($ mil.): 72
Current ratio: 0.80
Long-term debt ($ mil.): —
Dividends
Yield: —
Payout: —
Market value ($ mil.): —

CARE NEW ENGLAND HEALTH SYSTEM INC

Care New England Health System take pains to ease its patients' pain. The system operates four hospitals: Kent Hospital a general acute care facility with about 360 beds; the 290-bed Memorial Hospital of Rhode Island; psychiatric facility Butler Hospital; and Women & Infants Hospital of Rhode Island which specializes in obstetrics gynecology and newborn pediatrics. All told the system has more than 640 licensed beds. Care New England formed in 1996 by its three member hospitals also operates a home health agency and outpatient care facilities.

Geographic Reach

Based in Providence Rhode Island Care New England serves southeastern New England communities including Central Falls and Pawtucket Rhode Island and Plainville Massachusetts.

Operations

Three of the Care New England hospitals –Memorial Hospital Women & Infants and Butler –are teaching hospitals for Brown University's Warren Alpert Medical School. Altogether the organization's facilities handle more than 40000 inpatient discharges each year as well as 95000 emergency room visits and 9000 births. The organization provided $11 million in community benefits in 2012.

The organization's VNA of Care New England unit administers home health and hospice care as well as private duty nursing services for the elderly new mothers and terminally ill patients. The Care New England Wellness Center offers fitness and rehabilitation services. The health care network also includes physician practice locations and an adult day care center.

Strategy

The Care New England system is focused on five key initiatives: system strength clinical excellence physician alignment strategic partnerships and academic excellence. It is working to strengthen operations in clinical fields including cardiology emergency medicine behavioral health pathology pediatrics and women's health. In 2013 the company enhanced its mental health services by forming an affiliation with The Providence Center. In addition Kent Hospital launched the construction of a new ambulatory surgery and primary care center.

Mergers and Acquisitions

The Care New England organization added its fourth hospital in 2013 through the acquisition of Memorial Hospital of Rhode Island. The purchase added acute care and primary care capacity and expanded the organization's regional presence.

EXECUTIVES

President CEO and Director, John J. Hynes
Executive Vice President Behavioral, Patricia R. Recupero
Senior Vice President, Michael J. Dacey
Vice Chairman, Edward J. Cooney
President of Patient Care Services, Constance A. Howes
SVP Planning, Gail E. Costa
SVP General Counsel and Secretary, Thomas R. Courage
SVP Managed Care Contracting and Network Development, Domenic F. Delmonico
Senior Vice President Marketing Communications, May Kernan
SVP Human Resources, Marilyn J. Walsh
Associate VP Finance, Carleen P. Smith
Senior Vice President Chief Information Officer, Cedric J. Priebe III
Director Materials Management, Thomas W. Gardner
Chairman, Robert E. DeBlois
President Chief Executive Officer of VNA of Care New England, Nancy Roberts
Vice Chairman, Cynthia B. Patterson
Senior Vice President Chief Administrative Officer, Joseph DiPietro
Senior Vice President and Chief Nursing Officer, Rene Fischer
Senior Vice President Human Resources, David Campbell
Vice President Revenue Enhancement, Helen Reed
Chief Medical Officer, Joseph W. Spinale
President CEO and Director, John J. Hynes
EVP Behavioral Health Services and Director; President and CEO Butler Hospital, Patricia R. Recupero
Director, George W. Shuster
Director, Andrew M. Erickson
Vice Chairman, Edward J. Cooney
Director, Jonathan K. Farnum
EVP and Director; President and CEO Women & Infants Hospital, Constance A. Howes
Director, Charles R. Reppucci
Director, Allan H. Cicchitelli
Director, Robert G. Flanders Jr.
Director, Douglas Jacobs
Director, David A. Lowe
Vice Chairman, Cynthia B. Patterson
Director, Steven A. Rasmussen

LOCATIONS

HQ: CARE NEW ENGLAND HEALTH SYSTEM INC
45 WILLARD AVE, PROVIDENCE, RI 02905-3218
Phone: 401-453-7900
Web: WWW.VNACARENEWENGLAND.ORG

COMPETITORS

Baystate Health
Catholic Health East
Community Health Systems
Health Management Associates
Lifespan Corporation
Memorial Hospital of Rhode Island
Partners HealthCare
Roger Williams Medical Center
Southcoast Hospitals Group
Tenet Healthcare
Universal Health Services
Yale New Haven Health System

HISTORICAL FINANCIALS

Company Type: Private

Income Statement FYE: September 30

	ASSETS ($ mil.)	NET INCOME ($ mil.)	INCOME AS % OF ASSETS	EMPLOYEES
09/12	783	24	3.1%	6,500
09/04	472	7	1.5%	—
09/03	435	(1)	—	—
09/02	116	0	0.0%	—
Annual Growth	21.0%	207.6%	—	—

2012 Year-End Financials

Debt ratio: —
Return on equity: 2.80%
Cash ($ mil.): 62
Current ratio: 1.20
Long-term debt ($ mil.): —

Dividends
Yield: —
Payout: —
Market value ($ mil.): —

CAREALLIANCE HEALTH SERVICES

CareAlliance Health Services (doing business as Roper St. Francis Healthcare) knows that St. Francis may be the patron saint of animals but its medical centers are more concerned with humans. The company operates four hospitals –the 370-bed Roper Hospital the 200-bed Bon Secours St. Francis Hospital the 85-bed Mount Pleasant Hospital and the Roper Rehabilitation Hospital. It also operates outpatient emergency primary care and diagnostic facilities and it provides home health services. Roper St. Francis Healthcare serves Charleston South Carolina and surrounding communities. Its Roper St. Francis Physician Partners is one of the largest physician practices in the region.

Geographic Reach

Altogether Roper St. Francis Healthcare operates about 90 facilities in seven counties in the lowcountry region of South Carolina.

Operations

Roper St. Francis Healthcare has a medical staff of some 800 physicians. The Roper St. Francis Physician Partners organization has more than 180 physicians that offer primary and specialty care including family practice internal medicine and pediatrics.

Strategy

The health system is planning to add a fifth hospital to its roster after it completes construction of a 50-bed facility in Berkeley County to meet population growth demands in the blossoming region. Other facility expansions include the opening of two after-hours care centers in 2011 and 2012; it also started construction of a new data center in 2012 to help facilitate the implementation of its new electronic health record (EHR) system. Previously the health system opened the Mount Pleasant Hospital in November 2010.

Company Background

Roper St. Francis Healthcare was formed through the merger of Roper Hospital and Bon Secours St. Francis Hospital in 1998.

Roper St. Francis Physician Partners was formed through the 2009 combination of Roper St. Francis Physicians' Network and Lowcountry Medical Associates.

EXECUTIVES

President Chief Executive Officer, David L. Dunlap
VP and CIO, Mike Taylor
Vice President of Medical Affairs & Chief Medical Officer, Steven Shapiro
Senior Vice President & Chief Financial Officer, Bret Johnson
CEO Roper Hospital and SVP Operations, Matthew Severance
CEO Roper St. Francis Mount Pleasant Hospital and VP Operations, John Sullivan
Vice President Human Resources, Douglas Harrison
CEO Bon Secours St. Francis Hospital and SVP Operations, Allen Carroll
Chairman Roper St. Francis Foundation, John B. Holloway
Vice Chairman Roper St. Francis Foundation, Charles T. Cole
Treasurer, Edmund Puckhaber
Vice President General Counsel, Greg Edwards
Vice President Nursing & Senior, Lisa Irvin
Vice President Mission, Mark Dickson
Vice President Nursing & Senior Nurse Executive Bon Secours St. Francis, Pennie Peralta

Vice President Nursing & Senior Nurse Executive Roper Hospital, Lisa Schafer
CEO RSF Physician Partners & RSFH Vice President & Chief Strategy Officer, Douglas Bowling
Chief Nursing Officer & Vice President Patient Care Services Mount Pleasant Hospital, Diana Topjian
Vice President Nursing & Senior Nurse Executive, Bon St

LOCATIONS

HQ: CAREALLIANCE HEALTH SERVICES
315 CALHOUN ST STE 107, CHARLESTON, SC 29401-1115
Phone: 843-724-2000
Web: WWW.ROPERSAINTFRANCIS.COM

Selected South Carolina Facilities

Hospitals
- Mt. Pleasant Hospital Campus Mount Pleasant
- Roper Hospital Campus - Charleston
- Roper Rehabilitation Hospital
- St. Francis Campus - Charleston

Outpatient Centers
- After Hours Care - James Island
- Kiawah-Seabrook Medical & Urgent Care
- Roper Hospital Ambulatory Surgery - Berkeley
- Roper Hospital Ambulatory Surgery & Pain Management - James Island
- Roper Hospital Diagnostics & ER - Berkeley
- Roper Hospital Diagnostics & ER - Northwoods
- Roper Hospital Diagnostics - Farmfield
- Roper Hosptial Diagnostics - Goose Creek
- Roper Hosptial Diagnostics - James Island
- Roper Hosptial Diagnostics - Kiawah-Seabrook
- Roper Hosptial Diagnostics - Moncks Corner
- Roper Hospital Imaging - Wesley Drive
- Roper Hospital Imaging - Wingo Way

COMPETITORS

Beaufort Memorial Hospital
Conway Medical Center
Georgetown Hospital System
HCA
Health Management Associates
Medical University of South Carolina
Tenet Healthcare

HISTORICAL FINANCIALS

Company Type: Private

Income Statement FYE: December 31

	REVENUE ($ mil.)	NET INCOME ($ mil.)	NET PROFIT MARGIN	EMPLOYEES
12/09	682	56	8.3%	5,000
12/08	618	(51)	—	—
12/08	1,658	0	0.0%	—
Annual Growth	(58.8%)	13359378.7%	—	—

2009 Year-End Financials

Debt ratio: —
Return on equity: 8.30%
Cash ($ mil.): 25
Current ratio: 0.70
Long-term debt ($ mil.): —
Dividends
Yield: —
Payout: —
Market value ($ mil.): —

CAREGROUP INC.

Thanks to CareGroup there's well-bein' in Beantown. Formed through the 1997 union of several Boston-area health care organizations CareGroup serves Massachusetts residents through its flagship facility the 650-bed Beth Israel Deaconess Medical Center (BIDMC) and four other hospital campuses. With roughly 1100 beds total the system provides a comprehensive range of general acute care as well as specialty care in a number of areas including orthopedics obstetrics diabetes and cardiovascular disease. In addition to its hospitals CareGroup operates a network of outpatient clinics and physician practices in the Boston area. It is also heavily involved in biomedical research and medical education.

Geographic Reach

All of CareGroup's facilities are located in the Boston Massachusetts area.

Operations

The not-for-profit CareGroup organization operates five hospitals: BIDMC and its Beth Israel Deaconess Hospital-Needham and Beth Israel Deaconess Hospital-Milton (90 beds) satellite centers as well as the Beth Israel Deaconess New England Baptist Hospital and the Mount Auburn Hospital (210 beds). BIDMC and its two satellite hospitals employ 1250 physicians and handle some 50000 inpatient and 550000 outpatient visits each year.

BIDMC and the system's Mount Auburn Hospital are both teaching facilities for Harvard University's medical school while New England Baptist is affiliated with the medical schools of Harvard and Tufts University. BIDMC's biomedical research division receives roughly $200 million annually from the National Institutes of Health to help fund its research programs. BIDMC researchers conduct more than 850 active sponsored projects and 200 clinical trials. Research partners include the Dana-Farber Cancer Institute and the Joslin Diabetes Center. The BIDMC campus also includes the Harvard-Thorndike Laboratory which conducts clinical and medical lab research and has one of the most competitive residency and fellowship programs in the country.

Sales and Marketing

As its patient volume has continued to remain stable or even increase in recent years CareGroup has sought to expand and establish new clinical relationships with suburban providers in order to create a strong referral base in the communities surrounding Boston. Framingham's MetroWest Medical Center and BIDMC are establishing a cardiac service line while Mount Auburn is establishing its own primary care network.

CareGroup promotes its services through television print and outdoor advertising as well as direct mail and physician marketing campaigns.

Financial Performance

Revenues increased 3% to some $2.45 billion in 2012 on higher net patient service revenues and income sources despite a decline in investment income and research contributions. CareGroup is heavily reliant on BIDMC and its two satellite hospitals which account for about 75% of CareGroup's revenues.

Net income rose 180% to $131 million in 2012 due to the organization's new affiliation with the Milton hospital as well as from gains on limited partnership equity interests.

Strategy

CareGroup also known as CareGroup Healthcare System administers care to its member facilities in the form of consulting administrative and financial support. Though it offers such support services to its facilities each hospital operates autonomously with its own government and operational authority.

The system looks to grow by forming new affiliation agreements with area care providers as well as by expanding and improving services at existing facilities. By partnering with hospitals and clinics CareGroup aims to form a regional care organization to improve care management efficiency and quality for area residents. To expand its specialist services in 2013 the group launched construction of a new cancer center and surgical pavilion on the Beth Israel Deaconess Hospital-Needham campus.

Mergers and Acquisitions

BIDMC added a second satellite hospital when it formed an affiliation with Milton Hospital (now Beth Israel Deaconess Hospital-Milton) in 2012. The following year BIDMC entered an agreement to bring another Massachusetts medical center Jordan Hospital into the group. Through the affiliation Jordan Hospital will retain its independent management team and board of directors.

EXECUTIVES

SVP Human Resources, Lisa Zankman
CIO, John D. Halamka, age 51
President and CEO, Paul F. Levy

LOCATIONS

HQ: CAREGROUP INC.
375 LONGWOOD AVE FL 7, BOSTON, MA 02215-5395
Phone: 617-975-5000
Web: WWW.CAREGROUP.ORG

PRODUCTS/OPERATIONS

Selected Massachusetts Hospitals

Beth Israel Deaconess Medical Center (Boston)
Beth Israel Deaconess Hospital-Milton
Beth Israel Deaconess Hospital-Needham
Mount Auburn Hospital (Cambridge)
New England Baptist Hospital (Boston)

COMPETITORS

Baystate Health
Boston Medical Center
Brigham and Women's Hospital
Cambridge Health Alliance
Cape Cod Healthcare
Children's Hospital Boston
Lahey Health System
Massachusetts General Hospital
Milford Regional Medical Center
Partners HealthCare
Southcoast Health
St. Elizabeth's Medical Center
Steward Health Care
Winchester Healthcare

HISTORICAL FINANCIALS

Company Type: Private

Income Statement FYE: September 30

	REVENUE ($ mil.)	NET INCOME ($ mil.)	NET PROFIT MARGIN	EMPLOYEES
09/12	2,448	131	5.4%	12,000
09/11	2,380	46	2.0%	—
09/10	2,311	98	4.2%	—
09/09	2	0	2.2%	—
Annual Growth	938.6%	1288.8%	—	—

2012 Year-End Financials

Debt ratio: —
Return on equity: 5.40%
Cash ($ mil.): 284
Current ratio: 1.50
Long-term debt ($ mil.): —
Dividends
Yield: —
Payout: —
Market value ($ mil.): —

CARITAS NORWOOD HOSPITAL INC.

Caritas Norwood Hospital cares for hearts (and other body parts) of people in the greater Boston area. Operating as Norwood Hospital the facility is a community hospital with some 265 beds that serves patients in Norwood Massachusetts and surrounding towns. Founded in 1902 the acute care hospital has a medical staff of more than 450 that provides area residents with emergency and general health care and medical transport services. Norwood Hospital is also home to specialized programs including behavioral health services cancer treatment cardiology obstetrics/gynecology orthopedic medicine pediatrics rehabilitation sleep disorder treatment and surgery. Norwood Hospital is part of the Steward Health Care System.

Geographic Reach

Norwood Hospital serves a population of about 300000 people in Norwood and about 15 other area communities.

Operations

Norwood Hospital conducts a number of community health outreach programs including a cardiovascular disease education program a diabetes awareness program and a healthy nutrition program. The medical center also provides some $3.6 million in charity care to uninsured patients each year.

Strategy

To expand its specialty services in 2012 Norwood Hospital launched a knee surgery program. The MAKOplasty partial knee resurfacing program represents new technology advances in the orthopedic field.

EXECUTIVES

Medical Director, Eric Awtry
Vice President, Thomas Kenny
Chief Nursing Officer And Vice President Of Patient Care Services, Kathleen Davidson

LOCATIONS

HQ: CARITAS NORWOOD HOSPITAL INC.
800 WASHINGTON ST STE 1, NORWOOD, MA 02062-3487
Phone: 781-769-4000
Web: WWW.CARITASNORWOOD.ORG

PRODUCTS/OPERATIONS

Selected Services

Center for Cancer Care
Center for Cardiac and Vascular Care
Center for Weight Control
MAKOplasty (hip replacement)
Maternity
Orthopedics
Pediatrics

COMPETITORS

Boston Medical Center
Cambridge Health Alliance
CareGroup
Children' s Hospital Boston
Harrington Memorial Hospital
Northeast Health System
Partners HealthCare
South Shore Health
Sturdy Memorial

HISTORICAL FINANCIALS

Company Type: Private

Income Statement FYE: September 30

	REVENUE ($ mil.)	NET INCOME ($ mil.)	NET PROFIT MARGIN	EMPLOYEES
09/09	159	4	2.7%	1,800
09/08	151	(3)	—	—
09/06	153	15	9.8%	—
09/05	150	4	3.0%	—
Annual Growth	1.6%	(1.1%)	—	—

2009 Year-End Financials

Debt ratio: —
Return on equity: 2.70%
Cash ($ mil.): 7
Current ratio: 0.30
Long-term debt ($ mil.): —
Dividends
Yield: —
Payout: —
Market value ($ mil.): —

CARLE FOUNDATION HOSPITAL

Carle Foundation Hospital is a 345-bed acute-care facility that serves the residents of east central Illinois. The hospital includes the region's only Level I trauma center as well as a Level III perinatal center a neonatal ICU and centers devoted to cardiac and cancer care. It also runs a handful of specialty centers in the region. Carle Foundation Hospital is the primary teaching hospital for the University of Illinois College of Medicine at Urbana-Champaign. It is controlled by the not-for-profit Carle Foundation; sister company Carle Physician Group which boasts more than 330 physicians representing 50 specialties is one of the nation's largest private physician groups.

Geographic Reach

Carle Foundation Hospital's service area spans nine communities across east-central Illinois.

Operations

The hospital averages more than 20500 annual patient admissions and treats 63000-plus emergency room patients. It offers services related to bariatrics stroke sports medicine women's health and heart and cancer care.

Strategy

The hospital's affiliation with the Carle Physician Group has strengthened in recent years particularly when the Carle Foundation acquired the physician group in 2010 and became a not-for-profit entity. Prior to the deal Carle Foundation Hospital and Carle Physician Group already operated a number of collaborative facilities including specialty cancer cardiovascular and orthopedic clinics.

Construction has been key to Carle Foundation Hospital's growth in recent years. The hospital built a $6 million center for children with hearing loss; the center houses the Expanding Children's Hearing Opportunities Center and the Carle Auditory Oral School. Carle Foundation Hospital Research Institute opened an $11-million Biomedical Research Center that houses hospital and University of Illinois staff conducting research in breast cancer gastrointestinal and cardiovascular disease and neuroscience.

The hospital also started construction in 2011 on a $200 million addition to the main hospital center. The seven-story patient tower will house the heart and vascular institute and is scheduled for completion in 2013. The new patient capacity will replace patient beds in older parts of the hospital and provide for future growth opportunities.

EXECUTIVES

VP Medical Affairs, Napoleon B. Knight
President and CEO, James C. Leonard
Director Public Relations, Gretchen Robbins
VP of Research and Graduate Medical Education, James Dougherty

LOCATIONS

HQ: CARLE FOUNDATION HOSPITAL
611 W PARK ST STE 1, URBANA, IL 61801-2512
Phone: 217-383-3311
Web: WWW.CARLE.ORG

PRODUCTS/OPERATIONS

Selected Medical Services

Bariatrics
Cancer
Heart
Sports Medicine
Stroke
Women's Health

COMPETITORS

Advocate BroMenn
Crawford Memorial Hospital
Decatur Memorial Hospital
Hospital Sisters Health System
Iroquois Memorial Hospital
Memorial Health System
Morris Hospital
OSF Healthcare System
Provena Health
Sarah Bush Lincoln Health Center
Silver Cross Hospital
St. Elizabeth Regional Health
St. John' s Hospital (Illinois)
Union Hospital (Indiana)

HISTORICAL FINANCIALS

Company Type: Private

Income Statement FYE: December 31

	REVENUE ($ mil.)	NET INCOME ($ mil.)	NET PROFIT MARGIN	EMPLOYEES
12/12*	462	106	23.0%	2,500
06/09	365	30	8.4%	—
06/08	383	36	9.6%	—
Annual Growth	3.8%	23.7%	—	—

*Fiscal year change

CARNEGIE MELLON UNIVERSITY

If you can't act maybe Carnegie Mellon University can help. The university is known around the world for churning out award-winning actors from its highly regarded drama school. Drama isn't all Carnegie teaches though the school has seven colleges and schools that offer academic programs in areas such as psychology computer science engineering biology and public policy. It has more than 12000 students and 5000 faculty and staff and it has a relatively small student-teacher ratio of 10:1. Carnegie Mellon was founded by philanthropist and industrialist Andrew Carnegie who established the Carnegie Technical Schools in 1900 for the sons and daughters of Pittsburgh's blue-collar workers.

Geographic Reach

The school has locations in Pittsburgh (its main campus); Australia; Japan; Silicon Valley California; Singapore; Mexico; Greece; Portugal; and Doha Qatar.

Operations

Along with its undergraduate and graduate degree programs Carnegie offers working adults a chance to continue their learning through the Professional & Distance Learning arm of the school. Students there can hone their international business management skills and bone up on information technology health systems and human resources among other topics.

Carnegie prides itself on its innovation efforts and to support them operates about 120 research institutes and centers across its campus. Carnegie's CyLab is one of the largest university-based cybersecurity education and research centers in the country. Cylab focuses on seven primary areas of research and development spanning a wide range of technologies and systems and users.

Carnegie in 2012 established the Wilton E. Scott Institute for Energy Innovation a research and education initiative focused on improving energy efficiency and developing new clean and affordable energy sources. It also launched Initiative for Digital Entertainment Analytics which conducts research into questions raised by the emergence of digital distribution channels for entertainment content.

Financial Performance

The university experienced growth of 11% in 2012 due to increased retention in undergraduate programs and growth in graduate program tuition and international programs. The growth was also due to increase in investment income and income from auxiliary service.

However Carnegie experienced a 84% decline in net income in 2012 due to increases in operating expenses dining vendor expenses and software and maintenance licenses. Its bottom line was also hurt by a decrease in revenue from non-operating activities.

Company Background

Carnegie Tech merged with the Mellon Institute of Research to become Carnegie Mellon University in 1967.

EXECUTIVES

Vice Chairman, James E. (Jim) Rohr, age 65
Chairman, Raymond J. (Ray) Lane, age 67
President, Jared L. Cohon, age 66
EVP Provost and Chief Academic Officer; Interim CFO, Mark S. Kamlet
Vice President Chief Financial Officer, Deborah Moon
Vice Chairman, E. Kears Pollock
President, Subra Suresh
Dean Heinz College, Ramayya Krishnan
Chief Investment Officer, Charles A Kennedy
CIO, Steven K. (Steve) Huth
Director Marketing and Communications, Lara Steiner
Dean Carnegie Institute of Technology School of Engineering, James H. Garrett Jr.
Dean College of Fine Arts, Dan Martin
Dean Dietrich College of Humanities and Social Sciences, John Lehoczky
Dean Mellon College of Science, Fred Gilman
Dean School of Computer Science, Randall E. (Randy) Bryant
Dean Tepper School of Business, Robert M. Dammon
Vice Chairman, James E. (Jim) Rohr, age 65
President and Trustee, Jared L. Cohon, age 66
Vice Chairman, E. Kears Pollock
Auditors: Deloitte&ToucheLLP

LOCATIONS

HQ: CARNEGIE MELLON UNIVERSITY
5000 FORBES AVE, PITTSBURGH, PA 15213-3890
Phone: 412-268-8746
Web: WWW.HSS.CMU.EDU

Selected Locations

Adelaide Australia
Athens Greece
Aveiro and Coimbra Portugal
Doha Qatar
Kobe Japan
Lisbon Portugal
Los Angeles
Madeira Portugal
Minho and Porto Portugal
Mexico
Silicon Valley
Singapore

PRODUCTS/OPERATIONS

Selected Schools

Carnegie Institute of Technology
School of Computer Science
College of Fine Arts
College of Humanities & Social Sciences
H. John Heinz III College
Mellon College of Science
Tepper School of Business

HISTORICAL FINANCIALS

Company Type: Private

Income Statement FYE: June 30

	REVENUE ($ mil.)	NET INCOME ($ mil.)	NET PROFIT MARGIN	EMPLOYEES
06/12	1,061	44	4.2%	4,913
06/11	956	278	29.1%	—
06/10	899	97	10.8%	—
06/09	864	(366)	—	—
Annual Growth	7.1%	—	—	—

2012 Year-End Financials

Debt ratio: —
Return on equity: 4.20%
Cash ($ mil.): 162
Current ratio: —
Long-term debt ($ mil.): —
Dividends
Yield: —
Payout: —
Market value ($ mil.): —

CAROMONT HEALTH INC.

CaroMont Health is an independent not-for-profit health care system serving residents of North Carolina's Piedmont region. Anchoring CaroMont Health is Gaston Memorial Hospital a 435-bed medical and surgical facility that features a birthing center an inpatient psychiatric ward and specialized facilities for heart disease cancer sleep disorders diabetes and wound care. Other operations include a nearly 100-bed nursing home outpatient surgery and urgent care centers and a network of primary and specialty medical practices. CaroMont Health also provides home health and hospice care services. CaroMont Health is governed by the North Carolina Medical Care Commission.

Geographic Reach

CaroMont's primary facilities are located in Gastonia a community just west of Charlotte North Carolina. The health network also operates clinics and offices in Cleveland Mecklenburg Mountain Island Lake and Lincoln North Carolina as well as in York South Carolina.

Operations

CaroMont Health employs a total of some 3800 health professionals including about 450 physicians. Its CaroMont Medical Group physician practice organization includes 140 doctors that serve patients from 45 outpatient locations including primary and specialty practices surgery centers and urgent and immediate care clinics.

Financial Analysis

CaroMont Health reported operating revenues of some $472 million in 2011 nearly all of which came from patient service revenues. The organization also reported expenses of $446 million giving it an operating income of $26 million that year. CaroMont Health also reported $67 million in non-operating revenues giving it a total excess return of $93 million.

Strategy

Like many medical networks CaroMont Health is establishing urgent care and walk-in immediate care centers to offset un-necessary use of hospital emergency rooms. Such facilities help to lower costs and increase efficient patient care management. In 2011 CaroMont Health opened its first CLiC (convenient local immediate care) clinic in the nearby community of Mountain Island Lake; the CaroMont network already included two urgent care centers.

In other efforts to meet area population needs CaroMont began an expansion program to significantly increase the size of its Gaston Hospice facility.

EXECUTIVES

CFO, David O'Connor
COO, Terry Jones
Executive Vice President Chief Financial Officer, David O?
Vice President Human Resources, Libby McCraw
Vice President Chief Information Officer, Mike Johnson
Vice President Chief Nursing Officer, Bonnie Faust
Vice President Operations, Daniel Tuffy
Vice President Clinical Operations, Kathleen Besson
Vice President Wellness Development, Andrea Serra
Vice President Diagnostic and Support Services, Richard Blackburn
Vice President Patient Care & Post-Acute Services, Kathleen Harwell
Executive Vice President Chief Legal Officer, Maria Long
Executive Vice President Operational Integration & Chief Operating Officer Interim CEO, Douglas Luckett
Vice President Corporate Responsibility Officer, Donnetta Horseman
Vice President Patient Safety, Todd Davis

LOCATIONS

HQ: CAROMONT HEALTH INC.
2525 COURT DR, GASTONIA, NC 28054-2140
Phone: 704-834-2000
Web: WWW.CAROMONTHEALTH.ORG

PRODUCTS/OPERATIONS

Selected Service Areas

Cancer (oncology)
Diabetes
Emergency care
Heart and vascular
Hospice and palliative care
Immediate care
Long-term care
Mental health
Mobile screening
Neuroscience
Orthopedics
Pain management
Rehabilitation
Sleep medicine
Surgery
Trauma
Wellness programs
Women' s health
Wound care

COMPETITORS

Blue Ridge HealthCare
Carolinas HealthCare System
Community Health Systems
Health Management Associates
High Point Regional Health System
Mission Hospitals
New Hanover Regional Medical Center
Novant Health
Tenet Healthcare

HISTORICAL FINANCIALS

Company Type: Private

Income Statement FYE: June 30

	REVENUE ($ mil.)	NET INCOME ($ mil.)	NET PROFIT MARGIN	EMPLOYEES
06/11	471	94	20.1%	2,400
06/10	6	5	84.9%	—
06/08	10	0	8.5%	—
Annual Growth	255.6%	374.2%	—	—

2011 Year-End Financials

Debt ratio: —
Return on equity: 20.10%
Cash ($ mil.): 1
Current ratio: 0.60
Long-term debt ($ mil.): —
Dividends
Yield: —
Payout: —
Market value ($ mil.): —

CARPENTER CONTRACTORS OF AMERICA INC.

Carpenter Contractors of America has been working with wood for more than half of a century. The company manufactures roof trusses and wall panels and supplies building materials through its manufacturing facilities in Florida. The company also has offices in North Carolina and Illinois where it operates under the name R&D Thiel. The company's products and services are used in both residential and commercial construction. In 1955 brothers Robert and Donald Thiel founded the company as R&D Thiel in Belvidere Illinois. Carpenter Contractors of America filed for Chapter 11 bankruptcy in 2010.

EXECUTIVES

Chairman and CEO, Donald Thiel
VP Finance Secretary and Treasurer, Terrance B. (Terry) Smith
President Chicago, Donald W. (Don) Reiter
President, Billy D. (Bill) Fritsch

LOCATIONS

HQ: CARPENTER CONTRACTORS OF AMERICA INC.
3900 AVENUE D NW, WINTER HAVEN, FL 33880
Phone: 863-294-6449
Web: WWW.RDTHIEL.COM

COMPETITORS

Putnam Lumber & Export
Robbins Manufacturing Company
Roberts Lumber Company

HISTORICAL FINANCIALS

Company Type: Private

Income Statement FYE: February 3

	REVENUE ($ mil.)	NET INCOME ($ mil.)	NET PROFIT MARGIN	EMPLOYEES
02/07	353	12	3.5%	1,000
02/02	183	8	4.4%	—
02/01*	174	8	4.6%	—
01/00	159	5	3.2%	—
Annual Growth	12.1%	13.6%	—	—

*Fiscal year change

2007 Year-End Financials

Debt ratio: —
Return on equity: 3.50%
Cash ($ mil.): 28
Current ratio: 2.40
Long-term debt ($ mil.): —
Dividends
Yield: —
Payout: —
Market value ($ mil.): —

CARSON TAHOE REGIONAL HEALTHCARE

Carson Tahoe Regional Healthcare includes the Carson Tahoe Regional Medical Center (CTRMC) and serves Nevada's Carson Valley and surrounding areas. The not-for-profit CTRMC has 170 beds and provides acute general surgical specialty and outpatient care. The medical center also includes a rehabilitation center cardiovascular center surgical unit free-standing cancer center emergency room and women and children's center. Carson Tahoe Regional Healthcare also operates smaller urgent care behavioral health physical therapy and outpatient care centers in Carson City and nearby communities.

Geographic Reach

Carson Tahoe Health System's network of healthcare facilities services and programs are located in and around Northern Nevada and Eastern California.

Operations

The health system operates in 17 locations and serves a population of 250000. It has more than 240 board-certified physicians with expertise in more than 35 medical specialties.

Carson Tahoe Health's Behavioral Health Services division provides a diagnosis/multi disciplinary team approach to treating seniors adults adolescents and children experiencing behavioral and addictive disorders. It provides a broad range of inpatient and outpatient services that includes individual group and family counseling support groups medical model detoxification services and a 14-21 day addictive disorders rehabilitation program.

Company Background

The health system was established in 1949.

EXECUTIVES

President CEO and Trustee, Ed Epperson
VP Patient Care Services, Cathy Dinauer
Chair, Jeffrey D. Upton
VP and CFO, Ann Beck
Chief Medical Officer, Richard P. Rodriguez

LOCATIONS

HQ: CARSON TAHOE REGIONAL HEALTHCARE
1600 MEDICAL PKWY, CARSON CITY, NV 89703-4625
Phone: 775-445-8000
Web: WWW.CARSONTAHOE.COM

PRODUCTS/OPERATIONS

Operating Units
Behavioral Health Services Inpatient
Cancer Center
Carson Tahoe Cardiology Locations
Carson Tahoe Surgery Center
Dayton Medical Building
Eagle Medical Center
Holbrook Therapy
Minden Medical Center
Regional Medical Center
Sierra Surgery Hospital
Specialty Medical Center
Therapy at N. Roop Prof. Center
Urgent & Emergent Care
Walmart Clinics
Womens Health/Car

COMPETITORS

Dignity Health
HCA
Sutter Health
Universal Health Services

HISTORICAL FINANCIALS

Company Type: Private

Income Statement FYE: December 31

	REVENUE ($ mil.)	NET INCOME ($ mil.)	NET PROFIT MARGIN	EMPLOYEES
12/12	186	4	2.4%	1,500
12/09	195	18	9.4%	—
12/06	163	(8)	—	—
12/06	164	0	0.2%	—
Annual Growth	2.1%	55.4%	—	—

2012 Year-End Financials

Debt ratio: —
Return on equity: 2.40%
Cash ($ mil.): 4
Current ratio: 1.60
Long-term debt ($ mil.): —
Dividends
Yield: —
Payout: —
Market value ($ mil.): —

CASCADE ENGINEERING INC.

Ideas about plastic parts cascade down from Cascade Engineering's collection of companies ending up as practical components for many applications. The company manufactures and markets under the Cascade and other brands plastic injection molded products as well as parts for OEMs in the automotive truck material handling waste and recycling and home and office industries. Its auto lineup includes interior and exterior trim HVAC cases and ducts and acoustical parts along with heavy truck fairings fenders and grills. Catering to resource conservation markets Cascade also makes and services an eco-lineup comprising building-mountable wind turbines waste collection bins and water filtration systems.

Geographic Reach

Cascade Engineering serves its customers through 15 facilities spanning North America and Europe.

Operations

Cascade Engineering's operations are divided into 13 strategic business units serving the markets of automotive commercial truck and bus solid waste and recycling furniture material handling consumer products consulting and renewable energy. These units include CK Technologies Cascade Engineering Automotive Americas Cascade Engineering Automotive Europe Cascade Cart Solutions Xtreme RFID Capturit Cascade Engineering Commercial Products Invisible Waste Services Noble Polymers Decade Products Cascade Renewable Energy Cascade Consulting Group and Triple Quest.

Strategy

For growth the company has pursued a variety of public programs such as the Environmental Protection Agency's set-aside fund that supports job creation through green manufacturing. It launched a line of pink trash carts in 2010 garnering market awareness for breast cancer research as well as for the company.

In agriculture Cascade has partnered with an Israel company to form Decade Products a joint venture that manufactures harvesting bins touted as labor-saving for West Coast citrus and onion farmers. Fueling its renewable energy efforts Cascade has retrofitted a warehouse to accommodate an assembly line for wind turbine rotors used on top of houses. Research and development dollars are also being put into producing the Swift brand of lighter less expensive turbines.

Company Background

The company was founded by chairman and CEO Fred P. Keller in 1973.

EXECUTIVES

Chairman President and CEO, Frederick P. (Fred) Keller
VP Operations, David Williams
President, Mark Miller
VP, Kenyatta Brame
General Manager Cascade Cart Solutions, Jo-Anne Perkins

Director Cascade Consulting, Kelley Losey
Leader Invisible Waste Services, Max Hunsicker
Leader Xtreme RFID, Mike Lewis
Treasurer, Joe Maier

LOCATIONS

HQ: CASCADE ENGINEERING INC.
3400 INNOVATION CT SE, GRAND RAPIDS, MI 49512-2085
Phone: 616-975-4800
Web: WWW.CASCADERENEWABLEENERGY.COM

PRODUCTS/OPERATIONS

Selected Products and Brands

Automotive (acoustics chassis and powertrain interior and exterior trim)
Automotive aftermarket (portable consumer electronic devices for cars and trucks)
Commercial truck and bus (interior exterior functional systems)
Compounded polymers (thermoplastic polyolefins elastomers nanocomposites specialty polymers)
Furniture (seating products)
Material handling (reusable plastic containers and pallets)
Renewable energy (SWIFT wind turbine)
RFID systems tags and software
Solid waste and recycling (EcoCart)
Valet trash (Invisible Waster Services)
Water (HydrAid BioSand water filter)

COMPETITORS

ADAC Plastics
Delphi Automotive Systems
Fisher & Company
Johnson Controls
Key Plastics
Lear Corp
Nypro
Visteon

HISTORICAL FINANCIALS

Company Type: Private

Income Statement FYE: September 1

	REVENUE ($ mil.)	NET INCOME ($ mil.)	NET PROFIT MARGIN	EMPLOYEES
09/12*	238	0	—	1,200
08/11	238	0	—	—
08/10	238	0	—	—
08/09	0	0	—	—
Annual Growth			—	—

*Fiscal year change

2012 Year-End Financials

Debt ratio: —
Return on equity: —
Cash ($ mil.): 0
Current ratio: 0.60
Long-term debt ($ mil.): —
Dividends
Yield: —
Payout: —
Market value ($ mil.): —

CASE WESTERN RESERVE UNIVERSITY

Looking for a research-oriented university? Case Western Reserve University (CWRU) is a private research school with an enrollment of about 10000 students more than half of whom are graduate and professional students. CWRU offers about 200 undergraduate and graduate degree programs from its eight colleges and schools –business engineering law arts and sciences dentistry social work nursing and medicine –as well as a graduate school at its campus in Cleveland. The university has some 3000 faculty members and a student-to-teacher ratio of 10:1.

Geographic Reach

CWRU is located on the a 150-acre campus in Cleveland Ohio; the campus is located within the 500-acre University Circle district houses more than 40 educational medical cultural social and religious institutions. CWRU's students come from all 50 US states and more than 100 international countries.

Operations

The school receives close to $400 million in external funding each year to pay for its various research enterprises. CWRU provides research opportunities to about 4000 undergraduates and partners with corporations foundations and other universities to operate more than 100 research centers and institutes. Some of its priority research initiatives include energy and the environment culture creativity and design social justice and ethics. Medical studies are conducted in coordination with health care entities; its most predominant partner is the Cleveland Clinic.

Financial Performance

CWRU reported a 3% decrease in revenues to some $896 million in 2012 due to lower returns on operating investments and lower gifts and pledges income slightly offset by increased returns on long-term investment distributions. However the university reported a net loss of $149 million in 2012 due to increased expenses as well as from investment losses pension plan changes and depreciation.

Grants and contracts for research and training programs account for about 40% of CWRU's revenues while tuition income accounts for about one-third of revenues. Other sources of revenue include investment returns overhead cost recovery and gifts and pledges from private sources.

CWRU has an endowment is about $1.4 billion.

Strategy

CWRU's core priorities include enhancing its education and research programs advancing institutional resources strengthening partnerships and building a diverse community.

Company Background

The university's origins date back to 1826 in the Ohio region then known as the Western Reserve of Connecticut; its current structure was formed in 1967 with the combination of neighboring Case Institute of Technology and Western Reserve College.

EXECUTIVES

Vp Campus Services, Dick Jamieson
Vp Campus Planning And Operations, Kenneth A Basch
Vp University Planning, Christine Ash
Vp Commercial Development, Russell Berusch
Vp Research And Technology Management, Mark Coticchia
Vp Student Affairs, Glenn Nicholls
Vp University Relations, Lara Kalafatis
Director Media Relations, Lisa Chiu
President, Barbara R. Snyder, age 58
VP Information Technology Services and CIO, Lev S. Gonick
Dean School of Graduate Studies, Charles Rozek
Dean Undergraduate Studies, Jeffrey Wolcowitz
Chief Investment Officer, Sally J. Staley
Dean School of Dental Medicine, Jerold S. Goldberg
Dean Mandel School of Applied Social Sciences, Grover (Cleve) Gilmore
Provost and EVP, William A. (Bud) Baeslack
SVP Finance and CFO, John Sideras
Dean School of Medicine, Pamela Bowles Davis
Dean College of Arts and Sciences, Cyrus Taylor
VP University Marketing and Communications, Chris Sheridan
Dean Case School of Engineering, Jeffrey Duerk
Dean School of Law, Lawrence Mitchell
Dean Weatherhead School of Management, Robert E. Widing
Dean Frances Payne Bolton School of Nursing, Mary E. Kerr
Vp Inclusion Diversity And Equal Opportunity, Marilyn Sanders Mobley
Vice President And Chief Medical, Jeffrey Sunshine
Vp For Financial Planning, Ermia Melle
Vp Government Relations, David Bell
Chairman, Charles D. (Chuck) Fowler
Treasurer, Robert C Brown
Vice Chair, Joie A Gregor
Auditors: PricewaterhouseCoopersLLP

LOCATIONS

HQ: CASE WESTERN RESERVE UNIVERSITY
10900 EUCLID AVE, CLEVELAND, OH 44106-4901
Phone: 216-368-2000
Web: WWW.MSASS.CASE.EDU

PRODUCTS/OPERATIONS

Selected Schools and Programs

Case School of Engineering
College of Arts and Sciences
Cleveland Clinic (part of the School of Medicine)
Frances Payne Bolton School of Nursing
Mandel Center for Nonprofit Organizations
Mandel School of Applied Social Sciences
School of Dental Medicine
School of Graduate Studies
School of Law
School of Medicine
Weatherhead School of Management

HISTORICAL FINANCIALS

Company Type: Private

Income Statement FYE: June 30

	REVENUE ($ mil.)	NET INCOME ($ mil.)	NET PROFIT MARGIN	EMPLOYEES
06/11	1,052	75	7.2%	5,500
06/10	932	(15)	—	—
06/09	774	0	—	—
06/08	964	63	6.6%	—
Annual Growth	3.0%	5.7%	—	—

2011 Year-End Financials

Debt ratio: —
Return on equity: 7.20%
Cash ($ mil.): 105
Current ratio: —
Long-term debt ($ mil.): —
Dividends
Yield: —
Payout: —
Market value ($ mil.): —

CASH-WA DISTRIBUTING CO. OF KEARNEY INC.

This company keeps the Quik-E Marts in merchandise. Cash-Wa Distributing supplies food produce beverages equipment cleaning supplies and more to foodservice operators and convenience stores throughout Nebraska and in parts of eight other Upper Plains states. It operates three distribution centers and serves more than 3500 customers with an inventory of some 20000 items. The family-owned and -operated company was formed in 1934 as a candy and tobacco wholesaler and was purchased by the Henning family in 1957. Cash-Wa Distributing is a member of the UniPro distribution cooperative.

Geographic Reach

Cash-Wa Distributing's market area includes all or part of Nebraska Kansas Missouri Iowa Minnesota North and South Dakota Wyoming and Colorado. It has sales offices in Hays Kansas; Omaha and Sidney Nebraska; and Rapid City

South Dakota and distribution centers in Aberdeen South Dakota and Kearney and Lincoln Nebraska.

EXECUTIVES

Secretary and Treasurer, Gary Henning

LOCATIONS

HQ: CASH-WA DISTRIBUTING CO. OF KEARNEY INC.
401 W 4TH ST, KEARNEY, NE 68845-7825
Phone: 308-237-3151
Web: WWW.CASHWA.COM/ABOUT/PEOPLE

COMPETITORS

AMCON Distributing	MAINES
Affiliated Foods Midwest	McLane
Associated Wholesale Grocers	Meadowbrook Meat Company
C&S Wholesale	Nash-Finch
Core-Mark	Performance Food
Farner-Bocken	Performance Food Group
Hawkeye Foodservice Distribution	Reinhart FoodService
	Sysco
	US Foods

HISTORICAL FINANCIALS

Company Type: Private

Income Statement FYE: December 1

	REVENUE ($ mil.)	NET INCOME ($ mil.)	NET PROFIT MARGIN	EMPLOYEES
12/12	398	11	3.0%	539
12/11	306	5	1.8%	—
Annual Growth	30.0%	109.7%	—	—

2012 Year-End Financials

Debt ratio: —
Return on equity: 3.00%
Cash ($ mil.): 0
Current ratio: 1.00
Long-term debt ($ mil.): —
Dividends
Yield: —
Payout: —
Market value ($ mil.): —

CATAMOUNT CONSTRUCTORS INC.

A solid foundation is tantamount to Catamount's success. The company provides general contracting services for the construction of commercial industrial health care institutional and residential developments around the US. It offers services from conceptualization and design-build to construction management. Subsidiary CC Residential specializes in midrise multifamily residences including condominiums apartments and mixed-use developments. Catamount Constructors boasts a high customer return rate; it has provided services for such return clients as CarMax Walgreen and Chase Bank. CEO Geoff Wormer and other executives Kurt Kenchel Jeff Sidwell and Jeff Cochran founded the company in 1997.

Catamount Constructors has offices in metropolitan Denver and Atlanta two areas where it completes most of its projects.

EXECUTIVES

CEO, Geoffrey G. (Geoff) Wormer
President, Kurt T. Kenchel
President Atlanta Division, Scott A. Reynolds
VP Corporate Services, Jeffrey P. (Jeff) Sidwell
President Denver Division, Jeffrey L. (Jeff) Cochran
Vice President of Preconstruction & Business Development, Keith Rane
Division Vice President of Operations, Tom Seaman

LOCATIONS

HQ: CATAMOUNT CONSTRUCTORS INC.
1250 BERGEN PKWY B200, EVERGREEN, CO 80439-9584
Phone: 303-679-0087
Web: WWW.CATAMOUNTCONSTRUCTORS.COM

COMPETITORS

A.G. Spanos	J.E. Dunn Construction Group
Boran Craig Barber Engel	Peter Kiewit Sons'
Bovis Lend Lease	Skanska USA Building
Edward Rose	The Grupe Company
Imperial Construction Group	Turner Construction

HISTORICAL FINANCIALS

Company Type: Private

Income Statement FYE: December 31

	REVENUE ($ mil.)	NET INCOME ($ mil.)	NET PROFIT MARGIN	EMPLOYEES
12/08	226	4	1.9%	142
12/07	183	7	4.1%	—
12/06	156	0	—	—
Annual Growth	—	1499.4%	—	—

2008 Year-End Financials

Debt ratio: —
Return on equity: 1.90%
Cash ($ mil.): 4
Current ratio: 0.10
Long-term debt ($ mil.): —
Dividends
Yield: —
Payout: —
Market value ($ mil.): —

CATHOLIC HEALTH EAST

Catholic Health East (CHE) marries the physical and the spiritual in its vast network of not-for-profit health care facilities. As one of the largest religious health systems in the country CHE carries out its mission of healing the sick through more than 35 acute-care hospitals (7300 beds) four long-term acute care (LTAC) hospitals and 25 free-standing and hospital-based long-term care facilities as well as assisted living behavioral health and rehabilitation centers. Operating in 11 states along the East Coast from Maine to Florida CHE is also one of the country's largest providers of home health care services. The health care organization is sponsored by 10 religious congregations and ministries.

Geographic Reach

CHE operates hospitals in Alabama Connecticut Delaware Florida Georgia Massachusetts Maine New Jersey New York North Carolina and Pennsylvania.

Operations

In addition to its wholly owned hospitals CHE has a 50% stake in BayCare Health System in Florida and a one-third interest in New York's Catholic Health System.

Other operating divisions include Global Health Ministry Allegany Franciscan Ministries and Stella Maris Insurance Company.

Financial Performance

CHE reported a 7% increase in revenues to some $4.3 billion in 2011 due to higher net patient service revenues and other operating revenues. Net income also jumped by 179% to $398 million due to gains on asset sales and unrestricted contribution income.

Strategy

CHE announced in 2012 that it is exploring a merger with Michigan-based Trinity Health. The combination would create a health system serving 21 states from coast to coast with about 80 hospitals 90 continuing care facilities and home health and hospice programs that provide nearly 2.8 million visits annually. The system would have annual operating revenues of about $13.3 billion and assets of some $19.3 billion.

Like many other health care providers CHE has seen an influx of uninsured patients due to poor economic conditions in recent years. And with legislative health reform changes looming over the industry US health systems are struggling to control the cost of medical care while improving overall quality. In addition to forming partnerships with other area care providers to coordinate patient care (such as the potential merger with Trinity Health) CHE is working to improve quality through measures such as upgrading information technology systems and recruiting quality physicians.

CHE also looks to add new facilities through acquisitions and it conducts regular renovation and expansion efforts to improve services at its existing facilities. At the same time CHE regularly evaluates existing facilities and occasionally divests noncore medical centers.

Company Background

CHE was founded in 1998 when three regional Catholic health systems joined forces. It has since grown its network by adding affiliated hospitals to its network.

HISTORY

It was three easy pieces that made up Catholic Health East (CHE) in 1997. Allegany Health System Eastern Mercy Health System and Sisters of Providence Health System operated almost entirely in separate but adjacent geographic areas on the East Coast overlapping only in Florida.

CHE's history goes as far back as 1831 when the Sisters of Mercy was founded in Dublin Ireland by Catherine McAuley who established a poorhouse using her inheritance. Some of the sisters hopped the Pond in 1843 establishing the first Catholic hospital in the US the Mercy Hospital of Pittsburgh four years later. Over the years the Sisters of Mercy expanded throughout the US. By 1991 there were 25 Sisters of Mercy congregations; they united that year under the newly formed Institute of the Sisters of Mercy of the Americas.

The Sisters of Providence came from Kingston Ontario to found the first hospital in Holyoke Massachusetts. Having established their own ministry the sisters in Holyoke became a separate congregation in 1892. The congregation expanded slowly moving into North Carolina in 1956 eventually forming the Sisters of Providence Health System.

A Polish nun Mother Colette Hilbert formed a new congregation in Pittsburgh in 1897 after the other members of her former parish were recalled to Poland. The new congregation entered health care in 1926 establishing a home for the elderly in New York. In honor of Hilbert's favorite saint the order became the Franciscan Sisters of St. Joseph in 1934.

The Franciscan Sisters of St. Joseph and the Sisters of Mercy united to form the ministry that became Pittsburgh Mercy Health System in 1983. In 1986 the congregations formed Eastern Mercy Health System as a holding company for the health concern. The consolidation served to cut costs as well as to preserve the organization's religious mission.

The Franciscan Sisters of Allegany congregation got its start in 1859 teaching children in Buffalo New York. In 1883 the order took over St. Elizabeth Hospital in Boston expanding its health care services ministry throughout New York New Jersey and Florida by the 1930s. In 1986 the sisters organized the operations as Allegany Health System.

In the early 1990s Catholic health care systems underwent a round of consolidation. Allegany Health Systems and Eastern Mercy Health Systems combined services aiming to lower costs through economies of scale.

The mid-1990s also brought consolidation but this time operational costs weren't the major problem; Catholic health systems across the nation were facing a shortage of sisters. To have a sufficient number of sisters to keep the "Catholic" in Catholic health care the three health systems merged in 1997 becoming Catholic Health East (CHE).

After the merger the company continued to build its network through acquisitions including Mercy Health in Miami (1998) and a suffering secular Cooper Health System in Camden New Jersey (1999). In 2000 it gained control of two troubled hospitals in Palm Beach Florida only to sell them the following year.

CHE expanded in 2008 by acquiring two facilities: Saint Michael's Medical Center in Newark New Jersey and the Minnie G. Boswell Memorial Hospital an acute-care facility in Greene County Georgia.

CHE formed a partnership with Deborah Heart and Lung Center to develop a satellite emergency department on Deborah's campus in New Jersey in 2010.

EXECUTIVES

VP Advocacy Government Relations and Fund Development, Kenneth A. Becker
EVP Legal Services and General Counsel, Michael C. Hemsley
VP Capital Strategy and Management, Randal Schultz
VP Finance and Business Development CCMSN, Patricia Gathers
EVP Ministry Operations, H. Ray Welch Jr.
VP and CIO, Donette Herring
EVP Ministry Operations, John C. Johnson
EVP and COO, Peter L. (Pete) DeAngelis Jr.
President and CEO, Judith M. (Judy) Persichilli
VP Mission and Ethics, Philip J. Boyle
Director Quality Services, Pamela (Pam) Carroll-Solomon
VP Nursing Practice, Sharon Duffy
Executive Director Global Health Ministry, Sr. Mary Jo McGinley
VP Systems Communications, Scott Share
VP Supply Chain Management and Procurement, Florence Doyle
VP Leadership Development, Anita K. Jensen
President and CEO Continuing Care Management Services Network, John Capasso
VP Strategic Development, Anna Marie Butrie
VP Marketing and Sales CCMSN, Kathleen J. (Kay) Miller
VP Business Development, Scott Ash
VP Corporate Compliance and Internal Audit, Kim Lansford
EVP and Chief Nursing Officer, Nora Triola
EVP Finance and CFO, Jenny Barnett Sarpalius
EVP Shared Services and Chief Human Resource Officer, Clayton Fitzhugh
VP Chief Medical Information Officer, Michael J. McCoy
VP Regional Operations CCMSN, William J. Healy
VP Home and Community Services CCMSN, Joseph K. (Kelly) Hopkins
Director Information Technology CCMSN, Tony West
EVP Chief Medical Officer and Chief Quality Officer, Jeffry Komins
EVP Mission Integration, Sr. Mary Persico
Chairperson, Dennis Fitzpatrick
VP Clinical Informatics and Transformation, Virginia (Ginny) Davis
VP Revenue Management, Cynthia Fry
VP Information Services Administration, Sean Hughes
VP Accounting, Julia Puchtler
Executive Vice President Mission Integration, Juliana Casey
President and CEO, Judith M. (Judy) Persichilli
Director, Regina M. Benjamin
Director, Earle L. Bradford Jr.
Director, Judith A. Carey
Director, Edward J. Connors
Director, Kathleen Maire
Director, Mary Croghan
Director, Joel M. Ziff
Director, Mary Caritas Geary
Director, Patricia Wolf
Director, Barbara M. Wheeley
Director, Marlene Weidenborner
Director, Thomas J. Harvey
Director, William H. Izlar Jr.
Director, Christine McCann
Director, A. Diane Moeller
Director, Gladys Sharkey
Director, Rosemary J. Sgroi
Director, Daniel F. Russell
Director, Tim Porter-O?Grady
Auditors: PricewaterhouseCoopersLLP

LOCATIONS

HQ: CATHOLIC HEALTH EAST
3805 WEST CHESTER PIKE # 100, NEWTOWN SQUARE, PA 19073-2329
Phone: 610-355-2000
Web: WWW.CHE.ORG

Selected Facilities

Alabama
Mercy Medical (rehabilitation and nursing care Daphne)
Connecticut
Mercy Community Health (nursing care and senior living facilities West Hartford)
Delaware
St. Francis Healthcare Services (Wilmington)
Florida
BayCare Health Systems (50% Clearwater)
Holy Cross Hospital (Fort Lauderdale)
Georgia
Saint Joseph's Health System (Atlanta)
St. Mary's Health Care System Inc. (Athens)
Massachusetts
Sisters of Providence Health System (Springfield)
Maine
Mercy Health System of Maine (Portland)
New Jersey
Lourdes Health System (Camden)
Saint Michael's Medical Center (Newark)
St. Francis Medical Center (Trenton)
New York
Catholic Health System (Buffalo)
St. James Mercy Health System (Hornell)
St. Peter's Health Care Services (Albany)
North Carolina
St. Joseph of the Pines (senior living facility Southern Pines)
Pennsylvania
Maxis Health System (Carbondale)
Mercy Health System of Southeastern Pennsylvania (Conshohocken)
St. Mary Medical Center (Langhorne)

COMPETITORS

Albany Medical Center
Albert Einstein Healthcare Network
Ascension Health
Baptist Health South Florida
Baystate Medical Center
Bon Secours Health
Capital Health System
Catholic Health Initiatives
Christiana Care
Community Health Systems
HCA
Health Management Associates
Kaleida Health
Sun Health
Tenet Healthcare
Universal Health Services
University of Miami Hospital
University of Pennsylvania Health System

HISTORICAL FINANCIALS

Company Type: Private

Income Statement

FYE: December 31

	REVENUE ($ mil.)	NET INCOME ($ mil.)	NET PROFIT MARGIN	EMPLOYEES
12/10	4,057	142	3.5%	50,000
12/09	106	(3)	—	—
12/07	4,364	199	4.6%	—
12/06	4,175	199	4.8%	—
Annual Growth	(0.7%)	(8.1%)	—	—

2010 Year-End Financials

Debt ratio: —
Return on equity: 3.50%
Cash ($ mil.): 426
Current ratio: 0.90
Long-term debt ($ mil.): —

Dividends
Yield: —
Payout: —
Market value ($ mil.): —

CATHOLIC MEDICAL CENTER

Catholic Medical Center is a 330-bed hospital serving southern New Hampshire. Services include cancer treatment surgery rehabilitation treatments for sleep disorders and emergency medical services. Catholic Medical Center (CMC) offer 25 medical specialties through divisions including The Mom's Place (a birthing facility) and the New England Heart Institute. CMC has partnered with its community to extend health care and dental care to the uninsured and the homeless and has established a health clinic geared to help refugees being resettled in the area.

Geographic Reach

The hospital serves residents in and around Manchester New Hampshire as well as patients from across the state. Its primary service area includes the communities of Allenstown Auburn Bedford Candia Deerfield Dunbarton Goffstown Hooksett Manchester and New Boston.

Operations

CMC employs some 500 physicians. The hospital operates about a dozen outpatient and urgent care centers in its service territory as well as outreach programs including the Parish Nurse Program the Poisson Dental Facility the Westside Neighborhood Health Center and the Healthcare for the Homeless Project. As a not-for-profit institution CMC contributed some $88 million in community benefits during 2012.

Financial Performance

The hospital reported net patient service revenues of some $284 million in 2012 with Medicare and Medicaid policy reimbursements accounting for $94 million of sales.

Strategy

CMC focuses on enhancing and expanding its service offerings for area residents. It opened a heart and vascular intervention unit within the hospital facility in 2013 for instance and added neurology services as a new specialist offering. The hospital also expands by forming clinical care partnerships with other area medical centers.

In 2011 CMC canceled plans to merge with Dartmouth-Hitchcock Medical Center although the hospitals continue to collaborate at CMC's Special Care Nursery and D-H's Norris Cotton Cancer Center. CMC and Dartmouth-Hitchcock cited evolving changes in health care reforms behind their decision not to merge. The partnership was opposed by the New Hampshire attorney general on the grounds that it would violate state law and needed court approval.

Company Background

CMC was founded in 1974 through the merger of two Catholic-sponsored Manchester hospitals: Notre dame Hospital and Sacred Heart Hospital.

EXECUTIVES

President and CEO, Alyson Pitman Giles
VP Marketing Corporate Communication and Philanthropy, Gail Winslow-Pine
Vice Chairman, Maria Mongan

LOCATIONS

HQ: CATHOLIC MEDICAL CENTER
100 MCGREGOR ST, MANCHESTER, NH 03102-3770
Phone: 603-663-6888
Web: WWW.CATHOLICMEDICALCENTER.ORG

PRODUCTS/OPERATIONS

Selected Centers and Services

Behavioral Health Services
Breast Care Center
Cancer Care
Cholesterol Management Center
Community Health Services
Diabetes Resources Institute
Diagnostic Imaging
Emergency Department
Laboratory
New England Heart Institute
New England Sleep Center
Obesity Treatment Center
Primary Care Locations
Rehabilitation Services
Respiratory Services
Surgical Care Group
Surgical Services
The Mom' s Place
The Wellness Center
Urgent Care at Bedford
Wound Care Center

COMPETITORS

Beth Israel Deaconess Medical Center
Boston Medical Center
Brigham and Women' s Hospital
Cambridge Health Alliance
CareGroup
Caritas Holy Family Hospital
Concord Hospital
Elliot Health System
Exeter Health Resources
Frisbie Memorial Hospital
HealthSouth
Southern New Hampshire Medical Center

HISTORICAL FINANCIALS

Company Type: Private

Income Statement FYE: June 30

	REVENUE ($ mil.)	NET INCOME ($ mil.)	NET PROFIT MARGIN	EMPLOYEES
06/10	277	11	4.2%	1,500
06/09	241	(1)	—	—
06/09	88	0	0.0%	—
Annual Growth	215.6%	70399.5%	—	—

2010 Year-End Financials

Debt ratio: —
Return on equity: 4.20%
Cash ($ mil.): 40
Current ratio: 0.40
Long-term debt ($ mil.): —
Dividends
Yield: —
Payout: —
Market value ($ mil.): —

CEDARS-SINAI MEDICAL CENTER

Many a star has been born literally at Cedars-Sinai Medical Center. The 895-bed teaching and research hospital is located right where Los Angeles meets Beverly Hills and West Hollywood and has tended to the medical needs of a number of celebrities since its founding in 1902. However the center is also a major teaching hospital for UCLA's David Geffen School of Medicine and is engaged in hundreds of research programs in areas such as cancer neuroscience and genetics. It also includes two multi-specialty physician associations Cedars-Sinai Medical Group and Ceders-Sinai Health Associates and operates a number of community health centers and outreach programs (such as mobile health clinics).

Operations

The not-for-profit hospital's more than 2000 staff physicians represent just about every clinical specialty out there. Cedars-Sinai is consistently listed as a top-ranked hospital by U.S. News & World Report in such specialties as cancer cardiology endocrinology gastrointestinal disorders gynecology heart surgery kidney disease neurology orthopaedics and respiratory disorders.

Cedars-Sinai is the only private hospital with a Level 1 trauma center in Los Angeles County; as such the hospital sees about 1600 trauma patients a year. The hospital also provides a number of outpatient services.

Financial Analysis

Revenues from patient care and other sources totaled nearly $2.75 billion in fiscal 2012 while net income amounted to $132.6 million.

Strategy

To meet increasing patient demand and expand its capacity for research projects Cedars-Sinai opened a $600 million outpatient and research center (the Advanced Health Sciences Pavilion) in 2013. The hospital conducts some $100 million in medical and clinical research each year.

EXECUTIVES

President CEO, Thomas M. (Tom) Priselac
Senior Vice President Finance Chief Financial Officer, Edward M. Prunchunas
Senior Vice President for Human Resources and Organizational Development, Jeanne Flores
SVP Clinical Care Services and COO, Mark R. Gavens
Senior Vice President for Community Relations and Development, Arthur J. Ochoa
Senior Vice President Academic Affairs, Shlomo Melmed
Senior Vice President for Medical Affairs and Chief Medical Officer, Michael L. Langberg
Senior Vice President System Development, Richard B. Jacobs
SVP Medical Delivery Network, Thomas D. Gordon
Senior Vice President Legal Affairs, Peter E. Braveman
Chief of Staff and Director, William W. Brien
Secretary, Robert M. Eller
SVP Enterprise Information Systems and CIO, Darren Dworkin
Senior Development Officer Foundation Relations, Sharon Friedman
Vice Chairman, Vera Guerin
VP Nursing and Chief Nursing Officer, Linda Burnes Bolton
Chairman, James Klinenberg
Associate Program Director of Training, Amanda Ewing
Director of Research, Jerome Rotter
Research Scientist, Tripathi Rajavashisth
Vice President Academic Affairs, Richard Katzman
President of the nursing executives organization, Michelle Janney
Senior Vice President Chief Clinical Transformation Officer, Scott Weingarten
Director, Jay S. Wintrob, age 57
Director, Jeffrey Katzenberg, age 64
Director, Andy Heyward
Director, John M. Bendheim, age 59
Director, John G. Harold
Director, John C. Law
Director, James A. Nathan
Chief of Staff and Director, William W. Brien
Director, Steven D. Broidy
Director, Julian A. Gold
Director, Mark S. Greenfield
Director, Sue Neuman Hochberg
Director, Thomas J. Leanse
Director, Todd M. Morgan
Director, Richard Powell
Director, Marc Rapaport
Director, Mark S. Siegel
Director, Robert Silverstein
Director, Steven Spielberg
Director, Theodore Stein
Director, Leslie Vermut
Director, Walter Zifkin
Director, Paul Silka
Director, Robert Davidson
Vice Chairman, Vera Guerin
Director, Sheila Kar
Director, Beth Karlan
Director, Steven B. Nichols
Director, Luis Nogales
Director, Lynda Oschin
Director, Steven Romick
Director, David Saperstein
Director, Zab Mosenifar
Director Director, David Palestrant

LOCATIONS

HQ: CEDARS-SINAI MEDICAL CENTER
8700 BEVERLY BLVD, WEST HOLLYWOOD, CA 90048-1804
Phone: 310-423-4603
Web: WWW.CEDARS-SINAI.EDU

PRODUCTS/OPERATIONS

Selected Centers and Services

Ambulatory Care Center
Cedars-Sinai Center for Chest Disease
Cedars-Sinai Center for Digestive Diseases
Cedars-Sinai Heart Institute
Cedars-Sinai Institute Spine Center
Cedars-Sinai Health Associates (affiliated independent physician association)
Cedars-Sinai Medical Group (multi-specialty physicians group)
Cedars-Sinai Orthopedic Center
Diagnostic imaging center
Emergency department and trauma center
Hospice services
Kidney and pancreas transplant center
Neuroscience services
Pediatric services
Psychiatry and mental health services
Samuel Oschin Comprehensive Cancer Institute
Surgical services
Organ and bone marrow transplantation
Radiation therapy
Radiology
Stroke program
Pain management services
Women's health services

COMPETITORS

Adventist Health
Brotman Medical Center
Childrens Hospital Los Angeles
City of Hope
Community Health Systems

Dignity Health
Eisenhower Medical Center
Glendale Adventist Medical Center
Glendale Memorial Hospital
Golden State Health Centers
Good Samaritan Hospital (IN)
HCA
Hollywood Presbyterian Medical Center
Kaiser Permanente
Los Angeles County Health Department
Newhall Memorial Hospital
Pasadena Hospital Association
Providence Health System Southern California
Providence Saint Joseph Medical Center
Scripps health
Tenet Healthcare
UCSF Medical
White Memorial Medical Center

HISTORICAL FINANCIALS

Company Type: Private

Income Statement FYE: June 30

	REVENUE ($ mil.)	NET INCOME ($ mil.)	NET PROFIT MARGIN	EMPLOYEES
06/12	2,797	168	6.0%	8,000
06/11	2,658	210	7.9%	—
06/09	2,309	152	6.6%	—
06/09	1,962	88	4.5%	—
Annual Growth	12.5%	23.8%	—	—

2012 Year-End Financials

Debt ratio: —
Return on equity: 6.00%
Cash ($ mil.): 272
Current ratio: 0.40
Long-term debt ($ mil.): —
Dividends
Yield: —
Payout: —
Market value ($ mil.): —

CENTIMARK CORPORATION

Shout it from the rooftops CentiMark is one of the largest commercial and industrial roofing contractors in North America. The company provides roof installation inspection repair and emergency leak service. CentiMark typically works on flat roofs using EPDM rubber thermoplastic bitumen metal and coatings. Top customers include NASA and the US Army Corps of Engineers. Its QuestMark division offers commercial industrial and retail flooring do-it-yourself products and floor maintenance and cleaning products. Chairman and CEO Edward Dunlap founded CentiMark as an industrial cleaning business in 1967. The company which has about 70 offices throughout North America is owned by its employees.

Geographic Reach

Pittsburgh Pennsylvania-based CentiMark also does business in Canada through subsidiary CentiMark Ltd. which has offices in Calgary Edmonton Toronto and Vancouver.

Financial Performance

CentiMark's 2011 sales totaled more than $474 million a 17% increase vs. 2010.

Strategy

In response to customer demand for more energy-efficient options CentiMark has been increasing its use of spray polyurethane foam (which adds insulation and a waterproof barrier to roofs). The company also installs electricity-producing photovoltaic solar panels onto roofs. Other green options available from CentiMark include skylights and garden roofs.

The company also tries to stay ahead of the pack with technological innovations such as its MyCentiMark service. The online resource allows property owners to view invoices work authorizations before-and-after photos and recommendations for future roof maintenance.

Ownership

CentiMark is owned by its employees.

EXECUTIVES

Chairman and CEO, Edward B. Dunlap
President and COO, Timothy M. Dunlap
EVP and Northern Group Director, Robert J. Rudzik
EVP and Western Group Director, Steven M. Ferencz
EVP National and Regional Sales, John T. Godwin
EVP and CFO, John L. Heisey
EVP and Southern Group Director, Sherman L. Gaskins
SVP and CIO, Greg Wilson
EVP and QuestMark Flooring Group Director, John P. Scanlon
SVP and Eastern Group Director, Mark A. Cooper
VP and Canada Group Director CentiMark Ltd, Robert T. Penney

LOCATIONS

HQ: CENTIMARK CORPORATION
12 GRANDVIEW CIR, CANONSBURG, PA 15317-8533
Phone: 724-743-7777
Web: WWW.CENTIMARKLTD.COM

PRODUCTS/OPERATIONS

Selected Operations

CentiMark (roofing)
CentiMark ltd. (Canada roofing)
QuestMark (flooring)

COMPETITORS

Armstrong World Industries
Cabral Roofing & Waterproofing
D. C. Taylor
Duro-Last Roofing
Garcia Roofing
Holland Roofing
Pickens Roofing
Tecta America

HISTORICAL FINANCIALS

Company Type: Private

Income Statement FYE: April 30

	REVENUE ($ mil.)	NET INCOME ($ mil.)	NET PROFIT MARGIN	EMPLOYEES
04/13	484	38	8.0%	1,900
04/12	474	38	8.1%	—
04/10	404	31	7.8%	—
04/10	363	29	8.1%	—
Annual Growth	10.0%	9.7%	—	—

2013 Year-End Financials

Debt ratio: —
Return on equity: 8.00%
Cash ($ mil.): 67
Current ratio: 2.40
Long-term debt ($ mil.): —
Dividends
Yield: —
Payout: —
Market value ($ mil.): —

CENTRA HEALTH INC.

Centra Health is a constellation of hospitals and medical practices targeting the health care needs of residents in central and southern Virginia. At the not-for-profit entity's core are two acute care facilities in Lynchburg: the 360-bed Lynchburg General which is the region's main emergency center and specializes in orthopedic pediatric and cardiac care and Virginia Baptist a roughly 160-bed facility focused on surgery women's health infant care mental health and rehabilitation. Centra also operates a nearby community hospital and an array of primary care physician practices home health agencies retirement centers and other physical and behavioral health businesses.

Geographic Reach

Centra Health serves Lynchburg and surrounding communities in central Virginia including Farmville (located in Prince Edward County) Bedford Danville/Gretna Moneta/Smith Mountain Lake Virginia.

Operations

In addition to Lynchburg General and Virginia Baptist Centra's acute care facilities include Southside Community Hospital (Farmville). Southside Community Hospital serves as a central acute care and birthing facility for an eight-county region. Centra also operates the Bedford Memorial Hospital through a partnership with Carilion Health System.

Outside of its acute care operations Centra Health administers senior care services through The Summit assisted living and independent living facilities. The Summit offers senior residents private apartments medical care and personal assistance. Centra also operates a network of treatment centers for patients of all ages with behavioral and psychiatric disorders. The network includes facilities that specialize in treating children and adolescents with emotional and behavioral disorders.

Altogether the network handles some 300000 patient visits each year including more than 90000 emergency room visits and 5000 cardiac procedures. Its hospitals have a medical staff of about 500 doctors; it also operates the Centra Medical Group which includes about 140 primary care and specialist physicians.

Strategy

Centra Health is expanding its breadth of services as well as its network of facilities. It opened the Central Virginia Center for Simulation and Virtual Learning in 2012 to increase medical training services and it relocated its college of nursing in 2013 to provide larger classroom and laboratory spaces. The organization also expanded its orthopedic center at the Bedford Memorial Hospital during 2012 and it opened two new behavioral health facilities for adolescents and children.

In late 2012 Centra Health announced plans to build a new 50000-sq. ft. medical building in Gretna to meet growing health care needs in the region. The facility will include emergency medical diagnostic and transportation service facilities and would be located adjacent to the existing Gretna outpatient center.

Company Background

Centra Health was founded in 1987 through the merger of Lynchburg General and Virginia Baptist. Southside Community Hospital joined the network in 2006.

EXECUTIVES

Chairman, Kenneth S. White, age 74
Vice Chairman, Thomas W. Nygaard
President and CEO, Michael Bryant
Vice President Cancer Care Services, Curt Baker
Director, Robert D. Cook
Director, Rodger W. Fauber
Vice Chairman, Thomas W. Nygaard
Director, Consuella K. Woods
Director, Walker P. Sydnor Jr.
Director, Amy G. Ray
Director, Augustus A. Petticolas Jr., age 64
Director, Terry H. Jamerson
Director, Albert M. Baker
Director, Michael V. Bradford
Director, Kirsten L. Huber
Director, Stephen C. Keith
Director, Julie P. Doyle

LOCATIONS

HQ: CENTRA HEALTH INC.
1920 ATHERHOLT RD, LYNCHBURG, VA 24501-1120
Phone: 434-200-4700
Web: WWW.FOUNDATION.CENTRAHEALTH.COM

PRODUCTS/OPERATIONS

Selected Facilities

Bedford Memorial Hospital (Bedford Virginia; partnership with Carilion Health System)
Lynchburg General Hospital (Lynchburg Virginia)
Virginia Baptist Hospital (Lynchburg Virginia)
Southside Community Hospital (Farmville Virginia)
Physician Practices
- Altavista Medical Center (Altavista Virginia)
- Big Island Medical Center (North Big Island Virginia)
- Brookneal Family Medical Center (Brookneal Virginia)
- Gretna Medical Center (Gretna Virginia)
- Lynchburg Family Medicine Center (Lynchburg Virginia)

Other Facilities
- Bridges Treatment Center (Lynchburg Virginia)
- Fairmont Crossing Health and Rehabilitation Center (Amherst Virginia)
- Guggenheimer Health and Rehabilitation Center (Lynchburg Virginia)
- Piedmont Psychiatric Center (Lynchburg Virginia)
- Rivermont Schools (regional)
- The Summit (regional)

COMPETITORS

Alleghany Regional Hospital
Bon Secours Health
Carilion Clinic
Clinch Valley Medical Center
Danville Regional Medical Center
HealthSouth
Henrico Doctors' Hospital
Martha Jefferson Hospital
Mary Washington Healthcare
Montgomery Regional Hospital
Sentara Healthcare
University of Virginia Health System

HISTORICAL FINANCIALS

Company Type: Private

Income Statement FYE: December 31

	REVENUE ($ mil.)	NET INCOME ($ mil.)	NET PROFIT MARGIN	EMPLOYEES
12/09	534	16	3.1%	6,000
12/08	419	33	7.9%	—
12/04	331	10	3.3%	—
12/03	313	0	—	—
Annual Growth	9.3%	—	—	—

2009 Year-End Financials

Debt ratio: —
Return on equity: 3.10%
Cash ($ mil.): 21
Current ratio: 0.30
Long-term debt ($ mil.): —
Dividends
Yield: —
Payout: —
Market value ($ mil.): —

CENTRAL DUPAGE HOSPITAL ASSOCIATION

Central DuPage Hospital attends to the health needs of Windy City suburbanites. Located in DuPage County just west of Chicago the hospital has more than 310 beds and provides general medical and surgical care including specialty care in areas such as oncology cardiovascular disease neuroscience and orthopedics. The hospital is the focal point of a network of health services that include a physician medical group home health care services occupational care and about half a dozen urgent care centers. Central DuPage Hospital opened its doors in 1964.

Geographic Reach

DuPage County is a highly-populated community west of Chicago (and Cook County).

Operations

Central DuPage Hospital merged with neighboring Delnor Health System to create a new health system in 2011 called Cadence Health Foundation. The two facilities still operate independently with their own charitable money-raising foundations. Their affiliated community health operations were also moved into the system.

At the hospital network's urgent care centers which it calls Convenient Care Centers patients are able to obtain treatment for minor illnesses and injuries such as the flu and fractures as well as after-hours care. The idea behind the centers is to direct patients to the appropriate location for care rather than places such as expensive emergency rooms.

Strategy

Though it may not be the largest of hospitals Central DuPage has worked hard to keep up with the industry's technological advances and has an electronic medical records system that allows physicians to securely access a patient's clinical information from remote locations enabling them to spend less time filling out paperwork and more time providing medical care. The hospital also has a medication barcoding system that is used to confirm that patients receive the right medications at the right time reducing medical errors and improving patient outcomes which can lead to government-paid incentives.

Additionally nurses are able to electronically enter patient information at a patient's bedside through a computerized patient charting system reducing errors through lapse of memory as nurses make rounds of dozens of patients.

Central DuPage is also the first hospital in the county to use the da Vinci robotic surgical system to perform delicate prostate and gynecological procedures. Finally the hospital operates a telephone monitoring system for homebound patients to keep the hospital team aware of any issues prior to home visits.

Company Background

The hospital is one in the region that conducts clinical trials to help further our understanding of diseases and how they can be better treated. Some of its clinical trial areas include cardiology neonatal intensive care neuroscience oncology and many others.

EXECUTIVES

President CEO and Director, Luke McGuinness
VP and CIO, David (Dave) Printz
President Chief Executive Officer, Michael Vivoda
VP Operations, Robert Friedberg
EVP Strategy and Administration, Liz Rosenberg
VP and Chief Nursing Officer, Debra O'Donnell
EVP and CFO, James T. (Jim) Spear
Chair, Richard A. Mark
VP Finance and Controller, Maureen Taus
VP Quality and Safety, David Cooke
VP Legal Affairs and General Counsel, Michael Holzhueter
VP Marketing and Communications, Jill Brown
VP Medical Affairs, Kevin Most
VP Construction, Lawrence (Larry) Bell
VP Human Resources, Richard B. (Rick) Davis
VP Physician and Ambulatory Services, Andrew (Drew) Palumbo
VP and Treasurer, Brett Tande
Vice President of Human Resources, Rick Davis
President of Central DuPage Hospital, Brian Lemon
Vice President of Construction, Larry Bell
Vice President of Physician and Ambulatory Services, Drew Palumbo
VP of Operations and Business Development, Ann McMackin
President of Cadence Physician Group, Patrick Towne
President CEO and Director, Luke McGuinness
Director, Judith A. Whinfrey
Director, John R. Born
Director, James E. Comerford
Director, Bradley J. Kinsey
Director, Catherine E. Kozik
Director, C. William Pollard
Director, Gregory Osko
Director, Angelo Miele
Director, Matthew Ross
Auditors: KPMGLLP

LOCATIONS

HQ: CENTRAL DUPAGE HOSPITAL ASSOCIATION
25 N WINFIELD RD, WINFIELD, IL 60190-1295
Phone: 630-933-1600
Web: WWW.CDH.ORG

PRODUCTS/OPERATIONS

Selected Facilities

Cadence Health Foundation
Cadence Physician Group
Central DuPage Business Health (occupational health services)
Central DuPage Hospital
Central DuPage Physician Group
CNS Home Health and Hospice
Convenient Care Centers (urgent care)
HealthLab

COMPETITORS

Adventist Health System Sunbelt Healthcare
Advocate Health Care
Alexian Brothers Health System
Covenant Ministries
Elmhurst Memorial Healthcare
Gottleib Memorial Hospital
Loyola University Health System
Northwest Community Healthcare
Resurrection Health Care
Rush System for Health
St. Bernard Hospital and Health Care Center
University of Chicago Medical Center
Wheaton Franciscan Services

HISTORICAL FINANCIALS

Company Type: Private

Income Statement FYE: June 30

	REVENUE ($ mil.)	NET INCOME ($ mil.)	NET PROFIT MARGIN	EMPLOYEES
06/12	773	112	14.5%	3,431
06/11	667	25	3.9%	—
06/09	633	81	12.9%	—
06/09	596	72	12.2%	—
Annual Growth	9.0%	15.6%	—	—

2012 Year-End Financials

Debt ratio: —
Return on equity: 14.50%
Cash ($ mil.): 10
Current ratio: 1.30
Long-term debt ($ mil.): —
Dividends
Yield: —
Payout: —
Market value ($ mil.): —

CENTRAL GROCERS INC.

In a city of big stores Central Grocers helps neighborhood markets stay afloat. Founded in 1917 the cooperative wholesale food distributor is owned by some 225 members. It supplies 40000 food items and general merchandise to more than 400 independent grocery stores serving several states such as Illinois Indiana Iowa Michigan and Wisconsin. Central Grocers distributes products under both national brands and its own Centrella brand which is marketed exclusively to its member stores. The co-op also operates about 30 stores under a handful of banner names including Strack & Van Til Town & Country Key Market and the low-cost Ultra Foods chain.

Operations

As part of its business Central Grocers caters to its customers with the help of a fleet of 100 refrigerated trucks 300 dry trailers and about 70 Freightliner tractors.

Strategy

Central Grocers the 7th largest grocery cooperative in the US boasts the second-largest market share in the Chicago area. It specializes in serving Chicago independent supermarkets. Central Grocers supplies them with a comprehensive menu of groceries produce fresh meat service deli items frozen foods ice cream and items from its own Centrella brand.

Central Grocers expanded its distribution center by 15000-sq.-ft. to 940000-sq.-ft. of storage capacity in 2011. The reason for expansion was due to demand for produce and fresh meats.

Financial Performance

While privately-owned Central Grocers doesn't report financial results. The co-op rings up an estimated $2 billion in sales and it returns (in the form of dividends) to its members about $243 million.

Sales and Marketing

Central Grocers services a wide variety of store formats and ethnic groups including Hispanic Italian and African Americans. Besides older and smaller 5000-sq.-ft. stores its clients include large-scale warehouse discount stores that measure 75000 sq. ft. and large conventional stores that average 70000 sq. ft.

EXECUTIVES

CFO, Tim Kubis
Director Meat, Wally Locke
Auditors: Deloitte&ToucheLLP

LOCATIONS

HQ: CENTRAL GROCERS INC.
2600 HAVEN AVE, JOLIET, IL 604338467
Phone: 8155538800
Web: WWW.CENTRAL-GROCERS.COM

PRODUCTS/OPERATIONS

Selected Products

Fresh meat
Frozen foods
Groceries
Ice cream
Produce
Service deli items

COMPETITORS

ALDI
Albertsons
Alex Lee
Associated Wholesale Grocers
C&S Wholesale
Certco
Dearborn Wholesale Grocers
Kroger
Meijer
Nash-Finch
SUPERVALU
Safeway
Schnuck Markets
Wal-Mart
Winkler

HISTORICAL FINANCIALS

Company Type: Private

Income Statement FYE: July 28

	REVENUE ($ mil.)	NET INCOME ($ mil.)	NET PROFIT MARGIN	EMPLOYEES
07/07	1,197	(10)	—	2,300
07/06	1,108	5	0.5%	—
07/05	1,103	4	0.4%	—
07/04	1,047	0	—	—
Annual Growth	4.5%	—	—	—

2007 Year-End Financials

Debt ratio: —
Return on equity: (-0.90%)
Cash ($ mil.): 0
Current ratio: 0.20
Long-term debt ($ mil.): —
Dividends
Yield: —
Payout: —
Market value ($ mil.): —

CENTRAL IOWA POWER COOPERATIVE

Keeping a sharp eye out for the well-being of Iowa's citizens Central Iowa Power Cooperative provides electricity transmission and generation services to 13 member distribution cooperatives (12 rural electric cooperatives and one municipal cooperative) which in turn serve about 320000 residential and 7000 industrial and commercial customers. Central Iowa Power's member distribution cooperatives deliver power to commercial businesses farmsteads industrial parks manufacturers urban residences and other customers in a service area that stretches 300 miles diagonally across the state from Shenandoah in the southwest to the Mississippi River in the east.

The power cooperative serves 58 of of Iowa's 99 counties and 12 of its17 cities with populations of more than 25000.

More than 95% of the electric power provided by Central Iowa Power to its member cooperatives is generated in Iowa by coal gas hydroelectric nuclear oil and renewable energy power plants. An active advocate for reducing carbon dioxide emissions about 40% of its total power generation is fueled by non carbon-fuel sources (primarily nuclear and wind). In 2008 Central Iowa Power signed a 10-year contact to buy 42MW of wind power from FPL Energy's Story County Wind Energy Center.

HISTORY

h

EXECUTIVES

Chief Operating Officer And Vice President Of Business Operations, Craig Fricke
Auditors: KPMGLLP

LOCATIONS

HQ: CENTRAL IOWA POWER COOPERATIVE
1400 HIGHWAY 13, CEDAR RAPIDS, IA 524039060
Phone: 3193668011
Web: WWW.CIPCO.NET

HISTORICAL FINANCIALS

Company Type: Private

Income Statement FYE: December 31

	REVENUE ($ mil.)	NET INCOME ($ mil.)	NET PROFIT MARGIN	EMPLOYEES
12/13	193	12	6.3%	117
12/09	185	23	12.9%	—
12/08	164	6	4.0%	—
12/06	140	0	—	—
Annual Growth	4.6%	—	—	—

2013 Year-End Financials

Debt ratio: —
Return on equity: 6.30%
Cash ($ mil.): 20
Current ratio: 2.20
Long-term debt ($ mil.): —
Dividends
Yield: —
Payout: —
Market value ($ mil.): —

CENTRAL MICHIGAN UNIVERSITY

Academic advancement is central at Central Michigan University (CMU). It offers undergraduate graduate and professional coursework through eight colleges including business communication and fine arts medicine and education and human services. The university enrolls about 29000 students most of which attend the main campus in Mt. Pleasant. The institution also offers off-campus courses online and from about 50 locations throughout North America. Notable alumni include former US Senator Robert P. Griffin and actor Jeff Daniels. CMU was founded in 1892 as a teachers' college.

Operations

CMU has 1000 faculty members and a student-to-faculty ratio of 21:1. It offers about 400 academic programs for undergraduates and graduates. In addition the university has division I athletic programs for men and women and the CMU Public Broadcasting unit operates 10 television and seven radio stations.

Financial Performance

CMU experienced a 2% increase in revenues to $321.5 million in 2012 due to higher tuition earnings and auxiliary enterprise revenues as well as increased federal funding from various agencies. Tuition runs at about $18000 per student per year.

Net income fell 93% to $6.1 million in 2012 however due to higher expenses (from benefits and compensation supplies and other operating costs) as well as due to declining state appropriations Pell Grant income and investment income.

EXECUTIVES

Associate VP Human Resources, Lori Hella
Associate VP Financial Services and Reporting and Controller, Barrie J. Wilkes
Vice President Development and External Relations, Kathleen M. (Kathy) Wilbur
VP Technology and CIO, Roger Rehm
Director Financial Planning and Budgets, Carol Haas
VP Finance and Administrative Services, David A. Burdette
Executive Vice President Provost, E. Gary Shapiro
Director Administration, Dave Bunting
Associate VP Facilities Management, Stephen (Steve) Lawrence
Associate Vice President Residence & Auxiliary Services, John Fisher

Executive Director Alumni Relations, Marcie Otteman
Dean Libraries, Thomas Moore
President, George E. Ross
Vice President The Dow Chemical Company, Sarah R. Opperman
General Counsel, Manuel Rupe
Executive Assistant President, Mary Flanagan
Associate Vice President University Communications, Sherry Knight
Vice President Enrollment and Student Services, Steven Johnson
Interim Associate Vice President Diversity, Traci Guinn
CFO Vice President The Dow Chemical Company, William H. Weideman
Trustee, Brian W. Fannon, age 65
President, George E. Ross
Trustee, John D. Hurd
Trustee, Sarah R. Opperman

LOCATIONS

HQ: CENTRAL MICHIGAN UNIVERSITY
1200 S FRANKLIN ST, MOUNT PLEASANT, MI 48859-2001
Phone: 989-774-4000
Web: WWW.CMICH.EDU

PRODUCTS/OPERATIONS

Selected Colleges and Schools

College of Business Administration
College of Communication and Fine Arts
College of Education and Human Services
College of Graduate Studies
College of Health Professions
College of Humanities and Social and Behavioral Sciences
College of Medicine
College of Science and Technology
Global Campus & Online

HISTORICAL FINANCIALS

Company Type: Private

Income Statement FYE: June 30

	REVENUE ($ mil.)	NET INCOME ($ mil.)	NET PROFIT MARGIN	EMPLOYEES
06/13	319	32	10.1%	2,388
06/12	321	6	1.9%	—
06/10	329	90	27.4%	—
06/10	293	54	18.4%	—
Annual Growth	2.9%	(15.8%)	—	—

2013 Year-End Financials

Debt ratio: —
Return on equity: 10.10%
Cash ($ mil.): 64
Current ratio: 1.00
Long-term debt ($ mil.): —
Dividends
Yield: —
Payout: —
Market value ($ mil.): —

CENTRAL REFRIGERATED SERVICE INC.

No matter the weather conditions trucking company Central Refrigerated Service stays cool when it's on the move. The carrier provides temperature-controlled transportation and dry cargo services for major food suppliers and retailers across the US. It specializes in providing a wide array of offerings from private fleet conversion to inner city and solo driver deliveries to long haul truckload transportation services. Central Refrigerated operates a fleet of about 1800 tractors and 2700 refrigerated trailers or reefers. The company was acquired by truckload carrier Swift Transportation in mid-2013.

Change of Company Type

Central Refrigerated was owned by Jerry Moyes who also owns Swift Transportation. In August 2013 Swift acquired Central Refrigerated for $225 million in order to bolster its refrigerated transport and temperature-controlled offerings.

Operations Central Refrigerated Service estimates that 95% of its loads are food products. Through its Central Logistics division the company provides truckload capacity brokerage and dedicated fleet services.

Company Background Founded in 2002 as a unit of Central Freight Lines Central Refrigerated Service expanded that year by buying the assets of bankrupt Simon Transportation Services another Moyes-controlled company. Central Refrigerated Service was spun off from Central Freight Lines at the end of 2002.

EXECUTIVES

CEO, Jon F. Isaacson
VP Sales and Pricing, Tork A. Fulton
Southern California and Southwest Sales Manager, Brian Kilpatrick
Director Sales National Accounts, Charlie Bringle
Southeast Sales Manager, Mike Bailey
Director Customer Service, Mike Cafarelli
CFO, Bob Baer
Sales Manager, Al Aldrich
Sales Manager, Archie Tucker
Sales Manager, Joe Weber

LOCATIONS

HQ: CENTRAL REFRIGERATED SERVICE INC.
5175 W 2100 S, SALT LAKE CITY, UT 84120-1252
Phone: 801-924-7000
Web: WWW.CENTRALREFRIGERATED.COM

COMPETITORS

C.R. England
Covenant Transportation
Crete Carrier
Frozen Food Express
KLLM Transport Services
Marten Transport
Prime Inc.
Stevens Transport
Werner Enterprises
Willis Shaw Express

HISTORICAL FINANCIALS

Company Type: Private

Income Statement FYE: December 31

	REVENUE ($ mil.)	NET INCOME ($ mil.)	NET PROFIT MARGIN	EMPLOYEES
12/11	419	0	—	1,650
12/08	406	9	2.4%	—
12/07	361	6	1.8%	—
12/06	775	0	0.0%	—
Annual Growth	(11.6%)	—	—	—

CENTRASTATE HEALTHCARE SYSTEM INC

CentraState Healthcare System makes healing its central mission while serving residents of central New Jersey. The health system operates CentraState Medical Center an acute-care teaching hospital with more than 280 beds that offers emergency surgical and diagnostic imaging services as well as specialty services including cardiovascular care and women's health. Other CentraState Healthcare facilities include nursing homes wellness centers and outpatient clinics. CentraState Healthcare is an affiliate of the Robert Wood Johnson Health System and Network.

Operations

In addition to medical care CentraState Healthcare's main hospital provides medical training including a family medicine residency program through affiliations with the UMDNJ-Robert Wood Johnson Medical School and other colleges.

In addition to CentraState Medical Center the organization operates three nursing homes (Applewood Estates Manor Health and Monmouth Crossing) and the Star and Barry Tobias Ambulatory Campus which includes fitness and wellness centers. It also runs family medicine practices and its CentraState Healthcare Foundation supports the company's community health and expansion initiatives.

Strategy

CentraState has added on to its main medical campus over the years including the addition of the Star and Barry Tobias Ambulatory Campus a full-service outpatient care center located adjacent to the CentraState Medical Center. The company has also expanded its senior care facilities.

In 2012 it opened a new $160 million proton therapy clinic (one of ten such facilities in the US) through a partnership with Princeton Radiation Oncology and ProCure Cancer Centers. CentraState also expanded radiation oncology capabilities at CentraState Medical Center that year.

In partnership with other area hospitals CentraState Medical Center is working to improve efficiencies and reduce expenses during the care of Medicare and Medicaid patients. The program is called the Bundled Payments for Care Improvement initiative and is facilitated by the Centers for Medicare and Medicaid.

EXECUTIVES

Vp Human Resources, Frances Keane
Vp Planning & Business Devlpmnt, Richard Mackesy
Asst Vp Finance, Robert Nyman
Director Of Radiology, Barry Friedenberg
President and CEO, John T. Gribbin
SVP and CFO, John A. Dellocono
VP Patient Services, Linda Geisler
VP Senior Services, Jay S. Solomon
VP Clinical Services, Kim A. Kelly
VP and Chief Medical Officer, Jack H. Dworkin
VP Physician Practice Management, James Richvalsky
VP and Chief Information Officer, John W. Ulett
SVP and COO, Thomas W. Scott
Medical Director The Radiation Oncology Department, Edward M Soffen
Vice President And Manager Western Region Electric Distribution Division, Charles W Hayne
Director Of Pharmacy, John Dinattio
Asst Vp Quality & Performance, Carl B Ausfahl
Asst Vp Information Systems, Peg Kauth
Assit Vp Human Resources, Jacqueline Piccolini
Vice President Marketing, Valerie Critelli
Vice President Of Quality Corporate Compliance, Janice Breen
Asst Vp Corp Patnt Financl Srv, Jan McAvenia
Senior Vice President Director Medical, Benjamin Weinstein
Medical Director, David Frank
Senior Vice President Chief Medical, John Schaefer
Vice President Of Information Technology, Iris Mentle
Assistant Vice President Nursing, Cathleen Janzekovich

Chairperson, Joseph R. Iantosca
Vice Chairperson, Stephen J. Walsh
Board Of Directors, Casandra H Autry
Board Of Directors, Neha Shah

LOCATIONS

HQ: CENTRASTATE HEALTHCARE SYSTEM INC
901 W MAIN ST, FREEHOLD, NJ 07728-2537
Phone: 732-431-2000
Web: WWW.CENTRASTATE.COM

PRODUCTS/OPERATIONS

Selected Services

Cardiac catheterization lab
Cardiology services
Computed tomography (CT)
Coronary CTangiography (CTA)
Diabetes services (Novo Nordisk Diabetes Center)
Dialysis unit
Emergency services
Endovascular surgery
Inpatient psychiatric services
Magnetic resonance imaging (MRI)
Maternity care (single room) and special care nursery
Oncology
Radiation oncology
Rehabilitation
Short stay unit
Sleep disorders center
Women' s Health Center

COMPETITORS

Barnabas Health
Bergen Regional Medical
Capital Health System
JFK Health System
Princeton HealthCare
Raritan Bay Medical Center
Robert Wood Johnson University Hospital
Saint Peter' s University Hospital
Somerset Medical Center
St. Joseph' s Healthcare System
Trinitas Regional Medical Center

HISTORICAL FINANCIALS

Company Type: Private

Income Statement FYE: December 31

	REVENUE ($ mil.)	NET INCOME ($ mil.)	NET PROFIT MARGIN	EMPLOYEES
12/11	277	15	5.4%	2,527
12/10	259	15	5.9%	—
12/09	254	17	7.0%	—
12/08	260	(11)	—	—
Annual Growth	2.1%	—	—	—

2011 Year-End Financials

Debt ratio: —
Return on equity: 5.40%
Cash ($ mil.): 43
Current ratio: 1.40
Long-term debt ($ mil.): —
Dividends
Yield: —
Payout: —
Market value ($ mil.): —

CENTRIC BANK

LOCATIONS

HQ: CENTRIC BANK
4320 LINGLESTOWN RD, HARRISBURG, PA 171129532
Phone: 7175410721
Web: WWW.CENTRICBANK.COM

HISTORICAL FINANCIALS

Company Type: Private

Income Statement FYE: December 31

	ASSETS ($ mil.)	NET INCOME ($ mil.)	INCOME AS % OF ASSETS	EMPLOYEES
12/13	304	0	0.2%	40
12/08	125	(0)	—	—
Annual Growth	19.4%	—	—	—

2013 Year-End Financials

Debt ratio: —
Return on equity: 4.70%
Cash ($ mil.): 9
Current ratio: —
Long-term debt ($ mil.): —
Dividends
Yield: —
Payout: —
Market value ($ mil.): —

CERES SOLUTIONS LLP

Ceres Solutions is a growth business. The agricultural partnership provides farmers in about a dozen ,Âlndiana counties ,Âwith crop ,Âfarming support services and supplies. ,Âlt ,Âsells stores and distributes such goods as fertilizers and fuel (gasoline propane home-heating). The company's agronomy services include field mapping crop and pest management soil sampling and ,Âyield analysis. Ceres Solutions also offers crop-financing programs sells crop insurance and provides marketing services. Its Green Notes newsletter offers the state's farmers market and technical ,Âadvice and analysis.

Ceres Solutions which ,Â was formed in 2007 ,Âthrough the ,Âmerger of three agricultural cooperatives –,ÂWestland Growers and AgroKey. It operates primarily in the western region of Indiana through ,Âabout ,Â30 agronomy office ,Âlocations an energy office ,Âand its ,Âmain office which is located ,Âin Crawfordsville Indiana.

EXECUTIVES

Senior Vice President Marketing, Mark Kelp
Vp Of Agronomy, Dan Weber
Board Member, Morgan Dayhoff
Treasurer, Ron Monroe

LOCATIONS

HQ: CERES SOLUTIONS LLP
2112 INDIANAPOLIS RD, CRAWFORDSVILLE, IN 479333137
Phone: 7653626108
Web: WWW.CERESLLP.COM

COMPETITORS

ADM
Ag Processing Inc.
CHS
Cargill
GROWMARK
Premier AG Co-Op Inc.

HISTORICAL FINANCIALS

Company Type: Private

Income Statement FYE: July 31

	REVENUE ($ mil.)	NET INCOME ($ mil.)	NET PROFIT MARGIN	EMPLOYEES
07/14	412	22	5.4%	125
07/13	402	25	6.4%	—
07/12	399	22	5.6%	—
07/11	329	0	—	—
Annual Growth	7.8%	—	—	—

2014 Year-End Financials

Debt ratio: —
Return on equity: 5.40%
Cash ($ mil.): 16
Current ratio: 0.90
Long-term debt ($ mil.): —
Dividends
Yield: —
Payout: —
Market value ($ mil.): —

CERTCO INC.

Certco has built a business serving about 200 independent grocers in Minnesota Wisconsin Iowa and Illinois. The food distribution cooperative offers customers an inventory of more than 57000 items including bakery goods frozen foods meat products produce and general merchandise. It distributes products under the Shurfine Shurfresh and Top Care labels. Additionally Certco offers its member-operators such services as advertising accounting client data services warehousing merchandising store planning and design and other business support services. The cooperative was founded in 1930 as Central Wisconsin Cooperative Food Stores.

Geographic Reach

Based in Madison Wisconsin Certco operates in Minnesota and Wisconsin with an extended reach into parts of Iowa and Illinois.

Operations

To support its business Certco operates a nearly 1 million-sq.-ft. distribution center. Its brands include Shurfine Shurfresh Value Time Full Circle Topco and Top Care.

Sales and Marketing

Many of Certco's clients are Fortune 500 companies. It distributes the national brands of major companies such as Kraft General Mills Procter & Gamble and Johnson & Johnson. The company also distributes specialty items under the names Amy's Hodgson Mills Bob's Red Mill and Annie's that are only available through direct-store-delivery suppliers.

Company Background

Certco was established in 1930 when five Madison-area retailers formed an alliance to boost their combined purchasing muscle.

EXECUTIVES

Vice President, Antonio Hernandez

LOCATIONS

HQ: CERTCO INC.
5321 VERONA RD, FITCHBURG, WI 537116050
Phone: 6082782246
Web: WWW.CERTCOINC.COM

PRODUCTS/OPERATIONS

Selected Brands

Full Circle
Shurfine
Shurfresh
Top Care
Value Time

Selected Services

Advertising
Client data services
Retail accounting
Retail meetings/seminars
Retail support
Retail technology
Store planning & design
Trade shows
Value added services
Warehouses
Web architecture

COMPETITORS

Affiliated Foods Midwest
Associated Wholesale Grocers
C&S Wholesale
Central Grocers
Dearborn Wholesale Grocers
Kroger
Nash-Finch
Roundy' s
Winkler

HISTORICAL FINANCIALS

Company Type: Private

Income Statement FYE: April 26

	REVENUE ($ mil.)	NET INCOME ($ mil.)	NET PROFIT MARGIN	EMPLOYEES
04/14	640	5	0.9%	325
04/13	607	5	0.9%	—
04/12	569	5	0.9%	—
04/11	525	0	—	—
Annual Growth	6.8%	—	—	—

2014 Year-End Financials

Debt ratio: —
Return on equity: 0.90%
Cash ($ mil.): 11
Current ratio: 0.80
Long-term debt ($ mil.): —
Dividends
Yield: —
Payout: —
Market value ($ mil.): —

CGB ENTERPRISES INC.

The farmer in the delta relies on CGB Enterprises. Located in Louisiana near the shores of Lake Pontchartrain and the mouth of the Missisippi River the agricultural company provides US farmers with a range of services including grain handling storage and merchandising. It offers inland grain transportation by barge rail and truck and also markets and sells seeds agricultural chemicals and insurance. CGB's Consolidated Terminals and Logistics Co. (CTLC) subsidiary provides transportation logistics and bulk commodity services for both agricultural and non-agricultural customers. The company operates more than 95 locations across the US. Japanese trading conglomerates ITOCHU and ZEN-NOH own CGB.

Geographic Reach

From its headquarters in the city of Mandeville Louisiana CGB operates its business through more than 95 locations nationwide. It boasts grain facilities in nearly 10 states including Nebraska Oklahoma Arkansas Iowa Illinois Indiana Ohio Kentucky and Missouri. The company's fertilizer operations span Ohio Illinois Arkansas and Michigan.

Strategy

CGB has expanded its CTLC business in recent years. To give the unit an extended reach CTLC now serves the transportation bulk commodity and logistics needs of a global base of customers rather than just CGB's core businesses.

In 2013 the company entered a joint agreement with Riverland Ag to purchase and ship grain from Riverland's Savage Minnesota facility. The partnership allows Riverland to serve new markets.

CGB also regularly invests in its own holdings. The company is constructing a rail shipment facility in Defiance Ohio to boost its production capacity and existing transportation system.

Mergers and Acquisitions

Strengthening its foothold on the Mississippi River CGB acquired the grain and fertilizer assets of Twomey based in Smithshire Illinois. The deal consummated in 2011 added valuable loading capacity on the river and offered CGB with a solid customer base in northwestern Illinois.

Sales and Marketing

Besides its core services of inland grain transportation via barge rail and truck CGB markets and sells seeds agricultural chemicals and insurance as part of its operations.

Company Ownership

CGB is owned by a pair of Japanese trading conglomerates: ITOCHU and ZEN-NOH.

EXECUTIVES

President CEO, Kevin D. Adams
Manager Human Resources, Karen Hollis
VP Grain Group, Gregory Beck
Risk Manager Grain, Mark St. Clair
VP Diversified Services, Rodney L. Clark
General Manager Agri Financial Services, Alan Singleton
VP Soybean Processing, Doug Debelak
VP CTLC and Marine, Scott Leininger
Manager BioEnergy Services, Steve Burbrink
Manager Accounting, Robin Gerarve
Manager Information Systems, Sean Goodgion
Manager Legal, Sean Burke
Manager Credit, Randolph Hart
Manager Internal Audit, Jake Kavanaugh
General Manager Feed Ingredients, Marc Cruse
Director of Sales & Marketing, Brent Mahana

LOCATIONS

HQ: CGB ENTERPRISES INC.
1127 HWY 190 E SERVICE RD, COVINGTON, LA 70433-4929
Phone: 985-867-3500
Web: WWW.CGB.COM

PRODUCTS/OPERATIONS

Selected Business Units

Feed Ingredients
Fertilizer
Financial Services
Grain
Marine
Premium Grains
Risk Management
Soybean Processing
Terminals & Logistics

COMPETITORS

ADM
Ag Processing Inc.
Alabama Farmers Cooperative
Canal Barge Company
Cargill
Crosby Tugs
Jimmy Sanders
Kirby Corporation
Southern States
Tennessee Farmers Co-op

HISTORICAL FINANCIALS

Company Type: Private

Income Statement FYE: May 31

	REVENUE ($ mil.)	NET INCOME ($ mil.)	NET PROFIT MARGIN	EMPLOYEES
05/13	6,212	30	0.5%	1,250
05/12	6,108	53	0.9%	—
05/10	5,202	50	1.0%	—
05/10	4,157	47	1.1%	—
Annual Growth	14.3%	(14.1%)	—	—

2013 Year-End Financials

Debt ratio: —
Return on equity: 0.50%
Cash ($ mil.): 12
Current ratio: 0.40
Long-term debt ($ mil.): —
Dividends
Yield: —
Payout: —
Market value ($ mil.): —

CH2M HILL COMPANIES LTD.

LOCATIONS

HQ: CH2M HILL COMPANIES LTD.
9191 S JAMAICA ST, ENGLEWOOD, CO 801125946
Phone: 3037710900
Web: WWW.CH2M.COM

2012 Sales

$ in mil.		% of total
US	4,238	69
International	1,922	31
Total	**6,160**	**100**

PRODUCTS/OPERATIONS

2012 Sales

Energy water & facilities	3,474	56
Government environment &infrastructure	2,685	44

Selected Subsidiaries

CH2M HILL Alaska Inc.
CH2M HILL Canada Inc.
CH2M HILL Constructors Inc.
CH2M Hill Energy Ltd.
CH2M HILL Engineers Inc.
CH2M HILL Hanford Inc.
CH2M HILL Inc.
CH2M HILL International Ltd.
Halcrow Group Ltd.
HEBL Inc.

HISTORICAL FINANCIALS

Company Type: Private

Income Statement FYE: December 31

	REVENUE ($ mil.)	NET INCOME ($ mil.)	NET PROFIT MARGIN	EMPLOYEES
12/14	5,468	(318)	—	26,000
12/13	5,931	131	2.2%	—
12/12	6,224	98	1.6%	—
12/11	5,555	0	—	—
Annual Growth	(0.5%)	—	—	—

2014 Year-End Financials

Debt ratio: —
Return on equity: (-5.80%)
Cash ($ mil.): 131
Current ratio: 1.00
Long-term debt ($ mil.): —
Dividends
Yield: —
Payout: —
Market value ($ mil.): —

CHAMPLAIN VALLEY PHYSICIANS HOSPITAL

LOCATIONS

HQ: CHAMPLAIN VALLEY PHYSICIANS HOSPITAL
75 BEEKMAN ST, PLATTSBURGH, NY 129011438
Phone: 5185612000
Web: WWW.CVPH.ORG

HISTORICAL FINANCIALS

Company Type: Private

Income Statement FYE: December 31

	REVENUE ($ mil.)	NET INCOME ($ mil.)	NET PROFIT MARGIN	EMPLOYEES
12/08	204	(8)	—	2,000
12/05	178	2	1.3%	—
12/04	157	(1)	—	—
12/02	135	0	—	—
Annual Growth	7.1%	—	—	—

2008 Year-End Financials

Debt ratio: —
Return on equity: (-4.20%)
Cash ($ mil.): 12
Current ratio: 1.50
Long-term debt ($ mil.): —

Dividends
Yield: —
Payout: —
Market value ($ mil.): —

CHAPMAN UNIVERSITY

Chapman University enrolls 7000 students at campuses throughout California as well as in Washington State. From its main campus in Orange California the university offers traditional undergraduate graduate and professional programs at seven colleges and schools. It also confers bachelor and master's degrees and teaching credentials to non-traditional students at its two-dozen satellite campuses. The university offers some 50 undergraduate majors and 40 graduate programs. It has 650 faculty members and a student-to-teacher ratio of 15:1. Chapman University includes Brandman University a distance learning program for some 10000 working adults that operates two dozen locations and offers online courses.

Financial Performance

Chapman University reported a 9% increase in revenues to $304 million in 2011 due to higher income from tuition fees gifts grants and bequests. Net income also increased 27% to $70 million due to increased endowment returns offset slightly by increased general educational and auxiliary expenses.

Strategy

Chapman University is expanding programs to widen opportunities for students. In 2011 the School of Law launched a new business law program and in 2013 the Argyros School of Business and Economics opened a new financial center for real-time student investor trading and portfolio management training. Facilities expansions include the construction of a new center for the arts and a new health sciences campus; both projects were launched in 2012.

Company Background

Chapman University was founded in 1861 as Hesperian College; it was re-named Chapman College in 1934 in honor of philanthropist Charles C. Chapman.

EXECUTIVES

President, James L. (Jim) Doti, age 67
Associate VP Legal Affairs and University Counsel, Janine P. DuMontelle
Dean George L. Argyros School of Business and Economics, Arthur Kraft
EVP University Advancement, Sheryl A. Bourgeois
Director Institutional Research, Marisol Arredondo
Director Purchasing and University Services, Pamela Ames
Director Career Development Center, Barbara Hubert
Director Athletics, David Currey
Chancellor, Daniele C. Struppa
EVP and COO, Harold W. Hewitt Jr.
VP Campus Planning and Operations, Kris E. Olsen
Dean Leatherby Libraries, Charlene Baldwin
Dean Lawrence and Kristina Dodge College of Film and Media Arts, Robert Bassett
Dean School of Education, Donald N. Cardinal
Director Center for Global Education, James Coyle
Dean School of Law, John Eastman
Director Sponsored Research, Ronald DiMelfi
Dean Chapel, Ronald Farmer
Vice Chancellor Institutional Planning and Assessment, David Fite
Vice Chancellor Faculty Affairs, Karen R. Graham
Vice Chancellor Undergraduate Education, Jeanne Gunner
Dean College of Performing Arts, William D. Hall
Interim Dean College of Science, Janeen Hill
Dean Wilkinson College of Humanities and Social Sciences, Roberta Lessor
Vice Chancellor Enrollment Management, Mike Pelly
Vice Chancellor and Dean Students, Jerry Price
Vice Chancellor Academic Administration, Raymond Sfeir
Director Financial Aid, Gregory Ball
Registrar, John Snodgrass
Controller, Behzad Binesh
Chief Public Safety, Randy Burba
Equal Opportunity Officer, Eduardo A. Monge
Director Budget Planning, Michael C. Price
Director Development Education New Initiatives, Carol Bonner
Director Parent and Alumni Relations, David Moore
Director Communication and Media Relations, Mary Platt
operations Manager, Char Williams
account Manager, Carl Minor
Administrative Assistant, Angela Ruiz
Vice President, Mark Woodland
interim assistant Director alumni engagement, Alicia Vargas-Pharis
Executive Assistant, Karen Bustamante
senior Graphic Designer, Ryan Tolentino
art Director, Rosalinda Monroy
account Manager, Suzanne Meler
account Manager, Drew Farrington
Vice President of Human Resources, Becky Campos
Director Academic Technology and Digital Media, Mary Litch
Financial Operations Manager, Laura Baker
Dean School of Law, Tom Campbell
Dean Argyros School of Business & Economics, Reggie Gilyard
Dean Wilkinson College of Humanities and Social Sciences, Patrick Fuery
Chief Information Officer, Jack Robault
Vice President Michelle Larrimore, Steven Cometa

LOCATIONS

HQ: CHAPMAN UNIVERSITY
1 UNIVERSITY DR, ORANGE, CA 92866-1005
Phone: 714-744-7099
Web: WWW.CHAPMAN.EDU

PRODUCTS/OPERATIONS

Selected Colleges and Schools

College of Educational Studies
College of Performing Arts
George L. Argyros School of Business and Economics
Lawrence and Kristina Dodge College of Film and Media Arts
Schmid College of Science and Technology
School of Law
Wilkinson College of Humanities and Social Sciences

HISTORICAL FINANCIALS

Company Type: Private

Income Statement FYE: May 31

	REVENUE ($ mil.)	NET INCOME ($ mil.)	NET PROFIT MARGIN	EMPLOYEES
05/12	369	75	20.3%	3,300
05/11	303	70	23.1%	—
05/09	276	38	13.8%	—
05/09	196	0	—	—
Annual Growth	23.4%	—	—	—

2012 Year-End Financials

Debt ratio: —
Return on equity: 20.30%
Cash ($ mil.): 40
Current ratio: —
Long-term debt ($ mil.): —

Dividends
Yield: —
Payout: —
Market value ($ mil.): —

CHARLES C PARKS CO INC

The Charles C. Parks Company is a grocery distributor that primarily supplies convenience stores in more than half a dozen Southern states. It distributes a variety of food items and dry goods as well as beverages cigarettes candy and general merchandise. The company also offers support programs for in-store delis and other quick-service food operations. Carl C. Parks Jr. started the family-run business in 1934.

EXECUTIVES

SVP Sales, Gary Pickett
President, Crockett Parks III
Warehouse Manager, Donnie Vaughn
Manager Transportation, Jamie Davenport
CFO, Tom Cripps
EVP and COO, Bo Lanier
Sales Manager, Chris Pizzini
Food Service Director, Chuck Watkins
Purchasing Manager, Tim Flick
Information Technology Manager, David Lowery
Novelty Manager, Mike Pike

LOCATIONS

HQ: CHARLES C PARKS CO INC
500 N BELVEDERE DR, GALLATIN, TN 37066-5408
Phone: 615-452-2406
Web: WWW.CHARLESCPARKS.COM

COMPETITORS

Alex Lee
Atlantic Dominion
Core-Mark
Eby-Brown
H. T. Hackney
McLane
S. Abraham & Sons
SUPERVALU

HISTORICAL FINANCIALS

Company Type: Private

Income Statement FYE: April 30

	REVENUE ($ mil.)	NET INCOME ($ mil.)	NET PROFIT MARGIN	EMPLOYEES
04/13	275	0	0.2%	145
04/12	268	(0)	—	—
04/10	264	0	0.1%	—
04/10	292	1	0.5%	—
Annual Growth	(2.0%)	(32.8%)	—	—

2013 Year-End Financials

Debt ratio: —
Return on equity: 0.20%
Cash ($ mil.): 0
Current ratio: 2.50
Long-term debt ($ mil.): —

Dividends
Yield: —
Payout: —
Market value ($ mil.): —

CHARLES COUNTY BOARD OF EDUCATION

LOCATIONS

HQ: CHARLES COUNTY BOARD OF EDUCATION
5980 RADIO STATION RD, LA PLATA, MD 206463337
Phone: 3019326610
Web: WWW.CCBOE.COM

HISTORICAL FINANCIALS

Company Type: Private

Income Statement FYE: June 30

	REVENUE ($ mil.)	NET INCOME ($ mil.)	NET PROFIT MARGIN	EMPLOYEES
06/14	403	5	1.3%	5,000
06/13	393	9	2.5%	—
06/12	365	8	2.3%	—
06/10	355	0	—	—
Annual Growth	3.2%	—	—	—

2014 Year-End Financials

Debt ratio: —
Return on equity: 1.30%
Cash ($ mil.): 62
Current ratio: —
Long-term debt ($ mil.): —

Dividends
Yield: —
Payout: —
Market value ($ mil.): —

CHARLESTON AREA MEDICAL CENTER INC.

CAMC Health System is a catalyst for care in Charleston. The health network includes flagship facility Charleston Area Medical Center (CAMC) which is the largest hospital in West Virginia and consists of three campuses with some 840 beds total. The system also includes the CAMC Health Education and Research Institute which coordinates education programs for medical students from West Virginia University. In addition the health system operates smaller rural hospital CAMC Teays Valley and several urgent care and family practice clinics. CAMC Health System operates an online medical information system designed to communicate with health professionals statewide.

Operations The three campuses of CAMC include CAMC General Hospital CAMC Memorial Hospital and CAMC Women and Children's Hospital all of which are located in Charleston. Specialty services at the hospitals include cardiology kidney transplants trauma and pediatrics. The CAMC Institute conducts graduate and continuing education courses; it also connects education and health care through clinical research projects in areas such as cancer and cardiovascular studies. The Teays Valley Hospital is a 70-bed facility located in nearby Hurricane West Virginia.

EXECUTIVES

Vice President Human Resources, Beth Samples
President and CEO, David L. Ramsey
EVP and COO, Glen Crotty
EVP and CFO, Larry C. Hudson
VP CAMC Ambulatory Services, Jeff Goode
VP and Administrator CAMC Women and Children's Hospital, Andrew Weber
Administrator CAMC Memorial Hospital, Jeff Oskin
VP Information Services, Gregg Veltri
President CAMC Health Education and Research Institute, Sharon A. Hall
President Teays Valley Hospital, Randy Hodges
President CAMC Foundation, E. Gail Pitchford
VP Professional Practice; Chief Nursing Officer, Ron Moore
VP and Administrator CAMC General Hospital, Michael D. Williams
Chief Medical Officer, T. Pinckney McIlwain
Vp Of Quality Management, Dale Wood
Director Of Utilization Review, Janice Kiser
Vice President Human Resources, Kristy Snyder
Director Physician Recruitment, Carol Wamsley
Director Icu/coronary Care Unit, Sande Egnor
Director Of Operating Room, Phyllis Campbell
Director Of Operating Room, Marcy Myers
Vp, Dale Johnson
Infection Control Director, Sara Spencer
Operating Room Director, Glen Martin
Infection Control Director, Terrie Lee
Treasurer, Lisa Gerencir

LOCATIONS

HQ: CHARLESTON AREA MEDICAL CENTER INC.
501 MORRIS ST, CHARLESTON, WV 25301-1326
Phone: 304-348-5432
Web: WWW.CAMC.ORG

PRODUCTS/OPERATIONS

Selected Service Areas

Behavioral health
Cancer
Cardiac
Children's medicine
Craniofacial surgery
Endoscopy
Fertility
Gynecology
Hemophilia
Kidney transplant
Orthopedics
Palliative care
Perinatal
Plastic surgery
Stroke
Trauma
Urology
Vascular

COMPETITORS

Charleston Hospital
Ohio Valley Medical Center
Princeton Community Hospital
St. Mary' s Medical Center
WVUHS
Weirton Medical Center
West Virginia University Hospitals

HISTORICAL FINANCIALS

Company Type: Private

Income Statement FYE: December 31

	REVENUE ($ mil.)	NET INCOME ($ mil.)	NET PROFIT MARGIN	EMPLOYEES
12/07	703	9	1.3%	4,000
12/06	703	38	5.5%	—
12/05	406	0	—	—
Annual Growth	—13366.6%		—	—

2007 Year-End Financials

Debt ratio: —
Return on equity: 1.30%
Cash ($ mil.): 15
Current ratio: 0.80
Long-term debt ($ mil.): —

Dividends
Yield: —
Payout: —
Market value ($ mil.): —

CHARTER MANUFACTURING COMPANY INC.

Charter Manufacturing's magna carta calls for it to make steel products. The company and its divisions manufacture such steel products as special bar quality (SBQ) bar rod wire and stainless steel rod. The company also supplies precision cold-rolled custom profiles and engineered components including driveline engine and transmission parts for the automotive industry. It operates in the primarily in the US but also in Europe and Asia through subsidiaries Charter Steel (general steel products) Charter Wire Charter Dura-Bar (cast iron bar and bronze alloys); and Charter Automotive (engineered components for automotive applications).

Geographic Reach

Charter Manufacturing serves customers around the world and has plants in the US (Michigan Ohio and Wisconsin) China (one plant) and the UK (two plants).

Operations

The company manufactures special bar quality bar rod and wire as well as precision cold-rolled custom profiles flat wire and standard shapes and engineered components for use in engines transmissions and drivelines. Charter Steel is an integrated producer of special bar quality bar rod and wire products has an annual coil-making capacity of 1.2 million tons; Charter Dura-Bar is a leading producer of continuous cast iron bar stock and a distributor (through Dura-Bar Metal Services) of Dura-Bar products and bronze alloys; Charter Wire supplies precision cold-rolled custom profiles flat wire and standard shapes; while Charter Automotive supplies of engineered components for engine driveline and transmission applications.

Strategy

The company is looking to expand both geographically and in terms of product offerings. Growing its global footprint in 2012 the company expanded its European operations with the purchase of a 57000 sq.-ft. manufacturing plant in Burntwood UK. The expansion strengthens Charter Automotive's position as a global supplier to OEM automotive and powertrain industries and helps it meet the growing demands of customers in Europe and elsewhere.

Mergers and Acquisitions

In 2012 the company acquired Wells Manufacturing Company (owner of Dura-Bar and DuraBar Metal Services). The acquired assets (which added a fourth division to Charter Manufacturing's family of companies) focus on producing specialty iron bar and distributing bronze alloy products.

Company Background

Facing tough market conditions Charter Automotive closed part of its steelmaking operations in Milwaukee Wisconsin in 2010. The company ceased making steel dipsticks and tubes for cars and trucks as part of a wider response to global market trends. The company which kept its engine components operations elsewhere in Milwaukee active sold the Heather Avenue plant idled by this move.

Charter Manufacturing was founded in 1936.

EXECUTIVES

Chairman and CEO, John A. Mellowes, age 76
VP and General Manager Charter Wire, John W. Mellowes
VP and General Manager Charter Specialty Steel, Charles Mellowes

LOCATIONS

HQ: CHARTER MANUFACTURING COMPANY INC.
1212 W GLEN OAKS LN, MEQUON, WI 53092-3357
Phone: 262-243-4700
Web: WWW.CHARTERMFG.COM

PRODUCTS/OPERATIONS

Selected Operating Units

Charter Automotive
Charter Dura-Bar
Charter Steel
Charter Wire

Selected Mergers and Acquisitions

2012
Wells Manufacturing Company (owner of Dura-Bar—specialty iron bar and DuraBar Metal Services—bronze alloys)

COMPETITORS

AK Steel Holding Corporation
Federal-Mogul
Gerdau Ameristeel
Nucor
Republic Steel
Sumitomo Metal Industries
Timken
United States Steel

HISTORICAL FINANCIALS

Company Type: Private

Income Statement FYE: December 31

	REVENUE ($ mil.)	NET INCOME ($ mil.)	NET PROFIT MARGIN	EMPLOYEES
12/11	1,091	83	7.7%	2,000
12/10	903	74	8.3%	—
12/09	517	2	0.4%	—
12/08	996	26	2.7%	—
Annual Growth	3.1%	46.3%	—	—

2011 Year-End Financials

Debt ratio: —
Return on equity: 7.70%
Cash ($ mil.): 73
Current ratio: 1.10
Long-term debt ($ mil.): —
Dividends
Yield: —
Payout: —
Market value ($ mil.): —

CHECKERED FLAG MOTOR CAR COMPANY INC.

LOCATIONS

HQ: CHECKERED FLAG MOTOR CAR COMPANY INC.
5225 VIRGINIA BEACH BLVD, VIRGINIA BEACH, VA 234621899
Phone: 7574901111
Web: WWW.HONDA.CHECKEREDFLAG.COM

HISTORICAL FINANCIALS

Company Type: Private

Income Statement FYE: December 31

	REVENUE ($ mil.)	NET INCOME ($ mil.)	NET PROFIT MARGIN	EMPLOYEES
12/07	362	(0)	—	700
12/06	378	1	0.5%	—
12/05	365	44	12.3%	—
12/04	338	0	—	—
Annual Growth	2.4%	—	—	—

2007 Year-End Financials

Debt ratio: —
Return on equity: —
Cash ($ mil.): 3
Current ratio: 0.10
Long-term debt ($ mil.): —
Dividends
Yield: —
Payout: —
Market value ($ mil.): —

CHENEGA CORPORATION

An Alaska Native Corporation Chenega Corporation has gone from landowner to business titan. Representing the Chenega people residing in the central Alaskan Prince William Sound region it operates mostly through its subsidiaries. Chenega Integrated Systems and Chenega Technology Services offer information technology security training manufacturing research and development network engineering and military operation support services. Chenega Corporation's clients have included the Department of Defense Department of Homeland Security and EPA.

Geographic Reach

The company's headquarters are located in Anchorage Alaska. Chenega Corporation and its subsidiaries operate in 45 states and 11 countries.

Strategy

The company's growth strategy includes making acquisitions. In 2011 subsidiary Chenega Commercial Holdings acquired Alaska Based Hot Wire Inc. and its five Alaska based subsidiaries: Hot Wire Electric Inc. Hot Wire Communications Inc. Electric Inc. Redi Electric Inc. and Alaska Power & Communications LLC (55%). Hot Wire and its subsidiaries have been providing commercial and residential electrical and telecommunications contracting services since 1960 with extensive experience in both private and government construction throughout the US and internationally.

In late 2008 Chenega Corporation expanded its technical and management consulting services offerings by acquiring Time Solutions Corp. whose clients included government private industry national laboratories and universities.

Government contracts are another source of revenue growth. Chenega Corporation began to participate in the Government Services marketplace in 1997. In 2012 it was performing on more than 158 prime contracts and 100 principal sub-contracts through a combination of competitive and negotiated best-value awards.

Ownership

The corporation is owned by about 140 Native Alaskan shareholders.

Company Background

Chenega Corporation also owns the site of the original village of Chenega the oldest continually inhabited community in the area before it was destroyed by a tsunami in 1964. With some 80000 acres of land in the Prince William Sound region Chenega Corporation was the largest private landowner affected by the Exxon Valdez oil spill of 1989. It released about 60000 acres of land to federal and state agencies for environmental restoration in exchange for some $34 million. It retained ownership of some 20000 acres as well as some 10 land parcels held for tourism development.

The corporation was founded in 1974.

EXECUTIVES

Director Human Resources, Peggy O'Keefe

LOCATIONS

HQ: CHENEGA CORPORATION
3000 C ST STE 301, ANCHORAGE, AK 99503-3975
Phone: 907-277-5706
Web: WWW.CHENEGA.JOBS

PRODUCTS/OPERATIONS

Selected Services

Base operations and maintenance
Environmental management
Information technology
Intel and military operations
Light manufacturing
Logistics support
Telecommunications
Tourism and hospitality
Training services
Security services

COMPETITORS

Akal Security
Arctic Slope Regional Corporation
Computer Sciences Corp.
HP Enterprise Services
Halliburton
IBM Global Services
Parsons Corporation
TKC Communications
chugach alaska

HISTORICAL FINANCIALS

Company Type: Private

Income Statement FYE: September 30

	ASSETS ($ mil.)	NET INCOME ($ mil.)	INCOME AS % OF ASSETS	EMPLOYEES
09/12	414	8	2.1%	4,500
09/11	375	28	7.6%	—
09/10	370	28	7.7%	—
09/09	325	25	7.9%	—
Annual Growth	8.5%	(30.4%)	—	—

2012 Year-End Financials

Debt ratio: —
Return on equity: 0.80%
Cash ($ mil.): 2
Current ratio: 1.70
Long-term debt ($ mil.): —
Dividends
Yield: —
Payout: —
Market value ($ mil.): —

CHERRY CENTRAL COOPERATIVE INC.

Serving as a central hub for cherry pickers' crops Cherry Central Cooperative is a fruit marketing co-operative that consists of more than a dozen member cooperatives representing hundreds of growers in Michigan New York Utah Washington and Wisconsin. It processes cherries cranberries apples and other fruit products including the Indian Summer and Wilderness brands of apple and cherry juices and ciders. Its Oceana Foods unit makes dried fruit sold under the Traverse Bay label while its Dunkley International subsidiary makes fruit-processing equipment. Cherry Central's products are sold to retail foodservice and ingredient customers. The cooperative was formed in 1973.

Geographic Reach

From its base in Traverse City Michigan Cherry Central Cooperative directs fruit-growing activities in Michigan New York Utah Washington and Wisconsin serving customers nationwide in Canada and globally.

Operations

Besides its namesake cherry operations Cherry Central supplies customers with apples blueberries cranberries strawberries pomegranate arils and asparagus. The company makes Traverse Bay-brand dried fruit through its Shelby Michigan based Oceana Foods business. The cooperative makes equipment to process fruit at its Dunkley International subsidiary headquartered in Kalamazoo Michigan.

Strategy

To entice customers to continue to buy its products Cherry Central has been working to go to market with new shelf-stable and alternative products. Through a partnership inked in mid-2012 with Vancouver-based EnWave Corporation Cherry Central is evaluating and testing EnWave's Radiant Energy Vacuum (REV) technology. The cooperative anticipates that the collaboration will fuel the development and subsequent launch of a premium dehydrated cherry snack product as well as cherry and apple powders marketed as an alternative to conventional fruit purees. As part of the agreement Cherry Central licenses the REV technology for commercial distribution of these products.

Sales and Marketing

The cooperative organization sells products to retailers foodservice operators and ingredient customers.

EXECUTIVES

President of Cherry Central, Richard L. (Dick) Bogard
National Sales Manager Retail Brands, Brent Tackett
National Sales Manager Foodservice, David Barger
National Sales Manager Private Label, Frank Wolff
VP Operations, Steve Eiseler
Marketing Program Manager, Jamie Zmitko-Somers
VP-SIs, Mark McAuliffe

LOCATIONS

HQ: CHERRY CENTRAL COOPERATIVE INC.
1771 N US 31 S, TRAVERSE CITY, MI 49685-8748
Phone: 231-946-1860
Web: WWW.CHERRYCENTRAL.COM

PRODUCTS/OPERATIONS

Selected Frozen Ingredients

Apples
Blueberries
Cranberries
Damson Plums
Dark Sweet Cherries
Red Tart Cherries

Selected Frozen Fruit Varieties

Diced
Juice concentrate
IQF (Individually Quick Frozen)
Pitted or punch pitted
Pureed
Sliced
Solid or sugar pack
Whole

Selected Private Label and Co-pack Products

Applesauce
Formulas
Juice Flavors
Packaging

Selected Brands

Indian Summer
Traverse Bay Fruit Co.

COMPETITORS

Allens
California Giant
Chiquita Brands
Dole Food
Donio Produce
Encore Fruit Marketing
Fazio Marketing
Fresh Del Monte Produce
Graceland Fruit
Greenridge Fruit
Jasper Wyman & Son
Knouse Foods
Naturipe Farms
Pacific Coast Producers
Pro-Fac
Red Jacket Orchards
Seneca Foods
Shoreline Fruit
Sun World International
Sun-Maid
SunOpta
SunnyRidge Farm
Sunsweet Growers
Tree Top
Welch' s

HISTORICAL FINANCIALS

Company Type: Private

Income Statement FYE: April 30

	REVENUE ($ mil.)	NET INCOME ($ mil.)	NET PROFIT MARGIN	EMPLOYEES
04/13	185	1	0.6%	115
04/12	154	0	0.5%	—
04/10	144	0	0.1%	—
04/10	136	0	0.2%	—
Annual Growth	10.9%	73.6%	—	—

2013 Year-End Financials

Debt ratio: —
Return on equity: 0.60%
Cash ($ mil.): 0
Current ratio: 0.30
Long-term debt ($ mil.): —
Dividends
Yield: —
Payout: —
Market value ($ mil.): —

CHILDFUND INTERNATIONAL USA

ChildFund International (CFI) serves the little ones. The worldwide non-profit organization provides education medical care food and safe water to more than 13 million children –of all faiths –in about 30 countries in Africa Asia the Caribbean Eastern Europe Latin America and the US. It works in areas of early childhood development education family income generation nutrition and sanitation. The group also tries to get child soldiers away from the military and reintegrated into daily life. Founded in 1938 as China's Children Fund the group changed its name to Christian Children's Fund in 1951. In 2009 it again renamed itself ChildFund International.

Since its founding as an organization focused on orphans and orphanages CFI has become an international child development organization. More than 500000 sponsored children receive monthly contributions through the group; about 350000 of those sponsorships are supported by donors in the US. CFI also publishes newsletters booklets and studies on the effects of poverty and violence on children.

EXECUTIVES

VP Communications and Public Affairs, Cheri W. Dahl
President and CEO, Anne Lynam Goddard
Chief Financial Officer Vice President Finance & Operations, James M. Tuite
Chairman, Charles M. Caravati Jr.
Executive Vice President Programs, Isam M. Ghanim
Interim VP Global Programs, Dula C. James
VP People and Culture, Diane H. Willis
VP Marketing and Strategic Resources, Mike Pressendo
VP Global Programs, Anne Scott
Director Communications, Cynthia Price
Manager Communications, Ellie Whinnery
Chief Information Officer Vice President Information Technology, Scott Lemler
Executive Vice President CAO, Steve Stirling
Director, A. Hugh Ewing III
Director, Karen Hein
Director, Velma McBride Murry
Director, Thomas A. Siegfried
Director, Thomas Weisner
Director, Paul Hirschbiel
Auditors: Ernst&YoungLLP

LOCATIONS

HQ: CHILDFUND INTERNATIONAL USA
2821 EMERYWOOD PKWY, RICHMOND, VA 23294-3726
Phone: 804-756-2700
Web: WWW.CHILDFUND.ORG

HISTORICAL FINANCIALS

Company Type: Private

Income Statement FYE: June 30

	REVENUE ($ mil.)	NET INCOME ($ mil.)	NET PROFIT MARGIN	EMPLOYEES
06/12	230	3	1.5%	160
06/11	228	12	5.3%	—
06/09	215	4	2.2%	—
06/09	217	12	5.7%	—
Annual Growth	1.9%	(34.2%)	—	—

2012 Year-End Financials

Debt ratio: —
Return on equity: 1.50%
Cash ($ mil.): 32
Current ratio: 1.30
Long-term debt ($ mil.): —
Dividends
Yield: —
Payout: —
Market value ($ mil.): —

CHILDREN'S HOSPITAL MEDICAL CENTER

Cincinnati Children's Hospital Medical Center has a special place in its heart for kids –and vice versa. The pediatric health care facility offers specialty treatments for children and adolescents suffering from just about any malady including ailments of the heart and liver as well as blood diseases and cancer. Cincinnati Children's Hospital has some 590 beds and operates about a dozen outpatient care centers. Founded in 1883 the not-for-profit hospital runs the only Level 1 pediatric trauma center in the region and serves as a teaching and research facility for the University of Cincinnati College of Medicine.

Geographic Reach

Reaching beyond Cincinnati Cincinnati Children's Hospital also provides services to communities in southeastern Indiana and northern Kentucky through its network of outpatient clinics. The hospital serves patients from all 50 US states as well as from about 50 international countries. It has international research collaborations with institutions in Bangladesh Brazil China Honduras Israel Malawi Mexico Nepal and the United Arab Emirates.

Operations

With a staff of some 1500 physicians Cincinnati Children's Hospital serves more than 1 million patients each year including 120000 emergency room visits and 32000 surgical procedures. Its outpatient centers include community urgent and emergency care facilities and general and specialty physician practices as well as laboratory radiology dentistry and physical therapy clinics.

The Cincinnati Children's Research Foundation conducts research and clinical trials of pediatric medical innovations including new vaccines and surgical techniques. It has research partnerships with hospitals in Africa Asia Latin America and the Middle East. The hospital and research foundation's contributions to pediatric medicine include the rotavirus vaccine (approved in for use in the US in 2008) and Albert Sabin's discovery of the oral polio vaccine (first tested in 1960).

The hospital's educational programs are also renowned. More than 200 physicians from about 35 countries visited Cincinnati Children's Hospital for training and education during 2012.

Financial Performance

Cincinnati Children's Hospital increased operating revenues by 9% to nearly $1.9 billion in 2012 due to increase hospital patient service revenue professional service revenues and grants. As a result net income rose 141% that year to some $129 million.

Strategy

Cincinnati Children's Hospital regularly expands its facilities to improve medical services and enhance research and education programs. To expand its outpatient network it launched a Cincinnati center for kids with special needs and chronic ailments in 2010. In 2012 it began construction on a 425000-sq. ft. clinical sciences building on the main hospital campus to expand patient-oriented research capabilities; it also expanded its preterm birth prevention research program that year.

In addition the institution forms collaborations to expand its operations. In 2012 Cincinnati Children's Hospital formed a partnership with the Ben Gurion University in Israel. The two institutions will collaborate on the development of new pediatric medical devices.

The hospital has remained on the forefront of the digital revolution that has swept the health care industry. In recent years the organization has linked its emergency inpatient radiology pharmacy and specialty department patient data together to create an electronic medical record (EHR). The EHR system helps to reduce patient errors (such as medication errors) and improves communication between departments.

To prepare for health reform measures Cincinnati Children's Hospital is also reducing costs through workflow purchasing and care delivery improvement programs.

EXECUTIVES

Vice President Marketing, Phyllis Goodman
Dir Of Managed Care Contracts, Michael L Taylor
Vice President For Professional Develo, Joseph Fondacaro
President and CEO, Michael Fisher, age 55
EVP and COO, Scott J. Hamlin
SVP Information Services and CIO, Marianne F. James
CFO, Mark D. Mumford, age 52
Chief Medical Officer, Arnold W. Strauss
Vp Finance, Alma Helpling
Medical Director, Stavra A Xanthakos
Director Of Pharmacy, Dave Mayhaus
Asst Vp Ancillary Services, Jack Horn
Medical Director, David P Witte
Director Of Operating Room, Kahne Springborn
Clinical Director, Michael T Sorter
Assistant Vice President, Carolyn Karageorges
Vice President I S, Maryjo Zorb
Assistant Vice President, Courtney Saxton
Assistant Vice President, Karel Simbartl
Respiratory Therapy Director, Scott Pettinichi
Clinical Director, Victoria Decastro
Assistant Vice President Data And Analytics, Yiscah Bracha
Assistant Vice President Sponsored Programs And Research Accounting, Peter Koch
Senior Vice President Planning And Business Development, Dee Eilingwood
Assistant Vice President, James Page
Clinical Director, Connie Scully
Vice President Finance And Operations, Susan Laupola
Vice President Of Strategy, Ken Saporito
Assistant Vice President, Joseph Townsend
Assistant Vice President Ambulatory Services, Jackie Hausfeld
Assistant Vice President, Melissa Saladonis
Radiology Director, Carl Cordner
Clinical Director, Teresa Merk
Clinical Director, Shawna Langworthy
Assistant Vice President, Curtis Ohashi
Assistant Vice President Chief Patient Services Informatics Officer, Kristin Boggs
Assistant Vice President Patient Service, Deborah Browning
Associate Vice President (Aco) Medical Management, Amy Baldridge
Senior Vice President Production And Technical Operations, Sean Sweeney
Vice President And General Counsel, Elizabeth Stautberg
Assistant Vice President Patient Services, Barbara Tofani
Assistant Vice President, Courtney Campbell-saxton
Clinical Director, Laurie Webster
Vice President Business Development, Jim Barter
Clinical Director, Julie Clark
Chair, Thomas G. Cody, age 73
Board Member, Karen Salchli

LOCATIONS

HQ: CHILDREN' S HOSPITAL MEDICAL CENTER
3333 BURNET AVE, CINCINNATI, OH 45229-3039
Phone: 513-636-4200
Web: WWW.CINCINNATICHILDRENS.ORG

PRODUCTS/OPERATIONS

Selected Locations

Anderson
Batesville
Burnet Campus
Children's Health Care - Greensburg
College Hill Campus
Drake
Eastgate
Fairfield
Harrison
Hopple Street Center
Kenwood
Liberty Campus
Lindner Center of Hope (Mason)
Mason Campus
Northern Kentucky
Oak Campus

Selected Treatment Areas

Abdomen and Digestive Tract
Allergy Asthma Immunology
Anesthesia
Arthritis and Rheumatology
Babies / Infants
Bones Joints and Muscles
Brain Spinal Cord and Nerves
Cancer
Cerebral Palsy
Chest and Lungs
Craniofacial Anomalies
Dental and Oral Health
Developmental Disabilities
Ear Nose Throat
Endocrine Metabolism and Diabetes
Eyes
Genetics
Growth and Development
Heart
Hemangiomas and Vascular Malformations
Hematology and Blood
Infectious Diseases
Injuries and Poisonings
Kidney Bladder and Genitals
Liver
Medications
Mental Health
Nutrition and Diet
Pain Management
Rehabilitation
Safety and Injury Prevention
Skin
Speech
Sports Medicine
Surgery
Teen Health
X-Ray / Radiology

COMPETITORS

Bethesda North
Children' s Hospital of Philadelphia
Deaconess Associations
Kettering Health Network
Mercy Health (OH)
Nationwide Children' s Hospital
Nemours Foundation
Premier Health Partners
Shriners Hospitals For Children
St. Elizabeth Healthcare
St. Jude Children' s Research Hospital
The Christ Hospital Corporation
TriHealth
UC Health

HISTORICAL FINANCIALS

Company Type: Private

Income Statement FYE: June 30

	REVENUE ($ mil.)	NET INCOME ($ mil.)	NET PROFIT MARGIN	EMPLOYEES
06/11	1,693	53	3.2%	7,700
06/10	1,590	78	4.9%	—
06/09	1,487	(281)	—	—
06/05	912	19	2.2%	—
Annual Growth	10.9%	18.0%	—	—

2011 Year-End Financials

Debt ratio: —
Return on equity: 3.20%
Cash ($ mil.): 97
Current ratio: 1.40
Long-term debt ($ mil.): —
Dividends
Yield: —
Payout: —
Market value ($ mil.): —

CHILDREN'S MEDICAL CENTER OF DALLAS

Sick kiddos in North Texas who need specialized care don't have to travel far to find it. Children's Medical Center of Dallas treats children from birth to age 18 with various medical needs. Specialties include craniofacial deformities cystic fibrosis gastroenterology cancer and heart disease. Children's is also a major pediatric center for heart kidney bone marrow and other transplant procedures. The private not-for-profit hospital has about 600 beds and is the pediatric teaching facility for the University of Texas Southwestern Medical Center. Children's also operates a network of about 20 primary care and specialty clinics in and around Dallas in addition to its two full-service campuses.

Geographic Reach

Children's Medical Center's main campuses are located in Dallas and Plano Texas. It also has specialty centers in Dallas suburbs and area communities including Southlake.

Operations

Children's Medical Center's Dallas campus operates the city's only pediatric emergency room and the region's only pediatric-centered teaching hospital. It was also the first Level I trauma center for pediatrics in the state. Together the Dallas and Plano hospital campuses serve some 700000 patients annually and provide more than 50 sub-specialty programs. Additionally the organization provides primary health care services to the county's children living in under-served areas; some of these care services are provided through academic programs for doctors in training.

Children's Medical Center receives revenue from a mix of third-party payers including HMOs and PPOs as well as Medicaid and Medicare and the state Children's Health Insurance Program (CHIP). It also relies heavily on private donations and fundraising efforts but provides a hefty amount of charity care each year for the region's uninsured children.

Strategy

At any given time it seems Children's Medical Center is building one facility or another. In the four-year period between 2001 and 2005 the center spent more than $250 million on new construction and expansion projects. It opened a 72-bed Children's Legacy Hospital in nearby Plano in 2008 and in 2009 Children's completed construction of a new $150 million tower on its main Dallas campus to house its heart center cancer center and neonatal intensive care unit. In 2012 it also launched a multi-year $130 million renovation project that will add 50 new beds and expand the heart and cancer treatment units on the main campus to meet the growing demand for services.

The network also added several new MyChildren's primary care offices in 2012 and its latest satellite specialty center opened in 2011 in the suburb of Southlake.

In 2012 Children's Medical Center partnered with UT Southwestern Medical Center to establish a new research venture. The entities which already partner on educational programs will invest $150 million in research programs in various fields of science and medicine such as cancer metabolism and birth defects.

EXECUTIVES

President and CEO, Christopher J. (Chris) Durovich
VP, Thomas M. (Tom) Zellers
VP Legal Affairs, Anne E. Long
VP Quality, Fiona Howard Levy
Chief Nursing Officer, Mary Stowe
Director Medical Sevices, M. Douglas Baker
Chief Accounting Officer and Controller, Jerry Lee
Director Surgical Services, Robert Foglia
Auditors: Ernst&YoungLLP

LOCATIONS

HQ: CHILDREN' S MEDICAL CENTER OF DALLAS
1935 MEDICAL DISTRICT DR, DALLAS, TX 75235-7701
Phone: 214-456-7000
Web: WWW.CHILDRENS.COM

Children's Medical Center Selected Locations
Chase Bank Building Specialty Center (Dallas)
Children's Medical Center and Ambulatory Care Pavilion at Legacy (Plano)
Children's Medical Center of Dallas Main Campus
Dallas Ambulatory Care Pavilion
Irving Specialty Center
Mesquite Specialty Center
MyChildren's Primary Care (about 15 locations)
Pediatric Urology Clinic at Rockwall
Southlake Specialty Care Center
Walnut Hill Urology Clinic

PRODUCTS/OPERATIONS

Children's Medical Center Selected Services
Allergy/Immunology/Asthma
Audiology
Cystic fibrosis
Day surgery
Dentistry
Dermatology
Diabetes
Ear/Nose/Throat
Endocrinology
Gastroenterology
General surgery
Genetics/Metabolism
International adoption medicine
Laboratory services
Neurology
Nutrition
Obesity program
Occupational therapy
Ophthalmology
Orthodontics
Orthopaedics
Physical therapy
Plastic Surgery
Pulmonary function lab
Pulmonology
Radiology
Rheumatology
Sickle cell treatment
Sleep disorders
Speech therapy
Trauma
Urology

COMPETITORS

Baylor University Medical Center
Cook Children' s Health Care System
Dell Children' s Medical Center
HCA
Parkland Health & Hospital System
Tenet Healthcare
Texas Children' s Hospital

HISTORICAL FINANCIALS

Company Type: Private

Income Statement FYE: December 31

	REVENUE ($ mil.)	NET INCOME ($ mil.)	NET PROFIT MARGIN	EMPLOYEES
12/08	744	(4)	—	5,318
12/06	579	130	22.4%	—
Annual Growth	13.3%	—	—	—

2008 Year-End Financials

Debt ratio: ——
Return on equity: (-0.60%)
Cash ($ mil.): 43
Current ratio: 1.20
Long-term debt ($ mil.): —
Dividends
Yield: —
Payout: —
Market value ($ mil.): —

CHILDREN'S NATIONAL MEDICAL CENTER

Along with the National Archives and the National Mall Children's National Medical Center is a US capital city gem. Its flagship Children's Hospital which was founded in 1870 is an acute care facility with some 300 beds. It serves as a regional referral center for pediatric trauma cancer and other kinds of complex pediatric cases. Additionally it operates eight outpatient centers in DC and the Delmarva peninsula that provide specialized medical services (such as chemotherapy and outpatient surgery) and community health clinics that offer primary care to children and adolescents. Children's National Health Network links more than 900 community-based pediatricians with the specialists and sevices of the center.

Children's National is the only freestanding hospital dedicated to treating children between the cities of Philadelphia Pittsburgh Norfolk and Atlanta. The center completed a five-year strategy plan in 2010 that not only extended its reach through physical additions but added expertise through affiliations and partnerships. Also that year it achieved Magnet? status an international designation of quality care provided by nurses that only 5% of US hospitals have achieved.

The center is heavily engaged in research through its Children's Research Institute (CRI) its Clinical and Translational Science Istitute at Children's National and the Sheikh Zayed Institute for Pediatric Surgical Innovation also at Children's National. Research at CRI is divided into five specialties: cancer and immunology clinical and community genetic medicine molecular physiology and neuroscience. Children's National is engaged in more than 250 research projects studying a multitude of maladies including autism cerebral palsy HIV/AIDS and obesity to name just a few. Almost 90% of its annual research funding comes from federal agencies with more than 60% (and $60 million) from the National Institutes of Health.

The hospital is also a teaching institution providing clinical training for pediatric residents and fellows and other graduate trainees. Children's National also administers pediatric training to medical students from George Washington University Howard University and other medical schools.

EXECUTIVES

VP Finance, David Sparks
Executive Vice President and Chief Academic Officer, Mark Levitt Batshaw
SVP The Diana L. and Stephen A. Goldberg Center for Community Pediatric Health, Denice Cora-Bramble
Chief Risk Counsel, Mary Anne Hilliard
SVP Center for Heart Lung and Kidney Disease; Co-Director Children's National Heart Institute, Gerard R. Martin
President and CEO, Kurt D. Newman
SVP Center for Neuroscience and Behavioral Health, Roger J. Packer
EVP Patient Care Services, Nellie C. Robinson
Executive Vice President Chief Legal Officer, Raymond S. Sczudlo
Executive Vice President Chief Financial Officer Chief Operating Officer, Douglas T. (Doug) Myers
EVP and Chief Development Officer Children's Hospital Foundation, Pam King Sams
EVP and Chief People Officer, Darryl Varnado
SVP Child Health Advocacy Institute; Acting EVP and Chief Government and External Affairs Officer; Acting Chief Medical Officer, Joseph Wright
SVP Center for Hospital-Based Specialties, David Wessel
Chief Research Officer, Mendel Tuchman
Senior Vice President Operations, Roberta Alessi
Interim Chief Nursing Officer, Linda Talley
Chief Operations Officer Vice President of Patient Care Services, Kathleen E. Gorman
Chief Strategy Officer Vice President, Elizabeth Flury
Executive Vice President Chief Development Officer, Pam Sams
Interim Chief Information Officer, Brian Jacobs

LOCATIONS

HQ: CHILDREN' S NATIONAL MEDICAL CENTER
111 MICHIGAN AVE NW, WASHINGTON, DC 20010-2916
Phone: 202-476-5000
Web: WWW.CHILDRENSNATIONAL.ORG

PRODUCTS/OPERATIONS

Selected Departments and Programs

Back/spine surgery
Bone marrow transplant
Cancer

Cardiac surgery
Fetal medicine
Genetics and metabolism
Imaging/radiology
Neurosurgery
Obesity
Pediatric anesthesiology
Pediatric cardiology
Pediatric surgery
Weight loss surgery

2010 Research Funding by Source

	% of total
National Institutes of Health	63
Department of Defense	8
Internal	2
Other federal	17
Other non-federal	10
Total	100

COMPETITORS

Adventist HealthCare
Ascension Health
Children's Healthcare of Atlanta
Children's Hospital Boston
Children's Hospital of Philadelphia
Children's Hospital of Pittsburgh
Children's Hospital of Richmond
Children's Hospital of The King's Daughters
Children's Medical Center of Dallas
Cincinnati Children's Hospital
Dell Children's Medical Center
Georgetown University Hospital
HSC Pediatric Center
IU Health
Inova
Johns Hopkins Medicine
Kennedy Krieger Institute
MedStar Health
Providence Hospital (Washington DC)
Seattle Children's Hospital
Shriners Hospitals For Children
St. Jude Children's Research Hospital
Washington Hospital Center

HISTORICAL FINANCIALS

Company Type: Private

Income Statement FYE: June 30

	REVENUE ($ mil.)	NET INCOME ($ mil.)	NET PROFIT MARGIN	EMPLOYEES
06/09	516	16	3.2%	6,000
06/07	694	76	11.0%	—
Annual Growth	(13.8%)	(53.6%)	—	—

2009 Year-End Financials

Debt ratio: —
Return on equity: 3.20%
Cash ($ mil.): 65
Current ratio: 0.80
Long-term debt ($ mil.): —
Dividends
Yield: —
Payout: —
Market value ($ mil.): —

CHILDRENS HOSPITAL MEDICAL CENTER OF AKRON

What started as a nursery more than 100 years ago but has since turned into the largest pediatric health care system in northeast Ohio? If you guessed Akron Children's Hospital you'd be right on the money. The health system operates through about 80 locations scattered around the state including its flagship 250-bed hospital in Akron. Among Children's specialized services are cardiology orthopedics rehabilitation and home care. It also has a second 50-bed inpatient hospital called the Akron Children's Beeghly Campus. The main hospital's emergency department treats nearly 70000 patients each year. Its regional burn center sees about 3700 visits per year.

Geographic Reach

Akron Children's Hospital is a major teaching facility affiliated with Northeastern Ohio Universities College of Medicine and Pharmacy and offers nearly a dozen subspecialty fellowship training programs. Children's also runs one of the state's largest pediatric primary care networks with 15 offices in seven counties including Cuyahoga Medina Wayne Tuscawaras and Portage.

Financial Performance

The hospital's net revenue was about $580 million in fiscal 2012 with 90% of the hospital's revenue coming from patient services revenues.

Strategy

In 2012 the hospital broke ground on $200 million Akron campus expansion. Children's has expanded its Home Care Group in recent years as well.

EXECUTIVES

President and CEO, William H. (Bill) Considine
VP Medical Services; Clinical Leader Ohio Children's Hospitals Solutions for Patient Safety, Michael Bird
VP Managed Care, Karen Richter
VP Operations and COO, Grace Wakulchik
EVP, Shawn Lyden
VP Akron Children's Hospital Foundation, John Zoilo
Noah Miller Chair Department of Pediatrics, Norman C. Christopher
VP Akron Children's Mahoning Valley, Sharon Hrina
CFO, Michael Trainer
VP Patient Services and Chief Nursing Officer, Lisa Aurilio
CIO, Tom Ogg
VP Department of Pediatrics, Cindy Dormo
Chief Medical Information Officer, Amy Maneker
VP Surgical Subspecialty Practices, Craig McGhee
Chief Medical Officer, Robert McGregor
Evp, John P Stoner
Director Of Home Healthcare, Sally L Hartline
Director Of Nursing, Thomas S Turner
Medical Director, Jeffrey Hord
Avp Of Human Resources, Walt Schoeble
Medical Director, Laura A Pollauf
Director Of Nursing, Holly A Berchin
Director Physician Recruitment, Shawna Roach
Medical Records Director, Cheryl Sanders
Nurse Manager Of Psych Unit, Debbie Kilmer
Director Of Nursing, Les Sherman
Admissions Director, Ranee Hoffman
Vice President Corporate Services, Deborah Bonzak
Vice President Information Technology, Sandy Murvine
Senior Vice President, William Wooldredge
Vice President Information Technology, Joseph Caballero
Vice President Information Services, Jeffrey Beaver
Vice President Information Technology, Joseph Brown
Vice President Information Technology, Clay Murbine
Vice President Information Technology, Sandy Neva
Vice President Information Technology, Ray Broderick
Vice President Information Technology, Chris Rowe
Vice President Information Technology, Sandra Aloi
Treasurer, Ernie Douglas
Vice Chair Of Radiology And Radiology Residency Program Director, Azam Eghbal
Secretary, Mary Briggs
Board Member, J Attebery

LOCATIONS

HQ: CHILDRENS HOSPITAL MEDICAL CENTER OF AKRON
1 PERKINS SQ, AKRON, OH 44308-1063
Phone: 330-543-1000
Web: WWW.AKRONCHILDRENS.ORG

COMPETITORS

Akron General Medical Center
Aultman Health Foundation
Lake Health
Mercy Medical Center (NY)
MetroHealth System
Nationwide Children's Hospital
OhioHealth
Parma Community General Hospital
Robinson Memorial Hospital
Summa Health System
The Cleveland Clinic
University Hospitals Health System

HISTORICAL FINANCIALS

Company Type: Private

Income Statement FYE: December 31

	REVENUE ($ mil.)	NET INCOME ($ mil.)	NET PROFIT MARGIN	EMPLOYEES
12/12	579	46	8.1%	4,000
12/09	438	46	10.5%	—
12/06	387	(58)	—	—
12/06	308	24	7.9%	—
Annual Growth	11.1%	11.4%	—	—

2012 Year-End Financials

Debt ratio: —
Return on equity: 8.10%
Cash ($ mil.): 25
Current ratio: 1.20
Long-term debt ($ mil.): —
Dividends
Yield: —
Payout: —
Market value ($ mil.): —

CHRISTIAN FOUNDATION FOR CHILDREN AND AGING

EXECUTIVES

Chief Governing Officer, Scott Wasserman
President, Robert K. Hentzen
CEO, Francis (Paco) Wertin
Director International Programs, Paul Pearce
Treasurer, Ed Herman
Secretary, Father Allan Weinert
Director Church Relations, Larry Livingston
Director Communications, Loretta Shea Kline
Director Sponsor Outreach, Raelene Dietz
Director Sponsorship Operations, Elaine (Laney) Haake
Director of Finance, Martin Kraus
Director, Michael Alex
Director, Anne Ryder
Director, Louis A. Guillou
Director, Eileen Witaconis
Director, Rev Vince Haselhorst
Director, Carolyn Zimmerman

LOCATIONS

HQ: CHRISTIAN FOUNDATION FOR CHILDREN AND AGING
1 ELMWOOD AVE, KANSAS CITY, KS 661033719
Phone: 9133846500
Web: WWW.CFCAUSA.ORG

HISTORICAL FINANCIALS

Company Type: Private

Income Statement FYE: December 31

	REVENUE ($ mil.)	NET INCOME ($ mil.)	NET PROFIT MARGIN	EMPLOYEES
12/12	115	2	1.7%	130
12/11	110	0	0.7%	—
12/10	109	2	2.0%	—
12/09	107	0	—	—
Annual Growth	2.6%	—	—	—

2012 Year-End Financials

Debt ratio: —
Return on equity: 1.70%
Cash ($ mil.): 11
Current ratio: 7.30
Long-term debt ($ mil.): —
Dividends
Yield: —
Payout: —
Market value ($ mil.): —

CHRISTIAN HOSPITAL NORTHEAST - NORTHWEST

Christian or heathen if you're in the St. Louis area and need medical care Christian Hospital wants to help. The not-for-profit hospital which has nearly 500 beds is part of BJC HealthCare. Established in 1903 it specializes in a range of treatment areas including diabetes and cancer care and cardiothoracic surgery. Its more than 600 physicians also offer services in 40 other specialties from primary care to pulmonology. Christian Hospital offers a comprehensive mental health and substance abuse program that includes an inpatient option as well as specialization in geriatric mental wellness. The hospital is helmed by president Ron McMullen a long-time health care administrator.

Christian Hospital prides itself on being the first in the area to offer pioneering procedures. For example it was the first community hospital in the region to offer Video Assisted Thoracoscopic Surgery (VATS) lobectomy an advanced resectioning procedure to remove tumors in lung cancer patients.

Shortly before that Christian Hospital broke new ground by becoming the first community hospital in St. Louis to provide the Gliasite procedure. Gliasite is a brachytherapy (internal radiation therapy) procedure that treats patients with newly diagnosed metastatic or recurrent brain tumors.

EXECUTIVES

President, Ronald B. (Ron) McMullen
VP and Chief Medical Officer, Melanie Mueth
VP Human Resources, Bryan Hartwick
VP Finance, John Katsianis
Manager Public Relations and Internal Communications, Bret Berigan

LOCATIONS

HQ: CHRISTIAN HOSPITAL NORTHEAST - NORTHWEST
11133 DUNN RD, SAINT LOUIS, MO 63136-6119
Phone: 314-355-2300
Web: WWW.CHRISTIANHOSPITAL.ORG

COMPETITORS

Ascension Health
Barnes-Jewish Hospital
HCA
Memorial Hospital (Illinois)
Mercy Health
Mercy Hospital St. Louis
RehabCare
SSM Health Care
St. Anthony' s Medical Center
Tenet Healthcare

HISTORICAL FINANCIALS

Company Type: Private

Income Statement FYE: December 31

	REVENUE ($ mil.)	NET INCOME ($ mil.)	NET PROFIT MARGIN	EMPLOYEES
12/08	213	(24)	—	2,493
12/00	207	(20)	—	—
12/97	206	5	2.6%	—
Annual Growth	(0.0%)	—	—	—

CHRISTUS HEALTH

In CHRISTUS there is no east or west but plenty of care nonetheless. The not-for-profit Catholic health care system operates about 350 medical facilities from its more than 40 hospitals including general hospitals and long-term acute care facilities to clinics and outpatient centers. It operates mostly in Louisiana and Texas but also has facilities in Arkansas Georgia Missouri and New Mexico and in five states in Mexico. In addition to its acute care facilities CHRISTUS Health runs medical groups home health and hospice agencies and senior living facilities. Specialized services include oncology pediatrics rehabilitation and women's and children's health care.

Over the past several years CHRISTUS Health has engaged in cutting some of its operations and reining in costs to generate positive growth. In fiscal 2011 the health care system made modest gains ending the year with a more than 2% operating margin (compared to 1.6% the previous year) with its net operating income coming in at just under $1 billion up more than 40% from fiscal 2010.

CHRISTUS Health formed its CHRISTUS Continuing Care division in 2009 to advance the organization's plan to increase its non-acute care operations and house all of its non-acute care services. These services include home care hospice long-term care services residential senior services and its long-term acute care hospitals (many of which operate under the Dubuis brand name).

Another goal of CHRISTUS Health is to reduce overcrowding and such misuses as patients being seen for routine illnesses in its emergency rooms. To that end and to make primary care a bit more accessible the company has opened immediate care clinics in a number of Texas Wal-Mart stores. CHRISTUS Health has plans to expand the clinics into Wal-Marts in Louisiana.

Like many hospital companies the organization has struggled financially as a result of providing care (usually in the emergency room) for the indigent and for the growing ranks of uninsured especially in the hard-hit economic environment of 2008 and 2009. During that period the health care system's charity care (defined as unpaid services provided to the uninsured and indigent) was up nearly 35%.

As a result CHRISTUS Health has had to sell some money-losing facilities such as the St. Joseph Hospital in Houston which it sold to Hospital Partners of America (HPA) a company that allows doctors to take an ownership stake in its hospitals.

It also sold the CHRISTUS Medical Group-Southwest Community Health Center in Houston to Legacy Community Health Services in 2010 because Legacy is designated as a federally qualified health center (FQHC) and can operate the clinic as such (meaning it is eligible for more public-sector funding). FQHCs are not-for-profit or public entity community-owned health care providers serving low-income and medically underserved communities.

CHRISTUS Health has taken other steps to try to offset some costs of indigent care including pushing for the establishment of hospital districts to pay for charity care costs in some of its markets.

The organization has been focused on growing its operations in Mexico where it operates about a dozen hospitals and clinics in six states. CHRISTUS Health's Mexico operations are a majority-owned partnership with Monterrey-based Muguerza. The organization's main Monterrey facility became the first Mexican hospital to win accreditation from the Joint Commission International a unit of the organization that certifies US hospitals.

Because Mexican citizens overwhelmingly rely on public hospitals run by the national health care system CHRISTUS Muguerza markets itself as a "medical tourism" destination where Americans can go for cheaper and lower-hassle medical care. Services include acute and primary care dental care urgent care and post-surgical rehabilitation.

CHRISTUS Health was formed through the 1999 merger of Incarnate Word Health System and Sisters of Charity Health System. Both systems have their roots in the religious order Sisters of Charity of the Incarnate Word founded when three French nuns arrived in Texas in 1866 to care for the poor and sick.

EXECUTIVES

SVP and Chief Medical Officer, John Gillean
SVP Human Resource Services, Mary Lynch
SVP and CFO, Jay Herron
President and CEO CHRISTUS Santa Rosa Health Care, Patrick B. Carrier
President and CEO, Ernie W. Sadau
SVP Communications and Public Affairs, Linda McClung
SVP and CIO, George Conklin
SVP Business Strategy and Corporate Development, Peter Maddox
President and CEO CHRISTUS Health Gulf Coast and CHRISTUS Health Southeast Texas (CHRISTUS Hospital St. Elizabeth; CHRISTUS Hospital St. Mary and CHRISTUS Jasper Memorial Hospital), Ellen Jones
System Senior Director Strategic Marketing and Communications, Teri Cardenas
Senior Writer, Christie J. Fortune
President and CEO CHRISTUS Health Ark-La-Tex (CHRISTUS St. Michael Health System), Chris Karam
President and CEO CHRISTUS Health Central Louisiana (includes CHRISTUS Health Northern Louisiana CHRISTUS Health Central Louisiana and CHRISTUS Health Southwestern Louisiana), Stephen Wright
President and CEO CHRISTUS Health Utah (includes CHRISTUS St. Joseph Villa), Galen Ewer
Chairman, Richard L. (Dick) Clarke
Administrator CHRISTUS St. Joseph Village, Kim Bomgardner
President and CEO CHRISTUS Medical Group, Donna Mikulecky
Corporate VP Business Development and Managed Care, Jeff Puckett
Communications Specialist, Abby Lowe
Human Resources, Sandy York
Chief Development Officer, Kay Barnett
Vice President for Philanthropy, Karen Bonner

Regional Vice-President, Ivy Pate
VP Chief Development Officer, HarveyAnne Leimbrook
Regional Vice President, Michael Davis
Interim Executive Director, Stephanie Huff
Chief Development Officer, Susan Landreaux
Executive Vice President Chief Operating Officer, Eugene A. Woods
Senior Vice President - Mission Intregration & Leadership Formation, Gerard F. Heeley
Senior Vice President - Chief Strategy, Jeffrey M. Puckett
Director, Sister Kathleen Coughlin
Director, Robert Z. (Bob) Gussin
Director, Dennis Stine
Director, Sister Celeste Trahan
Director, Father Charles E. Bouchard
Director, Kenneth D. Wells
Director, Phyllis A. Cowling
Director, Sister Walter Maher
Director, Sister Hannah O'Donoghue

LOCATIONS

HQ: CHRISTUS HEALTH
919 HIDDEN RDG, IRVING, TX 75038-3813
Phone: 214-492-8500
Web: WWW.CHRISTUSHEALTH.ORG

PRODUCTS/OPERATIONS

2011 Revenues

	$ mil.	% of total
Patient services	3,410	90
Premium revenue	164	4
Other revenue	172	5
Equity in income of unconsolidated organizations	33	1
Total	**3,781**	**100**

2011 Payor Mix

	% of total
Managed care	37
Medicare	25
Self-pay	16
Medicaid	5
Commercial	4
Others	13
Total	**100**

2011 Payor Mix

	% of total
Managed care	37
Medicare	25
Self-pay	16
Medicaid	5
Commercial	4
Others	13
Total	**100**

Selected Facilities in Texas

CHRISTUS HomeCare - Corpus Christi
CHRISTUS HomeCare - Texarkana
CHRISTUS Hospital - St. Elizabeth
CHRISTUS Hospital - St. Mary
CHRISTUS Jasper Memorial Hospital
CHRISTUS Santa Rosa Alamo Heights Imaging Center
CHRISTUS Santa Rosa Ambulatory Surgery Center
CHRISTUS Santa Rosa Cancer Center
CHRISTUS Santa Rosa Children's Hospital
CHRISTUS Santa Rosa Hospital - City Centre
CHRISTUS Santa Rosa Hospital - Medical Center
CHRISTUS Santa Rosa Hospital New Braunfels
CHRISTUS Santa Rosa Hospital Westover Hills
CHRISTUS Santa Rosa Imaging Center
CHRISTUS Santa Rosa Outpatient Rehabilitation Center
CHRISTUS Santa Rosa Rehabilitation Hospital
CHRISTUS Santa Rosa Rehabilitation Services - Downtown
CHRISTUS Santa Rosa Rehabilitation Services - Medical Center
CHRISTUS Santa Rosa Wound Care and Hyperbaric Center - Downtown
CHRISTUS Santa Rosa Wound Care and Hyperbaric Center - Medical Center
CHRISTUS Spohn Family Center Northside
CHRISTUS Spohn Family Health Center
CHRISTUS Spohn Family Health Center Falfurrias
CHRISTUS Spohn Family Health Center Padre Island
CHRISTUS Spohn Family Health Center Robstown
CHRISTUS Spohn Family Health Center San Diego
CHRISTUS Spohn Family Health Center Westside
CHRISTUS Spohn Health System
CHRISTUS Spohn Hospital Alice
CHRISTUS Spohn Hospital Beeville
CHRISTUS Spohn Hospital Corpus Christi - Memorial
CHRISTUS Spohn Hospital Corpus Christi - Shoreline
CHRISTUS Spohn Hospital Corpus Christi - South
CHRISTUS Spohn Hospital Kleberg
CHRISTUS Spohn Medical Group - Obstetrics and Gynecology Associates
CHRISTUS St. Catherine Hospital
CHRISTUS St. John Hospital
CHRISTUS St. Michael Health System
CHRISTUS St. Michael Rehabilitation Hospital
CHRISTUS Transplant Institute
CHRISTUS Visiting Nurse Association - Houston
CHRISTUS Visiting Nurse Association - Nassau Bay
CHRISTUS Visiting Nurse Association - San Antonio
David Christopher Goldsbury Center for Children and Families
Dubuis Hospital of Beaumont
Dubuis Hospital of Bryan Texas
Dubuis Hospital of Corpus Christi
Dubuis Hospital of Houston Texas (long-term acute care)
Dubuis Hospital of Paris
Dubuis Hospital of Port Arthur Texas (long-term acute care)
Dubuis Hospital of Texarkana

Selected Other US Facilities

Advance Care Hospital of Fort Smith (Arkansas)
Advance Care Hospital of Hot Springs (Arkansas)
CHRISTUS Coushatta Health Care Center (Coushatta Louisiana)
CHRISTUS HomeCare - Jennings (Louisiana)
CHRISTUS HomeCare - Lake Charles (Louisiana)
CHRISTUS HomeCare - Shreveport (Louisiana)
CHRISTUS Hospice and Palliative Care - Alexandria (Louisiana)
CHRISTUS Schumpert Health System (Shreveport Louisiana)
CHRISTUS Schumpert Highland (Shreveport Louisiana)
CHRISTUS Schumpert St. Mary Place (Shreveport Louisiana)
CHRISTUS St. Frances Cabrini Hospital (Alexandria Louisiana)
CHRISTUS St. Patrick Hospital (Lake Charles Louisiana)
CHRISTUS St. Vincent (Santa Fe New Mexico)
Dubuis Hospital of Alexandria (Louisiana)
Dubuis Hospital of Lake Charles (Louisiana)
Dubuis Hospital of Shreveport (Louisiana)
Dubuis Hospital of St. Louis (Chesterfield Missouri)
Natchitoches Parish Hospital (Louisiana)
Southern Crescent Hospital for Specialty Care (Riverdale Georgia)

Selected Facilities in Mexico

CHRISTUS MUGUERZA Hospital Alta Especialidad (Monterrey Nuevo Leon)
CHRISTUS MUGUERZA Hospital Conchita (Monterrey Nuevo Leon)
CHRISTUS MUGUERZA Hospital Del Parque (Chihuahua)
CHRISTUS MUGUERZA Hospital Reynosa (Tamaulipas C.P.)
CHRISTUS MUGUERZA Hospital Saltillo (Coahuila)
CHRISTUS MUGUERZA Hospital Sur (Monterrey Nuevo Leon)
CHRISTUS MUGUERZA Hospital UPAEP (Puebla)

COMPETITORS

Ascension Health
Baylor Health
Catholic Health Initiatives
Community Health Systems
HCA
Health Management Associates
Iasis Healthcare
Intermountain Health Care
LifePoint Hospitals
MD Anderson Cancer Center
Memorial Health Services
Memorial Hermann Healthcare
Mercy Health
Methodist Hospital System
St. Luke' s Episcopal Hospital
Tenet Healthcare
Texas Children' s Hospital
Universal Health Services
University of Utah Hospitals & Clinics
Vanguard Health Systems

HISTORICAL FINANCIALS

Company Type: Private

Income Statement FYE: June 30

	REVENUE ($ mil.)	NET INCOME ($ mil.)	NET PROFIT MARGIN	EMPLOYEES
06/10	3,653	55	1.5%	25,000
06/09	3,466	(411)	—	—
06/09	0	0	—	—
Annual Growth	—	—	—	—

2010 Year-End Financials

Debt ratio: —
Return on equity: 1.50%
Cash ($ mil.): 537
Current ratio: 1.10
Long-term debt ($ mil.): —
Dividends
Yield: —
Payout: —
Market value ($ mil.): —

CHRISTUS HEALTH CENTRAL LOUISIANA

CHRISTUS St. Frances Cabrini Hospital provides a wide range of medical services to the denizens of Alexandria Louisiana. If you're ailing down south there's not much the hospital can't do to help especially in the area of cancer. Founded in 1950 the 240-bed St. Frances Cabrini Hospital has a staff of more than 320 physicians providing services that include emergency care women's health surgery and cardiology. For the insomniacs among us the hospital provides specialized care through its sleep center. St. Francis Cabrini's parent company is one of the nation's major hospital operators –with about 50 facilities located around the country.

LOCATIONS

HQ: CHRISTUS HEALTH CENTRAL LOUISIANA
3330 MASONIC DR, ALEXANDRIA, LA 71301-3841
Phone: 318-487-1122
Web: WWW.CHRISTUSHEALTH.ORG

COMPETITORS

General Health System
Lafayette General Medical Center
Lane Regional Medical Center
Our Lady of Lourdes
Our Lady of the Lake RMC
River Parishes Hospital
Woman' s Hospital

HISTORICAL FINANCIALS

Company Type: Private

Income Statement FYE: June 30

	REVENUE ($ mil.)	NET INCOME ($ mil.)	NET PROFIT MARGIN	EMPLOYEES
06/10	219	(0)	—	1,287
06/09	217	1	0.7%	—
06/09	1,027	0	—	—
Annual Growth	—	—	—	—

2010 Year-End Financials

Debt ratio: —
Return on equity: (-0.30%)
Cash ($ mil.): 24
Current ratio: 0.30
Long-term debt ($ mil.): —
Dividends
Yield: —
Payout: —
Market value ($ mil.): —

CHUGACH ALASKA CORPORATION

At the heart of Chugach Alaska Corporation is a vision of indigenous people running their own businesses on their own land. Chugach Alaska was formed following the activation of the Alaska Native Claims Settlement Act (which was passed by the US Congress in 1971) to provide land management services for the 928000-acre Chugach region of Alaska. The company derives the bulk of its sales from oil and gas production mining commercial timber and tourist activities that occur in the region and from its engagement in military base construction projects at more than 30 locations in Alaska the US Pacific Northwest and the Western Pacific. Chugach Alaska's shareholders consist of Aleut Eskimo and Indian natives.

Geographic Reach

With operations in Alaska the Pacific Northwest and the Western Pacific the company has major offices in Alabama Alaska Hawaii and Nevada.

Operations

In 2011 the company's Chugach World Services unit secured a $32 million contract (with the option for an additional $33 million) for housing and maintenance operations at Naval Base Guam and Andersen Air Force Base Guam.

In late 2010 the Chugach Alaska Services unit won a renewal of its existing oil spill prevention and response contract with Alyeska Pipeline Service Company. The new contract to service the Alaska Pipeline runs from 2011 to 2016.

Financial Performance

To raise cash in 2013 Chugach Alaska sold its three-story former headquarters building in downtown Anchorage.

Strategy

Developing and sustaining multiple revenues streams has been a key to the company's growth. Chugach Alaska is looking to continue to grow its Alaskan gas natural gas projects while diversifying into markets that are not traditional for the company such as the niche market of environmentally responsible guided tourism.

Expanding its global engineering footprint in 2012 the company acquired bankrupt Hawaii-based engineering firm Heide & Cook LLC.

Company Background

Chugach Alaska was founded in 1972 as an Alaska Native Claims Settlement Act Corporation. A nine-person board of directors elected from the corporation's more than 2300 shareholders oversees Chugach Alaska's management and operations. The company has gone from filing bankruptcy protection in 1990 (in the wake of the Exxon Valdez oil spill and a major cannery fire) to generating about $1 billion in annual revenues.

EXECUTIVES

President Government Contracting Division, Barney Uhart
VP Administration and House Counsel, Terri Bozkaya
Vice President of Cultural Resources, John F.C. Johnson
Chairman, Sheri D. Buretta
Director and Corporate Secretary, David J. Totemoff Sr.
Director Lands, David Phillips
Shareholder Services Supervisor and Executive Assistant to the Chairman, Trudi Komakhuk
Vice Chairman, Matthew P. McDaniel
VP Operations, Mel Lynch
Communications Specialist, Beth Welty
President Chugach Government Services, Chris Viramontes
President, Jerry Cole
Vice President of Operations, Scott Davis
VP Shareholder Development, Millie Johnson
Cultural Resources Project Coordinator, Angelina (Zippy) Sawden
President Chugach Federal Solutions, Dan Fenza
President Chugach Education Services, Mary Cohorst
President Chugach Support Services Chugach McKinley and Chugach Management Services, Matt Hayes
President, Mike Anderson
President Chugach Alaska Services, Peter Andersen
VP Business Development, Tim Hopper
VP Finance, Angie Astle
CEO, Gabriel Kompkoff
Operations Manager, John Kenyon
Director and Corporate Secretary, David J. Totemoff Sr.
Vice Chairman, Matthew P. McDaniel
Director, Julie E. Kitka
Director, Michael McCanna
Director, Violet F. Yeaton
Director, James Kvasnikoff
Director, Tim Christoffersen, age 47

LOCATIONS

HQ: CHUGACH ALASKA CORPORATION
3800 CENTERPOINT DR # 700, ANCHORAGE, AK 99503-5825
Phone: 907-563-8866
Web: WWW.CHUGACH-AK.COM

PRODUCTS/OPERATIONS

Selected Services

Base Operating Services
Construction Services
Educational Services
Engineering Services
IT/Telecommunications
Manufacturing Services
Oil and Gas Services

Selected Subsidiaries

Chugach Alaska Services Inc. (CASI)
Chugach Education Services Inc. (CESI)
Chugach Federal Solutions Inc. (CFSI)
Chugach Government Services Inc. (CGSI)
Chugach Industries Inc. (CII)
Chugach Information Technology Inc. (CITI)
Chugach Management Services Inc. (CMSI)
Chugach McKinley Inc. (CMI)
Chugach Support Services Inc. (CSSI)
Chugach Systems Integration Llc (CSI)
Chugach World Services Inc. (CWSI)
Heide & Cook LLC. (H&C)
Wolf Creek Federal Services Inc. (WCFS)

COMPETITORS

ConocoPhillips Alaska
Doyon
Fluor
Freegold Ventures
Jacobs Engineering
Sealaska
URS

HISTORICAL FINANCIALS

Company Type: Private

Income Statement FYE: December 31

	REVENUE ($ mil.)	NET INCOME ($ mil.)	NET PROFIT MARGIN	EMPLOYEES
12/12	708	20	2.9%	4,822
12/11	765	24	3.1%	—
12/09	936	26	2.8%	—
12/09	1,105	41	3.8%	—
Annual Growth	(13.8%)	(21.5%)	—	—

2012 Year-End Financials

Debt ratio: —
Return on equity: 2.90%
Cash ($ mil.): 79
Current ratio: 0.90
Long-term debt ($ mil.): —
Dividends
Yield: —
Payout: —
Market value ($ mil.): —

CIC GROUP INC.

CIC Group manages 20 or so diverse manufacturing and construction businesses. Its companies specialize in the manufacture maintenance and repair of equipment for the crude oil natural gas coal and other energy industries. Its largest subsidiary is Nooter/Eriksen which supplies heat recovery steam generators for combustion gas turbines worldwide. CIC's Nooter Construction is a construction contractor serving the refining petrochemical pulp and paper and power industries among others. The employee-owned holding company was formed in 2002.

Financial Performance Although privately held the company reported 2012 revenue of $1.2 billion up 30% from 2011. CIC anticipates revenue of $2 billion by 2017 or 2018.

EXECUTIVES

Director Human Resources, Joseph (Joe) Schomber
President Nooter/Eriksen, Vernon (Vern) Eriksen
CFO, Terry Jansing
Chairman President and CEO, Ross Osiek
President St. Louis Metallizing Company, Joseph Stricker
Office Manager, Virginia Van Jura
GM Megamet Solid Metals, Bruce Dionne

LOCATIONS

HQ: CIC GROUP INC.
530 MARYVILLE CENTRE DR, SAINT LOUIS, MO 63141-5825
Phone: 314-682-2900
Web: WWW.CICGROUP.COM

PRODUCTS/OPERATIONS

Selected Subsidiaries

ArcMelt
Delta Nooter
Megamet Sold Metals Co.
Nooter Construction
Nooter/Eriksen s.r.l.
Pressline Services
RMF Nooter
Schoeller Bleckmann Nooter GmbH
St. Louis Metallizing
Superior Corporate Travel
Wyatt Field Service Co.
Wyatt Virgin Islands

COMPETITORS

Clarkson Construction
Fred Weber
Phillips-Medisize
U.S. Pipe

HISTORICAL FINANCIALS

Company Type: Private

Income Statement FYE: November 30

	REVENUE ($ mil.)	NET INCOME ($ mil.)	NET PROFIT MARGIN	EMPLOYEES
11/12	1,149	0	—	1,062
11/11	838	0	—	—
11/08	758	0	—	—
11/08	1,120	0	—	—
Annual Growth	0.6%	—	—	—

2012 Year-End Financials

Debt ratio: —
Return on equity: —
Cash ($ mil.): 123
Current ratio: 1.30
Long-term debt ($ mil.): —
Dividends
Yield: —
Payout: —
Market value ($ mil.): —

CITATION OIL & GAS CORP.

Citation Oil & Gas is writing its own ticket to prosperity in the petroleum industry. The oil and gas development and production company has interests in about 15000 wells and reported 210 million barrels of proved oil equivalent reserves in 2012. Its oil fields are in the Mid-Continent Illinois basin Permian Basin and Rocky Mountain regions. Citation seeks out properties with high levels of crude oil declining production with long reserve life and low risk. The company uses a variety of techniques to recover oil and gas including waterflood and infill drilling. Subsidiary Citation Crude Marketing sells the company's products to refiners.

Geographic Reach

Citation explores for oil and gas in more than 480 fields in 13 states in the central third of the US with major holdings in the Illinois Basin Mid-Continent Permian Basin and Rocky Mountain regions. It has offices in Midland Texas; Gillette Wyoming; and Oklahoma City.

Operations

In the Rockies Citation is focusing on horizontal drilling in several fields. In Southern Oklahoma it is developing properties it acquired from Noble Energy and is also drilling deeper wells in the Shoveltum Hunton trend. West Texas activities are concentrated on the North Robertson and Jordan fields.

In addition to its upstream activities Citation is also engaged in crude oil marketing activities through its Citation Crude Marketing unit.

Strategy

For almost 30 years Citation has pursued a focused business strategy of acquiring and operating mature onshore oil (and some gas) properties in the US. In 2012 some 91% of its total proved reserves were oil.

Mergers and Acquisitions

In 2012 Citation acquired 100 additional leases and units in Kansas from Noble Energy near Citation's existing Fairport and Bemis-Schutts fields. This acquisition significantly expanded Citation's operations in Kansas boosting its production in that state by almost 300%.

Company Background

The company was formed in 1981 by Forrest E. Harrell Sr.

EXECUTIVES

SVP and CFO, Christopher A. Phelps, age 43
President and CEO, Curtis F. Harrell, age 50
Chairman, Forrest E. (Eddie) Harrell Sr.
VP Marketing and President CCMI, Forrest E. Harrell Jr.
SVP Engineering, Steve K. Anna
SVP Business Development and Land, Robert T. (Bobby) Kennedy
SVP CCMI, Jerry C. Martin
SVP Operations, Steven C. Pearson
SVP General Counsel and Secretary, Wayne Wiesen
VP Information Systems, Mark A. Anchondo
VP Administration, Nancy A. Anglin
VP Commercial Activities and Business Development, Scott A. Loosley
VP Taxation, Thomas E. Patrick
Vice President Controller, Craig K. Townsend

LOCATIONS

HQ: CITATION OIL & GAS CORP.
14077 CUTTEN RD, HOUSTON, TX 77069-2212
Phone: 281-891-1000
Web: WWW.COGC.COM

COMPETITORS

Adams Resources	EOG
Anadarko Petroleum	Exxon Mobil
Apache	Hunt Consolidated
BP	Jones Energy
Cabot Oil & Gas	Key Energy
Chesapeake Energy	National Fuel Gas
Chevron	Noble Energy
Cimarex	Pioneer Natural Resources
ConocoPhillips	
Devon Energy	Royal Dutch Shell

HISTORICAL FINANCIALS

Company Type: Private

Income Statement FYE: December 31

	REVENUE ($ mil.)	NET INCOME ($ mil.)	NET PROFIT MARGIN	EMPLOYEES
12/12	424	224	53.0%	507
12/11	449	251	56.0%	—
12/09	233	99	42.6%	—
12/08	364	219	60.1%	—
Annual Growth	3.9%	0.7%	—	—

2012 Year-End Financials

Debt ratio: —
Return on equity: 53.00%
Cash ($ mil.): 22
Current ratio: 0.50
Long-term debt ($ mil.): —
Dividends
Yield: —
Payout: —
Market value ($ mil.): —

CITIZENS ENERGY GROUP

EXECUTIVES

President and CEO, Carey B. Lykins
SVP and Chief Administrative Officer, M. Jean Richcreek
SVP Corporate and Legal Affairs, John R. Whitaker
VP Human Resources, Robert J. Hummel
VP Gas and Steam Operations, Lindsay C. Lindgren
SVP Operations, William A. (Bill) Tracy
Board President, Martha D. Lamkin
SVP and CFO, John Brehm
VP Customer Relationships, Michael Strohl
VP Community Relations, Yvonne Perkins
VP Engineering and Facilities Management, Jeffrey Harrison
General Manager Engineering and Facility Operations, Jamie Dillard
CEO, Jim Yelverton
Operations Manager United Water Services, Jim Pawlowski
President CEO, Lynn Engel
Owner, Marsha M. Oliver
President Indianapolis Neighborhood Housing Partnership, Moira Carlstedt
CEO, Steve Lains
Vice President Employee and Organization Development, Zaida Monell
President CEO, Brian Sanford
Director, Anne Nobles, age 57
Director, Anita J. Harden
Director, James M. McClelland
Auditors: PricewaterhouseCoopersLLP

LOCATIONS

HQ: CITIZENS ENERGY GROUP
2020 N MERIDIAN ST, INDIANAPOLIS, IN 462021306
Phone: 3179243341
Web: WWW.CITIZENSENERGYGROUP.COM

PRODUCTS/OPERATIONS

2012 Sales

Utility	650	93
Total	**696**	**100**

2012 Sales

Citizens Gas	37
Wastewater	22
Chilled Water	6
Resources	1

COMPETITORS

American States Water	NIPSCO
Duke Energy	Vectren
Indiana Municipal Power Agency	Veolia Environnement

HISTORICAL FINANCIALS

Company Type: Private

Income Statement FYE: September 30

	REVENUE ($ mil.)	NET INCOME ($ mil.)	NET PROFIT MARGIN	EMPLOYEES
09/13	711	(81)	—	1,100
09/12	696	(11)	—	—
09/11	463	32	7.0%	—
09/10	440	0	—	—
Annual Growth	17.3%	—	—	—

2013 Year-End Financials

Debt ratio: —
Return on equity: (-11.40%)
Cash ($ mil.): 194
Current ratio: 0.70
Long-term debt ($ mil.): —
Dividends
Yield: —
Payout: —
Market value ($ mil.): —

CITY OF MOBILE

LOCATIONS

HQ: CITY OF MOBILE
205 GOVERNMENT ST, MOBILE, AL 366020001
Phone: 2512087416
Web: WWW.CITYOFMOBILE.ORG

HISTORICAL FINANCIALS

Company Type: Private

Income Statement FYE: September 30

	REVENUE ($ mil.)	NET INCOME ($ mil.)	NET PROFIT MARGIN	EMPLOYEES
09/13	273	(11)	—	2,300
09/09	239	(44)	—	—
09/07	0	0	—	—
09/06	0	0	—	—
Annual Growth	—	—	—	—

CITY OF SALINAS

EXECUTIVES

Mayor, Dennis Donohue
Human Resources Officer, Teri Silva
City Manager, David Mora
City Attorney, Vanessa Vallarta
Director of Finance, Tom Kever
Deputy City Manager and City Engineer, Robert Russell
CEO Salinas Valley Chamber of Commerce, Tiffany DiTullio
Deputy City Manager, John Fair

LOCATIONS

HQ: CITY OF SALINAS
200 LINCOLN AVE, SALINAS, CA 939012639
Phone: 8317587256
Web: WWW.CITYOFSALINAS.COM

HISTORICAL FINANCIALS

Company Type: Private

Income Statement FYE: June 30

	REVENUE ($ mil.)	NET INCOME ($ mil.)	NET PROFIT MARGIN	EMPLOYEES
06/13	109	(7)	—	735
06/12	107	(4)	—	—
06/11	110	(1)	—	—
06/10	111	0	—	—
Annual Growth	(0.5%)	—	—	—

CITY PUBLIC SERVICES OF SAN ANTONIO

EXECUTIVES

Executive Vice President General Counsel, Carolyn E. Shellman
President Chief Executive Officer, Doyle N. Beneby, age 54
Executive Vice President Chief Financial Officer, Paula Gold-Williams
Executive Vice President Chief Administrative Officer, Jelynne L. Burley
Executive Vice President and Chief Strategy and Technology Officer, Cris Eugster
Senior Vice President of Energy Delivery Services, Frederick A. James
Senior Vice President of Customer Services, Maria Koudouris
Vice President of Business Operations, John Benedict
Senior Vice President of Energy Development, Richard Pe+?a
Vice President of Corporate Development & Planning, Frank Almaraz
Senior Vice President of Energy Supply & Market Operations, Richard Pe?a
Vice President of Communications & Medial Relations, Lisa Lewis
Vice President of External Relations, Rudy Garza

LOCATIONS

HQ: CITY PUBLIC SERVICES OF SAN ANTONIO
145 NAVARRO ST, SAN ANTONIO, TX 782052986
Phone: 2103532222
Web: WWW.CPSENERGY.COM

PRODUCTS/OPERATIONS

2013 Sales

Electric	90
Other	2

COMPETITORS

AEP
AES
Duke Energy
Energy Future
NextEra Energy
ONEOK

HISTORICAL FINANCIALS

Company Type: Private

Income Statement FYE: January 31

	REVENUE ($ mil.)	NET INCOME ($ mil.)	NET PROFIT MARGIN	EMPLOYEES
01/13	2,213	2	0.1%	3,743
01/12	2,258	21	0.9%	—
01/11	2,068	78	3.8%	—
01/10	1,930	0	—	—
Annual Growth	4.7%	—	—	—

2013 Year-End Financials

Debt ratio: —
Return on equity: 0.10%
Cash ($ mil.): 271
Current ratio: 0.90
Long-term debt ($ mil.): —
Dividends
Yield: —
Payout: —
Market value ($ mil.): —

CITY UTILITIES OF SPRINGFIELD MO

EXECUTIVES

Associate General Manager Operations, Wade Stinson
Associate General Manager Electric Supply, Scott Miller
Associate General Manager and General Counsel, John Black
Manager - Communications, Joel Alexander
Associate General Manager of Development, Dean Thompson
Associate General Manager - Finance, Mike Finch
Auditors: BKDLLP

LOCATIONS

HQ: CITY UTILITIES OF SPRINGFIELD MO
301 E CENTRAL ST, SPRINGFIELD, MO 658023858
Phone: 4178639000
Web: WWW.CITYUTIL.COM

PRODUCTS/OPERATIONS

2012 Sales

Electric	64
Water	9
Interest & other	3

HISTORICAL FINANCIALS

Company Type: Private

Income Statement FYE: September 30

	ASSETS ($ mil.)	NET INCOME ($ mil.)	INCOME AS % OF ASSETS	EMPLOYEES
09/13	1,760	14	0.8%	980
09/12	1,765	16	0.9%	—
09/11	1,776	18	1.0%	—
09/10	1,790	0	—	—
Annual Growth	(0.6%)	—	—	—

2013 Year-End Financials

Debt ratio: —
Return on equity: 3.60%
Cash ($ mil.): 32
Current ratio: 0.70
Long-term debt ($ mil.): —
Dividends
Yield: —
Payout: —
Market value ($ mil.): —

CITYSERVICEVALCON LLC

You don't have to live in the city to get the services of CityServiceValcon which markets and distributes petroleum products throughout the Inland Northwest and Rocky Mountain regions of the US as well as in the adjacent Plains states. Its products include gasoline diesel aviation fuels lubricants propane and heating oil. The company has diesel gasoline and heating oils for delivery through its network of bulk plants. CityServiceValcon also operates cardlock fueling facilities under the Pacific Pride brand name. Regional independent petroleum marketers City Service and Valcon merged their operations in 2003 to form CityServiceValcon.

Automotive gasoline brands represented by CityServiceValcon include Exxon Mobil Chevron and ConocoPhillips. The company also delivers aviation fuels (including Phillips 66 Aviation Fuels to Fixed Base Operators (FBOs) across the region.

Valcon Distributing has its roots in Kalispell Montana dating to the 1930s. City Service was cofounded by secretary and treasurer Dick Dasen in 1969.

LOCATIONS

HQ: CITYSERVICEVALCON LLC
640 W MONTANA ST, KALISPELL, MT 59901-3834
Phone: 406-755-4321
Web: WWW.CITYSERVICEVALCON.COM

COMPETITORS

Farstad Oil
Pettit Oil
Redwood Coast Petroleum
SPF Energy
Wilson Oil

HISTORICAL FINANCIALS

Company Type: Private

Income Statement FYE: September 30

	REVENUE ($ mil.)	NET INCOME ($ mil.)	NET PROFIT MARGIN	EMPLOYEES
09/08	625	4	0.6%	150
09/07	490	3	0.6%	—
09/06	459	4	1.0%	—
Annual Growth	16.6%	(8.0%)	—	—

2008 Year-End Financials

Debt ratio: —
Return on equity: 0.60%
Cash ($ mil.): 1
Current ratio: 1.20
Long-term debt ($ mil.): —
Dividends
Yield: —
Payout: —
Market value ($ mil.): —

CLARE ROSE INC.

EXECUTIVES

President and CEO, Lisa Rose, age 43
Chairman, Sean Rose
Sales Manager, George MacDonald
Director Safety and Health, Pat Costanzo
Director Human Resources, Christine Dunne
VP Operations and Procurement, Darwin Thomas
VP Information Technology, Gary Neumen
SVP, Kenneth (Ken) Meyer
VP Finance, Monica Wray

LOCATIONS

HQ: CLARE ROSE INC.
100 ROSE EXECUTIVE BLVD, SHIRLEY, NY 119671524
Phone: 6314752337
Web: WWW.CLAREROSE.COM

COMPETITORS

Empire Merchants
Manhattan Beer Distributors
Phoenix Beverages
Yuengling & Son

HISTORICAL FINANCIALS

Company Type: Private

Income Statement FYE: December 31

	REVENUE ($ mil.)	NET INCOME ($ mil.)	NET PROFIT MARGIN	EMPLOYEES
12/13	201	6	3.3%	267
12/12	209	9	4.5%	—
12/11	199	8	4.2%	—
12/10	200	0	—	—
Annual Growth	0.2%	—	—	—

2013 Year-End Financials

Debt ratio: —
Return on equity: 3.30%
Cash ($ mil.): 8
Current ratio: 1.00
Long-term debt ($ mil.): —
Dividends
Yield: —
Payout: —
Market value ($ mil.): —

CLAREMONT MCKENNA COLLEGE FOUNDATION

EXECUTIVES

VP and Dean Admission and Financial Aid, Richard C. Vos
VP Administration and Planning Registered In-House Counsel and Secretary of the College, Matthew Bibbens
Associate VP Admission and Financial Aid, Georgette R. DeVeres
VP Alumni and Parent Relations, John P. Faranda
VP Special Projects and Senior Associate Dean Faculty, Jerome Garris
Executive Director Information Technology Services CTO and Associate Professor Relgious Studies, Cynthia A. Humes
VP Student Affairs and Dean Students, Jefferson Huang
Director Human Resources, Susan Cozzitarto
Director Institutional Research and Registrar, Elizabeth Morgan
VP and Dean Faculty, Gregory Hess
VP Development and External Relations, William R. Lowery
Director of Human Resources, Andrea Gale
Associate Director of Human Resources, Agnes Sanchez
Senior Associate Director of Financial Aid, Abby Parsons
Assistant Director of Social Media and Multimedia Web Content, Benjamin Alden
Vice President for Student Affairs Office Manager, Julia Easley
Executive Director for Principal Gifts, Torrey Sun
Services Manager, Tatiana Shabelnik
Program Director for new Silicon Valley Program, Steve Siegel
Graphic Designer, Rebekah Roose
Associate Vice President for Development, Patrick Roche
Assistant Director of Development Services, Melissa Flanigan
Vice President for Development & External Relations, Ernie Iseminger
Administrative Assistant Vice President for Development & External Relations, Christina Montez-Rose
Administrative Assistant President, Christina Ranney
Secretary, Carlee Iverson
Administrative Assistant, Brenda Petrali
Associate Vice President, Max Benavidez
President Chief Financial Officer, Grant Kvalheim
Assistant Director of Development Services, Norene Black
Assistant Director of Financial Aid, Catherine Mayfield
Assistant Director of Annual Giving, Scott Kleinheksel
Assistant Director of Planned Giving, Susan Brinkama

LOCATIONS

HQ: CLAREMONT MCKENNA COLLEGE FOUNDATION
500 E 9TH ST, CLAREMONT, CA 917115929
Phone: 9096218088
Web: WWW.CLAREMONTMCKENNA.EDU

HISTORICAL FINANCIALS

Company Type: Private

Income Statement FYE: June 30

	REVENUE ($ mil.)	NET INCOME ($ mil.)	NET PROFIT MARGIN	EMPLOYEES
06/13	116	83	72.1%	370
06/12	154	22	14.8%	—
06/11	159	53	33.7%	—
06/10	109	0	—	—
Annual Growth	2.0%	—	—	—

2013 Year-End Financials

Debt ratio: —
Return on equity: 72.10%
Cash ($ mil.): 1
Current ratio: —
Long-term debt ($ mil.): —
Dividends
Yield: —
Payout: —
Market value ($ mil.): —

CLARKE POWER SERVICES INC.

LOCATIONS

HQ: CLARKE POWER SERVICES INC.
3133 E KEMPER RD, CINCINNATI, OH 452411516
Phone: 5137192388
Web: WWW.CLARKEPOWERSERVICES.COM

HISTORICAL FINANCIALS

Company Type: Private

Income Statement FYE: December 31

	REVENUE ($ mil.)	NET INCOME ($ mil.)	NET PROFIT MARGIN	EMPLOYEES
12/13	228	3	1.5%	600
12/12	216	2	1.1%	—
12/11	161	1	0.9%	—
12/10	135	0	—	—
Annual Growth	18.9%	—	—	—

2013 Year-End Financials

Debt ratio: —
Return on equity: 1.50%
Cash ($ mil.): 2
Current ratio: 0.60
Long-term debt ($ mil.): —
Dividends
Yield: —
Payout: —
Market value ($ mil.): —

CLASSIC STAR GROUP LP

LOCATIONS

HQ: CLASSIC STAR GROUP LP
6324 EDEN DR, HALTOM CITY, TX 761176129
Phone: 8178342868
Web: WWW.CLASSICSTARGROUP.COM

HISTORICAL FINANCIALS
Company Type: Private

Income Statement FYE: December 31

	REVENUE ($ mil.)	NET INCOME ($ mil.)	NET PROFIT MARGIN	EMPLOYEES
12/13	639	3	0.5%	17
12/12	555	2	0.4%	—
12/11*	530	1	0.3%	—
10/10	339	0	—	—
Annual Growth	23.5%	—	—	—

*Fiscal year change

2013 Year-End Financials

Debt ratio: —
Return on equity: 0.50%
Cash ($ mil.): 0
Current ratio: 0.70
Long-term debt ($ mil.): —
Dividends
Yield: —
Payout: —
Market value ($ mil.): —

CLAY ELECTRIC COOPERATIVE INC.

EXECUTIVES

General Manager and CEO, Bill Phillips
Director Member and Public Relations, Henry Barrow
Director of Engineering, Herman Dyal
Director of Finance and Administration, Mark Maxwell
Director of Information and Communication Technology, Bruce McHollan
Manager Energy Services, Sherman Phillips
Manager Communications, Larry E. Horne
Editor, Wayne Mattox
Video Services Coordinator, Tom Whitney
Director of Operations, Howard Mott
District Manager, Tommy Tomlinson
CEO and General Manager, Richard K. (Ricky) Davis
Director District Operations, Bill Thompson
District Manager, Kerry Page
District Manager, Jim Beeler
Communications Specialist, Amanda Hernandez
Manager Safety and Training, Lee Hicks
Safety and Training Coordinator, Mark Mosley
Director Human Resources, Chip Gray

LOCATIONS

HQ: CLAY ELECTRIC COOPERATIVE INC.
225 W WALKER DR, KEYSTONE HEIGHTS, FL 326567617
Phone: 3524734917
Web: WWW.CLAYELECTRIC.COM

COMPETITORS

Florida Power & Light
Florida Public Utilities
Gainesville Regional Utilities
JEA

HISTORICAL FINANCIALS
Company Type: Private

Income Statement FYE: December 31

	REVENUE ($ mil.)	NET INCOME ($ mil.)	NET PROFIT MARGIN	EMPLOYEES
12/13	339	11	3.4%	444
12/12	337	8	2.4%	—
12/11	356	20	5.7%	—
12/10	376	0	—	—
Annual Growth	(3.4%)	—	—	—

2013 Year-End Financials

Debt ratio: —
Return on equity: 3.40%
Cash ($ mil.): 6
Current ratio: 0.50
Long-term debt ($ mil.): —
Dividends
Yield: —
Payout: —
Market value ($ mil.): —

CLAYCO INC.

Clayco is a top US general building contractor that offers real estate architecture design engineering and construction services. The privately owned company serves a range of industries with a focus on industrial corporate government residential institutional and financial facilities. Projects include distribution and logistics centers industrial facilities and food and beverage industry warehouses and plants. Clayco also has constructed headquarters and operation centers call and data centers sports and education facilities and retail centers. Its Clayco Realty Group provides land development site selection and project financing. Clayco was founded in 1984 by CEO Robert Clark.

Geographic Reach

Missouri-based Clayco has offices in Chicago from St. Louis. The firm which is seeking to grow its global presence has major projects in 43 states and three countries.

Operations

Clayco operates through several businesses: Clayco Realty Group Forum Studio and Concrete Strategies.

Clayco Realty Group is a full-service real estate development firm that has been involved in the design-build development of 4000-plus acres of land and more than 19 million sq. ft. of commercial industrial residential mixed-use and hospitality space that altogether exceeds a value of $1.5 billion. Having partnered with Optimus Development on many projects Clayco in 2013 merged the Optimus business into its Clayco Realty Group.

Its other subsidiary Forum Studio is an architecture/planning/interior design firm. It serves both national and international clients.

Concrete Strategies a general contracting firm that specializes in concrete design provides US customers with architectural site cast concrete structural concrete flatwork site utilities and other concrete construction for commercial projects.

Financial Performance

Clayco's revenues exceeded $872 million in 2012 up from 2011's $820 million revenue figure.

Sales and Marketing

It has designed facilities for the Dow Chemical Company Amazon Caterpillar Procter and Gamble 3M and Chevron.

Strategy

Clayco has vaulted to the top ranks of US general building contractors by developing its own building technique of tilt-up a process of concrete building construction. The group specializes in building distribution/warehouse facilities and sports headquarters and training facilities.

Clayco which weathered the downturn in the construction business by relying on its diverse service offerings in a variety of geographic markets and taking on government-funded projects is seeking new projects in new markets across the country and abroad. To this end it completed its first project in Mexico in 2013 for Caterpillar Inc. Clayco built a 450000-sq.-ft. distribution center that features a full-service kitchen for employees soccer field and outdoor grill.

To support its growth the firm in 2014 moved its corporate headquarters to Chicago where it plans to double the number of employees there during the next several years. Clayco plans to hire new architects designers and project managers and expand its concrete and infrastructure business in Illinois.

It's also seeking to make acquisitions including a municipal engineering firm.

EXECUTIVES

Chairman and CEO, Robert G. (Bob) Clark
Chief Operating Officer & Partner, Steven R. (Steve) Sieckhaus
Principal Clayco Real Estate Services and Partner, Tom Schroyer
President Forum Studio, Chris Cedergreen
SVP and Partner, Kevin McKenna
SVP and Partner, P. Kirk Warden
SVP Financial Facilities Business Unit Leader, Paul Barrath
President, Russ Burns
SVP and Partner, Tom Sieckhaus
Chief Financial Officer, Tony Schofield
VP Preconstruction Services, Kurt Jaeger
President Concrete Strategies, Joe Vitale
EVP and Partner, Dave Moses
VP Education Business Unit Leader, Steve Street
President Clayco Realty Group, Chris McKee

LOCATIONS

HQ: CLAYCO INC.
35 E WACKER DR STE 1300, CHICAGO, IL 60601-2110
Phone: 312-658-0747
Web: WWW.CLAYCORP.COM

PRODUCTS/OPERATIONS

Selected Projects

308 Green Street
Air Products
BJC Administrative Office Building
Express Scripts 6
First Community - Richmond Heights
Gateway Plaza
Houston Police Federal Credit Union
Mercy Chesterfield Health Campus
Missouri Baptist Hospital Medical Office Building
Reinsurance Group of America
Stifel Nicolaus
University of Chicago Medical Center West Center for Care and Discovery Parking Garage
Washington University School of Medicine Scott McKinley Research Building
Zenithridge at Southpointe
Zurich North American Headquarters

Selected Subsidiaries

Clayco Realty Group
Concrete Strategies
Forum Studio Inc.

COMPETITORS

AECOM
Alberici
Alter Group
Amusement Leisure
Baker Concrete
Barton Malow
Bechtel
KHS&S
Kinsley Construction
Korte
M. A. Mortenson
McCarthy Building
Populous Inc.
Skanska USA Building

H&M Company
Hensel Phelps Construction
Hunt Construction
James G. Davis Construction
The Austin Company
Turner Corporation
Whiting-Turner

HISTORICAL FINANCIALS

Company Type: Private

Income Statement FYE: December 31

	REVENUE ($ mil.)	NET INCOME ($ mil.)	NET PROFIT MARGIN	EMPLOYEES
12/12	391	2	0.6%	500
12/11	511	2	0.5%	—
12/09	443	4	1.0%	—
12/09	450	6	1.3%	—
Annual Growth	(4.6%)	(26.4%)	—	—

2012 Year-End Financials

Debt ratio: —
Return on equity: 0.60%
Cash ($ mil.): 2
Current ratio: 1.00
Long-term debt ($ mil.): —
Dividends
Yield: —
Payout: —
Market value ($ mil.): —

CLEVELAND CONSTRUCTION INC.

Cleveland Construction Inc. (CCI) has ventured beyond Cleveland to offer its services nationwide and abroad. The company offers construction management services for commercial and institutional projects. It also is a top interior contractor in the US installing finishes such as drywall acoustic wall panels and specialty ceilings. Projects have included hospitals universities correctional facilities hotels convention centers sports complexes retail outlets and government buildings such as the Ohio State Stadium the George Bush Intercontinental Airport in Houston and Wal-Mart superstores in Florida. Founded in 1980 by CEO Richard Small and his sons the company remains family-owned.

EXECUTIVES

CEO, Richard G. Small
Purchasing, Steve Williams
CFO and VP Project Management, Mark T. Small
Estimating Interiors, Neal Keller
Estimating General Contracts, Edward Paradise
Project Management, Keith Ziegler
Sales and Marketing, Matthew Young
Safety Director, Mitch DaDante
Vice President of Construction, David S. Sawicki
Vice President CCI Interiors Division, Dave Kurilko
President, Dan Wireman

LOCATIONS

HQ: CLEVELAND CONSTRUCTION INC.
8620 TYLER BLVD, MENTOR, OH 44060-4348
Phone: 440-255-8000
Web: WWW.CLEVELANDCONSTRUCTION.COM

COMPETITORS

Albert M. Higley
The Austin Company
The Haskell Company
URS

HISTORICAL FINANCIALS

Company Type: Private

Income Statement FYE: December 31

	REVENUE ($ mil.)	NET INCOME ($ mil.)	NET PROFIT MARGIN	EMPLOYEES
12/11	218	4	2.2%	800
12/09	217	25	11.9%	—
12/08	186	24	12.9%	—
12/07	227	16	7.2%	—
Annual Growth	(1.1%)	(26.7%)	—	—

2011 Year-End Financials

Debt ratio: —
Return on equity: 2.20%
Cash ($ mil.): 10
Current ratio: 1.20
Long-term debt ($ mil.): —
Dividends
Yield: —
Payout: —
Market value ($ mil.): —

COAST CITRUS DISTRIBUTORS

LOCATIONS

HQ: COAST CITRUS DISTRIBUTORS
7597 BRISTOW CT, SAN DIEGO, CA 921547419
Phone: 6196617950
Web: WWW.COASTCITRUS.COM

COMPETITORS

A. Duda & Sons
Albert' s Organics
American Fruit & Produce
Borg Produce
Chiquita Brands
Fresh Del Monte Produce
FreshPoint
General Produce
Interfresh
The Oppenheimer Group

HISTORICAL FINANCIALS

Company Type: Private

Income Statement FYE: December 29

	REVENUE ($ mil.)	NET INCOME ($ mil.)	NET PROFIT MARGIN	EMPLOYEES
12/12	281	2	1.0%	389
12/11*	297	3	1.0%	—
01/11	294	4	1.4%	—
06/10	293	0	—	—
Annual Growth	(1.4%)	—	—	—

*Fiscal year change

2012 Year-End Financials

Debt ratio: —
Return on equity: 1.00%
Cash ($ mil.): 13
Current ratio: 1.60
Long-term debt ($ mil.): —
Dividends
Yield: —
Payout: —
Market value ($ mil.): —

COAST ELECTRIC POWER ASSOCIATION

EXECUTIVES

President and CEO, Robert J. (Bob) Occhi, age 63
Manager Financial and Administrative Services, John Holston
Manager Human Resources, Marilyn Sefton
VP Marketing and Public Relations, Ron Barnes
Manager Engineering and Western Division Operations, Steve Pitzer
Manager Eastern Division, David Hensley
Manager Safety and Compliance, Clement Ladner
Communications Specialist, April Lollar
Communications Specialist, Melissa Bryant
Marketing Executive, Janell Nolan
Vice President of Economic Development, Guy Johnson
Vice President of Procurement, Bruce Marie
Vice President of Pearl River County Operations, Louis Lee

LOCATIONS

HQ: COAST ELECTRIC POWER ASSOCIATION
18020 HIGHWAY 603, KILN, MS 395568487
Phone: 2283637000
Web: WWW.COASTEPA.COM

COMPETITORS

Entergy Mississippi
Mississippi Power
Southern Pine EPA

HISTORICAL FINANCIALS

Company Type: Private

Income Statement FYE: December 31

	REVENUE ($ mil.)	NET INCOME ($ mil.)	NET PROFIT MARGIN	EMPLOYEES
12/13	187	12	6.8%	238
12/12	184	13	7.2%	—
12/11	185	13	7.3%	—
12/10	196	0	—	—
Annual Growth	(1.6%)	—	—	—

2013 Year-End Financials

Debt ratio: —
Return on equity: 6.80%
Cash ($ mil.): 1
Current ratio: 0.30
Long-term debt ($ mil.): —
Dividends
Yield: —
Payout: —
Market value ($ mil.): —

COASTAL PACIFIC FOOD DISTRIBUTORS INC.

Coastal Pacific Food Distributors (CPF) fuels the military forces from facility to fork. The company is one of the top wholesale food distributors that primarily serves the US armed forces across the Western US and in the Far East. As part of its business CPF provides a full line of groceries to military bases run by the US Army Navy Air Force and Marines. It delivers a variety of products from distribution centers located in California Washington and Hawaii. CPF also offers information system programming services for its customers to track sales and shipping as well as procurement and logistics through partnerships in Iraq Kuwait and Saudi Arabia. The company was founded in 1986.

Geographic Reach

California-based CPF caters to the Western US as well as Alaska Hawaii Guam Japan Okinawa Korea Singapore Kwajalein Diego Garcia and the Philippines. Its business extends to the Middle East through partnerships for procurement and logistics with other companies. These additional areas include Iraq Kuwait and Saudi Arabia.

Operations

CPF has grown to become the second-largest worldwide military distributor of food and related products.

As part of its business CPF operates distribution centers in California Washington Hawaii and Canada. In California its largest Stockton facility spans more than 500000 sq. ft. while its Ontario center boasts 429000 sq. ft. Its distribution center in Fife Washington is 153000 sq. ft. A 45000-sq.-ft. facility in Hawaii delivers food to four military commissaries.

Strategy

The company works to support its existing markets. In 2013 CPF opened a new prime vendor platform in Calamba Luguna Philippines as it looks to serve future growth there. The platform supports Naval ships with dry chill and frozen items.

Sales and Marketing

Industry partners that keep CPF busy include the Defense Logistics Agency the Defense Commissary Agency Air Force NAF Purchasing Office Navy Exchange (NEXCOM) Army and Air Force Exchange Service (AAFES) and the American Logistics Association to name a few.

The company counts on food manufacturers to keep its customers happy. They include Kraft Foods Tyson Foods Procter & Gamble General Mills Nestle ConAgra Unilever Frito-Lay Campbell J.M. Smucker Global Military Marketing Mars S&K Sales Del Monte Corp. Georgia-Pacific Johnson & Johnson and Alder Foods.

EXECUTIVES

General Manager, Brian Murdoch
Vice President of Finance, Monika Bertke
CEO President, Frank Pecoraro
VP Business Development, Jeffrey King
Corporate Director of Merchandising, Bill Faucette
Business Manager, Debbie May
Senior Business Manager, Frank Costa
General Manager of Division, Marlin Vleet
Chief Financial Officer, Bill Ungerman
Chief Operating Officer, Terry F. Wood
Vice President of Distribution, Tim Tveitnes

LOCATIONS

HQ: COASTAL PACIFIC FOOD DISTRIBUTORS INC.
1015 PERFORMANCE DR, STOCKTON, CA 95206-4925
Phone: 209-983-2454
Web: WWW.CPFD.COM

PRODUCTS/OPERATIONS

Selected Products

Bakery
Candy
Deli
Fresh & frozen meats
Frozen foods
Pet foods
Refrigerated items
Sushi

Selected Brokers

Acosta Sales & Marketing
Alder Foods Inc.
Bisek & Co. Inc.
Dixon Marketing Inc.
Dunham & Smith Agencies
Elite Brands
Finnegan International Sales
First Wave Sales
Gateway Military LLC
Global Office Building
HI-PAC Ltd
Mid Valley
Overseas Service Corporation
Otis McAllister
Parra Sales Inc
Reese Group
S&K
S. Schwartz Sales Inc.
Turnkey Management
WEBCO General Partnership

COMPETITORS

AdvancePierre
JTM Provisions
Nash-Finch
Richmond Wholesale Meat

HISTORICAL FINANCIALS

Company Type: Private

Income Statement FYE: December 29

	REVENUE ($ mil.)	NET INCOME ($ mil.)	NET PROFIT MARGIN	EMPLOYEES
12/12	1,212	15	1.2%	459
12/11*	1,162	25	2.2%	—
01/11	1,113	17	1.6%	—
01/10	1,119	17	1.6%	—
Annual Growth	2.7%	(4.8%)	—	—

*Fiscal year change

2012 Year-End Financials

Debt ratio: —
Return on equity: 1.20%
Cash ($ mil.): 5
Current ratio: 1.20
Long-term debt ($ mil.): —
Dividends
Yield: —
Payout: —
Market value ($ mil.): —

COBB ELECTRIC MEMBERSHIP CORPORATION

Cobb Electric Membership Corporation (Cobb EMC) makes sure that Cobb County Georgia residents can cook corn on the cob (and anything else) using either electric power or natural gas. The utility distributes electricity to more than 200000 meters (more than 177000 residential commercial and industrial members) in Cobb County and four other north metro Atlanta counties. Cobb EMC operates about 10000 miles of power lines. The company's Gas South unit markets natural gas to customers who receive their service on Atlanta Gas & Light's natural gas distribution pipelines in Georgia.

Geographic Reach

One of the largest of Georgia's 41 EMCs Cobb EMC's distribution system covers approximately 1434 square miles (Cobb Bartow Cherokee Fulton and Paulding counties in the north metro Atlanta area and Randolph Calhoun Quitman and Clay counties in Southwest Georgia).

Operations

Its Cobb Energy Management provides administrative and labor support to Cobb EMC and offers phone and Internet services to Cobb EMC's customers primarily through subsidiaries. Cobb Energy Management provides call center training tree trimming and billing software services and other ancillary support to EMC's core activities.

Financial Performance

In 2012 the company reported a 46% increase in revenues thanks to a 10% rise in natural gas sales which outpaced a 2% decline in electric revenues. Net income grew by 194% in 2012 as a result of higher net sales and lower operating costs.

Strategy

Cobb EMC is a partner in Power4Georgians a consortium of six Georgia EMCs that collectively is developing a comprehensive strategy to provide reliable and affordable energy to the EMC members.

In 2013 as part of its ongoing transition out of non-energy businesses Cobb EMC announced today plans to cut its workforce by up to 20% percent through a company-wide offer of voluntary separation packages.

In 2012 Smart Energy Capital LLC and Jacoby Development Inc. signed a power purchase deal with Cobb EMC to provide power from the Azalea Solar Facility the largest solar power plant (10MW) in Georgia and one of the largest in the Southeast.

Company Background

The cooperative has been embroiled in litigation in recent years and in 2011 a Cobb County grand jury indicted Cobb EMC Dwight Brown on 31 counts of theft and racketeering. Brown was replaced as CEO by W.T. "Chip" Nelson.

The gas and support companies were merged into EMC as wholly owned units in 2009 as a way to streamline EMC's overall operations. The company has also sold a number of former assets to raise cash including Cooperative Business Ventures in 2009 for $2 million and the health and welfare brokerage business of Cooperative Benefits and Financial Services for a gain of $470000 in 2010.

Formed in 1938 Cobb EMC began life as an electric utility with 489 residential members and 14 commercial customers.

EXECUTIVES

President CEO and Director, Dwight Brown
Chairman, Larry N. Chadwick
Vice Chairman, Sarah Brown
Secretary Treasurer and Director, Alton R. (Al) Fortney Jr.
VP Public Relations, Sam Kelly
SVP Finance and Contracts, Frank Myers
President CEO and Director, Dwight Brown
Vice Chairman, Sarah Brown
Director, Donald W. (Don) Barnett
Director, David Herndon
Director, David McGinnis
Secretary Treasurer and Director, Alton R. (Al) Fortney Jr.
Director, Frank D. Boone
Director, Kay Anderson
Director, Henry Balkcom III
Director, Johnny Gresham
Auditors: McNairMcLemoreMiddlebrooks&Co.LLP

LOCATIONS

HQ: COBB ELECTRIC MEMBERSHIP CORPORATION
1000 EMC PKWY NE, MARIETTA, GA 30060-7908
Phone: 770-429-2100
Web: WWW.COBBEMC.COM

PRODUCTS/OPERATIONS

2012 Sales

Electric	419	67
Other	4	1

HISTORICAL FINANCIALS

Company Type: Private

Income Statement FYE: April 30

	REVENUE ($ mil.)	NET INCOME ($ mil.)	NET PROFIT MARGIN	EMPLOYEES
04/09*	641	3	0.6%	548
12/08	381	(0)	—	—
12/07	367	4	1.2%	—
12/06	344	10	3.0%	—
Annual Growth	36.4%	(40.9%)	—	—

*Fiscal year change

2009 Year-End Financials

Debt ratio: —
Return on equity: 0.60%
Cash ($ mil.): 35
Current ratio: 0.50
Long-term debt ($ mil.): —
Dividends
Yield: —
Payout: —
Market value ($ mil.): —

COBORN'S INCORPORATED

LOCATIONS

HQ: COBORN' ' S INCORPORATED
1445 HIGHWAY 23 E BLDG A, SAINT CLOUD, MN 563040952
Phone: 7633891350
Web: WWW.COBORNS.LIFEPICS.COM

PRODUCTS/OPERATIONS

Selected Store Formats

Convenience stores (Little Dukes Holiday)
Hardware stores (Ace)
Liquor stores
Pharmacies
Restaurants (Subway)
Supermarkets (Coborn' s Cash Wise Foods Save-A-Lot)
Video stores

COMPETITORS

ALDI
Couche-Tard
Cub Foods
Kowalski' s Markets
Kroger
Lunds
Target Corporation
Wal-Mart

HISTORICAL FINANCIALS

Company Type: Private

Income Statement FYE: December 28

	REVENUE ($ mil.)	NET INCOME ($ mil.)	NET PROFIT MARGIN	EMPLOYEES
12/13	1,246	30	2.5%	7,000
12/12	1,220	32	2.7%	—
12/11	1,191	29	2.4%	—
12/10	1,103	0	—	—
Annual Growth	4.1%	—	—	—

2013 Year-End Financials

Debt ratio: —
Return on equity: 2.50%
Cash ($ mil.): 21
Current ratio: 0.30
Long-term debt ($ mil.): —
Dividends
Yield: —
Payout: —
Market value ($ mil.): —

COC PROPERTIES INC.

LOCATIONS

HQ: COC PROPERTIES INC.
110 MACKENAN DR STE 300, CARY, NC 275117901
Phone: 9194621100
Web: WWW.CARYOIL.COM

HISTORICAL FINANCIALS

Company Type: Private

Income Statement FYE: December 31

	ASSETS ($ mil.)	NET INCOME ($ mil.)	INCOME AS % OF ASSETS	EMPLOYEES
12/13	77	3	4.4%	100
12/12	76	2	3.6%	—
12/11	76	2	2.7%	—
12/09	67	0	—	—
Annual Growth	3.6%	—	—	—

2013 Year-End Financials

Debt ratio: —
Return on equity: 0.20%
Cash ($ mil.): 2
Current ratio: 0.90
Long-term debt ($ mil.): —
Dividends
Yield: —
Payout: —
Market value ($ mil.): —

CODALE ELECTRIC SUPPLY INC.

Codale Electric Supply distributes lighting fixtures electrical supplies and datacomm products to wholesale customers through 11 locations in Nevada Utah Idaho and Wyoming. It stocks products from such manufacturers as Brad Harrison Chromalox Greenlee Philips Lighting Southwire and Western Tube & Conduit. The company sells to the aerospace construction mining healthcare schools government and utility markets. Codale Electric also offers consulting and training energy and safety audits and inventory management services. The company was founded in 1975 by CEO Dale Holt who owns nearly all of Codale Electric's equity.

In addition to expanding its service offerings beyond traditional wholesale distribution the company has added a division that provides modification and assembly of power substations for the utility industry.

HISTORY

odale

EXECUTIVES

Vice President, Nick Holt
V Pres Sec-treas, Jay Holt, age 59

LOCATIONS

HQ: CODALE ELECTRIC SUPPLY INC.
5225 W 2400 S, SALT LAKE CITY, UT 84120-1264
Phone: 801-975-7300
Web: WWW.CODALE.COM

COMPETITORS

Allied Electronics
Graybar Electric
MRC Global
W.W. Grainger
WESCO International

HISTORICAL FINANCIALS

Company Type: Private

Income Statement FYE: December 25

	REVENUE ($ mil.)	NET INCOME ($ mil.)	NET PROFIT MARGIN	EMPLOYEES
12/11	220	12	5.4%	230
12/10	175	6	3.4%	—
12/09	175	6	3.6%	—
12/08	235	16	6.9%	—
Annual Growth	(2.2%)	(9.8%)	—	—

2011 Year-End Financials

Debt ratio: —
Return on equity: 5.40%
Cash ($ mil.): 0
Current ratio: 0.90
Long-term debt ($ mil.): —
Dividends
Yield: —
Payout: —
Market value ($ mil.): —

COLLEGE ENTRANCE EXAMINATION BOARD

There are three letters every high school student must learn: S A and T. Who is responsible for making those letters so infamous? Why The College Board of course. The not-for-profit association owns and administers the Scholastic Assessment Test (SAT) College-Level Examination Program (CLEP) and the Advanced Placement Program (AP) at high schools nationwide. It also offers guidance counseling financial aid student assessment standardized testing and professional development courses. The College Board was founded in 1900; its members include nearly 6000 schools colleges universities and other educational institutions.

Geographic Reach

The College Board has main offices in New York City; Reston Virginia; and Washington DC. It also has six regional offices scattered across the US; these offices handle administrative duties for testing administrations in their respective regions. The organization's member institutions include schools in more than 60 countries; College Board exams are administered in more than 180 countries and territories worldwide.

Operations

The College Board's services reach more than 7 million students at 23000 high schools and 3800 colleges in the US and abroad. In 2012 the association administered some 3 million SAT exams. It also serves some 130000 AP teachers and administers 3.2 million AP exams annually. Some of the College Board's tests such as the SAT are administered at schools with support from third parties such as Educational Testing Services.

Strategy

In 2010 The College Board launched the College Board Advocacy & Policy Center to improve academic standards and support educators through a number of measures. It also seeks ways to improve college affordability and increase awareness of financial aid options among students and their families. In 2012 the center launched an affinity network designed to strengthen connections between K-12 and postsecondary education organizations and help students transition from high school to college.

Company Background

The College Board was created by a group of colleges as a way to expand access to higher education. The SAT (originally called the College Boards) was formed to help colleges and universities identify "deserving" students through shared entrance exams.

EXECUTIVES

President and Trustee, W. Gaston Caperton III, age 73
SVP Finance and CFO, Thomas (Tom) Higgins
VP Research and Development, Wayne J. Camara
Vice Chair, Shirley A. Ort
Chairman, Paul W. Sechrist, age 53
SVP Relationship Development, Peter Negroni
SVP Government Relations Grants Advocacy, Thomas Rudin
SVP Administration and General Counsel, Neil Lane
VP Organizational Effectiveness, Juliet Weissman
VP and Secretary, Dorothy Sexton
VP Membership, Mary C. Scott
Chairman, Maghan Keita
Chief Marketing Officer, Barbara Cooperman
COO, Jeremy Singer
SVP and CIO, Terri Shaw
President CEO and Trustee, David Coleman
President and Trustee, W. Gaston Caperton III, age 73
Vice Chair, Shirley A. Ort
Vice Chairman, Maghan Keita
President CEO and Trustee, David Coleman

LOCATIONS

HQ: COLLEGE ENTRANCE EXAMINATION BOARD
45 COLUMBUS AVE, NEW YORK, NY 10023-6917
Phone: 212-713-8000
Web: WWW.COLLEGEBOARD.ORG

PRODUCTS/OPERATIONS

Selected services

Advanced Placement (college readiness)
Big Future (college planning)
CLEP (College-Level Examination Program)
CollegeEd (college planning career guidance)
College Search (college readiness)
CSS/Financial Aid PROFILE (financial aid application service)
EXCELerator (school district consultation services college readiness)
PSAT/NMSQT (practice for SAT National Merit Scholarship Qualifying Test)
ReadiStep (middle school assessment high school readiness)
SAT SAT Subject Tests and SAT Readiness Tools
Scholarship Search (scholarship aid)
SpringBoard (pre-AP college readiness)
Student Search Service (sends student testing information to colleges and scholarship programs)

COMPETITORS

ACT Inc.	Educate
Bridges Transitions	Kaplan
College Coach	McGraw Hill Financial
ETS	Questar Assessment
Edmentum	The Princeton Review

HISTORICAL FINANCIALS

Company Type: Private

Income Statement FYE: June 30

	REVENUE ($ mil.)	NET INCOME ($ mil.)	NET PROFIT MARGIN	EMPLOYEES
06/13	779	93	12.0%	1,259
06/12	746	26	3.6%	—
06/10	705	102	14.5%	—
06/10	668	78	11.7%	—
Annual Growth	5.3%	6.1%	—	—

2013 Year-End Financials

Debt ratio: —
Return on equity: 12.00%
Cash ($ mil.): 147
Current ratio: 3.00
Long-term debt ($ mil.): —
Dividends
Yield: —
Payout: —
Market value ($ mil.): —

COLLEGE OF THE HOLY CROSS

College of The Holy Cross has some real Crusaders. The college with sports teams nicknamed the Crusaders is a liberal arts undergraduate institution in central Massachusetts with some 2900 students. Some of the school's more popular areas of study include liberal arts' favorites such as English history and political science but also multidisciplinary concentrations and specialty programs including biochemistry Latin American studies and women's studies. The school has more than 300 full- and part-time faculty with a 10:1 student-to-faculty ratio. Founded in 1843 by the Society of Jesus (Jesuits) Holy Cross is the oldest Catholic college in New England.

Geographic Reach

College of The Holy Cross is located on a 170-acre campus in Worcester Massachusetts. Its students come from throughout the US and more than 20 countries.

Financial Performance

College of the Holy Cross reported a 2% revenue increase to some $154 million in 2012 due to increased income from student tuition and fees auxiliary enterprises including living and dining services and external contributions. Tuition is the largest revenue contributor and falls at around $44000 annually per student. Net income fell into the red in 2012 however due to higher operating expenses and lower returns on investments.

EXECUTIVES

Chairman, P. Kevin Condron
Treasurer and Chief Investment Officer, William R. Durgin
VP Development and Alumni Relations, Paul E. Sheff
Director Human Resources, Donna C. Wrenn
Controller, Robert E. Grenon
SVP, Frank Vellaccio
VP Student Affairs and Dean Students, Jacqueline D. Peterson
VP Administration and Finance, Michael J. Lochhead
Director Public Safety, Christine Bernard-NcNamara
Manager Purchasing, Joan E. Anderson
Director Academic Services and Learning Resources, Christina Bi Chen
Bursar, Sheila E. Coakley
Director Library Services, James E. Hogan
Director Information Technology Services, Ellen J. Keohane
Director Athletics, Richard M. Regan Jr.
Director Public Affairs, Ellen Ryder
Head of Acquisitions and Cataloging, Nancy G. Singleton
Director Career Planning, John J. Winters Jr.
Director Development, Timm M. Zolkos
VP Academic Affairs and Dean College, Timothy R. Austin
General Counsel, Timothy F. Mines
Director Administrative Services and Acting Affirmative Action Officer, William J. Conley
Director Alumni Relations, Kristyn M. Dyer
President, Rev Philip L. Boroughs
President emeritus then a theology professor, John Brooks
Auditors: KPMGLLP

LOCATIONS

HQ: COLLEGE OF THE HOLY CROSS
1 COLLEGE ST, WORCESTER, MA 01610-2395
Phone: 508-793-2011
Web: WWW.OFFICES.HOLYCROSS.EDU

PRODUCTS/OPERATIONS

Selected Programs

Anthropology
Art History
Biology
Chemistry
Chinese
Classics
Computer Science
Economics
Economics and Accounting
Education
English
French
German
History
Italian
Mathematics
Modern Languages & Literatures
Music
Philosophy
Physics
Political Science
Psychology
Religious Studies
Russian
Sociology
Spanish
Studies in World Literature
Studio Art
Theatre
Career Programs
- Business
- Engineering
- Health Professions
- Law
- Teacher Education Program

Multidisciplinary and Specialty Programs
- Africana Studies
- Asian Studies
- Biochemistry
- Biological Psychology
- Education
- Environmental Studies
- Latin American and Latino Studies
- Naval Science
- Peace and Conflict Studies
- Women's and Gender Studies

COMPETITORS

Boston College	Fordham University
Fairfield University	Molloy College

HISTORICAL FINANCIALS

Company Type: Private

Income Statement FYE: June 30

	REVENUE ($ mil.)	NET INCOME ($ mil.)	NET PROFIT MARGIN	EMPLOYEES
06/12	154	(16)	—	949
06/11	151	96	63.6%	—
06/10	149	35	23.9%	—
06/09	144	(140)	—	—
Annual Growth	2.3%	—	—	—

2012 Year-End Financials

Debt ratio: —
Return on equity: (-10.60%)
Cash ($ mil.): 34
Current ratio: —
Long-term debt ($ mil.): —
Dividends
Yield: —
Payout: —
Market value ($ mil.): —

COLORADO SEMINARY

EXECUTIVES

Executive Director Newman Center for the Performing Arts, Stephen (Steve) Seifert

Chancellor, Robert D. (Bob) Coombe
Dean Josef Korbel School of International Studies, Christopher R. Hill
Vice Chancellor Business and Financial Affairs, Craig W. Woody
Director University Business Services Purchasing Services Department, Joe Benson
Controller and Assistant Treasurer, Margaret Henry
Dean Women's College, Lynn Gangone
Provost, Gregg Kvistad
Manager Technology and Security Services Department of Campus Safety, Steven J. Fay
Director Administrative Information Services University Technology Services, Susan L. Lutz
Chief Information Security Officer University Technology Services Department, Arlen M. Fletcher
Registrar, Dennis M. Becker
Dean Divisions of Arts Humanities and Social Sciences, Anne E. McCall
Dean and Professor of Management Daniels College of Business, Christine M. (Chris) Riordan
Dean Graduate School of Social Work, James H. Williams
Dean and Director Penrose Library, Nancy H. Allen
Dean University College, Jim Davis
Dean Sturm College of Law, Martin J. (Marty) Katz
Director Advising and Orientation, Niki Latino
Director Career Center, Mary Michael Hawkins
Dean Morgridge College of Education, Gregory M. (Greg) Anderson
Human Resources Coordinator, Sarah B. Childs
Human Resources Coordinator, Ashley N. Gross
Executive Director Intermodal Transportation Institute, Cathryne C. Johnson
Director International Human Rights Advocacy Center, Robert Golten
President of the CU Denver chapter, Maureen Ediger
Assistant Director of Financial Services, Denise Weber
Assistant Director of Budget & Human Resource Services, John Semple
Dean Graduate School of Professional Psychology, Shelly Smith-Acuna
Dean Natural Sciences and Mathematics, Andrei Kutateladze
Interim Dean Daniel Felix Ritchie School of Engineering and Computer Science, Michael Keables
Vice Chancellor Division of Marketing & COmmunications and Chief Marketing Officer, Kevin Carroll

LOCATIONS

HQ: COLORADO SEMINARY
2199 S UNIVERSITY BLVD, DENVER, CO 802104711
Phone: 3038712000
Web: WWW.DU.EDU

PRODUCTS/OPERATIONS

Selected Schools and Programs

Undergraduate Schools and Colleges
- Daniels College of Business
- Division of Natural Sciences & Mathematics
- Division of Arts Humanities and Social Sciences
- Josef Korbel School of International Studies
- Morgridge College of Education
- School of Engineering and Computer Science
- University College
- Women's College

Graduate and Professional Programs
Daniels College of Business
Divisions of Arts Humanities and Social Sciences
Divisions of Natural Sciences and Mathematics
Graduate School of Professional Psychology (GSPP)
Graduate School of Social Work (GSSW)
Graduate Tax Program
Interdisciplinary Degree Programs
Josef Korbel School of International Studies
Morgridge College of Education (MCE)
School of Engineering and Computer Science
The Sturm College of Law
University College

HISTORICAL FINANCIALS

Company Type: Private

Income Statement FYE: June 30

	REVENUE ($ mil.)	NET INCOME ($ mil.)	NET PROFIT MARGIN	EMPLOYEES
06/14	396	122	31.0%	2,770
06/12	367	56	15.5%	—
06/11	398	96	24.2%	—
06/10	469	0	—	—
Annual Growth	(4.2%)	—	—	—

2014 Year-End Financials

Debt ratio: —
Return on equity: 31.00%
Cash ($ mil.): 58
Current ratio: —
Long-term debt ($ mil.): —
Dividends
Yield: —
Payout: —
Market value ($ mil.): —

COLORADO STATE UNIVERSITY

Colorado State University (CSU) got its start as an agricultural college in 1870 six years before Colorado was even a state. The school still has agricultural and forestry programs as well as a veterinary medicine school but it also offers degrees in liberal arts business engineering and the sciences. True to its roots as a land-grant college CSU engages the larger community in research and outreach through statewide Cooperative Extension programs and centers like the Colorado Agricultural Experiment Station. More than 30000 students are enrolled at CSU about 80% of whom are Colorado residents. It employs about 1500 faculty members and has a student-to-teacher ratio of 19:1.

Geographic Reach

CSU's main campus and its nearby foothills agricultural and mountain campuses are located on about 5000 acres in Fort Collins Colorado. The university has more than 1200 international students and scholars from about 90 countries on its campus. Additionally about 900 CSU students travel abroad every year to participate in educational programs.

Operations

The school's student body is largely composed of undergraduate students (more than 80%) but also includes some graduate and professional veterinary medicine students. CSU's most popular undergraduate majors are business health and exercise science psychology biological science construction management and human development and family studies. Overall the university offers about 150 undergraduate graduate and professional degree programs through eight colleges.

CSU has extensive research programs in fields including atmospheric science clean energy the environment biomedicine and infectious diseases. The university's research programs attract some $300 million in external funding each year.

Financial Performance

CSU's revenues increased 8% in 2012 to $827 million from higher earnings on student tuition and fees grants and contracts auxiliary enterprises and other education activity sales and service income. Net income increased by 63% to $67 million that year as a result of the university's revenue growth.

CSU has primarily experienced an increase in revenues over the last five years with the exception a slight dip during 2010 caused by decreased state capital contributions and grants and contracts.

Student tuition and fees run at about $9000 per year for Colorado residents and $24000 for out-of-state students.

EXECUTIVES

VP Enrollment and Access, Robin Brown

LOCATIONS

HQ: COLORADO STATE UNIVERSITY
6003 CAMPUS DELIVERY, FORT COLLINS, CO 80523-6003
Phone: 970-491-1101
Web: WWW.CO.ADAMS.CO.US

PRODUCTS/OPERATIONS

Selected Colleges Schools and Programs

Colleges
- College of Agricultural Sciences
- College of Applied Human Sciences
- College of Business
- College of Engineering
- College of Liberal Arts
- College of Natural Sciences
- College of Veterinary Medicine and Biomedical Sciences
- Warner College of Natural Resources

Schools and Programs
- Graduate School
- International Programs
- Online Degrees and Courses (Online Plus)
- School of the Arts
- School of Biomedical Engineering
- School of Education
- School of Global Environmental Sustainability
- School of Social Work

HISTORICAL FINANCIALS

Company Type: Private

Income Statement FYE: June 30

	REVENUE ($ mil.)	NET INCOME ($ mil.)	NET PROFIT MARGIN	EMPLOYEES
06/08	740	(44)	—	1,306
06/06	562	26	4.7%	—
06/05	56,847	0	0.0%	—
Annual Growth	(76.5%)	—	—	—

2008 Year-End Financials

Debt ratio: —
Return on equity: (-6.00%)
Cash ($ mil.): 249
Current ratio: 2.20
Long-term debt ($ mil.): —
Dividends
Yield: —
Payout: —
Market value ($ mil.): —

COLQUITT ELECTRIC MEMBERSHIP CORPORATION

There's no quit in the electric service to Colquitt and surrounding counties in Georgia thanks to Colquitt Electric Membership Corporation (Colquitt EMC). The consumer-owned non-profit utility distributes electricity to more than 41000 members in Berrien Brooks Colquitt Cook Lowndes Tift and Worth counties. Colquitt EMC distributes electricity via more than 8020 miles of power line. In 1976 the cooperative changed its name from Colquitt County Rural Electric Company to Colquitt EMC. The utility is the largest EMC in south Georgia with some of the lowest electric rates in the state.

The cooperative which is pushing energy conservation to save its customers money ,Âserves about 61080 customer meters from six office locations.

Colquitt EMC was formed as Colquitt County Rural Electric Company in 1936 as part of the Rural Electrification Administration's drive to bring affordable power to rural areas across the US.

EXECUTIVES

Vice President Marketing, Richard Gaston
Treasurer, J Paulk
Board Member, Don Copeland

LOCATIONS

HQ: COLQUITT ELECTRIC MEMBERSHIP CORPORATION
15 ROWLAND DR, MOULTRIE, GA 317684169
Phone: 2299853620
Web: WWW.COLQUITTEMC.COM

HISTORICAL FINANCIALS

Company Type: Private

Income Statement FYE: December 31

	REVENUE ($ mil.)	NET INCOME ($ mil.)	NET PROFIT MARGIN	EMPLOYEES
12/13	127	0	—	164
12/09	109	2	2.6%	—
12/08	107	2	2.3%	—
12/07	106	0	—	—
Annual Growth	3.2%	—	—	—

2013 Year-End Financials

Debt ratio: —
Return on equity: —
Cash ($ mil.): 11
Current ratio: 2.50
Long-term debt ($ mil.): —
Dividends
Yield: —
Payout: —
Market value ($ mil.): —

COLSA CORPORATION

COLSA doesn't mind being called a little defensive. The company provides advanced technology systems and services to US government agencies such as the Missile Defense Agency and NASA. COLSA which specializes in radar and guidance system technology offers services including engineering and testing developing war games simulations analyzing radar technology and virtual prototyping. Its information systems services include integration maintenance and administration for large computer centers. COLSA also offers a software system for nuclear power plants and a gateway for sending simulation data to remote systems. COLSA was founded in 1980.

Geographic Reach

COLSA has offices in Alabama Arizona California Colorado Florida and Washington DC. About a third of COLSA's employees work directly at Redstone Arsenal home to the U.S. Army Aviation and Missile Command the Space and Missile Defense Command and components of the Defense Intelligence Agency and the Missile Defense Agency.

Sales and Marketing

Primarily working with defense agencies COLSA has sought to diversify its client base by adding other government bodies such as the Department of Justice. COLSA also plans to pursue international clients.

EXECUTIVES

Vice President Business Management, Susan Phillips
Vice President Advanced Research Center, John Welt
VP-Radar & Software Engrg, Ivan Garcia
Vice President Planning and Proposal Development, Penny Chilton
Vice President North Florida Operations, Joe Anderson
President Chief Operating Officer, Richard Amos
CEO, Francisco J. Collazo
VP-NASA Div, Phil Hodges
Vice President Federal Services Solutions, Jim Hunter
Vice President Business Development, Fred T. Fagan
Chairman, Stan Miller
Executive Vice President Chief Technical Officer, Tony DiRienzo

LOCATIONS

HQ: COLSA CORPORATION
6728 ODYSSEY DR NW, HUNTSVILLE, AL 35806-3305
Phone: 256-964-5555
Web: WWW.COLSA.COM

PRODUCTS/OPERATIONS

Selected Services

Information services
- Computer center design and engineering
- Computer center operation and maintenance
- Information assurance/security

Programmatic support
- Acquisition management
- Independent assessment
- Test support

System engineering
- Configuration management
- Modeling and simulation
- Software engineering
- Test engineering
- Testbed design development and operation

System integration
- Command control communications computers and intel (C4I) systems
- Hardware/software systems
- Security systems

COMPETITORS

CACI International
Computer Sciences Corp.
HP Enterprise Services
Northrop Grumman
Raytheon
SM&A
UNICOM Government

HISTORICAL FINANCIALS

Company Type: Private

Income Statement FYE: December 31

	REVENUE ($ mil.)	NET INCOME ($ mil.)	NET PROFIT MARGIN	EMPLOYEES
12/12	186	11	5.9%	890
12/11	152	11	7.8%	—
12/10	155	11	7.3%	—
12/09	151	8	5.8%	—
Annual Growth	7.2%	8.0%	—	—

2012 Year-End Financials

Debt ratio: —
Return on equity: 5.90%
Cash ($ mil.): 5
Current ratio: 1.30
Long-term debt ($ mil.): —
Dividends
Yield: —
Payout: —
Market value ($ mil.): —

COLUMBIA COLLEGE CHICAGO

Columbia College Chicago revels in its creative reputation. Specializing in arts and media the private not-for-profit school offers undergraduate and graduate degrees in the visual performing media and communication arts. The college offers more than 120 academic programs including architecture and interior design photography dance television theater film music composition journalism and marketing communications. Comedian Andy Richter and Wheel of Fortune host Pat Sajak are among the school's notable alumni. Founded in 1890 as the Columbia School of Oratory the college is located in several buildings in downtown Chicago and has about 12000 students. Average teacher to student ratio is 20:1.

Geographic Reach

Internationally-recognized Columbia College Chicago's student enrollment consists of students from all 50 states and more than 40 foreign nations. Its urban campus is located in Chicago's South Loop.

Operations

Columbia College Chicago welcomed a newly-constructed academic building in 2010. The Media Production Center includes a pair of sound stages a motion-capture studio an animation lab and classrooms. The college added the center to meet the demands of its more popular fields of study. Indeed its most popular majors include Film & Video Art & Design and Arts Entertainment & Media Management in that order.

Many of the college's students live on campus. About 2200 students live in four residence centers helping to make Columbia the second-largest college for out-of-state students in Illinois. The college pays the Education Advancement Fund (EAF) a corporation owned by Columbia College Chicago and two other Chicago educational institutions to develop operate and own the University Center of Chicago (UCC) about $11.5 million (including $3 million for its share of the residential life and meal plan expenses) toward its maximum rental liability in connection with its lease of 824 beds in fiscal year 2013. The UCC is managed by an international real estate management firm with the firm's chairman and CEO serving as a college board member.

Financial Performance

Rising tuition and fees (net of tuition allowances) and student housing (net of room allowances) as well as government grants and contracts all contributed to Columbia College Chicago's 2% revenue rise in fiscal 2012 as compared to 2011. Net income during the same reporting period dropped some 47% due to disappointing investment returns capital gifts for facilities and collections and expenses related to recognition of change in pension-funded status.

Strategy

The school is wrapping up a $100 million campaign that consisted of three parts: student scholarships support of building projects and endowment-building. Its top priority has been student scholarships. While the school focused on maintaining manageable costs its tuition still remains relatively high.

EXECUTIVES

Vice Chair, Richard P. (Dick) Kiphart, age 72
VP Administration Research and Planning, Anne E. Foley
President, Warrick L. Carter

VP Student Affairs, Mark Kelly
Associate VP Information Technology and CIO, Bernadette McMahon
Associate VP Business Affairs and Controller, Kevin Doherty
VP and General Counsel, Annice M. Kelly
Associate VP Academic Research and Dean of the Library, Jo Cates
Manager Benefits, Gabina Mora
Director Human Resources, Patricia Olalde
VP Business Affairs and CFO, Kenneth C. (Ken) Gotsch
Chairman, Allen M. Turner
Associate VP and Chief of Staff President's Office, Paul Chiaravalle
Director Purchasing, Thomas Russell
Associate Director Administrative Services, Theresa Kerr
National Director Alumni Relations, Joshua Culley-Foster
VP Academic Affairs and Interim Provost, Louise Love
Director Office of Budget and Reporting, Paula Scheiwe
Director Business Systems and Applications, Ann Kennedy
Director Enrollment Management Services, Maureen Herlehy
Associate VP Enrollment Management, Debra McGrath
Associate VP Facilities and Construction, John Kavouris
Executive Director Facilities and Operations, Katherine Dwyer
Associate VP and Dean of Students, Sharon Wilson-Taylor
VP Human Resources, Ellen Krutz
Director Telecommunications and Networking, Billy Cole
Director User Support, Dorothy Dare
Director Business Processes, Marsha J. Heizer
Executive Director of Development Institutional Advancement, Michael Anderson
Director Annual Giving Institutional Advancement, Dawn Baity
Associate VP Institutional Advancement, Kim Clement
Associate VP Public Relations Marketing and Advertising, Diane Doyne
Director Marketing, Brenda Berman
Director Internal Auditing, Greg Narlow
Director Payroll Office, Tracy Cargo
Director and Registrar Records Office, Marvin Cohen
Associate VP Safety and Security, Robert Koverman
VP Campus Environment, Alicia Berg
Vice President of Institutional Advancement, Eric Winston
Treasurer and Trustee, Ralph W. Gidwitz
Vice Chair, Sylvia Neil
Secretary and Trustee, Madeleine Moore Burrell
Executive Assistant Vice President Manager, Sherron Farrell
Vice-President Pan Papacosta, Peter Carpenter
Trustee, Lerone Bennett Jr.
Vice Chair, Richard P. (Dick) Kiphart, age 72
Trustee, Arthur M. Sussman
Trustee, Raymond J. Spencer, age 63
President and Trustee, Warrick L. Carter
Trustee, Robert A. Wislow
Trustee, Andrew Alexander
Trustee, Barry M. Sabloff
Treasurer and Trustee, Ralph W. Gidwitz
Trustee, Lester Coney
Trustee, Steve Devick
Trustee, Susan Downing
Trustee, Georgia Fogelson
Trustee, Sydney Smith Gordon
Trustee, Mary Louise Haddad
Trustee, Chester T. Kamin
Trustee, Pamela Kendall-Rijos
Trustee, Paul R. Knapp
Trustee, Bill Kurtis
Trustee, Averill Leviton
Trustee, Howard Mendelsohn
Vice Chair, Sylvia Neil
Trustee, Madeline Murphy Rabb
Trustee, Arlen Rubin
Trustee, Victor Skrebneski
Trustee, David S. Solomon
Trustee, Helena Chapellin Wilson
Secretary and Trustee, Madeleine Moore Burrell
Auditors: KPMGLLP

LOCATIONS

HQ: COLUMBIA COLLEGE CHICAGO
600 S MICHIGAN AVE FL 5, CHICAGO, IL 60605-1996
Phone: 312-663-1600
Web: WWW.COLUM.EDU

PRODUCTS/OPERATIONS

Selected Schools
School of Fine & Performing Arts
School of Liberal Arts & Sciences
School of Media Arts

HISTORICAL FINANCIALS

Company Type: Private

Income Statement FYE: August 31

	REVENUE ($ mil.)	NET INCOME ($ mil.)	NET PROFIT MARGIN	EMPLOYEES
08/10	244	18	7.6%	1,000
08/09	246	23	9.7%	—
08/09	0	0		—
Annual Growth	—112764.5%		—	—

2010 Year-End Financials

Debt ratio: —
Return on equity: 7.60%
Cash ($ mil.): 32
Current ratio: —
Long-term debt ($ mil.): —
Dividends
Yield: —
Payout: —
Market value ($ mil.): —

COMMAND TRANSPORTATION LLC

LOCATIONS

HQ: COMMAND TRANSPORTATION LLC
7500 FRONTAGE RD, SKOKIE, IL 600773213
Phone: 8472132200
Web: WWW.COMMANDTRANSPORTATION.COM

HISTORICAL FINANCIALS

Company Type: Private

Income Statement FYE: December 31

	REVENUE ($ mil.)	NET INCOME ($ mil.)	NET PROFIT MARGIN	EMPLOYEES
12/13	405	11	2.9%	550
12/12	329	13	4.1%	—
12/08	157	6	3.9%	—
12/07	101	0	—	—
Annual Growth	26.0%	—	—	—

2013 Year-End Financials

Debt ratio: —
Return on equity: 2.90%
Cash ($ mil.): 5
Current ratio: 6.80
Long-term debt ($ mil.): —
Dividends
Yield: —
Payout: —
Market value ($ mil.): —

COMMERCIAL CONTRACTING CORPORATION

LOCATIONS

HQ: COMMERCIAL CONTRACTING CORPORATION
4260 N ATLANTIC BLVD, AUBURN HILLS, MI 483261578
Phone: 2482090500
Web: WWW.CCCNETWORK.COM

HISTORICAL FINANCIALS

Company Type: Private

Income Statement FYE: December 31

	REVENUE ($ mil.)	NET INCOME ($ mil.)	NET PROFIT MARGIN	EMPLOYEES
12/13	253	0	—	300
12/12	253	0	—	—
12/11	0	0	—	—
12/10	0	0	—	—
Annual Growth	—	—	—	—

2013 Year-End Financials

Debt ratio: —
Return on equity: —
Cash ($ mil.): 19
Current ratio: 1.40
Long-term debt ($ mil.): —
Dividends
Yield: —
Payout: —
Market value ($ mil.): —

COMMUNICATIONS WORKERS OF AMERICA AFL-CIO CLC

CWA knows how to get its message across. Communications Workers of America is a labor union representing more than 700000 employees in the communications and media industries. Members work in a variety of sectors including telecommunications journalism publishing manufacturing and customer service. With about 1200 locals across the US Canada and Puerto Rico CWA is one of the most geographically diverse unions. It holds more than 2000 collective bargaining agreements guaranteeing wages benefits and good working conditions for members. The group is affiliated with the AFL-CIO the Canadian Labour Congress and Union Network International.

CWA has regional offices in Atlanta; Austin Texas; Cleveland Ohio; Denver; New York; Philadelphia; San Francisco; and Silver Spring Maryland. Major employers of union members have included AT&T many baby bells General Electric the Canadian Broadcasting Corporation US Airways and the University of California system.

EXECUTIVES

VP District 4, Seth Rosen
EVP, Annie Hill
Auditors: ThomasHaveyLLP

LOCATIONS

HQ: COMMUNICATIONS WORKERS OF AMERICA AFL-CIO CLC
501 3RD ST NW, WASHINGTON, DC 20001-2760
Phone: 202-434-1100
Web: WWW.CWA-UNION.ORG

HISTORICAL FINANCIALS

Company Type: Private

Income Statement FYE: May 31

	REVENUE ($ mil.)	NET INCOME ($ mil.)	NET PROFIT MARGIN	EMPLOYEES
05/11	155	2	1.3%	510
05/10*	156	9	5.9%	—
12/08	176	161	91.4%	—
05/06	182	38	21.1%	—
Annual Growth	(3.2%)	(44.5%)	—	—

*Fiscal year change

2011 Year-End Financials

Debt ratio: —
Return on equity: 1.30%
Cash ($ mil.): 18
Current ratio: 0.10
Long-term debt ($ mil.): —
Dividends
Yield: —
Payout: —
Market value ($ mil.): —

COMMUNITY ASPHALT CORP.

Community Asphalt provides paving services for the road more traveled. The company's services include grading and paving pavement milling surveying excavation on- and off-road hauling drainage utilities base finishing and highway sweeping. It also provides engineering contracting and design/build services; projects include parking lots industrial and retail complexes auto race tracks and airport runways. Formed in 1980 Community Asphalt has three asphalt plants in southeastern Florida. It also operates a limestone quarry and a fleet of dump trucks. In 2006 Community Asphalt and Spain's Obrascon Huarte Lain (OHL) made a stock purchase agreement which gave OHL a controlling interest in the company.

LOCATIONS

HQ: COMMUNITY ASPHALT CORP.
9725 NW 117TH AVE STE 110, MEDLEY, FL 33178-1213
Phone: 305-829-0700
Web: WWW.CACORP.NET

COMPETITORS

Angelo Iafrate
Baker Concrete
Boh Bros Construction
C.W. Matthews
Cherry Hill Construction
Megatran
Oldcastle Materials
The Middlesex Corporation

HISTORICAL FINANCIALS

Company Type: Private

Income Statement FYE: December 31

	REVENUE ($ mil.)	NET INCOME ($ mil.)	NET PROFIT MARGIN	EMPLOYEES
12/12	243	2	1.0%	640
12/11	260	3	1.2%	—
12/10	330	27	8.4%	—
12/09	291	16	5.5%	—
Annual Growth	(5.8%)	(47.1%)	—	—

2012 Year-End Financials

Debt ratio: —
Return on equity: 1.00%
Cash ($ mil.): 56
Current ratio: 1.50
Long-term debt ($ mil.): —
Dividends
Yield: —
Payout: —
Market value ($ mil.): —

COMMUNITY FIRST BANK

LOCATIONS

HQ: COMMUNITY FIRST BANK
200 E RIDGE AVE, HARRISON, AR 726014307
Phone: 8703918000
Web: WWW.COMMUNITYFIRSTBANK.COM

HISTORICAL FINANCIALS

Company Type: Private

Income Statement FYE: December 31

	ASSETS ($ mil.)	NET INCOME ($ mil.)	INCOME AS % OF ASSETS	EMPLOYEES
12/13	461	5	1.3%	150
12/09	561	2	0.5%	—
12/08	513	0	—	—
12/07	485	0	—	—
Annual Growth	(0.8%)	—	—	—

2013 Year-End Financials

Debt ratio: —
Return on equity: 21.60%
Cash ($ mil.): 7
Current ratio: —
Long-term debt ($ mil.): —
Dividends
Yield: —
Payout: —
Market value ($ mil.): —

COMMUNITY HOSPITAL OF ANDERSON AND MADISON COUNTY INCORPORATED

The folks of Madison County Indiana needn't race south to Indianapolis to find medical care. Community Hospital Anderson is an acute care facility with some 200 beds. Departments and services include a sleep analysis lab ECG (electrocardiogram) tests for cardiopulmonary conditions and specialized treatment for cancer and diabetes among other conditions. Community Hospital Anderson operates four intermediate and supervised care facilities in the area. The hospital is part of Community Hospitals of Indiana (also known as Community Health Network) a not-for-profit health care system that serves the health care needs of patients in Indiana.

In addition to the community-based long-term care facilities it operates Community Hospital Anderson has a 30-bed skilled nursing center on its fourth floor.

The hospital specializes in women's care maternity and cancer care services.

LOCATIONS

HQ: COMMUNITY HOSPITAL OF ANDERSON AND MADISON COUNTY INCORPORATED
1515 N MADISON AVE, ANDERSON, IN 46011-3453
Phone: 765-298-4242
Web: WWW.COMMUNITYANDERSON.COM

Facilities
Community Hospital Anderson (Anderson IN)
Community Northview Care Center (Anderson IN)
Community Parkview Care Center (Elwood IN)
Summit Convalescent Center (Summitville IN)
Monticello House (Anderson IN)

COMPETITORS

Daviess Community Hospital
Henry County Memorial Hospital
IU Health
Memorial Hospital & Health System
Memorial Hospital (Logansport)
Riverview Hospital
St. Vincent Health

HISTORICAL FINANCIALS

Company Type: Private

Income Statement FYE: December 31

	REVENUE ($ mil.)	NET INCOME ($ mil.)	NET PROFIT MARGIN	EMPLOYEES
12/12	152	35	23.3%	950
12/09	120	4	3.3%	—
12/06	58	1	2.0%	—
12/06	117	6	5.4%	—
Annual Growth	4.4%	33.3%	—	—

2012 Year-End Financials

Debt ratio: —
Return on equity: 23.30%
Cash ($ mil.): 25
Current ratio: 3.00
Long-term debt ($ mil.): —
Dividends
Yield: —
Payout: —
Market value ($ mil.): —

COMMUNITY HOSPITAL OF THE MONTEREY PENINSULA

Community Hospital of the Monterey Peninsula has a sunny disposition when it comes to medical care. The not-for-profit health care facility provides general medical and surgical services to residents of Monterey California. It has about 235 acute care and skilled nursing beds and offers specialty services including cardiac and cancer care obstetrics orthopedics and rehabilitation. In addition to its main facility the hospital operates several ancillary centers including a mental health clinic an inpatient hospice medical laboratory branches and several outpatient centers offering diagnostic imaging diabetes care and other services. Community Hospital of the Monterey Peninsula was founded in 1934.

Financial Performance

Community Hospital of the Monterey Peninsula reported net operating revenues of some $430 million in 2011 primarily from inpatient and outpatient care services. After operating expenses (including salaries and supplies) the hospital reported about $26 million remaining for facility and service improvements. However providing care for uninsured and under-insured patients continues to drag on the institution's earnings.

Strategy

As health care costs skyrocket in the US Community Hospital of the Monterey Peninsula has worked to lower its expenses. Between 2008 and 2011 the organization lowered annual costs by about $44 million.

To improve care in its service territory the hospital is working to increase best-practice sharing among physicians. It is also supporting information sharing by coordinating electronic health records (EHRs).

EXECUTIVES

Chief of Staff and Trustee, Michael Smith
President CEO, Steven J. Packer
Vice President Medical Affairs, Anthony D. Chavis
VP and CFO, Laura Zehm
VP Nursing, Terrill Lowe
VP, Tim Nylen
Vice President, Cynthia L. Peck
Communication Specialist, Lauren Elsensohn
Director Communication and Marketing, Mary Barker
Chair Board of Trustees, Ian Arnof
Vice Chairman Board of Trustees, Frank C. Amato
Secretary and Trustee, Laurie M. Benjamin
Auxiliary President and Trustee, Rita Echenique
Legal Counsel, Chuck Keller
Vice President Nursing, Terril Lowe
Chief of Staff and Trustee, Michael Smith
President CEO and Trustee, Steven J. Packer
Vice Chairman Board of Trustees, Frank C. Amato
Secretary and Trustee, Laurie M. Benjamin
Auxiliary President and Trustee, Rita Echenique
Trustee, Carsbia Anderson Jr.
Trustee, Ted J. Balestreri
Trustee, Shelley Claudel
Trustee, Stephen M. Dart
Trustee, James J. Didion
Trustee, H. James Griggs
Trustee, Jay Hudson
Trustee, Robert Kavner
Trustee, William W. Lewis
Trustee, Mark Vierra

LOCATIONS

HQ: COMMUNITY HOSPITAL OF THE MONTEREY PENINSULA
23625 HOLMAN HWY, MONTEREY, CA 93940-5902
Phone: 831-624-5311
Web: WWW.CHOMP.ORG

PRODUCTS/OPERATIONS

Selected Services

Bariatric Surgery
Behavioral Health Services
Carol Hatton Breast Care Center
Comprehensive Cancer Center
Diabetes
Diagnostic and Interventional Radiology
Emergency
Family Birth Center
Hospice of the Central Coast
Intermediate Intensive Care Nursery
Laboratory Services
Nutrition Therapy Program
Orthopedics
Outpatient Immunology Services
Outpatient Surgery Center
Pulmonary Wellness Services
Radiation Oncology
Rehabilitation Services
Sleep disorders
Social Services
Stroke Program
Tyler Heart Institute (Cardiac Care)
Westland House Skilled Nursing Facility
Wound Care and Hyperbaric Healing

COMPETITORS

Dignity Health
John Muir Health
Kaiser Permanente
Queen of the Valley Medical Center
Salinas Valley Memorial
Sequoia Healthcare District
Stanford Hospital and Clinics
Sutter Health
The Palo Alto Medical Foundation
UCSF Medical

HISTORICAL FINANCIALS

Company Type: Private

Income Statement FYE: December 31

	REVENUE ($ mil.)	NET INCOME ($ mil.)	NET PROFIT MARGIN	EMPLOYEES
12/12	442	81	18.4%	2,088
12/09	475	26	5.6%	—
12/06	406	32	8.0%	—
12/06	373	59	15.9%	—
Annual Growth	2.9%	5.4%	—	—

2012 Year-End Financials

Debt ratio: ——
Return on equity: 18.40%
Cash ($ mil.): 70
Current ratio: 1.70
Long-term debt ($ mil.): —

Dividends
Yield: —
Payout: —
Market value ($ mil.): —

COMMUNITY HOSPITALS OF INDIANA INC

Community Hospitals of Indiana (aka Community Health Network) has Indianapolis surrounded. The health care system includes about a half a dozen acute-care hospitals all operating under the Community Hospital moniker. One Community Hospital Anderson is located outside the state capital. It also runs the Community Heart and Vascular Hospital. Community Health Network whose origin reaches back to the 1950s has a total of about 1080 staffed beds and 1400-plus physicians. The network also includes more than 100 community care sites including physician practices community clinics surgery centers occupational health facilities a rehabilitation center and home health practices.

Operations

Together with its clinics health pavilions surgery centers and physician affiliations Community Health Network's service area covers an eight-county area in central Indiana. Various specialty centers treat digestive and joint ailments wounds spinal problems and gastrointestinal disease and also provide imaging services. Community's MedCheck clinics offer routine checkups and screenings in stand-alone locations while its MedCheck Express locations inside area Wal-Mart stores serve customers where they shop. Four Wellspring pharmacies all but one of which are located inside hospitals cover prescriptions patient education and wellness programs.

Among the system's notable features the Community Heart and Vascular Hospital (formerly Indiana Heart Hospital) which opened its doors in 2003 is an all-digital facility with digital equipment and wireless communications systems linking all its operations. Additionally the 42-bed neonatal intensive care room at Community Hospital North is one of the nation's largest labor delivery recovery and postpartum units and Westview Hospital is the state's only such facility offering osteopathic services.

Strategy

The health network is expanding in and around Indianapolis. In 2012 Community Healthcare Network (CHN) partnered with Johnson Memorial Hospital to build a $14 million70000-square-foot three-story medical facility Stones Crossing Health Pavilion which will house many outpatient services. The pavilion will also offer primary and specialty care physicians rehab and sports medicine services (including adult and pediatric rehabilitation) and lab services. The facility is scheduled to open in the summer of 2013. In 2011 CHN partnered with Centerre Healthcare of Nashville Tennessee to build a $23 million inpatient rehabilitation hospital in northeast Indianapolis. The new 63000-square-foot 60-bed facility is designed to serve the medical rehabilitation needs of neurological stroke and traumatic injury patients. Community's inpatient rehabilitation program Hook Rehabilitation will move its services and staff to the new rehabilitation hospital closing the unit located within Community Hospital East. The move will allow Community East to streamline operations and focus on its core services: emergency care cardiovascular and stroke care surgical services and the Center for Joint Health. The hospital is expected to open by mid-2013.

EXECUTIVES

President and CEO Community Health Network, William E. (Bill) Corley, age 71
President and CEO Community Hospital Anderson, William C. (Bill) VanNess II
President CEO of the network, Bryan A. Mills
Network VP Human Resources, Jill Parris
President and CEO, Michael C. (Mike) Blanchet
President Community Hospital North, Barbara (Barb) Summers
Network VP Legal Services and General Counsel, Karen Ann P. Lloyd
CIO Community Health Network, Ed Koschka
Network VP Ambulatory Development, Jon Fohrer
Network VP and CFO, Thomas P. Fischer
CEO Community Physicians of Indiana, Timothy L. Hobbs
Chief Nursing Officer, Janet M. Bingle
CEO Community Heart and Vascular, Thomas A. Malasto
Chief Medical Officer Community Health Network, Clif Knight
CEO Community Home Health Services, Jessie Westlund
President Community Hospital East, Robin Ledyard
President Community Hospital South, Anthony Lennen
President Chief Executive Officer, Beth Tharp
Network Purchasing Director, Kennon J. Thomas
Vice President, Kerry Sawin
Chief Information Officer, Ron Strachan

LOCATIONS

HQ: COMMUNITY HOSPITALS OF INDIANA INC
1500 N RITTER AVE, INDIANAPOLIS, IN 46219-3027
Phone: 317-355-1411
Web: WWW.ECOMMUNITY.COM

PRODUCTS/OPERATIONS

Selected Facilities and Affiliates

Community Health Pavilions
Community Heart and Vascular Hospital
Community Hospital Anderson
Community Hospital East
Community Hospital North
Community Hospital South
Community Imaging Centers
Community Physicians of Indiana network
Community Spine Center
Community Westview Hospital
Hook Rehabilitation Center
Indiana Surgery Centers
Indianapolis Endoscopy Center
MedCheck walk-in clinics
MedCheck Express clinics
Wellspring Pharmacy chain

COMPETITORS

Ball Memorial Hospital
Henry County Memorial Hospital
IU Health
IU Health Bloomington Hospital
Memorial Hospital (Logansport)
Riverview Hospital
St. Elizabeth Regional Health
St. Vincent Health
Wabash County Hospital

HISTORICAL FINANCIALS

Company Type: Private

Income Statement FYE: December 31

	REVENUE ($ mil.)	NET INCOME ($ mil.)	NET PROFIT MARGIN	EMPLOYEES
12/12	384	44	11.7%	5,000
12/09	679	35	5.2%	—
12/06	337	(89)	—	—
12/06	1,089	83	7.6%	—
Annual Growth	(15.9%)	(9.8%)	—	—

2012 Year-End Financials

Debt ratio: —
Return on equity: 11.70%
Cash ($ mil.): 76
Current ratio: 0.20
Long-term debt ($ mil.): —
Dividends
Yield: —
Payout: —
Market value ($ mil.): —

COMMUNITY INITIATIVES DEVELOPMENT CORPORATION

LOCATIONS

HQ: COMMUNITY INITIATIVES DEVELOPMENT CORPORATION
15375 BLUE FISH CIR, LAKEWOOD RANCH, FL 342025809
Phone: 9417561500

HISTORICAL FINANCIALS

Company Type: Private

Income Statement FYE: December 31

	ASSETS ($ mil.)	NET INCOME ($ mil.)	INCOME AS % OF ASSETS	EMPLOYEES
12/13	332	(13)	—	4
12/11	363	(14)	—	—
12/10	378	13	3.7%	—
12/08	323	0	—	—
Annual Growth	0.6%	—	—	—

2013 Year-End Financials

Debt ratio: —
Return on equity: (-108.90%)
Cash ($ mil.): 10
Current ratio: —
Long-term debt ($ mil.): —
Dividends
Yield: —
Payout: —
Market value ($ mil.): —

COMMUNITY UNIT SCHOOL DISTRICT 303

LOCATIONS

HQ: COMMUNITY UNIT SCHOOL DISTRICT 303
201 S 7TH ST, SAINT CHARLES, IL 601742664
Phone: 6305133030
Web: WWW.D303.ORG

HISTORICAL FINANCIALS

Company Type: Private

Income Statement FYE: June 30

	REVENUE ($ mil.)	NET INCOME ($ mil.)	NET PROFIT MARGIN	EMPLOYEES
06/13	215	18	8.4%	2,000
06/04	132	(3)	—	—
Annual Growth	5.5%	—	—	—

CONCORD HOSPITAL INC.

Concord Hospital is agreeably an acute care regional hospital serving central New Hampshire. The hospital has some 300 licensed beds and provides general inpatient and outpatient medical care as well as specialist centers for cardiology orthopedics cancer care urology and women's health. Concord Hospital operates other medical facilities either on its main campus or nearby including surgery imaging diagnostic hospice and rehabilitation facilities as well as physician practice locations. With roots reaching back to 1884 Concord Hospital is part of the Capital Region Health Care system which also offers mental health and home health care services.

Geographic Reach

Concord Hospital is located on a 110-acre campus in Concord New Hampshire. It provides services in area communities including Allenstown Andover Barnstead Boscawen Bow Bradford Canterbury Chichester Deering Dunbarton Epsom Henniker Hillsboro Hopkinton Loudon Northwood Pembroke Pittsfield Salsibury Warner Washington Weare Webster and Windsor.

Operations

With a staff of some 350 doctors Concord Hospital sees about 18000 patients performs more than 9000 surgeries and handles 67000 emergency room visits and 1300 births each year. The hospital provides services in about 40 specialty medical fields.

As part of Capital Region Health Care Concord Hospital shares education purchasing and outpatient service functions (and expenses) with its network sister entities which include the Concord Regional Visiting Nurse Association and the Riverbend Community Mental Health center. Through Capital Regional Health Care Concord Hospital also has affiliations with area organizations including Dartmouth-Hitchcock Medical Center Concord Ambulatory Center and Concord Imaging Center.

Concord Hospital is also part of collaborative network the Granite Healthcare Network (formed in 2011) with four regional New Hampshire health care providers: Elliot Health System (which operates the Elliot Hospital) LRGHealthcare (consisting of Lakes Region General Hospital and Franklin Regional Hospital) Southern New Hampshire Health System (operating the Southern New Hampshire Medical Center) and Wentworth-Douglass Hospital. Hospitals in the network remain independently managed and owned and have the option to participate or not participate in each of the group efforts.

Financial Performance

Annual operating revenues increased 1% to some $487 million due to higher net patient revenues and other operating earnings. Concord Hospital spent about $38 million that year on community care efforts including charity medical care for low-income and uninsured patients.

After a financially challenging year in 2010 (due to changes in state tax regulations for hospitals) Concord Hospital's cost-control and improvement efforts helped increase profits to some $27 million in 2011 (up more than 80% from 2010). However profits fell 26% to $20 million in 2012 due to increased expenses related to employee supply and service expenses.

Strategy

To help control the spiraling costs of medical care in the US as well as to meet health reform mandates Concord and its affiliated facilities are launching programs to share technology and administrative resources such as claims management software data storage linen service liability insurance pooling and Medicare patient management.

Concord Hospital has also launched independent initiatives to improve quality and patient safety programs including putting infection reduction protocols in place consolidating electronic health record (EHR) consolidation efforts and enacting medication management practices.

EXECUTIVES

President CEO, Michael B. Green
SVP Medical Affairs and Chief Medical Officer, David F. Green
SVP and COO, Joe Conley
Senior Vice President CFO, Bruce Burns
CIO, Deane Morrison
Vice President Operations & CNO, Diane E. Wood Allen
Vice President finance, Scott Sloane
Vice President operations, Kevin McCarthy
Vice President Physician Services, Marjo Mitchell
Vice President Community Affairs, Pamela Puleo
Vice President operations, Kristine Terrio
Vice President operations, James Thorne
Vice Chair, D. Thomas Akey
Secretary and Trustee, Mary E. Boucher
Chair, Christian Hallowell
Chief Human Resources Officer, Robin Moore
Vice President Facilities, Domenic Ciavarro
Vice President Behavioral, Louis Josephson
VP Acute Care Nursing, Jean Ten Haken
Chief Medical Information Officer, Joel Berman
Public Affairs and Marketing Coordinator, Andy Morse
Trustee; President Medical Staff, Stephen Imgrund
President, Gregory Thesing
Secretary and Treasurer Medical Staff, Lisa Atkinson
Director Public Affairs, Jennifer M. Dearborn
Trustee, Michelle L. Chicoine, age 57
Trustee, Philip Boulter
Trustee, James D. Cook
President CEO and ex officio Trustee, Michael B. Green
SVP CFO and ex officio Trustee, Bruce Burns
VP Operations Chief Nursing Officer and Trustee, Diane E. Wood Allen
Trustee, Jeffrey J. Zellers
Trustee, Rachel M. Rowe
Trustee, Jill K. Blackmer
Vice Chair, D. Thomas Akey
Secretary and Trustee, Mary E. Boucher
Trustee, C. Thomas Brown
Trustee, Gary S. Jones
Trustee, Jeffrey S. Kipperman
Trustee, Rt. Hon. Michael F. Sullivan
Trustee, Claudia Walker
Trustee, David Ruedig
Trustee, Muriel D. Schadee
Trustee, David A. Stevenson
Trustee, Sol Asmar
Trustee; President Medical Staff, Stephen Imgrund
Auditors: BakerNewman&Noyes

LOCATIONS

HQ: CONCORD HOSPITAL INC.
250 PLEASANT ST, CONCORD, NH 03301-2598
Phone: 603-227-7000
Web: WWW.CONCORDHOSPITAL.ORG

PRODUCTS/OPERATIONS

Selected Services

Ambulatory Care Center
Behavioral Health
Breast Care Center
Cancer
Cardiac
Center for Health Promotion
Child Life
Clinical Decision Unit
Day Surgery Center
Diabetes Self-Management Education
Concord Hospital Medical Group
Emergency Services
End Of Life
Family Health Centers
Infectious Disease
Intensive Care
Laboratory Services
Maternity
Neurology
Occupational Health
Orthopedics
Pediatrics
Primary Care
Radiology
Rehabilitation
Sleep Center
Surgery
Urology
Walk-in Urgent Care
Women' s Health
Wound Care

COMPETITORS

Cambridge Health Alliance
Catholic Medical Center
Elliot Health System
Exeter Health Resources
Frisbie Memorial Hospital
HCA
Partners HealthCare
Southern New Hampshire Medical Center
Steward Health Care

HISTORICAL FINANCIALS

Company Type: Private

Income Statement FYE: September 30

	REVENUE ($ mil.)	NET INCOME ($ mil.)	NET PROFIT MARGIN	EMPLOYEES
09/11	442	(9)	—	2,000
09/10	369	18	5.1%	—
09/09	349	0	—	—
09/08	331	16	4.9%	—
Annual Growth	10.1%	—	—	—

2011 Year-End Financials

Debt ratio: —
Return on equity: (-2.10%)
Cash ($ mil.): 8
Current ratio: 0.80
Long-term debt ($ mil.): —
Dividends
Yield: —
Payout: —
Market value ($ mil.): —

CONESTOGA BANK

LOCATIONS

HQ: CONESTOGA BANK
165 POTTSTOWN PIKE, CHESTER SPRINGS, PA 194259518
Phone: 6103216900
Web: WWW.CONESTOGABANK.COM

HISTORICAL FINANCIALS

Company Type: Private

Income Statement FYE: December 31

	ASSETS ($ mil.)	NET INCOME ($ mil.)	INCOME AS % OF ASSETS	EMPLOYEES
12/09	609	56	9.3%	309
12/08	703	4	0.6%	—
12/07	686	3	0.5%	—
Annual Growth	(5.8%)	296.2%	—	—

2009 Year-End Financials

Debt ratio: —
Return on equity: 170.20%
Cash ($ mil.): 55
Current ratio: —
Long-term debt ($ mil.): —
Dividends
Yield: —
Payout: —
Market value ($ mil.): —

CONNECTICUT CHILDREN'S MEDICAL CENTER

When their tiny tykes need some TLC Nutmeg Staters turn to Connecticut Children's Medical Center (CCMC). The 190-bed children's hospital is located on two campuses and provides a variety of pediatric services including surgery behavioral care and emergency medicine. Its facilities house pediatric trauma and intensive care units that receives referral patients from hospitals throughout the region. The medical center also conducts clinical research and provides pediatric training to health professionals. In addition CCMC operates outpatient facilities throughout Connecticut and a school for children with physical and behavioral challenges.

Geographic Reach

CCMC operates about 20 locations across Connecticut and portions of Massachusetts. Its main hospital campus is in Hartford while its secondary acute care center is in Waterbury (on the campus of Saint Mary's Hospital). Other locations include ambulatory surgery specialty care and general pediatric care offices.

Operations

At its main campus CCMC employs 1100 medical professionals practicing in more than 30 specialty care fields. The hospital handles about 7000 inpatient admissions more than 50000 emergency department visits and 11000 surgeries. The medical center also operates the Faculty Practice Plan an integrated full-service multi-specialty pediatric practice providing care to children and their families. The practice employs about 170 physicians and mid-level practitioners.

Founded in 1996 CCMC is the only academic medical center dedicated exclusively to pediatric care in western New England making it a popular destination for medical training and research program participants. As the primary teaching facility for the University of Connecticut School of Medicine's Department of Pediatrics the hospital is home to a number of clinical research and physician training programs including several two-year fellowships in pediatric subspecialties and a three-year fellowship in pediatric emergency medicine. Other hospital divisions conduct clinical trials in fields including oncology hematology endocrinology gastroenterology and infectious disease.

Strategy

CCMC grows by expanding its facilities and its range of patient services. It also strives to expand its services into new territories in southern New England including through partnerships with other area health care providers. In addition the medical center is working to increase its participation in basic and clinical research programs.

EXECUTIVES

Vice President Connecticut Childrens Medical Center Foundation, Elizabeth A. (Betsy) Rudden

Director Corporate Communications, Robert J. (Bob) Fraleigh
Treasurer, Gerald J. Boisvert Jr.
Executive Vice President Community Child, Paul H. Dworkin
Executive Vice President Chief Operating Officer, Theresa Hendricksen
Senior Vice President General Counsel, Ann Taylor
President Chief Executive Officer, Martin J. (Marty) Gavin
President Connecticut Childrens Medical Center Foundation, Martha E. Schall
Assistant Operations Manager, Linda Sogofsky
Vice President Strategic Planning, Thomas C. Richardson
Vice President Chief Human Resources Officer, Lawrence Milan
Senior Vice President Strategic Planning, Dean Rapoza
Vice President Clinical Services and Chief Nursing Officer, Cheryl Hoey
Treasurer, Gerald J. Boisvert Jr.
President Chief Executive Officer, Martin J. (Marty) Gavin

LOCATIONS

HQ: CONNECTICUT CHILDREN' S MEDICAL CENTER
282 WASHINGTON ST, HARTFORD, CT 06106-3322
Phone: 860-545-9000
Web: WWW.CONNECTICUTCHILDRENS.ORG

COMPETITORS

Backus
Baystate Health
Baystate Medical Center
Bridgeport Hospital
Bristol Hospital
Day Kimball Hospital
Griffin Health
Harrington Memorial Hospital
Hartford Health Care
Lawrence & Memorial Hospital
MidState Medical Center
New Milford Hospital
Saint Francis Hospital and Medical Center
St. Vincent' s Health Services
Yale-New Haven Hospital
Yale-New Haven Hospital Saint Raphael Campus

HISTORICAL FINANCIALS

Company Type: Private

Income Statement FYE: September 30

	REVENUE ($ mil.)	NET INCOME ($ mil.)	NET PROFIT MARGIN	EMPLOYEES
09/11	267	(2)	—	1,117
09/10	210	10	4.8%	—
09/09	192	6	3.6%	—
09/08	187	5	2.7%	—
Annual Growth	12.7%	—	—	—

2011 Year-End Financials

Debt ratio: —
Return on equity: (-0.90%)
Cash ($ mil.): 4
Current ratio: 0.60
Long-term debt ($ mil.): —
Dividends
Yield: —
Payout: —
Market value ($ mil.): —

CONNECTICUT STATE UNIVERSITY SYSTEM

EXECUTIVES

Vice Chancellor Finance and Administration and CFO, Pamela J. (Pam) Kedderis
Chief of Staff, Yvette Melendez
Senior Vice Chancellor Academic and Student Affairs, Louise H. Feroe
President Eastern Connecticut State University, Elsa Nu?ez
Associate Executive Officer Assessment and Learning, German Bermudez
Assistant Director Project Management and Engineering, Gerald Cotter
Interim Chief Financial Officer, Jim Howarth
Director Purchasing and Contract Compliance, Gary Ritchey
Contract Compliance Officer, Theresa O'Brien
Assistant Vice Chancellor Finance and Administration, Trevor Thorington
Director Accounting and Finance, Raymond Yirga
Manager Human Resources, Ellen Mantel
Director Telecommunications, William Aust Jr.
Director Technical Services, Richard Ellis
Manager Systems, Victor Semaska
Chancellor, David G. Carter Sr.
Associate Vice Chancellor Governmental Affairs and Communications, Jill E. Ferraiolo
Associate Vice Chancellor Strategic Planning Institutional Research Market Research and Analysis, William Gammell
Associate Vice Chancellor Human Resource and Labor Relations, David Trainor
Director Information Systems Applications, Scott Zak
Associate Executive Officer Information Technology, Debora Romano-Connors
President Central Connecticut State University, John W. (Jack) Miller
President Southern Connecticut State University, Cheryl J. Norton
President Western Connecticut State University, James W. (Jim) Schmotter, age 66
CIO, George Kahkedjian
Assistant Vice Chancellor Planning and Technical Services, Keith Epstein
Vice President for Real Estate, Cheryl Dahlman
Interim President of the Board of Regents, Philip E. Austin
Auditors: PricewaterhouseCoopersLLP

LOCATIONS

HQ: CONNECTICUT STATE UNIVERSITY SYSTEM
39 WOODLAND ST, HARTFORD, CT 061052337
Phone: 8604930000
Web: WWW.CT.EDU

HISTORICAL FINANCIALS

Company Type: Private

Income Statement FYE: June 30

	REVENUE ($ mil.)	NET INCOME ($ mil.)	NET PROFIT MARGIN	EMPLOYEES
06/11	428	55	13.0%	2,800
06/10	413	22	5.5%	—
Annual Growth	3.6%	143.9%	—	—

2011 Year-End Financials

Debt ratio: —
Return on equity: 13.00%
Cash ($ mil.): 176
Current ratio: 1.20
Long-term debt ($ mil.): —
Dividends
Yield: —
Payout: —
Market value ($ mil.): —

CONNEXUS ENERGY

EXECUTIVES

President and CEO, Mike Rajala
Vice Chair, Jim Leroux
Chair, Peter Wojciechowski
Secretary Treasurer and Director, Fran Bator
Assistant Secretary Assistant Treasurer and Director, Ken Fiereck
Communications Specialist, Samantha Neral
Vice Chair, Jim Leroux
Secretary Treasurer and Director, Fran Bator
Director, Jay Cain
Director, Derald Ewing
Director, Don Holl
Director, Don Jacobson
Director, Laurie Kerr
Director, Mark Ethen
Assistant Secretary Assistant Treasurer and Director, Ken Fiereck

LOCATIONS

HQ: CONNEXUS ENERGY
14601 RAMSEY BLVD NW, RAMSEY, MN 553036775
Phone: 7633232600
Web: WWW.CONNEXUSENERGY.COM

PRODUCTS/OPERATIONS

2012 Sales

Residential	51
Sales for resale	13
Other	1

COMPETITORS

ALLETE
Dakota Electric
Otter Tail

HISTORICAL FINANCIALS

Company Type: Private

Income Statement FYE: December 31

	REVENUE ($ mil.)	NET INCOME ($ mil.)	NET PROFIT MARGIN	EMPLOYEES
12/13	258	0	—	250
12/10	211	8	4.1%	—
12/09	213	11	5.4%	—
12/08	1,544	0	—	—
Annual Growth	(30.1%)	—	—	—

2013 Year-End Financials

Debt ratio: —
Return on equity: —
Cash ($ mil.): 0
Current ratio: 1.90
Long-term debt ($ mil.): —
Dividends
Yield: —
Payout: —
Market value ($ mil.): —

CONNOR CO.

EXECUTIVES

President, Warren P. Collins

LOCATIONS

HQ: CONNOR CO.
2800 NE ADAMS ST, PEORIA, IL 616032806
Phone: 3096937229
Web: WWW.CONNORCO.COM

COMPETITORS

Ferguson Enterprises
HD Supply
Lowe' s

HISTORICAL FINANCIALS

Company Type: Private

Income Statement FYE: December 31

	REVENUE ($ mil.)	NET INCOME ($ mil.)	NET PROFIT MARGIN	EMPLOYEES
12/07	109	6	5.8%	230
12/06	105	6	6.5%	—
12/05	100	4	4.8%	—
12/04	91	0	—	—
Annual Growth	6.2%	—	—	—

2007 Year-End Financials

Debt ratio: —
Return on equity: 5.80%
Cash ($ mil.): 6
Current ratio: 1.50
Long-term debt ($ mil.): —
Dividends
Yield: —
Payout: —
Market value ($ mil.): —

CONSERV FS INC.

LOCATIONS

HQ: CONSERV FS INC.
1110 MCCONNELL RD, WOODSTOCK, IL 600987310
Phone: 8153345950
Web: WWW.HOME.CONSERVFS.COM

HISTORICAL FINANCIALS

Company Type: Private

Income Statement FYE: August 31

	REVENUE ($ mil.)	NET INCOME ($ mil.)	NET PROFIT MARGIN	EMPLOYEES
08/14	241	8	3.6%	140
08/13	221	7	3.2%	—
08/12	221	4	1.9%	—
08/11	188	0	—	—
Annual Growth	8.6%	—	—	—

2014 Year-End Financials

Debt ratio: —
Return on equity: 3.60%
Cash ($ mil.): 2
Current ratio: 1.00
Long-term debt ($ mil.): —
Dividends
Yield: —
Payout: —
Market value ($ mil.): —

CONSIGLI CONSTRUCTION CO INC.

LOCATIONS

HQ: CONSIGLI CONSTRUCTION CO INC.
72 SUMNER ST, MILFORD, MA 017571663
Phone: 5084732580
Web: WWW.CONSIGLI.COM

HISTORICAL FINANCIALS

Company Type: Private

Income Statement FYE: December 31

	REVENUE ($ mil.)	NET INCOME ($ mil.)	NET PROFIT MARGIN	EMPLOYEES
12/12	616	34	5.6%	390
12/11	297	12	4.3%	—
12/10	0	0	—	—
12/09	297	0	—	—
Annual Growth	27.5%	—	—	—

2012 Year-End Financials

Debt ratio: —
Return on equity: 5.60%
Cash ($ mil.): 29
Current ratio: 0.20
Long-term debt ($ mil.): —
Dividends
Yield: —
Payout: —
Market value ($ mil.): —

CONSOLIDATED PIPE & SUPPLY COMPANY INC.

Consolidated Pipe and Supply lives up to its name: Its nine divisions supply pipe and pipeline materials to a swath of industries from energy to water and waste treatment chemical mining nuclear oil and gas and pulp and paper. Its industrial unit specializes in carbon and stainless alloy pipe valves and fittings. Vulcan makes all types of PVC. Corrosion resistant coatings are offered by a Line Pipe and Tubular unit and liquid applied coatings by Specialty Coatings. Its Consolidated Power Supply is the largest in the business of safety related metallic materials for commercial nuclear generation. Another unit caters to utilities. Consolidated also provides engineering services and inventory systems.

Geographic Reach

The company's reach extends to 19 US states including Alabama Arkansas Florida Georgia Illinois Indiana Kentucky Missouri Mississippi North Carolina Pennsylvania South Carolina Tennessee Texas and Virginia. It has nearly 50 sales offices in 15 states.

Operations

Consolidated Pipe and Supply is one of nearly 20 US Steel distributors authorized to sell seamless and electric resistance welded products in North America. Not limited to its branch and sales centers Consolidated Pipe and Supply's fitted semitrailers complete with area row and bin and bar coded shelving serve as mobile warehouses for construction customers requiring on-site materials management.

The company operates through nine divisions: Industrial Line Pipe Structural Pipeline Coatings Utility Products Specialty Coatings Consolidated Power Vulcan Plastics and Consolidated Controls.

EXECUTIVES

President, Howard J. Kerr
Secretary, Barry D. Howton

LOCATIONS

HQ: CONSOLIDATED PIPE & SUPPLY COMPANY INC.
1205 HILLTOP PKWY, BIRMINGHAM, AL 35204-5002
Phone: 205-323-7261
Web: WWW.CONSOLIDATEDPIPE.COM

PRODUCTS/OPERATIONS

Selected Industries Served

Chemical
Energy
Mining
Nuclear Generation
Oil and Gas
Petro-Chemical
Pulp and Paper
Water and Waste Treatment

Selected Divisions

Consolidated Controls (valves)
Consolidated Power (provides materials to energy industries)
Industrial (provides materials construction commercial energy pulp and paper chemical petro-chemical mining and fabrication industries)
Line Pipe (line pipe and tubular products)
Pipeline Coatings
Specialty Coatings (specialty linings for use in jet fuel and military applications)
Structural (1/8" through 48" structural and prime grades of carbon steel pipe)
Utility Products (provides utilities with products such as steel ductile iron PVC polyethylene and brass fittings and valves and steel PVC and polyethylene pipe)
Vulcan Plastics (water and sewer pipe)

COMPETITORS

American Cast Iron Pipe
Bristol Metals
Bull Moose Tube
Chicago Tube & Iron
Kelly Pipe Co. LLC
Phoenix Tube
Seymour Tubing
Southland Tube
Steel Ventures
U.S. Pipe

HISTORICAL FINANCIALS

Company Type: Private

Income Statement FYE: December 31

	REVENUE ($ mil.)	NET INCOME ($ mil.)	NET PROFIT MARGIN	EMPLOYEES
12/08	607	53	8.7%	700
12/05	387	20	5.3%	—
12/05	0	0	—	—
Annual Growth	—	—	—	—

2008 Year-End Financials

Debt ratio: —
Return on equity: 8.70%
Cash ($ mil.): 0
Current ratio: 0.80
Long-term debt ($ mil.): —
Dividends
Yield: —
Payout: —
Market value ($ mil.): —

CONSUMER PRODUCT DISTRIBUTORS INC.

Consumer Product Distributors helps convenience stores provide convenient services to their customers. The company which operates as J. Polep Distribution Services is a leading wholesale supplier serving more than 4000 convenience retailers in New York Pennsylvania and the New England states. J. Polep distributes a variety of products including cigarettes and other tobacco items candy dairy products frozen foods snack items and general merchandise as well as alcohol and other beverages. As part of its business J. Polep provides merchandising sales and marketing and technology services. The family-owned company was founded as Polep Tobacco in 1898 by Charles Polep.

Geographic Reach

The distribution company serves chain and independent retailers in six New England states as well as New York and Pennsylvania. Its distribution centers are located in Massachusetts Rhode Island and Connecticut.

Operations

Consumer Product Distributors ranks as one of the nation's top 12 convenience store distributors. To support its operations the company supplies customers with products through distribution centers located in Massachusetts (in Chicopee and Woburn) in Rhode Island (in Providence) and in Connecticut (in West Haven).

Mergers and Acquisitions

Company subsidiary Rachael's Food Corporation based in Chicopee Massachusetts entered the meat manufacturing business in late 2012 when the company acquired 122-year-old family-owned Grote and Weigel a hot dog and meat processor based in Bloomfield Connecticut. Soon after Rachael's Food Corporation also purchased family-owned meat processor Mucke's and transferred its operations to the Grote and Weigel unit. The 2012 purchases followed the company's acquisition of Springfield Smoked Fish. The food corporation's facilities are USDA-inspected and HACCP-certified.

EXECUTIVES

President, Jeffrey M. (Jeff) Polep

VP and Manager Information Systems and Technology, Paul Marusek

Vice President Chief Financial Officer, Bill Fitzsimmons

VP Human Resources, Stephen (Steve) Martin

LOCATIONS

HQ: CONSUMER PRODUCT DISTRIBUTORS INC.
705 MEADOW ST, CHICOPEE, MA 01013-4820

Phone: 413-592-4141

Web: WWW.JPOLEP.COM

PRODUCTS/OPERATIONS

Selected Products

Alcohol
- Spirits
- Wine

Automotive
- Branded Motor Oils
- Mag 1
- Additives
- Cleaning Supplies

Bakery/Pastry
- Rachael' s Gourmet
- Mrs. Freshley' s
- Dolly Madison
- Bon Appetite
- Bellow' s House
- Diana' s
- Table Talk

Beverages
- Poland Springs (Nestle Waters)
- Adirondack Soda
- Arizona
- Florida' s Natural
- Simply Juices
- Sweet Leaf Tea
- Trade Winds
- Daily Juice

Selected Services

Credit & Return Policy
Management Information Systems
Merchandising Support
Sales and Marketing Support

COMPETITORS

Atlantic Dominion
C&S Wholesale
Core-Mark
Eby-Brown
H. T. Hackney
Harold Levinson
McLane
Nash-Finch
SUPERVALU
Tripifoods

HISTORICAL FINANCIALS

Company Type: Private

Income Statement FYE: September 29

	REVENUE ($ mil.)	NET INCOME ($ mil.)	NET PROFIT MARGIN	EMPLOYEES
09/12*	804	3	0.4%	400
10/11	778	3	0.5%	—
10/10	736	3	0.5%	—
09/08	575	3	0.6%	—
Annual Growth	8.8%	(0.8%)	—	—

*Fiscal year change

2012 Year-End Financials

Debt ratio: —
Return on equity: 0.40%
Cash ($ mil.): 0
Current ratio: 0.70
Long-term debt ($ mil.): —
Dividends
Yield: —
Payout: —
Market value ($ mil.): —

CONSUMERS UNION OF UNITED STATES INC

Consumers Union of United States (CU) inspires both trust and fear. Best known for publishing Consumer Reports magazine the independent not-for-profit organization also serves as a consumer watchdog through other print publications and the Web (ConsumerReports.org). Its subscription site rates products ranging from candy bars to cars. CU tests and rates thousands of products annually through its National Testing and Research Center. CU accepts no advertising and derives income from the sale of Consumer Reports and other services and from non-commercial contributions grants and fees. CU traces its roots to 1926 when engineer Frederick Schlink organized a "consumer club" to rate products.

Geographic Reach

CU's magazines websites and newsletters have a combined subscription base of more than 8 million.

At its headquarters in Yonkers New York CU houses the Testing and Research Center which consists of 50 labs and offices. The organization also has an Auto Test Center in Connecticut; and three advocacy offices in Washington DC; Austin Texas; and San Francisco California.

Operations

CU testifies before legislative and regulatory entities and files lawsuits on behalf of consumers. The organization is governed by an 18-member board. Board members are elected by CU members and meet three times a year.

Sales and Marketing

The company's major industry markets include energy health care media and safety.

Financial Performance

CU reported revenue of $253.19 million in fiscal 2012 which was a slight increase compared to the previous year due to increased subscription newsstand and other products sales.

Strategy

To preserve its independence CU does not permit its ratings or comments to be used commercially.

In addition to its Consumer Reports publication CU publishes ShopSmart a magazine aimed at women who want a quick read on consumer items such as food beauty products and home and yard products. CU also covers health information through its ConsumerReportsHealth.org website and the Consumer Reports Health Ratings Center. It has a presence in the blogging world with Consumerist.com which provides snarky coverage of retail markups and shopper complaints. Rounding out its portfolio of offerings the organization delivers ratings of product categories to smart phones via its Consumer Reports Mobile service.

CU implemented cost-cutting measures in 2012 in order to reduce operating losses and position the organization for a return to operating profitability.

HISTORY

In 1926 engineer Frederick Schlink organized a "consumer club" (in White Plains New York) which distributed lists of recommended and non-recommended products. The lists led to the founding of Consumers' Research and a magazine devoted to testing products.

Schlink moved the group to Washington New Jersey in 1933. In 1935 three employees formed a union. Schlink fired them. Faced with another strike that year Schlink accused the strikers of being "Red" and responded with strikebreakers and armed detectives. The next year the strikers set up their own organization the Consumers Union of United States (CU).

CU's first magazine Consumers Union Reports came out three months later and rated products that the fledgling organization could afford to test such as soap and breakfast cereals. Subsequent issues focused on food and drug regulation and working conditions for women in textile mills.

The organization drew the wrath of both Reader's Digest and Good Housekeeping (which accused it in 1939 of prolonging the Depression). The next year the House Un-American Activities Committee put CU on its list of suspect organizations. CU cut staff and dropped "Union" from its magazine title but circulation remained low until after WWII.

By 1950 however Americans began consuming again helping to boost circulation to almost 400000. During the 1950s CU published a series of reports on the health hazards of smoking.

In 1960 CU helped found the International Organization of Consumers Unions (now Consumers International) to foster the consumer movement worldwide. Rhoda Karpatkin was hired as publisher in 1974. During the 1970s CU established consumer advocacy offices in California Texas and Washington DC.

Recession and an increase in not-for-profit mailing rates caused the organization to lose money in the early 1980s. CU looked to its readers who donated more than $3 million. The organization was hit by a 13-week strike in 1984 by union members calling for more say in management.

In 1996 CU slapped "not acceptable" ratings on the Isuzu Trooper and the Acura SLX. The next year the National Highway Traffic Safety Administration declared that CU's testing procedure of the Trooper was flawed but CU stood by its tests of the vehicle.

CU hit another bump in 1998 when it was compelled to retract a story on the nutritional value of Iams and Eukanuba pet food. Admitting its test results were incorrect CU's retraction of the story was something of a rarity –its last retraction had occurred almost 20 years earlier when the organization retracted a story on condoms.

A legal dispute broke out in 1999 between CU and automakers Isuzu and Suzuki which claimed negative reviews by Consumer Reports constituted defamation. The following year a jury found CU guilty of falsely reporting on the Isuzu but declined to impose fines on the publisher. (Suzuki eventually settled its case out of court in 2004.)

Karpatkin announced she would step down as president in 2001 and was replaced by chairman

James Guest. That same year CU agreed to license its content to Internet portal Yahoo! Retailer Sharper Image (later TSIC) sued CU over an article unflattering to the company's popular air purifier device but a judge threw out the suit in late 2004.

In 2006 CU launched ShopSmart a shopping magazine geared at women aged 30 to 45. The next year it launched ConsumerReportsHealth.org and the Consumer Reports Health Ratings Center. In 2009 the company entered the blogging world with Consumerist.com which it purchased from Gawker Media.

The following year it introduced its Consumer Reports Mobile service which delivers product ratings to cell phones. Feats for CU in 2010 include discoveries of a potential safety hazard of Toyota's Lexus GX460 and a signal-loss problem with Apple's phone 4 which resulted in a recall from Toyota and Apple's announcement of a free remedy.

EXECUTIVES

Svp Information Products, John J Sateja
Vice President For External Affairs And Information Services, Elizabeth Imholz
President and CEO, James A. (Jim) Guest
Director Policy Outreach and Southwest Office, Reggie James
Managing Director Consumer Reports Best Buy Drugs, Steve Findlay
Senior Administrative Assistant To Vp, Claudia Citarella
Vice President, Elizabeth Crow
Vice President Of Sales Western Region, Ellen Klosz
Vice President Group Client Director, Suzanne Mastrofski
Vice President Editorial Director, Julia Kagan
Vice President Digital Interactive Products And Services, Christian Nimsky
Vice President, Rahul Belani
Executive Vice President, Joel Gurin
Auditors: KPMGLLP

LOCATIONS

HQ: CONSUMERS UNION OF UNITED STATES INC
101 TRUMAN AVE, YONKERS, NY 107031057
Phone: 9143782000
Web: WWW.CONSUMERSUNION.ORG

PRODUCTS/OPERATIONS

2012 Sales

Subscriptions newsstand & other sales	231	91
Other	5	2

Content Areas
Autos
Food
Health Care
Money
Phones and Media
Product Safety

Selected Offerings

Magazines and newsletters
- Consumer Reports Magazine
- Consumer Reports Money Advisor (newsletter)
- Consumer Reports on Health (newsletter)
- ShopSmart

Websites
- ConsumerReports.org
- ConsumerReportsHealth.org
- Consumerist.com

COMPETITORS

Better Business Bureaus
Hearst Magazines
International Data Group
J.D. Power
Kelley Blue Book
National Technical Systems
Reader' s Digest
Reed Elsevier Group
Shopping.com
Underwriters Labs
Yelp

HISTORICAL FINANCIALS

Company Type: Private

Income Statement

FYE: May 31

	REVENUE ($ mil.)	NET INCOME ($ mil.)	NET PROFIT MARGIN	EMPLOYEES
05/13	259	3	1.4%	480
05/11	252	32	12.9%	—
05/10	242	9	3.7%	—
05/09	1,700	0	—	—
Annual Growth	(37.5%)	—	—	—

2013 Year-End Financials

Debt ratio: —
Return on equity: 1.40%
Cash ($ mil.): 21
Current ratio: 0.10
Long-term debt ($ mil.): —
Dividends
Yield: —
Payout: —
Market value ($ mil.): —

CONTI ENTERPRISES INC.

Conti Enterprises is continuing its tour of duty as a civil and heavy construction firm. Active primarily in the Northeast the company provides construction management general contracting and design/build services for a range of projects including commercial and industrial buildings power plants environmental remediation physical security upgrades and infrastructure such as dams roads bridges and rail systems. The company often participates in public-private partnerships. Clients have included the Army Corps of Engineers the EPA the FAA the Department of Energy Con Edison and Dominion Resources.

Conti Enterprises has entered the renewable energy market in a significant way. In recent years it has formed new firms —Alternity Power Alternity Wind Power and SunDurance Energy —to help customers implement green technologies to develop large-scale wind projects and to develop solar power respectively.

Conti Enterprises traces its roots to a company formed in 1906 by the great-grandfather of current CEO Kurt Conti. The company has offices in Massachusetts New Jersey Pennsylvania and Louisiana as well as in Israel.

EXECUTIVES

President and CEO, Kurt G. Conti
COO, William Picken
EVP Business Development, Jay Price
VP Construction, Mark Liebes
Vice President of Safety, Aldo Gonzalez
VP International Operations, Anthony LaBato
Vice President Construction, Glen Stasiak
VP Marketing & Proposals, Jeanine Wright
VP Human Resources, Kristen Olson
VP Purchasing & Contracts, Paul Force
VP Finance International, Richard Kenny
Vice President, Robert Scerbo
VP of Business Development Commercial & Industrial, Todd Martin

LOCATIONS

HQ: CONTI ENTERPRISES INC.
2045 LINCOLN HWY, EDISON, NJ 08817-3334
Phone: 732-520-5000
Web: WWW.CONTICORP.COM

PRODUCTS/OPERATIONS

Selected Affiliates

Alternity Wind Power (on-site clean energy generation)
Conti Federal Services (federal government contracting)
Conti Power & Industrial (power industry construction services)
Conti of New York LLC
Conti of Pennsylvania
Conti Services LLC (private sector design/build)
Lehigh Fabrication & Precast LLC (precast concrete and metal fabrication)
SunDurance Energy LLC (solar power solutions)

COMPETITORS

Andrew Velez Construction
BBL Construction Services
Barr & Barr
Burns and Roe
Colas Inc.
E.W. Howell
Foster Wheeler
Judlau Contracting

HISTORICAL FINANCIALS

Company Type: Private

Income Statement

FYE: December 31

	REVENUE ($ mil.)	NET INCOME ($ mil.)	NET PROFIT MARGIN	EMPLOYEES
12/09	198	0	—	250
12/08	198	0	—	—
12/05	123	0	—	—
12/04	115	0	0.2%	—
Annual Growth	11.4%	—	—	—

2009 Year-End Financials

Debt ratio: —
Return on equity: —
Cash ($ mil.): 11
Current ratio: 1.50
Long-term debt ($ mil.): —
Dividends
Yield: —
Payout: —
Market value ($ mil.): —

CONTINUUM ENERGY SERVICES L.L.C.

LOCATIONS

HQ: CONTINUUM ENERGY SERVICES L.L.C.
1323 E 71ST ST STE 300, TULSA, OK 741365068
Phone: 9184922840
Web: WWW.SEMINOLEENERGY.COM

HISTORICAL FINANCIALS

Company Type: Private

Income Statement

FYE: December 31

	REVENUE ($ mil.)	NET INCOME ($ mil.)	NET PROFIT MARGIN	EMPLOYEES
12/13	2,092	5	0.2%	159
12/12	1,558	16	1.0%	—
12/11	2,021	26	1.3%	—
12/10	2,009	0	—	—
Annual Growth	1.4%	—	—	—

2013 Year-End Financials

Debt ratio: —
Return on equity: 0.20%
Cash ($ mil.): 11
Current ratio: 1.00
Long-term debt ($ mil.): —
Dividends
Yield: —
Payout: —
Market value ($ mil.): —

CONTRACTORS STEEL COMPANY

EXECUTIVES

Chairman President CEO and Treasurer, Donald R. (Don) Simon

LOCATIONS

HQ: CONTRACTORS STEEL COMPANY
36555 AMRHEIN RD, LIVONIA, MI 481501182
Phone: 7344644000
Web: WWW.CONTRACTORSSTEEL.COM

COMPETITORS

Alro
Mill Steel
Peerless Steel

HISTORICAL FINANCIALS

Company Type: Private

Income Statement FYE: October 31

	REVENUE ($ mil.)	NET INCOME ($ mil.)	NET PROFIT MARGIN	EMPLOYEES
10/10	184	6	3.5%	250
10/09	153	(24)	—	—
10/08	632	0	0.0%	—
Annual Growth	(46.0%)	1889.7%	—	—

2010 Year-End Financials

Debt ratio: —
Return on equity: 3.50%
Cash ($ mil.): 15
Current ratio: 3.70
Long-term debt ($ mil.): —
Dividends
Yield: —
Payout: —
Market value ($ mil.): —

CONVERGINT TECHNOLOGIES LLC

It's IP for IT at Convergint Technologies. Convergint integrates IT (information technology) and physical security systems at both single- and multi-site facilities. Its security systems include IP (internet protocol) video and cameras biometrics card access and perimeter protection. The company designs installs as well as repairs electronic security fire alarm and life safety and building automation systems for a diverse group of commercial industrial and government customers. Clients have included Boeing and the Oregon Department of Transportation. As a value-added reseller (VAR) and partner Convergint installs products from such major OEMs as Honeywell Lenel and S2 Security.

Geographic Reach

Convergint serves customers across North America.

Strategy

Convergint Technologies' growth is based in part on its ability to delegate. Specifically each business unit is charged with developing a strategic direction. The company claims that as a result it has pursued new opportunities such as in health care technologies and even opened offices in promising markets.

Convergint Technologies is simultaneously focused on delivering tailor-made building system products and services. Unlike some competitors it strives to integrate physical security access systems with logical access control systems. Customers benefit from a more cost effective and efficient system infrastructure which can pave the way for Convergint Technologies to build sales.

EXECUTIVES

VP Electronic Security Division, Tony Varco
VP Fire Alarm and Life Safety Division, Barry Yatzor
VP and CFO, Wally Winkel
CEO, Dan Moceri
President and COO, Jim Boutwell

LOCATIONS

HQ: CONVERGINT TECHNOLOGIES LLC
1651 WILKENING RD, SCHAUMBURG, IL 60173-5323
Phone: 847-620-5000
Web: WWW.CONVERGINT.COM

PRODUCTS/OPERATIONS

Selected Services

Building automation
Electronic security
Fire alarm & life safety
Installation services
Support services

COMPETITORS

ADT
Advanced Security & Controls
Benson Systems
Henry Bros. Electronics
Professional Security Technologies

HISTORICAL FINANCIALS

Company Type: Private

Income Statement FYE: December 31

	REVENUE ($ mil.)	NET INCOME ($ mil.)	NET PROFIT MARGIN	EMPLOYEES
12/09	164	13	8.3%	1,000
12/08	151	6	4.3%	—
12/08	1,818	0	—	—
Annual Growth	—	5181649.0%	—	—

2009 Year-End Financials

Debt ratio: —
Return on equity: 8.30%
Cash ($ mil.): 24
Current ratio: 1.40
Long-term debt ($ mil.): —
Dividends
Yield: —
Payout: —
Market value ($ mil.): —

CONWAY HOSPITAL INC.

Conway Medical Center (CMC) finds a way to provide a wide range of health care services to residents of eastern South Carolina. The private not-for-profit 210-bed hospital (served by a medical staff of 200) provides services including primary diagnostic emergency surgical maternal and pediatric and rehabilitative care. CMC specializes in heart health hospice care and occupational health. Additionally CMC operates the Kingston Nursing Center an about 90-bed long-term nursing and rehabilitative care facility and the Conway Physicians Group which is home to about 10 physician practices offering a range of specialties.

Geographic Reach

The hospital system serves patients in eastern South Carolina.

Financial Analysis

CMC receives financial support in part through donations to the Conway Medical Center Foundation which was founded in 1988 to provide financial and voluntary staffing support to the hospital.

Company Background

The center expanded its operations in 2009 with the completion of a new patient tower with about 65 patient beds new nurses stations for streamlined patient care and updated technology.

EXECUTIVES

Chief Executive Officer, Philip A. (Phil) Clayton
Executive Vice President Fiscal Services, Bret Barr
VP Human Resources, Craig Hyman
Administrator Kingston Nursing Center/Medstar, Laura Fowler
VP Ancillary Services, Dwight Gentry
Executive Director Foundation, Berns Massey
VP Facility Management, Kevin Lovett
Vice-President Nursing Services, Tony Minshew
Vice-President Physician Services, Warren Ratley
Vice-President Medical Affairs, Preston Strosnider
Director IT, Mickey Waters

LOCATIONS

HQ: CONWAY HOSPITAL INC.
300 SINGLETON RIDGE RD, CONWAY, SC 29526-9142
Phone: 843-347-7111
Web: WWW.CONWAYMEDICALCENTER.COM

PRODUCTS/OPERATIONS

Selected Departments and Services

Center for Wound Healing
Critical Care Services
Diabetes Management
Diagnostic
Endoscopy
Heart Center
Hospice
Joint Replacement Center
Laboratory Services
Long Term Care
Mammography
Medical Services Center
Palliative Care
Pediatric Center
Pulmonary Rehabilitation
Rehabilitation
Senior Privileges Club
Sleep Disorders Center
Subacute
Surgical Services
The Birthplace
Weight Loss Surgery
Wellness & Fitness Center

COMPETITORS

Carolinas Hospital System
Georgetown Hospital System
Grand Strand Regional Medical Center
McLeod Health
Medical University of South Carolina
New Hanover Regional Medical Center
Roper St. Francis Healthcare

HISTORICAL FINANCIALS

Company Type: Private

Income Statement FYE: September 30

	REVENUE ($ mil.)	NET INCOME ($ mil.)	NET PROFIT MARGIN	EMPLOYEES
09/12	158	16	10.2%	1,200
09/11	149	13	8.9%	—
09/09	149	14	10.0%	—
09/06	126	3	2.4%	—
Annual Growth	3.9%	32.2%	—	—

2012 Year-End Financials

Debt ratio: —
Return on equity: 10.20%
Cash ($ mil.): 17
Current ratio: 1.40
Long-term debt ($ mil.): —
Dividends
Yield: —
Payout: —
Market value ($ mil.): —

COOPERATIVE ELEVATOR CO.

EXECUTIVES

President and CEO, Pat Anderson
VP Information Technology and Assistant Board Secretary, Barry Albrecht
VP Bean and Grain Divisions, Mike Janowicz
VP Finance and Board Treasurer, Mike Wehner
VP Petroleum, Tim Sielaff
VP Agronomy, Mark Boyne

LOCATIONS

HQ: COOPERATIVE ELEVATOR CO.
7211 E MICHIGAN AVE, PIGEON, MI 48755
Phone: 9894534500
Web: WWW.COOPELEV.COM

COMPETITORS

ADM
CHS
Cargill
Chippewa Valley Bean
Della Natura Commodities
Kelley Bean
Organic Bean & Grain
Star of the West
United Producers
Zeeland Farm

HISTORICAL FINANCIALS

Company Type: Private

Income Statement FYE: January 31

	REVENUE ($ mil.)	NET INCOME ($ mil.)	NET PROFIT MARGIN	EMPLOYEES
01/14	277	9	3.6%	136
01/13	293	12	4.4%	—
01/12	242	13	5.4%	—
01/11	166	0	—	—
Annual Growth	18.4%	—	—	—

2014 Year-End Financials

Debt ratio: —
Return on equity: 3.60%
Cash ($ mil.): 0
Current ratio: —
Long-term debt ($ mil.): —
Dividends
Yield: —
Payout: —
Market value ($ mil.): —

COOPERATIVE FOR ASSISTANCE AND RELIEF EVERYWHERE INC.

The Cooperative for Assistance and Relief Everywhere (CARE) strives to be the beginning of the end of poverty. The organization works to reduce poverty in about 85 countries by helping communities in areas such as health education economic development emergency relief and agriculture. CARE supports more than 1100 projects to combat poverty. ‚Ält also operates a small economic activity development (SEAD) unit that supports moneymaking activities. Through SEAD CARE ‚Âprovides technical training and savings and loans programs to help people – particularly ‚Âwomen –‚Âopen or expand small businesses. CARE was founded in 1945 to give aid to WWII survivors.

Geographic Reach

From its headquarters in Atlanta CARE serves poor communities in nearly 85 countries. It does not provide assistance in the US.

Operations

In addition to its home office in Georgia CARE maintains field offices in about 10 US cities including Boston Chicago Miami New York and Washington DC. The group's ‚Âinternational ‚Âfield offices are located in ‚Âmore than 55 countries.

CARE's 1100 projects reach 122 million people more than half of which are women. About 90% of the funds that CARE receives go toward its aid efforts. The organization helps people in the poorest communities of developing nations. (It does not provide assistance in the US.)

Strategy

CARE is supported by donations from thousands of individuals and dozens of corporations foundations and other charitable organizations in the US. Some of the participating organizations include ‚Â World Wildlife Fund ‚ÂCovance ‚ÂMerck ‚ÂMeredith Corporation and the ‚ÂWal-Mart Foundation. The group also receives funding and supplies from government agencies including the ‚ÂUnited Nations ‚Âand European Union. ‚Â As a result of the economic ‚Âdownturn CARE has ‚Âbeen ‚Âworking to raise contribution levels as governments businesses and individuals cut back their spending including charitable donations.

Financial Performance

CARE's revenue increased ‚Âa modest 1% to $590 million in fiscal 2011 as compared to 2010. While it logged a drop in revenues from the US government the organization saw a boost in private contributions –totaling $310 million –from CARE international members.

EXECUTIVES

Treasurer and Director, Dean C. Kehler, age 57
President CEO, Helene D. Gayle, age 59
SVP Finance and CFO, Vickie J. Barrow-Klein
COO, Jonathan (Jon) Mitchell
VP Individual Fundraising and Marketing, Lee Taliaferro (Tolli) Love
Vice President Of Human Resources, Daniel Berman
Vice President, Phil Mazzara
Senior Vice President Of Human, Barbara Murphy Warrington
Treasurer and Director, Dean C. Kehler, age 57
Chair, W. Bowman (Bo) Cutter
Vice Chair, Doris Meissner
Treasurer, Alex Cummings
Board Member, Charity Watch
Treasurer, Stephanie Badoud
Auditors: PricewaterhouseCoopersLLP

LOCATIONS

HQ: COOPERATIVE FOR ASSISTANCE AND RELIEF EVERYWHERE INC.
151 ELLIS ST NE FL 1, ATLANTA, GA 303032437
Phone: 4046812552
Web: WWW.CARE.ORG

PRODUCTS/OPERATIONS

Selected International Partner Organizations

Covance Inc.
Merck Foundation
Meredith Corporation
The Wal-mart Foundation
WWF

HISTORICAL FINANCIALS

Company Type: Private

Income Statement FYE: June 30

	REVENUE ($ mil.)	NET INCOME ($ mil.)	NET PROFIT MARGIN	EMPLOYEES
06/13	492	(18)	—	10,000
06/11	589	10	1.7%	—
06/08	713	40	5.6%	—
06/05	1,545	0	—	—
Annual Growth	—	—	—	—

2013 Year-End Financials

Debt ratio: —
Return on equity: (-3.80%)
Cash ($ mil.): 67
Current ratio: 0.70
Long-term debt ($ mil.): —
Dividends
Yield: —
Payout: —
Market value ($ mil.): —

COOPERATIVE REGIONS OF ORGANIC PRODUCER POOLS

Cooperative Regions of Organic Producers Pool (CROPP) is the largest organic farming cooperative in North America. The group's 1800-plus farmer/members produce the co-op's Organic Valley Family of Farms and Organic Prairie brands of fluid and shelf-stable milk along with cheese butter and soy milk. Beyond the dairy barn the cooperative also offers organic citrus juices produce eggs meats and poultry. Its Organic Valley products are sold by food retailers and its ingredients are marketed to other organic food processors. Wisconsin-headquartered CROPP's farmer/members are located in California Florida and the Northeast Northwest and Midwest regions of the US. The co-op was founded in 1988.

Geographic Reach

The cooperative's farmer members are located in 33 US states and four Canadian provinces.

Financial Performance

The co-op's sales increased 20% in 2012 to nearly $857 million compared with $715.6 million in 2011. In 2013 sales are expected to top $950 million. Sales have risen sharply along with the preference for organic milk and other dairy foods. Profitability is also on the rise. CROPP's gross margin grew to $110.1 million in 2012 versus $103 million in 2011.

Strategy

CROPP seeks to quench consumers' growing thirst for organic milk with new products including the 2012 launch of Organic Valley Grassmilk an organic specialty milk produced from cows that are 100% grass fed.

EXECUTIVES

CEO, George Siemon
VP Sales, Eric Newman
Chief Marketing Executive, Theresa Marquez
Central Retail and Foodservice Sales Manager, Steve Brandl
Chief Operating Officer, Louise Hemstead
Chief Financial Officer, Mike Bedessem
Sales Manager Eastern Natural Foods Division, Dennis O'Loughlin
Regional Sales Manager Northwestern States, Jack Lee

Regional Sales Manager Southern California Arizona and Hawaii, Camaryn Larramendy
Regional Sales Manager Midwest, David Butterfield
Regional Sales Manager Rocky Mountains and Plains, Matthew Provost
Regional Sales Manager Southwest, Calvin Daily
Regional Sales Manager Eastern Midwest, Sonny Luehrmann
Regional Sales Manager New England and Upstate New York, John Morrissey
Regional Sales Manager Mid-Atlantic and Metro New York, Dana Forsman
Regional Sales Manager Southeastern States, Beth Petrillo

LOCATIONS

HQ: COOPERATIVE REGIONS OF ORGANIC PRODUCER POOLS
1 ORGANIC WAY, LA FARGE, WI 54639-6604
Phone: 608-625-2602
Web: WWW.ORGANICVALLEY.COM

PRODUCTS/OPERATIONS

Selected Products

Butter
Cheese
Cottage cheese
Cream
Cream cheese
Eggs
Healthy snacks
Juice
Meat
Milk
Sour cream
Soy
Yogurt

COMPETITORS

Albert' s Organics	Land O' Lakes
Aurora Organic Dairy	Laura' s Lean Beef Co.
Berkeley Farms	Lifeway Foods
Chiquita Brands	Niman Ranch
Crowley Foods	Oberweis Dairy
Dairy Crest	Odwalla
Dairy Farmers of America	Organically Grown Company
Dakota Beef	Rachel' s Organic Dairy
Dannon	Rockview Dairies
Dean Foods	Sargento
Dole Food	Springfield Creamery
Egg Innovations	Stonyfield Farm
Foster Dairy Farms	Straus Family Creamery
Fresh Del Monte Produce	Stremicks Heritage Foods
Friendship Dairies	Turkey Hill Dairy
Galaxy Nutritional Foods	Tyson Foods
Garelick Farms	Tyson Fresh Meats
Great Lakes Cheese	United Natural
Jonathan Sprouts	Willow Wind Organic Farms
Keller' s Creamery	

HISTORICAL FINANCIALS

Company Type: Private

Income Statement FYE: December 31

	REVENUE ($ mil.)	NET INCOME ($ mil.)	NET PROFIT MARGIN	EMPLOYEES
12/11	715	13	1.9%	764
12/10	619	12	2.0%	—
12/08	527	3	0.7%	—
12/07	432	6	1.4%	—
Annual Growth	13.4%	20.9%	—	—

2011 Year-End Financials

Debt ratio: —
Return on equity: 1.90%
Cash ($ mil.): 17
Current ratio: 1.20
Long-term debt ($ mil.): —
Dividends
Yield: —
Payout: —
Market value ($ mil.): —

COPPER HILLS APARTMENTS L.P.

LOCATIONS

HQ: COPPER HILLS APARTMENTS L.P.
8265 ASPEN ST STE 100, RANCHO CUCAMONGA, CA 917303291
Phone: 9094832444

HISTORICAL FINANCIALS

Company Type: Private

Income Statement FYE: June 30

	ASSETS ($ mil.)	NET INCOME ($ mil.)	INCOME AS % OF ASSETS	EMPLOYEES
06/08*	61	0	0.4%	2
12/00	9	(0)	—	—
Annual Growth	29.8%	—	—	—

*Fiscal year change

2008 Year-End Financials

Debt ratio: —
Return on equity: 2.30%
Cash ($ mil.): 18
Current ratio: 20.60
Long-term debt ($ mil.): —
Dividends
Yield: —
Payout: —
Market value ($ mil.): —

CORE CONSTRUCTION INC.

EXECUTIVES

President, Howard L. Maurer
EVP, Shawn L. Maurer
VP Administration, JoAnn Dean
VP Finance, Dennis Barber
Treasurer, Steve Roeschley
Estimator, Marshall Wtizig
Director Business Development, Dennis Montague

LOCATIONS

HQ: CORE CONSTRUCTION INC.
3036 E GREENWAY RD, PHOENIX, AZ 850324414
Phone: 6024940800
Web: WWW.CORECONSTRUCT.COM

CORE Construction has a half dozen offices in Arizona Florida Illinois Nevada and Texas.

COMPETITORS

DPR Construction	Perini
Jaynes Companies	Summit Builders
Kitchell	Sundt
McCarthy Building	

HISTORICAL FINANCIALS

Company Type: Private

Income Statement FYE: December 31

	REVENUE ($ mil.)	NET INCOME ($ mil.)	NET PROFIT MARGIN	EMPLOYEES
12/13	219	0	—	60
12/12	162	0	—	—
12/11	206	0	—	—
12/10	244	0	—	—
Annual Growth	(3.5%)	—	—	—

2013 Year-End Financials

Debt ratio: —
Return on equity: —
Cash ($ mil.): 3
Current ratio: 0.10
Long-term debt ($ mil.): —
Dividends
Yield: —
Payout: —
Market value ($ mil.): —

CORPORATE TRAVEL CONSULTANTS INC

EXECUTIVES

CEO, Bonnie M. Lorefice
CFO, Gerry Lazar
President, Jane Batio
SVP, Lisa Donovan Berry
EVP, Jim Wasson
VP, Barb Lea-Maijala
Senior Vice President, Lisa Berry
COO, Mona Blankshain
Managing Director, Gina Maylath

LOCATIONS

HQ: CORPORATE TRAVEL CONSULTANTS INC
450 E 22ND ST STE 100, LOMBARD, IL 601486175
Phone: 6306919100
Web: WWW.CORPTRAV.COM

COMPETITORS

Adelman Travel	BCD Travel
Advantage Performance Network	Carlson Wagonlit
American Express	USTravel

HISTORICAL FINANCIALS

Company Type: Private

Income Statement FYE: December 31

	REVENUE ($ mil.)	NET INCOME ($ mil.)	NET PROFIT MARGIN	EMPLOYEES
12/14	222	1	0.7%	120
12/12	209	1	0.9%	—
12/10	135	0	0.4%	—
12/09	116	0		
Annual Growth	13.7%	—	—	—

2014 Year-End Financials

Debt ratio: —
Return on equity: 0.70%
Cash ($ mil.): 4
Current ratio: 3.00
Long-term debt ($ mil.): —
Dividends
Yield: —
Payout: —
Market value ($ mil.): —

COTTON STAPLE COOPERATIVE ASSOCIATION

Referred to as Staplcotn the Staple Cotton Co-operative has been a staple of its member-producers' business lives since 1921. One of the oldest and largest cotton marketing co-ops in the US it provides domestic and export marketing cotton warehousing and agricultural financing to some 9730 members in 47 states. As of 2011 the co-op handles nearly 14000 farm accounts in 10 states. Staplcotn's inventory is consigned by member-producers and averages from 2.5 million to 3 million bales of cotton a year. The co-op operates though 15 warehouses serving the mid-south and southeastern US to supply more than 25% of the cotton consumed by the US textile industry as well as the needs of textile mills overseas.

Staplcotn's operations currently draw members from all 11 cotton-producing states east of Texas. Georgia is the co-op's second largest in cotton production behind Texas. Staplcotn also holds 50% of the Mississippi crop market fourth in production nationwide in 2011. Members sign an agreement passing title for any cotton they produce on a particular farm to Staplcotn. The cotton is marketed in Staplcotn's name through the Mill Sales Program where large lots of cotton are offered for sale to attract better commodity prices.

The co-op's subsidiary Stapldiscount finances crops as well as farm equipment land purchases and improvements cotton gins and warehouses flying services and seed processors. It operates on a non-profit basis averaging a net interest rate less than the New York Prime Rate. Its accounts dot five states: Mississippi Louisiana Arkansas Tennessee and Missouri.

Although the co-op's cotton is sold mainly to domestic customers a decrease in demand for cotton in the US has led Staplcotn to pursue foreign sales mainly in Asia. In 2012 it was among several merchants that signed deals with Chinese mill owners for 220000 tons of cotton. Staplcotn's end-customers have included such clothing giants as Fruit of the Loom Levi Strauss and Hanes.

EXECUTIVES

VP Cotton Services, Sterling P. Jones
VP Systems and Controls; VP Systems and Controls Stapldiscount, L. A. (Larry) Gnemi
General Counsel and Secretary; General Counsel and Secretary Stapldiscount, Kenneth E. Downs
President Chief Executive Officer, Meredith B. Allen
VP Warehousing, Shane Stephens
Chairman of the Board, Woods E. Eastland
Vice President Chief Financial Officer, Charles Robertson
Director Internet Sales, Jason Ward
Senior Director Export Sales, Hank Reichle
VP Human Resources; VP Human Resources Stapldiscount, Russell Robertson
Vice President Chief Operating Officer, Tom Dillard
Director, Coley L. Bailey
President CEO and Director; President and CEO Stapldiscount, Woods E. Eastland
Director, Anderson W. Barham
Director, Laudies Dow Brantley Jr.
Director, W. P. Brown III
Director, Richard Bowen Flowers Jr.
Director, Fred Scott Franklin
Director, W. E. Harris
Director, Kenneth B. Hood
Director, John D. Hux Jr.
Director, Johnny Johnson
Director, Bernard Bryan Jones III
Director, John B. Laney Jr.
Director, Larry R. Mclendon
Director, Robert Mclendon
Director, Mike Newberry
Director, John Nolan Newcomb
Director, Thomas A. (Tap) Parker
Director, Kim Rentz
Director, Lowry Robinson
Director, Mike P. Sturdivant Jr.
Director, Warren W. (Tutt) Sullivan
Director, Hugh H. Summerville Jr.
Director, Kenneth M. (Mike) Tate
Director, Marty E. White
Director, John Willis
Director, B. E. (Sonny) Davis
Director, Cleve Mobley
Director, Lawrence Long
Director, George LaCour

LOCATIONS

HQ: COTTON STAPLE COOPERATIVE ASSOCIATION
214 W MARKET ST, GREENWOOD, MS 38930-4329
Phone: 662-453-6231
Web: WWW.STAPLCOTN.COM

PRODUCTS/OPERATIONS

Selected Services

Cotton services
- Loans
- Mill Sales Program

Marketing
Stapldiscount
Warehouse

COMPETITORS

Alabama Farmers Cooperative
Calcot
Cargill
Dunavant Enterprises
International Cotton Marketing
J.G. Boswell Co.
JB Cotton
King Ranch
Louis Dreyfus Group
Noble Group
Olam
Plains Cotton
Southern States
Tennessee Farmers Co-op
Weil Brothers Cotton

HISTORICAL FINANCIALS

Company Type: Private

Income Statement FYE: August 31

	REVENUE ($ mil.)	NET INCOME ($ mil.)	NET PROFIT MARGIN	EMPLOYEES
08/12	1,236	8	0.7%	201
08/11	963	875	90.8%	—
08/10	658	578	87.8%	—
08/09	773	693	89.7%	—
Annual Growth	16.9%	(77.3%)	—	—

2012 Year-End Financials

Debt ratio: —
Return on equity: 0.70%
Cash ($ mil.): 63
Current ratio: 0.50
Long-term debt ($ mil.): —
Dividends
Yield: —
Payout: —
Market value ($ mil.): —

COUNTRY PRIDE COOPERATIVE INC.

EXECUTIVES

President and General Manager, Carl Dickinson
Manager Human Resources, Laura Root
Controller, Marsha Lowry
Manager Energy and Safety, Mike Barfuss
Manager Feed and Grain Division, Rod Farley
Manager Retail Operations West, Ritch Hawranek
Manager Agronomy and Operations East, Bill Pape
Manager Progressive Marketing, Steve Koenig
Board President, Ross Plucker
Vice President of Feed, Leo Westendorf
Vice President of Human Resources Corporate Development, Linda Husher
CFO, Marsha Whetham
CEO, Mike Trosen
Vice President of Safety Risk Management, Tom Malek

LOCATIONS

HQ: COUNTRY PRIDE COOPERATIVE INC.
648 W 2ND ST, WINNER, SD 575801230
Phone: 6058422711
Web: WWW.COUNTRYPRIDECOOP.COM

COMPETITORS

ADM
CHS
Cargill
North Central Farmers Elevator
Northern Growers
South Dakota Wheat Growers

HISTORICAL FINANCIALS

Company Type: Private

Income Statement FYE: June 30

	REVENUE ($ mil.)	NET INCOME ($ mil.)	NET PROFIT MARGIN	EMPLOYEES
06/13	128	2	2.1%	200
06/12	170	3	2.0%	—
06/11	139	2	1.6%	—
06/10	109	0	—	—
Annual Growth	5.6%	—	—	—

2013 Year-End Financials

Debt ratio: —
Return on equity: 2.10%
Cash ($ mil.): 2
Current ratio: 0.60
Long-term debt ($ mil.): —
Dividends
Yield: —
Payout: —
Market value ($ mil.): —

COUNTRYMARK COOPERATIVE HOLDING CORPORATION

LOCATIONS

HQ: COUNTRYMARK COOPERATIVE HOLDING CORPORATION
225 S EAST ST STE 144, INDIANAPOLIS, IN 462024059
Phone: 8008083170
Web: WWW.COUNTRYMARK.COM

HISTORICAL FINANCIALS

Company Type: Private

Income Statement FYE: December 31

	REVENUE ($ mil.)	NET INCOME ($ mil.)	NET PROFIT MARGIN	EMPLOYEES
12/08	1,325	26	2.0%	425
12/07	964	56	5.9%	—
Annual Growth	37.5%	(52.4%)	—	—

2008 Year-End Financials

Debt ratio: —
Return on equity: 2.00%
Cash ($ mil.): 8
Current ratio: 0.30
Long-term debt ($ mil.): —
Dividends
Yield: —
Payout: —
Market value ($ mil.): —

COUNTY OF MARICOPA

LOCATIONS

HQ: COUNTY OF MARICOPA
9801 W VAN BUREN ST, TOLLESON, AZ 853532833
Phone: 6234784000
Web: WWW.TUHSD.ORG

HISTORICAL FINANCIALS

Company Type: Private

Income Statement FYE: June 30

	REVENUE ($ mil.)	NET INCOME ($ mil.)	NET PROFIT MARGIN	EMPLOYEES
06/14	1,750	(119)		919
06/13	1,797	(66)		—
06/12	1,820	(58)	—	—
06/99	25	0	—	—
Annual Growth	32.7%	—	—	—

2014 Year-End Financials

Debt ratio: —
Return on equity: (-6.80%)
Cash ($ mil.): 32
Current ratio: —
Long-term debt ($ mil.): —
Dividends
Yield: —
Payout: —
Market value ($ mil.): —

COVENANT HEALTH SYSTEM

Covenant Health System ties West Texas and Eastern New Mexico together with quality health care. The health services provider offers some 1100 beds in its five primary acute-care and specialty hospitals; it also manages about a dozen affiliated community hospitals. Covenant Health System part of the St. Joseph Health System also maintains a network of family health care and medical clinics. Covenant Health System's major facilities are Covenant Medical Center Covenant Specialty Hospital and Covenant Women's and Children's Hospital. The health system also includes some 20 clinics and 50 physician practices and its extensive outreach programs target isolated rural communities with mobile services.

Operations

The system's five hospitals include Covenant Medical Center Covenant Medical Center-Lakeside Covenant Specialty Hospital and Covenant Children's Hospital. It also operates three schools for healthcare careers in nursing radiography and surgical technology respectively.

Strategy

The Christian-based system which calls itself a ministry focuses on providing benefits to the community. Its key priorities include mental health dentistry diabetes home health management and childhood obesity.

Background

Covenant Health System was founded when two Lubbock hospitals St. Mary of the Plains Hospital (now known as Covenant Medical Center-Lakeside) and the Lubbock Methodist Hospital System (including the flagship Methodist Hospital which is now known as Covenant Medical Center) merged in 1998.

EXECUTIVES

VP, Sharon Prather
President and CEO, Richard H. Parks
Director Trauma Services, Tammy Jones
VP Mission Integration, Clarke Cochran
Chief Medical Officer, Scott Robins

LOCATIONS

HQ: COVENANT HEALTH SYSTEM
3615 19TH ST, LUBBOCK, TX 79410-1209
Phone: 806-725-1011
Web: WWW.STJHS.ORG

PRODUCTS/OPERATIONS

Selected Facilities

Covenant Heart and Vascular Institute
Covenant Hospital Levelland
Covenant Hosptial Plainview
Covenant Medical Center
Covenant NeuroScience Institute
Covenant Specialty Hospital
Covenant Women' s and Children' s Hospital (formerly Covenant Medical Center-Lakeside)
Joe Arrington Cancer Research and Treatment Center
Owens-White Outpatient Rehabilitation Center

Selected Schools

School of Nursing
School of Radiography
School of Surgical Technology

COMPETITORS

Baptist St. Anthony' s Health System
Baylor Health
Del Sol Medical Center
HealthSouth
Hunt Memorial
NW Texas Healthcare
Parkland Health & Hospital System
Tenet Healthcare
Texas Health Resources
The Methodist Health System
University Medical Center of El Paso

HISTORICAL FINANCIALS

Company Type: Private

Income Statement FYE: June 30

	REVENUE ($ mil.)	NET INCOME ($ mil.)	NET PROFIT MARGIN	EMPLOYEES
06/11	546	27	5.0%	5,700
06/09	1,185	(38)	—	—
06/08	572	8	1.5%	—
Annual Growth	(1.5%)	48.6%	—	—

2011 Year-End Financials

Debt ratio: —
Return on equity: 5.00%
Cash ($ mil.): 82
Current ratio: 0.70
Long-term debt ($ mil.): —
Dividends
Yield: —
Payout: —
Market value ($ mil.): —

COVENANT MEDICAL CENTER INC

EXECUTIVES

CEO, Spencer T. (Spence) Maidlow
CFO, Mark Gronda

LOCATIONS

HQ: COVENANT MEDICAL CENTER INC
1447 N HARRISON ST, SAGINAW, MI 486024727
Phone: 9895830000
Web: WWW.COVENANTHEALTHCARE.COM

PRODUCTS/OPERATIONS

Selected services

Bariatrics
Birth Center
Cancer Care
Cardiology - Center for the Heart
Childbirth Classes
da Vinci Robotic Surgery
Diabetes Self-Management Program
Emergency Care Center
Imaging and Diagnostics
Neonatal Intensive Care
Neurology
Osteoporosis
Orthopaedics
Pediatrics
Physical Medicine and Rehab.
Pulmonary/Respiratory Care
Sleep Center
Surgical Services
Trauma
Urologic Surgery
Women's Health
Wound Healing Center

COMPETITORS

Genesys Health System
Genesys Regional Medical Center
Hurley Medical Center
McLaren Bay
McLaren Health Care
Munson Healthcare
Sparrow Health System
University of Michigan Health System

HISTORICAL FINANCIALS

Company Type: Private

Income Statement FYE: June 30

	REVENUE ($ mil.)	NET INCOME ($ mil.)	NET PROFIT MARGIN	EMPLOYEES
06/13	513	31	6.2%	3,900
06/10	508	28	5.5%	—
06/09	467	(14)	—	—
06/08	1,608	0	—	—
Annual Growth	—	—	—	—

2013 Year-End Financials

Debt ratio: —
Return on equity: 6.20%
Cash ($ mil.): 42
Current ratio: 0.50
Long-term debt ($ mil.): —
Dividends
Yield: —
Payout: —
Market value ($ mil.): —

COVERALL NORTH AMERICA INC.

Coverall North America operating as Coverall Health-Based Cleaning System has commercial cleaning covered. Through more than 90 support centers and 9000 franchisees worldwide (including branches in Asia Australia the Middle East and the Americas) the company offers franchises that provides janitorial services to retail locations office buildings health care facilities manufacturing plants government facilities schools and airports. Services include routine cleaning decontamination cleaning carpet cleaning restroom sanitation and floor restoration. Prominent customers have included Fed Ex the United States Postal Service Orkin and Schenker. The company was founded in 1985.

The company continues to expand its franchise offerings domestically and internationally as facilities around the world need their floors scrubbed and their windows cleaned. The Coverall Health-

Based Cleaning System is specifically intended to reduce the spread of germs in public places and commercial environments. Organizations will always seek ways to eliminate lost productivity and reduce costs associated with illness and the Coverall Health-Based Cleaning System claims to reduce public health risks.

EXECUTIVES

VP Operations, Peter J. Sheldon Sr.
SVP, Kevin Derella
COO, Patrick Joyce
SVP and General Counsel, Jacqueline Vlaming
Regional Vice President, Laura Bach
CEO, Rick Ascolese
Owner, Tony PiLlanes
Auditors: Deloitte&ToucheLLP

LOCATIONS

HQ: COVERALL NORTH AMERICA INC.
350 SW 12TH AVE, DEERFIELD BEACH, FL 33442-3106
Phone: 561-922-2500
Web: WWW.COVERALL.COM

COMPETITORS

ABM Industries	Jani-King
ARAMARK	ServiceMaster
CleanNet USA	UGL Services UNICCO
ISS A/S	

HISTORICAL FINANCIALS

Company Type: Private

Income Statement FYE: December 31

	ASSETS ($ mil.)	NET INCOME ($ mil.)	INCOME AS % OF ASSETS	EMPLOYEES
12/11	72	(0)	—	476
12/07	56	13	23.5%	—
12/06	53	6	12.5%	—
12/05	50	1	2.9%	—
Annual Growth	6.4%	—	—	—

2011 Year-End Financials

Debt ratio: —
Return on equity: (-0.30%)
Cash ($ mil.): 1
Current ratio: 0.30
Long-term debt ($ mil.): —
Dividends
Yield: —
Payout: —
Market value ($ mil.): —

CREIGHTON ALEGENT HEALTH

Alegent Creighton Health (formerly Alegent Health) pledges allegiance to medical wellbeing in its corner of the Midwest. The not-for-profit health care system operates 11 hospitals with about 2000 beds in Omaha and surrounding communities in eastern Nebraska and southwestern Iowa including Bergan Mercy Medical Center and Immanuel Medical Center. Alegent Creighton Health's hospitals provide specialty services including cardiovascular orthopedic and cancer care; it also operates psychiatric long-term care home health and outpatient centers. The health system is sponsored by Catholic Health Initiatives and is affiliated with Creighton University.

Geographic Reach

The network's hospitals are located in Omaha (five medical centers) Papillion Plainview and Schuyler Nebraska as well as in Corning Council Bluffs and Missouri Valley Iowa.

Operations

Alegent Creighton Health is the primary provider of teaching locations for the Creighton University School of Medicine with academic programs in a number of fields including psychiatry women's health nursing and pharmacy. Its hospitals have some 1500 physicians on staff and include 10 acute care and one psychiatric hospital. Specialty units include an orthopedic hospital and skilled nursing centers.

In addition to its acute care facilities the organization provides primary and specialty outpatient care services through its Alegent Creighton Health Clinics unit. The division operates about 100 physician practices and clinics in Omaha and surrounding areas. There are also two Express Care clinics that offer urgent care for non-life-threatening ailments and six Quick Care clinics in Omaha (located in Hy-Vee retail stores) that provide minor medical ailment treatment as well as sports physicals and vaccinations. The idea behind the clinics is to divert patients who might otherwise end up at ERs with non-emergency symptoms (thus lowering hospital expenses).

Alegent Creighton Health spends some $66 million annually on community benefit programs including outreach programs community improvement efforts charity care and medical services for low-income families.

Strategy

The company changed its name to Alegent Creighton Health in 2012 to signify its presence as a unified regional health network following its acquisition of Creighton University Medical Center (CUMC). The purchase allows the company to better compete and thrive in the changing US health care landscape by expanding its facilities training programs and resources in the Omaha area. It also worked towards Alegent Creighton Health's long-term goal of providing meaningful quality care and integrated health management services –while simultaneously lowering medical expenses –within its regional service territories.

Other growth efforts include the formation of an intensive care partnership with Good Samaritan Hospital in 2013. The network has also opened several new community care clinics in recent years.

Mergers and Acquisitions

The company acquired the 400-bed CUMC from its former owners Tenet Healthcare (which owned 74% of CUMC) and Creighton University (26%) for around $60 million in September 2012 to expand its hospital network and educational programs. The network became the primary teaching hospital operator for Creighton University through the deal (it already provided some programs with the school prior to the transaction). The affiliated physician practice organization Creighton Medical Associates (CMA) was combined with the Alegent Health Clinic organization to create Alegent Creighton Health Clinics.

Ownership

Until late 2012 the Alegent Creighton Health organization operated as a joint venture between CHI which counts the Sisters of Mercy of Omaha among its sponsors and the Immanuel Healthcare System an organization sponsored by the Nebraska Synod of the Evangelical Lutheran Church in America. (The joint venture was first formed in 1996 when Immanuel Medical Center and Bergan Mercy Medical Center merged.) In 2012 however Immanuel Healthcare System transferred full sponsorship duties for Alegent Creighton Health to CHI.

EXECUTIVES

Vp-hr, Nancy Wallace
CFO, Jeanette M. Wojtalewicz
President and CEO, Cliff A. Robertson
SVP and COO, Joan Neuhaus
President and CEO Alegent Creighton Clinic, Richard (Rick) Rolston
SVP and Chief Quality Officer, Richard Miller
Director Of Health Information, Rosemary Borghoff
Vice President And System Chief Nursing, Jane Carmody
Regl Gen Coun & Vp Legal Svcs, Jason Yungtum
Vice President Of Operations, Chris Evans
Medical Director, Russell Cowles
Vice President Chief Development Officer, Kevin Bonney
Nursing Director, Kelly Houser
Vice President Mission Integration, Beth Llewellyn
Vice President Of Human Resources, Nancy Cahill-wallace
Director Of Operating Room, Barb Ricci
Associate Medical Director Midlevel Providers, Josette Gordon-simet
Nursing Director, Dee Ernesti
Medical Librarian, Cindy Perkins
Vice Chairman, Richard J. Vierk
Chairman, Michael T. DeFreece
Treas, Cindy Johnson

LOCATIONS

HQ: CREIGHTON ALEGENT HEALTH
12809 W DODGE RD, OMAHA, NE 68154-2155
Phone: 402-343-4300
Web: WWW.ALEGENT.COM

PRODUCTS/OPERATIONS

Selected Facilities and Operations

Alegent Creighton Health Clinics (primary care multiple locations in Iowa and Nebraska)
Alegent Creighton Health Urgent Care clinics (urgent care three locations in Nebraska)
Alegent Creighton Health Quick Care (minor care clinics; seven locations in Omaha Nebraska in Hy-Vee stores)
Alegent Health at Home (home health care)
Bergan Mercy Medical Center (Omaha Nebraska; 300 beds)
Community Memorial Hospital (Missouri Valley Iowa; 20 beds)
Creighton University Medical Center (Omaha Nebraska; 400 beds)
Immanuel Communities (independent and assisted living in Omaha and Lincoln)
Immanuel Fontenelle (nursing home in Omaha)
Immanuel Medical Center (Omaha Nebraska; 280 beds)
Immanuel Rehabilitation Center (Omaha Nebraska)
Lakeside Hospital (Omaha Nebraska; 160 beds)
Lasting Hope Recovery Center (Omaha Nebraska; psychiatric hospital with 120 beds)
Memorial Hospital (Schuyler Nebraska; 25 beds)
Mercy Corning Hospital (Corning Iowa; 20 beds)
Mercy Hospital (Council Bluffs Iowa; 160 beds)
Midlands Hospital (Papillion Nebraska; 50 beds)
Plainview Hospital (Plainview Nebraska)

COMPETITORS

BryanLGH Medical Center
Children's Hospital & Medical Center
Fremont Area Medical Center
Heartland Health
Iowa Health System
Madonna Rehabilitation Hospital
Mercy Health Network
Methodist Health System
Nebraska Medical Center
Saint Elizabeth Regional Medical Center
UNMC Physicians

HISTORICAL FINANCIALS

Company Type: Private

Income Statement FYE: June 30

	REVENUE ($ mil.)	NET INCOME ($ mil.)	NET PROFIT MARGIN	EMPLOYEES
06/11	262	26	10.2%	8,600
06/10	285	23	8.4%	—
06/09	3	0	—	—
06/08	5	(0)	—	—
Annual Growth	268.7%	—	—	—

2011 Year-End Financials

Debt ratio: —
Return on equity: 10.20%
Cash ($ mil.): 25
Current ratio: 0.10
Long-term debt ($ mil.): —
Dividends
Yield: —
Payout: —
Market value ($ mil.): —

CREIGHTON UNIVERSITY

Consistently ranked among the top universities in the Midwest Creighton University is a Jesuit Catholic university with an enrollment of approximately 8000 undergraduate graduate and professional students. With a student-to-faculty ratio of 11:1 it offers more than 70 majors through nine schools and colleges including institutions focused on arts and sciences business law medicine dentistry pharmacy and nursing. Its 130-acre campus is adjacent to the downtown business district of Omaha Nebraska. Creighton University was founded in 1878 and named after Omaha businessman Edward Creighton.

Geographic Reach

In addition to teaching international students from about 40 countries at its Omaha campus Creighton University offers hands-on service and learning programs in the Dominican Republic and the Middle East. It also has international affiliate or exchange programs with institutions in about 55 countries.

Operations

In addition to core curriculum the university has a long history of providing medical education. Many of its on-site medical training programs are provided at the facilities of medical care provider Alegent Creighton Health (formerly Alegent Health). Creighton University also has a partnership with the St. Joseph's Hospital and Medical Center in Phoenix Arizona. In addition the university conducts research programs in various scientific fields.

Following student tuition and fees which account for about 45% of annual revenue health services bring in about 20% of sales.

Financial Performance

Revenue fell 3% to $407.9 million in 2013 from lower health services revenue and grant and contract revenues which was partly offset by increased tuition and fee income. Net income of $84.5 million in fiscal 2013 showed a marked improvement over net losses reported in 2012; the profits were attributed to higher investment returns and other non-operating income sources.

Strategy

To expand its services for students Creighton University looks to launch new degree programs enhance facilities and increase partnerships with other educational medical and research institutions. In 2012 the university launched its first 100% online degree program (for a Bachelor of Science in Integrated Leadership) and in 2013 it opened the Creighton Business Institute to improve its business leadership development offerings.

Creighton University strengthened its partnership with the health network in 2012 when it sold its 26% stake in the 400-bed Creighton University Medical Center (CUMC) in Omaha to Alegent. Tenet Healthcare owned a majority stake in the hospital which was also acquired by Alegent. The transaction also made Alegent's network of care centers the primary teaching sites for Creighton University's School of Medicine and other health-related schools. Creighton University already partnered with Alegent on a number of health-related professional education and research programs prior to the deal and the university believes that its students will benefit from the expanded relationship.

EXECUTIVES

Vice Chairman, Bruce C. Rohde, age 65
President and Director, Rev John P. Schlegel
SVP Operations and Treasurer, Daniel E. Burkey
Controller, Michael A. Pille
VP Information Technology, Brian A. Young
VP Student Services and Dean Students, John C. Cernech
VP University Relations, Lisa D. Calvert
Senior General Counsel and Corporate Secretary, Greg D. Jahn
VP University Ministry, Rev Andrew F. Alexander
Director Career Center, Jim Bretl
Dean College of Business Administration, Anthony R. Hendrickson
Director Budget, Fred J. Nesler
Assistant VP Public Relations and Marketing, Kim B. Manning
Assistant VP Alumni Relations, Diane H. Dougherty Crowley
VP Institutional Relations, Patricia R. (Pat) Callone
Senior Associate VP Development and Campaign Director, Laura C. Simic
CEO Creighton Medical Associates, Todd Carlon
VP Academic Affairs and Interim Dean School of Law, Patrick J. Borchers
VP Health Services, Donald R. Frey
Associate VP Enrollment Management, Mary E. Chase
Director Environmental Health and Safety, John T. Baxter
University Registrar, John A. Krecek
Dean University College and Summer Sessions, Barbara J. Braden
Dean College of Arts and Sciences, Robert J. Lueger
Director Financial Aid, Robert D. Walker
Associate VP Faculty Development and Dean Graduate School, Gail M. Jensen
Dean School of Medicine, Rowen K. Zetterman
Dean School of Nursing, Eleanor V. Howell
Dean School of Pharmacy and Health Professions, J. Christopher Bradberry
Director Purchasing, Joseph J. Zaborowski
Associate VP Administration and Director Operational Planning, John L. Wilhelm
Director Human Resources, Jeffrey C. Branstetter
VP for General Counsel, Amy S. Bones
VP Research, Robert P. Heaney
Chairman, William A. Fitzgerald
Associate Director of Admissions, Monique Donahoe
Vice Chairman, Bruce C. Rohde, age 65
Director, James R. (Jim) Young, age 62
Director, Mogens C. Bay
Director, Patrick J. (Pat) Zenner, age 66
Director, Ronald B. (Ron) Gartlan
Director, W. Gary Gates, age 63
Director, Mark H. Rauenhorst, age 61
Director, Bruce E. Grewcock
Director, Joseph H. (Joe) Moglia, age 65
Director, George F. Haddix, age 75
Director, Michael R. (Mike) McCarthy, age 63
Director, Alan D. Simon
Director, Daniel P. Neary
Director, Howard L. Hawks
Director, Robert A. Reed Sr.
Director, Richard T. (Dick) Kizer
President and Director, Rev John P. Schlegel
Director, Floyd J. Malveaux
Director, Mimi A. Feller
Director, Frank L. Hayes
Director, Mark D. Huber
Director, Susan M. Jacques
Director, Melissa C. Kean
Director, Michael E. Kelly
Director, Rev Peter J. Klink
Director, Terry J. Kroeger
Director, Bruce R. Lauritzen
Director, Deborah A. Macdonald
Director, Chris J. Murphy
Director, Rev Roc O'Connor
Director, Rev Philip J. Rossi
Director, Constance M. Ryan
Director, Rev Gerard L. Stockhausen
Director, Gail Werner-Robertson
Auditors: Deloitte&ToucheLLP

LOCATIONS

HQ: CREIGHTON UNIVERSITY
2500 CALIFORNIA PLZ, OMAHA, NE 68178-0002
Phone: 402-280-2900
Web: WWW.MEDSCHOOL.CREIGHTON.EDU

PRODUCTS/OPERATIONS

2013 Revenue

	$ mil.	% of total
Student tuition & fees	190	46
Health care services	115	28
Auxiliary enterprises	31	8
Grants & contracts	27	7
Investment income	14	4
Contributions	11	3
Released assets	11	3
Other	5	1
Total	**407**	**100**

HISTORICAL FINANCIALS

Company Type: Private

Income Statement FYE: June 30

	REVENUE ($ mil.)	NET INCOME ($ mil.)	NET PROFIT MARGIN	EMPLOYEES
06/12	419	(28)	—	5,000
06/11	414	79	19.2%	—
06/10	405	36	8.9%	—
06/09	392	(79)	—	—
Annual Growth	2.2%	—	—	—

2012 Year-End Financials

Debt ratio: —
Return on equity: (-6.80%)
Cash ($ mil.): 32
Current ratio: —
Long-term debt ($ mil.): —
Dividends
Yield: —
Payout: —
Market value ($ mil.): —

CREST OPERATIONS LLC

Crest Operations part of Crest Industries distributes and installs electrical substations and transmission products for electric power generation and utility customers worldwide through its DIS-TRAN and Beta Engineering subsidiaries. Other subsidiaries grow pine and hardwood trees in Louisiana and Texas (Crest Natural Resources) and make wooden utility poles and cross arms. Crest's Mid-State Supply Company subsidiary is a

Louisiana-based distributor of electrical products that has showrooms for appliances and lighting. Crest Operations was founded in 1958.

EXECUTIVES

Human Resources, Kris Hickman

LOCATIONS

HQ: CREST OPERATIONS LLC
4725 HIGHWAY 28 E, PINEVILLE, LA 71360-4730
Phone: 318-448-8287

COMPETITORS

Consolidated Electrical
Graybar Electric
WESCO International

HISTORICAL FINANCIALS

Company Type: Private

Income Statement FYE: December 31

	REVENUE ($ mil.)	NET INCOME ($ mil.)	NET PROFIT MARGIN	EMPLOYEES
12/12	240	28	12.1%	300
12/11	196	16	8.2%	—
12/08	178	24	13.5%	—
12/07	138	18	13.5%	—
Annual Growth	11.7%	9.2%	—	—

2012 Year-End Financials

Debt ratio: —
Return on equity: 12.10%
Cash ($ mil.): 17
Current ratio: 0.30
Long-term debt ($ mil.): —
Dividends
Yield: —
Payout: —
Market value ($ mil.): —

CRISTA MINISTRIES

EXECUTIVES

Interim Asia Area Director, Robin Shell
President, David (Dave) Eller
Communications Officer, Derek Sciba
International Program Director, Meredith Long
Technical Support Director, Merry Fitzpatrick
Africa Area Director, Diane Bricker
Bolivia Country Director, Fatima Espinoza
Haiti Director, Christon Domond
Communications Officer, Cathy Herholdt
CFO, Michael Eggers
Senior Director of International Operations, Jacinta Tegman

LOCATIONS

HQ: CRISTA MINISTRIES
19303 FREMONT AVE N, SHORELINE, WA 981333800
Phone: 2065467200
Web: WWW.CRISTA.ORG

HISTORICAL FINANCIALS

Company Type: Private

Income Statement FYE: June 30

	REVENUE ($ mil.)	NET INCOME ($ mil.)	NET PROFIT MARGIN	EMPLOYEES
06/14	101	6	5.9%	1,200
06/13	102	1	1.4%	—
06/12	96	1	1.6%	—
06/09	132	0	—	—
Annual Growth	(5.2%)	—	—	—

2014 Year-End Financials

Debt ratio: —
Return on equity: 5.90%
Cash ($ mil.): 16
Current ratio: 1.60
Long-term debt ($ mil.): —
Dividends
Yield: —
Payout: —
Market value ($ mil.): —

CRITTENTON HOSPITAL MEDICAL CENTER

Crittenton Hospital Medical Center treats patients in the western counties of the suburban Detroit area. The not-for-profit hospital has 290 beds for acute care but also provides primary and specialist care. Crittenton offers such services as urgent pediatric care rehabilitative therapy inpatient psychiatric care joint replacement and sleep analysis. It is a fully accredited teaching campus and partners with area universities and medical providers. It also operates outpatient facilities including surgery imaging and therapy centers. With a heritage that reaches back to the early 1900s Crittenton Hospital Medical Center opened its doors in 1967.

Geographic Reach

Crittenton serves residents of Lapeer Macomb and Oakland counties. It has facilities in the Michigan communities of Auburn Hills Lake Orion Oxford Rochester Hills Sterling Heights Troy and Washington Township.

Operations

Crittenton has a medical staff of almost 500 physicians who practice in more than 50 specialist fields. The hospital treats more than 28000 patients each year capturing about 40% of the market share in its main service territory.

The hospital is the teaching facility for Wayne State University's medical school and conducts training programs including residencies for family medicine and ear nose and throat (ENT) practitioners. It also partners with Oakland University's School of Nursing. Other affiliations include a partnership with the University of Michigan Health System for electrophysiology and cardiovascular surgery.

Strategy

Crittenton has spent millions in recent years to expand its services and facilities. It is currently building a new south tower a six-story addition that will add about 90 private patient rooms. Past additions include the $16 million Karmanos-Crittenton Cancer Center (2010) and the Wayne State University Physicians Group Family Medicine Center (2008). In 2006 Crittenton completed an $86 million project that added north and south wings and increased capacity for emergency women's and children's services; it also upgraded administrative and information systems.

EXECUTIVES

Chief Strategy Officer, Michelle Hornberger
CFO, Donna M. Kopinski
CEO, Roy Powell
Chief Nursing Officer, Ken Sanger
Chief Medical Officer, Sheryl Wissman
Chairman, Robert J. Lenihan
Vice Chairman, Beverly Allen

LOCATIONS

HQ: CRITTENTON HOSPITAL MEDICAL CENTER
261 E MAPLE RD, BIRMINGHAM, MI 48009-6324
Phone: 248-652-5000
Web: WWW.CRITTENTON.COM

PRODUCTS/OPERATIONS

Selected Services

Behavioral Health
Bloodless Medicine
Cancer Services
Cardiovascular
Clinical Laboratory Services
Diabetes Services
Diagnostic Neurology (ENG)
Emergency Services
Endoscopy Services
Executive Medicine
Imaging Centers
Imaging Services
Medical Equipment
Occupational Medicine
Orthopedics
Palliative Care
Pediatrics
Pharmacy
Rehabilitation
Respiratory Therapy
Robotic Surgery
Senior Wellness
Sleep Center
Stroke Center
Surgical Services
Travel Medicine
Urology Services
Women' s Services
Wound Healing Center

COMPETITORS

Ascension Health
Beaumont Health System
Detroit Medical Center
Henry Ford Health System
Hurley Medical Center
Mount Clemens Regional Medical Center
Oakwood Healthcare
Providence Hospital and Medical Centers
Trinity Health (Novi)
University of Michigan Health System

HISTORICAL FINANCIALS

Company Type: Private

Income Statement FYE: December 31

	REVENUE ($ mil.)	NET INCOME ($ mil.)	NET PROFIT MARGIN	EMPLOYEES
12/09	223	(4)	—	1,515
12/08	200	(39)	—	—
Annual Growth	11.7%	—	—	—

2009 Year-End Financials

Debt ratio: —
Return on equity: (-1.90%)
Cash ($ mil.): 47
Current ratio: 0.60
Long-term debt ($ mil.): —
Dividends
Yield: —
Payout: —
Market value ($ mil.): —

CROSSLAND CONSTRUCTION COMPANY INC.

Crossland Construction has crossed the prairie transitioning from a local player in Columbus Kansas to a firm with a strong regional presence. The company designs builds and manages construction of government education healthcare retail and other buildings from a handful of offices in Kansas Missouri Arkansas Oklahoma Colorado and Texas. Customers have included Harley-Davidson SAM'S CLUB McCune Brooks Hospital Embassy Suites and a variety of school districts and municipalities. Crossland builds everything from office buildings and warehouses to veteran's memorials and airports. The company which often works in partnership with PBA Architects was founded by Ivan Crossland Sr. in 1978.

Sales and Marketing

Crossland Construction serves a variety of customer types such as Embassy Suites Harley-Davidson school districts and municipalities. In 2013 it's working with Pittsburgh State University to build a new Center for the Arts among other projects.

The construction firm's services include preconstruction construction management general construction services design build and self-performance capabilities.

Geographic Reach

With the capacity to perform work in more than 40 states Kansas-based Crossland Construction has offices in Kansas Texas Arkansas Oklahoma Colorado and Missouri.

Awards and Recognition

One of the top builders in the US Crossland Construction is ranked 95th among 400 Top US contractors by ENR Magazine.

Strategy

In recent years Crossland Construction has expanded its business to Colorado by establishing an office in Denver in 2012. To serve clients in the Oklahoma City and Edmond Oklahoma metropolitan area Crossland Construction opened a division office in Oklahoma City that is leveraging existing relationships with the lucrative and growing oil and gas industries in that market.

It also works to promote construction as a career path. Crossland Construction works to maintain a solid workforce by investing in education at two levels. The company's Crossland Academy offers current employees the chance to earn certificates in concrete welding heavy equipment operation and storm water protection in addition to a complete curriculum laid out by the National Center for Construction Education and Research (NCCER). Its Crossland Connection program helps elementary through high school students learn about careers in construction. High school students are offered the same NCCER curriculum as employees to prepare for a trade apprenticeship or to enter a college construction trades program.

EXECUTIVES

CEO, Ivan Crossland Jr.
President, Bennie Crossland
VP Texas Division, Mike Crossland
VP Business Development and Real Estate, Christopher Crossland
VP Special Projects, Patrick Crossland
Vice President Midwest Region, Danny Langerot
Chief Administrative Officer, David Allison
President Southwest Region, John Priest

LOCATIONS

HQ: CROSSLAND CONSTRUCTION COMPANY INC.
S HWY 19, COLUMBUS, KS 66725
Phone: 620-429-1414
Web: WWW.CROSSLANDCONSTRUCTION.COM

PRODUCTS/OPERATIONS

Selected Services

Pre-Construction
Construction Management
General Construction Services
Design Build
Self-Performance Capabilities

Selected Areas of Work

Distribution Centers
Educational
Healthcare
Heavy/civil
Hospitality
Manufacturing Plants
Meeting Spaces
Municipal
Office
Retail
Sporting Facilities

COMPETITORS

Austin Commercial
Austin Industries
Baldwin & Shell
C.F. Jordan
CDI Contractors
Cadence McShane
Dean Word
Fluor
Gilbane Building Company
Harvey Builders
JC General Contractors
KBR
Spawglass Holding
Structure Tone Southwest
Tellepsen Builders
Turner Construction
W.S. Bellows

HISTORICAL FINANCIALS

Company Type: Private

Income Statement FYE: July 31

	REVENUE ($ mil.)	NET INCOME ($ mil.)	NET PROFIT MARGIN	EMPLOYEES
07/11	363	2	0.6%	715
07/08	434	10	2.4%	—
07/07	336	11	3.4%	—
07/04	176	2	1.3%	—
Annual Growth	10.9%	(2.0%)	—	—

2011 Year-End Financials

Debt ratio: —
Return on equity: 0.60%
Cash ($ mil.): 34
Current ratio: 1.10
Long-term debt ($ mil.): —
Dividends
Yield: —
Payout: —
Market value ($ mil.): —

CROWDER CONSTRUCTION COMPANY INC

EXECUTIVES

Chairman President and CEO, Otis A. Crowder
Operations Manager, Mike Reisinger

LOCATIONS

HQ: CROWDER CONSTRUCTION COMPANY INC
6425 BROOKSHIRE BLVD, CHARLOTTE, NC 282160301
Phone: 7043723541
Web: WWW.CROWDERCC.COM

COMPETITORS

Alberici
English Construction Company
Hubbard Group
Oldcastle Materials
Rea Contracting
S. T. Wooten
Skanska USA Civil

HISTORICAL FINANCIALS

Company Type: Private

Income Statement FYE: March 31

	REVENUE ($ mil.)	NET INCOME ($ mil.)	NET PROFIT MARGIN	EMPLOYEES
03/14	233	0	—	900
03/13	233	0	—	—
03/12	222	0	—	—
03/11	186	0	—	—
Annual Growth	7.8%	—	—	—

2014 Year-End Financials

Debt ratio: —
Return on equity: —
Cash ($ mil.): 16
Current ratio: 0.50
Long-term debt ($ mil.): —
Dividends
Yield: —
Payout: —
Market value ($ mil.): —

CROWN BATTERY MANUFACTURING COMPANY

EXECUTIVES

President and CEO, Harold F. (Hal) Hawk Jr.
CFO, James Faist
President CEO, Bill Brooks
President Jeffery Allen, Ben Sverdlow
President Crown Battery Manufacturing Co, Hal Hawk

LOCATIONS

HQ: CROWN BATTERY MANUFACTURING COMPANY
1445 MAJESTIC DR, FREMONT, OH 434209190
Phone: 4193320563
Web: WWW.C-LINEBATTERY.COM

PRODUCTS/OPERATIONS

Selected Products

Batteries and Battery parts
Battery Chargers
Commercial
Deep Cycle
Marine
Sealed Lead Acid
Utility Starting
Industrial
- Lift Truck
- Rail Road
- Mining

Other
- Powerhouse Chargers
- Powerhouse Cleaners

COMPETITORS

C&D Technologies
Eagle-Picher
East Penn Manufacturing
EnerSys
Exide
GS Yuasa
Interstate Batteries
Johnson Controls Power Solutions
Ritar Power
Valence Technology

HISTORICAL FINANCIALS

Company Type: Private

Income Statement FYE: September 30

	REVENUE ($ mil.)	NET INCOME ($ mil.)	NET PROFIT MARGIN	EMPLOYEES
09/14	214	12	5.6%	550
09/13	196	10	5.5%	—
09/12	191	6	3.2%	—
09/11	215	0	—	—
Annual Growth	(0.2%)	—	—	—

2014 Year-End Financials

Debt ratio: —
Return on equity: 5.60%
Cash ($ mil.): 2
Current ratio: 1.10
Long-term debt ($ mil.): —
Dividends
Yield: —
Payout: —
Market value ($ mil.): —

CSI LEASING INC.

CSI Leasing provides computer products leasing for customers in the Americas Europe and Asia. The company targets businesses looking to lower operational costs by avoiding expenses related to ownership and upkeep of computer and communications network gear. It provides off-lease services through its EPC subsidiary which remarkets recycles and disposes of information technology equipment —and securely wipes and/or destroys the data on the equipment when it is returned. CSI serves clients in such industries as software financial services government and education. Majority-owned by employees and led by co-founder and chairman Ken Steinback the company was founded in 1972 as Computer Sales International.

CSI has been making moves in several directions as part of an expansion and diversification plan announced in 2010. The company operates domestically from more than 30 US sales offices but it has been looking increasingly to international clients to drive sales growth since US business has plateaued. To that end it boosted its presence in Singapore and added an office in Malaysia with the 2010 purchase of Fortis Lease Singapore and Fortis Lease Malaysia —bringing its number of international subsidiaries to about two dozen.

However the company is also looking for new growth in the US. In early 2011 it acquired Academic Capital Group a Chicago-based company that offers lease financing for cities and other government and educational institutions. Academic is becoming CSI Government and Education Finance a new division focusing on financing for commercial tax-exempt and proprietary vendors.

In 2009 CSI opened a subsidiary in Germany CSI Lifecycle Services to address demand there for IT systems planning implementation and support. The business is operated as a joint venture with ergoTrade a German IT products resale and related services provider. Also that year the company opened a new distribution and recycling facility in Toronto to better serve clients in eastern Canada. CSI has similar operations in St. Louis Kansas City Las Vegas and Columbia South Carolina.

EXECUTIVES

Senior Vice President Chief Information, Chris Schmidt
President and COO, Stephen G. (Steve) Hamilton, age 59
Vice Chairman and CEO, E. William (Bill) Gillula, age 69
President Executive Personal Computers, Dan Fuller
VP Marketing, Tim Tucker
Vice President General Counsel With Csi Leasing, Jeff Rousseau
Vp, Tom Brown
Vice President For International Adm, Paul Keefe
Senior Vice President Portfolio Mgmt, Mark K Schlichter
Senior Vice President General Couns, Lorraine Cherrick
Vice President, Karyn Voorhees
Vice President Media Finance, Bob Verzello
Vice President, Tony Ruggeri
Vice President, Dan Toscano
Vice President Marketing, Paul Rossan
Vice President, Angie Bader
Senior Vice President And Us Chief Credit Officer, Charles McDaniels
Svp Of Information Technology, Linda Miller
Vice President Lease Management, Kathie Haberstroh-nelke
Vice President, Michelle Thompson
Senior Vice President Sales, Chip Deson
Assistant Vice President Payroll Director, Dianne Kramlich
Assistant Vice President Finance, Matt Kersting
Vice President Accounting, Janine Todd
Marketing Vice President, Mark Crain
Assistant Vice President Finance, Ryan Bauer
Legal Secretary, Vanita Montgomery
Legal Secretary, Bonita Benda
Legal Secretary, Shannon Hulahan
Vice President And Associate Attorney, Joan Kersting
Assistant Vice President Of Applications Development, Bill Elmore
Executive Vice President Marketing, Lawrence Schinsky
Chairman, Kenneth B. (Ken) Steinback, age 72
Vice Chairman and CEO, E. William (Bill) Gillula, age 69
Manager Of Treasury, Aaron Tanaka
Auditors: Ernst&YoungLLP

LOCATIONS

HQ: CSI LEASING INC.
9990 OLD OLIVE STREET RD, SAINT LOUIS, MO 63141-5930
Phone: 314-997-7010
Web: WWW.CSILEASING.COM

PRODUCTS/OPERATIONS

Lifecycle Services
Leasing consultati
Financing options
Consolidation of leased assets from multiple manufactur
Online tracking of leased assets
Disposal of equipment and sanitizing of hard drives

COMPETITORS

Blackwell Consulting
CalFirst
Dell
HP Financial Services
IBM Global Financing
Ingram Micro
Pitney Bowes
Pomeroy IT
Syscap
ePlus

HISTORICAL FINANCIALS

Company Type: Private

Income Statement FYE: June 30

	REVENUE ($ mil.)	NET INCOME ($ mil.)	NET PROFIT MARGIN	EMPLOYEES
06/09	362	16	4.5%	540
06/03	531	14	2.7%	—
06/02	502	13	2.7%	—
06/01	576	10	1.9%	—
Annual Growth	(5.6%)	5.2%	—	—

2009 Year-End Financials

Debt ratio: —
Return on equity: 4.50%
Cash ($ mil.): 21
Current ratio: —
Long-term debt ($ mil.): —
Dividends
Yield: —
Payout: —
Market value ($ mil.): —

CUIVRE RIVER ELECTRIC COOPERATIVE INC.

EXECUTIVES

General Manager and CEO, Dan L. Brown
Manager Finance and Accounting, Susan Dollins
Manager Human Resources, Regina Creech
Manager Communications, Mary Jane Clark
Manager Member Services, Kevin Hurd
Manager Branch Offices, Keith Stone
Manager Administration and IT, Doug Tracy
Communications Specialist, Lonnie Tucker
Chairman, Don Schappe

LOCATIONS

HQ: CUIVRE RIVER ELECTRIC COOPERATIVE INC.
1112 E CHERRY ST, TROY, MO 633791518
Phone: 6365288261
Web: WWW.CUIVRERIVERELECTRICCOOPERATIVE.COM

HISTORICAL FINANCIALS

Company Type: Private

Income Statement FYE: December 31

	REVENUE ($ mil.)	NET INCOME ($ mil.)	NET PROFIT MARGIN	EMPLOYEES
12/12	107	5	4.9%	134
12/11	102	10	9.8%	—
12/09	101	8	8.4%	—
12/08	0	0	—	—
Annual Growth	344.1%	—	—	—

2012 Year-End Financials

Debt ratio: —
Return on equity: 4.90%
Cash ($ mil.): 2
Current ratio: —
Long-term debt ($ mil.): —
Dividends
Yield: —
Payout: —
Market value ($ mil.): —

CUMBERLAND COUNTY HOSPITAL SYSTEM INC.

Don't fear for a lack of medical services at Cumberland County Hospital System (doing business as Cape Fear Valley Health System). The medical provider comprises five acute-care and specialty hospitals with about 765 total beds and more than a dozen primary-care physician practices scattered throughou the region. The hospital system serves residents of coastal North Carolina providing general and specialized medical services such as cancer treatment open-heart surgery psychiatric care and rehabilitation. It also operates the HealthPlex fitness and wellness facility and provides home health and hospice services.

Geographic Reach

Cumberland County Hospital System's facilities include Cape Fear Valley Medical Center Highsmith-Rainey Specialty Hospital Cape Fear Valley Rehabilitation Center and Bladen County Hospital as well as several medical offices and clinics spread throughout the region.

Operations

Cumberland County Hospital System is the ninth largest health system in North Carolina with more than 935000 patient visits annually. It is also Cumberland County's largest non-government employer.

Company Background

The health system was founded in 1956 as a 200-bed one-building hospital. Flagship facility Cape Fear Valley Medical Center completed an expansion project in 2008 adding about 150 patient beds.

EXECUTIVES

CEO, Michael Nagowski
CFO, Sandra Williams
Chief Nursing Officer, Jana Stonestreet
Chief Medical Officer, Christopher Aul
Nursing Director, Jennifer Smith
Medical Director, Mark Graham
Chairman, Jerry Dean
Vice Chairman, Marion Gillis Olion
Treasurer, James Shearer

LOCATIONS

HQ: CUMBERLAND COUNTY HOSPITAL SYSTEM INC.
1638 OWEN DR, FAYETTEVILLE, NC 28304-3424
Phone: 910-609-4000
Web: WWW.CAPEFEARVALLEY.COM

PRODUCTS/OPERATIONS

Selected Services

Birth center
Healthplex
Heart and vascular
Imaging/diagnostics
Minority health
Neuroscience
Orthopedics
Outpatient services
Pediatrics
Physician practice
Rehabilitation
Scancer treatment
Surgical services
Weight loss surgery

COMPETITORS

Alamance Regional Medical Center
Annie Penn Hospital
Carolinas HealthCare System
Cone Health
Danville Regional Medical Center
Duke University Health System
High Point Regional Health System
Morehead Memorial Hospital
Rex Healthcare
Rowan Regional Medical Center
UNC Hospitals
Vidant Health
Wake Forest University Baptist Medical Center
WakeMed

HISTORICAL FINANCIALS

Company Type: Private

Income Statement FYE: September 30

	REVENUE ($ mil.)	NET INCOME ($ mil.)	NET PROFIT MARGIN	EMPLOYEES
09/07	504	23	4.6%	5,000
09/06	492	29	6.0%	—
09/05	1,753	0	0.0%	—
Annual Growth	(46.4%)	28202.0%	—	—

2007 Year-End Financials

Debt ratio: —	
Return on equity: 4.60%	Dividends
Cash ($ mil.): 11	Yield: —
Current ratio: 1.30	Payout: —
Long-term debt ($ mil.): —	Market value ($ mil.): —

CYSTIC FIBROSIS FOUNDATION

The Cystic Fibrosis Foundation funds cystic fibrosis (CF) research and medical programs. Founded in 1955 the organization supports clinical trials and specialized health-care centers provides grants for independent research operates university research centers encourages drug development through matching funds and offers CF-related information and educational materials. Its Cystic Fibrosis Foundation Therapeutics (CFFT) subsidiary partners with pharmaceutical companies and research facilities to develop CF drugs. The foundation provides funding training and accreditation for about 110 treatment centers in the US. It has about 75 chapters and branch offices nationwide.

EXECUTIVES

Director of Medical Communications, Carolyn A. Habbersett
Director Finance and Administration, Barb Gull
Auditors: PricewaterhouseCoopersLLP

LOCATIONS

HQ: CYSTIC FIBROSIS FOUNDATION
6931 ARLINGTON RD STE 200, BETHESDA, MD 20814-5269
Phone: 301-951-4422
Web: WWW.CFF.ORG

PRODUCTS/OPERATIONS

2010 Revenue Sources

	$ mil.	% of total
Pharmacy	137	44
Special events	81	26
Royalties	53	17
General contributions	37	11
Interest .6	1	
Other	2	1
Total	313	100

HISTORICAL FINANCIALS

Company Type: Private

Income Statement FYE: December 31

	REVENUE ($ mil.)	NET INCOME ($ mil.)	NET PROFIT MARGIN	EMPLOYEES
12/12	297	175	58.8%	550
12/08	138	(2)	—	—
12/06	246	219	89.1%	—
12/06	539	0	0.0%	—
Annual Growth	(9.4%)	369.4%	—	—

2012 Year-End Financials

Debt ratio: —	
Return on equity: 58.80%	Dividends
Cash ($ mil.): 89	Yield: —
Current ratio: —	Payout: —
Long-term debt ($ mil.): —	Market value ($ mil.): —

D W W CO. INC.

First Orange County then the world –or at least as far as Arizona and Mexico. Megadealer David Wilson Automotive Group has its roots in Orange County California with 16 branches that stretch to east to Scottsdale and now south to Puerto Vallarta Mexico. David Wilson's Automotive locations sell new and used Acura Ford Honda and Mazda cars as well as Toyota and Lexus brand vehicles. The group's dealerships also operate parts and service departments; some offer fleet services. Dealership Web sites allow customers to search inventory schedule service appointments and request quotes. David Wilson owns the company that bears his name

The company's growth strategy includes promoting form within. The owner hires sales managers only and promotes them to general managers over time as openings emerge. He also offers higher pay and benefits that many of his peers but demands that sales target are achieved.

Wilson graduated with from college in 1970 with a degree in religion and philosophy but found that his true calling was to the people on the highways not the ones in the pews. In 1985 Wilson bought Toyota of Orange and planted the seeds of his empire.

EXECUTIVES

Chairman and CEO, David Wilson

LOCATIONS

HQ: D W W CO. INC.
1400 N TUSTIN ST, ORANGE, CA 92867-3902
Phone: 714-639-6750
Web: WWW.DAVIDTOEWS.COM

COMPETITORS

AutoNation
Holman Enterprises
Marty Franich
Penske Motor Group
Tuttle-Click
piercey automotive

HISTORICAL FINANCIALS

Company Type: Private

Income Statement FYE: December 31

	REVENUE ($ mil.)	NET INCOME ($ mil.)	NET PROFIT MARGIN	EMPLOYEES
12/08	162	7	4.6%	135
12/07	199	7	3.8%	—
12/06	229	12	5.2%	—
12/05	214	10	4.7%	—
Annual Growth	(8.8%)	(9.2%)	—	—

2008 Year-End Financials

Debt ratio: —	
Return on equity: 4.60%	Dividends
Cash ($ mil.): 23	Yield: —
Current ratio: 0.20	Payout: —
Long-term debt ($ mil.): —	Market value ($ mil.): —

D/L COOPERATIVE INC.

Yes the farmer takes a wife then hi-ho the dairy-o the farmer takes membership in milk-marketing organizations such as Dairylea Cooperative. Owned by some 2000 dairy farmers in the northeastern US Dairylea processes and markets 6.3 billion pounds of milk for its farmers annually to dairy-product customers including food manufacturers. Its Agri-Services holding company provides members with a full range of financial and farm-management services as well as insurance. Its Empire Livestock Marketing unit operates regional livestock auction locations. Dairylea which was established in 1907 by New York dairy farmers merged with the US's largest milk marketing coop Dairy Farmers of America in 2014.

Ownership

Dairylea joined Kansas City Missouri-based Dairy Farmers of America (DFA) in April 2014 to expand its geographic coverage. Prior to joining DFA Dairylea has had a joint marketing venture (Dairy Marketing Services or DMS) with the national coop. DFA has 13000 members in 48 states. The Dairylea name became a brand of DFA and maintained a field office and staff in Syracuse.

Geographic Reach

Dairylea sells 6 billion pounds of raw milk annually through a milk-marketing network that stretches from Maine to Ohio to Maryland.

Services provided by holding company Agri-Services LLC include insurance coverage information management livestock marketing loan programs milk price risk management services business planning and consulting services purchasing programs and investment and retirement planning advice.

Operations

Through its DMS partnership with Dairy Farmers of America Dairylea sells and distributes raw milk. DMS serves both organizations as well as independent producers and cooperatives that produce 16 billion pounds of milk each year.

Financial Performance

Dairylea has annual sales of about $1 billion.

EXECUTIVES

CFO, Gregory I. (Greg) Wickham
President Chairman, William Beeman
Treasurer and Director, David R. Chamberlain
Assistant Treasurer and Director, Calvin Wood
Public Relations, Jennifer Huson
Media Contact, Karen Cartier
Executive Assistant, Krista Piper
Vice President, David White
Second VP Board of Directors and Secretary, William Beeman
Treasurer and Director, David R. Chamberlain
First VP Board of Directors, Raymond J. Diebold
Assistant Treasurer and Director, Calvin Wood
Director, Todd Hathorn
Director, G. Douglas Young
Director, James Madigan
Director, Sanford Stauffer
Director, Glen Gasstrom
Director, Lawrence Woodruff Jr.
Director, Edgar A. King
Director, Dale Van Erden
Director, Arnold Dueppengiesser
Director, Donald Risser
Director, Richard Baldwin

LOCATIONS

HQ: D/L COOPERATIVE INC.
5001 BRITTONFIELD PKWY, EAST SYRACUSE, NY 130579201
Phone: 3152331000
Web: WWW.DAIRYLEA.COM

PRODUCTS/OPERATIONS

Selected Affiliates & Subsidiaries

Agri-Edge Development
Agri-Max Financial Services
Agri-Services Agency
Dairy Risk Management Services
Eagle Dairy Direct
Empire Livestock Marketing Services

COMPETITORS

Agri-Mark
Associated Milk Producers
Dean Foods
Foremost Farms
Garelick Farms
Keller's Creamery
Land O' Lakes
Maryland & Virginia Milk Producers
Quality Chekd

HISTORICAL FINANCIALS

Company Type: Private

Income Statement FYE: March 31

	REVENUE ($ mil.)	NET INCOME ($ mil.)	NET PROFIT MARGIN	EMPLOYEES
03/11	1,333	1	0.1%	107
03/10	1,066	1	0.1%	
Annual Growth	25.1%	7.6%	—	—

2011 Year-End Financials

Debt ratio: —
Return on equity: 0.10%
Cash ($ mil.): 14
Current ratio: 0.60
Long-term debt ($ mil.): —
Dividends
Yield: —
Payout: —
Market value ($ mil.): —

DAKOTA ELECTRIC ASSOCIATION

The Dakota Electric Association delivers electricity to residents of southeastern Minnesota the Gopher State so they don't have to burrow underground to outlast those long cold winters. The member-owned utility serves more than 103000 customers in portions of Dakota Goodhue Rice and Scott counties south of Minneapolis-St. Paul. The co-op gets its power wholesale from transmission cooperative Great River Energy and distributes it more than 4010 miles of power lines nearly two-thirds of which are buried. Dakota Electric is pushing energy efficiency programs and products to help save its customers money.

Geographic Reach

The company serves parts of Dakota Goodhue Scott and Rice counties in southern Minnesota.

Operations

Dakota Electric purchases power from Great River Energy and distributes electricity to commercial residential farming street lighting and irrigation customers. It has 2792 miles of underground power lines and 1220 miles of overhead lines.

Financial Performance

In 2013 the company's revenue increased by 2%. Dakota Electric's commercial members accounted for 41% of revenues; residential and farming 58%; and street lighting and irrigation 1%.Its net income grew by 5% in 2013 thanks to higher revenues and the absence of a loss from discontinued operations.Dakota Electric's operating cash inflow increased to $13.13 million in fiscal 2013 (from $5.61 million in 2012) due to higher net income and a change in the working capital.

Strategy

The co-op seeks to maintain and upgrade its power infrastructure and service to its members while keep power costs low.

As part of this strategy Dakota Electric operates a for-profit subsidiary Midwest Energy Services. That unit's subsidiaries provides complementary services to Dakota Electric's main power delivery business. They offer standby power generator and solar panel installation and leasing services (Energy Alternatives) and substation engineering services (Consulting Engineers Group).

Company Background

Dakota Electric was formed in 1937 as part of the Roosevelt Administration's national rural electrification drive.

EXECUTIVES

Vice President, Dirk Rotty
Vice President Regulatory, Doug Larson
Vice Chair, Jerry Pittman
Secretary, Paul Trapp
Board Of Directors, Clay De Bogart
Board Of Directors, David Jones
Auditors: EideBaillyLLP

LOCATIONS

HQ: DAKOTA ELECTRIC ASSOCIATION
4300 220TH ST W, FARMINGTON, MN 550249583
Phone: 6514636212
Web: WWW.DAKOTAELECTRIC.COM

PRODUCTS/OPERATIONS

2010 Sales

	$ mil.	% of total
% of total		
Residential		59
Large		37
Small		3
Street lighting &		1
Total		100

2010 Energy Sources

% of total	
Coal	75
Purchased	9
Hydro	7
Wind	7
Natural gas &	2
Total	100

COMPETITORS

ALLETE
Connexus Energy
Otter Tail
Wisconsin Energy
Xcel Energy

HISTORICAL FINANCIALS

Company Type: Private

Income Statement FYE: December 31

	REVENUE ($ mil.)	NET INCOME ($ mil.)	NET PROFIT MARGIN	EMPLOYEES
12/13	205	8	4.2%	100,000
12/09	178	7	3.9%	—
12/08	185	6	3.8%	—
12/06	132	0	—	—
Annual Growth	6.4%	—	—	—

2013 Year-End Financials

Debt ratio: —
Return on equity: 4.20%
Cash ($ mil.): 0
Current ratio: 0.50
Long-term debt ($ mil.): —
Dividends
Yield: —
Payout: —
Market value ($ mil.): —

DAKOTA SUPPLY GROUP INC.

Dakota Supply Group (DSG) distributes electrical communications and mechanical equipment to customers through more than a dozen branch locations in Minnesota North Dakota and South Dakota. The company stocks approximately 25000 products. DSG carries products from 3Com 3M A. O. Smith Buckingham Manufacturing Corning

Emerson Electric Ferraz Shawmut General Electric Honeywell Hubbell Moen Schneider Electric and Zurn Industries among other manufacturers. The company was founded in 1898. An employee stock ownership plan holds nearly all of Dakota Supply.

EXECUTIVES

Territory Manager Northern Minnesota, Mike McNabb

LOCATIONS

HQ: DAKOTA SUPPLY GROUP INC.
2601 3RD AVE N, FARGO, ND 58102-4016
Phone: 701-237-9440
Web: WWW.DAKOTASUPPLYGROUP.COM

COMPETITORS

Border States Electric
J. H. Larson
Viking Electric

HISTORICAL FINANCIALS

Company Type: Private

Income Statement FYE: December 29

	REVENUE ($ mil.)	NET INCOME ($ mil.)	NET PROFIT MARGIN	EMPLOYEES
12/12	297	15	5.3%	450
12/11	211	13	6.6%	—
12/09	162	4	2.5%	—
12/08	168	8	5.2%	—
Annual Growth	15.2%	16.2%	—	—

2012 Year-End Financials

Debt ratio: —
Return on equity: 5.30%
Cash ($ mil.): 0
Current ratio: 1.00
Long-term debt ($ mil.): —
Dividends
Yield: —
Payout: —
Market value ($ mil.): —

DANA-FARBER CANCER INSTITUTE INC.

The Dana-Farber Cancer Institute fights cancer on two fronts: It provides treatment to cancer patients young and old and researches new cancer diagnostics treatments and preventions. The organization's scientists also research AIDS treatments and cures for a host of other deadly diseases. Patients receive treatment from Dana-Farber through its cancer centers operated in conjunction with Brigham and Women's Hospital Children's Hospital Boston and Massachusetts General Hospital. The institute is also a principal teaching affiliate of Harvard Medical School. Dana-Farber is funded by the National Cancer Institute the National Institute of Allergy and Infectious Diseases and private contributions.

Geographic Reach

The institute primarily serves patients in New England.

Operations

Dana-Farber reports more than 34800 patient visits a year is involved in some 700 clinical trials.

Financial Performance

The institute reported a 4% rise in revenues in 2012 thanks to an increase in patient service revenues unrestricted contributions and bequests and other operating revenues.

Revenues from Medicare accounted 23.6% of Dana-Farber's patient service revenues in 2012; Medicaid 6.5%.Net income increased by 100% in 2012 due to an increase in realized and unrealized gains on investments and investment gains.

Strategy

When it comes to patient care Dana-Farber emphasizes the importance of forming research and treatment partnerships with other health care organizations. To that end the institute has opened a handful of treatment clinics on other medical campuses including one at Faulkner Hospital in southwest Boston and another at Milford Regional Medical Center in Massachusetts.

Along with expanding on other campuses Dana-Farber built a new cancer care center on its main campus in Boston. The Yawkey Center for Cancer Care named in honor of long-time contributor The Yawkey Foundation opened in 2011 to serve a growing number of patients. The 275000-sq.-ft center's 14-stories house most of Dana-Farber's adult outpatient care. The building has more than 100 exam rooms about 140 infusion chairs and a number of consultation rooms for family and patients. It also connects Dana-Farber to other campus buildings and to its clinical partners Brigham and Women's Hospital and Children's Hospital Boston.

In 2013 the institute and Lawrence + Memorial Cancer Center opened a $34.5 million 47000 sq.-ft. cancer facility in Waterford Connecticut.

Although Dana-Farber directs its research efforts toward saving lives from deadly diseases some of its discoveries also bring in a tidy income as the company and its research partners occasionally license out their drug discoveries to pharmaceutical companies.

Company Background

Dana-Farber Cancer Institute was founded as a children's cancer research foundation in 1947 by Dr. Sidney Farber. The institute later expanded its services to provide programs for adults as well as children.

EXECUTIVES

EVP CFO and Assistant Treasurer, Dorothy E. Puhy, age 62
President and CEO, Edward J. Benz
Chair Department of Radiation Oncology, Jay R. Harris
Chair Department of Medical Oncology, James D. Griffin
Chair Department of Pediatric Oncology, Stuart H. Orkin
Chief Scientific Officer, Barrett J. Rollins
CFO, Karen Bird
Chief Department of Imaging, Annick D. Van den Abbeele
Chief Surgical Officer, Scott J. Swanson
Chair Department of Psychosocial Oncology and Palliative Care, Susan D. Block
Chief Medical Officer, Craig A. Bunnell
Chief Clinical Research Officer, Bruce E. Johnson
Vp Of Pharmacy Services, Sylvia Bartel
Director Of Health Information, Jacqueline Raymond
Director Of Infection Control, Susan O'Rourke
Vice President Human Resources, Deborah Hicks
Vice President Ambulatory Operations, Anne Gross
Medical Director, Lisa Manera
Vice President Clinical Bussiness, Elizabeth Liebow
Asst Vice President Dev Mkt Donor Rel, Jan Lawlor
Svp Patient Care Services And Chief Nursing Officer, Patricia Reid Ponte
Treasury, Joe Hawley

LOCATIONS

HQ: DANA-FARBER CANCER INSTITUTE INC.
450 BROOKLINE AVE STE 30, BOSTON, MA 02215-5450
Phone: 617-632-3000
Web: WWW.DANA-FARBER.ORG

PRODUCTS/OPERATIONS

2012 Sales

	% of total
Medicare	26
Blue	23
Harvard Pilgrim	10
Medicaid	6
Patients	1
Commercial &	34
Total	100

Selected Clinical Affiliations

Dana-Farber/Brigham and Women' s Cancer Center (outpatient services for adult cancer patients provided by Dana-Farber; and inpatient care provided by Brigham and Women' s Hospital)
Dana-Farber/Children' s Hospital Cancer Center (Dana-Farber Cancer Institute and Children' s Hospital Boston outpatient care for children provided at Dana-Farber' s Jimmy Fund Clinic)
Dana-Farber/Harvard Cancer Center (Beth Israel Deaconess Medical Center Brigham and Women' s Hospital Children' s Hospital Boston and Massachusetts General Hospital collaborate on research cancer prevention and treatments and therapies for cancer patients)
Dana-Farber/Lawrence + Memorial Cancer Center (cancer facility Waterford Connecticut).
Dana-Farber/Partners Cancer Care (consolidated adult oncology programs and clinical research of Dana-Farber Cancer Institute Brigham and Women' s Hospital and Massachusetts General Hospital)

Selected Satellite Centers

Dana-Farber/Brigham and Women' s Cancer Center at Faulkner Hospital in Jamaica Plain (southwest Boston area)
Dana-Farber/Brigham and Women' s Cancer Center at Milford Regional Medical Center (Massachusetts)
Dana-Farber/Brigham and Women' s Cancer Center in clinical affiliation with South Shore Hospital (South Weymouth Massachusetts)
Dana-Farber/New Hampshire Oncology-Hematology (Londonderry)
Adult Treatment Centers and Clinical Services
Blood Cancers
Breast Cancer
Cancer Genetics and Prevention
Cutaneous (Skin) Cancer
Gastrointestinal Cancer
Genitourinary Cancer
Gynecologic Cancer
Head and Neck Cancer
Hematology
Melanoma
Neuro-Oncology
Sarcoma
Thoracic (Lung) Cancer
Pediatric Treatment Centers and Clinical Services
Blood Disorders Center
Brain Tumor Center
Hematologic Malignancies Center
Solid Tumors Center
Stem Cell Transplant Center

COMPETITORS

Baystate Health
Beth Israel Deaconess Medical Center
Boston Medical Center
Brigham and Women' s Hospital
Care New England
CareGroup
Children' s National Medical Center
Emory Healthcare
Fox Chase Cancer Center
Johns Hopkins Medicine
MD Anderson Cancer Center
Mayo Clinic
Memorial Sloan-Kettering
Partners HealthCare
Roswell Park Cancer Institute
St. Elizabeth' s Medical Center
St. Jude Children' s Research Hospital

HISTORICAL FINANCIALS

Company Type: Private

Income Statement FYE: September 30

	REVENUE ($ mil.)	NET INCOME ($ mil.)	NET PROFIT MARGIN	EMPLOYEES
09/11	1,002	37	3.7%	3,000
09/10	894	16	1.9%	—
09/09	816	28	3.5%	—
09/08	808	85	10.5%	—
Annual Growth	7.4%	(24.0%)	—	—

2011 Year-End Financials

Debt ratio: —
Return on equity: 3.70%
Cash ($ mil.): 13
Current ratio: 0.20
Long-term debt ($ mil.): —
Dividends
Yield: —
Payout: —
Market value ($ mil.): —

DANE G HANSEN FOUNDATION INC

LOCATIONS

HQ: DANE G HANSEN FOUNDATION INC
110 W MAIN ST, LOGAN, KS 67646
Phone: 7856894816
Web: WWW.DANEHANSENFOUNDATION.ORG

HISTORICAL FINANCIALS

Company Type: Private

Income Statement FYE: September 30

	ASSETS ($ mil.)	NET INCOME ($ mil.)	INCOME AS % OF ASSETS	EMPLOYEES
09/12	84	0	0.8%	6
09/11	83	3	3.7%	—
09/10	80	3	4.2%	—
09/09	77	0	—	—
Annual Growth	3.0%	—	—	—

2012 Year-End Financials

Debt ratio: —
Return on equity: 9.10%
Cash ($ mil.): 3
Current ratio: —
Long-term debt ($ mil.): —
Dividends
Yield: —
Payout: —
Market value ($ mil.): —

DANIS BUILDING CONSTRUCTION COMPANY

Danis Building Construction can reach from the Buckeye state to the Sunshine state. The company provides commercial and industrial construction services in Ohio Indiana Kentucky Tennessee North Carolina Georgia and Florida. The third-generation family-owned company offers construction management design/build general construction and build-to-suit lease-back services. It specializes in public and private building and industrial projects such as offices health care facilities retail complexes hotels cultural facilities schools and industrial plants. Its projects have included the Cincinnati Children's Hospital and a federal courthouse in Kentucky. B.G. Danis established the company in 1916.

Danis Building Construction was once part of real estate and construction group The Danis Companies which built such notable Ohio landmarks as the Orville Wright home Kettering Tower and the University of Dayton Arena. In 1997 it became incorporated as an independent entity from The Danis Companies. Danis operates four offices in Cincinnati Columbus and Dayton Ohio and Jacksonville Florida.

EXECUTIVES

CFO, James (Jim) Fuller
Director Business Development Columbus Area, John Hartman

LOCATIONS

HQ: DANIS BUILDING CONSTRUCTION COMPANY
3233 NEWMARK DR, MIAMISBURG, OH 45342-5422
Phone: 937-228-1225
Web: WWW.DANIS.COM

COMPETITORS

Albert M. Higley
Bovis Lend Lease
Corna Kokosing Construction Company
Envoy Inc.
Gilbane Building Company
Messer Construction
Ruscilli Construction

HISTORICAL FINANCIALS

Company Type: Private

Income Statement FYE: December 31

	REVENUE ($ mil.)	NET INCOME ($ mil.)	NET PROFIT MARGIN	EMPLOYEES
12/08	217	0	—	475
12/07	208	0	—	—
12/06	0	0	—	—
12/04	0	0	—	—
Annual Growth	—	—	—	—

2008 Year-End Financials

Debt ratio: —
Return on equity: —
Cash ($ mil.): 21
Current ratio: 0.40
Long-term debt ($ mil.): —
Dividends
Yield: —
Payout: —
Market value ($ mil.): —

DATA RECOGNITION CORPORATION

LOCATIONS

HQ: DATA RECOGNITION CORPORATION
13490 BASS LAKE RD, MAPLE GROVE, MN 553113634
Phone: 9529387714
Web: WWW.DATARECOGNITION.COM

HISTORICAL FINANCIALS

Company Type: Private

Income Statement FYE: October 31

	REVENUE ($ mil.)	NET INCOME ($ mil.)	NET PROFIT MARGIN	EMPLOYEES
10/13	206	30	14.7%	629
10/12	178	28	16.0%	—
10/11	167	18	10.9%	—
10/10	168	0	—	—
Annual Growth	7.1%	—	—	—

2013 Year-End Financials

Debt ratio: —
Return on equity: 14.70%
Cash ($ mil.): 0
Current ratio: 0.60
Long-term debt ($ mil.): —
Dividends
Yield: —
Payout: —
Market value ($ mil.): —

DATS TRUCKING INC.

DATS Trucking specializes in less-than-truckload (LTL) freight transportation in the western US but that's not all there is to the company's operations. In addition to its LTL operations in which freight from multiple shippers is combined into a single trailer DATS Trucking provides truckload transportation. The company's tanker division Overland Petroleum transports gasoline diesel fuel and other petroleum products. Overall DATS Trucking operates a fleet of about 500 tractors and 2500 trailers. It offers LTL service outside its home territory via The Reliance Network a group of regional carriers that covers the US and Canada. President and CEO Don Ipson founded DATS Trucking in 1988.

The company operates from a network of about 40 terminals to serve destinations in Arizona California Colorado Idaho Nevada New Mexico Utah Texas and Wyoming. It has been gradually adding facilities in order to enhance its service offerings. Outside its core territory DATS Trucking serves portions of the Pacific Northwest and the southern US through partnerships with other carriers.

Along with its transportation operations DATS Trucking provides warehousing and distribution services.

EXECUTIVES

President and CEO, Don L. Ipson

LOCATIONS

HQ: DATS TRUCKING INC.
321 N OLD HIGHWAY 91, HURRICANE, UT 84737-3194
Phone: 435-673-1886
Web: WWW.DATSTRUCKING.COM

COMPETITORS

Bulkmatic
Central Freight Lines
Con-way Freight
FedEx Freight
J.B. Hunt
Kenan Advantage Group
Penn Tank Lines
Schneider National
Swift Transportation
UPS Freight
Werner Enterprises
YRC Worldwide

HISTORICAL FINANCIALS

Company Type: Private

Income Statement FYE: December 31

	REVENUE ($ mil.)	NET INCOME ($ mil.)	NET PROFIT MARGIN	EMPLOYEES
12/07	717	1	0.3%	475
12/06	658	7	1.2%	—
12/05	600	1	0.2%	—
12/04	391	1	0.4%	—
Annual Growth	22.3%	4.6%	—	—

DAVIDSON"S INC.

LOCATIONS

HQ: DAVIDSON' ' S INC.
6100 WILKINSON DR, PRESCOTT, AZ 863016162
Phone: 9287768055
Web: WWW.GALLERYOFGUNS.COM

HISTORICAL FINANCIALS

Company Type: Private

Income Statement FYE: November 30

	REVENUE ($ mil.)	NET INCOME ($ mil.)	NET PROFIT MARGIN	EMPLOYEES
11/14	322	15	4.7%	89
11/13	395	20	5.1%	—
11/12	265	11	4.4%	—
11/11	182	0	—	—
Annual Growth	21.0%	—	—	—

2014 Year-End Financials

Debt ratio: —
Return on equity: 4.70%
Cash ($ mil.): 1
Current ratio: 0.80
Long-term debt ($ mil.): —
Dividends
Yield: —
Payout: —
Market value ($ mil.): —

DE PAUL UNIVERSITY

In the land of da Bulls and da Bears there's DePaul. One of the largest private not-for-profit universities in the US DePaul has a total of about 25000 students attending classes at its five Chicago-area campuses. Also one of the country's largest Catholic institutions of higher learning the university offers more than 300 undergraduate and graduate programs through about a dozen colleges and schools including the Kellstadt Graduate School of Business and the College of Communication. It has a student teacher ratio of 17 to 1. DePaul was founded in 1898 by the Vincentian religious community and is named after 17th century French priest St. Vincent de Paul.

Geographic Reach

DePaul's five Chicago-area campuses are located in Lincoln Park the Loop Naperville Oak Forest and the O'Hare area.

EXECUTIVES

VP Teaching and Learning Resources; Senior Executive University Mission; and Secretary, Rev Edward R. Udovic
Chancellor, Rev John T. Richardson
VP Student Affairs, James R. (Jim) Doyle
SVP Enrollment Management and Marketing, David H. Kalsbeek
EVP, Robert L. (Bob) Kozoman
VP Finance, Bonnie Frankel
VP Facility Operations, Robert (Bob) Janis
President, Rev Dennis H. Holtschneider, age 52
VP Human Resources, William Seithel
SVP Advancement, Mary C. Finger
VP and General Counsel, Jose D. Padilla
Provost, Helmut P. Epp
Dean College of Commerce and Kellstadt Graduate School of Business, Ray Whittington
VP Institutional Diversity and Equity, Elizabeth F. Ortiz
Dean School for New Learning, Marisa Alicea
Dean School of Music, Donald E. Casey
Dean The Theatre School, John Culbert
Dean College of Computing and Digital Media, David Miller
Dean College of Liberal Arts and Sciences, Charles S. (Chuck) Suchar
Dean College of Communication, Jacqueline Taylor
Treasurer, Jeffrey (Jeff) Bethke
Chief of Staff and Senior Executive Presidential Administration, Jay Braatz
VP Development, David A. Lively
Dean School of Education, Paul Zionts
Interim Dean College of Law, Warren D. Wolfson
Controller, Mark Hawkins
VP Alumni Outreach and Engagement, Patricia O'Donoghue
VP Public Relations and Communications, Cheryl Procter-Rogers
Director Information Services, Bob McCormick
VP Community Government and International Affairs, J.D. Bindenagel
Interim Vice President for Human Resources, Kathryn Stieber
Vice President General Counsel, Jose D. Padilla

LOCATIONS

HQ: DE PAUL UNIVERSITY
1 E JACKSON BLVD, CHICAGO, IL 60604-2287
Phone: 312-362-8000
Web: WWW.ITUNES.DEPAUL.EDU

HISTORICAL FINANCIALS

Company Type: Private

Income Statement FYE: June 30

	REVENUE ($ mil.)	NET INCOME ($ mil.)	NET PROFIT MARGIN	EMPLOYEES
06/12	546	39	7.2%	3,895
06/11	535	94	17.7%	—
06/10	510	81	16.0%	—
06/09	477	(45)	—	—
Annual Growth	4.6%	—	—	—

2012 Year-End Financials

Debt ratio: —
Return on equity: 7.20%
Cash ($ mil.): 56
Current ratio: —
Long-term debt ($ mil.): —
Dividends
Yield: —
Payout: —
Market value ($ mil.): —

DEACONESS HOSPITAL INC

Deaconess Hospital provides benevolent medical assistance to residents of southern Indiana western Kentucky and southeastern Illinois. The not-for-profit hospital is a 365-bed acute care medical facility that is the flagship hospital of the Deaconess Health System. Specialized services include cardiovascular surgery cancer treatment orthopedics neurological and trauma care. The hospital also offers home health care hospice services and medical equipment rental and it operates outpatient family practice surgery wellness and community outreach centers. Founded in 1892 Deaconess Hospital is a teaching and research facility affiliated with the Indiana University School of Medicine.

Geographic Reach

Deaconess Hospital is located in Evansville Indiana and provides services to about 26 surrounding counties.

Operations

Deaconess handles about 18000 inpatient visits per year. It also sees about 350000 outpatients and 65000 emergency room visitors and it handles about 7500 annual surgery procedures.

Strategy

To improve services to area residents Deaconess Hospital is expanding its outpatient care facilities and enhancing its IT resources. For instance in 2013 it moved its urgent care center to a larger more efficient facility. The hospital is also pursuing recognition for specialist programs such as its stroke center which was certified as a level one facility in 2013.

EXECUTIVES

CFO, Richard M. (Rick) Stivers
Director Human Resources, Larry Pyle
Manager Public Relations, Sam Rogers
President and CEO, Harry L. Smith
COO, Shawn McCoy
Auditors: Ernst&YoungLLP

LOCATIONS

HQ: DEACONESS HOSPITAL INC
600 MARY ST, EVANSVILLE, IN 47710-1674
Phone: 812-450-5000
Web: WWW.DEACONESS.COM

Selected Services

24-hour Emergency Center
Cancer Services
Corporate Wellness
Family Medicine Clinic
Heart Services
Home Medical Equipment
Home-based Medical Care
Hospice Care
Inpatient and Outpatient Surgery
Mental Health Services
Neuro Services
Orthopedics
Pediatrics
Physician Referral Service
Radiology Services
Residency Program
Support Groups and Programs
Women' s Hospital

COMPETITORS

Ball Memorial Hospital
Baptist Health
Baptist Health Madisonville
Commonwealth Health Corporation
Community Hospitals of Indiana
Daviess Community Hospital
Good Samaritan Hospital (IN)
Henry County Memorial Hospital
Jewish Hospital & St. Mary' s HealthCare
Kosciusko Community Hospital
Memorial Hospital (Logansport)
Norton Healthcare
St. Mary' s Medical Center of Evansville

HISTORICAL FINANCIALS

Company Type: Private

Income Statement FYE: September 30

	REVENUE ($ mil.)	NET INCOME ($ mil.)	NET PROFIT MARGIN	EMPLOYEES
09/12	577	58	10.1%	4,357
09/11	550	49	9.0%	—
09/09	524	40	7.7%	—
09/09	533	0	—	—
Annual Growth	2.6%	—	—	—

2012 Year-End Financials

Debt ratio: —
Return on equity: 10.10%
Cash ($ mil.): 54
Current ratio: 0.40
Long-term debt ($ mil.): —

Dividends
Yield: —
Payout: —
Market value ($ mil.): —

DEKALB MEDICAL CENTER INC.

As far as DeKalb is concerned da healthier da better! Beginning as a rural hospital DeKalb Regional Health System now serves all of the Atlanta metropolitan area. The health system operating as DeKalb Medical is home to two acute-care hospitals DeKalb Medical at North Decatur and DeKalb Medical at Hillandale that have a combined total of about 550 beds. It also operates a 75-bed long-term rehabilitation hospital DeKalb Medical at Downtown Decatur. Specialty hospital services include oncology cardiology orthopedics and diabetes care. The health system which was founded in 1961 also operates primary specialty and mobile health care clinics partly through the DeKalb Medical Physicians Group.

Geographic Reach

In addition to its main facilities in Decatur and Hillandale the company has operations in Lilburn Lithonia Snellville Stone Mountain and Tucker.

Operations

The health network of three hospitals staffs more than 800 physicians who represent about 55 medical specialties including neurosurgery interventional radiology sports medicine endovascular surgery gynecology emergency medicine and infectious disease. Altogether DeKalb Medical's facilities conducted some 27000 inpatient visits 166000 outpatient encounter 109000 emergency room visits and 5000 births during 2012.

In addition to medical services DeKalb Medical offers educational residency programs in subjects including pharmacy nursing and podiatry. It also operates a school for radiology technicians.

Strategy

DeKalb Medical is a self-supporting not-for-profit community hospital that does not receive tax dollars as part of its funding. The hospital system's operating budget comes solely from patient fees; DeKalb Medical reinvests any excess income into expanding or updating its services and facilities to meet Atlanta's growing population. The DeKalb Medical Foundation was established in 1991 and since then has funded improvements in facilities technology and community outreach programs.

In 2012 the organization expanded its women's health center in Hillandale to meet increased demand for mammogram and biopsy services. It also announced plans to expand its Heart and Vascular Institute that year. In addition the company improved information technology systems through the implementation of an electronic medication management system across its three hospitals.

EXECUTIVES

President CEO and Director, Eric P. Norwood
Vice President Patient Care Services and Chief Nursing Officer, Susan Breslin
President and Chief Executive Officer, John A. Shelton Jr.
Vice President Marketing and Communications, Cheryl Iverson
VP Physician Support Services, C. Duane Barclay
Vice President of Patient Care Services for DeKalb Medical, Susan Parry
Vice President of Medical Affairs Chief Medical Officer, Reg Gilbreath
SVP and Chief Quality Officer, Cathleen Wheatley
Executive Vice President and Chief Operating Officer, Dane Henry
Senior Vice President and Chief Financial Officer, John Katsianis
VP and Administrator DeKalb Medical at Hillandale, J. Clay Fowler
Chairman, Oliver Lee
Secretary and Director, Robert E. Wilson
Treasurer and Director, David L. Jollay
Media Relations Coordinator DeKalb Medical, Tori Vogt
Executive Director The DeKalb Medical Foundation, Leigh Minter
Vice President Chief Information Officer, Mark Trocino
Executive Vice President Chief Operating Officer, Dane Henry
Senior Vice President Chief Financial Officer, John Katsianis
Vice President of Human Resources, LeRoy Walker
Vice President and Administrator DeKalb Medical at Hillandale, Susan Harris
Vice President DeKalb Medical Physicians Group, Stephen Thomas
Vice President Strategic Services and Managed Care, Jim Forstner
Vice President Legal Services and Chief Compliance Officer, Joel Schuessler
Vice President Strategic Services and Managed Care, Jim Forstner MSc
Chief Information Officer and Vice President of Information Systems, Elizabeth Patino MBA
President CEO and Director, Eric P. Norwood
Director, Susan Parry
Secretary and Director, Robert E. Wilson
Treasurer and Director, David L. Jollay
Director, Gulshan Harjee
Director, Gregory B. Levett Sr.

LOCATIONS

HQ: DEKALB MEDICAL CENTER INC.
2701 N DECATUR RD, DECATUR, GA 30033-5918
Phone: 404-501-1000
Web: WWW.DEKALBMEDICAL.ORG

PRODUCTS/OPERATIONS

Selected Specialties

Cancer Center
Community Programs
Corporate Health Services
Emergency Department
Heart and Vascular Services
Orthopedic Services
Podiatry
Radiology and Medical Imaging
Rehabilitation Services
Senior Services
Sleep Center
Surgical Weight Loss
Volunteers
Wellness Center
Women's Services
Workswell Services
Wound Care

COMPETITORS

Children' s Healthcare of Atlanta
Emory Healthcare
Grady Health System
Gwinnett Health System
HCA
Northside Hospital
Piedmont Healthcare
Saint Joseph' s Health System
St. Mary' s Health Care
WellStar Health System

HISTORICAL FINANCIALS

Company Type: Private

Income Statement FYE: June 30

	REVENUE ($ mil.)	NET INCOME ($ mil.)	NET PROFIT MARGIN	EMPLOYEES
06/11	422	0	0.2%	2,700
06/10	397	(15)	—	—
06/09	390	0	—	—
06/08	370	(11)	—	—
Annual Growth	4.5%	—	—	—

2011 Year-End Financials

Debt ratio: —
Return on equity: 0.20%
Cash ($ mil.): 21
Current ratio: 0.30
Long-term debt ($ mil.): —

Dividends
Yield: —
Payout: —
Market value ($ mil.): —

DELI MANAGEMENT INC.

This company knows a good sandwich when serves one. Deli Management operates Jason's Deli a chain of sandwich shops with more than 230 company-owned and franchised locations. The quick casual eateries specialize in deli-style sandwiches including such signature varieties as Bird to the Wise The New York Yankee and Rueben THE Great. The chain also serves panini and po'boy sandwiches pasta dishes soups and salads. Many Jason's outposts provide delivery and catering services as well as online ordering. President Joe Tortorice and partner Rusty Coco started the company in 1976.

Geographic Reach

The company has units in about 30 states throughout the US. Most of the restaurants are found in Texas and other parts of the South.

Strategy

Like other chains in the quick casual segment Jason's Deli aims to provide fast service while maintaining a higher quality of food. The company promotes its use of organic ingredients and removed high fructose corn syrup (HFCS) from all of the food items on its menu.

Within the quick casual segment Jason's Deli faces competition from leaders such as Panera Bread and Chipotle Mexican Grill. The quick-service sandwich market is dominated by leading brands Subway and Quiznos.

EXECUTIVES

Director Franchise Sales and Development, Gene Barber
Customer Relations Department Atlanta, Jeffrey Bigger
Human Resources Northern Region Florida and Alabama, Joe Loyd
Human Resources Southeast Region, Alex Cone
VP Operations, Peter J. (Pete) Verde

LOCATIONS

HQ: DELI MANAGEMENT INC.
2400 BROADWAY ST, BEAUMONT, TX 77702-1904
Phone: 409-838-1976
Web: WWW.JASONSDELI.COM

COMPETITORS

AFC Enterprises
Burger King
CKE Restaurants
Chick-fil-A
Chipotle
Church' s Chicken
Einstein Noah Restaurant Group
Jack in the Box
Jimmy John' s
Kahala
McAlister' s
McDonald' s
Panda Restaurant Group
Panera Bread
Potbelly Sandwich Shop
Quiznos
Schlotzsky' s
Sonic Corp.
Souper Salad
Subway
Thundercloud Inc.
Wendy' s
Whataburger
YUM!

HISTORICAL FINANCIALS

Company Type: Private

Income Statement FYE: December 31

	REVENUE ($ mil.)	NET INCOME ($ mil.)	NET PROFIT MARGIN	EMPLOYEES
12/08	344	5	1.7%	6,000
12/06	344	5	1.7%	—
12/05	1,402	0	0.0%	—
Annual Growth	(37.4%)	3425.2%	—	—

2008 Year-End Financials

Debt ratio: —
Return on equity: 1.70%
Cash ($ mil.): 1
Current ratio: 0.40
Long-term debt ($ mil.): —
Dividends
Yield: —
Payout: —
Market value ($ mil.): —

DELTA REGIONAL MEDICAL CENTER

If you're feeling bad down in the Lower Delta Delta Regional Medical Center can help perk you up. The only full service hospital and Level II trauma center in northwest Mississippi Delta Regional also serves as the tri-state Delta's safety-net hospital. The medical center provides such services as heart and vascular care a full service emergency room diagnostics center home care a sleep center a wound healing center maternal child center and inpatient psychiatric care. Founded as the Washington County General Hospital in 1953 the 325-bed Delta Regional Medical Center serves about 35000 patients each year. It has focused in recent years on Continuous Renal Replacement Therapy (CRRT).

Strategy

Delta Regional is the first hospital in the region to offer patients with acute kidney injury the CRRT in its intensive care unit. As one of only a few Mississippi hospitals to offer the therapy Delta Regional is better able to improve the healing process for its patients.

Geographic Reach

Delta Regional primarily serves those who reside in northwest Mississippi but acts as a support hospital for the Delta's tri-state region.

Company Background

The past decade has been rocky for Delta Regional. Under the direction of CEO Ray Humphreys Delta Regional decided to eliminate the closest competition by acquiring The King's Daughters Hospital for $21 million from Community Health Systems Inc. in 2005. The move breathed new life into the ailing hospital.

For years prior to the King's Daughters acquisition Delta Regional's demise seemed imminent and the hospital was facing two options: close or be sold. After some strategic maneuvering by the CEO and a $35 million cash infusion in 2007 in the form of a federal loan Delta Regional was revived. The hospital used the cash to pay off debt related to the King's Daughters buy and for expansion and renovation projects.

EXECUTIVES

SVP Nursing Services, Mazie Whalen
VP Finance, Courtney Phillips
Chairman, Billy Schultz
Trustee and Secretary, Mildred Crockett
VP Physician Practices, Peter Austin
VP Quality, Amy Dowdy
Medical Director, John Turner IV
VP West Campus, Lisa M. Zepponi
Vice President Quality, Amy Walker
Vice President Support Sevices, Chandler Ewing
CEO, J. Stansel Harvey
Trustee and Secretary, Mildred Crockett
Trustee, Henry Rucker
Trustee, James Hollowell
Trustee, Sam Newsom
Trustee, Sylvia G. Jackson
Trustee, Howard Sanders

LOCATIONS

HQ: DELTA REGIONAL MEDICAL CENTER
1400 E UNION ST, GREENVILLE, MS 38703-3246
Phone: 662-378-3783
Web: WWW.CAREERS.DELTAREGIONAL.COM

PRODUCTS/OPERATIONS

Selected Services

Allergy and Immunology
Ambulance Services
Anesthesiology
Cardiac Rehabilitation
Cardiology
Cardiovascular Surgery
Catheterization Lab
Colon Rectal Surgery
Critical Care ICU
Dermatology
ECHO
Emergency Room Physician
Family Practice
Gastroenterology
Gynecological Surgery
Hematology
Home Health and Hospice
Hyperbaric Medicine
Internal Medicine
Laboratory
Lifeline
Mammography
MRI
Nephrology
Neurology
Neurosurgery
Nuclear Medicine
Obstetrics
Occupational Therapy
Oncology
Ophthalmology
Orthopedic Surgery
Otolaryngology
Pain Management
Pathology
Pediatrics
Physical Therapy
Plastic and Reconstructive Surgery
Psychiatry
Pulmonology
Radiation Oncology
Radiology
Respiratory Therapy
Speech/Language Pathology
Stress Lab
Ultrasound
Urology
Vascular and Thoracic Surgery
Vascular Studies

COMPETITORS

Baptist Memorial Health Care
Jefferson Regional Medical Center of Pennsylvania
Natchez Regional Medical Center
North Mississippi Health Services

HISTORICAL FINANCIALS

Company Type: Private

Income Statement FYE: September 30

	REVENUE ($ mil.)	NET INCOME ($ mil.)	NET PROFIT MARGIN	EMPLOYEES
09/12	153	2	1.9%	1,000
09/06	116	0	0.3%	—
09/05	109	1	1.2%	—
09/04	167	0	0.0%	—
Annual Growth	(1.1%)	278.7%		

2012 Year-End Financials

Debt ratio: —
Return on equity: 1.90%
Cash ($ mil.): 17
Current ratio: 3.40
Long-term debt ($ mil.): —
Dividends
Yield: —
Payout: —
Market value ($ mil.): —

DENNIS K BURKE INC

LOCATIONS

HQ: DENNIS K BURKE INC
284 EASTERN AVE, CHELSEA, MA 021503318
Phone: 6178847800
Web: WWW.BURKEOIL.COM

HISTORICAL FINANCIALS

Company Type: Private

Income Statement FYE: April 30

	REVENUE ($ mil.)	NET INCOME ($ mil.)	NET PROFIT MARGIN	EMPLOYEES
04/13	858	7	0.8%	110
04/12	929	3	0.3%	—
04/11	807	0	0.1%	—
04/10	596	0	—	—
Annual Growth	12.9%	—	—	—

2013 Year-End Financials

Debt ratio: —
Return on equity: 0.80%
Cash ($ mil.): 0
Current ratio: 0.90
Long-term debt ($ mil.): —
Dividends
Yield: —
Payout: —
Market value ($ mil.): —

DEPAUW UNIVERSITY

EXECUTIVES

Chairman of the Board, R. David (Dave) Hoover, age 69
Executive Vice President CFO, Michael L. Smith, age 65
President, Brian W. Casey, age 50
President CEO, Thomas W. Boswell
Owner Manager Retired LETCO, Lee E. Tenzer
President, Bayard H. Walters
President Chief Executive Officer, R. Lee Wilson
Managing Director, Lawrence E. Young Jr.
VP Student Life and Dean of Students, Cindy Babington

CIO, Carol L. Smith
Executive Director Finance and Controller, Keith A. Archer
Executive Director Human Resources, Patricia A. (Pat) Bacon
VP Admission and Financial Aid, Daniel L. (Dan) Meyer
VP Advancement, Marcia S. Latta
Executive Director Alumni Relations, Jennifer C. Soster
General Manager Dining Services, Steve Santo
Director Office of Institutional Research, Bill Tobin
Executive Director Media Relations, Kenneth A. (Ken) Owen
VP Communications and Strategic Initiatives, Christopher J. Wells
Registrar, Ken Kirkpatrick
Director Sustainability, Carol Steele
Secretary, Donna Rust
Executive Director of Development, Jason Petrovich
Head, Jake Martin
President CEO, Jane Schlansker
Associate Vice President for Facilities, Richard Vance
Vice President of Finance, Brad Kelsheimer

LOCATIONS

HQ: DEPAUW UNIVERSITY
313 S LOCUST ST, GREENCASTLE, IN 461351736
Phone: 7656584800
Web: WWW.DEPAUW.EDU

PRODUCTS/OPERATIONS

Selected Academic Centers

Bartlett Reflection Center
Center for Student Engagement
Center for Teaching & Learning
Geographic Information Systems Lab
The Compton Center for Peace and Justice
The Compton Center for Peace and Justice
The Green Center for the Performing Arts
The Janet Prindle Institute for Ethics
The McDermond Center for Management and Entreprenuership
The Peeler Art Center
The Pulliam Center for Contemporary Media

HISTORICAL FINANCIALS

Company Type: Private

Income Statement FYE: June 30

	REVENUE ($ mil.)	NET INCOME ($ mil.)	NET PROFIT MARGIN	EMPLOYEES
06/13	246	94	38.4%	652
06/12	154	5	3.7%	—
06/11	147	2	1.7%	—
06/10	121	0	—	—
Annual Growth	26.4%	—	—	—

2013 Year-End Financials

Debt ratio: —
Return on equity: 38.40%
Cash ($ mil.): 29
Current ratio: 0.20
Long-term debt ($ mil.): —
Dividends
Yield: —
Payout: —
Market value ($ mil.): —

DESERET GENERATION AND TRANSMISSION CO-OPERATIVE

Its service area may be dry but it is not a power desert thanks to Deseret Generation and Transmission Cooperative (aka Deseret Power) which supplies wholesale electricity to its members (six retail distribution cooperatives) and other bulk energy customers in Arizona Colorado Nevada Utah and Wyoming. The member-owned utility operates 223 miles of transmission lines and it has interests in two power generation facilities in Utah that give it 550 MW of capacity. Deseret Power also operates its own coal mine which fuels its main power plant through subsidiary Blue Mountain Energy; other operations include the transportation of coal by railroad and the development of a limestone extraction facility.

The retail distribution cooperatives served by Deseret Power supply electricity to more than 45000 customers in their service areas. Deseret Power's Bonanza (500 MW) power plant in Utah has been ranked as one of the cleanest-burning coal-fired plants in the US.

The non-profit cooperative's key strategy revolves around its ownership operation and vertical integration of its primary assets and services – the coal mine where coal is extracted to fuel its power plants the power generation facilities as well the power lines used to transmit the electricity it produces. This integration and self-reliance allows it to manage costs and reinvest profits.

Deseret Power was formed in 1978 by six regional rural electric cooperatives.

EXECUTIVES

Controller, David (Dave) Carroll
President CEO, Kimball Rasmussen
Senior Vice President CFO, Soren Sorensen
VP Marketing, Curt Winterfeld
VP Operations and Chief Engineer, Ed Thatcher
VP and General Counsel, David Crabtree
Power Marketing Manager, Phil Tice
Retail Marketing Director, Keith Hill
Corporate Planning and Forecast Director, Rick Smith
Auditors: Deloitte&ToucheLLP

LOCATIONS

HQ: DESERET GENERATION AND TRANSMISSION CO-OPERATIVE
10714 S JORDAN GTWY # 300, SOUTH JORDAN, UT 84095-3922
Phone: 801-619-6500
Web: WWW.DESERETPOWER.COM

PRODUCTS/OPERATIONS

Member Distribution Cooperativ
Bridger Valley Electric Associatio
Dixie Escalante Rural Electric Associatio
Flowell Electric Associatio
Garkane Energy Associatio
Moon Lake Electric Associatio
Mt. Wheeler Power

COMPETITORS

Arch Coal
Bonneville Power
IPA
PacifiCorp
Peabody Energy
Utah Associated Municipal Power Systems

HISTORICAL FINANCIALS

Company Type: Private

Income Statement FYE: December 31

	REVENUE ($ mil.)	NET INCOME ($ mil.)	NET PROFIT MARGIN	EMPLOYEES
12/07	242	(9)	—	250
12/06	218	10	5.0%	—
12/05	1,732	0	0.0%	—
Annual Growth	(62.6%)	—	—	—

2007 Year-End Financials

Debt ratio: —
Return on equity: (-4.00%)
Cash ($ mil.): 12
Current ratio: 1.10
Long-term debt ($ mil.): —
Dividends
Yield: —
Payout: —
Market value ($ mil.): —

DEVCON CONSTRUCTION INCORPORATED

Devcon Construction has built a sturdy business from building in the Bay Area. One of the area's top general building contractors Devcon has constructed more than 30 million sq. ft. of office industrial and commercial space. Its focus is on Northern California mainly in the San Francisco Bay Area and Silicon Valley. The company provides engineering design/build and interior design services. It specializes in high-tech projects including data centers and industrial research and development facilities. In addition to building company facilities and offices Devcon works on such projects as hotels restaurants parking structures retail stores sports facilities and schools.

Geographic Reach

Based in Milpitas California Devcon maintains several satellite offices in California in Petaluma Stockton and Santa Cruz as well as an office in Reno Nevada.

Strategy

Although most of Devcon's work is in California the company also has completed projects in Nevada Oregon Idaho Texas Massachusetts and Florida. Recent projects in the San Francisco Forty Niners Stadium in Santa Clara San Jose Sharks Ice Center in Pleasanton and the Stanford Research Computing Facility.

The company partnered with US-based Central Concrete in 2012 to supply its high-performing low-CO_2 concrete for the new San Francisco 49er Stadium. The move showcases Devcon's focus on sustainability as part of its projects.

EXECUTIVES

VP and Controller, Bret Sisney
President, Gary Filizetti
Secretary, Justine Pereira
Vice President of Construction, Andy Schatzman
Vice President of Construction, Jonathan Harvey

LOCATIONS

HQ: DEVCON CONSTRUCTION INCORPORATED
690 GIBRALTAR DR, MILPITAS, CA 95035-6317
Phone: 408-942-8200
Web: WWW.DEVCON-CONST.COM

PRODUCTS/OPERATIONS

Selected Projects

1880 Mission Street San Francisco
3333 Scott Blvd. Buildings A B & C Santa Clara

Anderson Collection At Stanford University Stanford
Barnes & Nobles Palo Alto
Cisco Parking Structure 1 San Jose
Cisco Parking Structure 2 San Jose
Downtown Sunnyvale Town Center Sunnyvale
El Camino Family Housing South San Francisco
Fresno Hyatt Place Hotel Fresno
Friedenrich Center For Translational Research At 800 Welch Road
Lawson Lane East Buildings A & B Santa Clara
Oakland Air Traffic Control Tower (ATCT) Oakland
San Francisco 49ers Stadium Santa Clara
San Jose Earthquakes - MLS Soccer Stadium San Jose
SanDisk Milpitas
Santa Clara University Admissions & Enrollment Services Building Santa Clara
Sharks Ice Center Pleasanton
Stanford Research Computing Facility Stanford
The Plaza At Triton Park Foster City
University Plaza Palo Alto
Villa Siena Nursing Care Units Mountain View

COMPETITORS

Charles Pankow Builders
DPR Construction
Hathaway Dinwiddie Construction
Hensel Phelps Construction
KPRS Construction
Obayashi
Rudolph & Sletten
Structure Tone
Swinerton
Turner Corporation
Webcor Builders

HISTORICAL FINANCIALS

Company Type: Private

Income Statement FYE: December 31

	REVENUE ($ mil.)	NET INCOME ($ mil.)	NET PROFIT MARGIN	EMPLOYEES
12/12	779	3	0.5%	350
12/11	434	1	0.3%	—
12/09	469	1	0.2%	—
12/09	381	10	2.7%	—
Annual Growth	26.8%	(30.2%)	—	—

2012 Year-End Financials

Debt ratio: —
Return on equity: 0.50%
Cash ($ mil.): 17
Current ratio: 0.90
Long-term debt ($ mil.): —
Dividends
Yield: —
Payout: —
Market value ($ mil.): —

DEVEREUX FOUNDATION

Devereux Foundation endeavors to make a difference in the lives of people with behavioral psychological intellectual or neurological problems. A not-for-profit organization Devereux serves children adolescents and adults and their families through about 15 centers in about a dozen states. Its offerings include hospitalization group homes respite care family counseling and vocational training. Devereux also conducts behavioral health research and provides consulting services for other organizations with similar concerns. The group's work began in 1912 when Philadelphia educator Helena Devereux began working with three special education students in her parents' home.

Operations

The foundation's Institute of Clinical and Professional Training and Research (ICPTR) operates the Center for Effective Schools the Center for Resilient Children and Direct Care Training Resources to provide training for psychology psychiatry social work and special education professionals.

Geographic Reach

Devereux Foundation maintains facilities in Arizona California Colorado Connecticut Florida Georgia Massachusetts New Jersey New York Pennsylvania and Texas.

Devereux's revenue decreased by about 1% in 2013 to $391 million due to a decline in client revenue. Its net income increased 55% as salaries and benefits declined while other income (investments and donations) increased. That year the foundation provided $18.2 million in charity care.

Strategy

In 2012 as the foundation entered its second century of operation it began working on a comprehensive plan to set its strategic direction that would take into account not only new challenges but new opportunities present in the world today. Devereux is examining its centers and corporate departments while it continues to place the highest value on building relationships with the people and public agencies that use its services. Key elements to its strategic plan include quality management national branding and maintaining fiscal responsibility to ensure a strong balance sheet. The foundation is also looking to expand opportunities for its intellectual properties and services through partnerships with school systems and universities and through expanded services for people with autism and added community-based adult services. It is rolling out an electronic health record system and upgrading its accounting and billing systems.

Company Background

The organization's Institute of Clinical Training and Research was founded in 1938. It provides professional training in psychology psychiatry social work and special education.

EXECUTIVES

Vice President And General Counsel, Lori McLaughlin
V Pres-oper, Sarah E Lenahan
Vp Product Development, Martha Lindsay
Vp Human Resources, Chip McCloud
President CEO, Robert Q. (Bob) Kreider
Executive Director of CBHS, David Woodward
Vice President Of Operations, Sarah Chatani
Vice President Of Engineering, Denny Miller
Treasurer, Steven H Mansh, age 59
Vice Chairman, Thomas C. Hays
Vice Chairman, Samuel G. Coppersmith
Chairman, Francis (Skip) Genuardi
Treas, Stanley Kopala
Asst Sec, Roberta Louis

LOCATIONS

HQ: DEVEREUX FOUNDATION
444 DEVEREUX DR, VILLANOVA, PA 190851932
Phone: 6105203000
Web: WWW.DEVEREUX.ORG

PRODUCTS/OPERATIONS

2011 Revenue

	$ mil.	% of total
Client revenue	367	93
Investment income	8	2
Gifts & bequests	7	2
Other revenue	11	3
Total	**395**	**100**

Selected Services

After care programs
Community-based group homes
Family counseling and therapy
Foster care homes
Hospital inpatient and outpatient settings
Partial hospitalization
Preventive and post-discharge services
Residential and day treatment programs
Respite care programs
Special education day schools
Supervised apartments
Transitional living arrangements
Vocational and pre-vocational training

COMPETITORS

CIGNA Behavioral Health
CRC Health
Diakon Lutheran Social Ministries
FHC Health Systems
Hazelden Betty Ford
HealthSouth
Magellan Health
Mental Health Network
Northwestern Human Services
Physiotherapy Associates
Providence Service
Select Medical
UBH
Universal Health Services
Watson Institute
YAI National Institute for People with Disabilitie

HISTORICAL FINANCIALS

Company Type: Private

Income Statement FYE: June 30

	REVENUE ($ mil.)	NET INCOME ($ mil.)	NET PROFIT MARGIN	EMPLOYEES
06/13	391	3	0.9%	6,000
06/12	395	(5)	—	—
06/11	395	17	4.5%	—
06/08	384	0	—	—
Annual Growth	0.3%	—	—	—

2013 Year-End Financials

Debt ratio: —
Return on equity: 0.90%
Cash ($ mil.): 3
Current ratio: 0.90
Long-term debt ($ mil.): —
Dividends
Yield: —
Payout: —
Market value ($ mil.): —

DFB PHARMACEUTICALS INC.

DFB Pharmaceuticals contributes to drug development and manufacturing processes by providing essential ingredients. The company produces various pharmaceutical ingredients for its own use and for other drug makers through its Phyton Biotech subsidiary. Phyton Biotech uses its plant cell culture technology to make APIs (active pharmaceutical ingredients). DFB sold a majority stake in its contract manufacturing unit DPT Laboratories to Renaissance Acquisition Holdings in 2012. It also sold its Healthpoint subsidiary a maker of prescription drugs to prevent or treat disorders associated with skin and soft tissue to Smith & Nephew.

Operations Phyton Biotech which has produced taxanes for products such as anti-cancer drug Taxol (marketed by Bristol-Myers Squibb) focuses on producing plant-cell-culture-based ingredients used in chemotherapy drugs. Phyton Biotech provides taxane plant-cell fermentation and protein development services to help drugmakers formulate new APIs; it also offers rapid scale-up manufacturing services of ingredients as products are developed and commercialized.

Strategy The DPT and Healthpoint sales allow DFB to focus on the growth of its API operations. Through the DPT transaction completed in mid-2012 DFB Pharmaceuticals retained an interest in the DPT business and gained a seat on Renaissance's board.

In December 2012 Smith & Nephew acquired substantially all of the assets of DFB's Healthpoint affiliate for some $782 million. The unit had been facing a federal investigation into potential mismarketing activities.

EXECUTIVES

President and COO DPT Laboratories, Paul H. Johnson
President and COO Healthpoint, Travis E. Baugh, age 59
Chairman and CEO, H. Paul Dorman
Chief Medical Officer Healthpoint, Bert Slade

LOCATIONS

HQ: DFB PHARMACEUTICALS INC.
3909 HULEN ST, FORT WORTH, TX 76107-7253
Phone: 817-900-4050
Web: WWW.DFBHOLDING.COM

COMPETITORS

Ash Stevens	Johnson & Johnson
Collegium	Jubilant Life Sciences
ConvaTec	Lonza
Covance	Perrigo
Derma Sciences	Pharmaceutical Product Development
Formatech	Ranbaxy Laboratories
Galderma Laboratories	

HISTORICAL FINANCIALS

Company Type: Private

Income Statement FYE: December 31

	REVENUE ($ mil.)	NET INCOME ($ mil.)	NET PROFIT MARGIN	EMPLOYEES
12/11	344	0	—	700
12/10	322	0	—	—
12/08	318	0	—	—
12/07	355	0	—	—
Annual Growth	(0.7%)	—	—	—

2011 Year-End Financials

Debt ratio: —
Return on equity: —
Cash ($ mil.): 12
Current ratio: 0.80
Long-term debt ($ mil.): —
Dividends
Yield: —
Payout: —
Market value ($ mil.): —

DIALYSIS CLINIC INC.

Dialysis Clinic Inc. or DCI is dedicated to caring for patients with end-stage renal disease (ESRD). The not-for-profit company which operates a network of more than 210 dialysis centers serving more than 14000 patients in 27 states also provides kidney transplant assistance services. Affiliate DCI Donor Services is an organ and tissue procurement agency. DCI also funds kidney-related research and educational programs and is affiliated with various universities and teaching hospitals throughout the US including Tufts University the University of Arizona and Tulane University.

Geographic Reach

The company has its locations in Alabama Arizona Arkansas California Colorado Connecticut Florida Georgia Indiana Iowa Kentucky Louisiana Maine Massachusetts Missouri Montana Nebraska Nevada New Jersey New Mexico New York North Carolina Ohio Pennsylvania South Carolina Tennessee and Texas.

Strategy

DCI grows its network of facilities by forming partnerships with health care providers and other organizations. The company provides funding for construction and operation of the facility and it provides clinic support services including supply procurement and central laboratory services (through its DCI Lab subsidiary).

In 2012 the company opened a dialysis clinic in Albuquerque its first dialysis clinic in the South Valley region of New Mexico.

Company Background

DCI was established in 1971 by nephrologist Keith Johnson.

EXECUTIVES

Chairman, H. Keith Johnson
Director Corporate Contracts Sales and Marketing, Hal Whetstone
Director Reimbursement and Managed Care, Joe Swearingen
Controller, Andy Parker
Founder of the nations largest not-for-profit dialysis care, Camp Okawehna
Trustee, Nancy N. Johnson

LOCATIONS

HQ: DIALYSIS CLINIC INC.
1633 CHURCH ST STE 500, NASHVILLE, TN 37203-2948
Phone: 615-327-3061
Web: WWW.DCIINC.ORG

COMPETITORS

DaVita	Renal Advantage
FMCNA	U.S. Renal Care
Fresenius	

HISTORICAL FINANCIALS

Company Type: Private

Income Statement FYE: September 30

	REVENUE ($ mil.)	NET INCOME ($ mil.)	NET PROFIT MARGIN	EMPLOYEES
09/12	664	45	6.8%	5,000
09/11	642	48	7.5%	—
09/10	654	21	3.2%	—
09/09	631	(3)	—	—
Annual Growth	1.7%	—	—	—

2012 Year-End Financials

Debt ratio: —
Return on equity: 6.80%
Cash ($ mil.): 204
Current ratio: 3.90
Long-term debt ($ mil.): —
Dividends
Yield: —
Payout: —
Market value ($ mil.): —

DICKINSON COLLEGE

Located in Carlisle Pennsylvania Dickinson College is a private liberal arts college with a penchant for international study. The small but selective college has an annual enrollment of some 2400 students half of which study abroad in programs that span 24 countries on six continents. The college offers more than 40 programs in arts and humanities (including a significant foreign language program) social sciences and natural sciences. It also offers minors in fields including astronomy creative writing and film studies. Dickinson College traces its roots back to 1773; it is named for John Dickinson who signed the US Constitution and was known as "The Penman of the [American] Revolution."

EXECUTIVES

VP and CIO, Robert Renaud
Provost and Dean College, Neil B. Weissman
president, Nancy A. Roseman
Chair, Jennifer Ward Reynolds, age 76
Vice Chairman, Thomas L. Kalaris
Auditors: Deloitte&ToucheLLP

LOCATIONS

HQ: DICKINSON COLLEGE
COLLEGE & LOUTHER ST, CARLISLE, PA 17013
Phone: 7172451010
Web: WWW.DICKINSONATHLETICS.COM

HISTORICAL FINANCIALS

Company Type: Private

Income Statement FYE: June 30

	REVENUE ($ mil.)	NET INCOME ($ mil.)	NET PROFIT MARGIN	EMPLOYEES
06/14	173	51	29.4%	632
06/13	159	37	23.5%	—
06/12	115	(0)	—	—
06/11	159	0	—	—
Annual Growth	2.8%	—	—	—

2014 Year-End Financials

Debt ratio: —
Return on equity: 29.40%
Cash ($ mil.): 14
Current ratio: —
Long-term debt ($ mil.): —
Dividends
Yield: —
Payout: —
Market value ($ mil.): —

DIMEO CONSTRUCTION COMPANY

Dimeo Construction has built a reputation in New England. The company provides general contracting design/build and construction management services ranging from pre-planning to post-construction commissioning. It focuses on commercial education health care residential and public projects such as schools hospitals corporate headquarters research and development facilities and shopping centers. It also has worked on renovation projects such as The Mark Twain House & Museum and the Ocean House. The family-owned company was established in 1930 by Joseph Dimeo. Current CEO Brad Dimeo represents the third generation to lead the firm.

Dimeo Construction has offices in Boston; New Haven Connecticut; and Providence Rhode Island. The company has completed work for several of the region's Fortune 500 companies including CIGNA Hasbro and United Technologies Corporation. Its green side has emerged as well as it has completed eco-friendly projects for the likes of IKEA CVS Health and Yale University.

EXECUTIVES

Vp Operations, Paul G Aballo
Vp And Project Executive, Kosta Bitsis
Auditors: Ernst&YoungLLP

LOCATIONS

HQ: DIMEO CONSTRUCTION COMPANY
75 CHAPMAN ST, PROVIDENCE, RI 029055496
Phone: 4017819800
Web: WWW.DIMEO.COM

COMPETITORS

Gilbane Building Company	Konover Properties
Heery	Skanska USA Building
Imperial Construction Group	Turner Construction
	Walsh Brothers

HISTORICAL FINANCIALS

Company Type: Private

Income Statement FYE: June 30

	REVENUE ($ mil.)	NET INCOME ($ mil.)	NET PROFIT MARGIN	EMPLOYEES
06/12	373	6	1.7%	300
06/11	300	9	3.1%	—
06/10	356	9	2.7%	—
06/09	567	0	—	—
Annual Growth	(13.0%)	—	—	—

2012 Year-End Financials

Debt ratio: —
Return on equity: 1.70%
Cash ($ mil.): 78
Current ratio: 1.20
Long-term debt ($ mil.): —
Dividends
Yield: —
Payout: —
Market value ($ mil.): —

DIRECT RELIEF INTERNATIONAL INC

Direct Relief International wants to relieve the health problems of people around the world. The not-for-profit organization is dedicated to providing health care support and emergency relief to people in developing countries as well as victims of disasters and war. It gives medicine supplies and equipment through partnerships with local groups that make specific requests and coordinates distribution. Citing a "national health insurance and budgetary crisis" the group also has partnered with nonprofit clinics and commmunity health centers to provide medical care and medicine for homeless and low-income people in California. Direct Relief was founded in 1948 by Estonian immigrant William Zimdin.

The organization also has applied its experience with domestic relief efforts to help victims of hurricanes along the Gulf Coast.

Looking to maintain its funding during the economic downturn Direct Relief sought to appeal to Money magazine readers by being part of its November 2009 cover story "What to do with $1000 $10000 or $50000 Now." As part of the article Direct Relief cited that $10000 would purchase medical supplies for 800 victims of the next Gulf Coast hurricane.

EXECUTIVES

EVP and CFO, Bhupindarpal (Bhupi) Singh, age 55
President and CEO, Thomas Tighe
Director Operations, Rick Snekvik
VP Philanthropic Investment, Anthoula Randopoulos
Director Direct Relief USA, Damon Taugher
Director International Program Operations, Genevieve Bitter
Director Emergency Preparedness and Response, Brett Williams
COO, Annie Maxwell
Manager Logistics and Distribution, James Howard
Director Human Resources Administration and Compliance, Judy Gerrard Partch
Director Information Technology, Ross Comstock
Director Research and Analysis, Andrew Schroeder
Controller, Julie Aguiniga
Manager Media Relations, Jim Prosser
Manager Communications, Andrew Fletcher
VP Marketing and Development, Kerri Murray
System Administrator, George Linker
Manager SAP Applications, Saravanan Selvaraj

LOCATIONS

HQ: DIRECT RELIEF INTERNATIONAL INC
27 S LA PATERA LN, GOLETA, CA 93117-3251
Phone: 805-964-4767
Web: WWW.DIRECTRELIEF.ORG

HISTORICAL FINANCIALS

Company Type: Private

Income Statement FYE: June 30

	REVENUE ($ mil.)	NET INCOME ($ mil.)	NET PROFIT MARGIN	EMPLOYEES
06/12	299	(17)	—	2
06/11	405	95	23.6%	—
06/09*	164	0	—	—
03/08	201	(26)	—	—
Annual Growth	10.5%	—	—	—

*Fiscal year change

2012 Year-End Financials

Debt ratio: —
Return on equity: (-6.00%)
Cash ($ mil.): 0
Current ratio: 0.20
Long-term debt ($ mil.): —
Dividends
Yield: —
Payout: —
Market value ($ mil.): —

DISABLED AMERICAN VETERANS

Disabled American Veterans (DAV) helps ex-military men and women fight personal battles after the shooting stops. The nonprofit group strives to improve the quality of life for wounded veterans and their families by helping them navigate the US Department of Veterans Affairs system to obtain benefits. DAV also represents the political interests of veterans and provides various outreach and volunteer programs. The group which generates most of its revenue from tax-exempt contributions has about 1.3 million members. DAV was formed in 1920 and chartered by Congress in 1932.

EXECUTIVES

Treas, J M Burgess
Auditors: Deloitte&ToucheLLP

LOCATIONS

HQ: DISABLED AMERICAN VETERANS
3725 ALEXANDRIA PIKE, COLD SPRING, KY 41076-1712
Phone: 859-441-7300
Web: WWW.DAV.ORG

HISTORICAL FINANCIALS

Company Type: Private

Income Statement FYE: December 31

	REVENUE ($ mil.)	NET INCOME ($ mil.)	NET PROFIT MARGIN	EMPLOYEES
12/09	154	44	28.5%	615
12/08	151	(102)	—	—
12/07	185	24	13.0%	—
12/06	169	32	18.8%	—
Annual Growth	(3.1%)	11.2%	—	—

2009 Year-End Financials

Debt ratio: —
Return on equity: 28.50%
Cash ($ mil.): 4
Current ratio: 0.10
Long-term debt ($ mil.): —
Dividends
Yield: —
Payout: —
Market value ($ mil.): —

DLT SOLUTIONS LLC

DLT Solutions is a middleman for G-men. The company resells IT products and services primarily to local state and federal government clients in the US. The company sells and integrates hardware and software from such vendors as Autodesk Oracle NetApp Red Hat and Symantec. DLT's contracts are primarily with the US Department of Defense's Enterprise Software Initiative (ESI) and the US Navy. It also has more than a dozen other contracts with state and city governments. To a smaller extent it offers consulting network design application development training and other professional services. The company's areas of expertise include cloud computing data center consolidation cybersecurity and computer-aided design.

Strategy

As government budgets are tightened DLT is looking to higher-margin professional services such as cloud computing as an avenue for future growth. In 2013 it began offering Storage-as-a-Service (STaaS) with NetApp that allows federal agencies to store and protect their data while only paying for what they use.

EXECUTIVES

Vice President Of Human Resources, Chris Laggini
Svp, Ed Jones
EVP and CFO, Craig Adler
Chairman President and CEO, Rick Marcotte
EVP Sales and Marketing, Brian Strosser
CTO, Van Ristau
Chief Cloud Technologist, David Blankenhorn
Vice President Professional Services, Don Simpson
Senior Vice President Of Sales For Enterprise Applications Division, Kenneth Grimsley
Senior Vice President Enterprise, Steve Stratton
Sr Vice President Sales Entp, Ken Grimsley
Chairman President and CEO, Rick Marcotte
Board Member, Sam Katz

LOCATIONS

HQ: DLT SOLUTIONS LLC
13861 SUNRISE VALLEY DR # 400, HERNDON, VA 20171-6124
Phone: 703-709-7172
Web: WWW.DLT.COM

PRODUCTS/OPERATIONS

Selected Product Vendors

Akamai
Amazon Web Services
Autodesk
Blue Coat Systems
BMC Software
Google
Informatica
Quest Software
NetApp
Oracle
Red Hat
SolarWinds
Solera Networks
Symantec

COMPETITORS

A&T Systems
Apptis
CDW Government
ComGlobal Systems
Computer World Services
Daly Computers
GovConnection
Government Micro Resources
Melillo Consulting
Optimos
UNICOM Government
immixGroup

HISTORICAL FINANCIALS

Company Type: Private

Income Statement FYE: December 31

	REVENUE ($ mil.)	NET INCOME ($ mil.)	NET PROFIT MARGIN	EMPLOYEES
12/11	354	14	4.1%	253
12/10	447	13	2.9%	—
/ 0	0			
Annual Growth	—	—	—	—

2011 Year-End Financials

Debt ratio: —
Return on equity: 4.10%
Cash ($ mil.): 10
Current ratio: 0.70
Long-term debt ($ mil.): —

Dividends
Yield: —
Payout: —
Market value ($ mil.): —

DOCTOR'S ASSOCIATES INC.

You're more likely to catch a sub than a train at these Subway stations. Doctor's Associates owns the Subway chain of sandwich shops the world's largest quick-service restaurant chain by number of locations having surpassed burger giant McDonald's. It boasts about 39300 locations in more than 100 countries. Virtually all Subway restaurants are franchised and offer such fare as hot and cold sub sandwiches turkey wraps and salads. The eateries are located in freestanding buildings as well as in airports convenience stores sports facilities and other locations.

Geographic Reach

The company's network of eateries stretching from Afghanistan to Zambia is a testament to how effectively the franchising model can be used to expand a dining concept. Part of the reason for Subway's success is the portability and adaptability of the dining concept. The sandwich restaurants can be found in a vast array of locations including shopping center food courts suburban strip malls and even military bases. The company is particularly focused on expanding its international presence in Asia and Central Europe.

Operations

With the ability to fit one of its restaurants almost anywhere Subway can offer franchisees lower startup costs as compared to other concepts that require large areas for food preparation or dining space. Many of Subway's franchisees operate just a single location but a few oversee a large estate.

Local operators who own the individual restaurants use the Subway name in exchange for royalties and other fees. This allows Doctor's Associates to expand its sandwich business without the cost of construction and operation. (Domiciled in Florida the company operates its franchising business largely through Connecticut-based affiliate World Franchise Headquarters.)

Sales and Marketing

Like its fast-food brethren Subway relies heavily on continuous television advertising and sponsorships to promote itself. It has marketing partnerships with dozens of companies and celebrity spokespeople.

Strategy

The Subway chain has tapped into the health food and weight loss zeitgeist in the US prominently featuring in its advertising Jared Fogle a man who famously lost nearly 250 lbs. by switching to a Subway sandwich diet. The chain continues to tout the health benefits of its sandwiches over traditional burgers and fries by introducing new low-fat menu items.

In 2011 Subway began developing an upscale concept called Subway Cafe. The new format conceived for office buildings and other high-end locations is larger than the average Subway restaurant and features coffee espresso lattes and hot chocolate along with an expanded breakfast menu.

Ownership

Doctor's Associates is owned by co-founders Fred DeLuca and Peter Buck.

Company Background

Co-founders DeLuca and Buck opened the first Subway in 1965.

HISTORY

In 1965 17-year-old Fred DeLuca dreamed of becoming a doctor while working as a stock boy in a Bridgeport Connecticut hardware store to earn college tuition. It wasn't enough so he cornered family friend Peter Buck at a backyard barbecue and asked for advice. Buck a nuclear physicist suggested DeLuca open a submarine sandwich shop and put up $1000 to get him started.

As the summer of 1965 was coming to an end DeLuca rented a small location in a remote area of Bridgeport opened Pete's Super Submarines and there he sold foot-long sandwiches. On the first day the sandwiches were so popular that DeLuca hired his own customers to work behind the counter; by the end of the day he had sold out of all his supplies. The sandwiches continued to be popular for a while but within a few months the shop started losing money and DeLuca and Buck found that selling submarine sandwiches was a seasonal business. They decided they could create an illusion of success by opening a second location and then a third. The third store was finally successful partly because of its more visible location and increased marketing and partly because of a new name –Subway.

DeLuca and Buck had set a goal of 32 shops opened by 1975 but they had only 16 by 1974. They realized that the only way they could reach their goal in one year was to license the Subway name. The first franchise opened that year in Wallingford Connecticut and they opened 32 by the end of 1975. The partners hit 100 by 1978 then 200 by 1983 and DeLuca set a new goal: 5000 Subway shops by 1994. The first international Subway opened in Bahrain in 1984 and DeLuca achieved his goal of 5000 shops by 1990.

During the 1990s DeLuca experimented with several other franchise concepts including We Care Hair (budget styling salons) Cajun Joe's (spicy fried chicken) and Q Burgers. But none of these ventures fared as well as his sandwich empire. As Subway grew however controversy surrounding its treatment of franchisees began to surface. A Federal Trade Commission investigation of the company was dropped in 1993 but Subway continued to battle franchisees complaining about broken contracts market over-saturation (and therefore too much competition and self-cannibalization) and what the franchisees viewed as unreasonably high royalty fees.

In spite of its franchising troubles Subway kept growing. It expanded into Russia and China in the mid-1990s and opened its 11000th restaurant in 1995. In 1997 Subway inked deals with the Army Navy and Air Force exchange services to bring Subway units to military bases. Two years later the company opened its 14000th restaurant in Mount Gambier Australia an event that coincided with Subway's renewed push to expand internationally.

The company got some unexpected publicity in 1999 when 22-year-old Jared Fogle claimed that he dropped 245 pounds from his 425-pound frame by subsisting on a diet of Subway turkey sandwiches. Subway helped Fogle extend his 15 minutes of fame by featuring him and his oversized pants in a TV commercial. (The company has since built an entire campaign around Fogle that features other weight watchers attributing their success to Jared and Subway.) Subway introduced its largest menu initiative ever in 2000 when it unveiled its Subway Selects Gourmet Sandwiches adding 13 items to the menu. In April 2001 the company opened its 15000th store.

Also that year Buck retired as chairman but stayed on as a member of the board of directors. Becoming one of the fastest-growing franchises in the world Subway expanded from 16000 locations in 2002 to more than 22000 stores by the end of 2004.

All US Subway outlets switched from Pepsi to Coke products in 2005. Two years later the chain surpassed 21000 locations in the US.

EXECUTIVES

President Co-Founder, Frederick A. (Fred) DeLuca, age 66
Assistant Vp, Cindy Eadie, age 57
V Pres, Mildred Shinn
Vice President General Counsel, Leonard H Axelrod
Vice President, Chris Luth
Vice President, Fernando Kohler
Senior Vice President Department, Joseph Hofmann
Vice President Subway Purchasing, Joe Leahey
Vice President Of Human Resources, Dale Wiess
Vice President, Matthew Whelan
Senior Vice President Human Resources, Janet Boud

LOCATIONS

HQ: DOCTOR' S ASSOCIATES INC.
325 BIC DR, MILFORD, CT 06461-3072
Phone: 203-877-4281
Web: WWW.SUBWAY.CO.UK

COMPETITORS

Burger King	Panera Bread
CKE Restaurants	Papa John' s
Chick-fil-A	Popeyes
Chipotle	Potbelly Sandwich Shop
Church' s Chicken	Quiznos
Dairy Queen	Sonic Corp.
Domino' s	Starbucks
Jack in the Box	Tim Hortons
McDonald' s	Wendy' s
Panda Restaurant Group	YUM!

HISTORICAL FINANCIALS

Company Type: Private

Income Statement FYE: December 31

	ASSETS ($ mil.)	NET INCOME ($ mil.)	INCOME AS % OF ASSETS	EMPLOYEES
12/11	117	7	6.8%	650
12/10	114	7	6.5%	—
12/08	95	6	6.6%	—
12/07	73	5	7.7%	—
Annual Growth	12.5%	9.1%	—	—

2011 Year-End Financials

Debt ratio: —
Return on equity: 0.70%
Cash ($ mil.): 20
Current ratio: 0.50
Long-term debt ($ mil.): —

Dividends
Yield: —
Payout: —
Market value ($ mil.): —

DOCTORS' HOSPITAL INC.

Doctors Community Hospital is an acute care and surgical hospital serving the Washington DC area. The not-for-profit medical center admits 12000 patients each year and has some 220 beds and offers standard and specialty services such as diagnostics emergency and cardiac care diagnostics rehabilitation wound care and neurology. The hospital which has some 600 doctors on staff also includes a women's health center a sleep therapy division and the Joslin Diabetes Center. Established in 1975 Doctors Community Hospital provides community health services such as educational programs and support groups for specific medical conditions.

EXECUTIVES

President, Philip B. Down
Vice President Chief Financial Officer, Dennis Scanlon
VP Nursing and Patient Care Services, Paula L. Bruening
VP Human Resources, Charlene Lundgren
VP Medical Affairs, Gabriel Jaffe
VP Business Development, Scott B. Gregerson
Executive Vice President Chief Operating Officer, Paul R. Grenaldo
Vice President, Robyn M. Webb-Williams
Vice President of Doctors Community Hospital Foundation, Robyn M. Webb-Williams
Vice President Human Resources, Paul A. Hagens

LOCATIONS

HQ: DOCTORS' HOSPITAL INC.
8118 GOOD LUCK RD, LANHAM, MD 20706-3574
Phone: 301-552-8118
Web: WWW.DCHWEB.ORG

PRODUCTS/OPERATIONS

Selected Services

Bariatric services
Breast health
Cancer services
Cardiac services
Diabetes services
Diagnostic service
Emergency services
Neurosciences
Orthopedic services
Robotic surgery
Sleep center
Surgical services
Sears/nose/throat
Support groups
Therapy services
Wound care

COMPETITORS

Adventist HealthCare
Bon Secours Health
Calvert Memorial Hospital
Civista Health
Dimensions Healthcare
Johns Hopkins Medicine
MedStar Health
Providence Hospital (Washington DC)
Suburban Hospital

HISTORICAL FINANCIALS

Company Type: Private

Income Statement FYE: June 30

	REVENUE ($ mil.)	NET INCOME ($ mil.)	NET PROFIT MARGIN	EMPLOYEES
06/12	190	(0)		1,200
06/11	211	16	7.9%	—
06/10	198	(1)	—	—
06/09	179	(12)	—	—
Annual Growth	2.0%	—	—	—

2012 Year-End Financials

Debt ratio: —
Return on equity: (-0.20%)
Cash ($ mil.): 21
Current ratio: 1.20
Long-term debt ($ mil.): —
Dividends
Yield: —
Payout: —
Market value ($ mil.): —

DOOLEY''S PETROLEUM INC.

LOCATIONS

HQ: DOOLEY' ' S PETROLEUM INC.
304 MAIN AVE, MURDOCK, MN 562718033
Phone: 3208752641
Web: WWW.DOOLEYPETRO.COM

HISTORICAL FINANCIALS

Company Type: Private

Income Statement FYE: December 31

	REVENUE ($ mil.)	NET INCOME ($ mil.)	NET PROFIT MARGIN	EMPLOYEES
12/12	334	2	0.8%	110
12/11	359	2	0.6%	—
12/10	250	1	0.7%	—
12/09	205	0	—	—
Annual Growth	17.6%	—	—	—

2012 Year-End Financials

Debt ratio: —
Return on equity: 0.80%
Cash ($ mil.): 2
Current ratio: 0.60
Long-term debt ($ mil.): —
Dividends
Yield: —
Payout: —
Market value ($ mil.): —

DOYLESTOWN HOSPITAL HEALTH AND WELLNESS CENTER INC.

It takes a village to own a hospital and Doylestown Hospital is owned by the local women's civic organization Village Improvement Association. Founded in 1923 the hospital serves southeastern Pennsylvania and neighboring areas of New Jersey. With some 240 beds Doylestown Hospital provides a variety of acute and tertiary medical services. Specialties include cardiac surgery cancer care (as part of the University of Pennsylvania Cancer Network) and orthopedics. Affiliated with the hospital are two Pine Run nursing and assisted-living centers.

Geographic Reach

Doylestown Hospital serves Bucks and Montgomery counties in Pennsylvania (including northern suburbs of Philadelphia) and Hunterdon and Mercer counties in neighboring New Jersey.

Operations

The hospital employs some 420 doctors across 40 specialties including radiology gastroenterology urology and pulmonology. Doylestown is also a certified chest pain center (via The Woodall Chest Pain Center) and a joint commission-certified primary stroke center. Additional hospital departments cover emergency critical care birthing rehabilitation and robotic surgery services.

In addition to the main medical center Doylestown Hospital operates three outpatient locations: The Health and Wellness Center in Warrington an Open MRI center in Hartsville and The Pavilion outpatient building located adjacent to the hospital. The parent organization VIA Health runs the Pine Run retirement centers as well as community health facilities.

EXECUTIVES

President CEO, Richard A. Reif
VP Chief Medical Officer and Director, Scott S. Levy, age 56
VP Human Resources, Barb Hebel
Vice President Chief Financial Officer, Dan Upton
VP Development, Linda A. Plank
VP Patient Services and COO, Eleanor Wilson
Chair, Carolyn Della-Rodolfa
President CEO and Director, Richard A. Reif
VP Chief Medical Officer and Director, Scott S. Levy, age 56

LOCATIONS

HQ: DOYLESTOWN HOSPITAL HEALTH AND WELLNESS CENTER INC.
595 W STATE ST, DOYLESTOWN, PA 18901-2597
Phone: 215-345-2200
Web: WWW.DH.ORG

PRODUCTS/OPERATIONS

Selected Services

Hospice
Medical Imaging/Radiology
Outpatient Testing
Rehab/Therapy
Surgical Services
Visiting Nurse/Home Care
Women' s Services
Cardiac-Neuro Services
Diabetes Management
GI/Endoscopy
Fibromyalgia
Lab Services
Medical Library
Mammography
Nutrition Counseling - Healthy Directions

COMPETITORS

Abington Memorial Hospital
Children' s Hospital of Philadelphia
Jefferson Health System
Lehigh Valley Health Network
North Philadelphia Health System
Pennsylvania Hospital
Shore Memorial Hospital
St. Luke' s University Health Network
Tenet Healthcare
University of Pennsylvania Health System

HISTORICAL FINANCIALS

Company Type: Private

Income Statement FYE: June 30

	REVENUE ($ mil.)	NET INCOME ($ mil.)	NET PROFIT MARGIN	EMPLOYEES
06/11	238	22	9.5%	2,853
06/10	234	3	1.5%	—
06/09	202	6	3.1%	—
06/08	217	(1)	—	—
Annual Growth	3.2%	—	—	—

2011 Year-End Financials

Debt ratio: —
Return on equity: 9.50%
Cash ($ mil.): 32
Current ratio: 1.50
Long-term debt ($ mil.): —
Dividends
Yield: —
Payout: —
Market value ($ mil.): —

DPR CONSTRUCTION

From bio labs to wafer fabs DPR Construction runs the gamut for its high tech and health care clients. The employee-owned firm provides general contracting and construction management services for the advanced technology/mission critical life sciences healthcare higher education and corporate office markets. The construction firm specializes in developing retail stores hospitals data centers clean rooms laboratories manufacturing facilities and green buildings. Altogether DPR Construction boasts about 20 regional offices nationwide. Company head Doug Woods former CEO Peter Nosler and secretary/treasurer Ron Davidowski (the D P and R in DPR Construction) founded the firm in 1990.

Geographic Reach

To maintain a presence near customers DPR boasts nearly 20 regional offices. Its operations span 10 states including Arizona California Colorado North Carolina Florida Georgia Maryland Texas Virginia and Washington DC.

Sales and Marketing

DPR serves several core markets including advanced technology corporate offices healthcare higher education and life sciences. Customers have includes CHRISTUS Health Clif Bar & Company Intuit Facebook and Kaiser Permanente.

Strategy

The company is looking to leverage its expanded East Coast operations. In 2013 DPR added an office in Baltimore to supplement its existing offices in Richmond Virginia and Washington DC. The three offices also serve customers in Maryland West Virginia Delaware Pennsylvania and New Jersey.

DPR has been focusing on eco-friendly construction. More than 40% of its projects incorporate green building techniques or products and approximately one in four of its employees are Leadership in Energy and Environmental Design (LEED) certified.

Mergers and Acquisitions

DPR in 2013 purchased Atlanta-based Hardin Construction Company to extend its reach in the Southeast and Texas. Known as DPR Hardin in the Atlanta market (and as DPR Construction nationally) the combined company began work on half a dozen Georgia-based projects worth a total of $230 million.

EXECUTIVES

Management Committee, Jim Dolen
Management Committee, Peter A. Salvati
President, Douglas E. (Doug) Woods
Management Committee, Eric Lamb
Regional Manager Raleigh-Durham NC Office, Mark Whitson
Regional Manager Tampa FL Office, Page W. McKee
Regional Manager Redwood City, Jody Quinton
Regional Manager Baltimore and Washington DC, Greg Haldeman
Management Committee, George Pfeffer
Management Committee, Mike Ford
Regional Manager West Palm Beach, Deborah Beetson
Regional Manager Austin and Houston TX Offices, Gary Nauert
Regional Manager Phoenix, David Elrod
Regional Manager San Diego, Jay Leopold
Regional Manager Sacramento, Mark Cirksena
Regional Manager San Jose, Scott Greubel
CFO, Michele Leiva
Regional Manager San Francisco, Mike Humphrey
Regional Manager Richmond VA, Lisa Lingerfelt
Regional Manager Atlanta, Russ Brockelbank
Regional Manager Denver Office, Michael Devens
Regional Manager Newport Beach and Pasadena CA Offices, Dave Seastrom
Regional Manager Orlando FL Office, Scott Lyons
Vice President Of Operations, Carolyn Hunter
Vice President Engineering, Dustin Rothwell
Vice Chairman, Daniel Valentine

LOCATIONS

HQ: DPR CONSTRUCTION
1450 VETERANS BLVD OFC, REDWOOD CITY, CA 94063-2618
Phone: 650-474-1450
Web: WWW.DPRINC.COM

Selected Offices

Atlanta
Austin TX
Baltimore
Denver
Houston
Newport Beach CA
Orlando Florida
Pasadena CA
Phoenix
Raleigh-Durham NC
Redwood City CA
Richmond VA
Sacramento CA
San Diego CA
San Francisco CA
San Jose CA
Tampa Florida
Washington DC
West Palm Beach FL

COMPETITORS

Austin Industries
Bechtel
Bovis Lend Lease
Devcon Construction
Fluor
Hensel Phelps Construction
Hoffman Corporation
Jacobs Engineering
M. A. Mortenson
PC Construction
Skanska USA Building
Swinerton
Turner Corporation
Whiting-Turner

HISTORICAL FINANCIALS

Company Type: Private

Income Statement FYE: December 31

	REVENUE ($ mil.)	NET INCOME ($ mil.)	NET PROFIT MARGIN	EMPLOYEES
12/11	2,111	41	2.0%	2,300
12/08	1,836	68	3.7%	—
12/00	1,958	25	1.3%	—
Annual Growth	0.7%	4.5%	—	—

2011 Year-End Financials

Debt ratio: —
Return on equity: 2.00%
Cash ($ mil.): 161
Current ratio: 1.10
Long-term debt ($ mil.): —
Dividends
Yield: —
Payout: —
Market value ($ mil.): —

DRAKE UNIVERSITY

You won't find duck duck goose as part of the curriculum at Drake University. The Des Moines Iowa school provides undergraduate and graduate education programs for some 5500 students through its six colleges and schools: arts and sciences business and public administration education journalism and mass communications law and pharmacy and health sciences. It has a 15:1 student-to-faculty ratio. A private school Drake University was founded in 1881 with seed money from General Francis Marion Drake a Civil War general and former Iowa governor banker railroad builder and attorney. Drake University also hosts the Drake Relays one of the largest track and field events in the US.

Geographic Reach

Drake is located on a 150-acre campus in Des Moines Iowa. Its students hail from across the US and about 50 international countries.

Operations

The university offers more than 70 undergraduate programs as well as 20 graduate degrees. Drake employs 280 full-time faculty members. In addition to its main colleges and schools the university operates centers and institutes in fields including agricultural law finance humanities professional studies public policy scientific research and entrepreneurship.

Tuition and fees at the university runs at about $29000 each year and account for two-thirds of revenue.

Strategy

Expansion efforts at Drake include the opening of several new learning and laboratory facilities at the College of Pharmacy and Health Sciences in 2013. The university is also working to streamline administrative functions to control expenses.

EXECUTIVES

VP and Treasurer, Victoria F. Payseur
Dean of Students, Sentwali Bakari
Dean School of Law, Allan Vestal
Dean Cowles Library, Rodney Henshaw
Dean College of Business and Public Administration and School of Journalism and Mass Communications, Charles C. Edwards
VP Admission and Financial Aid, Tom Delahunt
VP Alumni and Development, John Smith
Provost, Michael J. Renner
Dean College of Arts and Sciences, Joseph Lenz
Dean School of Education, Janet McMahill
Dean College of Pharmacy and Health Sciences, Raylene Rospond
President, Keith Summerville
Chief Information Technology Officer, Ann Kovalchick
Administrative Assistant, Andrea McDonough
Director of financial aid, Susan Ladd
Vice President for business and finance treasurer&mdash, Deborah Newsom

Vice President for admission and financial aid&mdash, Thomas F. Delahunt

LOCATIONS

HQ: DRAKE UNIVERSITY
2507 UNIVERSITY AVE, DES MOINES, IA 50311-4505
Phone: 515-271-2011
Web: WWW.ARTSCI.DRAKE.EDU

PRODUCTS/OPERATIONS

2012 Operating Revenue

% of total	
Student tuition &	64
Auxiliary	16
Government grants &	7
Private	5
Endowment	5
Private grants &	1
Other	2
Total	**100**

Selected Services

College of Arts and Sciences
College of Business and Public Administration
College of Pharmacy and Health Sciences
Law School
School of Education
School of Journalism and Mass Communication

HISTORICAL FINANCIALS

Company Type: Private

Income Statement FYE: May 31

	REVENUE ($ mil.)	NET INCOME ($ mil.)	NET PROFIT MARGIN	EMPLOYEES
05/12	180	5	2.9%	830
05/10	123	21	17.6%	—
05/09	119	(39)	—	—
05/08	112	(2)	—	—
Annual Growth	12.6%	—	—	—

2012 Year-End Financials

Debt ratio: —
Return on equity: 2.90%
Cash ($ mil.): 45
Current ratio: —
Long-term debt ($ mil.): —
Dividends
Yield: —
Payout: —
Market value ($ mil.): —

DREXEL UNIVERSITY

Drexel doesn't want to train its dragons but to educate them in a wide range of disciplines. Drexel University (home of the Drexel Dragons) is a private coeducational institution of higher learning with an enrollment of more than 26000 undergraduate and graduate students and a student-teacher ratio of about 17:1. It operates more than a dozen schools and colleges in the US; the Drexel University College of Medicine is the one of the country's largest private medical schools. Drexel runs a mandatory co-operative education program that helps students gain real-world experience while supplying local employers with trained workers. Philadelphia financier and philanthropist Anthony Drexel founded the university in 1891.

Operations

One of the 15 largest private universities in the US Drexel offers more than 200 degree programs in 15 colleges and schools. Drexel Online was one of the first Internet-based distance education programs. It offers more than 100 degree programs. In research the university garners about $110 million in funding with about $88 million from federal sources.

Geographic Reach

Besides its three campuses in Philadelphia Drexel has educational operations in Malvern Pennsylvania and Sacramento California and it has research partnerships in China and Israel.

Financial Performance

For Drexel's fiscal 2013 (ends June) revenue increased nearly to $965 million and expenses came in a just under $900 million. Its assets grew to $1.1 billion in 2013 up from $946 million the previous year.

Strategy

Drexel is working with Amtrak and Brandywine Realty Trust to develop a mixed-use project on 75 acres around Philadelphia's 30th Street Station. Next door to that site Drexel is developing its Innovation Neighborhood project on 12 acres of its campus. That project is designed to attract and start high-tech businesses.

Drexel in 2014 opened a 23000-square-foot facility in Philadelphia's Center City that includes space for clinical services and research for its College of Nursing and Health Professions.

Mergers and Acquisitions

In September 2012 Drexel acquired the Academy of Natural Sciences of Philadelphia (ANS) establishing it as a not-for-profit subsidiary of the university.

EXECUTIVES

V Pres Enrollment Mgmt, Joan M Donald
Vice President Internal Audit, James K Seaman
Vice President Of Facilities, Robert Francis
President and CEO Academy of Natural Sciences of Drexel University, George W. Gephart
VP Information Resources and Technology, John A. Bielec
EVP Treasurer and CFO, Helen Y. Bowman
President, John A. Fry
Interim Provost, James Herbert
SVP Online Learning and President Drexel e-Learning, Susan C. Aldridge
Dean and SVP Medical Affairs College of Medicine, Daniel V. Schidlow
Vp Government And Community Relations, David E Wilson
Associate Vice President Chief, Kenneth Goldman
Vice President Of Compliance, Edward Longazel
Sr Assoc Vp Public Safety, Domenic Ceccanecchio
Senior Vice President Corporate Relations And Economic Development, Keith A Orris
Asst Vp Univ Procurement, Joe Campbell
Sr Vp University Communication, Lori Doyle
Vp Financial Plng/intrm Bursar, Amy Bosio
Asst Vp Admissions, Erin Finn
Sr Vp Inst Advancement, Elizabeth A Dale
Avp Advancement College Of Medicine, Donna Frithsen
Vp Finance/assoc Treasurer, Eric Olson
Sr Vp/executive Director, Brian Keech
Assistant Vice President, Kevin McNamara
Assistant Vice President Equality And Diversity, Michele Rovinsky
Assistant Vice President College Of Nursing And Health, Laura Valenti
Business Manager Vice President Government And Community Relations, Dimitrios Boufidis
Vice President Information Technology And Operations, Chris Shull
Clinical Director, Sheila Plungis
Vice President Of Membership And Recruitment Sigma Sigma Sigma, Christe Thompson
Vice President Of Finance, Jimmy Wong
Assistant Vice President External Affairs, Karen Lewis
Art Historian Department Head Art And Art History; Curator Pearlstein Gallery, Joseph Gregory
Associate Vice President And Director Of Investments, Catherine Ulozas
Chairman, Richard A. Greenawalt
Secretary, Xinlin Li
Auditors: Deloitte&ToucheLLP

LOCATIONS

HQ: DREXEL UNIVERSITY
3141 CHESTNUT ST, PHILADELPHIA, PA 191042875
Phone: 2158952000
Web: WWW.DREXEL.EDU

PRODUCTS/OPERATIONS

Selected Schools and Colleges

Antoinette Westphal College of Media Arts & Design
Bennett S. Lebow College of Business
College of Arts and Sciences
College of Engineering
The College of Information Science and Technology
College of Law
College of Nursing and Health Professions
Drexel University College of Medicine
Earle Mack School of Law
Pennoni Honors College
Richard C. Goodwin College of Professional Studies
School of Biomedical Engineering Science and Health Systems
School of Education
School of Public Health

HISTORICAL FINANCIALS

Company Type: Private

Income Statement FYE: June 30

	REVENUE ($ mil.)	NET INCOME ($ mil.)	NET PROFIT MARGIN	EMPLOYEES
06/13	965	107	11.1%	2,868
06/12	910	34	3.8%	—
06/11*	896	166	18.6%	—
12/08	0	0	—	—
Annual Growth	—	—	—	—

*Fiscal year change

2013 Year-End Financials

Debt ratio: —
Return on equity: 11.10%
Cash ($ mil.): 87
Current ratio: —
Long-term debt ($ mil.): —
Dividends
Yield: —
Payout: —
Market value ($ mil.): —

DTJ HOLDINGS INC.

EXECUTIVES

Director Purchasing, Cyndee Johnson
Manager Regional Trading Lumber Kansas, Brandon Alles
Regional Trading Manager Lumber Iowa, Alan Shearer
Regional Sales Manager Lumber Wisconsin, William (Bill) Johnson
Regional Trading Manager Lumber Illinois, Jim Jones
Assistant Regional Trading Manager Lumber Illinois, John Rich
Regional Trading Manager Lumber Illinois, Kerry Russell

LOCATIONS

HQ: DTJ HOLDINGS INC.
5034 GRAND RIDGE DR, WEST DES MOINES, IA 502655754
Phone: 5152626600
Web: WWW.ROBERTSDYBDAHL.COM

2009 Locations

	No.
Iowa	3
Illinois	2
Indiana	1

Kansas	1
Nebraska	1
Wisconsin	1
Total	**9**

COMPETITORS

84 Lumber
Babcock Lumber
Builders FirstSource
Edward Hines Lumber
HD Supply
Huttig Building Products
International Paper
Weekes Forest Products

HISTORICAL FINANCIALS

Company Type: Private

Income Statement FYE: December 31

	REVENUE ($ mil.)	NET INCOME ($ mil.)	NET PROFIT MARGIN	EMPLOYEES
12/12	220	1	0.7%	238
12/11	181	0	0.5%	—
12/10	187	1	0.8%	—
12/09	160	0	—	—
Annual Growth	11.2%	—	—	—

2012 Year-End Financials

Debt ratio: —
Return on equity: 0.70%
Cash ($ mil.): 2
Current ratio: 2.20
Long-term debt ($ mil.): —
Dividends
Yield: —
Payout: —
Market value ($ mil.): —

DUCON TECHNOLOGIES INC.

LOCATIONS

HQ: DUCON TECHNOLOGIES INC.
5 PENN PLZ STE 2403, NEW YORK, NY 100011848
Phone: 6316941700
Web: WWW.DUCON.COM

Ducon Technologies has operations in Australia Canada China India Italy Japan Kuwait Mexico the Netherlands Puerto Rico Qatar Taiwan and in the US.

PRODUCTS/OPERATIONS

Selected Subsidiaries

Ducon Environmental Systems
Ducon Fluid Transport
Environeering Environmental Company
MIP-Ducon
Thermal Process Construction Co.

HISTORICAL FINANCIALS

Company Type: Private

Income Statement FYE: December 31

	REVENUE ($ mil.)	NET INCOME ($ mil.)	NET PROFIT MARGIN	EMPLOYEES
12/12	479	4	0.9%	471
12/10	403	8	2.0%	—
12/09	412	7	1.7%	—
12/05	328	0	—	—
Annual Growth	5.5%	—	—	—

2012 Year-End Financials

Debt ratio: —
Return on equity: 0.90%
Cash ($ mil.): 5
Current ratio: 2.70
Long-term debt ($ mil.): —
Dividends
Yield: —
Payout: —
Market value ($ mil.): —

DUQUESNE UNIVERSITY OF THE HOLY SPIRIT

Duquesne University of The Holy Ghost keeps a keen eye on the spiritual as well as the academic. The school offers more than 100 undergraduate degree programs about 65 graduate and professional degree programs and more than 20 doctoral programs at schools of business education law liberal arts nursing pharmacy health sciences natural and environmental sciences music and leadership and professional advancement. Duquesne was founded in 1878 as the Pittsburgh Catholic College of the Holy Ghost. It has an annual enrollment of more than 10000 undergraduate graduate and law students.

EXECUTIVES

Vice President For Management Business, Stephen Schillo
Executive Vice President For, Sean M Hogan, age 74
Vice President Of Legal Affairs, Linda S Drago
Vp University Advancement, John P Plante
Vp Of Academics/provost, Ralph L Pearson
Vice President, Raymond French
Assoc Vp Financial Affairs, David Grousosky
Vice President, Michael Foglio
Vp Management/business, David Beaupre
Vice President Of Finance, Justin Battaglia
Vice President Of Membership Beta Alpha Psi, Emily Stephen
Board Member, Jean Anne Hattler
Auditors: KPMGLLP

LOCATIONS

HQ: DUQUESNE UNIVERSITY OF THE HOLY SPIRIT
600 FORBES AVE, PITTSBURGH, PA 152193016
Phone: 4123966000
Web: WWW.DUQ.EDU

HISTORICAL FINANCIALS

Company Type: Private

Income Statement FYE: June 30

	REVENUE ($ mil.)	NET INCOME ($ mil.)	NET PROFIT MARGIN	EMPLOYEES
06/13	357	20	5.7%	3,601
06/12	262	7	2.8%	—
06/11	333	21	6.6%	—
06/10	290	0	—	—
Annual Growth	7.2%	—	—	—

2013 Year-End Financials

Debt ratio: —
Return on equity: 5.70%
Cash ($ mil.): 40
Current ratio: 0.20
Long-term debt ($ mil.): —
Dividends
Yield: —
Payout: —
Market value ($ mil.): —

E-Z MART STORES INC.

E-Z Mart Stores aims to make filling gas tanks and stomachs EZR for small-town America. The regional convenience store chain operates about 295 stores across four neighboring states including Arkansas Louisiana Oklahoma and Texas. Rather than build its own stores the company usually expands through acquisitions. In addition to the standard hot dogs sodas coffee and cigarettes most E-Z Mart locations also offer Shell Conoco Phillips 66 or CITGO gasoline. E-Z Mart was founded in 1970 by Jim Yates in Nashville Arkansas. Yates died in 1998 when the plane he was piloting crashed leaving his daughter Sonja Hubbard at the company's helm as CEO.

Geographic Reach

Ranked #35 on Convenience Store News' "Top 100 Convenience Stores Report" E-Z Mart is a regional c-store chain that primarily serves Texas and Arkansas as well as Oklahoma and Louisiana.

Financial Performance

E-Z Mart's stores rang up an estimated $830 million in retail sales in 2013.

Sales and Marketing

Aiming to offer the chain's customers access to updated fuel prices a list of locations and in-store promotions among other items E-Z Mart in 2013 partnered with OpenStore by GasBuddy to roll out a new E-Z Mart website and mobile app. The fully integrated mobile app enables consumers to send feedback from their mobile phones and receive time-sensitive electronic mobile coupons.

Strategy

While E-Z Mart has trimmed its store count during the past decade or so including exiting markets such as Missouri it continues to make strategic acquisitions such as the purchase of eight stores in Arkansas from B-B-F Oil Co. in late 2010.

Like other convenience store operators seeking to boost in-store sales E-Z Mart is expanding its food and beverage offering adding fresh-brewed iced tea to all of its stores and installing freezers. Outside the company has a deal with Redbox to place its movie rental kiosks outside of E-Z Mart stores.

Company Ownership

E-Z Mart is privately-owned.

EXECUTIVES

CFO Secretary and Treasurer, Stacy Yates
CEO, Sonja Yates Hubbard
Chairman, FaEllen Yates
Manager Marketing and Public Relations, Kim Fowler
Assistant Controller, Jane Westbrook
Director Real Estate, Mike Ingram
VP Maintenance, Dale Sides
President and COO, Bob Hubbard
Director Human Resources and Risk Management, Amy Bowers
Controller, Les Smith
Manager Information Resources, Tom Withem
Category Manager Foodservice, James Culp
Catergory Manager Food Service, James Hudson
Category Manager Foodservice, Robert Goza
Category Manager Tobacco, Bob Richardson
Category Manager Beverages, Ron Gillion
Category Manager Candy and Snacks, Danna Huskey
VP Petroleum Operations, Liff Luthringer
VP Operations Division I, Lanny McAlester
VP Operations Division II, Harold Hicks
Director Environmental, Steve Launius

LOCATIONS

HQ: E-Z MART STORES INC.
602 FALVEY AVE, TEXARKANA, TX 75501-6677
Phone: 903-832-6502
Web: WWW.E-ZMART.COM

2013 Stores

	No.
Texas	99
Arkansas	95
Oklahoma	76
Louisiana	18
Total	**288**

COMPETITORS

7-Eleven
Love' s Country Stores

Allsup' s
Brookshire Grocery
Chevron
Exxon Mobil
Krause Gentle
QuikTrip
Racetrac Petroleum
Susser Holdings
Valero Energy

HISTORICAL FINANCIALS

Company Type: Private

Income Statement FYE: December 31

	REVENUE ($ mil.)	NET INCOME ($ mil.)	NET PROFIT MARGIN	EMPLOYEES
12/12	1,018	33	3.3%	2,100
12/11	961	13	1.4%	—
12/10	793	11	1.5%	—
12/09	102	9	9.5%	—
Annual Growth	114.6%	51.3%	—	—

2012 Year-End Financials

Debt ratio: —
Return on equity: 3.30%
Cash ($ mil.): 6
Current ratio: 0.40
Long-term debt ($ mil.): —
Dividends
Yield: —
Payout: —
Market value ($ mil.): —

E. C. BARTON & COMPANY

EXECUTIVES

President and CEO, Niel Crowson
Secretary and Treasurer, Tom Rainwater
VP Surplus Purchasing, Larry Chance
Chief Purchasing Officer, Greg Smith
VP Training and Development, John Tant
Manager Credit, Willis Tyler
M.I.S. Manager, Rick Cheshier
Executive Assistant, Judy Canada
Manager E.C.B. Brokerage, Wade Carpenter
District Manager, Ron Haynes
District Manager, David Herriman
Director Marketing, H. R. McDonough
Inventory Manager, Kevin Wooldridge
VP Finance and Administration Northern Division, Ron Bellas
Internal Communications, Jeff Chastain
Transportation Manager, Joe Crowson
Director Human Resources, Allen Devereux
Assistant Controller, Mitchell Fitts
District Manager, Travis Laurence
VP Operations, Kevin Pierce
Loss Prevention Manager, Tyson Teel
Manager Door Shop Northern Division, Russ Ashton
Buyer Northern Division, Rob Franklin
Buyer Northern Division, Mark Levin
Buyer Northern Division, Greg Peach
Store Auditor Northern Division, Nancy Willett
President Bargain Outlet, Tom Ford
Transportation Manager Northern Division, Doug Whitmarsh
Manager Marketing and Advertising Northern Division, Tom Dowd
Division Human Resource Manager Northern Division, Don Perry
Executive Assistant Northern Division, Gail Venti
Distribution Center Operations Manager Northern Division, Eric Dzialo
VP Store Operations Northern Division, Bill Ringelstein
Inventory and Replenishment Manager Bargain Outlet, Ken Thurston
Manager Builders Material Company, Steve Gage

LOCATIONS

HQ: E. C. BARTON & COMPANY
2929 BROWNS LN, JONESBORO, AR 724017208
Phone: 8709326673
Web: WWW.ECBARTON.COM

PRODUCTS/OPERATIONS

Selected Products

Bath
Ceiling fans and light kits
Ceilings
Composite decking
Doors
Driveway sealer
Electrical
Flooring
Kitchens
Lighting
Moulding
Outdoor living
Paint
Paint sundries
Pine / oak / vinyl boards
Roofing
Screws & nails
Tools & hardware
Wall planking plywood & shims
Water heaters
Windows

Selected Divisions

Barton' s
Builders Material Company
E.C.B. Brokerage and Surplus Purchasing
Grossman' s Bargain Outlet
Surplus Warehouse

COMPETITORS

84 Lumber
Ace Hardware
Builders FirstSource Southeast Group
Diamond Hill Plywood
Guardian Building Products Distribution
Home Depot
Lowe' s
Northern Tool
Snavely Forest Products
Stock Building Supply
True Value
WinWholesale

HISTORICAL FINANCIALS

Company Type: Private

Income Statement FYE: October 30

	REVENUE ($ mil.)	NET INCOME ($ mil.)	NET PROFIT MARGIN	EMPLOYEES
10/14	247	0	0.4%	700
10/13	241	(1)	—	—
10/12	265	(2)	—	—
10/11	263	0	—	—
Annual Growth	(2.1%)	—	—	—

2014 Year-End Financials

Debt ratio: —
Return on equity: 0.40%
Cash ($ mil.): 3
Current ratio: 0.40
Long-term debt ($ mil.): —
Dividends
Yield: —
Payout: —
Market value ($ mil.): —

EAST RIVER ELECTRIC POWER COOPERATIVE INC.

LOCATIONS

HQ: EAST RIVER ELECTRIC POWER COOPERATIVE INC.
211 S HARTH AVE, MADISON, SD 570422905
Phone: 6052564536
Web: WWW.EASTRIVER.COOP

HISTORICAL FINANCIALS

Company Type: Private

Income Statement FYE: December 31

	REVENUE ($ mil.)	NET INCOME ($ mil.)	NET PROFIT MARGIN	EMPLOYEES
12/13	226	0	0.2%	126
12/09	141	12	8.8%	—
Annual Growth	12.4%	(55.3%)	—	—

2013 Year-End Financials

Debt ratio: —
Return on equity: 0.20%
Cash ($ mil.): 1
Current ratio: 1.20
Long-term debt ($ mil.): —
Dividends
Yield: —
Payout: —
Market value ($ mil.): —

EAST TENNESSEE CHILDREN'S HOSPITAL ASSOCIATION INC.

ETCH has made a permanent mark on the lives of countless children over the years. Knoxville-based East Tennessee Children's Hospital (ETCH) with more than 150 beds provides a full range of health care services to children from eastern Tennessee and portions of surrounding states. Among its 30 specialized services are cardiology neonatal care orthopedics and psychiatry as well as cystic fibrosis and hearing impairment services. The hospital also offers support such as for families of children stricken by cancer. The hospital's roots are in the foundation of Knox County Crippled Children's Hospital in 1937 with less than 50 beds.

Geographic Reach

The medical center primarily serves 16 counties in eastern Tennessee: Anderson Blount Campbell Claiborne Cocke Grainger Hamblen Jefferson Knox Loudon Monroe Morgan Roane Scott Sevier and Union. It also provides services in other Tennessee counties and nearby portions of Kentucky North Carolina and Virginia.

Operations

With a total of about 450 physicians ETCH handles some 6000 inpatient visits per year while its emergency department treats some 70000 patients each year. The hospital is designated as a comprehensive regional pediatric center by the state of Tennessee. As such it operates a level III neonatal intensive care unit (ICU) and a level I trauma center and partners with smaller area hospitals in an effort to provide pediatric training support and patient transfer services. ETCH also partners with larger acute care hospitals including the University of Tennessee Medical Center to provide collaborative care services.

The medical center provides medical training services as well such as student internships nursing scholarships clinical rotations and residency programs. Some programs are offered through partnerships with area universities and colleges including the University of Tennessee and Lincoln Memorial University's DeBusk College of Osteopathic Medicine.

EXECUTIVES

Vice President for Legal Services & General Counsel, Bruce Anderson
President CEO, Keith D. Goodwin, age 59
VP Operations, Rudy McKinley
VP Medical Services, Joe Childs
VP Patient Care, Laura Barnes
Secretary Treasurer, Michael (Mike) Crabtree
Chief of Staff, John Buchheit
VP Finance and CFO, Zane Goodrich
Chief of Medicine, Lori Patterson
Vice President for Human Resources, Sue Wilburn
Vice President for Development and Community Services, Carlton M. Long

LOCATIONS

HQ: EAST TENNESSEE CHILDREN' S HOSPITAL ASSOCIATION INC.
2018 W CLINCH AVE, KNOXVILLE, TN 37916-2301
Phone: 865-541-8000
Web: WWW.ETCH.COM

PRODUCTS/OPERATIONS

Selected Services

Cancer
Cardiac
Emergency department
Hematology
Home health
Inpatient services
Intensive care unit (pediatric and neonatal)
Laboratory services
Mental health
Nutrition
Obesity
Orthopedics
Outpatient services
Radiology
Rehabilitation
Respiratory care
Sleep medicine
Surgical services
Sedation services
Transport service
Trauma

COMPETITORS

Akron Children' s Hospital
All Children' s Hospital
Children' s Hopsital of Chicago
Children' s Hospital Boston
Children' s Hospital Colorado
Children' s Hospital and Health System
Children' s Hospital of Philadelphia
Children' s Hospital of Richmond
Children' s Mercy Hospital
Cincinnati Children' s Hospital
Covenant Health
Dell Children' s Medical Center
Nationwide Children' s Hospital
Shriners Hospitals For Children
Tennova Healthcare
University Health System Inc.

HISTORICAL FINANCIALS

Company Type: Private

Income Statement FYE: June 30

	REVENUE ($ mil.)	NET INCOME ($ mil.)	NET PROFIT MARGIN	EMPLOYEES
06/13	216	37	17.4%	1,500
06/12	209	29	14.2%	—
06/10	183	19	10.5%	—
06/10	170	11	6.5%	—
Annual Growth	8.3%	50.3%	—	—

2013 Year-End Financials

Debt ratio: ——
Return on equity: 17.40%
Cash ($ mil.): 32
Current ratio: 2.40
Long-term debt ($ mil.): —
Dividends
Yield: —
Payout: —
Market value ($ mil.): —

EAST TEXAS MEDICAL CENTER REGIONAL HEALTHCARE SYST

East Texas Medical Center (ETMC) Regional Healthcare System works to meet the health care needs of residents of the Piney Woods. The not-for-profit health system operates more than a dozen hospitals across eastern Texas along with behavioral rehabilitation and home health care businesses. Its flagship 450-bed Tyler location serves as the hub and referral center for satellite medical centers located in more rural locations. The system also runs numerous primary care and outpatient clinics throughout the region. Serving more than 300000 patients each year ETMC operates an emergency ambulance service subsidiary and a clinical laboratory which provide services to the ETMC Regional Healthcare System.

Geographic Reach

ETMC serves the more than 1 million people who reside in East Texas communities. It caters to nearly 20 Texas counties including Anderson Camp Cherokee Ellis Franklin Freestone Henderson Hopkins Houston Panola Red River Rusk Shelby Smith Trinity Upshur Van Zandt and Wood. These communities range in size from fewer than 500 residents to more than 50000.

Operations

The flagship ETMC Tyler facility offers specialized care for cancer and cardiovascular and neurological conditions. It is a Level I regional trauma center and provides diagnostic and outpatient surgery services.

The system is organized so that primary care is provided in the rural health clinics. Secondary care is also provided locally in the ETMC affiliate hospitals. High-level secondary and tertiary care is provided at ETMC Tyler.

Strategy

To keep up with the needs of its residents the ETMC Regional Healthcare System works to expand its operations.

In 2013 ETMC Pittsburg broke ground on a 5000-sq.-ft. expansion of the hospital's surgery department. Its East Texas Medical Center Regional Healthcare System also added a pair of emergency transport helicopters valued at more than $9 million.

In 2012 the company completed $30-million expansion and renovation project at East Texas Medical Center Henderson including a new emergency department grand lobby and clinic space. It also wrapped up the second phase of an expansion project at ETMC Fairfield that involved adding a new entrance lobby clinic space cardiopulmonary rehabilitation facility and administrative suite.

Its 100-bed Henderson Memorial Hospital joined the network in 2009 as ETMC Henderson. Soon after becoming part of the network ETMC assisted its new affiliate with facility upgrades that included building new emergency department facilities renovating old rooms and installing new electrical and HVAC systems all completed in 2011. ETMC also expanded its Trinity facility with a 15-bed patient wing at the cost of $7.4 million and expanded its mammography services at ETMC Cedar Creek Lake. A $35 million ETMC Quitman facility is expected to be completed in 2013.

ETMC also concentrates on upgrading its information systems. The healthcare system's data exchange organization FirstNet Exchange received a grant from the state of Texas in 2011 to develop and operate a secure health information network to support hospitals and clinicians.

Sales and Marketing

The Medicare program accounted for 50% of net patient revenues in 2012; Medicaid contributed 12% of the same. Some 16% of total net patient service revenue came from commercial insurance carriers and preferred provider organizations.

Financial Performance

Due to an increase in patient service revenue ETMC's revenue rose by 6% to $942 million in 2012 from $888 million in 2011. Net income for the same reporting period dropped some 92% to $1.1 million from $16 million due to rising salaries and wages and employee benefits expenses as well as from an increase in loss from defined benefit pension adjustment.

EXECUTIVES

President and CEO, Elmer G. Ellis
SVP, Jerry Massey
SVP and CFO, Byron Hale
Corporate Director Marketing, Carrol Roge
VP Information Technology, Paula Anthony
SVP and Administrator East Texas Medical Center Tyler, Robert B. Evans
Secretary, Rebekah Morris

LOCATIONS

HQ: EAST TEXAS MEDICAL CENTER REGIONAL HEALTHCARE SYST
1000 S BECKHAM AVE, TYLER, TX 75701-1908
Phone: 903-531-8010
Web: WWW.ETMC.COM

PRODUCTS/OPERATIONS

Selected Health and Medical Services

Bariatric Surgery Center
Behavioral Health Center
Cancer Institute
Cardiovascular Institute
Digestive Disease Center
Emergency Services
Fitness Centers
Home Health
Neurological Institute
Orthopedic Institute
Plastic Surgery
Podiatry Care
Radiology and Imaging
Rehabilitation Center
Sleep Disorders Center
Specialty Hospital
Transplant Center
Urology Institute
Women's Health
Wound Healing Center

Selected East Texas Medical Center Hospitals

ETMC Athens

ETMC Carthage
ETMC Clarksville
ETMC Crockett
ETMC Fairfield
ETMC Gilmer
ETMC Henderson
ETMC Jacksonville
ETMC Lake Palestine
ETMC Mount Vernon
ETMC Pittsburg
ETMC Quitman
ETMC Rehabilitation Hospital (Tyler)
ETMC Specialty Hospital (Tyler)
ETMC Trinity
ETMC Tyler

COMPETITORS

Baylor Health
Community Health Systems
Essent Healthcare
Good Shepherd Health System
HCA
Hunt Memorial
Memorial Health System of East Texas
Tenet Healthcare
Trinity Mother Frances Hospital and Clinics
Wadley Regional Medical Center
Woodland Heights Medical Center

HISTORICAL FINANCIALS

Company Type: Private

Income Statement FYE: October 31

	REVENUE ($ mil.)	NET INCOME ($ mil.)	NET PROFIT MARGIN	EMPLOYEES
10/08	876	30	3.4%	7,600
10/07	827	40	4.8%	—
10/06	837	0	—	—
10/05	837	17	2.1%	—
Annual Growth	1.5%	20.4%	—	—

2008 Year-End Financials

Debt ratio: ——
Return on equity: 3.40%
Cash ($ mil.): 175
Current ratio: 2.90
Long-term debt ($ mil.): —
Dividends
Yield: —
Payout: —
Market value ($ mil.): —

EASTERN BAG AND PAPER COMPANY INCORPORATED

EXECUTIVES

President, James Sugarman
Chief Executive Officer, Meredith Baum Reuben
VP Marketing, Ken Rosenberg
VP and General Manager Tewksbury Division, John Mahon
CFO, William O'Donnell
VP Operations, Don Burton
CIO, Jack Jurkowski
VP Human Resources, Joseph F. Lopresti
VP and Sales Manager Healthcare Services, Dan Colcord
VP and Sales Manager Cleaning Services, Derek Wallace
VP Sales New Jersey Division, Matthew Sugarman
VP Purchasing, Eric Liebeskind

LOCATIONS

HQ: EASTERN BAG AND PAPER COMPANY INCORPORATED
200 RESEARCH DR, MILFORD, CT 064602880
Phone: 2038781814
Web: WWW.EASTERNBAG.COM

COMPETITORS

AFFLINK
MAINES
Penn Jersey
Perkins Paper
RDA Advantage
Sysco

HISTORICAL FINANCIALS

Company Type: Private

Income Statement FYE: December 31

	REVENUE ($ mil.)	NET INCOME ($ mil.)	NET PROFIT MARGIN	EMPLOYEES
12/13	182	2	1.1%	285
12/12	177	1	0.6%	—
12/11	174	0	—	—
12/08	0	0	—	—
Annual Growth	—	—	—	—

2013 Year-End Financials

Debt ratio: ——
Return on equity: 1.10%
Cash ($ mil.): 0
Current ratio: 1.70
Long-term debt ($ mil.): —
Dividends
Yield: —
Payout: —
Market value ($ mil.): —

EASTERN MICHIGAN UNIVERSITY

Eastern Michigan University (known affectionately as just plain Eastern) has long been an affordable place to study your way into a better career. The university began as a teachers' college in 1849 and it still graduates one out of every four teachers in Michigan. Eastern has an enrollment of more than 23000 students (90% are Michigan residents) who participate in undergraduate and graduate degree programs on its campus in the southeastern part of the state. Its 200 majors minors and concentrations are offered through colleges of arts and sciences business education technology and health and human services.

Geographic Reach

In addition to its 800-acre main campus in Ypsilanti Michigan which includes more than 120 buildings the university operates continuing education campuses in Brighton Detroit Flint Jackson Livonia Monroe and Traverse City. Students attending Eastern hail from across the US and some 85 international countries.

Operations

Eastern employs 700 full-time faculty members and has a student-to-teacher ratio of 19:1. In addition to its five academic colleges and an honors college the school has 14 research centers and institutes that conduct studies into fields including community development business development education textiles and product development. The university also gives students the opportunity to participate in more than 20 division I NCAA varsity sports teams. Annual tuition for state residents runs at about $9000 per year.

Sales and Marketing

To attract nontraditional students Eastern has created accelerated Continuing Education programs with classes held on weekends and evenings. It is also steadily adding online coursework and seeks to attract military personnel. Its Return to Learn program is specifically geared to serve displaced workers who need additional education to rejoin the workforce.

Financial Performance

The university reported operating revenue of $227 million in fiscal 2013 a slight increase (1%) from 2012 results on higher student tuition and fee revenue (prompted by a rate increased approved by the state board of regents in 2012).

Strategy

To meet its goal of expanding international student opportunities Eastern strengthened its partnerships with Wuhan University (China) and Korea National University of Education in 2012. It also has a collaboration with Tianjin University in China to provide joint business degrees. In addition the university has partnered with several Michigan community colleges to provide joint degree programs and it is expanding its online course offerings.

EXECUTIVES

Chief Government Relations Officer Office of Government Relations and Special Projects, Freman Hendrix
EVP Academic Affairs and Provost, Donald M. (Don) Loppnow
Vice President Secretary, Vicki Reaume
President, Susan W. Martin, age 63
Vice President FOR OPERATIONS AND FACILITIES, John Donegan
Athletic Director Intercollegiate Athletics, Derrick Gragg
Chief Financial Officer, John Lumm
Assistant Director of Athletics Marketing, Tyler Jones
Associate Vice President Marketing, Theodore Coutilish
Director of Baseball Operations, Kevin Wheeler
Director of Operations, Jed Dreher
Director of Football Operations, Jacob Kirkendall
Director of Basketball Operations, Victoria Sun
Vice President COMMUNICATIONS, Walter Kraft
Vice President OF ACADEMIC AND STUDENT AFFAIRS, Kim Schatzel
ASSISTANT Vice President Chief Information Officer, Carl Powell
Vice President ADVANCEMENT, Tom Stevick
Chief Human Resources Officer, James Gallaher
Member Board of Regents, James F. Stapleton
Member Board of Regents, Philip A. Incarnati, age 59
Member Board of Regents, Gary D. Hawks
Member Board of Regents, Francine (Fran) Parker, age 58
Member Board of Regents, Floyd Clack
Vice Chair Board of Regents, Roy E. Wilbanks
Member Board of Regents, Mohamed Okdie
Auditors: PricewaterhouseCoopersLLP

LOCATIONS

HQ: EASTERN MICHIGAN UNIVERSITY
202 WELCH HALL, YPSILANTI, MI 48197-2214
Phone: 734-487-2031
Web: WWW.EMICH.EDU

PRODUCTS/OPERATIONS

Selected Colleges Schools and Departments

College of Arts and Sciences
- African American Studies
- Art
- Biology
- Chemistry
- Communications and Theatre Arts
- Computer Science
- Economics
- English Language and Literature
- Foreign Languages and Bilingual Studies
- Geography and Geology
- History and Philosophy

Mathematics
Music and Dance
Physic and Astronomy
Political Science
Psychology
Sociology Anthropology and Criminology
College of Business
Accounting and Finance
Computer Information Systems
Management
Marketing
College of Education
Leadership and Counseling
Special Education
Teacher Education
College of Health and Human Services
School of Health Promotion and Human Performance
School of Health Sciences
School of Nursing
School of Social Work
College of Technology
Military Science and Leadership
School of Engineering Technology
School of Technology Studies

HISTORICAL FINANCIALS

Company Type: Private

Income Statement FYE: June 30

	REVENUE ($ mil.)	NET INCOME ($ mil.)	NET PROFIT MARGIN	EMPLOYEES
06/11	221	24	11.2%	2,000
06/10	217	(1)	—	—
06/09	211	5	2.5%	—
06/08	201	3	1.5%	—
Annual Growth	3.2%	101.3%	—	—

2011 Year-End Financials

Debt ratio: —
Return on equity: 11.20%
Cash ($ mil.): 4
Current ratio: 0.40
Long-term debt ($ mil.): —
Dividends
Yield: —
Payout: —
Market value ($ mil.): —

EASTERN SHIPBUILDING GROUP INC.

LOCATIONS

HQ: EASTERN SHIPBUILDING GROUP INC.
2200 NELSON AVE, PANAMA CITY, FL 324014969
Phone: 8507631900
Web: WWW.EASTERNSHIPBUILDING.COM

HISTORICAL FINANCIALS

Company Type: Private

Income Statement FYE: December 31

	REVENUE ($ mil.)	NET INCOME ($ mil.)	NET PROFIT MARGIN	EMPLOYEES
12/13	398	50	12.7%	975
12/12	304	44	14.6%	—
12/11	183	20	11.4%	—
12/08	170	0	—	—
Annual Growth	18.5%	—	—	—

2013 Year-End Financials

Debt ratio: —
Return on equity: 12.70%
Cash ($ mil.): 47
Current ratio: 0.80
Long-term debt ($ mil.): —
Dividends
Yield: —
Payout: —
Market value ($ mil.): —

EASTERN VIRGINIA MEDICAL SCHOOL

Eastern Virginia Medical School (EVMS) sends graduated physicians down the Hampton Roads. The school offers medical and doctoral degrees residencies and specialty programs such as reproductive medicine. The community-oriented school does not have a teaching hospital but rather partners with about a dozen regional hospitals. Its main campus is part of the Eastern Virginia Medical Center which is also home to Sentara Norfolk General Hospital and Children's Hospital of The King's Daughters located in the Hampton Roads region of southeastern Virginia. The south campus hosts pediatric and diabetes research programs. EVMS also has research programs devoted to cancer infectious diseases and heart disease.

Operations

Established in 1973 EVMS operates under a state charter and operates as a public institution. Its governing board is comprised of representatives from surrounding communities as well as appointees from the EVMS Foundation which conducts fundraising activities for the school.

The school enrolls some 350 students in its residency internship and fellowship programs which cover about 40 fields. It also provides professional education programs for about 450 students. EVMS has about 450 faculty members many of which are engaged in its extensive research programs. The school is the largest biomedical research organization in southeastern Virginia.

Financial Performance

EVPS reported a 5% decrease in operating revenue to $227 million in 2012 from lower state funding private gifts and interest income. Net income also fell 69% to $11.4 million as a result of lower revenue and increased expenses from instruction management and patient care costs.

Strategy

In 2012 EVMS entered discussions with the College of William & Mary over a possible merger or affiliation agreement. Under proposed terms of the deal which must be approved by Virginia's governing entities EVMS would join the College of William & Mary organization becoming known as the William & Mary School of Medicine. The two schools have worked together on projects in the past including conducting research collaborations. As they worked towards a merger the schools increased collaborative research programs in 2013.

In addition EVMS has been working to improve its facilities so that it can increase its enrollment numbers in both the physician assistant and medical doctorate programs. A new medical education and research building that meets this need was opened in mid-2011. The school also adds new programs such as a new biotechnology graduate program launched in 2012.

EXECUTIVES

VP Administration and Finance, Mark Babashanian
Dean and Provost, Gerald J. Pepe
President, Harry T. Lester
Director News, Doug Gardner
Director of Events Planning and Management, Ashlyn Brandt
General Counsel and Compliance Officer, Stacy Purcell
Director Office of Alumni Affairs, Melissa Lang
Director Office of Marketing and Communications, Vincent Rhodes
Chief Executive Officer, Jim Lind

LOCATIONS

HQ: EASTERN VIRGINIA MEDICAL SCHOOL
714 WOODIS AVE, NORFOLK, VA 23510-1026
Phone: 757-446-6052
Web: WWW.EVMS.EDU

HISTORICAL FINANCIALS

Company Type: Private

Income Statement FYE: June 30

	REVENUE ($ mil.)	NET INCOME ($ mil.)	NET PROFIT MARGIN	EMPLOYEES
06/12	226	17	7.5%	1,500
06/11	238	47	20.0%	—
06/10	211	15	7.2%	—
06/07	9	5	58.4%	—
Annual Growth	87.5%	24.5%	—	—

2012 Year-End Financials

Debt ratio: —
Return on equity: 7.50%
Cash ($ mil.): 2
Current ratio: 1.00
Long-term debt ($ mil.): —
Dividends
Yield: —
Payout: —
Market value ($ mil.): —

EBP SUPPLY SOLUTIONS

Eastern Bag and Paper Co. (dba EBP Supply) is a leading distributor of paper products in the northeastern US. In addition to disposable tableware and packaging the company offers food service products (including china and glassware) restaurant equipment (can openers refrigerators) personal care items (bath mats roll towels) and cleansers and maintenance supplies (air fresheners vacuums). Its products are used by the industrial health care food service and janitorial industries. Founded in 1918 by Samuel Baum the company is owned and run by CEO Meredith Baum Reuben.

Geographic Reach

The company operates three distribution centers in Connecticut Massachusetts and New Jersey and maintains a fleet of more than 70 trucks and trailers. EBP Supply's distribution area spans a dozen states from Maine to northern Virginia.

Strategy

In fall 2012 the company rebranded adopted a new logo and launched a new website EBPsupply.com to better convey its expanded product line. The rebranding was designed to focus on the company's customer-centric approach. In addition to the cleaning and restaurant supplies EBP Supply offers delivery consulting training and equipment repair services.

EXECUTIVES

President, James Sugarman
Chief Executive Officer, Meredith Baum Reuben
VP Marketing, Ken Rosenberg
VP and General Manager Tewksbury Division, John Mahon
CFO, William O'Donnell
VP Operations, Don Burton
CIO, Jack Jurkowski
VP Human Resources, Joseph F. Lopresti
VP and Sales Manager Healthcare Services, Dan Colcord
VP and Sales Manager Cleaning Services, Derek Wallace
VP Sales New Jersey Division, Matthew Sugarman
VP Purchasing, Eric Liebeskind

LOCATIONS

HQ: EBP SUPPLY SOLUTIONS
200 RESEARCH DR, MILFORD, CT 06460-8500
Phone: 203-878-1814
Web: WWW.EBPSUPPLY.COM

COMPETITORS

AFFLINK
MAINES
Penn Jersey
Perkins Paper
RDA Advantage
Sysco

HISTORICAL FINANCIALS

Company Type: Private

Income Statement FYE: December 31

	REVENUE ($ mil.)	NET INCOME ($ mil.)	NET PROFIT MARGIN	EMPLOYEES
12/12	177	1	0.6%	285
12/11	174	0	—	—
12/08	0	0	—	—
Annual Growth	—	—	—	—

2012 Year-End Financials

Debt ratio: ——
Return on equity: 0.60%
Cash ($ mil.): 0
Current ratio: 1.40
Long-term debt ($ mil.): —
Dividends
Yield: —
Payout: —
Market value ($ mil.): —

EBY-BROWN COMPANY LLC

Eby-Brown makes its money on such vices as munchies and nicotine. The company is a leading convenience store supplier that distributes more than 11000 products to some 13500 retail locations in 30 states mostly east of the Mississippi. Eby-Brown operates about half a dozen distribution centers (with total capacity of about 2 million sq. ft.) that supply such items as beverages candy and snack foods frozen and refrigerated foods tobacco products and general merchandise. The convenience store supplier also offers advertising and promotion services for its customers. Eby-Brown which is still family-owned was founded in 1887 by the Wake family.

Operations

Eby-Brown also operates subsidiary Wakefield Sandwich Company which distributes wholesale convenience products. Wakefield distributes products like deli sandwiches (subs and wedges) hand-wrapped frozen breakfast items (egg ham and cheese muffins and bacon egg and cheese bagels) hand-wrapped frozen lunches (bacon cheeseburgers and chicken and swiss) and heat-and-eat items (spicy chicken and double cheeseburgers).

Geographic Reach

Based in Illinois Eby-Brown operates nationwide with a presence in Wisconsin Illinois Michigan Ohio Indiana and Georgia.

Financial Performance

The company typically logs about $5 billion in sales each year.

Strategy

Although it offers a variety of products Eby-Brown is turning to tried-and-true customer favorites to help convenience stores boost their sales. The company is relying on the brand strength of popular candies and snacks like Snickers and M&Ms from Mars and Reese's peanut butter cups from Hershey because these provide a foundation for building revenues.

Mergers and Acquisitions

To extend its reach into northeast Wisconsin Eby-Brown in 2012 acquired the assets of privately-held convenience store supplier L.A. Edlbeck Co. of Green Bay Wisconsin.

Company Ownership

Eby-Brown is owned by members of the founding Wake family.

EXECUTIVES

Vice President Of Sales, Brent Shay
Vp Human Resources, John Hilton
CEO, Richard W. (Dick) Wake
CFO, Mark Smetana
Vice President Of Sales, Dennie Jezior
Position In Vice President Merchandising, John Roach
Senior Vice President Operations, Paul Lodics
Vice President Of Merchandising, John Scardina
Vice President Of Credit Management, Shirley Jaehrling
Vice President Sales, Mike McCormack
Vice President Merchandising Fast Foods, Sharon Kuncl
Vice President Business Development, Kenneth Denney
Vice President Business Development, Christina Larson
Executive Vice President Cigarettes, Jode Bunce
Vice President Merchandising, Andy Batt
Vp It, Barbara Gordon
Vice President Of Business Development, Dustin Snyder
Sales Vice President, Joe Roenna
Vice President Of Transportation, Lee Canon
National Account Manager Circle K Great Lakes, Betsy Turek
Vice President Sales, Jim Biser

LOCATIONS

HQ: EBY-BROWN COMPANY LLC
280 SHUMAN BLVD STE 280, NAPERVILLE, IL 60563-8106
Phone: 630-778-2800
Web: WWW.EBY-BROWN.COM

Selected Distribution Locations

Baltimore MD
Eau Claire WI
Montgomery IL
Plainfield IN
Rockmart GA
Springfield OH
Ypsilanti MI

PRODUCTS/OPERATIONS

Selected Services

Retailer
- Category management
- Customer service contracts
- Marketing solutions
- Publications viewer
- Recall notices
- Technology solutions

Supplier
- Marketing solutions
- SmartProcess of Category Management
- Supplier contracts

COMPETITORS

AMCON Distributing
Atlantic Dominion
C&S Wholesale
Core-Mark
Farner-Bocken
GSC Enterprises
H. T. Hackney
MAINES
McLane
Nash-Finch
S. Abraham & Sons

HISTORICAL FINANCIALS

Company Type: Private

Income Statement FYE: October 1

	REVENUE ($ mil.)	NET INCOME ($ mil.)	NET PROFIT MARGIN	EMPLOYEES
10/11	4,730	0	—	2,500
10/10*	4,730	0	—	—
09/08	0	0	—	—
09/07	0	0	—	—
Annual Growth	—	—	—	—

*Fiscal year change

2011 Year-End Financials

Debt ratio: ——
Return on equity: —
Cash ($ mil.): 6
Current ratio: 0.70
Long-term debt ($ mil.): —
Dividends
Yield: —
Payout: —
Market value ($ mil.): —

ECS FEDERAL INC.

Electronic Consulting Services (ECS) provides computer and telecommunications network consulting services primarily in the Eastern US. The company specializes in such areas as systems engineering enterprise communications project management and program support. It also offers information assurance help desk operations and Web development services. ECS primarily serves government agencies and defense contractors. Customers have included Lockheed Martin Titan the US Department of Housing and Urban Development and Advanced Technology Systems. The company has satellite offices in Florida Missouri North Carolina Pennsylvania and Washington D.C. Electronic Consulting Services was founded in 1993.

EXECUTIVES

Svp It Services, Jackie Marsteller
Vice President Business Development, Scott Weaver
Vice President Communications Publicity, Jeannette Baka
Vice President Army Programs, Randy Ball
Vice President Corporate Development, John Magee

LOCATIONS

HQ: ECS FEDERAL INC.
2750 PROSPERITY AVE # 600, FAIRFAX, VA 22031-4312
Phone: 703-270-1540
Web: WWW.ECS-FEDERAL.COM

COMPETITORS

Computer Sciences Corp.
HP Enterprise Group
IBM Global Services

HISTORICAL FINANCIALS

Company Type: Private

Income Statement FYE: December 31

	REVENUE ($ mil.)	NET INCOME ($ mil.)	NET PROFIT MARGIN	EMPLOYEES
12/12	208	16	7.9%	1,184
12/11	138	8	5.8%	—
12/10	112	11	9.9%	—
12/06	28	2	7.5%	—
Annual Growth	39.6%	40.9%	—	—

2012 Year-End Financials

Debt ratio: —
Return on equity: 7.90%
Cash ($ mil.): 0
Current ratio: 2.00
Long-term debt ($ mil.): —

Dividends
Yield: —
Payout: —
Market value ($ mil.): —

EDUCATIONAL CREDIT MANAGEMENT CORPORATION

LOCATIONS

HQ: EDUCATIONAL CREDIT MANAGEMENT CORPORATION
1 IMATION PL, SAINT PAUL, MN 551283422
Phone: 6512210566
Web: WWW.ECMCFOUNDATION.ORG

HISTORICAL FINANCIALS

Company Type: Private

Income Statement

FYE: December 31

	ASSETS ($ mil.)	NET INCOME ($ mil.)	INCOME AS % OF ASSETS	EMPLOYEES
12/11	802	87	10.9%	634
12/10	951	(15)	—	—
12/08	65	49	74.7%	—
12/04	193	0	—	—
Annual Growth	22.6%	—	—	—

2011 Year-End Financials

Debt ratio: —
Return on equity: 22.90%
Cash ($ mil.): 239
Current ratio: —
Long-term debt ($ mil.): —

Dividends
Yield: —
Payout: —
Market value ($ mil.): —

EDUCATIONAL TESTING SERVICE INC

Please completely fill in each circle on the answer sheet as prepared by Educational Testing Service (ETS). Founded in 1947 ETS develops and administers the Graduate Record Examinations (GRE) and Test of English as a Foreign Language (TOEFL). The not-for-profit group develops and administers more than 50 million achievement admissions academic and professional tests a year at some 9000 locations in more than 180 countries. It also develops assessment programs for corporations professional associations and state entities. ETS' research unit conducts education-focused analysis and policy studies; test-development firm Prometric is a for-profit subsidiary.

Geographic Reach

ETS serves US customers from offices in California Florida New Jersey Pennsylvania Puerto Rico Washington State and Washington DC. In addition ETS has direct operating subsidiaries in Canada China Korea and other countries in South America Asia Europe the Middle East and Africa; these offices provide services to customers in about 80 countries.

Operations

ETS' K-12 products include Advanced Placement (AP) exams and tests to meet individual state standards. Teachers are not forgotten –the company also develops and administers the Praxis Series assessments for teacher licensing and certifications. For college-bound scholars ETS supports The College Board's Scholastic Assessment Test (SAT) and the College Level Examination Program (CLEP).

Strategy

In addition to launching new graduate and college-preparation tests and online support programs of its own ETS teams with partners such as Pearson SchoolNet and the Kansas State Department of Education to develop new products such as online tutorials assessment tests for elementary and secondary-education students and teacher leadership assessments. ETS is also increasing security measures to ensure that test takers' identities are properly verified such as a voice recognition system launched for its TOEFL test in 2012.

ETS also works to increase the market share of its existing products. For instance ETS has been steadily nudging its way into the niche previously dominated by the Graduate Management Admission Council –which administers the GMAT for students heading to graduate business schools –by convincing a growing number of business schools that its GRE General Test is a valuable instrument and to accept the test for admissions. In 2011 the company opened several new customer support centers to support international customers seeking to take the TOEFL test.

Mergers and Acquisitions

The company bulked up its testing technology in early 2011 with the acquisition of Computerized Assessments and Learning (CAL). Operating as a subsidiary of ETS CAL offers assessment products for K-12 education systems.

To move beyond assessment and into actual education ETS acquired Edusoft an English language learning firm in 2011. The 2011 acquisition brought in Edusoft's English Discoveries Online product used around the world. The online product is designed to accompany and support classroom instruction with courses for general and technical English language instruction. Edusoft operates as a for-profit subsidiary.

EXECUTIVES

President and CEO, Kurt M. Landgraf, age 67
SVP Edmund W. Gordon Chair of ETS's PERC and heads Early Childhood Research Center, Michael T. Nettles
CIO and VP Scoring Reporting and Technology, Daniel Wakeman
VP Higher Education, Walt MacDonald
Frederic M. Lord Chair Measurement and Statistics, Robert J. (Bob) Mislevy
SVP and CFO, Jack Hayon
Vp Research Research Development Division, Scott G Paris
Vp Or Senior Vp, Sandra Hernandez
Vp, Ron Alden
Vice President Assessment Development, Marisa Farnum
Assistant Vice President Corporate, Emanuel Manny X Quiles
Associate Vice President For Statistics And Psychometrics, John Mazzeo
Vp Of Education, William Seibert
Vice President Group Executive Director, Nancy Kerins
Vice President Information Technology, Rebecca Pfund
Vp National Accounts, John Sikorski
Senior Vp, Mari Pearlman
Executive Vice President And Director, Len Dimmick
Vice President, Linda Tyler
Vice President & Controller, Michael Freddo
Vice President And Corporate Secretary, David Hobson
Asst Treas, Dawn Budd
Vp Treasurer, Jay Basehore
Treasury Manager, Rosalie McCracken

LOCATIONS

HQ: EDUCATIONAL TESTING SERVICE INC
666 ROSEDALE RD STOP 85D, PRINCETON, NJ 08540-2218
Phone: 609-921-9000
Web: WWW.ETS.ORG

PRODUCTS/OPERATIONS

Selected Testing Programs

Advanced Placement (AP)
Algebra end of course assessment (EOC)
California High School Exit Examination (CAHSEE)
California State University Placement Test (EPT/ELM)
College-Level Examination Program (CLEP)
ETS Literacy
ETS Proficiency Profile
EXADEP
Graduate Record Examinations (GRE)
High Schools That Work Assessment
iSkills Assessment
Major Field Tests (MFT)
Middle Grades Assessment (MGA)
National Assessment of Educational Progress (NAEP)
ParaPro Assessment
The Praxis Series: Professional Assessments for Beginning Teachers
Preliminary SAT/National Merit Scholarship Qualifying Test (PSAT/NMSQT)
Scholastic Aptitude Test (SAT)
School Leaders Licensure Assessment (SLLA)
School Leadership Series (SLS)
School Superintendent Assessment (SSA)
Secondary Level English Proficiency Test (SLEP)
Test Link Test Collection
TFI Test
Test of English as a Foreign Language (TOEFL)
Test of English for International Communication (TOEIC)

Selected Acquisitions

2011
Computerized Assessments and Learning (CAL assessment products for K-12 education systems)
Edusoft (English language learning programs)

COMPETITORS

ACT Inc.
Houghton Mifflin Harcourt
Kaplan
McGraw Hill Financial
Questar Assessment
Scantron
The Princeton Review
University of Iowa

HISTORICAL FINANCIALS

Company Type: Private

Income Statement

FYE: December 31

	REVENUE ($ mil.)	NET INCOME ($ mil.)	NET PROFIT MARGIN	EMPLOYEES
12/12	1,431	88	6.2%	2,614
12/11	1,357	70	5.2%	—
12/10	1,272	67	5.3%	—
12/09	1,224	44	3.6%	—
Annual Growth	5.3%	25.7%	—	—

2012 Year-End Financials

Debt ratio: —
Return on equity: 6.20%
Cash ($ mil.): 181
Current ratio: 0.80
Long-term debt ($ mil.): —

Dividends
Yield: —
Payout: —
Market value ($ mil.): —

EFFINGHAM EQUITY

LOCATIONS

HQ: EFFINGHAM EQUITY
201 W ROADWAY AVE, EFFINGHAM, IL 624012101
Phone: 2173424101
Web: WWW.EFFINGHAMEQUITY.COM

HISTORICAL FINANCIALS

Company Type: Private

Income Statement FYE: December 31

	REVENUE ($ mil.)	NET INCOME ($ mil.)	NET PROFIT MARGIN	EMPLOYEES
12/13	333	9	2.7%	348
12/10	51	12	23.8%	—
12/09	230	8	3.7%	—
12/08	1,692	0	—	—
Annual Growth	—	—	—	—

2013 Year-End Financials

Debt ratio: —
Return on equity: 2.70%
Cash ($ mil.): 11
Current ratio: 0.10
Long-term debt ($ mil.): —
Dividends
Yield: —
Payout: —
Market value ($ mil.): —

EIDE BAILLY LLP

Eide Bailly is how the West was audited. The company which was founded in 1917 provides clients with audit accounting tax and consulting services from more than 20 offices in 10 western and central US states. Eide Bailly's target industries include construction agricultural processing oil and gas real estate renewable energy government financial services manufacturing health care and not-for-profit organizations. Additional services are provided by subsidiaries and affiliates including Eide Bailly Technology Consulting. International services are provided through Eide Bailly's affiliation with HLB International. The firm serves some 40000 clients annually.

Geographic Reach

Fargo North Dakota-based Eide Bailly has offices in Arizona Colorado Idaho Iowa Minnesota Montana Oklahoma Utah and the Dakotas.

Financial Performance

Edie Bailly's net fees amounted to $158 million in fiscal 2012 (ends April) with the firm's audit and assurance and tax services businesses accounting for 43% and 38% of the total respectively.

Strategy

Edie Bailly is growing its business through the acquisition of regional accounting firms to better compete with larger national firms. The company expanded into Utah in 2012 with the purchase of Schmitt Griffiths Smith & Co. adding about $6 million in revenue to Edie Bailly's total. More significantly Edie Bailly announced plans to merge with fellow accountancy Milwaukee-based Wipfli in 2012. However the deal was called off later that year when the two firms could not reach an agreement on key terms.

Mergers and Acquisitions

Other recent purchases include Williston North Dakota-based CPA firm Voller Lee Seuss & Associates. The purchase which closed in December 2012 expands Edie Bailly's resources and services to clients in the rapidly-growing Bakken Oil Region in western North Dakota. Also in late 2012 the firm acquired Clark & Srsich LLC a boutique tax firm in Littleton Colorado. In 2010 the firm bought Denver-based R T Higgins & Associates boosting its oil and gas industry business an area of focus for the company.

EXECUTIVES

Managing Partner and CEO, Jerry A. Topp
Director Operations, LaRae E. Langerud
Partner amd Director Professional Practice, Jeff S. Strand
Chief Financial Officer, Karla R. Wilson
Director Communications, Elizabeth (Liz) Stabenow
Director Leadership Development, Candace Kane
COO, David L. (Dave) Stende
Chief Administrative Officer, Mike Astrup
Director Human Resources, Lisa R. Fitzgerald
Director Corporate Learning, Jason S. McKeever
Senior Manager, Chad Weber
Chairman, Roy Terwilliger
Controller, Kristine Wacker
Director of Financial Institutions, Linda Koerselman
Vice President of Finance, Laura Purfeerst
Controller, Chris Manger
Owner President, Craig Rickert
Vice President of Strategic Services, Ellen R. Davis

LOCATIONS

HQ: EIDE BAILLY LLP
4310 17TH AVE S, FARGO, ND 58103-3339
Phone: 701-239-8500
Web: WWW.EIDEBAILLY.COM

PRODUCTS/OPERATIONS

2012 Services by Category

	% of total
Assurance	43
Tax	38
Affiliates	2
Consulting and	17
Total	**100**

Selected Services

Accounting
Audit & assurance
Employee benefits
Enterprise risk management
Financial services
Forensic & valuation
International services
Tax
Technology consulting
Transaction services
Wealth management

COMPETITORS

BDO Seidman
BKD LLP
CliftonLarsonAllen
Crowe Horwath
Deloitte & Touche
Ernst & Young LLP
Grant Thornton
KPMG L.L.P.
PricewaterhouseCoopers US
RSM McGladrey

HISTORICAL FINANCIALS

Company Type: Private

Income Statement FYE: April 30

	REVENUE ($ mil.)	NET INCOME ($ mil.)	NET PROFIT MARGIN	EMPLOYEES
04/13	167	56	33.9%	1,270
04/12	148	51	34.5%	—
04/10	142	51	36.2%	—
04/10	144	48	33.6%	—
Annual Growth	5.1%	5.5%	—	—

2013 Year-End Financials

Debt ratio: —
Return on equity: 33.90%
Cash ($ mil.): 4
Current ratio: 1.00
Long-term debt ($ mil.): —
Dividends
Yield: —
Payout: —
Market value ($ mil.): —

EILEEN FISHER INC.

Eileen Fisher –the woman and the company – has an eye for clothing that's fashionable and comfortable. The company makes and sells upscale women's business and casual clothing (tops jackets pants skirts and dresses) made mostly from organic and natural fabrics. Fisher's unfussy forgivingly tailored block color lineup is sold through nearly 60 of its namesake stores in about 15 states Canada and the UK as well as through upscale department and specialty stores (including Nordstrom Saks Fifth Avenue and Neiman Marcus) nationwide. It also offers personal shopping services for US customers. After working in the fields of graphic arts and interior design Eileen Fisher founded the company in 1984.

Strategy

Despite the soft retail market for women's apparel the company has been expanding its store base by opening new shops in Tennessee and Maryland. It also extended its reach into the UK following the line's debut in Fenwick department stores in 2011. Eileen Fisher continues as well to test trends and new designs at a "lab store" in Irvington New York.

In addition to expanding its geographic presence the upscale fashion retailer hopes to grow by courting a clientele with an eco-friendly conscious. In 2012 the designer began asking customers to donate gently worn Eileen Fisher garments that the company cleans and resells at Green Eileen a new specialty shop that both helps consumers reduce their environmental impact and supports nonprofit organizations with programs for women and girls.

Eileen Fisher is also building its customer base through new designs and new product categories. (The over-50 set has long been the company's mainstay.) New looks include plus-size collections as well as leggings jeans and clingy tops designed to appeal to daughters as well as their mothers. Concurrently Eileen Fisher designs a Home Collection that includes bedding bath towels rugs and sleepware available in several of its boutiques as well as from catalog retailers including Garnet Hill (part of Cornerstone Brands).

Sales and Marketing

Besides its brick-and-mortar locations and e-commerce site (eileenfisher.com) Eileen Fisher sells its clothing nationwide through upscale department and specialty stores the likes of Nordstrom Saks Fifth Avenue and Neiman Marcus.

Company Ownership

Employees have owned about one-third of the company since Eileen Fisher sold its shares through an employee stock ownership plan in 2005. Fisher owns the rest.

EXECUTIVES

President, Eileen Fisher

LOCATIONS

HQ: EILEEN FISHER INC.
2 BRIDGE ST STE 230, IRVINGTON, NY 10533-3500
Phone: 914-591-5700
Web: WWW.EILEENFISHER.COM

PRODUCTS/OPERATIONS

Selected Products

Accessories
Bags and belts
Denim
Dresses
Handbags
Jackets
Leggings
Pants
Shoes
Skirts
Sweaters and cardigans
Tanks and camis
Tops and tees

COMPETITORS

Ann Taylor	J. Jill Group
Bernardo Fashions	Jones Group
Brand Matter	Lands' End
Calvin Klein	NEXT plc
Chico' s FAS	Ralph Lauren
Donna Karan	Talbots
Fifth & Pacific	Ted Baker
French Connection	Tory Burch
J. Crew	

HISTORICAL FINANCIALS

Company Type: Private

Income Statement FYE: December 31

	REVENUE ($ mil.)	NET INCOME ($ mil.)	NET PROFIT MARGIN	EMPLOYEES
12/08	272	2	1.0%	900
12/07	253	7	2.9%	—
12/07	1,361	0	0.0%	—
Annual Growth	(80.0%)	306258.7%	—	—

2008 Year-End Financials

Debt ratio: ——
Return on equity: 1.00%
Cash ($ mil.): 3
Current ratio: 0.20
Long-term debt ($ mil.): —
Dividends
Yield: —
Payout: —
Market value ($ mil.): —

EISENHOWER MEDICAL CENTER

The Eisenhower Medical Center is perhaps less known by its presidential name than by the name of a first lady: The not-for-profit medical campus is the home of the Betty Ford Center. In addition to the renowned alcohol and drug rehabilitation center Eisenhower Medical Center comprises the about 540-bed Eisenhower Memorial Hospital the Barbara Sinatra Children's Center and the Annenberg Center for Health Sciences. In addition to medical surgical and emergency services the hospital offers cancer care neurology orthopedics cardiology and rehabilitation. It also conducts training and research programs and it operates outpatient clinics in surrounding areas.

Geographic Reach

The Eisenhower Medical Center's main facilities are located on its 130-acre campus in Rancho Mirage California. Outpatient facilities are located in Rancho Mirage and area communities including Cathedral City La Quinta and Palm Springs.

Operations

Eisenhower Medical Center maintains the leading market share in its service location representing nearly 50% of the area.

In addition to patient services Eisenhower Medical Center provides residency programs for aspiring students through affiliations with the Keck School of Medicine (University of Southern California) and the Linda Loma University's School of Medicine. The physician training programs are offered through the newly established School of Graduate Medical Education and Research and include family medicine internal medicine and preliminary (one-year) residency programs.

Strategy

Eisenhower Medical Center's residency programs were launched in the summer of 2013 after the hospital received national accreditation. The hospital worked for several years to add medical training services to help meet the growing shortage of primary care physicians in the Coachella Valley. The establishment of the graduate school required capital improvements to the hospital's facilities causing it to launch a $32 million fundraising campaign that year.

The medical center has also been working to maintain its market share by launching a number of facility expansion campaigns in recent years. For instance in 2010 it completed construction of a $213 million addition to its main hospital that included 160 patient beds a cafeteria information systems and other departments. The addition was named the Eisenhower Walter and Leonore Annenberg Pavilion.

The medical center is expanding its outpatient care centers to provide greater services to surrounding communities and reduce the patient burden on hospital emergency rooms. For instance Eisenhower Medical Center opened a new primary and specialty outpatient care center in Palm Springs in 2013.

Eisenhower Medical Center faces some financial challenges due to a high volume of elderly Medicare patients. As a result it has made efforts to attract more self-pay patients to its facilities. In addition the hospital has incurred substantial debt due to its construction efforts; however it aims to recoup through increased revenues from the added facilities and through its successful fundraising efforts.

Company Background

Eisenhower Medical Center was dedicated in 1971 to honor former president Dwight Eisenhower who spent part of his retirement in the Coachella Valley. The late entertainer Bob Hope and his wife were the hospital's biggest benefactors having donated the original land for the hospital and continuing to help fundraising efforts until his death in 2003.

EXECUTIVES

Vice President Human Resources, Liz Guignier
Vp Of Engineering/maintenance, Ali Tourkaman
President and CEO, G. Aubrey Serfling
VP and CIO, David Perez
President Eisenhower Medical Center Foundation, Michael D. Landes
EVP and COO, Martin J. Massiello
VP Patient Care and Chief Nursing Officer, Ann Mostofi
SVP and CFO, Ken Wheat
Vp Information Systems, Don Mitchell
Bscc Vice President, William Osterman
Vice President Finance, Sharon Henderson
Director Of Radiology Services, Hilton S McCabe
Vice President, Joseph Scherger
Executive Vice President, Gene Richards
Vice President Management, Georgia Demarbiex
Director Of Him, Khalil Ismail
Vice President Ancillary Services, Andrew Flemer
Nursing Director, Sherri Ferguson
Pharmacy Manager, Tom Heitritter
Vice President, Robert Dufney
Assistant Vice President Sales, Pam Akin
Associate Vice President Patient Care, Mary Ann
Senior Vice President, David Crowl
Vice President Ancillary Services, Brian Helleland
Vice President Of Finance, Sharon Cisneros
Respiratory Therapy Director, Cynthia Molle
Director Of Patient Relations Public Relations Manager, Connie Norton
Vice President Marketing Publications And Pr, David Cash
Clinical Director, Janet Sullivan
Vice President Clinical Management, Kathleen Baugh
Medical Director, Leora Lanzkowsky
Managed Care Director, Melissa Reid
Operating Room Director, Ann Brooks
Vice President Cv Quality And Resources, Lynn Afton
Director Of Radiology, Scott Morgan
Director Of Nursing, Valerie Valente
Clinical Director, Philip Daly
Vp Finance, Nass Kamari
Director Of Radiology, Bernard Louvet
Vice President, Spiro Agnew
Vice President Foundation, Betty Wolf
Board Member, Alvin V Shoemaker, age 76
Board Trustee, Marvin B Brooks, age 75
Board Trustee, Karl A Schultz
Treasurer, Patricia Kent
Board Trustee, James Cullen
Secretary, Linda Lewis
Board Trustee, Willia Calkins
Board Trustee, Wallis Annenberg
Secretary, Adriana Trujillo
Board Trustee, S Barbara Sinatra
Board Trustee, Helene Galen
Assistant Treasurer, Sandra Schulz
Board Trustee, Susan Bales
Board Of Directors, Peter Solomon

LOCATIONS

HQ: EISENHOWER MEDICAL CENTER
39000 BOB HOPE DR, RANCHO MIRAGE, CA 92270-3221
Phone: 760-340-3911
Web: WWW.EMC.ORG

PRODUCTS/OPERATIONS

Selected Facilities

Eisenhower Medical Center (Rancho Mirage)
- Annenberg Center for Health Sciences (continuing education for health professionals)
- Barbara Sinatra Children' s Center (pediatrics)
- Betty Ford Center (alcohol and substance abuse)
- School of Graduate Medical Education and Research

Eisenhower George and Julia Argyros Health Center (La Quinta)
Eisenhower Health Centers at Plaza del Sol (Palm Springs)
Eisenhower Health Centers at Rimrock (Palm Springs)
Eisenhower Health Centers at Sunrock (Palm Springs)
Eisenhower Occupational Health (Cathedral City)
Eisenhower Physical and Occupational Health (La Quinta)
Rancho Mirage Medical Center (Rancho Mirage)

Selected Services

Adult Day Care
Bariatric Center
Center for Geropsychiatry
Cancer
Cardiovascular
Clinical Trials
Diabetes
Eisenhower Health Centers
Eisenhower Wellness Institute
Emergency Department
Imaging
Labtechniques
Neuroscience
Nutrition
Occupational Health
Orthopedics
Parkinson' s Center
Rehabilitation Services

Robotics Institute
Urgent Care
Wound Care Center

COMPETITORS

Anaheim Regional Medical Center	HCA
Arrowhead Medical Center	HealthSouth
Cedars-Sinai Medical Center	Memorial Health Services
Citrus Valley Health Partners	Palomar Health
Community Hospital of San Bernardino	Providence Health & Services
Dignity Health	Scripps health
Grossmont Hospital	Southwest Healthcare
	Tenet Healthcare
	UCSD Medical

HISTORICAL FINANCIALS

Company Type: Private

Income Statement FYE: June 30

	REVENUE ($ mil.)	NET INCOME ($ mil.)	NET PROFIT MARGIN	EMPLOYEES
06/10	411	6	1.7%	2,200
06/09	394	25	6.4%	—
06/09	0	0	—	—
Annual Growth	—	—	—	—

2010 Year-End Financials

Debt ratio: ——
Return on equity: 1.70%
Cash ($ mil.): 70
Current ratio: 0.30
Long-term debt ($ mil.): —
Dividends
Yield: —
Payout: —
Market value ($ mil.): —

EISNERAMPER LLP

Need help getting amped up to crunch numbers? EisnerAmper provides accounting and consulting services for clients (typically middle-market businesses) in the northeastern US. It specializes in industries and sectors including health sciences sports and entertainment not-for-profit financial services and technology. EisnerAmper provides auditing and accounting services tax planning legal support bankruptcy consulting corporate finance employee benefits plan services and IT consulting. Services outside the US are provided through Eisner's Cayman Islands office as well as through its affiliation with PKF International.

Geographic Reach

The company serves clients worldwide through about a dozen offices in California New Jersey New York Pennsylvania and the Cayman Islands.

Operations

As part of its services EisnerAmper specializes in structuring organizing and managing its clients' businesses as well as heading up their reporting requirements. It enlists the help of cross-border specialists who support the needs of multinational companies with a US presence. The company also serves wealthy clients providing them with services such as wealth management asset protection planning and tax advisory. Other primary service lines include human capital advisory employee benefit plan audits fund services litigation support and forensic accounting bankruptcy and insolvency and royalty audits.

The company provides full audit services to clients with off-shore needs through its PKF Cayman unit.

Sales and Marketing

The company provides services to more than 150 public companies and more than 1300 financial services entities and portfolio companies. EisnerAmper boasts more than 1000 hedge funds and more than 145 insurance companies as clients as well as banks and credit unions.

Strategy

In 2013 EisnerAmper opened a new Metropark location to help enhance its presence in New Jersey. In 2012 the firm launched a mobile website www.eisneramper.com to help its clients gain easy access to the company's resources including blogs events and service and industry expertise.

Ownership

EisnerAmper is an independent member of PKF International.

Company Background

EisnerAmper was created in 2010 through the combination of Eisner and Amper Politziner & Mattia similar accounting firms based in New Jersey. Now under one umbrella the company enjoys enhanced service capabilities and geographic reach.

EXECUTIVES

CEO, Charles (Charly) Weinstein
CFO, Brett James
Audit Partner Sports and Entertainment Services Group, Richard S. Nachmias
Director Operations Management Consulting Services Group, Victor Albanese
Principal Corporate Finance Group, Joel Barth
Partner-in-Charge Human Resources, Richard (Rick) Fisher
General Counsel, Lawrence (Larry) Goodman
Chairman, Howard Cohen
Principal and CIO, Gary Rosenberg
Chief Risk Officer, Peter Bible

LOCATIONS

HQ: EISNERAMPER LLP
750 3RD AVE FL 16TH, NEW YORK, NY 10017-2703
Phone: 212-949-8700
Web: WWW.EISNERAMPER.COM

PRODUCTS/OPERATIONS

Selected Services

Audit & accounting
Bankruptcy & insolvency
Business services
Corporate finance
Employee benefits plan services
Human resource strategies
Internal audit & risk management
Litigation consulting & forensic accounting
Resource staffing
Retirement solutions
Tax advisory
Wealth advisory

Selected Areas of Specialization

Automotive
Employee benefits
Financial services
Health care
Health sciences
Law firms
Litigation
Not-for-profit
Real estate
Sports media & entertainment
Technology industries
Wealth management

COMPETITORS

Anchin Block & Anchin	Grant Thornton
Citrin Cooperman	Heffler Radetich & Saitta
Crowe Horwath	KPMG L.L.P.
Deloitte & Touche	PricewaterhouseCoopers US
Ernst & Young Global	RSM McGladrey

HISTORICAL FINANCIALS

Company Type: Private

Income Statement FYE: January 31

	REVENUE ($ mil.)	NET INCOME ($ mil.)	NET PROFIT MARGIN	EMPLOYEES
01/13	247	55	22.5%	1,895
01/12	230	59	25.9%	—
01/11	173	40	23.4%	—
Annual Growth	19.4%	17.0%	—	—

2013 Year-End Financials

Debt ratio: ——
Return on equity: 22.50%
Cash ($ mil.): 32
Current ratio: 5.10
Long-term debt ($ mil.): —
Dividends
Yield: —
Payout: —
Market value ($ mil.): —

EL DORADO FURNITURE CORP

The road to El Dorado Furniture is covered in sand. The company sells home furnishings in South Florida through a dozen retail showrooms and a pair of outlets located in Broward Dade and Palm Beach counties. El Dorado Furniture stores offer wood upholstered and leather furniture for every room in the house as well as mattresses bedding and decorative accessories. Its stores are designed to look like small towns with building facades situated along a boulevard; some locations also feature cafes. Founded in 1967 and run by the Capo family El Dorado Furniture has become the nation's largest Hispanic-owned retail enterprises.

Geographic Reach

The retailer's showrooms and outlets are located in Florida's Palm Beach Broward and Dade counties.

Sales and Marketing

Unique to the furniture retailer its stores feature what it calls a Boulevard showroom which includes more than 20 individually themed storefronts open into specialized furniture shops. The marketing strategy remains one of the company's biggest draws for customers.

As part of the company's bricks-and-mortar business it produces and maintains an online catalog that's searchable by category product name or SKU.

Strategy

Besides its specialized showrooms El Dorado Furniture offers customers free home decorating advice from its design experts.

As Florida's real estate market rebounds post-recession El Dorado Furniture has worked to expand its business within the state by purchasing a shopping center on Florida's Gulf Coast in 2012. The purchase included a 179000-sq.-ft. shopping center to house a 70000-sq.-ft. El Dorado showroom. It's banking on a store of this caliber to bring in at least $10 million.

Awards and Recognition

El Dorado Furniture is ranked among the top 50 furniture retailers in the country.

LOCATIONS

HQ: EL DORADO FURNITURE CORP
4200 NW 167TH ST, MIAMI GARDENS, FL 33054-6112
Phone: 305-624-9700
Web: WWW.ELDORADOFURNITURE.COM

2013 Stores

	No.
Dade	7
Broward	3
Palm	2
Total	**12**

PRODUCTS/OPERATIONS

Selected Products

Furniture
Home office
Home decor & accents
Mattresses
Outdoor furniture

COMPETITORS

Baer' s Furniture
Carls Furniture
City Furniture
Havertys
La-Z-Boy
Leader' s Casual Furniture
Rooms To Go
W.S. Badcock

HISTORICAL FINANCIALS

Company Type: Private

Income Statement FYE: December 31

	REVENUE ($ mil.)	NET INCOME ($ mil.)	NET PROFIT MARGIN	EMPLOYEES
12/12	153	25	16.9%	705
12/11	152	23	15.5%	—
12/10	131	16	12.2%	—
12/09	126	14	11.7%	—
Annual Growth	6.7%	20.7%	—	—

2012 Year-End Financials

Debt ratio: —
Return on equity: 16.90%
Cash ($ mil.): 5
Current ratio: 0.50
Long-term debt ($ mil.): —
Dividends
Yield: —
Payout: —
Market value ($ mil.): —

ELECTRIC POWER BOARD OF THE METROPOLITAN GOVERNMENT OF NASHVILLE

The Electric Power Board of the Metropolitan Government of Nashville and Davidson County is a mouthful. Its operating name Nashville Electric Service (NES) sounds much better. And talking of sound the legendary "Nashville Sound" would be hard to hear without the resources of this power distributor which serves more than 360000 customers in central Tennessee. NES is one of the largest government-owned utilities in the US. The company is required to purchase all its power from another government-owned operator the Tennessee Valley Authority (TVA).

NES operates about 91000 distribution transformers more than 230 substations 5700 miles of power lines and more than 200000 utility poles.

It serves customers in the City of Nashville and Davidson County.

In 2011 the company posted a 13% jump in revenues thanks to a rate increase and stronger demand brought on by a warmer-than-usual summer. The higher revenues outpaced higher distribution costs and (coupled with lower administrative and general expenses) allowed NES to post a 35% spike in operating income for the year.

Anticipating deregulation both NES and TVA are expecting changes in their relationship. NES is ready to rock 'n' roll after the expected divorce. The company wants to cut its obligations to TVA and pursue other power sources including open-market purchasing and self-generation.

NES is also investing in educating its customers to reduce energy use as a way to cut carbon emissions and lower costs –through public education programs on conservation strategies and the use of renewables and green technology. Walking the talk in 2011 NES installed energy-efficient light bulbs and took other measures at its headquarters building to reduce electrical use by 11% and water use by 18%. It also recycles and reuses the oil in its transformer network.

EXECUTIVES

General Counsel, Eugene W. Ward
President and CEO, Decosta E. Jenkins
VP Information Systems and CIO, Victor L. (Vic) Hatridge
VP Operations Engineering, Paul H. Allen
Chairman, Robert A. (Rob) McCabe Jr., age 62
VP and Chief Customer Care Officer, Teresa Corlew
EVP and COO, Allen Bradley
VP Human Resources, Herb Deberry
VP Corporate Affairs, Laura S. Tidwell
VP and CFO, Teresa Broyles-Aplin
VP Operations Transmission and Distribution, Dennis Boehms
VP Operations, Eddie Andrews
Vice Chairman, Samuel Howard
Director, Robert A. (Rob) McCabe Jr., age 62
Vice Chair, Mary Jo Price
Director, Richard Courtney
Vice Chairman, Samuel Howard
Auditors: Deloitte&ToucheLLP

LOCATIONS

HQ: ELECTRIC POWER BOARD OF THE METROPOLITAN GOVERNMENT OF NASHVILLE
1214 CHURCH ST, NASHVILLE, TN 37246-0001
Phone: 615-747-3831
Web: WWW.NESPOWER.COM

PRODUCTS/OPERATIONS

2011 Sales

	$ mil.	% of total
Commercial & industrial	656	55
Residential	507	42
Street & highway lighting	16	1
Other	19	2
Total	**1,199**	**100**

COMPETITORS

AEP
AGL Resources
Constellation Energy Group
MLGW
Piedmont Natural Gas
Public Service Enterprise Group
SCANA
Southern Company

HISTORICAL FINANCIALS

Company Type: Private

Income Statement FYE: June 30

	REVENUE ($ mil.)	NET INCOME ($ mil.)	NET PROFIT MARGIN	EMPLOYEES
06/09	1,146	16	1.4%	990
06/08	1,030	33	3.2%	—
06/07	962	44	4.6%	—
06/06	903	34	3.8%	—
Annual Growth	8.3%	(22.5%)	—	—

2009 Year-End Financials

Debt ratio: —
Return on equity: 1.40%
Cash ($ mil.): 91
Current ratio: 1.30
Long-term debt ($ mil.): —
Dividends
Yield: —
Payout: —
Market value ($ mil.): —

ELECTRIC RELIABILITY COUNCIL OF TEXAS INC.

ERCOT works to ensure that Texas power grid errors are caught before triggering a massive blackout. The Electric Reliability Council of Texas (ERCOT) is responsible for the reliable operation of 550 generation units (74000 MW capacity) and a 40500-mile power transmission system carrying about 85% of the state's electric load and serving 23 million customers. A member of the North American Electric Reliability Council ERCOT functions as the independent system operator for the region. It also administers financial settlement for the competitive wholesale bulk-power market and oversees customer switching for 6.7 million Texans who live in areas where they have a competitive choice of power supplier.

Geographic Reach

ERCOT's territory covers about 75% of Texas' land area; it excludes most of the northern panhandle region and parts of West Texas (around El Paso) and East Texas (around Texarkana and Beaumont).

Operations

The council monitors and schedules the flow of wholesale energy on the grid balancing supply with demand and enabling fair competitive access. ERCOT maintains records on grid activities and market participants and schedules power on the electric grid connecting transmission lines and generation units.

Financial Performance

ERCOT reported a 1% to decline in revenues in 2012. It generates revenues from System administration fees; Nodal implementation surcharge; Reliability organization pass-through; and Membership fees and other. In 2012 System administration fees and Nodal implementation surcharge accounted for 93% of ERCOT's total revenues.

Strategy

In 2012 the council released a report pointing out that the combination of a fast-growing population and the closing of older coal-powered plants meant that power demand in Texas would begin to outstrip its power capacity and that new cleaner burning power plants would need to be built along with the use of renewable energy sources and the adoption of serious conservation measures in order to avoid future power interruptions.

To meet state and federal green energy requirements the organization is working on integrating wind power sources into its operating grid. Texas boasts 10000 MW of wind power generation the most in the country. In July 2012 ERCOT reported a record output of 8370 MW of wind energy or about 18% of its total load.

Texas state government has kept ERCOT physically isolated from other grid systems (primarily to avoid federal regulation and charges). However this policy came under scrutiny in early 2011 when a cold snap led to the loss of 50 generating units forcing rolling outages across Texas in order to lower demand and prompting ERCOT to access power from Mexico for a short time.

Ownership

ERCOT is a membership-based 501(c)(4) non-profit corporation.

Company Background

The entity is governed by a board of directors and subject to oversight by the Public Utility Commission of Texas and the Texas State Legislature. The Legislature restructured the Texas electric market in 1999.

EXECUTIVES

Vice Chairman, Michehl R. Gent
Vice President Finance and Treasury, Michael (Mike) Petterson
VP and CIO, Ronald J. (Ron) Hinsley
VP System Operations, Kent Saathoff
President and CEO, H. B. (Trip) Doggett
Media Relations, Dottie Roark
Vice President General Counsel Corporate Secretary, Bill Magness
SVP and COO, Mike Cleary
Chairman, Craven Crowell
Chairman, Donna Nelson
Vice President Commercial Operations Electric Reliability Council of Texas, Brad Jones
Vice President Chief Information Officer Electric Reliability Council of Texas, Jerry Dreyer
Vice President Grid Planning and Operations, Ken McIntyre
Vice President Credit and Enterprise Risk Management, Mark Ruane
Director, Clifton B. Karnei
Director, Jan L. Newton, age 60
Director, Miguel W. Espinosa, age 73
Vice Chairman, Michehl R. Gent
Director, Andrew J. Dalton
Director, Nikolaus (Nick) Fehrenbach
Director, Alton D. (Dee) Patton
Chairman, Craven Crowell
Auditors: Ernst&YoungLLP

LOCATIONS

HQ: ELECTRIC RELIABILITY COUNCIL OF TEXAS INC.
7620 METRO CENTER DR, AUSTIN, TX 78744-1613
Phone: 512-225-7000
Web: WWW.PLANNING.ERCOT.COM

PRODUCTS/OPERATIONS

2012 Sales

System administration fees	49	
Reliability organization pass-through	5	
Total	0	100

HISTORICAL FINANCIALS

Company Type: Private

Income Statement FYE: December 31

	REVENUE ($ mil.)	NET INCOME ($ mil.)	NET PROFIT MARGIN	EMPLOYEES
12/11	279	(1)	—	625
12/10	272	19	7.0%	—
12/08	206	28	13.9%	—
12/08	186	(5)	—	—
Annual Growth	14.4%	—	—	—

2011 Year-End Financials

Debt ratio: —
Return on equity: (-0.70%)
Cash ($ mil.): 660
Current ratio: 1.30
Long-term debt ($ mil.): —
Dividends
Yield: —
Payout: —
Market value ($ mil.): —

ELIXIR INDUSTRIES

EXECUTIVES

CEO, Christopher A. Sahm
Director International Sales, Julie Cameron
National Credit, Pat Hoeg
CFO, Bob Cuthbertson
VP Human Resources, Barbara Wright
President and COO, Dwight Knowles
Director New Business Development, John T. Willis
Director Information Technology, Roger Grant
National Accounts Coordinator, Bob Powers
Corporate Controller, Mary Leonard

LOCATIONS

HQ: ELIXIR INDUSTRIES
24800 CHRISANTA DR # 210, MISSION VIEJO, CA 926914833
Phone: 9498605000
Web: WWW.ELIXIRIND.COM

COMPETITORS

CertainTeed
Drew Industries
MW Manufacturers
Nortek

HISTORICAL FINANCIALS

Company Type: Private

Income Statement FYE: December 31

	REVENUE ($ mil.)	NET INCOME ($ mil.)	NET PROFIT MARGIN	EMPLOYEES
12/11	145	14	9.9%	700
12/05	221	0	—	—
Annual Growth	(6.7%)	—	—	—

2011 Year-End Financials

Debt ratio: —
Return on equity: 9.90%
Cash ($ mil.): 7
Current ratio: 1.40
Long-term debt ($ mil.): —
Dividends
Yield: —
Payout: —
Market value ($ mil.): —

ELKINS CONSTRUCTORS INC.

Elkins Constructors builds it all. The company one of Florida's largest privately held construction companies works on commercial industrial multi-family residential institutional and retail projects mainly in the Southeast. It offers general contracting design/build and construction management services and its retail market clients have included Lowe's British Airways and Castleton Beverage. Other projects include the ‚ÄAmerica Online ‚Äcall center and headquarters for ‚ÄPGA ‚ÄTour Productions. Elkins also has been named one of the top green contractors in the ‚ÄUS by Engineering News-Record. Founded in 1955 by Martin Elkins the company was acquired in 1984 by CEO Barry Allred and a team of investors.

EXECUTIVES

VP Operations, David (Dave) Scheele
Chairman and CEO, Barry L. Allred
President and COO, Matthew D. Welch
CFO, R. Joseph (Joe) Newell
VP Development, Gordon Steadman
Executive Vice President, David W. Hamilton
Senior Vice President Healthcare Senior Living, W. Scott Parker
SVP Institutional, J. Bill Stinson
VP Retail, J. Robert Crowe

LOCATIONS

HQ: ELKINS CONSTRUCTORS INC.
701 W ADAMS ST STE 1, JACKSONVILLE, FL 322041600
Phone: 9043536500
Web: WWW.ELKINSCONSTRUCTORS.COM

COMPETITORS

Brasfield & Gorrie
Choate Construction
Hunt Construction
McBride Construction

HISTORICAL FINANCIALS

Company Type: Private

Income Statement FYE: December 31

	REVENUE ($ mil.)	NET INCOME ($ mil.)	NET PROFIT MARGIN	EMPLOYEES
12/12	117	0	0.1%	126
12/08	285	10	3.6%	—
12/07	231	8	3.5%	—
12/06	60	0	—	—
Annual Growth	11.7%	—	—	—

2012 Year-End Financials

Debt ratio: —
Return on equity: 0.10%
Cash ($ mil.): 4
Current ratio: 0.90
Long-term debt ($ mil.): —
Dividends
Yield: —
Payout: —
Market value ($ mil.): —

ELLIOT HOSPITAL OF THE CITY OF MANCHESTER

Elliot Health System provides medical care to southern New Hampshire. The health care organization operates Elliot Hospital an acute care hospital with nearly 300 beds that is home to a regional cancer center a designated regional trauma center and a Level 3 neonatal intensive care unit (NICU). In addition to general and surgical care the hospital offers rehabilitation behavioral health obstetrics cardiology and lab services. The system also operates the Elliot Physician Network which operates primary care centers specialty clinics and surgery centers in various regional communities. Elliot Hospital was founded in 1890.

Strategy

Elliot Health System has expanded throughout the region by constructing new outpatient care centers in nearby towns. Most recently Elliot Health completed construction of satellite facilities including an ambulatory care center and a senior health center.

EXECUTIVES

President CEO, Douglas (Doug) Dean
SVP and CFO, Rick Elwell

VP Medical Staff and Trustee, Peter Kachavos
Chairman, John Hession
Medical Director Elliot Occupational Health Services, John A. Devine
President CEO and Trustee, Douglas (Doug) Dean
Trustee Emeritus, Mark Stebbins
Trustee Emeritus, Richard I. Winneg
Trustee, Wayne Robinson
Trustee, Robert J. Normandeau
Trustee, Selma Naccach-Hoff
Trustee, Rochelle H. Lindner
Trustee, Robert Lavery
VP Medical Staff and Trustee, Peter Kachavos
Trustee Emeritus, William S. Green
Trustee, Peter Cheung
Trustee, James Hood
Trustee, Richard Marcucci
Trustee, Edward Mitchell
Trustee, Robert Provencher Jr.
Trustee, Malcolm Widness

LOCATIONS

HQ: ELLIOT HOSPITAL OF THE CITY OF MANCHESTER
1 ELLIOT WAY, MANCHESTER, NH 03103-3502
Phone: 603-669-5300
Web: WWW.ELLIOTHOSPITAL.ORG

PRODUCTS/OPERATIONS

Selected Centers and Services

Aeronautics Medicine
Adult Day Programs
Bariatric Surgery
Behavioral Health
Breast Health Center
Cardiology Services
Center for Sleep Evaluation
Center for Wound Care & Hyberbaric Medicine
Childbirth And Family Education
Community Health and Wellness
Critical Care at The Elliot
Diabetes and Outpatient Nutrition Services
Diagnostic Imaging
Elliot 1-Day Surgery Center
The Elliot at Hooksett
Elliot Behavioral Health Services
Elliot Endocrinology Associates
Elliot Gastroenterology
Elliot General Surgical Specialists
Elliot Maternal Fetal Medicine
Elliot Medical Center at Londonderry
Elliot Neurology Associates
Elliot Obstetrics and Gynecology
Elliot Orthopaedic Surgical Specialists
Elliot Physician Network
Elliot Regional Cancer Center
Elliot Sports Medicine
Elliot Trauma Center
Elliot Wellness Center
Endoscopy Center
Health Education Library
Home Medical Equipment
Hospitalist Program
Infection Control Department
Inpatient Care/Nursing Units
Laboratory Services
Max K. Willscher Urology Center
Neurophysiology
New England EMS Institute
New Hampshire Arthritis Center
Nursing Units/Inpatient Care
Nutrition Services
Occupational Health & Wellness
Oral Maxillofacial Surgery Center
Oxygen Therapy
Pain Management Center
Pediatric Surgery
Pharmacy Services
Pulmonary Medicine
Pulmonary Rehabilitation
Physical Therapy
Rehabilitation
Respiratory Care
Senior Health Center
Sports Medicine
Surgery
Speech Therapy
Urgent Care - Londonderry
Urgent Care - Manchester
Visiting Nurse Association of Manchester & So. NH Inc.
Weight Management
Wellness Center
Women's & Children's Services
Wound Center

COMPETITORS

Caritas Holy Family Hospital
Catholic Medical Center
Concord Hospital
Exeter Health Resources
Frisbie Memorial Hospital
HCA
Lahey Health System
Southern New Hampshire Medical Center

HISTORICAL FINANCIALS

Company Type: Private

Income Statement FYE: June 30

	REVENUE ($ mil.)	NET INCOME ($ mil.)	NET PROFIT MARGIN	EMPLOYEES
06/10	324	7	2.4%	2,000
06/09	288	0	—	—
06/09	502	0	0.0%	—
Annual Growth	(35.4%)	47196.3%	—	—

2010 Year-End Financials

Debt ratio: —
Return on equity: 2.40%
Cash ($ mil.): 28
Current ratio: 0.20
Long-term debt ($ mil.): —
Dividends
Yield: —
Payout: —
Market value ($ mil.): —

ELLIS HOSPITAL

Schenectady-based Ellis Hospital serves the residents of New York's capital area as part of Ellis Medicine a 455-bed community and teaching healthcare system. The hospital provides emergency inpatient medical/surgical and psychiatric care including diagnostic primary and rehabilitative care. The hospital is also home to centers of excellence in the treatment of and care for heart and cardiovascular ailments cancer women's health issues stroke-related problems and behavioral health concerns. It also operates the Ellis Center the Bellvue Woman's Center and the satellite outpatient clinic Ellis Health Center.

Operations

Ellis Hospital is part of Ellis Medicine a 455-bed community and teaching healthcare system serving the Albany New York area. Ellis Medicine has three campuses - Ellis Hospital Ellis Health Center and Bellevue Woman's Center - five additional service locations and more than 700 affiliated physicians.

The hospital's specialty services include a nationally recognized Heart Center a New York State designated Stroke Center and advanced surgery programs such as cardiothoracic orthopedic neurological and vascular among others. The facility features diagnostic imaging a modern 36-bed Intensive Care Unit.

Ellis Hospital also operates academic programs to prepare students for careers in health care and nursing.

Geographic Reach

The hospital serves patients in the Albany Saratoga Schenectady counties of upstate New York.

Strategy

State health care reform measures mandated the closure of two area hospitals in 2007 and 2008. Ellis Hospital took over the duties of both facilities: St. Clare's Hospital became the outpatient Ellis Health Center (also known as the McClellan Campus) and the Bellvue Woman's Hospital is now Bellvue Woman's Center which still provides overnight services. As a group the facilities are known as Ellis Medicine.

All of the Schenectady facilities are undergoing expansion or improvement efforts to increase its service offerings and upgrade certain facilities. In 2010 the company opened the relocated nursing home and rehabilitation center. The Ellis Residential and Rehabilitation Center has more than double the rooms than the older facility with some 80 beds new activity and day rooms and a separate sub-acute care and short-stay rehabilitation unit.

EXECUTIVES

Vice President Human Resources, Joseph Giansante
Director Of Radiology Services, Areta Pibwerbetsky
VP Medical Affairs and Chief Medical Officer, David M. Liebers
President CEO and Trustee, James W. Connolly
EVP and COO, Paul A. Milton
VP Nursing and Chief Nursing Officer, Cecelia (CeCe) Lynch
VP and CFO, Daniel Rinaldi
VP Information Services and CIO, David H. Snyder
Medical Director, Ivan Shvachuk
Director Icu/coronary Care Unit, Jodi Hamel
Director Of Respiratory Therapy, Ed Stomski
Director Of Radiology, James Brown
Pharmacy Manager, Erin Buckley
Secretary, Robert M Liebers
Secretary and Trustee, Deborah Mullaney
President CEO and Trustee, James W. Connolly
Vice Chair, Stephen Pagano
Board Of Directors, William B Faubion
Secretary, Karen Reach
Board Member, Robert Murray

LOCATIONS

HQ: ELLIS HOSPITAL
1101 NOTT ST, SCHENECTADY, NY 12308-2489
Phone: 518-243-4000
Web: WWW.ELLISMEDICINE.ORG

PRODUCTS/OPERATIONS

Selected Services

Emergency
Cancer/Oncology
Neuroscience
Orthopedics
Primary care
Weight Loss
Women's Health

Selected Facilities

Bariatric Care Center
Bellevue Woman's Center
Ellis Health Center
Ellis Hospital
Medical Center Clifton Park
Primary Care
Clifton Park
Glenville
Latham
Schenectady (Nott St.)
Schenectady (McClellan St.)
School of Nursing

COMPETITORS

Albany Medical Center
Lifetime Health
Oneida Healthcare Center
SUNY Upstate Medical University
St. Joseph' s Hospital Health Center
St. Peter' s Health Partners
United Health Services Hospitals
Upstate University Hospital at Community General

HISTORICAL FINANCIALS

Company Type: Private

Income Statement FYE: December 31

	REVENUE ($ mil.)	NET INCOME ($ mil.)	NET PROFIT MARGIN	EMPLOYEES
12/09	373	14	4.0%	2,000
12/08	3	(0)	—	—
12/07	212	3	1.5%	—
12/06	0	0	2.3%	—
Annual Growth	1132.9%	1374.9%	—	—

2009 Year-End Financials

Debt ratio: —
Return on equity: 4.00%
Cash ($ mil.): 15
Current ratio: —
Long-term debt ($ mil.): —
Dividends
Yield: —
Payout: —
Market value ($ mil.): —

ELLSWORTH COOPERATIVE CREAMERY

EXECUTIVES

Plant Superintendent, Joe Hines
Plant Accountant and Human Resources, Lisa Radkey
Manager and CEO, Paul Bauer
Cheese Plant Supervisor, Doug Volenec
Whey Plant Supervisor, John Freyholtz
Field Supervisor, Tony Birkel
Maintenance Supervisor and Plant Engineer, Bob Radke

LOCATIONS

HQ: ELLSWORTH COOPERATIVE CREAMERY
232 N WALLACE ST, ELLSWORTH, WI 54011
Phone: 7152734311
Web: WWW.ELLSWORTHCHEESECURDS.COM

COMPETITORS

American Milk Products
Associated Milk Producers
Bel Brands USA
BelGioioso Cheese
California Dairies Inc.
Century Foods
Crystal Farms Refrigerated Distribution Company
Dairy Crest
Dairy Farmers of America
Foremost Farms
Friendship Dairies
Fromageries Bel
Great Lakes Cheese
Hiland Dairy
Kraft Foods Group Inc.
Lactalis USA
Land O' Lakes
Leprino Foods
MMPA
Marathon Cheese
Mondelez International
Organic Valley
Original Herkimer County Cheese Company
Prairie Farms Dairy
Saputo Cheese USA Inc.
Sargento
Schreiber Foods
Swiss Valley Farms
Swiss-American
Tillamook County Creamery Association
United Dairy Farmers
Uplands Cheese Company Inc.

HISTORICAL FINANCIALS

Company Type: Private

Income Statement FYE: December 31

	REVENUE ($ mil.)	NET INCOME ($ mil.)	NET PROFIT MARGIN	EMPLOYEES
12/07	145	3	2.4%	60
12/06	92	2	3.0%	—
12/05	116	0	—	—
Annual Growth	11.7%	185726.5%	—	—

2007 Year-End Financials

Debt ratio: —
Return on equity: 2.40%
Cash ($ mil.): 5
Current ratio: 1.10
Long-term debt ($ mil.): —
Dividends
Yield: —
Payout: —
Market value ($ mil.): —

ELMHURST MEMORIAL HOSPITAL INC

Elmhurst Memorial Healthcare operates Elmhurst Memorial Hospital an acute care facility located in DuPage County Illinois in the western suburbs of Chicago. Founded in 1926 the hospital provides a comprehensive range of medical services –from emergency care to specialty cancer and orthopedics care to behavioral health services. In addition to the 315-bed main hospital Elmhurst Memorial Healthcare operates several facilities such as doctors' offices outpatient centers occupational health programs and other ancillary health care operations. In 2011 the health system opened a new replacement facility for the Elmhurst Memorial Hospital.

Geographic Reach

Elmhurst Memorial Healthcare and its hospital serve the western suburbs of Chicago specifically the county residents of DuPage.

Operations

Aside from its Elmhurst Memorial Hospital Main Campus Elmhurst Memorial Healthcare operates several other facilities such as the Berteau Campus Center for Health Lombard Health Center Addison Health Center Elmhurst Memorial Sleep Center Occupational Health Services Wood Dale and an outpatient surgery center clinic primary care associates medical associates and hematology oncology associates offices under the Elmhurst banner.

The newer acute care hospital known as the Elmhurst Memorial Hospital Main Campus features about 260 private inpatient rooms as well as a high-tech emergency department and surgical and diagnostic imaging facilities. It includes the Elmhurst Memorial Center for Health which boasts outpatient clinics and a medical office building for general practice and specialty physicians.

Strategy

To provide its communities with quality cancer care Elmhurst Memorial Healthcare broke ground in late 2012 for the construction of a new 30000-sq.-ft. cancer center to be added to the 50-acre healthcare campus. Expected to open in fall 2013 the cancer care facility will boast medical oncologist offices an infusion center Cyberknife robotic radiosurgery system and radiation oncology services.

There are plans for the old Elmhurst Memorial Hospital campus known as the Berteau Campus. While the Berteau Campus' inpatient and emergency care operations were transferred to the new Main Campus the Berteau Campus' emergency room became an outpatient urgent care center. The campus also includes inpatient behavioral health and recovery facilities as well as outpatient cancer care physical therapy and occupational health clinics. For the long term Elmhurst Memorial Healthcare plans to transform the Berteau Campus into a senior health and housing center by closing or moving the existing operations to other or new locations.

EXECUTIVES

SVP Finance and CFO, Jim Doyle
System EVP & CFO, Vince Pryor
President Chief Executive Officer, W. Peter Daniels
Vice President Development, Sandra Nelson
Associate Vice President Patient Care Services, Jean Lydon
Vice President Medical Affairs, Connie Parker
VP Physician Practice Division, Mary Stull
Vice President Strategic Planning, Gail Warner
VP Human Resources, Lois Grubb
VP and CIO, Charles Colander
VP Legal Affairs and General Counsel, Mary Dano
Vice President COO/CNO Elmhurst Memorial Healthcare, Pamela Dunley
Vice President of Finance, Henry Zeisel
Vice President Marketing, J. Alex Bacchetti
Executive Vice President CFO, James Doyle
President & CEO Elmhurst Memorial Healthcare, Mary Lou Mastro
Vice President Marketing & Business Development, Alex Bacchetti
Vice President Legal Affairs and General Counsel, Mary Dano
Vice President Human Resources, Lois Grubb
System VP & CIO, Bobbie Byrn
Chief Medical Officer/VP Medical Affairs, Daniel Sullivan
System CEO, Pam Davis
System EVP & General Counsel, Chris Mollet
System EVP Human Resources, Susan Mitchell
System VP & Chief Marketing Officer, Brian Davis
System VP & CIO, Bobbie Byrne

LOCATIONS

HQ: ELMHURST MEMORIAL HOSPITAL INC
155 E BRUSH HILL RD, ELMHURST, IL 60126-5658
Phone: 331-221-1000
Web: WWW.EMHC.ORG

PRODUCTS/OPERATIONS

Selected Services

Breast Health Center
Cardiovascular Services
EMH Laboratory
Family Birthing Center
Home Health and Hospice
Immediate Care Centers
Occupational Health
Orthopedics
Radiology
Surgery
Cancer Center
Emergency Department

COMPETITORS

Adventist Health System Sunbelt Healthcare
Advocate Health Care
Alexian Brothers Health System
Central DuPage Hospital
Covenant Ministries
Gottleib Memorial Hospital
Loyola University Health System
Northwest Community Healthcare
Resurrection Health Care
Rush System for Health
University of Chicago Medical Center
Wheaton Franciscan Services

HISTORICAL FINANCIALS

Company Type: Private

Income Statement FYE: June 30

	REVENUE ($ mil.)	NET INCOME ($ mil.)	NET PROFIT MARGIN	EMPLOYEES
06/09	305	20	6.6%	2,444
06/08	345	(22)	—	—
06/07	341	43	12.7%	—
06/05	327	30	9.5%	—
Annual Growth	(1.7%)	(10.2%)	—	—

ELWYN

Elwyn isn't a character out of Harry Potter or Lord of the Rings. It's a not-for-profit organization that serves more than 12000 disabled and disadvantaged people of all ages at multiple sites through education rehabilitation and vocational counseling. The organization also operates residential communities including more than 80 group homes and apartments and provides a variety of health care services for persons with developmental physical and emotional disabilities. The group also publishes training materials and hosts conferences and seminars for human services professionals. Founded in 1852 as a school for children with mental retardation Elwyn is one of the oldest organizations of its kind in the US.

Geographic ReachElwyn's main campus is in Philadelphia with satellite locations in California New Jersey and Delaware.

Operations

Elwyn operates two for-profit subsidiaries. Its PEMS unit an applied technology service provides a variety of enhanced management services. The organization's Grace Pharmacy Inc. is a full-service pharmacy operation that specializes in long-term care clients.

Company Background

At a time when most people with mental disabilities were left to live on the streets or thrown in prison Dr. Alfred Elwyn proposed a special school to help "feeble-minded children." The school attracted the best minds of the time and grew quickly adding residential services and custodial care of adults in 1877.

EXECUTIVES

Vice Chairman, J. Richard Leaman Jr., age 79
President, Sandra S. Cornelius
Chair, Valaida S. Walker
Vice Chairman, Alan Wechsler
Treasurer, Jared G. Culotta
Secretary, H. Thomas Hollinger
Senior Vice President Chief Financial Officer, Daniel M. Reardon
Vice Chairman, J. Richard Leaman Jr., age 79
Vice Chairman, Alan Wechsler

LOCATIONS

HQ: ELWYN
111 ELWYN RD, MEDIA, PA 19063-4622
Phone: 610-891-2000
Web: WWW.ELWYN.ORG

PRODUCTS/OPERATIONS

Selected Services

Behavioral health services
Deaf services
Early childhood services
Education services
Research and health services
Supports for living
Work and adult day services

COMPETITORS

Res-Care

HISTORICAL FINANCIALS

Company Type: Private

Income Statement FYE: June 30

	REVENUE ($ mil.)	NET INCOME ($ mil.)	NET PROFIT MARGIN	EMPLOYEES
06/12	211	1	0.7%	2,500
06/11	264	14	5.5%	—
06/10	254	6	2.4%	—
06/09	192	0	—	—
Annual Growth	3.1%	—	—	—

2012 Year-End Financials

Debt ratio: —
Return on equity: 0.70%
Cash ($ mil.): 12
Current ratio: —
Long-term debt ($ mil.): —
Dividends
Yield: —
Payout: —
Market value ($ mil.): —

EMBRY-RIDDLE AERONAUTICAL UNIVERSITY INC.

Embry-Riddle Aeronautical University (ERAU) helps students solve the mysteries of space and flying. The not-for-profit corporation teaches aviation aerospace and engineering to about 24000 students a year (and a student-teacher ratio of about 15:1). ERAU which offers hands-on training through a fleet of 90 instructional aircraft has residential campuses in Daytona Beach Florida and Prescott Arizona. Its Embry-Riddle Worldwide program provides learning through more than 150 teaching centers and online training in the US Canada Europe and Middle East. It offers bachelor's master's and doctoral degrees in 35 areas.

Geographic Reach

ERAU's campuses provide instruction through more than 150 locations in Asia Canada Europe and the US through online learning.

Operations

The school has been adding non-degree programs to its curriculum in recent years in order to reach a broader range of students (such as working adults). Its worldwide campus houses the Center for Professional Education (CPE) which provides professional certification experience and training to corporate and professional adult learners. Many CPE programs are administered online; the school also offers a variety of seminars and workshops. ERAU's non-degree programs include English language training and aviation safety and security short courses.

Its fleet of more than 90 instructional aircraft includes American Champion Decathlon Cessna 150 Cessna 162 Cessna 172 G1000 Cessna 172R Cessna 172S Cessna 172S Nav III Cessna 182RG Diamond DA42 Diamond DA42NG Piper PA28R and Piper PA44. Embry-Riddle also has roughly 40 simulators at both campuses.

ERAU students enroll from 50 states and 120 nations with 14% of international students at the Daytona Beach campus and 4% at the Prescott campus.

Financial Performance

The annual operating budget of ERAU is about $297 million. From 2011 to 2012 it enjoyed a 6% increase in revenue due to a jump in tuition fees. However it posted a 4% decrease in net income in 2012 due to a spike in expenses related to student services flight instructions and auxiliary enterprises expenses. The decline was also due to a decrease in non-operating activities. Its net cash flow dipped by $20 million as a result of lower student deposits and advance payments.

Strategy

ERAU's growth strategy involves adding additional degree programs to its curriculum in order to increase the amount of tuitions. In 2013 it launched three new degree programs: astronomy; cyber intelligence; and security software engineering.

Also benefiting from additional offices ERAU opened a new location in the Fort Worth Alliance Airport in Texas in 2012. ERAU in 2011 expanded its Joint-Degree Pact with two Chinese universities to absorb growth in China's aviation sector.

Company Background

ERAU was founded to train pilots in 1925 by barnstormer John Paul Riddle and entrepreneur T. Higbee Embry.

EXECUTIVES

Chairman, Jim W. Henderson, age 67
SEVP and CFO, Eric B. Weekes
President, John P. Johnson
CIO, Cindy Bixler
EVP and Chief Academic Officer Daytona Beach Campus, Richard H. Heist
Chancellor Prescott Campus, Frank Ayers Jr.
Chancellor Worldwide Campus, John R. Watret
Vice President External Relations, Bernadine Douglas
Vice President Student Affairs, Nancee Bailey
Vice President Enrollment Management, Bill Hampton
Associate Vice President Academics, Robert Oxley
Trustee, James (Jim) Hagedorn, age 58
Trustee, Joseph R. (Joe) Martin, age 65
Trustee, Lawrence W. Clarkson, age 75
Trustee, Kenneth M. Dufour
Trustee, Jeffrey Feasel
Trustee, Mori Hosseini
Trustee, John E. O'Brien
Trustee, Glenn S. Ritchey
Trustee, David L. Robertson
Trustee, Jean G. Rosanvallon
Trustee, Louis C. Seno Jr.
Auditors: BDOUSALLP

LOCATIONS

HQ: EMBRY-RIDDLE AERONAUTICAL UNIVERSITY INC.
600 S CLYDE MORRIS BLVD, DAYTONA BEACH, FL 32114-3966
Phone: 386-226-6000
Web: WWW.DAYTONABEACH.ERAU.EDU

HISTORICAL FINANCIALS

Company Type: Private

Income Statement FYE: June 30

	REVENUE ($ mil.)	NET INCOME ($ mil.)	NET PROFIT MARGIN	EMPLOYEES
06/12	318	24	7.6%	4,719
06/11	359	46	12.9%	—
06/10	276	25	9.2%	—
06/09	270	3	1.4%	—
Annual Growth	5.5%	86.2%	—	—

2012 Year-End Financials

Debt ratio: —
Return on equity: 7.60%
Cash ($ mil.): 120
Current ratio: 2.20
Long-term debt ($ mil.): —
Dividends
Yield: —
Payout: —
Market value ($ mil.): —

EMERSON COLLEGE

Emerson College specializes in teaching subjects in the fields of communication and the arts in a liberal arts context. Areas of study include journalism; marketing; organizational and political communication; performing arts; visual and media arts; and writing literature and publishing. Its also has an acclaimed communication sciences and disorders program. The college enrolls about 3200 full-time undergraduates and 1000 full and part-time graduate students on its Boston-based campus. Among its alumni are producer Norman Lear talk show host Jay Leno and journalist Morton Dean. The college has additional facilities in Los Angeles and in the Netherlands. Emerson was founded in 1880 as a school of oratory.

EXECUTIVES

Executive Director Department of Professional Studies and Special Programs, Hank W. Zappala
President, Lee Pelton
Chair, Jeffrey Greenhawt
VP Information Technology, William Gilligan
Dean of Students, Ronald Ludman
VP Academic Affairs, Linda Moore
Vice Chair, Lawrence Rasky
VP Administration and Finance, Maureen Murphy
Executive Director Iwasaki Library, Robert Fleming
Dean Graduate Studies, Richard Zauft
VP Communications and Marketing, Andrew Tiedemann

LOCATIONS

HQ: EMERSON COLLEGE
120 BOYLSTON ST STE 414, BOSTON, MA 02116-4624
Phone: 617-824-8500
Web: WWW.EMERSONLIONS.COM

HISTORICAL FINANCIALS

Company Type: Private

Income Statement FYE: June 30

	REVENUE ($ mil.)	NET INCOME ($ mil.)	NET PROFIT MARGIN	EMPLOYEES
06/10	154	17	11.6%	425
06/09	147	15	10.8%	—
06/09	0	0	—	—
Annual Growth	—108806.9%		—	—

2010 Year-End Financials

Debt ratio: —
Return on equity: 11.60%
Cash ($ mil.): 51
Current ratio: —
Long-term debt ($ mil.): —
Dividends
Yield: —
Payout: —
Market value ($ mil.): —

EMERSON HOSPITAL

Emerson Hospital tends to the well-being of patients in and around historic Concord Massachusetts. The 180-bed community hospital is staffed by more than 300 doctors and specialists. Emerson partners with Massachusetts General on several specialty programs including pain management neonatology and radiation oncology which is housed within its Bethke Cancer Center. It also operates outpatient clinics serving residents in nearby communities such as Groton Sudbury and Westford. All told Emerson provides advanced medical services to more than 300000 people.

Geographic Reach

Emerson provides medical services to people in 25 communities in Massachusetts including Concord Groton Sudbury and Westford.

Operations

The hospital has more than 37500 emergency department visits per year. Emerson is well known for its outstanding nursing care and patient-centered facilities including the Bethke Cancer Center and the Birthing Center which has the area's only Special Care Level 2 Nursery for moderately ill newborns.

Strategy

To extend its coverage and skill base Emerson also partners with larger and/or specialist hospitals and medical facilities in the region including Boston IVF Brigham and Women's Hospital Children's Hospital Boston Hospice of the North Shore and Greater Boston and Massachusetts General.

Company Background

The hospital founded in 1911 is named for Charles Emerson a nephew of Ralph Waldo Emerson.

EXECUTIVES

Vice Chairman, Paul D. Birch, age 55
VP Development; Executive Director Emerson Healthcare Foundation, Jack Dresser
President CEO and Director, Christine C. Schuster
Vice President of Operations and Chief Human Resources Officer, Eric Stastny
Senior Vice President and Chief Financial Officer, Jack Wilhelm
Senior Vice President and Chief Medical Officer, C. Gregory Martin
Chairman, Ronald Johnson
Vice President for Patient Care Services and Chief Nursing Officer, Joyce Welsh
Vice President for Planning and Market Development, Christine Gallery
Vice Chairman, Paul D. Birch, age 55
President CEO and Director, Christine C. Schuster
Director, John M. Lowe III
Director, Michael J. Zak

LOCATIONS

HQ: EMERSON HOSPITAL
133 ORNAC, CONCORD, MA 01742-4169
Phone: 978-369-1400
Web: WWW.EMERSONHOSPITAL.ORG

PRODUCTS/OPERATIONS

Selected Facilities

Breast Health Center (Concord)
Center for Specialty Care (Concord)
Center for Sports Rehabilitation and Specialty Services (Concord)
Emerson Main Campus (Concord)
Emerson Medical at Bedford (Bedford)
Emerson Medical at Sudbury (Sudbury)
Groton Health Center (Groton)
Integrative Health and Wellness Center (Concord)
Laboratory Services (Concord)
Westford Health Center (Westford)

COMPETITORS

Lahey Health System
Newton-Wellesley Hospital
Steward Health Care
Winchester Healthcare

HISTORICAL FINANCIALS

Company Type: Private

Income Statement FYE: September 30

	REVENUE ($ mil.)	NET INCOME ($ mil.)	NET PROFIT MARGIN	EMPLOYEES
09/12	180	3	1.9%	1,450
09/09	0	0	—	—
09/06	146	3	2.2%	—
09/05	138	4	3.6%	—
Annual Growth	3.9%	(5.2%)	—	—

2012 Year-End Financials

Debt ratio: —
Return on equity: 1.90%
Cash ($ mil.): 33
Current ratio: 1.80
Long-term debt ($ mil.): —
Dividends
Yield: —
Payout: —
Market value ($ mil.): —

EMJ CORPORATION

EMJ does it all for the mall. Founded in 1968 by namesake Edgar M. Jolley the company specializes in building and renovating retail outlets and shopping centers throughout the US. It is also known for other building projects such as offices warehouses churches hotels multifamily residences hospitals and wind farms. Working from five offices nationwide EMJ provides general construction and construction management. The company's pre-construction services include creating detailed budgets and construction schedules and coordinating permitting utility companies and municipal requirements. To track a project's progress and monitor costs EMJ offers quality control and safety and warranty management.

Geographic Reach

From its base in Chattanooga Tennessee EMJ serves clients through a handful of US offices.

Operations

EMJ owns several operating divisions including Signal Energy which engineers and builds renewable energy projects such as wind farms and solar and biomass energy projects. Another division Accent Construction Management provides site selection budgeting scheduling and other services. Its RedStone Construction Services builds commercial retail hospitality healthcare government facilities and others. It is focused on fostering economic growth in Native American communities.

Sales and Marketing

EMJ has built more than 500 million sq. ft. of construction projects. Its client roster includes Academy Barnes & Noble Bed Bath & Beyond Blue Cross and Blue Shield Home Depot PetSmart and Winn-Dixie.

EXECUTIVES

CEO, Jay Jolley
CFO, David Keller
EVP, Doug Martin
President and COO, Burt Odom
EVP, Rob Eichelroth
EVP, Ray Catlin
EVP, Page Inman

LOCATIONS

HQ: EMJ CORPORATION
2034 HAMILTON PLACE BLVD # 400, CHATTANOOGA, TN 37421-6061
Phone: 423-855-1550
Web: WWW.EMJCORP.COM

PRODUCTS/OPERATIONS

Selected Projects
Airports
Education
Entertainment
Government/civic
Grocery
Healthcare
Hospitality
Industrial/warehouse
Lifestyle/mixed use development and retail
Native American tribal communities
Office buildings
Parking
Renewable energy
Renovations
Worship centers

Selected Services
Construction
Construction management
General contracting
Pre-construction services
Quality control
Safety consultation
Site evaluation
Warranty

COMPETITORS

Bovis Lend Lease
Case Contracting
Embree Construction
Fisher Development
Graycor
Hardaway Construction
Hardin Construction
Hayward Baker
Hoar Construction
JESCO
Rodgers Builders
S.D. Deacon
Skanska USA Building
Weis Builders
Workman Commercial

HISTORICAL FINANCIALS

Company Type: Private

Income Statement FYE: December 31

	REVENUE ($ mil.)	NET INCOME ($ mil.)	NET PROFIT MARGIN	EMPLOYEES
12/12	428	1	0.5%	210
12/11	437	0	0.1%	—
12/07	821	7	1.0%	—
12/07	959	10	1.1%	—
Annual Growth	(14.9%)	(28.2%)	—	—

2012 Year-End Financials

Debt ratio: —
Return on equity: 0.50%
Cash ($ mil.): 31
Current ratio: 1.10
Long-term debt ($ mil.): —
Dividends
Yield: —
Payout: —
Market value ($ mil.): —

EMPIRE SOUTHWEST LLC

EXECUTIVES

EVP, Chris Zaharis
Owner, Massey Ferguson
Founder, John Deere
Business Development Manager, Grant Taylor

LOCATIONS

HQ: EMPIRE SOUTHWEST LLC
1725 S COUNTRY CLUB DR, MESA, AZ 852106099
Phone: 4806334000
Web: WWW.EMPIRE-CAT.COM

PRODUCTS/OPERATIONS

Selected Industries Served
Agriculture
Demo and Scrap
Forestry
General Construction
Governmental
Heavy Construction
Landscaping
Marine
Mining
Oil and Gas
On-Highway Truck
Paving
Pipeline
Quarry and Aggregates
Waste

COMPETITORS

Arnold Machinery
CNH Global
Cashman Equipment
Cummins
Komatsu
Komatsu America
Multiquip
NES Rentals
RSC Equipment Rental
Sunbelt Rentals
United Rentals

HISTORICAL FINANCIALS

Company Type: Private

Income Statement FYE: October 31

	REVENUE ($ mil.)	NET INCOME ($ mil.)	NET PROFIT MARGIN	EMPLOYEES
10/12	881	53	6.1%	1,450
10/11	683	38	5.6%	—
10/10	528	22	4.3%	—
10/09	448	0	—	—
Annual Growth	25.3%	—	—	—

ENERGYUNITED ELECTRIC MEMBERSHIP CORPORATION

EXECUTIVES

Director, Ann M. Eller
Director, W. Max Walser
Treasurer Board of Directors, Jerry W. Anderson
Director, Glenn B. Smith
Director, Charles Hedrick
Director, C. Edgar Cartner
Secretary Board of Directors, Jeannette Overby
VP Board of Directors, N. Mack Shoaf
Director, Emory Windsor
Director, Richard C. Watts
Director, Ronnie Harrison
Director, Rufus Wyatt
Director, Eugene Dellinger

LOCATIONS

HQ: ENERGYUNITED ELECTRIC MEMBERSHIP CORPORATION
567 MOCKSVILLE HWY, STATESVILLE, NC 286258269
Phone: 7048735241
Web: WWW.ENERGYUNITED.COM

COMPETITORS

Duke Energy
Inergy
SCANA

HISTORICAL FINANCIALS

Company Type: Private

Income Statement FYE: December 31

	REVENUE ($ mil.)	NET INCOME ($ mil.)	NET PROFIT MARGIN	EMPLOYEES
12/14	274	9	3.5%	175
12/13	258	7	2.8%	—
12/12	245	13	5.5%	—
12/11	215	0	—	—
Annual Growth	8.4%	—	—	—

2014 Year-End Financials

Debt ratio: —
Return on equity: 3.50%
Cash ($ mil.): 8
Current ratio: 0.80
Long-term debt ($ mil.): —
Dividends
Yield: —
Payout: —
Market value ($ mil.): —

ERIEZ MANUFACTURING CO.

LOCATIONS

HQ: ERIEZ MANUFACTURING CO.
2200 ASBURY RD, ERIE, PA 165061402
Phone: 8148356000
Web: WWW.EN-US.ERIEZ.COM

HISTORICAL FINANCIALS

Company Type: Private

Income Statement FYE: December 31

	REVENUE ($ mil.)	NET INCOME ($ mil.)	NET PROFIT MARGIN	EMPLOYEES
12/12	229	22	9.9%	980
12/09	140	9	7.0%	—
12/08	157	10	6.9%	—
12/07	1,504	0	—	—
Annual Growth	(31.3%)	—	—	—

2012 Year-End Financials

Debt ratio: —
Return on equity: 9.90%
Cash ($ mil.): 37
Current ratio: 1.80
Long-term debt ($ mil.): —
Dividends
Yield: —
Payout: —
Market value ($ mil.): —

ESTES EXPRESS LINES INC.

Estes Express makes a business out of beating expectations. Founded during the Depression with a Chevy truck the company has grown into a multiregional less-than-truckload (LTL) freight hauler. Its fleet of some 6600 tractors and 24600 trailers operates via a network of 210 terminals dotting the US. Service in Canada is provided by TST Overland Express an ExpressLINK partner and in Mexico through affiliate Almex. Estes Express works with designated carriers to offer door-to-door delivery in the Caribbean and in Mexico. Subsidiary Estes Forwarding Worldwide services ocean/air freight forwarding. The company is owned and run by the family of founder W.W. Estes.

Geographic Reach

Estes Express offers regional service to all 50 US states. It also offers direct service to Canada Mexico and the Caribbean.

Operations

The company operates through several divisions and companies. Divisions include Estes Time-Critical (offering four levels of shipping) Level2 Logistics (business-to-business and business-to-consumer shipping) Estes Specialized Truckload and Delivery Services and Estes SureMove (customers load shipments themselves and Estes provides transportation). Companies include Estes Forwarding Worldwide Estes Brokerage Estes Leasing and Big E Transportation.

Strategy

Estes Express has continued to build out its LTL business by offering expedited delivery volume truckload transportation supply chain management nationwide brokerage services warehousing services and equipment leasing. The latter has provided such rental services as laundry trucks for the Department of Veterans Affairs. Its slate of services are supported by an upgraded wireless onboard pickup and delivery system featuring real-time data enabling terminals and drivers to process freight more efficiently. It has also formed a Mexico third-party logistics subsidiary Estes Logistica for managing freight consolidation and transportation to points south of the US border.

The company purchased about $180 million in equipment in 2014 with another $220 million planned for 2015. It is also upgrading its network to create new hubs breakbulks and bypass terminals to reduce rehandling stops.

Estes Express over the years has opened new offices in San Francisco Los Angeles Dallas Chicago Miami and New York. In 2014 it opened a 34-door terminal in North Chicago to support the continuing market growth in the Midwest. It also opened a new terminal in Oswego Illinois to accommodate increased demand for the company's services in the Chicagoland area.

Company Background

The company was formed in 1931.

EXECUTIVES

Vice President Human Resources, Tom Donahue
President and CEO, Rob W. Estes, age 62
V Pres, Patricia A Garland
Vp Pricing And Traffic, Paul J Dugent
Vice President Safety, Curtis Carr
Vp Corporate Sales And Strategic Planning, Pat Martin
Vice President Of Information, Nuno Valentine, age 51
President and CEO Estes Forwarding Worldwide, Scott Fisher
COO, Billy Hupp
VP and Chief Information Officer, Bob Fowler
Executive Vice President Of The Virginia, Dale Bennett
Sales And Marketing Vp, Legree Oswald
Vice President Operations Estes Air, John Eastland
Vice President National Accounts, Morton Mustian
Vice President Sales And Marketing Estes Air Forwarding, Mark Molloy
Vice President Of Operations, Al Bucher
Vice President International, Edward Alderman
Vice President Sales, Patricia Robinson
Vice President Marketing, Jeff Paseaur
Vice President Operations, John Son
Vice President, Ronald Taylor

LOCATIONS

HQ: ESTES EXPRESS LINES INC.
3901 W BROAD ST, RICHMOND, VA 232303962
Phone: 8043531900
Web: WWW.ESTES-EXPRESS.COM

PRODUCTS/OPERATIONS

Selected Services

Global (airfreight ocean international consolidation/deconsolidation customs brokerage international freight forwarding)
Less-than-truckload (regional national international/offshore)
Time critical (expedited guaranteed time/date definite)
Volume & truckload (LTL full loads backhaul services truckload brokerage dedicated truckload)

COMPETITORS

AAA Cooper Transportation
ArcBest
Averitt Express
Con-way Freight
FedEx Freight
Old Dominion Freight
Penske Truck Leasing
R+L Carriers
Ryder System
Saia
UPS Freight
Vitran
YRC Worldwide

HISTORICAL FINANCIALS

Company Type: Private

Income Statement FYE: December 31

	REVENUE ($ mil.)	NET INCOME ($ mil.)	NET PROFIT MARGIN	EMPLOYEES
12/13	1,958	71	3.6%	14,000
12/12	1,864	63	3.4%	—
12/11	1,738	52	3.0%	—
12/10	1,506	0	—	—
Annual Growth	9.1%	—	—	—

2013 Year-End Financials

Debt ratio: —
Return on equity: 3.60%
Cash ($ mil.): 53
Current ratio: 1.10
Long-term debt ($ mil.): —
Dividends
Yield: —
Payout: —
Market value ($ mil.): —

ETNA DISTRIBUTORS LLC

EXECUTIVES

President, R. David Potgeter
CEO, Russ Visner
Human Resources Manager, Angela Visner
Auditors: BDOSeidmanLLP

LOCATIONS

HQ: ETNA DISTRIBUTORS LLC
529 32ND ST SE, GRAND RAPIDS, MI 495482303
Phone: 6162454373
Web: WWW.ETNASUPPLY.COM

COMPETITORS

Fastenal
Ferguson Enterprises
HD Supply
Hajoca Corporation
Lowe' s
MSC Industrial Direct
Noland
Sid Harvey Industries Inc.
W.W. Grainger
Watsco
WinWholesale

HISTORICAL FINANCIALS

Company Type: Private

Income Statement FYE: December 31

	REVENUE ($ mil.)	NET INCOME ($ mil.)	NET PROFIT MARGIN	EMPLOYEES
12/13	149	2	1.6%	285
12/12	141	0	0.5%	—
12/11	132	0	0.6%	—
12/10	130	0	—	—
Annual Growth	4.6%	—	—	—

2013 Year-End Financials

Debt ratio: —
Return on equity: 1.60%
Cash ($ mil.): 0
Current ratio: 0.70
Long-term debt ($ mil.): —
Dividends
Yield: —
Payout: —
Market value ($ mil.): —

EVANGELICAL COMMUNITY HOSPITAL

Evangelical Community Hospital brings the good news of community health to residents in central Pennsylvania. Evangelical Community Hospital provides a wide range of medical services to the residents of Susquehanna Valley. Among its specialized services are home health care and hospice maternity oncology rehabilitation and pediatrics. The hospital delivers more than 1000 babies annually and treats more than 30000 patients in its emergency department each year. Its outreach network includes family practice offices and other medical services. Despite its name the hospital has no affiliation with any religious organization.

Geographic Reach

Evangelical Community Hospital serves patients in Northumberland Snyder and Union counties in Pennsylvania.

Operations

The hospital has 127 patient beds and 18 bassinets about 200 physicians on medical staff and about 900 clinical employees including lab technicians nurses therapists and radiology technicians.

Financial Performance

Evangelical Community Hospital reported a 9% increase in revenues in 2011 due to an increase an in patients visits investment income and funds raised.

Company Background

The hospital was established in 1926.

EXECUTIVES

VP Medical Affairs, J. Lawrence Ginsburg
Vice President ? Operations/COO, Kendra A. Aucker
VP Nursing Administration, Paul E. Tarves
VP Finance and CFO, James Stopper
Vice President - Information Systems, Dale Moyer
President CEO, Michael N. OKeefe

LOCATIONS

HQ: EVANGELICAL COMMUNITY HOSPITAL
1 HOSPITAL DR, LEWISBURG, PA 17837-9350
Phone: 570-522-2000
Web: WWW.EVANHOSPITAL.COM

COMPETITORS

Geisinger Health System
Lewistown Hospital
Mercy Health Partners Toledo
PinnacleHealth System

HISTORICAL FINANCIALS

Company Type: Private

Income Statement FYE: June 30

	REVENUE ($ mil.)	NET INCOME ($ mil.)	NET PROFIT MARGIN	EMPLOYEES
06/13	162	12	7.7%	1,360
06/12	154	9	6.2%	—
06/10	142	18	12.6%	—
06/10	122	13	10.8%	—
Annual Growth	9.7%	(2.1%)	—	—

2013 Year-End Financials

Debt ratio: —
Return on equity: 7.70%
Cash ($ mil.): 11
Current ratio: 1.10
Long-term debt ($ mil.): —
Dividends
Yield: —
Payout: —
Market value ($ mil.): —

EVERGREEN FS INC

Evergreen FS is an agricultural cooperative serving the needs of northern Illinois farmers. The co-op provides a full range of farm supplies and services including agronomy feed seed fertilizer fuel financing and marketing advice and products. It also operates six grain elevators. The co-op's 13000 member/owners operate farmland in the counties of McLean Woodford and Livingston. Evergreen FS is a member of the GROWMARK system.

EXECUTIVES

Vice President Of Research And Development, Gary Pavlich
Managing Director, David Burroughs
Vice President Of The Board, Rick Dickinson
Vice President Administration, Phil Willcoxon
Treas, Gary Schwartz
Treasurer, Paul Duzan
Director Board Of Directors, Ed Hoke
Treasurer, Paul Colfax
Secretary, Fred Gent
Vice Chairman, Rick Dickenson

LOCATIONS

HQ: EVERGREEN FS INC
402 N HERSHEY RD, BLOOMINGTON, IL 61704-3546
Phone: 309-663-2392
Web: WWW.HOME.EVERGREEN-FS.COM

COMPETITORS

ADM
ADM Alliance Nutrition
Ag Processing Inc.
Cargill
Land O' Lakes Purina Feed

HISTORICAL FINANCIALS

Company Type: Private

Income Statement FYE: August 31

	REVENUE ($ mil.)	NET INCOME ($ mil.)	NET PROFIT MARGIN	EMPLOYEES
08/11	307	10	3.4%	240
08/10	246	7	3.1%	—
08/09	0	0	—	—
08/07	204	3	1.9%	—
Annual Growth	10.7%	28.4%	—	—

2011 Year-End Financials

Debt ratio: —
Return on equity: 3.40%
Cash ($ mil.): 0
Current ratio: —
Long-term debt ($ mil.): —
Dividends
Yield: —
Payout: —
Market value ($ mil.): —

EWING IRRIGATION PRODUCTS INC.

You can thank Ewing Irrigation Products for that lush verdant golf course you occasionally call home. The company wholesales more than 13000 types of irrigation products for water management/conservation and erosion control for commercial and residential yards golf courses landscaping hardscape and turf maintenance. Ewing serves customers in the aquaculture food processing industrial process piping plumbing pool/spa construction and water treatment sectors. The company also supplies water features landscape lighting and pumps. Family owned Ewing operates through more than 195 branch locations in 22 states.

Strategy

Ewing has expanded in recent years opening new branch offices in Arkansas Alabama and South Carolina as well as by reorganizing its executive board to align with regional growth opportunities.

Company Background

Ewing was founded in 1922 as Atlas Lawn Sprinkler in San Francisco. King W. Ewing acquired and renamed the company in 1948. His family still owns and operates Ewing Irrigation Products.

EXECUTIVES

President and CEO, Douglas W. York
COO, Richard A. York
Director of Finance, Mark Finstad
SVP Marketing and Communications, Cliff Woodbury
VP-Credit, Rilus Graham

LOCATIONS

HQ: EWING IRRIGATION PRODUCTS INC.
3441 E HARBOUR DR, PHOENIX, AZ 85034-0908
Phone: 602-437-9530
Web: WWW.EWING1.COM

PRODUCTS/OPERATIONS

Selected Products

Erosion Control/Hydroseeding
Golf
Hardscape
Industrial Plastics
Landscape Lighting
Pumps
Residential and Commercial
Sports Fields
Turf Products
Water Features
Water Management/Conservation

COMPETITORS

Home Depot
Horizon Distributors
Lowe' s
Orbit Irrigation Products
Sears
Toro Company
Wal-Mart

HISTORICAL FINANCIALS

Company Type: Private

Income Statement FYE: June 29

	REVENUE ($ mil.)	NET INCOME ($ mil.)	NET PROFIT MARGIN	EMPLOYEES
06/12	315	10	3.2%	850
06/10	260	0	—	—
06/09	278	11	4.0%	—
06/08	306	11	3.7%	—
Annual Growth	0.7%	(2.6%)	—	—

2012 Year-End Financials

Debt ratio: —
Return on equity: 3.20%
Cash ($ mil.): 0
Current ratio: 0.40
Long-term debt ($ mil.): —
Dividends
Yield: —
Payout: —
Market value ($ mil.): —

EXEMPLA INC.

Exempla aims to provide exemplary health care to residents in the Denver area. The Exempla medical network operating as Exempla Healthcare includes three hospitals: Exempla Saint Joseph Hospital (570 beds) Exempla Lutheran Medical Center (400 beds) and Good Samaritan Medical Center (more than 230 beds). It also operates the Exempla Physician Network a chain of primary care clinics. The company employs more than 2100 physicians. Among its specialties are cardiovascular services and surgeries rehabilitation cancer care orthopedics and women's and children's services. Exempla Healthcare is sponsored by the Catholic faith-based Sisters of Charity of Leavenworth Health System (SCL Health System).

Strategy

Exempla is investing in expansion of the facilities at Lutheran Medical Center. It is also constructing a new building for Saint Joseph Hospital that is set to open in 2015.

Ownership

Exempla Healthcare was sponsored by two not-for-profit organizations –SCL Health System and the Lutheran-sponsored Community First Foundation –until 2012 when SCL Health System acquired the CFF interest in a deal worth some $275 million. SCL Health System had already gained management oversight of the Exempla facilities in 2009.

Company Background

Exempla Healthcare was formed in 1998 when Saint Joseph Hospital and Lutheran Medical Center combined.

EXECUTIVES

President CEO, Bain J. Farris, age 65
VP and CIO, David C. Pecoraro
President and CEO Exempla Good Samaritan Medical Center, David (Dave) Hamm
VP Payer Strategies and Legislative Affairs, Debbie Welle-Powell
Chief Operating Officer, Elisa (Lisa) Wetherbee
Senior Vice President Chief Financial Officer, Todd Conklin
Vice President Facilities Exempla, Al Davis
President and CEO Exempla Lutheran Medical Center, Grant Wicklund
President Sturm Financial Group and American National Bank, Koger L. Propst
Vice President Human Resources, Amy Pacey
President Group Operations West, Kaiser Permanente
Vice President Finance, John Higgins

Senior Vice President Chief Communications Officer, Christine Woolsey
Vice President Administrator Cardiovascular Services, Rick Harrell
Vice President Corporate Responsibility and Chief Compliance Officer, Mary L. Crumbaker
Director, Kathryn A. Paul, age 66
Director, Felix W. Cook Sr.

LOCATIONS

HQ: EXEMPLA INC.
2420 W 26TH AVE STE 100D, DENVER, CO 80211-5302
Phone: 303-813-5000
Web: WWW.EXEMPLA.COM

PRODUCTS/OPERATIONS

2009 Revenues

	$ mil.	% of total
Exempla Saint Joseph Hospital	377	40
Exempla Lutheran Medical Center	302	32
Exempla Good Samaritan Medical Center	217	23
Exempla Physician Network	22	2
Colorado Lutheran Home & Exempla West Pines Behavioral Health	22	2
Exempla Lutheran Collier Hospice	6	1
Total	**948**	**100**

COMPETITORS

Catholic Health Initiatives
Centura Health
Denver Health and Hospital Authority
HealthONE
Porter Adventist Hospital
Presbyterian/St. Luke' s Medical Center
Rose Medical Center
University of Colorado Hospital

HISTORICAL FINANCIALS

Company Type: Private

Income Statement FYE: December 31

	REVENUE ($ mil.)	NET INCOME ($ mil.)	NET PROFIT MARGIN	EMPLOYEES
12/09	597	7	1.3%	5,300
12/05	472	30	6.5%	—
12/04	335	37	11.2%	—
12/02	267	27	10.1%	—
Annual Growth	12.2%	(16.2%)	—	—

2009 Year-End Financials

Debt ratio: —
Return on equity: 1.30%
Cash ($ mil.): 53
Current ratio: 0.40
Long-term debt ($ mil.): —
Dividends
Yield: —
Payout: —
Market value ($ mil.): —

FAIRFIELD MEDICAL CENTER

Fairfield Medical Center is a more than 220-bed acute care hospital serving residents in southeastern and central Ohio. In addition to providing comprehensive medical and surgical care Fairfield Medical Center offers specialty services including cancer cardiovascular women's and children's health and rehabilitation services. The not-for-profit hospital also operates offsite facilities for physician practices as well as specialty diagnostic and laboratory services. The Center employs more than 250 physicians and is served by a number of volunteer organizations which help to support and operate it. The original hospital dates back to 1916.

Geographic Reach

The hospital serves the Ohio counties of Fairfield Perry Hocking and Athens.

Operations

Fairfield Medical Center handles some 10000 inpatient admissions each year. It also sees about 250000 outpatients and handles 2500 surgeries and 1000 birthing procedures.

Strategy

Fairfield Medical Center has launched a $38 million facility expansion program called Project BRIGHT (Build Revitalize and Innoate for Greater Health care Tomorrow). Through the project the medical center is adding a new hospital wing with 30 private patient rooms a surgery center and clinical support areas.

To further expand services and reach more patients the hospital is also forming collaborations and acquisitions. One such move was the hospital's entry into the convenient clinic market by pairing with Wal-Mart to open a seven-day walk-in clinic called the Clinic at Walmart in Canal Winchester Ohio in 2011. Two more Wal-Mart locations were added in Lancaster and Logan. The clinics offer school physicals immunizations treatment for common illnesses and other minor medical treatments.

Mergers and Acquisitions

On the acquisitions side Fairfield bought River View Surgery Center from a group of physician owners (70%) and Mount Carmel Health System (30%) for $8.5 million also in 2011. The hospital also paid about $1 million that year to buy out what had been a joint venture and gain full ownership of Fairfield Diagnostic Imaging.

EXECUTIVES

President and CEO, Mina H. Ubbing
VP and CFO, Sky Gettys
VP and Chief Nursing Officer, Cynthia Pearsall
VP Professional and Support Services, Howard D. Sniderman
VP and Chief Medical Officer, Jerome J. Roche
Foundation Director, Ricki Chenault

LOCATIONS

HQ: FAIRFIELD MEDICAL CENTER
401 N EWING ST, LANCASTER, OH 43130-3371
Phone: 740-687-8000
Web: WWW.FMCHEALTH.ORG

PRODUCTS/OPERATIONS

Selected Centers and Services

Bariatrics
Cancer Care
Emergency Care
Ewing Square Infusion Clinic
Fairfield Healthcare Professionals
Fairfield Medical Diagnostic Services
Heartburn Center
Internal Medicine Clinic
Maternity Care
Orthopedic Care
Outpatient Therapy Services / Sports Clinic / Worklife
Physical Therapy & Rehabilitative Services
River View Surgery Services
Snider Cardiovascular Institute
Southeast Ohio Sleep Disorder Center
Surgery
The Pavilion (Surgery and Medical Office)
Womens Health
Wound Clinic

COMPETITORS

Genesis HealthCare System (Ohio)
Licking Memorial Health Systems
Mount Carmel Health
Nationwide Children' s Hospital
OhioHealth

HISTORICAL FINANCIALS

Company Type: Private

Income Statement FYE: December 31

	REVENUE ($ mil.)	NET INCOME ($ mil.)	NET PROFIT MARGIN	EMPLOYEES
12/12	225	12	5.3%	2,200
12/09	197	7	3.8%	
12/07	187	(11)		
12/07	181	2	1.4%	
Annual Growth	4.5%	37.3%	—	—

2012 Year-End Financials

Debt ratio: —
Return on equity: 5.30%
Cash ($ mil.): 14
Current ratio: 1.40
Long-term debt ($ mil.): —
Dividends
Yield: —
Payout: —
Market value ($ mil.): —

FAIRFIELD UNIVERSITY

Fairfield University is a private Jesuit school with an enrollment of more than 5000 undergraduate and graduate students. It offers about 40 undergraduate majors as well as 40 graduate degree programs through six schools and colleges: College of Arts and Sciences; School of Nursing; School of Engineering; Dolan School of Business; Graduate School of Education and Allied Professions; and University College. With a faculty of about 550 professionals Fairfield University has one campus in Fairfield Connecticut and offers about 60 study abroad programs. The university was established by the Society of Jesus in 1942.

Geographic Reach

Fairfield University offers a variety of study abroad programs including courses in Italy Ireland Australia Brazil and Nicaragua. It also engages about 200 international students at its Connecticut campus.

Financial Performance

Fairfield University reported $187 million in revenues during fiscal 2012 an increase of about 6% over 2011. Most of the institution's earnings come from student tuition and fees. Net income dipped slightly into the red in 2012 (-$534000) down from $44 million in profits in 2011.

Strategy

The university aims to prepare students to take on leadership and service roles developing creativity and intelligence while fostering social responsibility and ethical and religious values. As part of its mission to create new opportunities for its students in 2011 Fairfield University added a new study abroad program in Brazil. In addition in 2012 it formed a partnership with Bridgeport Hospital to transition hospital RNs into the School of Nursing's Bachelor of Science degree program.

EXECUTIVES

President, Rev Jeffrey P. von Arx, age 67
Acting Senior Director Marketing and Communications, Cathleen Donahue
SVP Academic Affairs, Paul J. Fitzgerald
SVP Administration and Chief of Staff, Mark C. Reed
EVP and COO, Kevin Lawlor
CIO, Paige Francis
Dean Dolan School of Business, Donald E. Gibson
Dean College of Arts and Sciences, Robbin Crabtree
Dean Graduate School of Education and Allied Professions, Faith-Anne Dohm
Dean School of Engineering, Bruce Berdanier

Dean School of Nursing, Lynn Babington
Trustee, Ned C. Lautenbach, age 69
Trustee, David H. Chafey Jr., age 59
Trustee, Joseph F. Berardino, age 62
Trustee, William L. (Bill) Atwell, age 62
Trustee, Michele M. Macauda
Trustee, Kevin M. Conlisk, age 68
Trustee, Timothy J. Conway, age 58
Trustee, Michael E. McGuinness
Trustee, John F. Baldovin
Trustee, Terrence A. Baum
Trustee, Thomas G. Benz
Trustee, Stephen E. Bepler
Trustee, Joseph R. Bronson
Trustee, Frank J. Carroll III
Trustee, Thomas A. Franko
Trustee, Michael Garanzini
Trustee, Peter Gillen
Trustee, Patricia Glassford
Trustee, Brian Hull
Trustee, Jack L. Kelly
Trustee, Susan R. King
Trustee, William K. Lisecky
Trustee, William A. Malloy
Trustee, John C. Meditz
Trustee, Elner L. Morrell
Trustee, Rev George B. Murry
Trustee, Christopher C. Quick
Trustee, Lawrence C. Rafferty
Trustee, Eileen Rominger
Trustee, Rosellen Schnurr
Trustee, Jeffrey P. von Arx

LOCATIONS

HQ: FAIRFIELD UNIVERSITY
1073 N BENSON RD, FAIRFIELD, CT 06824-5195
Phone: 203-254-4000
Web: WWW.FAIRFIELD.EDU

HISTORICAL FINANCIALS

Company Type: Private

Income Statement FYE: June 30

	REVENUE ($ mil.)	NET INCOME ($ mil.)	NET PROFIT MARGIN	EMPLOYEES
06/13	191	39	20.7%	883
06/12	187	(0)	—	—
06/10	176	44	25.0%	—
06/10	172	26	15.6%	—
Annual Growth	3.6%	13.9%	—	—

2013 Year-End Financials

Debt ratio: —
Return on equity: 20.70%
Cash ($ mil.): 38
Current ratio: —
Long-term debt ($ mil.): —
Dividends
Yield: —
Payout: —
Market value ($ mil.): —

FAIRLEIGH DICKINSON UNIVERSITY

It's fair to say that Fairleigh Dickinson University (FDU) is the largest private university in New Jersey. It has an enrollment of approximately 12000 students and 260 full-time faculty members. It has a student-teacher ratio of 14:1 and offers more than 100 undergraduate and graduate degree programs as well as doctoral programs in clinical psychology and school psychology. In addition to its main Metropolitan Campus in Teaneck New Jersey; the university also offers degree programs at the College at Florham in Madison New Jersey; at FDU-Vancouver in Canada; and at Wroxton College in Oxfordshire England. Fairleigh Dickinson was founded in 1942.

Geographic Reach

The university operates a main Metropolitan Campus located in Teaneck New Jersey. It also has a campus in Vancouver Canada and offers degree programs to students through partnerships with other institutions such as the College at Florham in Madison Wisconsin and at Oxfordshire England's Wroxton College. FDU is the first American university to own and operate an overseas campus.

Operations

Some of the school's many disciplines include business education engineering hotel and restaurant management liberal arts (including communication criminal justice film and animation psychology and theater) nursing and allied health and the sciences.

Of its more than 260 full-time faculty members 85% hold a Ph.D. or terminal degree in their field.

Strategy

The school offers students combined degree programs that allow them to earn a master's or professional degree at an accelerated pace in more than a dozen disciplines. FDU boasts an interdisciplinary studies program in sports administration that began in 2009.

Entering agreements with universities worldwide has also given FDU the opportunity to exchange faculty conduct joint research projects and collaborate on educational initiatives. FDU is the first comprehensive university in the world to require its undergraduates to undergo distance learning. Such global partnerships include Galen University in Belize; Reims Management School in France; and Ross University Medical School in Dominica.

Looking to strengthen its position in the medical fields FDU in 2012 opened its new School of Pharmacy. The school represents New Jersey's first pharmacy school associated with a private university and the second of its kind in New Jersey.

Financial Performance

FDU logged marginal increases (1%) in fiscal 2012 as compared to 2011 citing net tuition and fees and auxiliary enterprises for the gains. Net income meanwhile dropped by 65% for the same reporting period due to rises in total educational and general expenses and declines in non-operating revenues.

EXECUTIVES

Chair, Patrick J. (Pat) Zenner, age 66
Executive Director Online Programs, David F. Epstein
VP Administration, Richard A. Riccio
Trustee and Interim President, Sheldon Drucker
VP Finance and Treasurer, Hania Ferrara
VP and CIO, Neal Sturm
Associate VP Communications and Marketing, Arthur E. (Art) Petrosemolo
SVP University Advancement, Richard P. Reiss
Associate VP Institutional Research and Assessment, Indira Govindan
Assistant VP Facilities, Michael Holland
Senior Development Officer University Advancement, Karen Lewis
Assistant VP Administration, Robert Valenti
Director University Advancement, Marilyn Adamczyk
Director Student Life, Sarah Azavedo
Executive Director Rothman Institute, James Barrood
Senior Program Director Continuing Education, Richard Bettencourt
Director Publications, Carol Black
Director Communications and Special Projects, Angelo Carfagna
Director School of Education, Vicki Cohen
Director of Financial Aid Operations, Theresa Coll
University Director Enrollment Services, Carol Creekmore
Director of Undergraduate Admissions Operations, Coleen Curtis
Director Information Systems and Technology, Brian Domenick
Director MFA in Creative Writing Program and Special Assistant to the President, Martin Donoff
Director Continuing Education, Jennifer Dudley
Director Bi-Campus Facilities, William Dyer
Director Office of Global Learning, Stuart Eisenstadt
Director Athletics and Administration, Scott Fisher
Director Internal Auditing, Peter Forman
Director Payroll and HRIS, Julie Friedman
Director Center for Student Academic Services, Rachel Friend
Director Academic Support Center, Patricia Geehr
Director University College Dean, June Anne Giardina
Director Sports Information, William Giglio
Director Freshman Intensive Studies, William Gillard
Director Vpia-Development, Christopher Groff
Director The EOF Program, Marjorie Hall-Jacques
Executive Assistant President, Karin Hamilton
Executive Director Human Resources, Gregory Hammill
Director Adult Education, Denise Hart
Director Aquatics, Tracy Holt
Executive Director Global Partnerships, Irwin Isquith
Director Public Relations, Gretchen Johnson
Director Transfer Students, Roger Kane
Executive Director Online Programs, Malavika Khullar
Director Management Information Systems, Saul Kleinman
Director Athletics, William Klika
Director Computing Services, Ralph Knapp
Director Telecommunications, Carl Kraus
Director Budgeting Service, Frank Lawson
Program Director Continuing Education, Joan Leder
Director Enhanced Freshman Experience, Rendell Mabey
Director Student Health Services, Ann Mahan
Director Petrocelli College, Anthony Mastropietro
Executive Director Development, Susan McConville
Director Financial Aid, Margaret McGrail
Director Vpia-Development, Andrew McKay
Director International Student Services, Jessica McMillan
Co-Director Student Counseling and Psychology Services, David Mednick
Director Campus Public Safety, David Miles
Co-Director Student Counseling and Psychology Services, Alice Mills
Director Residence Life, Bernard Montgomery
Senior Program Director Continuing Education, Diane Mora
Director Student Life, Craig Mourton
Director Adult and Part-time Studies, Andrew Nelson
Director Purchasing, Susan O'Connor
Director Computing Services, Robert Pelech
Director Operations, Helene Pier
Director Academic Advising Center, Deborah Pilipie
Director Donor Relations, Laura Reynolds
Director Educational Technology, Sandra Selick
Director International and Graduate Admissions, Thomas Shea
Director Grants and Sponsored Projects, Laurie Treleven
Budget Manager and Assistant to the Dean Petrocelli College, Denise Wisniewski
Accounts Payable Manager, Gregory Sarajian
Research and Records Manager, Dora Rodriguez

Print Shop Manager, Charlotte Morey
Manager Human Resources, Maureen Curry
Manager Software and Databases, Joseph Brancone
Systems Manager University Systems and Security, Christopher Bland
Campus Property Manager, Sal Vacirca
Executive Associate Dean Petrocelli College Administrative Science, Ronald Calissi
Assistant Dean Becton College, Elizabeth Feeley
Interim Campus Provost Metropolitan College, Robert Greenfield
Director Special Student Services, Brenda Jackson
Assistant Dean Students, Michelle McCroy Heins
Assistant Dean Students, Nestor Melendez
Associate Dean University College, Albert Schielke
Assistant Dean Silberman College, Janette Shurdom
Dean University College, John Snyder
Associate Dean Petrocelli College, Thomas Swanzey
Dean Petrocelli College, Kenneth Vehrkens
Campus Provost College at Florham, Kenneth Greene
SVP and Interim University Provost, Joseph J. Kiernan
Associate VP Human Resources, Rose D'Ambrosio
Associate Provost Academic Administration, Bonnie Diehl
Director Office of Government and Community Affairs, Richard D. Bronson
Campus Provost Fairleigh Dickinson University Vancouver, Ian Haslam
VP Enrollment Management, Jonathan Wexler
SVP Academic Affairs and Provost, Christopher A. Capuano
Dean Students, Brian Mauro
Dean Silberman College of Business, William M. Moore
Dean Maxwell Becton College of Arts and Sciences, Geoffrey Weinman
Trustee, Ronald J. Doerfler, age 73
Trustee, Vincent J. Naimoli
Trustee, Stewart Krentzman
Trustee and Interim President, Sheldon Drucker
Trustee, Kenneth Brier
Trustee, Guy F. Budinscak
Trustee, Robert Hallenbeck
Trustee, Gregory H. Olsen
Trustee, Robert Saltarelli
Trustee, Paul Santucci
Trustee, Mary Kay Stratis
Trustee, Skippy Weinstein
Trustee, Molly Easo Smith
Trustee, Anthony Ambrosio
Trustee, Curtis R. Artis
Trustee, Donna Del Prete Marki
Trustee, Ann Petrocelli
Auditors: PricewaterhouseCoopersLLP

LOCATIONS

HQ: FAIRLEIGH DICKINSON UNIVERSITY
1000 RIVER RD, TEANECK, NJ 07666-1914
Phone: 201-692-2000
Web: WWW.VIEW.FDU.EDU

Selected Global Partnerships

Belize
Galen University
Brazil
Centro Universitario (UNA)
Faculdades Integradas de Vitoria (FDV)
China
Northeastern University - Shenyang China
Shenyang University China
Capital University of Economics and Business (Beijing)
Colombia
Universidad Autonoma de Bucaramanga
Cyprus
Intercollege Cyprus
Dominica
Ross University Medical School
Dominican Republic
Pontificia Universidad Catolica Madre y Maestra
Ecuador
Universidad Catolica de Santiago de Guayaquil (Guayaquil)
France
IECS - Strasbourg Graduate School of Management
Reims Management School
Germany
Fachhochschule der Wirtschaft Germany
Hong Kong
Chinese University of Hong Kong
University of Hong Kong
Lignan University
Hungary
Central European University
India
Alliance Business School
Israel
Ben-Gurion University of the Negev (Beer-Sheva)
Korea
Kyungnam University
Sungkyungkwan University
Woosuk University
Lebanon
University of Balamand Lebanon
Malaysia
University College Sedaya International
Mexico
Universidad Autonoma de Guadalajara School of Medicine
Monaco
International University of Monaco
Philippines
University of the East
Poland
Karola Marcinkowski Medical School
Singapore
Republic Polytechnic- Singapore
Temasek Polytechnic Singapore
Spain
International University Study Center - Barcelona Spain
Universidad Alfonso X el Sabio - Madrid Spain
University of Cordoba

PRODUCTS/OPERATIONS

Selected Colleges

Becton College
Petrocelli College
Silberman College
University College

HISTORICAL FINANCIALS

Company Type: Private

Income Statement FYE: June 30

	REVENUE ($ mil.)	NET INCOME ($ mil.)	NET PROFIT MARGIN	EMPLOYEES
06/13	211	21	10.3%	1,505
06/12	204	7	3.9%	—
06/10	202	22	11.3%	—
06/10	191	13	7.2%	—
Annual Growth	3.3%	16.4%	—	—

2013 Year-End Financials

Debt ratio: ––
Return on equity: 10.30%
Cash ($ mil.): 58
Current ratio: —
Long-term debt ($ mil.): —

Dividends
Yield: —
Payout: —
Market value ($ mil.): —

FAIRVIEW HEALTH SERVICES

It's fair to say that when it comes to health care Fairview Health Services takes the long view. The not-for-profit health care system serves Minnesota's Twin Cities and nearby communities. Fairview Health Services is affiliated with the medical school of the University of Minnesota and counts among its 10 hospitals the University of Minnesota Medical Center. The hospitals house some 2500 beds and provide comprehensive medical and surgical services. The health system also operates a network of primary and specialty care clinics that provide preventive and wellness care. Additionally Fairview Health operates retail pharmacies and nursing homes and provides home health care and rehabilitation.

Operations

Fairview operates more than 40 primary care clinics seven urgent care clinics and more than 55 specialty service centers scattered across the state (plus one in Wisconsin). It employs more than 820 physicians. In 2011 the health system was one of the first in the nation to initiate a pay scheme for clinic doctors that rewards them for the manner in which they treat patients favorable satisfaction surveys and their ability to keep patients healthy and out of the hospital rather than simply for the number of tests run.

Fairview also provides a host of senior care options through its Ebenezer unit that include assisted and independent living adult day care and health services designed specifically for the elderly and administered by specialists that include geriatricians.

Financial Analysis

Fairview's revenues grew by 7% in 2011 due to an increase in revenues from agreements with third-party payors (which provide for payments to Fairview at amounts different from its established rates) and from the positive impact of acquisitions made in 2010.

Strategy

Fairview has grown through organic initiatives and via acquisitions.

In 2012 Fairview expanded its clinics' menu of virtual care including phone email and video visits through a partnership with Zipnosis to give online diagnosis and treatment for patients in Minnesota for certain conditions.

The company opened its newest hospital University of Minnesota Amplatz Children's Hospital in 2011. Part of the University of Minnesota Medical Center the 96-bed facility contains a pediatric ER with six operating suites and 2 trauma bays. The patients' rooms are all private and large enough to easily accommodate extended overnight stays by family members. The hospital also operates the only children's dialysis center in the state.

In 2011 the health system was one of the first in the nation to initiate a pay scheme for clinic doctors that rewards them for the manner in which they treat patients favorable satisfaction surveys and their ability to keep patients healthy and out of the hospital rather than simply for the number of tests run.

Mergers and Acquisitions

In 2011 the company acquired Bloomington Lake Clinic with locations in Minneapolis and Bloomington. In 2010 it bought the tumor-treating University of Minnesota Physicians Oncology Clinic.

Company Background

Fairview was founded in 1906.

EXECUTIVES

SVP Integrated Network and Payer Solutions and Chief Human Resources Officer, Paula H. Phillippe
Chairman, Charles W. (Chuck) Mooty, age 53
President CEO and Director, Mark A. Eustis, age 61
Executive Vice President Risk Management, Ann H. Hengel
Vice President and compliance counsel, Connie G. Weinman
President Fairview Community Hospitals, Daniel K. Anderson

President Senior Services, Mark F. Thomas
Systems Manager Media Relations, Ryan Davenport
Communications Consultant and Media Relations, Jennifer Amundson
SVP and General Counsel, George Chresand
Secretary and Director, Joanell Dyrstad
Chief Clinical Integration Officer, Mark J. Werner
President University of Minnesota Medical Center Fairview, Carolyn S. Wilson
SVP Strategy Marketing and Communication, Mark Hansberry
senior Vice President for transformation and chief information officer, Terry Carroll
President Fairview Medical Group, Brent Asplin
SVP and CFO, Daniel (Dan) Fromm
President Fairview Physician Associates, David Moen
Senior Vice President Human Resources, Karen Grabow
Vice President for, Aaron Friedman
Vice President of Fund Distribution, Mary Cooper
President Mary Schumacher, Pat Flug
President CEO and Director, Mark A. Eustis, age 61
Director, Ann H. Hengel
Director, Jon R. Campbell
Director, John Bjorklund
Secretary and Director, Joanell Dyrstad
Director, Douglas Dirks
Director, Michael Fay
Director, Rev Christopher Nelson
Director, Joanne Lofgren Ploetz
Director, Dan Dixon
Director, Carol Ley
Director, Mark Paller
Auditors: Ernst&YoungLLP

LOCATIONS

HQ: FAIRVIEW HEALTH SERVICES
2450 RIVERSIDE AVE, MINNEAPOLIS, MN 55454-1450
Phone: 612-672-6300
Web: WWW.UMPHYSICIANS.OIT.UMN.EDU

PRODUCTS/OPERATIONS

Revenue Sources

	% of total
Negotiated	46
Medicare	33
Medicaid	17
Commercial &	4
Total	**100**

Sales

	% of total
Net patient service	88
Other	12
Total	**100**

Selected Facilities

Bloomington Lake Clinic
Fairview Lakes Medical Center (Wyoming)
Fairview Maple Grove Medical Center
Fairview Northland Medical Center (Princeton)
Fairview Red Wing Medical Center
Fairview Ridges Hospital (Burnsville)
Fairview Southdale Hospital (Edina)
Fairview University Medical Center-Mesabi (Hibbing)
Maple Grove Hospital
University of Minnesota Amplatz Children's Hospital (Minneapolis)
University of Minnesota Medical Center (Minneapolis)

COMPETITORS

Abbott Northwestern Hospital
Allina Hospitals
Bethesda Hospital
Catholic Health Initiatives
CentraCare Health
HealthEast Care System
Mayo Clinic
North Memorial Health Care
Park Nicollet Health Services
Regions Hospital
St. John' s Hospital (Minnesota)

HISTORICAL FINANCIALS

Company Type: Private

Income Statement FYE: December 31

	REVENUE ($ mil.)	NET INCOME ($ mil.)	NET PROFIT MARGIN	EMPLOYEES
12/11	2,575	4	0.2%	18,000
12/09	2,744	281	10.2%	—
12/08	2,566	(182)	—	—
Annual Growth	0.1%	—	—	—

2011 Year-End Financials

Debt ratio: —
Return on equity: 0.20%
Cash ($ mil.): 47
Current ratio: 1.50
Long-term debt ($ mil.): —
Dividends
Yield: —
Payout: —
Market value ($ mil.): —

FAITH TECHNOLOGIES INC.

Keeping the faith in technology is a basic commitment of Faith Technologies one of the largest privately held electrical and specialty systems contractors in the US. The company's specialties include electrical contracting and service automated controls lighting security technology and preconstruction. It primarily serves clients in the commercial government industrial institutional health care manufacturing power residential retail transportation and data center sectors. The company has worked on a range of projects such as airports bridges correctional facilities government agencies hospitals restaurants and shopping centers.

Established in 1972 employee-owned Faith Technologies has around 15 locations in Georgia Kansas Minnesota Missouri Oklahoma and Wisconsin and is licensed to do business in some 45 states. In 2009 its Faith Technologies Tulsa division in Oklahoma merged with Alpha Electrical Services. Also that year the company completed the final phase of a nationwide transition by converting all 10 of its Town & Country Electric locations in Wisconsin under the Faith Technologies banner.

Faith Technologies opened its 15th location in Minneapolis in 2010.

EXECUTIVES

CEO, Roland G. (Rollie) Stephenson, age 68
President, Richard A. Schinke Jr.
CFO, Donald M. Stachowiak
VP Operations, George Van Der Linden
Chief Learning Officer, Terri Luebke
Service Manager, Tony Dohr
Service Project Manager, Aaron Bizub
Vice President - Springfield, Dave Klein
Executive Vice President, Darryl Betro
Regional Vice President, Bob Dakovich
Vice President - Preconstruction, Charlie Fredrickson
Director of Operations, Christine Rahlf
Vice President - Construction Services, Dan Siebers
Executive Vice President, David Jahner
Controller, Diane Kuehnl
Regional Vice President, Dick Merbach
Vice President - Madison, Heath Luedtke
Vice President - Preconstruction, Jack Brock
Vice President - Human Resources, Stephanie Guin

LOCATIONS

HQ: FAITH TECHNOLOGIES INC.
225 MAIN ST, MENASHA, WI 54952-3186
Phone: 920-738-1500
Web: WWW.FAITHTECHNOLOGIES.COM

COMPETITORS

Aldridge Electric
EEI
EMCOR
Guarantee Electrical
Sachs Electric

HISTORICAL FINANCIALS

Company Type: Private

Income Statement FYE: December 31

	REVENUE ($ mil.)	NET INCOME ($ mil.)	NET PROFIT MARGIN	EMPLOYEES
12/12	260	9	3.8%	1,547
12/11	248	4	1.9%	—
12/10	228	2	1.0%	—
12/09	219	5	2.6%	—
Annual Growth	5.9%	21.2%	—	—

2012 Year-End Financials

Debt ratio: —
Return on equity: 3.80%
Cash ($ mil.): 0
Current ratio: —
Long-term debt ($ mil.): —
Dividends
Yield: —
Payout: —
Market value ($ mil.): —

FAMILY EXPRESS CORPORATION

Convenience is all in the family at this Indiana chain. Family Express operates about 50 convenience store/gasoline stations in north central and northwestern Indiana (split almost evenly between city and rural locations). The chain's Cravin's Market in-house foodservice features fresh sandwiches fruits vegetables salads and a selection of floral items. Family Express also has launched its own proprietary brands including Java Wave gourmet coffees Squeeze Freeze carbonated beverages natural spring water and bread and milk products. In addition Family Express operates a small fleet of delivery trucks that say "moo." The company was founded in 1975.

EXECUTIVES

President and CEO, Gus Olympidis

LOCATIONS

HQ: FAMILY EXPRESS CORPORATION
213 S STATE ROAD 49, VALPARAISO, IN 46383-7976
Phone: 219-462-0144
Web: WWW.FAMILYEXPRESS.COM

COMPETITORS

7-Eleven
Casey' s General Stores
Chevron
Exxon Mobil
Speedway

HISTORICAL FINANCIALS

Company Type: Private

Income Statement FYE: December 31

	REVENUE ($ mil.)	NET INCOME ($ mil.)	NET PROFIT MARGIN	EMPLOYEES
12/12	379	5	1.4%	500
12/10	277	4	1.6%	—
12/09	244	2	1.2%	—
12/07	275	18	6.7%	—
Annual Growth	6.6%	(21.8%)	—	—

2012 Year-End Financials

Debt ratio: —
Return on equity: 1.40%
Cash ($ mil.): 6
Current ratio: 0.60
Long-term debt ($ mil.): —
Dividends
Yield: —
Payout: —
Market value ($ mil.): —

FAMILY HEALTH INTERNATIONAL INC

Known as FHI 360 Family Health International believes that health is wealth. From a handful of offices located in the US Asia-Pacific and South Africa FHI 360 funds and manages public health programs research education and other resources in more than 60 countries. Founded in 1971 as the International Fertility Research Program of the University of North Carolina at Chapel Hill FHI 360 primarily focuses on and supports HIV/AIDS prevention research reproductive health services and maternal and neonatal health programs. The organization works with governments private agencies and non-governmental organizations to develop the most appropriate programs for different areas.

Geographic Reach

Headquartered in Durham North Carolina the organization operates additional offices New York Boston and Washington DC. It extends its reach abroad with a pair of international offices: one in Pretoria South Africa that serves as its Southern regional office and another located in Bangkok to cover the Asia-Pacific region. Representatives from more than 110 countries travel to the US each year to take part in the organization's international exchange program.

Strategy

In 2011 Family Health International acquired the assets programs and expertise of Academy for Educational Development (AED) a Washington DC-based nonprofit organization that works globally in the areas of health education and social and economic development. AED implements more than 250 programs serving people in all 50 US states and more than 150 countries. As a result of the purchase AED was renamed FHI Development 360 and the larger organization is now known as FHI 360. The new moniker gets its meaning from the group's belief that a 360-degree perspective is necessary to address complex human development needs.

EXECUTIVES

Chief Human Resources Officer, Pamela (Pam) Myers
Chief Executive Officer, Albert J. Siemens
Executive Vice President General Counsel, Robert R. Price
President Research and Director, Willard Cates Jr.
President Public Health Programs and Director, Peter R. Lamptey
SVP Research and Strategic Coordination, Gary R. West
SVP, Sheila Mitchell
Chairman of the Board, Torrey C. Brown
Chief Administrative Officer, David Mein
VP Global Portfolio Management, Laura Kayser
SVP Strategic Development and Communications, Manisha Bharti
Vice Chairman, Edward W. Whitehorne
VP Business Development, Edward Dennison
COO, Marjorie Newman-Williams
Associate Director for Media Relations, Ramona Dubose
Chief Financial Officer, Robert Murphy
Chief Compliance Officer, Sean Temeemi
Chief Operating Officer, Patrick C. Fine
Vice President External Engagement & Social Responsibility, Helga Ying
Chief Executive Officer, Albert J. Siemens
President Research and Director, Willard Cates Jr.
President Public Health Programs and Director, Peter R. Lamptey
Director, R. Peyton Woodson III
Director, Torrey C. Brown
Director, Donald A. Collins
Director, Pramilla Senanayake
Vice Chairman, Edward W. Whitehorne
Director, Martin Mittag-Lenkheym

LOCATIONS

HQ: FAMILY HEALTH INTERNATIONAL INC
2224 E NC HIGHWAY 54, DURHAM, NC 27713-2208
Phone: 919-381-7040
Web: WWW.FHI360.ORG

PRODUCTS/OPERATIONS

Selected Services

Behavior-change communication
Capacity-building
Clinical trials services
Creative services
Data analysis
Quality assurance
Research services
Social marketing
Training and technical assistance

HISTORICAL FINANCIALS

Company Type: Private

Income Statement FYE: September 30

	REVENUE ($ mil.)	NET INCOME ($ mil.)	NET PROFIT MARGIN	EMPLOYEES
09/09	327	2	0.9%	4,000
09/08	369	3	0.9%	—
09/08	154	0	—	—
Annual Growth		—17716.7%	—	—

2009 Year-End Financials

Debt ratio: —
Return on equity: 0.90%
Cash ($ mil.): 42
Current ratio: 1.00
Long-term debt ($ mil.): —
Dividends
Yield: —
Payout: —
Market value ($ mil.): —

FARM CREDIT WEST

LOCATIONS

HQ: FARM CREDIT WEST
1478 STONE POINT DR # 450, ROSEVILLE, CA 956612869
Phone: 9167244800

HISTORICAL FINANCIALS

Company Type: Private

Income Statement FYE: December 31

	ASSETS ($ mil.)	NET INCOME ($ mil.)	INCOME AS % OF ASSETS	EMPLOYEES
12/13	6,925	156	2.3%	165
12/12	6,668	151	2.3%	—
12/11	6,282	176	2.8%	—
12/10	6,129	0		—
Annual Growth	4.2%	—	—	—

FARMERS COOPERATIVE COMPANY

EXECUTIVES

CEO, Roger Koppen
SVP Grain Marketing and Logistics, Jon Setterdahl
SVP and CFO, Mark Miner
COO, Chris Pearson
Seed Manager, Tom Hall
VP Agronomy Sales, Pat Zmolek
VP Feed Sales, John Malin
Business Development Manager, Lonnie Hansen
Marketing Manager, Dave Lemke
Sr. Vice President - Operations, Devin Mogler
Controller, Justin Nepper
Operations Manager, Justin Sollmann
Sr. Vice President of Grain Operations, Marvin Hodgson
Controller Manager, Molly Blanchfield
Business Development Manager serves our trade area, Ned Lenh
Marketing Manager, Ron Simmons
Sr. Vice President - Feed, Ron Hollenbeck
Operations Manager, Todd Scheer
Marketing Manager, Kirk Johnson
Chief Executive Officer, Jim Chism

LOCATIONS

HQ: FARMERS COOPERATIVE COMPANY
105 GARFIELD AVE, FARNHAMVILLE, IA 505386712
Phone: 5155443213
Web: WWW.FCCOOP.COM

PRODUCTS/OPERATIONS

Selected Departments

Agronomy
Feed
Grain
Seed

COMPETITORS

ADM
Ag Processing Inc.
CHS
Cargill
DeBruce Grain
Farm Service
Five Star Co-op
Gold-Eagle Cooperative
Heartland Co-op
Ingredion
NEW Cooperative
Scoular

Cooperative
Farmers Cooperative Society
Swiss Valley Farms
West Central Co-op

HISTORICAL FINANCIALS

Company Type: Private

Income Statement FYE: August 31

	REVENUE ($ mil.)	NET INCOME ($ mil.)	NET PROFIT MARGIN	EMPLOYEES
08/10	779	10	1.3%	450
08/09	894	13	1.5%	—
Annual Growth	(12.8%)	(19.9%)	—	—

2010 Year-End Financials

Debt ratio: —
Return on equity: 1.30%
Cash ($ mil.): 0
Current ratio: —
Long-term debt ($ mil.): —
Dividends
Yield: —
Payout: —
Market value ($ mil.): —

FARMERS COOPERATIVE SOCIETY

When farmers cooperate society benefits. Through its seven centers in northwest Iowa Farmers Cooperative Society offers its member/farmers a full range of agricultural growing and marketing products and services including crop-storage facilities and business consulting. Its feedlot with room for some 5500 head of cattle helps members buy and care for feeder cattle and provides discounts on grain for members. The co-op also operates a member-only How-To Building Store in Sioux Center Iowa that sells hardware lawn-care products lumber and paint as well as brand-name home appliances. Farmers Cooperative Society has roots dating back to 1907.

To provide the right product for its members the co-op's How-To Building store ,Âuses over 40 suppliers such as ,ÂAndersen ,ÂCertainTeed ,ÂToro and ,Â Weber-Stephen Products. ,Â The co-op ,Â also sells pork producers with products through suppliers like ,ÂAP Valco and Chore-time. The co-op also supplies pork producers through suppliers ,Âsuch as ,ÂAP Valco and Chore-time.

EXECUTIVES

Vice President, Mary Haynes
Secretary, Ann Venean

LOCATIONS

HQ: FARMERS COOPERATIVE SOCIETY
317 3RD ST NW, SIOUX CENTER, IA 512501897
Phone: 7127222671
Web: WWW.FARMERSCOOPSOCIETY.COM

COMPETITORS

AGRI Industries
Five Star Co-op
Gold-Eagle Cooperative
Heartland Co-op
Home Depot
Lowe' s
Miles Enterprises
Premier AG Co-Op Inc.
Sears
True Value
Wal-Mart
West Central Co-op

HISTORICAL FINANCIALS

Company Type: Private

Income Statement FYE: July 31

	REVENUE ($ mil.)	NET INCOME ($ mil.)	NET PROFIT MARGIN	EMPLOYEES
07/14	418	3	0.9%	160
07/13	496	4	1.0%	—
07/12*	434	8	1.9%	—
12/11	0	0	—	—
Annual Growth	—	—	—	—

*Fiscal year change

2014 Year-End Financials

Debt ratio: —
Return on equity: 0.90%
Cash ($ mil.): 2
Current ratio: —
Long-term debt ($ mil.): —
Dividends
Yield: —
Payout: —
Market value ($ mil.): —

FARMERS TELEPHONE COOPERATIVE INC.

EXECUTIVES

Customer Operations Manager FTC DSI, Lisa H. Ney

LOCATIONS

HQ: FARMERS TELEPHONE COOPERATIVE INC.
1101 E MAIN ST, KINGSTREE, SC 295564105
Phone: 8433822333
Web: WWW.FTC-I.NET

COMPETITORS

AT&T
AT&T Mobility
EarthLink
Sprint Communications
Verizon
tw telecom

HISTORICAL FINANCIALS

Company Type: Private

Income Statement FYE: June 30

	REVENUE ($ mil.)	NET INCOME ($ mil.)	NET PROFIT MARGIN	EMPLOYEES
06/10	131	8	6.6%	418
06/08	83	2	2.7%	—
06/07	1,597	0	0.0%	—
Annual Growth	(56.5%)	2582.1%	—	—

2010 Year-End Financials

Debt ratio: —
Return on equity: 6.60%
Cash ($ mil.): 38
Current ratio: 1.30
Long-term debt ($ mil.): —
Dividends
Yield: —
Payout: —
Market value ($ mil.): —

FARSTAD OIL INC.

When you are freezing in Fargo fuel is more than a luxury it's a necessity. Farstad Oil makes sure that gas stations lube shops and propane dealers are well stocked for those living through the cold winters in the Upper Midwest and West. Farstad Oil is a regional wholesale petroleum products distributor serving customers in North Dakota Montana Minnesota and Wyoming. The company a subsidiary of holding company SPF Energy wholesales about 250 million gallons of gas and fuel 20 million gallons of propane and 2.5 million gallons of lubricants each year. Its Minot operation is the largest lubricant plant in the region.

Farstad Oil was founded in 1938 as a family operated bulk oil business. It subsequently expanded to become a wholesale petroleum products distributor. In 2009 Farstad Oil was serving its customers through a fleet of more than 50 tanker trucks. The company has access to fuel supply from various suppliers (Exxon Mobil ConocoPhillips Sinclair Oil and Tesoro) at more than 100 terminals.

EXECUTIVES

COO, Dennis Krueger
General Manager Superpumper, Kris Wolla
CFO, Bruce Hest
Director Information Technology, Dan Olson

LOCATIONS

HQ: FARSTAD OIL INC.
100 27TH ST NE, MINOT, ND 58703-5164
Phone: 701-852-1194
Web: WWW.FARSTADOIL.COM

COMPETITORS

BP
HollyFrontier
Valero Energy

HISTORICAL FINANCIALS

Company Type: Private

Income Statement FYE: December 31

	REVENUE ($ mil.)	NET INCOME ($ mil.)	NET PROFIT MARGIN	EMPLOYEES
12/12	1,010	4	0.4%	125
12/11	1,034	3	0.4%	—
12/10	686	2	0.3%	—
12/09	476	1	0.3%	—
Annual Growth	28.5%	47.8%	—	—

2012 Year-End Financials

Debt ratio: —
Return on equity: 0.40%
Cash ($ mil.): 6
Current ratio: 0.90
Long-term debt ($ mil.): —
Dividends
Yield: —
Payout: —
Market value ($ mil.): —

FAYETTE COMMUNITY HOSPITAL INC.

If you do too much boogying at the Fayetteville Bluegrass Blast or slip in the sleet at the Christmas in Fayetteville festival Piedmont Fayette Hospital (PFH) is there to help. The acute care hospital is home to centers in cardiovascular medicine diabetes treatment sleep disorder therapy women's health fitness and rehabilitative care. With more than 500 physicians on staff the former Fayette Community Hospital has the ability to treat just about whatever comes through its doors –from ear nose throat problems to pediatric dentistry. The about 155-bed hospital opened in 1997 and is part of the not-for-profit Piedmont Healthcare network.

EXECUTIVES

CFO and Compliance Officer, John Miles

LOCATIONS

HQ: FAYETTE COMMUNITY HOSPITAL INC.
1255 HIGHWAY 54 W, FAYETTEVILLE, GA 30214-4526
Phone: 770-719-7000
Web: WWW.PIEDMONTNEWNAN.ORG

PRODUCTS/OPERATIONS

Selected Specialties

Anesthesiology
Cardiopulmonary services
Colon and rectal surgery
Dermatology
Emergency medicine
ENT (ear nose and throat)
Family practice
Gastroenterology
General surgery
Hematology
Internal medicine
Nephrology
Neurology
OB/GYN
Oncology
Ophthalmology
Orthopedic surgery
Pathology
Pediatric anesthesiology
Pediatric dentistry
Pediatric neurosurgery
Pediatrics
Plastic surgery
Pulmonology
Radiation oncology
Radiology
Urology
Vascular surgery

Selected Facilities

24-hour Emergency Department
Minor Emergency Care
Outpatient Diagnostic Center
Rehabilitation and Fitness Center
Sleep Order Laboratory
Women's Imaging Center

COMPETITORS

Adventist Health System Sunbelt Healthcare
DeKalb Medical
Emory Healthcare
Grady Health System
Gwinnett Health System
Northside Hospital
Saint Joseph' s Health System
Southern Regional Medical Center
Upson Regional Medical Center
WellStar Kennestone Hospital
West Georgia Health System

HISTORICAL FINANCIALS

Company Type: Private

Income Statement FYE: June 30

	REVENUE ($ mil.)	NET INCOME ($ mil.)	NET PROFIT MARGIN	EMPLOYEES
06/09	165	18	11.0%	1,045
06/08	163	12	7.7%	—
06/05	1,449	0	—	—
Annual Growth	—	2219.3%	—	—

2009 Year-End Financials

Debt ratio: —
Return on equity: 11.00%
Cash ($ mil.): 0
Current ratio: 0.80
Long-term debt ($ mil.): —
Dividends
Yield: —
Payout: —
Market value ($ mil.): —

FCI CONSTRUCTORS INC.

FCI Constructors focuses on commercial building and renovation projects in the Rocky Mountain and southwestern US. Its projects range from hospitals assisted living facilities municipal projects and recreation centers to office buildings banks churches and educational manufacturing warehouse correctional and postal facilities.The company has offices in Arizona Colorado and Wyoming. Projects include the Mesa County Justice Center in Phoenix Crossroads Urgent Psychiatric Care Hospital in Durango Colorado and the Denver Public Schools Bus Terminal. The company which was founded in 1978 by M. L. Francis is owned by CEO Ed Forsman EVP Ron Choate and its employees.

EXECUTIVES

President and CEO, Ed Forsman
Secretary and Treasurer, Terry Piland
EVP, Ron Choate
VP Western Slope Operations, Shane Haas
VP Arizona Operations, Joe Kelleher
VP Durango Operations, Mike Foutz
VP Wyoming Operations, Becket Hinson
Vice President of Front Range Operations, Jeff Erker

LOCATIONS

HQ: FCI CONSTRUCTORS INC.
3070 I-70 BUSINESS LOOP, GRAND JUNCTION, CO 81504-4468
Phone: 970-434-9093
Web: WWW.FCIOL.COM

PRODUCTS/OPERATIONS

Selected Services

Competitive bid
Construction management at risk (CM/GC)
Design
Project feasibility analysis
Site evaluation and planning
Value engineering

COMPETITORS

CORE Construction
Hensel Phelps Construction
Hunt Construction
Kitchell
McCarthy Building
PCL Construction Enterprises
PWI Construction
Sundt

HISTORICAL FINANCIALS

Company Type: Private

Income Statement FYE: March 31

	REVENUE ($ mil.)	NET INCOME ($ mil.)	NET PROFIT MARGIN	EMPLOYEES
03/12	248	1	0.5%	275
03/10	315	1	0.5%	—
03/09	379	3	0.9%	—
Annual Growth	(13.1%)	(30.1%)	—	—

2012 Year-End Financials

Debt ratio: —
Return on equity: 0.50%
Cash ($ mil.): 14
Current ratio: 1.20
Long-term debt ($ mil.): —
Dividends
Yield: —
Payout: —
Market value ($ mil.): —

FEED THE CHILDREN INC.

Tuppence a bag might feed some birds but it takes more to feed growing children. Feed The Children (FTC) is a not-for-profit Christian charity that distributes food medicine and other items. In the US FTC accepts bulk contributions of surplus food from businesses packages it in various ways at six main facilities nationwide and distributes it to food banks homeless shelters churches and other organizations that help feed the hungry. Overseas FTC works with organizations such as schools orphanages and churches to provide food medical supplies clothing and educational support to the needy. Larry and Frances Jones founded FTC in 1979.

While FTC has focused its efforts on feeding children the organization also concentrates on supplying them with support through outreach programs. FTC launched an educational initiative named H.E.L.P. (or Homeless Education and Literacy Program) which works with homeless outreach coordinators in elementary and middle schools to provide students with school supplies books and personal-care items in addition to food.

EXECUTIVES

Founder President and CEO, Larry Jones, age 70, $125,721 total compensation
CFO, Christy Tharp, $77,423 total compensation
VP and General Counsel, Larri Sue Jones, $109,022 total compensation
EVP, Frances Jones, $100,577 total compensation
Chairman, Dwight Powers
VP Management Information Systems, Larry Correa, $107,840 total compensation
VP International Public Relations, Steven Whetstone
VP Human Relations, Richard Gray
VP Operations, Travis Arnold
Director, Leo B. Fundaro Jr.
Founder President and CEO, Larry Jones, age 70
Director, George Q. Stevens
Director, Dan Mugg
Director, Linda Schluchter
Director, C. Earnest Wyat
Director, Rick England
Director, Leo B. Fundaro Jr.
Auditors: CapinCrouseLLP

LOCATIONS

HQ: FEED THE CHILDREN INC.
333 N MERIDIAN AVE, OKLAHOMA CITY, OK 73107-6507
Phone: 405-942-0228
Web: WWW.FEEDTHECHILDREN.ORG

PRODUCTS/OPERATIONS

2006 Support and Revenue

% of total	
Gifts-in-kind	78
Contributions	18
Gain on disposition of	1
Transportation	1
Investment	1
Other	100
Total	

2006 Distribution Expenditures

Program services	86	
Fundraising	11	
Management & support services	3	
Total	**0**	**100**

HISTORICAL FINANCIALS

Company Type: Private

Income Statement FYE: June 30

	REVENUE ($ mil.)	NET INCOME ($ mil.)	NET PROFIT MARGIN	EMPLOYEES
06/11	436	10	2.4%	160
06/10	520	(367)	—	—
06/09	1,189	0	—	—
06/08	1,183	34	2.9%	—
Annual Growth	(28.3%)	(32.6%)	—	—

2011 Year-End Financials

Debt ratio: —
Return on equity: 2.40%
Cash ($ mil.): 0
Current ratio: 0.10
Long-term debt ($ mil.): —

Dividends
Yield: —
Payout: —
Market value ($ mil.): —

FERRIS STATE UNIVERSITY

Going to college is no carnival but Ferris State University still hopes the experience is enjoyable. The career-oriented public university offers more than 180 degree programs including associate's bachelor's master's and doctoral degrees through the colleges of Allied Health Sciences Arts and Sciences Business Education and Human Services Optometry Pharmacy Technology and Kendall College of Art and Design. The school has some 14500 students on 21 campuses located across Michigan. Ferris State was founded in 1884 by Michigan educator and statesman Woodbridge N. Ferris.

EXECUTIVES

President, David L. Eisler
Manager Student and Administration Technology Services, Jeff Spedowski
Manager Business Operations, Paul M. Quick
Associate VP Human Resources, Warren Hills
Director Alumni Relations Annual Giving and Advancement Services; Executive Director FSU Alumni Association, Jeremy Mishler
Vice President for Extended and International Operations | Ferris State University, Don Green
Auditors: Plante&MoranPLLC

LOCATIONS

HQ: FERRIS STATE UNIVERSITY
1201 S STATE ST, BIG RAPIDS, MI 49307-2714
Phone: 231-591-2000
Web: WWW.OSPREY.FERRIS.EDU

HISTORICAL FINANCIALS

Company Type: Private

Income Statement FYE: June 30

	REVENUE ($ mil.)	NET INCOME ($ mil.)	NET PROFIT MARGIN	EMPLOYEES
06/13	164	15	9.3%	1,200
06/12	158	10	6.5%	—
06/10	153	44	29.3%	—
06/10	147	13	9.1%	—
Annual Growth	3.6%	4.3%	—	—

2013 Year-End Financials

Debt ratio: —
Return on equity: 9.30%
Cash ($ mil.): 56
Current ratio: 2.40
Long-term debt ($ mil.): —

Dividends
Yield: —
Payout: —
Market value ($ mil.): —

FERROUS PROCESSING AND TRADING COMPANY

LOCATIONS

HQ: FERROUS PROCESSING AND TRADING COMPANY
3400 E LAFAYETTE ST, DETROIT, MI 482074962
Phone: 3135822910
Web: WWW.FPT1.COM

HISTORICAL FINANCIALS

Company Type: Private

Income Statement FYE: May 31

	REVENUE ($ mil.)	NET INCOME ($ mil.)	NET PROFIT MARGIN	EMPLOYEES
05/14	1,154	14	1.2%	425
05/11	1,272	41	3.3%	—
05/10	915	23	2.6%	—
Annual Growth	6.0%	(11.9%)	—	—

2014 Year-End Financials

Debt ratio: —
Return on equity: 1.20%
Cash ($ mil.): 6
Current ratio: 2.00
Long-term debt ($ mil.): —

Dividends
Yield: —
Payout: —
Market value ($ mil.): —

FIESTA MART INC.

Fiesta Mart celebrates food every day of the year. The company runs some 60 stores in Texas that sell ethnic and conventional groceries including items popular with its target customers: Mexican- and Asian-Americans. Its stores are located mainly in the Houston area but Fiesta also has been adding stores in the Dallas/Fort Worth area and in Austin. Fiesta purchased three supermarkets from Winn-Dixie Stores when the grocer left Texas. At its supermarkets Fiesta leases kiosks to vendors who offer such items as jewelry and cell phones. The company also runs some 15 Beverage Mart liquor stores. Fiesta Mart founded in 1972 by Donald Bonham and O. C. Mendenhall is owned by grocery wholesaler Grocers Supply Co.

Geographic Reach

To capture market share in the crowded and competitive Texas grocery market Fiesta Mart is looking beyond its core Hispanic and Asia-American customers to serve other groups as well including shoppers the hail from India Southeast Asia and the Middle East.

Strategy

In addition to food geared towards Mexican and Asian-Americans Fiesta stores offer kosher and halal foods and some have dedicated aisles stocked only with international items. Indeed Fiesta's new 57000-square-foot store in Houston which opened in June 2012 stocks items from more than 60 countries and is one of the chain's most intensely international locations. The sheer size of the Hispanic market in Texas has prompted other local grocery chains to develop dedicated formats to serve Latino shoppers encroaching on Fiesta's niche. Examples include H-E-B's Mi Tienda ("my store" en Espa?ol) and Brookshire Grocery Co's. Ole Foods to name a few. Wal-Mart's supercenters and SAM'S CLUB also seek to cater to Hispanic shoppers.

Auditors: PricewaterhouseCoopers

LOCATIONS

HQ: FIESTA MART INC.
5235 KATY FWY, HOUSTON, TX 77007-2210
Phone: 713-869-5060
Web: WWW.FIESTAMART.COM

PRODUCTS/OPERATIONS

Selected Products and Services

Bakery (in selected locations)
Beer and wine
Check cashing
Clothing (in selected locations)
Delicatessens
Grocery products
International specialty foods and products
License tag purchases
Lottery tickets
Meat
Money orders
Natural foods (in selected locations)
Produce
Seafood
Soft goods (in selected locations)
Ticket purchases for concerts and sporting events
Utility bill payments

COMPETITORS

Brookshire Grocery
Costco Wholesale
Gerland' s Food Fair
H-E-B
Kroger
Randall' s
Wal-Mart
Whole Foods

HISTORICAL FINANCIALS

Company Type: Private

Income Statement FYE: January 3

	REVENUE ($ mil.)	NET INCOME ($ mil.)	NET PROFIT MARGIN	EMPLOYEES
01/10*	1,483	30	2.0%	8,200
12/06	1,137	21	1.9%	—
Annual Growth	9.3%	12.6%	—	—

*Fiscal year change

2010 Year-End Financials

Debt ratio: —
Return on equity: 2.00%
Cash ($ mil.): 25
Current ratio: 0.30
Long-term debt ($ mil.): —

Dividends
Yield: —
Payout: —
Market value ($ mil.): —

FINANCIAL INDUSTRY REGULATORY AUTHORITY INC.

FINRA is one of the long arms of the law for the securities industry. A non-governmental regulatory authority FINRA regulates all securities firms (roughly 4250) that conduct business in the US. Its activities include writing and enforcing rules; enforcing federal securities laws; licensing and registering brokerages and private equity firms; and providing educational information and arbitration services to investors. The regulator works with the SEC and the Fed and possesses the authority to issue fines and bar violators among other punitive actions. FINRA was formed in 2007 from the consolidation of the National Association of Securities Dealers and certain regulatory and enforcement elements of the NYSE.

Geographic Reach

FINRA operates from Washington DC and New York with 20 regional offices around the US. It also has more than 160000 branch offices and some 635000 registered securities representatives.

Operations

Under the oversight of the SEC FINRA brought 1541 disciplinary actions against registered people and firms in 2012 (an increase of 53 from 2011) levied fines totally more than $69 million and ordered payback in the amount of $34 million to investors (a record amount) that were harmed throughout the year.

Financial Performance

FINRA obviously benefits when lawmakers and regulators crack down on fraud and the breaking of securities laws that led up to the Great Recession. As such the bulk of its revenues (about 80%) come from the collection of regulatory user and contract service fees.

FINRA suffered a net loss of $84 million for 2011 mostly as a result of non-recurring costs related to the development of new data center facilities in New York and Maryland. The net loss was also due to increased integration expenses used to extend FINRA's cross market surveillance capabilities.

EXECUTIVES

President FINRA Dispute Resolution and Chief Hearing Officer, Linda D. Fienberg
Vice Chairman, Stephen I. Luparello
EVP and Chief Technology Officer, Martin P. Colburn
Executive Vice President and Chief Information Officer, Steven J. (Steve) Randich, age 52
EVP and General Counsel, T. Grant Callery
EVP Corporate Communications and Government Relations, Howard M. Schloss
EVP and General Counsel for Regulation, Marc Menchel
EVP Business Services and CIO, Samuel H. Gaer, age 47
EVP Member Regulation, Grace B. Vogel
Chairman and CEO, Richard G. Ketchum
EVP and CFO, Todd Diganci
EVP Member Regulation Sales Practice, Susan F. Axelrod
President FINRA Investor Education Foundation; SVP FINRA Investor Education, Gerri Walsh
Executive Vice President for Corporate Communications and Government Relations, F. Gregory Ahern
Auditors: Ernst&YoungLLP

LOCATIONS

HQ: FINANCIAL INDUSTRY REGULATORY AUTHORITY INC.
1735 K ST NW, WASHINGTON, DC 20006-1506
Phone: 202-728-8000
Web: WWW.FINRA.ORG

PRODUCTS/OPERATIONS

2012 Sales

	% of total
Regulatory	46
User	19
Contract services	15
Transparency services	6
Dispute resolution	5
Other	1
Total	**100**

HISTORICAL FINANCIALS

Company Type: Private

Income Statement FYE: December 31

	REVENUE ($ mil.)	NET INCOME ($ mil.)	NET PROFIT MARGIN	EMPLOYEES
12/12	878	10	1.2%	3,400
12/11	880	(84)	—	—
12/09	849	54	6.4%	—
12/09	1,097	48	4.4%	—
Annual Growth	(7.1%)	(40.0%)	—	—

2012 Year-End Financials

Debt ratio: —
Return on equity: 1.20%
Cash ($ mil.): 356
Current ratio: 0.60
Long-term debt ($ mil.): —
Dividends
Yield: —
Payout: —
Market value ($ mil.): —

FIRELANDS REGIONAL HEALTH SYSTEM

Firelands Regional Health System primarily operates through its Firelands Regional Medical Center (FRMC). The center serves eight counties in northern Ohio. It operates two hospital campuses with a total of 400 beds a medical office building and outpatient clinics throughout the region. FRMC's medical staff of 225 represents more than 35 specialties. The center's broad range of services include cardiovascular care home health care mental health services palliative care dialysis oncology care and chemical dependency programs. It also has hospital network and teaching affiliations with several area hospitals medical schools and community colleges. The medical center is supported by a non-profit foundation.

FRMC is the only breast imaging Center of Excellence in its service region. It is also an accredited chest pain center and a certified primary stroke center.

In 2012 Firelands Regional Health System expanded through the acquisition of the imaging center women's imaging center urgent care and occupational health center service lines that Northern Ohio Medical Specialists had previously operated. Firelands Physician Group now operates the urgent care service line with FRMC managing the other lines.

FRMC was ranked #1 in Ohio in 2011 and in the top 5% nationally for vascular surgery and overall orthopedic surgery. It also received other distinctions for patient safety (in the top 5% in the US) acute inpatient rehabilitation (in the top 10% in the country) and cardiovascular services (a Thomson Top 100 Hospital) that year.

The center achieved operating revenues of $3 million in 2010. FRMC's uncompensated care or charity care totaled more than $26 million most of which related to costs of services not covered by Medicare or Medicaid.

Improving the quality and breadth of its services as well as expanding accessibility to its services are cornerstones of Firelands Regional Medical Center's strategy for growth. Its commitment to these goals is evidenced by its standing among its peers in the region.

EXECUTIVES

VP Legal and General Counsel, Robert M. Moore
Executive Vice President Chief Financial Officer, Daniel J. Moncher
VP Information Systems and Telecommunications, Mike Canfield
SVP Operations and Chief Nursing Officer, Tamara L. Jackson
VP Human Resources, James A. Sennish
VP Marketing and Public Relations, Connie R. Lamb
President and CEO, Martin Tursky
VP Operations, Beverly J. Schrickel
Assistant VP Operations, Dru Meredith
VP Quality and Patient Satisfaction, Patricia S. Martin
VP Firelands Counseling & Recovery Services, Marsha Mruk

LOCATIONS

HQ: FIRELANDS REGIONAL HEALTH SYSTEM
1111 HAYES AVE, SANDUSKY, OH 44870-3323
Phone: 419-557-7400
Web: WWW.FIRELANDS.COM

Selected Counties Served

Firelands Counseling and Recovery Services
- Erie
- Huron
- Lorain
- Ottawa
- Sandusky
- Seneca
- Wyandot

Firelands Home Health Services
- Erie
- Huron
- Lorain
- Ottawa
- Richland
- Sandusky
- Seneca
- Wood

Firelands Regional Medical Center
- Erie
- Huron
- Ottawa
- Sandusky

PRODUCTS/OPERATIONS

Selected Services and Facilities

Behavioral health
Cancer Center
Clinics
Corporate health
Endocrine and diabetes
Dialysis Center
Digestive Health Center
Emergency room
Firelands 55+ Club
Healthy Lifestyles
Heart and Vascular Institute
Home health services
Imaging services
Infusion Center
Laboratory services
Maternity/Pediatrics
Pain relief
Pharmacy services
Rehabilitation
Respiratory services
Sleep disorders
Spine Center & Neurosciences
Surgical services
Women's health
Wound care programs

Selected Affiliations

Hospital Networks
- Community Care Five (five local independent hospitals collaborating within the region)
- University Hospitals Rainbow Babies & Children's Hospital (collaboration and pediatric hospitalist physician staffing agreement)
- University Hospitals Seidman Cancer Center (collaboration and physician staffing agreement

Teaching and Clinical
- BGSU Firelands
- Bowling Green State University
- Erie Huron Ottawa Vocational Education
- Lorain County Community College

Lourdes College (Sylvania Ohio)
Medical University of Ohio - Toledo
Midwestern University College of Osteopathic Medicine (Glendale Arizona)
Ohio University Heritage College of Osteopathic Medicine (Athens Ohio)
University of Health Sciences College of Osteopathic Medicine (Kansas City Missouri)
University of Osteopathic Medicine Health Sciences (Des Moines Iowa)
Sandusky Career Center
Terra Community College

COMPETITORS

Fairfield Medical Center
Kindred Healthcare
Lake Health
Mercy Health Partners Toledo
Mount Carmel Health
Nationwide Children' s Hospital
Oakwood Healthcare
OhioHealth
ProMedica
Robinson Memorial Hospital
Samaritan Regional Health System
The Cleveland Clinic
Toledo Hospital
University Hospitals Health System
University of Toledo Medical Center

HISTORICAL FINANCIALS

Company Type: Private

Income Statement FYE: December 31

	REVENUE ($ mil.)	NET INCOME ($ mil.)	NET PROFIT MARGIN	EMPLOYEES
12/11	230	11	5.0%	1,600
12/10	0	(0)	—	—
12/09*	0	0	—	—
06/09	0	(0)	—	—
Annual Growth	1723.7%	—	—	—

*Fiscal year change

2011 Year-End Financials

Debt ratio: —
Return on equity: 5.00%
Cash ($ mil.): 3
Current ratio: —
Long-term debt ($ mil.): —
Dividends
Yield: —
Payout: —
Market value ($ mil.): —

FIRST COOPERATIVE ASSOCIATION

LOCATIONS

HQ: FIRST COOPERATIVE ASSOCIATION
960 RIVERVIEW DR, CHEROKEE, IA 510121492
Phone: 7122255400
Web: WWW.FIRSTCOOP.COM

HISTORICAL FINANCIALS

Company Type: Private

Income Statement FYE: August 31

	REVENUE ($ mil.)	NET INCOME ($ mil.)	NET PROFIT MARGIN	EMPLOYEES
08/14	390	9	2.5%	130
08/03	121	(2)	—	—
08/02	111	1	1.0%	—
08/00	0	0	—	—
Annual Growth	—	—	—	—

2014 Year-End Financials

Debt ratio: —
Return on equity: 2.50%
Cash ($ mil.): 0
Current ratio: 0.20
Long-term debt ($ mil.): —
Dividends
Yield: —
Payout: —
Market value ($ mil.): —

FIRSTFLEET INC.

FirstFleet helps its customers move their freight –not just by the truckload but by providing fleets of trucks. The company offers dedicated contract carriage in which it supplies its customers with tractors and trailers and the drivers to operate them. In addition FirstFleet provides related fleet management logistics and maintenance services. The company operates a fleet of about 1450 trucks and tractors from facilities in some 30 states in the US and it provides transportation services throughout the 48 contiguous states and in Canada and Mexico. FirstFleet began operations in 1986.

EXECUTIVES

President, Gary Wilson
VP and CFO, David Beeny
VP Operations, Daniel Piper

LOCATIONS

HQ: FIRSTFLEET INC.
202 HERITAGE PARK DR, MURFREESBORO, TN 37129-1556
Phone: 615-890-9229
Web: WWW.FIRSTFLEETINC.COM

COMPETITORS

AAA Cooper Transportation
CRST International
Cardinal Logistics Management
Covenant Transportation
J.B. Hunt
Penske Truck Leasing
Ruan Transportation Management Systems
Ryder System
Schneider National
U.S. Xpress
Werner Enterprises

HISTORICAL FINANCIALS

Company Type: Private

Income Statement FYE: March 31

	REVENUE ($ mil.)	NET INCOME ($ mil.)	NET PROFIT MARGIN	EMPLOYEES
03/12	288	2	1.0%	2,000
03/10	259	0	0.2%	—
03/09	274	0	0.1%	—
03/08	288	1	0.5%	—
Annual Growth	0.1%	20.3%	—	—

2012 Year-End Financials

Debt ratio: —
Return on equity: 1.00%
Cash ($ mil.): 0
Current ratio: 1.10
Long-term debt ($ mil.): —
Dividends
Yield: —
Payout: —
Market value ($ mil.): —

FIRSTHEALTH OF THE CAROLINAS INC.

FirstHealth of the Carolinas maintains a health care network that extends to 15 counties across the mid-Carolinas. The health network includes three hospitals –Moore Regional Richmond Memorial and Montgomery Memorial –that provide emergency surgical acute care and diagnostic services and have a combined capacity of about 580 beds. Moore Regional its largest hospital includes an inpatient rehabilitation center and a heart hospital. FirstHealth of the Carolinas also operates satellite facilities including family practice clinics fitness centers and dental practices. The system's FirstCarolinaCare provides home health and hospice services emergency care medical transportation and health insurance.

Geographic Reach

FirstHealth serves those who reside in a 15-county region of the mid-Carolinas. Altogether it operates nearly 50 locations across North Carolina.

Operations

The health care network offers major medical and surgical specialties and subspecialties such as open-heart surgery bariatric weight-loss surgery neurosurgery and neonatology. To provide these specialties FirstHealth maintains an active medical staff of 290 of which 94% are board certified.

Strategy

Despite the downturn in the economy in recent years the health system worked to maintain its expansion efforts to meet the demand of area residents. On the Moore Regional campus it opened the 60-bed Reid Heart Hospital a cardiology and neurology facility in 2011. In Hoke County FirstHealth built a medical campus consisting of an urgent care center diagnostic facilities and physician offices. It is also constructing a new 65-bed acute care hospital in the area.

EXECUTIVES

CEO, David J. Kilarski
COO Moore Regional Hospital, Brian T. Canfield
Secretary, Victoria P. Brenner
Assistant Secretary, JoAn Moses
Treasurer, Jim Bulthuis

LOCATIONS

HQ: FIRSTHEALTH OF THE CAROLINAS INC.
155 MEMORIAL DR, PINEHURST, NC 28374-8710
Phone: 910-715-1000
Web: WWW.NCCANCERCARE.ORG

PRODUCTS/OPERATIONS

Selected Facilities

Montgomery Memorial Hospital (Troy North Carolina)
Moore Regional Hospital (Pinehurst North Carolina)
Richmond Memorial Hospital (Rockingham North Carolina)

COMPETITORS

Alamance Regional Medical Center
Carolinas HealthCare System
Cone Health
Cumberland County Hospital System
Duke University Health System
Health Management Associates
Morehead Memorial Hospital
Novant Health
Rex Healthcare
Stanly Medical Center
UNC Hospitals
Vidant Health
Wake Forest University Baptist Medical Center
WakeMed

HISTORICAL FINANCIALS

Company Type: Private

Income Statement FYE: September 30

	REVENUE ($ mil.)	NET INCOME ($ mil.)	NET PROFIT MARGIN	EMPLOYEES
09/13	569	51	9.0%	3,897
09/12	565	69	12.3%	—
09/11	507	12	2.4%	—
09/09	462	(9)	—	—
Annual Growth	5.4%	—	—	—

2013 Year-End Financials

Debt ratio: —
Return on equity: 9.00%
Cash ($ mil.): 21
Current ratio: 1.00
Long-term debt ($ mil.): —
Dividends
Yield: —
Payout: —
Market value ($ mil.): —

FIVE STAR COOPERATIVE

EXECUTIVES

General Manager, Ron Pumphrey, age 65
Location Manager and Agronomist Mason City, Tony Cockrell
Location Manager Dougherty, Rick Demaray
Region Grain Manager New Hampton, Judy Biwer
Chairman, Steve Laures
Vice-Chairman, Leon Zeien
Board Secretary, Terry Thomas
Project Manager and IT, Laura Schwickerath
Manager Agronomy, Olin Amundson
Manager Feed Department, John Winter
Location Manager Lawler, Dennis Lau
Location Manager Nashua, Mike Wedemeier
Location Manager North Washington, Bill Goss
Manager Petroleum, Bruce Halvorson
Manager Operations/Safety, Wayne Steven
Feed Mill Manager Klemme, Paul Larson
Agronomy Contact, Carmen Milliren
Location Manager Ventura, Dar Avery
Vice-Chairman, Leon Zeien
Director, Dave Newman
Director, John Eichenberger
Board Secretary, Terry Thomas
Director, Larry Eden
Director, Randy Greiman
Director, Don Chambers

LOCATIONS

HQ: FIVE STAR COOPERATIVE
1949 N LINN AVE, NEW HAMPTON, IA 506599406
Phone: 6413943052
Web: WWW.FIVESTAR.COOP

PRODUCTS/OPERATIONS

Selected Office Locations

Burchinal
Dougherty
Hanlontown
Ionia
Joice
Klemme
Lake Mills
Lawler
Mason City
Nashua
New Hampton
North Washington
Rockwell
Ventura

COMPETITORS

ADM Alliance Nutrition
DeBruce Grain
Farmers Cooperative Society
GROWMARK
Heartland Co-op
Orscheln Farm and Home
Rabo AgriFinance
West Central Co-op

HISTORICAL FINANCIALS

Company Type: Private

Income Statement FYE: June 30

	REVENUE ($ mil.)	NET INCOME ($ mil.)	NET PROFIT MARGIN	EMPLOYEES
06/14	364	7	2.0%	140
06/13	427	8	1.9%	—
06/12	479	9	2.0%	—
06/11	376	0	—	—
Annual Growth	(1.1%)	—	—	—

2014 Year-End Financials

Debt ratio: —
Return on equity: 2.00%
Cash ($ mil.): 0
Current ratio: 0.30
Long-term debt ($ mil.): —
Dividends
Yield: —
Payout: —
Market value ($ mil.): —

FLEMING GANNETT INC

Engineering firm Gannett Fleming has waded through water waste and sludge for nearly a century. Founded in 1915 the company focuses on serving the transportation water and wastewater facilities energy and environmental industries. Gannett Fleming operates through about a dozen subsidiaries that offer a variety of services that range from design/build construction management ground testing and soil strengthening site remediation structural rehabilitation electrical and mechanical installation geophysical mapping and surveying and 3D visualization. The company works on projects around the world and has more than 60 offices throughout North America and Middle East.

Operations

While the firm is heavily involved in traffic and transportation projects its water and wastewater infrastructure work is perhaps its hallmark. Gannett Fleming has worked on hundreds of treatment plants and pumping stations in addition to thousands of miles of water and sewer systems. It serves both the private and public sectors on such projects throughout the US and abroad. Clients have included JEA Washington Suburban Sanitary Commission and Chevron.

The company's long list of services has helped it endure dips in the economy. Its 25 lines of business include information technology transportation environmental resources facilities dams and hydraulics site development and construction management services.

Gannett Flemming's design practice GeoDecisions develops master plans for highways railroads bridges and airports. It also designs new dams and modifications on those needing repair.

Geographic Reach

Gannett Fleming has offices in the US Canada Mexico Qatar and the United Arab Emirates.

Mergers and Acquisitions

In early 2013 Gannett Fleming acquired Griffin Engineering and Technical Services which was added to its mechanical and electrical practices group. The purchase expands Gannett Fleming's presence in the Research Triangle region of North Carolina and its testing adjusting and balancing of HVAC systems which increases its reach into the biotech pharma and healthcare fields.

EXECUTIVES

VP and Senior Associate; National Practice Manager Marketing and Business Development Practice Leadership Team, Judy L. Hricak
Vice Chairman President and COO, Robert M. Scaer
SVP and Secretary, Chester L. Allen
SVP, Gene C. Koontz
Chairman and CEO, William M. Stout
SVP; Regional Office Manager South Plainfield NJ, Paul D. Nowicki
SVP, John R. Kenny
VP; Office Manager Tampa FL Kansas City KS and LaPlace LA, Jay H. L. Calhoun
VP; Regional Office Manager Austin TX and Office Manager Mexico City Mexico, Matthew J. Schiemer
SVP and National Director Transit and Rail, David B. Thomas
Manager, Paul Lewis
President Quantum Geophysics, Richard K. Lee
General Manager Abu Dhabi United Arab Emirates, Abdulilah Z. Zineddin

LOCATIONS

HQ: FLEMING GANNETT INC
207 SENATE AVE, CAMP HILL, PA 17011-2316
Phone: 717-763-7211
Web: WWW.GFNET.COM

PRODUCTS/OPERATIONS

Selected Services

Construction Management
- Bridges
- Commissioning Services
- Dams
- Facilities
- Roads and Highways
- Transit and Rail
- Water/Wastewater

Dams & Hydraulics
- Dam Investigations/Inspections
- Design
- Emergency Response Planning
- Hydrologic and Hydraulic Modeling
- Permitting

Environmental Resources
- Environmental Management
- Industrial Waste Management
- Oil and Gas Services
- Site Investigation and Remediation
- Solid Waste Management
- Water/Wastewater

Facilities
- Architectural
- Electrical
- Elevators and Escalators
- Facilities Management
- Healthcare Regulatory Compliance
- Industrial Process
- Information and Controls
- Mechanical
- Security Services
- Structural

GeoDecisions
- Application Design and Development
- Geographic Information Systems Mapping Analysis and Engineering Support
- Transportation Operations/ITS/Traffic
- Web Services

Geotechnical/Earth Sciences
- Earth Structures
- Foundations
- Geophysics
- Geotechnical Laboratory Services
- Ground Modification
- Groundwater and Hydrogeology
- Site Evaluation

Information Technology
- 3D Building Information Modeling (BIM)
- 3D Visualization and CADD
- Certified Training
- Digital Printing
- Graphics and Multimedia Design
- IT Services
- Reprographics

Planning
- Community
- Environmental
- Municipal Waste and Recycling
- Transportation

Site Development
- Bid/Construction Phase Services
- Drainage/Stormwater Management
- Environmental/Subsurface Investigations
- Green Design
- Land Development/Subdivision Plans
- Landscape Architecture
- Permitting/Agency Coordination
- Planning
- Traffic/Parking Studies
- Site/Roadway Designs
- Surveys
- Water and Sewer Systems

Sustainability
- Energy
- Facilities
- Industrial/Private
- Military
- Public/Government Agencies
- Technology
- Transportation
- Water Supply

Transportation
- Airports
- Bridges
- Highways
- Transit/Rail
- Transportation Operations/ITS/Traffic

Selected Subsidiaries & Affiliates

GANCOM (reprographics digital printing and graphic design)
Ganflec Architects & Engineers Inc. (general architectural and engineering design)
Gannett Fleming Pharmaceutical & Biotechnology Services (design and construction services on pharmaceutical and biotechnology facilities)
Gannett Fleming Project Development Corp. (design and construction management on commercial and industrial facilities)
Gannett Fleming Transit & Rail Systems (design and construction management on railway and rail transit systems)
Gannett Fleming Valuation and Rate Division (consulting to public utilities and railroads)
Gannett Fleming Williams Geotechnical Group (geotechnical engineering quality control testing construction inspection)
GeoDecisions (computerized mapping and database management services)
IT Services Division (computer consulting)
L.G. Hetager Drilling (exploratory drilling and testing services)
TerraSure (real estate remediation)
Vertical Transportation Excellence (consulting on elevator escalator moving walks material handling design and other specialty services)

COMPETITORS

AECOM
Bechtel
Black & Veatch Ltd.
CH2M HILL
Jacobs Engineering
K&M Engineering and Consulting
Louis Berger
MWH Global
Parsons Brinckerhoff
URS

HISTORICAL FINANCIALS

Company Type: Private

Income Statement FYE: December 31

	REVENUE ($ mil.)	NET INCOME ($ mil.)	NET PROFIT MARGIN	EMPLOYEES
12/11	286	4	1.6%	800
12/10	287	2	0.8%	—
12/09	283	13	4.8%	—
12/08	250	7	3.2%	—
Annual Growth	4.6%	(17.5%)	—	—

2011 Year-End Financials

Debt ratio: —
Return on equity: 1.60%
Cash ($ mil.): 6
Current ratio: 1.90
Long-term debt ($ mil.): —
Dividends
Yield: —
Payout: —
Market value ($ mil.): —

FLINT ELECTRIC MEMBERSHIP CORPORATION

The Native American inhabitants of Georgia may have used flint to spark the fires that brought light to their dwellings. Central Georgians today rely on the Flint Electric Membership Corporation which does business as Flint Energies to light their homes. Flint Energies serves 250000 residential commercial and industrial customers (through 82500 meters) in 17 counties Fort Benning and the city of Warner Robins. The customer-owned cooperative operates more than 6250 miles of distribution line and ,Âabout 50 ,Âsubstations. Flint Energies first flicked the switch in 1937.

As part of its commitment to green energy practices in 2009 Flint Energies teamed up with the ,ÂEPA's ENERGY STAR program to promote energy conserving appliances and strategies to its customers.

Georgia has 42 electric membership cooperatives; Flint Energies ranks as the seventh largest. It is also the 34th largest of the 990 electric cooperatives in the US.

EXECUTIVES

Svp Member And Community Services, Jimmy Autry
Auditors: McNairMcLemoreMiddlebrooks&Co.LLP

LOCATIONS

HQ: FLINT ELECTRIC MEMBERSHIP CORPORATION
3 S MACON ST, REYNOLDS, GA 310763104
Phone: 4788473415
Web: WWW.FLINTENERGIES.COM

COMPETITORS

Georgia Power
MEAG Power
Southeastern Power Administration

HISTORICAL FINANCIALS

Company Type: Private

Income Statement FYE: December 31

	REVENUE ($ mil.)	NET INCOME ($ mil.)	NET PROFIT MARGIN	EMPLOYEES
12/13	188	0	—	227
12/12	174	0	—	—
12/08	180	7	4.1%	—
12/07	148	0	—	—
Annual Growth	4.0%	—	—	—

2013 Year-End Financials

Debt ratio: —
Return on equity: —
Cash ($ mil.): 36
Current ratio: 0.30
Long-term debt ($ mil.): —
Dividends
Yield: —
Payout: —
Market value ($ mil.): —

FLORIDA HOSPITAL HEARTLAND MEDICAL CENTER

Florida Hospital Heartland Medical Center provides care to residents of central Florida. The not-for-profit 160-bed ,Âmedical center ,Âis the flagship facility of the Florida Hospital Heartland ,Âdivision of ,ÂAdventist Health System. ,Â Other ,Â facilities in the Heartland system ,Âinclude Florida Hospital Lake Placid (a 50-bed community hospital) Florida Hospital Wauchula (25 beds) various fitness centers medical clinics and counseling agencies. Together the facilities provide primary and acute care as well as specialty medical services including diagnostics obstetrics cardiac care and cancer treatment. The Florida Hospital Heartland Medical Center opened in 1997.

EXECUTIVES

Director Of Physical Therapy, Maggie Bobe
Managing Director, Roger L Wittum
Director Of Pharmacy, Felix Smith
Director Of Home Healthcare, Lucille Huber
Secretary, Tina Frost

LOCATIONS

HQ: FLORIDA HOSPITAL HEARTLAND MEDICAL CENTER
4200 SUN N LAKE BLVD, SEBRING, FL 338721986
Phone: 8633144466
Web: WWW.FHHEARTLAND.ORG

COMPETITORS

Baptist Health South Florida
Broward Health
DeSoto Memorial
HCA
Holy Cross Hospital Fort Lauderdale
Mount Sinai Medical Center of Florida
Munroe Regional Health System
South Broward Hospital District

HISTORICAL FINANCIALS

Company Type: Private

Income Statement FYE: December 31

	REVENUE ($ mil.)	NET INCOME ($ mil.)	NET PROFIT MARGIN	EMPLOYEES
12/08	126	0	0.0%	1,200
12/07	121	4	3.8%	—
12/06	124	3	3.2%	—
12/05	0	0	—	—
Annual Growth	—	—	—	—

2008 Year-End Financials

Debt ratio: —
Return on equity: —
Cash ($ mil.): 64
Current ratio: 2.30
Long-term debt ($ mil.): —
Dividends
Yield: —
Payout: —
Market value ($ mil.): —

FLORIDA HOSPITAL WATERMAN INC

Florida Hospital Waterman is a 270-bed community hospital serving the residents of Lake County Florida just north of Orlando. The hospital provides a full range of acute care services including cardiac and cancer care emergency services obstetrics pediatrics and rehabilitation. It also offers outpatient surgery diagnostic imaging laboratory and home health services. As part of its portfolio of services Florida Hospital Waterman operates a primary care clinic. Established in 1938 and named after the philanthropic leader of the Waterman Fountain Pen Company Florida Hospital Waterman has been part of the Adventist Health System since 1992.

Strategy

The Lake County area hospital has been focused on adding more beds to its facility after being at or above 80% occupancy for the past few years. In late 2012 it built out its sixth floor to expand its bed count by 60. The move was necessary to accommodate the growing influx of the area's winter residents. Florida Hospital Waterman is also expanding technologies and services to increase its offerings for area residents. In 2012 it improved orthopedic capabilities when it began using the newly developed MAKO Surgical RIO robotic surgery system and the Stryker Triathlon custom fit implant system.

As it works to continue to enhance quality safety and affordability for its patient community in 2012 Florida Hospital Waterman joined the Centers for Medicare & Medicaid Services Partnership for Patients program which is coordinated by group purchasing organization Premier. The alliance of medical companies is focused on health care performance improvements.

EXECUTIVES

President Chief Executive Officer, Kenneth R. (Ken) Mattison
Vice President Chief Financial Officer, Frances H. (Fran) Crunk
Chief of Staff, Rosemary Cirelli
Chairman, Michael H. Schultz
Senior Vice President Chief Operating Officer, Carrie L. Fish
Vice President Chief Nursing Officer, Patricia Dolan
Vice President Chief Medical Officer, Vinay Mehindru
President Chief Development Officer, Anita J. Young
President of the, Frank Waterman
President of the Florida Hospital Waterman Auxiliary, Marty Kotula

LOCATIONS

HQ: FLORIDA HOSPITAL WATERMAN INC
1000 WATERMAN WAY, TAVARES, FL 32778-5266
Phone: 352-253-3333
Web: WWW.FLORIDAHOSPITAL.COM

PRODUCTS/OPERATIONS

Selected Services

Cancer Institute
Child Care Center
Community Clinic
Diagnostic Imaging
Emergency Department
Foundation
Heart Center
Home Care
Laboratory
Joint Replacement Center
Nutrition
Partial knee resurfacing (MAKOplasty)
Pediatrics
Rehabilitation Institute
Respiratory Therapy
Stroke Center
Surgical Services
Support Groups
Vascular Center of Excellence
Women' s Health
Precious Beginnings

COMPETITORS

All Children' s Hospital
Baptist Health South Florida
Baptist Health System
Florida Hospital Heartland
Holmes Regional Medical Center
Mount Sinai Medical Center of Florida
Munroe Regional Health System
Nemours Foundation
Ocala Regional Medical Center
Orlando Health
UF&Shands

HISTORICAL FINANCIALS

Company Type: Private

Income Statement FYE: December 31

	REVENUE ($ mil.)	NET INCOME ($ mil.)	NET PROFIT MARGIN	EMPLOYEES
12/12	217	19	8.7%	1,200
12/09	211	18	8.9%	—
12/05	174	12	7.3%	—
12/05	1	0	—	—
Annual Growth	102.0%	—	—	—

2012 Year-End Financials

Debt ratio: —
Return on equity: 8.70%
Cash ($ mil.): 168
Current ratio: 6.80
Long-term debt ($ mil.): —
Dividends
Yield: —
Payout: —
Market value ($ mil.): —

FLOYD HEALTHCARE MANAGEMENT INC.

If you need heart help in the Heart of Dixie Floyd Healthcare Management is there for you. Its main hospital Floyd Medical Center has more than 300 beds and serves northwestern Georgia and northeastern Alabama. In addition to medical surgical and emergency care (including a Level II trauma center and level III neonatal intensive care unit) the hospital offers rehabilitation programs hospice and home health care. It also operates a 25-bed community hospital (Polk Medical Center) and the 50-bed Floyd Behavioral Health Center. Floyd Healthcare Management also operates outpatient centers including primary care surgery and urgent care locations. The organization was founded in 1942.

Geographic Reach

Floyd Healthcare Management serves Rome Rockmart and other communities in Polk and Floyd counties.

Operations

Floyd Healthcare Management's main hospital facility Floyd Medical Center employs 220 physicians and handles 76000 emergency visits each year. It also manages some 250000 outpatient visits and 2000 births and it specialized in fields including orthopedic surgery stroke care bariatric surgery and breast care. The system also operates about 30 primary care practices (housing 50 physician offices) and urgent care facilities in surrounding areas.

In partnership with the Floyd County Commission Floyd County Department of Family and Children Services (DFCS) and physicians in the community Floyd sponsors the Floyd County Clinic where low-income uninsured residents of Floyd County can receive free primary medical care services through the faculty and resident medical students enrolled in the Floyd Family Medicine Residency program.

Floyd Medical Center also provides community outreach programs through its mobile mammography vans and a range of other services aimed at improving access to health care throughout the service area.

Financial Performance

Sales increased 3% to $318 million in 2012 for Floyd Healthcare Management due to higher patient service revenue partly offset by a decline in other operating revenue. A majority of the company's sales come from patient revenue with about 30% of that sourced to Medicare reimbursements. Net income fell 18% to $9.8 million that year however due to lower investment income.

Strategy

The organization invests in improving care for its service territory. In 2012 it completed construction of a primary care and urgent care clinic in Rockmart (Floyd Primary Care and Floyd Urgent Care). Other 2012 enhancements include an expanded cardiac and pulmonary rehab program a renovated and expanded emergency care center at Floyd Medical Center and a new emergency station at the Polk Medical Center. The group launched a major construction project to rebuild the Polk Medical Center in 2013; the center will include all private rooms and an outpatient medical building.

In addition Floyd Healthcare Management enhanced its web services in 2012 to allow patients to pay medical bills online. The network launched another technology initiative in 2013 to implement a physician order entry system; the tool will help to reduce medical errors and improve patient care.

EXECUTIVES

President CEO, Kurt Stuenkel
Chief Medical Affairs, Dee B. Russell
SVP and COO, Warren A. (Sonny) Rigas
Vice President Chief Financial Officer, Rick Sheerin
VP, Alison Land
VP, Greg Polley
VP Market Development, Dan Sweitzer
VP and Chief Nursing Officer, Shelia Bennett
General Counsel, Wade Monk
Chief Medical Officer, Joe Biuso
Corporate Compliance Officer, Julie Rogers

LOCATIONS

HQ: FLOYD HEALTHCARE MANAGEMENT INC.
304 TURNER MCCALL BLVD SW, ROME, GA 30165-5621
Phone: 706-509-5000
Web: WWW.FLOYD.ORG

PRODUCTS/OPERATIONS

Selected Services

Bariatric Medicine Surgery and Aftercare
Behavioral Health
Cardiac Catheterization
Cardiology
Cardiac Rehabilitation
Diabetes Care
Echocardiography
Emergency Care
Family Medicine
Family Medicine Residency Program
Gynecology
Hospice
Hospitalist Care

- Hyperbarics and Wound Care
- Intensive Care
- Interventional Cardiology
- IV Therapy
- Laboratory
- Level III Neonatal Intensive Care Unit
- Level II Trauma Care
- Maternity
- Neurology
- Neuropsychology
- Neurosurgery
- Occupational Medicine
- Oncology
- Orthopedics
- Pediatrics
- Pediatric Intermediate Care
- Pharmacy Inpatient and Outpatient
- Pulmonary Rehabilitation
- Radiology
- Inpatient Rehabilitation
- Outpatient Rehabilitation
- Sleep Disorders
- Surgery Inpatient and Outpatient
- Urgent Care
- Vascular Surgery

COMPETITORS

- Gadsden Regional Medical Center
- Hutcheson Medical
- Redmond Regional Medical Center
- WellStar Kennestone Hospital

HISTORICAL FINANCIALS

Company Type: Private

Income Statement FYE: June 30

	REVENUE ($ mil.)	NET INCOME ($ mil.)	NET PROFIT MARGIN	EMPLOYEES
06/11	332	11	3.4%	2,400
06/10	288	8	3.0%	—
06/08	237	11	4.8%	—
06/06	215	2	0.9%	—
Annual Growth	9.0%	41.5%	—	—

2011 Year-End Financials

Debt ratio: ——
Return on equity: 3.40%
Cash ($ mil.): 10
Current ratio: 0.40
Long-term debt ($ mil.): —
Dividends
Yield: —
Payout: —
Market value ($ mil.): —

FOOD FOR THE POOR INC.

Food For The Poor feeds spiritual and physical hunger. The Christian charity provides health social economic and religious services for impoverished people in 17 countries in Latin America and the Caribbean. Food For The Poor believes its organization serves God by helping those most in need distributing requested goods through local churches and charities. The group works through Caritas the American-Nicaraguan Foundation and others to provide vocational training clinic and school construction educational materials feeding programs and medical supplies. Food For The Poor has distributed more than $3 billion in goods since its 1982 inception; the group uses 96% of its funds on programs.

Since its founding Food For The Poor has distributed more than 43900 tractor-trailer loads of aid to the poor built 50000 housing units and completed 568 water projects to provide clean water and sanitation for hundreds of thousands of villagers.

In 2008 to help hurricane battered residents in the Caribbean Food For The Poor sent more than 160 shipping containers of relief supplies including food water medical supplies personal care items and building materials. More than $7 million worth of aid was sent to storm-ravaged areas in Haiti Jamaica the Dominican Republic.

EXECUTIVES

President CEO and Director, Robin G. Mahfood
Executive Director, Angel A. Aloma
Chairman, P. Todd Kennedy
Secretary Treasurer and Director, David T. Price
Director Marketing and Public Relations, Alice Marino
Director Donor Relations, Michael Chin Quee
Director Donor Services, Sydney McFarlane
Director Speakers Bureau and Church and School Development Department, Vicki Kaufmann
President CEO and Director, Robin G. Mahfood
Secretary Treasurer and Director, David T. Price
Director, Grace Bonina
Director, Lynne G. Nasrallah
Director, Rev Lawrence A. Burke
Director, Rev Leopold Frade
Director, Rhonda Maingot
Director, Alvaro J. Pereira
Director, Rev Gregory Ramkissoon
Director, Bill Benson
Director, Rev Oscar Andres Rodriguez Maradiaga

LOCATIONS

HQ: FOOD FOR THE POOR INC.
6401 LYONS RD, COCONUT CREEK, FL 33073-3602
Phone: 954-427-2222
Web: WWW.FOODFORTHEPOOR.ORG

HISTORICAL FINANCIALS

Company Type: Private

Income Statement FYE: December 31

	REVENUE ($ mil.)	NET INCOME ($ mil.)	NET PROFIT MARGIN	EMPLOYEES
12/11	938	(12)	—	320
12/10	1,047	(3)	—	—
12/08	1,086	13	1.2%	—
12/08	1,514	(2)	—	—
Annual Growth	(14.7%)	—	—	—

2011 Year-End Financials

Debt ratio: ——
Return on equity: (-1.30%)
Cash ($ mil.): 7
Current ratio: 1.00
Long-term debt ($ mil.): —
Dividends
Yield: —
Payout: —
Market value ($ mil.): —

FORCE 3 INC.

In the world of federal IT contractors Force 3 aims to be a force to be reckoned with. The company provides integrated computer network systems for government agencies and to a smaller extent private industry customers. Force 3's services include consulting network design system integration training and support. The company also provides network security assessment services as well as business continuity and disaster recovery. The company specializes in military hospital network systems and has done work for more than 150 military medical facilities. Force 3 was founded in 1991 by Chairman Rocky Cintron.

Geographic Reach

Force 3 has offices in Crofton Maryland and Herndon Virginia.

Sales and Marketing

To provide its services Force 3 partners with notable technology companies like Apple Cisco Systems Citrix EMC NetApp and VMware.

The company has worked on IT contracts with the Department of Defense National Institutes of Health and the General Services Administration. In 2013 it won bids as a subcontractor on a $6.9 billion contract with the Navy and a $267 million contract with the GSA.

Mergers and Acquisitions

In 2012 Force 3 bought medical imaging technology provider secureRAD expanding its expertise to commercial and veterinary health care clients. The company sees the deal as an important one as it estimates the medical image storage and management market to be valued at around $6.6 billion.

EXECUTIVES

Chairman and President, Rocky D. Cintron
CEO, Les Trachtman
Vice Chairman, James B. (Jim) Bird
Chief Revenue Officer, Michael (Mike) Greaney
CTO, Chris Knotts

LOCATIONS

HQ: FORCE 3 INC.
2151 PRIEST BRIDGE DR # 7, CROFTON, MD 21114-2466
Phone: 301-261-0204
Web: WWW.FORCE3.COM

PRODUCTS/OPERATIONS

Selected Technology Partners

- Apple
- Cisco Systems
- Citrix
- EMC
- NetApp
- VMware

Selected Products and Services

- Borderless Networks
- Cisco Certified Training
- Communications and Collaboration
- Customer Innovation Center
- Cyber Security
- Data Center
- DISA Network STIG Assessment
- DISA Wireless Network STIG Assessment
- IM/IT Support Services
- Implementation Services
- Medical Image Management
- Virtualized Desktop Infrastructure
- VMware Ready Telework Solution

COMPETITORS

- Accenture
- CACI International
- Computer Sciences Corp.
- General Dynamics Information Technology
- HP Enterprise Services
- Infosys
- NTT DATA
- Raytheon
- Tata Consultancy
- Unisys
- Xerox

HISTORICAL FINANCIALS

Company Type: Private

Income Statement FYE: December 31

	REVENUE ($ mil.)	NET INCOME ($ mil.)	NET PROFIT MARGIN	EMPLOYEES
12/09	257	7	2.7%	300
12/08	325	5	1.8%	—
12/08	1,934	0	—	—
Annual Growth	(86.7%)	7971020.5%	—	—

2009 Year-End Financials

Debt ratio: —
Return on equity: 2.70%
Cash ($ mil.): 9
Current ratio: 1.20
Long-term debt ($ mil.): —
Dividends
Yield: —
Payout: —
Market value ($ mil.): —

FORDHAM UNIVERSITY

A private Catholic university Fordham offers its 15100 students –hailing from all 50 states and 50 foreign countries –degree programs through 10 graduate and undergraduate schools. Called the Jesuit University of New York Fordham has four locations including the original Rose Hill campus in the Bronx (often the scene of location shooting for movies TV shows and commercials) the Westchester campus the Lincoln Center campus in Manhattan as well as a biological field station in Armonk New York and international centers in China and the UK.

Operations

The Rose Hill campus is located on 85 acres in the Bronx and offers studies in business liberal arts science and religion. The Lincoln Center campus provides education business administration social services and legal training while the Westchester campus provides graduate programs in a variety of subjects. The Armonk field station is the headquarters for a number of university research programs.

The entering freshman class consists of almost 2000 students. The university offers more than 50 majors in liberal arts sciences and business. It has a student/faculty ratio of 14:1. It has more than 700 full-time instructors. Some 94% of its faculty holds a Ph.D. or other terminal degree.

Financial Performance

In fiscal year 2011 Fordham had $510.8 million in endowments and other investments.

Company Background

The school opened in 1841 as St. John's College. It officially changed its name to Fordham University in 1907.

EXECUTIVES

President and Trustee, Rev Joseph M. McShane
SVP and CFO, John J. Lordan
SVP and Chief Academic Officer, Stephen Freedman
Director University Libraries, James P. McCabe
Secretary, Margaret T. Ball
VP Administration, Brian J. Byrne
VP Student Affairs, Jeffrey L. Gray
VP Enrollment, Peter A. Stace
VP Finance, Frank Simio
Director Labor and Employee Relations, Angela Cioffi
Assistant VP Student Financial Services, Angela Van Dekker
Controller, Anthony Grono
Campus Director Student Financial Services, Barbara Wakie
Administrative Director Institute of International Humanitarian Affairs, Brendan Cahill
Chief of Operations Fordham University Emergency Medical Service (FUEMS), Brendan Ryan
Director Budget Operations, Carol Murabito
Business Office Manager, Casimira M. Stricker
Director Athletic Administration, Charles Elwood
Director Internet Services, Charles-Henri Sanson
Director Employer Relations, Christina Meincke
Director Treasury Operations, Conrad J. Obregon
President and CEO Graduate School of Arts and Sciences, David Reed
Associate VP Academic Affairs, David Stuhr
Legal Secretary, Diane Pinero
Assisant Dean and Director Admissions, Elaine Gerald
Director MBA Admissions, Frank Fletcher
Director Technical Operations, George J. Evans
Director Assessment and Accreditation, Gilbert Stack
Director Computer Services and Operations, Jason Benedict
Assistant VP Academic Affairs, Jerome A. Contee
Associate VP Government Relations, Joseph P. Muriana
Assistant VP Budgets and Logistics, Kevin Munnelly
Assistant VP Government Relations and State Affairs, Lesley Massiah
Associate VP Administration and Facilities, Marc Valera
Provost Marymount College, Mary Ann Quaranta
Director Information Technology Services Libraries, Michael Considine
Associate VP Student Affairs and Dean of Students Marymount, Michele C. Burris
Associate VP Academic Affairs, Ron Jacobson
Assistant VP Enrollment Services, Stephen Bordas
Director Office of Academic Effectiveness, Kristen Wenzel
Director Experiential Education Program, Bernard Stratford
VP Mission and Ministry, Rev Patrick Ryan
VP Technology and CIO, Frank Sirianni
VP Goverment Relations and Urban Affairs, Thomas A. Dunne
General Counsel, Thomas E. DeJulio
Director of Equity and Equal Oportunity, Georgina Calia Arendacs
Executive Director Human Resources, Michael C. Mineo
Trustee, Richard J. Buoncore, age 57
Vice Chair, Patricia M. Nazemetz, age 65
Trustee, Frank J. Petrilli, age 63
Trustee, Thomas P. Salice, age 55
Trustee, James E. Buckman, age 69
Trustee, Steven E. Sanderson
Trustee, Joel I. Picket, age 75
Trustee, Winston J. Churchill Jr., age 73
Trustee, Christine F. Driessen
Trustee, Robert B. McKeon, age 60
Trustee, Rev Michael J. Garanzini
President and Trustee, Rev Joseph M. McShane
Trustee, Stephen E. Bepler
Trustee, Donna M. Carroll
Trustee, John J. Cook Jr.
Trustee, Vincent M. Cooke
Trustee, Michael J. Cosgrove
Trustee, John R. Costantino, age 68
Trustee, Carolyn N. Dolan
Trustee, Kathleen Fagan
Trustee, William P. Frank
Trustee, Gerold F. L. Klauer
Trustee, Gerdenio Manuel
Trustee, Sylvester D. McClearn
Trustee, Francis J. Morison
Trustee, Nicholas A. Romano
Trustee, John S. Wilcha
Trustee, Robert A. Ferris
Trustee, Peter W. Howe
Trustee and Secretary, John P. Kehoe
Trustee, V. John Kriss
Trustee, Paul C. Saunders
Trustee, Christopher F. Fitzmaurice
Trustee, Darelene L. Jordan
Trustee, J. Thomas McClain
Trustee, Robert J. O'Shea
Trustee, Regina M. Pitaro
Trustee, Loretta A. Preska

LOCATIONS

HQ: FORDHAM UNIVERSITY
441 E FORDHAM RD, BRONX, NY 10458-9993
Phone: 718-817-1000
Web: WWW.BNET.FORDHAM.EDU

PRODUCTS/OPERATIONS

Selected Colleges

Graduate and Professional
- Graduate School of Arts and Sciences
- Graduate School of Business Administration
- Graduate School of Education
- Graduate School of Religion and Religious Education
- Graduate School of Social Services
- School of Law

Undergraduate
- Fordham College at Lincoln Center
- Fordham College at Rose Hill
- Fordham College of Liberal Studies
- Gabelli School of Business

HISTORICAL FINANCIALS

Company Type: Private

Income Statement FYE: June 30

	REVENUE ($ mil.)	NET INCOME ($ mil.)	NET PROFIT MARGIN	EMPLOYEES
06/12	518	60	11.6%	4,070
06/11	494	283	57.4%	—
06/10	568	17	3.0%	—
06/09	432	(103)	—	—
Annual Growth	6.2%	—	—	—

2012 Year-End Financials

Debt ratio: —
Return on equity: 11.60%
Cash ($ mil.): 3
Current ratio: —
Long-term debt ($ mil.): —
Dividends
Yield: —
Payout: —
Market value ($ mil.): —

FOREST SNAVELY PRODUCTS INC

EXECUTIVES

Chairman and CEO, Stephen V. Snavely
Chairman Emeritus, Chris M. Snavely
President and COO, John A. Stockhausen

LOCATIONS

HQ: FOREST SNAVELY PRODUCTS INC
600 DELWAR RD, PITTSBURGH, PA 152361351
Phone: 4128854000
Web: WWW.SNAVELYFOREST.COM

COMPETITORS

84 Lumber
ABC Supply
Builders FirstSource Southeast Group
Diamond Hill Plywood
E.C. Barton
Emco Corporation

Foxworth-Galbraith Lumber
Georgia-Pacific
Guardian Building Products Distribution
HD Supply
Hull Forest Products
Huttig Building Products
Jewett-Cameron Trading
Lumber Products
Pacific Coast Building Products
PrimeSource Building
Stock Building Supply
Weyerhaeuser

HISTORICAL FINANCIALS

Company Type: Private

Income Statement FYE: December 31

	REVENUE ($ mil.)	NET INCOME ($ mil.)	NET PROFIT MARGIN	EMPLOYEES
12/13	126	1	1.2%	145
12/12	114	1	1.1%	—
12/11	116	(0)	—	—
12/10	128	0	—	—
Annual Growth	(0.4%)	—	—	—

2013 Year-End Financials

Debt ratio: —
Return on equity: 1.20%
Cash ($ mil.): 0
Current ratio: 1.90
Long-term debt ($ mil.): —
Dividends
Yield: —
Payout: —
Market value ($ mil.): —

FORGE INDUSTRIES INC

Forge Industries connects a diverse group of businesses. Operating via several subsidiaries the family-owned private holding company distributes thousands of products from industrial gears and bearings to asphalt and concrete construction equipment. Businesses include construction/landscape equipment maker Miller Spreader and sister companies Akron Gear & Engineering and Bearing Distributors (BDI) Forge's global product and service distributor. Forge's lineup includes curb builders and hand tools as well as rebuild and repair gearboxes redesign customer equipment customize gear reducers and machining services. Customers work in the automotive package handling food processing and landscape industries.

LOCATIONS

HQ: FORGE INDUSTRIES INC
4450 MARKET ST, YOUNGSTOWN, OH 44512-1512
Phone: 330-533-5991
Web: WWW.FORGEINDUSTRIES.COM

COMPETITORS

Applied Industrial Technologies
Bosch Rexroth
DXP Enterprises
NTN Bearing Corp. of America
WESCO International

HISTORICAL FINANCIALS

Company Type: Private

Income Statement FYE: December 31

	REVENUE ($ mil.)	NET INCOME ($ mil.)	NET PROFIT MARGIN	EMPLOYEES
12/08	537	6	1.2%	2,000
12/07	605	0	—	—
12/06	0	0	—	—
12/05	404	73	18.1%	—
Annual Growth	9.9%	(56.0%)	—	—

2008 Year-End Financials

Debt ratio: —
Return on equity: 1.20%
Cash ($ mil.): 9
Current ratio: 0.90
Long-term debt ($ mil.): —
Dividends
Yield: —
Payout: —
Market value ($ mil.): —

FORREST COUNTY GENERAL HOSPITAL (INC)

Forrest General Hospital is the hub of health care in Hattiesburg Mississippi. Founded in 1952 the regional medical center serves southern Mississippi and its "Hub City" so named for its importance to early rail and lumber interests in the Pine Belt area. With some 400 acute care beds Forrest General offers general medical and surgical care as well as specialty care in heart disease cancer and women's health. Other facilities include the 90-bed Pine Grove behavioral health center for psychiatric and substance abuse treatment a 25-bed inpatient rehabilitation facility and an outpatient surgery center. The hospital system also operates a home health care agency and two nearby community hospitals.

Operations

In addition to the main inpatient and outpatient facilities Forrest General operates the nearby 100-bed Highland Community Hospital in Picayune. It also manages the Walthall County General Hospital in Tylertown through a lease management agreement. Within the Forrest General inpatient building a 30-bed long-term acute care hospital is operated by partner Regency Hospital Company. Altogether the system handles about 30000 inpatient visits and 100000 emergency room visits each year.

Company Background

Forrest General claims many area and state wide firsts including in 1969 the area's first emergency helicopter patient transport service. It is now the nation's longest continuously operating air ambulance. The hospital purchased Highland Community Hospital in 2006 and then constructed a new $76 million version of the hospital on a main state highway in 2009.

EXECUTIVES

President and CEO, Evan S. Dillard, age 60
Chief Medical Officer, Steven Farrell

LOCATIONS

HQ: FORREST COUNTY GENERAL HOSPITAL (INC)
6051 U S HIGHWAY 49, HATTIESBURG, MS 39401-7200
Phone: 601-288-7000
Web: WWW.FORRESTGENERAL.COM

PRODUCTS/OPERATIONS

Selected Services

Behavioral Health
Critical Care
Emergency
Heart and Vascular
Home Care
Hospice
Lithotripsy Center
Lifeline
LiveWell Center
Medicine
Neurology
Occupational Health
Oncology
Organ and Tissue Donation
Orthopedic
Radiology
Rehabilitation
Spirit of Women
Surgery
Trauma
Women and Children

COMPETITORS

Community Health Systems
HCA
Memorial Hospital at Gulfport
Natchez Regional Medical Center
North Mississippi Health Services
Southwest Mississippi Regional Medical Center

HISTORICAL FINANCIALS

Company Type: Private

Income Statement FYE: September 30

	REVENUE ($ mil.)	NET INCOME ($ mil.)	NET PROFIT MARGIN	EMPLOYEES
09/12	388	32	8.4%	4,030
09/06	346	31	9.0%	—
09/05	291	0	—	—
09/04	586	20	3.4%	—
Annual Growth	(5.0%)	6.2%	—	—

2012 Year-End Financials

Debt ratio: —
Return on equity: 8.40%
Cash ($ mil.): 105
Current ratio: 2.50
Long-term debt ($ mil.): —
Dividends
Yield: —
Payout: —
Market value ($ mil.): —

FOUNDATION FOR THE NATIONAL INSTITUTES OF HEALTH INC.

LOCATIONS

HQ: FOUNDATION FOR THE NATIONAL INSTITUTES OF HEALTH INC.
9650 ROCKVILLE PIKE, BETHESDA, MD 208143999
Phone: 3014025311
Web: WWW.FNIH.ORG

HISTORICAL FINANCIALS

Company Type: Private

Income Statement FYE: December 31

	ASSETS ($ mil.)	NET INCOME ($ mil.)	INCOME AS % OF ASSETS	EMPLOYEES
12/13	101	(1)	—	40
12/09	90	(0)	—	—
12/05	201	0	—	—
Annual Growth	(8.2%)	—	—	—

2013 Year-End Financials

Debt ratio: —
Return on equity: (-1.70%)
Cash ($ mil.): 21
Current ratio: 2.10
Long-term debt ($ mil.): —
Dividends
Yield: —
Payout: —
Market value ($ mil.): —

FOX HEAD INC.

Got a need for speed big jumps or crashes? Fox Racing makes and distributes motocross and other extreme sport apparel accessories and protective gear such as racewear pants jerseys gloves boots and helmets emblazoned with its fox head graphic logo. The company also offers bicycle motocross (BMX) and mountain bike apparel T-shirts hats jeans hoodies and pullovers and jackets. Line extensions include eyewear footwear and surf and wakeboard wear. Fox Racing sells its apparel through retail sporting goods and cycle and surf shops in the US. International offices are located in Canada and the UK. Founded in 1974 by Geoff Fox the company is family-owned and run by its second generation.

Geographic Reach

Based in Irvine California Fox Racing sells its products through specialty shops in the US Canada and the UK. The company with its Fox Head logo is an international leader in youth lifestyle clothing. It also operates additional offices in California and Spain.

Strategy

The company has been working to roll out more lifestyle-type products aside from its hard-core motocross offerings. To this end Fox Racing offers a line of casual wear and high-performance sunglasses and goggles for sports spectators. Its eyewear is made under an exclusive worldwide licensing agreement with sports accessories maker Oakley which is owned by behemoth Luxottica.

Particularly because more than 35% of the company's fans are under the age of 18 Fox Racing made its website available to smartphone users in late 2012 asserting that customers can buy products in fewer than 60 seconds.

As one of the best-selling brands of motocross apparel globally Fox Racing has worked with motocross riders including Ricky Carmichael James Stewart Damon Bradshaw Rick Johnson Mark Barnett Doug Henry Jeremy McGrath and Steve Lamson as part of its research and development efforts to provide them with maximum protection and performance as well as freedom of movement.

Fox Racing is looking at expanding its business across Europe. An alliance it inked in early 2013 with Cofton Maryland's Creative Logistics Solutions (CLS) will help the company with its goal. Fox Racing is leveraging CLS's InfoShip which communicates with Fox Racing's centralized InfoShip server located in California to process shipping transactions at its Netherlands site with remote support by CLS.

Sales and Marketing

To reinforce its presence in the motocross industry and spur young athletes to join the sports it supports Fox Racing keeps its brand in front of new and existing customers by sponsoring many professional riders.

Company Ownership

Fox Racing is family-owned and operated.

EXECUTIVES

V Pres, Greg Fox, age 50
CEO, Paul E. Harrington, age 52
Vp Of Marketing, Enich Harris
Vice President Performance Product, Wade Cleveland
Chairman, Scott Olivet

LOCATIONS

HQ: FOX HEAD INC.
18400 SUTTER BLVD, MORGAN HILL, CA 95037-2819
Phone: 408-776-8633
Web: WWW.FOXRACING.COM

PRODUCTS/OPERATIONS

Selected Sports Supported

Motocross (motorsport racing)
BMX (bicycle motocross)
MTB (mountain/trail motocross)
Surfing
Wakeboarding

COMPETITORS

Alliance Sports Group
American Recreation Products
Billabong
Columbia Sportswear
Oakley
Pacific Sunwear
Patagonia Inc.
Quiksilver
Vans
Volcom

HISTORICAL FINANCIALS

Company Type: Private

Income Statement FYE: December 31

	REVENUE ($ mil.)	NET INCOME ($ mil.)	NET PROFIT MARGIN	EMPLOYEES
12/09	216	20	9.4%	462
12/08	244	24	10.0%	—
12/07	444	0	—	—
Annual Growth	—	3430.2%	—	—

2009 Year-End Financials

Debt ratio: —
Return on equity: 9.40%
Cash ($ mil.): 34
Current ratio: 4.60
Long-term debt ($ mil.): —
Dividends
Yield: —
Payout: —
Market value ($ mil.): —

FOXWORTH GALBRAITH LUMBER COMPANY

Foxworth-Galbraith Lumber Company is helping to build out the Southwest. The company sells hardware lumber paint plumbing equipment tools and other building supplies through more than 20 locations across Texas New Mexico Arizona and Colorado (versus about 70 stores in 2006). Foxworth-Galbraith's main customers are residential and commercial builders; other clients include do-it-yourselfers specialty contractors and federal and state agencies. Foxworth-Galbraith is still owned and operated by the families of W.L. Foxworth and H.W. Galbraith who founded the company in Dalhart Texas in 1901 to take advantage of railroad construction.

Geographic Reach

Texas-based Foxworth-Galbraith covers the Southest in Arizona Colorado New Mexico and Texas.

Financial Performance

The company logged $198 million in gross sales in 2012.

Sales and Marketing

Foxworth-Galbraith serves several sectors providing services to sub-contractors repair and maintenance professionals landscapers and Realtors.

Operations

The company's commercial division supplies materials manufactured components engineered wood and specialty and environmental products for certain special projects that have included government light commercial and Native American projects. Completed building projects include Cheddar's (Independence Missouri) Jack In The Box (Broken Arrow Oklahoma) McDonald's (Englewood Colorado) and Well Fargo bank (Waco Texas).

Foxworth-Galbraith also provides other services such as project support (cabinet design custom paint matching and special-order products) and truss services (manufacturers and engineers trusses and wall panels) for residential and commercial projects. The firm also provides installation and delivery services.

Strategy

The decline in new home construction due to the economic downturn in the US led Foxworth-Galbraith to slash its store count by about 70% compared to its operations in the mid-2000s. The company also sold its headquarters building in 2011. The building supplies retailer's store count has held steady at about 20 locations (primarily in Texas and New Mexico) in recent years.

EXECUTIVES

Regional Vice President, Ken Frank

LOCATIONS

HQ: FOXWORTH GALBRAITH LUMBER COMPANY
4965 PRESTON PARK BLVD # 400, PLANO, TX 750935180
Phone: 9726652400
Web: WWW.FOXGAL.COM

2012 Stores

	No.
Texas	9
New	6
Arizona	3
Colorado	2
Total	20

PRODUCTS/OPERATIONS

Selected Product Categories

Building materials
Cabinets
Electrical
Hardware
Lawn and garden
Lumber
Paint
Plumbing
Tools

COMPETITORS

84 Lumber
A.C. Houston Lumber
Ace Hardware
BMC
Bison Building Materials
Builders FirstSource
Do it Best
Home Depot
Lowe' s
McCoy Corp.
Sears
Sherwin-Williams
Stock Building Supply
Sutherland Lumber
True Value

HISTORICAL FINANCIALS

Company Type: Private

Income Statement FYE: December 31

	REVENUE ($ mil.)	NET INCOME ($ mil.)	NET PROFIT MARGIN	EMPLOYEES
12/13	228	1	0.7%	2,500
12/12	197	0	0.4%	—
12/11	164	(3)	—	—
12/10	154	0	—	—
Annual Growth	13.9%	—	—	—

2013 Year-End Financials

Debt ratio: —
Return on equity: 0.70%
Cash ($ mil.): 0
Current ratio: —
Long-term debt ($ mil.): —
Dividends
Yield: —
Payout: —
Market value ($ mil.): —

FRANCIS SAINT MEDICAL CENTER

It may be guided by Catholic principles but you don't have to be a saint to get medical care at Saint Francis Medical Center. The hospital serves a five-state region from Missouri (its home base) to Arkansas with about 280 beds. Services include emergency medicine orthopedics cancer rehabilitation and women's health care. It also offers heart and neurosciences institutes as well as diabetes education and wound healing centers. The health care provider which was established in 1875 partners with Poplar Bluff Medical Partners to provide outpatient care at Poplar Bluff Medical Complex. Services include family practice OB-GYN and pain management.

Geographic Reach

Saint Francis Medical Center serves about 650000 people in Arkansas Kentucky Missouri Illinois and Tennessee.

Operations

Saint Francis Medical Center also partners with Landmark Holdings of Missouri to provide long-term acute care services through the 30-bed Landmark Hospital. The only facility of its kind between St. Louis and Memphis the hospital provides long-term care for patients who need complex medical care from catastrophic accidents or chronic diseases.

The hospital partners with the doctor-owned Physicians Alliance Surgery Center to provide outpatient surgery services in the region. Specialties provided at the center include gynecology ophthalmology orthopedic retinal and ENT (ear nose and throat) surgeries as well as general procedures.

Strategy

Saint Francis Medical Center completed construction of a 210000 sq. ft. heart hospital and cancer institute in 2012. It also broke ground on a major expansion and renovation project at the main hospital in late 2012. The $127 million project will be completed in 2016 and will add an orthopedic and neuroscience center a five-story patient tower and new surgery women's and children's health facilities.

EXECUTIVES

President and CEO, Steven C. Bjelich
CFO, Tony A. Balsano
VP Marketing and Referral Services, Barbara W. Thompson
VP Ambulatory Services, Alex Ogburn
VP Patient Care Services, Jeannette Fadler
President Professional Services, Marilyn K. Curtis
Chairman, Dennis Marchi
Vice Chairman, John A. Layton
Vice Chairman, Clyde Nenninger
VP Medical Affairs, James A. Schell II
CIO, Edward Duryee
Vice Chairman, John A. Layton
Vice Chairman, Clyde Nenninger

LOCATIONS

HQ: FRANCIS SAINT MEDICAL CENTER
211 SAINT FRANCIS DR, CAPE GIRARDEAU, MO 63703-5049
Phone: 573-331-3000
Web: WWW.CAREERS.SFMC.NET

COMPETITORS

Barnes-Jewish Hospital
Memorial Hospital (Illinois)
Southeast Missouri State University
Southern Illinois Healthcare
St. Anthony' s Medical Center
St. John' s Hospital (Illinois)

HISTORICAL FINANCIALS

Company Type: Private

Income Statement FYE: June 30

	REVENUE ($ mil.)	NET INCOME ($ mil.)	NET PROFIT MARGIN	EMPLOYEES
06/12	456	31	7.0%	1,500
06/11	423	48	11.4%	—
06/10	369	34	9.3%	—
06/09	313	(3)	—	—
Annual Growth	13.3%	—	—	—

2012 Year-End Financials

Debt ratio: —
Return on equity: 7.00%
Cash ($ mil.): 45
Current ratio: 0.50
Long-term debt ($ mil.): —
Dividends
Yield: —
Payout: —
Market value ($ mil.): —

FRANCISCAN ALLIANCE INC.

The Franciscan Alliance keeps watch over a family of hospitals. The not-for-profit organization operates more than a dozen hospitals in Indiana and south suburban Chicago. The hospitals house about 3500 beds and include specialist centers for cancer care heart and vascular care weight loss pediatrics and women's health. In addition to inpatient acute care services they operate numerous outpatient facilities and medical practices within their local service areas. Other subsidiaries and affiliates perform clinical laboratory tests offer home health services and provide support services to the system. Franciscan Alliance was founded and is sponsored by the Sisters of St. Francis of Perpetual Adoration.

Geographic Reach

Franciscan Alliance's hospitals are located in about ten communities in Indiana as well as in southern Chicago suburbs. The facilities serve patients in parts of Michigan as well. The organization also operates hundreds of outpatient clinics and physician offices in the area as well as a data center in Beech Grove Indiana.

Operations

Franciscan Alliance's hospitals handle about 100000 inpatient visits annually. The organization also handles about 3 million outpatient visits each year at its hospitals clinics and practice offices. Its physician practice organization includes about 700 doctors.

Along with providing a wide range of health care services Franciscan Alliance educates future health care providers through affiliations with area universities. The schools offer a variety of degree programs in fields including nursing medical technician and pharmacy residency.

Strategy

In 2011 the Sisters of St. Francis of Perpetual Adoration decided to change the name of the health system from Sisters of St. Francis Health Services to Franciscan Alliance to spread brand awareness and illustrate cohesiveness among the system's various facilities. The name change came after several months of consumer research and took about a year to be fully implemented across the entire system.

Franciscan Alliance also expanded through new construction in 2011 with the completion of the first phase of its Indianapolis Campus Expansion project. The health system moved a number of services into the new patient tower there including emergency services surgical suites and a wound care institute. In 2012 the company closed its Beech Grove hospital and consolidated services to the expanded Indianapolis center. It also opened a new short-stay hospital in Carmel that year.

In 2013 however the company announced that it is exploring options to sell all or part of its two Franciscan St. James Health hospitals. The organization seeks a partner that could invest in capital improvements at the facilities to ensure for strong services in the south suburbs of Chicago. Prior to the announcement Franciscan Alliance transferred the St. James occupational and environmental health clinic in southern Chicago to become part of its Franciscan WorkingWell network of clinics for area business employees.

Mergers and Acquisitions

In 2011 Franciscan Alliance grew its outpatient facilities by acquiring Surgical Hospital of Munster which serves as an outpatient surgery center of Franciscan Physicians Hospital.

EXECUTIVES

President CEO, Kevin Leahy
Regional Chief Executive Officer, Seth Warren
CEO Western Indiana Region, Terrance E. Wilson
CEO Central Indiana Region, Robert Brody

LOCATIONS

HQ: FRANCISCAN ALLIANCE INC.
1515 W DRAGOON TRL, MISHAWAKA, IN 46544-4710
Phone: 574-256-3935
Web: WWW.FRANCISCANALLIANCE.ORG

PRODUCTS/OPERATIONS

Selected Operations

St. Anthony Health (Crown Point and Michigan City Indiana)
St. Elizabeth Health (Crawfordsville Lafayette Central Lafayette East Indiana)
St. Francis Health (Carmel Indianapolis and Mooresville Indiana)
St. James Health (Chicago Heights and Olympia Fields Illinois)
St. Margaret Health (Hammond and Dyer Indiana)
Franciscan Healthcare Munster (formerly Physicians Hospital; Munster Indiana)

COMPETITORS

Advocate Health Care
Ascension Health
Community Hospitals of Indiana
Covenant Ministries
IU Health
Memorial Hospital & Health System
NorthShore University HealthSystem
Northwestern Memorial HealthCare
Porter Health Care System
Provena Health
Resurrection Health Care
Riverview Hospital
Rush System for Health
Sinai Health System
St. Bernard Hospital and Health Care Center
Union Hospital (Indiana)
University of Chicago Medical Center

HISTORICAL FINANCIALS

Company Type: Private

Income Statement FYE: December 31

	REVENUE ($ mil.)	NET INCOME ($ mil.)	NET PROFIT MARGIN	EMPLOYEES
12/07	2,065	204	9.9%	9,000
12/06	1,983	186	9.4%	—
Annual Growth	4.2%	9.5%	—	—

2007 Year-End Financials

Debt ratio: —
Return on equity: 9.90%
Cash ($ mil.): 141
Current ratio: 1.70
Long-term debt ($ mil.): —
Dividends
Yield: —
Payout: —
Market value ($ mil.): —

FRANKLIN AMERICAN MORTGAGE CO INC

Franklin American Mortgage is flying as high as a kite. The private mortgage bank is one of the country's largest and fastest-growing mortgage brokers. Franklin American Mortgage operates through three loan production channels. The correspondent lending division services lenders nationwide; the wholesale division funds and underwrites loans for mortgage brokers. Finally the retail division offers mortgages directly to individuals from about 20 offices (mostly located in the East and South). Franklin American Mortgage has a regional office in Texas in addition to its Tennessee headquarters. CEO Dan Crockett owns the company.

LOCATIONS

HQ: FRANKLIN AMERICAN MORTGAGE CO INC
501 CORP CNTRE DR STE 400, FRANKLIN, TN 37067
Phone: 615-778-1000
Web: WWW.FRANKLINAMERICAN.COM

COMPETITORS

Bank of America
CitiMortgage
Empire Equity
JPMorgan Chase
Residential Capital
Wells Fargo Home Mortgage

HISTORICAL FINANCIALS

Company Type: Private

Income Statement FYE: December 31

	ASSETS ($ mil.)	NET INCOME ($ mil.)	INCOME AS % OF ASSETS	EMPLOYEES
12/08	298	25	8.6%	700
12/07	206	5	2.7%	—
12/05	2	0	0.0%	—
Annual Growth	416.4%	29429.6%	—	—

2008 Year-End Financials

Debt ratio: —
Return on equity: 16.60%
Cash ($ mil.): 14
Current ratio: 0.10
Long-term debt ($ mil.): —
Dividends
Yield: —
Payout: —
Market value ($ mil.): —

FRANKLIN HOSPITAL

Franklin Hospital is part of the North Shore-Long Island Jewish Health System. The medical center has more than 300 beds and provides emergency and specialty care services. Franklin Hospital includes the 120-bed Orzac Center a long-term care rehabilitation unit as well as a 21-bed psychiatric unit and an adult day care center. Franklin Hospital also provides outpatient care –including pediatrics and women's health –and home health services. Established in 1963 as a small community hospital Franklin offers services and programs to the residents of Nassau and southeastern Queens Counties.

EXECUTIVES

VP Public Relations, Terry Lynam
President Medical Staff, Leonard Timpone
Human Resources Business Partner, Stacie Caplin
Director Rehabilitation Services, Alex Hellinger
Director Nutrition, Edward G. Cox
Director Radiology, Thomas Knichel
Chief Orthopedics, Norman Sveilich
Chief Executive Officer, Hervey Davis
Executive Director, Catherine Hottendorf
Acting Medical Director, Anthony Shallash
President Medical Staff, Gautam Reddy
CIO, John Bosco

LOCATIONS

HQ: FRANKLIN HOSPITAL
900 FRANKLIN AVE, VALLEY STREAM, NY 11580-2190
Phone: 516-256-6000
Web: WWW.CONCORDHOSPITAL.ORG

COMPETITORS

Catholic Health Services of Long Island
Catholic Healthcare System
Continuum Health Partners
Long Beach Medical Center
MediSys Health Network
New York City Health and Hospitals
New York Health Care
New York Hospital Queens

HISTORICAL FINANCIALS

Company Type: Private

Income Statement FYE: December 31

	REVENUE ($ mil.)	NET INCOME ($ mil.)	NET PROFIT MARGIN	EMPLOYEES
12/12	175	5	3.2%	1,300
12/08	169	(3)	—	—
12/01	0	(0)	—	—
12/01	103	0	0.1%	—
Annual Growth	5.0%	42.6%	—	—

2012 Year-End Financials

Debt ratio: —
Return on equity: 3.20%
Cash ($ mil.): 0
Current ratio: 0.30
Long-term debt ($ mil.): —
Dividends
Yield: —
Payout: —
Market value ($ mil.): —

FRANKLIN SQUARE HOSPITAL CENTER INC.

Franklin Square Hospital Center has made a declaration to care for the residents of eastern Baltimore County Maryland. The facility offers a wide range of specialties through some 700 doctors and about 375 beds. Since 1998 the hospital has been part of MedStar Health the region's largest integrated health system. As a teaching hospital Franklin Square offers a number of residency programs including internal and family medicine OB-GYN and surgery. The not-for-profit hospital's medical services are provided via six primary service lines: Medicine Surgery Women's and Children's Care Oncology Behavioral Health and Community Health and Wellness.

Geographic Reach

The only one of its kind in the region Franklin Square's Cancer Institute serves oncology patients by offering education and prevention services research and diagnostic treatment.

Strategy

The hospital which logs one of the highest numbers of cancer admissions in Maryland is working to expand its cancer services as it anticipates admissions to grow.

In fact the company is expanding other services as well also in anticipation of future patient demand. The hospital built a 300-bed patient tower on the campus which opened in 2010. Components of the new tower include an expanded emergency department dedicated pediatric and inpatient suites and an expanded 50-bed critical care unit.

EXECUTIVES

President and Director, Carl J. Schindelar
Senior Vice President of Operations, Glenn A. Visbeen
CFO, Bob Lally
Director Planning, Eric Slechter
VP Development and Community Relations, Janet Rafky
Assistant VP Public Relations Marketing and Community Affairs, Trina Adams
VP Medical Affairs, Anthony Sclama
VP Human Resources, Karen Robertson-Keck
VP Patient Care and Chief Nursing Officer, Larry Strassner
Chairman, G. Scott Barhight
Vice Chairman, Debra B. Doyle
Chief Pathology and Laboratory Medicine, Jerry J. Marty
Secretary and Treasurer, Vincent Martorana
President and Director, Carl J. Schindelar
Director, John Gontrum
Vice Chairman, Debra B. Doyle
Director, Hatem Abdo
Director, Khalid Al-Talib
Director, Michael Dietrich
Director, George J. Jabaji
Director, Patricia Norman
Director, Alexander (Bob) Page III
Director, Dennis F. Rasmussen
Director, Richard W. Single Sr.
Director, Michael D. Suter
Director, Deborah M. Turner
Director, Kenneth A. Samet, age 56

LOCATIONS

HQ: FRANKLIN SQUARE HOSPITAL CENTER INC.
9000 FRANKLIN SQUARE DR, BALTIMORE, MD 21237-3901
Phone: 443-777-7000
Web: WWW.FRANKLINSQUARE.ORG

COMPETITORS

Anne Arundel Medical Center
Bon Secours Health
GBMC
Good Samaritan Hospital of Maryland
Harbor Hospital
Johns Hopkins Bayview Medical Center
Johns Hopkins Health System
Johns Hopkins Medicine
LifeBridge Health
MedStar Union Memorial Hospital
Sinai Hospital of Baltimore
St. Agnes HealthCare
St. Joseph Medical Center
University of Maryland Medical System
Upper Chesapeake Health

HISTORICAL FINANCIALS

Company Type: Private

Income Statement FYE: June 30

	REVENUE ($ mil.)	NET INCOME ($ mil.)	NET PROFIT MARGIN	EMPLOYEES
06/12	471	(5)	—	3,019
06/11	452	18	4.0%	—
06/10*	439	31	7.1%	—
04/09	0	0		
Annual Growth	1028.5%	—	—	—

*Fiscal year change

2012 Year-End Financials

Debt ratio: —
Return on equity: (-1.20%)
Cash ($ mil.): 0
Current ratio: 1.10
Long-term debt ($ mil.): —
Dividends
Yield: —
Payout: —
Market value ($ mil.): —

FRAZIER INDUSTRIAL COMPANY

This company's racket is structural steel storage systems. Frazier Industrial Co. is a leading manufacturer of structural as opposed to roll-formed steel storage racks at about a dozen production centers in the US Canada and Mexico. These facilities can adapt production to demand and receive just-in-time delivery of raw materials. Customers use Frazier Industrial's storage racks in warehouses factories farms and other industrial and commercial facilities. Among the company's storage products is the Glide 'N Pick pallet cart that automatically rolls out for greater ease in retrieving items. Frazier Industrial is owned by CEO William Mascharka.

Geographic Reach

Frazier Industrial has manufacturing locations in Idaho New Jersey New York Pennsylvania South Carolina and Wisconsin. Outside the US it has plants in Mexicali and Monterrey Mexico and in Ontario Canada.

Strategy

Frazier Industrial is taking a stand for environmentally sound business practices as green initiatives become a focal point for customers such as Nestle Procter & Gamble and Unilever. Frazier sources all of its steel sections from North American mini-mills which only use recycled scrap material. Fittingly all of Frazier Industrial's scrap raw material is fully recyclable. Because the company receives preformed structural sections energy output is minimal; these structural parts require only cutting punching and welding. The location of Frazier Industrial's production centers helps to keep travel time and fuel expenses under control. They are all within 400 miles of the company's raw material suppliers and within 500 miles of major population centers in North America.

In 2013 the company launched a semi-automated high-density pallet mole system across North America. The pallet mole system a specific material handling technology maximizes available floor space enabling the storing of pallets up to 6-high and 50 positions deep while measurably increasing warehouse productivity.

Company Background

The company was founded in 1949.

EXECUTIVES

CEO, William L. Mascharka
President, Carlos Oliver
CFO, Walter Budzinski
National Sales Manager, Tony Reeves
National Account Manager, Tom Schenkenberger

LOCATIONS

HQ: FRAZIER INDUSTRIAL COMPANY
FAIRVIEW AVE, LONG VALLEY, NJ 07853
Phone: 908-867-7013
Web: WWW.FRAZIER.COM

PRODUCTS/OPERATIONS

Selected Products

Drive-In/Drive-Thru Storage
Frazier Design-Build
Glide-In Push-Back Storage
Glide N' Pick Order Picking Cart
Klamp-Fast Cantilever Rack
Pick-to-Belt Systems
Rack Supported Buildings
Safety Accessories
SelecDeck Carton Flow System
Sentinel Selective Pallet Rack
The Pallet Mole

COMPETITORS

Actionrack
Edsal Manufacturing
Interlake Mecalux
Lyon Workspace Products
Steel of West Virginia

HISTORICAL FINANCIALS

Company Type: Private

Income Statement FYE: December 31

	REVENUE ($ mil.)	NET INCOME ($ mil.)	NET PROFIT MARGIN	EMPLOYEES
12/12	183	2	1.6%	750
12/11	178	4	2.7%	—
12/09	133	3	2.8%	—
12/09	169	7	4.4%	—
Annual Growth	2.7%	(26.8%)	—	—

2012 Year-End Financials

Debt ratio: —
Return on equity: 1.60%
Cash ($ mil.): 1
Current ratio: 0.80
Long-term debt ($ mil.): —
Dividends
Yield: —
Payout: —
Market value ($ mil.): —

FREDERICK MEMORIAL HOSPITAL INC.

Frederick Memorial Healthcare System cares for the sick and unhealthy across The Old Line State. The system operates Frederick Memorial Hospital an acute care facility with some 240 beds and 20 satellite facilities in and around Frederick Maryland. Specialty services include cardiology oncology pediatrics and psychiatry. Other facilities in the system include FMH Immediate Care at Oak Street FMH Crestwood FMH Medical Fitness FMH Rose Hill FMH Wellness FMH Urbana Mt. Airy Health Services and the FMH Regional Cancer Therapy Center. The hospital traces its historical roots all the way back to 1902.

EXECUTIVES

CFO, Michelle Mahan
President and CEO, Thomas A. Kleinhanzl
VP Marketing and Development, Kenneth Coffey
Chairman, Anne-Herbert Rollins
Vice Chairman, E. James Reinsch
Secretary and Treasurer, Gerald Winnan
Chief of Staff, Neil Waravdekar
President FMH Auxiliary, Donna Tisdale
Auditors: Ernst&YoungLLP

LOCATIONS

HQ: FREDERICK MEMORIAL HOSPITAL INC.
400 W 7TH ST, FREDERICK, MD 21701-4593
Phone: 240-566-3300
Web: WWW.FMH.ORG

PRODUCTS/OPERATIONS

Selected Centers

FMH Crestwood
FMH Immediate Care at Oak Street
FMH Medical Fitness
FMH Regional Cancer Therapy Center
FMH Rose Hill
FMH Urbana
FMH Wellness
Frederick Memorial Hospital
Mt. Airy Health Services

Selected Medical Services

Behavioral Health
Cancer Care
Cardiac Rehabilitation
Cardiology Services
Diabetes Center
Emergency Services
Home Health Services
Hospice/Home Care Information
Hospitalist Care
Imaging Vascular Services
Laboratory Wellness Center
Medical Fitness Women and Children
Occupational Health
Orthopedic Services
Pain and Palliative Care
Pharmacy
Pulmonary Function Lab
Pulmonary Rehab Program
Rehabilitation
Robotics
Sleep Disorders
Smoking Cessation Program
Stroke Center
Surgical Services
Wound Care and Hyperbaric Medicine

COMPETITORS

Adventist HealthCare
Children' s National Medical Center
Johns Hopkins Medicine
Loudoun Healthcare
Meritus Health

HISTORICAL FINANCIALS

Company Type: Private

Income Statement FYE: June 30

	REVENUE ($ mil.)	NET INCOME ($ mil.)	NET PROFIT MARGIN	EMPLOYEES
06/12	355	(13)	—	2,600
06/11	348	15	4.6%	—
06/10	307	3	1.2%	—
06/09	279	(17)	—	—
Annual Growth	8.3%	—	—	—

2012 Year-End Financials

Debt ratio: —
Return on equity: (-3.70%)
Cash ($ mil.): 30
Current ratio: 1.30
Long-term debt ($ mil.): —
Dividends
Yield: —
Payout: —
Market value ($ mil.): —

FREEMAN HEALTH SYSTEM

Freeman Health System (FHS) offers comprehensive health and behavioral health services to the residents of Arkansas Kansas Missouri and Oklahoma through three hospitals with a total of more than 500 beds. Specialty facilities include a full-service cardiothoracic and vascular program at the Freeman Heart Institute and behavioral health services through its Ozark Health Center. Community-owned not-for-profit FHS also operates two urgent care centers a separate sleep center several doctors' office buildings and serves as a teaching hospital with three residency programs (ear nose and throat; emergency medicine; and internal medicine). FHS employs more than 300 physicians in 60 specialties.

Company Background

Located in Joplin Missouri –the site of the deadly E5 tornado that killed 161 people in May 2011—Freeman Health System was the only fully functional hospital in the aftermath of the disaster. Rival St. John's Regional Medical Center just two miles away was destroyed. However Ozark Health Center FHS's behavioral health division lost nine buildings in the disaster.

EXECUTIVES

President and CEO, Gary D. Duncan
Chief Financial Officer, Steve Graddy
Chief Information Officer, Sue Annesser
Chief Medical Officer, Richard D. Schooler
Vice President of Retail Service Operations, Debi Koelkebeck
Freeman President and Chief Executive Officer, Paula Baker
VP Administration, Phil Willcoxon
Media Coordinator, Heather Collier
VP Operations and Clinical, Jeffrey Carrier
Vice President of Business Development, Wes Braman
Vice President of Compliance, Carlos Haley
Chief Human Resources Officer, Deborah Chiodo

LOCATIONS

HQ: FREEMAN HEALTH SYSTEM
1102 W 32ND ST, JOPLIN, MO 64804-3503
Phone: 417-623-2801
Web: WWW.FREEMANHEALTH.COM

PRODUCTS/OPERATIONS

Selected Services

Autism Services
Behavioral/mental health
Bladder care
Cancer care
Children's Miracle Network Hospitals
Clinical trials
Cosmetic/reconstructive surgery
Critical Care (ICU)
Diabetes education
Digestive care
Emergency medicine
Family care
Family counseling
Geriatric medicine
Health screenings
Hearing services
Home care
Internal medicine
Internet Addiction Services
Kidney Care
Lung care
Maternity
Neonatal intensive care
Nephrology & dialysis
Neurology & neurosurgery
Occupational medicine
Orthopedics
Pain management
Palliative care
QuickMeds Pharmacy
Radiology
Rehabilitation
Senior Services
Skilled nursing
Sleep disorders
Sports medicine
Substance abuse services
Surgery
Tobacco cessation
Transitional Care Unit (TCU)
Urgent care
Women's Services
Wound care

COMPETITORS

Catholic Health Initiatives
Children' s Mercy Hospital
Heartland Regional Medical
Mercy Health

HISTORICAL FINANCIALS

Company Type: Private

Income Statement FYE: March 31

	REVENUE ($ mil.)	NET INCOME ($ mil.)	NET PROFIT MARGIN	EMPLOYEES
03/12	521	35	6.8%	3,887
03/11	452	7	1.7%	—
03/10	474	30	6.5%	—
03/09	460	(13)	—	—
Annual Growth	4.2%	—	—	—

2012 Year-End Financials

Debt ratio: —
Return on equity: 6.80%
Cash ($ mil.): 17
Current ratio: 1.50
Long-term debt ($ mil.): —
Dividends
Yield: —
Payout: —
Market value ($ mil.): —

FREIGHTQUOTE.COM INC.

Where should one go on the Web to find quotes for freight carriers? Freightquote.com silly. The company rates schedules and tracks all types of freight comparing numerous carriers in seconds through its free service. Freightquote serves customers across North America who use its services to schedule and track their shipments entirely on the Web. It also offers free online freight shipping quotes. Modes of freight transport include trucks airplanes and ships. The company moves more than one million shipments across North America per year. Freightquote was founded in 1998 by Timothy Barton. It has received funding from investment firms such as Menlo Ventures and Morgan Stanley Venture Partners.

Geographic Reach

The company operates throughout North America.

Operations

Freightquote organizes its freight solutions in categories that meet customer's different needs including truckload (TL) less than truckload (LTL freight) expedited LTL or intermodal (shipping by rail). The firm also offers custom logistics solutions such as project freight (a solution for projects with multiple-shipments) and freight spend analysis.

The company also operates subsidiary Rockwell Transportation Services a Pennsylvania-based transportation brokerage provider specializing in truckload less than truckload and intermodal solutions for shippers. Its transportation management system Freightview allows customers to streamline and automate the shipping process.

Financial Performance

Freightquote continues to maintain growth with large year-over-year revenue increases since 2004. In fiscal 2011 and fiscal 2012 annual sales were more than $500 million.

Strategy

To accommodate the company's recent growth Freightquote is moving its corporate headquarters to a larger facility in Kansas City Missouri. The new building will be 200000 square feet and is set to open in 2013. The move is a response to increased demand.

EXECUTIVES

Founder and Executive Chairman, Timothy A. (Tim) Barton
VP Enterprise Sales, Jason Beer
VP Human Resources, Luanne Eskew
VP and General Manager Rockwell Transportation Services, Lori Wittman
Chief Executive Officer, Tyler Ellison
Chief Financial Officer, Matt Druten
VP Business Solutions, Doug Grojean
VP Sales, Trent Flanary
VP Customer Service Operations, Lance Huggins
Vice President of Finance, Abbey Caton
Chief Information Officer, Byron Clymer
Vice President Financial Planning & Analysis and Investor Relations, Mike Collins
Vice President of Sales, Tracy Kenison
Chief Sales Officer, Sam Hastings

LOCATIONS

HQ: FREIGHTQUOTE.COM INC.
16025 W 113TH ST, LENEXA, KS 66219-5105
Phone: 913-642-4700
Web: WWW.FREIGHTQUOTE.COM

PRODUCTS/OPERATIONS

Selected Services

Truckload freight
Less-than-truckload (LTL) freight
Expedited LTL freight
Intermodal (rail) freight
Project freight (multiple shipments)
Dry van freight
Flatbed trucking
Refrigerated shipping
Air freight
Free online quotes

COMPETITORS

Expeditors
Phoenix International Freight Services
UBM Global Trade

HISTORICAL FINANCIALS

Company Type: Private

Income Statement FYE: December 31

	REVENUE ($ mil.)	NET INCOME ($ mil.)	NET PROFIT MARGIN	EMPLOYEES
12/12	573	0	—	1,200
12/11	385	0	—	—
12/10	0	0	—	—
12/09	359	0	—	—
Annual Growth	16.8%	—	—	—

2012 Year-End Financials

Debt ratio: —
Return on equity: —
Cash ($ mil.): 15
Current ratio: 1.20
Long-term debt ($ mil.): —

Dividends
Yield: —
Payout: —
Market value ($ mil.): —

FRESH MARK INC.

This company continues to make its mark in the processed meat market. Fresh Mark is a leading producer of smoked and processed meat products for the domestic and international retail and foodservice industries. From its three plants in Ohio the company makes and markets such products as deli meats hot dogs lunch meats hams and bacon sold under the names Superior's Brand and Sugardale. The company also produces private-label processed meat products for others and supplies the foodservice industry through its Sugardale Food Service business. Founded in 1920 Fresh Mark is owned and operated by the Genshaft family; Neil Genshaft is the meat producer's chairman and CEO.

Geographic Reach

Ohio-based Fresh Mark sells its products nationwide. It operates processing facilities in the Ohio cities of Canton Massillon and Salem.

Operations

Doing business as Superior's Brand Meats Fresh Mark makes and supplies smoked and processed meats for the US retail and foodservice industries. Products include bacon ham weiners dry sausages specialty meat items and deli and luncheon meats.

Some of its brands include Superior's Brand and Sugardale.

Sales and Marketing

The company's customers include major grocery chains and restaurant and foodservice operators across the US. It also distributes its products internationally and offers private-label services to customers.

Fresh Mark supports its brands through a variety of efforts such as marketing advertising public relations sports and event sponsorship merchandising and point-of-sale.

Strategy

One of the largest privately owned companies in its industry Fresh Mark has grown from a regional supplier of smoked and processed meats to a leading supplier nationwide. It's ranked among the top 40 of the nation's leading 150 meat and poultry companies as measured by National Provisioner magazine.

EXECUTIVES

Adm Vice President Chief Finc Ofc, David Cochenour

LOCATIONS

HQ: FRESH MARK INC.
1888 SOUTHWAY ST SE, MASSILLON, OH 44648
Phone: 3308343669
Web: WWW.FRESHMARK.COM

COMPETITORS

Birchwood Meat & Provision
Boar' s Head
Cargill Meat Solutions
Carl Buddig
Coleman Natural Foods
ConAgra
Farmland Foods
Hormel
Indiana Packers
JBS USA
Johnsonville Sausage
Kraft Foods Group Inc.
Smithfield Foods
Tyson Foods

HISTORICAL FINANCIALS

Company Type: Private

Income Statement FYE: January 1

	REVENUE ($ mil.)	NET INCOME ($ mil.)	NET PROFIT MARGIN	EMPLOYEES
01/11*	795	59	7.5%	2,300
12/07	534	31	5.8%	—
12/06	481	21	4.5%	—
12/05	481	0	—	—
Annual Growth	10.6%	—	—	—

*Fiscal year change

2011 Year-End Financials

Debt ratio: —
Return on equity: 7.50%
Cash ($ mil.): 4
Current ratio: 0.90
Long-term debt ($ mil.): —

Dividends
Yield: —
Payout: —
Market value ($ mil.): —

FROEDTERT MEMORIAL LUTHERAN HOSPITAL INC

Patients in southeastern Wisconsin count on Froedtert Memorial Lutheran Hospital for a full range of health services including trauma transplant sports medicine and senior care. The 500-bed hospital also known as Froedtert & The Medical College of Wisconsin is part of the Froedtert Health system (pronounced "fray-dert"). Specialty units include cancer dermatology neuroscience birthing fertility urology and vein clinics. The hospital also serves as a teaching facility for the Medical College of Wisconsin and it partners with the Children's Hospital of Wisconsin to provide pediatric services. Froedtert Hospital which was founded in 1980 operates the only adult Level One trauma center in the region.

Operations

Froedtert Health offers medical practice care in roughly 35 specialties and subspecialties. Beyond the hospital's walls it operates four diagnostic imaging centers as well as rehabilitation facilities and a handful of primary care clinics in the community. The Froedtert Health system also includes Community Memorial Hospital in Menomonee Falls; St. Joseph's Hospital in West Bend Wisconsin; and Froedtert Health Medical Group.

Strategy

In 2010 Froedtert Health acquired ProHealth Care Medical Associates practices in six Germantown Hartford and Menomonee Falls locations. The practices now operating as Froedtert Health included three general clinics specialty services behavioral health rehabilitation and a physician practice.

EXECUTIVES

President Froedtert Hospital, Catherine (Cathy) Buck
SVP Finance, Jeffrey Van De Kreeke
President and CEO Froedtert Health, Catherine A. Jacobson
Chief Medical Officer Froedtert Hospital, Lee Biblo
VP Marketing, Kathleen Perlewitz
COO Froedtert Health and President Community Memorial Hospital, Dennis Pollard
VP and CIO, Robert DeGrand
VP Perioperative Services, Gary Colpaert
VP Supply Chain and Pharmacy, James Klauck
VP Ambulatory Services, Katherine Bagemihl
VP Clinical Integration and Payer Strategies, Patricia Ruff
EVP, Peter Pruessing

LOCATIONS

HQ: FROEDTERT MEMORIAL LUTHERAN HOSPITAL INC
9200 W WISCONSIN AVE, MILWAUKEE, WI 53226-3522
Phone: 414-259-3000
Web: WWW.FROEDTERT.COM

PRODUCTS/OPERATIONS

Selected Departments Centers and Programs

Clinical Cancer Center
- Blood and Lymph Node Cancer Program
- Blood and Marrow Transplant Program
- Bone and Connective Tissue Cancer Program
- Brain and Spine Tumor Program
- Breast Cancer Program
- Cancer Genetics Screening Program
- Colorectal Cancer Program
- Endocrine Cancer Program
- Eye/Orbital Cancer Program
- Geriatric Oncology
- Gynecologic Cancer Program
- Head and Neck Cancer Program
- Liver Pancreas and Bile Duct Cancer Program
- Neuro-oncology Cognitive Clinic
- Palliative Care Program
- Plastic Surgery Center
- Prostate and Urologic Cancer Program
- Skin Cancer Center
- Thoracic Cancer Program (Lung and Esophageal Cancers)

Heart and Vascular Center
- Adult Congenital Heart Disease
- Advanced Heart Failure and Cardiac Transplantation
- Aortic Disease
- Arrhythmia and Atrial Fibrillation
- Coronary Artery Disease (CAD)
- Hereditary Hemorrhagic Telangiectasia (HHT)
- Hypertrophic Cardiomyopathy (HCM)
- Preventive Cardiology and Lipid Therapy
- Peripheral Arterial Disease (PAD)
- Pulmonary Hypertension
- Valvular Disease
- Venous Thrombotic Disease
- Venous and Vein Disease
- Women and Heart Disease

Neurosciences Center
- Brain Injury Program
- Brain and Spine Tumor Program
- Comprehensive Epilepsy Program
- Comprehensive Spasticity Management Program
- Memory Disorders Program
- Neuro-Oncology Cognitive Clinic
- Normal Pressure Hydrocephalus
- Parkinson's and Movement Disorders Program
- Sleep Disorders Program
- SpineCare Program
- Spinal Cord Injury Center
- Stroke and Neurovascular Program

COMPETITORS

Children's Hospital and Health System
Columbia St. Mary's Ministry Health Care
ProHealth Care
Rockford Health System
Waukesha Memorial
Wheaton Franciscan Services

HISTORICAL FINANCIALS

Company Type: Private

Income Statement FYE: June 30

	REVENUE ($ mil.)	NET INCOME ($ mil.)	NET PROFIT MARGIN	EMPLOYEES
06/12	1,057	101	9.6%	3,459
06/11	980	79	8.1%	—
06/09	894	59	6.7%	—
06/09	810	(28)	—	—
Annual Growth	9.3%	—	—	—

2012 Year-End Financials

Debt ratio: —
Return on equity: 9.60%
Cash ($ mil.): 39
Current ratio: 3.70
Long-term debt ($ mil.): —
Dividends
Yield: —
Payout: —
Market value ($ mil.): —

FRUIT GROWERS SUPPLY COMPANY INC

HISTORY

The company was formed in 1907 by the members of California Fruit Growers Exchange (now Sunkist Growers) and has grown with the expansion of citrus production in California.

EXECUTIVES

VP Northern Operations and Strategic Planning Timberlands, Charles Brown

LOCATIONS

HQ: FRUIT GROWERS SUPPLY COMPANY INC
14130 RIVERSIDE DR, SHERMAN OAKS, CA 914232313
Phone: 8059332723
Web: WWW.FRUITGROWERS.COM

PRODUCTS/OPERATIONS

Selected Products and Services

Agricultural Equipment
Cartons
Fertilizers and Pesticides
Grower Supplies
Harvesting Supplies
Irrigation Design and Installation
Lawn and Garden Supplies
Packaging
Packinghouse Supplies
Packing Services
Pallets
Powered Equipment
Small Engine Repair

COMPETITORS

Caraustar
Gibraltar Packaging
Green Bay Packaging
Pro-Fac
Rock-Tenn

HISTORICAL FINANCIALS

Company Type: Private

Income Statement FYE: December 31

	REVENUE ($ mil.)	NET INCOME ($ mil.)	NET PROFIT MARGIN	EMPLOYEES
12/13	203	5	2.8%	240
12/12	179	6	3.8%	—
12/11	177	6	3.9%	—
12/10	151	0	—	—
Annual Growth	10.4%	—	—	—

2013 Year-End Financials

Debt ratio: —
Return on equity: 2.80%
Cash ($ mil.): 0
Current ratio: 0.60
Long-term debt ($ mil.): —
Dividends
Yield: —
Payout: —
Market value ($ mil.): —

FURST-MCNESS COMPANY

LOCATIONS

HQ: FURST-MCNESS COMPANY
120 E CLARK ST, FREEPORT, IL 610323300
Phone: 8152356151
Web: WWW.MCNESS.COM

HISTORICAL FINANCIALS

Company Type: Private

Income Statement FYE: December 28

	REVENUE ($ mil.)	NET INCOME ($ mil.)	NET PROFIT MARGIN	EMPLOYEES
12/13	291	3	1.1%	245
12/12	270	3	1.3%	—
12/11	243	1	0.5%	—
12/10	176	0	—	—
Annual Growth	18.3%	—	—	—

2013 Year-End Financials

Debt ratio: —
Return on equity: 1.10%
Cash ($ mil.): 0
Current ratio: 0.90
Long-term debt ($ mil.): —
Dividends
Yield: —
Payout: —
Market value ($ mil.): —

G.M.P. EMPLOYERS RETIREE TRUST

LOCATIONS

HQ: G.M.P. EMPLOYERS RETIREE TRUST
5245 BIG PINE WAY STE 200, FORT MYERS, FL 339075924
Phone: 2399366242
Web: WWW.GMPTRUST.COM

HISTORICAL FINANCIALS

Company Type: Private

Income Statement FYE: December 31

	ASSETS ($ mil.)	NET INCOME ($ mil.)	INCOME AS % OF ASSETS	EMPLOYEES
12/09*	251	(24)	—	23
06/00	305	13	4.3%	—
06/99	268	35	13.4%	—
06/98	228	0	—	—
Annual Growth	0.8%	—	—	—

*Fiscal year change

2009 Year-End Financials

Debt ratio: —
Return on equity: (-116.90%)
Cash ($ mil.): 6
Current ratio: —
Long-term debt ($ mil.): —
Dividends
Yield: —
Payout: —
Market value ($ mil.): —

GAFFNEY-KROESE ELECTRICAL SUPPLY CORPORATION

LOCATIONS

HQ: GAFFNEY-KROESE ELECTRICAL SUPPLY CORPORATION
50 RANDOLPH RD, SOMERSET, NJ 088731240
Phone: 7328859000
Web: WWW.GAFFNEY-KROESE.COM

HISTORICAL FINANCIALS

Company Type: Private

Income Statement FYE: December 31

	REVENUE ($ mil.)	NET INCOME ($ mil.)	NET PROFIT MARGIN	EMPLOYEES
12/11	204	4	2.4%	260
12/10	155	3	2.1%	—
12/09	1,927	0	—	—
Annual Growth	—24778.6%	—	—	—

2011 Year-End Financials

Debt ratio: —
Return on equity: 2.40%
Cash ($ mil.): 1
Current ratio: 0.70
Long-term debt ($ mil.): —
Dividends
Yield: —
Payout: —
Market value ($ mil.): —

GAINESVILLE REGIONAL UTILITIES INC

Multi-service utility Gainesville Regional Utilities (GRU) started out small more than a century ago but has been gaining ground ever since. The company (now the fifth largest municipal electric utility in Florida) is the sole utilities provider in Gainesville and surrounding areas in Alachua County. The municipal utility distributes electric water wastewater natural gas and telecommunications services to approximately 93000 retail and wholesale customers. GRU has interests in power generation facilities that give it more than 600 MW of capacity. It also offers internet and other communications services. GRU gets the bulk of its revenues from its electric utility operations.

Operations

GRU operates electric water wastewater natural gas and telecommunications utilities. Its five utility power plants are Deerhaven Generating Station John R. Kelly Generating Station Kanapaha Water Reclamation Facility Main Street Water Reclamation Facility and Murphree Water Treatment Plant. In 2012 GRU also operated 752 miles of natural gas main lines and had 33200 natural gas customers.

Financial Performance

In 2012 GRU's operating sales and service revenues decreased 7% AS the result of lower consumption offset by higher rate increases implemented in October 2011 along with a decrease in fuel costs of $16 million. (Fuel costs are passed directly through to icustomers as part of a fuel adjustment charge which is reported as revenues).

The company's net income decreased by 46% in 2012.

GRU contributed more than $36 million to the City of Gainesville's General Fund in 2012.

Strategy

The multi-utility is pushing conservation and green energy as a way to increase operational efficiency reduce carbon emissions and help its customers save money. In order to help meet the state's clean energy requirements GRU installs photovoltaic panels on selected buildings and provides a solar water heating rebate program for its customers. It even offers customers a supply of woodchips (a by-product of the routine trimming done by GRU's Vegetation Management Department to reduce the number of tree-related electrical outages).

As part of its ongoing green energy push in 2011 GRU began offering its customers a 6% annual interest loan for pre-approved items including certified (ENERGY STAR) refrigerators efficient central air conditioning systems and solar photovoltaic systems.

Ownership

GRU is the City of Gainesville's combined municipal utility system.

Company Background

The company was founded in 1912.

Auditors: Ernst&YoungLLP

LOCATIONS

HQ: GAINESVILLE REGIONAL UTILITIES INC
301 SE 4TH AVE STE A105, GAINESVILLE, FL 32601-6857
Phone: 352-334-3400
Web: WWW.GRU.COM

HISTORICAL FINANCIALS

Company Type: Private

Income Statement FYE: September 30

	REVENUE ($ mil.)	NET INCOME ($ mil.)	NET PROFIT MARGIN	EMPLOYEES
09/09	369	33	9.1%	750
09/08	349	18	5.2%	—
Annual Growth	5.7%	83.0%	—	—

2009 Year-End Financials

Debt ratio: —
Return on equity: 9.10%
Cash ($ mil.): 9
Current ratio: 2.00
Long-term debt ($ mil.): —
Dividends
Yield: —
Payout: —
Market value ($ mil.): —

GALLAUDET UNIVERSITY

Gallaudet University (GU) gives deaf and hard-of-hearing students the chance to be in the majority. Designed to accommodate hearing-impaired students GU offers undergraduate and graduate degrees in more than 40 majors to about 2000 students annually. The bilingual university which uses both American Sign Language (ASL) and English admits a small number of hearing ASL-proficient students to each incoming freshman class. Through its Laurent Clerc National Deaf Education Center GU provides training and support for teachers and parents of hearing impaired children and operates demonstration schools. Founded in 1864 GU was named for Thomas Hopkins Gallaudet a pioneer in education for the deaf.

Operations

For the purposes of budgeting and operating its educational institution GU is divided into two major component programs: its university and the Laurent Clerc National Deaf Education Center. The center's primary focus as part of a federal mandate is to develop and disseminate innovative curriculum materials and teaching strategies to schools and programs nationwide. The center includes the Model Secondary School for the Deaf (MSSD) and the Kendall Demonstration Elementary School (KDES). MSSD serves students in grades nine through 12 while KDES serves infants and their parents continuing service through the eighth grade.

Also part of its operations the Gallaudet Research Institute studies the demographics and assessment of deaf and hard of hearing people in the educational system as well as language and learning processes. For its research the institute involves students in its studies.

Open to all students whether they're deaf hard of hearing or hearing GU's graduate programs include master of arts or master of science degrees specialist degrees certificates and doctoral degrees across several fields involving professional services to deaf and hard of hearing people.

Undergraduate tuition for GU runs about $13424 for US students.

Geographic Reach

From its 99-acre campus in Washington DC GU is a federally chartered university that caters to students nationwide as well as students in developing and non-developing countries (about 30 in total).

Strategy

GU is working through a five-year five-pronged strategic plan that runs through 2015. It includes a handful of lofty goals. GU is working to grow its enrollment of full-time undergraduates full- and part-time graduate students and continuing education students to 3000 by 2015. (In the fall of 2013 the university's enrollment was 1872.) GU's also focused on boosting its six-year undergraduate graduation rate to 50% refining a core set of undergraduate and graduate programs aimed at career success and positioning the university as the epicenter of research development and outreach. GU as its final and more far-reaching goal is concentrating on securing a sustainable revenue base by expanding and diversifying its funding partnerships while also increasing its operating efficiency. The university raised more than it goal of $3.2 million in new gifts and pledges for 2013.

EXECUTIVES

President, T. Alan Hurwitz
VP Administration and Finance, Paul Kelly
Provost, Stephen F. Weiner
Dean Student Affairs and Academic Support, A. Dwight Benedict
VP Laurent Clerc National Deaf Education Center, Edward (Ed) Bosso
Dean Graduate School Continuing Studies and International Affairs, Carol Erting
Dean School of Education Business and Human Services, Isaac Agboola
Dean College of Arts and Sciences, Genie Gertz
Vice President Of Gallaudet University, Kendall Hall
Coordinator Of Residence Education Vice President, Adrienne Morgan
Vice President, Gallaudet Intramurals
Mobile Vice President, Kevin Myers
Vice President, Shondra Mitchell

LOCATIONS

HQ: GALLAUDET UNIVERSITY
800 FLORIDA AVE NE, WASHINGTON, DC 200023600
Phone: 2026515000
Web: WWW.GALLAUDET.EDU

PRODUCTS/OPERATIONS

Selected Programs

Gallaudet Research Institute
Gallaudet University
Laurent Clerc National Deaf Education Center
Kendall Demonstration Elementary School
Model Secondary School for the Deaf

HISTORICAL FINANCIALS

Company Type: Private

Income Statement FYE: September 30

	REVENUE ($ mil.)	NET INCOME ($ mil.)	NET PROFIT MARGIN	EMPLOYEES
09/13	171	(0)	—	1,200
09/12	190	17	9.2%	—
09/11	177	4	2.7%	—
09/10	179	0	—	—
Annual Growth	(1.4%)	—	—	—

2013 Year-End Financials

Debt ratio: —
Return on equity: —
Cash ($ mil.): 16
Current ratio: 0.40
Long-term debt ($ mil.): —
Dividends
Yield: —
Payout: —
Market value ($ mil.): —

GALLERY MODEL HOMES INC.

EXECUTIVES

President, Jim (Mattress Mac) McIngvale

LOCATIONS

HQ: GALLERY MODEL HOMES INC.
6006 NORTH FWY, HOUSTON, TX 770764029
Phone: 7136921111
Web: WWW.GALLERYFURNITURE.COM

COMPETITORS

Chair King
Ethan Allen
Havertys
IKEA
Mattress Firm
Rooms To Go
Star Furniture

HISTORICAL FINANCIALS

Company Type: Private

Income Statement FYE: December 31

	REVENUE ($ mil.)	NET INCOME ($ mil.)	NET PROFIT MARGIN	EMPLOYEES
12/07	111	3	3.2%	400
12/06	129	1	0.8%	—
12/05	130	0	0.4%	—
12/04	115	0	—	—
Annual Growth	(1.1%)	—	—	—

GALLUP INC.

More than a pollster Gallup draws from its research and behavioral studies to offer consulting services related to performance management. Other specialties include branding marketing and recruiting. The company delivers its services on the Web through its Gallup University campuses and through about 40 global offices. It draws customers from a variety of industries including automotive business services health care hospitality manufacturing and retail. Despite its diversified business offerings the company is still most famous for its Gallup Poll surveys. It is owned by its employees.

Geographic Reach

Gallup's nearly 40 offices are spread around the Americas Asia Pacific Europe the Middle East and Africa.

Operations

Gallup has a staff of more than 2000 professionals. Gallup News reports on the world's 7 billion citizens based on Gallup's continuous polling in 160 countries.

Strategy

In addition to its famous polls and research surveys the company's Gallup Consulting division provides expertise in measuring employee satisfaction and engagement and in teaching managers and workers how to develop their strengths in order to be the best at their jobs. Gallup consultants help private and public sector organizations boost organic growth through measurement tools strategic advice and education.

Ownership

Gallup is an employee-owned company.

Company Background

The company was founded in 1935 by Dr. George Gallup a pioneer in the science of polling.

EXECUTIVES

CIO, Phil Ruhlman
Vice Chairman; Dean Gallup University, Connie Rath
Vice Chairman Research and Development, Gale D. Muller
General Counsel and Executive Publisher Gallup, Steve D. O'Brien
Director Corporate Communications, Sarah Van Allen
Chief Operating Officer, Jane E. Miller, age 49
Chief Marketing Officer; Executive Publisher Gallup Press, Lawrence M. (Larry) Emond
Chairman and CEO, Jim Clifton
CFO, James (Jim) Krieger
Editor-in-Chief Gallup, Frank M. Newport
Chief Economist, Dennis Jacobe
Regional Director Middle East and North Africa, Richard W. Burkholder Jr.
Regional Director Former Soviet Union Countries, Neli Esipova
Regional Director Latin America, Johanna Godoy
Senior Analyst and Executive Director Gallup Center for Muslim Studies, Dalia Mogahed
Regional Director Europe, Zsolt Nyiri
Regional Director Latin America, Jesus Rios
Regional Director Asia, Rajesh Srinivasan
Regional Director Sub-Saharan Africa, Robert D. Tortora
Chief Scientist, Jim Asplund
Chief Scientist, John H. Fleming
Chief Scientist, James K. Harter
Global Practice Leader Brand Engagement, William J. McEwen
Global Practice Leader Workplace and Leadership, Tom Rath
Senior Director Media Strategies, Eric Nielsen
Global Practice Leader Brand and Customer Engagement, Ed O'Boyle
Editorial Director Gallup Press, Geoffrey Brewer
Founder, George Gallup
Vice Chairman; Dean Gallup University, Connie Rath
Vice Chairman and CFO, James (Jim) Krieger
Auditors: KPMG

LOCATIONS

HQ: GALLUP INC.
901 F ST NW STE 400, WASHINGTON, DC 20004-1419
Phone: 202-715-3030
Web: WWW.GALLUP.COM

PRODUCTS/OPERATIONS

Selected Consulting Practice Areas

Customer relationship management
Employee development and training
Employee performance measurement
Employee relationship management
Executive coaching
Performance strategy analysis
Sales force training
Succession planning
Talent-based hiring

Selected Gallup Poll Topics

Business
Economics
Education
Government and public affairs
Healthcare
Lifestyle issues
Politics and elections
Religion and values
Other Products and Services
Books
Gallup University (management education)
Subscription publications

COMPETITORS

Abt Associates
Bain & Company
Booz Allen
Boston Consulting
Development Dimensions International
Edison Media Research
Harris Interactive
Hay Group
IBOPE Zogby International
International Demographics
J.D. Power
Kantar Group
Maritz
McKinsey & Company
ORC International

HISTORICAL FINANCIALS

Company Type: Private

Income Statement FYE: December 31

	REVENUE ($ mil.)	NET INCOME ($ mil.)	NET PROFIT MARGIN	EMPLOYEES
12/12	275	23	8.4%	2,000
12/11	303	34	11.2%	—
12/09	264	6	2.6%	—
12/08	300	21	7.0%	—
Annual Growth	(2.2%)	2.3%	—	—

2012 Year-End Financials

Debt ratio: —
Return on equity: 8.40%
Cash ($ mil.): 31
Current ratio: 0.70
Long-term debt ($ mil.): —
Dividends
Yield: —
Payout: —
Market value ($ mil.): —

GAVI FUND

LOCATIONS

HQ: GAVI FUND
1776 I ST NW STE 600, WASHINGTON, DC 200063765
Phone: 2024781050
Web: WWW.GAVIALLIANCE.ORG

HISTORICAL FINANCIALS

Company Type: Private

Income Statement FYE: December 31

	REVENUE ($ mil.)	NET INCOME ($ mil.)	NET PROFIT MARGIN	EMPLOYEES
12/08	306	(625)	—	100
12/06*	388	1,953	503.1%	—
06/01	18,546	16	0.1%	—
Annual Growth	(40.1%)	—	—	—

*Fiscal year change

2008 Year-End Financials

Debt ratio: —
Return on equity: (-203.70%)
Cash ($ mil.): 536
Current ratio: —
Long-term debt ($ mil.): —
Dividends
Yield: —
Payout: —
Market value ($ mil.): —

GEHAN HOMES LTD.

LOCATIONS

HQ: GEHAN HOMES LTD.
15725 DALLAS PKWY STE 300, ADDISON, TX 750013850
Phone: 9726639100
Web: WWW.GEHANHOMES.COM

HISTORICAL FINANCIALS

Company Type: Private

Income Statement FYE: December 31

	REVENUE ($ mil.)	NET INCOME ($ mil.)	NET PROFIT MARGIN	EMPLOYEES
12/07*	214	4	1.9%	175
11/02	150	13	9.1%	—
Annual Growth	7.4%	(21.8%)	—	—

*Fiscal year change

2007 Year-End Financials

Debt ratio: —
Return on equity: 1.90%
Cash ($ mil.): 6
Current ratio: 0.10
Long-term debt ($ mil.): —
Dividends
Yield: —
Payout: —
Market value ($ mil.): —

GELBER GROUP LLC

Gelber Group develops proprietary technology-based trading models for dealing in equities cash currencies commodities sovereign debt futures and related options markets. The company no longer has outside clients or investors; all of its trading activity is undertaken for its own account. Gelber Group which previously provided electronic trading services to individual professional traders was co-founded in 1982 by Brian Gelber (company chairman and president) and Frank Gelber (CFO). In addition to its Chicago Apparel Center headquarters the company also boasts offices in Connecticut New Jersey and New York as well as the UK and Switzerland.

Geographic Reach

With a home office in Chicago and offices in the US the UK and Switzerland Gelber Group trades across all major asset classes in the Americas Europe and Asia.

Strategy

Focusing on technology management and service as a leader in algorithmic trading Gelber Group works to expand its business globally to liquid electronic markets. The company looks to tap new trading opportunities across the world's financial and commodity markets.

Sales and Marketing

The investment firm serves individual professional traders trading groups or institutions.

EXECUTIVES

Chairman President CEO, Brian Gelber
Chief Technology Officer, Patrick Coffey

LOCATIONS

HQ: GELBER GROUP LLC
350 N ORLEANS ST FL 7, CHICAGO, IL 60654-1601
Phone: 312-253-0005
Web: WWW.GELBERGROUP.COM

PRODUCTS/OPERATIONS

Selected Markets

Cash
Commodities
Currencies
Equities
Futures
Sovereign debt

COMPETITORS

ADM Investor Services
Interactive Brokers
Investment Technology
Newedge
R.J. O' Brien
Rosenthal Collins
TradeStation

HISTORICAL FINANCIALS

Company Type: Private

Income Statement FYE: December 31

	ASSETS ($ mil.)	NET INCOME ($ mil.)	INCOME AS % OF ASSETS	EMPLOYEES
12/07	338	112	33.3%	300
12/04	106	70	65.8%	—
12/03	0	0	—	—
Annual Growth	—	811.0%	—	—

2007 Year-End Financials

Debt ratio: —
Return on equity: 50.30%
Cash ($ mil.): 1
Current ratio: —
Long-term debt ($ mil.): —
Dividends
Yield: —
Payout: —
Market value ($ mil.): —

GENESIS CORP.

Genesis Corp.'s raison d'etre is business and technology consulting. Focused on helping organizations streamline processes manage employees and minimize costs the company (doing business as Genesis10) provides services in areas such as project management application development enterprise systems integration staffing and management support. The company's managed service program assists businesses in managing its workforce as well as outsourced work. Genesis10 founded in 1999 also helps organizations with their hiring compliance and change management issues

Geographic Reach

Genesis10 operates from more than 20 sales and recruiting offices in the US and Canada. (This network includes five domestic delivery centers.)

Sales and Marketing

The company has over 150 clients the majority of whom are listed on the Fortune 500. Its customers reside in the financial services communications consumer products energy health care insurance manufacturing and technology industries.

EXECUTIVES

President Chief Financial Officer, Glenn Klein
CEO, Harley Lippman
EVP of Strategy, Walter Taylor
Senior Vice President National Delivery, Amy Drury

LOCATIONS

HQ: GENESIS CORP.
950 3RD AVE STE 2702, NEW YORK, NY 10022-2874
Phone: 212-688-5522
Web: WWW.GENESIS10.COM

PRODUCTS/OPERATIONS

Selected Products and Services

Business and technology staffing
G10 Associates (college hiring)
Project-based consulting
Veterans outreach

COMPETITORS

A.T. Kearney
Accenture
Bain & Company
Booz Allen
Boston Consulting
Deloitte Consulting
McKinsey & Company
Oliver Wyman
PA Consulting
Roland Berger

HISTORICAL FINANCIALS

Company Type: Private

Income Statement FYE: December 31

	REVENUE ($ mil.)	NET INCOME ($ mil.)	NET PROFIT MARGIN	EMPLOYEES
12/11	218	11	5.5%	2,105
12/10	173	10	6.1%	—
12/08	122	2	2.2%	—
12/07	130	3	2.5%	—
Annual Growth	13.7%	38.1%	—	—

2011 Year-End Financials

Debt ratio: —
Return on equity: 5.50%
Cash ($ mil.): 6
Current ratio: 1.30
Long-term debt ($ mil.): —
Dividends
Yield: —
Payout: —
Market value ($ mil.): —

GENESIS HEALTH SYSTEM

Genesis Health System operates three acute care hospitals in Iowa and Illinois that have more than 660 beds total and employ some 600 doctors. Genesis Medical Center in Davenport Iowa with more than 500 beds is the system's flagship facility; the hospital offers a range of general surgical and specialist health services. The system's Illini Campus in Silvis Illinois features an assisted-living center. The Genesis Medical Center Dewitt Campus serves that Iowa town and the surrounding area with its 13-bed hospital nursing home and related care facilities. Genesis Health System also operates physician practices outpatient centers and a home health agency.

Strategy In mid-2012 Genesis Health System joined with Wellmark Blue Cross and Blue Shield of Iowa to create an accountable care organization (ACO) in an effort to improve the quality and slow the costs of healthcare. In an ACO provider reimbursements are related to the quality of the care.

Company Background Genesis Health System had its genesis in 1869 with the establishment of Mercy Hospital (one of the first hospitals west of the Mississippi) and in the 1895 founding of St. Luke's Hospital. The two hospitals merged in 1994 to form the health system.

EXECUTIVES

VP Information Services and CIO, Robert (Rob) Frieden
VP; CEO Genesis Medical Center DeWitt, Jeffrey M. (Jeff) Cooper
VP Strategic Development, Robert (Bob) Travis
VP Quality, James Lehman
VP Corporate Communications and Business Development, Kenneth Croken
President and CEO, Douglas P. (Doug) Cropper
VP Medical Staff Affairs, Frank Claudy
VP Clinical Services, Rob Nelson
Medical Director, Bill Langley
VP Legal Affairs, Judith Mondello
Interim VP Patient Services, Judy Pranger
VP Finance and CFO, Mark Rogers
Vice President Support Services, Mike Sharp
Senior Vice President Genesis, Florence (Flo) Spyrow
Chief Medical Officer, Joseph Lohmuller
Vice President Human Resources, Heidi Kahly-McMahon
COO and President Genesis Medical Center Davenport, Wayne Diewald
Chief Nurse Executive, Jackie Anhalt
President Genesis Health Group, Richard Kishiue
VP Outpatient Services, Kevin Youmans

LOCATIONS

HQ: GENESIS HEALTH SYSTEM
1227 E RUSHOLME ST, DAVENPORT, IA 52803-2459
Phone: 563-421-1000
Web: WWW.GENESISHEALTHCLINIC.ORG

PRODUCTS/OPERATIONS

Selected Services

Bariatric Surgery
Behavioral Health
Birthing Services
Cancer
Cardiology
Home Health/Hospice
Neuroscience
Nursing Homes
Physical Medicine & Rehab
Senior Services

COMPETITORS

Blessing Hospital
Catholic Health Initiatives
Iowa Health System
McDonough District Hospital
Mercy Health Network
ORHC
OSF Healthcare System
University of Iowa Hospitals and Clinics

HISTORICAL FINANCIALS

Company Type: Private

Income Statement FYE: June 30

	REVENUE ($ mil.)	NET INCOME ($ mil.)	NET PROFIT MARGIN	EMPLOYEES
06/10	461	16	3.5%	5,000
06/09	993	0	—	—
06/09	1,643	0	0.0%	—
Annual Growth	(71.9%)	98808.6%	—	—

2010 Year-End Financials

Debt ratio: ——
Return on equity: 3.50%
Cash ($ mil.): 43
Current ratio: 0.80
Long-term debt ($ mil.): —
Dividends
Yield: —
Payout: —
Market value ($ mil.): —

GENESIS HEALTHCARE SYSTEM

Genesis HealthCare System doesn't need Phil Collins on drums to give it the medical touch. The health care system consists of two acute care hospitals (Genesis-Bethesda and Genesis-Good Samaritan Hospital) in Zanesville Ohio. In addition to general medical emergency and surgical care the hospitals' specialty areas include oncology trauma cardiovascular health orthopedics neurology and women's health. Genesis HealthCare also operates facilities for pharmacy child development and home health and hospice services as well as family practice and specialist offices. Genesis HealthCare is a not-for-profit system formed in 1997 when the Bethesda and Good Samaritan hospitals merged.

Geographic Reach

Genesis HealthCare serves residents of six counties in southeastern Ohio including the counties of Coshocton Guernsey Morgan Muskingum Noble and Perry.

Operations

Genesis HealthCare's outpatient facilities include the offices of some 300 physicians. Its Genesis HealthPlex provides a number of specialist services. The health system also operates the Community Ambulance Service as a joint venture between Genesis HealthCare and Community EMS. The service operates throughout Zanesville and is equipped with a computer-aided dispatch system that automatically monitors and records incoming calls and response times.

Strategy

In 2011 Genesis HealthCare announced plans to build a new state-of-the-art medical center with 260 beds on the grounds of the Bethesda Hospital. The $125 million project includes complete renovation of the existing hospital with a new patient tower an outpatient cancer center and a medical office building. Construction of the new Genesis Medical Center began in 2013 with completion expected in 2015.

Other expansion efforts include the addition of a breast care center at the outpatient center (HealthPlex) and a heart and vascular clinic at the Good Samaritan campus during 2012. To expand its network and help a smaller facility to remain independent the organization agreed to provide management services to the Coshocton County Memorial Hospital that year. It also partnered with other area organizations to build a recreational center in the community of Muskingum.

To further enhance its services Genesis HealthCare became a provisional Level III Trauma Center in 2010; its status was verified in 2012. The designation means that patients with serious trauma-related injuries are able to get specialized trauma care at the system's facilities.

In addition Genesis HealthCare is implementing an electronic health record (EHR) system that connects Genesis HealthCare hospitals and physician offices throughout the region. The total cost of the multi-year installation is roughly $50 million. In 2012 about 60 physicians at 20 practice locations were connected to the organization's EHR system (made by Epic Systems) and Genesis HealthCare boasted about 5400 active health professionals in the medical records (MyChart) feature of the Epic EHR. It also launched an Epic revenue cycle management program that year to improve registration scheduling and billing processes.

EXECUTIVES

Chief Financial Officer, Paul Masterson
Chief Development Officer, Al Burns
Vice Chair, Michael L. Bennett
Chair, Mark Moyer
Secretary, Walter E. Offinger
President CEO, Matt Perry
President CEO, Mathew Perry
Chief Human Resources Officer, Cassandra Palmer
Chief Nursing Officer, Pat Campbell
VP Quality, Gina Pennington
Chief Information Officer, Ed Romito
Chief Operating Officer, Richard Helsper
Vice Chair, Michael L. Bennett
Trustee, Robert D. Kessler
Trustee, William A. Phillips
Trustee, Walter Wielkiewicz
Trustee, Theresa Feldkamp
Trustee, Thomas H. Diehl
Trustee, James McDonald
Trustee, Jerry Nolder
President CEO, Matt Perry
Trustee, Erin Welch
Trustee, Brian W. Luft

LOCATIONS

HQ: GENESIS HEALTHCARE SYSTEM
800 FOREST AVE, ZANESVILLE, OH 43701-2821
Phone: 740-454-4000
Web: WWW.GENESISHCS.ORG

PRODUCTS/OPERATIONS

Selected Services

Cancer
Emergency and trauma
Heart and vascular
Neurosciences
Orthopedic care
Women' s health

Selected Facilities

Genesis-Bethesda Hospital
Genesis-Good Samaritan Hospital
Genesis CareGivers
Genesis Children' s Center
Genesis HomeCare
Genesis Lifestyle & Fitness Center
Northside Home Infusion
Northside Oxygen & Medical Equipment
Northside Pharmacy
Quality Care Partners

COMPETITORS

Catholic Health Initiatives
Catholic Health Partners
Fairfield Medical Center
Licking Memorial Health Systems
Mount Carmel Health
Nationwide Children' s Hospital
OhioHealth
Select Medical

HISTORICAL FINANCIALS

Company Type: Private

Income Statement FYE: December 31

	REVENUE ($ mil.)	NET INCOME ($ mil.)	NET PROFIT MARGIN	EMPLOYEES
12/11	380	(4)	—	3,500
12/10	369	15	4.2%	—
12/09	353	23	6.7%	—
12/07	259	8	3.3%	—
Annual Growth	10.0%	—	—	—

2011 Year-End Financials

Debt ratio: ——
Return on equity: (-1.30%)
Cash ($ mil.): 20
Current ratio: 1.70
Long-term debt ($ mil.): —
Dividends
Yield: —
Payout: —
Market value ($ mil.): —

GENICA CORPORATION

Think of Genica as computerdom's bargain basement. The company sells computer components peripherals and accessories —mainly overstocks and closeouts —over the Internet. It operates through two business units: Computer Geeks (which targets consumers through its geeks.com website) and Evertek Computer (which markets to small businesses and FORTUNE 500 firms). The company which offers more than 3000 brand name products was formed by the merger of online seller Computer Geeks with computer importer/distributor Evertek Computer and its Hong Kong-based sister firm Evertek Trading. Chairman and CEO Frank Segler owns a majority stake in Genica.

Geographic Reach

Temecula California-based Genica operates a 190000-sq.-ft. commercial property in Oceanside California —90% of which is dedicated to warehousing and fulfillment services. The company also has offices in Taiwan and Hong Kong.

Operations

Genica's wholesale unit Evertek Computer contributes about two-thirds of its sales while the consumer division Computer Geeks accounts for the rest.

EXECUTIVES

Vp International Operations, Randy Segler
Vice President Marketing, Chris Herzog
Vice President Of International, Kevin Segler
Vice President, Alan Hawkshaw
Vice President Controller, Patrick Thompson
Board Of Directors, Christine Lamarca

LOCATIONS

HQ: GENICA CORPORATION
43195 BUSINESS PARK DR, TEMECULA, CA 92590-3629
Phone: 855-433-5747
Web: WWW.GENICA.COM

COMPETITORS

Amazon.com
CDW
CompUSA
CompuCom
Enable Holdings
Insight Enterprises
Newegg
PC Connection
PC Mall
Systemax
Zones
eBay

HISTORICAL FINANCIALS

Company Type: Private

Income Statement FYE: December 31

	REVENUE ($ mil.)	NET INCOME ($ mil.)	NET PROFIT MARGIN	EMPLOYEES
12/09	172	5	3.2%	334
12/08	164	3	2.2%	—
12/08	672	0	—	—
Annual Growth	(74.4%)	29194636.8%	—	—

2009 Year-End Financials

Debt ratio: —
Return on equity: 3.20%
Cash ($ mil.): 0
Current ratio: 0.20
Long-term debt ($ mil.): —
Dividends
Yield: —
Payout: —
Market value ($ mil.): —

GEORGE E. WARREN CORPORATION

EXECUTIVES

President and CEO, Thomas L. Corr
CFO and Controller, Michael E. George
Director Human Resources, Cheryl Ernst
Vice President Operations, Timothy Smith

LOCATIONS

HQ: GEORGE E. WARREN CORPORATION
3001 OCEAN DR STE 203, VERO BEACH, FL 329631992
Phone: 7727787100
Web: WWW.GEWARREN.COM

COMPETITORS

Center Oil
ConocoPhillips
Crown Central
Exxon Mobil
Martin Resource Management
Penn Octane
Sun Coast Resources
Williams Companies

HISTORICAL FINANCIALS

Company Type: Private

Income Statement FYE: December 31

	REVENUE ($ mil.)	NET INCOME ($ mil.)	NET PROFIT MARGIN	EMPLOYEES
12/13	106	36	34.0%	35
12/12	156	56	35.9%	—
12/11	91	27	29.7%	—
12/10	79	0	—	—
Annual Growth	10.6%	—	—	—

2013 Year-End Financials

Debt ratio: —
Return on equity: 34.00%
Cash ($ mil.): 177
Current ratio: 0.80
Long-term debt ($ mil.): —
Dividends
Yield: —
Payout: —
Market value ($ mil.): —

GEORGIA SOUTHERN UNIVERSITY

Georgia Southern University shows students that higher education can be just peachy. Georgia Southern offers its student body more than 125 bachelor master and doctoral programs from eight colleges; academic fields include business education science and public health. One of 35 colleges and universities in the University System of Georgia it enrolls more than 20500 students most of which hail from Georgia. The average class size of lower division courses is about 43 upper division 23 and graduate level 11. The student to faculty ratio is 22:1.

Geographic Reach

Georgia Southern has a main campus Statesboro and graduate centers in Augusta Brunswick Dublin and Savannah; it also offers distance learning programs.

Operations

The university has some 3260 full time employees including faculty. Some 47% of its faculty are female 21% are minorities and 76% have doctorate level degrees. About 48% of the faculty are tenured while 24% are on tenure track.

Financial Performance

Georgia Southern saw an 8% increase in revenues in fiscal 2013 as the result of higher tuition and fees state appropriation grants contracts and other sources. It also reflected the impact of the acquisition of the Herty Advanced Material Center (transferred to Georgia Southern by the state legislature in 2012). Tuition and fees contributed about 50% of fiscal year 2013 revenues.

Strategy

Expanding its facilities in 2013 Georgia Southern opened a $41.4 million 158000 sq. ft. Biological Sciences Building (housing five active-learning classrooms 10 teaching labs and 15 research labs) for use by more than 1300 undergraduate and graduate biology students.

Company Background

Founded as a district agricultural school in 1906 the institution became a university in 1990.

EXECUTIVES

Vice President Business And Finance, Joseph Franklin
Secretary, Cindy Durden

LOCATIONS

HQ: GEORGIA SOUTHERN UNIVERSITY
1582 SOUTHERN DR, STATESBORO, GA 30458
Phone: 912-681-5224
Web: WWW.GSUSTORE.COM

HISTORICAL FINANCIALS

Company Type: Private

Income Statement FYE: June 30

	REVENUE ($ mil.)	NET INCOME ($ mil.)	NET PROFIT MARGIN	EMPLOYEES
06/12	185	0	0.5%	1,700
06/11	177	10	5.8%	—
06/10	151	9	6.0%	—
06/09	6	(0)	—	—
Annual Growth	201.0%	—	—	—

2012 Year-End Financials

Debt ratio: —
Return on equity: 0.50%
Cash ($ mil.): 44
Current ratio: 2.10
Long-term debt ($ mil.): —
Dividends
Yield: —
Payout: —
Market value ($ mil.): —

GEORGIA TRANSMISSION CORPORATION

With Georgia on its mind Georgia Transmission provides electric transmission services to power producers and distribution utilities. The company primarily transports power for its 39 member distribution cooperatives (out of Georgia's total of 42 coops) and their electricity supplier Oglethorpe Power. Georgia Transmission owns 3060 miles of transmission lines asn more that 640 substations. It jointly owns and plans the state's entire 17500 miles of transmission lines through the Integrated Transmission System in collaboration with Georgia Power MEAG Power and Dalton Utilities.

The economic downturn in 2008 and 2009 and unusually mild summers in 2009 and 2010 resulted in a slowing of the growth of the power load. Nevertheless Georgia Transmission is committed to upgrading its infrastructure to keep up with a growing population and to maintain regulatory compliance. It expects to add 1.2 million residnetial customers by 2020.

In 2010 Georgia Transmission built more than 190 projects including six new electrical substations and 45 miles of power line.

The entity collects revenues for network services from its Member Systems and Oglethorpe Power pursuant to long-term transmission agreements. In 2010 it reported an increase in revenues thanks to increased interest depreciation and other factors. Net margin was flat for the year.

Georgia Transmission was formed in 1974 as the transmission arm of Oglethorpe. In 1997 Georgia Transmission became a stand-alone power transmission cooperative.

EXECUTIVES

Sr. Vice President Chief Financial Officer, Barbara Hampton
Chairman, Charles R. Fendley, age 68
President and CEO, Michael (Mike) Smith
Human Resources, Shaunna Tyus
VP External Affairs and Member Relations, Tom Parker
Vice President Transmission Policy, Keith Daniel
Vice Chairman, Steve E. Rawl Sr.
President and CEO, Jerry Donovan
Vice President System Planning, Russ Schussler
VP Operations and Maintenance, David VanWinkle
Vendor and Contract Relations, Sonda Bradfield
Vice President Operations and Maintenance, David Winkle
Vice President, Angela Sheffield
Vice President Project Services, John Raese
Director, Ronnie Lee
Vice Chairman, Steve E. Rawl Sr.
Director, David Dunaway
Director, James Hubbard
Director, Kenneth Cook
Director, Everett Williams
Director, Jill Tietjen
Director, Gary Drake
Auditors: Ernst&YoungLLP

LOCATIONS

HQ: GEORGIA TRANSMISSION CORPORATION
2100 E EXCHANGE PL, TUCKER, GA 30084-5342
Phone: 770-270-7400
Web: WWW.GATRANS.COM

PRODUCTS/OPERATIONS

2010 Sales

	$ mil.	% of total
Network services	202	85
Other transmission	36	15
Total	**239**	**100**

HISTORICAL FINANCIALS

Company Type: Private

Income Statement FYE: December 31

	REVENUE ($ mil.)	NET INCOME ($ mil.)	NET PROFIT MARGIN	EMPLOYEES
12/09	229	14	6.3%	160
12/08	225	13	6.0%	—
12/08	0	0	—	—
Annual Growth	—	—	—	—

2009 Year-End Financials

Debt ratio: —
Return on equity: 6.30%
Cash ($ mil.): 28
Current ratio: 0.10
Long-term debt ($ mil.): —
Dividends
Yield: —
Payout: —
Market value ($ mil.): —

GERALD H. PHIPPS INC.

LOCATIONS

HQ: GERALD H. PHIPPS INC.
5995 GREENWOOD STE 100, GREENWOOD VILLAGE, CO 80111
Phone: 3035715377
Web: WWW.GHPHIPPS.COM

HISTORICAL FINANCIALS

Company Type: Private

Income Statement FYE: October 31

	REVENUE ($ mil.)	NET INCOME ($ mil.)	NET PROFIT MARGIN	EMPLOYEES
10/14	216	0	0.4%	350
10/13	226	(1)	—	—
10/12	215	1	0.5%	—
10/11	131	0	—	—
Annual Growth	18.0%	—	—	—

2014 Year-End Financials

Debt ratio: —
Return on equity: 0.40%
Cash ($ mil.): 9
Current ratio: 1.10
Long-term debt ($ mil.): —
Dividends
Yield: —
Payout: —
Market value ($ mil.): —

GIBBS DIE CASTING CORPORATION

There's plenty to die for at Gibbs Die Casting. The company manufactures aluminum and magnesium die-castings such as air conditioning compressor commercial refrigeration and engine and viscous clutch parts. Its Comac Machining Division provides precision machining and assembly work. The Audubon Tool Division uses fused deposition modeling prototyping equipment and CNC electrical discharge machines to build die-casting tools. Gibbs Engineering offers on-site product design prototype models and production tooling services. Gibbs Die Casting serves industries such as automobile and appliance manufacturing and alternative energy. Gibbs is owned by Koch Enterprises.

Geographic Reach

Based in Kentucky Gibbs Die Casting operates worldwide.

Operations

At its Kentucky headquarters Gibbs Die Casting maintains a manufacturing facility and technical center. Altogether Gibbs Die Casting operates eight plants (five for die-casting four for machining and one die building facility) with a total of more than 1.2 million sq. ft. of floor space across the US Brazil Hungary and China. The company performs its work using about 50 vertical and horizontal die casting machines that vary from 600 to 1600 tons.

Sales and Marketing

Gibbs Die Casting serves several sectors such as lawn and garden alternative energy small engine furniture and automotive. Automobile manufacturers –who are using more aluminum and magnesium parts to create lighter vehicles –account for about 90% of sales. Indeed Ford General Motors Fiat and Toyota are top customers.

Strategy

To keep up with the demand for lighter-weight aluminum die castings for the auto market Gibbs Die Casting is expanding its Comac Machining Division with new production lines at the Tech and Synchronous plants. The investment will cost the company $23 million.

Company Ownership

Koch Enterprises has owned Gibbs Die Casting since 1969.

Company Background

Gibbs Die Casting was founded in 1965 by Bob and Nick Gibbs.

EXECUTIVES

Assistant Treasurer and Director, Susan E. Parsons
Chairman, Robert L. (Bob) Koch II, age 75
Vice President, James H. (Jim) Muehlbauer
Treasurer and Director, William (Bill) Baxter
President, Steve A. Church
Marketing and Sales, Norm Wymer
Assistant Treasurer and Director, Susan E. Parsons
Director, James H. (Jim) Muehlbauer
Treasurer and Director, William (Bill) Baxter
Director, Thomas A. (Tom) Mowatt
Director, William L. (Bill) Haeberle
Director, Kevin R. Koch
President and Director, Steve A. Church

LOCATIONS

HQ: GIBBS DIE CASTING CORPORATION
369 COMMUNITY DR, HENDERSON, KY 42420-4397
Phone: 270-827-1801
Web: WWW.SUPPLIER.GIBBSDC.COM

PRODUCTS/OPERATIONS

Selected Services
Die building & design
Die casting
Engineering & prototyping
Machining
Value-added assembly

COMPETITORS

Anchor Mfg. Group
Atlantic Tool & Die
BuhlerPrince
Martinrea International
Peterson American
Shiloh Industries
WSI Industries
Wozniak Industries

HISTORICAL FINANCIALS

Company Type: Private

Income Statement FYE: December 31

	REVENUE ($ mil.)	NET INCOME ($ mil.)	NET PROFIT MARGIN	EMPLOYEES
12/12	175	0	—	1,299
12/11	187	0	—	—
12/10	210	0	—	—
12/09	158	0	—	—
Annual Growth	3.5%	—	—	—

2012 Year-End Financials

Debt ratio: —
Return on equity: —
Cash ($ mil.): 3
Current ratio: 0.90
Long-term debt ($ mil.): —
Dividends
Yield: —
Payout: —
Market value ($ mil.): —

GIRL SCOUTS OF THE UNITED STATES OF AMERICA

EXECUTIVES

Senior Vice President Human Resources, Michael Watson
Senior Vice President Chief Financial Officer, Florence Corsello
SVP Governance and Corporate Administration, Deborah Long
Chief Executive Officer, Kathy Cloninger
Second VP and Director, Linda P. Foreman
Chief of Staff, Jaclyn E. Libowitz
SVP Public Policy Advocacy and the Research Institute, Laurie A. Westley
Secretary and Director, Linda Mazon-Gutierrez
Treasurer and Director, Joan Wagnon
EVP Mission to Market, Norma I. Barquet
First VP and Director, Davia B. Temin
Honorary President, Michelle Obama
Chief Development Officer, Deb Taft
Chief Information Officer, Maggie Miller
Director, Harriet Edelman, age 58
Director, Marie C. Johns
Director, Vikki L. Pryor, age 60
Director, Sharon H. Matthews
Second VP and Director, Linda P. Foreman
Director, Nan C. Hillis, age 59
Secretary and Director, Linda Mazon-Gutierrez
Director, Debra Nakatomi
Director, Raquel (Rocky) Egusquiza
Director, Patricia Bowe Romines
Director, Sara L. Schwebel
Director, Marisa Tabizon Thompson
Treasurer and Director, Joan Wagnon
Director, Michelle L. Holiday
First VP and Director, Davia B. Temin
Director, Sylvia Acevedo
Director, Barbara F. Adachi
Director, Catherine Coughlin
Director, Ellen S. Fox
Director, Lisa Guillermin Gable
Director, John Hom
Director, Ingrid Saunders Jones
Director, Karen A. Maloney
Director, Robert L. Morris
Director, Susan P. Peters
Director, Rhea S. Schwartz
Director, Eileen Scott

Director, Gail M. Talbott
Director, Susan L. Taylor
Auditors: Ernst&YoungLLP

LOCATIONS

HQ: GIRL SCOUTS OF THE UNITED STATES OF AMERICA
420 5TH AVE FL 13, NEW YORK, NY 100182729
Phone: 2128528000
Web: WWW.GIRLSCOUTS.ORG

PRODUCTS/OPERATIONS

Girl Scout Programs	
Daisy Girl Scouts (ages	5
Brownie Girl Scouts (ages	6
Junior Girl Scouts (ages	8
Girl Scouts (ages	11

HISTORICAL FINANCIALS

Company Type: Private

Income Statement FYE: September 30

	REVENUE ($ mil.)	NET INCOME ($ mil.)	NET PROFIT MARGIN	EMPLOYEES
09/12	105	5	5.6%	500
09/11	129	(2)	—	—
09/10	80	(4)	—	—
09/09	66	0	—	—
Annual Growth	16.6%	—	—	—

2012 Year-End Financials

Debt ratio: —
Return on equity: 5.60%
Cash ($ mil.): 19
Current ratio: 0.50
Long-term debt ($ mil.): —
Dividends
Yield: —
Payout: —
Market value ($ mil.): —

GLENDALE ADVENTIST MEDICAL CENTER INC

Treating ladies from Pasadena and other patients throughout the suburbs of sunny Southern California Glendale Adventist Medical Center (GAMC) is a stalwart community member. The hospital is part of Adventist Health a group of about 20 hospitals and health care organizations in four western states. GAMC provides a range of specialty services including cancer treatment cardiology emergency medicine neuroscience home care psychiatry rehabilitation and women's healthcare. It also provides medical training and residency programs. The 515-bed hospital was founded in 1905 by the Seventh-Day Adventist Church.

Geographic Reach

GAMC is located in Glendale California and serves surrounding communities in Southern California.

Operations

GAMC employs more than 700 physicians and provides services to about 20000 inpatients each year. It also handles 46000 emergency department visits 20000 home health visits 280000 outpatient appointments and 2500 births each year. In addition the hospital provides more than $30 million in charity and community care services each year.

Strategy

GAMC is expanding its hospital facilities technologies and programs to enhance patient care. For instance it opened the final phase of its new West Tower in 2012 adding 60 beds and an expanded cardiovascular care center. The hospital also implemented its electronic health record (EHR) system including computerized order entry and bar code medication systems for improved patient safety. In addition GAMC introduced a new extended internship program for medical students studying clinical care fields.

EXECUTIVES

Sr. Vice President CFO, Kelly Turner
President and CEO, Morre Dean
SVP Operations and COO, Warren Tetz
President CEO, Kevin Roberts
Vice President Business Development, Mark J Newmyer
Senior Cno Vice President Clinical Services, Gwen Matthews
Vp Business Development, Kim Milstien
Sr Vice President And Cno, Judy Blair
Vice President, Gloria Santos
Vice President Of Information Technology, Michael Cann
Chairman, Arsen Danielian

LOCATIONS

HQ: GLENDALE ADVENTIST MEDICAL CENTER INC
1509 WILSON TER, GLENDALE, CA 91206-4007
Phone: 818-409-8000
Web: WWW.GLENDALEADVENTIST.COM

PRODUCTS/OPERATIONS

Selected Operations

Advanced Surgical Program
Cancer Services
Heart & Vascular Institute
Neuroscience Institute
Orthopedic Services
Physical Medicine & Rehabilitation
Spine Institute
Women's Services

COMPETITORS

Anaheim Regional Medical Center
Brotman Medical Center
Cedars-Sinai Medical Center
Childrens Hospital Los Angeles
City of Hope
Dignity Health
Glendale Memorial Hospital
Hollywood Presbyterian Medical Center
Long Beach Memorial
Los Angeles County Health Department
Methodist Hospital of Southern California
Pasadena Hospital Association
Tenet Healthcare
Western Medical Center - Santa Ana
White Memorial Medical Center

HISTORICAL FINANCIALS

Company Type: Private

Income Statement FYE: December 31

	REVENUE ($ mil.)	NET INCOME ($ mil.)	NET PROFIT MARGIN	EMPLOYEES
12/12	387	5	1.4%	2,600
12/09*	307	12	4.1%	—
06/05	273	0	0.1%	—
06/05	985	7	0.7%	—
Annual Growth	(11.0%)	(3.5%)	—	—

*Fiscal year change

2012 Year-End Financials

Debt ratio: —
Return on equity: 1.40%
Cash ($ mil.): 39
Current ratio: 3.10
Long-term debt ($ mil.): —
Dividends
Yield: —
Payout: —
Market value ($ mil.): —

GLENN O. HAWBAKER INC.

For Glenn O. Hawbaker (GOH) it's all about making the grade. Founded as an excavating and grading company GOH provides heavy construction concrete construction utility work asphalt production and heavy equipment rentals and sales. From its home base in Pennsylvania the company serves customers in the north-central portion of the state. As part of its business GOH operates two dozen quarries and eight asphalt production facilities in Pennsylvania New York and eastern Ohio (since 2012). Its Hawbaker Engineering subsidiary provides civil engineering services and site designs. The family-owned company was founded in 1952 by Glenn and Thelma Hawbaker the parents of president and CEO Daniel Hawbaker.

Geographic Reach

GOH targets customers in north-central Pennsylvania where it is headquartered. In Pennsylvania New York and eastern Ohio it operates quarries asphalt production facilities and four regional operations centers.

Operations

Besides its core operations GOH runs a construction materials recycling center in State College Pennsylvania that reuses and resells materials such as concrete asphalt wood bricks and yard waste. It also operates subsidiary Hawbaker Engineering a civil engineering and site design provider and Northeast Prestressed Products a unit that offers prestressed concrete bridge beams and precast products for transportation projects in eight northeastern states.

Strategy

GOH has been involved with the development of the Marcellus Shale gas reserve in central Pennsylvania. Drilling for gas trapped beneath layers of shale created a boom for the area and for GOH. It has built roads sold aggregates and performed other services for gas companies as they explore there. To boot the company opened a new quarry to service the gas industry. The project helped GOH weather the economic crisis as road projects and other construction projects ground to a halt. Government stimulus-funded infrastructure projects also helped the company make it through the recession.

Company Ownership

The company is owned by the Glenn and Thelma Hawbaker family.

EXECUTIVES

Vice President Operations, Ivan Hassinger
Regional Vice President Ohio Operations, Jeff Yeager
Vice President Of Sales And Estimating, Steve Taylor

LOCATIONS

HQ: GLENN O. HAWBAKER INC.
1952 WADDLE RD STE 203, STATE COLLEGE, PA 16803-1649
Phone: 814-237-1444
Web: WWW.GOH-INC.COM

Selected Locations

Eastern region
Montoursville office
Northeast region
Greens Landing office
Northern region
Turtle Point office
Ohio region
New Philadelphia office
Pleasant Gap office

State College Pennsylvania
Western region
Dubois office
Grove City office

PRODUCTS/OPERATIONS

Selected Services

Bridge Construction
Environmental Services
Equipment Rental
Equipment sales
Gas Field Services
Portadam Impoundments
Recycle Center State College
Roads & Highways
Sheeting Shoring & Piling
Site Development
Soil Stabilization
Utilities
Wetlands Remediation

Selected Locations

Eastern region
Montoursville office
Northeast region
Greens Landing office
Northern region
Turtle Point office
Ohio region
New Philadelphia office
Pleasant Gap office
State College Pensylvania
Western region
Dubois office
Grove City office

COMPETITORS

A & L
American Asphalt Paving
Balfour Beatty Infrastructure
Community Asphalt Corp.
Eastern Industries
Glasgow Inc.
Gohmann Asphalt & Construction
Kinsley Construction
Lane Construction
New Enterprise Stone & Lime
Peter Kiewit Sons'
Skanska USA Civil

HISTORICAL FINANCIALS

Company Type: Private

Income Statement FYE: December 31

	REVENUE ($ mil.)	NET INCOME ($ mil.)	NET PROFIT MARGIN	EMPLOYEES
12/12	251	0	0.4%	1,300
12/11	326	20	6.4%	—
12/10	337	25	7.5%	—
12/09	220	7	3.6%	—
Annual Growth	4.4%	(50.3%)	—	—

2012 Year-End Financials

Debt ratio: —
Return on equity: 0.40%
Cash ($ mil.): 0
Current ratio: 0.90
Long-term debt ($ mil.): —
Dividends
Yield: —
Payout: —
Market value ($ mil.): —

GLOBAL PACIFIC PRODUCE INC.

Global Pacific Produce is a leading exporter of fresh produce serving international retailers. It sources such goods as apples citrus grapes pears and stone fruit mostly from California and Mexico. The company supplies grocery store chains and other retailers in South America and Europe. Chris Kilvington originally from London started the business in 2000.

EXECUTIVES

President and CEO, Christopher (Chris) Kilvington
Manager Information Technology Finance and Controller, Spirou Khoury
Manager Commercial Export and Domestic, James Scott
Managing Director Global Pacific Europa, Adrian Bishton
Managing Director Global Skins UK, Chris Conroy
Manager Trading Latin America, Marco Nuques
Manager Logistics, Lee Cher
Managing Director KAS Foods, Matt Smith
Managing Director Global Pacific Chile, Luis F. Verela de la Carrera

LOCATIONS

HQ: GLOBAL PACIFIC PRODUCE INC.
11500 S EASTRN AVE 120, HENDERSON, NV 89052
Phone: 702-898-8051
Web: WWW.GLOBALPACIFICPRODUCE.COM

COMPETITORS

Altar Produce LLC
Chiquita Brands
Dole Food
Fresh Del Monte Produce
Gold Digger Apples

HISTORICAL FINANCIALS

Company Type: Private

Income Statement FYE: December 31

	REVENUE ($ mil.)	NET INCOME ($ mil.)	NET PROFIT MARGIN	EMPLOYEES
12/12	315	9	3.1%	250
12/11*	262	5	2.2%	—
01/11	192	4	2.3%	—
12/09	157	2	1.5%	—
Annual Growth	26.0%	60.6%	—	—

*Fiscal year change

2012 Year-End Financials

Debt ratio: —
Return on equity: 3.10%
Cash ($ mil.): 24
Current ratio: 1.40
Long-term debt ($ mil.): —
Dividends
Yield: —
Payout: —
Market value ($ mil.): —

GOLD-EAGLE COOPERATIVE

EXECUTIVES

General Manager, Brad Davis
Controller, John Stelzer
Manager Feed Mill, Brian Kelley
Manager Agronomy, Stu Pannkuk
Manager Seed Sales, Chris Petersen
Manager Transportation, Dennis Reed
Safety Director, Jeff Mericle

LOCATIONS

HQ: GOLD-EAGLE COOPERATIVE
415 LOCUST ST, GOLDFIELD, IA 505425092
Phone: 5158253161
Web: WWW.GOLDEAGLECOOP.COM

COMPETITORS

ADM
Ag Processing Inc.
Bunge Limited
CHS
Cargill
DeBruce Grain
Farmers Cooperative Society
GROWMARK
Heartland Co-op
JR Simplot
NEW Cooperative
West Central Co-op
Wilbur-Ellis

HISTORICAL FINANCIALS

Company Type: Private

Income Statement FYE: September 30

	REVENUE ($ mil.)	NET INCOME ($ mil.)	NET PROFIT MARGIN	EMPLOYEES
09/09	302	10	3.3%	170
09/08	304	9	3.2%	—
09/07	216	5	2.5%	—
09/06	131	0	—	—
Annual Growth	31.9%	—	—	—

2009 Year-End Financials

Debt ratio: —
Return on equity: 3.30%
Cash ($ mil.): 6
Current ratio: 0.60
Long-term debt ($ mil.): —
Dividends
Yield: —
Payout: —
Market value ($ mil.): —

GOLDEN VALLEY ELECTRIC ASSOCIATION INC.

LOCATIONS

HQ: GOLDEN VALLEY ELECTRIC ASSOCIATION INC.
758 ILLINOIS ST, FAIRBANKS, AK 997012919
Phone: 9074521151
Web: WWW.GVEA.COM

HISTORICAL FINANCIALS

Company Type: Private

Income Statement FYE: December 31

	REVENUE ($ mil.)	NET INCOME ($ mil.)	NET PROFIT MARGIN	EMPLOYEES
12/13	246	10	4.2%	270
12/12	273	13	4.8%	—
12/11	224	10	4.4%	—
12/10	224	0	—	—
Annual Growth	3.1%			

2013 Year-End Financials

Debt ratio: —
Return on equity: 4.20%
Cash ($ mil.): 9
Current ratio: 0.90
Long-term debt ($ mil.): —
Dividends
Yield: —
Payout: —
Market value ($ mil.): —

GOOD SAMARITAN HOSPITAL

LOCATIONS

HQ: GOOD SAMARITAN HOSPITAL
255 LAFAYETTE AVE, SUFFERN, NY 109014869
Phone: 8453685000
Web: WWW.GOODSAMHOSP.ORG

PRODUCTS/OPERATIONS

Selected Services

Clinical Services
Cardiology
Cardiac Surgery
Comprehensive Sleep Center
Diagnostic Imaging (Radiology)
Emergency Services
ENT (Ear Nose & Throat)
Gamma Knife
Gastroenterology
Laboratory
Neurosciences
Oncology (Cancer)
Ophthalmology and Retinal Medicine
Orthopedics
Physical Medicine
Podiatry
Pulmonary Medicine and Respiratory Care
Radiation Oncology
Surgery
Women' s Health and Newborn Services
Urology

HISTORICAL FINANCIALS

Company Type: Private

Income Statement FYE: December 31

	REVENUE ($ mil.)	NET INCOME ($ mil.)	NET PROFIT MARGIN	EMPLOYEES
12/08*	254	(12)	—	1,600
06/05	118	(1)	—	—
08/03	159	(0)	—	—
12/02	150	0	—	—
Annual Growth	9.2%	—	—	—

*Fiscal year change

2008 Year-End Financials

Debt ratio: —
Return on equity: (-4.80%)
Cash ($ mil.): 0
Current ratio: 1.00
Long-term debt ($ mil.): —

Dividends
Yield: —
Payout: —
Market value ($ mil.): —

GOOD SAMARITAN HOSPITAL

Good Samaritan Hospital provides a full slate of healthcare services to both southwest Indiana and southeast Illinois. Its services include cardiology emergency care orthopedics women's health and pediatrics among others. The 230-bed hospital is located a few blocks from the Wabash River which forms the border between the Hoosier and Prairies states. Good Samaritan operates specialty units as well including same-day surgery breast care behavioral health radiology sleep cancer care and rehabilitation centers. It also provides home health and hospice services. Established in 1908 with 25 beds Good Samaritan was Indiana's first county hospital.

Geographic Reach

Located in Vincennes Indiana Good Samaritan serves residents along the neighboring southern borders of both Indiana and Illinois.

Operations

Busy regional hospital Good Samaritan logs more than 458000 outpatient visits each year as well as an additional 35950 visits to its emergency room. It boasts an Imaging Center Dayson Heart Center and Cancer Pavilion with a 25000-sq.-ft. comprehensive oncology care center.

Good Samaritan is a member of the Voluntary Hospital Association Indiana Hospital Association and Genesis Health.

Sales and Marketing

The hospital uses TV advertising to market its services.

Strategy

While Good Samaritan is focused on serving patients as an outpatient facility the regional hospital is nearing completion of a new inpatient tower. It's building a 200000-sq.-ft. five-story 120-bed inpatient tower at the cost of $109 million. As part of this BEACON project Good Samaritan is redesigning key healthcare service areas and upgrading its critical engineering systems. Project completion dates span 2014 to late 2016 for the BEACON project.

To make information more readily available to its patients Good Samaritan in 2012 rolled out an Indiana Health Information Exchange clinical messaging service called DOCS4DOCS. The service provides a portal for accessing lab results radiology reports transcripts pathology and hospital admissions reports and discharge and transfer reports. Good Samaritan is one of several thousand participating hospitals along with physician practices labs and radiology centers.

EXECUTIVES

President and CEO, Robert McLin
VP Medical Affairs, Charles C. Hedde
VP Professional and Support Services, Fred J. England

LOCATIONS

HQ: GOOD SAMARITAN HOSPITAL
520 S 7TH ST, VINCENNES, IN 47591-1038
Phone: 812-882-5220
Web: WWW.GSHVIN.ORG

PRODUCTS/OPERATIONS

Selected Centers

Dayson Heart Center
Cancer Pavilion
Imaging Center

COMPETITORS

Daviess Community Hospital
Deaconess Health System
IU Health
Southern Illinois Healthcare
St. John' s Hospital (Illinois)
St. Mary' s Medical Center of Evansville
Wabash County Hospital

HISTORICAL FINANCIALS

Company Type: Private

Income Statement FYE: December 31

	REVENUE ($ mil.)	NET INCOME ($ mil.)	NET PROFIT MARGIN	EMPLOYEES
12/12	191	12	6.6%	1,700
12/11	175	8	4.8%	—
12/10	156	10	6.4%	—
12/09	143	9	6.8%	—
Annual Growth	10.1%	9.0%	—	—

2012 Year-End Financials

Debt ratio: —
Return on equity: 6.60%
Cash ($ mil.): 53
Current ratio: 3.50
Long-term debt ($ mil.): —

Dividends
Yield: —
Payout: —
Market value ($ mil.): —

GOODFELLOW BROS. INC.

The good men at Goodfellow Bros. build everything from golf courses to runways to dams and residences. The family-owned company specializes in heavy construction infrastructure transportation systems and housing and recreation facilities in the western continental US and Hawaii. Goodfellow Bros. also offers earth moving and paving services. Its Blasting Technologies subsidiary blasts drills and demolishes rock and other structures. The company was founded in 1921 by brothers Jack Bert and Jim Sr. Their early business included the first excavation work on the Grand Coulee Dam in 1933. Now the company has a number of planned communities public facilities ,Â and other projects ,Âunder its belt. ,Â

EXECUTIVES

Vice President Finance, Ronald Lester
Assistant Vice President, Henry Kennedy

LOCATIONS

HQ: GOODFELLOW BROS. INC.
1407 WALLA WALLA AVE, WENATCHEE, WA 988011530
Phone: 5096679095
Web: WWW.GOODFELLOWBROS.COM

Goodfellow Bros. has offices in Kihei Maui Hawaii; Maple Valley and Wenatchee Washington; and Portland Oregon.

PRODUCTS/OPERATIONS

Projects and Services
Airports
Blasting
Crushing paving and grading
Landfills
Highways
Golf Courses
Public and private facilities
Heavy mechanical and infrastruc
Reservoirs and dams
Environmental and emergency responses
Harbors and marinas
Private developments and planning communitie

COMPETITORS

Bechtel
C.C. Myers
GLY Construction
Granite Construction
Harnish Group
J.F. Shea
Macro-Z-Technology Co.
PCL Construction Enterprises
Parsons Corporation
S.D. Deacon

HISTORICAL FINANCIALS

Company Type: Private

Income Statement FYE: December 31

	REVENUE ($ mil.)	NET INCOME ($ mil.)	NET PROFIT MARGIN	EMPLOYEES
12/13	203	7	3.6%	1,050
12/09	240	19	8.2%	—
12/08	0	0	—	—
12/07	519	0	—	—
Annual Growth	(14.5%)	—	—	—

2013 Year-End Financials

Debt ratio: —
Return on equity: 3.60%
Cash ($ mil.): 32
Current ratio: 0.90
Long-term debt ($ mil.): —

Dividends
Yield: —
Payout: —
Market value ($ mil.): —

GOODWILL INDUSTRIES OF SOUTHEASTERN WISCONSIN INC.

LOCATIONS

HQ: GOODWILL INDUSTRIES OF SOUTHEASTERN WISCONSIN INC.
5300 N 118TH CT, MILWAUKEE, WI 532253084
Phone: 4148474159
Web: WWW.GOODWILLSEW.COM

HISTORICAL FINANCIALS

Company Type: Private

Income Statement FYE: December 31

	REVENUE ($ mil.)	NET INCOME ($ mil.)	NET PROFIT MARGIN	EMPLOYEES
12/13	347	13	3.9%	3,391
12/12	255	13	5.4%	—
12/11	293	11	3.9%	—
12/10	277	0	—	—
Annual Growth	7.7%	—	—	—

2013 Year-End Financials

Debt ratio: —
Return on equity: 3.90%
Cash ($ mil.): 21
Current ratio: 1.20
Long-term debt ($ mil.): —
Dividends
Yield: —
Payout: —
Market value ($ mil.): —

GPM INVESTMENTS LLC

GPM Investments is where it's at for convenience store operators Fas Mart and Shore Stop. The investment firm operates more than 465 company-owned stores and some 145 independent convenience stores in 10 states mainly on the East Coast. The company has a high concentration of Fas Mart and Shore Stop stores in Virginia; others are located in nine states from Connecticut to Tennessee. The stores sell BP Exxon Marathon and Valero brand gas. (GPM's petroleum wholesaling business delivers petro to independent dealers.) In addition to the usual beer smokes and snacks the stores sell hot foods for breakfast lunch and dinner including the company's own brand of fried Fas Chicken at cafe sites.

Geographic Reach

Richmond Virginia-based GPM operates more than 600 convenience stores in Virginia North Carolina Delaware Maryland Pennsylvania New Jersey Connecticut Rhode Island South Carolina and Tennessee.

Operations

In addition to convenience stores GPM also operates 15 Subway franchises one Taco Bell franchise and 50 restaurants that serve Southern fried chicken.

Strategy

To help fund investments in new capital improvement projects and in acquisitions GPM entered into a $35 million credit facility with PNC Bank N.A. in 2012. Maturing in November 2016 the credit facility allows GPM to open new stores and improve existing locations. To this end the convenience store operator has offered to buy a 50% stake in EZ Energy Ltd. based in Ramat Gan Israel for $15 million. The company typically uses funding received through credit facilities to improve its locations with brighter interior and exterior lighting wider aisles and cleaner stores. It is also increasing its marketing efforts through social media to target younger shoppers.

Fast-growing GPM Investments in growing through acquisitions. Indeed in 2013 the company made its largest acquisition to date propelling its store count to more than 600 locations in 10 states.

Mergers and Acquisitions

In August 2013 GPM acquired the Southeastern division of VPS Convenience Store Group from Sun Capital Partners. The regional division operates more than 260 stores and 33 dealer sites and was cobbled together from acquisitions that included the Scotchman Young's Li'l Cricket Everyday Shop and Cigarette City banners. Most of the newly-acquired stores are in the Carolinas where GPM's retail presence is thin. Earlier in August GPM purchased five stores operating under the Get & Zip banner in Virginia. Most of the

EXECUTIVES

CFO, Don Bassell
Controller, Alison Douglas

LOCATIONS

HQ: GPM INVESTMENTS LLC
8565 MAGELLAN PKWY # 400, RICHMOND, VA 23227-1172
Phone: 804-266-1363
Web: WWW.FASMART.COM

Selected Locations

Connecticut
Delaware
Maryland
New Jersey
North Carolina
Pennsylvania
Rhode Island
South Carolina
Tennessee
Virginia

COMPETITORS

7-Eleven
Cumberland Farms
Exxon Mobil
Gate Petroleum
Racetrac Petroleum
Sheetz
The Pantry
Wawa Inc.

HISTORICAL FINANCIALS

Company Type: Private

Income Statement FYE: December 31

	REVENUE ($ mil.)	NET INCOME ($ mil.)	NET PROFIT MARGIN	EMPLOYEES
12/08	1,249	(1)	—	1,300
12/07	891	3	0.4%	—
Annual Growth	40.2%	—	—	—

2008 Year-End Financials

Debt ratio: —
Return on equity: (-0.10%)
Cash ($ mil.): 12
Current ratio: 0.40
Long-term debt ($ mil.): —
Dividends
Yield: —
Payout: —
Market value ($ mil.): —

GRAEBEL COMPANIES INC.

Graebel can move your table ... and just about anything else you need relocated. Offering both domestic and international household and commercial relocation services most of the company's business comes from firms transferring employees but it also provides individual household moving services and storage as well as freight forwarding. Graebel operates from service centers throughout the US and from international forwarding offices at major ports. It provides transportation services in Asia Europe the Middle East and Africa through hubs in Prague and Singapore and elsewhere in the world via a network of partners. Chairman Dave Graebel founded the family-run company in 1950.

Geographic Reach

Graebel has operations in Colorado and other locations throughout the US; it provides moving services in 165 countries and maintains an international presence in the Czech Republic Prague Singapore and Shanghai.

Operations

In addition to providing its moving services the company offers storage services freight forwarding and move management. Because the company insists on tight background checks and security measures Graebel serves specialized industries as well as high-end customers.

Additionally Graebel handles relocations for libraries hotels health care facilities and the entertainment industry. To serve its customers better the company offers its Graebel Relocation app (application) which gives clients their relocation facts and status of their transfers via an iPhone or iPad tablet computer; in 2011 it added an Android app.

EXECUTIVES

Chief Executive Officer, William (Bill) Graebel
Chairman, David (Dave) Graebel
President Move Management Graebel Van Lines and Graebel Forwarders, Craig Broback
CFO, Brad Siler
SVP Marketing and Public Relations, Carolyn White
President Graebel Transportation & Logistics, Jim Petzel
COO, Tim Callahan
CIO, Ron Dunlap
Vice President of Business Development, Donald Rankin

LOCATIONS

HQ: GRAEBEL COMPANIES INC.
16346 AIRPORT CIR, AURORA, CO 80011-1558
Phone: 303-214-6683
Web: WWW.GRAEBELMOVING.COM

PRODUCTS/OPERATIONS

Selected Services

Bar-coded inventory and asset management
Corporate headquarters office and one-time office relocation
Healthcare industry relocation project services
High density filing systems storage solutions
Hospitality industry furniture fixtures and equipment (FF&E) services
Just-In-Time deliveries
MAC management
Project management
Records storage and disposal
Relocation services
Single-source logistic services and management
Sub-contractor data telephony electrical coordination

Systems furniture transport delivery installation and reconfiguration
Warehouse and distribution services
Worldwide air ocean transportation including less-than-truckload truckload / padded van services

COMPETITORS

A-1 Freeman Moving & Storage
ALTAIR Global Relocation
Ace Relocation Systems
Arpin Van Lines
Atlas World Group
Bekins
Brookfield Global Relocation
Business Relocation Services
Move Solutions
National Van Lines
Paxton Van Lines
Prudential
SIRVA
Seino Transportation Co
Suddath
TheMIGroup
UniGroup
Weichert Relocation Resources
Wheaton Van Lines

HISTORICAL FINANCIALS

Company Type: Private

Income Statement FYE: December 31

	REVENUE ($ mil.)	NET INCOME ($ mil.)	NET PROFIT MARGIN	EMPLOYEES
12/12	341	4	1.3%	1,771
12/11	322	3	0.9%	—
12/09	260	(3)	—	—
12/06	334	0	0.1%	—
Annual Growth	0.4%	54.2%	—	—

2012 Year-End Financials

Debt ratio: —
Return on equity: 1.30%
Cash ($ mil.): 3
Current ratio: 1.00
Long-term debt ($ mil.): —
Dividends
Yield: —
Payout: —
Market value ($ mil.): —

GRAND VIEW HOSPITAL

Grand View Hospital (GVH) hopes to give patients a glimpse of great health care. The hospital provide emergency inpatient surgery and specialty services including cardiology orthopedics sleep diagnostic rehabilitation women's and children's care and other medical services to the Bucks County region of Pennsylvania. GVH's oncology program is affiliated with the Fox Chase Cancer Center in Philadelphia. The medical center also operates primary care and outpatient clinics in the region and it provides home health hospice fitness and community outreach programs. Founded in 1913 the hospital has about 200 beds.

Geographic Reach

In addition to its main hospital in Sellersville Pennsylvania GVH operates outpatient centers in Sellersville Harleysville and Pennsburg as well as a cancer center in Chalfont.

Financial Performance

In 2012 GVH reported revenues of some $175 million up 2% from 2011. About 80% of the company's earnings came from commercial managed care insurance and Medicare reimbursements. Other patient revenues come from self-pay customers. Operating expenses in 2012 were about $168 million.

Strategy

GVH has grown in recent years by expanding its medical facilities and services. In 2010 it opened a new labor and delivery unit and in 2012 it began offering neonatology services through a partnership with the Children's Hospital of Philadelphia.

EXECUTIVES

Secretary, William S. Aichele, age 63
CEO, Stuart H. Fine
VP and CIO, Jane D. Loveless
VP Quality, Darla Weaver

LOCATIONS

HQ: GRAND VIEW HOSPITAL
700 LAWN AVE, SELLERSVILLE, PA 18960-1548
Phone: 215-453-4000
Web: WWW.GVH.ORG

PRODUCTS/OPERATIONS

Selected Services and Centers

Acute Rehabilitation Unit
Ambulance/Transport Services
Case Management
Child Immunization Clinic
Children's Center - Daycare
Clinical Research
Diabetes Education
Emergency Department
Grand View Information Line
Health Promotion and Wellness
Healthy Beginnings Plus
Home Health Care Services
Industrial Medicine
Laboratory (Blood Work) Services at Grand View Hospital
Lifestyle Fitness Center
Medical Equipment and Supplies
Men's Health
Nutritional Counseling Services
Pediatric Weight Management (Grand New Youth)
Physical Medicine & Rehabilitation
Pulmonary Rehabilitation
Radiology Services (X-ray) Senior Services
Stoneridge Sleep Center
Sports Medicine
Support Groups & Consultations
Weight Management (Grand New You)
Wound Care Center

COMPETITORS

Abington Memorial Hospital
Children' s Hospital of Philadelphia
Doylestown Hospital
Jefferson Health System
Lehigh Valley Health Network
North Philadelphia Health System
St. Luke' s University Health Network
Tenet Healthcare
University of Pennsylvania Health System

HISTORICAL FINANCIALS

Company Type: Private

Income Statement FYE: June 30

	REVENUE ($ mil.)	NET INCOME ($ mil.)	NET PROFIT MARGIN	EMPLOYEES
06/13	168	31	18.7%	1,600
06/12	169	(26)	—	—
06/10	177	10	5.7%	—
06/10	182	7	4.1%	—
Annual Growth	(2.7%)	60.8%	—	—

2013 Year-End Financials

Debt ratio: —
Return on equity: 18.70%
Cash ($ mil.): 25
Current ratio: 1.80
Long-term debt ($ mil.): —
Dividends
Yield: —
Payout: —
Market value ($ mil.): —

GRAVES OIL COMPANY

LOCATIONS

HQ: GRAVES OIL COMPANY
226 PEARSON ST, BATESVILLE, MS 386062428
Phone: 6625610940
Web: WWW.GRAVESOIL.COM

HISTORICAL FINANCIALS

Company Type: Private

Income Statement FYE: February 28

	REVENUE ($ mil.)	NET INCOME ($ mil.)	NET PROFIT MARGIN	EMPLOYEES
02/14	279	0	0.0%	146
02/13	246	0	0.0%	—
02/12	229	0	0.1%	—
02/11	165	0	—	—
Annual Growth	19.1%	—	—	—

2014 Year-End Financials

Debt ratio: —
Return on equity: —
Cash ($ mil.): 1
Current ratio: 0.70
Long-term debt ($ mil.): —
Dividends
Yield: —
Payout: —
Market value ($ mil.): —

GREAT NORTHERN CORPORATION

LOCATIONS

HQ: GREAT NORTHERN CORPORATION
395 STROEBE RD, APPLETON, WI 549148782
Phone: 9207393671
Web: WWW.GREATNORTHERNCORP.COM

HISTORICAL FINANCIALS

Company Type: Private

Income Statement FYE: December 31

	REVENUE ($ mil.)	NET INCOME ($ mil.)	NET PROFIT MARGIN	EMPLOYEES
12/13	392	31	8.0%	1,032
12/07	231	16	7.2%	—
12/05	196	12	6.3%	—
12/04	1,389	0	—	—
Annual Growth	(13.1%)	—	—	—

2013 Year-End Financials

Debt ratio: —
Return on equity: 8.00%
Cash ($ mil.): 0
Current ratio: 1.00
Long-term debt ($ mil.): —
Dividends
Yield: —
Payout: —
Market value ($ mil.): —

GREATER BALTIMORE MEDICAL CENTER INC.

Greater Baltimore Medical Center also known as GBMC operates an integrated health system for residents of Baltimore and surrounding counties.

The 280-bed medical center provides surgery women's health oncology cardiology and other specialty and general medical services. In addition to inpatient and outpatient services it provides teaching services through an affiliation with Johns Hopkins University. GBMC also includes area clinics and physician practice locations. The GBMC Foundation coordinates fundraising for the health network.

Geographic Reach

The main 70-acre hospital campus is located in the suburban Baltimore town of Towson. The GBMC campus includes three physician practice pavilions and the organization operates several clinics in area communities including Bel Air Hunt Manor Hunt Valley Mays Chapel Owings Mills Perry Hall and Pikesville.

Operations

GBMC handles some 27000 inpatient cases each year as well as about 60000 emergency room visits 30000 surgeries and 4000 births. It has a staff of 1300 doctors and 1200 nurses (including hospice staff). In addition to the main hospital inpatient and outpatient care operations the GBMC organization includes medical and community outreach facilities operated by Greater Baltimore Medical Associates Gilchrist Hospice Care and GBMC Foundation.

Strategy

In 2010 the hospital opened a palliative care unit in its Berman Cancer Institute. The unit funded through GBMC's Gilchrist Hospice Care unit offers guidance and support to cancer patients and their families; it also serves as an in-hospital end-of-life care option. Another hospice option launched in 2010 was Gilchrist Kids the state's only hospice program exclusively for children.

In addition to expanding its facilities GBMC is working to enhance its information technology systems to support its clinical financial and operational reporting needs. For instance it is integrating a new electronic health record (EHR) program into its clinical information system to connect outpatient and inpatient records. The organization is also working to recruit new primary care physicians.

Ownership

Greater Baltimore Medical Center is owned and operated by GBMC HealthCare a private not-for-profit organization.

Company Background

GBMC was born out of two hospitals. The Hospital for the Women of Maryland of Baltimore City was the nation's second hospital for women's care when it opened in 1882. The Presbyterian Eye Ear and Throat Charity Hospital began in 1887 as a clinic run by a civil war surgeon in his carriage house. The two joined to create GBMC in 1960; the new hospital opened in 1965.

EXECUTIVES

Vp Of Facilities Engineering, Michael A Forthman
Director Of Radiology Services, Phillip Komenda
Director Of Surgery, Gary Cohen
Director Physician Recruitment, Mary Larson
Director Of Nursing, Alan Ziman
Clinical Director, Gretchen Bell
Co Director, Marc Dubin
Director Icu/coronary Care Unit, Justine Kellar
Director Of Infection Control, Karen Mackie
Admissions Director, Dawn Ward
Medical Director, Natalie Facmg
Vice President, Robert Roca
Secretary, Vanta Brewster

LOCATIONS

HQ: GREATER BALTIMORE MEDICAL CENTER INC.
6701 N CHARLES ST, BALTIMORE, MD 21204-6808
Phone: 443-849-2000
Web: WWW.GBMC.ORG

PRODUCTS/OPERATIONS

Selected Facilities

GBMC at Hunt Manor
GBMC at Hunt Valley
GBMC at Joppa Road
GBMC at Owings Mills
GBMC at Perry Hall
GBMC at Timonium-Texas Station
GBMC Medicine for Adults
GBMC Primary Care Physicians

Selected Services

Anesthesiology
Bone Density (Dexa)
Cancer Services
Cardiology
Cleft Lip and Palate Clinic
Clinical Trials
Dermatology
Diabetes (Geckle Diabetes and Nutrition Center)
Digestive Disorders
Domestic Violence
Ear Nose and Throat (ENT)
Emergency/Urgent Care
Endocrinology
Family Care Associates
Gastroenterology
General Surgery
General Internal Medicine
Genetic Services
Gynecology
Hearing/Vision
Hematology
Hospice
Hyperbaric Medicine/HBO Unit
Infectious Disease
Infusion Therapy
Labor and Delivery
Milton J. Dance Jr. Head and Neck Center
Minimally Invasive/Robotics
Neonatal Intensive Care Unit (NICU)
Neurosurgery
Obesity Management Program
Obstetrics
Oncology Clinical Trials
Ophthalmology
Orthopedics
Otolaryngology
Pathology and Laboratory Medicine
Pediatrics
Physical/Occupational Therapy
Plastic Surgery
Primary Care
Pulmonary Diseases
Radiation Oncology
Radiology
Rheumatology
SAFE Program
Sandra and Malcolm Berman Cancer Institute
Senior Services
Sleep Services
Stroke Center
Surgery
Thyroid Center
Urology
Voice Center
Women' s Services
Wound Care

COMPETITORS

Anne Arundel Medical Center
Bon Secours Health
Dimensions Healthcare
Franklin Square Hospital Center
Harbor Hospital
Johns Hopkins Health System
Johns Hopkins Medicine
LifeBridge Health
University of Maryland Medical System
Upper Chesapeake Health

HISTORICAL FINANCIALS

Company Type: Private

Income Statement FYE: June 30

	REVENUE ($ mil.)	NET INCOME ($ mil.)	NET PROFIT MARGIN	EMPLOYEES
06/11	416	25	6.1%	—
06/10	403	20	5.1%	—
06/09	388	0	—	—
06/08	392	8	2.1%	—
Annual Growth	2.0%	45.7%	—	—

2011 Year-End Financials

Debt ratio: —
Return on equity: 6.10%
Cash ($ mil.): 44
Current ratio: 0.40
Long-term debt ($ mil.): —
Dividends
Yield: —
Payout: —
Market value ($ mil.): —

GREENSTONE FARM CREDIT SERVICES ACA

One of the largest associations in the Farm Credit System GreenStone offers FARM CREDIT SERVICES (FCS) provides short intermediate and long-term loans; equipment and building leases; appraisal services; and life and crop insurance to farmers in Michigan and Wisconsin. It serves about 15000 members and has nearly 40 locations. Through an alliance with AgriSolutions a farm software and consulting company Greenstone provides income tax planning and preparation services farm business consulting and educational seminars. FCS Mortgage provides residential loans for rural properties as well as loans for home improvement construction and refinancing.

Dairy and cash crop loans each account for nearly a quarter of GreenStone FCS' loan portfolio which is rounded out by rural residential real estate and greenhouses hogs and other commodities.

EXECUTIVES

Regional Vice President East Region, Randy Stec
Allegan County Mi Board Vp, Darl E Evers, age 71
Chief Credit Officer Senior Vp, Gerald Brian
Vice President Customer Support, Jack Kelly, age 62
Exec V Pres, Melissa A Stolicker
Vp Chief Appraiser, James Garvey
Exec V Pres, Peter L Lemmer
Regional Vp West Region, Bert Sheridan
Vice President Of Sales And Customer Relations, Ben Mahlich
Senior Vice President Capital Markets, Al Compton
Vice President Human Resources, Bethany L Barker
Vice President Credit, Grabitz Mark
Regional Vice President, Erin Dubois
Vice President Financial Services, Leo Pasch
Regional Vice President, David Ballman
Regional Vice President, Tim McTigue
Vice President Credit, Steve Kluemper
Senior Vice President Sales, Brad Henion
Vice President Commercial Lending, Larry Urban
Regional Vice President, Ian McGonigal
Vice President Of Information Services, Dominic Roberts
Vice President Credit, Kevin Emison
Vice President Commercial Lending, Thomas Wilson
Vp Commercial Lending, Daniel Gitter

Second Vice President, Shane Kenner
Vice President Commercial Credit, Gayle Olson
Vice Chairperson, Catherine L Webster, age 70
Lending Officer, Brad Wright
Auditors: PricewaterhouseCoopersLLP

LOCATIONS

HQ: GREENSTONE FARM CREDIT SERVICES ACA
3515 WEST RD, EAST LANSING, MI 48823-7312
Phone: 517-318-2290
Web: WWW.GREENSTONEFCS.COM

COMPETITORS

COUNTRY Financial
FB BanCorp
Rabobank Group

HISTORICAL FINANCIALS

Company Type: Private

Income Statement FYE: December 31

	ASSETS ($ mil.)	NET INCOME ($ mil.)	INCOME AS % OF ASSETS	EMPLOYEES
12/07	4,317	69	1.6%	380
12/06	3,691	63	1.7%	—
Annual Growth	17.0%	8.9%	—	—

GREENWICH HOSPITAL ASSOCIATION INC

LOCATIONS

HQ: GREENWICH HOSPITAL ASSOCIATION INC
5 PERRYRIDGE RD, GREENWICH, CT 068304697
Phone: 2038633000
Web: WWW.GREENHOSP.ORG

HISTORICAL FINANCIALS

Company Type: Private

Income Statement FYE: September 30

	REVENUE ($ mil.)	NET INCOME ($ mil.)	NET PROFIT MARGIN	EMPLOYEES
09/13	312	27	8.9%	1,600
09/09	307	22	7.3%	—
09/05	1	0	—	—
09/03	188	0	—	—
Annual Growth	5.2%	—	—	—

2013 Year-End Financials

Debt ratio: —
Return on equity: 8.90%
Cash ($ mil.): 25
Current ratio: 1.20
Long-term debt ($ mil.): —
Dividends
Yield: —
Payout: —
Market value ($ mil.): —

GROSSMONT HOSPITAL CORPORATION

Residents of the eastern San Diego community of La Mesa California depend on Grossmont for medical care. Grossmont Hospital is a 540-bed not-for-profit health care facility. The hospital which opened in 1955 has a staff of about 700 physicians. The full-service acute care facility provides specialty services in the areas of cardiology oncology mental health orthopedics pediatrics physical therapy sleep therapy hospice and women's health care. The Grossmont Hospital Corporation is a subsidiary of Sharp HealthCare; it operates the Grossmont Hospital through a lease agreement with state-owned Grossmont Hospital District.

Strategy

Grossmont Hospital is undergoing expansion and improvement efforts. Current projects include renovation efforts (including energy and utility upgrades) on the existing hospital and the construction of new hospital wings and buildings on the surrounding grounds. In 2012 the company began work on a new $60 million heart and vascular center that will include diagnostic laboratory and surgery space.

An earlier $80 million stage of the hospital's expansion project was completed in 2009 and included construction of a five-story critical care and emergency center tower (adding 90 beds) as well as other renovations and utility upgrades. The improvement efforts are funded by public general obligation bonds approved in 2006 and overseen by a citizens' board and the Grossmont Hospital District which will fund a total of up to $247 million in construction efforts by 2016.

Company Background

The property and buildings of Grossmont Hospital are owned by the Grossmont Hospital District which was formed in 1952. The Grossmont Hospital Corporation was created in 1991 as a subsidiary of Sharp HealthCare exclusively to run a 30-year lease (expiring in 2021) of state-owned Grossmont Hospital District.

EXECUTIVES

R.N. Board Secretary, Gloria A. Chadwick
Chief Executive Officer, Barry Jantz
Chairman, Robert Klaiber
Board Vice President, Gloria A. Chadwick
Director, Deborah McElravy
Director, Michael Emerson
Director, Michael T. Long
CEO and Director, Barry Jantz

LOCATIONS

HQ: GROSSMONT HOSPITAL CORPORATION
5555 GROSSMONT CENTER DR, LA MESA, CA 91942-3077
Phone: 619-740-6000
Web: WWW.SHARP.COM

COMPETITORS

Adventist Health
Eisenhower Medical Center
Kaiser Permanente
Palomar Health
Paradise Valley Hospital
Rady Children' s Hospital
Scripps health
Tenet Healthcare
Tri-City Healthcare District
UCSD Medical

HISTORICAL FINANCIALS

Company Type: Private

Income Statement FYE: September 30

	REVENUE ($ mil.)	NET INCOME ($ mil.)	NET PROFIT MARGIN	EMPLOYEES
09/09	500	41	8.3%	2,697
09/08	452	37	8.3%	—
09/04	327	4	1.4%	—
09/03	309	18	5.9%	—
Annual Growth	8.3%	14.6%	—	—

2009 Year-End Financials

Debt ratio: —
Return on equity: 8.30%
Cash ($ mil.): 37
Current ratio: 0.80
Long-term debt ($ mil.): —
Dividends
Yield: —
Payout: —
Market value ($ mil.): —

GROWMARK INC.

EXECUTIVES

SVP Member Services, Dennis Farmer
Chairman and President, Daniel T. (Dan) Kelley
Vice Chairman, John Reifsteck
Vice Chairman, Rick Nelson
CEO, Jeff Solberg
Secretary of the Board, Chet Esther Jr.
VP and General Counsel, Brent Bostrom
VP Eastern Retail Operations, Steve Buckalew
VP Finance and Risk Management; CFO, Marshall Bohbrink
VP Energy, Kevin Carroll
VP Midwest Retail and Acquisitions, Shelly Kruse
VP Agromony, Jim Spradlin
VP Grain, Brent Ericson
VP Human Resources and Compliance, Gary Swango
Director of propane operations, Randy Miller
marketing Manager, Randy Holthaus
Vice Chairman, John Reifsteck
Vice Chairman, Rick Nelson
Director, Bill Hanson
Director, Gary Leber
Director, Randy Newcomb
Director, Bob Phelps
Director, Ray Steffens
Director, David Watt
Director, Matt Heitz
Director, Evert (Ed) Benjamins
Director, Allen Tanner
Director, Larry Garlisch
Director, Denis Bourdeau
Director, Jim Williams
Auditors: Ernst&YoungLLP

LOCATIONS

HQ: GROWMARK INC.
1701 TOWANDA AVE, BLOOMINGTON, IL 617012057
Phone: 3095576000
Web: WWW.GROWMARK.COM

PRODUCTS/OPERATIONS

Selected Retail Products and Operations

COMFORT PRO (propane heating oil)
FAST STOP (fuel facilities)
FS (farm supplies)
Green Yard (turf seed fertilizer)
Seedway (farm turf and vegetable seed)

Selected Member Cooperatives and Subsidiaries

AgVantage FS Inc.
AgView Grain LLC
Evergreen FS Inc.
GROWMARK FS LLC
MID-CO COMMODITIES
Northern Grain Marketing LLC
Seedway LLC
Total Grain Marketing LLC
Western Grain Marketing LLC

COMPETITORS

ADM
AGRI Industries
Ag Processing Inc.
BP
Barkley Seed
Bayer CropScience
Marathon Oil
NC Hybrids
Orscheln Farm and Home
Pfister Hybrid Corn
Pioneer Hi-Bred
Rabo AgriFinance

CHS	Sakata Seed
Cargill	Seed Enterprises
Chevron	Southern States
Costco Wholesale	Terra Nitrogen
DeBruce Grain	Wal-Mart
Exxon Mobil	Wilbur-Ellis

HISTORICAL FINANCIALS

Company Type: Private

Income Statement FYE: August 31

	REVENUE ($ mil.)	NET INCOME ($ mil.)	NET PROFIT MARGIN	EMPLOYEES
08/14	10,372	166	1.6%	1,036
08/13	10,171	189	1.9%	—
08/12	10,057	249	2.5%	—
08/11	8,597	0	—	—
Annual Growth	6.5%	—	—	—

2014 Year-End Financials

Debt ratio: —
Return on equity: 1.60%
Cash ($ mil.): 83
Current ratio: 0.80
Long-term debt ($ mil.): —

Dividends
Yield: —
Payout: —
Market value ($ mil.): —

GRUNLEY CONSTRUCTION CO. INC.

Founded in 1955 Grunley Construction Company provides general contracting engineering architectural and construction management services and specializes in the renovation restoration and modernization of historic buildings in the Washington DC area. Its projects range from prestigious undertakings –the Smithsonian Institution the Washington Monument and the US Treasury building –to more mundane endeavors such as office buildings apartment buildings schools and power plants. The company also has lent its services to the construction of embassies airports and military facilities.

EXECUTIVES

Chairman, Martin Grunley
President, Kenneth (Ken) Grunley
Chief Estimator, Andrew Phillips
Strategic Planning Business Development and New Technology, Joel Zingeser
Communications Manager, Donna Duncan
HR Generalist, Gloria Nokes
Project Manager, Rodney Nichols
Project Manager, Daniel L. Patete
Superintendent, Robert Dalton
Estimating Assistant, Michael Ann Balloch
President He, Greg Druga
VP Special Projects Group, John Greenwell
Director Preconstruction Services, Walker Tom
Project Executive, Chip Scott
Vice President of Pre-Construction Services, Tom Walker

LOCATIONS

HQ: GRUNLEY CONSTRUCTION CO. INC.
15020 SHADY STE 500, ROCKVILLE, MD 20850
Phone: 240-399-2000
Web: WWW.GRUNLEY.COM

COMPETITORS

Hega Construction Company	Parsons Transportation
	S. W. Rodgers

HISTORICAL FINANCIALS

Company Type: Private

Income Statement FYE: December 31

	REVENUE ($ mil.)	NET INCOME ($ mil.)	NET PROFIT MARGIN	EMPLOYEES
12/12	317	0	—	330
12/11	323	0	—	—
12/10	310	0	—	—
12/09	310	0	—	—
Annual Growth	0.7%	—	—	—

2012 Year-End Financials

Debt ratio: —
Return on equity: —
Cash ($ mil.): 12
Current ratio: 0.90
Long-term debt ($ mil.): —

Dividends
Yield: —
Payout: —
Market value ($ mil.): —

GUARANTEE ELECTRICAL COMPANY

EXECUTIVES

Chairman and Chief Executive Officer, Frederick J. (Rick) Oertli
Chairman, Charles W. (Chuck) Oertli
Vice Chairman, Fred G. Oertli Jr.
Executive Vice President Missouri Operations, Roger Oertli
President, Douglas (Doug) Mertzlufft
Business Development and Marketing, Julie TenEyck
Senior Vice President Colorado Operations, Steve Juan
VP and Senior Project Manager, Dipak Kapadia
Director Construction, Steve Kellenberger
President GECO Engineering, Gary Schaeffer
Senior Vice President Preconstruction & Engineering Services, David M. Gralike
Chief Financial Officer, Josh Voegtli, age 37

LOCATIONS

HQ: GUARANTEE ELECTRICAL COMPANY
3405 BENT AVE, SAINT LOUIS, MO 631162601
Phone: 3147725400
Web: WWW.GECO.COM

PRODUCTS/OPERATIONS

Selected Projects

Alton Memorial Hospital expansion
Southern Illinois Office of Guarantee Electrical
SunCoke Energy Inc. coke oven plant
Saint Louis Art Museum expansion
Emerson Data Center
River City Casino
Express Scripts Technology & Innovation Center

COMPETITORS

Conti Electric	MDU Construction Services
Dycom	Quanta Services
EMCOR	
Integrated Electrical Services	

HISTORICAL FINANCIALS

Company Type: Private

Income Statement FYE: September 30

	REVENUE ($ mil.)	NET INCOME ($ mil.)	NET PROFIT MARGIN	EMPLOYEES
09/14	168	0	—	700
09/13	169	0	—	—
09/12	135	0	—	—
09/11	119	0	—	—
Annual Growth	12.1%	—	—	—

2014 Year-End Financials

Debt ratio: —
Return on equity: —
Cash ($ mil.): 3
Current ratio: 1.40
Long-term debt ($ mil.): —

Dividends
Yield: —
Payout: —
Market value ($ mil.): —

GUEST SERVICES INC.

Guest Services satisfies hungry and sleepy patrons. The company provides contract food services and hospitality-management services nationwide. It operates cafeterias and onsite restaurants and offers catering to businesses hotels hospitals conference centers and government operations including the US Supreme Court the US House of Representatives and the National Park Service. For leisure and resort facilities Guest Services also provides special-event catering and offers management services such as marketing human resources procurement quality-assurance and information technology services. Guest Services was founded in 1917 as a private company to serve governmental agencies.

Geographic Reach

Based in Fairfax Virginia Guest Services serves a variety of customers nationwide.

Sales and Marketing

Guest Services serves several clients including government and business dining facilities museums hotels resorts conference centers luxury condominiums senior living centers health care systems state and national park recreation school and university dining facilities specialty retail stores and full-service restaurants.

Customers have included Washington DC's National Mall and Memorial Park. It also manages food lodging and recreation services at stake parks in West Virginia New York and California.

Operations

As part of its business Guest Services serves some 250 facilities across the US and more than 25 million guests each year.

It operates Lancaster Foods one of the largest wholesale produce companies in the mid-Atlantic region as a wholly owned subsidiary.

Strategy

Guest Services has been expanding its portfolio of premium properties. It already owns and manages the DoubleTree Suites by Hilton Naples. In 2013 Guest Services acquired The Lodge and Spa at Breckenridge which overlooks Colorado's Breckenridge Village. With 45 rooms the property is a popular destination for weddings and corporate events. It's adding food and beverage service in-house catering and event planning to the property's services.

EXECUTIVES

Vp Hotel Division South, Barry G Trice
Assistant Vice President Operations Div, Rick Wayland

LOCATIONS

HQ: GUEST SERVICES INC.
3055 PROSPERITY AVE, FAIRFAX, VA 220312290
Phone: 7038499300
Web: WWW.GUESTSERVICES.COM

PRODUCTS/OPERATIONS

Selected Services

Audits
Corporate Support Services
Financial Accounting Systems
Food Safety and Health
Human Resources
IT
Maintenance Support
Management Information Systems
Marketing
Onsite Test Kitchen
PeopleSoft Processing
Procurement
Quality Assurance
Safety
Security
Test Kitchen
Training

COMPETITORS

ARAMARK
Centerplate
Compass Group USA
Delaware North
Sodexo USA
Valley Services

HISTORICAL FINANCIALS

Company Type: Private

Income Statement FYE: December 31

	REVENUE ($ mil.)	NET INCOME ($ mil.)	NET PROFIT MARGIN	EMPLOYEES
12/13	387	2	0.6%	3,500
12/12	377	2	0.7%	—
12/11	369	0	0.0%	—
12/10	346	0	—	—
Annual Growth	3.8%	—	—	—

2013 Year-End Financials

Debt ratio: —
Return on equity: 0.60%
Cash ($ mil.): 2
Current ratio: 0.90
Long-term debt ($ mil.): —
Dividends
Yield: —
Payout: —
Market value ($ mil.): —

GUNDERSEN LUTHERAN MEDICAL CENTER INC.

At the heart of the Gundersen Lutheran health system Gundersen Lutheran Medical Center serves residents of nearly 20 counties that stretch across the upper Midwest. The clinical campus for the University of Wisconsin's medical and nursing schools operates a 325-bed teaching hospital with a Level II Trauma and Emergency Center. Focused on caring for patients in western Wisconsin the hospital boasts several specialty services such as bariatrics behavioral health cancer care orthopedics palliative care pediatrics rehabilitation and women's health. The physician-led not-for-profit medical center is affiliated with a group of regional clinics and specialty centers.

Geographic Reach

From its main campus in La Crosse Wisconsin as well as a satellite outpatient center in Onalaska the hospital serves communities located in 19 counties throughout western Wisconsin northeastern Iowa and southeastern Minnesota.

Operations

Gundersen Lutheran Medical Center has a staff of some 700 doctors dentists and other professionals. As part of Gundersen Lutheran (also known as Gundersen Health System) the hospital's sister entities include the Gundersen Clinic and the Gundersen Lutheran Administrative Services entity.

Strategy

To offer advanced training to residents and physicians Gundersen Lutheran Medical Center developed and opened a high-tech training center in 2012. The Cleary Kumm Simulation and Training Labs offer mock operating rooms and simulation labs for use by local doctors and nationwide medical professionals for training or conferences. Gundersen Lutheran Medical Center is banking on the simulation and training facility to draw interest talent and outside funds.

The Gundersen Lutheran organization also expands though partnerships such as an alliance with the Allen Hospital in Iowa to enhance regional cardiovascular services in 2013. The medical center is also working to upgrade its infrastructure to enable 100% energy independence in 2014.

Company Background

Gundersen Lutheran Medical Center was founded in 1995 through the merger of Gunderson Clinic and Lutheran Hospital-La Crosse.

EXECUTIVES

Chairman and CEO, Jeffrey E. (Jeff) Thompson
SVP Operations and Human Resources, Kathy Klock
EVP, Julio J. Bird
Senior Vice President Business Services, Jerry Arndt
Vice President Team 3, Marilu Bintz
Medical VP Team 2, Michael J. Dolan
VP Nursing Systems, Mary Lu Gerke
Medical VP Team 1 and Regional System, Sigurd B. Gundersen III
VP Team 1 and Regional System, Mary Jo Klos
Chief of Corporate Ventures Partnerships and Investments, Daryl Applebury
Chief Quality Officer, Jean Krause
Chief Learning Officer, Mary Ellen McCartney
Clinic Administrator and CIO, Deb Rislow
Vice President Team, Jan DeHaan
Executive Director Human Resources, Monty Clark
Chief Business Development and Marketing Officer, Pamela Maas
Chairman Gundersen Lutheran Medical Foundation, Mark V. Connelly
Chief Medical Officer, Greg Thompson
CFO, Gordon Edwards
Vice President of Supply Chain and Gundersen, Cathy Fischer
Vice President Team 1, Bryan Erdmann
Vice President Team 1 & Regional System, Mary Kuffel
Vice President Team 2, Scott Rathgaber
Senior Vice President Strategy, Bob Trine
Vice President Team 4, Kelly Barton
Chief Compliance Officer, Kari Adank

LOCATIONS

HQ: GUNDERSEN LUTHERAN MEDICAL CENTER INC.
1910 SOUTH AVE, LA CROSSE, WI 54601-5467
Phone: 608-782-7300
Web: WWW.GUNDERSENHEALTH.ORG

PRODUCTS/OPERATIONS

Selected Services

Advance care planning
Apnea
Audiology
Autism Spectrum Disorder
BioBank
Brain disorders
Cardiac services
Children's health
Cleft Lip & Palate Clinic
Endocrinology
Hospice
Eye care
Gynecology
Hand surgery
Heart Institute
LASIK eye surgery
Massage
Neck surgery
Neurosciences
Oral and maxillofacial surgery
Pediatrics
Radiation oncology
Rehabilitation
Urgent care
Urology
Weight management
Wound care

COMPETITORS

Dean Health Systems Inc.
Franciscan Skemp Healthcare
Luther Midelfort
Mayo Clinic
Meriter Health Services
Ministry Health Care
Olmsted Medical
Sacred Heart Hospital
Tomah Memorial Hospital
University of Wisconsin Hospital and Clinics

HISTORICAL FINANCIALS

Company Type: Private

Income Statement FYE: December 31

	REVENUE ($ mil.)	NET INCOME ($ mil.)	NET PROFIT MARGIN	EMPLOYEES
12/12	396	116	29.3%	4,500
12/11	431	49	11.5%	—
Annual Growth	(8.2%)	134.2%	—	—

2012 Year-End Financials

Debt ratio: —
Return on equity: 29.30%
Cash ($ mil.): 15
Current ratio: 0.50
Long-term debt ($ mil.): —
Dividends
Yield: —
Payout: —
Market value ($ mil.): —

GUSTAVUS ADOLPHUS COLLEGE

EXECUTIVES

VP Finance and Treasurer, Kenneth C. Westphal
Assistant VP College Relations, Stacia Senne
Controller, Kelly Waldron
Registrar, Kristianne Reinholtzen
Director Alumni Relations, Randall Stuckey
Director Human Resources, Kirk Beyer
Director Safety and Security, Raymond H. Thrower Jr.
Director Gustavus Technology Services, Bruce Aarsvold
Academic Dean, Eric Eliason
Academic Dean, Mariangela McGuire
President, Jack R. Ohle
VP Academic Affairs and Provost, Mary E. Morton Strey
VP College Relations, Gwendolyn Freed
VP Institutional Advancement, Thomas Young
VP Admission and Student Financial Assistance, Mark Anderson
VP Student Affairs and Dean Students, Henry Toutain

LOCATIONS

HQ: GUSTAVUS ADOLPHUS COLLEGE
800 W COLLEGE AVE, SAINT PETER, MN 560821498
Phone: 5079337508
Web: WWW.GUSTAVUS.EDU

HISTORICAL FINANCIALS

Company Type: Private

Income Statement FYE: May 31

	REVENUE ($ mil.)	NET INCOME ($ mil.)	NET PROFIT MARGIN	EMPLOYEES
05/13	103	21	20.6%	700
05/12	134	9	6.7%	—
05/11	97	19	20.0%	—
05/10	106	0	—	—
Annual Growth	(1.1%)	—	—	—

2013 Year-End Financials

Debt ratio: —
Return on equity: 20.60%
Cash ($ mil.): 26
Current ratio: —
Long-term debt ($ mil.): —
Dividends
Yield: —
Payout: —
Market value ($ mil.): —

H. J. RUSSELL & COMPANY

H.J. Russell & Company one of the nation's largest minority-owned enterprises helps shape southeastern cities. It's a general contractor construction manager property manager and developer that specializes in affordable multifamily housing and mixed-use communities. It also has expertise in building airports hospitals office towers retail stores and schools. Its development arm Russell New Urban Development offers such services as feasibility analysis land development and asset management; it has more than $500 million in development underway. H.J. Russell also manages more than 6000 apartment and public housing units. The family-owned company was founded by chairman Herman J. Russell in 1952.

Geographic Reach

Firmly rooted in Atlanta H.J. Russell conducts much of its business in Georgia. The company has increasingly looked outside of the state to diversify its projects. Beyond Atlanta Russell has offices in Chicago Dallas Florida New York North Carolina Ohio and Phoenix.

Operations

H.J. Russell & Company is active on many fronts. Its menu of interconnected services includes: Real Estate Development; Program Management (established 1976); Construction (est. 1962); and Property Management. More than half of the firm's employees work in its development division Russell New Urban Development which is closely intertwined with the construction side of the family business. It is a formula that the firm relies on for growth.

Strategy

The downturn in the construction market during the recession left H.J. Russell depending on its various service offerings and geographic diversity to weather the storm. Facing lagging revenues the company cut costs and reduced staff as it waited for the economy to rebound.

H.J. Russell also looked for more non-residential work. The company keeps its non-residential client and project roster diverse serving the commercial institutional and public sectors. Some of the company's key projects include the $1.9 billion Dallas/Fort Worth International Airport Atlanta's $6.2 billion Hartsfield-Jackson Development the $1.6 billion Maynard H. Jackson Jr. International Terminal the US headquarters of The Coca-Cola Company Howard University and the Birmingham Civil Rights Institute. It also regularly builds stores for retail giants Target and The Home Depot.

Company Background

After leading the group for more than 50 years Herman Russell stepped down as CEO and handed the reins of the company to his children in 2004.

EXECUTIVES

Vp Education Construction, Darrell Stallings
Vp Joint Ventures Program Management Construction, James Willie
Vp Residential Construction Division, Greg Dixon
CEO, Michael Russell
CFO, Eddie Bradford
Vice President, T D Smith
Vice President Development And Construction Chief Operating Officer, William Campbell
Vice President Of Information, Joe Hardiman
CFO, Eddie Bradford

LOCATIONS

HQ: H. J. RUSSELL & COMPANY
504 FAIR ST SW, ATLANTA, GA 303131206
Phone: 4043301000
Web: WWW.HJRUSSELL.COM

PRODUCTS/OPERATIONS

Services
Construction
Program management
Property management
Real estate developmen

COMPETITORS

Barton Malow
Batson-Cook
Brasfield & Gorrie
Brice Building
Choate Construction
Comstock Holding
Cousins Properties
Hardin Construction
Shelco
Weitz
Winter Construction

HISTORICAL FINANCIALS

Company Type: Private

Income Statement FYE: December 31

	REVENUE ($ mil.)	NET INCOME ($ mil.)	NET PROFIT MARGIN	EMPLOYEES
12/09	170	2	1.2%	733
12/08	222	3	1.8%	—
12/07	321	0	—	—
Annual Growth	—	64434.9%	—	—

2009 Year-End Financials

Debt ratio: —
Return on equity: 1.20%
Cash ($ mil.): 17
Current ratio: 1.30
Long-term debt ($ mil.): —
Dividends
Yield: —
Payout: —
Market value ($ mil.): —

H. LEE MOFFITT CANCER CENTER & RESEARCH INSTITUTE HOSPITAL INC.

The H. Lee Moffitt Cancer Center and Research Institute founded in 1986 is a National Cancer Institute-designated Comprehensive Cancer Center located on the Tampa campus of the University of South Florida. The institute carries it out its stated mission of contributing to the prevention and cure of cancer through patient care research and education. It operates a 210-bed medical and surgical facility as well as outpatient treatment programs and a blood and marrow transplant program. Its research programs include study in the areas of molecular oncology immunology risk assessment health outcomes and experimental therapeutics.

Geographic Reach

Through its main campus and numerous outpatient sites Moffitt Cancer Center primarily serves residents of seven Florida counties: Hernando Hillsborough Manatee Pasco Pinellas Polk and Sarasota. It also serves patients from other areas of Florida and neighboring states.

Operations

The Moffitt Cancer Center sees more than 9000 cancer inpatients each year; it also handles some 325000 outpatient visits annually. In addition to its 40-bed blood and marrow transplant center which performs 400 annual transplants the hospital includes more than a dozen operating rooms and extensive diagnostic radiology and radiation therapy labs. The Cancer Screening and Prevention Center offers genetic testing for certain kinds of hereditary cancers (breast ovarian colon and melanoma).

The Moffitt Research Institute conducts a wide range of cancer studies and some of its drug discovery research programs are managed through partnerships with pharmaceutical companies and other research laboratories. The research institute also relies on funding grants from organizations such as the National Institutes of Health. It has received over $80 million in grant funding and participated in some 300 clinical trials.

The Moffitt Cancer Center likewise has educational and health care alliances with a number of Florida hospitals and colleges including a three-way cancer care and research partnership with Shands HealthCare and the University of Florida. Through its affiliated network program (the Moffitt Oncology Network) Moffitt works with community doctors and centers across Florida to provide enhanced cancer services throughout the state. It also operates a number of outpatient clinics in surrounding areas.

Sales and Marketing

HMO and PPO plans account for about 45% of patient service revenues while reimbursements from Medicare and Medicaid plans account for another 40% of sales.

Financial Performance

Revenue at Moffitt Cancer Center and Research Institute increased by 4% to $772 million in 2012 due to higher patient service revenues. The organization reported a net loss that year however due to higher operating expenses and provisions for bad debts (unpaid medical bills).

Strategy

The medical facility conducts expansion and facility improvement projects to enhance services for its cancer patients. For instance in 2011 the organization completed construction of a two-story Moffitt Cancer Center at International Plaza to provide satellite outpatient care; its former outpatient clinic located at Tampa General Hospital relocated to the new location. Moffitt Cancer Center launched construction of a new $74 million outpatient facility at the current McKinley office site in 2013; the location is near the main campus and will provide surgery infusion imaging research and other services.

Moffitt Cancer Center completed a major hospital expansion project in 2009 that added patient beds and physician office capacity as well as new radiation treatment units and more space for the blood and marrow transplant unit.

EXECUTIVES

VP and CIO, Mark Hulse
President and CEO, Alan List
executive Vice President of clinical affairs, Douglas Letson

LOCATIONS

HQ: H. LEE MOFFITT CANCER CENTER & RESEARCH INSTITUTE HOSPITAL INC.
12902 USF MAGNOLIA DR, TAMPA, FL 33612-9416
Phone: 813-745-4673
Web: WWW.MOFFITT.USF.EDU

PRODUCTS/OPERATIONS

Selected Services

Chemotherapy
Diagnosis
Emotional Support
Integrative Medicine
Labwork Scans and Biopsy
Other Patient Services
Pain Management
Radiation
Screening and Genetics
Spiritual Support
Surgical Care
Well-Being

Selected Research Fields

Basic Science Division
- Cancer Imaging and Metabolism
- Drug Discovery
- Immunology
- Integrated Mathematical Oncology
- Molecular Oncology
- Tumor Biology

Population Science Division
- Biostatistics and Bioinformatics
- Cancer Epidemiology
- Health Outcomes & Behavior

COMPETITORS

All Children' s Hospital
Baptist Hospital of Miami
Bay Medical Center
Boca Raton Regional Hospital
Dana-Farber
Fox Chase Cancer Center
Jackson County Hospital of Florida
MD Anderson Cancer Center
Manatee Memorial Hospital
Mayo Clinic Jacksonville
Memorial Sloan-Kettering
Oak Hill Hospital
Roswell Park Cancer Institute
Sacred Heart Health System
South Georgia Medical Center
St. Vincent' s Health System

HISTORICAL FINANCIALS

Company Type: Private

Income Statement FYE: June 30

	REVENUE ($ mil.)	NET INCOME ($ mil.)	NET PROFIT MARGIN	EMPLOYEES
06/13	779	26	3.4%	3,700
06/12	771	(7)	—	—
06/10	744	22	3.0%	—
06/10	676	19	2.9%	—
Annual Growth	4.8%	10.2%	—	—

2013 Year-End Financials

Debt ratio: —
Return on equity: 3.40%
Cash ($ mil.): 86
Current ratio: 1.50
Long-term debt ($ mil.): —
Dividends
Yield: —
Payout: —
Market value ($ mil.): —

H.D.R. INC.

With projects ranging from restoring the Pentagon and the Everglades to working on the Hoover Dam Bypass project HDR has left its mark on the US. HDR is an architecture engineering and consulting firm that specializes in such projects as bridges water- and wastewater-treatment plants and hospitals. The company also provides mechanical and plumbing services construction and project management and utilities planning. It has completed projects nationwide and in some 60 countries through its more than 200 global locations. The employee-owned company was founded as Henningson Engineering in 1917 to build municipal plants in the rural Midwest.

Geographic Reach

Headquartered in Omaha Nebraska HDR has completed projects in 60 countries and maintains some 200 offices worldwide. It operates in the Americas Asia Australia Europe and the Middle East.

Strategy

HDR is looking to extend its reach globally. The company opened an office in Dubai where it has worked on a $1.5 billion hospital and where it anticipates future projects. In 2011 HDR expanded to Australia. The company opened an office in Melbourne which provides business commercial financial risk and project management services to clients in Australia New Zealand the Middle East and Asia.

Mergers and Acquisitions

It is also focused on expanding its capabilities through acquisitions. The acquisition of architectural practice Rice Daubney in late 2013 enhances the company's position in the Australian market while purchases in 2012 (Wyoming's Stetson Engineering) and 2011 (New Jersey's HydroQual) extended its water capabilities. Other areas of concentration include engineering (Schiff Associates in 2011 and iTrans Consulting in 2009) healthcare (Cooper Medical in 2011) and expansion into Canada (Amnis Engineering in 2011 and Devine Tarbell & Associates in 2009).

EXECUTIVES

Chief Executive Officer, Richard R. (Dick) Bell
Chairman and CEO, George A. Little
CFO, Terence C. (Terry) Cox
Manager Media Relations HDR Inc., Jackie Fox
EVP and Director Federal Energy and Resource Management, Elwin Larson
EVP and Director Water Program, Gary L. Bleeker
Vice Chairman; President HDR Engineering Inc., Eric L. Keen
Senior Vice President, Brian K. Hoppy
President Manager, Kevin Keller
President HDR Architecture Inc., Doug S. Wignall
CIO, Michael Geppert
Director Communications HDR Architecture, Katie Sosnowchik
Director Science and Technology HDR Architecture, Steven Riojas
EVP and Director Transportation, Charles O'Reilly
SVP and Director Corporate Communications, Rex Fisher
Vice Chairman, Ronald L. HarrisFormer
Vice President Global Market Sector Director Freight Railroads, Scott Goehri
Vice President Director Private Development, Jim Lee
Vice President Aviation Market Sector Director, Duane Hippe
President Manager Richmond Hill Traffic Practice, David Argue
Vice President Transit Market Sector Director, Steve Beard

LOCATIONS

HQ: H.D.R. INC.
8404 INDIAN HILLS DR, OMAHA, NE 68114-4098
Phone: 402-399-1000
Web: WWW.HDRINC.COM

PRODUCTS/OPERATIONS

Selected Mergers and Acquisitions

FY2103
- Rice Daubney (Australia architecture design for healthcare retail defense markets)

FY2012
- Stetson Engineering (Wyoming projects in water sewer storm water hydrology and transportation)

FY2011
- Amnis Engineering (Canada)
- Cooper Medical (Healthcare design/build specialist)
- HydroQual (New Jersey water resource management)
- Schiff Associates (California engineering)

FY2009
- Devine Tarbell & Associates (Maine now named HDR|DTA)
- iTrans Consulting (Toronto-based engineering firm)

Selected Markets

Architecture
- Academic
- Civic
- Corporate
- Healthcare
- Justice
- Science and Technology

Energy
- Oil and Gas
- Power Delivery
- Power Generation
- Renewable Energy

Federal
- Federal Architecture
- Federal Engineering
- Federal Planning
- Federal Environmental
- Federal Energy
- Federal Construction
- HDR SeaPort-e

Private Land Development
- Commercial
- Industrial
- Institutional
- Residential
- Resorts and Hotels

Resource Management
- Community Planning & Consulting
- Environmental Sciences & Permitting
- Fisheries Science & Design
- Mining
- Natural Resource Management
- Waste Management and Industrial

Transportation
- Aviation
- Freight Rail
- Highways and Local Roads
- Maritime

- Transit
- Water
  - Water
  - Wastewater
  - Water Planning
  - Industrial

Selected Services

Analytical consulting
Architectural design
Coastal engineering and restoration
Consulting
Design/build
Environmental monitoring
Finished water storage facility services
Interior design
Landscape architecture
Master planning
Power facility engineering
Pump stations and flow control
Security services
Utility master planning and modeling
Water resources
Water treatment systems

COMPETITORS

AECOM
Black & Veatch
Brown and Caldwell
CH2M HILL
Epstein
Fuscoe Engineering
Gensler
Geotechnics
HBE Corporation
HKS Inc.
Interior Architects
Jacobs Engineering
KPA Associates
Kimley-Horn and Associates
Lee Burkhart Liu
Leo A Daly
MCG Architects
MWH Global
Michael Baker
Nasland Engineering
Perkowitz + Ruth
RMJM
RTKL Associates
SAIC Energy Environment & Infrastructure
STV
Tetra Tech
The Austin Company
URS
Western Summit Constructors
Willdan Group

HISTORICAL FINANCIALS

Company Type: Private

Income Statement

FYE: December 29

	REVENUE ($ mil.)	NET INCOME ($ mil.)	NET PROFIT MARGIN	EMPLOYEES
12/12	1,760	90	5.2%	7,800
12/11	1,691	54	3.2%	—
12/10	1,553	61	3.9%	—
12/09	1,486	17	1.2%	—
Annual Growth	5.8%	72.5%	—	—

2012 Year-End Financials

Debt ratio: ——
Return on equity: 5.20%
Cash ($ mil.): 221
Current ratio: 0.50
Long-term debt ($ mil.): —

Dividends
Yield: —
Payout: —
Market value ($ mil.): —

HABITAT FOR HUMANITY INTERNATIONAL

Thanks to Habitat for Humanity more than 3 million people worldwide know there's no place like home. The mission of the not-for-profit ecumenical Christian organization is to provide adequate and affordable shelter. It has built more than 600000 houses at cost for families who demonstrate a need and are willing to invest "sweat equity" during construction. Homeowners make payments on no-interest mortgages; Habitat for Humanity funnels the funds back into the construction of homes for others. The group operates in all 50 states the District of Columbia Guam and Puerto Rico in addition to affiliates in more than 90 countries. It was founded in 1976 by Linda Fuller and her late husband Millard.

Geographic Reach

Georgia-based Habitat for Humanity International operates in Africa and the Middle East the Asia-Pacific Region Europe and Central Asia Latin America and the Caribbean and throughout North America.

Operations

In addition to its home building and rehabbing operations Habitat for Humanity supports recovery efforts following natural disasters. In fall 2012 it launched its first fleet of mobile response units to assist victims of superstorm Sandy. The vans carried tools and equipment to assist families with critical home repairs. While the quick-response vans are addressing the short-term needs of storm victims the organization will provide long-term assistance as well. Previously the organization responded to the January 2010 7.0-magnitude earthquake that hit Haiti. Habitat for Humanity's support included providing starter kits for making immediate home repairs and preparing emergency shelter cleaning up debris and identifying salvageable materials and rebuilding with improved construction methods.

Financial Analysis

Habitat for Humanity's fiscal 2012 (ends June) revenue increased by 4% vs. the prior year to nearly $300 million. It was the second straight year of revenue growth following the downturn in the economy which led to a dip in donations for many nonprofit organizations. Indeed the $300 million in 2012 revenue was well below Habitat's peak in 2007 of about $355 million.

While revenue from contributions fell by 10% in fiscal 2012 vs. 2011 donations in-kind and government grants increased by 19% and 26% respectively. Fiscal 2012 marked the fifth consecutive year of unprofitability for Habitat.

In late 2012 Thrivent Financial for Lutherans committed nearly $7 million to help build 113 Habitat for Humanity houses across the US in 2013.

Strategy

Habitat for Humanity nascent turnaround is credited to changes made at the beginning of the recession. Faced with a depressed housing market in many US states Habitat for Humanity shifted gears to get the most for its money. It refocused its efforts on rehabbing homes rather than building new as renovating is less costly than building from the ground up. Also the organization began to repurpose a growing number of foreclosed and empty homes by buying and renovating them then selling them to low-income families at reduced prices. It also pared down its operations. As a result the housing group has slashed expenses and shed staff in hopes of being able to reach out to more of those in need with less overhead.

EXECUTIVES

Executive Vice President International Field Operations, Michael (Mike) Carscaddon
Secretary, Henry G. Cisneros, age 66
Senior Vice President Marketing and Communications, Chris Clarke
President CEO and Director, Jonathan T. M. Reckford, age 51
Chair, Elizabeth Crossman
SVP Development, Kymberly Wolff
Senior Vice President U.S. and Canada, Larry Gluth
VP Europe and Central Asia Area, Don Haszczyn
Senior Public Relations and Media Relations Specialist, Nakia Fowler
Communications Coordinator Africa and Middle East, Lee Martin
Director Communications Latin America and Caribbean, Steve Little
Treasurer, Eduardo Tabush
VP Africa and Middle East Region, Gregory Foster
Manager Public Relations and Media Europe and Central Asia, Katerina Bezgachina
SVP Strategy, Dave McMurty
CIO, Gail Hyde
VP Operations US and Canada, Sue Henderson
Director, John O. Gilbert
Director, Edward H. (Ed) Bastian, age 55
Director, Kathleen M. Bader, age 62
Vice Chairman, Theodore A. (Ted) Dosch, age 53
Secretary, Henry G. Cisneros, age 66
President CEO and Director, Jonathan T. M. Reckford, age 51
Director, Mary Kazunga
Chairman, Ken Klein
Vice Chairman, Tony Lanigan
Vice Chairman, Anugerah Pekerti
Director, Nabil Abadir
Director, Paul Ekelschot
Director, Janet Huckabee
Director, Ed Schreyer
Director, Juel Shannon Smith
Director, John Stack
Secretary and Director, Elizabeth Crossman
Director, Vicken Aykasian
Director, Renee L. Glover
Director, Chainarong Monthienvichienchai
Treasurer, Eduardo Tabush
Director, Alex Silva
Director, Emil Constantinescu
VP Operations US and Canada, Sue Henderson
Auditors: Ernst&YoungLLP

LOCATIONS

HQ: HABITAT FOR HUMANITY INTERNATIONAL
121 HABITAT ST, AMERICUS, GA 31709-3498
Phone: 800-422-4828
Web: WWW.HABITAT.ORG

PRODUCTS/OPERATIONS

2012 Revenue

	$ mil.	% of total
Contributions	141	47
Government grants	77	26
Donations-in-kind	57	19
Other	23	8
Total	**299**	**100**

HISTORICAL FINANCIALS

Company Type: Private

Income Statement FYE: June 30

	REVENUE ($ mil.)	NET INCOME ($ mil.)	NET PROFIT MARGIN	EMPLOYEES
06/12	292	(31)	—	1,500
06/11	1	0	7.0%	—
Annual Growth	22681.2%	—	—	—

2012 Year-End Financials

Debt ratio: —
Return on equity: (-10.80%)
Cash ($ mil.): 40
Current ratio: —
Long-term debt ($ mil.): —
Dividends
Yield: —
Payout: —
Market value ($ mil.): —

HACKENSACK UNIVERSITY MEDICAL CENTER

Hackensack University Medical Center (HUMC) is an acute care teaching and research hospital that serves the residents of northern New Jersey and parts of New York. The hospital has about 775 beds and staffs more than 2200 medical professionals. HUMC administers general medical surgical emergency and diagnostic care. The medical center also includes specialized treatment centers including a children's hospital a women's hospital a cancer center and a heart and vascular hospital. HUMC is part of the Hackensack University Health Network which also includes a physician practice group and a joint venture that operates two community hospitals.

Operations

HUMC helps train future dentists and doctors through its affiliation with the University of Medicine and Dentistry of New Jersey. It expanded its education programs in 2012 by partnering with the Stevens Institute of Technology to offer joint biomedical training programs.

The hospital also performs research through the David Joseph Jurist Research Center for Tomorrow's Children. The center has roughly 475 research programs in operation at any given time.

Financial Performance

Medicare accounts for 29.5% of HUMC's funding; HMOs 28%; and Blue Cross 28%.

Strategy

The company grows organically and through acquisitions partnerships and affiliations.

To expand its services HUMC broke ground on a $35 million project to expand and renovate its trauma and emergency facilities in 2012 (scheduled to open in 2015).

Hackensack University Health Network is increasing its partnerships and affiliations with other regional care providers following the trend of US hospitals seeking to improve and lower the cost of health care through shared services and resources. The network partnered up with Texas-based LPH Hospital Group in 2012 to reenovate the Pascack Valley Hospital (now HackensackUMC Pascack) in Westwood New Jersey. Hackensack took over the bankrupt facility's ER back in 2007 and in 2012 the joint venture launched a $90 million project to revamp the rest of the 130-bed acute-care community hospital. It reopened in 2013.

Hackensack University Health Network also formed a joint venture with an area physician group to open two ambulatory surgery centers in 2012 and it entered a collaboration with CVS Caremark's MinuteClinic to open new urgent care centers.

That year HUMC formed a joint venture partnership with community physicians and United Surgical Partners International to buy and operate ambulatory surgery centers in Bergen County: Hackensack Endoscopy Center and the Endoscopy Center of Bergen County.

Mergers and Acquisitions

To extend its network of facilities in the region in 2012 the joint venture between Hackensack University Health Network and Legacy Partners acquired Mountainside Hospital (now Hackensack-UMC Mountainside) a 365-bed hospital located in Montclair from Merit Health Systems for some $190 million.

Company Background

To simplify its operations HUMC sold its hospice operations to Amedisys in 2011. The health provider previously sold its home health agency to Amedisys in 2009 to generate revenue and control costs after struggling with financial losses throughout the year due to declining admissions.

HUMC completed construction of its new John Theurer Cancer Center in late 2010 giving it one of the largest comprehensive cancer centers in the US. The center includes diagnostic and treatment units that focus on specific types of cancers.

HUMC was founded as a hospital in 1888 with 12 beds.

EXECUTIVES

Chairman Department of Ophthamology, Michael Rosenberg
Auditors: Deloitte&ToucheLLP

LOCATIONS

HQ: HACKENSACK UNIVERSITY MEDICAL CENTER
30 PROSPECT AVE STE 1, HACKENSACK, NJ 07601-1912
Phone: 201-996-2000
Web: WWW.HACKENSACKUMC.ORG

PRODUCTS/OPERATIONS

Selected Facilities

Donna A. Sanzari Women's Hospital
Hackensack University Medical Center Mountainside
Hackensack University Medical Center Pascack
Heart & Vascular Hospital
John Theurer Cancer Center
Joseph M. Sanzari Children's Hospital
Tomorrows Children's Institute for Cancer and Blood Disorders

COMPETITORS

Bergen Regional Medical
Bronx-Lebanon Hospital
Catholic Health East
Continuum Health Partners
Englewood Hospital and Medical Center
Hospital for Special Surgery
Lenox Hill Hospital
Montefiore Medical
NewYork-Presbyterian Healthcare
Newark Beth Israel Medical Center
St. Joseph' s Healthcare System
Valley Health System

HISTORICAL FINANCIALS

Company Type: Private

Income Statement FYE: December 31

	REVENUE ($ mil.)	NET INCOME ($ mil.)	NET PROFIT MARGIN	EMPLOYEES
12/08	1,037	(86)	—	7,175
12/07	1,183	48	4.1%	—
12/05	1,004	26	2.6%	—
12/04	873	40	4.7%	—
Annual Growth	4.4%	—	—	—

2008 Year-End Financials

Debt ratio: —
Return on equity: (-8.30%)
Cash ($ mil.): 275
Current ratio: 1.50
Long-term debt ($ mil.): —
Dividends
Yield: —
Payout: —
Market value ($ mil.): —

HACKLEY HOSPITAL

Medical professionals at Hackley Hospital aim to heal. Operating as as Mercy Health Partners Hackley Campus the hospital is a 210-bed acute care facility that serves patients living in Muskegon opposite the thumb on Michigan's shoreline. The teaching hospital offers such services as behavioral health care a sleep analysis lab a bariatric treatment center a cancer center stroke care emergency medicine and rehabilitation therapies. Mercy Health Partners Hackley Campus is part Mercy Health Partners Muskegon.

Operations

Mercy Health Muskegon is a Trinity Health division that operates three additional Michigan hospitals as well as outpatient care centers. Together the Mercy Health Muskegon division employs about 375 doctors and serves 21000 inpatients each year; it also handles some 137000 emergency and urgent care patients.

Strategy

To improve quality of care and process efficiencies Mercy Health Muskegon implemented an electronic health record (EHR) system during 2011. The network also expands by adding new facilities specialty services and affiliations in the region.

Company Background

The medical center opened in 1904. In 2008 Hackley Hospital's former parent (Hackley Health System) merged with Mercy General Health Partners to form Mercy Health Partners Muskegon.

EXECUTIVES

Regional President & CEO - Trinity Health West Michigan, Roger W. Spoelman, age 61
CFO, Gary Allore
Interim VP Human Resources, Greg Loomis
Chief Medical Officer, F. Remington Sprague
President & CEO Lakeshore Campus, Jay Bryan
Chief Nursing Officer & VP Patient Care Services, Kimberly A Maguire
Interim President & COO, Gregory A Loomis

LOCATIONS

HQ: HACKLEY HOSPITAL
1700 CLINTON ST, MUSKEGON, MI 49442-5591
Phone: 231-728-4950
Web: WWW.MERCYHEALTHMUSKEGON.COM

PRODUCTS/OPERATIONS

Selected Centers and Services

Aesthetics
Athletic Performance Center

Bariatric Surgery
Behavioral Health
Birth Center
Bladder Control Clinic
Diabetes Management Clinic and Education
Emergency and Urgent Care
Healthcare Equipment
Imaging Center of Excellence
Johnson Family Cancer Center
Laboratories
Life Counseling
Lymphedema Therapy
Memory Clinic
Muskegon Community Health Project
Neurosurgery
Orthopedics
Orthotics and Prosthetics
Pain Clinic
Pharmacies
Primary Care
Rehabilitation and Sports Medicine
Safe Kids West Michigan
Sleep Disorders Center
Spine Services
The Dan and Mavis Thill Heart and Vascular Institute
Weight Management
Women' s Health
Workplace Health

COMPETITORS

Borgess Health
Borgess Medical Center
Bronson Battle Creek
Bronson Health Care
Children' s Hospital of Michigan
Covenant HealthCare
Gerber Memorial
Holland Community Hospital
McLaren Bay
Sheridan Community Hospital
Shriners Hospitals For Children
Sparrow Health System
Spectrum Health
University of Michigan Health System
Zeeland Community Hospital

HISTORICAL FINANCIALS

Company Type: Private

Income Statement FYE: June 30

	REVENUE ($ mil.)	NET INCOME ($ mil.)	NET PROFIT MARGIN	EMPLOYEES
06/11	166	1	1.1%	1,500
06/10	151	(42)	—	—
06/09	144	(6)	—	—
06/08	306	12	4.0%	—
Annual Growth	(18.5%)	(47.1%)	—	—

2011 Year-End Financials

Debt ratio: —
Return on equity: 1.10%
Cash ($ mil.): 2
Current ratio: 1.80
Long-term debt ($ mil.): —
Dividends
Yield: —
Payout: —
Market value ($ mil.): —

HAGGEN INC.

EXECUTIVES

VP-Mktg, Scott Smith
Owner, Donald E. (Don) Haggen
President and CEO, Clarence J. (Gabe) Gabriel Jr., age 60
VP Marketing and Strategy, Becky Skaggs
VP-Perishables, Mike Lobaugh
Director of Marketing, Andy Tudor
Founder, Katie Stagliano

LOCATIONS

HQ: HAGGEN INC.
2211 RIMLAND DR STE 300, BELLINGHAM, WA 982265699
Phone: 3607338720
Web: WWW.HAGGEN.COM

2011 Stores

Washington	24
Oregon	4
Total	**28**

PRODUCTS/OPERATIONS

2013 Stores

TOP Food & Drug	15
Haggen Food & Pharmacy	13
Total	**28**

Selected Departments and Services

Bakery
Banking
Blockbuster Video
Cash machines
Deli
Dry cleaning
Full-service floral department
Garden supplies
In-store home economist
Just for Kids child-care center
Library book drop off
Market Street Cafe
Meat
Orient Express
Parcel pickup
Pharmacy
Produce
Seafood
Service deli catering
Starbucks Coffee shop
Sushi
Wine

COMPETITORS

Costco Wholesale
Fred Meyer Stores
Grocery Outlet
Quality Food
SUPERVALU
Safeway
Sam' s Club
Smart & Final
Target Corporation
Trader Joe' s
Wal-Mart
Walgreen
WinCo Foods

HISTORICAL FINANCIALS

Company Type: Private

Income Statement FYE: December 31

	REVENUE ($ mil.)	NET INCOME ($ mil.)	NET PROFIT MARGIN	EMPLOYEES
12/07	787	8	1.1%	3,900
12/06	758	6	0.9%	—
12/05	164	0	—	—
Annual Growth	—	20237.1%	—	—

2007 Year-End Financials

Debt ratio: —
Return on equity: 1.10%
Cash ($ mil.): 6
Current ratio: 0.30
Long-term debt ($ mil.): —
Dividends
Yield: —
Payout: —
Market value ($ mil.): —

HAMPTON UNIVERSITY

Hampton University is composed of six undergraduate schools as well as a graduate college and a college of continuing education. It offers some 70 bachelor's degree programs more than 25 master's degree programs and several doctoral or professional degrees in nursing physics atmospheric and planetary science physical therapy and pharmacy. It also includes the Scripps Howard School of Journalism and Communications. The school has an enrollment of about 5000 students. Hampton University has more than 300 full-time faculty members and a student-to-teacher ratio of 16:1.

Geographic Reach

Hampton University's campus includes some 120 buildings located on about 300 acres at mouth of the Chesapeake Bay in Virginia. It serves students from nearly all 50 US states and some 35 global countries.

Operations

The university's six undergraduate schools focus on business engineering and technology liberal arts and education nursing pharmacy and science. Hampton University is supported by a $190 million endowment. Tuition runs at about $18000 per year.

Strategy

To expand its programs in 2012 Hampton University partnered with the School of Dental Medicine of the University of Pennsylvania to offer a joint dental surgery and biology degree. In addition in 2013 Hampton's Journalism school partnered with Bloomberg to create a career development program in fields of communication.

Company Background

A historically black college Hampton was founded in 1868 during Reconstruction to educate newly-freed people with the support of the Freedman's Bureau Northern philanthropists and religious groups. It was originally named Hampton Normal and Agricultural Institute. Its name was changed to Hampton Institute in 1940 and again to Hampton University in 1984.

EXECUTIVES

Vp For Development, Laron Clark
Asst Vp For Development, Harriet Frink-davis
Vice President, Claude Alexander
Exec Vice President, Jo Ann Haysbert
Vice President For Business Affairs And Treasurer, Theresa Spells
Assistant Vice President For Development, Evelyn Oakley
Vp Business Affs/treasurer, Doretha J Spells
Secretary, Ebony Majeed
Auditors: KPMGLLP

LOCATIONS

HQ: HAMPTON UNIVERSITY
100 E QUEEN ST, HAMPTON, VA 236680108
Phone: 7577275000
Web: WWW.HAMPTONU.EDU

HISTORICAL FINANCIALS

Company Type: Private

Income Statement FYE: June 30

	REVENUE ($ mil.)	NET INCOME ($ mil.)	NET PROFIT MARGIN	EMPLOYEES
06/11	140	(1)	—	1,050
06/10	140	(1)	—	—
06/09	0	0	—	—
Annual Growth	—	—	—	—

2011 Year-End Financials

Debt ratio: —
Return on equity: (-1.10%)
Cash ($ mil.): 5
Current ratio: —
Long-term debt ($ mil.): —
Dividends
Yield: —
Payout: —
Market value ($ mil.): —

HARLAND M. BRAUN & CO. INC.

EXECUTIVES

President, Mike Hamilton
VP Sales, Dick Veale
Office Manager Finance, Karen Thareererg
Controller, Brian Jung
Documentation Assistant, Christine Cho
Production Supervisor Manufacturing, Sergio Novo
Logistics Manager, Brenda A. Ho
General Manager, Roland Sebastian
Quality Control Operator, Gene Beenders
Sales Manager, Rene Buchhammer
Sales Assistant, Chad Robertson
Documentation Supervisor, Ryan Tang
Founder, Harland Braun

LOCATIONS

HQ: HARLAND M. BRAUN & CO. INC.
4010 WHITESIDE ST, LOS ANGELES, CA 900631617
Phone: 3232639275
Web: WWW.BRAUNEXP.COM

COMPETITORS

Danier Leather
Pittards
Prime Tanning Co.
S. B. Foot Tanning

HISTORICAL FINANCIALS

Company Type: Private

Income Statement FYE: October 31

	REVENUE ($ mil.)	NET INCOME ($ mil.)	NET PROFIT MARGIN	EMPLOYEES
10/13	307	0	0.0%	30
10/12	277	0	0.2%	—
10/11	290	0	0.0%	—
10/10	212	0		
Annual Growth	13.1%	—	—	—

2013 Year-End Financials

Debt ratio: —
Return on equity: —
Cash ($ mil.): 1
Current ratio: 0.70
Long-term debt ($ mil.): —
Dividends
Yield: —
Payout: —
Market value ($ mil.): —

HARTFORD SAVINGS BANK

LOCATIONS

HQ: HARTFORD SAVINGS BANK
1400 SCHAUER DR, HARTFORD, WI 530271983
Phone: 2626732390
Web: WWW.HARTFORDSHOMETOWNBANK.COM

HISTORICAL FINANCIALS

Company Type: Private

Income Statement FYE: December 31

	ASSETS ($ mil.)	NET INCOME ($ mil.)	INCOME AS % OF ASSETS	EMPLOYEES
12/10	218	0	0.2%	46
12/09	221	0	0.0%	—
12/08	4	0	0.0%	—
Annual Growth	578.1%	19704.2%	—	—

2010 Year-End Financials

Debt ratio: —
Return on equity: 4.30%
Cash ($ mil.): 25
Current ratio: —
Long-term debt ($ mil.): —
Dividends
Yield: —
Payout: —
Market value ($ mil.): —

HARVEST LAND COOPERATIVE

LOCATIONS

HQ: HARVEST LAND COOPERATIVE
711 FRONT ST, MORGAN, MN 56266
Phone: 5072493196
Web: WWW.HARVESTLAND.COM

HISTORICAL FINANCIALS

Company Type: Private

Income Statement FYE: August 31

	REVENUE ($ mil.)	NET INCOME ($ mil.)	NET PROFIT MARGIN	EMPLOYEES
08/13	289	9	3.2%	150
08/12	263	9	3.5%	—
08/11	226	6	2.9%	—
08/10	183	0	—	—
Annual Growth	16.5%	—	—	—

2013 Year-End Financials

Debt ratio: —
Return on equity: 3.20%
Cash ($ mil.): 2
Current ratio: —
Long-term debt ($ mil.): —
Dividends
Yield: —
Payout: —
Market value ($ mil.): —

HATCH MOTT MACDONALD GROUP INC.

Hatch Mott MacDonald builds North America's underlying framework. The engineering firm which is a subsidiary of Mott MacDonald offers planning project development analysis design construction management facility maintenance and asset management for all types of infrastructure projects in North America. It specializes in tunnels wastewater systems pipelines rail and transit systems buildings and utilities. Customers are both private companies and municipalities. The company was formed in 1996 after Hatch Associates of Canada merged with Mott MacDonald. The company has more than doubled in size since the merger and now includes some 70 offices in the US and Canada.

Geographic Reach

New Jersey-based Hatch Mott MacDonald has offices in about two dozen US states including California Florida Massachusetts New York and Texas as well as in Alberta British Columbia New Brunswick Newfoundland and Labrador Nova Scotia and Ontario Canada.

Strategy

Hatch Mott MacDonald (HMM) is growing by acquiring smaller engineering firms across a variety of specialty practices and regions. Most recently the company acquired Canadian consulting specialist Engineering Northwest in May 2012. The Thunder Bay Ontario-based firm is focused on highway municipal water and wastewater engineering and project and construction management services. Also in 2012 HMM extended its reach to New Orleans with the purchase of Lambert Engineers an engineering and architectural firm there. With its extensive infrastructure needs New Orleans is a fertile market for HMM's services and complements the firm's other Gulf Coast offices from Florida to Texas.

Previously HMM acquired Richard P. Arber Associates a professional consulting engineering firm in Lakewood Colorado to expand its water and wastewater practice in the western US in 2011. Also that year it purchased North Carolina-based transportation firm Gibson Engineers.

EXECUTIVES

Principal, John Davenport
Owner, Mott MacDonald
Senior Vice President and Rail &, Nathan Higgins
CEO President, Nicholas DeNichilo

LOCATIONS

HQ: HATCH MOTT MACDONALD GROUP INC.
27 BLEEKER ST, MILLBURN, NJ 07041-1414
Phone: 973-379-3400
Web: WWW.HATCHMOTT.COM

PRODUCTS/OPERATIONS

Selected Services

Asset management
Aviation
Environment
Highways & bridges
Information management
Life-safety & security
Model-based Design/BIM
Pipelines
Ports
Project delivery
Rail & transit
Site development
Sustainability
Transportation planning
Tunnels
Wastewater
Water

COMPETITORS

AREVA NP
Bechtel
Black & Veatch Ltd.
Burns and Roe
CDI Engineering Solutions
E M C Engineers
Fagen Inc.
Fluor
Lauren Engineers
Sargent & Lundy

HISTORICAL FINANCIALS

Company Type: Private

Income Statement FYE: December 31

	REVENUE ($ mil.)	NET INCOME ($ mil.)	NET PROFIT MARGIN	EMPLOYEES
12/12	477	27	5.7%	1,800
12/11	440	25	5.8%	—
12/10	374	20	5.5%	—
12/09	343	18	5.3%	—
Annual Growth	11.6%	14.7%	—	—

2012 Year-End Financials

Debt ratio: ——
Return on equity: 5.70%
Cash ($ mil.): 25
Current ratio: 1.20
Long-term debt ($ mil.): —
Dividends
Yield: —
Payout: —
Market value ($ mil.): —

HAWAI I PACIFIC HEALTH

Hawaii may be paradise but even paradise's residents get sick sometimes. That's when Hawai'i Pacific Health (HPH) surfs in to save the day. HPH is a not-for-profit health care system consisting of four hospitals (Kapi'olani Medical Center for Women & Children Pali Momi Medical Center Straub Clinic & Hospital and Wilcox Memorial Hospital) across the islands with a combined capacity of 550 beds. The system offers a full array of tertiary specialty and acute care services through its hospitals which also serve as teaching and research centers as well as about 50 outpatient centers. Specialized services offered by HPH include cardiac care maternity services oncology orthopedics and pediatric care.

Operations

HPH supplies a wide range of primary and specialty medical services through its physician organizations. The Kapi'olani Medical Specialists group for instance comprises more than 100 physicians and partners with Kapi'olani Medical Center for Women & Children to care for patients from infancy through adulthood. The center also functions as the women's health and pediatric teaching hospital for the University of Hawaii School of Medicine. Its Visiting Specialists group provides care to the islands where HPH doesn't have primary care facilities.

The system has partnered with Surgical Care Affiliates to build an outpatient surgical center in Honolulu in an effort to meet growing demand there. The center dubbed Surgicare of Hawai'i offers an array of medical services including orthopedics pain management ophthalmology general surgery and podiatry; the facility opened in 2010.

Also in 2010 the hospital system embarked on a 6-year $580 million master facility plan to make expansion and improvement efforts at some of its primary hospital locations. The first stage includes new intensive care units and parking capacity at the Kapi'olani Medical Center.

Company Background

The organization was formed through the 2001 merger of three entities: Kapi'olani Health Straub Clinic & Hospital and Wilcox Health System.

EXECUTIVES

CEO Straub Clinic & Hospital, Art Gladstone, age 50
Executive Vice President Chief Medical Officer, Kenneth B. Robbins
President and CEO, Raymond P. Vara Jr.
EVP and CFO, David Okabe
General Counsel Vice President Hawaii Pacific, Bob Ching
EVP Strategic Business Development, Ginny Pressler
CEO Pali Momi Medical Center, Jen Chahanovich
CEO Kapi'olani Medical Center for Women & Children, Martha Smith
President and CEO Wilcox Memorial Hospital; CEO Kauai Medical Clinic, Kathy Clark
EVP and CIO Revenue Management and IT, Steve Robertson
Chief Medical Officer, Geri Young
Chief Operating Officer, Lynne Joseph

LOCATIONS

HQ: HAWAI I PACIFIC HEALTH
55 MERCHANT ST FL 27, HONOLULU, HI 96813-4333
Phone: 808-535-7350
Web: WWW.KAPIOLANI.ORG

PRODUCTS/OPERATIONS

Selected Facilities

Kapi'olani Medical Center for Women & Children (Honolulu)
Kaua'i Medical Clinics (Kaua'i)
Pali Momi Medical Center (Aiea)
Straub Clinic & Hospital (Honolulu)
Straub Family Health Centers (Honolulu)
Visiting Specialists (Hilo Kaua'i Lana'i Maui Moloka'i Walmea)
Wilcox Memorial Hospital (Lihue Kaua'i)

COMPETITORS

Adventist Health
Kuakini Health System
Queen' s Medical Center
Rehabilitation Hospital of the Pacific

HISTORICAL FINANCIALS

Company Type: Private

Income Statement FYE: June 30

	REVENUE ($ mil.)	NET INCOME ($ mil.)	NET PROFIT MARGIN	EMPLOYEES
06/11	901	75	8.4%	5,400
06/10	112	1	1.5%	—
06/09	812	(8)	—	—
06/08	716	(2)	—	—
Annual Growth	8.0%	—	—	—

2011 Year-End Financials

Debt ratio: ——
Return on equity: 8.40%
Cash ($ mil.): 66
Current ratio: 1.20
Long-term debt ($ mil.): —
Dividends
Yield: —
Payout: —
Market value ($ mil.): —

HAWKINS CONSTRUCTION COMPANY

Hawkins Construction provides both commercial building and heavy/highway contracting services. The diversified contractor has a project portfolio that includes regional ,Âbanks warehouses schools churches and prisons. It also works on highways bridges site developments and parking structures and is one of ,Â the Midwest's largest ,Âroad builders. Clients include the ,ÂUniversity of Nebraska ,Â Mutual of Omaha and ,ÂHewlett-Packard. ,ÂThe family-owned company began with a successful contract bid in 1922 by Kenneth Hawkins and his brother Earl for what is now Lincoln Nebraska's Memorial Stadium; the firm was incorporated in 1960 by Kenneth and his son Fred.

EXECUTIVES

Evp Commercial And Building Projects, Dudley Rinaker, age 64
V Pres, David Langenberg
V Pres, Bob Bloechle, age 77
V Pres, Tom Crockett, age 54
V Pres, Chris Harnly
V Pres, Kurt Peyton
V Pres, Chris Grojean
Senior Vice President Discovery, Feng Malloy
Assistant Vice President, Josh Bridges

LOCATIONS

HQ: HAWKINS CONSTRUCTION COMPANY
2516 DEER PARK BLVD, OMAHA, NE 681053771
Phone: 4023424455
Web: WWW.HAWKINS1.COM

COMPETITORS

Oldcastle Materials
Pepper Construction
Peter Kiewit Sons'
Turner Corporation
Walsh Group

HISTORICAL FINANCIALS

Company Type: Private

Income Statement FYE: December 31

	REVENUE ($ mil.)	NET INCOME ($ mil.)	NET PROFIT MARGIN	EMPLOYEES
12/13	160	9	5.6%	400
12/12	0	0	50.1%	—
12/08	238	16	6.7%	—
12/07	223	0	—	—
Annual Growth	(5.3%)	—	—	—

2013 Year-End Financials

Debt ratio: ——
Return on equity: 5.60%
Cash ($ mil.): 23
Current ratio: 1.20
Long-term debt ($ mil.): —
Dividends
Yield: —
Payout: —
Market value ($ mil.): —

HAWTHORNE MACHINERY CO.

Leader of the track Hawthorne Machinery a Caterpillar dealership sells and rents more than 300 CAT equipment models including tractors trucks loaders compactors harvesters graders excavators and power systems. It also provides parts and repair services for industrial and construction contractors and other public and private customers around San Diego County. Hawthorne Machinery offers new and used equipment and rentals of brand-name equipment by such blue chip OEMs as Kubota Spartan and Sullair. The company was founded in 1956 by Tom Hawthorne.

Geographic Reach

Outside of San Diego Hawthorne has 20 locations in Hawaii Guam American Samoa and Saipan.

Sales and Marketing

Hawthorne sells rents and provides parts and services to various industries including general building construction landscaping marine paving and power generation.

EXECUTIVES

Chief Financial Officer, Brian Verhoeven
Vice President, Howard Blaire
Associate Corporate Counsel Assistant Treasurer, Paul Dombrowski

LOCATIONS

HQ: HAWTHORNE MACHINERY CO.
16945 CAMINO SAN BERNARDO, SAN DIEGO, CA 92127-2499
Phone: 858-674-7000
Web: WWW.HAWTHORNECAT.COM

PRODUCTS/OPERATIONS

Selected Products

Farrow systems
Machinery
- Articulated trucks
- Backhoe loaders
- Cold planers
- Compact track & multi terrain loaders
- Compactors
- Feller bunchers
- Forest machines
- Forwarders
- Harvesters
- Hydraulic excavators
- Industrial loaders
- Knuckleboom loaders
- Material handlers
- Motor graders
- Off-highway trucks
- Paving equipment
- Pipelayers
- Road reclaimers
- Skid steer loaders
- Skidders
- Telehandlers
- Track loaders
- Track-type tractors
- Underground mining
- Wheel dozers
- Wheel excavators
- Wheel loaders
- Wheel tractor-scrapers

Power systems
- Air compressors
- Electric power (generator sets)
- Marine (commercial & pleasure craft engines auxiliary generator sets)

Work tool attachments
- Augers
- Backhoes
- Blades
- Brooms
- Brushcutters
- Buckets
  - Backhoe front/rear
  - Compact wheel loader
  - Excavator
  - Loader
  - Skid steer loader
  - Telehandlers
- Cold Planers
- Compactors
- Couplers
  - Backhoe rear
  - Excavator
  - Loader
- Felling heads
- Forks
  - Backhoe loader
  - Compact wheel loader
  - Loader
  - Skid steer loader
  - Telehandlers
- Grapples
- Hammers
- Harvester heads
- Lift groups
- Material handling arms
- Mulchers
- Multi-processors
- Rakes
- Rippers
- Saws
- Scarifiers
- Shears
- Snow blowers
- Snow plows & snow wings
- Stump grinders
- Thumbs
- Tillers
- Trenchers
- Truss booms

COMPETITORS

AMECO
Johnson Machinery
Pacific Rim Capital
Peterson Power
Small Parts Manufacturing
Sunbelt Rentals
United Rentals

HISTORICAL FINANCIALS

Company Type: Private

Income Statement FYE: December 31

	REVENUE ($ mil.)	NET INCOME ($ mil.)	NET PROFIT MARGIN	EMPLOYEES
12/07	338	0	0.1%	1,000
12/06	377	7	2.0%	—
12/03	170	44	26.2%	—
12/02	176	0	—	—
Annual Growth	13.9%	—	—	—

2007 Year-End Financials

Debt ratio: —
Return on equity: 0.10%
Cash ($ mil.): 10
Current ratio: 0.30
Long-term debt ($ mil.): —
Dividends
Yield: —
Payout: —
Market value ($ mil.): —

HAYS MEDICAL CENTER INC.

Hays Medical Center brings big city health care to rural Kansas. The not-for-profit hospital which has more than 220 beds provides both acute and tertiary medical care to the Midwestern plains serving more than 13000 emergency patients each year. In addition to medical surgical and pediatric care Hays Medical Center offers home care hospice skilled nursing rehabilitation and behavioral health services. It operates centers for cardiac care (the DeBakey Heart Institute) and cancer treatment (the Dreiling/Schmidt Cancer Center). The organization also operates specialty and rural health clinics.

Strategy

The medical center has grown its business through selective acquisitions and hospital expansion projects. At the tune of $18.5 million Hays Medical Center in 2011 began to add about 65000 sq. ft. of both office and clinical space to the hospital's main building while also remodeling a handful of exisiting departments. Due to be completed in 2013 the plan includes the $3.8 million expansion of the Dreiling/Schmidt Cancer Institute and Breast Care Center which began construction in 2012.

Hays Medical Center has also added reconstructive surgery services with the addition of a cosmetic surgeon and expanded its surgical capabilities by agreeing to assist with operations at nearby St. Joseph Memorial Hospital.

Sales and Marketing

Hays Medical Center maintains a local market share of nearly 90% with total primary/secondary/tertiary service at 25%.

Company Background

The medical center was formed in 1991 through the merger of a pair of religiously affiliated facilities.

EXECUTIVES

Vice President Chief Development, Jodi A Schmidt
President and CEO, John H. Jeter
COO, Bryce A. Young
Chief Nursing Officer, Terry J. Siek
SVP CFO and Chief Information Officer, William J. (Bill) Overbey
VP Regional Operations, Shae C. Veach
Chief Medical Officer, Larry Watts
CFO, George Harms
Director Physician Recruitment, Myron Applequist
Medical Director, Robert H Cox
Vice President Of Support Services, Dale A Montgomery
Director Of Operating Room, William Norris
Infection Control Director, Richard Matzke
Vice President Of Health Care, John L Miller
Cota, Cari Readle
Vice President Sales And Application Development, Kim Meier
Medical Dir, Thomas McDonald

LOCATIONS

HQ: HAYS MEDICAL CENTER INC.
2220 CANTERBURY DR, HAYS, KS 67601-2370
Phone: 785-623-5000
Web: WWW.HAYSMED.COM

PRODUCTS/OPERATIONS

Selected Departments

Billing/Financial
Dietary
Education
Emergency Department
Fitness Center
Hospice
Hospitalists
Imaging
Lifeline
Occupational Therapy
Palliative Care
Pharmacy
Rehabilitation
- In-Patient
- Out Patient

Respiratory Therapy
Senior Focused Care
Sexual Assault Response Team
Sleep and Neurodiagnostic
Special Nursing Services
Sports Medicine
Volunteer Services
Wound Healing and Hyperbaric Center
Weight Loss Surgery
WorkSMART

COMPETITORS

Adventist Health System Sunbelt Healthcare
Sisters of Charity of Leavenworth
Stormont-Vail HealthCare
University of Kansas Medical Center
Via Christi Health System

HISTORICAL FINANCIALS
Company Type: Private

Income Statement FYE: June 30

	REVENUE ($ mil.)	NET INCOME ($ mil.)	NET PROFIT MARGIN	EMPLOYEES
06/13	199	17	8.5%	1,178
06/12	209	17	8.1%	—
06/10	189	9	4.8%	—
06/10	184	9	5.1%	—
Annual Growth	2.6%	22.0%	—	—

2013 Year-End Financials

Debt ratio: —
Return on equity: 8.50%
Cash ($ mil.): 7
Current ratio: 1.90
Long-term debt ($ mil.): —
Dividends
Yield: —
Payout: —
Market value ($ mil.): —

HDC DISTRIBUTING LTD.

LOCATIONS

HQ: HDC DISTRIBUTING LTD.
7100 HIGH LIFE DR, HOUSTON, TX 770663713
Phone: 2818802730

HISTORICAL FINANCIALS
Company Type: Private

Income Statement FYE: December 31

	REVENUE ($ mil.)	NET INCOME ($ mil.)	NET PROFIT MARGIN	EMPLOYEES
12/11	203	11	5.9%	2
12/10	197	9	4.9%	—
Annual Growth	3.0%	24.7%	—	—

2011 Year-End Financials

Debt ratio: —
Return on equity: 5.90%
Cash ($ mil.): 3
Current ratio: 0.40
Long-term debt ($ mil.): —
Dividends
Yield: —
Payout: —
Market value ($ mil.): —

HEALTH PARTNERS OF PHILADELPHIA INC..

Health Partners wants to partner up with Pennsylvanians in need of health care. The company is a not-for-profit health plan that provides health benefits to some 170000 Medicaid recipients in the Philadelphia area. Its HealthChoices plans for Medicaid participants cover medical dental prescription and vision costs. Its KidzPartners program is provided in partnership with the state of Pennsylvania's Children's Health Insurance Program (CHIP). Its provider network includes about 4400 primary and specialty care doctors and 30 hospitals in the region. The company also provides community outreach and wellness programs. Health Partners was founded in 1985 by a group of hospitals in the Philadelphia area.

Strategy

Health Partners has been working to enhance its community health programs in recent years. In 2012 it launched its Computer Health Care Management Education program to provide free monthly computer lessons combined with tutorials about healthy lifestyle programs. In addition in 2011 the organization launched a new Nurse Advice Line to further enhance customer service in both its children's and its adult plans.

In 2012 Health Partners teamed up with the Norcom Community Center to offer HealthChoices and KidzPartners members fitness benefits at the facility; the company has a total of more than 20 fitness centers in its expanding provider network. The KidzPartners program which provides free or affordable insurance coverage to childrens and teens who don't qualify for Medicaid was first launched in 2009. Also in 2009 Health Partners opened a new community outreach office to enhance customer service; the location's employees answer health benefit questions and provide community programs such as computer training.

Ownership

The area hospitals that own Health Partners are Albert Einstein Medical Center Aria Health Temple University Hospital Episcopal Hospital and two Tenet Healthcare facilities (Hahnemann University Hospital and St. Christopher's Hospital for Children).

EXECUTIVES

Senior VP Chief Operating Officer, Elaine T. Markezin
SVP Health Care Management and Chief Medical Officer, Mary Stom
President CEO, Mary Brainerd
Vice President General Counsel, Barb TrethewaySr
Executive Vice President Chief Marketing Officer, Andrea Walsh
Vice President of Finance and Chief Financial Officer, Rolando J. Portocarrero

LOCATIONS

HQ: HEALTH PARTNERS OF PHILADELPHIA INC..
901 MARKET ST STE 500, PHILADELPHIA, PA 19107-3144
Phone: 215-849-9606
Web: WWW.HEALTHPART.COM

COMPETITORS

Aetna
CIGNA
Coventry Health Care
Gateway Health Plan
Health Net
Highmark
Independence Blue Cross
Keystone Mercy
UnitedHealth Group

HISTORICAL FINANCIALS
Company Type: Private

Income Statement FYE: December 31

	REVENUE ($ mil.)	NET INCOME ($ mil.)	NET PROFIT MARGIN	EMPLOYEES
12/12	1,034	(1)	—	500
12/09	805	2	0.4%	—
12/08	702	(0)	—	—
12/07	1,203	0	—	—
Annual Growth	(3.0%)	—	—	—

2012 Year-End Financials

Debt ratio: —
Return on equity: (-0.20%)
Cash ($ mil.): 97
Current ratio: 0.50
Long-term debt ($ mil.): —
Dividends
Yield: —
Payout: —
Market value ($ mil.): —

HEALTH RESEARCH INC.

Health Research Inc. (HRI) knows where the money is. The group is a not-for-profit organization that helps the New York State Department of Health and its affiliated Roswell Park Cancer Institute solicit evaluate and administer financial support. Sources of that support come from federal and state government sources other non-profits and businesses. HRI's Technology Transfer office also assists the Department of Health in sharing its research findings with other public and private institutions and finding ways to create biomedical technologies through private sector development. HRI was founded in 1953 and has administered $7 billion over its lifetime.

HRI's Technology Transfer office has aided several research organizations in recent years such as ones studying prostate specific antigen (or the PSA test) photodynamic therapy and pox virus vectors among others. ,Â

EXECUTIVES

Executive Director, Michael Nazarko
Associate Director Technology Transfer, Robert (Bob) Gallo

LOCATIONS

HQ: HEALTH RESEARCH INC.
150 BROADWAY STE 560, MENANDS, NY 122042736
Phone: 5184311200
Web: WWW.HEALTHRESEARCH.ORG

HISTORICAL FINANCIALS
Company Type: Private

Income Statement FYE: March 31

	REVENUE ($ mil.)	NET INCOME ($ mil.)	NET PROFIT MARGIN	EMPLOYEES
03/14	703	13	1.9%	1,400
03/13	665	25	3.9%	—
03/12	661	(10)	—	—
03/11	665	0	—	—
Annual Growth	1.9%	—	—	—

2014 Year-End Financials

Debt ratio: —
Return on equity: 1.90%
Cash ($ mil.): 137
Current ratio: 0.30
Long-term debt ($ mil.): —
Dividends
Yield: —
Payout: —
Market value ($ mil.): —

HEALTHEAST ST JOHN'S HOSPITAL

St. John's Hospital provides health care to folks residing the suburbs of the Twin Cities. The hospital has about 185 beds and is an acute-care facility with emergency inpatient and outpatient medicine departments. Its facilities include specialty centers for breast care cancer care heart health maternity services and orthopedics among other offerings. St. John's started in 1910 with a private home that was converted into a 25-bed hospital. St. John's Hospital is part of the HealthEast Care System which includes other hospitals and health centers in the Minneapolis/St. Paul metropolitan area.

LOCATIONS

HQ: HEALTHEAST ST JOHN' S HOSPITAL
1575 BEAM AVE, SAINT PAUL, MN 55109-1126
Phone: 651-232-7000
Web: WWW.STJOHNSHOSPITAL-MN.ORG

COMPETITORS

Allina Hospitals
Catholic Health Initiatives
Fairview Health
Mayo Clinic
Park Nicollet Health Services
Regions Hospital

HISTORICAL FINANCIALS

Company Type: Private

Income Statement FYE: August 31

	REVENUE ($ mil.)	NET INCOME ($ mil.)	NET PROFIT MARGIN	EMPLOYEES
08/09	252	18	7.4%	713
08/06	203	14	7.1%	—
08/05	190	11	6.1%	—
08/02	168	21	12.6%	—
Annual Growth	6.0%	(1.8%)	—	—

2009 Year-End Financials

Debt ratio: —
Return on equity: 7.40%
Cash ($ mil.): 0
Current ratio: 2.20
Long-term debt ($ mil.): —
Dividends
Yield: —
Payout: —
Market value ($ mil.): —

HEARTLAND HEALTH

Heartland Health provides medical care in the heart of the Midwest. The integrated health care system serves residents of northwest Missouri as well as bordering areas of Kansas and Nebraska. Its flagship facility is Heartland Regional Medical Center a 350-bed acute-care hospital that features an emergency room and Level II trauma center as well as specialty care programs in heart disease cancer and obstetrics. Heartland Health also provides primary care through a multi-specialty medical practice (Heartland Clinic) and it offers home health hospice and long-term care services from the primary medical center facility. The company's Community Health Improvement Solutions unit is an HMO health insurer.

Strategy In 2012 Heartland Health joined the Mayo Clinic Care Network which will enable to it to tap the knowledge and expertise of Mayo Clinic physicians to better serve its patients.

Company Background Heartland Health was formed in 1984 through the merger of two St. Joseph Missouri hospital: Methodist Medical Center and St. Joseph's Hospital. The two facilities trace their roots back to 1924 and 1861 respectively.

EXECUTIVES

Chief Operating Officer, Curt Kretzinger
Chief Financial Officer, John Wilson
Vice Chairman, Carol Roever
Chairman, Alfred L. Purcell
Chief Business Development, Dirck Clark
Coordinator Media and Communications, Marcy George

LOCATIONS

HQ: HEARTLAND HEALTH
5325 FARAON ST, SAINT JOSEPH, MO 64506-3488
Phone: 816-271-6000
Web: WWW.HEARTLAND-HEALTH.COM

PRODUCTS/OPERATIONS

Selected Affiliates

Atchison Hospital (Atchison KS)
Community Hospital (Fairfax MO)
Community Medical Center (Falls City NE)
Dental Clinic (St. Joseph MO)
Laser Cosmedic Center (Platte City MO)
North Kansas City Hospital (North Kansas City MO)
The Surgery Center (St. Joseph MO)

COMPETITORS

Ascension Health
BJC HealthCare
Blue Cross and Blue Shield of Kansas City
Catholic Health Initiatives
Children' s Mercy Hospital
CoxHealth
HCA
Mercy Health
Mercy Hospital Springfield
Saint Luke' s Health System
Shawnee Mission Medical Center
Sisters of Charity of Leavenworth
St. John' s Health System
Truman Medical Centers
University of Kansas Medical Center

HISTORICAL FINANCIALS

Company Type: Private

Income Statement FYE: June 30

	REVENUE ($ mil.)	NET INCOME ($ mil.)	NET PROFIT MARGIN	EMPLOYEES
06/13	572	76	13.4%	32,000
06/12	584	10	1.8%	—
06/03	528	69	13.1%	—
06/03	309	5	1.6%	—
Annual Growth	6.4%	31.2%	—	—

2013 Year-End Financials

Debt ratio: —
Return on equity: 13.40%
Cash ($ mil.): 15
Current ratio: 1.30
Long-term debt ($ mil.): —
Dividends
Yield: —
Payout: —
Market value ($ mil.): —

HEARTLAND REGIONAL MEDICAL CENTER

EXECUTIVES

Vice Chairman, Carol Roever
Chairman, Alfred L. Purcell
Purchasing Secretary, Sharon Erickson
Auditors: KPMGLLP

LOCATIONS

HQ: HEARTLAND REGIONAL MEDICAL CENTER
5325 FARAON ST, SAINT JOSEPH, MO 645063488
Phone: 8162717211

PRODUCTS/OPERATIONS

Selected Services

Appendectomy
Cholecystectomy
Colon Resection
Hernia Repair
Nephrectomy
Assisted Vaginal Hysterectomy
Peritoneal Dialysis Catheter Placement
Pyloromyotomy
Tubal Ligation
Abdominal Perineal Resection
Adrenalectomy
Colostomy
Gastric Banding
Gastric Bypass
Gastric Sleeve
Gastrostomy Tube Placement
Laser Lysis of Adhesions/Endometriosis
Nissan Fundoplication
Salpingo-Oophorectomy
Prostatectomy

COMPETITORS

Ascension Health
BJC HealthCare
Catholic Health Initiatives
Children' s Mercy Hospital
CoxHealth
Mercy Health
Saint Luke' s Health System
Shawnee Mission Medical Center
Sisters of Charity of Leavenworth
St. John' s Health System
Truman Medical Centers
University of Kansas Medical Center

HISTORICAL FINANCIALS

Company Type: Private

Income Statement FYE: June 30

	REVENUE ($ mil.)	NET INCOME ($ mil.)	NET PROFIT MARGIN	EMPLOYEES
06/13	604	44	7.4%	2,600
06/12	564	11	2.0%	—
06/11	514	72	14.0%	—
06/10	483	0	—	—
Annual Growth	7.7%	—	—	—

2013 Year-End Financials

Debt ratio: —
Return on equity: 7.40%
Cash ($ mil.): 12
Current ratio: 0.30
Long-term debt ($ mil.): —
Dividends
Yield: —
Payout: —
Market value ($ mil.): —

HEIDTMAN STEEL PRODUCTS INC.

Steel life is an art at Heidtman Steel Products a provider of steel processing services such as blanking leveling and pickling. One of the largest privately held flat-rolled steel service networks in the US the company processes more than five million tons of steel annually. Services include hot-rolling cold-rolling and steel coating a full-range of slitting capabilities and galvanizing. Heidtman Steel operates plants in five mainly Midwestern states that serve automotive bus and truck manufacturers as well as furniture and appliance makers. The company is an approved steel supplier to Caterpillar and Ford.

Geographic Reach

The company operates plants in Indiana Illinois Michigan Maryland and Ohio.

Operations

Looking to ramp up its activities Heidtman Steel participates in several joint ventures. The company's investments include Fulton County Processing with VanPoppel Enterprises and Kelco Metals and American Roll Coating and Cleaning Co. (Arcco) with Universal Metals. Together the company and its affiliates operates nine steel processing plants.

Sales and Marketing

The company serves customers in a range of industries including automotive truck and bus manufacturers appliance furniture and HVAC makers and other steel service centers.

Its hot rolled cold rolled and coated steel products and first operation blanks are marketed through its Toledo blank location.

Strategy

Improving its customer service operations in 2013 Heidtman Steel launched the Quick Ship Program to help customers to order products online in a variety of coating weights and thicknesses in either coil or sheet form. In 2012 the company installed a Bradbury leveler in its Cleveland Ohio pickling line enabling the plant to provide end products with superior flatness shape and surface conditions.

Company Background

Heidtman Steel Products was formed in 1954 by William Heidtman and offered leveling and shearing services during its first few years of operation. It introduced steel slitting equipment in 1971 and flat rolled steel service in 1979.

EXECUTIVES

Vice President Of Eastern Region, Greg Glenn
Vice President Of Quality, Doug McFarland
Vice President Purchasing, Darlene Dotson

LOCATIONS

HQ: HEIDTMAN STEEL PRODUCTS INC.
2401 FRONT ST, TOLEDO, OH 43605-1199
Phone: 419-691-4646
Web: WWW.HEIDTMAN.AVATARSYN.COM

PRODUCTS/OPERATIONS

Selected Products and Services

Blanking and shearing
Coated products
- Aluminized
- Culvert stock
- Electrogalvanized
- Galvannealed
- Hot-dipped galvanized
- Painted

Cold-rolled applications
Culvert applications
Cut-to-length
Edging
Excess and secondary steel (through Steel spider)
First operation blanks
Galvanizing
Galvannealing
Hot-rolled applications
Leveling
Pickling
Slitting
Smooth Clean Surface (SCS) steal processing
Temper/one pass processing

Selected Markets

Agricultural
Appliances
Automotive OEM
Automotive suppliers
Components manufacturers
Construction
Fasteners
Furniture
Hardware
Heavy truck manufacturers
HVAC
Lawn and garden
Metal building
Metal tank
Pipe and tube
Power distribution
Steel service centers
Storage racks/Store fixtures
Truck trailer manufacturers

COMPETITORS

Feralloy
Metalcraft
Nucor
O' Neal Steel
Olympic Steel
United States Steel

HISTORICAL FINANCIALS

Company Type: Private

Income Statement FYE: March 31

	REVENUE ($ mil.)	NET INCOME ($ mil.)	NET PROFIT MARGIN	EMPLOYEES
03/07	637	14	2.2%	1,000
03/06	599	(0)	—	—
03/05	679	5	0.8%	—
03/04	443	1	0.3%	—
Annual Growth	12.8%	114.4%	—	—

2007 Year-End Financials

Debt ratio: —
Return on equity: 2.20%
Cash ($ mil.): 2
Current ratio: 0.60
Long-term debt ($ mil.): —
Dividends
Yield: —
Payout: —
Market value ($ mil.): —

HELEN KELLER INTERNATIONAL

Helen Keller International (HKI) has vision. The organization fights blindness by working with doctors government agencies partner groups and individuals in 22 countries citing that 80% of all blindness is avoidable. Its core areas of focus are eye health overall health and nutrition and poverty reduction. HKI distributes antibiotics performs cataract surgery and provides eye screenings glasses and education. The group works to combat malnutrition by promoting prenatal care supplying Vitamin A and helping others set up sustainable gardens and nutrition programs. It aims to reduce poverty through projects for literacy preschool and clean water and offers entrepreneurial support for women.

Geographic Reach

Based in New York City HKI offers its services through programs in 22 countries worldwide specifically 13 in Africa and eight in Asia Pacific and the US.

Operations

HKI besides its operations in the US boasts regional offices in Africa's Senegal and in Cambodia; it has an office in France through affiliate Helen Keller International Europe.

Financial Performance

HKI generated $220 million in revenue in fiscal 2012 up from $162 million in 2011 and $112 million in 2010. Of this government grants comprised some 70% with contributions from individuals corporations and foundations (including gifts in kind) accounting for the balance. The group spends 85% of its funds on programs to prevent blindness and malnutrition.

Strategy

In recent years HKI has expanded its ChildSight program which makes it easier for struggling school children to get prescription eyeglasses. Already active in the US for nearly two decades and having reached 1.4 million students the program is now getting traction in Indonesia's underserved communities. In Indonesia ChildSight has trained more than 1500 teachers who've conducted vision screenings for 85000 children –16500 of which have received eyeglasses. To leverage the successes of the ChildSight program a similar program has since been rolled out in Vietnam.

Company Background

HKI began in 1915 as an organization to help soldiers blinded in World War I. Focus on prevention including nutritional causes of blindness didn't come until 1966.

EXECUTIVES

President and CEO, Kathy Spahn
VP and Regional Director Africa, Shawn K. Baker
VP Eye Health, Nicholas Kourgialis
Chairman, L. Bradford Perkins
VP and Regional Director Asia-Pacific, Nancy Haselow
SVP Programs, Victoria Quinn
VP Development and Communications, Jennifer S. Klopp
Managing Director Helen Keller International Europe, Alix de Nicolay
Vice Chair and Secretary, Nancy Smith Lione
Director for Finance, Lily Natalia
Chief Financial Officer, Patricia Manyari
Vice President for Information and Operations Systems, Ric Plaisance
Vice President of Development, Peggy ONeill

LOCATIONS

HQ: HELEN KELLER INTERNATIONAL
352 PARK AVE S FL 12, NEW YORK, NY 10010-1723
Phone: 212-532-0544
Web: WWW.HKI.ORG

PRODUCTS/OPERATIONS

2012 Revenue

	% of total
Contributions - Medical supplies medicines & other	77
Grants - US government	10
Contributions - Corporations foundations &	7
Grants - Non-US government	6
Dividends & interest —	
Legacies & —	
Program & other —	
Total	100

HISTORICAL FINANCIALS

Company Type: Private

Income Statement FYE: June 30

	REVENUE ($ mil.)	NET INCOME ($ mil.)	NET PROFIT MARGIN	EMPLOYEES
06/12	220	2	1.0%	600
06/11	162	(0)	—	—
06/10	94	(2)	—	—
06/09	39	0	1.5%	—
Annual Growth	76.7%	55.5%	—	—

2012 Year-End Financials

Debt ratio: —
Return on equity: 1.00%
Cash ($ mil.): 11
Current ratio: 3.60
Long-term debt ($ mil.): —
Dividends
Yield: —
Payout: —
Market value ($ mil.): —

HENRICKSEN & COMPANY INC.

Henricksen & Company wants your company to be comfortable. The firm is an office furniture distributor selling mid- and high-end office furnishings such as desks chairs filing systems and partitions from manufacturers including Allsteel Gunlocke and HON. Henricksen also offers furniture warehousing installation maintenance and cleaning as well as reconfiguration design and space planning services. It leases furniture as well. Customers have included Cray Huron Consulting

Restaurant Technologies SXC Health Solutions and Roundy's.The company was founded by the Henricksen family in the 1960s.

Geographic Reach

Henricksen has three Chicago-area offices (Chicago Naperville and Itasca) as well as locations in Brookfield and Madison Wisconsin; Minneapolis; and Peoria Illinois.

Financial Performance

Although privately held the company reports annual sales of around $130 million.

EXECUTIVES

Chairman, Stephen E. (Steve) McPartlin
VP, Russell Frees
Director Business Development, Mark Dalton
VP and General Manager Minneapolis, Dick Nash
CFO Treasurer, Tim Osborn
President, Michael D. Assell
Executive Vice President Secretary, Richard D. Failla
Vice President General Manager Principal, Chris Knoeppel

LOCATIONS

HQ: HENRICKSEN & COMPANY INC.
1070 ARDMORE AVE, ITASCA, IL 60143-1366
Phone: 630-250-9090
Web: WWW.HENRICKSEN.COM

PRODUCTS/OPERATIONS

Selected Products

Architectural Products
Benching
Casegoods & Desking
Conference
Design Classics
Education Furniture
Ergonomics
Filing/Storage
Floor Coverings
Healthcare Furniture
Lounge Seating
Multi-Purpose Seating
Reception
Systems
Tables
Task Seating

Selected Services

Asset Management/Storage
AutoCAD/Product Application
Buy Back
Install/Reconfigure
Leasing Options
Move and Change
Nationwide Services
Ongoing Maintenance
Online Corporate Standards
Repair/Refurbish

COMPETITORS

Aaron' s Inc.
Corporate Concepts
OEC Business Interiors
Office Concepts
Office Depot
OfficeMax
Staples
Target Commercial Interiors

HISTORICAL FINANCIALS

Company Type: Private

Income Statement FYE: April 30

	REVENUE ($ mil.)	NET INCOME ($ mil.)	NET PROFIT MARGIN	EMPLOYEES
04/13	157	0	0.1%	197
04/12	147	0	0.1%	—
04/10	129	0	0.2%	—
04/10	114	0	0.1%	—
Annual Growth	11.1%	(10.3%)	—	—

2013 Year-End Financials

Debt ratio: —
Return on equity: 0.10%
Cash ($ mil.): 0
Current ratio: 0.80
Long-term debt ($ mil.): —
Dividends
Yield: —
Payout: —
Market value ($ mil.): —

HENRY FORD HEALTH SYSTEM

Built around a hospital founded by Detroit's favorite son the not-for-profit Henry Ford Health System (HFHS) is a hospital network that is also involved in medical research and education. The system's half-dozen hospitals –including the flagship Henry Ford Hospital as well as Henry Ford Wyandotte Hospital and mental health facility Kingswood Hospital –are home to roughly 2200 beds. HFHS also operates a 1200-doctor-strong medical group (with more than 40 specialities) as well as nursing homes hospice and a home health care network. The system's Health Alliance Plan of Michigan provides managed care and health insurance to about half a million members.

Geographic Reach

HFHS serves patients in Detroit and southeastern Michigan.

Operations

Along with its hospitals large and small the system also operates more than 30 medical centers and maintains partnerships with community health services. About 20% of ambulatory care and 10% of acute care services in the region are provided by HFHS. In 2011 its hospitals took in 106590 patients handled more than 405100 emergency room visits and delivered more than 7440 babies. It also conducts more than 300000 home health care visits annually.

For patients who need more than an ambulance to get them to the hospital the Henry Ford Hospital provides air ambulance transportation. The flagship hospital provides transport for critically ill and trauma patients within a 150-mile radius of Detroit (in Michigan Ohio and Ontario) via its Air Med 1 aeromedical helicopter.

Affiliated with Wayne State University's School of Medicine the health system is a leading education and research center with ongoing research in areas such as stroke heart disease cancer and diabetes. Wayne State and HFHS have agreed to expand their affiliation by increasing the number of medical students who train at Henry Ford working together on research projects and opening a new research center. HFHS trains more than 1500 future physicians every year. Henry Ford Hospital is responsible for many of those providing about 45 accredited programs to medical students.

Financial Performance

HFHS has a fairly diverse payer mix. In 2011 it derived about 32% of its third-payer income from its Health Alliance Plan 29% from Medicare 16% from Blue Cross Blue Shield and the rest from Medicaid and other contracts including Aetna and United Health.

Strategy

HFHS grows organically and through partnerships. In 2012 it teamed up with Presbyterian Villages of Michigan forming a joint venture to operate the Center for Senior Independence. The Center was part of HFHS and is now a separate non-profit organization with Presbyterian is expected to increase by 2016 to nearly 1000 seniors from the current 230 patients.

In 2012 the company opened its 32nd medical center in southeast Michigan with a new site in Bloomfield Hills.

HFHS has increased its physician base by launching a subsidiary the Henry Ford Physician Network which is composed of private practice and hospital-employed physicians as well as the existing Henry Ford Medical Group.

The company also increased its home health equipment sales by opening its own retail home health store in 2010. The store (which it calls a self-health consulting center) sells a wide range of products including ambulatory aids respiratory therapy equipment wound care products and blood pressure and diabetes supplies.

Company Background

Automaker Henry Ford founded Henry Ford Hospital in 1915.

EXECUTIVES

Chairman, Anthony F. Earley Jr., age 64
President Emeritus, Gail L. Warden, age 75
EVP Finance and Administration and CFO, James M. Connelly
CEO, Nancy M. Schlichting, age 60
EVP and Chief Medical Officer; CEO Henry Ford Medical Group, Mark A. Kelley
President and COO, Robert G. (Bob) Riney
Director Medical Records Henry Ford Hospital, Karen Schmidt
EVP and Chief Medical Officer, John Popovich Jr., age 64
CEO Community Care Services, John J. Polanski
Senior Vice President of Philanthropy, Jon M. Fitzgerald
Director Workforce Diversity and Affirmative Action, Jocelyn Giangrande
Vice President General Manager for The Ritz-Carlton Hotel Company, Gerard van Grinsven, age 53
EVP and Chief Quality Officer; CEO Henry Ford Medical Group, William A. Conway
VP and COO Henry Ford Medical Group, Thomas S. Nantais
SVP Communications and Chief Marketing Officer, Rose M. Glenn
VP and Chief Diversity Officer, Randy D. Walker
President and CEO Henry Ford Wyandotte Hospital, Denise Brooks-Williams
SVP Pathology and Laboratory Medicine, Richard J. Zarbo
VP Supply Chain Management, Jim O'Connor
SVP and Chief Human Resources Officer, Kathleen M. (Kathy) Oswald
SVP Strategic Business Development, William R. (Bill) Schramm
EVP; President and CEO Health Alliance Plan, William R. (Bill) Alvin
VP Governance and Secretary, Edith L. Eisenmann
Chief Nursing Officer; COO Henry Ford Hospital, Veronica M. Hall
VP Planning and Performance Improvement, Susan S. Hawkins
Vice President General Counsel, David B. Lee
President and CEO Henry Ford Macomb Hospitals, Barbara W. Rossmann
President and CEO Henry Ford Wyandotte Hospital, James J. Sexton
VP Community Health Education and Wellness, Kimberlydawn Wisdom
Director Media Relations Henry Ford Health System and Henry Ford West Bloomfield Hospital, Dwight Angell
Manager Media Relations, David Olejarz
Chairman, Sandra E. Pierce
Chair Biostatistics and Research Epidemiology, Christine Cole Johnson
VP Total Rewards, Noel R. Baril
SVP and CIO, Mary Alice Annecharico
Operations Manager, Fiona MacPhail

Vice President, John Carey
President Henry Ford Kingswood Hospital, Nichole Stromberg
Vice President of patient care services and chief nursing officer, Karen Harris
Honorary Trustee, William C. (Bill) Ford Jr., age 56
Honorary Trustee, Walter E. Douglas
Honorary Trustee, Douglas T. McClure
Trustee, Allan D. Gilmour, age 79
Honorary Trustee, Edsel B. Ford II, age 65
CEO, Nancy M. Schlichting, age 59
Trustee, Marwan S. Abouljoud
Trustee, Charles H. (Chuck) Podowski
Trustee, Lynn Ford Alandt
Trustee, N. Charles Anderson
Trustee, Manuel L. Brown
Trustee, James Grosfeld
Trustee, David M. Hempstead
Trustee, Joseph R. Jordan
Trustee, Alan M. Kiriluk
Trustee, David B. Lewis
Trustee, Albert L. Lorenzo
Trustee, John C. Plant
Honorary Trustee, Richard R. Vlasic
Honorary Trustee, E. Paul Casey
Honorary Trustee, Martha F. Ford
Honorary Trustee, Morton E. Harris
Trustee, Edward J. Bagale
Trustee, Stephanie W. Bergeron
Trustee, Steven D. Harrington

LOCATIONS

HQ: HENRY FORD HEALTH SYSTEM
1 FORD PL, DETROIT, MI 48202-3450
Phone: 313-916-2600
Web: WWW.HENRYFORD.COM

PRODUCTS/OPERATIONS

2011 Payer Distribution

Health Alliance Plan	32
Medicare	29
Blue Cross	16
Other	8

Selected Operations

Hospitals
- Henry Ford Hospital
- Henry Ford Macomb Hospitals
- Henry Ford West Bloomfield Hospital
- Henry Ford Wyandotte Hospital
- Kingswood Hospital (mental health care)

Other
- Greenfield Health Systems (dialysis provider)
- Health Alliance Plan of Michigan (health plan)
- Henry Ford Continuing Care (nursing homes)
- Henry Ford Health Products (medical supply retailer)
- Henry Ford Home Health Care (home health)
- Henry Ford Medical Centers and Urgent Care (urgent care)
- Henry Ford Medical Group (physician's group)
- Henry Ford OptimEyes (eye care services)
- Hospices of Henry Ford (hospice)

COMPETITORS

Ascension Health
Beaumont Health System
Blue Cross Blue Shield of Michigan
Crittenton Hospital
Detroit Medical Center
Garden City Hospital
Harper-Hutzel Hospital
HealthPlus of Michigan
McLaren Health Care
Mount Clemens Regional Medical Center
Oakwood Healthcare
OmniCare Health Plan
St. John Health
Total Health Care
Trinity Health (Novi)
University of Michigan Health System

HISTORICAL FINANCIALS

Company Type: Private

Income Statement FYE: December 31

	REVENUE ($ mil.)	NET INCOME ($ mil.)	NET PROFIT MARGIN	EMPLOYEES
12/09	2,118	26	1.3%	23,000
12/08	1,083	(122)	—	—
12/07	1,820	80	4.4%	—
12/06	3,245	134	4.2%	—
Annual Growth	(13.3%)	(41.6%)	—	—

2009 Year-End Financials

Debt ratio: —
Return on equity: 1.30%
Cash ($ mil.): 513
Current ratio: —
Long-term debt ($ mil.): —
Dividends
Yield: —
Payout: —
Market value ($ mil.): —

HENRY MAYO NEWHALL MEMORIAL HOSPITAL

Had a bit too much mayo? Arteries feeling a bit clogged? Henry Mayo Newhall Memorial Hospital exists for just this reason (among others). The hospital serves the healthcare needs of the Santa Clarita Valley in northern Los Angeles County. The not-for-profit community hospital houses more than 220 beds and provides general medical and surgical care as well as trauma services (it is a Level II trauma center) outpatient services psychiatric care and emergency services among other specialties. In operation since 1975 the hospital was built to serve the needs of the at-the-time unincorporated City of Santa Clara on land donated by The Newhall Land and Farming Company.

Henry Mayo Memorial's physicians offer patients more than 70 different medical specialties that range from a widely hailed cancer program to an advanced primary stroke center spine and joint program an acute rehab unit growing cardiology services outpatient wound care services and physical and occupational therapies. The hospital also offers extensive maternity programs that include lactation support and childbirth education programs.

The hospital is undergoing a number of expansions including the addition of more intensive care unit (ICU) beds a larger emergency room expanded surgery department the construction of two helipads to receive patients via helicopter and the development of a new Neonatal Intensive Care Unit (NICU). All of the construction is part of Henry Mayo Memorial's 15-year master plan to expand and upgrade to accommodate a growing patient population.

Henry Mayo Hospital is also building an inpatient hospital to house up to another 120 hospital beds. The hospital addition will operate 24 hours a day seven days a week and its development will provide Santa Clarita residents with close to 360 total patient beds. Opening is anticipated for 2016.

To sum up the 15 year development plan includes the inpatient building up to three medical office buildings a new central plant and up to four parking structures. Other campus modifications include additional acute care beds in the pavilion one helipad on a parking structure and one on the new inpatient building. The plan also includes the new ICU NICU expanded imaging services new operating rooms and centers of excellence. The entire project is expected to cost $300 million and is being funded through operations bonds philanthropy and private investments.

EXECUTIVES

President CEO and Director, Roger E. Seaver
SVP and COO, John Schleif
Chair, James D. Hicken
Vice Chair, Craig Peters
Chief of Staff and Director, Mark Sender
Manager Public Relations, Laura Young
Director Women's Services, Sally McGann
Director, Margaret M. (Marlee) Lauffer, age 53
Treasurer and Director, Donald L. (Don) Kimball, age 55
President CEO and Director, Roger E. Seaver
Director, Elizabeth Hopp
Director, Vinod Assomull
Secretary and Director, Judy Fish
Deputy Chief of Staff and Director, Chand Khanna
Vice Chair, Craig Peters
Director, Douglas R. Sink
Director, Cecelia Hann
Chief of Staff and Director, Mark Sender
Director, Mark Liker
Director, Dale Donohoe
Director, Graciela Freixes
Auditors: StonefieldJosephsonInc.

LOCATIONS

HQ: HENRY MAYO NEWHALL MEMORIAL HOSPITAL
23845 MCBEAN PKWY, SANTA CLARITA, CA 91355-2001
Phone: 661-253-8011
Web: WWW.HENRYMAYO.COM

COMPETITORS

Aptium Oncology
Brotman Medical Center
Cedars-Sinai Medical Center
Childrens Hospital Los Angeles
Glendale Adventist Medical Center
Good Samaritan Hospital (Los Angeles)
HCA
Hoag Memorial Hospital
Hollywood Presbyterian Medical Center
Kaiser Permanente
Los Angeles County Health Department
Marin General Hospital
Methodist Hospital of Southern California
Providence Saint Joseph Medical Center
Tenet Healthcare
United Surgical Partners

HISTORICAL FINANCIALS

Company Type: Private

Income Statement FYE: September 30

	REVENUE ($ mil.)	NET INCOME ($ mil.)	NET PROFIT MARGIN	EMPLOYEES
09/12	223	14	6.4%	1,000
09/09	205	11	5.8%	—
09/05	145	10	6.9%	—
09/05	131	127	97.1%	—
Annual Growth	7.9%	(26.8%)	—	—

2012 Year-End Financials

Debt ratio: —
Return on equity: 6.40%
Cash ($ mil.): 30
Current ratio: 1.60
Long-term debt ($ mil.): —
Dividends
Yield: —
Payout: —
Market value ($ mil.): —

HENRY MODELL & COMPANY INC.

EXECUTIVES

CEO, Mitchell B. (Mitch) Modell, age 60
VP Information Technology, Hans Kantor
VP Logistics, Steve Ondrejack

LOCATIONS

HQ: HENRY MODELL & COMPANY INC.
498 7TH AVE FL 20, NEW YORK, NY 100186704
Phone: 2128221000
Web: WWW.MODELLS.COM

PRODUCTS/OPERATIONS

Selected Product Categories

Accessories
Apparel
Baseball
Basketball
Boxing/martial arts
Camping/hiking
Cycling
Electronics/optics
Fan shop-pro/college
Field hockey
Fishing
Fitness
Football
Footwear
Games
Golf
Ice/roller hockey
In-Line/roller skating
Lacrosse
Optics/telescopes
Outdoor recreation
Paintball
Pilates
Racquetball/squash
Roller hockey
Rugby
Running
Scooters
Skateboarding
Snow sports
Soccer
Softball
Tennis
Water recreation
Winter recreation
Wrestling
Yoga

COMPETITORS

Athleta
Dick' s Sporting Goods
Dunham' s
Eastern Mountain Sports
Foot Locker
Hat World
Olympia Sports
Sears
Sports Authority
Target Corporation
Wal-Mart

HISTORICAL FINANCIALS

Company Type: Private

Income Statement

FYE: February 1

	REVENUE ($ mil.)	NET INCOME ($ mil.)	NET PROFIT MARGIN	EMPLOYEES
02/14	604	(4)	—	5,430
02/13*	607	0	0.1%	—
01/12	570	(3)	—	—
01/11	558	0	—	—
Annual Growth	2.7%	—	—	—

*Fiscal year change

2014 Year-End Financials

Debt ratio: ——
Return on equity: (-0.80%)
Cash ($ mil.): 5
Current ratio: 0.10
Long-term debt ($ mil.): —
Dividends
Yield: —
Payout: —
Market value ($ mil.): —

HENSEL PHELPS CONSTRUCTION CO

Hensel Phelps Construction builds it all from the courthouse to the big house. The employee-owned general contractor provides a full range of development pre-construction and construction services for commercial institutional and government projects throughout the US and abroad. Its project portfolio includes prisons airports arenas laboratories government complexes offices and more. Major public and private clients have included the US Army Corps of Engineers IBM United Airlines The University of Texas Kodak and Whole Foods. Hensel Phelps founded the eponymous company as a homebuilder in 1937.

Geographic Reach

Colorado-based Hensel Phelps Construction has seven regional offices throughout the continental US including two in California. In 2012 the firm opened a branch in Honolulu that oversees operations in Hawaii Guam the Marshall Islands and Asia. The company operates internationally most often for US federal projects but also for foreign governments and private enterprises.

Financial Performance

One of America's largest private companies Hensel Phelps reported $2.1 billion in revenue in 2012.

Strategy

Hensel Phelps ranks in the top three (by Engineering News Record) among general contractors and construction managers in the US in the aerospace government and "green" government office sectors. The company self performs (as opposed to subcontracting) most of the work tied to a specific project. That ability helps keep costs and schedules in check. Its construction services include concrete work quality control safety management waste management among others.

Recent big projects include many for the Smithsonian Institution and the US Navy including the new Homeport Ashore Bachelor Quarters (BEQ) at Naval Base San Diego. The 161000 square foot BEQ will house about 645 sailors while their ship is docked in San Diego. Other notable projects include a new central library in Austin Texas.

Ownership

Hensel Phelps Construction is owned by its employees.

EXECUTIVES

President Phelps Development, Eric L. Wilson
CFO, Stephen J. (Steve) Carrico
CEO and President, Jerry L. Morgensen
EVP, Wayne S. Lindholm
EVP, Jon W. Ball
President and CEO, Jeffrey K. (Jeff) Wenaas
Director Project Planning and Development Mid-Atlantic District, Brent Helmandollar
Chief Estimator Northern California District, Dale A. Weislak
Manager Preconstruction Services Southeast District, Ken Petterson
VP-South Central District, Mark T. Baugh
EVP Central Division, Edwin L. Calhoun
Director Diversity and Project Development Capitol District, Charles Eaton
Chief Estimator Southeast District, Bryan L. Butcher
Chief Estimator Southern California District, Mike Verrastro
EVP, Michael J. Choutka
Project Development Manager Northern California District, Jeff A. Bennett
VP and Manager Western District, Steve Grauer
VP Southern California District, Cuyler R. McGinley
VP and Manager Southwest District, Thomas D. Fisher
VP and District Manager Southeast, Kirk J. Hazen
EVP, Richard G. Tucker
Project Development Manager, Andrew Millar
Project Development Manager, Jeff Stoddard
Project Development Manager, Stephen J. Friar
District Manager Vice President Larry Gonda Chief Estimator, Allan J. Bliesmer
District Manager Vice President, Bran Jeanneret
Vice President - Services Group, Mo Luqman
President Hensel Phelps Services, Edwin (Glen) Miller
Auditors: KPMGLLP

LOCATIONS

HQ: HENSEL PHELPS CONSTRUCTION CO
420 6TH AVE, GREELEY, CO 80631-2332
Phone: 970-352-6565
Web: WWW.HENSELPHELPS.COM

PRODUCTS/OPERATIONS

Selected Services

Construction
- Change management
- Construction waste management
- LEED project registration
- Quality control
- Safety management
- Scheduling
- Self-perfoming concrete
- Status reporting
- Subcontractor management
- Sustainability audits
- Quality control

Development
- Feasibility studies
- Financing
- Green building planning/education
- Land acquisition
- Leasing
- Pro forma review

Post-construction
- As-built documentation
- Building operations
- Certificate of occupancy
- Commissioning and warranty programs
- LEED project certification
- Moving services

Preconstruction
- Bid packaging
- Budgeting/cost modeling
- Design management
- Estimating
- Green building and planning/education
- Phasing plans
- Regulatory investigation
- Scheduling
- Status reporting
- Subcontractor prequalification
- Value engineering

Selected Markets

Commercial
Education
High technology
Industrial
International
Justice
Leisure
Medical
Multiresidence
Public
Transportation

COMPETITORS

Balfour Construction
C.F. Jordan
CH2M HILL
Clark Construction Group
Fluor
Gilbane
Hunt Construction
Jacobs Engineering
KBR
M. A. Mortenson
McCarthy Building
PCL Employees Holdings
Rooney Holdings
Skanska USA Building
Turner Corporation
Tutor Perini
Walbridge Aldinger
Walsh Group
Whiting-Turner

HISTORICAL FINANCIALS

Company Type: Private

Income Statement FYE: December 31

	REVENUE ($ mil.)	NET INCOME ($ mil.)	NET PROFIT MARGIN	EMPLOYEES
12/12*	1,220	35	2.9%	2,800
05/12	2,178	54	2.5%	—
05/11	2,494	152	6.1%	—
05/10	3,012	237	7.9%	—
Annual Growth	(26.0%)	(46.8%)	—	—

*Fiscal year change

2012 Year-End Financials

Debt ratio: —
Return on equity: 2.90%
Cash ($ mil.): 205
Current ratio: 0.90
Long-term debt ($ mil.): —
Dividends
Yield: —
Payout: —
Market value ($ mil.): —

HERSHEY ENTERTAINMENT & RESORTS COMPANY

EXECUTIVES

CEO, Theodore J. (Ted) Kleisner, age 69
Director Corporate Relations, Garrett Gallia
Executive Vice President, Kim Schaller
Chief Financial Officer Secretary Treasurer, Dave Lavery
Vice President of Operations, John Lawn
President Chief Operating Officer, William Simpson
Vice President of Marketing, Lisa Hultquist
Vice President Human Resources, Nathan Douty

LOCATIONS

HQ: HERSHEY ENTERTAINMENT & RESORTS COMPANY
100 HOTEL RD, HERSHEY, PA 170339507
Phone: 7175343131
Web: WWW.THEHOTELHERSHEY.COM

PRODUCTS/OPERATIONS

Selected Operations

Amusement parks
- Hersheypark
- ZooAmerica

Hotels
- Hershey Lodge
- The Hotel Hershey
  - The Spa At The Hotel Hershey

Other
- Giant Center
- Hershey Golf Collection
- Hershey Highmeadow Campground
- Hersheypark Stadium

COMPETITORS

Adventureland
Cedar Fair
Disney Parks & Resorts
Great Wolf
Herschend Entertainment
Kennywood
LEGO
SeaWorld
Six Flags
Universal Parks

HISTORICAL FINANCIALS

Company Type: Private

Income Statement FYE: December 31

	REVENUE ($ mil.)	NET INCOME ($ mil.)	NET PROFIT MARGIN	EMPLOYEES
12/09	270	6	2.6%	7,100
12/08	273	13	5.1%	—
12/07	1,333	0	0.0%	—
Annual Growth	(54.9%)	16391.2%	—	—

2009 Year-End Financials

Debt ratio: —
Return on equity: 2.60%
Cash ($ mil.): 2
Current ratio: 0.20
Long-term debt ($ mil.): —
Dividends
Yield: —
Payout: —
Market value ($ mil.): —

HICKMAN WILLIAMS & COMPANY

LOCATIONS

HQ: HICKMAN WILLIAMS & COMPANY
250 E 5TH ST STE 300, CINCINNATI, OH 452024198
Phone: 5136211946
Web: WWW.HICWILCO.COM

HISTORICAL FINANCIALS

Company Type: Private

Income Statement FYE: March 31

	REVENUE ($ mil.)	NET INCOME ($ mil.)	NET PROFIT MARGIN	EMPLOYEES
03/14	245	0	—	93
03/13	287	5	2.0%	—
03/12	0	0	—	—
03/11	299	0	—	—
Annual Growth	(6.4%)	—	—	—

2014 Year-End Financials

Debt ratio: —
Return on equity: —
Cash ($ mil.): 22
Current ratio: 2.30
Long-term debt ($ mil.): —
Dividends
Yield: —
Payout: —
Market value ($ mil.): —

HIGH INDUSTRIES INC.

High Industries has ascended to the top of the steel and construction business. Doing business as High Companies its subsidiaries are active in heavy construction and materials. Its High Steel Structures is one of North America's largest steel bridge fabricators. Other group companies include High Steel Service Center (metal processing) High Concrete Group (precast concrete) High Transit (specialty hauler) and High Structural Erectors (field erection services). Affiliates of High Companies such as High Hotels are active in real estate. The group mostly does business along the East Coast tracing its roots to a welding shop founded by Sanford H. High in 1931. It is controlled by the High Family Council.

Geographic Reach

Headquartered in Lancaster Pennsylvania High Industries caters to clients across the US's East Coast.

Sales and Marketing

High Industries serves a diverse group of customers throughout the Eastern and Midwestern US.

Operations

The company is controlled by the High Family Council which comprises three members including third-generation High family members. The council is supported by two boards of directors and an executive committee.

High Industries operates High Steel Structures High Steel Service Center High Concrete Group High Hotels and High Transit a specialty hauler that serves all affiliated companies of High Industries. When High Transit isn't busy hauling for its parent it offers specialty services for companies in the civil construction manufacturing transportation building construction Marcellus Shale and heavy equipment industries. High Industries formed High Structural Erectors in 2013. It provides erection services to the infrastructure commercial institutional and industrial markets.

Most well known for its steel work High Steel Structures is the largest steel bridge girder manufacturer in the US serving as a fabricator and erector of more than 6000 bridges since 1980. Bridge projects include the Arthur Ravenel Jr. Bridge in South Carolina and the Frederick Douglass - Susan B. Anthony Memorial Bridge in New York. Its biggest project was the $85-million high-occupancy lanes on the I045 Virginia Capital Beltway.

Strategy

The slowdown in the economy caused lower demand in the construction industry. High Companies weathered the recession by seeking out work in the public sector and completed more school university transportation and military projects.

EXECUTIVES

Vp-corp Tax, Dean Glick
CEO, Nevin D. Cooley
SVP and CFO, Michael W. Van Belle
President and COO High Real Estate Group LLC, Mark C. Fitzgerald
President and COO, Jeffrey L. Sterner
Vice President Of Information, Ronnie Medlock
V Pres And Controller, Karen A Biondolillo
Vice President, Michael J Lorelli
Vice President Of Services, Darryl P Gordon
Vice President Finance, Jim Brubaker
Vice President Of Marketing, Brian Reichert
Senior Vice Presiden, Jim Holthouser
Vice President, Brian Urban
Senior Vice President, Brad Mowbray
Senior Vice President, Michael Kelly
Chairman and President, S. Dale High
Secretary, Robin D Stauffer
Board Member, Steve Gaul
Asst Sec, Elaine A Richard

LOCATIONS

HQ: HIGH INDUSTRIES INC.
1853 WILLIAM PENN WAY, LANCASTER, PA 17601-6713
Phone: 717-293-4444
Web: WWW.HIGHINDUSTRIES.ORG

PRODUCTS/OPERATIONS

Selected Affiliates

High Industries Inc.
- High Concrete Group LLC
- High Steel Service Center Inc.
- High Steel Structures Inc.
- High Structural Erectors LLC
- High Transit LLC

High Real Estate Group LLC
- Greenfield Architects Ltd.
- High Associates Ltd.
- High Construction Company
- High Environmental Health & Safety Consulting Ltd.
- High Hotels Ltd.
- High Investors Ltd.

COMPETITORS

AK Steel Holding Corporation
American Bridge Company
Dukane Precast
Flatiron Construction
New Era Builders
Nucor
Peter Kiewit Sons'
Schuff
Skanska USA Civil
United States Steel
Walsh Group
Williams Industries

HISTORICAL FINANCIALS

Company Type: Private

Income Statement FYE: December 31

	ASSETS ($ mil.)	NET INCOME ($ mil.)	INCOME AS % OF ASSETS	EMPLOYEES
12/09	230	0	—	2,107
12/08	272	31	11.7%	—
12/07	266	23	8.7%	—
12/06	297	25	8.7%	—
Annual Growth	(8.2%)	—	—	—

2009 Year-End Financials

Debt ratio: ——
Return on equity: —
Cash ($ mil.): 26
Current ratio: 1.30
Long-term debt ($ mil.): —
Dividends
Yield: —
Payout: —
Market value ($ mil.): —

HIGH POINT REGIONAL HEALTH SYSTEM

Hospital stays are usually not the high point of one's life but High Point Regional Health System aims to make patients comfortable. Its main facility is High Point Regional Hospital a medical/surgical facility with about 380 beds serving the Piedmont Triad region of North Carolina. The private not-for-profit health care system also operates the Carolina Regional Heart Center Neuroscience Center Piedmont Joint Replacement Center Emergency Center Culp Women's Center and Hayworth Cancer Center. Other operations include primary care physician practices mental health wound care and home health care services. The hospital was founded in 1904. It became part of the UNC Health Care System in 2013.

Change in Company Type

The hospital became part of the UNC Health Care System (also known as University of North Carolina Hospitals) in 2013 through a merger transaction. Through the deal UNC Health will invest $150 million in capital improvements at High Point Regional as well as $50 million in community health initiatives. High Point Regional remains a not-for-profit entity with its own supporting foundation.

Geographic Reach

High Point Regional Hospital is located in High Point North Carolina and serves the Piedmont Triad region.

Operations

High Point Regional Hospital has a medical staff of about 2300 workers (including 400 physicians) and serves 120000 patients annually. It handles some 63000 emergency room visits 185000 outpatient care visits and 1500 births each year. The hospital also provides more than $40 million in community care programs including charity medical programs.

Other services offered through the Health System include diabetes treatment mental health bariatrics fitness wound care imaging and rehabilitation. It also operates Regional Physicians Multispecialty Group (a physicians practice organization) High Point Surgery Center and the Millis Regional Health Education Center.

Sales and Marketing

High Point Regional Hospital uses television commercials and social media to promote its services in the region.

Financial Performance

High Point reported a modest 6% revenue gain due to higher patient payments. Net income rose sharply due to a change in investment reporting while cash flow held steady.

Strategy

The organization began looking for a strategic partner in 2012 with the goal of leveraging its position in the changing US health care landscape. It formed an agreement with UNC Health Care later that year and the merger was completed in April 2013.

Prior to that High Point had signed an agreement with Duke Medicine to expand services for oncology and cardiovascular patients.

EXECUTIVES

President Chief Executive Officer, Jeffrey S. (Jeff) Miller
SVP, Linda M. Roney, age 65
COO, Gregory W. Taylor
VP and Chief Nursing Officer, Tammi Mengel
VP People Services, Katherine Burns
VP Foundation Public Relations and Marketing, Denise Potter
Vice President Chief Nursing Officer, Tammi-Erving Mengel

LOCATIONS

HQ: HIGH POINT REGIONAL HEALTH SYSTEM
601 N ELM ST, HIGH POINT, NC 27262-4398
Phone: 336-878-6000
Web: WWW.HIGHPOINTREGIONAL.COM

PRODUCTS/OPERATIONS

Selected Centers and Services

Primary Centers
- The Carolina Regional Heart Center
- Culp Women' s Center
- The Emergency Center
- Hayworth Cancer Center
- The Neuroscience Center
- The Piedmont Joint Replacement Center

Other Centers
- Adult Health
- Behavioral Health
- Diabetes Self-Care Management Center
- The Fitness Center at High Point Regional
- The Fitness Center at Kernersville
- Heart Strides
- Millis Regional Health Education Center
- MRI and Open MRI
- Online Nursery
- PET Imaging
- Premier Imaging
- Regional Center for Bariatric Surgery
- Regional Physicians
- Regional Wound Center
- Rehab Services
- Robotic Surgery
- The Stroke Center
- Vascular Services

COMPETITORS

Alamance Regional Medical Center
Carolinas HealthCare System
Cone Health
Health Management Associates
Tenet Healthcare
UNC Hospitals
Wake Forest University Baptist Medical Center

HISTORICAL FINANCIALS

Company Type: Private

Income Statement FYE: September 30

	REVENUE ($ mil.)	NET INCOME ($ mil.)	NET PROFIT MARGIN	EMPLOYEES
09/12	274	1	0.7%	2,338
09/11	276	(13)	—	—
09/10	296	0	0.3%	—
09/09	302	(1)	—	—
Annual Growth	(3.2%)	—	—	—

2012 Year-End Financials

Debt ratio: ——
Return on equity: 0.70%
Cash ($ mil.): 1
Current ratio: 0.60
Long-term debt ($ mil.): —
Dividends
Yield: —
Payout: —
Market value ($ mil.): —

HIGH STEEL STRUCTURES INC.

Steel fabricator High Steel Structures helps to build bridges —literally. The company manufactures structural steel beams and girders used to build bridges and elevated roads in the US. High Steel also makes steel structures for buildings such as manufacturing plants power plants and sports arenas and offers erection services and emergency repair services. Working with contractors such as Balfour Beatty Skanska and Middlesex High Steel has fabricated steel for thousands of bridges mainly along the East Coast. The company has four fabrication plants in Pennsylvania and is a part of High Industries. High Steel traces its roots back to 1931 when it was founded as High Welding Company.

High Steel was challenged in the past few years when the construction industry declined and the price of steel rose. But the company is working on projects with stimulus dollars as state departments of transportation begin awarding contracts for new roads and bridges.

EXECUTIVES

President, Jeffery L. Sterner

LOCATIONS

HQ: HIGH STEEL STRUCTURES INC.
1915 OLD PHILADELPHIA PIKE, LANCASTER, PA 17602-3410
Phone: 717-299-5211
Web: WWW.HIGHSTEEL.COM

COMPETITORS

American Bridge Company
Commercial Metals
Hirschfeld Steel
L. B. Foster
Schuff
Stupp Bros.
Williams Industries

HISTORICAL FINANCIALS

Company Type: Private

Income Statement FYE: December 31

	REVENUE ($ mil.)	NET INCOME ($ mil.)	NET PROFIT MARGIN	EMPLOYEES
12/09	180	0	—	600
12/08	131	7	5.4%	—
12/07	135	5	4.4%	—
Annual Growth	15.4%	—	—	—

2009 Year-End Financials

Debt ratio: —
Return on equity: —
Cash ($ mil.): 0
Current ratio: 0.80
Long-term debt ($ mil.): —

Dividends
Yield: —
Payout: —
Market value ($ mil.): —

HILAND DAIRY FOODS COMPANY. LLC

EXECUTIVES

President, Gary L. Aggus

LOCATIONS

HQ: HILAND DAIRY FOODS COMPANY. LLC
1133 E KEARNEY ST, SPRINGFIELD, MO 658033435
Phone: 4178629311
Web: WWW.HILANDDAIRY.COM

Selected Plant Locations

Chandler Oklahoma
Fayetteville Arkansas
Fort Smith Arkansas
Kansas City Missouri
Little Rock Arkansas
Norfolk Nebraska
Norman Oklahoma
Omaha Nebraska
Springfield Missouri
Wichita Kansas

PRODUCTS/OPERATIONS

Selected Products

Butter
Cheese
Cottage cheese
Cravelatte (milk and coffee)
Creams/Half-and-Half
Dips
Egg nog
Egg substitute
Fruit-flavored drinks
Ice cream
Juice
Lactose-free milk
Lemonade
Milk
Sour cream
Tea
To-go drinks
Water
Yogurt

COMPETITORS

Agri-Mark
Associated Milk Producers
Blue Bell
ConAgra
Dairylea
Dean Foods
Dreyer' s
Fonterra
Great Lakes Cheese
Hornell Brewing
Kemps LLC
Land O' Lakes
MMPA
Nestle
Oberweis Dairy
Organic Valley
Roberts Dairy
Saputo
Sargento
Smith Dairy
Snapple
Wells' Dairy

HISTORICAL FINANCIALS

Company Type: Private

Income Statement FYE: September 30

	REVENUE ($ mil.)	NET INCOME ($ mil.)	NET PROFIT MARGIN	EMPLOYEES
09/11	958	8	0.9%	1,350
09/10	588	24	4.2%	—
09/09	2,110	0	—	—
Annual Growth	(32.6%)	35387.7%	—	—

2011 Year-End Financials

Debt ratio: —
Return on equity: —
Cash ($ mil.): 19
Current ratio: 0.90
Long-term debt ($ mil.): —

Dividends
Yield: —
Payout: —
Market value ($ mil.): —

HILL PHYSICIANS MEDICAL GROUP INC

Hill Physicians Medical Group is the doctors' answer to HMOs. The company is an independent practice association (IPA) serving some 300000 health plan members in northern California. The company contracts with managed care organizations throughout the region –including HMOs belonging to Aetna CIGNA and Health Net –to provide care to health plan members through its provider affiliates. Its network includes about 3700 primary care and specialty physicians 36 hospitals and 15 urgent care centers. The company also provides administrative services for doctors and patients. PriMed a management services organization created Hill Physicians Medical Group in 1984 and still runs the company.

Geographic Reach

Hill Physicians Medical Group's member facilities are located in Alameda Contra Costa El Dorado Placer Sacramento San Francisco San Joaquin San Mateo Solano and Yolo counties in northern California.

Financial Analysis

Hill Physicians Medical Group reported a 6% increase in 2011 to about $481 million due to higher health plan revenues and investment income. Net income grew by 114% to some $12 million that year due to higher revenues and cost savings programs.

Strategy

Hill Physicians Medical Group has been working to enhance its technology systems to improve coordination of care including installing electronic prescription and referral management systems. It is also forming partnerships with area insurers and hospitals to improve communication among regional providers as well as to control overall health care costs. For instance the company teamed up with Dignity Health and Blue Shield of California to form an accountable care organization (ACO).

Mergers and Acquisitions

In 2010 Hill Physicians Medical Group expanded its physician network by acquiring another IPA the Physicians Integrated Medical Group.

EXECUTIVES

Chief Administrative Officer, Dan Robinson
CIO, Craig Lanway
COO, David Joyner
CEO, Darryl Cardoza
Chief Medical Services Officer, Rosaleen Derington
CFO, Rick Messman
Chairman, Bruce A. Bob
Treasurer and Director, Robert C. Feldman
Vice Chairman, Elisabeth H. Renner
Chief Medical Officer and Director, Thomas Long
VP Legal Services and Chief Privacy Officer, Wendy Chow
VP Medical Group Services, Terry Hill
Director, Bruce A. Bob
Director, Dean J. Nickles
Treasurer and Director, Robert C. Feldman
Secretary and Primary Care Medical Director; Board Member, Elisabeth Renner
Director, Sean P. Hennessey
Director, Alvin M. Sockolov
Director, Thomas J. Imperato
Chief Medical Officer and Director, Thomas Long
Director, Larry G. Strieff
Director, Andrew W. Moyce
Director, Richard B. Ward
Director, Harpreet S. Grewal
Director, Michael J. McNamara
Director, Joshua S. (Josh) Adler
Auditors: KPMG

LOCATIONS

HQ: HILL PHYSICIANS MEDICAL GROUP INC
2409 CAMINO RAMON, SAN RAMON, CA 94583-4285
Phone: 925-820-3536

PRODUCTS/OPERATIONS

Selected Health Plan Partners

Aetna of California
Alliance CompleteCare
Anthem/Blue Cross of California
Blue Shield of California
Blue Shield 65 Plus
CIGNA Healthcare of California
Health Net of California
Health Net Medicare
United Healthcare West (formerly Pacificare)
SCAN
Secure Horizons by United Healthcare
Western Healthcare Advantage

COMPETITORS

Alta Bates Summit Medical Center
Beaver Medical Group
HealthCare Partners
Kaiser Permanente
Orion HealthCorp
Prospect Medical
The Palo Alto Medical Foundation

HISTORICAL FINANCIALS

Company Type: Private

Income Statement FYE: December 31

	REVENUE ($ mil.)	NET INCOME ($ mil.)	NET PROFIT MARGIN	EMPLOYEES
12/11	480	11	2.4%	488
12/10	427	5	1.2%	—
12/06	427	5	1.2%	—
12/05	414	7	1.9%	—
Annual Growth	2.5%	6.9%	—	—

2011 Year-End Financials

Debt ratio: —
Return on equity: 2.40%
Cash ($ mil.): 68
Current ratio: 1.50
Long-term debt ($ mil.): —

Dividends
Yield: —
Payout: —
Market value ($ mil.): —

HINES INTERESTS LIMITED PARTNERSHIP

EXECUTIVES

EVP; CEO Europe/Middle East Region, Michael J. G. Topham
EVP; CEO West Region, James C. (Jim) Buie Jr.
EVP, Kenneth W. (Ken) Hubbard
EVP; CEO Midwest and Southeast Regions, C. Kevin Shannahan
Chairman, Gerald D. Hines
SVP Corporate Communications, George C. Lancaster
SVP and Chief Administration Officer, David LeVrier
Vice Chairman and Chief Investment Officer, C. Hastings (Hasty) Johnson
President and CEO, Jeffery C. (Jeff) Hines
CFO, Charles M. Baughn
Senior Vice President Corporate Finance, Kay P. Forbes
SVP Human Resources, Stephanie Fore
SVP Southwest, John Mooz
EVP Conceptual Construction, Jerrold P. Lea
EVP; CEO Southwest Region, Mark Cover
SVP Midwest, Thomas (Tom) Danilek
SVP Midwest, David McGinnis
SVP and CIO, Jesse Carrillo
SVP Midwest, Thomas G. D'Arcy
SVP Midwest, Greg Van Schaack
SVP Midwest, Chuck Watters
Director Hines Europe, Patrick Albrand
Director Hines Europe; President Hines France Sovacim, Olivier de Dampierre
Director Hines Europe, Mietek Godzisz
Director Hines Europe, Simon O'Donnell
VP Hines Europe, Jay Wyper
SVP West, Jim Morrison
SVP West, Paul Paradis
CEO Investment Management, Colin Shepherd
SVP East, Bill Alsup
SVP East, Tommy Craig
Vice President Manager HCB Interests I & II LP, Steve Dolman
CEO Capital Markets and East Region, Christopher D. Hughes
Director Hines Germany, Karl Wambach
SVP Southwest, Charles Elder
Senior Managing Director and Chief Risk Officer Investments, Tom Owens
Senior Vice President Engineering Services, Clayton Ulrich
Senior Vice President Corporate Operations Services, Ilene Allen
CFO European Region/MENA, Lars Huber
Senior Vice President, David J. Congdon
Vice President, Avi Tesciuba
Vice President, Ponce Leon
Vice President Manager HCC Interests, Simon Shen
Senior Vice President, Thomas Kruggel
Senior Vice President and Corporate Controller, Keith Montgomery
Senior Vice President Worldwide Ta, Jeanine Hutchens
Senior Vice President Risk Management, Rick Vance

LOCATIONS

HQ: HINES INTERESTS LIMITED PARTNERSHIP
2800 POST OAK BLVD # 4800, HOUSTON, TX 770566118
Phone: 7136218000
Web: WWW.HINES.COM

PRODUCTS/OPERATIONS

Selected Services

Acquisition & Disposition Services
- Building pro forma
- Cash flow pro forma
- Closing
- Financing
- Investor pro forma
- Market evaluation
- Property evaluation
- Risk analysis
- Strategic planning

Asset & Property Management Services
- Acquisition & sales coordination
- Budgeting accounting & control
- Construction management
- Energy management
- Facility management
- Marketing & leasing
- Parking management
- Preventative maintenance programs
- Project development & redevelopment
- Project financing
- Property management
- Public relations
- Real estate & market assessments
- Risk management
- Security
- Strategic planning project positioning & repositioning
- Tax analysis & administration
- Tenant relations
- Vendor contract negotiations

Development Services
- Accounting control & reporting
- Architectural & engineering contract negotiations
- Budget development & administration
- Conceptual construction
- Construction buyout
- Construction management
- Design coordination
- Environmental evaluation
- Feasibility & market analysis
- Governmental approval coordination
- Marketing & public relations
- Operations & maintenance planning
- Pro forma development
- Scheduling
- Site evaluation
- Tenant construction management

Marketing & Leasing Services
- Broker relations
- Investment market assessment
- Lease negotiations
- Market assessment
- Marketing plan development
- National Tenant Program coordination
- Project assessment
- Public relations
- Repositioning strategy
- Tenant prospecting

COMPETITORS

Brookfield Office Properties
CBRE Group
Captec
Cencor Realty
Equity Office
Grubb & Ellis
Jones Lang LaSalle
Lincoln Property
Mack-Cali
Shorenstein
Tishman Speyer
Transwestern Commercial Services

HISTORICAL FINANCIALS

Company Type: Private

Income Statement FYE: December 31

	REVENUE ($ mil.)	NET INCOME ($ mil.)	NET PROFIT MARGIN	EMPLOYEES
12/10	234	0	—	3,200
12/09	200	0	—	—
12/08	1,216	0	—	—
Annual Growth	—	—	—	—

2010 Year-End Financials

Debt ratio: —
Return on equity: —
Cash ($ mil.): 229
Current ratio: 2.60
Long-term debt ($ mil.): —

Dividends
Yield: —
Payout: —
Market value ($ mil.): —

HINSHAW & CULBERTSON LLP

Hinshaw & Culbertson's 500 lawyers offer a wide range of legal services though the firm specializes in commercial and defense litigation and corporate environmental employment and construction law. It represents professionals dealing with corporate health care taxation malpractice white collar crime insurance coverage immigration intellectual property securities and real estate liability and risk management issues. The firm also offers legal advisement services to architects engineers and people residing in the financial services sector. Hinshaw & Culbertson has about 25 offices throughout 12 states in the US. The firm was founded in 1934.

Geographic Reach

Hinshaw & Culbertson has offices in Arizona California Florida Illinois Indiana Massachusetts Minnesota Missouri New York Oregon Rhode Island and Wisconsin.

Sales and Marketing

The firm represents clients in investigations by state and federal agencies such as the US Department of Justice and the US Securities and Exchange Commission.

Strategy

The firm's lawyers include several former federal and state prosecutors with extensive experience concerning white collar crime. In 2012 Hinshaw & Culbertson launched its White Collar Crime & Internal Investigations Blog. The blog addresses legal issues events and other news involving internal investigations white collar crime fraud and abuse.

Also in 2012 Hinshaw & Culbertson relocated its Miami office to a larger facility representing an approximately 50% increase the amount of space it occupies. The firm made the move as part of its continued expansion strategy in south Florida.

Mergers and Acquisitions

Hinshaw & Culbertson expanded its offerings when it acquired the strategic and management consulting business unit of Buckley Companies in 2012. The firm now offers Buckley's consulting services across its national network of offices through a subsidiary. Services include providing economic and financial analysis of business issues to local governments institutions private enterprises and the professional firms that serve them.

EXECUTIVES

Chairman, Donald L. Mrozek
Managing Partner, J. William Roberts
Partner-In-Charge Tampa, Bruce W. Bennett
Vice Chairman, Kevin Joseph Burke
Partner-In-Charge St. Louis, Terese A. Drew
Partner-In-Charge Portland, Peter R. Jarvis
Partner-In-Charge Miami, Ronald L. Kammer
Partner-In-Charge Appleton, Patrick F. Koenen
Partner-In-Charge New York, Hal R. Lieberman
Partner-In-Charge Milwaukee, Michael P. Malone
Partner-In-Charge Indiana, Renee J. Mortimer
Partner-In-Charge Minneapolis, David R. Mylrea
Chief Financial Officer, Robert P. Johnson
Vice President Moderates, Theresa L. Concepcion

LOCATIONS

HQ: HINSHAW & CULBERTSON LLP
222 N LASALLE ST STE 300, CHICAGO, IL 60601
Phone: 312-704-3000
Web: WWW.HINSHAWLAW.COM

PRODUCTS/OPERATIONS

Selected Practices
Construction law
Corporate and business Law
Environmental law
Government
Health care
Insurance services
Labor and employment
Litigation
Professional liability
School law

Selected Industries Served
Construction
Financial services
Health care
Insurance
Legal
Manufacturing
Real estate
Retail
Transportation

COMPETITORS

Baker & McKenzie
Chapman and Cutler LLP
Jenner & Block
Kirkland & Ellis
Schiff Hardin
Seyfarth Shaw
Sidley Austin

HISTORICAL FINANCIALS

Company Type: Private

Income Statement FYE: December 31

	REVENUE ($ mil.)	NET INCOME ($ mil.)	NET PROFIT MARGIN	EMPLOYEES
12/10	202	98	48.5%	1,010
12/03	124	53	43.1%	—
12/02	116	50	43.2%	—
12/01	108	44	40.6%	—
Annual Growth	7.2%	9.4%	—	—

2010 Year-End Financials

Debt ratio: —
Return on equity: 48.50%
Cash ($ mil.): 9
Current ratio: 3.00
Long-term debt ($ mil.): —
Dividends
Yield: —
Payout: —
Market value ($ mil.): —

HITT CONTRACTING INC.

HITT Contracting hits the nail on the general contracting head. The group provides turnkey construction services for corporate base building aviation legal hospitality technology research medical and institutional and governmental facilities. Projects have included construction and design for the Federal Reserve DirecTV and Greenpeace. In addition to general contracting HITT offers design interior paint preconstruction and construction management services. It handles eco-friendly projects historic renovations and infrastructure refits. HITT which operates in more than 30 states is a family-owned and -operated firm that was founded in 1937 as W.A. Hitt Decorating Co. by Warren and Myrtle Hitt.

Geographic Reach

HITT operates from its headquarters in Virginia and has offices in Atlanta Charleston Baltimore and South Florida. The company is opening a new office in Denver.

Strategy

The company has experienced a decline in revenues due to lagging demand in the construction industry. However HITT's experience in serving a variety of industries as well as its geographic diversity has helped the company maintain a healthy backlog. The company often uses its own money to partially fund projects and buys materials supplies and equipment. The strategy has helped HITT to better control quality and deliver projects on time.

In 2011 the company launched HITT Hospitality which specializes in hotel renovation and construction. The unit focuses on the mid-Atlantic and other US markets. Projects include work for hotel brands including Hilton Marriott Hyatt Four Seasons and W Hotels.

EXECUTIVES

Chairman, Russell A. Hitt
Co-President, Brett R. Hitt
Co-President, James E. Millar
EVP Institutional, Yogen R. Patel
EVP Technology, John W. Kane
SVP Denver, Kevin L. Ott
EVP Government, John M. Britt
SVP Paint and Service, David R. Kane
SVP Charleston, Carson P. Knizevski
SVP Hospitality, Peter T. Lanfranchi
EVP National Accounts, Steven E. Richbourg
SVP Atlanta, R. Ryan Bixler
SVP Healthcare, Nick D. Raico
EVP Corporate Base Building, Jeremy S. Bardin
SVP Corporate Interiors, Brian S. Kriz
SVP Law Firms, Joseph P. LaFonte Jr.
SVP South Florida, John Planz
SVP Government, R. James Whitney

LOCATIONS

HQ: HITT CONTRACTING INC.
2900 FAIRVIEW PARK DR # 300, FALLS CHURCH, VA 22042-4513
Phone: 703-846-9000
Web: WWW.HITT-GC.COM

PRODUCTS/OPERATIONS

Selected Markets
Base building
Interiors
Government
Health care
Hospitality
Institutional
Law firms
Major projects
Technology

COMPETITORS

Branch & Associates
Donohoe Companies
Hayward Baker
James G. Davis Construction
KBS
Rodgers Builders
SMCI
Skanska USA Building
Turner Corporation

HISTORICAL FINANCIALS

Company Type: Private

Income Statement FYE: December 31

	REVENUE ($ mil.)	NET INCOME ($ mil.)	NET PROFIT MARGIN	EMPLOYEES
12/12	827	18	2.3%	600
12/11	976	30	3.1%	—
12/10	706	25	3.6%	—
12/09	767	33	4.4%	—
Annual Growth	2.6%	(17.9%)	—	—

2012 Year-End Financials

Debt ratio: —
Return on equity: 2.30%
Cash ($ mil.): 54
Current ratio: 0.90
Long-term debt ($ mil.): —
Dividends
Yield: —
Payout: —
Market value ($ mil.): —

HO-CHUNK INC.

Ho-Chunk Inc. (HCI) the economic development corporation run by the Winnebago Tribe of Nebraska manages about 18 subsidiaries in the fields of communications construction distribution gasoline and convenience store retail (under the Heritage Express banner in Iowa and Nebraska) government contracting lodging (The WinnaVegas Inn) marketing used-vehicle sales and more. The profits from these businesses are in turn managed by the Ho-Chunk Community Development Corporation a not-for-profit organization that directs commercial growth and community infrastructure development for the tribe. "Ho-Chunk" is a modernized form of Hochungra the Winnebago tribe's traditional name.

Ho-Chunk does business in seven US states and the District of Columbia as well as three foreign countries: Afghanistan Iraq and Mexico.

EXECUTIVES

President and CEO, Lance Morgan
VP and COO, Annette Hamilton
Executive Director Ho-Chunk Community Development Corporation, Judi Meyer
Director Human Resources and Secretary, Sarah Snake
Manager Operations, Sharon Bass
Chairman, John Blackhawk
CFO, Dennis Johnson
Vice Chairman, Brian Chamberlain
Director, Kenny Mallory
Director, Lauren Buchanan
Auditors: McGladreyLLP

LOCATIONS

HQ: HO-CHUNK INC.
1 MISSION DR, WINNEBAGO, NE 68071
Phone: 402-878-2809
Web: WWW.HOCHUNKINC.COM

HISTORICAL FINANCIALS

Company Type: Private

Income Statement FYE: December 31

	ASSETS ($ mil.)	NET INCOME ($ mil.)	INCOME AS % OF ASSETS	EMPLOYEES
12/09	53	4	8.4%	310
12/07	46	1	2.3%	—
12/06	41	0	1.6%	—
12/05	39	0	1.7%	—
Annual Growth	7.6%	59.6%	—	—

2009 Year-End Financials

Debt ratio: —
Return on equity: 2.90%
Cash ($ mil.): 6
Current ratio: 1.10
Long-term debt ($ mil.): —
Dividends
Yield: —
Payout: —
Market value ($ mil.): —

HOLIDAY BUILDERS INC.

Holiday Builders is out to make buying a new home a vacation-like experience. The company a 100% employee-owned enterprise since 1999 builds single-family detached homes throughout Florida and in Alabama South Carolina and Texas. Since its inception the company has built more than 30000 homes sold primarily to first-time and value-conscious buyers. The company offers full homebuying services to its clients through HBI Title Company Holiday Builders Real Estate HB Designs and a partnership with Shelter Mortgage. Holiday Builders was founded in 1983.

EXECUTIVES

President and CEO, Bruce Assam

LOCATIONS

HQ: HOLIDAY BUILDERS INC.
2293 W EAU GALLIE BLVD, MELBOURNE, FL 32935-3184
Phone: 321-610-5156
Web: WWW.HOLIDAYBUILDERS.COM

COMPETITORS

Adams Homes
David Weekley Homes
Gehan Homes
Lennar
PulteGroup

HISTORICAL FINANCIALS

Company Type: Private

Income Statement FYE: December 31

	REVENUE ($ mil.)	NET INCOME ($ mil.)	NET PROFIT MARGIN	EMPLOYEES
12/07	234	(26)	—	101
12/06	699	40	5.8%	—
12/05	1,030	0	—	—
Annual Growth	—	—	—	—

2007 Year-End Financials

Debt ratio: —
Return on equity: (-11.20%)
Cash ($ mil.): 57
Current ratio: 1.00
Long-term debt ($ mil.): —
Dividends
Yield: —
Payout: —
Market value ($ mil.): —

HOLIDAY WHOLESALE INC.

EXECUTIVES

President, Bernard E. (Bud) Gussel
VP Finance, Pam Rudoll
VP Human Resources, Darrell Vogel
VP Marketing, Ed Wognicz

LOCATIONS

HQ: HOLIDAY WHOLESALE INC.
225 PIONEER DR, WISCONSIN DELLS, WI 539658397
Phone: 6082530404
Web: WWW.HOLIDAYWHOLESALE.COM

COMPETITORS

Affiliated Foods Midwest
Central Grocers
Certco
Nash-Finch
Roundy' s

HISTORICAL FINANCIALS

Company Type: Private

Income Statement FYE: February 28

	REVENUE ($ mil.)	NET INCOME ($ mil.)	NET PROFIT MARGIN	EMPLOYEES
02/09	126	0	0.5%	250
02/08	120	0	0.6%	—
02/07	113	0	0.7%	—
02/06	111	0	—	—
Annual Growth	4.3%	—	—	—

2009 Year-End Financials

Debt ratio: —
Return on equity: 0.50%
Cash ($ mil.): 0
Current ratio: 1.00
Long-term debt ($ mil.): —
Dividends
Yield: —
Payout: —
Market value ($ mil.): —

HOLLAND COMMUNITY HOSPITAL INC

Holland Community Hospital (HCH) provides a comprehensive range of health services to residents of western Michigan's Lakeshore region. The 190-bed not-for-profit hospital provides a variety of medical care and health services including primary emergency diagnostic surgical rehabilitative and inpatient behavioral health care. HCH is home to centers of excellence in the treatment of sleep disorders cancer women's health issues and cardiovascular ailments. The hospital provides community health and wellness education programs and operates a regional community health clinic. Founded in 1917 HCH employs some 330 physicians across 14 medical specialties.

EXECUTIVES

President CEO, Dale Sowders
VP Human Resources and Operations Support and Director, Chuck Kohlruss
VP CFO and Director, Terry Steele
VP Ancillary Services and Quality and Director, Mark Pawlak
VP Nursing Chief Nursing Officer and Director, Patti VanDort
Secretary and Director, William (Bill) Frauenheim
Chairman, Chuck DePree
VP Medical Affairs and Director, William (Bill) Vander Vliet
President CEO and Director, Dale Sowders
VP Human Resources and Operations Support and Director, Chuck Kohlruss
VP CFO and Director, Terry Steele
VP Ancillary Services and Quality and Director, Mark Pawlak
Secretary and Director, William (Bill) Frauenheim
Chairman, Chuck DePree
Director, Becca Dernberger
Director, Donald (Don) Komejan
VP Medical Affairs and Director, William (Bill) Vander Vliet
Director, Roger Gamache
Director, Kristen Manos
Director, Dawn Garcia Ward
Auditors: Plante&MoranPLLC

LOCATIONS

HQ: HOLLAND COMMUNITY HOSPITAL INC
602 MICHIGAN AVE, HOLLAND, MI 49423-4999
Phone: 616-748-9346
Web: WWW.HOLLANDHOSPITAL.ORG

Selected Locations

Holland Hospital Main Campus (Holland Michigan)
Holland Hospital Medical Building (Zeeland Michigan)
Lakeshore Medical Campus (Holland Michigan)
Holland Hospital Laboratory & Rehabilitation Services (Douglas Michigan)
854 South Washington Medical Offices (Holland Michigan)
844 South Washington Medical Offices (Holland Michigan)
Holland Hospital Center for Good Health (Holland Michigan)
Surgery Center of Western Michigan (Holland Michigan)
Lakeshore Area Radiation Oncology Center (Holland Michigan)
Community Health Center (Holland Michigan)

COMPETITORS

Mercy Health Hackley
Spectrum Health
Zeeland Community Hospital

HISTORICAL FINANCIALS

Company Type: Private

Income Statement FYE: March 31

	REVENUE ($ mil.)	NET INCOME ($ mil.)	NET PROFIT MARGIN	EMPLOYEES
03/12	201	16	8.4%	1,500
03/10*	170	10	6.2%	—
12/08	0	0	—	—
03/07	142	32	22.9%	—
Annual Growth	7.2%	(12.3%)	—	—

*Fiscal year change

2012 Year-End Financials

Debt ratio: —
Return on equity: 8.40%
Cash ($ mil.): 20
Current ratio: 0.60
Long-term debt ($ mil.): —
Dividends
Yield: —
Payout: —
Market value ($ mil.): —

HOLLINGSWORTH OIL CO. INC.

The Hollingsworth Companies meets companies' industrial-strength needs. The company develops and builds industrial parks and facilities in the southeastern US. It provides build-to-suit and finish-to-suit structures primarily on its SouthPoint Business Park pad-ready sites located in Alabama North Carolina Tennessee and Virginia. Developments typically range from 50000 sq. ft. to 500000 sq. ft. Hollingsworth also provides facility expansion and funding services. All of the company's SouthPoint properties are located in areas convenient to interstate highways and airport services. CEO and owner Joe Hollingsworth Jr. founded The Hollingsworth Companies in 1986.

Both contractor and developer The Hollingsworth Companies is able to complete custom-built facilities in as little as three months.

Joe Hollingsworth's book The Southern Advantage published in 2003 establishes the South as an increasingly desirable region for industrial manufacturing due to lower tax burdens rapidly growing population and Right-to-Work protections.

EXECUTIVES

CEO The Hollingsworth Companies, Joe A. Hollingsworth Jr.
SVP Architecture and Business Development, Tom Wortham
Director Industrial Real Estate, Warren Green

Director Industrial Real EstateNorth Carolina, Chip Sisk
Director Industrial Real Estate Alabama, Tommy Marr
Internal Operations Manager, Amanda Hensley
CFO, Timothy Lennon

LOCATIONS

HQ: HOLLINGSWORTH OIL CO. INC.
1503 MEMORIAL BLVD STE B, SPRINGFIELD, TN 37172-3269
Phone: 615-242-8466
Web: WWW.HOLLINGSWORTHCOMPANIES.COM

COMPETITORS

American Buildings
Belz
Childress Klein
Crescent Resources
Gladstone Commercial
Highwoods Properties
Varco Pruden Buildings

HISTORICAL FINANCIALS

Company Type: Private

Income Statement FYE: December 31

	REVENUE ($ mil.)	NET INCOME ($ mil.)	NET PROFIT MARGIN	EMPLOYEES
12/12	584	0	0.0%	300
12/11	593	0	0.1%	—
12/09	501	0	0.1%	—
12/09	432	0	0.2%	—
Annual Growth	10.5%	(58.9%)	—	—

2012 Year-End Financials

Debt ratio: —
Return on equity: —
Cash ($ mil.): 0
Current ratio: 0.30
Long-term debt ($ mil.): —
Dividends
Yield: —
Payout: —
Market value ($ mil.): —

HOLMES REGIONAL MEDICAL CENTER INC.

If you're a Great Space Coaster you might depend on Holmes Regional Medical Center in times of medical need. The general acute-care hospital which houses about 515 beds and provides comprehensive medical and surgical care serves residents of Brevard County on Florida's Space Coast. A member of not-for-profit health care system Health First Holmes Regional Medical Center offers specialty care in a number of areas including trauma oncology cardiology orthopedics pediatrics and women's health. It also operates an air ambulance service a stroke care center a full-service endoscopy unit and an outpatient diagnostic facility as well as advanced robotic surgery and joint replacement centers.

EXECUTIVES

COO Health First, Larry F. Garrison
CFO Health First, Robert C. Galloway
VP Human Resources Health First, Robert W. Suttles
First Vice Chairman, James C. Shaw
President CEO and Director, Judy Killebrew
Chairman, Catherine A. Ford
Treasurer and Director, William C. Potter
VP Marketing and Corporate Communications Health First, Keith Lundquist
President, Sean J. Gregory
Executive Vice President Chief Operations Officer, Stuart Mitchell
First Vice Chairman, James C. Shaw
President CEO and Director, Judy Killebrew
Director, Eugene S. (Gene) Cavallucci, age 66
Director, A. Thomas Hollingsworth
Director, Harry L. Deffebach
Director, Pamela A. Gatto
Treasurer and Director, William C. Potter
Director, Judith (Judy) Gizinski
Director, Patrick J. Domkowski

LOCATIONS

HQ: HOLMES REGIONAL MEDICAL CENTER INC.
1350 HICKORY ST, MELBOURNE, FL 32901-3224
Phone: 321-434-7000
Web: WWW.HOLMESREGIONALMEDICALCENTER.ORG

PRODUCTS/OPERATIONS

Selected Centers and Services

The Birth Suites
Cancer care
da Vinci robotics surgery
Diabetes
Emergency room
First Flight aeromedical helicopter
Family library
The Heart Center (cardiac care and rehabilitation services)
Holmes Trauma Center
Interventional neuroradiology (stroke care)
Interventional radiology/Y-90
Outpatient services
Orthopedics
QuickCare walk-in clinic
VitalWatch (eICU)

COMPETITORS

Adventist Health System Sunbelt Healthcare
HCA
Nemours Foundation
Orlando Health
UF&Shands
Wuesthoff Health System

HISTORICAL FINANCIALS

Company Type: Private

Income Statement FYE: September 30

	REVENUE ($ mil.)	NET INCOME ($ mil.)	NET PROFIT MARGIN	EMPLOYEES
09/12	411	63	15.3%	2,778
09/06	0	0	0.3%	—
09/05	0	0	17.0%	—
09/04	1,990	0	0.0%	—
Annual Growth	(17.9%)	366.5%	—	—

2012 Year-End Financials

Debt ratio: —
Return on equity: 15.30%
Cash ($ mil.): 125
Current ratio: 2.10
Long-term debt ($ mil.): —
Dividends
Yield: —
Payout: —
Market value ($ mil.): —

HOLY CROSS HOSPITAL INC.

Holy Cross Hospital's patients have more than just doctors on their side. Holy Cross is a Catholic community hospital serving the Ft. Lauderdale Florida area. The hospital has about 560 beds and offers inpatient and outpatient medical services along with a cancer treatment center heart and vascular center women's health center orthopedic unit and home health division as well as outpatient imaging centers. It also operates family health and specialist clinics in the region. Established in 1955 Holy Cross Hospital is sponsored by the Sisters of Mercy religious order and is part of Catholic Health East.

Geographic Reach

The hospital operates in South Florida's Broward and Palm Beach counties.

Operations

Holy Cross Hospital employs some 600 physicians including specialists in about 40 medical fields. The organization's Holy Cross Medical Group physician practice group has more than 150 doctors working at about 30 clinics. The hospital also operates the Holy Cross HealthPlex which includes an orthopedic institute a women's health center a wound healing center diagnostic imaging and laboratory facilities and an outpatient surgery center.

Strategy

To enhance service offerings and bring in more area residents Holy Cross Hospital is working to enhance its facilities and improve its technologies. For instance in 2012 it added a new surgery device for aneurysm embolization treatment procedures. In addition the medical center opened a new meditation chapel and healing garden. The following year Holy Cross Hospital built a new urgent care and diagnostic imaging center in Fort Lauderdale's Rio Vista community to improve patient access to outpatient services.

To align itself with the goals of US federal health reform measures in 2013 Holy Cross Hospital joined the accountable care organization (ACO) facilitated by Blue Cross and Blue Shield of Florida. The ACO aims to coordinate care for area Medicare residents in order to improve care quality and lower medical costs in the region.

Ownership

Holy Cross Hospital is part of Catholic Health East (CHE)'s Southeast division. CHE announced in late 2012 that is exploring a merger with Michigan-based Trinity Health. While consolidation talks are non-binding the two parties look to reach a definitive agreement during 2013.

EXECUTIVES

Senior Vice President Chief Financial Officer, Linda Wilford
President Chief Executive Officer, Patrick A. Taylor
Vice President Sponsorship and Mission Effectiveness, Sister Rita Levasseur
Senior Vice President & Administrator, Mark R. Dissette
Senior Vice President Chief Operating Officer, Luisa Gutman
VP Operations Holy Cross Medical Group, James Desmarteau
Vice President & Chief Nursing Officer, Margaret Scheaffel
Chief Medical Officer, Kenneth Homer
Auditors: Ernst&YoungLLP

LOCATIONS

HQ: HOLY CROSS HOSPITAL INC.
4725 N FEDERAL HWY, FORT LAUDERDALE, FL 33308-4668
Phone: 954-771-8000
Web: WWW.HOLY-CROSS.COM

PRODUCTS/OPERATIONS

Selected Services

Back Pain Management
Bariatrics
Cancer
Center for Optimal Health
Comprehensive Stroke Center
Diagnostic Imaging
Emergency
Epilepsy Monitoring Unit
Heart and Vascular
Heart Research

Home Health
International Services
Maternal/Child Health
Medical Group
Neurology and Spine
Orthopedics
Outpatient Services
Rehabilitation Institute
Robotics
Sleep Disorder Lab
Spine Center
Wellness Pavilion
Women's Center
Wound Healing and Hyperbarics

COMPETITORS

Adventist Health System Sunbelt Healthcare
Ascension Health
Baptist Health South Florida
Broward Health
Florida Hospital Heartland
HCA
Lawnwood Medical Center
Mount Sinai Medical Center of Florida
Northwest Medical Center
Oak Hill Hospital
Palms West Hospital
Plantation General
Raulerson Hospital
South Broward Hospital District
St. Lucie Medical
Tenet Healthcare

HISTORICAL FINANCIALS

Company Type: Private

Income Statement FYE: December 31

	REVENUE ($ mil.)	NET INCOME ($ mil.)	NET PROFIT MARGIN	EMPLOYEES
12/12	426	21	5.0%	2,300
12/09*	420	7	1.7%	—
04/05	373	(25)	—	—
04/05	0	0	97.4%	—
Annual Growth	141.0%	66.1%	—	—

*Fiscal year change

2012 Year-End Financials

Debt ratio: —
Return on equity: 5.00%
Cash ($ mil.): 17
Current ratio: 1.00
Long-term debt ($ mil.): —
Dividends
Yield: —
Payout: —
Market value ($ mil.): —

HOLY SPIRIT HOSPITAL OF THE SISTERS OF CHRISTIAN CHARITY

Holy Spirit Health tends to the health of the incarnate. The Holy Spirit Health System (HSHS) provides cardiology women's health care pediatric care and other acute and emergency medical services to the residents of greater Harrisburg in south-central Pennsylvania. The flagship Holy Spirit Hospital has some 315 beds as well as a level III neonatal intensive care unit. The hospital also operates an adjoining cardiac treatment facility and it has a network of affiliated family practice urgent care surgical and specialty health clinics. HSHS was established in 1963 and is operated by the Sisters of Christian Charity.

Geographic Reach

HSHS operates in a five-county service territory surrounding Harrisburg in south-central Pennsylvania. It has facilities in Camp Hill Carlisle Chambersburg Dillsburg Duncannon Harrisburg Lemoyne Marysville Mechanicsburg New Cumberland New Kingstown and Shippensburg.

Operations

The Holy Spirit Hospital employs some 500 physicians and operates specialty care centers include an endoscopy clinic a hyperbaric wound healing unit and women's post-surgical recovery unit. Outpatient facilities include cardiology clinics family medicine centers surgery clinics and pediatric and women's health centers. Altogether HSHS handles some 16000 inpatient admissions 250000 outpatient visits 52000 emergency room visits and 1200 births.

HSHS employs a number of hospitalists who follow the patient's progress from admission to discharge and ensure follow-up care. The hospital also provides community health seminars to educate the public on common health concerns and the benefits of preventative care.

Sales and Marketing

Reimbursements from Medicare policies account for 30% of revenue while Blue Cross Blue Shield plans bring in another 28%. Self-pay customers and other commercial and government insurance sources account for the remainder of patient income.

Strategy

HSHS has undergone a number of expansions in recent years opening numerous outpatient centers to deliver care closer to home in the communities in which it serves. Also many hospitals are growing their outpatient services because they tend to bring in more income and help compensate for downward pricing on inpatient hospital stays from private and public health care payers.

The organization expanded clinical services in areas including cryoablation cardiac rehabilitation sleep diagnostics and urgent care during 2012 and 2013. It also opened a new data center increase and improve use of electronic health record (EHR) systems.

EXECUTIVES

President and CEO, Sister Romaine Niemeyer
SVP Strategic and Business Development, Richard E. LaVanture
VP Patient Services and Chief Nursing Officer, Lisa Lewis
Director Quality and Organizational Performance, Karen G. Sloan
COO, Richard A. (Rick) Schaffner Jr.
Director Volunteer Services, Kristi Ondo

LOCATIONS

HQ: HOLY SPIRIT HOSPITAL OF THE SISTERS OF CHRISTIAN CHARITY
503 N 21ST ST, CAMP HILL, PA 17011-2288
Phone: 717-763-2100
Web: WWW.HSH.ORG

PRODUCTS/OPERATIONS

Selected Centers and Services

Atrial Fibrillation Center
Behavioral Health
Broad Street Family Health Center
Cancer Care
Capital Cardiovascular Associates
Cardiac Rehab
Carlisle Family Health Center
Centers for Women' s Health - OB/GYN
Devonshire Family Health Center
Diabetes Services
Diagnostic
Dillsburg Family Health Center
Duncannon Family Health Center
Emergency Services
Gastrointestinal Services
Green Hill Family Health Center
Heart Care
Holy Spirit Endocrinology Center
Home Health Care
Hospitalist Program
Imaging Services
Internal Medicine of Mechanicsburg
Kunkel Group' s LAP-BAND Program
Kunkel Surgical Group
Laboratory Services
Lewin & Nadar Cardiology Associates
Magill Family Health Center
Maternal Assistance Program
Maternity
Medical Outreach
Nutrition Services
Occupational Health
Orthopedics
Palliative Care
Pharmacy Services
Physical Therapy
Preparing for Your Appointment
Research & Clinical Trials
Ryder Barnes and Associates (pediatrics)
Silver Creek Family Health Center
Sleep Studies
Snoke Family Health Center
Speech Therapy
Spirit Urgent Care
Surgical Services
Travel Health Services
Vascular Associates
Women' s Services
Wound Healing & Hyperbarics

COMPETITORS

Hershey Medical Center
PinnacleHealth System
Pocono Health System
Saint Vincent Health System
Sharon Regional Health System
University of Pennsylvania Health System
WellSpan Health

HISTORICAL FINANCIALS

Company Type: Private

Income Statement FYE: June 30

	REVENUE ($ mil.)	NET INCOME ($ mil.)	NET PROFIT MARGIN	EMPLOYEES
06/10	271	11	4.2%	2,698
06/09	5	0	—	—
06/09	1,650	0	0.0%	—
Annual Growth	(83.5%)	69255.8%	—	—

2010 Year-End Financials

Debt ratio: —
Return on equity: 4.20%
Cash ($ mil.): 8
Current ratio: —
Long-term debt ($ mil.): —
Dividends
Yield: —
Payout: —
Market value ($ mil.): —

HOMELAND ENERGY SOLUTIONS LLC

LOCATIONS

HQ: HOMELAND ENERGY SOLUTIONS LLC
2779 HIGHWAY 24, LAWLER, IA 52154
Phone: 5632385555
Web: WWW.HOMELANDENERGYSOLUTIONS.COM

HISTORICAL FINANCIALS

Company Type: Private

Income Statement FYE: December 31

	REVENUE ($ mil.)	NET INCOME ($ mil.)	NET PROFIT MARGIN	EMPLOYEES
12/14	330	68	20.8%	42
12/13	400	28	7.1%	—
12/12	359	0	0.1%	—
12/11	419	0	—	—
Annual Growth	(7.6%)	—	—	—

2014 Year-End Financials

Debt ratio: —
Return on equity: 20.80%
Cash ($ mil.): 32
Current ratio: 0.80
Long-term debt ($ mil.): —
Dividends
Yield: —
Payout: —
Market value ($ mil.): —

HOMEWISE INC.

LOCATIONS

HQ: HOMEWISE INC.
1301 SILER RD STE D, SANTA FE, NM 875073540
Phone: 5059839473
Web: WWW.HOMEWISE.ORG

HISTORICAL FINANCIALS

Company Type: Private

Income Statement FYE: March 31

	ASSETS ($ mil.)	NET INCOME ($ mil.)	INCOME AS % OF ASSETS	EMPLOYEES
03/14	74	2	3.5%	28
03/11	51	2	4.9%	—
03/10	42	0	0.6%	—
03/09	2	0	—	—
Annual Growth	99.0%	—	—	—

2014 Year-End Financials

Debt ratio: —
Return on equity: 28.30%
Cash ($ mil.): 5
Current ratio: 5.10
Long-term debt ($ mil.): —
Dividends
Yield: —
Payout: —
Market value ($ mil.): —

HOOSIER ENERGY RURAL ELECTRIC COOPERATIVE INC

Who's yer daddy? In terms of providing electricity for many Indianans (and some residents of Illinois) that would be Hoosier Energy Rural Electric Cooperative which provides wholesale electric power to 18 member distribution cooperatives in 48 central and southern Indiana counties and 11 counties in southeastern Illinois. These electric cooperatives serve 750000 residents businesses industries and farms in a 15000 sq. ml. service area. Hoosier Energy operates six power plants and a 1700-mile transmission system and maintains the Tuttle Creek Reservoir in Southwest Indiana. Hoosier Energy is part of the Touchstone Energy network of electric cooperatives.

Geographic Reach

The company delivers power to member distribution cooperatives in central and southern Indiana and southeastern Illinois.

Operations

Hoosier Energy operates coal- natural gas- and renewable energy-generation plants. It delivers electricity via a 1700-mile transmission network including 21 major substations and more than 350 delivery points.

Financial Performance

In 2012 the power coop's revenues decreased by 0.3% due t a decline in nonmember revenues. Net income dropped by 8% as the result of to lower net sales and higher operating costs.

Strategy

To advance its push for more renewable sources Hoosier Energy is pursuing cost-effective generating projects and supply contracts including the Clark-Floyd Landfill Methane Generation plant which has four landfill/coal bed methane projects and which has purchased power agreements for wind and hydropower. These measures are expected to provide 7% of member energy sales annually beginning in 2014.

In 2011 the coop was operating a 2.5 MW landfill methane generation facility in addition to buying 25 MW of wind energy.

Expanding its geographic coverage in 2011 Hoosier Energy began to supply power to the Wayne-White Counties Electric Cooperative when that coop's contract with an independent power supplier ended. The distribution coop serves 13500 residential farm and business consumers in 11 counties in southeastern Illinois.

Company Background

Hoosier Energy was formed in 1948 as part of the nationwide rural electrification drive initiated by the Roosevelt administration in the 1930s.

EXECUTIVES

President and CEO, J. Steven Smith
SVP Marketing and Business Development, R. M. (Mike) Rampley
Director Public Affairs, Randy Haymaker
Chairman, Eugene Roberts
Vice Chairman, Dale Walther
VP Management Services, Robert I. Richhart
VP Power Supply, David W. Sandefur
VP Finance, Donna L. Snyder
Vice Chairman, Darin Duncan
Chairman, James Weimer
Attorney, Christopher Goffinet
Owner of MPI Solar and contractor for the installation, Dave Mann
VP Power Production, Robert C. Hochstetler
VP Member Services and Communication, Tom Van Paris
Vice Chairman, Dale Walther
Auditors: Deloitte&ToucheLLP

LOCATIONS

HQ: HOOSIER ENERGY RURAL ELECTRIC COOPERATIVE INC
7398 N STATE ROAD 37, BLOOMINGTON, IN 47404-9424
Phone: 812-876-2021

PRODUCTS/OPERATIONS

2012 Sales

Members	532	82
Other	0	-

Member Cooperativ
Bartholomew County REMC
Clark County REMC
Decatur County REMC
Daviess-Martin County REMC
Dubois REC Inc.
Harrison REMC
Henry County REMC
Jackson County REMC
Johnson County REMC
Orange County REMC
RushShelby Energy
South Central Indiana REMC
Southeastern Indiana REMC
Southern Indiana Power
Utilities District of Western Indiana REMC
Wayne-White Counties Electric Cooperativ
WIN Energy REMC
Whitewater Valley REMC

COMPETITORS

IPALCO Enterprises
Indiana Michigan Power
Indiana Municipal Power Agency

HISTORICAL FINANCIALS

Company Type: Private

Income Statement FYE: December 31

	REVENUE ($ mil.)	NET INCOME ($ mil.)	NET PROFIT MARGIN	EMPLOYEES
12/12	647	27	4.3%	450
12/11	649	30	4.7%	
12/09	575	16	2.9%	
12/08	566	19	3.5%	
Annual Growth	3.4%	9.2%		

2012 Year-End Financials

Debt ratio: —
Return on equity: 4.30%
Cash ($ mil.): 50
Current ratio: 0.30
Long-term debt ($ mil.): —
Dividends
Yield: —
Payout: —
Market value ($ mil.): —

HORIZON RESOURCES

LOCATIONS

HQ: HORIZON RESOURCES
317 2ND ST W, WILLISTON, ND 588015903
Phone: 7015722171
Web: WWW.HORIZONRESOURCES.COOP

HISTORICAL FINANCIALS

Company Type: Private

Income Statement FYE: December 31

	REVENUE ($ mil.)	NET INCOME ($ mil.)	NET PROFIT MARGIN	EMPLOYEES
12/12	470	25	5.3%	150
12/11	379	15	4.1%	—
12/10	238	15	6.4%	—
12/09	161	0	—	—
Annual Growth	42.8%	—	—	—

2012 Year-End Financials

Debt ratio: —
Return on equity: 5.30%
Cash ($ mil.): 15
Current ratio: 0.90
Long-term debt ($ mil.): —
Dividends
Yield: —
Payout: —
Market value ($ mil.): —

HORRY TELEPHONE COOPERATIVE INC.

EXECUTIVES

Chief Executive Customer Operations, Brent Groome
VP and Director, Morris Graham
Secretary and Director, Betty F. Jordan
President and Director, Ken Summerall
Chief Executive Officer, Michael Hagg
Chief Executive Plant Operations, Scott Everett
Chief Exective Human Resourcs, Glenda Page
Treasurer and Director, Cynthia J. Cannon
VP and Director, Morris Graham
Secretary and Director, Betty F. Jordan
President and Director, Ken Summerall
CEO and Director, Michael Hagg
Treasurer and Director, Cynthia J. Cannon
Director, Theron Bellamy
Director, James R. Clarkson
Director, Kevin Elliott
Director, Russell Grainger
Director, Charles Whaley

LOCATIONS

HQ: HORRY TELEPHONE COOPERATIVE INC.
3480 HIGHWAY 701 N, CONWAY, SC 295265702
Phone: 8433652151
Web: WWW.HTCINC.NET

COMPETITORS

Comcast
Comporium Communications
DIRECTV
DISH Network
Hargray
Sprint Communications
T-Mobile USA
Time Warner Cable
U.S. Cellular
Verizon

HISTORICAL FINANCIALS

Company Type: Private

Income Statement FYE: December 31

	REVENUE ($ mil.)	NET INCOME ($ mil.)	NET PROFIT MARGIN	EMPLOYEES
12/13	177	21	12.2%	690
12/09	172	4	2.5%	—
12/08	162	3	2.2%	—
12/07	1,361	0	—	—
Annual Growth	—	—	—	—

2013 Year-End Financials

Debt ratio: —
Return on equity: 12.20%
Cash ($ mil.): 18
Current ratio: 0.90
Long-term debt ($ mil.): —
Dividends
Yield: —
Payout: —
Market value ($ mil.): —

HOSPITAL OF CENTRAL CONNECTICUT

The Hospital of Central Connecticut an acute care facility serves the communities of central Connecticut from two campuses. With approximately 415 beds and 500 physicians the hospital offers a full range of diagnostic and treatment services as well as education and prevention programs. Its diabetes treatment program is an affiliate of the Boston-based Joslin Diabetes Center; the hospital is also affiliated with the University of Connecticut School of Medicine and other universities. Central Connecticut Health Alliance (CCHA) is the parent company of The Hospital of Central Connecticut and is part of the Hartford Health Care network.

Geographic Reach

The Hospital of Central Connecticut's two Connecticut locations are the Bradley Memorial Campus in Southington and the New Britain General Campus in New Britain.

Operations

In addition to its 415 acute-care beds the two Hospital of Central Connecticut campuses have about 30 bassinets. Through its university affiliations the hospital facilities provide residency and training programs in fields including critical care internal medicine gastroenterology general surgery and pulmonary medicine. It also conducts medical research including clinical trials in fields such as diabetes mental health and cancer treatment.

Affiliates that are part of the CCHA organization include Alliance Occupational Health Central Connecticut Senior Health Services Central Connecticut Physical Medicine and Central Connecticut VNA. CCHA affiliates provide a wide range of whole-life services throughout the region.

Strategy

In 2011 CCHA and Hartford Health Care (HHC) created an affiliation to improve the region's quality of care and improve local access to care. CCHA and HHC have 20-year history of collaboration and the affiliation will provide for increased efficiencies and reduced costs through shared resources including information technology platforms (including electronic health record or EHR systems) and group purchasing tools.

To expand its care network in 2012 Hospital of Central Connecticut opened a new primary care medical practice in Southington. In addition the organization enhanced its New Britain campus by opening a new family enrichment center and by launching a $40 million construction project to build a new cancer center.

Company Background

The Hospital of Central Connecticut was formed through the merger of New Britain General Hospital and Bradley Memorial Hospital.

EXECUTIVES

Vice President Human Resources, Mary Morgan
Director Physician Recruitment, Patti Lowicki
Clinic Manager, Kathy Scalise
Medical Director, Justin Lundbye
Pharmacy Manager, Richard Sullivan
Director Of Nursing, Karen McAvoy
Regional Vp Of Finance, Carolyn Freiheit
Vice Chairman Board Of Director, John J Patrick, age 55
Board Member, Judy Jennings
Board Member, Jillian Wanik
Board Member, Lisa King
Advisory Board Member, Kathleen Yuskis
Auditors: Ernst&YoungLLP

LOCATIONS

HQ: HOSPITAL OF CENTRAL CONNECTICUT
100 GRAND ST, NEW BRITAIN, CT 06052-2016
Phone: 860-224-5011
Web: WWW.THOCC.ORG

PRODUCTS/OPERATIONS

Selected Centers and Services

Bariatric surgery
Breast care
Cancer Center
Cardiovascular
Clinical research
Diabetes care
Emergency services
Endocrine and bone health
Family Enrichment Center
Healthy Aging Center
Joint and Spine Center
Laboratory
Lifeline
Maternity
Medical services
Nursing
Occupational health
Occupational therapy
Outpatient services
Pain management
Palliative care
Pediatrics
Physical medicine
Primary care and specialty practices
Psychiatry
Radiology
Sleep disorders
Speech therapy
Stroke Center
Surgical services
Vascular Center
Weigh Your Options
Wellness programs
Wound care

COMPETITORS

Bristol Hospital
Lawrence & Memorial Hospital
Saint Francis Hospital and Medical Center
Waterbury Hospital
Western Connecticut Health Network
Yale New Haven Health System

HISTORICAL FINANCIALS

Company Type: Private

Income Statement FYE: September 30

	REVENUE ($ mil.)	NET INCOME ($ mil.)	NET PROFIT MARGIN	EMPLOYEES
09/09	401	(71)	—	2,500
09/08	358	8	2.5%	—
09/06	83	0	0.0%	—
Annual Growth	69.1%	—	—	—

2009 Year-End Financials

Debt ratio: —
Return on equity: (-17.80%)
Cash ($ mil.): 22
Current ratio: 0.80
Long-term debt ($ mil.): —
Dividends
Yield: —
Payout: —
Market value ($ mil.): —

HOUSING AUTHORITY OF THE CITY OF TAMPA

LOCATIONS

HQ: HOUSING AUTHORITY OF THE CITY OF TAMPA
5301 W CYPREFL ST STE 100, TAMPA, FL 33607
Phone: 8133419101
Web: WWW.THAFL.COM

HISTORICAL FINANCIALS

Company Type: Private

Income Statement FYE: March 31

	REVENUE ($ mil.)	NET INCOME ($ mil.)	NET PROFIT MARGIN	EMPLOYEES
03/14	417	(0)	—	233
03/03	74	9	13.2%	—
03/02	49	10	21.6%	—
03/99	3	0	—	—
Annual Growth	37.3%	—	—	—

2014 Year-End Financials

Debt ratio: —
Return on equity: (-0.10%)
Cash ($ mil.): 24
Current ratio: 3.00
Long-term debt ($ mil.): —

Dividends
Yield: —
Payout: —
Market value ($ mil.): —

HOUSTON SAM STATE UNIVERSITY

Part of the Texas State University System Sam Houston University has an enrollment of nearly 18500 students. It consists of six schools: Business Administration Criminal Justice Education Fine Arts and Mass Communications Humanities and Social Sciences and Sciences. The university offers some 130 undergraduate and master programs as well as doctoral programs in counselor education criminal justice educational leadership reading and clinical psychology. It offers more than 20 undergraduate and graduate degrees entirely online. Sam Houston State was founded as Sam Houston Normal Institute in 1879 and is named after Texas hero General Sam Houston.

Geographic Reach

From its campus in Huntsville Texas Sam Houston State serves a diverse student body that represents about 60 countries. It also offers degrees for both undergraduates and graduates through its online educational system.

Operations

With a student/faculty ratio of 19:1 and an average class size of about 30 students Sam Houston State boasts a modest full-time undergraduate tuition and fees rate of approximately $2700. About 72% of the university's faculty members hold doctoral or terminal degrees.

Sales and Marketing

Sam Houston State sources its student population globally. Across its undergraduates and graduates the university's students hail from some 60 countries. The educational institution is also working to expand its online student system which it has developed in recent years to support the needs of students unable to attend classes on campus.

EXECUTIVES

VP Finance and Operations, Jack C. Parker
Director Human Resources, Ted Michael
VP Academic Affairs and Provost, David E. Payne
VP University Advancement, Frank R. Holmes
VP Student Services, Frank Parker
Associate VP Research and Special Programs, Jerry Cook
Dean College of Criminal Justice, Vincent Webb
Dean College of Humanities and Social Sciences, John de Castro
Director Newton Gresham Library, Ann Holder
Associate VP Information Resources, Mark Adams
Director Public Safety, Kevin H. Morris
VP Enrollment Management, Heather Crowson
President for Enrollment Management, Diane McCormick
Vice President Estill Building, Heather Thielemann

LOCATIONS

HQ: HOUSTON SAM STATE UNIVERSITY
1806 AVE J, HUNTSVILLE, TX 77341-0001
Phone: 936-294-1092
Web: WWW.SAMHOUSTON.STATEUNIVERSITY.COM

PRODUCTS/OPERATIONS

Selected Colleges

College of Business Administration (COBA)
College of Criminal Justice (CJ)
College of Education (COE)
College of Fine Arts and Mass Communication (COFAMC)
College of Humanities & Social Sciences (CHSS)
College of Sciences (COS)

HISTORICAL FINANCIALS

Company Type: Private

Income Statement FYE: August 31

	REVENUE ($ mil.)	NET INCOME ($ mil.)	NET PROFIT MARGIN	EMPLOYEES
08/11	160	29	18.4%	2,200
08/08	136	63	46.5%	—
08/07	128	14	11.6%	—
08/06	255	0	—	—
Annual Growth	(8.9%)	2011.7%	—	—

2011 Year-End Financials

Debt ratio: —
Return on equity: 18.40%
Cash ($ mil.): 66
Current ratio: 0.90
Long-term debt ($ mil.): —

Dividends
Yield: —
Payout: —
Market value ($ mil.): —

HOVENSA LLC

HOVENSA brings together US and Latin American know-how and operations to produce oil products in the US Virgin Islands. HOVENSA is a joint venture of Hess and Venezuelan oil giant PDVSA (its major crude oil supplier). The largest private employer in the US Virgin Islands the company operates a 500000-barrels-per-day crude oil refinery on St. Croix along with two specialized oil processing complexes a 150000-barrels-per-day fluid catalytic cracking unit and a 58000-barrels-per-day delayed coker unit. It is Hess' only crude oil refinery. Hess also owns and operates a 70000-barrels-per-day fluid catalytic cracking unit in Port Reading New Jersey to supply its retail outlets in the Northeast.

The St. Croix refinery's strategic location and 55-ft. deep harbor enables it to receive crude oil tanker deliveries from Venezuela and around the world and export refined products to the US Gulf Coast and East Coast markets.

HOVENSA's delayed coking unit enables the manufacture of gasoline and heating oil using lower-cost heavy crude oil. The company also has the capacity to store 32 million barrels of oil and petroleum products.

In 2008 HOVENSA reported a decline in its refinery throughput due to market conditions and a prolonged maintenance downtime of its fluid catalytic cracker unit. In 2009 the global economic downturn depressed demand for oil caused a further dip in production and prompted the company to lay off 270 employees (about 21% of its total contract workers).

In 2009 Hess obtained 45% of the refined products it sells from HOVENSA and the Port Reading plant. The rest was acquired from third parties.

EXECUTIVES

President and COO, Lawrence J. (Larry) Kupfer
EVP, Alexander A. (Alex) Moorehead
VP and Deputy COO, Marco Crovesi
VP Environmental Health and Safety, Richard (Dick) Smullen
VP Refinery Operations, Peter (Pete) Barba
Finance Manager, Mike Fennessey
Purchasing Manager, Gary Miller
President Chief Operating Officer of HOVENSA, Brian K. Lever

LOCATIONS

HQ: HOVENSA LLC
1 ESTATE HOPE, CHRISTIANSTED, VI 00820
Phone: 340-692-3000
Web: WWW.HOVENSALLC.COM

COMPETITORS

Chevron
ConocoPhillips
Exxon Mobil
Marathon Oil
Royal Dutch Shell
Sunoco
Valero Energy

HISTORICAL FINANCIALS

Company Type: Private

Income Statement FYE: December 31

	REVENUE ($ mil.)	NET INCOME ($ mil.)	NET PROFIT MARGIN	EMPLOYEES
12/09	10,048	(451)	—	1,300
12/08	17,479	94	0.5%	—
12/08	0	0	—	—
Annual Growth	—	—	—	—

2009 Year-End Financials

Debt ratio: —
Return on equity: (-4.50%)
Cash ($ mil.): 77
Current ratio: 0.20
Long-term debt ($ mil.): —

Dividends
Yield: —
Payout: —
Market value ($ mil.): —

HOWARD UNIVERSITY INC.

Howard University is a predominantly African-American university enrolling some 11000 students in Washington DC. The university offers undergraduate graduate and professional degrees in 120 areas including engineering education divinity dentistry law medicine history political science music and social work through its 12 schools and colleges. It has about 1000 full-time faculty members and has a low student-to-teacher ratio of about 8:1. Established in 1867 the school was named after one of its founders General Oliver O. Howard a Civil War hero who was commissioner of the Freedman's Bureau.

Operations

Medical students at Howard University have the convenience of using Howard University Hospital (located right on the school's campus) for their training and residency programs. The not-for-profit hospital offers students training in a full range of medical specialties including Level 1 Trauma care. The hospital is also a research facility giving students the opportunity to participate in clinical and research work.

Notable alumni at Howard University include choreographer Debbie Allen former US Supreme Court Justice Thurgood Marshall former New York City mayor David Dinkins Nobel laureate Toni Morrison and singer Roberta Flack.

Financial Performance

Howard University reported a 2% increase in revenue to some $851 million in 2012 due to higher tuition and fees patient services and other income. The university reported net income losses of $149 million that year (it also posted a loss in 2011) due to higher operating expenses and restructuring costs as well as lower investment returns.

Howard University's endowment is about $400 million. Its operating budget is nearly $885 million.

EXECUTIVES

President, Sidney A. Ribeau, age 65
VP and General Counsel, Kurt L. Schmoke, age 64
SVP and Secretary, Artis G. Hampshire-Cowan
VP Student Affairs, Barbara L.J. Griffin
Founder President CEO, Harold P. Freeman
SVP Strategic Planning and External Affairs, Hassan Minor
VP Development and Alumni Relations, Nesta H. Bernard
Vice Chairwoman, Renee Higginbotham-Brooks
Chairman, A. Barry Rand
Senior Vice President Chief Financial Officer Treasurer, Robert Tarola
Executive Vice President Chief Operating Officer, Troy Stovall
Trustee, Wayman F. Smith III
Trustee, Stacey J. Mobley, age 68
Trustee, Robert L. Lumpkins, age 70
Trustee, John A. Thain, age 58
Trustee, Vernon E. Jordan Jr., age 78
Trustee, John D. Zeglis, age 66
Trustee, Earl G. Graves Sr., age 79
Trustee, Floretta D. McKenzie
Trustee, Gerald D. Prothro, age 71
Trustee, Charisse R. Lillie, age 61
Trustee, Elizabeth G. Early
Vice Chairwoman, Renee Higginbotham-Brooks
Trustee, Charles J. McDonald
Trustee, Cornell Leverette Moore
Trustee, Jessye Norman
Trustee, M. Kasim Reed
Trustee, Gregory A. White
Trustee, L. Douglas Wilder, age 83

LOCATIONS

HQ: HOWARD UNIVERSITY INC.
2400 6TH ST NW, WASHINGTON, DC 20059-0002
Phone: 202-806-6100
Web: WWW.HOWARD.EDU

PRODUCTS/OPERATIONS

Selected Schools and Colleges

Arts and Sciences
Business
Communications
Dentistry
Divinity
Education
Engineering Architecture and Computer Sciences
Graduate School
Law
Medicine
Nursing and Allied Health Sciences
Pharmacy
Social Work

HISTORICAL FINANCIALS

Company Type: Private

Income Statement FYE: June 30

	REVENUE ($ mil.)	NET INCOME ($ mil.)	NET PROFIT MARGIN	EMPLOYEES
06/12	851	(148)	—	5,600
06/11	989	11	1.2%	—
06/10	941	10	1.1%	—
06/09	844	835	98.9%	—
Annual Growth	0.2%	—	—	—

2012 Year-End Financials

Debt ratio: —
Return on equity: (-17.50%)
Cash ($ mil.): 35
Current ratio: —
Long-term debt ($ mil.): —
Dividends
Yield: —
Payout: —
Market value ($ mil.): —

HPS LLC

LOCATIONS

HQ: HPS LLC
3275 N M 37 HWY, MIDDLEVILLE, MI 493339126
Phone: 2697953308
Web: WWW.HPSNET.NET

HISTORICAL FINANCIALS

Company Type: Private

Income Statement FYE: June 30

	REVENUE ($ mil.)	NET INCOME ($ mil.)	NET PROFIT MARGIN	EMPLOYEES
06/14	862	0	0.1%	38
06/13	898	0	0.1%	—
06/12	705	0	0.0%	—
06/11	755	0	—	—
Annual Growth	4.5%	—	—	—

2014 Year-End Financials

Debt ratio: —
Return on equity: 0.10%
Cash ($ mil.): 4
Current ratio: 1.50
Long-term debt ($ mil.): —
Dividends
Yield: —
Payout: —
Market value ($ mil.): —

HUMAX USA INC.

Humax USA prefers to connect with its customers through its products. The company develops and manufactures flat-panel TV sets and digital set-top boxes for satellite cable and terrestrial connections. Humax USA is the US-based subsidiary of Korean consumer electronics manufacturing firm Humax Co. which was founded in 1989. The brand has become one of the most popular worldwide among set-top boxes. Humax's products are available in more than 90 countries as well as in the US. The company primarily serves customers in Asia and Europe.

To expand its presence in the US market Humax USA has partnered with the likes of DIRECTV and TiVo to offer products integrated with their technology.

EXECUTIVES

Chairman and CEO, Dae Gyu Byun
President Humax USA, T.H. Kim
SVP Sales and Marketing Humax USA, Christopher C. Cudina

LOCATIONS

HQ: HUMAX USA INC.
17501 VON KARMAN AVE, IRVINE, CA 92614-6207
Phone: 949-251-5200
Web: WWW.HUMAXDIGITAL.COM

COMPETITORS

DIRECTV
SANYO
Samsung Electronics
Sony USA
TiVo

HISTORICAL FINANCIALS

Company Type: Private

Income Statement FYE: December 31

	REVENUE ($ mil.)	NET INCOME ($ mil.)	NET PROFIT MARGIN	EMPLOYEES
12/12	290	0	0.2%	26
12/11	347	1	0.4%	—
12/10	268	0	0.1%	
12/09	116	0	0.2%	
Annual Growth	35.5%	28.2%	—	—

2012 Year-End Financials

Debt ratio: —
Return on equity: 0.20%
Cash ($ mil.): 2
Current ratio: 0.80
Long-term debt ($ mil.): —
Dividends
Yield: —
Payout: —
Market value ($ mil.): —

HURLEY MEDICAL CENTER INC.

A community hospital owned by the City of Flint Hurley Medical Center is a teaching hospital serving Genesee Lapeer and Shiawassee counties in eastern Michigan. The 440-bed acute care facility is affiliated with the medical schools of Michigan State University and The University of Michigan. It provides care in areas such as cancer mental health rehabilitation surgery and women's health and it is a regional center for pediatrics. Hurley Medical Center also offers advanced specialty care such as trauma care neonatal intensive care kidney transplantation burn medicine and bariatric (weight loss) surgery. The center was founded in 1908 and is owned by the state of Michigan.

Operations

Hurley Medical Center has a physician health organization (PHO) partnership with the Professional Medical Corporation. The Hurley PHO of Mid-Michigan is a multi-specialty physician group that contracts with managed care organizations to provide care.

The hospital has an affiliation partnership with the Henry Ford Health System; the two health care providers offer a joint kidney transplantation program. Hurley Medical Center also operates the Genesys Hurley Cancer Institute in partnership with the Genesys Regional Medical Center.

Financial Performance

Hurley's revenue increased 3% in 2013 as it took in more patient payments. It reported a net loss of $2.3 million due to increased expenses including salaries unrealized losses on investments.

Strategy

The medical center works to update and expand its services on a regular basis. In 2012 it doubled in size with the opening of the Paul F. Reinhart Emergency Trauma Center.

EXECUTIVES

Senior Vice President Chief Financial Officer, Cass Wisniewski
Vice President of Patient Care Services, Amy Benko
President Chief Executive Officer, Melany Gavulic
Interim Vice President for, Beth Brophy
Vice President of Service Line Development, Michael Burnett
Treasurer, Carl Bekofske

LOCATIONS

HQ: HURLEY MEDICAL CENTER INC.
1 HURLEY PLZ, FLINT, MI 48503-5902
Phone: 810-257-9000
Web: WWW.HURLEYMC.COM

COMPETITORS

Covenant HealthCare
Crittenton Hospital
Detroit Medical Center
Genesys Regional Medical Center
Henry Ford Health System
McLaren Health Care
Munson Healthcare
Sparrow Health System
St. John Health
Trinity Health (Novi)

HISTORICAL FINANCIALS

Company Type: Private

Income Statement FYE: June 30

	REVENUE ($ mil.)	NET INCOME ($ mil.)	NET PROFIT MARGIN	EMPLOYEES
06/08*	350	3	1.1%	2,884
03/08	250	0	0.1%	
Annual Growth	***********	%***********	%—	—

*Fiscal year change

2008 Year-End Financials

Debt ratio: —
Return on equity: 1.10%
Cash ($ mil.): 24
Current ratio: 1.10
Long-term debt ($ mil.): —
Dividends
Yield: —
Payout: —
Market value ($ mil.): —

HUSKER AG LLC

LOCATIONS

HQ: HUSKER AG LLC
54048 HIGHWAY 20, PLAINVIEW, NE 687694072
Phone: 4025824446
Web: WWW.HUSKERAG.COM

HISTORICAL FINANCIALS

Company Type: Private

Income Statement FYE: December 31

	REVENUE ($ mil.)	NET INCOME ($ mil.)	NET PROFIT MARGIN	EMPLOYEES
12/13	216	17	8.1%	52
12/12	202	(1)	—	—
12/11	237	20	8.5%	—
12/10	146	0	—	—
Annual Growth	13.8%	—	—	—

2013 Year-End Financials

Debt ratio: —
Return on equity: 8.10%
Cash ($ mil.): 0
Current ratio: 0.30
Long-term debt ($ mil.): —
Dividends
Yield: —
Payout: —
Market value ($ mil.): —

HY-VEE INC.

Give Hy-Vee a high five for being one of the largest privately owned US supermarket chains despite serving some modestly sized towns in the Midwest. The company runs some 235 stores in eight Midwestern states. About half of its supermarkets are in Iowa as are most of its 20-plus Hy-Vee drugstores. It distributes products to its stores through several subsidiaries including Lomar Distributing (specialty foods) and Perishable Distributors of Iowa (fresh foods). Other activities include construction and specialty pharmacies. Charles Hyde and David Vredenburg founded the employee-owned firm in 1930. It takes its name from a combination of its founders' names.

Geographic Reach

Hy-Vee's stores are located in Illinois Iowa Kansas Minnesota Missouri Nebraska South Dakota and Wisconsin. The company supplies its stores from distribution centers in Chariton and Cherokee Iowa.

Operations

In addition to its food and drug retail operations Hy-Vee offers customers financial products. Adding to its menu of financial services Hy-Vee subsidiary Midwest Heritage Bank in 2011 acquired Iowa-based L&K Insurance a full-line insurance agency. L&K changed its name to Midwest Heritage Insurance Services post sale.

Financial Performance

Hy-Vee's 235 stores ring up more than $8 billion in annual sales.

Strategy

Hy-Vee is gradually expanding in several key markets in the Midwest including Chicago Minneapolis-St. Paul and Madison Wisconsin. To that end the regional grocery chain in 2014 announced plans to enter the Twin Cities market. In 2013 the chain opened its second supermarket in Madison after entering the Madison market in 2009. To cater to local tastes the company says the 80000-sq.-ft. Madison store has the largest cheese selection of any Hy-Vee supermarket. Hy-Vee is also testing a smaller-format store (about 20000-25000 sq. ft. with no pharmacies) in select locations. It's also adding stores in its core Iowa market with a supermarket slated to open in Winterset in 2014.

Going beyond traditional grocery fare Hy-Vee in 2013 acquired its joint venture partner's stake in Hy-Vee Weitz Company a construction firm based in Des Moines. The grocery store operator renamed the company Hy-Vee Construction and plans to expand the in-house construction management group. The company also teamed up with specialty pharmacy operator Amber Pharmacy to form a new company (called Hy-Vee Pharmacy Solutions) to provide services for patients with complex and chronic health problems including Crohn's disease hemophilia psoriasis and other chronic ailments. The grocery chain has also been focusing on adding Hy-Vee Gas convenience units (some 80 locations include these) wine and spirits stores pharmacies and Hy-Vee HealthMarket departments.

Ric Jurgens in 2012 retired as chairman and CEO after 43-years with Hy-Vee. He was succeeded by president and COO Randy Edeker.

EXECUTIVES

Asst Vp Advertising, Jason Sheridan
Vp, Stephen P Meyer, age 68
Assistant Vice President Real Estate, David A Bailie
SVP Marketing, Jon S. Wendel, age 51
VP Management Information Systems, Eric Smith
VP Perishables, Paula K. Correy, age 48
VP Petroleum Marketing, Thomas E. (Tom) Watson
Store Manager Madison Wisconsin, Rob Budd
Chairman President and CEO, Randall B. (Randy) Edeker, age 52
Vice President Retail Information Technology, Julie Proffitt
Assistant Vice President Application Development, Jason Mikesell
Vice President, Matt Dougan
Assistant Vp Operations, Jim Watters
Pharmacy Manager, Danielle Scott
Vp-employee Benefits, Kristine Hennings
Vice President, Karl Kruse
Assistant Vice-president, Angie Rosenberger
Assistant Vice-president, Rob Eslick
Assistant Vice President Data Warehousing, Tom Settle
Vp Information Systems, Darren Baty
Assistant Vice-president, Tony Byington
Asst Vice President Trans Human Resrcs, Lisa Stowater
Senior Vice President Of Purchasing, Ken Waller
Assistant Vice President Compliance And Food Safety, Charles Seaman
Assistant Vice President Construction, Mark Brauer
Asst Vp General Mdse, Matt Beenblossom
Assistant Vice-president, Dave Kozak
Pharmacy Manager, Tom Bride
Assistant Vice President Network Systems, Luke Tingley
Assistant Vice President Risk Management, Janet Crocker
Assistant Vice-president, Kenan Judge
Assistant Vice President Engineering, Adam Bishop
Assistant Vice-president, Erin Bailey
Assistant Vice President Retail Systems, Christy Myers
Asst Vp Wine Spirits, Jay Wilson
Assistant Vice President Marketing Communications, Donna Tweeten
Assistant Vice-president, Dan Wampler
Vp Sales, Katie Graham
Assistant Vice-president, Tony Kaska
Chairman President and CEO, Randall B. (Randy) Edeker, age 52
Secretary Treasurer, James Siemens
Board Member, Bree Cooper
Treasurer, Jennifer Tucker
Assisant Treasurer, Jeff Pierce

LOCATIONS

HQ: HY-VEE INC.
5820 WESTOWN PKWY, WEST DES MOINES, IA 502668223
Phone: 5152672800
Web: WWW.HY-VEE.COM

PRODUCTS/OPERATIONS

2012 Stores

	No.
Supermarkets	212
Drugstores	22
Total	**234**

Selected Subsidiaries

D & D Foods Inc. (salads dips and meats)
Florist Distributing Inc. (flowers plants and florist supplies)
Hy-Vee Construction L.C. (construction)
Hy-Vee Pharmacy Solutions (specialty pharmacy services)
Hy-Vee Weitz Construction L.C. (construction)
Lomar Distributing Inc. (specialty foods)
Midwest Heritage Bank FSB (banking)
Perishable Distributors of Iowa Ltd. (meat fish seafood and ice cream)

COMPETITORS

ALDI
Nash-Finch

Associated Wholesale Grocers	Niemann Foods
Ball' s Food	Rite Aid
CVS	Roundy' s
Casey' s General Stores	SUPERVALU
Dahl' s Foods	Save-A-Lot Food Stores
Fareway Stores	Target Corporation
Kmart	Wal-Mart
Kroger	Walgreen

HISTORICAL FINANCIALS

Company Type: Private

Income Statement FYE: September 28

	REVENUE ($ mil.)	NET INCOME ($ mil.)	NET PROFIT MARGIN	EMPLOYEES
09/14	8,014	0	—	62,000
09/13	8,014	0	—	—
09/12*	7,682	0	—	—
10/11	0	0	—	—
Annual Growth	—	—	—	—

*Fiscal year change

2014 Year-End Financials

Debt ratio: —
Return on equity: —
Cash ($ mil.): 7
Current ratio: 0.20
Long-term debt ($ mil.): —

Dividends
Yield: —
Payout: —
Market value ($ mil.): —

ILLINOIS INSTITUTE OF TECHNOLOGY

Chicago has some cool architecture due in part to the Illinois Institute of Technology (IIT). The school offers more than 100 undergraduate and graduate degree programs in engineering science psychology architecture business law humanities and design. In addition to three campuses in Chicago IIT also has locations in Summit-Argo (Moffet campus) and Wheaton (Daniel F. and Ada L. Rice campus). The institute has an enrollment of some 8000 undergraduate graduate business school and law school students with a student-to-faculty ratio of 8:1. IIT was created in 1940 by the merger of Armour Institute (founded in 1893) with Lewis Institute (established in 1895).

Operations

IIT's heritage includes the innovative Bauhaus tradition that set up shop at the university in the 1930's. These days its innovation is expressed in the form of interdisciplinary research on such themes as Energy and Sustainability Improving the Quality of Life and Perfect Power. IIT maintains about 30 research institutes with major centers focused on the study of sustainable energy electricity innovation and biomedical science and engineering and food safety and health.

Financial Performance

IIT reported $250 million in revenues in fiscal 2012 up 1% over results in 2011 as the university met its growth targets for tuition and enrollment. However net income fell into the red in 2012 as the university reported a loss of about $7 million down from profits of nearly $32 million in 2011.

Strategy

IIT regularly evaluates its offerings and adds new degree programs to meet the needs of a changing society. In 2011 it added five new degree programs in fields including biology physics and sociology and in 2012 it introduced a Master's degree program for cyber forensics and security majors.

In addition to expand its research capacity and reflect the growing importance of food safety research IIT opened a new center for food safety and technology research in 2011 upgrading the previous nutritional research center's status to institute. The move will help the university increase services to government and industry partners. IIT also opened a new startup business center that year to help transition research discoveries into commercial business stages.

EXECUTIVES

Vice Chair, David J. Vitale, age 67
Vice Chair, Craig J. Duchossois
CIO, Ophir Trigalo
Chair, John W. Rowe, age 68
Vice Provost New Initiatives, Dennis A. Roberson, age 65
VP External Affairs, David Baker
VP Business and Operations, John P. Collins
Senior Vice President and Director, David McCormick
VP International Affairs, Darsh Wasan
President, John L. Anderson
Senior Vice President for Academic Affairs, Alan W. Cramb
IIT Vice President and IFSH Director/Co-Director National Center for Food Safety and Technology, Robert E. Brackett
VP Institutional Advancement, Elizabeth J. Hughes
VP Community Affairs and Outreach Programs, Leroy Kennedy
Director Enterprise Systems, Wesley Matthews
Director Programming and Customer Service, James Meyer
Dean Libraries, Christopher Stewart
Director Finance, Patricia A. Grow
VP Research and Dean Graduate College, Ali Cinar
Associate Provost Undergraduate Affairs, Michael R. Gosz
Director Alumni Relations, Tara L. Anderson
Vice Provost Undergraduate Admission and Financial Aid, Gerald P. Doyle
Vice President for Marketing and Communications, Jeanne Hartig
Dean of IIT Armour College of Engineering, Natacha DePaola
VP Finance and Administration, Patricia Laughlin
Senior Director of Communications, Evan Venie
Vice President for Facilities and Public Safety, Bruce Watts
Vice Chair, David J. Vitale, age 67
Vice Chair, Craig J. Duchossois

LOCATIONS

HQ: ILLINOIS INSTITUTE OF TECHNOLOGY
10 W 35TH ST, CHICAGO, IL 60616-3717
Phone: 312-567-3000
Web: WWW.IIT.EDU

PRODUCTS/OPERATIONS

Selected Schools and Colleges

Armour College of Engineering
ChicagoKent College of Law
College of Architecture
College of Psychology
College of Science and Letters
Institute of Design
School of Applied Technology (SAT)
Stuart School of Business

HISTORICAL FINANCIALS

Company Type: Private

Income Statement FYE: May 31

	REVENUE ($ mil.)	NET INCOME ($ mil.)	NET PROFIT MARGIN	EMPLOYEES
05/12	249	(6)	—	1,662
05/11	305	8	2.9%	—
05/10	333	41	12.4%	—
05/09	190	0	—	—
Annual Growth	9.4%	—	—	—

2012 Year-End Financials

Debt ratio: —
Return on equity: (-2.80%)
Cash ($ mil.): 18
Current ratio: —
Long-term debt ($ mil.): —

Dividends
Yield: —
Payout: —
Market value ($ mil.): —

IMMIXGROUP INC.

immixGroup offers a blend of information technology (IT) business development and consulting services to help tech firms do business with federal state and local government agencies. Through its technology sales division the company is a hardware and software reseller for such manufacturers as IBM Oracle and Hewlett-Packard. It also offers customized public sector channel development programs outsourced government contract management and IT consulting and execution. Other services include market intelligence sales training and recruiting. immixGroup serves more than 250 tech manufacturers and its government partner network includes more than 600 resellers systems integrators and other providers.

EXECUTIVES

EVP, Stephen G. (Steve) Charles
VP Technology Sales Division, David Stewart
VP Government Channels Division, Skip Liesegang
Vice President Corporate Development & General Counsel, Scott Needleman
VP Operations, William (Bill) Bottoms
VP IT Solutions Division, Phill Magaro
VP Marketing, Allan Rubin
Account Manager, Kristy Williams
Senior Account Manager, Stacy Cole
Account Manager Renewals, Sarah Stone
Account Manager, Andrew Keeney
Account Manager, Chase Bartalone
Account Manager, Neil Michaels
Senior Account Manager, Elizabeth Mulhern
Chairman and CEO, Jeff Copeland
President, Art Richer
Vice President of Business Development, Ron Breland
Chief Financial Officer, Noel Samuel

LOCATIONS

HQ: IMMIXGROUP INC.
8444 WESTPARK DR STE 200, MC LEAN, VA 22102-5112
Phone: 703-752-0610
Web: WWW.IMMIXGROUP.COM

COMPETITORS

Accenture
BAE Systems Technology Solutions
Booz Allen
CACI International
Computer Sciences Corp.
HP Enterprise Services
Honeywell Technology Solutions
IBM Global Services

Lockheed Martin Information Systems
ManTech
McKinsey & Company
Northrop Grumman Info Systems
Raytheon Intelligence Information and Services
SAIC
SRA International
Unisys

HISTORICAL FINANCIALS

Company Type: Private

Income Statement FYE: May 31

	REVENUE ($ mil.)	NET INCOME ($ mil.)	NET PROFIT MARGIN	EMPLOYEES
05/12	502	13	2.6%	201
05/11	43	16	37.9%	—
05/10	563	11	2.1%	—
05/09	403	6	1.7%	—
Annual Growth	7.5%	24.3%	—	—

2012 Year-End Financials

Debt ratio: —
Return on equity: 2.60%
Cash ($ mil.): 24
Current ratio: 1.10
Long-term debt ($ mil.): —
Dividends
Yield: —
Payout: —
Market value ($ mil.): —

IMPERIAL IRRIGATION DISTRICT

Imperial Irrigation District (IID) keeps the lights on and the water flowing. A public agency IID is the six largest public power utility in the state of California providing generation transmission and distribution services to more than 145000 residential commercial and industrial customers. It is also the largest irrigation district in the US with more than 3000 miles of canals and drains delivering water to active farmland and providing wholesale water to local municipalities primarily in the Southern California desert corridors of Imperial Valley and Coachella Valley. The district is governed by a five-member board of directors elected by district residents.

Strategy

In the area of renewable energy IID is part of a statewide effort to significantly increase solar energy development and production by the year 2017. In 2011 it announced a public-private partnership with renewable energy generators. The partnership involves the signing of interconnection and transmission service agreements among IID CalEnergy Generation 8minuteenergy Ormat Technologies and the Los Angeles Department of Water and Power. It's the first step in a renewable energy transmission expansion plan to increase capacity enough to support more than a dozen renewable energy construction projects.

In addition IID offers a variety of programs to assist its customers in reducing their personal energy consumption including rebates for buying select energy efficient products online home energy audits and funding for residential projects that involve installing solar technologies such as photovoltaic (PV) systems.

Financial Performance

IID saw its revenues increase 6% from $530 million in 2011 to $562 million in 2012. The growth was driven by a 12% surge in water revenue; this was due to a rise in water transfer rates and a volume increase in water transferred to the San Diego County Water Authority and the Coachella Valley Water District of about $5 million. Power revenues also climbed 4% in 2012 due to a spike in energy sales mainly from residential customers.

Company Background

Founded in 1911 IID acquired properties from the financially struggling California Development Company and its Mexican subsidiary. By 1922 it had purchased 13 mutual water companies each of which had developed and operated distribution canals in the Imperial Valley. Principal water customers today include farm operators and municipalities that treat the water and resell it to their residential and business customers. The district entered the power business in 1936 to utilize the hydroelectric generation of the All-American Canal. Since that time IID has added geothermal natural gas coal and solar to its energy generation portfolio. Its electric services account for majority of IID's annual revenues.

EXECUTIVES

CFO, Greg Broeking
Vice President, Alfonso Juarez
Vice President Of Finance, Cora Cervantes
Auditors: MossAdamsLLP

LOCATIONS

HQ: IMPERIAL IRRIGATION DISTRICT
333 E BARIONI BLVD, IMPERIAL, CA 922511773
Phone: 8003037756
Web: WWW.IID.COM

PRODUCTS/OPERATIONS

2012 Sales

Power	405	72
Total	**562**	**100**

HISTORICAL FINANCIALS

Company Type: Private

Income Statement FYE: December 31

	REVENUE ($ mil.)	NET INCOME ($ mil.)	NET PROFIT MARGIN	EMPLOYEES
12/07	524	151	29.0%	1,300
12/06	503	108	21.5%	—
12/05	408	62	15.3%	—
12/04	367	0	—	—
Annual Growth	12.6%	—	—	—

2007 Year-End Financials

Debt ratio: —
Return on equity: 29.00%
Cash ($ mil.): 165
Current ratio: 1.00
Long-term debt ($ mil.): —
Dividends
Yield: —
Payout: —
Market value ($ mil.): —

INDIANA UNIVERSITY FOUNDATION INC.

EXECUTIVES

Vice Chairman, August M. (Gus) Watanabe, age 73
President CEO and Director, Curtis R. Simic
SVP and CFO, James P. (Jim) Perin
Executive Director Finance and Controller, Gina Reel
SVP Development, Kent Dove
Chairman, Adam W. Hebert Jr.
VP Indianapolis, William G. Heller
VP Regional Campuses, James E. Smith
VP and Chief Investment Officer, Gary A. Stratten
Secretary, Karen J. Pieper
SVP Development, Marti Heil
Vice Chairman, August M. (Gus) Watanabe, age 73
Director, David I. Klapper, age 65
Director, David C. Evans
Director, William G. Mays, age 68
Director, Stephen A. Stitle, age 65
Director, Alecia A. DeCoudreaux, age 59
President CEO and Director, Curtis R. Simic
Director, Jay B. Hunt, age 75
Director, Stephen L. (Steve) Ferguson
Director, Randall C. Morgan Jr.
Director, Patrick A. Shoulders
Director, Kathryn Ryan Booth
Director, Bill C. Brown
Director, William P. Carmichael
Director, Gayle C. Cook
Director, Clarence H. Doninger
Director, David G. Elmore
Director, Richard E. Ford
Director, Ezra H. (Zeke) Friedlander
Director, Jack M. Gill
Director, Moses W. Gray
Director, Ann L. Harrison
Director, V. William Hunt
Director, Needham S. Hurst
Director, Robert W. Lanum
Director, Dale Ellen Leff
Director, Jane Halagiere Martin
Director, Joseph T. Morrow
Director, John D. Peterson
Director, N. E. (Ned) Pfau
Director, Thomas D. Rush
Director, Scott C. Schurz
Director, Richard C. Searles
Director, Julie Inskeep Simpson
Director, James G. Sinclair
Director, Cynthia Simon (Cindy) Skjodt
Director, Fred G. Steingraber
Director, Milton R. (Milt) Stewart
Director, Gregg T. Summerville
Director, W. Michael (Mike) Wells
Director, Desmond C. Wong, age 63
Director, Richard E. Woosnam
Auditors: Deloitte&ToucheLLP

LOCATIONS

HQ: INDIANA UNIVERSITY FOUNDATION INC.
1500 N STATE ROAD 46 BYP, BLOOMINGTON, IN 47408
Phone: 8128558311
Web: WWW.IUFOUNDATION.IU.EDU

HISTORICAL FINANCIALS

Company Type: Private

Income Statement FYE: June 30

	ASSETS ($ mil.)	NET INCOME ($ mil.)	INCOME AS % OF ASSETS	EMPLOYEES
06/13	2,277	107	4.7%	220
06/12	2,105	(11)	—	—
06/11	2,054	255	12.4%	—
06/10	1,767	0	—	—
Annual Growth	8.8%	—	—	—

2013 Year-End Financials

Debt ratio: —
Return on equity: 40.80%
Cash ($ mil.): 154
Current ratio: —
Long-term debt ($ mil.): —
Dividends
Yield: —
Payout: —
Market value ($ mil.): —

INDIANA UNIVERSITY HEALTH BLOOMINGTON INC

Indiana University Health Bloomington wants to put a bloom back in patients' cheeks. The facility operating as IU Health Bloomington provides care in a ten-county region in south central Indiana. The not-for-profit hospital –which includes a 350-bed main campus in Bloomington and a 25-bed rural hospital in Paoli –provides care in a number of medical specialties including cardiovascular disease cancer orthopedics and neuroscience. It also runs home health and hospice urgent care lab and specialty care facilities as well as physician practices under the name Southern Indiana Physicians. IU Health Bloomington is part of the Indiana University Health (IU Health) system.

Geographic Reach

IU Health Bloomington has a customer base of about 415000 patients in a 10-county area in south central Indiana. The hospital serves as a regional referral center for other hospitals in the area.

Operations

The company's operations include Indiana University Health Paoli (Paoli) Indiana University Health Morgan Hospital (Morgan) and Indiana University Health White Memorial Hospital (White).

Strategy

Like most hospitals IU Health Bloomington enters partnerships to extend its patient reach. In 2012 IU Health Bloomington and a Monroe County YMCA collaborated to provide a new space in a new northwest YMCA dedicated to IU Health for physical therapy orthopedic services sports medicine and health and wellness services.

Company Background

After several years of negotiations IU Health Bloomington officially became an integrated part of the Clarian network at the start of 2010. Then at the beginning of 2011 Clarian changed its name to IU Health to clarify its relationship with Indiana University and to provide a unified brand to connect all of its facilities.

EXECUTIVES

Vice President Of Marketing, Brian Witman
Director Physician Recruitment, John Lee
Medical Librarian, Patty Booker
Vice President Iu Health, Rhonda Volk
President CEO, Mark E. Moore
CFO, James (Jim) Myers
CIO, Mark McMath
VP Fund Development; Executive Director Bloomington Hospital Foundation, Chris Molloy
VP; CEO Bloomington Hospital Orange County, Gene Perry
VP Marketing Business Development and Community Relations, F. Brian Whitman
Executive Director Regional Orthopedics Center and Regional Neuroscience Institute, Myron Lewis
Executive Vice President and Chief Nurse Executive, Linda Q. Everett
Executive Vice President Chief Operating Officer, Dennis Murphy
President Bloomington Hospital Foundation, Jon W. Barada
Medical Director, Mark Bauman
Director Of Respiratory Therapy, Ted Jackson
Vp Marketing, Holly Vonderheit
Department Head, Vicki Trueblood
Clinic Supervisor, Sherryl Yake
Vice President Chief Nursing Officer, Linda Chase
Nursing Director, Pam Hoppe
Chief Nursing Executive Vice President Of Patient Care Services, Joshua Fleming
Director Of Nursing, Pam Adams
Vice President And Chief Nursing Officer, Lori Knarr
Vice President Human Resources, Koreen Kyhnell
Vice President Of Sales, Julie Hedden
Member Board Of Directors, Kent Rodgers
Vice Chairman, Cam Malloy
Secretary, Karen Tveten

LOCATIONS

HQ: INDIANA UNIVERSITY HEALTH BLOOMINGTON INC
601 W 2ND ST, BLOOMINGTON, IN 47403-2317
Phone: 812-353-9830
Web: WWW.BLOOMINGTONHOSPITAL.ORG

PRODUCTS/OPERATIONS

Selected Services

Anticoagulation Center
Assisted Medical Transportation
Behavioral Health
Cancer
Cardiovascular
Children's Therapy Center
Diabetes Center
Emergency
Home Care
Home Medical Equipment
Hospice
Laboratory
Neuroscience
Occupational
Orthopedics
Pain Center
Primary Care
Radiology
Rehabilitation
Sleep Lab
Surgical
Urgent Care Centers
Women and Children's
Wound Center

COMPETITORS

Ascension Health
Community Hospitals of Indiana
Daviess Community Hospital
Franciscan Alliance
Henry County Memorial Hospital
Memorial Hospital (Logansport)
Riverview Hospital
St. Vincent Health
Union Hospital (Indiana)
Wabash County Hospital

HISTORICAL FINANCIALS

Company Type: Private

Income Statement FYE: December 31

	REVENUE ($ mil.)	NET INCOME ($ mil.)	NET PROFIT MARGIN	EMPLOYEES
12/11	391	22	5.7%	3,200
12/10	359	30	8.4%	—
12/09	346	31	9.1%	—
12/08	321	(5)	—	—
Annual Growth	6.8%	—	—	—

2011 Year-End Financials

Debt ratio: —
Return on equity: 5.70%
Cash ($ mil.): 69
Current ratio: 2.50
Long-term debt ($ mil.): —

Dividends
Yield: —
Payout: —
Market value ($ mil.): —

INDIANA UNIVERSITY HEALTH INC.

Indiana University Health cares about health care for all in the state of Indiana. As one of the largest health systems in the state not-for-profit IU Health owns or is affiliated with more than 20 hospitals and health centers throughout the state including three major hospitals –Methodist Hospital Indiana University Hospital and Riley Hospital for Children –that serve the downtown Indianapolis area. The largest Methodist Hospital features the Methodist Research Institute which conducts research and clinical trials. The system's hospitals also serve as teaching facilities for Indiana University's medical school.

Operations

IU Health partners with Indiana University School of Medicine to give patients access to innovative therapies. The organization is comprised of hospitals physicians and other care providers dedicated to offering quality care throughout Indiana and beyond.

The system has more than 3500 beds and more than 3700 physicians. In addition to hospitals the health system offers additional services through a network of primary and specialty care clinics and a home health care business. In 2012 Indiana University Health reported more than 144000 total patient admissions and more than 2.5 million outpatient visits.

IU Health is not only an educational establishment it's considered a major research hub with total grant research funding of close to $270 million. It has about 1000 residents and fellows conducting roughly 2600 research studies. Together Indiana University Health and Indiana University School of Medicine work together to train physicians using a blended curriculum of research and treatments on actual patients.

Financial Performance

In 2012 IU Health reported a nearly 30% increase in revenue due to a bump in patient revenue. Net income jumped 120% due to better investments. Cash flow followed with a $310 million improvement.

Strategy

The company changed its name from Clarian Health Partners to Indiana University Health in 2011 to reflect its growing relationship with the university and to unify branding of its facilities which also began to operate under the Indiana University Health (or IU Health) moniker.

The system's growth strategy includes expanding into the city's growing (and affluent) suburbs with majority-owned for-profit facilities located in Avon and Carmel. The system (along with the Indiana University School of Medicine) is investing $100 million to increase its neuroscience services. As part of the investment plan the two are building a Neuroscience Center of Excellence near the Methodist Hospital slated to open in 2014.

While it continues to expand in 2013 the organization responded to the changing health care landscape in the US by announcing plans to cut about 800 hospital jobs and realign certain service offerings. The moves come as part of an effort to reduce expenses by about $1 billion over a five-year period during a time when large-scale health organizations across the US look to control medical costs.

Mergers and Acquisitions

In 2013 IU Health purchased Wipperman Occupational Health a South Bend clinic offering occupational health and wellness to area employers.

The facility was rebranded IU Health Occupational Services Wipperman Clinic.

Company Background

IU Health was formed in 1997 as Clarian Health Partners.

EXECUTIVES

Chairman, V. William (Bill) Hunt, age 68
President CEO and Director, Daniel F. (Dan) Evans Jr., age 65
EVP and COO Clarian Health Indianapolis Operations, Samuel L. (Sam) Odle, age 65
President Chief Executive Officer, Jonathan R. (Jon) Goble, age 56
EVP and Chief Medical Officer, Richard Graffis
SVP Values Ethics and Pastoral Services, Steven Ivy
VP Business Development, Scott Black
Public Relations Coordinator, Gene H. Ford
EVP and Chief Nurse Executive, Linda Q. Everett
Vice Chairman, Thomas W. Chapman
SVP Engagement and External Affairs, Ron Stiver
President Chief Executive Officer, Matt Bailey
Director Public Relations and Communications, Holly Vonderheit
Manager Public Relations, Margie Smith-Simmons
Public Relations Coordinator, Kit Werbe
Vice President of Human Resources and Development, Cindy Smale
Vice President of Patient Services, Brenda Davis
Vice President of Finances, Charles Shetler
Senior Vice President Secretary General Counsel, Thomas V. Easterday
Director, Charles E. Golden, age 67
President CEO and Director, Daniel F. (Dan) Evans Jr., age 65
Director, William R. Cast
Director, D. Craig Brater
Vice Chairman, Thomas W. Chapman
Director, David W. Goodrich
Director, James E. Lingeman
Director, Angela Barron McBride
Director, Gene E. Robbins
Director, Michael A. McRobbie
Director, Michael J. Coyner

LOCATIONS

HQ: INDIANA UNIVERSITY HEALTH INC.
1701 N SENATE BLVD, INDIANAPOLIS, IN 46202-1239
Phone: 317-962-2000
Web: WWW.IUHEALTH.ORG

PRODUCTS/OPERATIONS

Selected Facilities

INDIANAPOLIS-AREA HOSPITALS
Indiana University Hospital (dba IU Health University Hospital Indianapolis)
Methodist Hospital (dba IU Health Methodist Hospital Indianapolis)
Riley Hospital for Children (dba Riley Hospital for Children at IU Health Indianapolis)
IU Simon Cancer Center
Clarian North Medical Center (dba IU Health North Hospital Carmel)
Clarian West Medical Center (dba IU Health West Hospital Avon)
STATEWIDE PARTNERS
Clarian Arnett Health (dba IU Health Arnett Hospital Lafayette)
Ball Memorial Hospital (dba IU Health Ball Memorial Hospital Muncie)
Bedford Regional Medical Center (dba IU Health Bedford Hospital Bedford)
Blackford Community Hospital (dba IU Health Blackford Hospital Hartford City)
Bloomington Hospital (dba IU Health Bloomington Hospital Bloomington)
Bloomington Hospital of Orange County (dba IU Health Paoli Hospital Paoli)
Goshen Health System (dba IU Health Goshen Hospital Goshen)
LaPorte Regional Health System (dba IU Health LaPorte Hospital La Porte)
Midwest Proton Radiotherapy Institute (dba IU Health Proton Therapy Center Bloomington)
Starke Memorial Hospital (dba IU Health Starke Hospital Knox)
Tipton Hospital (dba IU Health Tipton Hospital Tipton)
METHODIST MEDICAL PLAZAS (outpatient centers)
Georgetown Medical Plaza
Methodist Medical Plaza Eagle Highlands
Methodist Medical Plaza North
Methodist Medical Plaza South

COMPETITORS

Ascension Health
Banner Health
Catholic Health Initiatives
Community Hospital Anderson
Community Hospitals of Indiana
Daviess Community Hospital
Franciscan Alliance
Good Samaritan Hospital (IN)
Henry County Memorial Hospital
MedStar Health
Riverview Hospital
St. Elizabeth Regional Health
St. Vincent Health
Tenet Healthcare
Union Hospital (Indiana)

HISTORICAL FINANCIALS

Company Type: Private

Income Statement FYE: December 31

	REVENUE ($ mil.)	NET INCOME ($ mil.)	NET PROFIT MARGIN	EMPLOYEES
12/12	2,425	762	31.4%	17,242
12/08	1,889	(23)	—	—
12/05	2,478	159	6.4%	—
12/05	2,281	68	3.0%	—
Annual Growth	0.9%	41.0%	—	—

2012 Year-End Financials

Debt ratio: ——
Return on equity: 31.40%
Cash ($ mil.): 472
Current ratio: 1.00
Long-term debt ($ mil.): —
Dividends
Yield: —
Payout: —
Market value ($ mil.): —

INDYNE INC.

InDyne offers out-of-this-world technology expertise. The company provides information technology science and engineering and technical and administrative services primarily to US government agencies including NASA. It develops custom software designs Web sites and builds computer networks. InDyne's science and engineering division designs aerospace systems provides space mission support and crew training and offers structural and fluid analysis. Its technical and administrative services unit handles imagery operations data management media services and operations support. The company's project have included the development of custom database software for the CDC and the Department of Transportation.

Geographic Reach

The company has offices across the US often on or near government facilities. Its locations include Alabama California Florida New Mexico Ohio Virginia and Washington DC.

EXECUTIVES

President CEO, C. Donald Bishop
Director Human Resources, Margaret James
CFO, Robert (Bob) Miller
VP Strategic Programs, Jeff Riemer
VP-Ops, Skip Olson

LOCATIONS

HQ: INDYNE INC.
11800 SUNRISE VALLEY DR # 250, RESTON, VA 20191-5300
Phone: 703-903-6900
Web: WWW.INDYNEINC.COM

PRODUCTS/OPERATIONS

Selected Services

Range Services
Base Operations Maintenance
Security Systems
Communication Services
Information Technology
Multimedia Services

COMPETITORS

Affiliated Computer Services
Alion
CACI International
Computer Sciences Corp.
Dynamics Research
General Dynamics Information Technology
HP Enterprise Services
IBM Global Services
Leidos
Lockheed Martin Information Systems
ManTech
Northrop Grumman Info Systems
Raytheon IIS
SRA International
UNICOM Government
Unisys

HISTORICAL FINANCIALS

Company Type: Private

Income Statement FYE: December 31

	REVENUE ($ mil.)	NET INCOME ($ mil.)	NET PROFIT MARGIN	EMPLOYEES
12/11	240	6	2.8%	1,700
12/10	260	6	2.6%	—
12/09	255	7	3.0%	—
12/08	288	8	3.1%	—
Annual Growth	(5.8%)	(8.9%)	—	—

2011 Year-End Financials

Debt ratio: —
Return on equity: 2.80%
Cash ($ mil.): 3
Current ratio: 0.20
Long-term debt ($ mil.): —
Dividends
Yield: —
Payout: —
Market value ($ mil.): —

INFINITE ENERGY INC.

Infinite wisdom? No. Infinite energy? Yes. Infinite Energy does not provide its customers with the natural high of endorphins or with the latest health diet but with the more prosaic commodity of natural gas. The company supplies natural gas to clients in Florida Georgia and New York. Wholesale customers include municipalities institutions and utilities; Infinite Energy also sells to large and small commercial establishments (including restaurants) and to residential customers.

Former utility energy buyers Darin Cook and Rich Blaser established Infinite Energy in 1994. It started up operations that year in Florida and in Georgia in 1998.

In 2004 the company launched operations in New York.

In 2007 in a innovative marketing move it offered residential customers in New York and New Jersey two month of free gas supply in a bid to attract new customers.

EXECUTIVES

Director Traderoom Operations, Michael (Mike) Jones

LOCATIONS

HQ: INFINITE ENERGY INC.
7001 SW 24TH AVE, GAINESVILLE, FL 32607-3704
Phone: 352-331-1654
Web: WWW.INFINITEENERGY.COM

COMPETITORS

Florida Gas Transmission
National Grid USA
New Jersey Natural Gas
Northeast Utilities
Piedmont Natural Gas
SCANA

HISTORICAL FINANCIALS

Company Type: Private

Income Statement FYE: December 31

	REVENUE ($ mil.)	NET INCOME ($ mil.)	NET PROFIT MARGIN	EMPLOYEES
12/09	477	13	2.7%	250
12/05	583	4	0.8%	—
12/04	474	8	1.8%	—
12/03	335	3	0.9%	—
Annual Growth	6.0%	26.7%	—	—

2009 Year-End Financials

Debt ratio: —
Return on equity: 2.70%
Cash ($ mil.): 12
Current ratio: 0.70
Long-term debt ($ mil.): —
Dividends
Yield: —
Payout: —
Market value ($ mil.): —

INGALLS & SNYDER LLC

LOCATIONS

HQ: INGALLS & SNYDER LLC
1325 AVENUE OF THE AMERIC, NEW YORK, NY 100196074
Phone: 2122697800
Web: WWW.INGALLS.NET

HISTORICAL FINANCIALS

Company Type: Private

Income Statement FYE: September 30

	ASSETS ($ mil.)	NET INCOME ($ mil.)	INCOME AS % OF ASSETS	EMPLOYEES
09/08	57	20	35.3%	80
09/07	73	19	26.5%	—
09/06	64	22	35.4%	—
09/03	48	0	—	—
Annual Growth	3.4%	—	—	—

2008 Year-End Financials

Debt ratio: —
Return on equity: 35.40%
Cash ($ mil.): 12
Current ratio: —
Long-term debt ($ mil.): —
Dividends
Yield: —
Payout: —
Market value ($ mil.): —

INOVA HEALTH SYSTEM

Inova Health Foundation provides financial support and assistance to the Inova Health System which operates a network of not-for-profit community hospitals in northern Virginia. It also supports home health services heart care programs clinical research and trials emergency and urgent care centers family practice locations and rehabilitation centers. To raise funds for the hospital system the foundation organizes special events such as galas golf tournaments and silent auctions. Donors can also make contributions through the Inova website. The foundation took in $15.8 million in contributions in 2012.

EXECUTIVES

CFO, Richard Magenheimer
Chairman, Terry D. McCallister
VP, John Fay
Director Leadership Giving Inova Fair Oaks Hospital, Dayna Kuhar
Director Leadership Giving Inova Loudoun Hospital Foundation, Pam Maroulis
Chairman, Fred Sachs
Senior Director Foundation Services Finance and Gift Administration, Paige Moses
Manager Gift Administration, Sandra White
Development Specialist Gift Administration, Amalia Arbulu
Manager Finance, Barbara Beard
Manager Prospect Research, Leslie Cronen
Senior Director Development Services Gift and Estate Planning, Linda Robertson
Development Specialist Gift and Estate Planning, Patricia Bowen
Director Constituent Relations Constituent Relations, Bonnie Roberts
Director Development Special Events, Kim Perry
Director Development Annual Programs, Tim Cronen
Development Specialist Annual Programs, Alexandra Obrand
Director Leadership Giving Inova Alexandria Hospital Foundation, Mary Myers
Manager Inova Alexandria Hospital Foundation, Lori Powell
Manager Inova Loudoun Hospital Foundation, Ginny Hamson
Executive Director Inova Fairfax Hospital Campus, Judy Bilicki
Development Officer Inova Fairfax Hospital for Children, Kristin O?Brien
Development Specialist Inova Mount Vernon Hospital - Special Foundation Projects, Bonnie Stauber
Director Leadership Giving Nursing Education - Inova VNA Home Health, Maureen Zutz

LOCATIONS

HQ: INOVA HEALTH SYSTEM
8110 GATEHOUSE RD 200E, FALLS CHURCH, VA 22042-1217
Phone: 703-289-2072
Web: WWW.INOVACAREERS.ORG

HISTORICAL FINANCIALS

Company Type: Private

Income Statement FYE: December 31

	REVENUE ($ mil.)	NET INCOME ($ mil.)	NET PROFIT MARGIN	EMPLOYEES
12/08	2,140	147	6.9%	16,000
12/06	1,978	0	0.0%	—
Annual Growth	4.0%	1842.2%	—	—

2008 Year-End Financials

Debt ratio: —
Return on equity: 6.90%
Cash ($ mil.): 292
Current ratio: 0.50
Long-term debt ($ mil.): —
Dividends
Yield: —
Payout: —
Market value ($ mil.): —

INSTITUTE FOR DEFENSE ANALYSES INC

The Institute for Defense Analyses founded in 1947 to provide technical analyses of weapons is a federally funded organization that works for the US government's defense agencies as well as for other government entities. The institute's focus areas include war and defense systems evaluations materials and information technology assessments resource cost and readiness analyses and force and strategy assessments. The Institute for Defense Analyses' Science and Technology Policy Institute analyzes global science and tech trends to help the US government formula policy.

EXECUTIVES

Vice President Finance, Ruth L Greenstein, age 68
President and CEO, David S.C. Chu
Vice President Research And Development, Judith Hautala
Chair, Suzanne H. (Sue) Woolsey, age 73

LOCATIONS

HQ: INSTITUTE FOR DEFENSE ANALYSES INC
4850 MARK CENTER DR, ALEXANDRIA, VA 22311-1882
Phone: 703-845-2000
Web: WWW.IDA.ORG

COMPETITORS

Charles Stark Draper Laboratory
Lawrence Livermore Lab
QinetiQ
Quantum Research
Sandia National Laboratories

HISTORICAL FINANCIALS

Company Type: Private

Income Statement FYE: September 28

	REVENUE ($ mil.)	NET INCOME ($ mil.)	NET PROFIT MARGIN	EMPLOYEES
09/12	221	23	10.5%	1,500
09/11	226	0	0.0%	—
09/10	227	11	5.1%	—
09/09	227	6	2.9%	—
Annual Growth	(0.8%)	52.4%	—	—

2012 Year-End Financials

Debt ratio: —
Return on equity: 10.50%
Cash ($ mil.): 23
Current ratio: 0.90
Long-term debt ($ mil.): —
Dividends
Yield: —
Payout: —
Market value ($ mil.): —

INTELLIGENT SOFTWARE SOLUTIONS INC.

Intelligent Software Solutions is no dummy when it comes to software development and IT systems analysis. The privately-held company develops and integrates custom software used for such applications as data visualization and analysis pattern detection and mission planning for the aerospace defense and maritime industries. It also provides on-site product and development support and training. As a government contractor it serves a range of public sector agencies within the US Department of Defense US Department of Homeland Security and US Air Force. Intelligent Software Solutions corporate clients have included Lockheed Martin Northrop Grumman and Leidos.

With expertise in counter-terrorism homeland security intelligence and special operations the company has about 100 projects under dozens of contracts. In 2012 Intelligent Software Solutions won $120 million in new contracts with the Air Force Research Labs to support several US government clients with data integration and analysis and reporting software used for situational awareness.

The company is expanding its geographic footprint to better serve key clients outside of its home state of Colorado. It opened a new office in New York state the previous year and an office in Florida in 2010 adding to other satellite locations in Massachusetts Virginia and Washington DC. The Rome New York office was established to better support its client there the Air Force Research Labs while its Tampa Florida facility houses part of the company's combat systems division that support the US Central Command (CENTCOM).

Intelligent Software Solutions also does some business overseas. In 2011 the company was awarded a contract with awarded a contract from the UK's Ministry of Defence to develop predictive reasoning and pattern-analysis software for improving the British military's situational awareness in theaters around the world. In late 2012 it acquired the assets of New Jersey-based Xpect Software which offers a complementary product suite (Dfuze) and expands Intelligent Software Solutions into new international markets.

Intelligent Software Solutions was established in 1997 by four former engineers from GTE Government Systems (which was acquired by General Dynamics in 1999).

EXECUTIVES

Co-Founder President of Intelligent Software Solutions, Jay Jesse
Vice President Strategic Initiatives & Advanced Technology, Carl Houghton
Senior Vice President Co-Founder, Dennis Linn
Vice President Federal Systems, Rob Rogers
Vice President of Programs and Operations, David A. Coker
Senior Vice President Co-Founder Chief Architect, Jesse Miller
CFO, Nikki Herman
Vice President Global Enterprise Solutions, Kevin Moffatt
Vice President C2ISR Systems, Marcus Featherston
Vice President Xpect Solutions, Laine Napier

LOCATIONS

HQ: INTELLIGENT SOFTWARE SOLUTIONS INC.
5450 TECH CENTER DR # 400, COLORADO SPRINGS, CO 80919-2339
Phone: 719-452-7000
Web: WWW.ISSINC.COM

COMPETITORS

Affiliated Computer Services
BAE SYSTEMS
Booz Allen
CACI International
CIBER
Camber Corp.
ComGlobal Systems
Computer Sciences Corp.
Computer Technology Associates
General Dynamics Information Technology
Jacobs Engineering
L-3 Communications
Leidos
ManTech
MetroStar Systems
Northrop Grumman
QinetiQ
Raytheon
SRA International
UNICOM Government

HISTORICAL FINANCIALS

Company Type: Private

Income Statement FYE: December 28

	REVENUE ($ mil.)	NET INCOME ($ mil.)	NET PROFIT MARGIN	EMPLOYEES
12/12	195	14	7.2%	650
12/11	167	12	7.5%	—
12/09	121	7	6.2%	—
12/09	78	6	8.0%	—
Annual Growth	35.3%	30.4%	—	—

2012 Year-End Financials

Debt ratio: —
Return on equity: 7.20%
Cash ($ mil.): 3
Current ratio: 1.20
Long-term debt ($ mil.): —
Dividends
Yield: —
Payout: —
Market value ($ mil.): —

INTERBOND CORPORATION OF AMERICA

EXECUTIVES

CFO, Eric Beazley
Chairman, Robert Perlman
President, Michael Perlman
Auditors: KaufmanRossin&Co.

LOCATIONS

HQ: INTERBOND CORPORATION OF AMERICA
3200 SW 42ND ST, FORT LAUDERDALE, FL 333126813
Phone: 9547974000
Web: WWW.PROD.BRANDSMARTUSA.COM

2013 Stores

	No.
Florida	5
Georgia	4
Total	9

PRODUCTS/OPERATIONS

Selected Products

Appliances
Blu-rays & DVDs
Headphones
Home audio
Car audio & GPS
Computers
Fitness
Games
Home security
Mobile phones
Office products
Personal care
Tablets
Toys
TVs
Wellness

Selected Brands

Bose
Dell
Electrolux
Epson
Frigidaire
iRobot
LG
Logitech
Samsung
Sharp
Sony

COMPETITORS

Best Buy
Costco Wholesale
Fry' s Electronics
Home Depot
RadioShack
Sears
Wal-Mart
hhgregg

HISTORICAL FINANCIALS

Company Type: Private

Income Statement FYE: September 24

	REVENUE ($ mil.)	NET INCOME ($ mil.)	NET PROFIT MARGIN	EMPLOYEES
09/11	743	3	0.5%	2,400
09/10	800	7	0.9%	—
09/08	320	0	0.0%	—
Annual Growth	32.3%	2377.1%	—	—

2011 Year-End Financials

Debt ratio: —
Return on equity: 0.50%
Cash ($ mil.): 1
Current ratio: —
Long-term debt ($ mil.): —
Dividends
Yield: —
Payout: —
Market value ($ mil.): —

INTERMOUNTAIN HEALTH CARE INC

If you whoosh down the side of one of Idaho's majestic mountains and take a nasty spill Intermountain Health Care (dba Intermountain Healthcare) will pick you up and put you back together. From air ambulance services to urgent care clinics and general hospitals Intermountain has all the tools to mend skiers (and non-skiers alike) in Utah and southern Idaho. The not-for-profit health system operates 22 hospitals and more than 800 physicians and 185 urgent care clinics as well as home health care agencies and rehabilitation centers. Its hospitals have a combined total of about 2700 licensed beds.

Geographic Reach

Intermountain serves the healthcare needs of Utah and Idaho residents.

Operations

Its hospitals range from general surgical to specialty care including orthopedic and pediatric facilities. Along with the full spectrum of physical health care services Intermountain also offers comprehensive mental health and substance abuse programs for patients of all ages. The organization's spectrum of care includes acute inpatient residential treatment day treatment chemical dependency inpatient/detoxification and intensive outpatient programs. To serve the the region's uninsured and low-income residents Intermountain owns or supports 18 community and school primary care clinics.

The organization conducts cancer research through its partnership with Huntsman Cancer Institute at the University of Utah. The two share data best practices funding and co-conduct clinical trials. They also operate a number of cancer-specific treatment centers including multi-disciplinary tumor-specific clinics designed to provide one-stop service for cancer patients to meet with different cancer specialists on the same day for a more comprehensive treatment plan. Other areas of research include cardiovascular intensive medicine surgical care and behavioral health.

On the physician side the Intermountain Medical Group administers multi-specialty health care services through more than 800 doctors in clinics located throughout the region. The group also operates urgent care clinics under the ExpressCare InstaCare and KidsCare banners.

Entering itself into the "what doesn't Intermountain do?" category the health system also provides health and dental insurance plans through its SelectHealth division. SelectHealth provides coverage for large and small employer groups runs the state Children's Health Insurance Program and administers a high-risk insurance pool for the state of Utah.

In 2012 Intermountain reported 482013 emergency room visits; 140141 acute patient admissions; 41002 inpatient surgeries; and 30873 births. Insurance provider SelectHealth had 600000 members.

Financial Performance

The health care system reported slightly higher revenue in 2012 as it took in a bit more for patient services and spent a bit less on services for patients who were unable to pay. As a non-profit it allocated all those funds by spending a bit more on salaries supplies and funds for future improvements.

Strategy

Intermountain strives to improve clinical quality and establish efficiency enhancements to manage costs.

In 2013 it teamed up with several leading IT companies (including Xi3 Intel Dell and NetApp) to form Intermountain's Healthcare Transformation Lab on the campus of its flagship hospital Intermountain Medical Center in Murray Utah. The lab researches develops and measures new ideas to improve patient care. The same year it worked with GE to established a research center to reduce radiation during tomography procedures.

In 2012 the system opened a new high-tech 327000-square-foot distribution warehouse and office facility in Midvale.

Intermountain has also joined such peers as the Mayo Clinic Cleveland Clinic and others in the High Value Healthcare Collaborative to share information to improve health care manage and save costs and extend best practices out to physicians clinics and hospitals throughout the US. By streamlining its purchasing storage and distribution processes the company was also able to save about $55 million in supply chain costs in 2012.

The company is also collaborating with the Centers for Medicare and Medicaid Services and other health systems to examine ways to improve health care safety and reduce costs by preventing patient injuries and complications.

Company Background

Intermountain was formed in 1975 when the Church of Jesus Christ of Latter Day Saints donated 15 hospitals to local communities.

EXECUTIVES

Vp Of Human Resources, Dan Zuhlke
Svp, Joseph R Horton
Assistant Vice President Financial And Administration System Intermountain Health Care Inc, Craig M Jacobsen
Vice President Corporate Communications Executive, Clark P Jensen
CEO Intermountain Medical Group, Linda C. Leckman
President and CEO SelectHealth, Patricia R. Richards
EVP and CFO, Bert R. Zimmerli
EVP and COO, Laura S. Kaiser
VP and CIO, Marc Probst
Chief Development Officer, David L. Flood
President and CEO, Charles W. Sorenson
VP Supply Chain and Support Services; Chief Purchasing Officer, Brent Johnson
CEO Park City Medical Center, Robert Allen
VP Clinical Operations and Chief Nursing Officer, Kim Henrichsen
CEO Urban North Region and McKay-Dee Hospital Center, Timothy T. Pehrson
Chief Medical Officer, Brent E. Wallace
CEO Primary Children ,Â's Medical Center, Katherine A. (Katy) Welkie
President Weber State University, Ann Millner
Medical Director, Anthony R Wallin
Medical Director, Scott F Hansen
Medical Director, Gregory L Gochnour
Vice President, Richard A Segal
Nurse Manager Of Psych Unit, Peggy Carrico
Director Of Infection Control, Eileen Jackson
Assistant Vice President Of Risk Management Services, Harlan Hammond
Medical Director Primary Children's Medical Center Foundation, Edward B Clark
Vice President Revenue Cycle Organization, Todd Craghead
Medical Director, David Pombo
Asst Vice President Rev Cyc Organizatio, Michael Jex
Vice President Information Technology, Matt Weed
Clinic Manager, Summer Rees
Medical Director, Terry Clemmer
Director Of Radiology Services, Shelli Richardson
Vice President, Rick L Rose
Medical Director, Keith Robbins
Medical Director, Douglas Esplin
Pharmacy Manager, Robb Dengg
Assistant Vice President Communications, Tom Vitelli
Assistant Vice President Quality And Patient Safet, Robin Betts
Vice President, George Hamilton
Medical Director, Eugene Worth
Medical Director, Wesley Valdes
Assistant Vice President, Kathleen Konishi
Vice President Of Engineering, Craig Bedford
Director Of Pharmacy, Alan Lodder
Pharmacy Manager, Brenda Winger
Director Of Pharmacy, Scott Yardley
Vice President Management, Jim Darrington
Director Of Admissions, Louise Green
Medical Director, Frank Thomas
Assistant Vice President Physician Relations And M, Susan Dubois
Medical Director, Craig Marsden
Vp Of Finance, Greg Johnson
Nursing Director, Rebecca Allen
Respiratory Therapy Director, Vrena Flint
Vice President Marketing And Communication, Todd Frehse
Assistant Vice President Clinical, Tammy Madsen
Director Of Respiratory Therapy, Jeffrey Sargent
Vice President Engineering, Tamie Jensen
Medical Librarian, Don McFall
Vice President Information Technology, Karl West
Director Of Nursing, Debbie Shelley
Medical Director, Frank Yanowitz
Pharmacy Manager, Tom Shelley
Pharmd, Greg Myers
Vice Chairman, Bruce T. Reese
Chairman, A. Scott Anderson
Secretary, Heidi Rasmussen

LOCATIONS

HQ: INTERMOUNTAIN HEALTH CARE INC
36 S STATE ST STE 2300, SALT LAKE CITY, UT 84111-1471
Phone: 801-442-2000
Web: WWW.INTERMOUNTAINHEALTHCARE.ORG

PRODUCTS/OPERATIONS

Selected Hospitals

Alta View Hospital (Sandy UT)
American Fork Hospital (Utah)
Bear River Valley Hospital (Tremonton UT)
Cassia Regional Medical Center (Burley ID)
Delta Community Medical Center (Utah)
Dixie Regional Medical Center (St. George UT)
Fillmore Community Medical Center (Utah)
Garfield Memorial Hospital (Panguitch UT)
Heber Valley Medical Center (Heber City UT)
Intermountain Medical Center (Murray UT)
LDS Hospital (Salt Lake City)
Logan Regional Hospital (Orem UT)
McKay-Dee Hospital Center (Ogden UT)
  McKay-Dee Behavioral Health Institute
Orem Community Hospital (Utah)
Park City Medical Center (Park City UT)
Primary Children' s Medical Center (Salt Lake City)
Riverton Hospital (Riverton UT)
Sanpete Valley Hospital (Mt. Pleasant UT)
Sevier Valley Hospital (Richfield UT)
TOSH - The Orthopedic Specialty Hospital (Murray UT)
Utah Valley Regional Medical Center (Provo UT)
Valley View Medical Center (Cedar City UT)

Selected Other Facilities

Northern Idaho and Utah
- Clinics
  - Bear River Clinic
  - Budge Clinic
  - Canyon View Orthopedics & Associates
  - Isom Plastic Surgery
  - Logan Clinic
  - South Cache Valley Clinic
  - Summit Clinic
- Home Health Hospice and Home Medical Equipment
  - Cassia
  - Logan
  - Tremonton
- InstaCare and KidsCare
  - Logan InstaCare
- WorkMed
  - Burley
  - Logan
  - Tremonton

Davis - Weber
- Clinics
  - Bountiful Clinic
  - Calton/Harrison Orthopedic Clinic
  - Endocrine Diabetes
  - Herefordshire Clinic
  - Layton Clinic
  - McKay-Dee Cardiology Clinic
  - McKay-Dee Dermatology & Plastic Surgery
  - McKay-Dee ENT Clinic
  - McKay-Dee Foot and Ankle Clinic
  - McKay-Dee Internal Medicine Clinic
  - McKay-Dee Rheumatology Clinic
  - McKay-Dee Urogynecology Clinic
  - North Ogden Clinic
  - Northern Utah Pediatrics
  - Northern Utah Surgeons
  - Ogden Cardiovascular Associates
  - South Ogden Clinic
  - Sports Medicine Specialists - Bountiful
  - Summit Orthopedics
  - Syracuse Clinic
  - Wasatch OB/GYN
- Home Health Hospice and Home Medical Equipment
  - Ogden
- InstaCare and KidsCare
  - Bountiful InstaCare
  - Bountiful KidsCare
  - Herefordshire InstaCare
  - Layton InstaCare
  - Layton KidsCare
  - North Ogden InstaCare
  - North Ogden KidsCare
  - South Ogden InstaCare
  - Syracuse InstaCare
- ExpressCare
  - Smith's Food & Drug - Farmington
- WorkMed
  - Layton
  - Ogden

Greater Salt Lake Valley
- Clinics
  - Alta View Specialty Clinic

Avenues Specialty Clinic
Bryner Clinic
Central Valley ENT Head & Neck Surgery
Central Valley Thyroid & Parathyroid Clinic
Cottonwood Endocrine & Diabetes Center
Cottonwood Family Practice
Cottonwood Internal Medicine
Gorang Family Practice
Heart and Lung Surgical Associates
Hillcrest Pediatrics
Holladay Clinic
Holladay Pediatrics
Holladay Pediatrics - North
Internal Medicine Associates
Medical Tower Family Practice
Memorial Clinic
Mountain View Pediatrics
Noyes Surgical Oncology
Obstetrics & Gynecology Specialists
Orthopedic Specialty Group Clinics
Park City Specialty Clinic
Plastic Surgery Center
Pulmonology Clinic
Salt Lake Clinic
Sandy Clinic
Sandy OB/GYN
South Jordan Clinic
South Sandy Clinic
Southridge Clinic
Southridge OB/GYN
Southridge Pediatrics
Surgical Specialists
Taylorsville Clinic
Utah Heart Clinic
Urological Institute Clinics
West Jordan Clinic
Home Health Hospice and Home Medical Equipment
Salt Lake City
InstaCare and KidsCare
Holladay InstaCare
Memorial InstaCare
Memorial KidsCare
Mountain View Pediatrics KidsCare
Murray InstaCare
Sandy InstaCare
Southridge InstaCare
Southridge KidsCare
Taylorsville InstaCare
Taylorsville KidsCare
West Jordan InstaCare
West Jordan KidsCare
ExpressCare
Smith's Food & Drug - Draper
Smith's Food & Drug - Salt Lake City
WorkMed
Murray
Salt Lake City
Greater Utah Valley
Clinics
American Fork Internal Medicine & Dermatology
American Fork Pulmonary Clinic
American Fork Surgical Associates
Central Orem Clinic
Heber Valley Clinic
Highland Clinic
Legacy OB/GYN Clinic
North Canyon Family Practice
North Orem Clinic
North Valley Pediatrics
Physical Medicine & Rehabilitation
Provo Neurological Clinic
Saratoga Springs Clinic
Springville Clinic
Utah Valley Ear Nose & Throat
Utah Valley Heart & Lung Surgical Associates
Utah Valley Internal Medicine Clinic
Utah Valley Orthopaedics & Sports Medicine
Utah Valley Pediatric Specialists
Utah Valley Pulmonary Clinic
Utah Valley Vein Clinic
Home Health Hospice and Home Medical Equipment
Heber City
Orem
Urgent Care
Highland InstaCare
North Orem InstaCare
Provo InstaCare
Saratoga Springs InstaCare
Springville InstaCare
WorkMed
Orem
Springville
Central Utah
Clinics
Ephraim Clinic
Fillmore Clinic
Manti Family Clinic
Moroni Clinic
Mt. Pleasant Clinic
North Sevier Medical Clinic
Richfield Family Practice
Sevier Valley Family Practice
Home Health Hospice and Home Medical Equipment
Delta
Fillmore
Mt. Pleasant
Richfield
WorkMed
Moroni
Mt. Pleasant
Southern Utah
Clinics
Canyon View Family Practice
Cardiovascular & Thoracic Surgery St. George
Cedar City Clinic
Dixie Plastic & Reconstructive Surgery
Hurricane Valley Clinic
Pulmonary Medicine Clinic - St. George
Redrock Pediatrics
Rim Rock Orthopaedics & Sports Medicine
River Road Family Practice
River Road Internal Medicine
Southern Utah Behavioral Health
Southern Utah Surgical Associates
Southwest Cardiology - St. George
Southwest Neurology Associates
Southwest Regional Cancer Clinic
Southwest Rheumatology Associates
Southwest Spine & Pain Center
Sunset Clinic
Valley View Heart Clinic
Women's Health Specialists
Zion Orthopaedics & Sports Medicine
Home Health Hospice and Home Medical Equipment
Cedar City
St. George
InstaCare and KidsCare
Cedar City InstaCare
Hurricane Valley InstaCare
River Road InstaCare
Sunset InstaCare
WorkMed
Cedar City
St. George

COMPETITORS

CHRISTUS Health
HCA
HealthSouth
Iasis Healthcare
LifePoint Hospitals
Ogden Regional Medical Center
Regence BlueCross BlueShield of Utah
St. Mark's
University of Utah Hospitals & Clinics

HISTORICAL FINANCIALS

Company Type: Private

Income Statement FYE: December 31

	REVENUE ($ mil.)	NET INCOME ($ mil.)	NET PROFIT MARGIN	EMPLOYEES
12/12	4,700	546	11.6%	23,000
12/11	4,049	6	0.2%	—
12/10	4,381	716	16.3%	—
12/09	3,568	1,032	28.9%	—
Annual Growth	9.6%	(19.1%)	—	—

2012 Year-End Financials

Debt ratio: —
Return on equity: 11.60%
Cash ($ mil.): 463
Current ratio: 0.70
Long-term debt ($ mil.): —
Dividends
Yield: —
Payout: —
Market value ($ mil.): —

INTERMOUNTAIN RURAL ELECTRIC ASSOCIATION

LOCATIONS

HQ: INTERMOUNTAIN RURAL ELECTRIC ASSOCIATION
5496 N US HIGHWAY 85, SEDALIA, CO 801358600
Phone: 3036883100
Web: WWW.INTERMOUNTAIN-REA.COM

HISTORICAL FINANCIALS

Company Type: Private

Income Statement FYE: December 31

	REVENUE ($ mil.)	NET INCOME ($ mil.)	NET PROFIT MARGIN	EMPLOYEES
12/13	279	0	—	176
12/09	199	2	1.4%	—
12/08	212	0	—	—
12/04	152	0	—	—
Annual Growth	7.0%	—	—	—

2013 Year-End Financials

Debt ratio: —
Return on equity: —
Cash ($ mil.): 36
Current ratio: 4.20
Long-term debt ($ mil.): —
Dividends
Yield: —
Payout: —
Market value ($ mil.): —

INTERNATIONAL BROTHERHOOD OF TEAMSTERS

One of the largest and best-known labor unions in the US the International Brotherhood of Teamsters has 1.4 million members. The Teamsters represents workers in some 20 industry sectors including airlines freight parcel delivery industrial trades and public service. More than 200000 of the union's members are employees of package delivery giant United Parcel Service. Besides negotiating labor contracts with employers on behalf of its members the union oversees pension funds and serves as an advocate in legislative and regulatory arenas. The union and its affiliates have about 1900 local chapters in the US and Canada including about 475 Teamsters locals. The Teamsters union was founded in 1903.

Teamsters chief James P. Hoffa (son of assumed-dead union leader Jimmy Hoffa) is working to improve the union's image after implementing ethics policies aimed at rooting out internal corruption and ties to organized crime. Hoffa first elected in 1998 wants the Teamsters to police themselves and to put an end to the government supervision under which the union has operated since 1989.

The Teamsters have packed up and moved out from under the AFL-CIO umbrella and joined fellow unions Unite Here (textile hotel and restaurant workers) Service Employees International (SEIU) United Food and Commercial Workers and others in the rival Change to Win Coalition. The group hopes to reverse the decline of labor jobs and union membership in the US by focusing its time and money on recruiting rather than on participating in political campaigns. Other key issues for Change to Win include health care immigration and retirement security.

HISTORY

Two rival team-driver unions the Drivers International Union and the Teamsters National Union merged to form the International Brotherhood of Teamsters in 1903. Led by Cornelius Shea the Teamsters established headquarters in Indianapolis. Daniel Tobin (president for 45 years starting in 1907) demanded that union locals obtain executive approval before striking. Membership expanded from the team-driver base prompting the union to add Chauffeurs Stablemen and Helpers to its name (1909).

Following the first transcontinental delivery by motor truck (1912) the Teamster deliverymen traded their horses for trucks. The union then recruited food processing brewery and farm workers among others to augment Teamster effectiveness during strikes. It joined the American Federation of Labor in 1920.

Until the Depression the Teamsters was still a small union of predominantly urban deliverymen. Then Farrell Dobbs a Trotskyite Teamster from Minneapolis organized the famous Minneapolis strikes in 1934 to protest local management's refusal to allow the workers to unionize. Workers clashed with police and National Guard units for 11 days before management acceded to the workers' demands. The strikes demonstrated the potential strength of unions and Teamsters membership swelled. Although union power ebbed during WWII the union continued to grow. It moved its headquarters to Washington DC in 1953.

The AFL-CIO expelled the Teamsters in 1957 when Teamster ties to the mob became public during a US Senate investigation. New Teamsters boss Jimmy Hoffa eluded indictment and took advantage of America's growing dependence on trucking to negotiate the powerful National Master Freight Agreement (1964). Hoffa also organized industrial workers. He used a union pension fund to make mob-connected loans and was later convicted of jury tampering and sent to prison. In 1975 four years after his release Hoffa vanished without a trace and is believed to have been the victim of a Mafia hit.

The Teamsters rejoined the AFL-CIO in 1987 and the following year settled a racketeering lawsuit filed by the US Justice Department by allowing government appointees to discipline corrupt union leaders help run the union and oversee its elections. The election of self-styled reformer Ronald Carey in 1991 (he received 49% of the vote) seemed to portend real changes for the union; each of his six predecessors had been accused of or imprisoned for criminal activities. However membership dropped by 40000 in both 1991 and 1992.

Carey won re-election as union president in 1996 over rival and son of former boss Jimmy Hoffa James P. Hoffa (whom Carey accused of having ties to organized crime). A 15-day strike by the Teamsters' UPS employees in 1997 led to the delivery company's agreement to combine part-time jobs into 10000 new full-time positions. That year Carey's re-election was overturned amid a campaign finance investigation that netted guilty pleas from three Carey associates and the Teamsters leader was disqualified from running for re-election in 1998. Carey was officially expelled from the Teamsters by the federal government and Hoffa won the 1998 election over Tom Leedham (who was backed by the union's reform wing).

Promising to fight corruption Hoffa hired former federal prosecutor Edwin Stier and several former FBI agents to help him operate Project RISE (respect integrity strength and ethics) a new in-house anti-corruption program. In 2002 the union began lobbying against plans to allow Mexican trucking companies to transport goods across the US.

In 2005 the Teamsters joined four other unions representing more than 5 million workers to call for sweeping reform in the AFL-CIO. They released a proposal to revitalize the labor movement by focusing on growth and empowerment. When AFL-CIO president John Sweeney failed to heed their calls the Teamsters joined the Service Employees International Union in boycotting the umbrella group's annual convention and joining the Change to Win Coalition.

EXECUTIVES

Vice President, James P Hoffa
Vp Eastern Region, John F Murphy
Vp Central Region, Gordon Sweeton
General Secretary and Treasurer, C. Thomas (Tom) Keegel
Vp At-large, Randy Cammack
VP Canada; President Teamsters Canada, Robert Bouvier
VP At-Large Western Region, Fred Potter
Chairman of the Board Chief Executive Officer Chairman, Bryan Bedford
Vp Operations Production Mfg, Iain Gold
Corporate Vice President Human Resources, Joena Berrios

Central Region Vice President, Cheryl Johnson
Vice President Eastern Region, Richard Hall
Vice President Information Technology, Myron Sharp
Vice President Business Representative, Don Givens
Vice President Operations, Sydney Goldstein
Vice President Canada, Garnet Zimmerman
Vice President Local 697, David Yoders
Legal Secretary, Timika Long
Vice President Business Representative, Hernan Gomez
Secretary & Treasurer, Ken Hall
General Secretary and Treasurer, C. Thomas (Tom) Keegel
Secretary, Galen Munroe
Secretary Treasurer, Mark Harrington
Secretary Treasurer, Robert Morales
Secretary, Sue Fickas
Secretary Treasurer, Mike Goebel

LOCATIONS

HQ: INTERNATIONAL BROTHERHOOD OF TEAMSTERS
25 LOUISIANA AVE NW, WASHINGTON, DC 20001-2130
Phone: 202-624-6800
Web: WWW.TEAMSTER.ORG

PRODUCTS/OPERATIONS

Trade Divisions
Airline
Bakery and Laundry
Brewery and Soft Drink
Building Material and Constructi
Carhaul
Dairy
Food Processing
Freight
Graphic Communicat
Industrial Trades
Motion Picture and Theatrical Trade
Newspaper Magazine and Electronic Media
Parcel and Small Package
Port
Public Services
Rail
Solid Waste
Tankhaul
Trade Show and Convention Centers
Warehouse

HISTORICAL FINANCIALS

Company Type: Private

Income Statement FYE: December 31

	REVENUE ($ mil.)	NET INCOME ($ mil.)	NET PROFIT MARGIN	EMPLOYEES
12/11	179	30	16.9%	649
12/09	172	12	7.2%	—
12/08	155	(22)	—	—
12/07	186	24	13.2%	—
Annual Growth	(1.0%)	5.3%	—	—

2011 Year-End Financials

Debt ratio: —
Return on equity: 16.90%
Cash ($ mil.): 28
Current ratio: 0.70
Long-term debt ($ mil.): —
Dividends
Yield: —
Payout: —
Market value ($ mil.): —

ITA GROUP INC

ITA Group (doing business as ITAGroup) bets it can make your company better. Specializing in performance marketing ITAGroup (standing for "Ideas to Action") builds and manages programs that help clients increase sales and customer satisfaction through incentives and training. The company's services include research and program design administration fulfillment and measurement for employee recognition and rewards programs business-to-business loyalty programs and sales incentive programs. ITAGroup also provides business meeting and event planning services.

Geographic Reach

ITAGroup is based in West Des Moines Iowa with a dozen sales offices located across the US in Boca Raton Chicago Dallas Detroit Indianapolis Los Angeles Minneapolis Philadelphia San Francisco and the greater New York City area.

Strategy

ITAGroup's Emerging Markets Division consults with companies on corporate recognition and incentive programs. The unit is focused specifically on helping middle market businesses effectively use incentive and recognition programs to create loyalty among employees and customers.

Sales and Marketing

ITAGroup offers a specially designed app for companies using Salesforce CRM.

Company Background

The company was originally founded in 1963.

EXECUTIVES

President and CEO, Thomas J. Mahoney Jr.
Senior Vice President Chief Financial Officer, Richard Rue
SVP and CFO, Brent VanderWaal
Senior Vice President - Sales, Doug Stine
VP and CIO, John Rose
Senior Vice President Event Management, Mary Z. Bussone
Vice President Marketing Communications Group and Individual Awards, Kent Schlawin

LOCATIONS

HQ: ITA GROUP INC
4800 WESTOWN PKWY STE 300, WEST DES MOINES, IA 50266-6719
Phone: 515-326-3400
Web: WWW.ITAGROUP.COM

COMPETITORS

All Star Incentive Marketing
Marketing Innovators
Motivcom

Alliance Data Systems
Korman Marketing Group
LoyaltyOne
Loyaltyworks
Maritz Loyalty & Motivation
Pitney Bowes Marketing Solutions
Points International
Schoeneckers
TharpeRobbins

HISTORICAL FINANCIALS

Company Type: Private

Income Statement FYE: August 31

	REVENUE ($ mil.)	NET INCOME ($ mil.)	NET PROFIT MARGIN	EMPLOYEES
08/12	288	0	—	500
08/11	233	0	—	—
08/10	0	0	—	—
08/09	0	0	—	—
Annual Growth	—	—	—	—

2012 Year-End Financials

Debt ratio: —
Return on equity: —
Cash ($ mil.): 45
Current ratio: 1.00
Long-term debt ($ mil.): —
Dividends
Yield: —
Payout: —
Market value ($ mil.): —

J M SMITH CORPORATION

EXECUTIVES

Chairman and CEO, William (Bill) Cobb
CFO, James C. Wilson Jr.

LOCATIONS

HQ: J M SMITH CORPORATION
101 W SAINT JOHN ST # 305, SPARTANBURG, SC 293065179
Phone: 8645429419
Web: WWW.QS1.COM

Selected Office Locations

Altamonte Springs FL
Brandon MS
Columbia SC
Dallas TX
Fairmont WV
Gray ME
Hermitage PA
Houston TX
Indianapolis IN
Lexington KY
Mechanicsburg PA
Miami FL
Morrisville GA
Paragould AR
Perry GA
Pleasant Hill MO
Richmond VA
Seattle WA
Spartanburg SC
St. Paul MN
Sturbridge MA
Valdosta GA
Valencia CA
Wake Forest NC

PRODUCTS/OPERATIONS

Selected Divisions

Integral Solutions Group
Norgenix Pharmaceuticals
QS/1
RxMedic
Smith Drug Company
Smith Premier Services

COMPETITORS

AmerisourceBergen
CVS Caremark
Cardinal Health
Express Scripts
Fiserv
H. D. Smith Wholesale Drug
HP Enterprise Services
Kinray
McKesson
PharMerica

HISTORICAL FINANCIALS

Company Type: Private

Income Statement FYE: February 28

	REVENUE ($ mil.)	NET INCOME ($ mil.)	NET PROFIT MARGIN	EMPLOYEES
02/14	2,370	38	1.6%	1,050
02/13	2,362	26	1.1%	—
02/12	2,479	25	1.0%	—
02/11	2,437	0	—	—
Annual Growth	(0.9%)	—	—	—

2014 Year-End Financials

Debt ratio: —
Return on equity: 1.60%
Cash ($ mil.): 153
Current ratio: 1.20
Long-term debt ($ mil.): —
Dividends
Yield: —
Payout: —
Market value ($ mil.): —

J. D. STREETT & COMPANY INC.

EXECUTIVES

Sales Manager, Chuck Whelehon
Sales Manager Unbranded Fuel Sales Rep, Tom Irwin
Operations General Manager, William Starbuck
Auditors: BKDLLP

LOCATIONS

HQ: J. D. STREETT & COMPANY INC.
144 WELDON PKWY, MARYLAND HEIGHTS, MO 630433100
Phone: 3144326600
Web: WWW.JDSTREETT.COM

COMPETITORS

BP Lubricants USA
Fuchs Lubricants
Lubrizol
PetroLiance
U.S. Venture
Vesco Oil

HISTORICAL FINANCIALS

Company Type: Private

Income Statement FYE: December 31

	REVENUE ($ mil.)	NET INCOME ($ mil.)	NET PROFIT MARGIN	EMPLOYEES
12/13	316	5	1.8%	240
12/12	342	(11)	—	—
12/11	366	3	0.8%	—
12/10	313	0	—	—
Annual Growth	0.3%	—	—	—

2013 Year-End Financials

Debt ratio: —
Return on equity: 1.80%
Cash ($ mil.): 1
Current ratio: 0.80
Long-term debt ($ mil.): —
Dividends
Yield: —
Payout: —
Market value ($ mil.): —

J. F. WHITE CONTRACTING COMPANY

From excavating the foundation for the Harvard Business School to working on Boston's Big Dig project J.F. White Contracting has been a key player in heavy civil construction in New England for over 80 years. The group has civil design/build mechanical electrical and fiber optic/telecom divisions to provide a large range of engineering construction infrastructure and equipment and wiring installation services. J.F. White also has a diving division (marine construction) to complement its heavy civil construction operations. The company was founded in 1924 by Joseph F. White Sr.

EXECUTIVES

Evp And Chief Engineer, Kevin K Egan
Vice President Operations Electrical Division, James Fratto
Vice President Management Information, Steve Wuerfl

LOCATIONS

HQ: J. F. WHITE CONTRACTING COMPANY
10 BURR ST, FRAMINGHAM, MA 01701-4692
Phone: 508-879-4700
Web: WWW.JFWHITE.COM

COMPETITORS

Commodore Builders
Fluor
Gilbane
Granite Construction
Lane Construction
Skanska USA Civil
The Middlesex Corporation
Tutor Perini
Wayne J. Griffin Electric

HISTORICAL FINANCIALS

Company Type: Private

Income Statement FYE: September 30

	REVENUE ($ mil.)	NET INCOME ($ mil.)	NET PROFIT MARGIN	EMPLOYEES
09/12	271	0	—	400
09/11	374	0	—	—
09/09	251	0	—	—
09/08	0	0	—	—
Annual Growth	—	—	—	—

2012 Year-End Financials

Debt ratio: —
Return on equity: —
Cash ($ mil.): 22
Current ratio: 0.90
Long-term debt ($ mil.): —
Dividends
Yield: —
Payout: —
Market value ($ mil.): —

J. H. FINDORFF & SON INC.

EXECUTIVES

Chairman, Curt Hastings
VP Finance and CFO, Daniel L. (Dan) Petersen
EVP, Dave Beck-Engel
VP Operations, Mike Dillis

VP Administration, Tim Stadelman
Owner, Wayne Dishaw
President CEO, William T. Montei
Vice President Business Development, Jeffrey A. Tubbs
Vice President Dan Basile Business Development, Jim Yehle
Auditors: McGladreyLLP

LOCATIONS

HQ: J. H. FINDORFF & SON INC.
300 S BEDFORD ST, MADISON, WI 537033622
Phone: 6082575321
Web: WWW.FINDORFF.COM

PRODUCTS/OPERATIONS

Selected Services

Preconstruction
Construction management
General contracting
Design/Build
Self-performed trades
Special projects
Building information modeling

COMPETITORS

Boldt
C. G. Schmidt
C.D. Smith
Hunt Construction
Hunzinger Construction
Market & Johnson
Miron Construction
Walsh Group
Weis Builders

HISTORICAL FINANCIALS

Company Type: Private

Income Statement FYE: September 30

	REVENUE ($ mil.)	NET INCOME ($ mil.)	NET PROFIT MARGIN	EMPLOYEES
09/12	320	4	1.3%	500
09/11	209	0	0.1%	—
09/08	322	3	1.2%	—
09/06	248	0	—	—
Annual Growth	4.4%	—	—	—

2012 Year-End Financials

Debt ratio: —
Return on equity: 1.30%
Cash ($ mil.): 74
Current ratio: 1.20
Long-term debt ($ mil.): —
Dividends
Yield: —
Payout: —
Market value ($ mil.): —

J.D. ABRAMS L.P.

EXECUTIVES

Chairman President and CEO, Jon F. Abrams
VP Operations, Brad Everett
VP Contract Administration, Barry Rollman
Chief Estimator, Martin Poduska
CFO, Kelly Gallagher
VP Human Resources and Safety, Dean Bernal
VP Project Development and Director Strategic Initiative, William G. (Bill) Burnett
Controller, Ron Konkol
SVP; Area Manager Dallas, C. P. (Pat) Worrell
President Austin Prestress, Jim Abrams Jr.
Manager Austin Prestressed, Nick Lujan
Equipment Supervisor Transmountain Equipment, Don Mouser
Area Manager Houston, William G. (Bill) Duguay
Special Project Manager, William (Bill) Mahrer
Manager El Paso, Alfonso (Al) Fernandez
Director of Human Resources, Sandy Lindberg

LOCATIONS

HQ: J.D. ABRAMS L.P.
111 CONGRESS AVE STE 2400, AUSTIN, TX 787014298
Phone: 5122433317
Web: WWW.JDABRAMS.COM

COMPETITORS

C.F. Jordan
Holloman
Sterling Construction
Zack Burkett

HISTORICAL FINANCIALS

Company Type: Private

Income Statement FYE: December 31

	REVENUE ($ mil.)	NET INCOME ($ mil.)	NET PROFIT MARGIN	EMPLOYEES
12/13	155	(2)	—	750
12/12	176	(2)	—	—
12/09	307	15	4.9%	—
12/08	42	0	—	—
Annual Growth	29.3%	—	—	—

2013 Year-End Financials

Debt ratio: —
Return on equity: (-1.70%)
Cash ($ mil.): 34
Current ratio: 1.70
Long-term debt ($ mil.): —
Dividends
Yield: —
Payout: —
Market value ($ mil.): —

J.H. WILLIAMS OIL COMPANY INC.

LOCATIONS

HQ: J.H. WILLIAMS OIL COMPANY INC.
1237 E TWIGGS ST, TAMPA, FL 336023139
Phone: 8132287776
Web: WWW.JHWOIL.COM

HISTORICAL FINANCIALS

Company Type: Private

Income Statement FYE: December 31

	REVENUE ($ mil.)	NET INCOME ($ mil.)	NET PROFIT MARGIN	EMPLOYEES
12/13	395	0	0.1%	35
12/12	382	(0)	—	—
12/11	355	(0)	—	—
12/10	278	0	—	—
Annual Growth	12.4%	—	—	—

2013 Year-End Financials

Debt ratio: —
Return on equity: 0.10%
Cash ($ mil.): 0
Current ratio: 0.50
Long-term debt ($ mil.): —
Dividends
Yield: —
Payout: —
Market value ($ mil.): —

JACKSON ELECTRIC MEMBERSHIP CORPORATION

Jackson EMC distributes electricity to more than 197800 individual customers (more than 210200 meters) in 10 counties around Atlanta and in northeastern Georgia. The majority of customers are residential with commercial and industrial customers accounting for 42% of fiscal year 2013 revenues. One of the largest nonprofit power cooperatives in the US and the largest electric cooperative in Georgia Jackson EMC is owned by its members. The cooperative's generation and transmission partners include Oglethorpe Power Corp. Georgia Systems Operation and Georgia Transmission Corp.

Operations

Jackson EMC operates 86 substations and more than 13550 miles of power line.

Financial Performance

Normal 0 false false false EN-US X-NONE X-NONE

/* Style Definitions */ table.MsoNormalTable {mso-style-name:"Table Normal"; mso-tstyle-rowband-size:0; mso-tstyle-colband-size:0; mso-style-noshow:yes; mso-style-priority:99; mso-style-parent:""; mso-padding-alt:0in 5.4pt 0in 5.4pt; mso-para-margin-top:0in; mso-para-margin-right:0in; mso-para-margin-bottom:10.0pt; mso-para-margin-left:0in; line-height:115%; mso-pagination:widow-orphan; font-size:11.0pt; font-family:"Calibri""sans-serif"; mso-ascii-font-family:Calibri; mso-ascii-theme-font:minor-latin; mso-hansi-font-family:Calibri; mso-hansi-theme-font:minor-latin;}

Normal 0 false false false EN-US X-NONE X-NONE

/* Style Definitions */ table.MsoNormalTable {mso-style-name:"Table Normal"; mso-tstyle-rowband-size:0; mso-tstyle-colband-size:0; mso-style-noshow:yes; mso-style-priority:99; mso-style-parent:""; mso-padding-alt:0in 5.4pt 0in 5.4pt; mso-para-margin-top:0in; mso-para-margin-right:0in; mso-para-margin-bottom:10.0pt; mso-para-margin-left:0in; line-height:115%; mso-pagination:widow-orphan; font-size:11.0pt; font-family:"Calibri""sans-serif"; mso-ascii-font-family:Calibri; mso-ascii-theme-font:minor-latin; mso-hansi-font-family:Calibri; mso-hansi-theme-font:minor-latin;}In fiscal 2013 the coop reported a revenue increased of 1%. Net income declined slightly by 0.3%. That year the non-profit coop returned $5.5 million in margin refunds to nearly 201000 members.

Strategy

Among other initiatives Jackson EMC is promoting conservation and green energy options as a way to slow energy growth and reduce greenhouse gas emissions. Initiatives include advocating the use of more efficient light bulbs and the widespread use of solar panels for power generation.

Ownership

The cooperative is owned by its members.

Company Background

Although the county of Jackson is named after a Georgia statesman from the Revolutionary War era Jackson Electric Membership Corporation (Jackson EMC) can trace its roots more directly to US president Franklin Roosevelt whose frequent trips to Warm Springs alerted him to the shortage of affordable electric power outside of major cities.

Jackson EMC was founded in 1938 as part of the Roosevelt government's national rural electrification drive.

EXECUTIVES

Controller And Vice President, Bob Hill
Auditors: McNairMcLemoreMiddlebrooks&Co.LLP

LOCATIONS

HQ: JACKSON ELECTRIC MEMBERSHIP CORPORATION
850 COMMERCE RD, JEFFERSON, GA 305493329
Phone: 7063675281
Web: WWW.JACKSONEMC.COM

PRODUCTS/OPERATIONS

2013 Sales

% of total	
Residential	58
Commercial/industrial	42
Total	**100**

HISTORICAL FINANCIALS

Company Type: Private

Income Statement FYE: December 31

	REVENUE ($ mil.)	NET INCOME ($ mil.)	NET PROFIT MARGIN	EMPLOYEES
12/13*	472	0	—	445
05/13	475	21	4.6%	—
05/12	472	21	4.6%	—
05/11	462	0	—	—
Annual Growth	0.7%	—	—	—

*Fiscal year change

2013 Year-End Financials

Debt ratio: —
Return on equity: —
Cash ($ mil.): 57
Current ratio: 1.30
Long-term debt ($ mil.): —
Dividends
Yield: —
Payout: —
Market value ($ mil.): —

JACKSON ENERGY AUTHORITY

Jackson Energy Authority has the power and the authority to provide for all of Jackson Tennessee's energy needs. The municipal utility distributes electricity natural gas and water and provides wastewater services to about 40000 residential commercial and industrial customers in Jackson and surrounding areas. Jackson Energy also sells propane and offers broadband telecommunications services (cable Internet and telephone). Other services provided by Jackson Energy Authority include the sale of outdoor security lights surge protection systems gas grills and decorative lights.

As part of its strategy to reduce carbon emission conserve energy and help its customers cut costs Jackson Energy Authority's Wise Energy program provides practical energy saving advice to gas power and water users.

The company was formed by the City of Jackson in 1959 to combine its three separate utilities (natural gas electricity and water/wastewater) under one utility operation. A five-member Board of Directors appointed by the Mayor and City Council of Jackson governs Jackson Energy Authority.

EXECUTIVES

Svp Water And Wastewater Division, Steve Raper
Vice President Information Systems, George Flew
Vp Customer Service, Rowland Fisher
Senior Vice President, Tommy Nanney
Vice President Operations, David Hoffman
Vice President Of Information Technology, Michael Baughn

LOCATIONS

HQ: JACKSON ENERGY AUTHORITY
119 E COLLEGE ST, JACKSON, TN 38301-6201
Phone: 731-422-7500
Web: WWW.JAXENERGY.COM

HISTORICAL FINANCIALS

Company Type: Private

Income Statement FYE: December 31

	REVENUE ($ mil.)	NET INCOME ($ mil.)	NET PROFIT MARGIN	EMPLOYEES
12/11*	243	22	9.4%	425
06/10	218	10	5.0%	—
06/09	237	4	1.8%	—
06/08	210	9	4.4%	—
Annual Growth	3.7%	25.4%	—	—

*Fiscal year change

2011 Year-End Financials

Debt ratio: —
Return on equity: 9.40%
Cash ($ mil.): 49
Current ratio: 2.20
Long-term debt ($ mil.): —
Dividends
Yield: —
Payout: —
Market value ($ mil.): —

JACO OIL COMPANY

Jaco Oil Company is jockeying for its piece of the convenience store pie. The company's Fastrip Food Stores subsidiary operates more than 50 convenience stores and gas stations primarily in and around Bakersfield California but also in Arizona. In addition to traditional convenience store fare which includes coffee milk beer snacks tobacco and the like the Fastrip chain offers a full range of grocery items in-store financial service centers which provide check cashing payday loans wire transfer services via The Western Union Company and other services at many locations. Jaco Oil Company was founded in 1970.

Geographic Reach

Jaco Oil operates nearly 50 stores in Bakersfield and Kern counties as well as Fresno Sacramento and the Chico area. It also has four stores in Arizona located in Bullhead Casa Grande and Nogales.

Strategy

Fastrip seeks to distinguish itself from other convenience store chains by stocking a complete assortment of grocery items including such staples as sugar flour salt cake mix and even green beans. The chain bills itself as a Mini Grocery Store a strategy that other retailers including Dollar General and drugstore-giant Walgreen have adopted.

EXECUTIVES

Vp Operations, Lee Jamieson

LOCATIONS

HQ: JACO OIL COMPANY
3101 STATE RD, BAKERSFIELD, CA 93308-4931
Phone: 661-393-7000
Web: WWW.FASTRIP.COM

PRODUCTS/OPERATIONS

2012 Stores

	No.
California	49
Arizona	4
Total	**53**

COMPETITORS

7-Eleven
Chevron
Couche-Tard
Dollar General
Exxon Mobil
Ralphs Grocery
Stater Bros.
Vons
Walgreen

HISTORICAL FINANCIALS

Company Type: Private

Income Statement FYE: December 31

	REVENUE ($ mil.)	NET INCOME ($ mil.)	NET PROFIT MARGIN	EMPLOYEES
12/12	829	28	3.5%	350
12/11	794	20	2.6%	—
12/08	644	10	1.6%	—
12/08	517	7	1.5%	—
Annual Growth	12.5%	38.4%	—	—

2012 Year-End Financials

Debt ratio: —
Return on equity: 3.50%
Cash ($ mil.): 52
Current ratio: 2.10
Long-term debt ($ mil.): —
Dividends
Yield: —
Payout: —
Market value ($ mil.): —

JAMES MADISON UNIVERSITY INC.

James Madison is known as the Father of the Constitution and America's fourth president but he also has a public institution of higher education named after him. James Madison University (JMU) offers some 70 undergraduate and 40 graduate degrees through more than a half-dozen colleges including arts and letters business education visual and performing arts and science and mathematics. The university enrolls about 20000 students mostly undergrads with a faculty of 1200 teachers and a student-to-faculty ratio of 16:1. JMU also has extensive men's and women's athletic programs. JMU was established in 1908 in Harrisonburg Virginia.

Geographic Reach

James Madison University is located on on a 470-acre campus in Harrisonburg located in the Shenandoah Valley of Virginia. Altogether the university operates more than 112 building on 720 acres. More than 70% of its students are residents of Virginia while the rest pay out-of-state tuition fees.

Strategy

In 2012 James Madison University increased the number of colleges from seven to eight (including the graduate school) when it broke up its College of Integrated Science and Technology into two new schools. The new College of Health and Behavioral Studies includes the psychology health sciences nursing social work and communication disorders programs while the College of Integrated Science and Engineering includes computer science integrated science and technology engineering programs. The move helps the university meet the growing need for education programs for health and human behavior professionals.

EXECUTIVES

President, Linwood H. Rose
Provost and VP Academic Affairs, Douglas T. Brown
Senior Vice President Administration and Finance, Charles W. King Jr.
SVP Student Affairs and University Planning, Mark Warner
SVP University Advancement, Joanne Carr
Dean College of Education, Phillip M. Wishon
Dean College of Science and Mathematics, David F. Brakke
Dean University Studies, Linda Cabe Halpern
Dean Libraries and Educational Technologies, Ralph A. Alberico
Dean College of Business, Robert D. Reid
Director Athletics, Jeffrey T. Bourne
Rector Board of Visitors, Meredith Strohm Gunter
Vice Rector Board of Visitors, James E. (Jim) Hartman
Dean The Graduate School, Reid Linn
Dean College of Arts and Letters, David K. Jeffrey
Speaker Faculty Senate and Faculty Representative to Board of Visitors, Steven Garren
Dean College of Visual and Performing Arts, George E. Sparks
Director Public Affairs and University Spokesman, Don Egle
Media Relations Manager, Bill Wyatt
Community Affairs Manager, Rachael Walters
Administrative Assistant, Machelle Rader
Member Board of Visitors, Charles H. (Charlie) Foster Jr., age 71
Member Board of Visitors, Stephen R. Leeolou, age 55
Member Board of Visitors, Fred Thompson
Member Board of Visitors, Joseph F. Damico, age 60
Executive Assistant President, Donna L. Harper
Member Board of Visitors, Mark T. Bowles
Vice Rector Board of Visitors, James E. (Jim) Hartman
Member Board of Visitors, Wharton B. (Zie) Rivers Jr., age 65
Member Board of Visitors, Judith (Judy) Strickler
Speaker Faculty Senate and Faculty Representative to Board of Visitors, Steven Garren
Member Board of Visitors, Elizabeth V. Lodal
Member Board of Visitors, Joseph K. Funkhouser II
Member Board of Visitors, Lois Forbes
Member Board of Visitors, Vanessa M. Evans
Member Board of Visitors, Ronald C. Devine

LOCATIONS

HQ: JAMES MADISON UNIVERSITY INC.
MSC 5719, HARRISONBURG, VA 22807-0001
Phone: 540-568-6433
Web: WWW.JMU.EDU

PRODUCTS/OPERATIONS

Selected Schools

College of Arts and Letters
College of Business
College of Education
College of Health and Behavioral Studies
College of Integrated Science and Engineering
College of Science and Mathematics
College of Visual and Performing Arts
The Graduate School

Selected Degrees

Bachelor of Arts (BA)
Bachelor of Science (BS)
Bachelor of Music Education (BMEd)
Bachelor of Business Administration (BBA)
Bachelor of General Studies (BGS)
Bachelor of Music (BM)
Bachelor of Social Work (BSW)
Bachelor of Science in Nursing (BSN)
Doctor of Psychology (PsyD)
Master of Arts (MA)
Master of Fine Arts (MFA)
Master of Science (MS)
Master of Business Administration (MBA)
Master of Science in Education (MSEd)
Master of Arts in Teaching (MAT)
Master of Education (MEd)
Master of Music (MM)
Master of Public Administration (MPA)
Educational Specialist (EdS)
Doctor of Audiology (AUD)
Doctor of Philosophy (PhD)
Doctor of Musical Arts (DMA)
Master o Science in Nursing (MSN)
Master of Occupational Therapy (MOT)
Master of Physician Assistant Studies (MPAS)

HISTORICAL FINANCIALS

Company Type: Private

Income Statement FYE: June 30

	REVENUE ($ mil.)	NET INCOME ($ mil.)	NET PROFIT MARGIN	EMPLOYEES
06/11	323	56	17.5%	1,700
06/08	270	69	25.6%	—
06/07	248	78	31.5%	—
06/06	1,980	0	—	—
Annual Growth	(30.4%)	—	—	—

2011 Year-End Financials

Debt ratio: ——
Return on equity: 17.50%
Cash ($ mil.): 117
Current ratio: 1.50
Long-term debt ($ mil.): —
Dividends
Yield: —
Payout: —
Market value ($ mil.): —

JEFFERSON HEALTH SYSTEM INC.

This health care system's freedom-loving namesake might approve of its work to preserve the people's freedom of choice in health care. Jefferson Health System is a not-for-profit network that includes three health systems with hospitals specialty clinics and other medical facilities serving communities in the greater Philadelphia area. Members include the Thomas Jefferson University Hospital family (one of the system's founders) Main Line Health (the other founding organization) and Magee Rehabilitation. The Jefferson network has some 2435 beds and 3400 medical staff members and is affiliated with Thomas Jefferson University.

Operations

Main Line Hospitals include The Bryn Mawr Hospital; The Lankenau Hospital; Paoli Hospital); Lankenau Institute of Medical Research; Main Line Diversified Services; Bryn Mawr Rehabilitation Hospital and other related organizations. TJUH includes Thomas Jefferson University Hospitals (Thomas Jefferson University Hospital and its subsidiaries; the Jefferson Hospital for Neuroscience and the Methodist Hospital Division.)

Thomas Jefferson University Hospitals has 969 licensed acute care beds and provides services in at five locations - the main hospital facility and Jefferson Hospital for Neuroscience both in Center City Philadelphia; Methodist Hospital in South Philadelphia; Jefferson at the Navy Yard just past the sports complex; and Jefferson-Voorhees in South Jersey. Magee Rehabilitation Hospital is a physical rehabilitation hospital specializing in the treatment of spinal cord injury brain injury stroke and orthopedic. Main Line Health offers a range of medical surgical obstetric pediatric psychiatric and emergency services.

Financial Analysis

The company's revenues increased by 5% in fiscal 2012 due to a growth in patient services and other revenues. The patient services revenues increase was primarily due to a growth in Medicare and Medical Assistance fee-for-service program revenues. The increase in other income was due to receipts received for the initial payment of the incentive relating to Main Line Health implementing an electronic health records program as part of the American Recovery and Reinvestment Act of 2009.

Net income increased by 2% in fiscal 2012 primarily due to higher revenues.

Strategy

Jefferson Health System has realigned its relationship with former member Aria Health (formerly Frankford Health Care System) after the two organizations decided they too could better serve customers as separate entities. While Aria Health is no longer a direct member of the Jefferson Health System the two health networks maintain an affiliate relationship through which they collaborate in some areas of care.

EXECUTIVES

EVP CFO and COO, Kirk E. Gorman, age 63
President and CEO Main Line Health, John J. (Jack) Lynch III
President and CEO, Joesph T. Sebastianelli, age 65
EVP and Chief Legal Officer, David F. Simon, age 59
Auditors: PricewaterhouseCoopersLLP

LOCATIONS

HQ: JEFFERSON HEALTH SYSTEM INC.
259 N RADNOR CHESTER RD # 290, RADNOR, PA 19087-5240
Phone: 610-225-6200
Web: WWW.JEFFERSONHEALTH.ORG

PRODUCTS/OPERATIONS

2011 Sales

	$ mil.	% of total
Patient services	2,781	94
Other	159	6

Selected Members

Magee Hospital for Convalescents (or Magee Rehabilitation Philadelphia)
Main Line Health (Bryn Mawr Pennsylvania)
Thomas Jefferson University Hospital System (Philadelphia)

COMPETITORS

Abington Memorial Hospital
Albert Einstein Healthcare Network
Crozer-Keystone Health System
Lancaster General
Lehigh Valley Health Network
Memorial Hospital (PA)
Mercy Health System
North Philadelphia Health System
TUHS
University of Pennsylvania Health System
Virtua Health

HISTORICAL FINANCIALS

Company Type: Private

Income Statement FYE: June 30

	REVENUE ($ mil.)	NET INCOME ($ mil.)	NET PROFIT MARGIN	EMPLOYEES
06/13	3,047	472	15.5%	17,485
06/12	3,101	(28)	—	—
06/11	2,950	422	14.3%	—
Annual Growth	1.6%	5.7%	—	—

2013 Year-End Financials

Debt ratio: —
Return on equity: 15.50%
Cash ($ mil.): 133
Current ratio: 1.10
Long-term debt ($ mil.): —
Dividends
Yield: —
Payout: —
Market value ($ mil.): —

JEFFERSON HOMEBUILDERS INC.

Culpeper Wood Preservers may sound like the name of an environmental non-profit but this Virginia-based building materials supplier has more commercial interests in mind. The company manufactures and distributes pressure-treated lumber from plants located in the midwestern and northeastern US (pressure treating protects wood from damage by moisture and insects). Products include standard dimensional lumber decking boards plywood and timbers. The company also makes such specialty products as deck accessories lattice fencing moulded products and landscaping items.

In response to increased demand the company has locations in Virginia Indiana Maryland and South Carolina. Culpeper sells about 500 million board feet of lumber annually.

Culpeper established in 1972 is owned and operated by brothers Joe and Ronald Daniel who serve respectively as president and vice president of the company.

EXECUTIVES

Yard Manager, Mike Elliott
CEO, Joseph R. (Joe) Daniel Sr.
Treasurer, Doris Batiste
Treating Supervisor, Duane McDaniel
President, Joseph R. (Josh) Daniel Jr.
VP, Larry Lang
Director Marketing and Executive Assistant to President, Yvonne Gooding

LOCATIONS

HQ: JEFFERSON HOMEBUILDERS INC.
501 N MAIN ST, CULPEPER, VA 22701-2607
Phone: 540-825-5898
Web: WWW.CULPEPERWOOD.COM

COMPETITORS

Georgia-Pacific
Louisiana-Pacific
Weyerhaeuser

HISTORICAL FINANCIALS

Company Type: Private

Income Statement — FYE: September 30

	REVENUE ($ mil.)	NET INCOME ($ mil.)	NET PROFIT MARGIN	EMPLOYEES
09/07	157	3	2.0%	177
09/06	165	5	3.1%	—
09/05	912	0	0.0%	—
Annual Growth	(58.5%)	19522.0%	—	—

JEFFERSON HOSPITAL ASSOCIATION INC.

Jefferson Regional Medical Center (JRMC) provides acute care and other health services to residents of Pine Bluff and an 11-county area of southern Arkansas. The not-for-profit community-owned hospital has about 470 acute care beds and offers general medical and surgical care as well as services in a range of specialties including urology orthopedics cardiology and oncology. It also has a 25-bed skilled nursing unit that cares for patients transitioning to long-term care or home care. A network of clinics offers outpatient surgery diagnostic imaging wound care and other ambulatory health services. Additionally the health system operates a nursing school and home health and hospice agencies.

To bring its operations up to speed with modern technology requirements in the health care industry JRMC has implemented an electronic health record (EHR) system and is employing that system to comply with meaningful use guidelines from the US government. In fact JRMC was a frontrunner in the movement to bring medical records online first moving to install EHR systems in 2003.

The hospital also expanded its services for the southern Arkansas region by becoming certified as a Level II trauma center in 2010. JRMC has also expanded and upgraded its wellness centers to serve the exercise needs of the community.

EXECUTIVES

Dir Of Maternal Health Programs, Susan Sweat
Director Of Him, Barbara Grant

LOCATIONS

HQ: JEFFERSON HOSPITAL ASSOCIATION INC.
1600 W 40TH AVE, PINE BLUFF, AR 71603-6301
Phone: 870-541-7100
Web: WWW.DAVISLIFECARE.ORG

COMPETITORS

Arkansas Heart Hospital
Baptist Health (Arkansas)
Conway Regional Health System
Medical Park Hospital
Sparks Health System
St. Vincent Health System
University of Arkansas
Weirton Medical Center
White County Medical Center

HISTORICAL FINANCIALS

Company Type: Private

Income Statement — FYE: June 30

	REVENUE ($ mil.)	NET INCOME ($ mil.)	NET PROFIT MARGIN	EMPLOYEES
06/10	198	11	5.6%	1,800
06/09	5	(4)	—	—
06/09	941	0	—	—
Annual Growth	—	7385623.0%	—	—

2010 Year-End Financials

Debt ratio: —
Return on equity: 5.60%
Cash ($ mil.): 45
Current ratio: 1.20
Long-term debt ($ mil.): —
Dividends
Yield: —
Payout: —
Market value ($ mil.): —

JEFFERSON REGIONAL MEDICAL CENTER

Jefferson Regional Medical Center serves the South Hills area of Pittsburgh. The hospital has about 370 beds. In addition to primary care Jefferson Regional Medical Center offers such specialized services as a heart institute for treating cardiovascular conditions and a physical rehabilitation and sports medicine center. Its emergency department treats more than 55000 patients each year. Jefferson Regional Medical Center also provides home health care and emergency helicopter transportation services and it operates nearby outpatient clinics and physician offices.

Geographic Reach

Jefferson Regional Medical Center provides comprehensive medical and surgical services and primary care medicine in 14 community-based locations throughout southwestern Pennsylvania. It operates outpatient centers in Baldwin Belle Vernon Bethel Park Brentwood Charleroi Clairton Homestead Pleasant Hills Squirrel Hill and Uniontown.

Operations

Jefferson Regional Medical Center has 400 physicians representing more than 40 specialties. Its main location includes inpatient and outpatient surgical services as well as The Heart Institute The Radiation Oncology Center The Joint Care Center The Women's Diagnostic Center The Sleep Disorder Center and Physical Therapy.

It offers a range of community education programs including the Diabetes Education Program and the Dr. Dean Ornish Program for Reversing Heart Disease. It also offers seminars to help manage depression and osteoporosis; support groups for cancer kidney failure or stroke; and wellness programs for everything from nutrition to stress management.

Strategy

The company is looking to expand its capacity to keep up with demand. In 2012 Jefferson Regional Medical Center signed a strategic partnership with Blue Cross and Blue Shield licensee Highmark to expand and enhance its services. As a part of the deal the medical center will build a 35000-square-foot addition at Jefferson Regional Bethel Park Campus to expand its services.

During 2011 Jefferson Regional Medical Center opened three new centers for Diagnostic Services including The Bethel Park campus and centers in Charleroi and Belle Vernon.

Company Background

The company was created in 1973 by the merger of St. Joseph's and Homestead Hospitals.

EXECUTIVES

Vice President Human Resources, Rosanne C Saunders
SVP and CFO, JoAnne R. Hahey
Vice President, James W Backstrom
Senior Vice President Physician Strategy, Marcie S Caplan
Senior Executive Vice President, James Cooper
Vice President, Michael J Evans
Vice President Ids Planning, Dorothy E Bellhouse
Vice President Finance, Nathan Genderen
Vice President Of Cardiovascular Services And Oncology Programming, Mary Kaplan
Vice President, Todd Goodnight
Vice President Marketing, Todd Blodgett
Medical Director, Chris Richter
Director Of Home Healthcare Svs, Monica Rozier
Nurse Manager Of Psych Unit, Diane Boyd

Physical Therapy Director, Robert Stahara
Chief Operating Officer Executive Vp, Robert Horn
Director Of Clinical Services, Bill Bledsoe
Vice President Of Medical Staff, Benjamin Albano
Vice President, Mike Evans
Treasurer, Albert J Ragan
Co Vice Chairperson Department Of Diagnostic Imaging, Mark Jablonski
Board Member, Bill McKenna

LOCATIONS

HQ: JEFFERSON REGIONAL MEDICAL CENTER
565 COAL VALLEY RD, CLAIRTON, PA 15025-3703
Phone: 412-469-5000
Web: WWW.JEFFERSONREGIONAL.COM

COMPETITORS

Butler Health System
Excela Health
Heritage Valley Health
Ohio Valley General
St. Clair Health
UPMC
West Penn Allegheny Health System

HISTORICAL FINANCIALS

Company Type: Private

Income Statement FYE: June 30

	REVENUE ($ mil.)	NET INCOME ($ mil.)	NET PROFIT MARGIN	EMPLOYEES
06/09	204	(19)	—	2,000
06/08	216	(19)	—	—
06/07	1,736	0	0.0%	—
Annual Growth	(65.7%)	—	—	—

2009 Year-End Financials

Debt ratio: —
Return on equity: (-9.40%)
Cash ($ mil.): 7
Current ratio: 1.30
Long-term debt ($ mil.): —
Dividends
Yield: —
Payout: —
Market value ($ mil.): —

JERNIGAN OIL CO. INC.

LOCATIONS

HQ: JERNIGAN OIL CO. INC.
415 MAIN ST E, AHOSKIE, NC 279103421
Phone: 2523322131
Web: WWW.JERNIGANOIL.COM

HISTORICAL FINANCIALS

Company Type: Private

Income Statement FYE: December 31

	REVENUE ($ mil.)	NET INCOME ($ mil.)	NET PROFIT MARGIN	EMPLOYEES
12/13	232	(0)	—	350
12/12	226	0	0.1%	—
12/11	218	0	0.1%	—
12/10	168	0	—	—
Annual Growth	11.3%	—	—	—

2013 Year-End Financials

Debt ratio: —
Return on equity: (-0.10%)
Cash ($ mil.): 1
Current ratio: 0.50
Long-term debt ($ mil.): —
Dividends
Yield: —
Payout: —
Market value ($ mil.): —

JERSEY CITY MEDICAL CENTER INC

With roots extending back to 1882 Jersey City Medical Center (JCMC) may have history but it's not stuck in the past. The 350-bed acute-care hospital serves residents of New Jersey's Hudson County area. Operated by Liberty Healthcare the hospital includes a trauma center a perinatal center and a heart institute. JCMC also offers pediatric women's health rehabilitation and ambulatory care and it is a teaching affiliate for the Mount Sinai School of Medicine. JCMC's modern incarnation came about in the Great Depression when it was constructed by a political ally of Franklin Roosevelt.

Geographic Reach

The 15-acre JCMC campus which overlooks the New York Harbor and the Liberty State Park is also home to the Wilzig Hospital and the Provident Bank Ambulatory Center. JCMC offers a Mobile Health Screening Unit that will travel to underserved areas throughout Hudson County. The hospital is the primary medical facility serving New York's Hudson Essex and Union counties.

Operations

JCMC operates as a regional referral center meaning that it takes on complicated cases from smaller community hospitals in the area. As an area teaching hospital the hospital offers medical residency programs in internal medicine and nursing. It also offers continuing education courses to keep its medical residents up on the latest medical developments.

JCMC's mobile outreach program provides health and wellness screenings dispense care and offer health education. It is funded through a grant provided by The New Jersey Department of Health and Senior Services. Among other things the van will provide diabetes HIV and mental health screenings as well as perform blood pressure checks offer preventive care and educate people on the streets of Hudson County and Jersey City. The van travels to health fairs and regularly scheduled outreach events such as at schools and senior centers.

Strategy

In mid-2013 JCMC announced that it has entered an agreement to become part of the Barnabas Health system. The merger was expected to close by the end of 2013 following regulatory approval.

JCMC focuses on expanding and improving services for area residents. The hospital opened a hand and upper extremity unit in 2013 to address the needs of patients with pain and functional difficulties related to arthritis carpal tunnel syndrome injuries and other conditions. It also added about 200 new physicians during 2012 to enhance patient access to general and specialty care. It opened a new gastrointestinal disorder center on the main campus in 2012 and it expanded its cardiac care services with the opening of a new electrophysiology lab.

In 2012 it announced plans to renovate and reopen the former Greenville Hospital campus in Jersey City as an outpatient facility to meet the rising needs for ambulatory care in the area.

Auditors: Ernst&Young

LOCATIONS

HQ: JERSEY CITY MEDICAL CENTER INC
355 GRAND ST, JERSEY CITY, NJ 07302-4321
Phone: 201-915-2000
Web: WWW.LIBERTYHEALTH.ORG

PRODUCTS/OPERATIONS

Selected Locations

Emergency Services at JCMC
Family Regional Perinatal Center
Fannie E. Rippel Foundation Heart Institute
General Pediatrics at JCMC
Nursing at JCMC
Provident Bank Ambulatory Center
Port Authority Heroes of Sept 11 Trauma Center
The Rehabilitation Services Department
Volunteer Services at JCMC
Wilzig Hospital

COMPETITORS

Bergen Regional Medical
Bronx-Lebanon Hospital
Catholic Health East
Continuum Health Partners
Englewood Hospital and Medical Center
Hackensack University Medical Center
Hospital for Special Surgery
Lenox Hill Hospital
Montefiore Medical
Newark Beth Israel Medical Center
Robert Wood Johnson University Hospital at Rahway
St. Joseph' s Healthcare System
The Valley Hospital
Valley Health System

HISTORICAL FINANCIALS

Company Type: Private

Income Statement FYE: December 31

	REVENUE ($ mil.)	NET INCOME ($ mil.)	NET PROFIT MARGIN	EMPLOYEES
12/12	294	29	9.9%	1,942
12/08	249	8	3.3%	—
12/01	202	0	0.2%	—
12/01	195	1	0.9%	—
Annual Growth	3.8%	29.4%	—	—

2012 Year-End Financials

Debt ratio: —
Return on equity: 9.90%
Cash ($ mil.): 35
Current ratio: 1.10
Long-term debt ($ mil.): —
Dividends
Yield: —
Payout: —
Market value ($ mil.): —

JEWISH COMMUNAL FUND

LOCATIONS

HQ: JEWISH COMMUNAL FUND
575 MADISON AVE STE 703, NEW YORK, NY 100228591
Phone: 2127528277

HISTORICAL FINANCIALS

Company Type: Private

Income Statement FYE: June 30

	ASSETS ($ mil.)	NET INCOME ($ mil.)	INCOME AS % OF ASSETS	EMPLOYEES
06/13	1,179	110	9.3%	14
06/12	1,012	(57)	—	—
06/11	1,086	42	3.9%	—
06/10	971	0	—	—
Annual Growth	6.7%	—	—	—

2013 Year-End Financials

Debt ratio: —
Return on equity: 28.30%
Cash ($ mil.): 354
Current ratio: —
Long-term debt ($ mil.): —
Dividends
Yield: —
Payout: —
Market value ($ mil.): —

JFK HEALTH SYSTEM INC.

EXECUTIVES

COO JFK Medical Center, J. Scott Gebhard
President and CEO, Raymond F. Fredericks
Director Public Relations and Marketing, Steven Weiss
Chair, Michael Kleiman

LOCATIONS

HQ: JFK HEALTH SYSTEM INC.
65 JAMES ST, EDISON, NJ 088203947
Phone: 7323217000

Selected Facilities

JFK At Home
JFK Hartwyck Nursing and Rehabilitation Centers
JFK Johnson Rehabilitation Institute
JFK Medical Center
JFK MediPlex Surgery Center
JFK Muhlenberg Campus
JFK Muhlenberg Harold B. & Dorothy A. Snyder Schools
JFK New Jersey Neuroscience Institute
Whispering Knoll Assisted Living

COMPETITORS

Atlantic Health
Barnabas Health
Catholic Health East
CentraState Healthcare System
Continuum Health Partners
East Orange General Hospital
NewYork-Presbyterian Healthcare
Newark Beth Israel Medical Center
Raritan Bay Medical Center
Robert Wood Johnson University Hospital
Saint Peter' s University Hospital
Somerset Medical Center
St. Joseph' s Healthcare System
Staten Island University Hospital
Trinitas Regional Medical Center

HISTORICAL FINANCIALS

Company Type: Private

Income Statement

FYE: December 31

	REVENUE ($ mil.)	NET INCOME ($ mil.)	NET PROFIT MARGIN	EMPLOYEES
12/12	481	9	2.1%	6,735
12/11	509	11	2.2%	—
12/10	500	(12)	—	—
12/09	488	0	—	—
Annual Growth	(0.5%)	—	—	—

2012 Year-End Financials

Debt ratio: —
Return on equity: 2.10%
Cash ($ mil.): 48
Current ratio: 1.40
Long-term debt ($ mil.): —
Dividends
Yield: —
Payout: —
Market value ($ mil.): —

JOHN C. LINCOLN HEALTH NETWORK

John C. Lincoln Health Network takes care of the health of John Q. Public in Arizona. The not-for-profit health care network serves the northern Phoenix area and is home to two hospitals: John C. Lincoln Deer Valley Hospital with more than 200 beds and John C. Lincoln North Mountain Hospital with roughly 260 beds. The system also features a children's care facility various physician and dental clinics a food bank and assisted living facilities for the elderly all operating under the Desert Mission moniker. The John C. Lincoln Health Foundation is the fundraising arm of the organization. John C. Lincoln Health Network has a staff of about 1100 physicians.

Operations

In addition to its hospital locations the network includes physician practices for primary and specialty care as well as medical imaging and research centers. John C. Lincoln's facilities serve about 750000 patients each year and provide specialty services in fields including cardiology pulmonary care neuroscience and women's health. The Deer Valley Hospital is also home to Mendy's Place the North Valley's only 24-hour hospital emergency center exclusively for children and an accredited Chest Pain Center.

The health system's Desert Mission Food Bank distributed roughly 41000 emergency food boxes to members of its community in 2012. Other locations providing community outreach services include the Community Health Center Children's Dental Clinic Lincoln Learning Center Adult Day Health Care and Neighborhood Renewal. The Marley House Behavioral Health Clinic provides mental health and related services for children and adults on a sliding scale basis in English and Spanish. The John C. Lincoln Health Foundation conducts philanthropic efforts.

Strategy

To strengthen its footing in the Arizona marketplace in 2013 John C. Lincoln announced that intends to form an affiliation with Scottsdale Healthcare. If the networks combine they would operate under the moniker Scottsdale Lincoln Health Network. The merger would create a five-hospital system with some 3700 affiliated physicians and an extensive outpatient services network.

In addition in 2013 John C. Lincoln moved to expand by breaking ground on a new emergency center and outpatient clinic in Phoenix. The $18 million project will include an emergency department medical practice and diagnostic imaging facilities.

Company Background

The hospital gained its first real funding in 1933 from millionaire entrepreneur John C. Lincoln the founder of Lincoln Electric.

EXECUTIVES

President CEO and Director, Dan C. Coleman
CIO, Robert Israel
CEO John C. Lincoln North Mountain Hospital, Bruce Pearson
President, Rhonda Forsyth
CEO John C. Lincoln Deer Valley Hospital, John L. Harrington Jr.
Chairman, Thomas M. Batson
CEO John C. Lincoln Physician Network Development & Accountable Care, Nathan Anspach
VP Patient Care Services John C. Lincoln Deer Valley Hospital, Colleen Scharneck
VP Patient Care Services John C. Lincoln North Mountain Hospital, Sue Hanauer
VP Clinical and Support Services John C. Lincoln North Mountain Hospital, Catherine (Cathy) Lindstrom
EVP and CEO John C. Lincoln Health Foundation, Elaine Hugunin
Chief Compliance Officer, Christina Galbo
Vice President Clinical & Support Services, David Price
Research Manager, Jennie Miller
Executive Assistant, Chrysa Callaghan
Development Manager, Mallory Lebovitz
Director of Development & Operations, Scott Showers
Vice President Partner, Martin Aronson
Chairman, David C. Lincoln
Senior Vice President of Sales, Frank Pugh
Vice President & Chief Nursing Officer, Kristin Schmidt
Chairman Vice President Chief Financial Officer, Larry Seay
Chief Nursing Officer, Maggi Griffin
CEO John C. Lincoln Health Foundation, Marcia L. Mintz
Vice President & Chief Nursing Officer, Jessica Rivas
Vice President Clinical & Support Services, Wayne Gillis
President CEO and Director, Dan C. Coleman
Chairman, David C. Lincoln
Auditors: BKDLLP

LOCATIONS

HQ: JOHN C. LINCOLN HEALTH NETWORK
250 E DUNLAP AVE, PHOENIX, AZ 85020-2825
Phone: 602-943-2381
Web: WWW.JCL.COM

PRODUCTS/OPERATIONS

Selected Centers and Services

Breast Health and Research Center
Cancer Treatment
Cardiac Care
Deep Vein Thrombosis Program
Emergency Care
Heartburn Program
Level I Trauma Center
Medical Imaging
Neurosciences
Orthopedics
Outpatient Surgery Centers
Pediatrics
Pulmonary Program
Reconstructive Plastic Surgery
Scarless Surgery
Uterine Fibroid Treatment
Varicose Vein Treatment

COMPETITORS

Banner Health
Community Health Systems
Dignity Health
Flagstaff Medical Center
Iasis Healthcare
Northern Arizona Healthcare
Phoenix Children' s Hospital
Scottsdale Healthcare
Universal Health Services
University of Arizona Health Network
Vanguard Health Systems
Yuma Regional Medical Center

HISTORICAL FINANCIALS

Company Type: Private

Income Statement FYE: December 31

	REVENUE ($ mil.)	NET INCOME ($ mil.)	NET PROFIT MARGIN	EMPLOYEES
12/12	509	32	6.4%	3,500
12/11	486	17	3.6%	—
12/10	551	19	3.5%	—
12/09	516	12	2.5%	—
Annual Growth	(0.4%)	36.6%	—	—

2012 Year-End Financials

Debt ratio: —
Return on equity: 6.40%
Cash ($ mil.): 25
Current ratio: 1.40
Long-term debt ($ mil.): —
Dividends
Yield: —
Payout: —
Market value ($ mil.): —

JOHN D ARCHBOLD MEMORIAL HOSPITAL

LOCATIONS

HQ: JOHN D ARCHBOLD MEMORIAL HOSPITAL
915 GORDON AVE, THOMASVILLE, GA 317926699
Phone: 2292282000
Web: WWW.ARCHBOLD.ORG

HISTORICAL FINANCIALS

Company Type: Private

Income Statement FYE: September 30

	REVENUE ($ mil.)	NET INCOME ($ mil.)	NET PROFIT MARGIN	EMPLOYEES
09/13	301	24	8.0%	2,700
09/12	230	26	11.3%	—
09/09	342	33	9.9%	—
09/06	296	0	—	—
Annual Growth	0.2%	—	—	—

2013 Year-End Financials

Debt ratio: —
Return on equity: 8.00%
Cash ($ mil.): 8
Current ratio: 0.30
Long-term debt ($ mil.): —
Dividends
Yield: —
Payout: —
Market value ($ mil.): —

JOHN F KENNEDY CENTER FOR THE PERFORMING ARTS

The John F. Kennedy Center for the Performing Arts also known as The Kennedy Center traces its roots to 1958 when president Dwight Eisenhower signed the National Cultural Center Act calling for a privately funded venture featuring a variety of classic and contemporary programming with an educational focus. The center was a pet project and fund raiser beneficiary of president Kennedy; it was named as a living memorial to him after his death. Located on 17 acres overlooking the Potomac River in Washington D.C. the center opened in 1971 and presents some 2000 events a year including musicals dance performances and jazz and orchestral concerts. It also produces TV programming workshops and lectures.

EXECUTIVES

Chairman, David M. Rubenstein, age 65
President, Michael M. Kaiser
VP-Mktg & Sls, David Kitto

LOCATIONS

HQ: JOHN F KENNEDY CENTER FOR THE PERFORMING ARTS
2700 F ST NW, WASHINGTON, DC 20566-0002
Phone: 202-416-8000
Web: WWW.KENNEDY-CENTER.ORG

COMPETITORS

Nederlander Producing Company
Smithsonian
The National Gallery

HISTORICAL FINANCIALS

Company Type: Private

Income Statement FYE: September 30

	REVENUE ($ mil.)	NET INCOME ($ mil.)	NET PROFIT MARGIN	EMPLOYEES
09/10	182	21	11.9%	1,144
09/09	156	(7)	—	—
09/08	186	(16)	—	—
09/07	138	24	17.6%	—
Annual Growth	9.7%	(3.5%)	—	—

2010 Year-End Financials

Debt ratio: —
Return on equity: 11.90%
Cash ($ mil.): 22
Current ratio: 0.60
Long-term debt ($ mil.): —
Dividends
Yield: —
Payout: —
Market value ($ mil.): —

JOHN T MATHER MEMORIAL HOSPITAL OF PORT JEFFERSON NEW YORK INC.

Shipbuilder John T. Mather envisioned a legacy that would keep his community of Port Jefferson in good health and John T. Mather Memorial Hospital came to fruition in 1929 one year after it's namesake's death. The not-for-profit hospital has some 250 beds and provides a variety of health care services to the residents of Port Jefferson New York and surrounding areas of Suffolk County. Services include emergency care occupational therapy psychiatry and radiology. Mather Hospital is a member of Long Island Health Network an association of about a dozen affiliated hospitals all serving Long Island.

Operations

Mather Hospital has some 600 physicians both full-time employees and affiliates who serve some 12000 inpatient customers annually. The emergency room handles about 44000 visits per year. The hospital's specialty service units include the Fortunato Breast Health Center which provides outpatient diagnostics to 15000 patients annually as well as centers for sleep disorder treatment bariatrics wound care and stroke management.

In addition to its membership in the Long Island Health Alliance Mather Hospital has formed a partnership with nearby St. Charles Hospital and Rehabilitation Center to provide tandem services in some areas including cancer and pediatric care.

EXECUTIVES

President, Kenneth D. (Ken) Roberts
Vice Chairperson, Konrad J. Kuhn
Vice Chairperson, Betsy Noyes Britton
Vice Chairperson, Harold Tranchon Jr.
Chairman, Kenneth A. Jacoppi
Co-Chairman Public Affairs Committee, Alan D. Beck
Coordinator Public Affairs, Julie Parenti
Chairman Public Affairs Committee and Secretary, Gene Gerrard
Treasurer, John R. Sini
VP Medical Staff; Vice Chairwoman Medical Board, Kara H.V. Kvilekval
Vice Chairperson, Konrad J. Kuhn
Vice Chairperson, Betsy Noyes Britton
Vice Chairperson, Harold Tranchon Jr.
Co-Chairman Public Affairs Committee, Alan D. Beck
Director, Gary Cress
Director, James Danowski
Director, M. Cecile Forte
Director, Judith A. Fortunato
Director, Frederick C. Johs
Director, Thomas Kohlmann
Director, Richard Lusak
Director, Wayne Rampone
Director, Leo Sternlicht
Director, Edward J. Weiss
Director, Kathryn B. Frey
Chairman Public Affairs Committee and Secretary, Gene Gerrard
VP Medical Staff; Vice Chairwoman Medical Board, Kara H.V. Kvilekval

LOCATIONS

HQ: JOHN T MATHER MEMORIAL HOSPITAL OF PORT JEFFERSON NEW YORK INC.
75 N COUNTRY RD, PORT JEFFERSON, NY 11777-2119
Phone: 631-473-1320
Web: WWW.MATHERHOSPITAL.ORG

PRODUCTS/OPERATIONS

Selected Centers and Services

Bariatric Surgery Center of Excellence
Behavioral Health Services
Breast Health Center
Critical Care
Emergency Department
Hospitalists
Hyperbaric Oxygen Therapy Unit
Imaging Services/Radiology
Infusion Center
Intensivists
Joint Replacement Program
Laboratory
Lithotripsy
Lymphedema Program
Pain Management Program
Palliative Medicine
Physical Therapy
Prostate Health Program
Respiratory Therapy
Transitional Care Unit
Sleep Disorders Center
Surgical Services
Wound Treatment Center

COMPETITORS

Catholic Health Services of Long Island
Catholic Healthcare System
Long Island College Hospital
New York City Health and Hospitals

NewYork-Presbyterian Healthcare
North Shore-Long Island Jewish Health System
Peconic Bay Medical Center

HISTORICAL FINANCIALS

Company Type: Private

Income Statement FYE: December 31

	REVENUE ($ mil.)	NET INCOME ($ mil.)	NET PROFIT MARGIN	EMPLOYEES
12/12	238	(0)	—	1,700
12/08	192	2	1.3%	—
12/05	181	3	1.9%	—
12/05	351	0	0.0%	—
Annual Growth	(5.4%)	—	—	—

2012 Year-End Financials

Debt ratio: —
Return on equity: (-0.40%)
Cash ($ mil.): 6
Current ratio: 1.00
Long-term debt ($ mil.): —

Dividends
Yield: —
Payout: —
Market value ($ mil.): —

JOHNS HOPKINS HEALTH SYS CORP

Named after philanthropist Johns Hopkins the Johns Hopkins Health System (JHHS) gifts Baltimore residents with an array of health care services. The health system is an affiliate of world-renowned Johns Hopkins Medicine and oversees six hospitals: All Children's Hospital Johns Hopkins Hospital Bayview Medical Center Howard County General Hospital Sibley Memorial Hospital and Suburban Hospital. The not-for-profit teaching hospitals offer inpatient and outpatient health services that include general medicine emergency/trauma care pediatrics maternity care senior care and numerous specialized areas of medicine. It also community health and satellite care facilities.

Geographic Reach

The JHHS inpatient and outpatient facilities are located throughout Maryland and the Washington DC-area as well as in Florida. Johns Hopkins Health System operates a handful of outpatient surgery and imaging centers as well. The group's hospitals serve visitors from all over the world.

Operations

JHHS facilities handle 2.8 million patient encounters each year including 120000 inpatient admissions and 350000 emergency room visits. In addition to the six Johns Hopkins Medicine hospitals the JHHS organization includes four surgery centers two dozen primary care clinics associated with the Johns Hopkins Community Physicians practice organization and a home health care services agency. JHHS offers unified shared services to its members including advertising purchasing finance legal and other administrative functions.

The Johns Hopkins name is well-known for health care but is probably equally as well-known for its medical education and research initiatives. The health system's hospitals are affiliated with Johns Hopkins University offering physicians-in-training a whole host of residency options.

Financial Performance

JHHS reported revenues of $4.7 billion in 2012 a 16% increase over 2011 results due to higher patient service revenues (and increased earnings from other sources). The health system also reported a net loss of $22 million that year due to lower contributions and investment returns as well as higher expenses (related to wages salaries benefits purchasing expenses and provisions for unpaid medical bills) down from profits $1.5 billion in 2011.

Strategy

In 2012 JHHS opened a new $1 billion building at the Johns Hopkins Hospital campus. The facility includes two 12-story patient towers (one for pediatrics and one for adult care) 560 all-private patient rooms 33 high-tech operating rooms and expansive new adult and pediatric emergency departments. The organization regularly expands through small to large construction efforts as well as acquisitions.

Mergers and Acquisitions

The system added its sixth hospital through the purchase of All Children's Hospital in Florida in 2011; the move added an all-pediatric medical center to the JHHS network. The organization was a four-hospital system until late 2010 when it acquired Washington DC-based Sibley Hospital which expanded Johns Hopkins reach in the nation's capital and gave Sibley access to Johns Hopkins world-class research and clinical programs.

EXECUTIVES

Svp, Steven J (Steve) Thompson, age 55
VP Management Systems and Information Services, Stephanie L. Reel
President, Ronald R. Peterson, age 66
VP and General Counsel and Chief of Staff, Joanne E. Pollak
VP Finance and Treasurer Johns Hopkins Health System and The Johns Hopkins Hospital, Ronald J. Werthman
VP Operations Integration; EVP and COO The Johns Hopkins Hospital, Judy A. Reitz
SVP; President and CEO of Suburban Hospital, Brian A. Gragnolati
VP Marketing and Communications, Dalal Haldeman
VP Innovation and Patient Safety, Richard O. Davis
VP Supply Chain, Kenneth Grant
VP Facilities, Sally W. MacConnell
V Pres-medical Affairs, Beryl Rosenstein
Vice President Corporate Security, Harry Koffenberger
Vice Chairman, Edward D. Miller, age 72
President, Ronald R. Peterson, age 66
VP Finance and Treasurer Johns Hopkins Health System and The Johns Hopkins Hospital, Ronald J. Werthman
Vice Chairman, Paul B. Rothman
Vp/ General Counsel/ Secretary, Daniel G Shealer

LOCATIONS

HQ: JOHNS HOPKINS HEALTH SYS CORP
600 N WOLFE ST, BALTIMORE, MD 21287-0005
Phone: 410-955-5000
Web: WWW.JHMI.EDU

PRODUCTS/OPERATIONS

Selected Facilities

All Children' s Hospital (St. Petersburg FL)
Bayview Medical Center (Baltimore MD)
Howard County General Hospital (Columbia MD)
Johns Hopkins at Cedar Lane (Columbia MD)
Johns Hopkins at Greenspring Station (Lutherville MD)
Johns Hopkins at Odenton (Odenton MD)
Johns Hopkins at White Marsh (White Marsh MD)
Johns Hopkins Hospital (Baltimore MD)
Johns Hopkins Outpatient Center (Baltimore MD)
Sibley Memorial Hospital (Washington DC)
Suburban Hospital (Bethesda MD)

COMPETITORS

Anne Arundel Medical Center
Ascension Health
Bon Secours Health
LifeBridge Health
MedStar Health
MedStar Union Memorial Hospital
Carilion Clinic
Christiana Care
Dimensions Healthcare
Franklin Square Hospital Center
GBMC
Good Samaritan Hospital of Maryland
Harbor Hospital
Levindale Hospital
Sinai Hospital of Baltimore
St. Agnes HealthCare
St. Joseph Medical Center
University of Maryland Medical System
Upper Chesapeake Health

HISTORICAL FINANCIALS

Company Type: Private

Income Statement FYE: June 30

	REVENUE ($ mil.)	NET INCOME ($ mil.)	NET PROFIT MARGIN	EMPLOYEES
06/07	2,438	163	6.7%	13,000
06/06	0	0	2.5%	—
06/05	106	6	6.0%	—
06/03	1,599	28	1.8%	—
Annual Growth	11.1%	54.9%	—	—

2007 Year-End Financials

Debt ratio: —
Return on equity: 6.70%
Cash ($ mil.): 322
Current ratio: 1.30
Long-term debt ($ mil.): —

Dividends
Yield: —
Payout: —
Market value ($ mil.): —

JOHNSON & WALES UNIVERSITY INC

Things are a little upside-down at Johnson & Wales University and that's just the way they like it. The private not-for-profit accredited institution provides what it calls an upside-down curriculum allowing students to take courses in their major during the first year so they learn right away if their career choice is right for them. At the end of two years of study students earn an associate's degree and the opportunity to go on to earn a bachelor's degree. Founded in 1914 the school enrolls more than 17000 students across its four campuses in Colorado Florida North Carolina and Rhode Island. It offers degrees in business education foodservice hospitality culinary arts and technology.

Geographic Reach

The university's campuses as located in (Providence) Rhode Island (North Miami) Florida (Denver) Colorado and (Charlotte) North Carolina.

Operations

Undergraduate tuition at Johnson & Wales University runs more than $26000.

Financial Performance

Johnson & Wales University in 2012 logged revenue increases of 3% as compared to 2011 due to net student fees. The educational institution points to increases in tuition and fees residence and dining and scholarships for the gains. Net income meanwhile dropped by 94% for the same reporting period thanks to rising operating expenses and declining non-operating activities attributable to weak investment returns.

Sales and Marketing

The university sources its student body from nearly 100 countries. Its top 10 international populations (among its more than 1800 international students) hail from China South Korea Taiwan Saudi Arabia India Morocco Turkey the Bahamas the Netherlands and Malaysia.

EXECUTIVES

Director Human Resources, Diane D'Ambra
Chancellor, John J. Bowen
Vice Chancellor, Thomas L. G. Dwyer
President Charlotte Campus, Arthur J. Gallagher
VP Enrollment Management, Kenneth F. DiSaia
President and COO Providence Campus, Mim L. Runey
Treasurer Chief Financial Officer, William F. McArdle
VP Facilities Management, Christopher O. Placco
VP Information Technology and CIO, John A. Smithers
Executive Director Student Financial Services, Lynn M. Robinson
President North Miami Campus, Loreen Chant, age 46
Provost, Veera S. Gaul
Executive Director Campus Safety and Security, Michael P. Quinn
VP Student Affairs and Dean Students, Ronald Martel
VP Student Services and University Registrar, Marie Bernardo-Sousa
Vice President of human resources, Diane H. DAmbra
Trustee, Don W. Hubble, age 73
Trustee, Richard L. Bready, age 69
Trustee, Peter H. (Pete) Coors, age 66
Trustee, James H. (Jim) Hance Jr., age 68
Trustee, Merrill W. Sherman, age 64
President and Trustee, John J. Bowen
Trustee, Walter L. Isenberg
Trustee, John H. White Jr.
Trustee, Edward P. Grace III, age 62
Trustee, Sylvia E. Robinson
Trustee, Gerald A. Fernandez
Trustee, Emeril J. Lagasse
Trustee, Edward P. Triangolo Jr.
Trustee, David F. Brochu
Trustee, Michele Bailey DiMartino
Trustee, Laura Freid
Trustee, William E. Trueheart
Auditors: MayerHoffmanMcCannP.C.

LOCATIONS

HQ: JOHNSON & WALES UNIVERSITY INC
8 ABBOTT PARK PL, PROVIDENCE, RI 02903-3775
Phone: 401-598-1000
Web: WWW.JWU.EDU

PRODUCTS/OPERATIONS

Selected Colleges and Schools

The Alan Shawn Feinstein Graduate School
College of Business
College of Culinary Arts
The Hospitality College
School of Technology

Selected Operations

CAFE LLC
Griffin Realty Enterprises Inc.
Griffin Realty of Rhode Island-Florida Inc.
Harborside Enterprises Inc.
J.W.C. Corporation
J&W Corporation
Johnson & Wales Alumni Services Corporation
Johnson & Wales University
Johnson & Wales University Club

HISTORICAL FINANCIALS

Company Type: Private

Income Statement FYE: June 30

	REVENUE ($ mil.)	NET INCOME ($ mil.)	NET PROFIT MARGIN	EMPLOYEES
06/12	353	4	1.2%	1,400
06/11	343	75	22.0%	—
06/10	427	33	7.8%	—
06/09	407	10	2.7%	—
Annual Growth	(4.6%)	(27.4%)	—	—

2012 Year-End Financials

Debt ratio: —
Return on equity: 1.20%
Cash ($ mil.): 15
Current ratio: —
Long-term debt ($ mil.): —
Dividends
Yield: —
Payout: —
Market value ($ mil.): —

JOHNSON SUPPLY AND EQUIPMENT CORPORATION

Global warming? Bring it on! Keeping Texas and Louisiana residents cool is no easy task but Johnson Supply does what it can. Through about two dozen locations in hot spots like Houston and Lake Charles Louisiana Johnson Supply distributes air-conditioning and refrigeration equipment controls parts and supplies from more than 200 manufacturers. Since those places also get cold relatively speaking the company sells heating and ventilation equipment as well. Its 200 suppliers include names like York Friedrich Warren Mueller and Johnson Controls. The company was founded in 1953 by Carl I. Johnson Sr.

Geographic Reach

The company has more than 20 locations in Texas and two branches in Lafayette and Lake Charles Louisiana.

EXECUTIVES

V Pres, Darrell Simoneaux, age 65
V Pres, Sonia Mendiola
Vice President Of Operations, Douglas Domgard
V Pres, James B Cook, age 55

LOCATIONS

HQ: JOHNSON SUPPLY AND EQUIPMENT CORPORATION
10151 STELLA LINK RD, HOUSTON, TX 770255398
Phone: 7138302300
Web: WWW.JOHNSONSUPPLY.COM

PRODUCTS/OPERATIONS

2012 Locations

	No.
Texas	22
Louisiana	2
Total	**24**

COMPETITORS

American Residential Services
Comfort Systems USA
Entech Sales and Service
Service Experts
Yazaki Energy Systems

HISTORICAL FINANCIALS

Company Type: Private

Income Statement FYE: March 31

	REVENUE ($ mil.)	NET INCOME ($ mil.)	NET PROFIT MARGIN	EMPLOYEES
03/08	103	24	23.9%	270
03/05	110	80	72.6%	—
03/04	105	22	21.2%	—
03/03	97	0	—	—
Annual Growth	1.2%	—	—	—

2008 Year-End Financials

Debt ratio: —
Return on equity: 23.90%
Cash ($ mil.): 0
Current ratio: 1.00
Long-term debt ($ mil.): —
Dividends
Yield: —
Payout: —
Market value ($ mil.): —

JOHNSTON ENTERPRISES INC.

Johnston Enterprises serves the harvesters of America's amber waves of grain. The company offers farmers in Oklahoma and other Midwestern states grain-processing and storage facilities and inland water transportation services through its Johnston Grain and Johnston Port Terminals divisions. Its Johnston Seed subsidiary sells wildflower and turf wild forage and native grass seed and wildlife feed. The company was founded in 1893 by W. B. Johnston and is owned and operated by the founder's descendants president Lew Meibergen and COO Butch Meibergen.

EXECUTIVES

Chairman, J. L. (Lew) Meibergen II
President and CEO, J. L. (Butch) Meibergen III, age 54
Vice President, Steve Taylor
COO, Dennis Craig
VP, Joey Meibergen

LOCATIONS

HQ: JOHNSTON ENTERPRISES INC.
411 W CHESTNUT AVE, ENID, OK 73701-2057
Phone: 580-233-5800
Web: WWW.JEINC.COM

COMPETITORS

ADM
Ag Processing Inc.
Andersons
Bartlett and Company
CGC
CHS
Cargill
DeBruce Grain
Owensboro Grain
Scoular
Stewart Grain

HISTORICAL FINANCIALS

Company Type: Private

Income Statement FYE: April 30

	REVENUE ($ mil.)	NET INCOME ($ mil.)	NET PROFIT MARGIN	EMPLOYEES
04/13	334	1	0.5%	280
04/12	297	1	0.5%	—
04/10	289	1	0.5%	—
04/10	140	0	0.2%	—
Annual Growth	33.6%	84.3%	—	—

2013 Year-End Financials

Debt ratio: —
Return on equity: 0.50%
Cash ($ mil.): 2
Current ratio: 0.10
Long-term debt ($ mil.): —
Dividends
Yield: —
Payout: —
Market value ($ mil.): —

JOINT COMMISSION ON ACCREDITATION OF HEALTHCARE ORGANIZATIONS

With an eye on improving performance and patient care the Joint Commission on Accreditation of Health Care Organizations is a nonprofit that provides accreditation and certification services. The group evaluates and accredits more than 20000 health care providers in the US. Its board of commissioners includes doctors nurses consumers and administrators. They evaluate hospitals health care networks nursing homes and other long-term care facilities laboratories and health-related groups. The Joint Commission's Quality Check website includes each accredited organization's quality review. The group also known simply as The Joint Commission was founded in 1951.

Geographic Reach

The Joint Commission on Accreditation of Health Care Organizations restricts the reach of its operations to US health care providers.

Operations

The commission is health care's oldest and largest standards-setting and accrediting body nationwide. To earn and maintain The Joint Commission's Gold Seal of Approval an organization must undergo an onsite survey by a Joint Commission survey team at least every three years.

The commission's corporate members include the American College of Physicians the American College of Surgeons the American Dental Association the American Hospital Association and the American Medical Association.

Strategy

Looking to help improve performance on ORYX core measures of patient care the Joint Commission in 2012 integrated performance expectations on accountability measures into its accreditation standards. Hospitals accredited by the Joint Commission are now expected to meet a new performance improvement requirement that establishes an 85% composite compliance target rate for performance on ORYX accountability measures.

EXECUTIVES

Senior Vice President, Paul Schyve
Vice President Standards Division And Survey Methods, Robert Wise
CFO, Paige A. Rodgers
EVP Business Development Government and External Relations, Charles A. (Chuck) Mowll
EVP Public Policy and Government Relations, Margaret A. VanAmringe
President and CEO, Mark R. Chassin
EVP Support Operations and Chief of Staff, Anne Marie Benedicto
EVP Customer Relations, Ann Scott Blouin
EVP and Chief Medical Officer, Ana Pujols McKee
VP and Chief Medical Officer, Erin S. DuPree
CIO and Enterprise Security Officer, John C. Mache
COO Accreditation and Certification Operations, Mark G. Pelletier
President and CEO Joint Commission International and Joint Commission Resources, Paula Wilson
Vice President Consulting Services Joint Commission Resources And Joint Commission International, Anne Rooney
Director Of Clinical Services, Leslie Duffy
Board Member, Khin Aungthein
Secretary, Orzella Wells
Secretary, Jan Burgess

LOCATIONS

HQ: JOINT COMMISSION ON ACCREDITATION OF HEALTHCARE ORGANIZATIONS
1 RENAISSANCE BLVD, OAKBROOK TERRACE, IL 60181-4805
Phone: 630-792-5000

PRODUCTS/OPERATIONS

Selected Programs and Services

Accreditation
- Ambulatory Health Care
- Behavioral Health Care
- Critical Access Hospitals
- Home Care
- Hospital
- Laboratory Services
- Nursing and Rehabilitation Center
- International Accreditation

Certification
- Disease-Specific Care Certification
- Advanced Disease-Specific Care Certification
- Advanced Certification for Palliative Care
- Health Care Staffing Services Certification

Programs
- Advanced Certification
- Ambulatory Health Care
- Behavioral Health Care
- Critical Access Hospitals
- Disease-Specific Care
- Health Care Staffing Services
- Home Care
- Hospitals
- Laboratory Services
- Nursing and Rehabilitation Center

HISTORICAL FINANCIALS

Company Type: Private

Income Statement FYE: December 31

	REVENUE ($ mil.)	NET INCOME ($ mil.)	NET PROFIT MARGIN	EMPLOYEES
12/11	180	8	4.6%	936
12/02	115	12	10.8%	—
12/01*	122	8	7.2%	—
03/01	1,045	0	0.0%	—
Annual Growth	(14.8%)	150.0%	—	—

*Fiscal year change

2011 Year-End Financials

Debt ratio: —
Return on equity: 4.60%
Cash ($ mil.): 31
Current ratio: 1.70
Long-term debt ($ mil.): —
Dividends
Yield: —
Payout: —
Market value ($ mil.): —

JORDAN CF INVESTMENTS LLP

A high-flier in construction services C.F. Jordan is a top building contractor that offers preconstruction design/build development and project management services. The company has traditionally built hotels and resorts but has diversified into military residential highway and school construction. Its contracts include projects for the Immigration and Naturalization Service for border patrol stations health care centers and detention centers. Other works have included Sea World in San Antonio the Insights Science Museum in El Paso and the Pearl Harbor Commissary and Exchange in Hawaii. Chairman Charles "Paco" Jordan started the Texas-based firm in 1988.

C.F. Jordan has worked throughout Texas as well as 30 other states and in Mexico. Its civil construction division works extensively on Texas Department of Transportation projects in West Texas and builds other highway and road construction projects in New Mexico. Its concrete division pours slabs and builds concrete garages in Texas and southern New Mexico.

EXECUTIVES

President and CEO, Darren G. Woody, age 50
Chairman, Charles F. (Paco) Jordan III
EVP El Paso, Paul Bauer
Secretary and CFO, J. Robert (Rob) Hutchison
EVP Dallas Commercial Division, Denis E. Gee
EVP San Antonio, David E. Baer
EVP Residential, Mark Lear
VP Risk and Safety Management, Patricia Kagerer
EVP Civil and Concrete Divisions, John Goodrich
EVP, Mike Miller
VP Houston, Jay F. Nelson
VP Corporate Estimating, James M. Roach
Controller, Cynthia Rogers
Executive Vice President Houston, Bob Richardson
Executive Vice President Central South Texas, Leland Rocchio

LOCATIONS

HQ: JORDAN CF INVESTMENTS LLP
7700 CF JORDAN DR, EL PASO, TX 79912-8808
Phone: 915-877-3333
Web: WWW.CFJORDAN.COM

COMPETITORS

Centex
Constructors & Associates
D.E. Harvey
D.R. Horton
Hensel Phelps Construction
Hunt Companies
Hunt Construction
J.D. Abrams
JC General Contractors
Manhattan Construction
Perini
Summit Builders
Turner Corporation

HISTORICAL FINANCIALS

Company Type: Private

Income Statement FYE: December 31

	REVENUE ($ mil.)	NET INCOME ($ mil.)	NET PROFIT MARGIN	EMPLOYEES
12/11	299	0	0.3%	500
12/09	337	3	1.1%	—
12/08	337	3	1.1%	—
12/05	259	2	1.0%	—
Annual Growth	2.4%	(16.0%)	—	—

2011 Year-End Financials

Debt ratio: —
Return on equity: 0.30%
Cash ($ mil.): 7
Current ratio: 0.20
Long-term debt ($ mil.): —
Dividends
Yield: —
Payout: —
Market value ($ mil.): —

JORDAN R. L. OIL CO OF NC INC

R. L. Jordan Oil Company takes gas from hot spots and sells it –and lots more –at Hot Spots. The company operates a chain of more than 50 convenience stores and gas stations under the Hot Spots banner as well as about 10 fast food restaurants under the Hardee's and Subway names. It operates in the Carolinas. About 75% of the company's stores are located in South Carolina. The family-owned and -operated company was founded by its namesake and former chairman in 1950 the late R. L. Jordan. As part of its operations the Jordan family also owns a real estate business Jordan Properties which operates several hotels and properties in North Carolina.

Operations

Besides convenience stores with gas stations and fast food establishments Jordon Oil Company extends its reach into the real estate business. The company manages properties such as the Crown Reef Resort Mountain High Motel and Tropical Seas Hotel.

Strategy

In recent years the convenience store operator has braced for the impact of a state cigarette tax hike of 50 cents per pack in South Carolina. (The price of a pack of cigarettes in the state has risen from $4.09 in 2009 to $5.21 on July 1 2010 as a result of recent federal and state tax increases.) The tax hike which took effect in July 2010 is expected to have a negative impact on sales. According to Jordan Oil cigarettes account for about 25% of sales at its South Carolina Hot Spot stores.

History

The foundation of Jordan Oil Company was built in 1950 from a small country store in Franklin North Carolina. Under the name Jordan's Self Serve the company represented the first gasoline station in its market to provide less expensive and unbranded gasoline.

EXECUTIVES

President, Dan Durbin
Director of HR, Deanna Williamson

LOCATIONS

HQ: JORDAN R. L. OIL CO OF NC INC
1451 FERNWOOD GLENDALE RD, SPARTANBURG, SC 29307-3044
Phone: 864-585-2784
Web: WWW.HOTSPOTCSTORE.COM

2012 Stores

	No.
South	41
North	13
Total	**54**

COMPETITORS

7-Eleven
Colonial Group
Cumberland Farms
Exxon Mobil
McDonald' s
Mountain Empire Oil
Quiznos
Racetrac Petroleum
Spinx
The Pantry

HISTORICAL FINANCIALS

Company Type: Private

Income Statement FYE: September 30

	REVENUE ($ mil.)	NET INCOME ($ mil.)	NET PROFIT MARGIN	EMPLOYEES
09/07	278	(0)	—	900
09/06	270	(1)	—	—
09/05	1,428	0	—	—
Annual Growth	—	—	—	—

2007 Year-End Financials

Debt ratio: —
Return on equity: (-0.10%)
Cash ($ mil.): 4
Current ratio: 0.60
Long-term debt ($ mil.): —
Dividends
Yield: —
Payout: —
Market value ($ mil.): —

JOSEPH B WHITEHEAD FOUNDATION

LOCATIONS

HQ: JOSEPH B WHITEHEAD FOUNDATION
191 PEACHTREE ST NE # 3540, ATLANTA, GA 303031740
Phone: 4045226755

HISTORICAL FINANCIALS

Company Type: Private

Income Statement FYE: December 31

	ASSETS ($ mil.)	NET INCOME ($ mil.)	INCOME AS % OF ASSETS	EMPLOYEES
12/12	94	0	0.4%	12
12/10	94	(0)	—	—
12/09*	94	1	1.6%	—
06/09	92	0	—	—
Annual Growth	0.5%	—	—	—

*Fiscal year change

2012 Year-End Financials

Debt ratio: —
Return on equity: 1.00%
Cash ($ mil.): 13
Current ratio: —
Long-term debt ($ mil.): —
Dividends
Yield: —
Payout: —
Market value ($ mil.): —

JOYCE LESLIE INC.

LOCATIONS

HQ: JOYCE LESLIE INC.
170 W COMMERCIAL AVE, MOONACHIE, NJ 070741706
Phone: 2018047800
Web: WWW.JOYCELESLIE.COM

2011 Stores

	No.
New	24
New	19
Pennsylvania	5
Connecticut	3
Total	**51**

COMPETITORS

A & E Stores
Ascena Retail
Big M
Cato
Charlotte Russe
Deb Shops
Forever 21
H&M
Pacific Sunwear
TJX Companies
Target Corporation
Urban Outfitters
Wet Seal
Zara
dELiA*s

HISTORICAL FINANCIALS

Company Type: Private

Income Statement FYE: January 30

	REVENUE ($ mil.)	NET INCOME ($ mil.)	NET PROFIT MARGIN	EMPLOYEES
01/10	101	1	1.3%	900
01/09	100	1	1.2%	—
01/08	1,654	0	0.0%	—
Annual Growth	(75.3%)	786.8%	—	—

2010 Year-End Financials

Debt ratio: —
Return on equity: 1.30%
Cash ($ mil.): 9
Current ratio: 0.90
Long-term debt ($ mil.): —
Dividends
Yield: —
Payout: —
Market value ($ mil.): —

JUPITER MEDICAL CENTER INC.

Nope no hospital on the fifth planet from the Sun. Located just north of West Palm Beach Jupiter Medical Center provides specialty services that include cancer treatment cardiology orthopedics emergency medicine wound care birthing and pain management. Not-for-profit Jupiter Medical Center consists of more than 160 private acute-care beds and 120 long-term rehab and hospice beds. The hospital is affiliated with the University of Miami's Miller School of Medicine. Established in 1956 as the convalescence center for a retirement village the medical center was transformed into a full-service acute-care hospital in 1979.

Strategy

In a climate of industry reformation Jupiter Medical Center is stretching out to make a transformational change beyond acute care strengthening its position by focusing on improving its services outcomes and costs. To that end the company launched NuVista Living in 2011 to become a partner in NuVista's Institute for Healthy Living Life Science and Research project under development. The $70 million facility expected to open in the spring of 2013 will expand the northern Palm Beach County community's access to a full spectrum of rehabilitative and long-term care while adding about 150 new jobs in the area.

EXECUTIVES

VP Marketing and Strategic Business Development, Stacey Brandt
VP and COO, Teresa (Terri) Wentz
VP Physician Services, Paula M. Zalucki
VP Long Term Care and Rehabilitative Services/Pavilion Administrator, Betsy Heartfield
President and CEO, John D. Couris, age 46
VP and CIO, Mike Fehr
VP Finance and CFO, Dale Hocking
VP Patient Care Services and Chief Nursing Officer, Steven Seeley
Vice President Human Resources, Peter Gloggner

Vice President General Counsel, Kelly Sullivan
Auditors: Deloitte&ToucheLLP

LOCATIONS

HQ: JUPITER MEDICAL CENTER INC.
1210 S OLD DIXIE HWY, JUPITER, FL 33458-7205
Phone: 561-747-2234
Web: WWW.JUPITERMED.COM

PRODUCTS/OPERATIONS

Selected Medical Services

Cancer Services
Cardiology
Clinical Research
Children's and Women's / OB
Comprehensive Breast Care
Diabetes Education
Digestive Health
Emergency Services
Health and Rehabilitation
Hospice Care
Imaging
Laboratory Services
Men's Health
Occupational Health
Orthopedic and Spine
Outpatient Medical Nutrition Therapy
Pain Management
The Pavilion
Sleep Center
Stroke Program
Surgical Services
Robotic Surgery
Thoracic Surgery
Travel Immunizations
Urgent Care
Weight Loss (Bariatrics)
Wound Care / Hyperbarics

COMPETITORS

Boca Raton Regional Hospital
Broward Health
Columbia Hospital
HCA
Heart & Family Health Institute
Lawnwood Medical Center
Northwest Medical Center
Palms West Hospital
Raulerson Hospital
South Broward Hospital District
St. Lucie Medical
Tenet Healthcare

HISTORICAL FINANCIALS

Company Type: Private

Income Statement FYE: September 30

	REVENUE ($ mil.)	NET INCOME ($ mil.)	NET PROFIT MARGIN	EMPLOYEES
09/12	174	6	3.8%	1,500
09/11	185	4	2.5%	—
09/09	176	16	9.1%	—
09/09	174	(0)	—	—
Annual Growth	0.1%	—	—	—

2012 Year-End Financials

Debt ratio: —
Return on equity: 3.80%
Cash ($ mil.): 9
Current ratio: 1.70
Long-term debt ($ mil.): —
Dividends
Yield: —
Payout: —
Market value ($ mil.): —

KADLEC REGIONAL MEDICAL CENTER

Kadlec Regional Medical Center is an acute care hospital facility serving southeastern Washington and northeastern Oregon. In addition to providing comprehensive medical surgical and emergency services the hospital provides neonatal intensive care cardiopulmonary rehabilitation interventional cardiology neurology cancer care and other specialist services. The not-for-profit Kadlec Regional Medical Center founded in 1944 has some 270 in-patient beds including pediatric intensive intermediate and critical care capacity. It also operates outpatient physician offices and clinics in surrounding areas.

Geographic Reach

Kadlec Regional Medical Center has hospital and clinic locations in Hermiston Kennewick Pasco Pendleton Prosser and Richland.

Operations

Kadlec Regional's cardiovascular programs include open heart surgery and interventional cardiology. The hospital also operates an all-digital outpatient imaging center and the region's only level III neonatal intensive care unit (NICU). Area specialist practices include centers for dermatology colorectal surgery nephrology pediatrics women's health ENT (ear nose and throat) and foot and ankle practices. Kadlec Regional also operates satellite urgent care and family practice clinics.

Financial Performance

The hospital reported revenue of $312 million in 2012 consisting of $305 million in net patient service earnings and other revenue of some $7.5 million. Kadlec Regional brought in profits of some $29 million.

Strategy

The hospital has undergone aggressive expansion efforts adding a new patient tower with diagnostic outpatient and intermediate care and surgery rooms. Kadlec Regional is enhancing its specialty service units in fields to attract specialists and increase revenue. For instance the organization launched a project to expand its NICU unit in 2013; the effort will add 27 private and semi-private rooms and new observation gathering and lactation areas.

It is also expanding outpatient service facilities such as a new $19 million three-story specialty physician practice office that opened in Richland in 2013. The new building increases collaboration between various surgical and medical specialists in the Kadlec Clinic organization.

The regional center also forms affiliations with area providers; for instance in 2011 it partnered with the nearby PMH Medical Center to increase collaboration and specialist referrals between the two hospitals. The partnership extends the reach of Kadlec's medical specialists to additional communities and is bringing PMH online with Kadlec's new electronic health record (EHR) system. Both hospitals remain independently run.

EXECUTIVES

Vice President Human Resources, Jeffrey Clark
Vice President Of Finance Svs, Julie Meek
Director Of Respiratory Therapy, Angela Mohondro
Director Icu/coronary Care Unit, Nancy Dahlberg
Director Of Infection Control, Cathy Johnson
Director Of Patient Relations, Debra Langston
Ambulatory Services Dir, Renee Sams
Auditors: MossAdamsLLP

LOCATIONS

HQ: KADLEC REGIONAL MEDICAL CENTER
888 SWIFT BLVD, RICHLAND, WA 99352-3514
Phone: 509-946-4611
Web: WWW.KADLEC.ORG

PRODUCTS/OPERATIONS

Selected Services

The Birth Center
Bloodless Medicine and Surgery
Cancer Care
Cardiac Care
Cardiac Catheterization
CardioPulmonary Rehabilitation
Cardiovascular and Thoracic Surgery
CaringBridge
Clinical Decision Unit
Coumadin Clinic
Diabetes Learning Center
Diagnostic Imaging
Don and Lori Watts Pediatric Center
Emergency Department
Emergency Room-Kennewick
Home Health Care
Imaging
Inpatient Rehabilitation and Therapy
Intensive Care Unit
Joint Care Center
Kadlec Academy
Kadlec Healthy Ages
Kadlec Medical Associates
Neonatal Intensive Care Unit
Occupational Medicine
Occupational Therapy
Ostomy Support Group
Outpatient Imaging Center
Outpatient Procedures
Physical Therapy
Planetree
Rehabilitation and Therapy Services
Speech Therapy
Urgent Care
Water Therapy
Wound Healing Center

COMPETITORS

Adventist Health
Asante Health System
Legacy Health System
PeaceHealth
Providence Health & Services
Sacred Heart Medical Center
Salem Hospital
Wenatchee Valley Medical Center
Yakima Valley Memorial

HISTORICAL FINANCIALS

Company Type: Private

Income Statement FYE: December 31

	REVENUE ($ mil.)	NET INCOME ($ mil.)	NET PROFIT MARGIN	EMPLOYEES
12/12	312	16	5.2%	2,668
12/10	277	3	1.3%	—
12/09	255	27	10.6%	—
12/08	216	(13)	—	—
Annual Growth	9.6%	—	—	—

2012 Year-End Financials

Debt ratio: —
Return on equity: 5.20%
Cash ($ mil.): 37
Current ratio: 1.80
Long-term debt ($ mil.): —
Dividends
Yield: —
Payout: —
Market value ($ mil.): —

KAISER FOUNDATION HOSPITALS INC

Kaiser Foundation Hospitals is on a roll. The hospital group one part of the Kaiser Permanente health care consortium operates three dozen acute care hospitals and almost 600 medical offices in nine states (California Colorado Georgia Hawaii Maryland Ohio Oregon Virginia and Washington) and Washington D.C. The company's largest presence is in California where the majority of its hospitals are located. Hawaii and Oregon are home to one hospital each; altogether its hospitals have more than 8500 beds. Specialty facilities include three behavioral health and chemical dependency clinics the Denver area and more than a dozen dental clinics in Oregon and Washington.

Kaiser Permanente is also made up of its doctors' group controlled by Permanente Medical Groups and its HMO offered through Kaiser Foundation Health Plan. Altogether about 8.8 million members are enrolled in its HMO.

LOCATIONS

HQ: KAISER FOUNDATION HOSPITALS INC
1 KAISER PLZ STE 2600, OAKLAND, CA 94612-3673
Phone: 510-271-5800
Web: WWW.HEALTHY.KAISERPERMANENTE.ORG

PRODUCTS/OPERATIONS

Selected Hospitals

Antioch Medical Center
Fremont Medical Center
Fresno Medical Center
Hayward Medical Center
Manteca Medical Center
Modesto Medical Center
Oakland Medical Center
Redwood City Medical Center
Richmond Medical Center
Roseville Women and Children's Center
San Jose Medical Center
Santa Clara Medical Center
Sacramento Medical Center
South San Francisco Medical Center
South Sacramento Trauma Center
Santa Rosa Medical Center
San Francisco Medical Center
San Rafael Medical Center
Vacaville Medical Center
Vallejo Medical Center
Walnut Creek Medical Center
Baldwin Park Medical Center
Downey Medical Center
Fontana Medical Center
Los Angeles Medical Center
Moreno Valley Community Hospital
Orange County - Anaheim Medical Center
Orange County - Irvine Medical Center
Panorama City Medical Center
Riverside Medical Center
San Diego Medical Center
Harbor City (South Bay Medical Center)
Woodlands Hills Medical Center
West Los Angeles Medical Center
Sunnyside Medical Center (Portland Oregon area)
Moanalua Medical Center (Hawaii)

COMPETITORS

Adventist Health
Ascension Health
Banner Health
CHRISTUS Health
Catholic Health Initiatives
Catholic Health Partners
Community Health Systems
Dignity Health
HCA
Health Management Associates
LifePoint Hospitals
Sutter Health
Tenet Healthcare
The Cleveland Clinic
Universal Health Services

HISTORICAL FINANCIALS

Company Type: Private

Income Statement

FYE: December 31

	REVENUE ($ mil.)	NET INCOME ($ mil.)	NET PROFIT MARGIN	EMPLOYEES
12/09	14,795	429	2.9%	49,000
12/08	0	0	99.0%	—
12/05	9,852	774	7.9%	—
Annual Growth	10.7%	(13.7%)	—	—

2009 Year-End Financials

Debt ratio: —
Return on equity: 2.90%
Cash ($ mil.): 57
Current ratio: —
Long-term debt ($ mil.): —
Dividends
Yield: —
Payout: —
Market value ($ mil.): —

KALEIDA HEALTH

EXECUTIVES

Vice Chair, Robert M. Zak, age 56
SVP Legal Services and General Counsel, Robert Nolan
Chair, John R. Koelmel, age 61
President CEO and Director, James R. (Jim) Kaskie, age 61
SVP Operations Buffalo General Medical Center, Cheryl Klass, age 58
VP; President DeGraff Memorial Hospital; President Millard Fillmore Suburban Hospital, Christopher T. (Chris) Lane
SVP Business Development, Donald (Don) Boyd
VP and Chief Marketing Officer, Michael P. (Mike) Hughes
EVP and Chief Medical Officer, Margaret Paroski
President Millard Fillmore Gates Circle Hospital, Tamara (Tammy) Owen
VP Long Term Care, Maureen Caruana
EVP and CFO, Joseph (Joe) Kessler
President of Buffalo General, Lawrence (Larry) Zielinski
Chief Nursing Executive, Mary Beth Campo
VP Clinical Engineering, David Croston
President of DeGraff, Anthony (Tony) Zito
EVP and Chief Human Resources Officer, Toni L. Booker
President VNA, Judy Baumgartner
Vice Chair, Robert M. Zak, age 56
Director, Robert Halonen
President CEO and Director, James R. (Jim) Kaskie, age 61
Director, James A.W. McLeod
Director, Herman S. Mogavero Jr.
Director, Dale N. Schumacher
Director, Evan Evans
Director, Muriel Howard
Director, Francisco M. Vasquez
Director, David A. Milling
Director, James Budny
Director, Rev Matthew L. Brown
Director, Joyce P. Korzen
Auditors: KPMGLLP

LOCATIONS

HQ: KALEIDA HEALTH
726 EXCHANGE ST, BUFFALO, NY 142101484
Phone: 7168598000
Web: WWW.KALEIDAHEALTH.ORG

PRODUCTS/OPERATIONS

Selected Facilities

Buffalo General Hospital (Buffalo)
Deaconess Center (Buffalo)
DeGraff Memorial Hospital (North Tonawanda)
Gates Vascular Institute (Buffalo)
Millard Fillmore Suburban Hospital (Williamsville)
VNA Home Care Services (Allegany County Chautauqua County Erie County Genesee County Niagara County)
Women and Children's Hospital of Buffalo (Buffalo)

COMPETITORS

Catholic Health East
Catholic Health System
Ellis Hospital
Hamot Medical Center
Kane Community Hospital
Lifetime Health
Oneida Healthcare Center
SUNY Upstate Medical University
St. Joseph' s Hospital Health Center
St. Peter' s Health Partners
St. Vincent Health System
Titusville
United Health Services Hospitals
Unity Health System
Upstate University Hospital at Community General

HISTORICAL FINANCIALS

Company Type: Private

Income Statement

FYE: December 31

	REVENUE ($ mil.)	NET INCOME ($ mil.)	NET PROFIT MARGIN	EMPLOYEES
12/09	1,155	75	6.5%	9,000
12/08	1,102	(208)	—	—
12/07	1,059	81	7.7%	—
12/06	997	0	—	—
Annual Growth	5.0%	—	—	—

2009 Year-End Financials

Debt ratio: —
Return on equity: 6.50%
Cash ($ mil.): 118
Current ratio: 0.70
Long-term debt ($ mil.): —
Dividends
Yield: —
Payout: —
Market value ($ mil.): —

KAMO ELECTRIC COOPERATIVE INC.

LOCATIONS

HQ: KAMO ELECTRIC COOPERATIVE INC.
500 S KAMO DR, VINITA, OK 743014613
Phone: 9182565551
Web: WWW.KAMOPOWER.COM

HISTORICAL FINANCIALS

Company Type: Private

Income Statement

FYE: December 31

	REVENUE ($ mil.)	NET INCOME ($ mil.)	NET PROFIT MARGIN	EMPLOYEES
12/13	372	24	6.6%	154
12/12	354	21	6.2%	—
12/11	361	19	5.3%	—
12/10	332	0	—	—
Annual Growth	3.9%	—	—	—

2013 Year-End Financials

Debt ratio: —
Return on equity: 6.60%
Cash ($ mil.): 5
Current ratio: 0.30
Long-term debt ($ mil.): —
Dividends
Yield: —
Payout: —
Market value ($ mil.): —

KANSAS ELECTRIC POWER COOPERATIVE INC.

If Dorothy lived in rural Kansas today she'd probably hear that tornado warning and reach safety thanks to the power supplied by Kansas Electric Power Cooperative (KEPCo). KEPCo operates power plants and purchases additional energy for its 19 member distribution cooperatives which serve more than 110000 rural customers. The generation and transmission utility's assets include a 6% stake in Wolf Creek Nuclear Operating Corporation which operates Kansas' Wolf Creek Generating Station. Subsidiary KSI Engineering provides utility construction and infrastructure services. KEPCo which was formed in 1975 is part of the alliance of Touchstone Energy Cooperatives.

KEPCo generates 70 MW of power. Additional resources include the Sharpe Generating Station in Coffey County (20MW) hydroelectric power purchases of 100 MW from the Southwestern Power Administration and 14 MW from the Western Area Power Administration. It also purchases power from regional utilities as needed. With an eye on the increasing requirements of environmental regulations some 50% of its energy mix is from non-carbon emitting sources (nuclear and hydroelectric).

Securing a long term energy supply deal in 2007 the company signed a 38-year agreement with Westar Energy to supply the bulk of its power needs.

EXECUTIVES

EVP and CEO, Stephen E. Parr
VP Energy and Technical Services, Robert (Bob) Bowser
Business Development Coordinator, Loren Medley
Director Member Services and External Affairs, Phil Wages
Member Executive Committee, Melroy Kopsa
VP Finance and Controller, Coleen Wells
Manager Engineering; VP KSI Engineering, Mark Barbee
VP Administration and General Counsel, J. Michael Peters
President, Kenneth J. (Ken) Maginley
SVP and COO, Tom Grennan
VP Power Supply, Les Evans
Senior Engineer, John Payne
Member Executive Committee, Robert Reece
VP, Kirk Thompson
Member Executive Committee, Harlow Haney
Accounting Payroll and Benefits Specialist, Shari Koch
Manager Officer Services and Executive Assistant, Rita Petty
Treasurer, Bryan Coover
Secretary, Gordon Coulter
System Operator, Paul Stone
Operations Manager, Leah Tindle
Auditors: KPMGLLP

LOCATIONS

HQ: KANSAS ELECTRIC POWER COOPERATIVE INC.
600 SW CORPORATE VW, TOPEKA, KS 66615-1233
Phone: 785-273-7010
Web: WWW.KEPCO.ORG

HISTORICAL FINANCIALS

Company Type: Private

Income Statement FYE: December 31

	REVENUE ($ mil.)	NET INCOME ($ mil.)	NET PROFIT MARGIN	EMPLOYEES
12/11	162	10	6.7%	24
12/10	140	7	5.4%	—
12/08	122	9	7.6%	—
12/08	121	5	4.5%	—
Annual Growth	10.1%	25.6%	—	—

2011 Year-End Financials

Debt ratio: —
Return on equity: 6.70%
Cash ($ mil.): 8
Current ratio: 0.10
Long-term debt ($ mil.): —
Dividends
Yield: —
Payout: —
Market value ($ mil.): —

KANSAS STATE UNIVERSITY

K-State is a big deal in the Little Apple. Located in Manhattan Kansas (aka the Little Apple) Kansas State University (K-State) is a land grant institution that has an enrollment of some 24000 students. It offers more than 250 undergraduate majors 65 master's degrees 45 doctoral degrees and more than 20 graduate certificate programs. Major fields of study include agriculture technology and veterinary medicine. Notable alumni include former White House press secretary Marlin Fitzwater and actor Gordon Jump. Along with the University of Kansas and other universities technical schools and community colleges in the state K-State is governed by The Kansas Board of Regents.

Geographic Reach

K-State has its main campus on 670-acres in Manhattan Kansas. It also has satellite campuses in Salina and Olathe. It also has agricultural and research centers at five Kansas locations. The university's students come from all 50 US states and more than 90 countries.

Operations

With a student-to-faculty ratio of 20:1 K-State ranks among top US colleges and has one of the highest levels of prestigious scholarship winners (including Rhodes Marshall and Truman scholars) in the US. The university also has several notable research organizations in fields including agriculture and genetic science.

K-State is also big on sports and is part of the Big 12 Conference of collegiate athletics.

Financial Performance

K-State increased revenues by 9% to $541 million in 2012 due to higher income from student fees; government and non-government grants and contracts (for research and athletic activities); and auxiliary enterprises. Net income decreased 24% to $47 million due to higher operating expenses and lower non-operating revenues which was attributed to lower state appropriation levels and higher interest expenses.

Strategy

K-State is expanding its facilities and programs to meet the needs of its students. It completed the first $22 million phase of its National Bio and Agro-Defense Facility in 2012 as well as work on a new student recreational housing classroom and athletics facilities. In 2011 it added a new bachelor's degree program in social work. It also expanded its partnership with the Chinese scholarship council to allow additional students from China to study at K-State.

Company Background

K-State was established in 1858 as Bluemont Central College; five years later it was one of the first colleges in the US to be designated a land-grant school.

EXECUTIVES

VP Administration and Finance, Bruce Shubert
VP Research, Ronald W. (Ron) Trewyn
SVP Academic Affairs, Ruth Dyer
SVP and Provost, April Mason
VP Communications and Marketing, Jeffery (Bob) Morris
President, Kirk Schulz
VP Student Life and Dean of Students, Pat Bosco
Senior Vice-President, K-State Provost

LOCATIONS

HQ: KANSAS STATE UNIVERSITY
ANDERSON HALL 110, MANHATTAN, KS 66506
Phone: 785-532-6210
Web: WWW.FOUND.KSU.EDU

PRODUCTS/OPERATIONS

Selected Colleges and Departments

College of Agriculture
- Agricultural Economics
- Agronomy
- Animal Sciences and Industry
- Entomology
- Food Science Institute
- Grain Science and Industry
- Plant Pathology

College of Architecture Planning and Design
- Architecture
- Interior Architecture and Product Design
- Landscape Architecture/Regional and Community Planning

College of Arts and Sciences
- Aerospace Studies
- American Ethnic Studies
- Art
- Biochemistry
- Chemistry
- Economics
- English
- Geography
- Geology
- History
- International and Area Studies
- Journalism and Mass Communications
- Kinesiology
- Mathematics
- Military Science
- Modern Languages
- Music
- Philosophy
- Physics
- Political Science
- Psychology
- Statistics
- Women's Studies

College of Business Administration
- Accounting
- Finance
- Management
- Marketing

College of Education
- Educational Leadership
- Elementary Education
- Secondary Education
- Special Education Counseling and Student Affairs

College of Engineering
- Architectural Engineering and Construction Science
- Biological and Agricultural Engineering
- Chemical Engineering
- Computing and Information Science
- Electrical and Computer Engineering
- Mechanical and Nuclear Engineering

College of Human Ecology
- Apparel Textiles and Interior Design
- Gerontology
- Human Nutrition

College of Technology and Aviation
- Arts Sciences and Business
- Aviation Technology

College of Veterinary Medicine
- Anatomy and Physiology
- Clinical Sciences

COMPETITORS

Baylor University
Iowa State University
Oklahoma State
Texas A&M
Texas Tech
The University of Kansas
University of Colorado
University of Missouri
University of Nebraska
University of Oklahoma
University of Texas
Wichita State University

HISTORICAL FINANCIALS

Company Type: Private

Income Statement FYE: June 30

	REVENUE ($ mil.)	NET INCOME ($ mil.)	NET PROFIT MARGIN	EMPLOYEES
06/10	459	50	11.0%	5,168
06/09	420	10	2.6%	—
06/09	1,988	0	0.0%	—
Annual Growth	(76.9%)	18858724.3%	—	—

2010 Year-End Financials

Debt ratio: —
Return on equity: 11.00%
Cash ($ mil.): 133
Current ratio: 1.90
Long-term debt ($ mil.): —
Dividends
Yield: —
Payout: —
Market value ($ mil.): —

KBS INC.

EXECUTIVES

VP Operations, Richard (Rich) Lee

LOCATIONS

HQ: KBS INC.
8050 KIMWAY DR, RICHMOND, VA 232282831
Phone: 8042620100
Web: WWW.KBSGC.COM

COMPETITORS

Branch & Associates
Hitt
Milestone Construction
SMCI
W.M. Jordan

HISTORICAL FINANCIALS

Company Type: Private

Income Statement FYE: September 30

	REVENUE ($ mil.)	NET INCOME ($ mil.)	NET PROFIT MARGIN	EMPLOYEES
09/13	151	1	1.2%	130
09/12	192	2	1.1%	—
09/11	159	2	1.8%	—
09/10	153	0	—	—
Annual Growth	(0.4%)	—	—	—

2013 Year-End Financials

Debt ratio: —
Return on equity: 1.20%
Cash ($ mil.): 7
Current ratio: 1.00
Long-term debt ($ mil.): —
Dividends
Yield: —
Payout: —
Market value ($ mil.): —

KEENAN HOPKINS SUDER & STOWELL CONTRACTORS INC.

LOCATIONS

HQ: KEENAN HOPKINS SUDER & STOWELL CONTRACTORS INC.
5109 E LA PALMA AVE STE A, ANAHEIM, CA 928072066
Phone: 7146953670
Web: WWW.KHSS.COM

HISTORICAL FINANCIALS

Company Type: Private

Income Statement FYE: December 31

	REVENUE ($ mil.)	NET INCOME ($ mil.)	NET PROFIT MARGIN	EMPLOYEES
12/09	265	5	1.9%	2,000
12/08	325	17	5.4%	—
12/07	824	0	0.0%	—
Annual Growth	(43.3%)	16724.4%	—	—

2009 Year-End Financials

Debt ratio: —
Return on equity: 1.90%
Cash ($ mil.): 2
Current ratio: 1.30
Long-term debt ($ mil.): —
Dividends
Yield: —
Payout: —
Market value ($ mil.): —

KELLSTROM AEROSPACE LLC

Does the spell-check at aircraft parts inventory service Kellstrom Aerospace correct "enginuity"? Using its ingenuity to specialize in engines made by CFM International General Electric Pratt & Whitney and Rolls-Royce the company supplies new and overhauled products for military and commercial aircraft. Kellstrom doing business as Kellstrom Industries also provides maintenance for military and commercial aircraft components. Customers include commercial airlines US and foreign military forces and maintenance repair and overhaul facilities. Kellstrom Aerospace was established in 1990 and has been privately owned since 2002.

Geographic Reach

Kellstrom has offices in Austria Denmark Finland Germany Greenland Iceland Ireland Norway Sweden Switzerland Israel Cyprus Greece Turkey the UK and the US.

Operations

The company operates through two primary business segments. Commercial Aerospace supplies aircraft parts as well as provides logistics and material management support to customers that have included Delta Air Lines Eagle Services-Asia and Beaver Aerospace. Its Defense Aerospace segment focuses on the T-56 engine as well as engines for the C-130 Hercules P-3 Orion F-16 Fighting Falcon.

Strategy

Kellstrom strengthened its market presence in mid-2013 through the purchase of AirLiance Materials a supplier of high-quality surplus parts to the global air transport and MRO industry. The deal fortified Kellstrom's Commercial Aerospace segment and augmented its customer base to more than 1000 customers.

Ownership

Investment firm Inverness Management owns a controlling stake in Kellstrom. It led a group that bought the assets in 2002 of Kellstrom Industries which had filed for Chapter 11 bankruptcy earlier that year.

EXECUTIVES

President and CEO, Dennis A. Zalupski

LOCATIONS

HQ: KELLSTROM AEROSPACE LLC
3701 S FLAMINGO RD, MIRAMAR, FL 33027-2934
Phone: 954-538-2000
Web: WWW.ARROWHEAD.KELLSTROM.COM

PRODUCTS/OPERATIONS

Selected Products and Services

Aerospace Distribution - Aftermarket Parts
Commercial Aerospace
- Commercial airframes
- Commercial engines
- Inventory management & support
- Purchasing management
- Repair management & support

Defense Aerospace
- Engines
  - C-130
  - P-3
  - F-16
  - T-56
- Military aircraft and parts
- Repair

Kellstrom Power Group - Aeroderivative gas turbines
Repair & Repair Management - High Tech Avionics and Accessories
- Air data computers
- Auto pilots
- FAA approved repair and overhaul
- Flight control systems
- Flight management computers
- Mode control panels
- TCAS computers

COMPETITORS

AAR Corp.
Banner Aerospace
First Aviation
Thales Communications
Triumph Group
Willis Lease

HISTORICAL FINANCIALS

Company Type: Private

Income Statement FYE: December 31

	REVENUE ($ mil.)	NET INCOME ($ mil.)	NET PROFIT MARGIN	EMPLOYEES
12/12	180	6	3.5%	262
12/11	155	0	0.6%	—
12/10	149	2	1.8%	—
12/09	163	1	1.1%	—
Annual Growth	3.4%	53.9%	—	—

KENERGY CORP.

Kenergy kens energy as the Scots might say. Electric distribution cooperative Kenergy serves about 55000 customers in 14 counties (Breckinridge Caldwell Crittenden Daviess Hancock Henderson Hopkins Livingston Lyon McLean Muhlenberg Ohio Union and Webster) in Western Kentucky. Kenergy serves its customer base of households commercial enterprises and industries via more than 6700 miles of power lines. The customer-owned company is part of Touchstone Energy Cooperatives a national alliance of more than 600 local consumer-owned electric utility cooperatives.

EXECUTIVES

VP Operations, Gerald J. Ford, age 67
VP Engineering, John Newland
VP Finance and Accounting, Steve Thompson
VP Human Resources, Keith Ellis
President and CEO, Sanford (Sandy) Novick
Auditors: RineyHancock&Co.PSC

LOCATIONS

HQ: KENERGY CORP.
6402 OLD CORYDON RD, HENDERSON, KY 42420-9392
Phone: 270-926-4141
Web: WWW.KENERGYCORP.COM

COMPETITORS

Duke Energy Kentucky
Kentucky Utilities
Warren RECC

HISTORICAL FINANCIALS

Company Type: Private

Income Statement FYE: December 31

	REVENUE ($ mil.)	NET INCOME ($ mil.)	NET PROFIT MARGIN	EMPLOYEES
12/12	495	0	0.0%	155
12/11	426	0	0.0%	—
12/02	402	5	1.5%	—
12/09	350	2	0.8%	—
Annual Growth	12.2%	(64.4%)	—	—

2012 Year-End Financials

Debt ratio: ——
Return on equity: —
Cash ($ mil.): 1
Current ratio: 0.30
Long-term debt ($ mil.): —
Dividends
Yield: —
Payout: —
Market value ($ mil.): —

KENNEDY HEALTH SYSTEM INC.

Like its namesake The Kennedy Health System is all about service to the public. The Kennedy Health System operates three acute care hospitals with more than 600 beds in southern interior New Jersey. Its operations include several outpatient centers and wellness programs cancer care dialysis centers primary care facilities and a nursing home. Its outpatient services are vast and varied. They range from behavioral and occupational health centers to balance centers (to treat dizziness and balance problems) and sleep centers. The system is affiliated with the University of Medicine and Dentistry of New Jersey (UMDNJ). The Kennedy Health System was founded in 1965 as John F. Kennedy Hospital.

Geographic Reach

Kennedy Health serves residents in the New Jersey counties of Burlington Camden and Gloucester. Its southern New Jersey hospitals are located in Cherry Hill Stratford and Washington Township.

Operations

Kennedy Health employs more than 4000 health care professionals and associates including 900 physicians. Its Kennedy University Hospital in Washington Township has specialist centers for wound care diagnostics stroke and neonatal care some of which are nationally recognized. Through its affiliation with UMDNJ the organization provides one of the largest physician training programs in New Jersey.

In addition to the hospitals 600 acute care beds the system's Kennedy Health Care Center is a 130-bed skilled nursing and rehabilitation home for seniors.

Financial Performance

The health system reported revenues of $457 million in 2011.

Strategy

In 2013 Kennedy Health expanded the Kennedy Cancer Center by adding a TrueBeam linear accelerator which allows doctors to perform more precise cancer treatment procedures. The system also expanded its outpatient wound care program by partnering with Accelecare to operate an advanced wound care and hyperbaric oxygen therapy center on the Kennedy University Hospital campus.

EXECUTIVES

Director Orthopedic Service Line, John K. Mariani
President & Chief Executive Officer, Martin A. Bieber
VP Medical Affairs/GME, Christopher J. Barone
VP Marketing, Frances G. Atkinson
President & Chief Executive Officer, Joseph W. Devine
VP Ambulatory Services, Richard Koss
Senior Vice President and Chief Medical Officer for Kennedy University Hospital, David V. Condoluci
Chairman, John P. Silvestri
Treasurer, Michele A. Fletcher
Secretary, Barry M. Weinberg
VP Information Systems and Technology and CIO, Thomas J. Balcavage
Senior Vice President Clinical Operations Chief Nursing Officer, Linda A. Carrick
Vice President of Human Resources, Anneliese McMenamin
Senior Vice President Chief Finance Officer, Gary Terrinoni
Vice President of Finance, Gui Valladares
Vice President Hospital Operations, Lisa A. Dutterer
Senior Vice President Clinical Integration, Carman Ciervo
Senior Vice President & Chief Financial Officer, Gary Terrinoni
Senior Vice President Chief Legal Officer, Edward Sullivan
VP-Performance Improvement, Patricia Wallace
Vice President of Clinical Services, Jonathan McCarthy
Vice President of Planning, Louis Liebhaber
Vice President of Facilities Management, James Huynh
Vice President Clinical Services, Helene Burns
Chief Administrative Officer, Jim Mullen
Director, Harry T. Gamble
Director, Donald A. Barone
Director, Stanley J.C. Giberson Sr.
Director, John H. Lucas
Director, Joseph A. Maressa
Director, Bruce J. Paparone
Director, Daniel J. Ragone
Director, Albert E. Smith
Vice Chairman, John F. Durante

LOCATIONS

HQ: KENNEDY HEALTH SYSTEM INC.
1099 WHITE HORSE RD, VOORHEES, NJ 08043-4405
Phone: 856-488-6500
Web: WWW.KENNEDYHEALTH.ORG

PRODUCTS/OPERATIONS

Selected Services and Units

Ambulatory Services
Balance Center
Bariatric Surgery
Behavioral Health
Cancer Center
Diabetes Control Center
Kennedy Health Alliance
Kennedy Foundation
Kennedy Neuroscience Center
Laboratory Services
Medical Imaging
Robotic Surgery
Sleep Center
STAT Medical Transport
Women' s and Children' s Services

COMPETITORS

Albert Einstein Healthcare Network
Capital Health System
Children' s Hospital of Philadelphia
Crozer-Keystone Health System
Fox Chase Cancer Center
Inspira Health Network
Lourdes Health
Our Lady of Lourdes Medical Center
Princeton HealthCare
Shore Memorial Hospital
Tenet Healthcare
The Cooper Health System
University of Pennsylvania Health System
Virtua Health

HISTORICAL FINANCIALS

Company Type: Private

Income Statement FYE: September 30

	REVENUE ($ mil.)	NET INCOME ($ mil.)	NET PROFIT MARGIN	EMPLOYEES
09/09*	355	10	3.1%	3,030
12/08	455	(15)	—	—
12/07	16	0	—	—
Annual Growth	—23787.8%		—	—

*Fiscal year change

2009 Year-End Financials

Debt ratio: ——
Return on equity: 3.10%
Cash ($ mil.): 23
Current ratio: 0.70
Long-term debt ($ mil.): —
Dividends
Yield: —
Payout: —
Market value ($ mil.): —

KENTUCKY MEDICAL SERVICES FOUNDATION INC.

Does the mailbox at your old Kentucky home contain doctors' bills? They might be from Kentucky Medical Services Foundation Inc. The physician's practice group provides billing and other administrative services for the more than 600 physicians and other health care providers affiliated with the University of Kentucky's medical center which offers more than 80 specialty services and programs.

EXECUTIVES

Executive Director, Darrell Griffith
IT Manager, Jamie Tillett

Associate Director Business Operations, Peggy Halcomb
Human Resources Manager, Garland Strang

LOCATIONS

HQ: KENTUCKY MEDICAL SERVICES FOUNDATION INC.
2333 ALUMNI PARK PLZ # 200, LEXINGTON, KY 40517-4012
Phone: 859-257-7910
Web: WWW.KMSF.ORG

COMPETITORS

Appalachian Regional Healthcare
Baptist Health
Catholic Health Initiatives
Jewish Hospital & St. Mary' s HealthCare
Norton Healthcare

HISTORICAL FINANCIALS

Company Type: Private

Income Statement FYE: June 30

	REVENUE ($ mil.)	NET INCOME ($ mil.)	NET PROFIT MARGIN	EMPLOYEES
06/10	196	(4)	—	150
06/09	189	2	1.4%	—
06/09	1,523	0	—	—
Annual Growth	(87.1%)	—	—	—

2010 Year-End Financials

Debt ratio: —
Return on equity: (-2.30%)
Cash ($ mil.): 27
Current ratio: 0.60
Long-term debt ($ mil.): —
Dividends
Yield: —
Payout: —
Market value ($ mil.): —

KETTERING MEDICAL CENTER

Kettering Health Network keeps Ohio in a healthy state. The network named for famed inventor Charles F. Kettering is an Ohio-based health care system comprised of about 90 facilities including seven acute care hospitals: Kettering Medical Center Grandview Medical Center Sycamore Medical Center Southview Medical Center Fort Hamilton Hospital Greene Memorial Hospital and Soin Medical Center. Other facilities include a mental health hospital (Kettering Behavioral Hospital) and multiple outpatient diagnostic senior care and urgent care clinics. Among its specialized services are heart care rehabilitation orthopedics women's health and emergency medicine.

Geographic Reach

Kettering Health's facilities are located in Dayton Ohio and surrounding towns including Beavercreek Hamilton Kettering Miamisburg and Xenia.

Operations

Kettering Health has been named to the Thomson Reuter's list of the Top 10 US Healthcare Systems several times in recent years.

As a not-for-profit entity Kettering Health provides some $120 million in community care benefits each year including health screenings education programs charity care for uninsured patients and covering Medicare/Medicaid shortfalls for under-insured patients).

Strategy

Kettering makes capital investments in its medical centers to better serve its communities. In 2012 it opened a new hospital the Soin Medical Center to serve the Dayton-area community of Beavercreek. The $135 million construction project created a five-story 95-bed medical center featuring emergency maternity orthopedic and surgery units.

Kettering works to improve specialty units and equipment at its existing inpatient hospitals as well as technologically advanced hospitals tend to attract better physicians and therefore patients. The company launched a $5 million improvement project to enhance emergency room services at the Fort Hamilton Hospital in 2012 including physician recruitment efforts and new service provisions. A 5000-sq. ft. facility addition will also increase the department's capacity from 36000 patients to 52000 patients per year.

The health network is also intent on expanding its outpatient facility network. For instance in 2011 it added a new emergency department to the Huber Health Center an outpatient care center in Huber Height to enhance care for area residents. The $9 million expansion effort added 40 new health professionals to the facility. In addition the company added a new primary care office in Liberty Township in 2012.

Mergers and Acquisitions

Kettering Health added another hospital in 2010 when the 175-bed Fort Hamilton Hospital joined its ranks. Fort Hamilton had exited its former affiliation with UC Health (previously named The Health Alliance) and joined the Kettering network to gain the benefits of belonging to a larger organization such as group purchasing and pooled administrative functions.

EXECUTIVES

President and CEO, Francisco J. (Frank) Perez
CEO, Fred Manchur
President Kettering and Sycamore Hospital, Roy Chew
President Grandview and Southview Hospital, Richard Haas
President Soin and Greene Hospital, Terry Burns
President Kettering Health Network, Terri Day
President Fort Hamilton Hospital, Mark Smith

LOCATIONS

HQ: KETTERING MEDICAL CENTER
3535 SOUTHERN BLVD, KETTERING, OH 45429-1298
Phone: 937-298-4331
Web: WWW.KETTERINGHEALTH.ORG

PRODUCTS/OPERATIONS

Selected Ohio Facilities

Acute Care Hospitals
Fort Hamilton Hospital (Hamilton)
Grandview Medical Center (Dayton)
Greene Memorial Hospital (Xenia)
Kettering Medical Center (Kettering)
Soin Medical Center (Beavercreek)
Southview Medical Center (Dayton)
Sycamore Medical Center (Miamisburg)
Other
Adolescent Recovery Center of Hope
Beavercreek Health Center
Beavercreek Health Park
Charles H. Huber Health Center
Corwin M. Nixon Health Center
Englewood Community Medical Center
Kettering Behavioral Hospital (Dayton)
Sugarcreek Health Center
Sycamore Glen Health Center
Sycamore Glen Retirement Center
Sycamore Primary Care Center
Urgent Care Centers (regional)

COMPETITORS

AdCare
Adena Health System
Catholic Health Partners
Cincinnati Children' s Hospital
MetroHealth System
Mount Carmel Health
OhioHealth
Premier Health Partners
Regency Hospital
Fairfield Medical Center
Licking Memorial Health Systems
MedCath
Select Medical
TriHealth
UC Health
University Hospitals Health System

HISTORICAL FINANCIALS

Company Type: Private

Income Statement FYE: December 31

	REVENUE ($ mil.)	NET INCOME ($ mil.)	NET PROFIT MARGIN	EMPLOYEES
12/09	531	40	7.6%	3,100
12/04	628	40	6.4%	—
12/03	568	561	98.6%	—
12/02	496	5	1.1%	—
Annual Growth	1.0%	33.4%	—	—

2009 Year-End Financials

Debt ratio: —
Return on equity: 7.60%
Cash ($ mil.): 13
Current ratio: 0.20
Long-term debt ($ mil.): —
Dividends
Yield: —
Payout: —
Market value ($ mil.): —

KEY COOPERATIVE

LOCATIONS

HQ: KEY COOPERATIVE
13585 620TH AVE, ROLAND, IA 502368061
Phone: 5153884341
Web: WWW.KEYCOOP.COM

HISTORICAL FINANCIALS

Company Type: Private

Income Statement FYE: September 30

	REVENUE ($ mil.)	NET INCOME ($ mil.)	NET PROFIT MARGIN	EMPLOYEES
09/14	371	4	1.1%	180
09/13	531	10	2.0%	—
09/12	541	8	1.5%	—
09/11	451	0	—	—
Annual Growth	(6.3%)	—	—	—

2014 Year-End Financials

Debt ratio: —
Return on equity: 1.10%
Cash ($ mil.): 5
Current ratio: 0.80
Long-term debt ($ mil.): —
Dividends
Yield: —
Payout: —
Market value ($ mil.): —

KEY FOOD STORES CO-OPERATIVE INC.

EXECUTIVES

Senior Director Nonperishables, Paul Orecchia
SVP, Jerry Cesaro
Senior Director Finance, Chet Koby
CEO, Dean Janeway
Controller, Barbara Leonardis

LOCATIONS

HQ: KEY FOOD STORES CO-OPERATIVE INC.
1200 SOUTH AVE, STATEN ISLAND, NY 103143413
Phone: 7183704200
Web: WWW.KEYFOODS.COM

PRODUCTS/OPERATIONS

Selected Banners

Food Dynasty
Food World
Holiday Farms
Key Food
Key Food Marketplace
Key Fresh & Natural
Locust Valley
Milford Farms
Urban Market

COMPETITORS

A&P
D' Agostino Supermarkets
Food Emporium
Fresh Direct
Gristede' s Foods
King Kullen Grocery
Walgreen

HISTORICAL FINANCIALS

Company Type: Private

Income Statement FYE: April 26

	REVENUE ($ mil.)	NET INCOME ($ mil.)	NET PROFIT MARGIN	EMPLOYEES
04/14	753	0	0.0%	66
04/11	537	(0)	—	—
04/10	0	0	—	—
Annual Growth	—	—	—	—

2014 Year-End Financials

Debt ratio: —
Return on equity: —
Cash ($ mil.): 6
Current ratio: 0.90
Long-term debt ($ mil.): —
Dividends
Yield: —
Payout: —
Market value ($ mil.): —

KEYSTONE EQUIPMENT FINANCE CORP.

LOCATIONS

HQ: KEYSTONE EQUIPMENT FINANCE CORP.
433 NEW PARK AVE, WEST HARTFORD, CT 061101141
Phone: 8602333663
Web: WWW.KEYSTONEEFC.COM

HISTORICAL FINANCIALS

Company Type: Private

Income Statement FYE: December 31

	ASSETS ($ mil.)	NET INCOME ($ mil.)	INCOME AS % OF ASSETS	EMPLOYEES
12/08	51	1	3.8%	26
12/07	61	3	5.5%	—
12/06	0	0	12.7%	—
Annual Growth	1904.1%	998.6%	—	—

2008 Year-End Financials

Debt ratio: —
Return on equity: 10.10%
Cash ($ mil.): 4
Current ratio: —
Long-term debt ($ mil.): —
Dividends
Yield: —
Payout: —
Market value ($ mil.): —

KIMBALL HILL INC

LOCATIONS

HQ: KIMBALL HILL INC
5999 NEW WILKE RD STE 306, ROLLING MEADOWS, IL 600084503
Phone: 8473647300
Web: WWW.KHHCORP.COM

HISTORICAL FINANCIALS

Company Type: Private

Income Statement FYE: September 30

	REVENUE ($ mil.)	NET INCOME ($ mil.)	NET PROFIT MARGIN	EMPLOYEES
09/07	900	(220)	—	900
09/05	1,146	86	7.6%	—
09/04	927	55	6.0%	—
09/03	786	0		
Annual Growth	3.4%	—	—	—

2007 Year-End Financials

Debt ratio: —
Return on equity: (-24.50%)
Cash ($ mil.): 31
Current ratio: —
Long-term debt ($ mil.): —
Dividends
Yield: —
Payout: —
Market value ($ mil.): —

KING COUNTY PUBLIC HOSPITAL DISTRICT NO 2

LOCATIONS

HQ: KING COUNTY PUBLIC HOSPITAL DISTRICT NO 2
12040 NE 128TH ST, KIRKLAND, WA 980343013
Phone: 4258991000

HISTORICAL FINANCIALS

Company Type: Private

Income Statement FYE: December 31

	REVENUE ($ mil.)	NET INCOME ($ mil.)	NET PROFIT MARGIN	EMPLOYEES
12/07	301	6	2.3%	2,800
12/04	229	(7)	—	—
Annual Growth	9.5%	—	—	—

2007 Year-End Financials

Debt ratio: —
Return on equity: 2.30%
Cash ($ mil.): 6
Current ratio: 0.80
Long-term debt ($ mil.): —
Dividends
Yield: —
Payout: —
Market value ($ mil.): —

KINGSBROOK JEWISH MEDICAL CENTER INC

Kingsbrook Jewish Medical Center (KJMC) cares for the health needs of all Brooklyn residents. Founded in 1925 to serve the area's Jewish community the campus includes an acute care hospital with about 320 inpatient beds and an adult and pediatric long-term care facility with 540 beds. KJMC provides emergency surgical cardiology gastroenterology pulmonary wound care and diagnostic imaging services as well as skilled nursing services. The hospital also serves as a training facility for medical dental and pharmacy residents. It also operates a primary and specialty care outpatient center and a rehabilitation institute.

Geographic Reach

KJMC is located in the East Flatbush neighborhood of Brooklyn. The hospital also operates the Pierre Toussaint Family Health Center in Brooklyn.

Operations

KJMC's specialty inpatient units include its Traumatic Brain Injury and Coma Recovery Unit (part of the Kingsbrook Rehabilitation Institute). Other centers of excellence include a geriatric inpatient psychiatry program to serve the borough's mentally challenged elderly residents as well as centers for radiology wound healing orthopedic surgery women's health and pharmacy services. The outpatient center provides family practice services and specialist care in about 20 medical fields.

KJMC's skilled nursing facility known as Rutland Nursing Home provides skilled nursing care physical rehabilitation comprehensive wound care a specialty unit for ventilator-dependent residents and a range of sub-acute services. Rutland Nursing Home also has a dedicated pediatric long-term care unit for children with severe developmental and metabolic disorders. Because it is located on the KJMC campus all of the medical center's resources are available to the residents.

Strategy

KJMC is making investments in its facilities to better serve the growing needs of its community. To that end in 2011 the center broke ground on a new emergency department increasing its capacity to handle about 6000 additional ER visits per year. It is also renovating its ambulatory care facilities and expanding community programs (such as its adult day health services program). In addition in 2012 the hospital opened a new outpatient specialty care facility; the project took two years to complete and incorporates new processes for the efficient coordination of care for patients with multiple medical conditions.

The hospital is also upgrading its data systems to improve efficiencies. In 2013 it selected the ClearDATA health cloud platform to host its offsite backup system. Shifting its IT infrastructure to the platform will help KJMC reduce capital expenses and minimize risk.

Other efforts at KJMC include initiatives to reduce patient readmissions and hospital-acquired conditions.

EXECUTIVES

President CEO, Linda Brady
Director Marketing and Public Affairs, Enid Dillard
CIO, Nympha Meindel
VP Operations and COO, Kevin Molloy

LOCATIONS

HQ: KINGSBROOK JEWISH MEDICAL CENTER INC
585 SCHENECTADY AVE STE 2, BROOKLYN, NY 11203-1809
Phone: 718-604-5000
Web: WWW.KINGSBROOK.ORG

PRODUCTS/OPERATIONS

Selected Centers of Excellence

Comprehensive Wound Healing and Hyperbaric Center
Department of Physical Medicine and Rehabilitation
Geriatric Psychiatry

Gynecological Services / Minimally Invasive
Laparoscopic Surgery
Non-Invasive Vascular Laboratory
Ophthalmology and Neuro-ophthalmology
Orthopedics and Joint Replacement
Pharmacy
Radiology
Rutland Adult Day Health Care Center
Rutland Nursing Home
Traumatic Brain Injury and Coma Recovery Unit
Vascular Center of Excellence

Selected Clinical Services

Cardiovascular
Cardiac Cath Lab
Emergency Services
Emergency Department
Neurosciences
Electroencephalography (EEG)
Oncology
Chemotherapy
Orthopedics
Arthroscopy
Radiology Nuclear Medicine and Imaging
Computed Tomography (CT)
Magnetic Resonance Imaging (MRI)
Single Photon Emission Computerized Tomography (SPECT)
Rehabilitation
Physical Therapy
Special Care
Coronary Intensive Care (CCU)
Intensive Care Unit (ICU)
Subprovider Units
Psychiatric
Rehabilitation
Skilled Nursing (SNF)
Wound Care
Hyperbaric Oxygen
Wound care

COMPETITORS

Brookdale University Hospital
Brooklyn Hospital Center
Lutheran HealthCare
Maimonides Medical Center
MediSys Health Network
Montefiore Medical
New York City Health and Hospitals
New York Methodist Hospital
NewYork-Presbyterian Healthcare
North Shore-Long Island Jewish Health System
SUNY Downstate
Wyckoff Heights Medical Center

HISTORICAL FINANCIALS

Company Type: Private

Income Statement FYE: December 31

	REVENUE ($ mil.)	NET INCOME ($ mil.)	NET PROFIT MARGIN	EMPLOYEES
12/12	247	(5)	—	2,100
12/08	241	(3)	—	—
12/02	227	(14)	—	—
12/02	1,184	0	0.0%	—
Annual Growth	(14.5%)	—	—	—

2012 Year-End Financials

Debt ratio: —
Return on equity: (-2.20%)
Cash ($ mil.): 6
Current ratio: 0.60
Long-term debt ($ mil.): —
Dividends
Yield: —
Payout: —
Market value ($ mil.): —

KINNEY DRUGS INC.

Founded by Burt Orrin Kinney who opened the company's first drugstore in 1903 Kinney Drugs has grown to number about 95 stores in central and northern New York and Vermont. Most of the company's stores are free-standing units with pharmacies one-hour photo developing services and a growing selection of convenience foods. The 100%-employee-owned company maintains its own distribution warehouse and offers about 800 different products including Kinney-branded over-the-counter medicines. Pharmacy accounts for 75% of sales. Besides retail stores the firm operates ProAct prescription benefit management firm HealthDirect institutional pharmacy services and HealthDirect mail order pharmacy services.

Financial Analysis

Kinney Drugs rang up about $810 million in sales in 2011 a nearly 3% increase vs. the prior year. Prescription drugs sales totaled $616 million or 76% of total sales. Sales per store at Kinney averaged $5.5 million.

Strategy

To distinguish itself from its national competitors including Walgreen CVS and Wal-Mart the regional retailer strives to maintain a hometown feel. To that end it launched the KinneyCare Discount Prescription Plan for its insured and uninsured pharmacy customers. Under the plan more than 350 generic prescriptions are available for $12 for a 90-day supply. The plans costs $10 a year to enroll. The chain's ReadyScripts automated refill program sends messages to remind patients to pick up their prescriptions and offers free delivery to the mobility-impaired customers

With the worst of the recession –and concurrent decrease in spending on health care and prescription drugs –behind it Kinney acquired four independent pharmacies in central New York and Vermont in mid-2012 bringing its store count to 94.

EXECUTIVES

VP Marketing, James R. Wuest
Chairman and CEO, Craig C. Painter
President Kinney Healthcare Services, Bridget-Ann Hart
President of ProAct, David B. Warner
Vice President of MIS, Wayne Jones
EVP and CFO, Stephen P. McCoy
SVP Pharmacy Procurement, Owen W. Halloran
VP of Pharmacy Operations, Michael D. Duteau
Director Asset Protection, Lew Kimball
Founder, Burt Orrin
Vice President of Real Estate, David McClure
VP Information Services and CIO, Jeffrey A. Rorick
Vice President Financial Planning and Treasury, Michael Burgess
Vice President of Human Resources, Rich McNulty
President of, Larry Greco
COO Kinney Drug Store Division, James Spencer
General Manager Healthcare Services, John Dyer
President Health Direct Institutional Services, Brian Scott

LOCATIONS

HQ: KINNEY DRUGS INC.
520 E MAIN ST, GOUVERNEUR, NY 13642-1562
Phone: 315-287-1500
Web: WWW.KINNEYDRUGS.COM

2012 Stores

New York	73	
Vermont	21	
Total	**0**	**94**

COMPETITORS

BJ' s Wholesale Club
CVS Caremark
Costco Wholesale
Kmart
Rite Aid
Stop & Shop
Target Corporation
Wal-Mart
Walgreen

HISTORICAL FINANCIALS

Company Type: Private

Income Statement FYE: December 31

	REVENUE ($ mil.)	NET INCOME ($ mil.)	NET PROFIT MARGIN	EMPLOYEES
12/08	711	10	1.5%	3,000
12/07	666	11	1.8%	—
12/06	606	9	1.6%	—
12/05	525	9	1.8%	—
Annual Growth	10.6%	2.7%	—	—

2008 Year-End Financials

Debt ratio: —
Return on equity: 1.50%
Cash ($ mil.): 3
Current ratio: 0.40
Long-term debt ($ mil.): —
Dividends
Yield: —
Payout: —
Market value ($ mil.): —

KIRBY RISK CORPORATION

Kirby Risk sees nothing risky about helping harness a little electrical energy. The company named after one of its co-founders ,Âsupplies electrical products (process automation products drives and motors lighting fuses wire and cable) and services ,Âto the Midwestern US. The company operates through four business units comprising Electrical Supply Service Center Mechanical Solutions and Service and Precision Machining. The Electrical Supply distribution unit handles more than 20000 products from some 500 manufacturers including ,ÂGE ,ÂThomas & Betts and ,ÂRockwell Automation. Other operations include ARCO Electric Products (phase converters). CEO James Risk III owns the company that was founded in 1926.

Operations

The company's Electrical Supply division stocks lighting and power instruments while the ,ÂKirby Risk Service Center makes custom wiring harnesses control panels subassemblies and kits for ,Âindustrial customers. Mechanical ,ÂSolutions and Service is the repair ,Âend of the business it also sells motors power transmissions and generators.

Kirby Risk Precision Machining offers precision machining using CNC (computer numerical control) technology. ARCO ,Â manufactures rotophase converters which are rotary-type generators (different from static phase converters) as well as power factor correction capacitors. ,Â

Sales and Marketing

The company has roughly 35 customer service locations throughout Illinois Indiana and Ohio.

Company Background

Otto Keiffer and J. Kirby Risk founded the company as the Keiffer-Risk Battery Company in 1926 in an abandoned blacksmith shop in Lafayette Indiana.

EXECUTIVES

Vice President Of Human Resources, Doug Gutridge

LOCATIONS

HQ: KIRBY RISK CORPORATION
1815 SAGAMORE PKWY N, LAFAYETTE, IN 479041765
Phone: 7654484567
Web: WWW.KIRBYRISK.COM

PRODUCTS/OPERATIONS

Selected Divisions

Arco Electric Products
Electrical supply
Mechanical solutions and service
Precision machining
Service center

COMPETITORS

Anixter International
Consolidated Electrical
Graybar Electric
Hagemeyer North America
Premier Farnell
Rexel Inc.
SUMMIT Electric Supply
Skyworks
W.W. Grainger
WESCO International

HISTORICAL FINANCIALS

Company Type: Private

Income Statement

FYE: December 31

	REVENUE ($ mil.)	NET INCOME ($ mil.)	NET PROFIT MARGIN	EMPLOYEES
12/13	401	0	—	950
12/12	398	0	—	—
12/11	377	0	—	—
12/10	399	0	—	—
Annual Growth	0.1%	—	—	—

2013 Year-End Financials

Debt ratio: —
Return on equity: —
Cash ($ mil.): 38
Current ratio: 2.40
Long-term debt ($ mil.): —
Dividends
Yield: —
Payout: —
Market value ($ mil.): —

KITCHELL CORPORATION

EXECUTIVES

President Kitchell Development Co., Jeff Allen
President Kitchell Capital Expenditure Managers Inc., Russell Fox
President and CEO, James T (Jim) Swanson
President Kitchell Contractors Inc., Dan Pierce
President hardison/downey construction inc., Nick Crisci
President American Refrigeration Supplies Inc., Steve Martin
Auditors: MayerHoffmanMcCannP.C.

LOCATIONS

HQ: KITCHELL CORPORATION
1707 E HIGHLAND AVE # 100, PHOENIX, AZ 850164668
Phone: 6022644411
Web: WWW.KITCHELL.COM

PRODUCTS/OPERATIONS

Selected Services

Construction services
  Custom homes
  Engineering & architectural services
  Environmental services
  Facilities development
  General contracting
  Program/project/construction management
Fleet services
Property management
Real estate development
Refrigeration supplies

Selected Subsidiaries

American Refrigeration Supplies
FDI Planning Consultants
hardison/downey
Kitchell Capital Expenditure Managers
Kitchell Contractors
Kitchell Development Company

COMPETITORS

Balfour Beatty
CORE Construction
Flintco
Gilbane
Jacobs Engineering
McCarthy Building
Summit Builders
Sundt
Swinerton
Turner Corporation
Tutor Perini

HISTORICAL FINANCIALS

Company Type: Private

Income Statement

FYE: December 31

	REVENUE ($ mil.)	NET INCOME ($ mil.)	NET PROFIT MARGIN	EMPLOYEES
12/10	480	0	—	946
12/09	677	0	—	—
12/08	1,027	0	0.0%	—
Annual Growth	(31.6%)	—	—	—

2010 Year-End Financials

Debt ratio:
Return on equity: —
Cash ($ mil.): 65
Current ratio: 1.10
Long-term debt ($ mil.): —
Dividends
Yield: —
Payout: —
Market value ($ mil.): —

KNIGHTS OF COLUMBUS

Good Knight! The Knights of Columbus is a formidable volunteer group boasting about 14000 councils made up of 1.8 million Roman Catholic male members in the US Canada Mexico Cuba the Philippines Poland and several other countries. The organization is also a force to be reckoned with in the insurance world providing life insurance annuities and long-term care insurance to its members and their families. In addition the group manages the Knights of Columbus Museum in New Haven Connecticut featuring exhibits of religious art and history. The Knights of Columbus was founded in New Haven by Father Michael J. McGivney in 1882 and has been selling insurance since its founding.

Geographic Reach

The Knights of Columbus comprises more than 14000 local councils throughout the US Canada Mexico Puerto Rico Guam and the U.S.Virgin Islands. It also has councils in the Bahamas Cuba the Dominican Republic Guatemala Panama the Philippines Poland and Saipan.

Operations

The Knights of Columbus is also engaged in religious education the support of public policy issues (including immigration reform marriage protection opposing abortion) and charitable activities such as disaster relief. Indeed The Gulf States relief efforts led the Knights to a record year of charitable giving with more than 64 million hours and $139 million dollars donated overall. Also the organization underwrote the cost of restoration work done on the gravesite of President John F. Kennedy in Arlington National Cemetery in 2010.

Financial Performance

During the past decade the charity has raised more than $1.4 billion. Total charitable contributions totaled $154.6 million in 2011 exeeding 2010's total by more than $3.4 million.

EXECUTIVES

Supreme Knight, Carl A. Anderson
Supreme Chaplain, Bishop William E. Lori
Deputy Supreme Knight, Dennis Savoie
Supreme Treasurer, Logan T. Ludwig
Supreme Secretary, Charles E. Maurer Jr.
Supreme Advocate and General Counsel, John A. Marrella
Director Catholic Information Service, Michelle Borras

LOCATIONS

HQ: KNIGHTS OF COLUMBUS
1 COLUMBUS PLZ STE 1700, NEW HAVEN, CT 06510-3326
Phone: 203-752-4000
Web: WWW.KOFC.ORG

PRODUCTS/OPERATIONS

2011 Charitable Contributions

	$ mil.	% of total
State and local affiliates	125	81
Supreme Council	29	19
Total	154	100

HISTORICAL FINANCIALS

Company Type: Private

Income Statement

FYE: December 31

	REVENUE ($ mil.)	NET INCOME ($ mil.)	NET PROFIT MARGIN	EMPLOYEES
12/12	2,148	127	5.9%	2,300
12/11	2,059	81	3.9%	—
12/10*	1,937	86	4.5%	—
06/09	0	(0)	—	—
Annual Growth	1157.2%	—	—	—

*Fiscal year change

2012 Year-End Financials

Debt ratio: —
Return on equity: 5.90%
Cash ($ mil.): 466
Current ratio: —
Long-term debt ($ mil.): —
Dividends
Yield: —
Payout: —
Market value ($ mil.): —

KNOUSE FOODS COOPERATIVE INC.

Is there a Knouse in the house? Might be. With retail brand names such as Apple Time Lucky Leaf Musselman's Lincoln and Speas Farm Knouse Foods Cooperative's apple products are in many a pantry. The company is a growers' co-op made up of some 150 Appalachian Mountain and Midwestern grower/members. It processes its members' apples for sale as canned and bottled applesauce juice cider vinegar apple butter pie fillings and snack packs all of which are available nationwide. In addition to stocking supermarket shelves Knouse founded in 1949 supplies foodservice operators and industrial-ingredient companies with bulk apple and other fruit products. It also offers private-label and co-packing services.

Geographic Reach

The company operates half a dozen processing plants in Pennsylvannia –covering nearly 2.4 million sq. ft. on about 300000 acres –and a single plant in Paw Paw Michigan.

Operations

The company's business segments include: retail; foodservice which supplies restaurants cafeterias healthcare facilities and other institutional customers; an industrial/ingredient division that provides customized products for industrial clients; and co-packing.

Knouse gets an A for all things Apple but also makes the grade with foodservice cheese sauces dessert toppings and fillings and puddings. And along with apple its pie fillings include apricot blackberry blueberry cherry lemon peach pineapple raisin raspberry and strawberry.

Strategy

In recent years companies like Knouse have been focused on packaging to make its products more portable. To this end Knouse in 2014 introduced Musselman's Squeezables single-serve apple sauce.

EXECUTIVES

National Sales Manager, Barbara A Williams
V Pres, Emery C Etter
Treas, Craig M Hinkle, age 45

LOCATIONS

HQ: KNOUSE FOODS COOPERATIVE INC.
800 PACH GLEN IDAVILLE RD, PEACH GLEN, PA 173750001
Phone: 7176778181
Web: WWW.KNOUSEFOODSERVICE.COM

PRODUCTS/OPERATIONS

Selected Products

Apple butter
Apple juice & cider
Apple sauce
Pie filling
Specialty fruit (cherriessliced apples)

COMPETITORS

BakeMark
Big Heart Pet Brands
Birds Eye
Chelan Fruit Company
Chiquita Brands
Dole Food
Eagle Family Foods
H. J. Heinz Limited
Monster Beverage
Mott' s
Naked Juice
Ocean Spray
Odwalla
Old Orchard
Seneca Foods
Shamrock Foods
Smucker
Snapple
Sun-Rype
Tree Top
TreeHouse
Tropicana
Wet Planet Beverages

HISTORICAL FINANCIALS

Company Type: Private

Income Statement FYE: June 30

	REVENUE ($ mil.)	NET INCOME ($ mil.)	NET PROFIT MARGIN	EMPLOYEES
06/08	270	7	2.8%	1,200
06/07	259	2	0.8%	—
06/06	248	2	1.0%	—
06/05	239	0	—	—
Annual Growth	4.2%	—	—	—

2008 Year-End Financials

Debt ratio: —
Return on equity: 2.80%
Cash ($ mil.): 0
Current ratio: 0.40
Long-term debt ($ mil.): —
Dividends
Yield: —
Payout: —
Market value ($ mil.): —

KOCH ENTERPRISES INC.

Koch gets straight A's for diversification; it's a private holding company active in automobile parts manufacturing metals recycling wholesale distribution and equipment design and construction. Subsidiaries include Audubon Metals (processes aluminum) George Koch Sons (engineers installs and services auto finishing systems) Koch Air (distributes Carrier HVAC equipment) Gibbs Die Casting (parts for making cars lighter) Brake Supply (repairs brakes and hydraulic systems for auto and mining equipment) and Uniseal (makes structural adhesives thermoplastics and sealant systems for industrial and auto markets). George Koch founded the company in 1873.

Geographic Reach

Koch has operations in Brazil China Hungary India the UK and the US.

Operations

The company operates in four industry markets: automotive parts manufacturing (37% of total sales) equipment design and construction (9%) metal recycling (28%) and wholesale distribution (26%).

Financial Performance

Ever since bottoming out during the Great Recession Koch has seen steady growth over the last four years. Its net revenue reached $943 million in 2012 one of the highest totals it has generated in the company's history.

Strategy

Koch's business strategy centers around owning diverse businesses which are in different stages of maturity and perform in complementary business cycles. This strategy has enabled it to maintain a strong financial position and to continue growing over many years.

A large portion of Koch's revenues are from manufacturing automobile parts for such major auto OEM suppliers as Visteon and Delphi. Koch has continued to focus on developing greener lighter more cost-effective vehicle-related components. Its investment has helped to sustain its competitive position and improve the profit margins of core lines.

Simultaneously Koch is expanding its geographic footprint. Its UK auto finishing systems venture George Koch Sons Europe in 2010 purchased a 51% stake in Kurion Technologies also based in the UK. Kurion supplies systems for wastewater treatment water recycling and resource recovery. The deal gave George Koch access to new eco-friendly technologies diversifying and deepening its international presence.

Ownership

Koch Enterprises is family owned.

EXECUTIVES

CFO Secretary and Treasurer, Susan E. Parsons
Chairman and CEO, Robert L. (Bob) Koch II, age 75
Vice Chairman, James H. (Jim) Muehlbauer
President Audubon Metals, Jim Butkus
Director; President and CEO Koch Air, Brad J. Muehlbauer
President and Director, Kevin R. Koch
Director; President and CEO Brake Supply Co., David M. Koch
Director; President & CEO Gibbs Die Casting Corp., Steven A. Church
President George Koch Sons, Chris Brack
President SWC, Todd Lucy
President Uniseal, Randy Zahn
President CEO and Director, Robert L. (Bob) Koch II, age 74
Director, Lawrence J. (Larry) Kremer, age 72
Director, Alan W. Braun, age 68
Director, P. Daniel (Dan) Miller, age 65
Vice Chairman, James H. (Jim) Muehlbauer
Director, Stephen G. Jennings
Director; President and CEO Koch Air, Brad J. Muehlbauer
President and Director, Kevin R. Koch
Director; President and CEO Brake Supply Co., David M. Koch
Director, Jeffrey A. (Jeff) Bosse
Director; President & CEO Gibbs Die Casting Corp., Steven A. Church

LOCATIONS

HQ: KOCH ENTERPRISES INC.
14 S 11TH AVE, EVANSVILLE, IN 47712-5020
Phone: 812-465-9800
Web: WWW.KOCHENTERPRISES.COM

PRODUCTS/OPERATIONS

Selected Products and Services

Aluminum and magnesium die castings
Brake linings
Cellular rubber parts
Financing for contractors and dealers
Heating and air-conditioning equipment
Hydraulics
Paint finishing systems
PIPECONX (pipe connectors)
Powder coating systems
Security communications and controls system integration
Specialty sealants
Structural adhesives

COMPETITORS

Alcoa
Alumasc Group
Arlington Industries
Dana Holding
ESCO
Graco
Hitchiner Manufacturing
Illinois Tool Works
Kaiser Aluminum
Magna International
Nordson
Rio Tinto Alcan
Siemens Water Technologies
Sika Corporation
Sun Hydraulics
U.S. Paint

HISTORICAL FINANCIALS

Company Type: Private

Income Statement FYE: December 31

	REVENUE ($ mil.)	NET INCOME ($ mil.)	NET PROFIT MARGIN	EMPLOYEES
12/12	942	0	—	2,482
12/11	915	0	—	—
12/10	851	22	2.7%	—
12/09	830	0	—	—
Annual Growth	4.3%	—	—	—

2012 Year-End Financials

Debt ratio: —
Return on equity: —
Cash ($ mil.): 35
Current ratio: 1.10
Long-term debt ($ mil.): —
Dividends
Yield: —
Payout: —
Market value ($ mil.): —

KPH HEALTHCARE SERVICES INC.

EXECUTIVES

VP Marketing, James R. Wuest
Chairman and CEO, Craig C. Painter
President Kinney Healthcare Services, Bridget-Ann Hart
President of ProAct, David B. Warner
Vice President of MIS, Wayne Jones
EVP and CFO, Stephen P. McCoy
SVP Pharmacy Procurement, Owen W. Halloran
VP of Pharmacy Operations, Michael D. Duteau
Director Asset Protection, Lew Kimball
Founder, Burt Orrin
Vice President of Real Estate, David McClure
VP Information Services and CIO, Jeffrey A. Rorick
Vice President Financial Planning and Treasury, Michael Burgess
Vice President of Human Resources, Rich McNulty

President of, Larry Greco
COO Kinney Drug Store Division, James Spencer
General Manager Healthcare Services, John Dyer
President Health Direct Institutional Services, Brian Scott

LOCATIONS

HQ: KPH HEALTHCARE SERVICES INC.
520 E MAIN ST, GOUVERNEUR, NY 136421561
Phone: 3152871500
Web: WWW.KINNEYDRUGS.COM

2012 Stores

New York		73
Vermont		21
Total	**0**	**94**

COMPETITORS

BJ' s Wholesale Club
CVS Caremark
Costco Wholesale
Kmart
Rite Aid
Stop & Shop
Target Corporation
Wal-Mart
Walgreen

HISTORICAL FINANCIALS

Company Type: Private

Income Statement FYE: December 31

	REVENUE ($ mil.)	NET INCOME ($ mil.)	NET PROFIT MARGIN	EMPLOYEES
12/08	711	10	1.5%	3,000
12/07	666	11	1.8%	—
12/06	606	9	1.6%	—
12/05	525	0	—	—
Annual Growth	10.6%	—	—	—

2008 Year-End Financials

Debt ratio: —
Return on equity: 1.50%
Cash ($ mil.): 3
Current ratio: 0.40
Long-term debt ($ mil.): —
Dividends
Yield: —
Payout: —
Market value ($ mil.): —

KRONES INC.

Krones is in the business of keeping things all bottled up. The company develops manufactures and installs packaging machinery and systems that design clean rinse and fill bottles cans and plastic containers. Its offerings include labeling and sealing machines inspection and monitoring systems and mixing and carbonating systems. Krones caters to companies in North and Central America and the Caribbean in the food and beverage beer wine and spirits health and cosmetic pharmaceutical and household goods industries. Established in 1966 Krones is a subsidiary of KRONES owned largely by the founding Kronseder family.

Operations

Krones' major products and brands include its Krones LitePac pack strapping technology used for PET containers its Sleevematic labeler used for handling stretch-sleeve films and The Contiform 3 the latest generation of the company's stretch blow-molding machines.

EXECUTIVES

Chairman, Volker Kronseder
Marketing Manager, Konie Brenneman
President Chief Executive Officer Chief Financial Officer, Holger Beckmann, age 45
Executive Vice President, Timothy (Tim) Raymond, age 52
Regional Service Coordinator Central and West Region USA, Jodi Stefanski
COO, Michael Wiebe
VP Sales Special Projects USA East, Patrick Carroll
VP Sales Eastern Division USA East, John Muha
Manager Regional Sales USA East, Sean Madden
Manager Regional Sales USA Central, Wayne Confiant
Manager Regional Sales USA West, Casey Farrell
Manager Regional Sales USA West, Bjoern Wissling
Manager Regional Sales USA Central, Don Soich
Manager Regional Sales USA Central, Gary Burnside
VP Sales Central America and Caribbean Division, Walid Eid
Manager Regional Sales, Jose Rojas
Regional Sales Manager, Brad Cardell
Vice President of Supply Operations, Jerry Tidwell
General Manager Director of Sales, Sebastian Delgado
Regional Sales Manager, Thomas Costantini
Chairman, Volker Kronseder
President Chief Executive Officer Chief Financial Officer, Holger Beckmann, age 45

LOCATIONS

HQ: KRONES INC.
9600 S 58TH ST, FRANKLIN, WI 53132-9107
Phone: 414-409-4000
Web: WWW.KRONESUSA.COM

PRODUCTS/OPERATIONS

Selected Products

Cleaning technology
Conveyor system
Filling technology
Handling parts
Inspection technology
Intralogistics (block warehouse high-bay warehouse)
Labeling technology
Line expertise
Packing and palletising technology
Plastics technology
Process technology (beer water milk soft drink spirits)
Product treatment technology

COMPETITORS

CarnaudMetalbox
Consolidated Container
Husky Injection Molding Systems
Industria Macchine Automatiche
Intertape Polymer
KUKA
Klockner-Werke
SIG Combibloc
Sidel

HISTORICAL FINANCIALS

Company Type: Private

Income Statement FYE: December 31

	REVENUE ($ mil.)	NET INCOME ($ mil.)	NET PROFIT MARGIN	EMPLOYEES
12/08	363	5	1.6%	499
12/07	359	6	1.9%	—
12/06	364	2	0.6%	—
12/05	383	1	0.4%	—
Annual Growth	(1.7%)	58.2%	—	—

2008 Year-End Financials

Debt ratio: —
Return on equity: 1.60%
Cash ($ mil.): 9
Current ratio: 0.40
Long-term debt ($ mil.): —
Dividends
Yield: —
Payout: —
Market value ($ mil.): —

KRUEGER INTERNATIONAL INC.

Krueger International can be found in cubicles classrooms cafeterias and college dorms. The company which does business as KI makes ergonomic seating cabinets and other furniture used by businesses healthcare organizations government agencies and educational institutions. The company offers everything from benches and beds to desks and tables not to mention shelving filing systems movable walls and trash bins. KI markets its products through sales representatives furniture dealers architects and interior designers worldwide. Founded in 1941 KI was purchased in the 1980s by its managers who later allowed employees to buy stock. Today KI is 100% employee owned.

Geographic Reach

Based in Wisconsin KI operates manufacturing facilities and sales offices in the US Canada China and India as well as throughout Europe Latin America and Asia. It has subsidiaries based in the UK Canada India and Malaysia.

Sales and Marketing

KI sells its products worldwide through furniture dealers sales representatives architects and interior designers.

Operations

Along with its impressive geographic reach KI operates a variety of subsidiaries including KI UK Ltd. KI East Asia Sdn. Bhd KI Nova Scotia KI Canada and KI India.

KI also owns three subsidiaries: AWP Wood Products Pallas Textiles and Spacesaver. Quebec-based AWP Wood Products makes architectural wood doors for the office partition industry. Pallas Textiles which operates out of Wisconsin creates textile products for contract upholstery panel systems and wall-coverings healthcare environments and casements. Spacesaver Corporation also located in Wisconsin makes high-density mobile storage systems for office institutional and industrial applications and is a major supplier of steel shelving systems rotary storage systems and storage accessories.

The company maintains several manufacturing sites. Besides its four locations in Wisconsin (in Bonduel Fort Atkinson Green Bay and Manitowoc) KI operates production facilities in High Point North Carolina; Penmroke Ontario Canada; and Tupelo Mississippi. In 2012 KI expanded its Green Bay Wisconsin plant (at the tune of $3.3 million) by more than 100000 sq. ft. for additional elbow room devoted to manufacturing shipping receiving and warehousing.

KI is well-regarded in the classroom furniture market and is a leading supplier for both K-12 schools and universities. The company has outfitted classrooms lecture halls administrative offices computer labs media centers residence halls and student unions. KI has been a government vendor for more than six decades and provided furnishings for an assortment of federal agencies including all branches of the military. KI's corporate products are ergonomically designed to help individuals work more comfortably and efficiently. In addition to these core customer groups KI has also installed its furnishings in outdoor public spaces sports arenas conference centers and airports.

Strategy

The company has been expanding its network of showrooms in the US and abroad. KI added a showroom in Houston in 2010 to boost its US presence which includes about 10 locations in half a dozen states. To better serve its Asian and European customers the company operates through a showroom in Shanghai China. KI has international showrooms in London Malaysia Mexico Puerto Rico and Toronto.

As its showroom presence grows KI has also formed new sales partnerships. The company tapped Heartland Furniture Group a contract furniture representative in 2011 to take care of existing customer accounts and broker sales in Kansas Missouri and southern Illinois.

Mergers and Acquisitions

It's also looking to acquisitions to extend the reach of its business. In 2011 KI purchased Sebel Furniture Limited from GWA Group Ltd. a top supplier of building fixtures in Australia. The $24 million deal has given KI a foothold in the commercial furniture business in Australia New Zealand the UK and Hong Kong.

Company Ownership

KI is 100% employee-owned.

EXECUTIVES

President and CEO, Richard J. Resch
VP Education Markets, Nat Porter
VP Healthcare, Debbie Breunig
Product Manager Movable Walls, Rob Witt
VP Sales Eastern Region, John Duffy
Seating Product Manager, Leo Welter
Dealer Representative Southern California, Gregg Kent
VP Business Markets, Jonathan Webb
VP Sales, Richard Butrym
EVP, Brian Krenke
Manager Government Marketing, Randy Hoople
Associate Product Marketing Manager, Ryan Usiak

LOCATIONS

HQ: KRUEGER INTERNATIONAL INC.
1330 BELLEVUE ST, GREEN BAY, WI 54302-2197
Phone: 920-468-8100
Web: WWW.KI.COM

PRODUCTS/OPERATIONS

Selected Products

Auditorium seating
Beds
Benches
Bookcases
Carrels
Chairs
Desks
File cabinets
Lecterns
Movable walls
Planters
Power and data connections
Receptacles
Recliners
Residence hall furniture
Sleepers
Special events seating
Stools
Tables

COMPETITORS

ABCO Office Furniture
Allsteel
Bretford
CFGroup
Columbia Manufacturing
Edsal Manufacturing
Global Group
HNI
Haworth Inc.
Herman Miller
Inscape corp
Kewaunee Scientific
Kimball International
Knoll Inc.
La-Z-Boy
Norstar Office Products
Royal Seating
Sagus
Steelcase
Trendway
Virco Mfg.

HISTORICAL FINANCIALS

Company Type: Private

Income Statement FYE: December 31

	REVENUE ($ mil.)	NET INCOME ($ mil.)	NET PROFIT MARGIN	EMPLOYEES
12/11	649	56	8.8%	2,300
12/10	615	59	9.6%	—
12/08	1,377	0	0.0%	—
Annual Growth	(22.2%)	4991.3%	—	—

2011 Year-End Financials

Debt ratio: —
Return on equity: 8.80%
Cash ($ mil.): 3
Current ratio: 0.80
Long-term debt ($ mil.): —
Dividends
Yield: —
Payout: —
Market value ($ mil.): —

KWIK TRIP INC.

Midwesterners who need to make a quick trip to get gas or groceries cigarettes or donuts race on over to Kwik Trip stores. Kwik Trip owns and operates about 400 Kwik Trip and Kwik Star convenience stores throughout Iowa Minnesota and Wisconsin. The company also runs about a dozen Hearty Platter restaurants and cafes some 40 Tobacco Outlet Plus (TOP) cigar stores and car washes at some Kwik Trip store locations. All Kwik Trip stores built since 1990 are owned by Convenience Store Investments a separate company which leases the land and stores to Kwik Trip. Kwik Trip which opened its first store in 1965 in Eau Claire Wisconsin is owned by the family of CEO Don Zietlow.

Operations

To supply its stores with baked goods and other foods Kwik Trip operates a 60000-square-foot commissary and research facility at its headquarters in southwestern Wisconsin. The bakery produces the Kwickery Bake Shoppe line of bagels buns cookies donuts muffins and more and its dairy packages the Nature's Touch brand of fresh milk ice cream orange juice and water. The company is building a new 65000-square-foot dairy facility in its hometown of La Crosse to supply its own stores (and those owned by others) with ice cream yogurt and other dairy products. Longer term the company hopes to develop its own plastic bottle manufacturing plant. Food service currently accounts for about a third of the company's annual profit ahead of fuel.

Kwik Trip vertically integrates by processing its own gasoline and producing and packaging products to be sold in its convenience stores.

Strategy

Kwik Trip is growing quickly. The convenience store chain expects to add about 2000 jobs across the company by late 2013 to staff and supply its growing number of stores. Kwik Trip is testing a new 5000-square-foot store format designed to appeal to soccer moms and other female customers. The new more upscale look includes wood fixtures and subdued florescent lighting combined with accent lighting. To supply its larger store base the company is building a new 65000-square-foot dairy facility in its hometown of La Crosse.

To compensate for shrinking fuel and tobacco margins the regional convenience store chain has been expanding its food offerings —adding soup and chili to its menu of pizza tacos salads and other hot and fresh items -and plans to enter the take-home meals market with entrees such as lasagna chicken beef pork fish and meat loaf. Indeed over the past several years the company has greatly expanded its food production activities and has begun selling food on a wholesale basis to other retailers including noncompeting retailers and school districts. The company estimates that by 2030 the wholesale business could account for as much as half of the food that Kwik Trip produces.

Company Background

The John Hansen family founded Kwik Trip in Eau Claire Wisconsin in 1965. In 2000 the Hansens sold their interest in Kwik Trip to the Zietlow family for $120 million. The two families had jointly owned Kwik Trip since 1972.

EXECUTIVES

President and CEO, Donald P. (Don) Zietlow, age 79
VP and Director Petroleum Operations, Steve Zietlow

LOCATIONS

HQ: KWIK TRIP INC.
1626 OAK ST, LA CROSSE, WI 54603-2308
Phone: 608-781-8988
Web: WWW.KWIKTRIP.COM

PRODUCTS/OPERATIONS

Selected Banners

Hearty Platter
Kwik Star
Kwik Trip
Tobacco Outlet Plus

COMPETITORS

7-Eleven
Brinker
Carlson Restaurants
Casey' s General Stores
Chevron
Couche-Tard
Cub Foods
Denny' s
Exxon Mobil
Hy-Vee
Krause Gentle
Northern Tier Energy
Roundy' s

HISTORICAL FINANCIALS

Company Type: Private

Income Statement FYE: September 27

	REVENUE ($ mil.)	NET INCOME ($ mil.)	NET PROFIT MARGIN	EMPLOYEES
09/08	3,640	23	0.7%	10,500
09/04	1,887	24	1.3%	—
Annual Growth	17.9%	(0.8%)	—	—

2008 Year-End Financials

Debt ratio: —
Return on equity: 0.70%
Cash ($ mil.): 1
Current ratio: 0.40
Long-term debt ($ mil.): —
Dividends
Yield: —
Payout: —
Market value ($ mil.): —

LA FRANCE CORP.

Viva LaFrance! would make a nice nameplate and this company could design it. LaFrance Corp. makes nameplates trim plastic enclosures metal letters and other products through several divisions. Its Benmatt Industries unit makes a range of customized products including key fobs license plate frames and trailer hitch covers that are used as promotional items by auto dealerships. The company's J.A.T. Creative Products division provides products like bottle openers bottle and can huggers and keychains to promote and advertise companies and special events. PacTec is a producer of standard and custom modified plastic electronic enclosures.

Geographic Reach

In addition to its headquarters in Concordville Pennsylvania the company has an 85000 sq. ft. manufacturing and distribution facility in Sarasota Florida. Its Asian headquarters is located in Shenzhen China and LaFrance has an additional office in the country located in Guangzhou. Two other international offices are located in Tokyo and Hong Kong.

Operations

LaFrance offers metal letters aluminum nameplates and trims stainless steel logos coined aluminum domed products die cast nameplates plastic products custom modified plastic electronic enclosures license plate frames key fobs and on-car advertising and promotional products.

The company operates through several divisions. Benmatt Industries manufacturers key fobs license plate frames and trailer hitch covers that are used by auto dealerships. J.A.T. Creative Products provides bottle openers and bottle and can huggers while PacTec is a leading producer of standard (more than 350 sizes) and custom modified plastic electronic enclosures.LaFrance's Industrial Design works with clients' product placement and brand strategy when supporting the creation of designs. It utilizes a variety of 2D and 3D modeling programs to create and review the design with our customers prior to creating the specific parts.

Sales and Marketing

The company serve a diverse range of consumer and professional product manufacturers who produce such items as computers motorcycles appliances cell phones eye ware and cosmetics. Customers include Dell Dirt Devil LG Mizuno and Zyliss.

Company Background

LaFrance was founded in 1946 by Joseph Teti.

EXECUTIVES

Vp, Brian McHenry
V Pres, Peter Peroni, age 84
Executive Vice President, Alan Grodnitzky
Vice President Line Sales Manager, Jerry Helbein

LOCATIONS

HQ: LA FRANCE CORP.
1 LAFRANCE WAY, CONCORDVILLE, PA 19331
Phone: 6103614300
Web: WWW.LAFRANCECORP.COM

PRODUCTS/OPERATIONS

Selected Products

Aluminum
Buttons and Keys
Camera Bezels
Clocks
Coined Aluminum
Combo
Die Cast Zinc
Domed
Electroform
Metal Letters
Nameplates
Plastic
Speedometers
Stainless Steel

COMPETITORS

Agion Technologies
Chromalox
GM Nameplate
Mcloone metal graphics
StreetGlow
Tanury Industries
ZF Electronics

HISTORICAL FINANCIALS

Company Type: Private

Income Statement FYE: December 31

	REVENUE ($ mil.)	NET INCOME ($ mil.)	NET PROFIT MARGIN	EMPLOYEES
12/13	131	10	7.8%	1,827
12/12	115	10	9.5%	—
Annual Growth	14.1%	(5.8%)	—	—

2013 Year-End Financials

Debt ratio: —
Return on equity: 7.80%
Cash ($ mil.): 6
Current ratio: 1.20
Long-term debt ($ mil.): —
Dividends
Yield: —
Payout: —
Market value ($ mil.): —

LAFAYETTE GENERAL MEDICAL CENTER INC

Serving the people of Acadiana (southern Louisiana) Lafayette General Medical Center (LGMC) provides general inpatient medical and surgical care as well as highly specialized services such as trauma care and neonatal intensive care. The not-for-profit hospital which has more than 350 beds also offers home health services outpatient care occupational medicine and mental health care. LGMC is a member of group purchasing organization Premier and has affiliations with other health care institutions including two small community hospitals –St. Martin Hospital in St. Martin Parish and Abrom Kaplan Memorial Hospital in Vermilion Parish –to which it provides management services.

Lafayette General has evolved from a six-bed sanitarium that opened in 1911 to become the region's only community-owned and managed hospital. At the dawn of its centennial the hospital completed a $70 million renovation program to expand its facilities by almost 15000 sq. ft. with total renovations throughout its facilities affecting close to 162000 sq. ft. Expenditures for buildings equipment and technology in 2010 alone exceeded $43 million.

The 10-floor hospital now has larger rooms bathrooms and showers. It has also updated the Louisiana Extended Care Hospital its long-term acute care unit as well as its adult emergency department. New pediatric treatment and waiting areas were added to the emergency department and a new in-patient rehab unit was created.

Like many health care providers facing reforms in the industry the hospital is developing a new patient-centered model of care delivery using evidenced-based practices and collaboration between patients their families and clinical ancillary and support staff members to improve outcomes and gain efficiencies.

A strong community member Lafayette General not only makes financial contributions to further medical education and research it also coordinates events and provides free screenings to the public it serves.

EXECUTIVES

Vice President / Chief Nursing Officer, Rebecca (Becki) Benoit
CEO / VP University Hospital & Clinics, Jared Stark
Executive Vice President / CEO Lafayette General Medical Center, Patrick W. Gandy Jr.
Senior Vice President / Chief Financial Officer, Roger Mattke
Vice President Information Systems / Chief Information Officer, Edwina Mallery
President and CEO, David L. Callecod
Vice President Marketing Business Development, Carolyn Huval
Vice President of Cancer Services, Craig Ortego
Vice Chairman, Edward J. Krampe
General Counsel and Chief Compliance Officer, Gordon Rountree
Assistant Vice President Network Development, Paul Molbert
Chairman, Clay M. Allen
Chief Medical Officer, Ziad Ashkar
CEO / VP St. Martin Hospital, Katie Hebert

LOCATIONS

HQ: LAFAYETTE GENERAL MEDICAL CENTER INC
1214 COOLIDGE BLVD, LAFAYETTE, LA 70503-2621
Phone: 337-289-7991
Web: WWW.LAFAYETTEGENERAL.COM

PRODUCTS/OPERATIONS

Selected Affiliates

Abrom-Kaplan Hospital
Cancer Center of Acadiana
Cardiovascular Institute of the South
CyberKnife Louisiana
Family Health Plaza (Minor Emergency Clinic) - River Ranch
Family Health Plaza South - Sugar Mill Pond Youngsville
Lafayette General Imaging
Lafayette General Surgical Hospital
Neuroscience Center
Opelousas General Health System
Savoy Medical Center - Mamou
St. Martin Hospital

COMPETITORS

Baton Rouge General
CHRISTUS St. Frances Cabrini Hospital
HCA
LifePoint Hospitals
Our Lady of Lourdes
Women & Children's Hospital

HISTORICAL FINANCIALS

Company Type: Private

Income Statement FYE: September 30

	REVENUE ($ mil.)	NET INCOME ($ mil.)	NET PROFIT MARGIN	EMPLOYEES
09/12	268	25	9.6%	1,626
09/09	181	1	1.1%	—
09/05	177	11	6.3%	—
09/05	152	7	5.2%	—
Annual Growth	8.4%	18.2%	—	—

2012 Year-End Financials

Debt ratio: —
Return on equity: 9.60%
Cash ($ mil.): 21
Current ratio: 0.50
Long-term debt ($ mil.): —
Dividends
Yield: —
Payout: —
Market value ($ mil.): —

LAFAYETTE PARISH SCHOOL BOARD

LOCATIONS

HQ: LAFAYETTE PARISH SCHOOL BOARD
113 CHAPLIN DR, LAFAYETTE, LA 705082101
Phone: 3375217000
Web: WWW.LPSSONLINE.COM

HISTORICAL FINANCIALS

Company Type: Private

Income Statement FYE: June 30

	REVENUE ($ mil.)	NET INCOME ($ mil.)	NET PROFIT MARGIN	EMPLOYEES
06/13	339	45	13.5%	3,400
06/10	322	8	2.7%	—
06/09	326	15	4.9%	—
06/08	0	0	—	—
Annual Growth	—	—	—	—

2013 Year-End Financials

Debt ratio: —
Return on equity: 13.50%
Cash ($ mil.): 126
Current ratio: —
Long-term debt ($ mil.): —
Dividends
Yield: —
Payout: —
Market value ($ mil.): —

LAKE HOSPITAL SYSTEM INC.

The aptly named Lake Hospital System (doing business as Lake Health) serves several northeast Ohio communities located along Lake Erie and throughout Lake County. The system comprises two main hospital campuses (TriPoint Medical Center and West) which together house more than 350 beds as well as a dozen ancillary facilities offering rehabilitative care outpatient surgery urgent care services primary care and specialist doctors' offices and diagnostic imaging. The system's Lake Health Physician Group includes physicians ranging from family practitioners to vascular surgeons. A not-for-profit health system Lake Health was founded in 1902 by the Daughters of the American Revolution.

Company Background

Lake Health opened the TriPoint Medical Center in 2009. The $155 million medical center replaced the aging 100-year-old LakeEast Medical Center. The modern four-story TriPoint hospital features 119 private patient rooms as well as digital technology and integrative medicine therapies like healing touch and music therapy.

EXECUTIVES

President Chief Executive Officer, Cynthia Moore-Hardy
Senior Vice President Administrative Services, Steven R. Karns
Vice President of government and community affairs of, Gary Robinson
VP Information Technologies and CIO, Jerry Peters
VP Human Resources, Craig Ghidotti
SVP Medical Affairs, Theodore Nichols
SVP Patient Care Services and Chief Nursing Officer, Mary L. Ogrinc
Vice President Critical Care Services/, Leslie Manzo
Vice President Clinical Services, Janie Racer
Corporate Director Decision Support, Ferole Parmelee
Chair, Bruce M. Kephart
Senior Vice President Business Development, Richard Cicero
VP Quality and Chief Quality Officer, Joyce Taylor
VP Support Services, Ted Hoffman
CFO, Michael E. Kittoe
Founder, Jim Glisson
Vice President Corporate Finance, Charles Josey
SVP Medical Affairs and Chief Medical Officer, Michael R. Goler
Vice President, David Rollins
Vice President Perioperative Care, Andrea Wasdovich
Trustee, John F. Platz
Trustee, Susan Tullai-McGuinness
Trustee, Thomas P. Jubek
Trustee, I. James Hackenberg
Trustee, Robert G. Schiebli

LOCATIONS

HQ: LAKE HOSPITAL SYSTEM INC.
7590 AUBURN RD, PAINESVILLE, OH 44077-9176
Phone: 440-354-2400
Web: WWW.LAKEHEALTH.ORG

Selected Facilities

Lyndhurst Diagnostics
Madison Campus
Madison Emergency Room
Mentor Campus
Mentor Diagnostics
Mentor Physical Therapy
Painesville Quick Care Center
The Clinic At Madison
The Clinic At Middlefield
Tyler Urgent Care Center
TriPoint Medical Center
West Medical Center
Willoughby Hills Diagnostics
Willoughby Physical Therapy
Chardon Campus
Willowick Campus

PRODUCTS/OPERATIONS

Selected Services

Anti-Coagulation Clinic
Cancer Services
Cardiac Services
Chronic Kidney Disease Clinic
Congestive Heart Failure Clinic
Diabetes Care Center
Emergency Services
Family Birthing Center
Geriatric Psychiatry
Home Health
Imaging Services
Integrated Medicine
Men's Health
Occupational Health
Orthopedics/Sports Medicine
Pain Management
Senior Services
Sleep Center
Surgical Services
Women's Services
Wound Care Center

COMPETITORS

Akron Children' s Hospital
Akron General Health System
Akron General Medical Center
MetroHealth System
Parma Community General Hospital
Robinson Memorial Hospital
Summa Health System
The Cleveland Clinic
University Hospitals Health System

HISTORICAL FINANCIALS

Company Type: Private

Income Statement FYE: December 31

	REVENUE ($ mil.)	NET INCOME ($ mil.)	NET PROFIT MARGIN	EMPLOYEES
12/12	315	5	1.7%	2,200
12/11	360	23	6.5%	—
12/01	278	(31)	—	—
12/02	184	5	2.8%	—
Annual Growth	5.5%	0.4%	—	—

2012 Year-End Financials

Debt ratio: —
Return on equity: 1.70%
Cash ($ mil.): 10
Current ratio: 1.30
Long-term debt ($ mil.): —
Dividends
Yield: —
Payout: —
Market value ($ mil.): —

LAKESIDE INDUSTRIES INC.

Lakeside Industries is one of the largest highway contractors in the Pacific Northwest. A leading asphalt paving contractor and manufacturer the company works on municipal commercial and industrial sites as well as residential projects. It also sells hot-mix and cold asphalt to other paving contractors. It has about a dozen offices in western Washington northwestern Oregon and central Idaho. Owned by the founding Lee family Lakeside Industries was established when the family combined their mining sand and gravel asphalt and trucking businesses in 1972.

EXECUTIVES

CFO Secretary and Treasurer, Henry R. (Hank) Waggoner
Director Information Technology, Mike Smith
President, Mike Lee
Shop Manager, Craig Nachatilo

LOCATIONS

HQ: LAKESIDE INDUSTRIES INC.
6505 226TH PL SE STE 200, ISSAQUAH, WA 98027-8905
Phone: 425-313-2600
Web: WWW.LAKESIDEIND.COM

Selected Locations

Aberdeen WA
Anacortes WA
Bellevue ID
Centralia WA
Kent WA
Lacey WA
Longview WA
Monroe WA
Port Angeles WA
Portland OR
Seattle
Vancouver WA

COMPETITORS

Balfour Beatty Infrastructure
Koch Industries Inc.
Peter Kiewit Sons'
The Cruz Corporation

HISTORICAL FINANCIALS

Company Type: Private

Income Statement FYE: November 30

	REVENUE ($ mil.)	NET INCOME ($ mil.)	NET PROFIT MARGIN	EMPLOYEES
11/07	205	0	—	750
11/05	147	5	4.0%	—
11/04	0	0	—	—
11/03	136	0	—	—
Annual Growth	10.9%	—	—	—

2007 Year-End Financials

Debt ratio: —
Return on equity: —
Cash ($ mil.): 21
Current ratio: 1.90
Long-term debt ($ mil.): —
Dividends
Yield: —
Payout: —
Market value ($ mil.): —

LANCASTER GENERAL HEALTH

Lancaster General Health (LG Health) is a 623-bed integrated health care delivery system serving residents of Lancaster County Pennsylvania and surrounding areas. Its flagship Lancaster General Hospital (LGH) - opened in 1893 - is known for its cardiology orthopedic and intensive care specialties. A separate Women & Babies hospital cares for those just making it into the world. The system also includes multiple outpatient clinics a rehab hospital home care services and a nursing center and healthcare college as well as a medical group of more than 100 physicians operating from 20 offices throughout the area.

Strategy LG Health continues to make strategic investments to better serve its patients and the community. In 2010 it began a $100 million electronic records initiative which included the launch of the MyLGHealth online program for accessing records communicating with doctors and requesting appointments. The following year the health system began construction on the Ann B. Barshinger Cancer Center which is scheduled to open in mid-2013.

EXECUTIVES

Senior Vice President Business Development & Ambulatory Services, Susan Wynne
EVP Lancaster General Health; President Lancaster General Hospital, Marion A. McGowan
Senior Vice President Chief Financial Officer Treasurer, F. Joseph Byorick III
President and CEO, Thomas E. (Tom) Beeman
Executive Vice President Chief Operating Officer, Jan L. Bergen
SVP Chief Administrative and Legal Officer and Corporate Secretary, Robert P. Macina
Senior Vice President of Operations, Geoffrey W. Eddowes
SVP and Chief Physician Executive, Lee M. Duke II
SVP Chief Quality Officer and Chief Marketing Officer, Norma J. Ferdinand
SVP Human Resources and Chief Leadership Officer, Regina Mingle
Vice Chairman, Clair McCormick
Chief Financial Officer Treasurer, Joseph Byorick
Senior Vice President Chief Information Officer, Gary Davidson
Senior Vice President Hospital Operations & Nurse Executive, Karen Flaherty-Oxler

LOCATIONS

HQ: LANCASTER GENERAL HEALTH
555 N DUKE ST, LANCASTER, PA 17602-2250
Phone: 717-544-5511
Web: WWW.LANCASTERGENERAL.ORG

PRODUCTS/OPERATIONS

Selected Specialties

Cardiology
Emergency medical
Intensive care
Neurology
Oncology
Radiology
Rehabilitation
Urology

COMPETITORS

Altoona Regional
Ascension Health
Catholic Health Initiatives
Evangelical Community Hospital
Hanover Healthcare
Holy Spirit
Jefferson Health System
Lewistown Hospital
Memorial Hospital (PA)
PinnacleHealth System
Saint Vincent Health System
St. Luke' s University Health Network
University of Pennsylvania Health System
WellSpan Health

HISTORICAL FINANCIALS

Company Type: Private

Income Statement FYE: June 30

	REVENUE ($ mil.)	NET INCOME ($ mil.)	NET PROFIT MARGIN	EMPLOYEES
06/12	852	31	3.7%	5,000
06/11	838	(113)	—	—
06/10	828	31	3.8%	—
06/09	815	48	5.9%	—
Annual Growth	1.5%	(13.2%)	—	—

2012 Year-End Financials

Debt ratio: —
Return on equity: 3.70%
Cash ($ mil.): 5
Current ratio: 1.20
Long-term debt ($ mil.): —
Dividends
Yield: —
Payout: —
Market value ($ mil.): —

LASSUS BROS OIL INC

LOCATIONS

HQ: LASSUS BROS OIL INC
1800 MAGNAVOX WAY, FORT WAYNE, IN 468041540
Phone: 2604361415

HISTORICAL FINANCIALS

Company Type: Private

Income Statement FYE: September 30

	REVENUE ($ mil.)	NET INCOME ($ mil.)	NET PROFIT MARGIN	EMPLOYEES
09/11	209	0	0.2%	375
09/10	0	0	21.9%	—
09/09	0	0	—	—
Annual Growth	—	338.4%	—	—

2011 Year-End Financials

Debt ratio: —
Return on equity: 0.10%
Cash ($ mil.): 0
Current ratio: 0.40
Long-term debt ($ mil.): —
Dividends
Yield: —
Payout: —
Market value ($ mil.): —

LATEX CONSTRUCTION COMPANY INC

LOCATIONS

HQ: LATEX CONSTRUCTION COMPANY INC
1353 FARMER RD NW, CONYERS, GA 300123488
Phone: 7707600820
Web: WWW.LATEXCONSTRUCTION.COM

HISTORICAL FINANCIALS

Company Type: Private

Income Statement FYE: December 31

	REVENUE ($ mil.)	NET INCOME ($ mil.)	NET PROFIT MARGIN	EMPLOYEES
12/08	431	50	11.8%	400
12/07	272	40	14.7%	—
12/06	1,870	0	—	—
Annual Growth	—	5471.5%	—	—

2008 Year-End Financials

Debt ratio: —
Return on equity: 11.80%
Cash ($ mil.): 74
Current ratio: 2.00
Long-term debt ($ mil.): —
Dividends
Yield: —
Payout: —
Market value ($ mil.): —

LAWRENCE & MEMORIAL HOSPITAL INC.

Lawrence & Memorial Hospital (L&M) connects residents of Connecticut with health care whether they're near the Rhode Island border or enjoying the Connecticut River. The not-for-profit hospital founded in 1912 provides services to a ten-town region on the Connecticut shoreline and neighboring areas in the Northeast. L&M has roughly 280 beds and provides general acute care including medical surgical rehabilitative pediatric psychiatric and obstetrical services. The hospital also runs about a dozen community physician practices and specialty clinics.

Geographic Reach

L&M serves patients in eastern Connecticut as well as Washington County in Rhode Island and the Fishers Island region of New York State.

Operations

Each year L&M sees some 84000 patients in its emergency room. It also admits about 16000 inpatients and conducts some 7000 surgeries annually. The hospital's specialty facilities include a cardiac catheterization lab a cancer center a sleep disorder unit and a the region's only neonatal ICU.

Affiliates of the L&M system include Joslin Diabetes Center L&M Physicians the Visiting Nurse Association of Southeastern Connecticut and Hospice Southeastern Connecticut.

Strategy

The changing economy and health care landscape in the US has prompted many independent hospitals to seek affiliations with other medical providers as a means of controlling spending and enhancing care and L&M is no exception.

The hospital is moving towards expansion by acquiring neighboring 125-bed Westerly Hospital (an affiliate of Yale New Haven Health) in Westerly Rhode Island. The two hospitals began negotiations in 2011 but were suspended briefly when the struggling Westerly Hospital filed for receivership. In mid-2012 the deal resumed when L&M submitted a bid to acquire Westerly Hospital for some $69 million.

In addition L&M is planning to grow its service offerings through other means. In 2012 the care provider began construction of a $35 million cancer center in Waterford Rhode Island.

EXECUTIVES

President CEO and Director, Bruce D. Cummings
Secretary and Director, Marilynn R. (Lynn) Malerba, age 61
VP Chief Medical & Clinical Operations Officer, Daniel Rissi
VP and CIO, Kimberly Kalajainen
Vice President Development and Community Relations, William A. Stanley
VP and Chief HR Officer, Donna Epps
Director Information Services, Helen Favello
Chairman, Ulysses B. Hammond
Vice Chairman, Granville Morris
Vice President General Counsel, Maureen Anderson
President Medical Staff, Henry Amdur
President Medical Staff, Donald Felitto
Treasurer and Director, Fred Conti
Vice President and Chief Financial and Support Services Officer, Lou Inzana
Vice President and Physician Practice Management, Pamela Kane
Vice President Marketing, Crista Durand
Vice President and Chief Transformation Officer, Chris Lehrach
Director, Leon J. (Lee) Olivier, age 65
Director, Scott D. Bates
President CEO and Director, Bruce D. Cummings
Secretary and Director, Marilynn R. (Lynn) Malerba, age 61
Director, Timothy D. Bates
Vice Chairman, Granville Morris
VP and General Counsel, Maureen Anderson
Director, John E. Allen
Director, L. James Carroll
Treasurer and Director, Fred Conti
Director, Mary Ellen Jukoski
Director, Robert Keltner
Director, Daniel P. O?Shea
Director, Carol Ridgway
Director, Kathy Steamer
Auditors: Ernst&YoungLLP

LOCATIONS

HQ: LAWRENCE & MEMORIAL HOSPITAL INC.
365 MONTAUK AVE, NEW LONDON, CT 06320-4769
Phone: 860-442-0711
Web: WWW.LMHOSPITAL.ORG

PRODUCTS/OPERATIONS

Selected Services

Core Services
- Cardiac Care
- Maternity Care
- Cancer Care
- Surgery
- Occupational Health Care

Other Services
- Behavioral Medicine
- Chronic Pain
- Diagnostic Imaging
- Emergency Services
- Gastroenterology
- Hand Center
- Infectious Diseases
- Joint Replacement Center
- Joslin Diabetes Center
- Laboratory
- Neurosurgery
- Pulmonary Disorders
- Pulmonary Rehabilitation
- Rehabilitation - Acute Inpatient
- Rehabilitation - Signature Outpatient
- Sleep Center
- Social Work
- Women's and Infants Services
- Wound and Hyperbaric Center

COMPETITORS

Backus
Care New England
Connecticut Children' s Medical Center
Day Kimball Hospital
Harrington Memorial Hospital
Hartford Health Care
Hospital of Central Connecticut
Kent Hospital
Roger Williams Medical Center
Saint Francis Hospital and Medical Center
Sturdy Memorial
University of Connecticut Health Center
Waterbury Hospital
Yale New Haven Health System

HISTORICAL FINANCIALS

Company Type: Private

Income Statement FYE: September 30

	REVENUE ($ mil.)	NET INCOME ($ mil.)	NET PROFIT MARGIN	EMPLOYEES
09/11	336	3	1.0%	2,200
09/10	324	8	2.6%	—
09/09	293	(11)	—	—
09/08	278	(17)	—	—
Annual Growth	6.6%	—	—	—

2011 Year-End Financials

Debt ratio: —
Return on equity: 1.00%
Cash ($ mil.): 41
Current ratio: 1.40
Long-term debt ($ mil.): —
Dividends
Yield: —
Payout: —
Market value ($ mil.): —

LEAVITT GROUP ENTERPRISES INC

LOCATIONS

HQ: LEAVITT GROUP ENTERPRISES INC
216 S 200 W, CEDAR CITY, UT 847203207
Phone: 4355861555
Web: WWW.LEAVITT.COM

HISTORICAL FINANCIALS

Company Type: Private

Income Statement FYE: December 31

	REVENUE ($ mil.)	NET INCOME ($ mil.)	NET PROFIT MARGIN	EMPLOYEES
12/13	207	4	1.9%	1,272
12/12	185	2	1.5%	—
12/09	196	0	0.0%	—
12/08	186	0	—	—
Annual Growth	2.2%	—	—	—

2013 Year-End Financials

Debt ratio: —
Return on equity: 1.90%
Cash ($ mil.): 16
Current ratio: 0.30
Long-term debt ($ mil.): —
Dividends
Yield: —
Payout: —
Market value ($ mil.): —

LEE BANK

LOCATIONS

HQ: LEE BANK
75 PARK ST, LEE, MA 012381726
Phone: 4132430117
Web: WWW.LEEBANK.COM

HISTORICAL FINANCIALS

Company Type: Private

Income Statement FYE: December 31

	ASSETS ($ mil.)	NET INCOME ($ mil.)	INCOME AS % OF ASSETS	EMPLOYEES
12/13	280	1	0.5%	46
12/09	282	1	0.6%	—
12/08	297	1	0.5%	—
12/07	286	0	—	—
Annual Growth	(0.3%)	—	—	—

2013 Year-End Financials

Debt ratio: —
Return on equity: 10.10%
Cash ($ mil.): 5
Current ratio: —
Long-term debt ($ mil.): —
Dividends
Yield: —
Payout: —
Market value ($ mil.): —

LEE COUNTY ELECTRIC COOPERATIVE INC.

If you are a Floridian who is a really early riser or a night owl Lee County Electric Cooperative (LCEC) may help light your way. The electric cooperative provides power to more than 198880 residential and commercial customers across five counties in southwestern Florida (Lee County and parts of Collier Hendry Charlotte and Broward counties. The member-owned non-profit electric utility operates more than 8000 miles of transmission and distribution lines and more than 20 substations. Tampa-based Seminole Electric Cooperative serves as LCEC's wholesale power supplier.

Geographic Reach

The company's service territory includes Cape Coral North Fort Myers Marco Island Sanibel and Captiva Islands Pine Island Everglades City Immokalee and parts of Lehigh Acres.

Financial Performance

In 2012 LCEC's revenues declined by 0.3% as the result of abnormally mild weather and conservation efforts by customers coupled with ongoing economic uncertainty all of which trimmed demand. Net income decreased by 11% in 2012 as the drop in net sales outpaced only slightly lower operating costs for the year.

As part of its non-profit charter LCEC returns surplus equity to its current and former members. In 2012 its Board of Trustees approved $12.9 million in equity distribution.

Strategy

The cooperative is working on a number of strategic initiatives in order to keep up with the demands of the growing population in its service area: maintain power quality enhance disaster recovery competency keep up with regulatory compliance requirements implement mobile workforce technology and keep employees engaged.

To better support its customers that year LCEC upgraded its website with improved navigation and additional energy management tips and tools.

Company Background

Under the leadership of Homer Welch (and as part of a nationwide rural electrification drive) LCEC began operations with 15 miles of distribution line and 158 members or about 1% of Lee County's 1940 population of 17500.

EXECUTIVES

Vp Marketing, Joe Padgett

LOCATIONS

HQ: LEE COUNTY ELECTRIC COOPERATIVE INC.
4980 BAYLINE DR, FORT MYERS, FL 339173998
Phone: 8005992356
Web: WWW.LCEC.NET

HISTORICAL FINANCIALS

Company Type: Private

Income Statement FYE: December 31

	REVENUE ($ mil.)	NET INCOME ($ mil.)	NET PROFIT MARGIN	EMPLOYEES
12/13	405	2	0.5%	400
12/12	404	2	0.6%	—
Annual Growth	0.3%	(12.7%)	—	—

2013 Year-End Financials

Debt ratio: ——
Return on equity: 0.50%
Cash ($ mil.): 2
Current ratio: 1.00
Long-term debt ($ mil.): —
Dividends
Yield: —
Payout: —
Market value ($ mil.): —

LEE LEWIS CONSTRUCTION INC.

General builder Lee Lewis Construction has waltzed across Texas and beyond to keep in step with the top US contractors. The company provides construction-related services and construction management for commercial institutional and industrial projects. Among its projects is the Garland ISD Special Events Center in Garland Texas; it also worked on the Grand Floridian Resort at Walt Disney World. The company earns much of its revenue from projects for Texas school systems. Projects for hometown neighbor Texas Tech University have generated a significant portion of the company's business. CEO Lee Lewis founded the company in 1976.

EXECUTIVES

CEO, Lee Lewis
President, Tom E. Ferguson
Treasurer, Jeanette Howell
Secretary, Judy Ward
Marketing Coordinator, Allison Lee
Human Resources, Mona Wiley

LOCATIONS

HQ: LEE LEWIS CONSTRUCTION INC.
7810 ORLANDO AVE, LUBBOCK, TX 79423-1942
Phone: 806-797-8400
Web: WWW.LEELEWIS.COM

COMPETITORS

Austin Industries
Beck Group
Centex
Flint Industries
Hensel Phelps Construction
Hunt Construction
Manhattan Construction
Skanska USA Building
Turner Construction

HISTORICAL FINANCIALS

Company Type: Private

Income Statement FYE: June 30

	REVENUE ($ mil.)	NET INCOME ($ mil.)	NET PROFIT MARGIN	EMPLOYEES
06/09	229	6	2.8%	200
06/06	245	4	1.8%	—
06/05	176	2	1.3%	—
06/04	138	0	0.6%	—
Annual Growth	10.6%	47.7%	—	—

2009 Year-End Financials

Debt ratio: ——
Return on equity: 2.80%
Cash ($ mil.): 25
Current ratio: 1.50
Long-term debt ($ mil.): —
Dividends
Yield: —
Payout: —
Market value ($ mil.): —

LEESBURG REGIONAL MEDICAL CENTER INC.

LOCATIONS

HQ: LEESBURG REGIONAL MEDICAL CENTER INC.
600 E DIXIE AVE, LEESBURG, FL 347485999
Phone: 3523235762
Web: WWW.CFHALLIANCE.ORG

HISTORICAL FINANCIALS

Company Type: Private

Income Statement FYE: June 30

	REVENUE ($ mil.)	NET INCOME ($ mil.)	NET PROFIT MARGIN	EMPLOYEES
06/13	237	14	5.9%	1,900
06/12	245	15	6.5%	—
06/11	246	9	3.9%	—
06/10	241	0	—	—
Annual Growth	(0.5%)	—	—	—

2013 Year-End Financials

Debt ratio: ——
Return on equity: 5.90%
Cash ($ mil.): 35
Current ratio: 0.60
Long-term debt ($ mil.): —
Dividends
Yield: —
Payout: —
Market value ($ mil.): —

LEGACY EMANUEL HOSPITAL & HEALTH CENTER

Legacy Emanuel Hospital and Health Center part of the Legacy Health System provides acute and specialized health care to residents of Portland Oregon and surrounding communities. The 400-bed teaching hospital's operations include centers devoted to trauma treatment burn care oncology birthing neurosurgery orthopedics and cardiology. It also houses a pediatric hospital and operates the region's Life Flight Network service which is owned by a consortium of local hospitals. Legacy Emanuel Hospital was established in 1912 by the Lutheran Church.

Operations

Legacy Emanuel's trauma and burn centers are level I designated facilities meaning they receive severe trauma and burn cases from other area hospitals. The hospital's burn center is the only one of its kind in an area stretching from Seattle to Sacramento and Salt Lake City. Other specialist facilities at Legacy Emanuel include its maternity center and its diagnostic imaging and screening units.

The medical center sees more than 18000 inpatients each year. Its staff includes about 140 full-time doctors and dentists as well as 700 full-time registered nurses. The Randall Children's Hospital located within Legacy Emanuel has about 600 affiliated pediatricians and specialists on its staff and handles about 100000 patient encounters each year including 20000 emergency room visits.

Strategy

The hospital is undergoing massive expansion efforts. The hospital completed construction of the new Randall Children's Hospital facilities in 2012 making it one of the largest pediatric facilities in the state. The new pediatric center is four times as large as the past facilities. Other expansion efforts in recent years include new acute and intensive care capacity.

To expand its medical transportation services Legacy Emanuel and other owners of LFN teamed up to purchase 15 new helicopters in 2012.

EXECUTIVES

SVP and Chief Medical Officer, George A. (Jack) Cioffi, age 53
SVP and CIO, Richard (Dick) Gibson, age 59
Chief Administrative Officer, Lori Morgan
VP-Community Rels & Mktg, Wayne Clark

LOCATIONS

HQ: LEGACY EMANUEL HOSPITAL & HEALTH CENTER
2801 N GANTENBEIN AVE, PORTLAND, OR 97227-1623
Phone: 503-413-2200
Web: WWW.LEGACYHEALTH.ORG

PRODUCTS/OPERATIONS

Selected Centers and Services

Burn care
Cancer care
Children' s care
Diabetes and nutrition
Emergency services
Family birth center
Gardens
High-risk obstetrics
Imaging

Injury prevention
Intensive care
Interventional and diagnostic cardiology
Level I trauma center
Life flight network
Maternal-fetal medicine
Neurology and neurosurgery including spine surgery
Orthopedics
Pediatrics
Rehabilitation (inpatient and outpatient)
Radiation oncology
Stroke
Surgery (including minimally invasive surgery)
Vascular clinic
Wound and ostomy clinic
Wound care and outpatient burn clinic

COMPETITORS

Adventist Health
Asante Health System
Dignity Health
Kadlec Regional Medical Center
Kaiser Permanente
PeaceHealth
PeaceHealth Southwest Medical Center
Providence Health & Services
Salem Hospital

HISTORICAL FINANCIALS

Company Type: Private

Income Statement FYE: March 31

	REVENUE ($ mil.)	NET INCOME ($ mil.)	NET PROFIT MARGIN	EMPLOYEES
03/12	571	(6)	—	3,619
03/10*	573	13	2.4%	—
04/05	0	0	—	—
03/04	383	12	3.2%	—
Annual Growth	5.1%	—	—	—

*Fiscal year change

2012 Year-End Financials

Debt ratio: —
Return on equity: (-1.10%)
Cash ($ mil.): 0
Current ratio: 1.30
Long-term debt ($ mil.): —
Dividends
Yield: —
Payout: —
Market value ($ mil.): —

LEGACY HEALTH

EXECUTIVES

SVP and Chief Nursing Officer, Carol Bradley
VP Community Relations and Marketing, Wayne L. Clark
Vice Chair, Colleen A. Cain
President and CEO, George J. Brown
Chief Administrative Officer Legacy Meridian Park Medical Center, Allyson Anderson
Chief Administrative Officer Legacy Salmon Creek Medical Center, Jonathan Avery
Chief Administrative Officer Randall Children?s Hospital at Legacy Emanuel, Carla D. Harris
SVP and CIO, John Kenagy
Chief Administrative Officer Legacy Medical Group, Will Mowe, age 59
Chief Administrative Officer Legacy Emanuel Medical Center, Lori Morgan
SVP and Chief Development Officer, Maureen Bradley
SVP and CFO, David Eager
SVP and COO, Mike Newcomb
SVP and Chief Medical Officer, Lewis Low
Chief Administrative Officer Legacy Good Samaritan Medical Center, Tony Melaragno
Chief Administrative Officer Legacy Mount Hood Medical Center, Gretchen Nichols
Director, Duane C. McDougall, age 61
Director, Ronald S. King
Director, Jack L. Orchard
Director, Judith A. Andersen
Vice Chair, Colleen A. Cain
Director, Barbara K. Ferre
Director, Hollis J. Hendricks
Director, John W. Winter Jr.
Director, Jeffrey D. Gordon
Director, Corliss McKeever
Director, David (Dave) Brauer-Rieke
Director, Robert L. Cornie
Director, Rev William Lupfer
Director, Steven Newberry
Director, Christopher S. Thoming

LOCATIONS

HQ: LEGACY HEALTH
1919 NW LOVEJOY ST, PORTLAND, OR 972091503
Phone: 5034155600
Web: WWW.LEGACYHEALTH.ORG

PRODUCTS/OPERATIONS

Selected Facilities

Hospitals
- Legacy Emanuel Medical Center (Portland Oregon)
- Legacy Good Samaritan Medical Center (Portland Oregon)
- Legacy Meridian Park Medical Center (Tualatin Oregon)
- Legacy Mount Hood Medical Center (Gresham Oregon)
- Legacy Salmon Creek Medical Center (Vancouver Washington)
- Randall Children' s Hospital At Legacy Emanuel (Portland Oregon)

Clinics
- Legacy Medical Group - Battle Ground
- Legacy Medical Group - Bridgeport
- Legacy Medical Group - Broadway
- Legacy Medical Group - Canby
- Legacy Medical Group - Cornell
- Legacy Medical Group - Firwood
- Legacy Medical Group - Fisher' s Landing
- Legacy Medical Group - Forest Heights
- Legacy Medical Group - Good Samaritan
- Legacy Medical Group - Lake Oswego
- Legacy Medical Group - Mount Hood
- Legacy Medical Group - Northeast
- Legacy Medical Group - Northwest
- Legacy Medical Group - Tualatin
- Legacy Medical Group - West Linn
- Legacy Medical Group - Woodburn
- Salmon Creek Family Medicine (Vancouver Washington)
- Salmon Creek Internal Medicine (Vancouver Washington)
- Urgent Care St. Helens (St. Helens Oregon)

COMPETITORS

Adventist Health
Asante Health System
Dignity Health
Kadlec Regional Medical Center
Kaiser Permanente
PeaceHealth
PeaceHealth Southwest Medical Center
Providence Health & Services
Salem Hospital

HISTORICAL FINANCIALS

Company Type: Private

Income Statement FYE: March 31

	REVENUE ($ mil.)	NET INCOME ($ mil.)	NET PROFIT MARGIN	EMPLOYEES
03/14	183	9	5.2%	8,000
03/12*	1,326	(0)	—	—
08/10	1,249	192	15.4%	—
03/10	1,249	0	—	—
Annual Growth	(38.1%)	—	—	—

*Fiscal year change

2014 Year-End Financials

Debt ratio: —
Return on equity: 5.20%
Cash ($ mil.): 69
Current ratio: 1.30
Long-term debt ($ mil.): —
Dividends
Yield: —
Payout: —
Market value ($ mil.): —

LEHIGH UNIVERSITY

Lehigh University (LU) nestled in eastern Pennsylvania's Lehigh Valley offers about 90 undergraduate programs and majors at colleges of arts and sciences business and economics engineering and applied sciences and education. It also offers more than 40 masters and doctoral degree programs as well as certificate programs. Tuition is more than $40000 per year; more than half of students receive financial aid. LU has an enrollment of nearly 7000 undergraduate and graduate students. The university was founded in 1865 by entrepreneur and philanthropist Asa Packer.

Geographic Reach

One of the most selective schools in the nation it accepts about 3600 students per year out of the more than 12000 who apply; about a third of those accepted matriculate at LU.

Operations

The student to faculty ratio is 10:1 and the average class size is 27. The students are instructed by about 700 faculty memebrs.

EXECUTIVES

President, John D. Simon
Provost and VP Academic Affairs, Patrick V. Farrell
VP Finance and Administration, Patricia A. Johnson
Dean College of Arts and Sciences, Donald E. Hall
Dean College of Business and Economics, Georgette C. Phillips
Dean College of Education, Gary M. Sasso
Dean P.C. Rossin College of Engineering and Applied Science, S. David Wu
Avp University Marketing, K Sivakumar
Vp For Advancement, Joseph P Kender
Vice Chairman, Kevin L. Clayton, age 52
Vice Chairman, Jane P. Jamieson
Chairman, Brad E. Scheler
Board Member, Donald Talhelm

LOCATIONS

HQ: LEHIGH UNIVERSITY
27 MEMORIAL DR W UNIT 8, BETHLEHEM, PA 18015-3005
Phone: 610-758-3000
Web: WWW.LEHIGH.EDU

HISTORICAL FINANCIALS

Company Type: Private

Income Statement FYE: June 30

	REVENUE ($ mil.)	NET INCOME ($ mil.)	NET PROFIT MARGIN	EMPLOYEES
06/12	423	23	5.5%	4,000
06/07*	316	169	53.6%	—
03/06	0	(0)	—	—
06/05	272	74	27.2%	—
Annual Growth	6.5%	(15.2%)	—	—

*Fiscal year change

2012 Year-End Financials

Debt ratio: —
Return on equity: 5.50%
Cash ($ mil.): 57
Current ratio: —
Long-term debt ($ mil.): —
Dividends
Yield: —
Payout: —
Market value ($ mil.): —

LEHIGH VALLEY HEALTH NETWORK

Residents of the Lehigh Valley seeking medical care head uptown to facilities operated by the Lehigh Valley Health Network (LVHN). The not-for-profit health care provider operates through three hospital campuses housing a total of about 1000 licensed beds. The medical center serves as a regional referral center for trauma and burn care and organ transplantation as well as specialty care in numerous areas such as cardiology women's health and pediatric surgery. LVHN also boasts a network of physician practices and community health centers as well as home health and hospice units.

Geographic Reach

The LVHN system's main facilities are located in Allentown and Bethlehem. It provides services to residents of a four-county territory in Pennsylvania.

Operations

The company's hospitals provide care in about 95 specialist fields including pediatric care burn treatment trauma care organ transplant cardiovascular care oncology and neurology. Its children's hospital includes inpatient emergency and specialist units. LVHN also conducts medical training programs and performs research in a range of different areas including cancer cardiovascular and infectious disease; a number of these programs are conducted through partnerships with entities including the H. Lee Moffitt Cancer Center and the University of South Florida's Morsani College of Medicine.

In addition to its core hospital operations the health organization has an alliance with the Sacred Heart Hospital of Allentown through which it provides Sacred Heart with certain services in the areas of cardiac care primary care telehealth services and mental health care. The two hospitals discussed but ultimately dismissed the possibility of a formal merger settling on being affiliated instead.

LVHN's 40 community clinics administer primary and specialty care for area residents including facilities for low-income patients. For patients (insured or not) who need care for minor ailments and routine tests LVHN operates a handful of retail health clinics under the Careworks brand. In addition the network includes a system of medical laboratories (Health Network Laboratories).

Financial Performance

Revenues for LVHN for 2012 increased 6% to $1.6 billion on higher earnings from patient service and support operations. The growth was partially offset by lower net assets released from restrictions.

Strategy

LVHN expanded its pediatric service offerings in 2011 when it added the region's first pediatric emergency department at its Cedar Crest campus. The new center houses about a dozen beds and is staffed by pediatric emergency physicians and nurses as well as a child life specialist. To further expand its emergency capabilities in 2013 the organization added emergency transportation services to its offerings.

LOCATIONS

HQ: LEHIGH VALLEY HEALTH NETWORK
1247 S CEDAR CREST BLVD 104A, ALLENTOWN, PA 18103-6298
Phone: 610-402-8000
Web: WWW.LVH.COM

PRODUCTS/OPERATIONS

Selected Facilities

Community Health Centers
- Hamburg Community Health Center
- Lehigh Valley Health Center at Bath
- Lehigh Valley Health Center at Bethlehem Township
- Lehigh Valley Health Center at Hellertown
- Lehigh Valley Health Center at Kutztown
- Lehigh Valley Health Center at Saucon Valley
- Lehigh Valley Health Center at Trexlertown
- Upper Bucks Health & Diagnostic Center (in partnership with Grand View Hospital Quakertown)

Hospitals
- Lehigh Valley Hospital - 17th St. (short-stay hospital Salisbury Township in Allentown)
- Lehigh Valley Hospital - Cedar Crest (Allentown)
- Lehigh Valley Hospital - Muhlenberg (Bethlehem)

COMPETITORS

Abington Memorial Hospital
Ascension Health
Community Health Systems
Doylestown Hospital
Grand View
Jefferson Health System
Mercy Health System
Moses Taylor Hospital
North Philadelphia Health System
Pennsylvania Hospital
Reading Hospital and Medical Center
Sacred Heart Hospital of Allentown
Shore Memorial Hospital
St. Luke' s University Health Network
Tenet Healthcare
University of Pennsylvania Health System
Wyoming Valley Health Care System

HISTORICAL FINANCIALS

Company Type: Private

Income Statement FYE: June 30

	REVENUE ($ mil.)	NET INCOME ($ mil.)	NET PROFIT MARGIN	EMPLOYEES
06/12	1,620	(63)	—	7,000
06/11	1,524	314	20.6%	—
06/10	1,399	58	4.2%	—
06/09	1,291	(177)	—	—
Annual Growth	7.8%	—	—	—

2012 Year-End Financials

Debt ratio: —
Return on equity: (-3.90%)
Cash ($ mil.): 26
Current ratio: 1.40
Long-term debt ($ mil.): —
Dividends
Yield: —
Payout: —
Market value ($ mil.): —

LEO A. DALY COMPANY

EXECUTIVES

Vice President Managing Principal Vice President and operations principal, Lloyd A. Meyer
VP and CFO, Robert L. (Bob) Luhrs
EVP, Charles D. Dalluge
Corporate Director Public Relations, Sian Imber
VP and Managing Principal Honolulu Office, Edward Z. Pskowski
Vice President Director of Design, Francis X. Dumont
President Lockwood Andrews & Newman, Dennis W. Petersen
Vice President Managing Principal, Patricia Miller
Vice President Managing Principal, Mary Morissette
Vice President Director of Design, Michael Walden
Vice President Managing Principal Director of operations, Ted Redmond
Vice President Director of Design, Walt Geiger
Vice President Director of Design, Bill Baxley
Vice President Director of Design, Brian Titus
Vice President Managing Principal Director of operations and Walter Geiger, David N. Zelig

LOCATIONS

HQ: LEO A. DALY COMPANY
8600 INDIAN HILLS DR, OMAHA, NE 681144039
Phone: 8085218889
Web: WWW.LEODALY.COM

PRODUCTS/OPERATIONS

Selected Services

Architecture
Engineering
Industrial refrigeration
Interiors
Infrastructure
Integrated design
Planning

COMPETITORS

Cannon Design	HOK
Einhorn Yaffee	Heery
Epstein	Interior Architects
Gensler	RTKL Associates
HDR	Skidmore Owings
HKS Inc.	SmithGroupJJR
HNTB Companies	Thorton Tomasetti

HISTORICAL FINANCIALS

Company Type: Private

Income Statement FYE: February 28

	REVENUE ($ mil.)	NET INCOME ($ mil.)	NET PROFIT MARGIN	EMPLOYEES
02/14	100	(3)	—	750
02/13	162	1	0.7%	—
02/12	131	(5)	—	—
02/11	114	0	—	—
Annual Growth	(4.3%)	—	—	—

2014 Year-End Financials

Debt ratio: —
Return on equity: (-3.30%)
Cash ($ mil.): 2
Current ratio: 0.60
Long-term debt ($ mil.): —
Dividends
Yield: —
Payout: —
Market value ($ mil.): —

LESTER E. COX MEDICAL CENTERS

Where health care in the Ozarks is concerned Lester is more. Lester E. Cox Medical Centers (dba CoxHealth) provides a myriad of medical services to people in Missouri and Arkansas. CoxHealth's network includes five acute care hospitals with some 950 beds and more than 80 physician clinics. Centers for cardiac care cancer treatment orthopedics mental health and women's health are among CoxHealth's specialized care options. Other operations include an ambulance service offering both ground and air transportation the Cox Health Systems HMO the Oxford HealthCare home health agency and educational programs. The organization was named after its primary fundraiser in the 1940s.

Operations

Each year CoxHealth handles about 500000 outpatient visits; 1560000 emergency urgent care and trauma visits; 28000 ground ambulance transports; and 4000 births. Its hospitals include Cox

Medical Center South Cox Medical Center Branson Cox North Hospital Cox Monett Hospital and the Meyer Orthopedic and Rehabilitation Hospital. Its specialty clinics include centers for cancer orthopedics cardiovascular care women's and children's health outpatient surgery and diagnostic imaging.

Geographic Reach

CoxHealth serves about 25 communities in 25 counties in southwestern Missouri and northwestern Arkansas. Major facilities are located in Branson Monett and Springfield Missouri.

Sales and Marketing

The organization primarily receives income from commercial insurance reimbursements which account for about 60% of patient revenue. Other payer sources include Medicare and Medicaid plans and self-pay patients.

Financial Performance

Revenue for CoxHealth increased 4% to $1.1 billion in 2012 on higher patient service income premiums and other revenue sources as well as net assets released from restrictions.

Strategy

Enduring through blizzards and tornadoes CoxHealth strives to improve its services and the health of its community.

Expanding its geographic coverage in 2013 CoxHealth completed a partnership deal with Skaggs Regional Medical Center which changed its name to Cox Medical Center Branson. CoxHealth plans to invest about $100 million into medical facilities in Branson. In addition the company formed an affiliation with Texas County Memorial Hospital in 2012 to enhance clinical collaboration between the two organizations.

The company also expands by adding or expanding facilities. It started construction of a new patient tower addition on the Cox Medical Center South facility in 2013; the wing will house facilities for neuroscience pediatrics and women's health. Other initiatives include upgrading clinical processes and information technology systems.

Company Background

CoxHealth was founded as Burge Deaconess Hospital in 1908. It became Lester E. Cox Medical Centers in 1968 following the death of Cox a St. Louis businessman who led a series of major fund raising campaigns in the 1940s critical to the survival and growth of the hospital.

EXECUTIVES

Vice President and Chief Medical Officer; and Medical Director Oxford Hospice, Dan Sontheimer
Senior Vice President Chief Hospital Officer, John Duff
Vice President and Chief Nursing Officer, Karen Kramer
Vice President Human Resources, John D. Hursh
Senior Vice President and Chief Financial Officer, Jacob McWay
Vice President and Chief Information Officer, Bruce Robison
VP and Chief Business Development Officer, Brian Williams
President Cox HealthPlans, Jeffrey C. (Jeff) Bond
Vice President and Chief Clinical Officer, Ron Prenger
Executive Director, Tim Siebert
Vice President Corporate Integrity, Betty S. Breshears
Controller, DeAnna Maples
Vice President; President Cox Monett, Genny Maroc
Vice President; President Oxford Healthcare, Karen Thomas
Chairman Joint Operations Committee and Chief Integrated Physicians, Kenneth Powell
Vice President President Home Parenteral Services, H. Lynn Kelley
Vice President Clinical Services, Pete Leer
Vice President Ferrell-Duncan Clinic, Robert L. Ferguson
Vice President Facilities Management, Rod Schaffer
President and CEO; Director, Steven D. (Steve) Edwards
Vice President Clinical Services, Tyler Hedden
President CoxHealth Foundation, Lisa Alexander
President Cox College, Anne Liners Brett

LOCATIONS

HQ: LESTER E. COX MEDICAL CENTERS
1423 N JEFFERSON AVE, SPRINGFIELD, MO 65802-1917
Phone: 417-269-3000
Web: WWW.COXHEALTH.COM

PRODUCTS/OPERATIONS

Selected Services

Air Care
Alzheimer' s Disease
Behavioral Health
Brain and Spine Disorders
Breast Care
Cancer Services
Children' s Health
Diabetes
Dialysis
Ear Nose and Throat (ENT)
Emergency Department
Fitness Centers
Food and Nutrition
Heart and Vascular
Home Health
Hyperbaric Medicine and Wound Care
Neuroscience
Occupational Medicine
Orthopedics
Parenting
Parkinson' s Clinic
Pharmacy
Physical Medicine
Pregnancy
Radiology
Rehabilitation
Respiratory Care
Robotic Surgery
Sleep Disorders
Smoking Cessation
Specialty Services
Sports Medicine
Stroke
Trauma Services
Urgent Care
Weight Loss
Wellness Consultations
Women' s Health
Workers' Compensation

COMPETITORS

Ascension Health
BJC HealthCare
Catholic Health Initiatives
Children' s Mercy Hospital
HCA
Mercy Health
Mercy Hospital Springfield
Saint Luke' s Health System
Shawnee Mission Medical Center
Sisters of Charity of Leavenworth
St. Anthony' s Medical Center
St. John' s Health System
Tenet Healthcare
Truman Medical Centers
Universal Health Services
University of Kansas Medical Center

HISTORICAL FINANCIALS

Company Type: Private

Income Statement FYE: September 30

	REVENUE ($ mil.)	NET INCOME ($ mil.)	NET PROFIT MARGIN	EMPLOYEES
09/09	876	29	3.4%	9,100
09/08	900	46	5.2%	—
09/04	0	0	—	—
09/03	677	4	0.7%	—
Annual Growth	4.4%	36.1%	—	—

2009 Year-End Financials

Debt ratio: —
Return on equity: 3.40%
Cash ($ mil.): 336
Current ratio: 1.00
Long-term debt ($ mil.): —
Dividends
Yield: —
Payout: —
Market value ($ mil.): —

LEWIS & CLARK COLLEGE

EXECUTIVES

VP and Provost, Jane Monnig Atkinson
President, Thomas Hochstettler
Vice President Secretary General Counsel, David Ellis
Associate Vice President for Campus Life, Michael Ford
Associate VP Facilities, Richard J. Bettega
Assistant Director Systems and Technical Services Aubrey R. Watzek Library, Mark Dahl
Head of Special Collections and Archivist Aubrey R. Watzek Library, Doug Erickson
Coordinator Reference Services Aubrey R. Watzek Library, Joanna Haney
Director Aubrey R. Watzek Library, Jim Kopp
Associate Provost, Mervyn Brockett
Administrative Assistant, Rosslyn Nayer
VP Business and Finance and Treasurer, Carl B. Vance
Dean College of Arts and Sciences, Julio C. de Paula
Director Student Financial Services, Glendi Gaddis
VP Institutional Advancement, Gregory A. Volk
Associate Director Human Resources and Manager Benefits, Kris Codron
Registrar, Diane Crabtree
Director Alumni and Parent Programs, Andrew McPheeters
President, Barry Glassner
Dean College of Arts and Sciences, Tuajuanda Jordan
Dean Law School, Robert Klonoff
Dean Graduate School of Education and Counseling, Scott Fletcher
CIO, Adam Buchwald
Vice President Millennium Ventures, Libby McCaslin
Executive Vice President of Marketing, Peter Chang
Executive Assistant Vice President Secretary General Counsel, Bonny Paralegal

LOCATIONS

HQ: LEWIS & CLARK COLLEGE
0615 SW PALATINE HILL RD, PORTLAND, OR 972197879
Phone: 5037687000
Web: WWW.GRADUATE.LCLARK.EDU

HISTORICAL FINANCIALS

Company Type: Private

Income Statement FYE: May 31

	REVENUE ($ mil.)	NET INCOME ($ mil.)	NET PROFIT MARGIN	EMPLOYEES
05/14	115	11	10.2%	800
05/13	116	29	24.9%	—
05/12	113	(19)	—	—
05/11	173	0	—	—
Annual Growth	(12.6%)	—	—	—

2014 Year-End Financials

Debt ratio: —
Return on equity: 10.20%
Cash ($ mil.): 4
Current ratio: —
Long-term debt ($ mil.): —
Dividends
Yield: —
Payout: —
Market value ($ mil.): —

LEXA INTERNATIONAL CORPORATION

LOCATIONS

HQ: LEXA INTERNATIONAL CORPORATION
1 LANDMARK SQ STE 407, STAMFORD, CT 069012601
Phone: 2033265200
Web: WWW.AXELJOHNSON.COM

HISTORICAL FINANCIALS

Company Type: Private

Income Statement FYE: December 31

	ASSETS ($ mil.)	NET INCOME ($ mil.)	INCOME AS % OF ASSETS	EMPLOYEES
12/09	1,118	6	0.6%	1,204
12/08	1,241	4	0.4%	—
Annual Growth	(9.9%)	47.8%	—	—

2009 Year-End Financials

Debt ratio: —
Return on equity: 0.20%
Cash ($ mil.): 43
Current ratio: 0.90
Long-term debt ($ mil.): —
Dividends
Yield: —
Payout: —
Market value ($ mil.): —

LICKING MEMORIAL HEALTH SYSTEMS

Here to help Buckeye Staters lick disease is Licking Memorial Health Systems. The health care provider operates the 230-bed Licking Memorial Hospital. Specialty services at the hospital include cancer care home health occupational health cardiology rehabilitation and obstetrics. Licking Memorial Hospital administers behavioral health care (including substance abuse treatments) through its Shepherd Hill department. The health system also includes area outpatient medical practices largely through the multi-specialty physician group Licking Memorial Health Professionals. Licking Memorial Health Systems was founded in 1898 by the Newark Hospital Association.

Operations

In 2012 Licking Memorial handled more than 9000 inpatient admissions as well as nearly 60000 emergency room visits 7000 surgeries and 1100 births. The hospital employs about 160 active staff members. The physicians' group operates through about 40 practices with 100 doctors spanning over about a seven-town area.

Strategy

The opening of urgent care clinics helps health networks like Licking Memorial decrease the crowding and offset costs of hospital emergency room visits especially when it comes to caring for uninsured or under-insured patients. To expand its services in the field of outpatient emergency care Licking Memorial opened its second urgent care facility in 2012. The company also expanded its outpatient care capacity by acquiring an ambulatory care facility from the nearby Medical Center of Newark that year.

To expand its breadth of specialty services at the main Licking Memorial Hospital location the company added a new acute inpatient rehabilitation unit in 2012. The center focuses on helping patients regain independence after suffering from disabilities caused by injuries or illnesses.

EXECUTIVES

President and CEO, Robert A. Montagnese
VP Development and Public Relations, Veronica Link
VP Information Systems, Sallie Arnett
VP Medical Affairs, Craig Cairns
VP Patient Care Services, Deborah Young
VP Physician Practices, Christine McGee
Chairman, William N. Mann
Secretary Treasurer and Director, John Hinderer
VP Financial Services, Cindy Webster
Vice Chairman, Judith B. Pierce
President CEO and Director, Rob Montagnese
Secretary Treasurer and Director, John Hinderer
Director, Walter Gemmell

LOCATIONS

HQ: LICKING MEMORIAL HEALTH SYSTEMS
1320 W MAIN ST, NEWARK, OH 43055-1822
Phone: 740-348-4000
Web: WWW.LMHEALTH.ORG

PRODUCTS/OPERATIONS

Selected Services

Behavioral Health Services
Cancer Care
Case Management
Child Wellness and Pediatric Care
Classes and Events
Clinics and Outpatient Services
Critical Care Units
Diabetes Care and Nutrition
Emergency Department
Endoscopy Services
Heart Care
Home Care Services
Infection Prevention
Laboratory Services
Medical Pediatric and Surgical Inpatient Units
Maternal Child
Pastoral Care
Radiology Services
Rehabilitation Services
Renal Dialysis
Respiratory Care
Sleep Laboratory
Surgical Services
Women' s Health

COMPETITORS

Fairfield Medical Center
Genesis HealthCare System (Ohio)
Mount Carmel Health
Nationwide Children' s Hospital
OhioHealth

HISTORICAL FINANCIALS

Company Type: Private

Income Statement FYE: December 31

	REVENUE ($ mil.)	NET INCOME ($ mil.)	NET PROFIT MARGIN	EMPLOYEES
12/11	184	(7)	—	1,600
12/10	198	4	2.2%	—
12/09	199	12	6.1%	—
12/08	34	0	—	—
Annual Growth	75.3%	—	—	—

2011 Year-End Financials

Debt ratio: —
Return on equity: (-4.20%)
Cash ($ mil.): 11
Current ratio: 1.30
Long-term debt ($ mil.): —
Dividends
Yield: —
Payout: —
Market value ($ mil.): —

LIFEBRIDGE HEALTH INC.

Like a bridge over troubled waters LifeBridge Health links ailing patients to care and healing. Serving the Baltimore region the not-for-profit company operates two general hospitals –Sinai Hospital of Baltimore and Northwest Hospital – with specialties including oncology neurology pediatrics and sports medicine. The LifeBridge Health network also provides long-term care at the Levindale Hebrew Geriatric Center and Hospital (nursing subacute and adult day care services) and the Courtland Gardens Nursing & Rehabilitation Center. Altogether the health system boasts some 1190 beds. LifeBridge's Health Wellness division includes a health and fitness program and community fitness center.

Operations

Sinai Hospital is a teaching hospital with residency programs for medical students training at Johns Hopkins University and University of Maryland. Levindale also serves as a teaching facility for medical dental nursing and social work students pursuing training to serve geriatric populations.

EXECUTIVES

EVP and President Sinai Hospital, Amy Perry
SVP; President Sinai Hospital of Baltimore, Neil M. Meltzer
SVP and CFO, Charles (Chuck) Orlando
President and CEO, Warren Green
SVP; President Northwest Hospital Center, Erik G. Wexler
VP and CIO, Karen Barker
VP Marketing and Community Relations, Rudy Miller
VP and CIO, Tressa Springmann
VP Human Resources, Taylor Foss
Vice President, Barbara Epke
Chairman, Benjamin S. Schapiro
VP Operations Engineering, Ev Amaral
Vice President Physician Services, Christine DeAngelis
SVP and CFO, David Krajewski
Vice President Government Relations and Advocacy, Martha Nathanson
Vice President and Legal Counsel, Joel Suldan
VP Capital Improvements and Campus Services, Peter Arn
Vice President Development, Julie Cox
VP Revenue Cycle, Tony Morris

SVP and President Northwest Hospital, Brian White
Chief Operating Officer, Jeff Watson
Vice President Chief Medical Officer, Daniel Silverman
Vice President Facilities, Lionel Weeks
Vice President Human Resources, Cheryl Boyer
SVP and President Levindale Hebrew Geriatric Center and Hospital and Courtland Gardens Nursing and Rehabilitation Center, Aric Spitulnik
Vice Chairman, Walter G. Amprey
Vice President Chief Nursing Officer, Diane Johnson

LOCATIONS

HQ: LIFEBRIDGE HEALTH INC.
2401 W BELVEDERE AVE, BALTIMORE, MD 21215-5216
Phone: 410-601-5653
Web: WWW.LIFEBRIDGEHEALTH.ORG

PRODUCTS/OPERATIONS

Selected Locations

Courtland Gardens Nursing & Rehabilitation Center
Levindale Hebrew Geriatric Center and Hospital
Northwest Hospital
Sinai Hospital

Selected Services

Bariatric and Minimally Invasive Surgery
Brain & Spine Institute
Cancer Institute
Hospitalist Program
Rubin Institute for Advanced Orthopedics
Vascular Institute

COMPETITORS

Anne Arundel Medical Center
Ascension Health
Bon Secours Health
Franklin Square Hospital Center
GBMC
Johns Hopkins Health System
MedStar Health
MedStar Union Memorial Hospital
University of Maryland Medical System

HISTORICAL FINANCIALS

Company Type: Private

Income Statement

FYE: June 30

	REVENUE ($ mil.)	NET INCOME ($ mil.)	NET PROFIT MARGIN	EMPLOYEES
06/12	1,051	28	2.7%	6,000
06/11	99	(3)	—	—
06/10	95	(2)	—	—
06/09	97	0	—	—
Annual Growth	120.8%	—	—	—

2012 Year-End Financials

Debt ratio: —
Return on equity: 2.70%
Cash ($ mil.): 159
Current ratio: 1.50
Long-term debt ($ mil.): —
Dividends
Yield: —
Payout: —
Market value ($ mil.): —

LIFEWAY CHRISTIAN RESOURCES OF THE SOUTHERN BAPTIST CONVENTION

LifeWay Christian Resources of the Southern Baptist Convention helps to spread the teachings of Jesus. The company is a not-for-profit Christian publisher. It also sells Bibles CDs gifts software church furniture signs and other supplies. In addition to its 165 LifeWay Christian Stores located in more than 25 states the retailer sells products online and through its catalog. LifeWay operates two of the nation's largest Christian conference facilities and summer camps. LifeWay Ridgecrest Conference Center in North Carolina and LifeWay Glorieta Conference Center in New Mexico together welcome some 2000 conference and overnight guests each year. LifeWay was founded in 1891 by Dr. J.M. Frost.

Geographic Reach

Based in Nashville LifeWay boasts offices and conference centers in three states: Tennessee New Mexico and North Carolina. In Nashville the company has more than 1.3 million sq. ft. of office retail parking conference and warehouse space that covers 14.6 acres. As part of its operations LifeWay has a 350000-sq.-ft. warehouse on 44 acres in Lebanon Tennessee that supports the LifeWay Christian Stores the company operates nationwide in more than 25 states and extends its reach globally through its website and catalogs.

Operations

The B&H Publishing Group produces Bibles books Sunday school teaching materials and audio and video products which are sold to bookstores and other retailers. Its Holman Christian Standard Bible is one of the best-selling versions in the US. As part of its digital outreach efforts Lifeway provides ministry services-related Digital Church which can be accessed through Lifeway's website and offers an array of resources for ministries including downloadable worship music and a video publishing utility.

Its Executive Communications and Relations division produces LifeWay's news and information services directs corporate events builds corporate relations and supports the office of the president. It works with state conventions and other evangelical organizations as well. The Technology division offers strategic retail enterprise and Internet services. The company's Research and Ministry Development division is where LifeWay conducts its research and explores new ministry ventures it calls "blue oceans." LifeWay's Finance and Business Services division which runs a conference center in Ridgecrest North Carolina oversees the company's financial policies and general accounting as well as directs business services such as legal investment purchasing real estate strategic planning corporate services and human resources.

Strategy

Chasing after promising growth in digital media the organization in 2011 acquired a pair of Bible software companies —WORDsearch and QuickVerse —to increase its share of the digital media market in the Christian publishing niche. WORDsearch based in Austin Texas offers more than 4200 volumes of electronic books for Christian pastors teachers and laypeople through its WORDsearch Bible Explorer LESSONmaker WORDsearchToGo and InstaView software. The QuickVerse software offers SermonBuilder a resource for thousands of Bible-related stories quotes and anecdotes. As part of its growth strategy LifeWay Christian Resources of the Southern Baptist Convention continues to seek opportunities to expand its digital media business.

It's also considering selling its 2100-acre Glorieta Conference Center located in New Mexico. California evangelical educational institution Olivet University has stepped up as a potential purchaser. In the meantime Olivet University rents portions of the facility to house 200 students faculty and staff.

EXECUTIVES

VP LifeWay Christian Stores, Tim Vineyard
VP Finance and Business Services; CFO, Jerry Rhyne
President and CEO, Thom S. Rainer
EVP, Brad Waggoner
VP B&H Publishing Group, Selma Wilson
VP Insights Division, Ed Stetzer
VP Church Resources Division, Eric Geiger
VP and CIO, Tim Hill
Vice President Lifeway Christian Stores, Mark Scott
Vice President Of Operations, Bruce Munns
Vice President Store Operations, Mick Houston
Vice President, Micah Fries
Vice President Business Operations, Eric Glover
Vice President Information Technology, Regina Thompson
Senior Vice President Ancillary Services, Cathy Brown
Vice President Of International Sales, Bob Vanfleteren
Vice President Marketing And Sales, Jim Baird

LOCATIONS

HQ: LIFEWAY CHRISTIAN RESOURCES OF THE SOUTHERN BAPTIST CONVENTION
1 LIFEWAY PLZ, NASHVILLE, TN 372341001
Phone: 6152512000
Web: WWW.LIFEWAY.COM

2013 Stores

	No.
Texas	26
Tennessee	21
North	14
Alabama	11
Georgia	11
Virginia	9
Florida	8
Kentucky	8
Arkansas	6
Mississippi	6
South	6
Louisiana	5
Minnesota	5
Missouri	5
Ohio	4
Pennsylvania	3
California	2
Illinois	2
Kansas	2
Maryland	2
Oklahoma	2
Washington	2
Colorado	1
Indiana	1
New	1
Oregon	1
Utah	1
Total	**165**

PRODUCTS/OPERATIONS

Selected Divisions

B&H Publishing Group
Church Resources
Executive Communications and Relations
Finance and Business Services
LifeWay Christian Stores
Research and Ministry Development

Technology

Selected Products

Apparel
Audio
Bibles
Books
Church supplies
Curriculum
eBooks
Events
Gifts
Magazines
Movies
Music
Video

COMPETITORS

Amazon.com
Baker Publishing
Barnes & Noble
Deseret Management
Family Christian Stores
United Methodist Publishing
Wal-Mart

HISTORICAL FINANCIALS

Company Type: Private

Income Statement FYE: September 30

	REVENUE ($ mil.)	NET INCOME ($ mil.)	NET PROFIT MARGIN	EMPLOYEES
09/14	500	(25)	—	2,477
09/13	481	79	16.5%	—
09/12	488	(35)	—	—
09/11	468	0	—	—
Annual Growth	2.2%	—	—	—

2014 Year-End Financials

Debt ratio: —
Return on equity: (-5.10%)
Cash ($ mil.): 1
Current ratio: 0.60
Long-term debt ($ mil.): —
Dividends
Yield: —
Payout: —
Market value ($ mil.): —

LINCOLN CENTER FOR THE PERFORMING ARTS INC.

One of the world's largest cultural hubs Lincoln Center presents live music theater dance and opera performances from its 16-acre complex in New York City. The Center also offers educational programming and provides a home base for such organizations as the School of American Ballet the New York Philharmonic the Metropolitan Opera and The Film Society of Lincoln Center. More than 5000 performances and educational programs are presented and more than 5 million people visit each year. The Lincoln Center was conceived by New York City movers and shakers including Robert Moses Robert F. Wagner Jr. and John D. Rockefeller III; construction of the complex took place between 1959 and 1972.

Financial Performance

The Lincoln Center reported 2012 support and revenue of about $120 million up nearly 20% from the prior year as it saw increases in contributions box office sales and services and rental income among other areas.

Strategy

The organization has made some $1.2 billion in renovations to the facility in recent years as part of the Transforming Lincoln Center initiative. The Center paid for the improvements through fundraising efforts including $240 million pledged by New York City. The renovations opened up Broadway to more pedestrians and made the Lincoln Center grounds more welcoming to tourists; the redevelopment also included the modernization of its performance halls.

EXECUTIVES

Vice President Human Resources And Administrative Services, Liza Parker
Vice President General Counsel And Secretary, Lesley Rosenthal
Managing Director Lincoln Center Global, Kara M Barnett
Vice President, Leslie Powell
Vice President, Alex Tiscareno
Evp Planning And Development, Tamar C Podell
Vice President, Rita Edwards
Vp Manufacturing, Jane S Moss
Vice President Public Relations, Betsy Vorce
Vice-chairman, Gary W Parr
First Assistant Treasurer Of Alice Tully Hall Box Office, Tod Schreiber
Assistant Treasurer Of Alice Tully Hal, Russell Hammel
Assistant Treasurer, Nat Francisco
Assistant Treasurer Of Alice Tully Hall Box Office, Donna Schreiber
Treasurer, Gerald Levine

LOCATIONS

HQ: LINCOLN CENTER FOR THE PERFORMING ARTS INC.
70 LINCOLN CENTER PLZ # 9, NEW YORK, NY 10023-6548
Phone: 212-875-5000
Web: WWW.NYPHIL.ORG

HISTORICAL FINANCIALS

Company Type: Private

Income Statement FYE: June 30

	REVENUE ($ mil.)	NET INCOME ($ mil.)	NET PROFIT MARGIN	EMPLOYEES
06/11	169	(17)	—	525
06/10	205	(28)	—	—
06/09	246	0	—	—
06/06	196	78	40.0%	—
Annual Growth	(2.8%)	—	—	—

2011 Year-End Financials

Debt ratio: —
Return on equity: (-10.10%)
Cash ($ mil.): 44
Current ratio: 0.10
Long-term debt ($ mil.): —
Dividends
Yield: —
Payout: —
Market value ($ mil.): —

LITCHFIELD BANCORP

LOCATIONS

HQ: LITCHFIELD BANCORP
294 WEST ST, LITCHFIELD, CT 067593404
Phone: 8605679401
Web: WWW.LITCHFIELDBANCORP.COM

HISTORICAL FINANCIALS

Company Type: Private

Income Statement FYE: December 31

	ASSETS ($ mil.)	NET INCOME ($ mil.)	INCOME AS % OF ASSETS	EMPLOYEES
12/13	216	0	0.2%	50
12/12	211	0	0.3%	—
12/09	212	0	0.3%	—
12/07	198	0	—	—
Annual Growth	1.5%	—	—	—

2013 Year-End Financials

Debt ratio: —
Return on equity: 5.00%
Cash ($ mil.): 4
Current ratio: —
Long-term debt ($ mil.): —
Dividends
Yield: —
Payout: —
Market value ($ mil.): —

LITTLE SIOUX CORN PROCESSORS LLC

LOCATIONS

HQ: LITTLE SIOUX CORN PROCESSORS LLC
4808 F AVE, MARCUS, IA 510357070
Phone: 7123762800
Web: WWW.LITTLESIOUXCORNPROCESSORS.COM

HISTORICAL FINANCIALS

Company Type: Private

Income Statement FYE: September 30

	REVENUE ($ mil.)	NET INCOME ($ mil.)	NET PROFIT MARGIN	EMPLOYEES
09/13	346	4	1.3%	45
09/11	329	9	2.9%	
/ 0	0	—	—	
Annual Growth		—	—	—

2013 Year-End Financials

Debt ratio: —
Return on equity: 1.30%
Cash ($ mil.): 0
Current ratio: 0.60
Long-term debt ($ mil.): —
Dividends
Yield: —
Payout: —
Market value ($ mil.): —

LOGICALIS INC.

Logicalis believes enterprise technology should operate in a straightforward fashion. The company provides a variety of IT services such as consulting implementation systems integration staffing network design and training. Logicalis also offers managed services for tasks such as network security IT infrastructure management and monitoring and application management. Customers come from a variety of fields including manufacturing financial services and health care. In the US Logicalis operates from more than 20 offices. It is a subsidiary of UK-based Logicalis Group. Both are owned by South Africa-based Datatec Limited.

EXECUTIVES

COO, Rob Evans, age 48
President and CEO, Mark Rogers
Sr V Pres Solutions And Servic, Mike Martin

LOCATIONS

HQ: LOGICALIS INC.
1 PENN PLZ STE 5130, NEW YORK, NY 10119-5160
Phone: 212-596-7160
Web: WWW.US.LOGICALIS.COM

COMPETITORS

Accenture
Agilysys
Black Box
Capgemini North America
Cognizant Tech Solutions
Computer Sciences Corp.
Forsythe Technology
HP Enterprise Services
IBM Global Services
RCM Technologies
Sapient
Sirius Computer Solutions
Sogeti USA LLC
TCS America
Unisys

HISTORICAL FINANCIALS

Company Type: Private

Income Statement FYE: February 29

	REVENUE ($ mil.)	NET INCOME ($ mil.)	NET PROFIT MARGIN	EMPLOYEES
02/12	384	4	1.1%	700
02/11	357	5	1.4%	—
02/10	338	0	0.2%	—
02/09	409	8	2.1%	—
Annual Growth	(2.1%)	(21.3%)	—	—

2012 Year-End Financials

Debt ratio: —
Return on equity: 1.10%
Cash ($ mil.): 1
Current ratio: 0.50
Long-term debt ($ mil.): —
Dividends
Yield: —
Payout: —
Market value ($ mil.): —

LONG BEACH MEMORIAL MEDICAL CENTER

Long Beach Memorial Medical Center (LBMMC) is an old-timer in the Long Beach health care market. A subsidiary of Memorial Health Services LBMMC provides a full range of health services to residents of the Long Beach California area. The medical center a more than 460 bed acute-care hospital was founded in 1907 and is one of the largest private hospitals on the West Coast. Services include primary emergency diagnostic surgical therapeutic and rehabilitative care. The hospital is home to centers for treatment of cancer heart stroke and women's and children's health concerns. It also provides home and hospice care programs as well as occupational health services.

Geographic Reach

Long Beach Memorial Medical Center (LBMMC) is one of the largest private hospitals on the West Coast of the US.

Operations

The medical center is 460 bed acute-care hospital. LBMMC installed an electronic medical record (EMR) system in 2010 that connects the hospital and all of its affiliated physicians and pharmacies so that they can transfer patient information electronically between different care providers and locations.

Strategy

Hospitals that use an EMR are eligible for incentives and higher reimbursements from the federal government. Additionally EMRs reduce medical errors and increase patient safety by eliminating things like medication interactions and duplicate patient records.

The hospital is expanding its cancer services by building a dedicated outpatient cancer facility. The MemorialCare Todd Cancer Institute is being built because the current center has reached capacity. With the new MemorialCare Todd Cancer Institute pavilion LBMMC will expand its cancer care technology and capacity.

LBMMC has also expanded its robotics program beyond cardiology and the hospital recently established a new intensivist program in the Intensive Care Unit (ICU). The ICU program integrates teaching from the University of California Irvine residents and interns.

EXECUTIVES

CIO, Scott Joslyn
CFO, Wendy Dorchester
Chief Medical Officer, S. Gainer Pillsbury
Chief Nursing Officer, Judy Fix
Director Public Relations, Colleen Reinhart
Vice President Development, Thomas Poole
President Chief Executive Officer, Barry Arbuckle

LOCATIONS

HQ: LONG BEACH MEMORIAL MEDICAL CENTER
2801 ATLANTIC AVE, LONG BEACH, CA 90806-1701
Phone: 562-933-2000
Web:
WWW.SUPPORTLONGBEACH.MEMORIALCARE.ORG

COMPETITORS

Adventist Health
Aptium Oncology
Brotman Medical Center
Cedars-Sinai Medical Center
Childrens Hospital Los Angeles
Dignity Health
Glendale Adventist Medical Center
Good Samaritan Hospital (Los Angeles)
HCA
Hoag Memorial Hospital
Hollywood Presbyterian Medical Center
Los Angeles County Health Department
Methodist Hospital of Southern California
Newhall Memorial Hospital
Pasadena Hospital Association
Providence Health & Services
Providence Health System Southern California
Sutter Health
Tenet Healthcare
Torrance Memorial Medical Center
Trinity Health (Novi)
Western Medical Center - Santa Ana

HISTORICAL FINANCIALS

Company Type: Private

Income Statement FYE: June 30

	REVENUE ($ mil.)	NET INCOME ($ mil.)	NET PROFIT MARGIN	EMPLOYEES
06/11	1,083	63	5.9%	—
06/09	446	53	12.0%	—
06/08	843	73	8.7%	—
06/06	696	62	8.9%	—
Annual Growth	9.2%	0.4%	—	—

2011 Year-End Financials

Debt ratio: —
Return on equity: 5.90%
Cash ($ mil.): 4
Current ratio: 1.50
Long-term debt ($ mil.): —
Dividends
Yield: —
Payout: —
Market value ($ mil.): —

LONG ISLAND UNIVERSITY

Long Island University (LIU) helps students see a long future in professional fields including medicine and business. LIU has an enrollment of more than 24000 students at multiple locations in New York State. The university employs more than 600 full-time faculty members and has a 12:1 student-to-teacher ratio. LIU offers 575 degree programs and certificates in fields including pharmacy nursing health sciences education liberal arts sciences business and information studies. The school traces its roots to 1886 when the Brooklyn College of Pharmacy was founded.

Geographic Reach

LIU has eight campuses in New York located in Brooklyn Brookville Brentwood Riverhead Rockland and Westchester). Internationally LIU Global offers study abroad programs in Asia Australia the Middle East and South America.

Strategy

LIU has expanded its offerings in recent years to meet current demands. It has added degree programs in fields such as digital game design computer information systems health sciences and human resource management.

EXECUTIVES

Dean Richard L. Conolly College of Liberal Arts and Sciences, David Cohen
President, David J. Steinberg
VP Finance and Treasurer, Robert N. (Rob) Altholz
Provost LIU Brooklyn, Gale Stevens Haynes
Chairman, Edward Travaglianti
VP Information Technology, George Baroudi
Senior Vice Chair, Thomas L. Pulling
Provost LIU Post, Paul H. Forestell
Dean LIU Global, Robert Glass
Dean School of Business Public Administration and Information Sciences, Ken Colwell
Dean College of Education Information and Technology, Robert Hannafin
Dean School of Education, Cecilia Traugh
Dean College of Liberal Arts and Sciences, Katherine Hill-Miller
Dean College of Management, Andrew J. Rosman
Dean Hudson Graduate Centers, Sylvia Blake
Dean Arnold & Marie Schwartz College of Pharmacy and Health Sciences, David R. Taft
Dean School of Health Professions, Barry S. Eckert
Dean School of Visual and Performing Arts, Noel Zahler
Dean School of Health Professions and Nursing, MaryAnn Clark
Dean School of Nursing, Shirley Girouard
Dean University Libraries, Valeda F. Dent
Vice President - Long Island University, Jackie Nealon

LOCATIONS

HQ: LONG ISLAND UNIVERSITY
700 NORTHERN BLVD, GREENVALE, NY 11548-1327
Phone: 516-299-2535
Web: WWW.LIU.EDU

HISTORICAL FINANCIALS

Company Type: Private

Income Statement FYE: August 31

	REVENUE ($ mil.)	NET INCOME ($ mil.)	NET PROFIT MARGIN	EMPLOYEES
08/12	484	4	0.9%	3,300
08/11	468	2	0.5%	—
08/09	370	(1)	—	—
08/09	363	(26)	—	—
Annual Growth	10.0%	—	—	—

2012 Year-End Financials

Debt ratio: —
Return on equity: 0.90%
Cash ($ mil.): 89
Current ratio: —
Long-term debt ($ mil.): —
Dividends
Yield: —
Payout: —
Market value ($ mil.): —

LOOP LLC

LOOP (Louisiana Offshore Oil Port) offloads crude oil from tankers stores it and routes it to pipelines and refineries along the Gulf Coast and the Midwest. It is also the storage and terminalling facility for the MARS pipeline system and its supply of offshore Gulf of Mexico crude oil. Oil is stored in eight underground caverns leached out of a naturally occurring salt dome. These caverns are capable of storing about 50 million barrels of crude oil. The company is owned by Marathon Ashland Pipe Line Murphy Oil and Shell Oil. In addition to other services LOOP has an aboveground tank farm made up of six 600000 barrel tanks.

The company's port facility is located 18 miles south of Grand Isle Louisiana in 110 feet of water and is the only port in the US capable of offloading deep draft tankers. Although battered by Hurricane Katrina in 2005 LOOP's operations were only temporarily interrupted.

LOOP is connected to more than 50% of US refinery capacity and has offloaded more than 7 billion barrels of foreign crude oil in the past 27 years. LOOP was established in 1972 and converted to a limited liability company in 1996.

EXECUTIVES

President, Thomas L. Shaw

LOCATIONS

HQ: LOOP LLC
137 NORTHPARK BLVD, COVINGTON, LA 70433-5071
Phone: 985-276-6100
Web: WWW.LOOPLLC.COM

COMPETITORS

Chemoil
Martin Midstream Partners
Sunoco
World Point Terminals

HISTORICAL FINANCIALS

Company Type: Private

Income Statement FYE: December 31

	REVENUE ($ mil.)	NET INCOME ($ mil.)	NET PROFIT MARGIN	EMPLOYEES
12/09	243	87	35.8%	128
12/08	265	79	29.8%	—
12/06	235	104	44.2%	—
12/05	184	73	40.2%	—
Annual Growth	7.3%	4.2%	—	—

2009 Year-End Financials

Debt ratio: —
Return on equity: 35.80%
Cash ($ mil.): 0
Current ratio: —
Long-term debt ($ mil.): —
Dividends
Yield: —
Payout: —
Market value ($ mil.): —

LOS ANGELES DEPARTMENT OF WATER AND POWER

The Los Angeles Department of Water and Power (LADWP) keeps the movie cameras running and the swimming pools full. The largest municipally owned utility in the US LADWP provides electricity to 1.4 million residential and business customers and water to 666000 customers. The company has power plant interests that give it more than 7220 MW of generating capacity; it also buys and sells wholesale power. Most of the city's water supply is transported through two aqueduct systems from the Sierra Nevada Mountains; other water sources include wells and local groundwater basins. Because LADWP is city-owned its retail monopoly status has been unaffected by utility deregulation in California.

Financial Performance

LADWP's operations are entirely financed by the sale of water and electric services. The multi-utility transfers about 7% of its annual electric revenues and 5% of its water revenues to the City of Los Angeles general fund.

Strategy

Residential customers form the largest client group of the utility's water service unit; commercial customers the largest customer class of the power segment. To enhance operating efficiencies and conserve energy the department has launched a 10-year $1 billion Smart Grid program to automate and upgrade the City's grid.

It is also pushing to increase the amount of energy it generates from renewable sources (mainly wind and solar power) to meet state and federal clean air goals. LADWP got only 5% of it power from renewables in 2005 but has upped that amount to more than 20%. LADWP plans to sell its Navajo Generating Station in Arizona (by 2014) which will cut carbon emissions by a further 26%

In 2013 LADWP signed a decade-long power purchase agreement to purchase renewable geothermal power (about 34 MW) from the Imperial Valley (enough to provide enough clean energy to serve 47600 Los Angeles homes).

In addition as the Western US states battle a prolonged drought the utility is negotiating with water agencies across the region to ensure a reliable future supply for its citizens.

Ownership

The department is part of the City of Los Angeles.

Company Background

LADWP was founded in 1902.

EXECUTIVES

Generation, Eric Tharp
CFO, Ronald O. Vazquez
Director Economic Development, Bernadette S. Kirkwood
Assistant General Manager, Pamela T. Porter
Manager Water Conservation, Tom Gackstetter
Manager Media and Community Relations, Darlene Battle
Resource Planning Procurement and Development, Randy S. Howard
Manager Environmental Communications and Educational Services Affairs, Walter Zeisl
City Attorney Water and Power, Richard Brown
Assistant General Manager Employee Relations, Hal D. Lindsey
Manager Risk Management, Avery Neaman
COO, Raman Raj
Environmental Affairs, James H. Caldwell Jr.
Senior Assistant General Manager Power System, Aram Benyamin
Engineering Services, Marvin Moon
Power Operation and Maintenance, Michael A. Coia
Power Transmission and Distribution, Darrell G. Mathis
Power System Planning and Development, Mo Beshir
Power Control and Business Systems, Ali Morabbi
Water Resources, Thomas M. Erb
Water Distribution, Steven Malinoski
Water Engineering and Technical Services, Glen C. Singley
Commissioner, Thomas S. (Tom) Sayles, age 62
VP Board of Water and Power Commissioners, Edith Ramirez
Commissioner, Forescee Hogan-Rowles
President Board of Commissioners, Lee K. Alpert
Auditors: KPMGLLP

LOCATIONS

HQ: LOS ANGELES DEPARTMENT OF WATER AND POWER
111 N HOPE ST, LOS ANGELES, CA 90012-2607
Phone: 213-367-4211

PRODUCTS/OPERATIONS

2012 Sales

Electric	75	
Total	0	100

COMPETITORS

AES
American States Water
Avista
California Water Service
Calpine
Duke Energy
Edison International
PG&E Corporation
Sacramento Municipal Utility
Sempra Energy
SouthWest Water

HISTORICAL FINANCIALS

Company Type: Private

Income Statement FYE: June 30

	REVENUE ($ mil.)	NET INCOME ($ mil.)	NET PROFIT MARGIN	EMPLOYEES
06/12	3,081	118	3.8%	8,000
06/11	3,125	57	1.8%	—
06/10	812	67	8.3%	—
Annual Growth	94.8%	32.5%	—	—

2012 Year-End Financials

Debt ratio: —
Return on equity: 3.80%
Cash ($ mil.): 417
Current ratio: 0.80
Long-term debt ($ mil.): —
Dividends
Yield: —
Payout: —
Market value ($ mil.): —

LOYOLA MARYMOUNT UNIVERSITY INC

Loyola Marymount University (LMU) in Los Angeles is a Jesuit (Catholic) institution with an enrollment of more than 9000 students. It offers more than 115 graduate and undergraduate programs through four colleges: Bellarmine College of Liberal Arts College of Business Administration College of Communication and Fine Arts and Seaver College of Science and Engineering. There is also the School of Education and School of Film and Television. Other programs include the Graduate Division Continuing Education Program and Loyola Law School. LMU has an 11:1 student-to-faculty ratio. The university was formed in 1973 by the merger of Loyola College (founded in 1911) and Marymount Junior College.

Geographic Reach

LMU is located on a 140-acre campus in Los Angeles.

Operations

LMU offers about 60 majors and 55 minor study programs to its undergraduate students. The university also offers about 35 master's degrees two doctorates and a dozen certification programs. In total LMU employs about 1700 faculty and staff members.

LMU has partnerships with about a dozen public and private elementary and secondary schools in the Los Angeles area. Through the LMU Family of Schools model school demonstration program the university provides professional development and educational resources to the schools.

Financial Performance

LMU experienced a 4% increase in revenues to $320 million in 2012 due to higher net tuition and fee income auxiliary enterprise revenue and investment returns designated for operations. Tuition runs at some $39000 annually plus some $13000 in room and board. However the company reported a net income loss in 2012 due to increased operating expenses and lower returns on investments (after amounts designated for operations).

Strategy

To increase student access to its programs LMU launched a new scholarship initiative in 2012. Through the program the university seeks to raise some $100 million for new scholarships through donations and endowment returns over a three-year period.

EXECUTIVES

President, Father Robert B. Lawton
Jr. Senior Vice President Chief Financial Officer, Thomas O. Fleming Jr.
SVP Student Affairs, Elena M. (Lane) Bove
EVP and Provost, David W. Burcham
Dean School of Education, Shane P. Martin
VP Communications and Government Relations, Kathleen Flanagan
Director Athletics, William S. Husak
Chancellor, Father Patrick J. Cahalan
Senior Vice President and Dean of Loyola Law School, Victor J. Gold
Director Financial Aid, Catherine Graham
Executive Vice President, Joseph Provost
Vice President for Mission and Ministry, Robert V. Caro
Auditors: PricewaterhouseCoopersLLP

LOCATIONS

HQ: LOYOLA MARYMOUNT UNIVERSITY INC
1 LMU DR STE 100, LOS ANGELES, CA 90045-2677
Phone: 310-338-2700
Web: WWW.LMU.EDU

PRODUCTS/OPERATIONS

Colleges and Schools
Bellarmine College of Liberal Arts
College of Business Administra
College of Communication and Fine Arts
Graduate Division
LMU Extension
Loyola Law School
School of Education
School of Film and Television
Seaver College of Science and Engineerin

HISTORICAL FINANCIALS

Company Type: Private

Income Statement FYE: May 31

	REVENUE ($ mil.)	NET INCOME ($ mil.)	NET PROFIT MARGIN	EMPLOYEES
05/12	320	(16)	—	1,449
05/07	254	93	36.7%	—
05/06	234	51	21.9%	—
05/05	0	0	—	—
Annual Growth	—	—	—	—

2012 Year-End Financials

Debt ratio: —
Return on equity: (-5.10%)
Cash ($ mil.): 12
Current ratio: —
Long-term debt ($ mil.): —
Dividends
Yield: —
Payout: —
Market value ($ mil.): —

LOYOLA UNIVERSITY MARYLAND INC.

Loyola University in Maryland is a Jesuit Catholic university that offers studies in liberal arts and sciences. In addition to its undergraduate programs Loyola has graduate degree programs in education speech pathology finance psychology modern studies pastoral counseling and engineering science. The university annually enrolls about 3500 undergraduate and some 2600 graduate students. The school has more than 300 full-time faculty and a student-teacher ratio of about 12:1. Loyola was founded in 1852 by Father John Early and eight other Jesuits.

EXECUTIVES

Chairman, H. Edward (Ed) Hanway, age 62
Dean College of Arts and Sciences, James Buckley
VP Finance and Treasurer, Randall D. Gentzler
President, Rev Brian Linnane, age 58
VP Administration, Terrence Sawyer
EVP, Susan Donovan
Director Library, John McGinty
Assistant VP Administration, Joan Flynn
Assistant VP Human Resources, George (Skip) Casey
VP Advancement, Megan Gillick
Dirtector Alumni Relations, Brian M. Oakes
Assistant VP and CIO, Louise Finn
Assistant VP Facilitites and Campus Services, Helen Schneider
Director The Career Center, CreSaundra Sills
Controller, Kelly Nelson
Dean Sellinger School of Business and Management, Karyl B. Leggio
Director Facilities Operations, Charles Riordan
Director and Assistant VP Financial Aid, Mark Lindenmeyer
Digital Access Librarian, Danielle Whren
Assistant VP Marketing and Communications, Sharon Higgins
VP Academic Affairs, Timothy Law Snyder
VP Enrollment Management and Communications, Marc M. Camille
assistant Director of parent relations, Nancy Panepento
Assistant Director of Recruitment, Katlyn E. Good
Associate Director for Program Operations, Heather Moore
Executive Assistant, Candra Healy
Administrative Assistant, Antoinette Lobdell
Executive Assistant, JoAnn Smoot
Director of program operations, Dan McClain
Administrative Assistant, Jeanne Muscella
Administrative Assistant, Jennifer Lyall
VP Student Development and Dean of Students, Sheilah Shaw Horton
Dean of First-Year Students & Academic Services, Ilona McGuiness
Dean School of Education, Joshua Smith
Dean College of Arts and Sciences, Rev James J. Miracky
Chairman of the Board Chief Investment Officer, Brian C. Rogers
Chief Executive Officer, Randall M. Griffin
Founder President, Eddie C. Brown
President Verizon-Maryland, William R. Roberts

LOCATIONS

HQ: LOYOLA UNIVERSITY MARYLAND INC.
4501 N CHARLES ST, BALTIMORE, MD 21210-2601
Phone: 410-617-2000
Web: WWW.LOYOLA.EDU

HISTORICAL FINANCIALS

Company Type: Private

Income Statement FYE: May 31

	REVENUE ($ mil.)	NET INCOME ($ mil.)	NET PROFIT MARGIN	EMPLOYEES
05/12	185	(2)	—	2,066
05/11	238	11	5.0%	—
05/10	221	9	4.1%	—
05/09	196	0	—	—
Annual Growth	(2.0%)	—	—	—

2012 Year-End Financials

Debt ratio: —
Return on equity: (-1.20%)
Cash ($ mil.): 34
Current ratio: —
Long-term debt ($ mil.): —
Dividends
Yield: —
Payout: —
Market value ($ mil.): —

LOYOLA UNIVERSITY NEW ORLEANS INC

EXECUTIVES

Executive Director Information Technology, Bret Jacobs
President, Rev Kevin W. Wildes
Director Graduate Development Program, Brenda Joyner
VP Finance and Administration, Jay Calamia
VP Institutional Advancement, Victoria Frank
VP Student Affairs and Associate Provost, M. L. (Cissy) Petty

Director Public Affairs and External Relations, Meredith Hartley
VP Academic Affairs and Provost, Edward J. Kvet
Interim Dean College Music and Fine Arts, Anthony DeCuir
VP Office of Mission and Ministry, Rev Ted Dziak

LOCATIONS

HQ: LOYOLA UNIVERSITY NEW ORLEANS INC
6363 SAINT CHARLES AVE, NEW ORLEANS, LA 701186195
Phone: 5048652011
Web: WWW.LOYNO.EDU

PRODUCTS/OPERATIONS

Selected Colleges
College of Business
College of Humanities and Natural Sciences
College of Law
College of Music and Fine Arts
College of Social Sciences

COMPETITORS

Boston College
Fordham University
Loyola Marymount University
Loyola University
Loyola University in Maryland
University of New Orleans

HISTORICAL FINANCIALS

Company Type: Private

Income Statement FYE: July 31

	REVENUE ($ mil.)	NET INCOME ($ mil.)	NET PROFIT MARGIN	EMPLOYEES
07/14	135	3	2.4%	1,000
07/13	154	26	17.0%	—
07/12	126	(16)	—	—
07/11	129	0	—	—
Annual Growth	1.4%	—	—	—

2014 Year-End Financials

Debt ratio: —
Return on equity: 2.40%
Cash ($ mil.): 1
Current ratio: —
Long-term debt ($ mil.): —
Dividends
Yield: —
Payout: —
Market value ($ mil.): —

LUDWIG INSTITUTE FOR CANCER RESEARCH

LOCATIONS

HQ: LUDWIG INSTITUTE FOR CANCER RESEARCH
666 3RD AVE FL 28, NEW YORK, NY 100174030
Phone: 2124501500
Web: WWW.LUDWIGCANCER.ORG

HISTORICAL FINANCIALS

Company Type: Private

Income Statement FYE: December 31

	REVENUE ($ mil.)	NET INCOME ($ mil.)	NET PROFIT MARGIN	EMPLOYEES
12/13	227	761	335.0%	703
12/12	205	647	315.9%	—
12/11	13	561	4169.4%	—
12/10	191	0	—	—
Annual Growth	5.9%	—	—	—

2013 Year-End Financials

Debt ratio: —
Return on equity: 335.00%
Cash ($ mil.): 8
Current ratio: 0.30
Long-term debt ($ mil.): —
Dividends
Yield: —
Payout: —
Market value ($ mil.): —

LUMBER PRODUCTS AN OREGON CORPORATION

Lumber Products pines to get hammered. Operating through about 15 locations in 10 states throughout the Northwest and intermountain region Lumber Products distributes hard-wood counter tops doors edge banding glue insulation jambs lumber mouldings mdf particle boards and overlays plywood and sidings to home-improvement centers building material dealers home manufacturers and others. Brands include JELD-WEN and Masonite. Among the company's lumber offerings are pine Douglas fir hemlock and mahogany. Founded in 1938 by Ernest E. Hall (grandfather of Peter Hall great-grandfather of Craig Hall) Lumber Products is employee-owned.

EXECUTIVES

President, Peter J. Hall
COO, Craig Hall
Branch Manager Tualatin, Tess Landis
Branch Manager Medford, Jerry Fitzpatrick
Branch Manager Eugene, Keith Lambright
Branch Manager Boise, Cal Emerson
Manager MaC, Ken Gloss
Branch Manager Denver, Tom Ludwig
Branch Manager Kent, Bill Plummer
Branch Manager Spokane, Randy McComas
Branch Manager Renton, Craig Edholm
Manager Sunrise Wood Products, Scott Richner
Branch Manager Bozeman, Brad Butterfield
Branch Manager Las Vegas, Robert Cleland
Branch Manager Albuquerque, Stan Kitts
Branch Manager Chandler, Mike Stump
Branch Manager Salt Lake City, Trace Cunningham
Branch Manager Sacramento, Keith Wambold
Manager Doors Division, John Myers
CFO, Bart Walker
Auditors: PricewaterhouseCoopers

LOCATIONS

HQ: LUMBER PRODUCTS AN OREGON CORPORATION
19855 SW 124TH AVE, TUALATIN, OR 970628007
Phone: 5036923322

COMPETITORS

ABC Supply
Arthur Lumber
Foxworth-Galbraith Lumber
Georgia-Pacific
Guardian Building Products Distribution
HD Supply
Huttig Building Products
Jewett-Cameron Trading
Pacific Coast Building Products
PrimeSource Building
Snavely Forest Products
Stock Building Supply
Weyerhaeuser

HISTORICAL FINANCIALS

Company Type: Private

Income Statement FYE: December 31

	REVENUE ($ mil.)	NET INCOME ($ mil.)	NET PROFIT MARGIN	EMPLOYEES
12/07	437	2	0.6%	540
12/06	442	10	2.3%	—
12/05	398	13	3.5%	—
12/04	345	0	—	—
Annual Growth	8.1%	—	—	—

2007 Year-End Financials

Debt ratio: —
Return on equity: 0.60%
Cash ($ mil.): 1
Current ratio: 0.50
Long-term debt ($ mil.): —
Dividends
Yield: —
Payout: —
Market value ($ mil.): —

LVI SERVICES INC.

Asbestos lead-based paint nuclear materials and toxic mold don't scare LVI Services one of the top environmental contractors in the US with more than 30 offices across the country. The privately-held company provides integrated facility services such as remediation of hazardous materials decontamination and demolition. It caters to clients in a wide range of business segments from hotels and retail to commercial industrial and institutional. It also serves government and education segments. Customers have included AT&T IBM Marriott Prudential and Raytheon.

Geographic Reach

Headquartered in New York City the company works in all 50 US states. It has more than 30 offices nationwide.

Operations

LVI Services offers design-build general construction program management hazardous material and mold abatement infection control fireproofing demolition as wells as emergency response/disaster recovery and services.

Subsidiary NorthStar Recovery Services provides emergency response and recovery services that help clients minimize damage and disruption following disasters.

Sales and Marketing

LVI Services serves customers in the commercial education government health care hospitality industrial oil and gas power and retail segments.

Strategy

In addition to its core business activities LVI Services offers complementary services that leverage its expertise in remediation such as lead abatement decontamination and decommissioning and drying and dehumidification.

It has provided services to aid in detecting and interdicting nuclear and radioactive threats for three federal agencies: the US Department of Homeland Security the US Department of Energy and the US Customs and Border Protection Agency.

In 2012 LVI Services completed the decommissioning of the University of Arizona's 52-year-old Nuclear Reactor Laboratory.

Mergers and Acquisitions

In 2012 the company acquired Washington State-based Randolph Construction Services which provides design-build contracting services for commercial industrial and government clients.

Company Background

Major stockholder CHS Capital moved in 2010 to merge LVI Services with another of its companies Penhall International which specializes in highway excavations. However Penhall ran into debt problems which squelched the deal and sent LVI Services to the bond market to restructure its debt.

LVI Services was founded in 1986.

EXECUTIVES

Vp Preconstruction Services, Michael Marcheschi
Vice President And General Counsel, Gregory G Dicarlo
Treasurer, Joseph M Annarumma, age 62

LOCATIONS

HQ: LVI SERVICES INC.
150 W 30TH ST FL 8, NEW YORK, NY 10001-4151
Phone: 212-951-3660
Web: WWW.LVISERVICES.COM

PRODUCTS/OPERATIONS

Selected Services

Asbestos abatement
Demolition
Emergency/disaster response
Drying and dehumidification
Biological and chemical decontamination
Mold remediation
Infection control
Lead abatement
Decontamination and decommissioning
Fireproofing
Power and Petroleum

Selected Industries

Commercial
Government
Industrial
Retail
Health care
Education
Hospitality

COMPETITORS

Bechtel
CH2M HILL
Controlled Demolition
Corvera Abatement
Dallas Contracting
ENSR International
ERM
Fluor
Native Environmental
Parsons Corporation

HISTORICAL FINANCIALS

Company Type: Private

Income Statement FYE: December 31

	REVENUE ($ mil.)	NET INCOME ($ mil.)	NET PROFIT MARGIN	EMPLOYEES
12/12	404	7	1.9%	3,500
12/11	339	(6)	—	—
12/10	250	65	26.1%	—
12/09	265	0	—	—
Annual Growth	15.1%	—	—	—

2012 Year-End Financials

Debt ratio: —
Return on equity: 1.90%
Cash ($ mil.): 2
Current ratio: 1.10
Long-term debt ($ mil.): —
Dividends
Yield: —
Payout: —
Market value ($ mil.): —

LYDIG CONSTRUCTION INC.

LOCATIONS

HQ: LYDIG CONSTRUCTION INC.
11001 E MONTGOMERY DR, SPOKANE VALLEY, WA 992064714
Phone: 5095340451
Web: WWW.LYDIG.COM

HISTORICAL FINANCIALS

Company Type: Private

Income Statement FYE: December 31

	REVENUE ($ mil.)	NET INCOME ($ mil.)	NET PROFIT MARGIN	EMPLOYEES
12/12	241	0	0.2%	130
12/10	206	7	3.8%	—
12/09	313	12	4.1%	—
Annual Growth	(8.4%)	(65.8%)	—	—

2012 Year-End Financials

Debt ratio: —
Return on equity: 0.20%
Cash ($ mil.): 45
Current ratio: 1.00
Long-term debt ($ mil.): —
Dividends
Yield: —
Payout: —
Market value ($ mil.): —

LYNDON BAINES JOHNSON FOUNDATION

LOCATIONS

HQ: LYNDON BAINES JOHNSON FOUNDATION
2313 RED RIVER ST, AUSTIN, TX 787055737
Phone: 5122322266
Web: WWW.LBJFOUNDATION.ORG

HISTORICAL FINANCIALS

Company Type: Private

Income Statement FYE: August 31

	ASSETS ($ mil.)	NET INCOME ($ mil.)	INCOME AS % OF ASSETS	EMPLOYEES
08/14	178	16	9.2%	26
08/13	161	(2)	—	—
08/12	158	4	2.7%	—
08/10	140	0	—	—
Annual Growth	6.1%	—	—	—

2014 Year-End Financials

Debt ratio: —
Return on equity: 66.10%
Cash ($ mil.): 4
Current ratio: 288.30
Long-term debt ($ mil.): —
Dividends
Yield: —
Payout: —
Market value ($ mil.): —

M & H ENTERPRISES INC.

What M & H Enterprises builds in Vegas stays in Vegas. Also known as Martin-Harris Construction the company provides design/build general construction and construction management services to commercial institutional and industrial projects throughout the Southwest. In addition to its home state Martin-Harris also provides general contracting services in New Mexico Texas Colorado and Utah. Martin-Harris has completed office retail hospitality entertainment high-rise condominium and public works projects for clients such as Neiman Marcus Embassy Suites and US Air Force. The company was founded in 1976 by president and CEO Frank Martin. It has offices in Las Vegas and Phoenix.

EXECUTIVES

President and CEO, Frank Martin
President MHC Texas with a dedicated team of project managers, Kevin Zahm
VP Estimating, Frank (Guy) Martin

LOCATIONS

HQ: M & H ENTERPRISES INC.
3030 S HIGHLAND DR, LAS VEGAS, NV 89109-1047
Phone: 702-385-5257
Web: WWW.MARTINHARRIS.COM

COMPETITORS

Balfour Construction
Bovis Lend Lease
Turner Corporation

HISTORICAL FINANCIALS

Company Type: Private

Income Statement FYE: December 31

	REVENUE ($ mil.)	NET INCOME ($ mil.)	NET PROFIT MARGIN	EMPLOYEES
12/12*	179	1	0.9%	140
11/11	119	1	1.2%	—
12/09	168	1	0.9%	—
12/09	165	1	1.1%	—
Annual Growth	2.6%	(4.7%)	—	—

*Fiscal year change

2012 Year-End Financials

Debt ratio: —
Return on equity: 0.90%
Cash ($ mil.): 16
Current ratio: 0.90
Long-term debt ($ mil.): —
Dividends
Yield: —
Payout: —
Market value ($ mil.): —

M & M SERVICE CO INC

LOCATIONS

HQ: M & M SERVICE CO INC
130 N CHILES ST, CARLINVILLE, IL 626261684
Phone: 2178544516
Web: WWW.MMSERVICE.COM

HISTORICAL FINANCIALS

Company Type: Private

Income Statement FYE: August 31

	REVENUE ($ mil.)	NET INCOME ($ mil.)	NET PROFIT MARGIN	EMPLOYEES
08/14	294	4	1.5%	165
08/13	256	3	1.5%	—
08/12	296	2	0.9%	—
08/11	292	0	—	—
Annual Growth	0.2%	—	—	—

2014 Year-End Financials

Debt ratio: —
Return on equity: 1.50%
Cash ($ mil.): 2
Current ratio: 0.70
Long-term debt ($ mil.): —
Dividends
Yield: —
Payout: —
Market value ($ mil.): —

M. B. KAHN CONSTRUCTION CO. INC.

One of the largest construction companies in the southeastern US M. B. Kahn Construction Co. works on commercial institutional and industrial projects including hospitals airports shopping centers and manufacturing plants. Additionally it is rated as one of the top builders in the nation's education market. The company provides general contracting and design/build delivery services as well as construction management and program management services. Russian immigrant Myron B. Kahn founded the company in 1927. It is now chaired by Alan Kahn his grandson. The group operates through divisions in South Carolina and Georgia.

The purchase of South Carolina-based general contractor Chancel Construction increased the company's customer base in the Carolina's. Since then M.B. Kahn has been busy building and designing business parks arts centers and jails in the region.

EXECUTIVES

Executive Vp, Rick Ott
Vice President, Dave Burrell
Senior Executive Vice President, Charles Jordan
Vp Of Finance, Kynn Harris
Executive Vice President, Michael Satterwhite

LOCATIONS

HQ: M. B. KAHN CONSTRUCTION CO. INC.
101 FLINTLAKE RD, COLUMBIA, SC 29223-7851
Phone: 803-736-2950
Web: WWW.MBKAHN.COM

PRODUCTS/OPERATIONS

Selected Projects and Customers

Commercial
- Blue Cross/Blue Shield South Carolina
- South Carolina Bank & Trust
- Hilton Hotel
- South Carolina Bank and Trust headquarters

Education
- Barbara Bush Center at Columbia College
- Camden High School
- New Marietta High School
- West Ashley High School

Health Care
- Hollings Cancer Institute
- Roper Hospital
- Steadman Hawkins Clinic of the Carolinas

Industrial
- Bose Corporation
- Caterpillar
- Fruit of the Loom
- John Deere
- Komatsu America

Public Sector
- Greenville County Detention Center
- Horry County Courthouse
- Lexington County Judicial Center
- Pamlico County Detention Center

Religous
- Riverland Hills Baptist Church
- Pelham Road Baptist Church
- Saxe Gotha Presbyterian Church Facility

Water Works
- Columbia Wastewater Treatment Plant
- Hartwell Water Treatment Plant

COMPETITORS

Brasfield & Gorrie
Choate Construction
Gilbane Building Company
Hardin Construction
Parsons Infrastructure & Technology
Rodgers Builders
Shelco
Skanska USA Building
Tetra Tech Tesoro
Turner Corporation

HISTORICAL FINANCIALS

Company Type: Private

Income Statement FYE: December 31

	REVENUE ($ mil.)	NET INCOME ($ mil.)	NET PROFIT MARGIN	EMPLOYEES
12/12	251	6	2.8%	429
12/11	248	3	1.6%	—
12/10	184	8	4.7%	—
Annual Growth	16.8%	(10.0%)	—	—

2012 Year-End Financials

Debt ratio: —
Return on equity: 2.80%
Cash ($ mil.): 13
Current ratio: 0.30
Long-term debt ($ mil.): —
Dividends
Yield: —
Payout: —
Market value ($ mil.): —

M. C. GILL CORPORATION

LOCATIONS

HQ: M. C. GILL CORPORATION
4056 EASY ST, EL MONTE, CA 917311054
Phone: 6264436094
Web: WWW.MCGILLCORP.COM

HISTORICAL FINANCIALS

Company Type: Private

Income Statement FYE: December 28

	REVENUE ($ mil.)	NET INCOME ($ mil.)	NET PROFIT MARGIN	EMPLOYEES
12/13	207	48	23.6%	475
12/12	176	40	22.8%	—
12/11	153	29	18.9%	—
12/10	126	0	—	—
Annual Growth	17.9%	—	—	—

2013 Year-End Financials

Debt ratio: —
Return on equity: 23.60%
Cash ($ mil.): 27
Current ratio: 2.00
Long-term debt ($ mil.): —
Dividends
Yield: —
Payout: —
Market value ($ mil.): —

M. M. FOWLER INC.

LOCATIONS

HQ: M. M. FOWLER INC.
4220 NEAL RD, DURHAM, NC 277052322
Phone: 9193092925
Web: WWW.FAMILYFARECONVENIENCESTORES.COM

HISTORICAL FINANCIALS

Company Type: Private

Income Statement FYE: December 31

	REVENUE ($ mil.)	NET INCOME ($ mil.)	NET PROFIT MARGIN	EMPLOYEES
12/10	407	9	2.4%	28
12/09	332	6	2.1%	—
12/08	1,313	0	—	—
Annual Growth	(44.3%)	40616.0%	—	—

2010 Year-End Financials

Debt ratio: —
Return on equity: 2.40%
Cash ($ mil.): 21
Current ratio: 1.20
Long-term debt ($ mil.): —
Dividends
Yield: —
Payout: —
Market value ($ mil.): —

MACOMB OAKLAND REGIONAL CENTER INC

Michigan's disabled citizens have more than a friend in MORC. The Macomb-Oakland Regional Center (MORC) advocates for adults and children with developmental physical or psychiatric disabilities hoping to improve the lives of its clients. In addition to finding homes and jobs and coordinating recreational activities for the disabled the not-for-profit organization helps connect customers with support services including psychology nursing and medical care. It also holds community education seminars and it provides home health visitation and rehabilitation therapy services through its MORC Home Care and MORC Rehab divisions. Founded in 1972 MORC serves over 4000 clients in the state.

EXECUTIVES

President and Executive Director, Gerald (Jerry) Provencal
Secretary and Director, Thomas (Tom) Marchand
CFO Treasurer and Director, Richard Stone
Chairman, Joseph Erwin
Chairman, David Reece
President and Executive Director, Gerald (Jerry) Provencal
Secretary and Director, Thomas (Tom) Marchand
CFO Treasurer and Director, Richard Stone
Director, Mark Stilwell
Director, Lynda Wolf
Director, Michael Switalski
Chairman, David Reece
Auditors: GrantThorntonLLP

LOCATIONS

HQ: MACOMB OAKLAND REGIONAL CENTER INC
16200 19 MILE RD, CLINTON TOWNSHIP, MI 48038-1103
Phone: 586-263-8700
Web: WWW.THEAMORC.ORG

COMPETITORS

Gentiva
HealthSouth
Magellan Health
NHC
Sun Healthcare

HISTORICAL FINANCIALS

Company Type: Private

Income Statement FYE: September 30

	REVENUE ($ mil.)	NET INCOME ($ mil.)	NET PROFIT MARGIN	EMPLOYEES
09/12	193	0	0.1%	300
09/10	186	0	0.2%	—
09/09	181	0	0.1%	—
09/08	328	0	—	—
Annual Growth	—	65.0%	—	—

2012 Year-End Financials

Debt ratio: —
Return on equity: 0.10%
Cash ($ mil.): 7
Current ratio: 0.50
Long-term debt ($ mil.): —
Dividends
Yield: —
Payout: —
Market value ($ mil.): —

MADISON BANK

LOCATIONS

HQ: MADISON BANK
1001 HIGHLANDS DR, RICHMOND, KY 404753497
Phone: 8596268008

HISTORICAL FINANCIALS

Company Type: Private

Income Statement FYE: December 31

	ASSETS ($ mil.)	NET INCOME ($ mil.)	INCOME AS % OF ASSETS	EMPLOYEES
12/13	126	0	0.3%	43
12/08	141	0	0.4%	—
12/06	135	0	0.7%	—
12/05	0	0	—	—
Annual Growth	100.9%	—	—	—

2013 Year-End Financials

Debt ratio: —
Return on equity: 5.00%
Cash ($ mil.): 6
Current ratio: —
Long-term debt ($ mil.): —
Dividends
Yield: —
Payout: —
Market value ($ mil.): —

MADISON CAPITAL MANAGEMENT LLC

LOCATIONS

HQ: MADISON CAPITAL MANAGEMENT LLC
5619 DTC PKWY STE 800, GREENWOOD VILLAGE, CO 801113139
Phone: 3039572000
Web: WWW.MADISONCAP.COM

HISTORICAL FINANCIALS

Company Type: Private

Income Statement FYE: December 31

	ASSETS ($ mil.)	NET INCOME ($ mil.)	INCOME AS % OF ASSETS	EMPLOYEES
12/08	531	21	4.1%	70
12/07	21	0	—	—
12/06	1	0	0.0%	—
Annual Growth	1776.9%	74021.5%	—	—

2008 Year-End Financials

Debt ratio: —
Return on equity: 84.50%
Cash ($ mil.): 29
Current ratio: —
Long-term debt ($ mil.): —
Dividends
Yield: —
Payout: —
Market value ($ mil.): —

MAIMONIDES MEDICAL CENTER INC

The name is a mouthful but if you choke while trying to get it out Maimonides Medical Center can help. The not-for-profit hospital offers emergency medicine surgical procedures psychiatric treatment and other traditional hospital services to patients in Brooklyn New York. It has more than 710 beds and more than 70 subspecialty treatment programs for a range of conditions including cancer cardiac stroke neurological pediatric and women's health ailments. It also operates outpatient family health and specialty clinics. Maimonides Medical Center is an independent teaching hospital that serves as a training facility for SUNY-Brooklyn St. George's University and other schools.

Financial Performance

Maimonides Medical Center reported a revenue increase of 2% in 2012 primarily due to increase in government grant income and electronic health records incentive payments.

It had net income of $15 million in 2012 (compared to a loss in 2011) thanks to income from change in captive insurance program interest rate shortfall and a change in captive insurance program.

Strategy

Maimonides Medical Center works to keep its utilization rates up (the number of patients it sees) and make itself attractive to doctors by making capital investments in its facilities and technology systems on a regular basis. In 2012 it opened a new $8.6 million breast cancer facility to better meet the needs of specialty care patients; it also opened a pediatric outpatient center that year.

The hospital uses a fully-implemented electronic health record (EHR) system that includes a computerized physician order entry system (CPOE) that reduces prescription errors and a picture archival communications system (PACS) to store digital radiology images. The use of such technology is becoming increasingly tied to how the government reimburses hospitals for the services they provide especially in the new health care reform laws.

Mergers and Acquisitions

Reflecting an increasing consolidation among hospitals across the city in 2013 Maimonides Medical Center and fellow Brooklyn-based institution Brookdale University Hospital and Medical Center began exploring a possible merger or formal affiliation.

Company Background

Maimonides Medical Center traces its roots to the New Utrecht Dispensary which opened in 1911. The medical center later merged with Beth Moses and United Israel Zion hospitals in 1947. It is named after 12th-century philosopher Rabbi Moshe Ben Maimon.

EXECUTIVES

Exec Vp Of Clinical Affairs, David I Cohen
Sr Vp Of Psychiatry Svs, Marcel Biberfeld
Vp External Affairs, Barry Ensminger
President and CEO, Pamela S. (Pam) Brier, age 68
EVP and CFO, Robert Naldi
VP Management Information Systems and CIO, Walter J. Fahey
EVP and COO, Dominick Stanzione
Medical Director, Barry S Rand
Medical Director, Seyed E Hashemi
Medical Director, Edward K Chapnick
Vp Of Nursing, Camille Scarciotta
Vp Of Cancer Center, Paulette Cirillo
Vp Of Utilization Review, Madeline Rivera
Director Of Respiratory Therapy, Angel Lora
Assistant Vice President Marketing, Maureen O'Connor
Director Of Infection Control, Mary O'Keefe
Vice Presidentprofessional Affairs, Karen Kobus
Director Of Nursing, Kathy Peterson
Vice President Of Human Resources, Brigid Klein
Vp Of Purchasing Services, Wade Wilson
Senior Vice President Intg Delvr Sys, Karen Nelson
Sr Vp Human Resources, Thomas Doherty
Medical Director, Jeffrey Goldberg
Vp Perioperative Services, David L Feldman
Medical Director, Anna Skiandos
Medical Director, Pui Wong
Medical Director, Rosa Reizis
Medical Director, Vladimir Klebanov
Director Of Radiology, Dennis Dejesus
Medical Director, Joseph Carmody
Medical Director, Joseph Squitieri
Pharmacy Manager, Anne Monarch
Vice President Support Services, Bob Cruz
Associate Vice President Finance, John Scanlan
Medical Director, John Lops
Medical Director, David Inwood
Medical Director, Melanie Schwarz
Medical Director, Denise Miles
Assistant Vice President Of Fin Reimb, Yun Tzeng
Medical Director, Kenneth Harris
Executive Assistant To The Vp, Antoinette Baker
Vice President, Andrew Leguelof
Vice President Of Nursing, Dorothy Hannah
Assistant Vice President Primary Care Services And Chief Of Clinical Network Development, Jenny Quinn
Executive Assistant To The Senior Vice President Of Legal Affairs, Terry Battipaglia
Medical Director, Miriam Zibkoff
Vice President Information Technology, Kip Peterson
Vice President Human Resources, Linda Issacs
Vice President Of Public Affairs, Vicki Ciampa
Vice President Business Innovation And Operations, Alice Peterson
Vice President And Chief Information, Theresa Sawhney
Senior Vice President Chief Information, Walter Womack
Senior Vice President Integrated, Karen Menix
Assistant To The Executive Vice President Finance And Chief Financial Officer, Elaine Swiontak
Assistant Vice President Emergency, William Howe
Intern With The Senior Vice President, Christina Cellante
Vice President Information Technology, Tom Pennanen
Assistant Vice President Labor, Gaitre Lorick

Medical Director, Szymon Hyzak
Vice President Of Patient Accounts, Frank Degratto
Director Of Health Information, Sylvia Scmenskaya
Chair Department Of Medicine, Stephan Kamholz
Chairman, Martin D. Payson, age 77
Associate Vice Chairman For Operations Department Of Emergency Medicine, Kenneth Sable
Secretary, Wanda Ortiz
Secretary, Anna Pidoto
Secretary, Rose Brooke
Secretary, Migdalia Concepcion
Secretary, Jeannette Collazo
Secretary, Rosalyn Levin
Secretary, Millie Gutierrez
Board Member, Elly Kleinman
Secretary, Kathy Reyna
Auditors: Ernst&YoungLLP

LOCATIONS

HQ: MAIMONIDES MEDICAL CENTER INC
4802 10TH AVE, BROOKLYN, NY 11219-2916
Phone: 718-283-6000
Web: WWW.MAIMONIDESMED.ORG

PRODUCTS/OPERATIONS

Selected Brooklyn Locations

Adult Primary Care
Ambulatory Health Services
Bay Parkway Multi-Specialty
Manfredi Family Health Center
Newkirk Family Health Center
Outpatient Eye Clinic
Pediatric Primary Care
Primary Health Services
Sheepshead Bay
Women's Primary Care Services

COMPETITORS

Beth Israel Medical Center
Bronx-Lebanon Hospital
Brookdale University Hospital
Brooklyn Hospital Center
Catholic Healthcare System
Continuum Health Partners
Jamaica Hospital Medical Center
Kingsbrook Jewish Medical Center
Long Island College Hospital
Lutheran HealthCare
Montefiore Medical
New York City Health and Hospitals
New York Methodist Hospital
NewYork-Presbyterian Hospital
North Shore University Hospital
SUNY Downstate
Staten Island University Hospital
Wyckoff Heights Medical Center

HISTORICAL FINANCIALS

Company Type: Private

Income Statement FYE: December 31

	REVENUE ($ mil.)	NET INCOME ($ mil.)	NET PROFIT MARGIN	EMPLOYEES
12/10	997	47	4.7%	6,382
12/09	928	37	4.0%	—
12/08	926	12	1.4%	—
12/06	0	0	—	—
Annual Growth	—	—	—	—

2010 Year-End Financials

Debt ratio: —
Return on equity: 4.70%
Cash ($ mil.): 135
Current ratio: 1.20
Long-term debt ($ mil.): —
Dividends
Yield: —
Payout: —
Market value ($ mil.): —

MAIN LINE HEALTH INC.

Part of the Jefferson Health System Main Line Health serves constituents in the Philadelphia area. The health system consists of four acute-care facilities (Bryn Mawr Hospital Lankenau Medical Center Paoli Hospital and Riddle Hospital) with a total of more than 1100 beds. It also operates physician practices a research institute a 150-bed rehabilitation hospital (Bryn Mawr Rehab Hospital) an addiction recovery facility (Mirmont Treatment Center) and various other facilities. Main Line Health provides home health care services and care for the elderly through senior programs. It operates several ambulatory-care centers and provides occupational health as well.

Geographic Reach

Main Line Health serves Philadelphia and the western suburbs of Philadelphia.

Operations

The organization's affiliated physician practices are part of Main Line HealthCare a multi-specialty provider network. Meanwhile the group's research programs are conducted through the Lankenau Institute for Medical Research on the Lankenau Medical Center campus. Fields of research include cancer cardiovascular disease and other conditions.

Altogether Main Line Health employs 2000 physicians at its four acute care medical centers. Bryn Mawr Hospital and Lankenau Medical Center both serve as physician training facilities while Paoli Hospital serves as a level II regional trauma center and Riddle Hospital specializes in transitional care.

Strategy

To expand medical resources for area children Bryn Mawr Hospital expanded its partnership with Alfred I. duPont Hospital for Children in 2012. Also in 2012 Lankenau Medical Center expanded orthopedic care when it opened a new spine center. Main Line Health is also opening new outpatient care facilities in the region.

Company Background

Main Line Health was organized in 1985.

EXECUTIVES

President and CEO, John J. (Jack) Lynch III
Chairman, George W. Gephart Jr.
VP and CIO, Karen Thomas
SVP Human Resources, Eileen McAnally
EVP and CFO, Michael J. (Mike) Buongiorno
President Bryn Mawr Hospital, Andrea F. Gilbert
SVP and General Counsel, Brian T. Corbett
President Lankenau Hospital, Elaine C. Thompson, age 57
President Paoli Hospital, Barbara J. Tachovsky
President Lankenau Medical Center, Phillip D. Robinson
SVP Marketing and Public Affairs, Sarah A. Peterson
President Bryn Mawr Rehab Hospital and Affiliates, Donna M. Phillips
SVP Development, Kenneth E. Kirby
SVP Facilities Design and Construction, JoAnn M. Magnatta
VP Planning and Business Development, Joel A. Port
President and CEO Lankenau Institute of Medical Research, George C. Prendergast
President Paoli Hospital, Jim Paradis
Chief Nursing Officer, Nancy Valentine
Senior Vice President and Chief Nursing Officer, Barbara Wadsworth
Manager Public Relations, Frieda Schmidt
President and CEO Riddle Memorial Hospital, Daniel E. Kennedy
President Riddle Hospital, Gary L. Perecko
SVP Medical Affairs and Chief Medical Officer, Donald C. Arthur
VP and Chief Medical Information Officer, Harm J. Scherpbier
Assistant Manager Public Relations, Bridget Therriault
SVP and Chief Medical Officer, Andrew J. Norton
SVP Marketing and Business Development, Lydia Hammer
President Mirmont Treatment Center, Thomas F. (Tom) Cain

LOCATIONS

HQ: MAIN LINE HEALTH INC.
130 S BRYN MAWR AVE, BRYN MAWR, PA 19010-3121
Phone: 484-337-3000
Web: WWW.MAINLINEHEALTH.ORG

PRODUCTS/OPERATIONS

Selected Operations

Bryn Mawr Hospital (Bryn Mawr Pennsylvania)
Bryn Mawr Rehab Hospital (Malvern Pennsylvania)
Lankenau Medical Center (Wynnewood Pennsylvania)
Mirmont Treatment Center (Lima Pennsylvania)
Paoli Hospital (Paoli Pennsylvania)
Riddle Hospital (Media Pennsylvania)

COMPETITORS

Abington Memorial Hospital
Christiana Care
Crozer-Keystone Health System
Doylestown Hospital
Kennedy Health System
Mercy Health System
North Philadelphia Health System
The Cooper Health System
University of Pennsylvania Health System

HISTORICAL FINANCIALS

Company Type: Private

Income Statement FYE: June 30

	REVENUE ($ mil.)	NET INCOME ($ mil.)	NET PROFIT MARGIN	EMPLOYEES
06/12	1,475	193	13.1%	5,840
06/11	1,405	112	8.0%	—
06/10	1,361	111	8.2%	—
06/08	1,224	118	9.6%	—
Annual Growth	4.8%	13.1%	—	—

2012 Year-End Financials

Debt ratio: —
Return on equity: 13.10%
Cash ($ mil.): 153
Current ratio: 1.50
Long-term debt ($ mil.): —
Dividends
Yield: —
Payout: —
Market value ($ mil.): —

MAIN LINE HOSPITALS INC.

Bryn Mawr Hospital a member of the Main Line Health network is an acute care facility providing a variety of inpatient and outpatient services for the western suburbs of Philadelphia. With some 320 beds Bryn Mawr Hospital is recognized nationally for its orthopedic program. Founded in 1893 by Dr. George Gerhard the hospital also provides cancer cardiac surgical pediatric reproductive health diagnostic imaging psychiatric bariatric and wound care services. Bryn Mawr Hospital and the other Main Line Health facilities are part of community based not-for-profit network Jefferson Health System.

Operations

Based in Pennsylvania Bryn Mawr Hospital boasts specialized departments such as a Comprehensive Breast Center; Wound Healing Center at Bryn Mawr Hospital; Outpatient Imaging Center; Center for Reproductive Medicine; Cancer Center; Main Line Health Heart Center; Center for Addictive Diseases; Level III Neonatal Intensive Care Unit; and Nemours Pediatric Partners at Bryn Mawr Hospital. It provides care to more than 2000 newborns each year.

The hospital also operates another health center in Newton Square that offers a range of outpatient services and medical practices.

Strategy

Like many hospitals Bryn Mawr Hospital aims to expand its outpatient services and connect to medical practices. The practice helps to boost the number of referrals to its facility and grow physician relations throughout the community.

Bryn Mawr Hospital collaborates with Nemours/Alfred I. duPont Hospital for Children to provide 24/7 pediatric care for the pediatric inpatient unit and the pediatric emergency department with added board-certified emergency medicine physicians.

Company Ownership

Bryn Mawr Hospital is part of the Jefferson Health System a community based not-for-profit network.

Awards and Recognition

Bryn Mawr Hospital has Magnet designation from the American Nurses Credentialing Center for excellence in nursing care. The hospital has also been nationally recognized by Press Ganey Thomson Reuters The Joint Commission and other healthcare ratings organizations for its high quality patient care. In 2012 the hospital was named among US News & World Report's Best Hospitals for the Philadelphia metro area.

EXECUTIVES

Chairman, George W. Gephart Jr.
VP and CIO, Karen Thomas
VP Finance and Treasurer, Michael J. (Mike) Buongiorno
President, Andrea F. Gilbert
SVP and General Counsel, Brian T. Corbett
VP Patient Services, Claire Baldwin
VP Operations, Michael (Mike) Reno
Director Human Resources, Terry Dougherty

LOCATIONS

HQ: MAIN LINE HOSPITALS INC.
130 S BRYN MAWR AVE, BRYN MAWR, PA 19010-3121
Phone: 610-526-3000
Web: WWW.MAINLINEHEALTH.ORG

PRODUCTS/OPERATIONS

Selected Clinical Programs and Health Centers

American Day Treatment Center
Behavioral Health Inpatient Unit
Bryn Mawr Hospital/duPont Children' s Health Program
Comprehensive Breast Center
Cancer Center/Radiation Oncology including IMRT
Cardiac/Pulmonary Rehabilitation
Center for Reproductive Medicine
Clinical Laboratory and Pathology
Clinical Research including but not limited to a Community Clinical Oncology Program (CCOP) grant sponsored by the National Cancer Institute and Heart Center research trials.
Community Services offering screenings wellness and educational programs
Critical Care
Diabetes Management Program
Emergency Services
Enterostomal Therapy
Family Centered Maternity Unit with Labor/Delivery/Recovery Rooms
Family Practice
General Surgery and Subspecialties
Geriatric Services
Main Line Health Heart Center from prevention to surgery
Internal Medicine and Subspecialties
Interventional Radiology
Kidney Dialysis
Level III Neonatal Intensive Care Unit
Neurodiagnostic Center
Neurosciences
Nutritional Services
Occupational/Employee Health Services
Orthopedics/Joint Replacement Program
Pain Management Services
Pediatricians and Dedicated Pediatric Inpatient Unit
Perinatal Testing Center
Physical Medicine/Rehabilitation and Therapy
Pulmonary Diagnostic and Wellness Center
Diagnostic and Therapeutic Radiology includingMRI CT Special Procedures Nuclear Medicine PET/CT
Sleep Medicine Services
Surgicenter
Travelers' Services
Wound Healing Center

COMPETITORS

Abington Memorial Hospital
Albert Einstein Healthcare Network
Catholic Health East
Christiana Care
Crozer-Keystone Health System
Doylestown Hospital
Jefferson Health System

Memorial Hospital (PA)
Moses Taylor Hospital
North Philadelphia Health System
Tenet Healthcare
University of Pennsylvania Health System
Virtua Memorial

HISTORICAL FINANCIALS

Company Type: Private

Income Statement FYE: June 30

	REVENUE ($ mil.)	NET INCOME ($ mil.)	NET PROFIT MARGIN	EMPLOYEES
06/10	953	114	12.0%	3,353
06/08	11	2	19.2%	—
06/08	0	0	—	—
Annual Growth	—	—	—	—

2010 Year-End Financials

Debt ratio: —
Return on equity: 12.00%
Cash ($ mil.): 53
Current ratio: 1.50
Long-term debt ($ mil.): —
Dividends
Yield: —
Payout: —
Market value ($ mil.): —

MAINEGENERAL HEALTH

If you're aching or ailing within shouting distance of the Kennebec River in Maine then MaineGeneral Health is the place to head. The comprehensive health care organization features acute care hospitals outpatient clinics and physicians' practices long-term care centers and home health and hospice agencies. Its flagship facilities are the three main campuses (in state capital Augusta and Waterville farther north) of MaineGeneral Medical Center together featuring about 290 inpatient beds. MaineGeneral Health also runs nursing homes with some 270 beds in all as well as senior living apartments lab and imaging centers and inpatient rehabilitation and mental health facilities.

Operations MaineGeneral has a number of operations aimed at reaching underserved populations in rural parts of its service area. For instance the organization includes a small rural facility in northern Somerset County with an emergency room outpatient center and nursing home. And its HealthReach Network works with area hospitals and health care providers to ensure that some services (particularly home health care substance abuse treatment and mental health services) reach rural residents. Similarly the health care system hosts periodic specialty clinics that bring in doctors in medical specialties not represented on its own staff. Strategy In 2009 MaineGeneral announced plans to build a new 225-bed medical center in north Augusta that would consolidate the inpatient operations of its hospital campuses. Two of the medical center campuses would close (Augusta Campus and Seton Campus) while the third (Thayer Campus) would become an outpatient/emergency care facility. Construction of the $322 million hospital began in 2011 with a completion date in late 2013.

EXECUTIVES

President CEO and Director, Scott B. Bullock, age 62
President and CEO MaineGeneral Medical Center, Charles Hays
Chair, Barbara Mayer
Vice Chair, Robert Marden
President CEO and Director, Scott B. Bullock, age 62
Director, Conrad L. Ayotte, age 59
Vice Chair, Robert Marden
Director, William (Bro) Adams
Director, Charles Danielson
Director, Jeffrey Hubert
Director, Gordon Pow
Director, William Sprague
Director, Peter Alfond
Director, Diane Campbell
Director, Frederick (Ted) LaRochelle
Director, Roy Miller
Director, Kenneth Viens
Director, Douglas Cutchin
Director, Peter Guzzetti
Director, Elizabeth Mitchell
Director, Tobi Schneider
Auditors: PricewaterhouseCoopersLLP

LOCATIONS

HQ: MAINEGENERAL HEALTH
35 MEDICAL CENTER PKWY, AUGUSTA, ME 04330-8160
Phone: 207-626-1000
Web: WWW.OURNEWHOSPITAL.ORG

COMPETITORS

Eastern Maine Healthcare Systems
Franklin Community Health Network
Maine Coast Memorial Hospital
MaineHealth
Mercy Health System of Maine
Parkview Hospital
St. Joseph Healthcare

HISTORICAL FINANCIALS

Company Type: Private

Income Statement FYE: June 30

	REVENUE ($ mil.)	NET INCOME ($ mil.)	NET PROFIT MARGIN	EMPLOYEES
06/12	440	(2)	—	3,800
06/11	421	46	10.9%	—
06/10	401	15	3.8%	—
06/09	378	(35)	—	—
Annual Growth	5.2%	—	—	—

2012 Year-End Financials

Debt ratio: —
Return on equity: (-0.50%)
Cash ($ mil.): 19
Current ratio: 0.70
Long-term debt ($ mil.): —

Dividends
Yield: —
Payout: —
Market value ($ mil.): —

MANAGEMENT AND TRAINING CORPORATION

Management & Training Corporation (MTC) prepares prison inmates for re-entry into society. It provides a variety of academic vocational and social-skills training in rehabilitation-oriented private prisons. Its holistic education model offers programs to help inmates avoid substance abuse as they also boost their engagement in community service find work and increase their cognitive skills. As part of its services MTC operates about two dozen correctional facilities in eight states through a contract with the Department of Labor. The company also operates Job Corps centers and provides health care related services to correctional facilities.

Operations

Founded in 1981 MTC operates through four divisions: Correctional Job Corps MTC Medical and International Development. Its correctional division operates facilities that house more than 30000 inmates and is one of the largest US correctional contractors for the Department of Labor. Its Job Corps division is the largest single operator of Job Corps centers in the US with more than 120 centers across the US. Job Corps is a government funded job-training program for 16-to-24-year-old children and adults.

The company's MTC Medical unit provides subcontracted health care services to correctional facilities by employing a range of medical providers including dentists optometrists psychiatrists and psychologists and physicians. The International Development division offers research retraining and vocational training through contracts with organizations around the globe.

The company trains its supervisors senior managers and executives through its MTC Corporate University while its MTC Institute performs research into forming best practices related to addressing issues facing those who work with Job Corps youth and prison inmates.

Geographic Reach

The company's main offices are located in Centerville Utah and it has satellite centers in Georgia Texas and Washington DC. MTC operates through contracts in about 20 states including correctional facility contracts in Arizona California Florida Idaho Ohio New Mexico Mississippi and Texas.

MTC operates internationally providing governments NGOs ministries and private entities with customized training programs designed to help develop workforces. Its international unit has assisted clients in Africa Asia Australia the Middle East and North America.

Sales and Marketing

In addition to the Department of Labor the company has held contracts with the US Agency for International Development the African Development Bank UNICEF and other organizations. It also serves state agencies such as the Texas Department of Criminal Justice.

Financial Performance

MTC reported gross revenues of some $704 million in 2012.

Strategy

MTC expands by recruiting and retaining quality educators health professionals and international consultants. To maximize its employees' potential the company conducts leadership development programs for all of its employees. MTC also expands by adding new contracts with state correctional agencies.

EXECUTIVES

Chairman, Robert Marquardt
President, R. Scott Marquardt
Senior Vice President CFO Secretary, Lyle J. Parry
SVP Training, John Pederson
VP Human Resources, Teresa Aramaki
VP Corrections Marketing, Mike Murphy
Vice President Regional Operations Corrections, Al Murphy
VP Communication, Celeste McDonald
VP Information Systems, Rich Skeen
VP and General Counsel, Dawn Call
Senior Vice President Corrections, Odie Washington
Director Corrections, Mark Lee
Director Corporate Communications, Issa Arnita
Senior Director Medical Operations, David Meeker
Administrative Assistant, Teresa Anderson
Vice President Regional Operations Corrections, Neil Adler
Vice President Central Region Job Corps, Anita Sharp
Vice President Program Development, Craig Sudbury
Vice President Southeast Intermountain Region Job Corps, Dean Hoffman
Vice President Western Region Job Corps, Elizabeth M. Lopez
Senior Vice President Training Programs, John Pedersen
Vice President Regional Operations Corrections, Rich Gansheimer
Vice President North Central Region Job Corps, Tom Fitzwater
Vice President Contract Administration, Virleen Ferre
Vice President Development, Lynette Greenwell
Senior Vice President Business Development & Administration, Sergio Molina

LOCATIONS

HQ: MANAGEMENT AND TRAINING CORPORATION
500 N MARKET PLACE DR # 100, CENTERVILLE, UT 84014-1708
Phone: 801-693-2600
Web: WWW.MTCTRAINS.COM

PRODUCTS/OPERATIONS

Selected Services

Communicate through formal and informal channels
Develop custom training for students clients & offenders
Manage facilities
Provide community connections
Provide data solutions

COMPETITORS

Avalon Correctional Services
Community Education Centers
Conmed Healthcare
Corizon
Corrections Corporation of America
G4S
GEO Group
MHM Services
Res-Care
Wexford Health

HISTORICAL FINANCIALS

Company Type: Private

Income Statement FYE: December 31

	REVENUE ($ mil.)	NET INCOME ($ mil.)	NET PROFIT MARGIN	EMPLOYEES
12/12	704	45	6.5%	7,800
12/11	687	30	4.4%	—
12/10	667	24	3.6%	—
12/09	672	20	3.0%	—
Annual Growth	1.6%	30.8%	—	—

2012 Year-End Financials

Debt ratio: —
Return on equity: 6.50%
Cash ($ mil.): 19
Current ratio: 1.60
Long-term debt ($ mil.): —

Dividends
Yield: —
Payout: —
Market value ($ mil.): —

MAR-JAC POULTRY INC.

From farm to table Mar-Jac Poultry's business is "poultry in motion." The company is one of the major processors of chicken sold to the domestic fast-food restaurant and foodservice market. Its operations include a hatchery to raise birds and a feed mill that churns 8500 tons of feed a week for some 200 farmers in Georgia who contract with the company to grow its chicks and broilers. Mar-Jac's plant processes about two million chickens a week which are vacuum-packed in its cold storage facility prior to shipment to mostly local distributors in the US and some international export customers. Mar-Jac was started by brothers Marvin and Jackson McKibbon in 1954 and later acquired by a group of poultry farmers.

Despite its humble origins the company has confronted a number of complex legal and regulatory issues. In 2011 the poultry farm appealed a federal court ruling that dismissed its claim for libel slander and product disparagement against CBS. A 60 Minutes program was covering a government investigation that implicated Mar-Jac in an alleged plot to launder money for terrorists using the chicken production industry as a cover. Mar-Jac also faced $380000 in OSHA fines for multiple willful safety and health violations in 2009.

EXECUTIVES

VP Finance, Mahoud D. Mohamed
VP Poultry Operations, Pete Martin
Manager Live Production, Tony Gravitt

LOCATIONS

HQ: MAR-JAC POULTRY INC.
1020 AVIATION BLVD, GAINESVILLE, GA 30501-6839
Phone: 770-531-5000
Web: WWW.MARJACPOULTRY.COM

PRODUCTS/OPERATIONS

Selected Products

Boneless
- Butterflies
- Filets
- Tenders
- Thigh meat

Fast food
- 6 piece
- 8 piece
- 9 piece
- Quarters
- Splits

Parts
- Cut Wings
- Drums

Gizzards
Leg quarters
Livers
Paws (export only)
Split breasts
Thighs
Whole legs
Whole wings
Whole birds
With giblets
Without giblets

COMPETITORS

Eberly Poultry	Plainville Farms
Foster Farms	Rose Acre Farms
Mountaire Farms	Sanderson Farms
Perdue Incorporated	Shelton' s
Petaluma Poultry	Tecumseh Poultry
Pilgrim' s Pride	Tyson Foods

HISTORICAL FINANCIALS

Company Type: Private

Income Statement FYE: April 27

	REVENUE ($ mil.)	NET INCOME ($ mil.)	NET PROFIT MARGIN	EMPLOYEES
04/12	283	8	2.9%	1,200
04/11	257	11	4.4%	—
04/10*	262	29	11.4%	—
05/09	263	12	4.7%	—
Annual Growth	2.5%	(13.1%)	—	—

*Fiscal year change

2012 Year-End Financials

Debt ratio: ——
Return on equity: 2.90%
Cash ($ mil.): 36
Current ratio: 2.90
Long-term debt ($ mil.): —
Dividends
Yield: —
Payout: —
Market value ($ mil.): —

MARCH OF DIMES FOUNDATION

The March of Dimes Foundation has been lending a hand since 1938. Established by President Franklin Roosevelt to fight polio the organization has evolved into an advocate for the prevention of birth defects and infant mortality. Its focus areas include genetic birth defects premature birth parent education and expanding access to health care. The foundation provides information and support services for professionals and the public and supports research efforts. Most of the foundation's revenue comes from contributions to its signature March for Babies event and other fundraisers.

Financial Performance

In 2012 March of Dimes reported revenue of $219 million an increase of nearly 10% from 2011. A rise in investment gains was enough to offset a small decline in bequests and major gifts. The March for Babies raised just over $106 million nearly half of the organization's total revenue that year. In addition special events and direct response brought in a combined $90+ million while major gifts accounted for about $12 million.

Overall the foundation invested some $30 million in research to study premature birth defects and infant mortality in 2012. The research money is also used for medical treatments and prevention.

Company Background

The organization originally called The National Foundation for Infantile Paralysis owes its name to comedian Eddie Cantor. In an early fundraiser for the group Cantor appealed to radio listeners nationwide to send dimes to the White House. He called the campaign the March of Dimes after the popular newsreel feature The March of Time. The campaign was a success and The National Foundation for Infantile Paralysis formally became the March of Dimes in 1979.

EXECUTIVES

President and CEO, Jennifer L. Howse
EVP and COO, Jane E. Massey
SVP General Counsel and Assistant Secretary, Lisa E. Bellsey
Vice Chairman, David R. Smith
Medical Director, Alan R. Fleischman
Chairman and Trustee, Kenneth A. (Ken) May, age 53
SVP CFO and Assistant Treasurer, Richard E. Mulligan
Trustee and Secretary, Laverne H. Council
Vice Chairman of the Maryland FBLA Board of Directors, Janice Icenhower
Trustee, Frederick W. Telling, age 61
Trustee, J. Joseph (Joe) Hale Jr.
Trustee, Robert F. (Rob) Friel, age 58
Trustee, F. Robert (Bob) Woudstra, age 70
Trustee, Thomas A. (Tom) Russo, age 69
Trustee, Marc G. Guild, age 61
Trustee, Jerome T. Lienhard II
Trustee, Timothy E. (Tim) Kelly, age 55
Trustee, Beth E. Ford
Trustee, Joseph W. (Joe) Wood, age 66
Trustee, Carol J. Evans
Vice Chairman, David R. Smith
Trustee, Michael E. Mohnsen
Trustee, Alfred B. Childs
Trustee and Secretary, Laverne H. Council
Trustee, Michele Fabrizi
Trustee, G. Brent Minor
Trustee, Judith A. Nolte
Vice Chairman, Mark Selcow
Trustee, John Burbank, age 50
Trustee, Troy Ruhanen
Trustee, Miriam Arond
Trustee, Kathy Behrens
Trustee, Harris Brooks
Trudtee, Harvey Cohen
Trustee, Jose F. Cordero
Trustee, Virginia Davis Floyd
Trustee, Don Germano
Trustee, Elizabeth Roosevelt Johnston
Trustee, Jon Spector
Trustee, Roger C. Young
Auditors: KPMGLLP

LOCATIONS

HQ: MARCH OF DIMES FOUNDATION
1275 MAMARONECK AVE, WHITE PLAINS, NY 10605-5298
Phone: 914-428-7100
Web: WWW.WALKAMERICA.ORG

PRODUCTS/OPERATIONS

2012 Revenues

	$ mil.	% of total
Contributions	186	85
Investment gain	14	6
Bequests and major gifts	9	4
Grants	3	2
Other	5	3
Total	**218**	**100**

HISTORICAL FINANCIALS

Company Type: Private

Income Statement FYE: December 31

	REVENUE ($ mil.)	NET INCOME ($ mil.)	NET PROFIT MARGIN	EMPLOYEES
12/09	214	35	16.4%	1,200
12/08	236	0	—	—
12/06	236	9	4.1%	—
12/05	226	12	5.5%	—
Annual Growth	(1.4%)	29.4%	—	—

2009 Year-End Financials

Debt ratio: ——
Return on equity: 16.40%
Cash ($ mil.): 9
Current ratio: 0.10
Long-term debt ($ mil.): —
Dividends
Yield: —
Payout: —
Market value ($ mil.): —

MARIST COLLEGE

Marist College is a gem among small private US colleges. The liberal arts college has a enrollment of more than 6300 students and a student-faculty ratio of 16-to-1. It offers more than 40 bachelor's and a dozen master's programs as well as some 20 certificate programs. It seven schools specialize in communication and the arts computer science and math continuing education liberal arts management science and social and behavioral sciences. In addition to its main 210-acre campus along the shores of the Hudson River the college has several off-campus extension sites that mainly cater to adult students. Marist was founded in 1929 to train new members in the Marist Brothers order of Catholic priests.

Operations

Marist College has recently been recognized by publications including Kiplinger's Private Finance magazine which named Marist as one of the best value private college in the US. It has also been on the Princeton Review's best colleges list with a special recognition for its extensive study abroad programs (including a branch campus in Florence Italy) as well as its business teaching criminal justice fashion and communication programs. Marist College also offers advanced IT resources to its students through a partnership with IBM which is also located in southeastern New York State.

Financial Performance

The college has an annual operating budget of $160 million.

In 2014 Marist College reported a 9% rise in revenues thanks to an increase in student tuition and fees as well as more grants and other income.

Company Background

Marist College was founded in 1929 as a training center for the brothers of the Roman Catholic Marist order.

EXECUTIVES

President, Dennis J. Murray
VP and CIO, William (Bill) Thirsk
EVP, Geoffrey L. Brackett
VP Business Affairs and CFO, John Pecchia
VP Academic Affairs and Dean of Faculty, Thomas Wermuth
Vice President Of The Black Student Union, Jionne McMichael
Assoc Vp Academic Affairs, John Ritschdorff
Executive Vice President, Jeffrey Brackett
Vp Of Admiss/enroll Planning, Sean Kaylor
Executive Secretary To Vice President For College Advancement, Claire Horton

Associate Vice President For Human Resources, Deborah Raikes
Dean Of Faculty And Vice President For Academic Affairs, Artin Arslanian
Vice President Of Information Technology And Chief Information Officer, Bill Thrisk
Vice President Of Finance, Jeanie Plecenik
Chairman, Ellen M. Hancock, age 70
Vice Chairman, Ross A. Mauri
Secretary, Joan Nies
Secretary, Betty Moody

LOCATIONS

HQ: MARIST COLLEGE
3399 NORTH RD, POUGHKEEPSIE, NY 126011387
Phone: 8455753000
Web: WWW.CLUBS.MARIST.EDU

PRODUCTS/OPERATIONS

Majors
Accounting
American Studies
Applied Mathematic
Athletic Training
Biochemistry (B.A.)
Biochemistry (B.S.)
Biology
Biology Education
Biomedical Sciences
Business Administra
Finance
Human Resource Management
International Business
Marketing
Chemistry (B.A.)
Chemistry (B.S.)
Communication
Advertising
Communication Studies
Journalism
Public Relations
Sports Communicat
Computer Science
Computer Science/Game Design
Criminal Justice
Digital Media
Economics
Education
Adolescence Education (Grades 7
Childhood/Special Education (Grades 1
English
Literature
Theatre
Writing
Environmental Science
Policy
Science
Fashion Design
Fashion Merchandis
Fine Arts
Art History
Studio Art
History
Information Technology and Systems
Information Systems
Information Technology
Mathematics
Media Studies and Production
Medical Technology
Modern Languages and Cultures
French
Italian
Spanish
Philosophy
Religious Studies
Political Science
International Studies
Public Affairs
Psychology
Psychology/Dual Certification/Special Education (1-6)
Social Work
Graduate Programs
Accounting MBA
MA in Communicat
MA in Integrated Marketing Communicat
MA in Mental Health Counseling
MA in Museum Studies
MA in School Psychology
Master of Arts in Educational Psychology
Master of Education (Initial Teaching Certificat
MBA- Master of Business Administra
MPA- Master of Public Administra
MS in Information Systems
MS in Software Developmen
Advanced Certificate in Information Systems

HISTORICAL FINANCIALS

Company Type: Private

Income Statement FYE: June 30

	REVENUE ($ mil.)	NET INCOME ($ mil.)	NET PROFIT MARGIN	EMPLOYEES
06/13	228	33	14.7%	750
06/10	211	47	22.3%	
06/09	159	0	—	—
06/08	0	0	—	—
Annual Growth	—	—	—	—

2013 Year-End Financials

Debt ratio: —
Return on equity: 14.70%
Cash ($ mil.): 49
Current ratio: 0.40
Long-term debt ($ mil.): —
Dividends
Yield: —
Payout: —
Market value ($ mil.): —

MARITZ HOLDINGS INC.

Maritz may not send your employees on business trips but it will motivate them to go. The company's mission is to understand enable and motivate people to unleash their hidden potential enabling people to do things differently by developing their strengths knowledge and confidence. The Steve Maritz-owned company designs employee incentive and reward programs (including incentive travel rewards) and customer loyalty programs. It also plans corporate trade shows and events and offers traditional market research services such as the creation of product launch campaigns. Its programs are designed to help its clients improve workforce quality and customer satisfaction.

HISTORY

Edward Maritz an entrepreneur of Swiss-French descent founded the E. Maritz Jewelry Manufacturing Company in St. Louis in 1894. By 1900 the wholesaler and manufacturer of men's and women's jewelry was supplying retail jewelers across the South and West. By 1921 Maritz had become a major importer of Swiss watches which it sold to retail jewelers under the Merit Cymrex and Record brands. In the 1920s the company added diamond jewelry and silverware to its product mix. Edward Maritz died in 1929.

To drum up new business during the Depression Edward's son James began trying to sell watches and jewelry to large corporations for use as sales and service awards pioneering the incentive market. The first sale for a nationwide employee incentive campaign was to Caradine Hat a St. Louis hatmaker in 1930. In 1948 Maritz handled a $2 million incentive program for Chevrolet.

In 1950 the Maritz family split the business into two operations. Brother Lloyd handled the jewelry business (it died in 1955 when Lloyd died); James took over the incentive operations which flourished. In the 1950s James expanded his company's offerings to include merchandise awards and in 1958 travel incentive awards (arranged through the newly acquired Holiday House Travel Center of Detroit). The enterprise adopted the corporate name Maritz Inc. in 1961. During the 1960s and early 1970s Maritz made a series of acquisitions closely allied with its motivation endeavors including Lee Creative Research the nucleus of what would become its market research operations (1973). The organization expanded internationally with the opening of Maritz offices in the UK and Mexico in 1974.

In 1980 the company acquired the Wilding division of Bell & Howell which it merged with another unit to form Maritz Communications Co. James died in 1981. Maritz beefed up its travel operations in the 1980s acquiring corporate travel agency Traveler's Service (St. Louis 1981) Byfield Travel (Chicago 1984) Beverly Hills Travel (Los Angeles 1986) and Travel Counselors International (Virginia 1986).

These acquisitions led to record sales in 1989 but sliding results in the early 1990s prompted the company to streamline its operations by cutting overlapping units. After a family boardroom tussle in 1993 William Maritz expanded his control by buying out his sister's 50% stake in the company and putting his two sons on the board. His son Stephen Maritz subsequently took over as president.

As part of its international expansion strategy Maritz acquired The Research Business Group the UK's largest independently owned marketing research firm (1993) and BLC the largest performance-improvement company in France (1994). In 1997 the company established an office in Manila its first in Asia.

In 1998 William Maritz stepped down as CEO and retained the title of chairman; his son Stephen succeeded him. In 1998 and 1999 the company boosted its international presence with acquisitions in Canada (group travel firm Partners in Performance marketing research firm Thompson Lightstone & Co.) and the Netherlands (Maritz B.V.).

Facing heat from online incentive programs the company launched its own online service e-Maritz in 2000. It also started Heybridge an e-commerce subsidiary that helps small and midsized businesses sell over the Internet. In 2001 Maritz purchased Librix Learning an online learning company.

The following year it purchased travel and incentive business McGettigan (later to be renamed Martiz McGettigan) to add depth to its client offerings. Also that same year Peter and Philip Maritz (brothers of chairman and CEO Steve Maritz) sued the company purportedly seeking a greater role in managing the family business. In the summer of 2003 the brothers again filed suit against Steve alleging that the purchase of McGettigan cost $10 million more than what was originally presented to the board. Peter and Philip's suits are an attempt to cash out of the family business –which they feel lost value because of the McGettigan purchase –at a better price than they'd get now.

In early 2004 Maritz sold its data collection unit Delve to St. Louis-based Bush O'Donnell Capital Partners. The same year Maritz sold its TQ3 Travel Solutions division to Carlson Wagonlit Travel.

Steve Maritz became the sole owner of the company in 2006 after buying out his other family members' shares.

Maritz also expanded its product offerings and geographic reach in 2008 when it acquired Cascade Promotion Corporation a marketing and fulfillment business operating out of Boston Las Vegas and St. Louis. With Cascade catering to the gaming and technology industries the buyout gave Maritz access to growing niche markets.

Making ground into what it considers a high-growth market Maritz solidified its position in the prepaid card sector in 2010 when it acquired full ownership of American Express Incentive Services (AEIS). For more than a decade AEIS operated as a joint venture between Maritz and a subsidiary of American Express. AEIS is an independent issuer of prepaid products such as cards and American Express Travelers Cheques on the American Express network. The products are used for employee recognition consumer promotions and sales incentives.

EXECUTIVES

Chairman and CEO, W. Stephen (Steve) Maritz, age 57
President and COO, Dennis Hummel
SVP and CIO, Gil Hoffman
CFO, Rick Ramos
Cams Chief Compliance Officer And Vice President Corporate Legal, Wendy Harp-lewis
Vice President Director, Mary McEuen
Vice President For Auto Research Group, Gary Eversole
Vp Public Relations And Corporate Communications, Beth Rusert
Corporate Vice President Senior Vice President M, John Luby
Senior Vice President Maritz Research Information Technology, Joe Ziegler
Vice President Technology, Alan Hunsaker
Vice President Sales And Marketing Services, Karen Korn
Vice President Sales, Jack Stiehr
Vice President Marketing, Ken Abendschein
Vice President Internal Audit, John Farley
Vice President Group Business Manager, Terry Erwin
Divisional Vice President Customer Operation, Valerie Reedy
Division Vice President Maritz Research, Lisa Weaner
Vice President Of Sales, Mark Alt
Vice President Of Finance And Assistant Treasurer, Matt Glazer
Vice President Of Business Development, Greg Bogue
Vice President, Alfredo Legorreta
Vice President Pharma Sector, Dave Caldwell
Vice President Of Sales And Marketing, Carrie Nolan
Vice President, Jim Payne
Vice President Awards, Jill Eichwald
Division Vice President Automotive Research Group Maritz Research, Dale Drerup
Divisional Vp Client Services, Beth Schelske
Vice President, Paula Schapp
Vp Sales, Jim Messina
Vice President Client Services, Michelle Ubell
Senior Vice President Chief Operating Officer, Chip Schafer
Division Vice President Research Services Retail And Technology Sector, Britt Robertson
Vice President Finance, Dan Sanders
Vice President, Dick O'Connor
Vice President Development Services, Julie Parent
Chairman and CEO, W. Stephen (Steve) Maritz, age 57
Assistant Treasurer, Thomas Sizemore
Treasurer, Cindy Dolan
Board Member, Ron Zika

LOCATIONS

HQ: MARITZ HOLDINGS INC.
1375 N HIGHWAY DR, FENTON, MO 630990001
Phone: 6368274000
Web: WWW.MARITZTRAVEL.COM

PRODUCTS/OPERATIONS

Selected Services

Marketing Research
- Custom marketing research
- Customer satisfaction and customer value analysis
- Data collection (focus groups telephone interviews)
- Maritz Polls and Maritz Research Reports
- Syndicated buyer research
- Telecommunications research

Performance Improvement
- Communications
- e-Learning
- Fulfillment
- Internet consulting
- Loyalty marketing
- Measurement and feedback
- Rewards and recognition

Travel
- Consulting services
- Corporate travel management
- Group travel services
- Travel award programs

COMPETITORS

Franklin Covey	J.D. Power
Gallup	JTB Corp.
GiftCertificates.com	Kantar Group
Harris Interactive	Motivcom
IMS Health	Nielsen
Information Resources Inc.	ORC International

HISTORICAL FINANCIALS

Company Type: Private

Income Statement FYE: March 31

	REVENUE ($ mil.)	NET INCOME ($ mil.)	NET PROFIT MARGIN	EMPLOYEES
03/14	1,218	113	9.3%	2,955
03/13	1,256	42	3.3%	—
03/12	1,155	47	4.1%	—
03/11	1,158	0	—	—
Annual Growth	1.7%	—	—	—

2014 Year-End Financials

Debt ratio: —
Return on equity: 9.30%
Cash ($ mil.): 116
Current ratio: 0.80
Long-term debt ($ mil.): —
Dividends
Yield: —
Payout: —
Market value ($ mil.): —

MARKET & JOHNSON INC.

EXECUTIVES

President and CEO, Dan R. Market
VP Finance, Steve Breitenfeldt
VP Operations, Donald (Don) Carlson
VP, Jerry Shea
CFO, Kevin Monson
Director Business Development, Jason Plante
Senior Project Manager, Matthew (Matt) Faulkner
Vice President Chief Operation Officer, Dan Adams
Director of Vertical Operations, Larry Dahl
Director of Operations, Joe Breid
CEO, Charles Grossklaus
Vice President, Dennis A. Olson
Auditors: WipfliUllrichBertelsonLLP

LOCATIONS

HQ: MARKET & JOHNSON INC.
2350 GALLOWAY ST, EAU CLAIRE, WI 547033441
Phone: 6087849651
Web: WWW.MARKET-JOHNSON.COM

COMPETITORS

Boldt	Hunzinger Construction
C. G. Schmidt	J.H. Findorff & Son
C.D. Smith	Tutor Perini
F.A. Wilhelm	Weis Builders
Hill International	
Hunt Construction	

HISTORICAL FINANCIALS

Company Type: Private

Income Statement FYE: December 31

	REVENUE ($ mil.)	NET INCOME ($ mil.)	NET PROFIT MARGIN	EMPLOYEES
12/13	104	4	4.8%	250
12/12	107	6	5.8%	—
12/11	84	1	1.8%	—
12/10	116	0	—	—
Annual Growth	(3.7%)	—	—	—

2013 Year-End Financials

Debt ratio: —
Return on equity: 4.80%
Cash ($ mil.): 5
Current ratio: 0.20
Long-term debt ($ mil.): —
Dividends
Yield: —
Payout: —
Market value ($ mil.): —

MARKET AMERICA INC.

Calling itself a cross between Amazon and QVC Market America is an Internet marketer and broker of products and services from a variety of categories including apparel beauty and personal care electronics entertainment nutrition and sports. Market America sells more than 2500 of its own branded products (such as Isotonix Motives and Snap) and spotlights the offerings of 3000 other retailers (including Sears Staples and Wal-Mart). In addition the company manages UnFranchise a network marketing business with more than 180000 independent shopping consultants. The company was founded in 1992 by president and CEO James "JR" Ridinger.

Geographic Reach

Based in North Carolina the company has a presence in several global markets including the US Canada Australia Hong Kong Taiwan the UK and Mexico. It's expanding into Latin America. Through its website Market America provides access to its brands to consumers in 200-plus countries.

Operations

Market America's independent shopping consultants operate under the company's UnFranchise business model also referred to as "one-to-one marketing." The UnFranchise platform comes complete with a business plan customizable Web portal merchandising materials and management system. To develop community relations consultants can provide online assistance to shoppers in their areas and recruit potential UnFranchise consultants. Consultants earn commissions when shoppers purchase products and services through their Market America shopping portals. In 2010 Market America opened its UnFranchise business model to nonprofits. The company said individuals following its business model have netted more than $2 billion in commissions and retail profits since it was established.

Strategy

Operating in seven global markets Market America looks to expand into Spain Colombia Costa Rica Ecuador and the Dominican Republic. It's working to extend the reach of its UnFranchise business model to Latino entrepreneurs. The move marks the company's largest expansion in its history.

To bolster its position in Internet retailing Market America has been expanding its operations outside the US. The company has international branches in Canada Australia Hong Kong Taiwan and the Philippines. It plans to extend its reach to the UK Mexico Latin America and other markets where it does not yet have a presence.

Mergers and Acquisitions

Market America acquired e-tailer SHOP.COM in late 2010 to blend its marketing and brokering expertise with SHOP.COM's strength in technology and merchandising. The result creates a "social shopping" movement capable of challenging some of the Internet's leading shopping destinations. As part of the deal the two firms agreed to operate their websites separately.

Financial Performance

Market America boasts more than $3.8 billion in accumulated retail sales and more than $2.2 billion in retail profit and commissions.

Ownership

Market America Inc. operates as a subsidiary of Market America Worldwide Inc.

EXECUTIVES

Senior Vice President, Loren Ashley Ridinger
Executive Vice President, Dennis Franks
Executive Vice President, Marty Weissman
Executive Vice President of International Development, Joe Bolyard
Vice President of One-To-One Marketing & Field Training, Kevin Buckman
Vice President of Communications, Anthony Akers
Public Relations Specialist, Mark Miller
Sr. Director of Marketing, Valerie Brown

Independent Chairman of the Board, Scott Booth
Chief Technology Officer, Eric Orme
Chief Executive Officer, Carrie Ferman
Chief Operating Officer; General Counsel; Corporate Secretary, Bradley Zimmer
Vice President of Human Resources, Beth Cox
Vice President of Operations, Brandi Quinn
Vice President of Sales, Jim Winkler
Chief Technology Officer, Michael Brady
Vice President of Internet Marketing, Steve Ashley
Vice President of Project Management, Eugene Wallace
Vice President of Research & Development, Sam Ritchie
Chief Financial Officer, Kirk Wall

LOCATIONS

HQ: MARKET AMERICA INC.
1302 PLEASANT RIDGE RD, GREENSBORO, NC 27409-9415
Phone: 336-605-0040
Web: WWW.MARKETAMERICA.COM

PRODUCTS/OPERATIONS

Selected Brands

Cellular Laboratories
Custom Cocktail
Fixx
Gene SNP DNA Analysis
Heart Health
Isotonix
MA Capital Resources
MA Webcenters
Matriskin
Motives
NutriClean
Pentaxyl
Pet Health
Prime
Royal Spa
Snap
Timeless Prescriptions
TLS Weight Loss Solution
Ultimate Aloe

Selected Product Categories

Anti-aging
Apparel jewelry and shoes
Automotive and tools
Baby products
Beauty products cosmetics
Books movies and video games
Cameras
Cell phones and communications
Computers
Consumer electronics
Crafts
Grocery
Health and nutrition
Home and Garden
Jewelry
Music
Party supplies
Pet supplies
Tickets
Toys

COMPETITORS

AMS Health Sciences
Amazon.com
Amway
Astral Brands
Avon
Buy.com
HSN
Mannatech
Melaleuca
NexTag
Overstock.com
PriceGrabber.com
QVC
Shaklee
Shopzilla
USANA Health Sciences
ViSalus
Yahoo!
eBay

HISTORICAL FINANCIALS

Company Type: Private

Income Statement FYE: December 31

	REVENUE ($ mil.)	NET INCOME ($ mil.)	NET PROFIT MARGIN	EMPLOYEES
12/09	224	15	7.0%	650
12/08	228	3	1.5%	—
12/08	218	0	0.0%	—
Annual Growth	3.0%	112585779%	—	—

2009 Year-End Financials

Debt ratio: —
Return on equity: 7.00%
Cash ($ mil.): 55
Current ratio: 4.10
Long-term debt ($ mil.): —
Dividends
Yield: —
Payout: —
Market value ($ mil.): —

MARQUETTE UNIVERSITY

EXECUTIVES

Opus Dean College of Engineering, Stanley V. Jaskolski
Chairman, Charles M. (Chuck) Swoboda, age 47
Vice Chairman, John F. Ferraro
interim President of Marquette University, Rev Robert A. Wild
SVP, Gregory J. (Greg) Kliebhan
President, Rev Scott R. Pilarz
Vice President for Public Affairs, Rana H. Altenburg
VP and General Counsel, Cynthia M. Bauer
VP Finance, John C. Lamb
Executive Director University Mission and Identity, Stephanie Russell
Vice President for Administration, Arthur F. Scheuber
VP University Advancement, Julie Tolan
Secretary and Assistant to the President, Steven W. Frieder
Vice Provost Undergraduate Programs and Teaching, Margaret L. Bloom
Vice Provost Research and Dean Graduate School, William R. Wiener
Dean University Libraries, Janice S. Welburn
VP Marketing and Communications, Tricia Geraghty
Provost, John J. Pauly
Dean Admissions and Enrollment Planning, Roby Blust
Dean College of Nursing and Interim Provost, Margaret Faut Callahan
Dean College of Health Sciences, William E. Cullinan
Dean College of Professional Studies, Robert J. Deahl
Dean College of Education, William A. Henk
Dean Law School, Joseph D. Kearney
Dean School of Dentistry, William K. Lobb
VP Student Affairs, L. Christopher Miller
Senior Associate Vice President, Anne O'Brien
Dean Graduate School, Jeanne Hossenlopp
Dean James H. Keyes College of Business Administration, Linda M. Salchenberger
Interim Dean J. William and Mary Diederich College of Communication, Lynn H. Turner
Director University Communication, Brigid O'Brien Miller
Senior Director University Communication, Mary Pat Pfeil
Vice Provost Undergraduate Programs and Teaching, Gary Meyer
Secretary, Ethel Woods
Secretary, Mary Jennings
Secretary, Jane Hanley
Secretary, Judith Koerner
Vice President of Human Resources, Cas Castro
Senior Vice President Chief Administrative Officer, Kristine Rappe
EVP, Mary DiStanislao
VP Marketing and Communication, Dave Murphy
Dean Diederich College of Communication, Lori Bergen
Dean College of Engineering, Robert H. Bishop
Dean Klingler College of Arts and Sciences, Richard C. Holz
Associate Vice President, Daniel S. Hendrickson
Vice President of Planning and University Architect, Thomas P. Ganey
Senior Vice President Fidelity Investments, Alfred C. McGuire
Auditors: Deloitte&ToucheLLP

LOCATIONS

HQ: MARQUETTE UNIVERSITY
1250 W WISCONSIN AVE, MILWAUKEE, WI 532332225
Phone: 4142887223
Web: WWW.MARQUETTE.EDU

PRODUCTS/OPERATIONS

Selected Schools and Colleges

College of Business Administration
College of Education
College of Engineering
College of Health Sciences
College of Nursing
College of Professional Studies
Graduate School
Graduate School of Management
Helen Way Klingler College of Arts and Sciences
J. William and Mary Diederich College of Communications
Law School
School of Dentistry

HISTORICAL FINANCIALS

Company Type: Private

Income Statement FYE: June 30

	REVENUE ($ mil.)	NET INCOME ($ mil.)	NET PROFIT MARGIN	EMPLOYEES
06/13	391	37	9.5%	3,000
06/12	385	9	2.4%	—
06/11	383	90	23.7%	—
06/10	449	0	—	—
Annual Growth	(4.5%)	—	—	—

2013 Year-End Financials

Debt ratio: —
Return on equity: 9.50%
Cash ($ mil.): 41
Current ratio: —
Long-term debt ($ mil.): —
Dividends
Yield: —
Payout: —
Market value ($ mil.): —

MARS SUPER MARKETS INC

EXECUTIVES

President, Carmen V. D'Anna Jr.
VP and CFO, Phil Hanlon
EVP and Secretary, Christopher P. (Chris) D'Anna
EVP, Theodore (Teddy) D'Anna
Director Information Technology Services, Jeffrey Nassner
Controller, Jerry Seuell

LOCATIONS

HQ: MARS SUPER MARKETS INC
9627 PHILADELPHIA RD, BALTIMORE, MD 212374154
Phone: 4105900500
Web: WWW.MARSFOOD.COM

COMPETITORS

7-Eleven
ALDI
Acme Markets
Costco Wholesale
Food Lion
Giant Food
SUPERVALU
Safeway
Shoppers Food Warehouse
Wal-Mart
Weis Markets

HISTORICAL FINANCIALS

Company Type: Private

Income Statement FYE: December 26

	REVENUE ($ mil.)	NET INCOME ($ mil.)	NET PROFIT MARGIN	EMPLOYEES
12/09	280	6	2.3%	1,700
12/06	300	11	3.8%	—
12/05	267	14	5.3%	—
12/04	0	0	—	—
Annual Growth	—	—	—	—

2009 Year-End Financials

Debt ratio: —
Return on equity: 2.30%
Cash ($ mil.): 25
Current ratio: 1.40
Long-term debt ($ mil.): —
Dividends
Yield: —
Payout: —
Market value ($ mil.): —

MARSHALL UNIVERSITY

If "You Are Marshall" you know that Marshall University is a state-supported non-profit educational institution serving about 14000 students including 3500 graduate and medical students. The university offers about 55 baccalaureate and more than 50 graduate programs through more than a dozen colleges and schools. It also offers two Associate Programs two Ed.S four Doctoral Degree Programs and three First Professional programs. Marshall students attend classes either at the university's main campus in Huntington West Virginia; at its regional campuses; or online.

Geographic Reach

Marshall has locations in Huntington West Virginia (its main campus) as well as in South Charleston Campus Mid-Ohio Valley Center Teays Valley Center and Beckley Center. The university enrolls students from all counties in West Virginia 46 US states and the District of Columbia as well as from about 50 countries worldwide.

Operations

The university enrolls about 19% of the students from out of state. It has an undergraduate student/faculty ratio of 19:1 and the average class size is 23.

Financial Performance

Marshall reported flat revenues in fiscal year 2013 as an increase in revenues from students tuition and fees interest on loans receivables and sales and services of educational activities was partially offset by lower revenues from federal contracts and grants and from auxiliary enterprises.Net income increased by 38% in fiscal year 2013 due to a decline in operating expenses and higher investment income.

Strategy

In 2013 the university expanded its program portfolio with the introduction of master's degree in public administration and a bachelor of science degree in medical imaging with an emphasis in diagnostic medical sonography. That year Marshall continued building its $50 million new engineering complex on the Huntington campus as part of its strategy to upgrade facilities on its main campus.

Company Background

Named for former Chief Justice John Marshall the university was established in 1837. The 2006 movie "We Are Marshall" dramatizes the aftermath of the 1970 plane crash that killed most of Marshall's Thundering Herd football team.

EXECUTIVES

Director Alumni Development Services, Debra Elliotte
Director Human Resources Services, James R. (Jim) Stephens
Director Residence Services, Winston A. Baker
SVP Information Technology and CIO, Jan I. Fox
SVP Academic Affairs and Provost, Sarah N. Denman
President, Stephen J. Kopp
SVP Executive Affairs and General Counsel, Layton Cottrill
Assistant VP Administration, Karen Kirtley
Business Manager, Jim Hodges
Head, Jim Schroer
Auditors: Deloitte&ToucheLLP

LOCATIONS

HQ: MARSHALL UNIVERSITY
1 JOHN MARSHALL DR, HUNTINGTON, WV 25755-0003
Phone: 304-696-2385
Web: WWW.MARSHALL.EDU

PRODUCTS/OPERATIONS

Selected Colleges and Schools

College of Business
College of Education and Human Services
College of Fine Arts
College of Health Professionals
College of Information Technology and Engineering
College of Liberal Arts
College of Science
Community and Technical College
Graduate College
School of Extended Education
School of Journalism and Mass Communications
School of Medicine
University College

HISTORICAL FINANCIALS

Company Type: Private

Income Statement FYE: June 30

	REVENUE ($ mil.)	NET INCOME ($ mil.)	NET PROFIT MARGIN	EMPLOYEES
06/12	175	19	11.1%	1,632
06/08	172	25	15.0%	—
06/07	163	23	14.3%	—
06/06	60	44	72.5%	—
Annual Growth	19.3%	(12.8%)	—	—

2012 Year-End Financials

Debt ratio: —
Return on equity: 11.10%
Cash ($ mil.): 101
Current ratio: 2.90
Long-term debt ($ mil.): —
Dividends
Yield: —
Payout: —
Market value ($ mil.): —

MARTIN & BAYLEY INC.

EXECUTIVES

Vice Chairman, Charles Martin
Chairman, Mark Bayley
Chairman Emeritus, Frank Bayley
CEO, Todd Jenney
Vice Chairman, Charles Martin
Chairman Emeritus, Frank Bayley

LOCATIONS

HQ: MARTIN & BAYLEY INC.
1311A W MAIN ST, CARMI, IL 628211389
Phone: 6183822334
Web: WWW.MARTINANDBAYLEY.COM

PRODUCTS/OPERATIONS

2013 Stores

Illinois	55
Kentucky	18
Tennessee	2

Selected Product Lines

Godfathers Pizza
5 Buck Huck
Bigg Swigg
Coffee
Deli Express
Fresh Brewed Ice Tea
Hot to Go at Huck' s
Sweet Street

COMPETITORS

7-Eleven
Casey' s General Stores
Chevron
Couche-Tard
Exxon Mobil
Krause Gentle
TravelCenters of America

HISTORICAL FINANCIALS

Company Type: Private

Income Statement FYE: March 29

	REVENUE ($ mil.)	NET INCOME ($ mil.)	NET PROFIT MARGIN	EMPLOYEES
03/11	528	7	1.4%	1,500
03/10	466	5	1.1%	—
03/09	1,579	0	—	—
Annual Growth	—12031.5%		—	—

2011 Year-End Financials

Debt ratio: —
Return on equity: 1.40%
Cash ($ mil.): 13
Current ratio: 0.50
Long-term debt ($ mil.): —
Dividends
Yield: —
Payout: —
Market value ($ mil.): —

MARTIN"S POINT HEALTH CARE INC.

LOCATIONS

HQ: MARTIN' ' S POINT HEALTH CARE INC.
331 VERANDA ST STE 1, PORTLAND, ME 041035544
Phone: 2078282402
Web: WWW.MARTINSPOINT.ORG

HISTORICAL FINANCIALS

Company Type: Private

Income Statement FYE: December 31

	REVENUE ($ mil.)	NET INCOME ($ mil.)	NET PROFIT MARGIN	EMPLOYEES
12/13	489	10	2.1%	729
12/09	267	30	11.3%	—
12/07	200	42	21.0%	—
12/06	168	0	—	—
Annual Growth	16.4%	—	—	—

2013 Year-End Financials

Debt ratio: —
Return on equity: 2.10%
Cash ($ mil.): 68
Current ratio: 1.10
Long-term debt ($ mil.): —
Dividends
Yield: —
Payout: —
Market value ($ mil.): —

MARVIN ENGINEERING CO. INC.

EXECUTIVES

President, Howard Gussman
President Geotest (Marvin Test Systems), Steve Sargeant
President Aerospace Dynamics International, John Cave
Chairman and CEO, Jerry Friedman
President Flyer Defense LLC, Oded Nechustan

LOCATIONS

HQ: MARVIN ENGINEERING CO. INC.
261 W BEACH AVE, INGLEWOOD, CA 903022904
Phone: 3106745030
Web: WWW.MARVINGROUP.COM

PRODUCTS/OPERATIONS

Selected Products

Ejector racks
Launchers
  Air-to-air missile launchers
  Air-to-ground missile launchers
Machined components
Power supplies
Pylons

Selected Services

Assembly
  Cable Assemblies
  Digital Tray Assemblies
  Electro-Hydraulic
  Electro-Mechanical
  Electronic and Electrical
  Firing Lanyards
  Mechanical
  Printed Circuit Boards
  Wire Harnesses (Striping and Automatic Lead Forming)
Environmental Testing
  Burst and Leak
  Continuity
  DWV
  Electrical
  Electronic
  Gas Chromatograph
  Humidity and Salt Fog
  IR
  Live Fire
  Temperature and Altitude
  Vibration
Machining
  Axis high-speed machining
  N/C /turning
  Vertical and horizontal
Miscellaneous Capabilities
  Electron Beam Welding
  MIG TIG and Heli-Arc
  Wave Soldering
  Welding
NC Programming Systems
  AutoCAD
  CATIA
  Pro-Engineer
  Vericut

COMPETITORS

American Pacific
BAE SYSTEMS
Boeing
Breeze-Eastern
CIC International
GenCorp
General Dynamics
Kaman
Lockheed Martin Missiles
MBDA
Northrop Grumman
RUAG Holding

HISTORICAL FINANCIALS

Company Type: Private

Income Statement FYE: January 31

	REVENUE ($ mil.)	NET INCOME ($ mil.)	NET PROFIT MARGIN	EMPLOYEES
01/09	133	(3)	—	700
01/08	105	0	0.6%	—
01/07	205	0	0.0%	—
Annual Growth	(19.3%)	—	—	—

2009 Year-End Financials

Debt ratio: —
Return on equity: (-2.60%)
Cash ($ mil.): 12
Current ratio: 0.40
Long-term debt ($ mil.): —
Dividends
Yield: —
Payout: —
Market value ($ mil.): —

MARYLAND AND VIRGINIA MILK PRODUCERS COOPERATIVE ASSOCIATION INC

Milk is "Mar-VA-lous" for the members of the Maryland & Virginia Milk Producers Cooperative Association. Known as Maryland & Virginia the co-op processes and sells milk for nearly 1500 member/farmers with dairy herds in the southeastern US and mid-Atlantic region. Maryland & Virginia produces fluid milk ice cream and cultured dairy products for retail sale under the Marva Maid Maola and Valley Milk brands. Its butter condensed milk and milk-powder products are sold primarily to food manufacturers. As a co-op it also offers agricultural supplies to its members. Maryland & Virginia operates three fluid-milk processing plants a manufacturing plant and an equipment-supply warehouse.

Geographic Reach

The co-op gets its milk from member farmers in Delaware Florida Georgia Kentucky Maryland North Carolina Ohio Pennsylvania South Carolina Tennessee Virginia and West Virginia. Its fluid processing plants are located in Newport News Virginia; Landover Maryland; and New Bern North Carolina. It has manufacturing facilities in Laurel Maryland and Strasburg Virginia and a warehouse in Frederick Maryland.

Operations

Maryland & Virginia operates three fluid processing plants a single manufacturing plant and a farm supply equipment division. It also owns a majority stake in Valley Milk LLC. The co-op transports more than 300 tanker truckloads of milk daily to nearly 30 different plants. Member farms range in size from fewer than 100 cows to more than 2000. Combined Maryland & Virginia members produce three billion pounds of milk annually.

Sales and Marketing

In addition to supermarkets the co-op counts customers such as Walgreens Starbucks Sheetz convenience stores and Dairy Queen among its customers.

Financial Performance

The co-op's revenue decreased by 5% to $1.3 billion in 2012 versus $1.4 billion in 2011 due to a decline in milk dairy and other products as well as sales of equipment and supplies partially offset by an increase in sales of its members' and nonmembers' raw milk. Despite the decline in sales the Maryland & Virginia reported a profit of $5.5 million in 2012 versus a loss of $2.8 million the prior year. Like other milk producers Maryland & Virginia has been contending with sluggish milk sales due to decreasing milk consumption beginning in the 1970s.

EXECUTIVES

Vice President Engineering And Technical Support, Grant Gayman
Board Member Vice President, Richard C Mosemann
Board Member, Rodney Carson
Board Member, Samuel G Tressler
Board Member, Robert Gammon
Board Member, Steve Mellott
Board Member, W W Sanford

Board Member, David Graves
Board Of Directors, Carolina Virginia

LOCATIONS

HQ: MARYLAND AND VIRGINIA MILK PRODUCERS COOPERATIVE ASSOCIATION INC
1985 ISAAC NEWTON SQ W # 200, RESTON, VA 201905031
Phone: 7037426800
Web: WWW.MDVAMILK.COM

COMPETITORS

Associated Milk Producers
Dairy Farmers of America
Dairy Manufacturers
Dairylea
Dean Foods
Foremost Farms
Land O' Lakes

HISTORICAL FINANCIALS

Company Type: Private

Income Statement FYE: December 31

	REVENUE ($ mil.)	NET INCOME ($ mil.)	NET PROFIT MARGIN	EMPLOYEES
12/13	1,372	5	0.4%	550
12/12	1,296	5	0.4%	—
12/11	1,362	(2)	—	—
12/10	1,219	0	—	—
Annual Growth	4.0%	—	—	—

2013 Year-End Financials

Debt ratio: —
Return on equity: 0.40%
Cash ($ mil.): 0
Current ratio: 0.90
Long-term debt ($ mil.): —
Dividends
Yield: —
Payout: —
Market value ($ mil.): —

MARYLAND SOUTHERN ELECTRIC COOPERATIVE INC

EXECUTIVES

President and CEO, Austin J. Slater Jr.
SVP Information and Customer Services; CIO, Joseph Trentacosta
SVP Engineering and Operations; COO, Kenneth Capps
Chairman, Joseph V. (Joe) Stone Jr.
Secretary Treasurer and Director, Kenneth L. (Kenny) Dyson
Vice Chairman, Samuel J. (Jack) Hammett
SVP Financial Economic and Employee Services; CFO, Sonja M. Cox
Secretary Treasurer and Director, Kenneth L. (Kenny) Dyson

LOCATIONS

HQ: MARYLAND SOUTHERN ELECTRIC COOPERATIVE INC
15035 BURNT STORE RD, HUGHESVILLE, MD 206372699
Phone: 3012743111
Web: WWW.SMECO.COM

PRODUCTS/OPERATIONS

2012 Sales

Residential	66
Transmission	1
Street lights	1

HISTORICAL FINANCIALS

Company Type: Private

Income Statement FYE: December 31

	REVENUE ($ mil.)	NET INCOME ($ mil.)	NET PROFIT MARGIN	EMPLOYEES
12/10	492	17	3.5%	375
12/09	462	3	0.7%	—
12/08	2,121	0	0.0%	—
Annual Growth	(51.8%)	17166.9%	—	—

2010 Year-End Financials

Debt ratio: —
Return on equity: 3.50%
Cash ($ mil.): 9
Current ratio: 0.50
Long-term debt ($ mil.): —
Dividends
Yield: —
Payout: —
Market value ($ mil.): —

MASSACHUSETTS HIGHER EDUCATION ASSISTANCE CORPORATION

EXECUTIVES

President CEO, Paul Combe
EXECUTIVE Vice President COO, Michael Finn
VP Lender and School Services, Susan Nathan
VP Strategic Services, Shelley Saunders
VP Business Development, Debra Chromy
VP Human Resources, Lauren Rolfe
VP Borrower Services, Michael Ryan
Auditors: GrantThorntonLLP

LOCATIONS

HQ: MASSACHUSETTS HIGHER EDUCATION ASSISTANCE CORPORATION
100 CAMBRIDGE ST STE 1600, BOSTON, MA 021142518
Phone: 6177284507
Web: WWW.ASA.ORG

COMPETITORS

Access Group
Bank of America
Discover
First Marblehead
JPMorgan Chase
Nelnet
Pennsylvania Higher Education Assistance Agency
Sallie Mae

HISTORICAL FINANCIALS

Company Type: Private

Income Statement FYE: June 30

	ASSETS ($ mil.)	NET INCOME ($ mil.)	INCOME AS % OF ASSETS	EMPLOYEES
06/13	375	48	12.9%	580
06/10	170	34	20.0%	—
06/09	148	0	—	—
06/08	19	0	—	—
Annual Growth	80.3%	—	—	—

2013 Year-End Financials

Debt ratio: —
Return on equity: —
Cash ($ mil.): 111
Current ratio: 8.30
Long-term debt ($ mil.): —
Dividends
Yield: —
Payout: —
Market value ($ mil.): —

MASSACHUSETTS PORT AUTHORITY

Massachusetts Port Authority (Massport) operates three airports: Boston Logan International Hanscom Field and Worcester Regional. Logan is home to 50 airlines and is New England's largest airport and the first port of call for many international flights entering the US. (It accounts for the majority of Massport's revenues.) Hanscom Field operates as the region's main aviation airport and offers niche commercial services while Worcester Regional primarily supports commercial flight services. Massport also oversees various waterfront properties of the Port of Boston. The agency was created by the Commonwealth of Massachusetts in 1956. The governor of Massachusetts appoints the agency's board members.

Operations

Massport's business consists of two distinct operating departments: Aviation and the Port. Logan airport catered to 29.4 million aviation passengers and 369000 cruise passengers in 2013. Its shipping operations serviced more than 110000 containers of products at its port.

Financial Performance

Massport's net revenues have steadily climbed over the years. Revenues jumped 2% from $1.78 billion in 2012 to $1.83 billion in 2013 thanks mainly to parking concession ground services and other revenue from nearly 125000 more passengers at Logan. The overall revenue increase for 2013 was generated by operating revenues exceeding operating expenses by $2.4 million.

EXECUTIVES

CEO and Executive Director, Thomas J. (Tom) Kinton
CIO, Francis X. Anglin
CFO, John Pranckevicius
Chairman, Richard Davey
Auditors: PricewaterhouseCoopersLLP

LOCATIONS

HQ: MASSACHUSETTS PORT AUTHORITY
1 HARBORSIDE DR STE 200S, BOSTON, MA 021282905
Phone: 6175611600
Web: WWW.MASSPORT.COM

2011 Sales

	$ mil.	% of total
% of total		
Airports		
Logan		85
Hanscom		2
Worcester		-
Maritime		9
Maritime real		4
Total		100

HISTORICAL FINANCIALS

Company Type: Private

Income Statement FYE: June 30

	REVENUE ($ mil.)	NET INCOME ($ mil.)	NET PROFIT MARGIN	EMPLOYEES
06/07	526	49	9.3%	1,102
06/06*	497	74	15.0%	—
12/05	0	0	11.5%	—
06/04	414	0	—	—
Annual Growth	8.3%	—	—	—

*Fiscal year change

2007 Year-End Financials

Debt ratio: —
Return on equity: 9.30%
Cash ($ mil.): 71
Current ratio: 0.40
Long-term debt ($ mil.): —
Dividends
Yield: —
Payout: —
Market value ($ mil.): —

MATTINGLY FOODS INC.

LOCATIONS

HQ: MATTINGLY FOODS INC.
302 STATE ST, ZANESVILLE, OH 437013200
Phone: 7404540136
Web: WWW.MATTINGLYCASHNCARRY.COM

COMPETITORS

Dot Foods
Edward Don
Ellenbee-Leggett
Gordon Food Service
I Supply
Meadowbrook Meat Company
Performance Food
Reinhart FoodService
Sysco
US Foods
Van Eerden

HISTORICAL FINANCIALS

Company Type: Private

Income Statement FYE: December 29

	REVENUE ($ mil.)	NET INCOME ($ mil.)	NET PROFIT MARGIN	EMPLOYEES
12/07	263	1	0.4%	240
12/06	290	1	0.4%	—
12/05	301	3	1.0%	—
12/04	309	0	—	—
Annual Growth	(5.2%)	—	—	—

2007 Year-End Financials

Debt ratio: —
Return on equity: 0.40%
Cash ($ mil.): 0
Current ratio: 0.70
Long-term debt ($ mil.): —
Dividends
Yield: —
Payout: —
Market value ($ mil.): —

MAVERICK FUNDING CORP.

LOCATIONS

HQ: MAVERICK FUNDING CORP.
1160 PARSIPPANY BLVD # 200, PARSIPPANY, NJ 070541811
Phone: 9735856099
Web: WWW.MAVERICKWHOLESALE.COM

HISTORICAL FINANCIALS

Company Type: Private

Income Statement FYE: December 31

	ASSETS ($ mil.)	NET INCOME ($ mil.)	INCOME AS % OF ASSETS	EMPLOYEES
12/13	94	1	1.5%	98
12/12	126	12	10.2%	—
12/11*	50	1	2.7%	—
09/10	40	0	—	—
Annual Growth	33.2%	—	—	—

*Fiscal year change

MAXIM HEALTHCARE SERVICES INC.

Good health as the maxim goes is one of life's greatest blessings and Maxim Healthcare Services aims to promote that principle by offering medical staffing and home health care as well as immunizations and other wellness services to clients nationwide. The company provides medical and administrative personnel for hospitals school systems nursing homes and correctional facilities. The company's staffing division offers contract per diem and travel assignments. Maxim Healthcare's consultants are available 24 hours a day seven days a week to provide assistance for clients. The company which operates from more than 360 locations nationwide was established in 1988.

Operations

The company's Maxim Health Systems division established in 1996 provides immunizations health screenings and health fairs. Each year the division's immunization program is responsible for vaccinating millions of people across more than 40000 clinics.

Other major Maxim Healthcare divisions include Maxim Staffing Solutions (Nurse Allied Health and Administrative Staffing) Maxim Government Services Maxim Physician Resources Timeline Recruiting Maxim Coders Maxim Pediatric Services; Logix Healthcare Search Partners and StaffAssist.

EXECUTIVES

VP and Chief Culture Officer, Timothy (Tim) Kuhn
CIO, Kevin Apperson
CFO, William J. (Bill) Butz
COO Maxim Staffing Solutions, Chris Powell
CEO, W. Bradley (Brad) Bennett
VP and COO, Paula Sotir
VP Chief Medical Officer and Chief Quality Officer, W. John Langley
VP and Chief Compliance Officer, Jacqueline (Jackie) Baratian
Vice President of Compliance, Shane Campbell

LOCATIONS

HQ: MAXIM HEALTHCARE SERVICES INC.
7227 LEE DEFOREST DR, COLUMBIA, MD 21046-3236
Phone: 410-910-1500
Web: WWW.MAXIMHEALTHCARE.COM

PRODUCTS/OPERATIONS

Selected Services

Allied Health staffing
Facility nurse staffing
Flu and wellness services
Government services
Health information services
International nursing
Home healthcare
HME/pharmacy services
Habilitation services
Physician services
Travel nursing

Selected Divisions

CareFocus
CareFocus Companion Services
Centrus Premier Homecare
Logix Healthcare Search Partners
Maxim Coders
Maxim Government Services
Maxim Health Information Services
Maxim Health Systems
Maxim Healthcare Services (Homecare)
Maxim Home Health Resources
Maxim Pediatric Services
Maxim Physician Resources
Maxim Staffing Solutions - Administrative Staffing
Maxim Staffing Solutions - Allied Health
Maxim Staffing Solutions - Nurse Staffing
Orbis Clinical
Reflectx Services
StaffAssist
TimeLine Recruiting
TravelMax

COMPETITORS

American HomePatient
Apria Healthcare
Cross Country Healthcare
MedStaff
Medical Staffing Network
Medsearch Staffing Services
PHS Correctional Healthcare
Team Health
TeamStaff

HISTORICAL FINANCIALS

Company Type: Private

Income Statement FYE: December 31

	REVENUE ($ mil.)	NET INCOME ($ mil.)	NET PROFIT MARGIN	EMPLOYEES
12/12	1,241	(21)	—	35,000
12/11	1,341	(12)	—	—
12/09	1,390	51	3.7%	—
12/09	1,369	(62)	—	—
Annual Growth	(3.2%)	—	—	—

2012 Year-End Financials

Debt ratio: —
Return on equity: (-1.80%)
Cash ($ mil.): 6
Current ratio: 1.60
Long-term debt ($ mil.): —
Dividends
Yield: —
Payout: —
Market value ($ mil.): —

MAXOR NATIONAL PHARMACY SERVICES CORPORATION

Maxor National Pharmacy Services provides health care and pharmacy services including retail and mail order prescriptions (Maxor Pharmacies) pharmacy benefits management (MaxorPlus) pharmacy consulting (Maxor Pharmacy Consulting Services) and infusion and injection services (IV-Solutions). The company operates about a dozen Maxor Pharmacy stores mostly in Texas and Washington but also in Colorado and New York. Its correctional division provides services to more than 330000 offenders in more than 250 correctional facilities in 26 states through direct management contracts or via its pharmacy services division. Founded in 1926 as a single pharmacy in Amarillo Maxor put itself up for sale in 2013.

Change in Company Type

Privately-owned Maxor put itself up for sale seeking a private equity buyer in July 2013. Maxor's chairman and primary shareholder is looking to cash out of part of his investment and is seeking additional capital to grow the company.

Geographic Reach

Amarillo Texas-based Maxor has regional offices in Colorado Maryland New York Washington and South Texas. The company's drugstores are located in Texas New York Colorado and Washington. The firm also operates in Puerto Rico.

Operations

The company expanded its geographic and customer reach in 2011 when its Maxor Correctional Pharmacy Services business was awarded a contract worth $110 million over three years from the Michigan Department of Corrections. The contract guarantees that Maxor will provide pharmacy services for some 43000 prisoners at 31 correctional facilities and two residential facilities.

Maxor's specialty pharmacy business is growing. In mid-2013 the unit announced that the Jackson Health System (JHS) introduced its specialty pharmacy to patients employees and their families. Maxor currently manages five pharmacies for JHS in Miami-Dade County.

Strategy

Maxor sees great potential for its PickPoint technology division to expand in Puerto Rico over the next five years with the aim of becoming the dominant pharmacy solution there.

Mergers and Acquisitions

The company acquired California-based PickPoint Corp. in 2011 to expand its technology services offering. PickPoint designs manufactures and distributes software that improves the accuracy safety and efficiency of medication delivery. Its Will Call System uses an LED light-guided system to easily identify prescription hangers via wireless technology.

Ownership

Maxor's primary shareholder is its chairman Jerry Hodge.

EXECUTIVES

Chairman, Jerry H. Hodge
President, Carl Birdsong
EVP MaxorPlus, Steve Smith
CFO, Jerry Havard
Executive Director Correctional Pharmacy Services, Deleca Reynolds-Barnes
VP Operations, Angela Serio Harney
Vice President of Marketing and Sales, Heath Hodge
VP Marketing and Sales, John Fabrizio
VP Operations IV Solutions, Jan Robinson
Vice President Mail Service Pharmacy, Rick Pollard
SVP Correctional Services, James (Jim) Riley
CEO, John Ward
VP Correctional Administration, Allen Sapp
VP Mail Service Pharmacy, Andrew Campbell
Vice President of Contract Administration, Angela Harney

LOCATIONS

HQ: MAXOR NATIONAL PHARMACY SERVICES CORPORATION
320 S POLK ST STE 100, AMARILLO, TX 79101-1436
Phone: 806-324-5400
Web: WWW.MAXOR.COM

PRODUCTS/OPERATIONS

Selected Operations

IV Solutions (infusion therapy services)
Maxor Administrative Services (employee benefits)
Maxor Pharmacies (retail pharmacies)
MaxorPlus (pharmacy benefit management)
Maxor Specialty (specialty pharmaceuticals infusion therapy services chronic injectables)
PickPoint (pharmacy technology products)

COMPETITORS

CVS Caremark
H-E-B
Rite Aid
Wal-Mart
Walgreen

HISTORICAL FINANCIALS

Company Type: Private

Income Statement FYE: December 31

	REVENUE ($ mil.)	NET INCOME ($ mil.)	NET PROFIT MARGIN	EMPLOYEES
12/09	223	0	—	481
12/07	176	0	—	—
12/06	0	0	—	—
12/05	118	0	—	—
Annual Growth	17.2%	—	—	—

2009 Year-End Financials

Debt ratio: —
Return on equity: —
Cash ($ mil.): 8
Current ratio: 1.70
Long-term debt ($ mil.): —
Dividends
Yield: —
Payout: —
Market value ($ mil.): —

MAXYIELD COOPERATIVE

LOCATIONS

HQ: MAXYIELD COOPERATIVE
313 3RD AVE NW, WEST BEND, IA 505978572
Phone: 5158877211
Web: WWW.MAXYIELDCOOPERATIVE.COM

HISTORICAL FINANCIALS

Company Type: Private

Income Statement FYE: July 31

	REVENUE ($ mil.)	NET INCOME ($ mil.)	NET PROFIT MARGIN	EMPLOYEES
07/14	324	5	1.7%	157
07/13	372	7	2.1%	—
07/12	387	6	1.8%	—
07/11	241	0	—	—
Annual Growth	10.4%	—	—	—

2014 Year-End Financials

Debt ratio: —
Return on equity: 1.70%
Cash ($ mil.): 26
Current ratio: 0.80
Long-term debt ($ mil.): —
Dividends
Yield: —
Payout: —
Market value ($ mil.): —

MAYER ELECTRIC SUPPLY COMPANY INC.

EXECUTIVES

Chairman Emeritus, Charles A. Collat Sr.
CFO, David L. Morgan
Chairman and CEO, Nancy Collat Goedecke
President, Wes Smith
EVP Sales and Marketing, Glenn Goedecke
Vice Chairman, Jim Summerlin
Chairman and CEO, Nancy Collat Goedecke

LOCATIONS

HQ: MAYER ELECTRIC SUPPLY COMPANY INC.
3405 4TH AVE S, BIRMINGHAM, AL 352222300
Phone: 2055833500
Web: WWW.MAYERELECTRIC.COM

PRODUCTS/OPERATIONS

Selected Services

Basic distributor services
Construction partner
Maintenance repair and operations

Selected Products

Ballasts
Batteries
Cable and wire
Circuit breakers
Conduit
Factory automation products
Fan boxes
Fasteners
Fuses
LED lighting systems
Lenses
Lighting fixtures
Locks
Low-voltage lighting systems
Meters
Motors
Panelboards
Power supplies
Relays
Switches
Surge protection devices
Terminal blocks
Tools
Transformers
Voltage regulators

COMPETITORS

Anixter International
Consolidated Electrical
Crescent Electric Supply
Gexpro
Graybar Electric
Independent Electric Supply
Rexel Inc.
W.W. Grainger
WESCO International
Wholesale Supply Group

HISTORICAL FINANCIALS

Company Type: Private

Income Statement FYE: December 28

	REVENUE ($ mil.)	NET INCOME ($ mil.)	NET PROFIT MARGIN	EMPLOYEES
12/13	672	6	1.0%	900
12/12	606	6	1.1%	—
12/11*	623	7	1.2%	—
01/11	565	0	—	—
Annual Growth	6.0%	—	—	—

*Fiscal year change

2013 Year-End Financials

Debt ratio: —
Return on equity: 1.00%
Cash ($ mil.): 2
Current ratio: 1.70
Long-term debt ($ mil.): —
Dividends
Yield: —
Payout: —
Market value ($ mil.): —

MAYVILLE ENGINEERING CO INC

EXECUTIVES

Chairman President and CEO, Robert Kamphuis
Director Sales and Marketing, Jim Sokoly

Manager Estimating, Rick Hartwig
Manager New Product Development, Tom Williams
VP Operations, Doug Smith
Director Information Services, Brian Post
VP Administration, Barry Hoops
Benefits Coordinator, Marleen Lechner
Controller, Glenn Helmbrecht
Regional Vice President, Don Barbos
VP-Admin, Barry Hoopes

LOCATIONS

HQ: MAYVILLE ENGINEERING CO INC
715 SOUTH ST, MAYVILLE, WI 530501823
Phone: 9203874500

PRODUCTS/OPERATIONS

Selected Products and Services

Assembly
Brake press
Coatings
Coatings
Equipment
Fabrication
Laser and Plasma Cutting
Machining and Turning
Metal Fastening
Punch press
Stamping
Tube Bending
Tube Bending and Forming
Welding

COMPETITORS

Kuhl Machine Shop
Kurt Manufacturing
MetoKote
Smith & Wesson Holding
Valmont Industries

HISTORICAL FINANCIALS

Company Type: Private

Income Statement FYE: December 31

	REVENUE ($ mil.)	NET INCOME ($ mil.)	NET PROFIT MARGIN	EMPLOYEES
12/11	177	6	3.9%	1,925
12/10*	153	15	10.3%	—
03/10	1,003	0	—	—
Annual Growth	—23640.9%	—	—	—

*Fiscal year change

2011 Year-End Financials

Debt ratio: —
Return on equity: 3.90%
Cash ($ mil.): 7
Current ratio: 1.20
Long-term debt ($ mil.): —
Dividends
Yield: —
Payout: —
Market value ($ mil.): —

MCCARTHY BUILDING COMPANIES INC.

A company that was in construction before Reconstruction McCarthy Building Companies is one of the oldest and largest privately-held builders in the US. The general contractor and construction manager ranks among the top builders of health care and education facilities in the country. Contracts include heavy construction projects (bridges and water- and waste-treatment plants) commercial projects (retail and office buildings) and institutional projects (airports schools and prisons). Subsidiary MC Industrial handles energy auto and other manufacturing projects. Founded by Timothy McCarthy in 1864 the company is 100% employee owned.

Geographic Reach

Headquartered in Saint Louis McCarthy Building Companies has offices in Newport Beach San Francisco Sacramento and San Diego California; Albuquerque New Mexico; Las Vegas; Phoenix; St. Louis; Atlanta; Dallas; Houston; and Illinois. It does business in about 45 states.

Financial Performance

Ranked among the Top 10 commercial builders in the US McCarthy generates about $3 billion in annual revenues.

Strategy

McCarthy is steadily building its presence across the US. To that end the firm opened offices in Utah in an effort to grow in the Intermountain region and diversify its geographic footprint.

The firm gets more than 70% of its work from repeat clients. They include McCarthy Building Companies' clients have included Kaiser Permanente California State University and Bally's Casino Resort. Its projects include The Platinum condominium/hotel tower in Las Vegas expansion at M.D. Anderson Cancer Center and renovation and expansion of the National Baseball Hall of Fame and Museum in Cooperstown New York.

In 2013 Clark McCarthy Healthcare Partners II the company's joint venture with Clark Construction Group was awarded a $648 million contract by the US Army Corps of Engineers to build the Fort Bliss Replacement Hospital in El Paso Texas. The 1.1 million-square-foot healthcare campus will consist of a seven-story hospital two clinics and a building with biosafety level three laboratories among other structures and is slated to be finished in 2016.

Ownership

McCarthy Building Companies was sold it its employees in 2002 by the great grandson of the founder. The firm is now 100% employee owned.

EXECUTIVES

Chief Executive Officer Chairman, Michael D. (Mike) Bolen
President and COO, Derek W. Glanvill
President Northern Pacific Division, Richard A. Henry
President Southwest Region, Robert (Bo) Calbert
President Texas Region, Michael J. McWay
President California Region, Randy Highland
President Southeast Division, Kevin Kuntz
President MC Industrial, Tom Felton
President Central Division, Scott Wittkop
President Houston Division, Jim Stevenson
EVP, Ray Sedey
Vice President Chief Information Officer, Mike Oster
Chief Financial Officer, Doug Audiffred
Senior Vice President Of Education, Mark Mardock
Vp-bus Dev-healthcare, Jeff Clarkson
Vice President Of Operations, Adam Knoebel
Vice President Science And Technology, Kevin Williams
Vice President Of Operations Our Crews, Justin Kelton
Vice President Of Operations Houston Office, Ben Johanneman
Vice President M Ep, Jaime Perera
Vice President, Paul Kinsley
Secretary, Lisa Signorelli
Auditors: Ernst&YoungLLP

LOCATIONS

HQ: MCCARTHY BUILDING COMPANIES INC.
1341 N ROCK HILL RD, SAINT LOUIS, MO 631241441
Phone: 3149683300
Web: WWW.MCCARTHY.COM

PRODUCTS/OPERATIONS

Selected Markets

Commercial
Education K-12
Health care
Heavy/civil/transportation
Higher education
High performance/green
Hospitality/entertainment
Industrial
Native American
Parking structures
Science and technology
Water/wastewater

Selected Services

Negotiated general contracting
Construction management
Hard bid (lump sum contract for services)
Design/build
Construction management/general contracting

COMPETITORS

Alberici
Barton Malow
Bechtel
Bovis Lend Lease
Clayco
DPR Construction
Gilbane
HBE Corporation
Hensel Phelps Construction
Korte
Peter Kiewit Sons'
Primus Builders
S. M. Wilson
Skanska
Swinerton
Turner Corporation
Tutor Perini

HISTORICAL FINANCIALS

Company Type: Private

Income Statement FYE: December 31

	REVENUE ($ mil.)	NET INCOME ($ mil.)	NET PROFIT MARGIN	EMPLOYEES
12/13	2,991	0	—	2,438
12/12	2,816	0	—	—
12/11	2,331	0	—	—
12/10	2,379	0	—	—
Annual Growth	7.9%	—	—	—

2013 Year-End Financials

Debt ratio: —
Return on equity: —
Cash ($ mil.): 287
Current ratio: 1.30
Long-term debt ($ mil.): —
Dividends
Yield: —
Payout: —
Market value ($ mil.): —

MCMILLIN COMPANIES LLC

LOCATIONS

HQ: MCMILLIN COMPANIES LLC
2750 WOMBLE RD STE 200, SAN DIEGO, CA 921066114
Phone: 6194774117
Web: WWW.MCMILLIN.COM

HISTORICAL FINANCIALS

Company Type: Private

Income Statement FYE: December 31

	ASSETS ($ mil.)	NET INCOME ($ mil.)	INCOME AS % OF ASSETS	EMPLOYEES
12/12	196	(1)	—	300
12/11	209	(17)	—	—
12/10	257	11	4.6%	—
12/09	331	0	—	—
Annual Growth	(16.0%)	—	—	—

2012 Year-End Financials

Debt ratio: —
Return on equity: (-1.40%)
Cash ($ mil.): 20
Current ratio: —
Long-term debt ($ mil.): —
Dividends
Yield: —
Payout: —
Market value ($ mil.): —

MCNAUGHTON-MCKAY ELECTRIC CO.

Getting connected at work has a completely different meaning at McNaughton-McKay. Its more than 10000 customers can buy electrical supplies sensors and controls and automation and security software online or through 22 branches in five US states and two offices in Germany. One of the largest employee-owned companies in the US McNaughton-McKay distributes some 300 product lines from manufacturers such as Hubbell GE Brady Belden Coleman Cable Leviton Thomas & Betts Cognex Specter Instruments and Rockwell Automation. It sells to the construction commercial government and industrial automation markets.

Geographic Reach

The company serves more than 10000 customers in the US and Germany.

Sales and Marketing

The company sells its products from its sales offices and as well as eSales Centers. In addition to the industrial automation commercial and construction markets McNaughton-McKay supports government customers on a Federal State and Local level by providing hundreds of electrical products and MRO supplies with local support and inventory. McNaughton-McKay's customers include supplyFORCE Vanguard National Alliance and Vantage Group.

Strategy

McNaughton-McKay –informally known as Mc-Mc –has grown by expanding its product lineup and increasing its purchasing power through buying and marketing groups such as Affiliated Distributors supplyFORCE and Vantage Group. The distributor has also added a group dedicated to green products primarily energy-efficient lighting and power distribution products along with an Engineered Solutions Group that sells and installs solar and wind energy through partnerships with companies that include Schletter and Ohio Green Wind.

Ownership

McNaughton-McKay is owned by its employees.

Company Background

Founded in 1910 the Bull and McNaughton families ran McNaughton-McKay until 2006. It established a sales office in Germany in 2004.

EXECUTIVES

EVP and, Donald D. (Don) Slominski

LOCATIONS

HQ: MCNAUGHTON-MCKAY ELECTRIC CO.
1357 E LINCOLN AVE, MADISON HEIGHTS, MI 480714126
Phone: 2485412805
Web: WWW.MC-MC.COM

PRODUCTS/OPERATIONS

Selected Products

Bar code scanners and systems
Communication input/output (I/O) networks
Computers and peripherals
Convenience panels (cables and equipment)
Cordsets
Data-collection terminals and software
Drives and motor controllers
Engineered products
I/O products (AC/DC modules)
Motion-control products
- CNC controls
- Servos
- Spindles

Motors (AC)
PLC processors
Radio-frequency identification (RFID) products
Safety products
- Gate switches
- Light curtains
- Mats
- Relays

Sensors
Software
Vision products (inspection equipment)

COMPETITORS

Anixter International
Border States Electric
Consolidated Electrical
Crescent Electric Supply
Dealers Electrical
Electrocomponents
Graybar Electric
Hite Company
Kendall Electric
Madison Electric
Medler Electric
OneSource Distributors
Rexel Inc.
SUMMIT Electric Supply
Steiner Electric
Stuart C. Irby
W.W. Grainger
WESCO International

HISTORICAL FINANCIALS

Company Type: Private

Income Statement FYE: December 31

	REVENUE ($ mil.)	NET INCOME ($ mil.)	NET PROFIT MARGIN	EMPLOYEES
12/13	663	0	—	725
12/12	641	0	—	—
12/11	603	0	—	—
12/10	493	0	—	—
Annual Growth	10.4%	—	—	—

2013 Year-End Financials

Debt ratio: —
Return on equity: —
Cash ($ mil.): 16
Current ratio: 1.50
Long-term debt ($ mil.): —
Dividends
Yield: —
Payout: —
Market value ($ mil.): —

MCNEILUS STEEL INC.

LOCATIONS

HQ: MCNEILUS STEEL INC.
702 2ND AVE SE, DODGE CENTER, MN 559278903
Phone: 5073746336
Web: WWW.MCNEILUS.COM

HISTORICAL FINANCIALS

Company Type: Private

Income Statement FYE: September 30

	REVENUE ($ mil.)	NET INCOME ($ mil.)	NET PROFIT MARGIN	EMPLOYEES
09/13	441	22	5.1%	475
09/12	443	21	4.9%	—
09/11	360	22	6.3%	—
09/10	245	0	—	—
Annual Growth	21.6%	—	—	—

2013 Year-End Financials

Debt ratio: —
Return on equity: 5.10%
Cash ($ mil.): 1
Current ratio: 1.60
Long-term debt ($ mil.): —
Dividends
Yield: —
Payout: —
Market value ($ mil.): —

MCNICHOLS COMPANY

McNichols Company manufactures metal products that are full of holes ... by design. Its products include perforated and expanded metals wire mesh bar and plank gratings fiberglass grating floorings handrail components ladder rungs and mattings. Its perforated metal (aka "hole") products are sold under the brand names Eco-Mesh Grate-Lock Perf-O-Grip Safplate and Vinylmesh among many others. The company also provides custom fabrication services. McNichols operates is business through some 20 service centers nationwide. It was founded in 1952 by the late Robert McNichols grandfather of current president Scott McNichols. The McNichols family runs the firm based on Christian principles.

Geographic Reach

Tampa Florida-based McNichols Company operates its business in the US Mexico Canada the Caribbean and Central and South America.

Operations

The company's specialties range from shearing sawing notching banding and welding to a variety of finishes including powder coating and galvanizing. McNichols is one of the nation's largest distributors of perforated and expanded metals wire mesh bar plant and safety gratings stair treads matting and more. The company's architectural products are used on building facades and interiors including the Tampa Museum of Art Kaufmann Stadium in Kansas City and Baltimore's Mercy Medical Center.

Financial Performance

McNichols Company reported sales of about $167 million in fiscal 2013 (ended September) and increase of $7 million over the prior year due to the impact of a single big contract from Burgerfi a fast-growing hamburger chain which sourced its metal ceiling panels from the company.

EXECUTIVES

Vice President Of Sales, John Farley
V Pres, Jennifer McNichols
Senior Vice President Sales, Ben Carlson
Senior Vice President Sales, Dave Brenneman
Exec V Pres-asst Sec-treas, Larry Jones, age 68

LOCATIONS

HQ: MCNICHOLS COMPANY
2502 N ROCKY POINT DR # 750, TAMPA, FL 336071421
Phone: 8132823828
Web: WWW.MCNICHOLS.COM

PRODUCTS/OPERATIONS

Selected Products

Expanded metal products (decorative flattened and standard)
Floorings
Gratings
Handrail components
Ladder rungs
Perforated metal products
Stair tread
Stair tread covers
Structural shapes
Trench drain systems
Wire mesh

Selected Services

Cutouts
Cutting
Metal finishes
Print takeoffs
Stair treads
Welding

COMPETITORS

Alabama Metal Industries Corporation
Macsteel Service Centers USA
Redman Fisher Engineering

HISTORICAL FINANCIALS

Company Type: Private

Income Statement FYE: December 31

	REVENUE ($ mil.)	NET INCOME ($ mil.)	NET PROFIT MARGIN	EMPLOYEES
12/09	140	0	—	325
12/08	209	3	1.8%	—
12/07	376	0	0.0%	—
Annual Growth	(38.8%)	—	—	—

2009 Year-End Financials

Debt ratio: —
Return on equity: —
Cash ($ mil.): 0
Current ratio: 0.50
Long-term debt ($ mil.): —
Dividends
Yield: —
Payout: —
Market value ($ mil.): —

MEDCO L.L.C.

LOCATIONS

HQ: MEDCO L.L.C.
3700 DADEVILLE RD, ALEXANDER CITY, AL 35010
Phone: 2562153889

HISTORICAL FINANCIALS

Company Type: Private

Income Statement FYE: June 30

	REVENUE ($ mil.)	NET INCOME ($ mil.)	NET PROFIT MARGIN	EMPLOYEES
06/09*	854	(173)	—	225
09/02	4	0	13.6%	—
09/00	2	0	13.7%	—
12/99	0	0	—	—
Annual Growth	—	—	—	—

*Fiscal year change

2009 Year-End Financials

Debt ratio: —
Return on equity: (-20.30%)
Cash ($ mil.): 0
Current ratio: 1.40
Long-term debt ($ mil.): —
Dividends
Yield: —
Payout: —
Market value ($ mil.): —

MEDICAL SERVICES OF AMERICA INC.

LOCATIONS

HQ: MEDICAL SERVICES OF AMERICA INC.
171 MONROE LN, LEXINGTON, SC 290723904
Phone: 8039570500
Web: WWW.MSA-CORP.COM

HISTORICAL FINANCIALS

Company Type: Private

Income Statement FYE: September 30

	REVENUE ($ mil.)	NET INCOME ($ mil.)	NET PROFIT MARGIN	EMPLOYEES
09/10	248	9	3.7%	3,000
09/08	232	15	6.6%	—
09/07	1,450	0	—	—
Annual Growth	(44.5%)	5674.8%	—	—

2010 Year-End Financials

Debt ratio: —
Return on equity: 3.70%
Cash ($ mil.): 30
Current ratio: 2.20
Long-term debt ($ mil.): —
Dividends
Yield: —
Payout: —
Market value ($ mil.): —

MEDSTAR HEALTH INC.

Whether you're seeing stars or are just plain sickly MedStar Health can cater to you. The not-for-profit organization runs 10 hospitals and about 20 other health-related businesses across Maryland and the Washington DC area including Union Memorial and Georgetown University Hospital. With more than 3000 beds and 5600 affiliated physicians MedStar has a comprehensive service offering including acute and long-term sub-acute care emergency services home health care and rehabilitation. It also operates emergency clinics and assisted living and nursing homes maintains a primary care and specialist physician network (MedStar Physician Partners) and conducts research and medical education activities.

Operations

Along with its 10 hospitals and a dizzying array of inpatient and outpatient services MedStar Health also operates a Medicaid managed care program called MedStar Family Choice.

Its Nascott Orthotics and Prosthetics division provides adult and pediatric prosthetic services and devices to patients in Washington DC and Baltimore. The company provides a continuum of care from initial measurement to fabrication of the device and maintenance through four locations scattered throughout the service areas.

MedStar Health's Visiting Nurse Association (VNA) administers home health care infusion services private duty nursing and hospice as well as immunizations. The VNA increased its home care capabilities a couple of years ago when it began using telemonitoring services to keep tabs on home care patients without having to physically visit each patient's home.

Strategy

Despite its already hefty size MedStar Health is not adverse to getting bigger. It grows usually through acquisitions of existing facilities but also through alliances with other health care providers.

In 2011 MedStar partnered with Cleveland Clinic to form an Innovation Alliance designed to benefit patients through collaborative innovation projects research clinical investigation and commercialization. Initially the alliance is focusing on developing and rapidly deploying new technologies. MedStar Health has acquired several hospitals in recent years including St. Mary's Hospital with 100 beds in southern Maryland and Montgomery General Hospital a 150-bed general acute care facility located in Montgomery County Maryland.

MedStar Health has also entered the growing quick-care and urgent care market by partnering with Rite Aid to establish walk-in health clinics in a number of Rite Aid pharmacies throughout the Baltimore and Washington DC markets.

EXECUTIVES

Executive Vice President Planning, Christine M. Swearingen
President MedStar Physician Partners, Edward D. Miller Jr., age 72
Chairman, Edward S. (Ed) Civera, age 63
Executive Vice President External Affairs & Diversified Operations, Eric R. Wagner
EVP Operations Baltimore, Carl J. Schindelar
Executive Vice President Chief Administrative and Financial Officer, Michael J. Curran
Chair-Elect, William R. Roberts
President MedStar Montgomery Medical Center & Senior Vice President, Peter W. (Pete) Monge
EVP Operations Washington, M. Joy Drass, age 67
President MedStar Union Memorial Hospital & Senior Vice President, Bradley S. Chambers
SVP Development, Bruce A. Bartoo
Senior Vice President Chief Information Officer, Catherine Szenczy, age 59
President MedStar Georgetown University Hospital & Senior Vice President, Richard Goldberg
President MedStar Good Samaritan Hospital & Senior Vice President, Jeffrey A. Matton
President CEO, Kenneth A. Samet, age 56
President MedStar Visiting Nurse Association, Traci K. Anderson-Araujo
VP Medical Affairs Georgetown University Hospital, Stephen Evans
President MedStar Harbor Hospital & Senior Vice President, Dennis W. Pullin
President MedStar National Rehabilitation Network & Senior Vice President, John D. Rockwood
President MedStar, Neil J. Weissman
President St. Mary's Hospital, Christine Wray
Director, Stephen D. Harlan, age 79
Chair-Elect, William R. Roberts
Director, William J. Oetgen
Director, Catherine Meloy
Director, Mark T. Jensen
President CEO and Director, Kenneth A. Samet, age 56
Director, Drew Berry
Director, Chandralekha Banerjee
Director, F. Donald Cooney
Director, John J. DeGioia
Director, Donovan Dietrick
Director, Barbara R. Heller
Director, John R. Kirkpatrick
Director, Roberta M. Loker
Director, Stuart F. Seides
Director, Sara E. Watkins
Director, Rt. Hon. Togo D. West Jr.
Director, Marc N. Duber
Auditors: PricewaterhouseCoopersLLP

LOCATIONS

HQ: MEDSTAR HEALTH INC.
5565 STERRETT PL STE 500, COLUMBIA, MD 21044-2679
Phone: 410-772-6500
Web: WWW.MEDSTARHEALTH.ORG

Selected Facilities

Maryland
- Franklin Square Hospital Center (Baltimore)
- Good Samaritan Hospital (Baltimore)
- Harbor Hospital (Baltimore)
- Montgomery General Hospital (Olney)
- St. Mary's Hospital (Leonardtown)
- Union Memorial Hospital (Baltimore)

Washington DC
- Georgetown University Hospital
- National Rehabilitation Hospital
- Washington Hospital Center

PRODUCTS/OPERATIONS

Selected Affiliates/Operations

Clinical Research
- Georgetown University Medical Center (Washington DC)
- MedStar Research Institute (Hyattsville Maryland)

Home Health Care
- MedStar Health VNA (Washington DC)
- MedStar Health Infusion (Elkridge Maryland)
- MGH Community Health (Olney Maryland)

Managed Care
- MedStar Family Choice (Baltimore Maryland)

Nursing Homes/Senior Living
- Franklin Woods (Rosedale Maryland)
- Good Samaritan Nursing Center (Baltimore Maryland)
- Belvedere Green (Baltimore Maryland)
- Woodbourne Woods (Baltimore Maryland)

Primary Care
- MedStar Physician Partners (Washington DC)

Outpatient Surgery Centers
- MedStar Surgery Center (Washington DC)
- Harbor Hospital HealthPark (Pasadena Maryland)
- SurgiCenter at Pasadena (Pasadena Maryland)

COMPETITORS

Adventist HealthCare
Anne Arundel Medical Center
Ascension Health
Bon Secours Health
Carilion Clinic
Children' s National Medical Center
Christiana Care
Civista Health
Franklin Square Hospital Center
GBMC
Harbor Hospital
Inova
Johns Hopkins Health System
Johns Hopkins Medicine
Kaiser Foundation Health Plan of the Mid-Atlantic
Levindale Hospital
LifeBridge Health
MedStar Union Memorial Hospital
Providence Hospital (Washington DC)
Sinai Hospital of Baltimore
Suburban Hospital
Trinity Health (Novi)
University of Maryland Medical System
Valley Health
Virginia Hospital Center

HISTORICAL FINANCIALS

Company Type: Private

Income Statement FYE: June 30

	REVENUE ($ mil.)	NET INCOME ($ mil.)	NET PROFIT MARGIN	EMPLOYEES
06/12	4,175	(181)	—	24,100
06/11	4,011	271	6.8%	—
/ 0	0	—	—	
Annual Growth	—	—	—	—

2012 Year-End Financials

Debt ratio: —
Return on equity: (-4.40%)
Cash ($ mil.): 568
Current ratio: 1.30
Long-term debt ($ mil.): —

Dividends
Yield: —
Payout: —
Market value ($ mil.): —

MEDSTAR-GEORGETOWN MEDICAL CENTER INC.

Georgetown University Hospital part of MedStar Health is a 609-bed acute care teaching hospital serving residents of the greater Washington DC area including Maryland and Virginia. The hospital's staff of more than 1100 physicians represents a wide range of medical specializations including cardiology oncology neurology/neurosurgery and surgical transplantation. Georgetown University Hospital (also known as Medstar Georgetown University Hospital) provides a comprehensive array of inpatient outpatient surgical and rehabilitative care services. The hospital is part of a local network of affiliated primary care providers.

Georgetown University Hospital's Transplant Institute is one of a handful of centers in the US that offers living-donor liver transplants. Also Georgetown Neurosciences is the sixth unit nationwide to provide CyberKnife stereotactic radiosurgery for the treatment of tumors and lesions of the brain neck and spine.

In 2011 Georgetown University Hospital became the first health system in the area to offer bloodless surgery to patients who prefer not to receive someone else's blood usually for religious reasons. There are three primary approaches to performing bloodless surgeries: before during and after surgery. Before surgery the hospital gives the patient medications such as iron supplements or epoprotein to boost the blood's hemoglobin level. During surgery the hospital is precise as it can be with its surgical techniques to limit blood loss and there are anesthesia techniques to lower blood pressure so patients bleed less. There is also a machine called Cell Saver that is used during surgery that collects blood lost suctions it into a canister washes and filters it and then returns it directly into the patient as a product that is about 60-percent pure red blood cells.

After surgery medications are used to raise blood levels and medical providers avoid taking multiple blood draws for blood tests.

EXECUTIVES

Vice President of Public Affairs and Marketing, Karen Alcorn
President, Richard Goldberg
CFO, Paul Warda
Director Lombardi Comprehensive Cancer Center, Louis M. Weiner
Director Media Relations, Marianne Worley
VP and Executive Director Georgetown Physician's Group, Michael (Mike) Sachtleben

LOCATIONS

HQ: MEDSTAR-GEORGETOWN MEDICAL CENTER INC.
3800 RESERVOIR RD NW, WASHINGTON, DC 20007-2113
Phone: 202-444-2000
Web: WWW.MEDSTARGEORGETOWN.ORG

COMPETITORS

Adventist HealthCare
Bon Secours Health
Calvert Memorial Hospital
Children' s National Medical Center
Chindex International
Dimensions Healthcare
Doctors Community Hospital
Inova Alexandria Hospital
Providence Health & Services
Providence Hospital (Washington DC)
Suburban Hospital
Upper Chesapeake Health

HISTORICAL FINANCIALS

Company Type: Private

Income Statement FYE: June 30

	REVENUE ($ mil.)	NET INCOME ($ mil.)	NET PROFIT MARGIN	EMPLOYEES
06/11	809	43	5.4%	4,000
06/10	782	45	5.8%	—
Annual Growth	3.4%	(3.7%)	—	—

2011 Year-End Financials

Debt ratio: —
Return on equity: 5.40%
Cash ($ mil.): 3
Current ratio: 0.90
Long-term debt ($ mil.): —

Dividends
Yield: —
Payout: —
Market value ($ mil.): —

MEMORIAL HEALTH SYSTEM OF EAST TEXAS

Memorial Health System of East Texas operates deep in the heart of East Texas. The system is anchored by the 270-bed Memorial Medical Center-Lufkin a full-service general acute care hospital offering everything from rehabilitative and diabetes care to specialized centers in heart disease and cancer treatment. The Lufkin hospital also includes Memorial Specialty Hospital a long-term ward for critically ill patients. In addition Memorial Health System of East Texas features two critical access hospitals that offer limited services including emergency care and diagnostic imaging. Additionally the system operates several primary care clinics throughout its service area.

Geographic Reach

The main hospital is in Lufkin Texas while Memorial Health System of East Texas' critical access facilities are located in Livingston and San Augustine. The system operates outpatient clinics in all three towns.

Operations

Specialty services provided by Memorial Health System of East Texas include orthopedics wound care kidney treatment sleep disorder therapy women's health pediatrics stroke care robotic surgery and home health care. It also has diagnostic facilities including the Express Lab and the Temple Imaging Center. The organization handles about 250000 patient encounters each year including 67000 emergency room visits 7500 inpatient and outpatient surgeries and 1000 births.

Financial Performance

Memorial Health System of East Texas reported an 8% increase in 2012 revenues (to some $192 million) due to higher net patient service income and a reduced provision for uncollectable medical bills. The company reported net loss in 2011 and 2012 but the loss figure declined to $5.9 million in 2012 (from $18.7 million in 2011) due to higher revenues and lower expenses.

Strategy

Memorial Health System of East Texas is expanding to meet the needs of its growing regional population. The system opened a new specialty medical center the Cardiovascular & Stroke Center of East Texas in 2012. To improve medical technologies the Memorial Medical Center purchased Texas' first DaVinci high-definition robotic surgery system and updated diagnostic systems to include new 4D ultrasound and cardiac imaging system equipment that year. Furthermore the Livingston campus invested $1.6 million in new imaging equipment during 2013.

Affiliations are also key to growth and in 2012 the organization created an affiliation with the Methodist Hospital of Houston to provide more comprehensive stroke care services.

Company Background

The not-for-profit health system was founded in 1949.

EXECUTIVES

Second Vice Chairman, John (Jay) Glick
President and CEO, Bryant H. Krenek Jr.
President and CEO, Gary Looper
Director Marketing and Public Relations, Yana Ogletree
Interim CEO Memorial Medical Center Livingston, Earl Denning
Administrator Memorial Specialty Hospital, Les Leach
VP Patient Services, Mario B. Estrella
Administrator Memorial Medical Center San Augustine, Darlene Williams
CFO, Kristi Gay
Interim Vice President of Human Resources, Tyane Dietz
Vice President of Human Resources, Don Morris
VP Business Development, Rick Hefner
Chairman, Jack Sweeny
First Vice Chairman, Gibson (Gip) Friesen
COO, Peggy Mortensen
Interim Chief Nursing Officer Livingston, Mary Kay DeGroot
Second Vice Chairman, John (Jay) Glick
First Vice Chairman, Gibson (Gip) Friesen

LOCATIONS

HQ: MEMORIAL HEALTH SYSTEM OF EAST TEXAS
1201 W FRANK AVE, LUFKIN, TX 75904-3357
Phone: 936-634-8111
Web: WWW.MEMORIALHEALTH.US

PRODUCTS/OPERATIONS

Selected Texas Locations

Memorial Medical Center-Livingston
Memorial Medical Center-Lufkin
Memorial Medical Center-San Augustine
Memorial Specialty Hospital (long-term acute care hospital)

Selected Services

Ambulatory Services
Cancer Center
Cardiovascular & Stroke Center
Diabetes
Emergency
Express Lab
Homecare
Inpatient & Outpatient Therapy
Imaging
Intensive Care
Infusion Center
Orthopedics
Robotic Surgery
SANE
Sleep Lab
Social Services
Stroke
Surgery
Women' s & Children' s Center
Wound Care & Hyperbaric Oxygen

COMPETITORS

Community Health Systems
East Texas Medical Center Regional Healthcare
Good Shepherd Health System
LifePoint Hospitals
Trinity Mother Frances Hospital and Clinics
Wadley Regional Medical Center

HISTORICAL FINANCIALS

Company Type: Private

Income Statement

FYE: December 31

	REVENUE ($ mil.)	NET INCOME ($ mil.)	NET PROFIT MARGIN	EMPLOYEES
12/09	192	22	11.6%	940
12/08	8	0	—	—
/ 0	0	—	—	
Annual Growth	—	—	—	—

2009 Year-End Financials

Debt ratio: ——
Return on equity: 11.60%
Cash ($ mil.): 55
Current ratio: —
Long-term debt ($ mil.): —
Dividends
Yield: —
Payout: —
Market value ($ mil.): —

MEMORIAL HEALTH UNIVERSITY MEDICAL CENTER INC.

Memorial Health University Medical Center wants to provide memorable health care to residents of Savannah Georgia and surrounding areas. An affiliate of Mercer University School of Medicine the tertiary care facility provides such services as cardiac and trauma care and rehabilitation. Also known as Memorial University Medical Center (MUMC) the hospital has some 620 beds and includes the MUMC Children's Hospital. It also operates specialty cancer care and women's health centers as well as research programs. Founded in 1955 MUMC is the flagship facility in a broader system of entities known as Memorial Health which includes affiliated primary and specialty care clinics in the region.

Geographic Reach

MUMC serves a 35-county region in southeastern Georgia and southern South Carolina. The medical center serves as a regional referral center for several smaller community hospitals in the area. Affiliates include Bacon County Hospital Evans Memorial Hospital and Liberty Regional Medical Center.

Operations

MUMC's cancer center the Curtis and Elizabeth Anderson Cancer Institute provides cancer treatment and surgical procedures; it also conducts research efforts to discover and develop new cancer therapies. The Women's Health Institute offers obstetrics gynecology and neonatology. MUMC also includes a level I trauma center and a Heart and Vascular Institute as well as programs in orthopedics neurology gastroenterology urology and pulmonary care. The affiliated Memorial Health University Physicians (MHUP) group operates primary and specialty care offices in the area.

Strategy

In 2012 Memorial Health formed an affiliation with Novant Health. The partnership will help the MUMC organization cut costs provide for future growth opportunities and improve its operational infractructure. By joining the Novant Health Shared Services group MUMC will gain access to a larger base of supply chain clinical engineering information technology and best practices resources.

EXECUTIVES

Director Community Benefits, Peter Doliber
SVP Oncology and Research, William (Bill) Hoskins
SVP Memorial Health Foundation, Hall Powell
SVP and Chief Medical Officer, Ramon V. Meguiar
President CEO and Director, Margaret (Maggie) Gill
VP Continuous Quality Improvement and Chief Patient Safety Officer, Frank Carlton
VP Women's and Children's Services, Jean Wright
VP Government Affairs, Amy H. Hughes
SVP Administration, S. Hart Williford
VP Clinical Oncology, Trib Vats
VP Finance and Associate CFO, Darcy J. Davis
SVP Physician Services, John Angstadt
Vice Chair, Kay A. Ford
SVP Chief Nursing Officer and COO, Mary Chatman
Ethics Officer, Mary Ann Bowman Beil
VP Strategy Business Development and The Children's Hospital, William (Bill) Lee III
VP Memorial Health Foundation, Phoenicia Miracle
VP Perioperative Services, Deborah (Debbie) Hattrich
Treasurer, Harry Haslam
Development Manager, Anne Cordeiro
Vice President for Oncology Programs, Guy Petruzzelli
Vice President Physician Services, Sharon Bromley
Senior Vice President Administration and General, Ira P. Berman
Chairman, Jacqueline Rabinowitz
Operations Manager, Monique Williams
Vice President Chief Communications Officer, Rebecca Keightley
Vice President of Finance, Laura Dow
Vice President Chief Information Officer, Robert Tynan
Vice President Memorial, Brett Waress
Director, Curtis G. Anderson, age 73
Director, Southwood J. (Woody) Morcott, age 76
Director, Jack M. Jones, age 75
President CEO and Director, Margaret (Maggie) Gill
Director, John R. Duttenhaver
Director, Gus H. Bell
Director, William J. Degenhart
Director, Helen Dean Downing
Director, Harold P. DuCloux Jr.
Director, Mark E. Murphy
Director, William L. (Bill) Lyght
Vice Chairman, William T. (Bill) Daniel
Director, Charles F. McMillan
Vice Chair, Kay A. Ford

LOCATIONS

HQ: MEMORIAL HEALTH UNIVERSITY MEDICAL CENTER INC.
4700 WATERS AVE, SAVANNAH, GA 31404-6283
Phone: 912-350-8000
Web: WWW.MEMORIALHEALTH.COM

COMPETITORS

Appling
Beaufort Memorial Hospital
Doctors Hospital of Augusta
Liberty Regional Medical Center
Redmond Regional Medical Center
South Georgia Medical Center
St. Joseph' s/Candler Health System
Tift Regional Medical Center
Universal Health Services
University Health Services
Walton Rehabilitation Hospital

HISTORICAL FINANCIALS

Company Type: Private

Income Statement FYE: December 31

	REVENUE ($ mil.)	NET INCOME ($ mil.)	NET PROFIT MARGIN	EMPLOYEES
12/08*	453	(29)	—	5,000
06/05	447	39	8.8%	—
12/02	344	0	0.0%	—
Annual Growth	4.7%	—	—	—

*Fiscal year change

2008 Year-End Financials

Debt ratio: —
Return on equity: (-6.50%)
Cash ($ mil.): 16
Current ratio: 1.10
Long-term debt ($ mil.): —
Dividends
Yield: —
Payout: —
Market value ($ mil.): —

MEMORIAL HERMANN HEALTH SYSTEM

Memorial Hermann Healthcare System is a Texas-sized operation. As Houston's largest not-for-profit health care system it includes a dozen hospitals (one is a children's hospital) with more than 3500 beds and dozens of specialty treatment centers. The system also operates three managed acute care hospitals and a retirement community. Through Memorial Hermann Regional Healthcare Services the company is affiliated with more than 20 community hospitals and health centers most serving rural areas within 150 miles of the Houston area. Other services and programs include substance abuse treatment home health services air ambulances medical training and imaging; it also offers health insurance coverage.

Geographic Reach

Memorial Hermann's various facilities serve Southeast Texas and the Greater Houston community.

Operations

In the insurance arena the company's subsidiary MHealth provides health plans underwritten by UniCare Life & Health Insurance; it also offers administration of self-funded health care benefits and administers wellness programs. Memorial Hermann chose to start offering health care benefits as a way to help employers and individuals cut healthcare costs.

Sales and Marketing

Memorial Herman markets its services through a variety of outlets including social media which is somewhat unusual for a health care provider.

Financial Performance

Memorial Hermann's revenue increased by 7% to $3.6 billion in fiscal 2013 compared to fiscal 2012. The spike was largely due to increased net patient service revenue. Memorial Hermann's net income increased by 146% to $221 million in fiscal 2013 compared to fiscal 2012 while cash flow increased by $375 million in fiscal 2013 compared to the previous period due to a decline in investments.

Strategy

As Houston (one of the nation's largest cities) sprawls into the suburbs so has Memorial Hermann. The system's facilities were previously confined to the downtown medical plaza known as Texas Medical Center and other metropolitan locations but Memorial Hermann has branched out to serve the surrounding areas and now operates eight suburban hospitals. Partnerships with other area providers are another way in which Memorial Hermann enhances its service offerings.

Memorial Herman is also upgrading information technology systems at its facilities to provide consistency of care across its network. For instance Memorial Hermann launched the first health information exchange (HIE) in the Houston area. Such systems are designed to let area health provider access a patient's medical history through electronic health records (EHRs) in order to make faster diagnoses and avoid un-necessary medical costs.

EXECUTIVES

President CEO of Memorial, Daniel J. Wolterman
COO, Charles D. (Chuck) Stokes, age 60
Chief Medical Officer, M. Michael Shabot
Physician-In-Chief, Keith Fernandez
CEO Memorial Hermann Heart and Vascular Institute, Paul O'Sullivan
Chief Compliance Officer, Charles Bumpass

LOCATIONS

HQ: MEMORIAL HERMANN HEALTH SYSTEM
909 FROSTWOOD DR STE 2100, HOUSTON, TX 77024-2301
Phone: 713-338-4179
Web: WWW.MEMORIALHERMANN.ORG

PRODUCTS/OPERATIONS

Selected Facilities

Children's Memorial Hermann Hospital
Memorial Hermann Katy Hospital
Memorial Hermann Memorial City Medical Center
Memorial Hermann Northeast Hospital
Memorial Hermann Northwest Hospital
Memorial Hermann Rehabilitation Hospital - Katy
Memorial Hermann Southeast Hospital
Memorial Hermann Southwest Hospital
Memorial Hermann Sugar Land Health Center
Memorial Hermann - Texas Medical Center
Memorial Hermann The Woodlands Hospital
Memorial Hermann Wellness Center and Garden Spa
Neighborhood Health Center
TIRR Memorial Hermann (Houston)
University Place Retirement Community and Nursing Center (Houston)
Affiliates
Huntsville Memorial Hospital
Memorial Hermann Baptist Hospitals (Beaumont)
Triumph Healthcare (Houston)

COMPETITORS

CHRISTUS Health
Dynacq Healthcare
HCA
Health Management Associates
LifePoint Hospitals
MD Anderson Cancer Center
Memorial Sloan-Kettering
Methodist Hospital System
St. Luke' s Episcopal Health System
Tenet Healthcare
Texas Children' s Hospital

HISTORICAL FINANCIALS

Company Type: Private

Income Statement FYE: June 30

	REVENUE ($ mil.)	NET INCOME ($ mil.)	NET PROFIT MARGIN	EMPLOYEES
06/08	2,841	16	0.6%	16,505
06/07	2,506	209	8.4%	—
Annual Growth	13.4%	(92.3%)	—	—

2008 Year-End Financials

Debt ratio: —
Return on equity: 0.60%
Cash ($ mil.): 327
Current ratio: 1.20
Long-term debt ($ mil.): —
Dividends
Yield: —
Payout: —
Market value ($ mil.): —

MEMORIAL HOSPITAL OF BURLINGTON COUNTY (INC)

Virtua Memorial Hospital of Burlington County provides acute care to patients in southern New Jersey and the Philadelphia metropolitan area. Part of the Virtua Health network the hospital has more than 430 beds and is well-known for its women's and children's health services and stroke care. Other specialty programs include a sleep center cardiac rehabilitation diabetes treatment and wound care. Virtua Memorial provides a full range of cancer treatments through its collaboration with Philadelphia's Fox Chase Cancer Center and operates an in-hospital hospice center for terminally ill patients through a partnership with Samaritan Hospice.

Strategy Virtua Memorial is part of Virtua Health's massive expansion plans which include technology upgrades through a partnership with GE. The health system is investing in new construction including a $9.5 million 13-bed pediatric pavilion scheduled to open on the Virtua Memorial campus in Mt. Holly New Jersey in the spring of 2013.

EXECUTIVES

VP Medical Staff, Ira Smith

LOCATIONS

HQ: MEMORIAL HOSPITAL OF BURLINGTON COUNTY (INC)
175 MADISON AVE, MOUNT HOLLY, NJ 08060-2038
Phone: 609-267-0700
Web: WWW.VIRTUA.ORG

PRODUCTS/OPERATIONS

Selected Specialties

Cardiac care
Emergency care
General surgery
Maternal-fetal medicine
Obstetrics
Oncology
Orthopedics
Radiation oncology
Spine care
Stroke care
Total joint replacement

COMPETITORS

AtlantiCare
Atlantic Health
Crozer-Keystone Health System
Inspira Health Network
Kennedy Health System
Lourdes Health
Meridian Health
North Philadelphia Health System
Shore Memorial Hospital
The Cooper Health System
University of Pennsylvania Health System

HISTORICAL FINANCIALS

Company Type: Private

Income Statement FYE: December 31

	REVENUE ($ mil.)	NET INCOME ($ mil.)	NET PROFIT MARGIN	EMPLOYEES
12/08	328	25	7.9%	1,450
12/06	283	39	13.8%	—
12/05	0	0	—	—
12/02	614	17	2.9%	—
Annual Growth	(9.9%)	6.7%	—	—

2008 Year-End Financials

Debt ratio: —
Return on equity: 7.90%
Cash ($ mil.): 0
Current ratio: —
Long-term debt ($ mil.): —
Dividends
Yield: —
Payout: —
Market value ($ mil.): —

MERCY CHILDREN'S HOSPITAL

When you've got sick grumpy kids on your hands beneficence may not be the first word that comes to mind that is unless you're a doctor at The Children's Mercy Hospital. The pediatric hospital offers health care for youngsters in and around Kansas City Missouri. Specialized services include home health endocrinology genetics heart surgery neonatology and rehabilitation. Founded in 1897 the hospital has about 335 beds. The Children's Mercy health care system also includes a small suburban campus outpatient clinics outreach clinics and research facilities.

Geographic Reach

Children's Mercy Hospital is the only Level I pediatric trauma center between St. Louis Missouri and Denver Colorado.

It is a teaching hospital affiliated with University of Missouri-Kansas City Medical School University of Kansas the Stowers Institute and Midwest Research Institute.

Operations

The hospital has more than 40 pediatric subspecialty clinics and a medical staff of roughly 700 pediatric specialists. Its main campus has 335 beds; there are an additional 54 at the Children's Mercy Hospital South suburban campus. Of the total number of beds about 90 are special care beds composed of about 30 pediatric intensive care and the rest neonatal intensive care.

Strategy

Children's Mercy Hospital is undergoing a 15-year $800 million expansion designed to more than double the size of the hospital increase the number of patient beds by 50% add a new emergency room six new operating rooms new heart catheterization labs new educational buildings clinics and doctors' offices.

A large part of the funding for the expansion comes from philanthropic donations. Since the project began growth at the health system has included new urgent and specialty care centers a Pediatric Research Center new primary care centers and additional patient units and beds. The hospital has also undergone remodeling and expansion of certain existing facilities.

Company Background

The Children's Mercy Hospital is part of The Children's Mercy Hospital and Clinics a not-for-profit free-standing pediatric health system that also offers low-income families a low- or no-cost health plan through Kansas Healthwave and MO HealthNet Managed Care.

The Children's Mercy Family Health Partners insurance plan contracts with the states of Missouri and Kansas to provide coverage to patients who are eligible for Medicaid or the State Children's Health Insurance Plan (SCHIP).

EXECUTIVES

President CEO and Director, Randall L. O'Donnell
Vice President Human Resources, Dan Wright
Executive Vice President Co-Chief Operating Officer, Karen Cox
EVP and Co-COO, Jo Stueve
VP Facilities Management, Lonnie Breaux
Vice President Medical Administration, Joe Galeazzi
Executive Medical Director/Executive Vice President, Charles C. Roberts
Vice President General Counsel, Sally Surridge
EVP and CFO, Sandra A. J. Lawrence
Vice President Government Relations, Genny Nicholas
VP and Chief Nursing Officer, Cheri Hunt
Director, Jack Ovel
Vice President Audit and Compliance, Kimberly Brown
Senior Vice President Strategy and Innovation, David Westbrook
VP Market Development and Outreach, Warren Dudley
Vice President/General Counsel, Robin Foster
President CEO and Director, Randall L. O'Donnell
Director, William Daniels

LOCATIONS

HQ: MERCY CHILDREN' S HOSPITAL
2401 GILLHAM RD, KANSAS CITY, MO 64108-4698
Phone: 816-234-3000
Web: WWW.CMH.EDU

Selected locations

Children's Mercy Hospital Hill (Kansas City)
Children's Mercy Northland (Kansas City)
Children's Mercy South (Overland Park MO)
Children's Mercy Teen Clinic (Kansas City)
Children's Mercy College Boulevard Clinics (Overland Park MO)

COMPETITORS

Ascension Health
CoxHealth
Liberty Hospital
Saint Luke' s Health System
Shawnee Mission Medical Center
Shriners Hospitals For Children
Sisters of Charity of Leavenworth
Truman Medical Centers
University of Kansas Medical Center

HISTORICAL FINANCIALS

Company Type: Private

Income Statement FYE: June 30

	REVENUE ($ mil.)	NET INCOME ($ mil.)	NET PROFIT MARGIN	EMPLOYEES
06/11	816	13	1.6%	3,000
06/10	787	43	5.6%	—
06/09	582	22	3.9%	—
06/08	2	(0)	—	—
Annual Growth	597.0%	—	—	—

2011 Year-End Financials

Debt ratio: —
Return on equity: 1.60%
Cash ($ mil.): 188
Current ratio: 2.90
Long-term debt ($ mil.): —
Dividends
Yield: —
Payout: —
Market value ($ mil.): —

MERCY COLLEGE

Mercy College is a private Catholic school founded by the Sisters of Mercy in 1950. The college provides higher education to some 9000 undergraduate and graduate students in the New York City area. Mercy College offers 90 degrees in fields including business accounting civic and cultural studies computer science education health professions literature language communication natural sciences and social sciences. The institution also provides some online courses as well as professional certification programs. Mercy College employs some 200 full-time faculty members.

Geographic Reach

The main Mercy College campus is in Dobbs Ferry (of Westchester County) New York with branch campuses in the Bronx Yorktown Heights and Manhattan. Students on the main campus come from some 35 US states and about 40 countries.

Operations

Mercy College provides its academic programs through five schools: Business Education Health and Natural Sciences Liberal Arts and Social and Behavioral Sciences. Most of the programs are bachelors and master's degrees; Mercy College also offers a doctorate in physical therapy. More than 70% of the college's student base is female.

Financial Performance

Mercy College reported $154 million in total operating revenues and support in 2012. The figure was up by 6% from 2011 results of $145.5 million. Revenues primarily come from student tuition and fees (90%); other sources include auxiliary activities government grants and private contributions.

EXECUTIVES

Dean Libraries Instructional Technology and Online Learning, Dr. Braddlee
Interim President, Concetta M. Stewart

LOCATIONS

HQ: MERCY COLLEGE
555 BRDWY, DOBBS FERRY, NY 10522
Phone: 914-693-4500
Web: WWW.MERCY.EDU

PRODUCTS/OPERATIONS

2012 Operating Revenues & Support

	% of total
Net tuition &	90
Auxiliary	5
Government grants &	4
Contributions private grants &	1
Total	**100**

Selected Schools

Business
Education
Health and Natural Sciences
Liberal Arts
Social and Behavioral Sciences

HISTORICAL FINANCIALS

Company Type: Private

Income Statement FYE: June 30

	REVENUE ($ mil.)	NET INCOME ($ mil.)	NET PROFIT MARGIN	EMPLOYEES
06/11	177	39	22.2%	500
06/10	154	28	18.3%	—
06/09	128	0	—	—
06/08	99	1	1.4%	—
Annual Growth	21.1%	206.7%	—	—

2011 Year-End Financials

Debt ratio: —
Return on equity: 22.20%
Cash ($ mil.): 69
Current ratio: —
Long-term debt ($ mil.): —
Dividends
Yield: —
Payout: —
Market value ($ mil.): —

MERCY CORPS

Mercy Corps is dedicated to helping the poor and oppressed in developing countries. The not-for-profit organization offers emergency relief and economic support as well as assistance in building sustainable communities. It also develops curriculum guides to introduce students to various topics ranging from Kurdish history and Afghan henna art to the worldwide clean water campaign. Since its founding Mercy Corps programs have provided about $1.5 billion in assistance to people in 106 nations. Originally the organization was named Save the Refugees Fund when it was founded by Dan O'Neill in response to the plight of Cambodian refugees in 1979.

Mercy Corps boasts offices in North America and Europe as well as several field offices in more troubled regions. The group's daily efforts reach more than 16 million people in some 35 countries.

EXECUTIVES

Chair, Linda A. Mason, age 60
Founder and Director, Daniel W. (Dan) O'Neill
CEO and Director, Neal L. Keny-Guyer
VP Financial Services and CFO, Steve Mitchell
President and Director, Nancy E. Lindborg
SVP, Paul D. Hart
VP Program Operations, Jim White
VP Marketing and Communications, Jeremy Barnicle
VP Development, Johanna Thoeresz
Senior Director Development, Christine Tye
Director Corporate and Foundation Partnerships, Graham Craft
Senior Development Officer, Jennifer Schmidt
Director Development Seattle, Karen Donahue Robinson
Director Development Cambridge, Cully Lundgren
CIO, Chip Carter
Director Public Affairs, Heather Hanson
Director Global Emergency Operations, Randy Martin
Director Strategy and Learning, Anna Young
Communications Officer, Lindsay Murphy
Director, David L. Mahoney, age 60
Founder and Director, Daniel W. (Dan) O'Neill
CEO and Director, Neal L. Keny-Guyer
President and Director, Nancy E. Lindborg
Director, Phyllis Dobyns
Director, Mark Gordon
Director, Allen Grossman
Director, Michael O. (Mike) Maerz, age 68
Director, Anita Bekenstein
Director, Scott Brown
Director, Gun Denhart
Director, Rick Little
Director, Melissa Waggener Zorkin
Director, Ned Lamont
Director, Henry P. Vigil

LOCATIONS

HQ: MERCY CORPS
45 SW ANKENY ST, PORTLAND, OR 97204-3500
Phone: 503-796-6800
Web: WWW.MERCYCORPS.ORG.UK

HISTORICAL FINANCIALS

Company Type: Private

Income Statement FYE: June 30

	REVENUE ($ mil.)	NET INCOME ($ mil.)	NET PROFIT MARGIN	EMPLOYEES
06/12	232	(7)	—	450
06/11	268	1	0.6%	—
06/10	244	2	1.0%	—
06/09	196	(0)	—	—
Annual Growth	5.8%	—	—	—

2012 Year-End Financials

Debt ratio: —
Return on equity: (-3.30%)
Cash ($ mil.): 48
Current ratio: 2.20
Long-term debt ($ mil.): —
Dividends
Yield: —
Payout: —
Market value ($ mil.): —

MERCY HOSPITAL AND MEDICAL CENTER

EXECUTIVES

President CEO and Director, Sister Sheila Lyne
Chief Operating Officer, Rick Cerceo
CFO, Tom Garvey
Vice President Business Development, Barbara Townsend
Vice President Spirituality and Mission, Rev Martin Hebda
VP Human Resources and Risk Management, Nancy Hill
Vice President Marketing & Public Relations, Constance (Connie) Murphy
Vice Chair and Secretary, Susan G. Gallagher
Chairman, John McCarthy
Secretary and Director, William A. Brown
Chief Nursing Officer, Carla Campbell
President Medical Staff, Pierre Noisette
Vice President Human Resources, Nancy L. Davis
President Medical Staff, Charles Lawler
President Chief Executive Officer, Carol L. Schneider
President Elect, Charles Bower
President CEO and Director, Sister Sheila Lyne
Vice Chair and Secretary, Susan G. Gallagher
Secretary and Director, William A. Brown

LOCATIONS

HQ: MERCY HOSPITAL AND MEDICAL CENTER
2525 S MICHIGAN AVE, CHICAGO, IL 606162332
Phone: 3125672201
Web: WWW.MERCY-CHICAGO.ORG

PRODUCTS/OPERATIONS

Selected Centers

The Birth Place
Cancer Center
Center for Weight Management
Comprehensive Breast and Women' s Healthcare Center
Diabetes Treatment Center
Ear Nose & Throat Center
Heart & Vascular Center
Orthopedics
Spine & Back Care
Stroke Center

Selected Treatment Options

Cardiac rehabilitation
Clinical trials
Emergency medicine
Immediate care
Integrative medicine & wellness
Minimally invasive surgery
Pulmonary rehabilitation
Rehabilitation and therapy
Robotic surgery

Selected Specialty Care Centers

Behavioral health services
Center for urinary health
Diagnostic imaging/radiology
Dizziness & balance center
Eye center
Family health center
Gastroenterology
Laboratory & pathology
Lap-band program
Occupational health
Pain management
Pediatrics
Pre-birth center
Sleep center
Vitas hospice
Wound management

COMPETITORS

Covenant Ministries
NorthShore University HealthSystem
Northwestern Memorial HealthCare
Rush System for Health
Silver Cross Hospital
Sinai Health System
St. Bernard Hospital and Health Care Center
Swedish Covenant
SwedishAmerican Health System
University of Chicago Medical Center
Vanguard MacNeal Hospital
Weiss Memorial Hospital

HISTORICAL FINANCIALS

Company Type: Private

Income Statement FYE: June 30

	REVENUE ($ mil.)	NET INCOME ($ mil.)	NET PROFIT MARGIN	EMPLOYEES
06/13	265	4	1.5%	1,550
06/10	250	9	3.6%	—
06/09	235	2	1.1%	—
06/08	1,500	0	—	—
Annual Growth	—	—	—	—

2013 Year-End Financials

Debt ratio: —
Return on equity: 1.50%
Cash ($ mil.): 81
Current ratio: 1.70
Long-term debt ($ mil.): —
Dividends
Yield: —
Payout: —
Market value ($ mil.): —

MERCY HOSPITAL OF BUFFALO

LOCATIONS

HQ: MERCY HOSPITAL OF BUFFALO
565 ABBOTT RD, BUFFALO, NY 142202095
Phone: 7168267000
Web: WWW.MERCYHOSPFOUND.ORG

HISTORICAL FINANCIALS

Company Type: Private

Income Statement FYE: December 31

	REVENUE ($ mil.)	NET INCOME ($ mil.)	NET PROFIT MARGIN	EMPLOYEES
12/12	337	13	4.0%	2,000
12/08	249	6	2.6%	—
12/05	205	6	3.2%	—
Annual Growth	7.4%	10.9%	—	—

2012 Year-End Financials

Debt ratio: —
Return on equity: 4.00%
Cash ($ mil.): 59
Current ratio: 1.10
Long-term debt ($ mil.): —
Dividends
Yield: —
Payout: —
Market value ($ mil.): —

MERCY HOSPITAL SPRINGFIELD

Mercy Hospital Springfield is an 890-bed acute-care hospital in the Mercy Health system. The facility provides health care to southwestern Missouri and northwestern Arkansas and includes the Mercy Children's Hospital Springfield. Other hospital specialties include cardiology and stroke care as well as women's and seniors' health cancer emergency trauma burn neuroscience rehabilitation and sports medicine. In addition to its hospital in Springfield Mercy Hospital Springfield operates a number of community clinics and specialty care centers in the area.

Operations

Mercy Hospital Springfield has about 700 doctors on its medical staff. The center sees some 575000 patient visits per year as well as 85000 emergency room visits and 30000 surgeries. Specialty units feature a level I trauma and burn center (the highest ranking in the US) a neonatal intensive care unit a nationally certified stroke center and high-tech surgery suites (including da Vinci robotic surgery and CyberKnife radiosurgery centers). It also operates an air ambulance service.

Financial Performance

Mercy Hospital Springfield reported $822 million in operating revenue in 2011. The hospital spends some $50 million on charity care and community benefit programs each year.

Strategy

Mercy Hospital Springfield broke ground on a new Mercy Orthopedic Hospital in 2011 with the new facility scheduled for completion by the end of 2013. In 2012 the medical center also completed a major renovation of Mercy Children's Hospital Springfield which is located in the six-story East Wing of the main hospital building. The revamped pediatric hospital includes a new Ronald McDonald House to provide housing for family members of sick children.

In addition in 2013 the hospital began construction of a $28 million 63000-sq. ft. Mercy Rehabilitation Hospital Springfield facility for patients recovering from strokes amputations injuries (brain spinal cord or orthopedic) and other conditions. The facility will have 60 beds.

Formerly St. John's Regional Health Center the hospital's name changed to Mercy Hospital Springfield in 2012; the move coincided with the parent organization's efforts to to unify its brand identity. (The parent group's named changed as well from Sisters of Mercy Health System to Mercy Health.)

Company Background

The hospital was founded in 1891 by the Sisters of Mercy.

EXECUTIVES

CEO St. John's Health System, Kim Day
COO, Michele Schaefer
Executive Vice President Chief Operating Officer, Michael McCurry
Executive Vice President Chief Financial Officer, Randy Combs
Executive Vice President Organizational Effectiveness, Shannon Sock

LOCATIONS

HQ: MERCY HOSPITAL SPRINGFIELD
1235 E CHEROKEE ST, SPRINGFIELD, MO 65804-2203
Phone: 417-820-2000
Web: WWW.STJOHNS.COM

PRODUCTS/OPERATIONS

Selected Services

Bariatric Surgery
Cancer Care
Children' s Care
Heart Care
Integrative Medicine
Mother and Baby Care
Neurosciences
Orthopedic and Sport Care
Palliative Care
Pastoral Care
Senior Care
Trauma and Burn Care
Women' s Care

COMPETITORS

Allina Hospitals
Ascension Health
BJC HealthCare
Baxter Regional Medical Center
Boone Hospital Center
Catholic Health Initiatives
Christian Hospital
CoxHealth
HCA
Heartland Health
Liberty Hospital
OhioHealth
Tenet Healthcare
Truman Medical Centers
UC Health
Universal Health Services
University of Kansas Medical Center

HISTORICAL FINANCIALS

Company Type: Private

Income Statement FYE: June 30

	REVENUE ($ mil.)	NET INCOME ($ mil.)	NET PROFIT MARGIN	EMPLOYEES
06/12	968	112	11.6%	4,400
06/11	880	86	9.8%	—
06/09	68	5	8.1%	—
06/09	644	98	15.3%	—
Annual Growth	14.5%	4.5%	—	—

2012 Year-End Financials

Debt ratio: —
Return on equity: 11.60%
Cash ($ mil.): 26
Current ratio: 1.10
Long-term debt ($ mil.): —
Dividends
Yield: —
Payout: —
Market value ($ mil.): —

MERCY MEDICAL CENTER

Overlooking Long Island's Hempstead Lake State Park Mercy Medical Center offers healthcare services to patients just east of Manhattan. The not-for-profit Catholic hospital has expertise in weight loss and orthopedic surgeries mammograms and breast health and women's health services. It also provides outpatient services such as family and mental health care. With about 380 beds the medical center employs some 700 physicians who deliver about 1300 babies each year. Its acute care facilities include a suburban branch of Memorial Sloan-Kettering Cancer Center. Mercy Medical Center established in 1913 by the Sisters of the Congregation of the Infant Jesus is part of Catholic Health Services of Long Island.

EXECUTIVES

President and CEO, Alan D. Guerci
Director Public Relations and Marketing, Mel Granick
SVP and COO, Ron Steimel
Senior Vice President Chief Financial Officer, William Armstrong
EVP and Chief Administrative Officer, Aaron E. Glatt

LOCATIONS

HQ: MERCY MEDICAL CENTER
1000 N VILLAGE AVE, ROCKVILLE CENTRE, NY 11570-1000
Phone: 516-562-6907
Web: WWW.MERCYMEDICALCENTER.CHSLI.ORG

PRODUCTS/OPERATIONS

Selected Services

Bariatric Surgery
Behavioral Health
Cancer Program
Cardiovascular Care
Drug and Alcohol
Emergency Care
Geriatrics
Mother Baby Services
Neurology
Neurosurgery
Orthopedic Surgery
Pediatrics
Physical Medicine and Rehabilitation
Podiatry
Procedures/Testing
Radiology and Imaging
Respiratory Health
Support Services
Surgery

COMPETITORS

Brookhaven Memorial Hospital Medical Center
Long Beach Medical Center
Long Island College Hospital
Long Island Jewish Medical Center
New York City Health and Hospitals
NewYork-Presbyterian Healthcare
North Shore-Long Island Jewish Health System
Southside Hospital

HISTORICAL FINANCIALS

Company Type: Private

Income Statement FYE: December 31

	REVENUE ($ mil.)	NET INCOME ($ mil.)	NET PROFIT MARGIN	EMPLOYEES
12/09	197	(8)	—	1,610
12/08	178	(8)	—	—
12/06	206	(3)	—	—
12/05	191	(14)	—	—
Annual Growth	0.8%	—	—	—

2009 Year-End Financials

Debt ratio: —
Return on equity: (-4.10%)
Cash ($ mil.): 8
Current ratio: 0.20
Long-term debt ($ mil.): —
Dividends
Yield: —
Payout: —
Market value ($ mil.): —

MERITER HEALTH SERVICES INC.

Meriter Health Services believes that the health concerns of its patients merits its careful attention. A teaching affiliate of the University of Wisconsin the Madison-based system serves residents of southern Wisconsin and northwestern Illinois. Its flagship facility is the 450-bed Meriter Hospital a not-for-profit community hospital providing general medical and surgical care as well as pediatric mental health services through its Child and Adolescent Psychiatric Hospital unit. Meriter Health Services also operates primary care clinics a home health care provider and clinical laboratories. It owns two-thirds of Physicians Plus Insurance a regional HMO.

Geographic Reach

In addition to its flagship hospital the company operates a network of clinics in the Greater Madison area which include DeForest-Windsor Clinic Deming Way Clinic Fitchburg Clinic McKee Clinic Middleton Clinic Monona Clinic Stoughton Clinic and West Washington Clinic.

Operations

Along with providing a full spectrum of medical services Meriter Health participates in an array of clinical research trials. Its trials include those for heart conditions mental health and vascular care as well as ways to improve information flow at the hospital.

Strategy

To advance its commitment to high-quality local patient care through shared best practices in 2014 the system affiliated with UnityPoint Health an integrated health system based in West Des Moines Iowa.

In 2013 Meriter Health won the National Research Corporation's Innovative Best Practice award Top Rated Adult Doctors award and Top Rated Pediatric Doctors award.

Meriter Health has been involved in a frenzy of expansion activity in recent years. In 2013 the system opened its three-story Birthing Center. In 2012 it opened one floor (5 North) in its Family Care Center with 24 private rooms and it also opened Meriter Stoughton a new clinic that is part of a growing group of eight primary care clinics located throughout the Madison-area.

Meriter Health also in 2012 adopted the technically advanced da Vinci Surgical System. It features high definition 3D vision wristed instrumentation and a natural motion enabling surgeons to perform with more agility. It also began offering neurology services that year.

Mergers and Acquisitions

At the beginning of 2012 Wisconsin Heart & Vascular Institute joined Meriter Medical Group. The practice which included 16 cardiologists vascular surgeons and mid-level providers experienced in all areas of cardiovascular care was subsequently renamed Meriter Wisconsin Heart.

Company Background

Meriter Health's roots can be traced all the way back to 1898 as Madison General Hospital. However it wasn't until 1987 that the hospital was given the Meriter moniker when General Health Services and Methodist Health Services (parent companies of Madison General Hospital and Methodist Hospital) merged to become Meriter Health Services. The combination of the two hospitals made Meriter Hospital.

In 2011 the company opened Meriter DeForest-Windsor a new clinic offering primary care medical imaging and lab and therapy services.

EXECUTIVES

President and CEO, James L. Woodward
CIO, Kerra Guffey
President Physicians Plus Insurance Corporation, Linda Hoff
Chief Medical Officer, Geoffrey Priest
Chairman, Virginia Graves
President Meriter Foundation, Fran Petonic
Chief Nursing Officer, Pat Grunwald
CFO, Kevin Boren
Chief Marketing and Planning Officer, Mary Reinke
Vice President - Professional Services, Sue Erickson
President Meriter Medical Group, Robert Turngren
President Meriter Foundation, Marilyn Rhodes
Vice Chairman, George Kamperschroer
Director, Pat Richter
Director, Holly Cremer Berkenstadt, age 58
Director, James L. Woodward
Director, Bradley L. Manning
Director, Paul Peercy
Director, Cathy Durham

LOCATIONS

HQ: MERITER HEALTH SERVICES INC.
202 S PARK ST, MADISON, WI 53715-1507
Phone: 608-267-5811
Web: WWW.MERITERFOUNDATION.ORG

PRODUCTS/OPERATIONS

Selected Medical Services

Allergy and Immunology
Birthing Center
Dermatology
Digestive Health
Emergency Services
Endocrinology and Diabetes Care
General Surgery
Gynecology and Obstetrics
Heart and Vascular
Hospitalist Program
Laboratories
Medical Imaging Services
Medical Psychology
Home Health
Neuroscience
Newborn Intensive Care Unit
Oncology
Orthopedics
Palliative Care
Patient and Family Services
Pediatric Services
Plastic Surgery
Primary Care
Pharmacy
Psychiatry Program
Pulmonary Diagnostics
Sexual Assault Nurse Examiner Program
Sleep Clinic and Lab
Smoking Cessation Programs
Spiritual Care
Substance Use Treatment Program
Therapy for Adults
Therapy for Children
Women and Infants

COMPETITORS

Aspirus
Beaver Dam Community Hospitals
Beloit Health System
Dean Health Systems Inc.
Franciscan Skemp Healthcare
Marshfield Clinic Health System
Ministry Health Care
SSM Health Care
Stoughton Hospital
ThedaCare Inc.
Tomah Memorial Hospital
University of Wisconsin Hospital and Clinics

HISTORICAL FINANCIALS

Company Type: Private

Income Statement FYE: December 31

	REVENUE ($ mil.)	NET INCOME ($ mil.)	NET PROFIT MARGIN	EMPLOYEES
12/12	774	12	1.6%	3,330
12/11	773	(16)	—	—
12/09	725	351	48.5%	
12/09	687	71	10.4%	—
Annual Growth	4.1%	(43.7%)	—	—

2012 Year-End Financials

Debt ratio: —
Return on equity: 1.60%
Cash ($ mil.): 71
Current ratio: 0.90
Long-term debt ($ mil.): —

Dividends
Yield: —
Payout: —
Market value ($ mil.): —

METHODIST HOSPITAL OF SOUTHERN CALIFORNIA

If you're dehydrated in the Valley Methodist Hospital of Southern California can help. The hospital provides medical care to the residents of California's central San Gabriel Valley. The healthcare facility boasts some 600 beds and is part of Southern California Healthcare Systems. The not-for-profit hospital provides comprehensive acute care including surgical pediatric and intensive care units as well as a wide range of specialty services include cardiology oncology neurology bariatrics and orthopedics. The hospital opened its doors in 1903 with five beds.

Geographic Reach

Methodist Hospital is located in Arcadia California in the northeastern corner of the Los Angeles metropolitan area; it serves patients from surrounding communities as well.

Operations

In addition to typical acute care services Methodist Hospital's cardiac care center provides complete cardiovascular services including open-heart surgery. The medical facility's intensive care units include both neonatal and adult centers. Its cardiovascular stroke and cancer centers are certified by various national medical specialist organizations. The hospital employs about 615 medical staff members.

It also operates a rehabilitation clinic and a long-term recovery facility for patients requiring transitional care.

Strategy

In 2012 a grant from the H.N. and Frances C. Berger Foundation allowed the hospital to install a state-of-the-art hyperbaric (high-pressure oxygen) chamber in the hospital's Wound Healing Center. The chamber will help treat diabetic patients suffering from chronic wounds as well as wounds resulting from immune deficiencies and will help patients suffering from decompression sickness or the "bends" as a result of diving accidents.

During 2013 Methodist Hospital continued with its infrastructure expansion and improvement projects with a focus on expanding its emergency department.

EXECUTIVES

Senior Vice President And Chief, Marc L Boom, age 49
President CEO and Director, Dan F. Ausman, age 59
SVP CFO and Assistant Treasurer, William E. Grigg
SVP and COO, Steven A. Sisto
President Methodist Hospital Foundation, Michael Driebe
CIO, Kara Marx
Chair Department of Emergency Medicine, Jacob Fakoory
Chair Department of Ob/Gyn/Peds, Shaun Grady
Director Of Pharmacy, Dorothy Wong
Director Of Medical Records, Bridgitte Didier
Vice President Infrastructure, Steve Burns
Sr V Pres, Clifford R Daniels
Vice President, Tony Marino
Respiratory Therapy Director, Mark Ung
Vice President Leadership Development Talent Manager, Carrie Courtney
Medical Director, Edward Bartkus
Nursing Director, Debbie Pirih
Director Of Physical Therapy, Regina Schultheis
Ambulatory Services Dir, Barbara Murphy
Director Managed Care, Gabriela Ornelas
Senior Management (Senior Vice President General Manager Director), Jeff Stack
Or Director Vice President Clin Services, Connie Smith
Assistant Secretary, Kathryn Saldivar
Director, Michael Hoover
President CEO and Director, Dan F. Ausman, age 59
Director, Kathleen Ellison
SVP CFO and Assistant Treasurer, William E. Grigg
Secretary, Katie Martinez
Secretary, Debra Jones
Treasurer, Doug McEachern

LOCATIONS

HQ: METHODIST HOSPITAL OF SOUTHERN CALIFORNIA
300 W HUNTINGTON DR, ARCADIA, CA 91007-3402
Phone: 626-898-8000
Web: WWW.METHODISTHOSPITAL.ORG

PRODUCTS/OPERATIONS

Selected Services

Cardiology
Diabetes Services
Emergency Services
Maternal Child Health
Neurology
Oncology
Orthopedics
Outpatient Services
Rehabilitation Services
Senior Services
Surgical Services
Stroke
Transitional Care Unit
Weight Loss Surgery
Wound Healing Center

COMPETITORS

Citrus Valley Health Partners
Dignity Health
Glendale Adventist Medical Center
Good Samaritan Hospital (Los Angeles)
HCA
Hollywood Presbyterian Medical Center
Los Angeles County Health Department
Memorial Health Services
Newhall Memorial Hospital
Providence Saint Joseph Medical Center
St. Joseph Health System
Tenet Healthcare

HISTORICAL FINANCIALS

Company Type: Private

Income Statement FYE: December 31

	REVENUE ($ mil.)	NET INCOME ($ mil.)	NET PROFIT MARGIN	EMPLOYEES
12/12	281	0	0.3%	2,200
12/11	245	(4)	—	—
12/07	271	7	2.9%	—
12/08	245	(12)	—	—
Annual Growth	3.5%	—	—	—

2012 Year-End Financials

Debt ratio: —
Return on equity: 0.30%
Cash ($ mil.): 64
Current ratio: 2.30
Long-term debt ($ mil.): —

Dividends
Yield: —
Payout: —
Market value ($ mil.): —

METHODIST HOSPITALS OF DALLAS INC

Methodist Hospitals of Dallas serves the health care needs of North Texas —from Mansfield to McKinney. The church-affiliated organization which does business as Methodist Health System operates more than a dozen hospitals clinics and medical facilities in and around the area deemed by locals as Big D. The original hospital Methodist Dallas Medical Center opened in 1927. The 515-bed teaching and referral hospital boasts a Level II trauma center and an organ transplant program. Other facilities include the 300-bed Methodist Charlton Medical Center the 80-bed Methodist Mansfield Medical Center and the 200-bed Methodist Richardson Medical Center.

Geographic Reach

Methodist Hospitals of Dallas serves the residents of several communities located in and around the North Dallas area such as Midlothian Grand Prairie Cedar Hill Richardson Plano Garland Wylie and McKinney.

Operations

The Methodist Dallas liver kidney and pancreas transplant program is one of the largest and most active transplant centers in the southwestern part of the country performing hundreds of kidney pancreas and liver transplants each year.

Both Methodist Hospital for Special Surgery and Methodist McKinney are part of two separate joint venture agreements made between Methodist Health System and Nueterra Healthcare a health care facilities management and development company.

Strategy

In recent years Methodist Health System has grown through a series of acquisitions (such as the Methodist Mansfield Medical Center and the Methodist Richardson Medical Center) as well as through organic expansion efforts such as the construction of about 50 rooms and new surgery suites in the Methodist Charlton hospital.

In late 2012 the health care provider began to expand its Methodist Richardson Medical Center - Bush/Renner hospital. Scheduled to open in fall 2014 the new 125-bed hospital will reach four stories high and serve the northeast Dallas communities of Richardson Garland Murphy Plano Sachse Wylie and other surrounding areas. It will boast a women's pavilion level III neonatal intensive care unit advanced neurosciences program outpatient surgical services such as the robotic da Vinci surgical system and other specialty services.

EXECUTIVES

Senior Vice President Chief Human Resources Officer, Deanna Kenard
President Methodist Mansfield Medical Center, John E. Phillips
President and CEO, Stephen L. (Steve) Mansfield
EVP and CFO, Michael J. Schaefer, age 63, $370,759 total compensation
VP Public Relations and Marketing, Kathleen Beathard
EVP and Chief Legal Officer, Michael O. (Mickey) Price, $219,359 total compensation
SVP External Affairs; President and CEO Methodist Health System Foundation, April B. Chamberlain
SVP and CIO, Pamela G. McNutt
President Methodist Dallas Medical Center, Michael A. Mayo
President Methodist Dallas Medical Center, Laura Irvine
VP and Chief Medical Informatics Officer, Sam Bagchi
EVP and COO, Pamela (Pam) Stoyanoff
SVP and Chief Development Officer, Michael W. Arvin
EVP System Alignment and Integration, Tim B. Kirby
President Methodist Charlton Medical Center, Jonathan S. Davis
President Methodist Richardson Medical Center, E. Kenneth Hutchenrider Jr.
SVP and Chief Medical Officer, Adam L. Myers
SVP and Chief Nursing Officer; Chief Nursing Officer Methodist Dallas Medical Center, Nancy E. Simon
Senior Vice President and Chief Human Resources Officer Methodist Health System, Cheryl Flynn SPHR

LOCATIONS

HQ: METHODIST HOSPITALS OF DALLAS INC
1441 N BECKLEY AVE, DALLAS, TX 75203-1201
Phone: 214-947-8181
Web: WWW.METHODISTHEALTHSYSTEM.ORG

PRODUCTS/OPERATIONS

Selected Services

Back and Spine
Behavioral Health and Addiction Recovery
Cancer Services
Cardiovascular
da Vinci Surgical System
Diabetes
Digestive Diseases
Ear Nose & Throat (ENT) Services & Allergy Treatments
Emergency and Trauma Care
Fitness Programs
Home Health
Imaging and Radiology
The Liver Institute
Neurosurgery and Neurology
Ophthalmology
Orthopedics
Pain Management
Palliative Care
Physical Therapy and Rehabilitation
Prostate Screening and Awareness Program
Sleep Disorders
Transplant
Urology
Weight Management
Women and Children's Services
Women's Imaging and Mammography
Wound Care and Hyperbaric Center

Selected Facilities

Golden Cross Academic Clinic
Methodist Dallas Medical Center
Methodist Charlton Medical Center
Methodist Family Health Centers

Cedar Hill
Central Grand Prairie
Dallas
Midlothian
South Grand Prairie
Methodist Hospital for Surgery
Methodist Mansfield Medical Center
Methodist McKinney Hospital
Methodist Midlothian Health Center (imaging)
Methodist Richardson Medical Center
Methodist Richardson Medical Center Bush/Renner
Methodist Rehabilitation Hospital

COMPETITORS

Baylor Health
CHRISTUS Health
Children' s Medical Center of Dallas
Community Health Systems
Cook Children' s Health Care System
HCA
Harris Methodist Fort Worth Hospital
Health Management Associates
Hunt Memorial
JPS Health Network
NW Texas Healthcare
Parkland Health & Hospital System
Presbyterian Hospital of Dallas
Southwestern Medical Center
Tenet Healthcare
Texas Health Denton
Texas Health Resources

HISTORICAL FINANCIALS

Company Type: Private

Income Statement FYE: September 30

	REVENUE ($ mil.)	NET INCOME ($ mil.)	NET PROFIT MARGIN	EMPLOYEES
09/12	969	165	17.1%	4,804
09/11	985	51	5.3%	—
09/10	889	88	10.0%	—
09/09	747	37	5.0%	—
Annual Growth	9.0%	63.6%	—	—

2012 Year-End Financials

Debt ratio: —
Return on equity: 17.10%
Cash ($ mil.): 45
Current ratio: 1.90
Long-term debt ($ mil.): —
Dividends
Yield: —
Payout: —
Market value ($ mil.): —

METHODIST LE BONHEUR HEALTHCARE

Methodist Le Bonheur Healthcare is happy to take care of sick people. Founded in 1918 by John Sherard the not-for-profit health care system serves the Memphis area with seven hospitals; multiple minor medical surgical and diagnostic health centers; and home health agencies. The system has more than 1700 beds. In addition to traditional health services Methodist Healthcare offers extended care services sleep disorder centers and physical therapy. It also operates physician practices and a physician referral service. The system's flagship hospital Methodist University Hospital has about 700 beds and is a teaching hospital affiliated with the University of Tennessee Health Science Center.

Operations

Along with the University of Tennessee Methodist Healthcare is affiliated with a number of organizations throughout the state including the University of Memphis The Medical Education and Research Institute and Health Choice (the exclusive managed care provider for the system in Memphis and the Mid-South).

Strategy

Methodist Healthcare in 2011 acquired Penn Marc Internal Medicine a small physician practice in Memphis in order to expand its reach throughout the community. Some of Methodist Healthcare's other physician office purchases have included Foundation Medical Group Lakeland Family Medicine McGee General Surgery Clinic Sutherland Cardiology Clinic and The CardioVascular Center.

In 2012 Methodist Healthcare partnered with BlueShield of Tennessee in a five-year arrangement that enhanced its new care and payment models. It also opened a Methodist Healthcare Comprehensive Sickle Cell Center as an expansion strategy to provide better service to patients.

EXECUTIVES

President Chief Executive Officer, Gary S. Shorb
Senior Vice President of Corporate Affairs, Cato Johnson
EVP, Donna A. Abney
President of the Methodist, Paula Jacobson
EVP Finance, Chris McLean
VP Marketing and Communications, Michelle B. Collis
Vice President of Materials Management, Larry Fogarty
CTO, Gene Fernandez
Administrator and CEO Methodist Extended Care Hospital, Sandra Bailey
CEO Methodist Olive Branch Hospital, David Baytos
CEO Methodist Le Bonheur Germantown Hospital, William A. Kenley
President of Affiliated Services, Mitch Graves
EVP and COO, Michael Ugwueke
President CEO, Meri Armour
Administrator and CEO Methodist Fayette Hospital, David Crislip
CEO Methodist South Hospital, James L. (Jay) Robinson III
Chief Healthcare Information Officer, Alastair MacGregor
CEO Crittenden Regional Hospital, Eugene K. Cashman III
Chief Medical Officer, Howard Scott
Chief Financial Officer, Jane George
Senior Vice President Strategic Planning and Marketing, Ed Rafalski
Interim Senior Vice President Faith, Harry Durbin

LOCATIONS

HQ: METHODIST LE BONHEUR HEALTHCARE
1211 UNION AVE STE 700, MEMPHIS, TN 38104-6600
Phone: 901-516-7000
Web: WWW.CAREERS.METHODISTHEALTH.ORG

PRODUCTS/OPERATIONS

Selected Hospitals

Le Bonheur Children's Health Center (Memphis)
Methodist Extended Care Hospital (Memphis)
Methodist Fayette Hospital (Somerville)
Methodist Le Bonheur Germantown Hospital (Germantown)
Methodist North Hospital (Memphis)
Methodist Olive Branch Hospital (Olive Branch)
Methodist South Hospital (Memphis)
Methodist University Hospital (Memphis)

COMPETITORS

Ascension Health
Baptist Memorial Health Care
Catholic Health Partners
Community Health Systems
HCA
Health Management Associates
HealthSouth
LifePoint Hospitals
Mercy Health
North Mississippi Health Services
Shelby County Health Care
St. Jude Children' s Research Hospital
Tenet Healthcare
UT Medical Group
Universal Health
Kindred Healthcare
Services

HISTORICAL FINANCIALS

Company Type: Private

Income Statement FYE: December 31

	REVENUE ($ mil.)	NET INCOME ($ mil.)	NET PROFIT MARGIN	EMPLOYEES
12/08	1,232	(266)	—	11,459
12/06	1,181	142	12.0%	—
12/02	870	(35)	—	—
12/01	934	15	1.6%	—
Annual Growth	4.0%	—	—	—

2008 Year-End Financials

Debt ratio: —
Return on equity: (-21.60%)
Cash ($ mil.): 46
Current ratio: 1.60
Long-term debt ($ mil.): —
Dividends
Yield: —
Payout: —
Market value ($ mil.): —

METROPOLITAN UTILITIES DISTRICT OMAHA NEBRASKA.

EXECUTIVES

President Secretary and Director, Thomas A. (Tom) Wurtz
SVP Administration and Treasurer, Ronald E. (Ron) Bucher
VP Water Operations, Joel G. Christensen
SVP Operations, Scott L. Keep
Chairman, Jack C. Frost
Chairman, Tim Cavanaugh
SVP and CIO, Mark Doyle
President Secretary, Douglas R. (Doug) Clark
SVP and CIO, Mark W. Weiss
Vice Chairperson, Amy Lindsay
SVP and CFO, Debra A. Schneider
Director, Michael W. (Mike) McGowan
President Secretary and Director, Thomas A. (Tom) Wurtz
Director, Tim Cavanaugh
Director, Thomas F. Dowd
Vice Chairperson, Amy Lindsay
Auditors: KPMGLLP

LOCATIONS

HQ: METROPOLITAN UTILITIES DISTRICT OMAHA NEBRASKA.
1723 HARNEY ST, OMAHA, NE 681021960
Phone: 4025546666
Web: WWW.MYACOUNT.MUDOMAHA.COM

PRODUCTS/OPERATIONS

2012 Sales

	$ mil.	% of total
Gas	182	62
Water	110	38
Total	**292**	**100**

HISTORICAL FINANCIALS

Company Type: Private

Income Statement FYE: December 31

	REVENUE ($ mil.)	NET INCOME ($ mil.)	NET PROFIT MARGIN	EMPLOYEES
12/13	341	47	13.7%	852
12/12	292	46	15.8%	—
12/11	311	15	4.9%	—
12/09	308	0	—	—
Annual Growth	2.6%	—	—	—

2013 Year-End Financials

Debt ratio: —
Return on equity: 13.70%
Cash ($ mil.): 64
Current ratio: 1.30
Long-term debt ($ mil.): —
Dividends
Yield: —
Payout: —
Market value ($ mil.): —

MFA INCORPORATED

EXECUTIVES

Senior Vice President Corporate and Member Services Corporate Secretary, Janice Schuerman
SVP CFO and Treasurer, Allen Floyd
Executive Assistant and Assistant Secretary, Larna Lavelle
Senior Vice President Corporate Operations, J. Brian Griffith
President MFA Incorporated, Bill Streeter
VP Plant Foods Marketing and Transportation Division, Charles (Charlie) Cott
Vice President Feed Operations Animal, Alan Wessler
Controller, Ernie Verslues
Sales Manager, Brandon Graupman
Treasurer, John Akridge
Sales Manager, Ryan Mauzey
Vice President Plant Foods Transportation, Bill Coen
Vice President Crop Protection Seed Farm Supply, Don Houston
Sales Manager, Kenny Schlitt
Founder, William Hirth
Director, Tim Lichte
Vice Chairman, Phil Becker
Director, Harry Thompson
Director, Randy Ludwig
Director, Kendall Kircher
Director, John Moffitt
Director, Tim Engemann
Director, Don Mills
Director, Glen Cope
Director, Barry Kagay
Director, Carlton Spence
Director, David Callis
Director, Julius Fraley

LOCATIONS

HQ: MFA INCORPORATED
201 RAY YOUNG DR, COLUMBIA, MO 652013599
Phone: 5738745111
Web: WWW.CALIFORNIAMFA.COM

COMPETITORS

ADM
Andersons
Cargill
Farm Service Cooperative
Farmers Cooperative Company
GROWMARK
Heartland Co-op
Missouri Farm Bureau
Orscheln Farm and Home
Tennessee Farmers Co-op
United Producers

HISTORICAL FINANCIALS

Company Type: Private

Income Statement FYE: August 31

	REVENUE ($ mil.)	NET INCOME ($ mil.)	NET PROFIT MARGIN	EMPLOYEES
08/14	1,510	18	1.2%	1,393
08/13	1,510	15	1.0%	—
08/12	1,470	22	1.5%	—
08/11	1,354	0	—	—
Annual Growth	3.7%	—	—	—

MFA OIL COMPANY

EXECUTIVES

Chairman, Benny Farrell
President, Jerome (Jerry) Taylor
Director Break Time Operations, Jackie Maxwell
Director, Joey Massey
Director, Ronald Felten
Director, Ralph Schallert

LOCATIONS

HQ: MFA OIL COMPANY
1 RAY YOUNG DR, COLUMBIA, MO 652013506
Phone: 5734420171
Web: WWW.MFAOIL.COM

COMPETITORS

Ag Processing Inc.
BioFuel Energy
Green Plains
Jordan Oil Company
Lykins
Shell Oil Products
Valero Energy
WilcoHess

HISTORICAL FINANCIALS

Company Type: Private

Income Statement FYE: August 31

	REVENUE ($ mil.)	NET INCOME ($ mil.)	NET PROFIT MARGIN	EMPLOYEES
08/14	1,471	40	2.8%	1,500
08/13	1,300	55	4.2%	—
08/12	1,255	34	2.7%	—
08/11	1,275	0	—	—
Annual Growth	4.9%	—	—	—

2014 Year-End Financials

Debt ratio: —
Return on equity: 2.80%
Cash ($ mil.): 39
Current ratio: 0.90
Long-term debt ($ mil.): —
Dividends
Yield: —
Payout: —
Market value ($ mil.): —

MIAMI UNIVERSITY

Not that Miami the other one. Named for the Miami Indian Tribe that inhabited the area now known as the Miami Valley Region of Ohio Miami University emphasizes undergraduate study at its main campus in Oxford (35 miles north of Cincinnati) as well as at commuter campuses in Hamilton Middletown and West Chester Ohio and a European Center in Luxembourg. The school offers bachelors masters and doctoral programs in areas including business administration arts and sciences engineering and education. Its student body includes more than 15000 undergraduates on the Oxford campus; 2500 graduate students; and another 5700 students attending satellite campuses. Miami University was established in 1809.

Financial Performance

Miami University's 2011 revenue increased 3% vs. 2010 due to a corresponding increase in undergraduate tuition on its three campuses and a rising rates for room and board. Net income at the public university rose 25% over the same period on higher revenue and lower operating expenses due primarily to a reduction in the number of positions and no salary increases. The rise in tuition for Ohio residents in 2011 was the first in four years. Also investment income rose in 2011 for the second consecutive year.

Company Background

Miami University celebrated its bicentennial in 2009. The school was chartered in February of 1809 by the State of Ohio but the first classses were not held until 1824.

EXECUTIVES

VP University Advancement; Executive Director Miami University Foundation, Jayne E. Whitehead
Associate VP University Communications and Marketing, Deedie Dowdle
Senior Associate VP Business Services and Auxiliary Enterprises, Adolph Haislar
Dean Farmer School of Business, Roger L. Jenkins
Dean and University Librarian, Judith A. Sessions
President, David C. Hodge
General Counsel, Robin Leigh Parker
University Registrar, Dave Sauter
Associate Provost and Interim Dean Graduate School, Jeffrey A. Potteiger
VP Finance and Business Services and Treasurer, David Creamer
VP Information Technology, Debra Allison
VP Student Affairs, Barbara Jones
Executive Assistant to the President and Secretary, Stephen D. Snyder
Dean College of Arts and Science, Karen Maitland Schilling
Dean School of Education Health and Society, Carine Feyten
Dean School of Fine Arts, James P. Lentini
Dean Graduate School, Bruce Cochrane
Dean John E. Dolibois European Campus, Ekkehard F. R. Stiller
Dean Miami University Hamilton, Daniel E. Hall
Dean Miami University Middletown, Kelly Cowan
Treasurer, David F. Herche
Director News and Public Information Office, Claire Wagner
Provost and EVP Academic Affairs, Conrado M. (Bobby) Gempesaw
Associate VP Institutional Diversity, Ronald B. Scott
Associate VP Enrollment Management, Michael Kabbaz
Secretary and Executive Assistant to the President, Ted Pickerill
Dean Regional Campuses, G. Michael Pratt
Assistant Director News and Public Information, Carole Johnson
Trustee, Lolita M. McDavid
Trustee, David M. Shade
Trustee, Fred G. Wall
Trustee, Jay L. Henderson
Trustee, John S. Christie
Trustee, S. Kay Geiger
Trustee, Donald L. Crain
Trustee, Peter Lawson Jones
Trustee, Harry T. Wilks
Trustee, Kerry McCormack
Trustee, Heath R. Ingram
Auditors: KPMGLLP

LOCATIONS

HQ: MIAMI UNIVERSITY
501 E HIGH ST, OXFORD, OH 45056-1846
Phone: 513-529-1809
Web: WWW.MIAMI.MUOHIO.EDU

HISTORICAL FINANCIALS

Company Type: Private

Income Statement FYE: June 30

	REVENUE ($ mil.)	NET INCOME ($ mil.)	NET PROFIT MARGIN	EMPLOYEES
06/12	440	32	7.5%	6,600
06/11	418	120	28.8%	—
06/10	404	85	21.2%	—
06/09	396	(102)	—	—
Annual Growth	3.6%	—	—	—

2012 Year-End Financials

Debt ratio: —
Return on equity: 7.50%
Cash ($ mil.): 282
Current ratio: 2.80
Long-term debt ($ mil.): —
Dividends
Yield: —
Payout: —
Market value ($ mil.): —

MIAMI VALLEY HOSPITAL

Don't go to Florida looking for this hospital! Miami Valley Hospital (MVH) is an acute care facility serving the residents of Dayton Ohio and surrounding areas through two campuses. MVH and MVH South have roughly 850 beds and offer 50 primary and specialty care practices through its Regional Adult Burn Center the MVH Cancer Center MVH Sports Medicine Center and behavioral health units for outpatient and inpatient chemical dependency therapy and other psychiatric services. MVH also offers Level I trauma services an air ambulance program and blood marrow and kidney transplant services. The hospital formed in 1890 is part of the Premier Health Partners network.

Operations

In addition to Miami Valley Hospital the Premier Health Partners network consists of Good Samaritan Hospital (also stationed in Dayton Ohio) Atrium Medical Center in nearby Middletown and Upper Valley Medical Center in Troy. Collectively the multi-hospital health system houses about 1800 inpatient beds and around 65 facilities.

EXECUTIVES

CIO, Mikki Clancy
SVMedical Affairs and Chief Medical Officer, Gary S. Collier
VP Operations and Chief Nursing Officer, Deb Mals
VP and CFO, Scott Shelton
President and CEO, Bobbie Gerhart
EVP and COO, Barbara Johnson
VP Miami Valley Hospital South (MVHS) Hospital Operations, Joann Ringer
Auditors: Ernst&YoungLLP

LOCATIONS

HQ: MIAMI VALLEY HOSPITAL
1 WYOMING ST, DAYTON, OH 45409-2711
Phone: 937-208-8000
Web: WWW.MIAMIVALLEYHOSPITAL.ORG

PRODUCTS/OPERATIONS

Selected Services and Specialties

Ablation (Cardiology)
Access and Transfer Center (physicians)
Alcoholism Drug Dependency and Addiction Treatment
Aneurysm (Neurosciences)
Ankle Surgery
Arterial Interventions
Audiology
Bariatrics/Weight Loss Surgery
Behavioral Services
Biotherapy/Targeted Therapy
Blood and Marrow Transplant Program
Brachytherapy
Brain Conditions and Treatments
Brain Injury Rehabilitation
Breast Cancer Navigators
Breast Center
Breast Center
Brethen Center for Surgical Advancement (physicians)
Bull Family Diabetes Center
Burn Center
Cancer Care
Cancer Care (Oncology)
Cardiac Electrophysiology Lab
Cardiac Rehabilitation
Cardiology
Cardiology
Cardiothoracic Surgery
CareFlight - Medical Transportation
Catheterization Lab Procedures
Center for Sleep and Wake Disorders
Chemoembolization
Chemotherapy and Infusion Therapy
Childbirth Education
Colon Cancer
Colorectal Cancer
Complementary Medicine (Cancer)
Comprehensive Outpatient Rehab Program (CORP)
Counseling/Pastoral Care
Craniectomy (Neuroscience)
Craniotomy (Neuroscience)
Cryoablation
CT scan (Imaging)
Dental Center
Depression/Anxiety Treatment
Diabetes
Dialysis Services
Discectomy
Drug Addiction Treatment
Elder Care
Emergency & Trauma Center (ETC)
Foot Surgery
Fractures (Athletes)
Fusion (spinal treatment)
Gastric Bypass
Genetic Testing
Gynecologic Cancer
Gynecology
Hand Therapy
Head and Neck Cancer
Heart Care
Heart Surgery
High Risk Breast Cancer Center
Hip Surgery
Hormone Therapy
Hospitalists/Medical Professionals
Hyperbaric Oxygen Therapy Center
Image Guided Radiation Therapy (IGRT)
Injury Prevention Center
Inpatient Rehabilitation
Intensity Modulated Radiation Therapy (IMRT)
Intensive Care Unit (ICU)
Interventional Radiology
Joint replacements
Kidney Transplant
Knee Surgery
Kyphoplasty
Leukemia
Lung Cancer
Lymphoma
Mammography Screenings
Maternal-Fetal Medicine
Maternity
Maternity
Medical Professionals/Hospitalists
Medical Transportation - CareFlight
Mental Health Services
Minimally Invasive Surgery
Mother and Baby Services
MRI (Imaging)
Nanoknife
Neonatal Intensive Care
Neuro Rehabilitation
NeuroInterventional Center
Neuroscience
Neurosciences
Nutrition Services
OB-GYN
Obstetrics
Occupational Rehabilitation
Occupational Therapy
Oncology
Organ Transplant
Orthopedics
Orthopedics
Outpatient Physical Therapy
Pain Management
Palliative Care
Pancreatic Cancer
Perinatal Intensive Care
PET Scan (Imaging)
Pharmacy
Physiatry
Physical Therapy
Pre-Admission Testing
Premier HeartWorks
Preventive Cardiology
Prostate Cancer
Pulmonary Services
Radiofrequency ablation
Radiology
Radionuclide scan
Rehabilitation
Rehabilitation Institute of Ohio
Respiratory Care
Robotic Surgery
Shoulder Surgery
Shunt (Neuroscience)
Skin Cancer
Sleep Center
Solitaire Revascularization Device (Neurosciences)
Speech-Language Pathology
Spinal decompression surgery
Spinal disc replacement
Spinal fracture treatment
Spinal tumor surgery
Spine and back injuries (Orthopedics)
Spine Conditions and Treatments (Neuroscience)
Sports Medicine
Sports Medicine
Stereotaxis
Stomach Cancer
Stroke Treatments
Surgery Center
Surgical Oncology
Thoracic Surgery
Throat Cancer
Trauma
Ultrasound (Imaging)
Urological Cancer
Urology
Vascular Services
Venous Interventions
Vertebroplasty
Weight Loss Surgery (Bariatrics)
Weight Loss Surgery/Bariatrics
Wheelchair Clinic
Women' s Health
Women' s Heart Services
Women's Services
Wound Therapy
X-rays (Imaging)
Y-90 Radioembolization

COMPETITORS

Cincinnati Children' s Hospital
Deaconess Associations
Good Samaritan Hospital (IN)
Greene Memorial Hospital
HealthSouth
Kettering Health Network
MedCath
OhioHealth
The Christ Hospital Corporation
TriHealth
UC Health

HISTORICAL FINANCIALS

Company Type: Private

Income Statement FYE: December 31

	REVENUE ($ mil.)	NET INCOME ($ mil.)	NET PROFIT MARGIN	EMPLOYEES
12/07	622	44	7.1%	6,000
12/05	502	(0)	—	—
Annual Growth	11.3%	—	—	—

2007 Year-End Financials

Debt ratio: —
Return on equity: 7.10%
Cash ($ mil.): 9
Current ratio: 1.10
Long-term debt ($ mil.): —
Dividends
Yield: —
Payout: —
Market value ($ mil.): —

MICHIGAN MILK PRODUCERS ASSOCIATION

EXECUTIVES

Data Processing, Gregory Schulkey
Director Human Resources, Cindy Tilden
Director Manufactured Product Sales, Clayton Galarneau
Manager Credit and Insurance, Cheryl Schmandt
Director Milk Sales, Carl Rasch
Controller, Joseph Diglio
Director Member Relations and Public Affairs, Sheila Burkhardt
General Manager, John Dilland
President, Kenneth (Ken) Nobis
Manager Laboratory, Patti Huttula
VP, Bob Kran Jr.
Supervisor Merchandise, Joe Mishler
Treasurer, Velmar Green
Director, Earl Horning
Director, Tim Hood
Director, Dan Javor
Director, James Reid
Director, Deanna Stamp
Director, John Kronemeyer
Director, Rodney Daniels
Director, Mark Halbert
Director, Brent Wilson
Director, Eric Frahm
Auditors: Deloitte&ToucheLLP

LOCATIONS

HQ: MICHIGAN MILK PRODUCERS ASSOCIATION
41310 BRIDGE ST, NOVI, MI 483751302
Phone: 2484746672
Web: WWW.MIMILK.COM

PRODUCTS/OPERATIONS

Selected Products

Condensed skim milk
Condensed whole milk
Dried buttermilk
Dried whole milk
Ice cream mixes
Instant nonfat dry milk
Nonfat dry milk
Standardized cream
Standardized milk
Sweet condensed milk
Sweet cream butter

COMPETITORS

Associated Milk Producers
Dairy Farmers of America
Dean Foods
Foremost Farms
Land O' Lakes
Main Street Ingredients
Quality Chekd
Saputo

HISTORICAL FINANCIALS

Company Type: Private

Income Statement FYE: September 30

	REVENUE ($ mil.)	NET INCOME ($ mil.)	NET PROFIT MARGIN	EMPLOYEES
09/12	854	5	0.7%	200
09/11	870	6	0.7%	—
09/10	698	6	1.0%	—
09/09	556	0	—	—
Annual Growth	15.3%	—	—	—

2012 Year-End Financials

Debt ratio: —
Return on equity: 0.70%
Cash ($ mil.): 17
Current ratio: 1.20
Long-term debt ($ mil.): —
Dividends
Yield: —
Payout: —
Market value ($ mil.): —

MIDDLE TENNESSEE STATE UNIVERSITY

Middle Tennessee State University (MTSU) founded in 1911 as a school for teacher training offers bachelor's and master's degrees through its eight university colleges. The educational institution boasts basic and applied sciences business education and behavioral science honors liberal arts mass communication and graduate studies. The school bestows master's degrees in eight areas including business and education. MTSU also confers a Specialist in Education degree and doctorate degrees. It has an enrollment of more than 25000 students. MTSU is part of the State University and Community College System of Tennessee.

Geographic Reach

With its campus in Murfreesboro Tennessee Middle Tennessee State University is the oldest and largest public university in Middle Tennessee with more than 500 acres.

Strategy

To expand the types of degrees it confers MTSU in recent years has added to its doctoral programs. Besides a doctorate in Philosophy it now offers a doctorate in Computational Science Molecular Biosciences and Math & Science Education.

Financial Performance

Revenue increased 7% in fiscal 2012 as compared to 2011 due to rising tuition and fees thanks to a nearly 10% fee increase for the 2011-2012 academic year as well as an increase in grants and contracts. Net income dropped by 85% however during the same reporting period attributable to rising operating expenses due to the completion of building projects and routine expenses. It also logged a decline in non-operating revenues and expenses attributable to lower capital appropriation.

Operations

Notable alumni include Nobel Laureate James Buchanan (class of '40) and the late Senator Albert Gore Sr. (class of '32).

EXECUTIVES

VP Information Technology and CIO, Bruce Petryshak
President, Sidney A. McPhee
VP Student Affairs and Vice Provost Enrollment and Academic Services, Robert K. (Bob) Glenn
SVP, John W. Cothern
VP Development and University Relations, William J. (Joe) Bales
Provost, Brad Bartel

LOCATIONS

HQ: MIDDLE TENNESSEE STATE UNIVERSITY
1301 E MAIN ST, MURFREESBORO, TN 37132-0002
Phone: 615-898-2300
Web: WWW.MTSU.EDU

PRODUCTS/OPERATIONS

Selected Colleges

Basic and Applied Sciences
Behavioral and Health Sciences
Business
Education
Graduate Studies
University College
Liberal Arts
Mass Communication
University Honors

HISTORICAL FINANCIALS

Company Type: Private

Income Statement FYE: June 30

	REVENUE ($ mil.)	NET INCOME ($ mil.)	NET PROFIT MARGIN	EMPLOYEES
06/12	218	18	8.4%	2,610
06/06	5	0	—	—
06/05	5	(0)	—	—
06/03	116	0	0.0%	—
Annual Growth	7.2%	91.9%	—	—

2012 Year-End Financials

Debt ratio: —
Return on equity: 8.40%
Cash ($ mil.): 65
Current ratio: 1.40
Long-term debt ($ mil.): —
Dividends
Yield: —
Payout: —
Market value ($ mil.): —

MIDWEST ENERGY INC.

Some rural residents of the Sunflower State rely on Midwest Energy for their power and gas needs. The multi-utility serves approximately 48000 electricity customers and 42000 natural gas customers in central and western Kansas. It also has some power generation operations; it purchases most of its electric supply from wholesale marketers. The company's Midwest United Energy subsidiary is a competitive natural gas supplier in four states and its WestLand Energy unit sells propane to Kansas consumers. Midwest Energy has seen its power sales grow by 23% since 2006 and its natural gas sales by 17%.

A strong advocate of green energy as a way to cut carbon emissions comply with regulations and conserve energy Midwest Energy got 9% of its power from wind-generated sources in 2011. It also offers its customers How$mart program which allows residents to pay for energy-saving projects with no upfront costs through utility bills.

Investing heavily infrastructure both to keep up with demand and to replace aging systems in 2011 the company invested more than $26 million in electric construction and about $3 million in gas construction.

Midwest Energy reported a 14% jump in revenues in 2011 led by higher rates and very hot summer which increased power demand. Its net margin went up 11% thanks to the higher revenues a drop in per-capita gas costs (due to lower gas prices) and lower interest expenses.

The Central Kansas Electric Cooperative was formed in 1939 to provide electric service to customers in the rural counties surrounding Great Bend Kansas. Midwest Energy was formed in 1981 when the Central Kansas Electric Cooperative acquired investor-owned Central Kansas Power.

EXECUTIVES

VP Finance and CFO, Tom Meis
VP Customer Service, Pat Parke
President and General Manager, Earnie Lehman
Executive Assistant, Brenda Hutchison
VP Administrative Services, Sharon Dreher
VP Energy Management and Supply, Bill Dowling
Director Information Technology, Ed Rempe
Senior Accountant, Todd Gabel
Purchasing Agent, Deanna Wellbrock
Capital Credits Clerk, Vicki Schippers
Manager Corporate Communications, Bob Helm
Director Customer Service, Mchael Sadeghi
Director Economic and Community Development Hays, Bob Muirhead
Key Account Manager Great Bend, James Wright
Manager Energy Services Hays, Brian Dreiling
Energy Analyst and Account Manager Hays, Curtis (Curt) Carl
Energy Analyst and Account Manager Colby, Les Loker
Director Regulatory and Energy Services, Michael Volker
Rates and Services Representative, Kay Unruh
Compensation and Benefits Manager, Wanda Kuhn
Network Administrator, Ron VanEpps
IT Specialist, Gloria Aust
IT Specialist, Ann Schmidtberger
IT Support Specialist, Darren Stieben
Meter Reading Coordinator, Janet Ekberg
VP Engineering, Ray Harold
VP Operations, Fred Taylor
Operations Manager Hays, Brett Albert
Area Superintendent Colby, Jerry Schoenfeld
Area Superintendent Hays, Roger Mettlen
Energy Management Analyst, Nancy Urban
Field Service Representative Atwood, Chad Zimmerman
Field Service Representative Atwood, Todd Unruh
Field Operations Assistant Hays, Jackie Jones
Field Operations Assistant Hays, Kaye Hoffman
Field Operations Assistant Great Bend, Debbie Allen
Field Service Representative Great Bend, Dan Guesnier
Energy Analyst and Account Manager Hays, Greg Swob
Energy Analyst and Account Manager Great Bend, Mike Ruppe
Web Developer, Justin Cook
Safety Manager, Charles Staab
Operations Manager Great Bend, Don Augustine
Research Analyst, Michael Billinger
Senior Gas Scheduler, Dixie Riedel
Manager Transmission Operations and Scheduling, Aaron Rome
Field Service Representative Great Bend, Don Sherman
Field Service Representative Hays and WaKeeney, Craig Augustine
Field Service Representative Hays, Arlen Flax
Field Service Representative Phillipsburg, Brett Miles

LOCATIONS

HQ: MIDWEST ENERGY INC.
1330 CANTERBURY DR, HAYS, KS 67601-2708
Phone: 785-625-3437
Web: WWW.MWENERGY.COM

PRODUCTS/OPERATIONS

2011 Sales

	% of total
Electric	76
Gas	24
Total	**100**

2011 Fuel Mix

	% of total
Contract	55
Contract	31
Wind	9
Gneration	2
Market	2
Hydro	1
Total	**100**

COMPETITORS

AES
Black Hills
Edison International
Great Plains Energy
Westar Energy

HISTORICAL FINANCIALS

Company Type: Private

Income Statement FYE: December 31

	REVENUE ($ mil.)	NET INCOME ($ mil.)	NET PROFIT MARGIN	EMPLOYEES
12/12	197	16	8.4%	274
12/11	197	14	7.5%	—
12/10	176	13	7.7%	—
12/09	156	10	6.5%	—
Annual Growth	7.9%	17.7%	—	—

2012 Year-End Financials

Debt ratio: —
Return on equity: 8.40%
Cash ($ mil.): 0
Current ratio: 0.70
Long-term debt ($ mil.): —
Dividends
Yield: —
Payout: —
Market value ($ mil.): —

MIDWEST PETROLEUM COMPANY

LOCATIONS

HQ: MIDWEST PETROLEUM COMPANY
6760 SOUTHWEST AVE, SAINT LOUIS, MO 631432624
Phone: 3146475550
Web: WWW.MIDWESTPETRO.COM

HISTORICAL FINANCIALS

Company Type: Private

Income Statement FYE: December 31

	REVENUE ($ mil.)	NET INCOME ($ mil.)	NET PROFIT MARGIN	EMPLOYEES
12/09	203	1	0.7%	450
12/08	248	1	0.7%	—
12/07	1,530	0	0.0%	—
Annual Growth	(63.5%)	10392.4%	—	—

2009 Year-End Financials

Debt ratio: —
Return on equity: —
Cash ($ mil.): 1
Current ratio: 0.20
Long-term debt ($ mil.): —
Dividends
Yield: —
Payout: —
Market value ($ mil.): —

MILES HEALTH CARE INC

Miles Health Care provides acute and specialty health care service to the residents of Maine's Lincoln County. The not-for-profit company operates Miles Memorial Hospital –known as LincolnHealth Miles Campus –a rural medical center with about 40 beds and has emergency intensive care surgery and birthing departments. In addition Miles Health Care operates outpatient and specialty practice clinics physician practice offices and home health rehabilitation and hospice programs. It also provides long-term senior care through its nursing assisted and independent living facilities. Miles Health Care is a member of Lincoln County Healthcare (LincolnHealth) which is part of the MaineHealth network.

Change in Company Type

In 2013 parent MaineHealth combined two of its hospitals –Miles Memorial Hospital and St. Andrews Hospital –to form the two-campus LincolnHealth organization. The merger aimed to reduce operating expenses by more than $6 million annually as well as a more than $5 million increase revenue due to the combined organization's new status as a critical access hospital (which leads to higher reimbursements from Medicare and Medicaid plans). The increased earnings will allow the LincolnHealth campuses to reduce the price of services including x-rays laboratory tests and minor surgeries and procedures.

Geographic Reach

The LincolnHealth Miles Campus is located in Lincoln County Maine in the town of Damariscotta (which is north of Portland). The LincolnHealth St. Andrews Campus is located in Boothbay Harbor.

Operations

In addition to the two main hospital campuses LincolnHealth includes physician practices operated by the Lincoln Medical Partners as well as family care and urgent care centers. It also continues to operate nursing home health hospice and assisted-living organizations.

Strategy

Both the Miles and St. Andrews medical centers began using electronic health record (EHR) systems in 2010 which allows doctors to access a patient's past medical and diagnostic experiences to make the best decisions on current treatment plans and avoid duplication. Such EHR systems are part of an initiative to lower the cost of medical care in the US.

Company Background

Miles Health Care was established in 1941. Miles has historically been governed by a board of trustees (the Lincoln County Healthcare Board of Trustees) that also oversee the nearby St. Andrews Hospital; as an independently governed member of MaineHealth Miles has received planning consulting capital and group purchasing benefits. In 2013 St. Andrews Hospital and Miles Memorial Hospital were officially merged to serve as dual campuses of the single LincolnHealth hospital.

LOCATIONS

HQ: MILES HEALTH CARE INC
35 MILES ST, DAMARISCOTTA, ME 04543-4047
Phone: 207-563-1234
Web: WWW.MILESHEALTHCARE.ORG

PRODUCTS/OPERATIONS

Selected Centers and Services

Chase Point Adult Day Services
Chase Point Assisted Living
Cove' s Edge
Emergency Services
Family Support Services
General Surgery
Internal Medicine
Mammography
Miles & St. Andrews Home Health & Hospice
Miles Family Medicine
MMH BabyNet
Obstetrics
Orthopedic Services
Pediatric Services
Schooner Cove
Senior Services
Waldoboro Family Medicine
Wellness and Rehabilitation
Wiscasset Family Medicine
Women' s Services

COMPETITORS

Eastern Maine Healthcare Systems
MaineGeneral Health
Mercy Health System of Maine
Parkview Hospital
St. Joseph Healthcare

HISTORICAL FINANCIALS

Company Type: Private

Income Statement FYE: September 30

	REVENUE ($ mil.)	NET INCOME ($ mil.)	NET PROFIT MARGIN	EMPLOYEES
09/09	1,042	12	1.2%	800
09/08	14	0	3.9%	—
09/06	58	3	5.9%	—
09/05	52	(0)	—	—
Annual Growth	111.6%	—	—	—

2009 Year-End Financials

Debt ratio: —
Return on equity: 1.20%
Cash ($ mil.): 0
Current ratio: 0.70
Long-term debt ($ mil.): —
Dividends
Yield: —
Payout: —
Market value ($ mil.): —

MILHELM ATTEA & BROS. INC.

LOCATIONS

HQ: MILHELM ATTEA & BROS. INC.
1509 CLINTON ST, BUFFALO, NY 142063008
Phone: 7168221665

HISTORICAL FINANCIALS

Company Type: Private

Income Statement FYE: December 31

	REVENUE ($ mil.)	NET INCOME ($ mil.)	NET PROFIT MARGIN	EMPLOYEES
12/08	206	3	1.8%	30
12/06	226	1	0.7%	—
12/05	192	2	1.0%	—
12/04	237	0	—	—
Annual Growth	(3.4%)	—	—	—

2008 Year-End Financials

Debt ratio: —
Return on equity: 1.80%
Cash ($ mil.): 6
Current ratio: 21.10
Long-term debt ($ mil.): —
Dividends
Yield: —
Payout: —
Market value ($ mil.): —

MILLER ELECTRIC COMPANY

Miller Electric ‚ÂCompany flips the switch for projects primarily in the Southeast. The Florida-based electrical contractor provides services ‚Âincluding construction installation renovation and maintenance of electrical systems. ‚ÂThe company serves ‚Âmany industries including the communications construction health care and transportation segments. Outside of ‚ÂFlorida the company has offices ‚Âin Alabama Arkansas Georgia North Carolina Virginia Texas ‚Âand Washington DC. Clients have included ‚Â Anheuser Busch ‚Â Bank of America ‚Â Blue Cross and Blue Shield and the ‚ÂUniversity of North Florida. Miller Electric was founded by Henry G. Miller in 1928.

Miller has found success by providing a myriad of installation services to the growing data center and Intelligent Transportation Systems (ITS) fields. ‚ÂITS technologies are used ‚Âto manage vehicle traffic and include intersection traffic signals dynamic message signs vehicle detection systems weather advisory systems and highway advisory radios. The company also installs the required power services and switching stations.

Most recently Miller also has diversified into the renewable energy market. In 2010 the company built a high tech solar project in Jacksonville that provides more than 12 megawatts of power for the city.

EXECUTIVES

V Pres, Daniel Brown
Vice President Roadway And Uty, Tom Lesso
Vice President, Eddie Ohalloran

LOCATIONS

HQ: MILLER ELECTRIC COMPANY
2251 ROSSELLE ST, JACKSONVILLE, FL 322043125
Phone: 9043888000
Web: WWW.MECOJAX.COM

PRODUCTS/OPERATIONS

Selected Services

Access control
Audio/visual systems
Building Information Modeling (BIM)
Communications systems and services
Control systems
Electrical construction and repair
Fiber optic network installation
Fire protection systems
Maintenance Services
Network cabling installation and maintenance Specialty systems
Paging and intercom
Site lighting
UPS and generator installation and maintenance

COMPETITORS

Dycom
Edd Helms
Honshy Electric
Johnson Contractors
Megatran
Pike Corporation
Tri-City Electrical Contractors

HISTORICAL FINANCIALS

Company Type: Private

Income Statement FYE: September 30

	REVENUE ($ mil.)	NET INCOME ($ mil.)	NET PROFIT MARGIN	EMPLOYEES
09/14	216	6	3.0%	691
09/13	204	2	1.3%	—
09/12	183	0	0.1%	—
09/11	183	0	—	—
Annual Growth	5.7%	—	—	—

2014 Year-End Financials

Debt ratio: —
Return on equity: 3.00%
Cash ($ mil.): 4
Current ratio: 1.60
Long-term debt ($ mil.): —
Dividends
Yield: —
Payout: —
Market value ($ mil.): —

MILLER TRANSPORTATION SERVICES INC.

No beer here. Tank truck carrier Miller Transporters hauls bulk commodities such as chemicals and petroleum products from a network of more than ‚Â20 ‚Âterminals in the eastern half of the US. The company operates a fleet of some 500 tractors and 1100 trailers and carries cargo domestically as well as between the US and Canada and Mexico. ‚ÂA sister company Miller Intermodal Logistics arranges the transportation of liquid bulk cargo worldwide. The company that became Miller Transporters was founded in 1942 by Harold Dewey Miller. ‚ÂIts founder's family still owns Miller Transporters.

EXECUTIVES

VP Finance, Joe Hegi
VP Operations, Larry Bagwell

VP Human Resources and Insurance, Terry Malone
EVP, Hal Miller III
President, Lee Miller
VP Sales and Marketing, Steven Tapscott

LOCATIONS

HQ: MILLER TRANSPORTATION SERVICES INC.
5500 HIGHWAY 80 W, JACKSON, MS 392093507
Phone: 6018566526
Web: WWW.MILLERT.COM

COMPETITORS

Groendyke Transport
Quality Distribution
Superior Bulk Logistics
Trimac

HISTORICAL FINANCIALS

Company Type: Private

Income Statement FYE: December 31

	REVENUE ($ mil.)	NET INCOME ($ mil.)	NET PROFIT MARGIN	EMPLOYEES
12/13	102	0	0.7%	1,000
12/12	102	1	1.1%	—
12/11	96	0	0.4%	—
12/10	87	0	—	—
Annual Growth	5.6%	—	—	—

2013 Year-End Financials

Debt ratio: —
Return on equity: 0.70%
Cash ($ mil.): 0
Current ratio: 0.60
Long-term debt ($ mil.): —
Dividends
Yield: —
Payout: —
Market value ($ mil.): —

MILLMAN LUMBER COMPANY

LOCATIONS

HQ: MILLMAN LUMBER COMPANY
9264 MANCHESTER RD, SAINT LOUIS, MO 631442636
Phone: 3149616195
Web: WWW.MILLMANLUMBER.COM

HISTORICAL FINANCIALS

Company Type: Private

Income Statement FYE: October 31

	REVENUE ($ mil.)	NET INCOME ($ mil.)	NET PROFIT MARGIN	EMPLOYEES
10/14	255	2	1.0%	80
10/13	245	2	0.9%	—
10/12	197	2	1.1%	—
10/11	158	0	—	—
Annual Growth	17.2%	—	—	—

2014 Year-End Financials

Debt ratio: —
Return on equity: 1.00%
Cash ($ mil.): 2
Current ratio: 0.70
Long-term debt ($ mil.): —
Dividends
Yield: —
Payout: —
Market value ($ mil.): —

MILLS-PENINSULA HEALTH SERVICES

With health facilities south of San Francisco Mills-Peninsula Health Services provides care to communities in and around Burlingame California. The group includes the 240-bed Mills-Peninsula Medical Center an acute-care hospital in Burlingame; Mills Health Center an outpatient diagnostic surgery and rehabilitation facility in San Mateo; and physician practice offices in surrounding areas. The facilities provide specialty services such as cancer care cardiovascular therapy behavioral health radiology respiratory care and senior services. Mills-Peninsula Health Services is part of the Sutter Health network.

Operations

Along with sister company Palo Alto Medical Foundation Mills-Peninsula forms the Peninsula Coastal Region division of Sutter Health. Together the organizations operate collaborative medical clinic and physician practice locations.

Strategy

The organization opened the doors on its newly constructed Mills-Peninsula Medical Center in Burlingame in 2011. The $618 million project added a new 240-bed main hospital facility (to replace the aging Peninsula Medical Center facility) with all private patient rooms as well as a 180000 sq. ft. medical office building and a parking garage. The new hospital is compliant with California's new earthquake safety requirements. The hospital enhanced its surgical capabilities in 2013 with the addition of a da Vinci Si robotic system for surgical procedures.

Company Background

Founded in 1908 the Mills hospital was named for philanthropist Elizabeth Mills Reid who helped to fund the medical facility. The Peninsula facility was founded as a public hospital district in 1954. The two hospitals merged in 1985 and became part of Sutter Health the following year.

EXECUTIVES

CEO, Robert W. (Bob) Merwin
CFO, Iftikhar Hussain
COO, Dolores Gomez
Medical Director, Michael Wood
Director Of Surgery Services, Sheila Littrell

LOCATIONS

HQ: MILLS-PENINSULA HEALTH SERVICES
1501 TROUSDALE DR, BURLINGAME, CA 94010-4506
Phone: 650-696-5400
Web: WWW.MILLS-PENINSULA.ORG

COMPETITORS

Alta Bates Summit Medical Center
California Pacific Medical Center
Dignity Health
Good Samaritan Hospital (San Jose)
John Muir Health
Marin General Hospital
Sequoia Healthcare District
The Palo Alto Medical Foundation
UCSF Medical

HISTORICAL FINANCIALS

Company Type: Private

Income Statement FYE: December 31

	REVENUE ($ mil.)	NET INCOME ($ mil.)	NET PROFIT MARGIN	EMPLOYEES
12/11	572	(34)	—	2,200
12/09	533	56	10.6%	—
12/02	274	18	6.6%	—
12/01	267	20	7.5%	—
Annual Growth	7.9%	—	—	—

2011 Year-End Financials

Debt ratio: —
Return on equity: (-5.90%)
Cash ($ mil.): 25
Current ratio: 1.50
Long-term debt ($ mil.): —
Dividends
Yield: —
Payout: —
Market value ($ mil.): —

MINERS INCORPORATED

EXECUTIVES

General Counsel, Bruce Sanderson

LOCATIONS

HQ: MINERS INCORPORATED
5065 MILLER TRUNK HWY, HERMANTOWN, MN 558111442
Phone: 2187295882
Web: WWW.SUPERONEFOODS.COM

2013 Stores

	No.
Minnesota	21
Wisconsin	6
Michigan	5
North	1
Total	33

PRODUCTS/OPERATIONS

2013 Stores

	No.
Super One	29
U-Save	3
Marketplace	1
Total	33

COMPETITORS

Cub Foods
IGA
Kroger
Meijer
Roundy' s
Spartan Stores
Target Corporation
Wal-Mart

HISTORICAL FINANCIALS

Company Type: Private

Income Statement FYE: June 29

	REVENUE ($ mil.)	NET INCOME ($ mil.)	NET PROFIT MARGIN	EMPLOYEES
06/13	530	30	5.7%	2,300
06/12	501	31	6.3%	—
06/11	475	30	6.4%	—
06/10	463	0	—	—
Annual Growth	4.6%	—	—	—

2013 Year-End Financials

Debt ratio: —
Return on equity: 5.70%
Cash ($ mil.): 7
Current ratio: 0.30
Long-term debt ($ mil.): —
Dividends
Yield: —
Payout: —
Market value ($ mil.): —

MINNKOTA POWER COOPERATIVE INC.

The Minnkota Power Cooperative keeps the juice flowing to power users in northwestern Minnesota and eastern North Dakota. The generation and transmission cooperative supplies electricity to its 11 member-owner distribution cooperatives and as operating agent for the ,ÂNorthern Municipal Power Agency ,Âto 12 municipal systems to serve more than 118000 retail customers in a 34500-sq.-mi. region. Minnkota owns and operates ,Âthe 235 MW lignite coal-fired generation Unit ,Â 1 of the ,ÂMilton R. Young plant ,Âin Center North Dakota and 30% of the 400 MW lignite coal-fired Coyote Station near Beulah. ,ÂThe company also has wind power assets.

Minnkota ,Âoperates the 455 MW unit 2 at the Milton R. Young plant (owned by Square Butte Cooperative) on behalf of the Northern Municipal Power Agency. ,Â

To meet emission standards and diversify its portfolio ,Â Minnkota is pushing green power through its ownership stakes in ,Âtwo wind turbine projects. In 2010 ,ÂMinnkota had ,Â239 MW of wind capacity in its power supply portfolio enough to meet about 30% of its overall power distribution obligations.

Planning for the long term in 2010 ,Âthe cooperative ,Âsigned a strategic agreement with utility ,ÂMinnesota Power ,Âto secure additional energy (227.5 MW) ,Âfrom the Milton R. Young plant between 2013 and 2026. Minnesota Power will use a 465-mile transmission line bought from Square Butte Cooperative to deliver wind energy that is developed by Minnkota.

A 5% rate hike and a surcharge lifted sales in 2010 and topped increased operating expenses allowing ,Âthe company to post a healthy net margin.

Minnkota was founded in 1940 as part of the rural electrification drive of the Depression-era administration of Franklin D. Roosevelt.

EXECUTIVES

Vp Transmission, Wally Lang
Auditors: BradyMartz&AssociatesP.C.

LOCATIONS

HQ: MINNKOTA POWER COOPERATIVE INC.
1822 MILL RD, GRAND FORKS, ND 582031536
Phone: 7017954000
Web: WWW.MINNKOTACGF.COM

PRODUCTS/OPERATIONS

2010 Sales

	$ mil.	% of total
Energy		
Members	181	73
Other	10	4
Other	56	23
Total	**249**	**100**

COMPETITORS

Basin Electric Power
Black Hills Power
Great River Energy

HISTORICAL FINANCIALS

Company Type: Private

Income Statement FYE: December 31

	REVENUE ($ mil.)	NET INCOME ($ mil.)	NET PROFIT MARGIN	EMPLOYEES
12/14	145	2	1.7%	355
12/13	317	7	2.4%	—
12/12	137	2	1.7%	—
12/08	200	0	—	—
Annual Growth	(5.2%)	—	—	—

2014 Year-End Financials

Debt ratio: —
Return on equity: 1.70%
Cash ($ mil.): 10
Current ratio: 0.70
Long-term debt ($ mil.): —
Dividends
Yield: —
Payout: —
Market value ($ mil.): —

MISSION PHARMACAL COMPANY

EXECUTIVES

EVP, James K. Walsdorf
President, Neil B. Walsdorf Jr.
CEO, Neill Walsdorf Sr.
President Commercial Operations, Terry Herring

LOCATIONS

HQ: MISSION PHARMACAL COMPANY
10999 W IH 10 STE 1000, SAN ANTONIO, TX 782301355
Phone: 2106968400
Web: WWW.MISSIONPHARMACAL.COM

PRODUCTS/OPERATIONS

Selected Products

Dermatology
- Eletone
- Texacort

Pediatrics
- Asmalpred
- Dr. Smith' s
- Lycell
- Texacort

Urology
- Lithostat
- Thiola
- Uribel
- Urocit-K

Women' s health
- Calcet
- CitraNatal
- Ferralet 90
- Natafort
- Tindamax
- Uribel

COMPETITORS

Actavis Inc.
Alere
Bayer AG
Chattem
Contract Pharmacal
Depomed
Eli Lilly
Endo
GlaxoSmithKline
HealthTronics
Hi-Tech Pharmacal
Johnson & Johnson
Mylan
Nature' s Sunshine
Nutraceutical International
Perrigo
Sandoz International GmbH
Teva
Upsher-Smith
Warner Chilcott
Xanodyne Pharmaceuticals

HISTORICAL FINANCIALS

Company Type: Private

Income Statement FYE: April 30

	REVENUE ($ mil.)	NET INCOME ($ mil.)	NET PROFIT MARGIN	EMPLOYEES
04/14	152	(1)	—	495
04/13	124	7	6.2%	—
04/12	118	18	15.5%	—
04/11	95	0	—	—
Annual Growth	16.9%	—	—	—

2014 Year-End Financials

Debt ratio: —
Return on equity: (-1.10%)
Cash ($ mil.): 4
Current ratio: 0.50
Long-term debt ($ mil.): —
Dividends
Yield: —
Payout: —
Market value ($ mil.): —

MISSISSIPPI COUNTY ELECTRIC COOPERATIVE INC.

EXECUTIVES

President and CEO, Larry Hellums
SVP Cooperative Services, Pat O'Neal
VP Finance and Accounting, Mike Parrish
COO, Brad Harrison
Billing and Office Supervisor, Annette Parish
Operations Supervisor, Keeley Wheeler
Construction Supervisor, Tommy Jones
Chairman, Robert Davis
Secretary Treasurer, Steve West
Vice Chairman, Neil Burge

LOCATIONS

HQ: MISSISSIPPI COUNTY ELECTRIC COOPERATIVE INC.
510 N BROADWAY ST, BLYTHEVILLE, AR 723152732
Phone: 8707634563
Web: WWW.MCECI.COM

HISTORICAL FINANCIALS

Company Type: Private

Income Statement FYE: December 31

	REVENUE ($ mil.)	NET INCOME ($ mil.)	NET PROFIT MARGIN	EMPLOYEES
12/13	157	0	0.2%	16
12/09	88	2	2.4%	—
12/08	150	4	3.1%	—
12/07	141	0	—	—
Annual Growth	1.7%	—	—	—

2013 Year-End Financials

Debt ratio: —
Return on equity: 0.20%
Cash ($ mil.): 4
Current ratio: 1.40
Long-term debt ($ mil.): —
Dividends
Yield: —
Payout: —
Market value ($ mil.): —

MISSOURI STATE UNIVERSITY

When Missouri students say "show me" Missouri State University happily obliges. It is the state's second-largest university (after University of Missouri) with an enrollment of 23000 students. The school offers about 88 undergraduate majors 133 undergraduate minors and 50 graduate majors including 14 masters 3 doctoral degrees and one specialist degree. The university' coursework includes accounting biology criminology and physical geography. Missouri State awarded almost 4370 degrees in 2012. It also hosted some 16 NCAA Division One sports teams that year.

Geographic Reach

In addition to its main campus in Springfield the university has campuses in Mountain Grove and West Plains. Missouri State also operates various other special facilities including the Darr Agricultural Center (southwest Springfield) the Jordan Valley Innovation Center (downtown Springfield) the Bull Shoals Field Station near Forsyth Baker's Acres and Observatory near Marshfield and the Missouri State University Graduate Center in Joplin. The university also has a branch campus at Liaoning Normal University in Dalian China.

Operations

The university has six Academic colleges one School of Agriculture and one Graduate College. It has 4000 faculty and staff members. The student-to-faculty ratio is approximately 19:1. Missouri State enrolls students from all 50 US states and 85 foreign countries. The Extended Campus provides learning opportunities through telecourses Internet-based instruction and through BearNet an interactive video network.

Financial Performance

Missouri State's revenues increased by 2% in 2012 due to higher tuition and fees and better returns from sales and services and auxiliary enterprises. Organic growth helped to lift revenues every year between 2009 and 2012.

However net income dropped by 55% in 2012 due to a decline in non-operating revenues caused by a drop in state appropriations federal grants and contracts and investment income.

Company Background

The school was founded in 1905 as the Fourth District Normal School a teacher training institution; it changed its name to Missouri State University 100 years later.

EXECUTIVES

President, Michael T. (Mike) Nietzel, age 62
VP Administrative and Information Services, Greg Burris
VP Research and Economic Development, Jim Baker
Dean College of Business Administration, Ron Bottin
Provost, Belinda R. McCarthy
General Counsel, Clif Smart
Assistant VP Enrollment Management and Services and Director Admissions, Don Simpson
Executive Director Alumni Relations, Julie Ebersold
President for University Advancement, Brent Dunn
Associate Dean of Library Services, Neosha Mackey
Director Facilities Management, Bob Eckels
Acting Dean of Students, Mike Jungers
Director Career Center, Jack Hunter
CFO, Nila Hayes
General Counsel, Penni Groves
President for Administrative and Information Services, Ken McClure
President - Missouri State University, Earle Doman
President for Diversity and Inclusion, Kenneth Coopwood
Assistant Director of Human Resources, Paula M. Wilhelm
Board Member, Michael J. (Mike) Duggan, age 63
VP Board of Governors, Mary Sheid
Board Member, Phyllis Washington
Board Member, Ryan Sivill
Board Member, James H. Buford
Board Member, John L. Winston
Board Member, Brian Hammons

LOCATIONS

HQ: MISSOURI STATE UNIVERSITY
901 S NATIONAL AVE, SPRINGFIELD, MO 65897-0001
Phone: 417-836-5000
Web: WWW.MISSOURISTATE.EDU

HISTORICAL FINANCIALS

Company Type: Private

Income Statement FYE: June 30

	REVENUE ($ mil.)	NET INCOME ($ mil.)	NET PROFIT MARGIN	EMPLOYEES
06/12	201	16	8.4%	2,066
06/11	190	33	17.7%	—
06/10	189	30	16.0%	—
06/09	177	12	6.9%	—
Annual Growth	4.3%	11.4%	—	—

2012 Year-End Financials

Debt ratio: —
Return on equity: 8.40%
Cash ($ mil.): 81
Current ratio: 2.10
Long-term debt ($ mil.): —
Dividends
Yield: —
Payout: —
Market value ($ mil.): —

MMR GROUP INC.

Specialty contractor MMR Group provides electrical contracting instrumentation and technical services worldwide to clients in the oil and gas; power generation; chemical and petrochemical; and industrial manufacturing industries. It also offers services in offshore marine and platform environments. Its MMR Power Solutions division specializes in constructing on site power generation systems for manufacturing plants and other facilities. Clients include Chevron Shell BP Merck Air Liquide DuPont and 3M. MMR Group which was founded in 1990 has offices in the US mostly near the Gulf of Mexico but also in California Arizona and Colorado. It has international offices in Venezuela.

Subsidiary Southwestern Power Group in Arizona typically constructs and operates gas-fired power plants. It also has partnered with four other companies to construct a 500-mile transmission line called the SunZia Southwest Transmission Project. The line spanning Arizona and New Mexico will provide 3000 megawatts of capacity generated from wind solar and geothermal energy sources. The project to be complete in 2013 is designed to meet the growing need for clean renewable energy. Another project the $1 billion Bowie Power Station in Arizona will utilize clean-burning natural gas.

EXECUTIVES

CEO, James R. Rutland
EVP, Allen R. Boudreaux
VP Marketing, Grady Saucier

LOCATIONS

HQ: MMR GROUP INC.
15961 AIRLINE HWY, BATON ROUGE, LA 70817-7412
Phone: 225-756-5090
Web: WWW.MMRGRP.COM

PRODUCTS/OPERATIONS

Selected Services

Instrumentation
- Air supply installation
- Control room equipment installation
- Instrument installation
- Process leads
- Panel fabrication
- Signal wiring

Electrical
- Controls
- Electrical equipment setting
- Grounding
- Lighting
- Power distribution

Technical
- Calibration
- Commissioning
- Detail design
- High voltage testing
- Instrument procurement
- Loop check
- Maintenance
- Start up assistance
- System analysis

Selected Divisions

MMR Constructors
MMR International
MMR Power Solutions
MMR Offshore Services
MMR Technical Services
Southwestern Power Group

COMPETITORS

Alberici
EMCOR
Fisk Electric
Industrial Specialty Contractors
MYR Group
Matrix Service
Turner Industries

HISTORICAL FINANCIALS

Company Type: Private

Income Statement FYE: December 31

	REVENUE ($ mil.)	NET INCOME ($ mil.)	NET PROFIT MARGIN	EMPLOYEES
12/12	501	19	3.9%	2,500
12/11	254	11	4.4%	—
12/10	0	0	—	—
12/09	0	0	—	—
Annual Growth	—	—	—	—

2012 Year-End Financials

Debt ratio: —
Return on equity: 3.90%
Cash ($ mil.): 0
Current ratio: 1.40
Long-term debt ($ mil.): —
Dividends
Yield: —
Payout: —
Market value ($ mil.): —

MNP CORPORATION

If you are fascinated with fasteners then MNP will galvanize your senses. MNP manufactures a plethora of precision fasteners and cold formed components including screws rivets washers small stampings as well as screw machine parts. Its services range from plating to annealing flat-rolling pickling hot-dip galvanizing and coatings. General Fasteners Cadon Plating & Coatings Marathon Metals and Ohio Pickling & Processing are a few of MNP's affiliated companies that produce a medley of metal parts and jointly operate the GFC/MNP Engineering Center in Michigan. The company serves the automotive heavy truck military and industrial markets. Founder and chairman Larry Berman owns the company.

Operations

MNP is considered a Tier One supplier to the Big Three automobile makers in Detroit and operates four production facilities within its Fastener Manufacturing division. The company has grown to encompass a dozen operating and support divisions and subsidiaries which provide steel and wire fabricating steel treating washer manufacture tool and die capabilities dip/spin coatings cold forming as well as engineering and design services.

Strategy

MNP is counting on the prediction that fasteners for aerospace and construction (especially residential building) applications are expected to outpace standard fasteners. (It develops and manufactures fasteners for both applications.) The company's biggest competition comes from alternative fastening products such as industrial adhesives and clinching and welding. It also contends with falling raw material prices which cause fastener prices to decrease.

Company Background

MNP was founded in 1970 as Michigan Nut Products.

EXECUTIVES

President CEO, Thomas (Tom) Klein
Executive Vice President CFO, Craig L. Stormer
Chairman, Larry S. Berman
VP Sales and Marketing, David Cronovich
VP Processing Divisions, Floyd Cushman
VP Human Resources and Purchasing, Randall G. (Randy) Allison
Auditors: KleimanCarney&Greenbaum

LOCATIONS

HQ: MNP CORPORATION
44225 UTICA RD, UTICA, MI 48317-5464
Phone: 586-254-1320
Web: WWW.MNP.COM

PRODUCTS/OPERATIONS

Selected Products and Services

Engineering and design
- Cold forming tooling
- Engineered product applications and solutions
  - Alternative cam bolt assembly design
  - Automated pre-assembly of fasteners and other cylindrical parts
  - Bolt retainer
  - Cold formed specials
  - Isolator bolt
  - Rotatable captured nut
  - VTR bolt pre-located bolts for assembly
- Engineered stamping and fastener assemblies
- Joint design and problem solving
- Stamping tooling

Fastener and metal part coatings
- Organic coatings
- Phosphate based coatings
- Plating - mechanical and electroplated metals

Fastener and metal part heat treating
- Carburize
- Quench and temper

Male threaded fasteners
- Specialty engineered fasteners
- Standard fasteners
- Licenses
  - Bolt Retainer
  - Lo-Driv
  - MAThread
  - REMFORM
  - Taptite
  - Torx and Torx Plus
  - VTR Bolt

Stampings
- Powder metal parts
- Small metal parts
- Washers

Steel sales and processing
- Rod and wire

Tooling and repair parts
- Machine repair

COMPETITORS

A. Raymond Tinnerman
AZZ Galvanizing Services
Anixter Fasteners
Chicago Rivet
Federal Screw Works
Handy & Harman
Illinois Tool Works
LISI
Lawson Products
MacLean-Fogg
Metric & Multistandard
Nucor
Park-Ohio Holdings
PennEngineering
Porteous Fastener
TriMas
Valmont Industries
Worthington Industries
Wurth Group

HISTORICAL FINANCIALS

Company Type: Private

Income Statement FYE: November 30

	REVENUE ($ mil.)	NET INCOME ($ mil.)	NET PROFIT MARGIN	EMPLOYEES
11/12	182	10	6.0%	1,000
11/11	173	8	4.7%	—
11/10	150	5	3.7%	—
11/09	94	1	1.3%	—
Annual Growth	24.4%	105.7%	—	—

2012 Year-End Financials

Debt ratio: ——
Return on equity: 6.00%
Cash ($ mil.): 0
Current ratio: 1.10
Long-term debt ($ mil.): —
Dividends
Yield: —
Payout: —
Market value ($ mil.): —

MODERN WOODMEN OF AMERICA

No need to pitch a tent to have Modern Woodmen in your camp. One of the largest fraternal benefit societies in the US Modern Woodmen of America provides annuities life insurance and other financial savings products to more than 770000 members through some 1500 agents. The group founded in 1883 is organized into "camps" (or chapters) that provide financial social recreational and service benefits to members. Founder Joseph Cullen Root chose the society's name to compare pioneering woodmen clearing forests to men using life insurance to remove the financial burdens their families could face upon their deaths.

Operations

The organization claims some 2300 family and summit chapters and more than 870 youth clubs nationwide. In addition to financial services the chapters also offer social activities and community service opportunities for members and their families. In addition to life insurance and annuities the company offers retirement accounts including IRAs college savings plans investment assistance and other insurance products.

Subsidiary MWA Financial Services offers securities and brokered insurance products. The MWA-Bank (dba Modern Woodmen Bank) division provides retail banking services.

Financial Performance

All told the company has more than $12 billion in assets and roughly $35 billion of life insurance in force. In 2010 the society's total premium income exceeded $1 billion for the first time. Premiums in 2011 and 2012 came in at around $1.1 billion.

Benefit payouts to members during 2012 totaled $712.7 million a 2% increase over 2012 and member life and annuity policy dividends amounted to another $15.7 million. Net operating gain was reported at $56.5 million bringing the surplus and reserve levels above the $1.3 billion mark.

Strategy

The company enhances its operations by adding new products as well as through marketing efforts for existing products. For instance in 2012 Modern Woodsmen's financial representatives increased promotional efforts for life insurance products leading to a 5% increase in certificates and a 12% rise new policies that year. The increase in life insurance sales was also attributed to the Planning for Life program a system introduced in 2011 to help members understand the role of life insurance in financial planning.

Mergers and Acquisitions

In 2012 Modern Woodmen grew its membership by more than 17000 through the acquisition of Equitable Reserve Association. Through the combination Modern Woodmen assumed the assets liabilities and operations of Equitable Reserve.

Company Background

Although Modern Woodmen's roots are tangled with Woodmen of the World Life Insurance Society the two fraternal benefit societies are not related.

EXECUTIVES

Vice President Information Services, Rick Click
Vice President Marketing And Public, Steven Haack

LOCATIONS

HQ: MODERN WOODMEN OF AMERICA
1701 1ST AVE, ROCK ISLAND, IL 61201-8779
Phone: 309-793-5537
Web: WWW.MODERN-WOODMEN.ORG

PRODUCTS/OPERATIONS

Selected Products

Annuities (fixed immediate and variable; through MWA Financial Services)

Banking (MWABank)
- Certificates of Deposit
- Checking and savings accounts
- Credit cards and gift cards
- First mortgage and refinancing home loans
- Home equity loans

Insurance (through MWAGIA)
- Dental and vision insurance
- Disability income insurance
- Group employee benefits
- Group voluntary benefits
- Impaired risk life insurance
- International life and health insurance
- Long-term care insurance
- Major medical insurance
- Medicare supplement insurance

Investment (through MWA Financial Services)
- Brokerage services
- College savings plans
- Mutual funds
- Retirement plans

Life Insurance
- Term life insurance
- Term life insurance for children
- Universal life insurance
- Whole life insurance

COMPETITORS

Allstate
MassMutual
MetLife
Nationwide Financial
New York Life
Northwestern Mutual
Prudential
Reliance Standard
Royal Neighbors Of America
State Farm
Thrivent Financial
Woodmen of the World Life Insurance

HISTORICAL FINANCIALS

Company Type: Private

Income Statement FYE: December 31

	ASSETS ($ mil.)	NET INCOME ($ mil.)	INCOME AS % OF ASSETS	EMPLOYEES
12/07	8,318	96	1.2%	2,100
12/06	7,928	99	1.3%	—
Annual Growth	4.9%	(2.6%)	—	—

2007 Year-End Financials

Debt ratio: —
Return on equity: 9.10%
Cash ($ mil.): 40
Current ratio: —
Long-term debt ($ mil.): —
Dividends
Yield: —
Payout: —
Market value ($ mil.): —

MONMOUTH MEDICAL CENTER INC.

Monmouth Medical Center is a 530-bed tertiary care teaching hospital providing comprehensive health care to residents of central New Jersey. The not-for-profit medical center offers services ranging from orthopedics diagnostics and obstetric care to surgery dentistry and geriatric services. The medical center campus also includes a children's hospital a cancer center a neuroscience institute an outpatient care clinic and hospice and home health facilities. Monmouth Medical Center is a major teaching affiliate of the Drexel University College of Medicine in Philadelphia. The hospital is an affiliate of the Saint Barnabas Healthcare System.

Geographic Reach

Monmouth Medical Center is located on about 20 acres in Long Branch New Jersey near the Atlantic Ocean. The campus includes the main 16-wing hospital and and about 16 other buildings including resident physician dwellings a day care center a medical education and training facility and a Ronald McDonald House.

The hospital serves a territory consisting of Monmouth Ocean and Middlesex counties with a total of about one million residents. It has outpatient locations in Colts Neck Howell Long Branch Ocean Township and Shrewsbury.

Operations

Monmouth Medical Center handles 19000 inpatient admissions each year as well as 49000 emergency room visits. Its outpatient clinic handles some 126000 appointments annually. The hospital has 700 doctors representing 60 specialties on its staff.

Strategy

The hospital has conducted recent expansion projects including additions of new a new cancer center surgical suites and a family center. In 2013 it opened a new postpartum wing and newborn nursery as well as a larger neonatal ICU. Monmouth Medical Center also extended its pediatric and oncology programs by forming partnerships with other area hospitals in 2012.

Company Background

Monmouth Medical Center was founded in 1887. It has expanded over the years to provide a number of specialist services including high-tech offerings such as robotic surgery.

EXECUTIVES

Chairman Director, Michael Goldfarb
Program Director, Debra LaRusso
Vice-President System Corporate Finance, Thomas G. Scott

LOCATIONS

HQ: MONMOUTH MEDICAL CENTER INC.
300 2ND AVE, LONG BRANCH, NJ 07740-6395
Phone: 732-222-5200

PRODUCTS/OPERATIONS

Selected Centers and Services

Anesthesiology Services
Behavioral Health Network
Brain Tumor Center (David S. Zocchi)
The Breast Center (Jacqueline M. Wilentz Comprehensive)
Burn Center
Cancer Services
Cardiac Services
Cardiac Surgery
Children' s Hospital at Monmouth (Pediatrics)
Cleft Palate Center
Cord Blood Banking Program
Cosmetic Surgery
Cranmer Ambulatory Surgery Center
Critical Care Services
Diabetes Education - Center for Diabetes Education
Dental Medicine
Diagnostic Imaging Services
The Eisenberg Family Center
Emergency Services
Epilepsy Monitoring Program
Extracorporeal Membrane Oxygenation Program (ECMO)
The Gamma Knife Center
Geriatric Emergency Medicine (GEM) Unit
Geriatric Health Center
Head & Neck Surgery
Hernias Repair Institute for the Treatment of Complex
HIV/AIDS Program
Home Health Care
Home Infusion Care
Hospice
Hyperbaric Oxygen Therapy
Integrative Medicine (Center for)
Joint Replacement and Spine Center
Medical Records
Medical Alert/Lifeline
Medicine (Department of)
Minimally Invasive Surgery
Monmouth Family Health Center
Neonatal Intensive Care Unit (Regional Newborn Center)
Neuroscience Institute
Nutritional Counseling
Obstetrics/Gynecological Services
Occupational Medicine
Orthopaedic Services
Outpatient Services Location
Pain Management Program
Palliative Care
Pastoral Care
Pathology & Laboratory Services
Pediatric Services
Pediatric Subspecialty Center at Toms River The
Pediatric Surgery
Pharmacy Department
Plastic Surgery
Podiatry Services
Pre-Admission Testing Services
Psychiatric Services
Pulmonary Services
Radiation Oncology
Rehabilitation Services
Renal Services
Renal Transplantation
Respiratory Services
Robotic Surgery
Senior Services Program
Sleep Disorders Center
Spine Center
Surgical Services
Total Joint Replacement
Urogynecology
Urology
Valerie Fund Cancer Center (Pediatrics)
Vascular Surgery
The Weight Loss Institute of New Jersey
Wound Treatment Center

COMPETITORS

Atlantic Health
Bergen Regional Medical
Capital Health System
CentraState Healthcare System
JFK Health System
Meridian Health
Princeton HealthCare
Saint Peter' s University Hospital
Shore Memorial Hospital
St. Joseph' s Healthcare System
Trinitas Regional Medical Center
Valley Health System

HISTORICAL FINANCIALS

Company Type: Private

Income Statement FYE: December 31

	REVENUE ($ mil.)	NET INCOME ($ mil.)	NET PROFIT MARGIN	EMPLOYEES
12/09	287	14	5.0%	2,400
12/08	262	(11)	—	—
12/04	228	9	4.3%	—
12/03	221	3	1.6%	—
Annual Growth	4.4%	26.3%	—	—

MONOGRAM FOOD SOLUTIONS LLC

Monogram Food Solutions is focused on M E A and T. As a manufacturer of meat and meat snack products the company produces beef jerky sausage hot dogs bacon and other processed food items. Its brands include Circle B King Cotton and Trail's Best Meat Snacks. Through several special licensing agreements Monogram Food Solutions also sells Jeff Foxworthy Jerky Products NASCAR Jerky and Steak Strips and Bass Pro Uncle Buck's Licensed Products. The company which distributes its products nationwide operates facilities in Minnesota Indiana and Virginia. Founded in 2004 Monogram Food Solutions was formed through the merger of assets (King Cotton and Circle B) previously owned by Sara Lee Corp.

Geographic Reach

From its headquarters in Memphis Tennessee Monogram Food Solutions directs the operation of additional facilities in (Chandler) Minnesota (Muncie and Bristol) Indiana and (Martinsville) Virginia. The company distributes its products nationwide.

Strategy

Licensing agreements have helped Monogram Food Solutions build a firm foundation for its business. Aside from its deal with Bass Pro Shops and Jeff Foxworthy the company enjoys licensing partnerships with Johnsonville Sausage and Glory Foods. Its alliance with Johnsonville Sausage inked in 2012 gave Monogram Food Solutions the go-ahead to produce and market Johnsonville Deli Bites Bacon Jerky and other meat snacks innovations.

Beginning in 2010 the company began manufacturing and selling meat snacks for the energy drink maker DNA Beverages Corporation under the DNA brand. Geared toward a younger consumer the DNA beef products gives Monogram a larger demographic for its products.

Mergers & Acquisitions

Since its founding the company has quickly built itself up by buying established meat product manufacturers and processing plants. In 2009 it acquired three companies including beef jerky maker Wild Bill's Foods and Al Pete's Meats (and the Pete's Pride brand name). It also acquired the Hannah's Bull's O'Brien's and Dakota meat snack brands from meat processing company American Foods Group.

In late 2012 Monogram Food Solutions purchased Hinsdale Farms of Bristol Indiana. As one of the nation's largest makers of corn dogs Hinsdale also has a hand in serving retail private label customers and co-packing for other manufacturers. The deal added a fourth manufacturing plant for processing meat. As part of the acquisition Monogram Food Solutions is working to integrate the Hinsdale business into its manufacturing and sales systems.

EXECUTIVES

Chief People Officer, Raymond R. Stitle
Chairman and CEO, Karl A. Schledwitz
CFO, David (Dave) Dunavant
President, Wes Jackson
COO, Don Brunson
Chief, Mark Olivito
VP Marketing, Kathy Mullins
President and COO Monogram Meat Snacks, Ches Jackson
Vice President of operations, George Roden

LOCATIONS

HQ: MONOGRAM FOOD SOLUTIONS LLC
930 S WHITE STATION RD, MEMPHIS, TN 38117-5703
Phone: 901-685-7167
Web: WWW.MONOGRAMFOODS.COM

PRODUCTS/OPERATIONS

Selected Brands

Circle B
Hannah' s
King Cotton
O' Brien' s Meat Snacks/Sausages
Wild Bill' s

COMPETITORS

Bridgford Foods
Carl Buddig
Clemens Family Corporation
ConAgra
Hormel
Jerky Snack Brands
Link Snacks
Oberto Sausage Company
Weaver Meats

HISTORICAL FINANCIALS

Company Type: Private

Income Statement FYE: December 29

	REVENUE ($ mil.)	NET INCOME ($ mil.)	NET PROFIT MARGIN	EMPLOYEES
12/12	197	1	0.9%	790
12/11	173	3	1.8%	—
Annual Growth	13.8%	(43.6%)	—	—

2012 Year-End Financials

Debt ratio: —
Return on equity: 0.90%
Cash ($ mil.): 0
Current ratio: 0.80
Long-term debt ($ mil.): —
Dividends
Yield: —
Payout: —
Market value ($ mil.): —

MONTANA STATE UNIVERSITY INC

Montana State University helps develop young minds in Big Sky Country. The university located in Bozeman serves more than 14500 students most of whom are undergraduates from Montana. The school offers baccalaureate degrees in 60 fields master's degrees in 45 fields and doctoral degrees in about 20 fields. The school offers primarily a liberal arts education though it is also strong in agriculture and the fine arts. The university provides courses in fields ranging from English to political science to engineering. It has a teaching staff of more than 1150 including 781 full-time and 373 part-time faculty and department heads. Tuition and fees for a resident student is $6705; a non-resident $20062.

Geographic Reach

The university has campuses located in Bozeman Billings Great Falls and Havre as well as the Montana Agricultural Experiment Station Montana Extension Service and the Fire Services Training School.

Operations

Montana State University's expenditures from sponsored research programs reached $112 million in 2012. That year it had an enrollment of 14660 students and a faculty/student ratio of 17:1.

Financial Performance

The university saw a 5% increase in revenues in 2012 due to a rise in tuition and fees a growth in revenues from auxiliary enterprises and other revenues. These were partially offset by a decline in grant and contract operating revenues.

Net income grew by 46% in 2012 thanks to an increase in capital gifts grants and contributions partially offset by higher expenses and a decline in non-operating revenues.

Montana State University was supported by endowments of $7.8 million in 2012.

Higher tuition and fees helped to lift the university's revenues between 2009 and 2012.

Company Background

The university was founded in 1893.

Montana State University is one of only 108 institutions (out of 4600) designated as "very high research activity" by the Carnegie Foundation for the Advancement of Teaching.

EXECUTIVES

President, Geoffrey Gamble
VP Student Affairs, Allen Yarnell
VP Administration and Finance, Craig Roloff
VP Academic Affairs and Provost, David M. Dooley
VP Research Creativity and Technology Transfer, Thomas McCoy
VP Inter-Campus Affairs, Rolf Groseth
Senior Vice Provost, Joseph Fedock
VP Communications and Public Affairs, Cathy Conover
Associate Vice President for Financial Services, Laura Humberger
Director Financial Aid Services, Brandi Payne
University Legal Counsel, Leslie Taylor
Director Personnel and Payroll Services, Susan Alt
Director Purchasing, Shawna Lanphear
Director Admissions and Registrar, Charles Nelson
Director University Marketing, Julie Kipfer
Director Human Resources and Affirmative Action, Marjorie (Marj) Brown
Director Safety and Risk Management, Jeff Shada
Director Career Services, Carina Beck
Vice President for Administration & Finance, Terry Leist
Chief Human Resources Officer, Dennis Defa
Chief Information Officer, Dewitt Latimer
Human Resources Director Montana State University, Diane Letendre
President CEO, Jaynee Groseth

LOCATIONS

HQ: MONTANA STATE UNIVERSITY INC
901 W GARFIELD ST, BOZEMAN, MT 59717
Phone: 406-994-4361
Web: WWW.FLATHEAD.MT.GOV

PRODUCTS/OPERATIONS

2012 Revenues

	% of total
Tuition &	28
Grant & contract	23
State & local	20
Auxiliary	8
Pell	6
Capital grants &	4
Gifts	3
Federal	1
Land grant & investment	1
Othwe	6
Total	**100**

Schools Colleges
College Agricultur
College of Arts Architectu
College Business
College of Education Health & Developmen
College Engineerin
College of Letters Science
College Nursing
Gallatin College
The School
University College

HISTORICAL FINANCIALS

Company Type: Private

Income Statement FYE: June 30

	REVENUE ($ mil.)	NET INCOME ($ mil.)	NET PROFIT MARGIN	EMPLOYEES
06/12	334	24	7.4%	2,500
06/11	318	16	5.3%	—
06/08	302	17	5.8%	—
06/07	302	23	7.7%	—
Annual Growth	2.0%	1.2%	—	—

2012 Year-End Financials

Debt ratio: —
Return on equity: 7.40%
Cash ($ mil.): 182
Current ratio: 2.70
Long-term debt ($ mil.): —
Dividends
Yield: —
Payout: —
Market value ($ mil.): —

MONTCLAIR STATE UNIVERSITY

With its roots as a teaching college it's fitting that today Montclair State University (MSU) is one of a handful of universities in the US offering a doctorate in pedagogy (the art and science of teaching). For more than 100 years MSU has provided a comprehensive curriculum for future educators as well as other students studying a variety of subjects. With an enrollment of some 19000 students MSU operates through six schools and colleges: College of the Arts College of Education and Human Services College of Humanities and Social Sciences College of Science and Mathematics School of Business and the Graduate School.

Geographic Reach

MSU's main campus is located on 250-acres in Montclair New Jersey.

Operations

MSU's more than 400 fields of study include about 60 undergraduate and 50 graduate majors as well as numerous certificate programs and niche concentrations. Programs include molecular biology applied linguistics nutrition bioinformatics environmental management and justice studies. The university has a student-to-faculty ratio of 17:1.

Financials

Revenues for MSU have risen over the last few years due to higher enrollment levels and tuition rates including a 6% increase to $267 million in 2012. Growth in 2012 was also attributed to higher income from food services offset slightly by a decrease in housing revenues. Net income also increased by 35% to $29 million due to increased revenues capital gifts and grants partly offset by a decrease in non-operating revenues.

Strategy

MSU is growing quickly and in recent years the school has spent more than $300 million on new buildings to accommodate that growth. In 2012 the university completed the renovation of Finley Hall (classroom facilities); the building was renamed as the Conrad J. Schmitt Hall after the construction was completed. In 2011 MSU also opened a new student housing and dining facility; the new center is called The Heights and accommodates nearly 2000 students.

Company Background

MSU was founded in 1908 as a two-year college named Montclair State Normal School. It became a four-year institution in 1927 when it became known as Montclair State Teachers College; it gained its final name of Montclair State College in 1958.

EXECUTIVES

VP Finance and Treasurer, Donald D. Cipullo
President, Susan A. Cole
VP and CIO, Edward P. Chapel
VP Student Development and Campus Life, Karen Pennington
VP Human Resources, Judith Hain
VP University Advancement, Thomas Haynes
VP University Facilities, Gregory Bressler
Assistant VP Finance and Controller, Catherine A. Coryat
Provost and VP Academic Affairs, Willard P. Gingerich
VP University Advancement, John T. (Jack) Shannon

LOCATIONS

HQ: MONTCLAIR STATE UNIVERSITY
1 NORMAL AVE, MONTCLAIR, NJ 07043-1624
Phone: 973-655-4000
Web: WWW.BUSINESS.MONTCLAIR.EDU

PRODUCTS/OPERATIONS

Selected Schools and Colleges

College of the Arts
College of Education and Human Services
College of Humanities and Social Sciences
College of Science and Mathematics
School of Business
The Graduate School

HISTORICAL FINANCIALS

Company Type: Private

Income Statement FYE: June 30

	REVENUE ($ mil.)	NET INCOME ($ mil.)	NET PROFIT MARGIN	EMPLOYEES
06/13	280	6	2.3%	2,000
06/12	266	29	11.0%	—
06/07	200	24	12.4%	—
06/07	179	23	13.0%	—
Annual Growth	7.7%	(19.1%)		

2013 Year-End Financials

Debt ratio: —
Return on equity: 2.30%
Cash ($ mil.): 51
Current ratio: 0.80
Long-term debt ($ mil.): —
Dividends
Yield: —
Payout: —
Market value ($ mil.): —

MORROW-MEADOWS CORPORATION

Today and tomorrow Morrow-Meadows Corp. provides electrical contracting services including work on data communications and power distribution systems for commercial and industrial facilities in the western US primarily in California and Oregon. Its divisions include Oregon-based Cherry City Electric and Morrow-Meadows Corp. Northern California. The company provides project development design engineering and construction services on a range of projects such as shopping malls office buildings medical centers hotels parking garages theme parks and water treatment plants. The company counts among its customers Disney Intel Stanford University Hewlett-Packard and Kaiser Permanente.

Operations

The company's Datacom Division provides custom installations for customers and provides such services as design engineering and the installation of voice data and video communications systems.

Company Background

Chairman J. Robert Meadows was a contributing founder of the enterprise in 1964. President Karen Price joined Morrow-Meadows in 1973 and became president in 1992. The company is a woman-owned business enterprise certified by the City of Los Angeles.

EXECUTIVES

President, Karen V. Price
EVP Operations, Robert E. Meadows
VP Estimating, Ed Slingluff
CFO Secretary and Treasurer, Tim Langley
VP Project Development, Rick Lane
VP Corporate Marketing, Mark Freedman
VP Preconstruction, Joseph Babcock
VP Construction, Rick Jarvis
VP Purchasing, Bob Atkinson
VP and General Manager Cherry City Electric, Ray Ellis
Vice President General Manager, Gary Deadmon
Chairman, Elizabeth (Betty) Meadows
Board Of Directors, Cathleen Vick

LOCATIONS

HQ: MORROW-MEADOWS CORPORATION
231 BENTON CT, CITY OF INDUSTRY, CA 91789-5213
Phone: 909-598-7700
Web: WWW.MORROW-MEADOWS.COM

PRODUCTS/OPERATIONS

Selected Services

Construction
Data communication
Instrumentation
Prefabrication
Energy services
SPG/Service

COMPETITORS

Barri Electric Company
Christenson Electric
Cupertino Electric
Helix Electric
Oregon Electric Construction
Rosendin Electric

HISTORICAL FINANCIALS

Company Type: Private

Income Statement FYE: October 31

	REVENUE ($ mil.)	NET INCOME ($ mil.)	NET PROFIT MARGIN	EMPLOYEES
10/11	312	0	—	1,200
10/04	177	0	0.5%	—
10/01	201	4	2.4%	—
10/00	158	3	2.5%	—
Annual Growth	6.4%	—	—	—

MORSE OPERATIONS INC.

Morse Operations (dba Ed Morse Automotive Group) has been selling cars and trucks long enough to know the code of the road. It owns about a dozen new car dealerships across Florida most of them operating under the Ed Morse name. Dealerships house more than 15 franchises and 10 domestic and import car brands including Cadillac Fiat Chevrolet Buick GMC Scion Honda Mazda and Toyota. The company's Bayview Cadillac in Fort Lauderdale is one of the world's largest volume sellers of Cadillacs. Morse Operations also sells used cars provides parts and service and operates a fleet sales division. Founder and auto magnate the late Ed Morse entered the automobile business in 1946 with a 20-car rental fleet.

Geographic Reach

The dealership network serves customers throughout Florida along the East and West coasts and in Central Florida.

Operations

Ed Morse Fleet Sales offers vehicles from about 10 different brands including Honda Cadillac Fiat Chevrolet Buick GMC Scion Mazda and Toyota. To date annual fleet sales have reached 100000 vehicles.

Fleet customers include daily rental companies such as National Car Rental Avis and Alamo Rent A Car.

EXECUTIVES

EVP and COO, Carmine Colella
President and CEO, Ted Morse

LOCATIONS

HQ: MORSE OPERATIONS INC.
2850 S FEDERAL HWY, DELRAY BEACH, FL 33483-3216
Phone: 561-276-5000
Web: WWW.EDMORSE.COM

PRODUCTS/OPERATIONS

Selected Dealerships

Brandon Auto Mall
Ed Morse Auto Plaza - Port Richey
Ed Morse Bayview Cadillac
Ed Morse Cadillac - Delray Beach
Ed Morse Cadillac - Tampa
Ed Morse Cadillac - Brandon
Ed Morse Delray Toyota/Scion
Ed Morse Honda Blue Heron
Ed Morse Mazda - Lakeland
Ed Morse Sawgrass

COMPETITORS

AutoNation
Braman Management
Buchanan Automotive
Ferman Automotive
Holman Enterprises
Island Lincoln-Mercury
JM Family Enterprises
March/Hodge
Penske Automotive Group
Scott-McRae

HISTORICAL FINANCIALS

Company Type: Private

Income Statement FYE: December 31

	REVENUE ($ mil.)	NET INCOME ($ mil.)	NET PROFIT MARGIN	EMPLOYEES
12/12	604	(6)	—	1,295
12/11	513	4	0.8%	—
12/08	550	0	0.1%	—
12/08	619	(2)	—	—
Annual Growth	(0.6%)	—	—	—

2012 Year-End Financials

Debt ratio: —
Return on equity: (-1.00%)
Cash ($ mil.): 3
Current ratio: 0.20
Long-term debt ($ mil.): —
Dividends
Yield: —
Payout: —
Market value ($ mil.): —

MORTGAGE INVESTORS CORPORATION

LOCATIONS

HQ: MORTGAGE INVESTORS CORPORATION
6090 CENTRAL AVE, SAINT PETERSBURG, FL 337071622
Phone: 7273471930
Web: WWW.MORTGAGEINVESTORS.COM

HISTORICAL FINANCIALS

Company Type: Private

Income Statement FYE: December 31

	ASSETS ($ mil.)	NET INCOME ($ mil.)	INCOME AS % OF ASSETS	EMPLOYEES
12/12	115	75	65.8%	1,200
12/11	165	6	4.1%	—
12/10	120	23	19.5%	—
12/09	73	0	—	—
Annual Growth	16.5%	—	—	—

2012 Year-End Financials

Debt ratio: —
Return on equity: 1.10%
Cash ($ mil.): 13
Current ratio: —
Long-term debt ($ mil.): —
Dividends
Yield: —
Payout: —
Market value ($ mil.): —

MOSAIC

Mosaic creates color in the lives of the disadvantaged. The not-for-profit organization provides individualized support and advocacy services living facilities education and employment for people with disabilities. The Christian organization serves some 3500 clients through 40 agencies across the US as well as select international locations. Services include case management foster care vocational training and supervised living arrangements. Mosaic also offers senior independent living services and support at select facilities. The organization is affiliated with the Evangelical Lutheran Church in America.

Geographic Reach

Mosaic serves clients in 250 communities in 10 US states (Arizona Colorado Connecticut Delaware Illinois Indiana Iowa Kansas Nebraska and Texas). It also partners with organizations in other countries such as Romania and Tanzania to provide services.

Strategy

The organization has been expanding its international efforts through its participation in international Lutheran network IMPACT. Through the alliance Mosaic serves as the representative in Romania and Tanzania. Other participants in the project include Lutheran organizations in Germany Norway and the UK.

Company Background

Mosaic is affiliated with the Evangelical Lutheran Church in America and came into being when Bethpage Inner Mission Association and Martin Luther Homes consolidated in 2003.

EXECUTIVES

Senior Vice President, Keith H Schmode
Vp Financial Operations, Dean Wilson
Vice President Of Church Relations, David Defreese
Finance Director For Nebraska Region Senior Vice President Of Finance, Scott Hoffman
Vice President Of Human Resources, Sue Loerts
Senior Vice President Of Operations, Holly Morrison
Senior Vice President Public Policy, Richard Carman
Regional Vice President, Tammy Westfall
Vice President Talent Management, Yvette Gillett
Vice President Of Employee Relations, Paula Burton
Vice President Special Projects, Amy Stevens
Vice President Of Accounting, Kristin Rossow
Vice President Legal Supports, Mike Lyons
Vice President Of Mission Advancement, Brenda Solomon
Board Of Directors, Jed Osborn

LOCATIONS

HQ: MOSAIC
4980 S 118TH ST, OMAHA, NE 68137-2200
Phone: 402-896-3884
Web: WWW.MOSAICINFO.ORG

PRODUCTS/OPERATIONS

Selected Services

Affordable and Accessible Housing
Case Management
Children' s Services
Day Services
Host Homes/Foster Care
Residential
Senior Supported Living
Supported/Intermittent

COMPETITORS

Brookdale Senior Living
Care UK
Elwyn
GEO Group
HCR ManorCare
Kindred Healthcare
Life Care Centers
Magellan Health
Providence Service
Res-Care
Sunrise Senior Living

HISTORICAL FINANCIALS

Company Type: Private

Income Statement FYE: June 30

	REVENUE ($ mil.)	NET INCOME ($ mil.)	NET PROFIT MARGIN	EMPLOYEES
06/13	234	(0)	—	3,500
06/12	212	4	1.9%	—
06/10	212	11	5.3%	—
06/10	197	7	4.0%	—
Annual Growth	6.0%	—	—	—

2013 Year-End Financials

Debt ratio: —
Return on equity: (-0.20%)
Cash ($ mil.): 17
Current ratio: 1.40
Long-term debt ($ mil.): —
Dividends
Yield: —
Payout: —
Market value ($ mil.): —

MOUNT CARMEL HEALTH SYSTEM

Mount Carmel Health System cares for the sick in the greater Columbus area and central Ohio. The health care system boasts 1500 physicians at three general hospitals and a specialty surgical hospital offering a comprehensive range of medical and surgical services including cardiovascular care. Mount Carmel Health also operates outpatient centers including primary care and specialty physicians' practices and it offers home health care services. The hospital group is part of Trinity Health one of the largest Catholic health care systems in the US.

Operations

Mount Carmel's facilities include the acute care Mount Carmel East Mount Carmel West and Mount Carmel St. Ann's hospitals as well as the Mount Carmel New Albany a surgical hospital specializing in orthopedic neurological and musculoskeletal treatments. The system also operates several freestanding emergency and surgery centers and other outpatient and community care centers. Its HealthProviders subsidiary manages about two dozen primary care and specialty practices with more than 100 physicians in central Ohio.

In the realm of education Mount Carmel Health operates six medical residency programs for physicians and its Mount Carmel College of Nursing is one of the largest in the state.

Strategy

In 2012 the company launched a $110 million facilities improvement project (Project GRACE) which includes the renovation of the St. Ann's hospital. Mount Carmel Health plans for the upgraded St. Ann's facility to serve as a regional medical center.

In 2010 Mount Carmel completed construction of a new freestanding emergency center in the town of Canal Winchester through a partnership with Fairfield Medical Center. The center features both general emergency and pediatric urgent care facilities. In time the center might expand into a larger hospital facility.

Company Background

Mother M. Angela and Sister M. Rufina Dunn of the Congregation of the Sisters of the Holy Cross of Notre Dame founded Mount Carmel in 1886.

EXECUTIVES

President CEO, Claus P. von Zychlin
CIO, Cindy Sheets
VP Managed Care, Skip Turner
COO; COO Mount Carmel East Hospital, Ronald E. Whiteside
Vice President Medical Education, Charles E. Sanders

LOCATIONS

HQ: MOUNT CARMEL HEALTH SYSTEM
6150 E BROAD ST, COLUMBUS, OH 43213-1574
Phone: 614-546-4100
Web: WWW.MOUNTCARMELHEALTH.COM

PRODUCTS/OPERATIONS

Selected Facilities

Hospitals
- Mount Carmel East
- Mount Carmel New Albany
- Mount Carmel St. Ann' s
- Mount Carmel West

Other Facilities
- Anticoagulation Centers
- Atrial Fibrillation Center
- Cardiac Rehabilitation
- Diley Ridge Medical Center
- Mount Carmel Grove City Medical Center
- Geriatrics Center
- Health Centers
- Heart Failure Centers
- Home Medical Equipment
- Imaging Centers
- Mount Carmel Medical Group
- Occupational Health Centers
- Outpatient Cancer Treatment
- Outpatient Labs
- Physician Offices
- Rehab and Sports Medicine Services
- Sleep Medicine
- Surgery Centers
- Urgent Care Centers
- Women' s Health Centers
- Wound Centers

COMPETITORS

Adena Health System
Catholic Health Partners
Fairfield Medical Center
Genesis HealthCare System (Ohio)
Licking Memorial Health Systems
Nationwide Children' s Hospital
OhioHealth
Regency Hospital

HISTORICAL FINANCIALS

Company Type: Private

Income Statement FYE: June 30

	REVENUE ($ mil.)	NET INCOME ($ mil.)	NET PROFIT MARGIN	EMPLOYEES
06/11	201	13	6.7%	8,000
06/10	198	2	1.2%	—
06/09	167	0	—	—
06/05	0	0	—	—
Annual Growth	—	—	—	—

2011 Year-End Financials

Debt ratio: —
Return on equity: 6.70%
Cash ($ mil.): 17
Current ratio: —
Long-term debt ($ mil.): —
Dividends
Yield: —
Payout: —
Market value ($ mil.): —

MOUNT CLEMENS REGIONAL MEDICAL CENTER INC.

Mount Clemens Regional Medical Center (doing business as McLaren Medical Center-Macomb) is an general acute care hospital serving the Macomb County area of suburban Detroit. With about 290 beds the hospital offers such specialties as cardiac and cancer care family practice services home and hospice care and emergency care. The McLaren Health Care-controlled company also operates three prompt care centers in nearby townships as well as a wound treatment clinic. Of the more than 420 physicians on staff at the hospital more than 100 are family medicine and internal medicine specialists who provide primary care.

Geographic Reach

The hospital system serves Michigan patients in the Macomb County area of suburban Detroit.

Strategy

Growing its geographic network of services in 2012 McLaren Medical Center-Macomb opened a new facility in Richmond-Lenox its offers includes physical therapy X-ray/diagnostic imaging and a laboratory blood draw station.

That year it also expanded its technological capabilities with the addition of the da Vinci? Si HD Surgical System robotic technology. The acquisition was part of a long history of adopting surgical advancements.

Ownership

Mount Clemens Regional Medical Center was acquired by McLaren Health Care in 2006 to expand its reach into southeastern Michigan. In 2012 the medical center changed its name to McLaren Medical Center-Macomb.

Company Background

The hospital was founded in 1944.

EXECUTIVES

Treasurer, Thomas P. Schwanitz
Secretary and Trustee, Carolyn Dorian
Vice Chair, James C. George
Chief of Staff and Trustee, James E. Johnson
Secretary and Trustee, Carolyn Dorian
Chief of Staff and Trustee, James E. Johnson

LOCATIONS

HQ: MOUNT CLEMENS REGIONAL MEDICAL CENTER INC.
1000 HARRINGTON ST, MOUNT CLEMENS, MI 48043-2920
Phone: 586-493-8000
Web: WWW.MCRMC.ORG

PRODUCTS/OPERATIONS

Selected Departments and Services

- Bariatrics
- Behavioral Health
- Blood Conservation
- Cancer Services
- Cardiac
- Diabetes
- Diagnostic Imaging
- Dialysis Services
- Emergency Care
- EMS
- Family BirthPlace
- Fitness Centers
- Free Clinics
- Health Insurance
- Home Care
- Hospice
- Immunizations
- Implantable Hearing Solutions
- Infectious Disease
- Infusion Center
- Intensive Care
- Internal Medicine
- Laboratory and Pathology
- Lifeline
- Medical Library
- Medical Supplies & Equipment
- Neurosciences
- Nutritional Counseling
- Ophthalmology
- Orthopedics
- Pain Management
- Pediatrics
- Pharmacy Services
- Primary Care
- Proton Therapy
- Pulmonary and Respiratory
- Rehabilitaton and Therapy
- Robotic Surgery
- Sleep Medicine
- Stroke Center
- Surgical and Endoscopy Services
- Trauma
- Urology
- Walk-in Clinics
- Women's Services
- Wound Care

COMPETITORS

Beaumont Health System
Crittenton Hospital
St. John Hospital & Medical Center
St. John Macomb-Oakland Hospital

HISTORICAL FINANCIALS

Company Type: Private

Income Statement FYE: September 30

	REVENUE ($ mil.)	NET INCOME ($ mil.)	NET PROFIT MARGIN	EMPLOYEES
09/12	256	28	11.0%	2,249
09/09*	277	11	4.2%	—
05/05	264	14	5.5%	—
05/05	0	0	—	—
Annual Growth	—	—	—	—

*Fiscal year change

2012 Year-End Financials

Debt ratio: —
Return on equity: 11.00%
Cash ($ mil.): 7
Current ratio: 0.70
Long-term debt ($ mil.): —
Dividends
Yield: —
Payout: —
Market value ($ mil.): —

MRIGLOBAL

MRIGlobal provides contract research services for government and private-sector clients in fields such as agricultural and food safety analytical chemistry biological sciences energy engineering environment health sciences information technology and national defense. The institute operates laboratories and agricultural research centers in Florida Kansas Maryland Missouri North Carolina and Washington DC. MRIGlobal also manages the US Department of Energy's National Renewable Energy Laboratory in Golden Colorado. Work related to biological and chemical defense accounts for most of MRIGlobal's sales. The not-for-profit organization was founded in 1944.

EXECUTIVES

Vice Chairman, James L. Spigarelli, age 69
EVP; Director National Renewable Energy Lab, Dan E. Arvizu
President and CEO, Michael F. Helmstetter

VP and CFO, Fred Cornwell
General Counsel and Corporate Secretary, Jeanie Latz
Chairman, Richard C. Green Jr.
VP Business Development, John S. Stanley
Director, A. Drue Jennings, age 65
Director, Jonathan M. Kemper, age 58
Director, Louis W. Smith, age 69
Director, Thomas M. Bloch, age 58
Director, Thomas M. (Tom) Hoenig, age 65
Vice Chairman, James L. Spigarelli, age 69
Director, Ben D. McCallister
Director, Charles W. Battey
Director, David M. Clarke
Director, Robert A. Kipp
Director, Robert A. Long
Director, William C. Nelson

LOCATIONS

HQ: MRIGLOBAL
425 VOLKER BLVD, KANSAS CITY, MO 64110-2241
Phone: 816-753-7600
Web: WWW.MRIGLOBAL.ORG

HISTORICAL FINANCIALS

Company Type: Private

Income Statement FYE: June 30

	REVENUE ($ mil.)	NET INCOME ($ mil.)	NET PROFIT MARGIN	EMPLOYEES
06/13	497	1	0.4%	2,547
06/12	17	(0)	—	—
06/11	625	6	1.0%	—
06/10	547	4	0.8%	—
Annual Growth	(3.1%)	(22.9%)	—	—

2013 Year-End Financials

Debt ratio: —
Return on equity: 0.40%
Cash ($ mil.): 19
Current ratio: 0.20
Long-term debt ($ mil.): —
Dividends
Yield: —
Payout: —
Market value ($ mil.): —

MULTICARE HEALTH SYSTEM

MultiCare Health System is a not-for-profit health system that serves the residents of four counties in the southern Puget Sound region and southwestern Washington. Altogether the system's five hospitals have more than 1000 beds. The largest facility Tacoma General boasts 390 beds and provides specialized cancer cardiac orthopedic and trauma care in addition to general medical and surgical care. Other medical centers include Good Samaritan Hospital (with 225 beds) Allenmore Hospital (130 beds) and Mary Bridge Children's Hospital (70 beds). The health system also operates dozens of primary care specialty care and urgent care clinics in the region as well as home health and hospice care agencies.

Geographic Reach

MultiCare Health System serves those who reside in Washington's Pierce South King Thurston and Kitsap counties.

Strategy

MultiCare has been busy adding to its health system through acquisitions and expansion efforts. MultiCare added a fifth hospital to its network when it acquired Auburn Regional Medical Center from Universal Health Services in 2012. The purchase added a 210-bed hospital facility as well as outpatient clinics.

It also expanded by opening a new emergency care clinic at the MultiCare outpatient center in Covington (where it also plans to build a new hospital) during 2012. The company added a new patient tower to its Good Samaritan Hospital in 2011.

EXECUTIVES

President and CEO, Diane Cecchettini
SVP and CFO, Vincent (Vince) Schmitz
SVP Community Services, Lois I. Bernstein
SVP Human Potential, Sarah M. Horsman
SVP and General Counsel, Erik Rasmussen
EVP and CIO, Florence Chang
VP and Chief Nurse Executive, Kate Bechtold
President East Pierce Region, Glenn Kasman
SVP Quality, Lester Reed
President West Pierce Region, Shelly Mullin

LOCATIONS

HQ: MULTICARE HEALTH SYSTEM
315 MARTIN LUTHER KING, TACOMA, WA 98405-4234
Phone: 253-403-1000
Web: WWW.MULTICARE.ORG

PRODUCTS/OPERATIONS

Selected Facilities

Hospitals
- Allenmore Hospital (Tacoma)
- Auburn Medical Center (Auburn)
- Good Samaritan Hospital (Puyallup)
- Mary Bridge Children's Hospital and Health Center (Tacoma)
- Tacoma General Hospital (Tacoma)

Other facilities
- Allenmore Medical Center
- Auburn MultiCare Clinic
- Covington MultiCare Clinic
- Lakewood Urgent Care Clinic
- Kent MultiCare Clinic
- MultiCare Home Services
- Spanaway MultiCare Clinic
- Tacoma Family Medicine
- University Place Urgent Care Clinic
- Westgate Urgent Care Clinic

COMPETITORS

Catholic Health Initiatives
Franciscan Health System
Harrison Medical Center
Overlake Hospital
PeaceHealth
Providence Health & Services
Seattle Children' s Hospital
Swedish Health Services
Yakima Valley Memorial

HISTORICAL FINANCIALS

Company Type: Private

Income Statement FYE: December 31

	REVENUE ($ mil.)	NET INCOME ($ mil.)	NET PROFIT MARGIN	EMPLOYEES
12/12	1,563	245	15.7%	6,510
12/11	1,384	27	2.0%	—
12/10	1,384	146	10.6%	—
12/09	1,094	118	10.8%	—
Annual Growth	12.6%	27.3%	—	—

2012 Year-End Financials

Debt ratio: —
Return on equity: 15.70%
Cash ($ mil.): 74
Current ratio: 1.10
Long-term debt ($ mil.): —
Dividends
Yield: —
Payout: —
Market value ($ mil.): —

MUNROE REGIONAL HEALTH SYSTEM INC.

Munroe Regional Health System operates the Munroe Regional Medical Center and affiliated facilities serving residents of north central Florida's Marion County and surrounding areas. Munroe Regional Medical Center is a 420-bed acute care hospital that offers comprehensive medical surgical and emergency care along with programs devoted to cardiovascular care stroke prevention and care orthopedics and women's health. The hospital is operated under a lease agreement with the Marion County Hospital District. Munroe Regional Health System also provides home health services and operates outpatient clinics providing primary care diagnostic and rehabilitation therapy services.

Geographic Reach

Munroe Regional Health System serves those who reside in the north central Florida county of Marion as well as its surrounding areas.

Operations

Munroe Regional Medical Center employs some 450 physicians. Its staff members handle more than 21000 inpatient admissions each year as well as 100000 emergency room visits and 50000 outpatient care visits.

Strategy

Munroe Regional Health System has expanded its services by partnering with other health care providers and by forming strategic joint ventures. Such partners include Clinical Lab Solutions Heart of Florida Health Center Medical Imaging Center Munroe HealthCare TimberRidge Imaging Center TimberRidge Nursing and Rehabilitation and Women's Imaging Center.

For access to four additional operating rooms a pair of procedure rooms and a 6% market share Munroe Regional Health System in late 2012 agreed to acquire a 20% stake in Surgery Center of Ocala. The surgery center which performs some 4200 procedures each year will benefit as well from the health system's greater purchasing power for its supplies and medicine.

In mid-2013 hospital operator Health Management Associates (HMA) announced that it entered a letter of intent to lease and operate the Munroe Regional organization. If successful the agreement would bring Munroe Regional under HMA's clinical affiliation with the University of Florida Shands Hospital. Munroe Regional would continue to operate under the guidance of a local board of trustees.

EXECUTIVES

SVP and COO, Paul Clark
Interim President & CEO, Richard D. (Rich) Mutarelli
VP and CIO, Carl Candullo Jr.
President and CEO, Stephen A. (Steve) Purves, age 58
Vice President Human Resources, Dan O'Connor
VP Strategic Planning and Marketing, Mike G. Robertson
VP and Chief Nursing Officer, Pam Michell
Senior Vice President Physician Services, Marc J. Miller
SVP Medical Affairs and Chief Quality Officer, Lon McPherson
Vice President Human Resources, Dan OConnor
Vice President Finance, Rhonda Kautz
Chairman, Ron Ewers
Vice Chairman, Charles Dassance

Senior Vice President of Medical Affairs & Chief Quality Officer, Lon H. McPherson

LOCATIONS

HQ: MUNROE REGIONAL HEALTH SYSTEM INC.
1500 SW 1REST AVE RST, OCALA, FL 34471
Phone: 352-351-7200
Web: WWW.MUNROEREGIONAL.COM

PRODUCTS/OPERATIONS

Selected Services

Diabetes Healthways
Emergency Care
LifeTime Wellness
Advanced Technology
Midwives of Ocala
Speech & Hearing
Stroke Center
Urology
Women's Center

COMPETITORS

Adventist Health System Sunbelt Healthcare
Baptist Health South Florida
Baptist Health System
Bay Medical Center
Florida Hospital Heartland
HCA
Jackson County Hospital of Florida
Kindred Healthcare
Mount Sinai Medical Center of Florida
Orlando Health
Tallahassee Memorial HealthCare
UF&Shands

HISTORICAL FINANCIALS

Company Type: Private

Income Statement FYE: September 30

	REVENUE ($ mil.)	NET INCOME ($ mil.)	NET PROFIT MARGIN	EMPLOYEES
09/09	313	(7)	—	2,179
09/08	312	(3)	—	—
09/06	263	4	1.5%	—
09/05	267	0	—	—
Annual Growth	4.0%	—	—	—

2009 Year-End Financials

Debt ratio: —
Return on equity: (-2.40%)
Cash ($ mil.): 52
Current ratio: 0.60
Long-term debt ($ mil.): —
Dividends
Yield: —
Payout: —
Market value ($ mil.): —

MUSCULAR DYSTROPHY ASSOCIATION INC.

The Muscular Dystrophy Association (MDA) is a not-for-profit health agency that supports research into more than 40 neuromuscular diseases including including muscular dystrophy and Lou Gehrig's disease (also known as ALS). MDA believes more than one million Americans have some form of muscular dystrophy. The organization operates more than 200 health care clinics across the US runs summer camps for kids provides funding for research publishes educational materials and engages in national advocacy. It also sponsors more than 200 hospital-affiliated clinics and funds some 330 research projects globally. Founded in 1950 MDA is funded by private contributions.

Along with private contributions MDA is also funded by corporate sponsorships such as 7-Eleven Burger King CITGO Harley Davidson and Safeway.

The organization also publishes print and online magazines such as Quest and MDA/ALS Newsmagazine.Both Quest and MDA/ALS published quarterly and a subscribership of over 130000 provides important stories and facts to people with neurological diseases like tips for better independent living resources available to people with disabilities medical treatment and procedures and and new medical treatments.

After serving 49 years as the host and fundraiser for the MDA the organization parted ways with comedian Jerry Lewis in 2011.

EXECUTIVES

Treasurer, Suzanne Lowden, age 61
Chairman, R. Rodney Howell
Vice Chairman, Lois R. West
Vice Chairman, Lois R. West
Director, Stanley H. Appel
Director, Robert M. Bennett
Director, Leon I. Charash
Director, Bart Conner
Director, Harold C. Crump
Director, Benjamin F. Cumbo
Director, Joseph S. DiMartino
Director, Louis M. Kunkel
Director, Maureen McGovern
Director, Ed McMahon
Director, Olin F. Morris
Director, Christopher J. Rosa
Director, Charles D. Schoor
Auditors: Ernst&YoungLLP

LOCATIONS

HQ: MUSCULAR DYSTROPHY ASSOCIATION INC.
3300 E SUNRISE DR, TUCSON, AZ 85718-3299
Phone: 520-529-2000
Web: WWW.MDA.ORG

HISTORICAL FINANCIALS

Company Type: Private

Income Statement FYE: December 31

	REVENUE ($ mil.)	NET INCOME ($ mil.)	NET PROFIT MARGIN	EMPLOYEES
12/12	159	(11)	—	950
12/11	159	(53)	—	—
12/09	178	(7)	—	—
12/09	190	5	2.9%	—
Annual Growth	(5.9%)	—	—	—

2012 Year-End Financials

Debt ratio: —
Return on equity: (-7.50%)
Cash ($ mil.): 6
Current ratio: 0.20
Long-term debt ($ mil.): —
Dividends
Yield: —
Payout: —
Market value ($ mil.): —

MUSEUM OF FINE ARTS

In a city known for its erudite inhabitants the The Museum of Fine Arts (MFA) Boston seeks to entertain and educate. The MFA offers a wide range of collections such as Art of Americas Art of Europe Art of the Ancient World Contemporary Art Textile and Fashion Arts and Musical Instruments. The museum also provides public programs for children and adults including art classes and workshops. With approximately 70000 member households the MFA attracts some 1.2 million visitors annually. Founded in 1870 the museum through a partnership opened the Nagoya/Boston Museum of Fine Arts in 1999.

Financial Performance

The MFA reported 2012 support and revenue of about $106 million up 5% from the prior year. Support (including gifts contributions and grants) accounts for less than 10% of that total. Growth continues to come from increased attendance –the 1.2 million attendance number for 2012 is some 20% above the MFA's 10-year average attendance.

Strategy

The Museum is focused on expanding its public offerings and boosting attendance. In late 2011 it opened the Linde Family Wing for Contemporary Art which includes seven galleries showcasing some 250 works. That followed the late 2010 openings of the Art of the Americas Wing and the Ruth and Carl J. Shapiro Family Courtyard.

EXECUTIVES

Ann and Graham Gund Director, Malcolm Rogers
Director Public Relations, Dawn Griffin
Chairman, Stokley P. Towles
President Board of Trustees, Barbara Alfond

LOCATIONS

HQ: MUSEUM OF FINE ARTS
465 HUNTINGTON AVE, BOSTON, MA 02115-5597
Phone: 617-267-9300
Web: WWW.MFA.ORG

HISTORICAL FINANCIALS

Company Type: Private

Income Statement FYE: June 30

	REVENUE ($ mil.)	NET INCOME ($ mil.)	NET PROFIT MARGIN	EMPLOYEES
06/11	157	12	7.8%	1,000
06/10	122	7	5.9%	—
06/09	69	(49)	—	—
06/08	226	64	28.5%	—
Annual Growth	(11.5%)	(42.5%)	—	—

2011 Year-End Financials

Debt ratio: —
Return on equity: 7.80%
Cash ($ mil.): 71
Current ratio: 0.40
Long-term debt ($ mil.): —
Dividends
Yield: —
Payout: —
Market value ($ mil.): —

MUSTANG FUEL CORPORATION

Like a good mustang Mustang Fuel is independent –an independent oil and gas exploration production transportation and marketing company that is. The company owns and operates 200 properties and owns non-operated interests in more than 1300 other properties. It also controls more than 100000 net undeveloped leasehold acres in a four-state service region. Mustang Fuel also owns natural gas gathering and transporting pipelines operates one of the largest gas processing facilities in Oklahoma and has a fleet of trucks that transports petroleum products. It also markets gas. Subsidiaries include Mustang Fuel Marketing Company and Mustang Gas Products LLC.

Geographic Reach

The company has operations in Colorado Kansas Oklahoma Texas and Utah.

Operations

Mustang Fuel operates upstream (exploration and production) and midstream assets.

Mustang Fuel Marketing Company (first formed in 1990 as Eagle Gas Marketing) serves several independent gas producers with a focus on the intrastate natural gas pipelines in Oklahoma.

Mustang Gas Products LLC (formed in 2002 to buy gas gathering and processing assets from ONEOK) operates four gas processing facilities in Oklahoma and owns 4000 miles of gas gathering pipeline. The unit's cryogenic gas plants daily process about 110 million cu. ft. of natural gas and 450000 gallons of natural gas liquids.

Strategy

The company has primarily grown through developing its own properties and by acquiring strategic complementary properties.

To better serve its customers in 2011 and 2012 Mustang Gas Products expanded its Rodman gas gathering and processing capability in Kay and Noble counties in Oklahoma.

Ownership

Mustang Fuel is privately owned.

Company Background

Korean War veteran Edward Joullian III founded Mustang Fuel (as Westoc Oil & Gas Company) in 1949 and became chairman and president of the closely-held oil and gas company in 1964. He died in 2006. His son (E. Carey Joullian IV) took charge of the company

EXECUTIVES

SVP Secretary General Counsel and COO, Rand Phipps
Chairman President and CEO, E. Carey Joullian IV
VP Gas Marketing and Supply, J. Paul Belflower
VP and CIO, Bradley R. Jordan
VP Gas Operations, Gary Sump
VP Gas Supply, Brian Tibbs
Gas Control Manager Mustang Fuel Marketing Company, Rick Riggs
Vice President Controller of Mustang Fuel Corporation and its subsidiary, Carrie Brower
VP Gas Operations, John Hogsett
Senior Vice President Chief Financial Officer Treasurer of Mustang Fuel Corporation and its subsidiaries, Scott Chap
SVP CFO and Treasurer, M. Scott Chapline
Auditors: Ernst&YoungLLP

LOCATIONS

HQ: MUSTANG FUEL CORPORATION
9800 N OKLAHOMA AVE, OKLAHOMA CITY, OK 73114-7406
Phone: 405-748-9400

COMPETITORS

Anadarko Petroleum
Apache
Chesapeake Energy
Newfield Exploration
Noble Energy
OGE Energy
Occidental Petroleum
Pioneer Natural Resources
SandRidge Energy
Southwestern Energy

HISTORICAL FINANCIALS

Company Type: Private

Income Statement FYE: December 31

	REVENUE ($ mil.)	NET INCOME ($ mil.)	NET PROFIT MARGIN	EMPLOYEES
12/09	240	13	5.7%	124
12/08	482	43	9.0%	—
12/05	441	24	5.6%	—
12/04	313	1	0.5%	—
Annual Growth	(5.2%)	52.7%	—	—

2009 Year-End Financials

Debt ratio: —
Return on equity: 5.70%
Cash ($ mil.): 37
Current ratio: 2.20
Long-term debt ($ mil.): —
Dividends
Yield: —
Payout: —
Market value ($ mil.): —

MWH GLOBAL INC.

If it's wet MWH Global will make it work. The environmental engineering construction and management firm specializes in water-related projects or "wet infrastructure." Typical projects include building water treatment or desalination plants water transmission systems or storage facilitates. MWH also provides general building services for transportation energy mining ports and waterways and industrial projects. The company is active in some 35 countries and serves governments public utilities and private sector clients. Affiliates of the employee-owned company include software provider Innovyze business and government relations firm mCapitol and MWH Laboratories which conducts research.

Geographic Reach

When it comes to projects MWH Global lives up to its name. The Colorado-based firm operates from 180 offices in 35 countries on six continents. It is focusing on expansion especially in South America the Asia/Pacific region Asia/Pacific region the Middle East Africa and Europe.

Operations

As a global leader in the infrastructure sector the company's portfolio contains plenty of high-profile clients such as the US government and projects. The firm is the lead designer for the Panama Canal's navigation locks which will double the canal's capacity. The projects is slated for completion in 2014. MWH Global also is working on the largest energy infrastructure program in the UK. The firm is managing the project for National Grid an international electricity and gas company.

MWH also was awarded a contract to design a drainage master plan in Qatar. The project will provide a roadmap for future investment into water and wastewater treatment and other water-related infrastructure programs over the next 50 years.

In the United States MWH completed recovery work in New Orleans in the aftermath of Hurricane Katrina. The company was responsible for removing debris cleaning the storm drains and inspecting the city's sewer and water infrastructure for damage. The work which was completed in 2010 also included expediting the reconstruction of city facilities such as police and fire stations recreation centers libraries and other municipal projects.

Other US contracts include drought protection and water quality improvements in Nevada and work in the Florida Everglades with joint venture partner Jacobs Engineering.

Financial Performance

MWH Global reported $236.3 million in total revenue in 2012 and was ranked 60th among the Top 100 Design-Build Firms in 2013 by Engineering News Record.

Company Background

MWH Global formed after the 2001 merger of Montgomery Watson and Harza. The company has deep roots. Predecessor Ames Crosta Company was founded in 1820.

EXECUTIVES

CFO, David G. Barnes, age 51
Vice President Of Finance, Michael Hanf
President Energy and Industry, Joseph (Joe) Adams
Chairman and CEO, Alan J. Krause, age 60
President Innovyze, Paul F. Boulos
President Business Solutions, Dan McConville
President MWH Constructors, Blair Lavoie
President Europe Africa Government and Infrastructure, Wim Drossaert
President Government and Infrastructure Americas and Asia Pacific, Marshall Davert
CIO, Claire Rutkowski
Managing Director United Kingdom, Catherine Schefer
Chief Strategy Officer, David A. Smith
Vice President Director Of Industrial, Thomas Demayo
Vice President Of Finance, Rodney Edmonds
Svp And Managing Executive The Asset Group (Tag), Ed Carter
Executive Vice President, Donald L Smith
Financial Controller Vice President, Clint Rivet
Vice President, Norman Bishop
Vice President, Glen Grant
Vice President, Joe Hegna
Vice President Of Information Technology, Greg Clark
Vice President, Bruno Trouille
Vice President Engrg, Mike Rozenblatt
Vice President, Garry Wohlgemuth
Vice President, Craig Wilcox
Vice President, Frank Tam
Vice President, Vito Dicosola
Vice President, Lawrence Bailey
Vice President, Maura Horn
Vice President, Timothy Wolfe
Vice President Of Information Systems, Babak Bozorgy
Senior Vice President And Chief, Garry Sanderson
Vice President And Corporate Controller, Chad Scherer
Vice President, Shannon Rowley
Principal Engineer And Senior Vp, Robert Aaserude
Vice President And Director For Nrii, Finis Mario
Vice President Marketing Government And Infrastructure, Roger Austin
Vice President, Bob Parent
Vice President, Simon Bluestone Bces
Vice President And Principal Ecologist, Ed Redente
Vice President, Greg Tate
Vice President Of Technology Systems, Carlos Claros
Vice President, Sandra Shuster
National Sales Manager, Richard Leigh
Vice President Client Services Manager, Tom Boehnke
Vice President And Regional Manager, John Robinson
Vice President, Eugene Minnick
Vice President Program Director, Richard Maurer
Vice President Global Geotechnical, Peter Dickson
Vice President Business Development, Douglas G Smith
Vice President, Paul Blaszczyk
Vice President, Michael Bruen
Vice President Management Consulting, Martin Hodell
Vice President Director Of Marketing, Diane Jones
Vice President Of Ethics, Kimberly Strong
Senior Structural Engineer Vp, James Witnik
Vice President, Janet Sheldon
Vice President Business Development, Eric Kastner
Vice President, Dean P Bell
Vice President Sr Client Services, Becky Hachenburg
Vice President And Location Manager, Kimberly Kesler Arnold
Vice President Marketing, Jacques Perret
Vice President, Donald Erpenbeck
Vice President Global Ethics And Compliance, Corey Sanchez
Vice President Business Solutions, Philip Smith

Vice President, Rick Adcock
Vice President, Gregory Tate
Vice President Networking, Ed Kimura
Vice President, Khalid Nazeer
Vice President, Joseph Wojslaw
Treas, Thomas Payne
Chairman Emeritus, Bill Carol
Chairman and CEO, Alan J. Krause, age 60
Board Member, Richard Wankmuller
Treasurer, Sandi White
Secretary, Debi Lewis
Board Member, Jerry Henry

LOCATIONS

HQ: MWH GLOBAL INC.
380 INTERLOCKEN CRES, BROOMFIELD, CO 80021-8022
Phone: 303-533-1900
Web: WWW.MWHGLOBAL.COM

PRODUCTS/OPERATIONS

Selected Services

Construction
- Airports
- General building
- Industrial
- Highways bridges roads
- Marine and port facilities

Engineering and technical services
Facilities development
Government relations
Program management and management consulting
Research and testing
Renewable energy and sustainability
- Chemical and soil remediation
- Hazardous waste
- Hydroelectric power
- Non-hydro renewable energy
- Power distribution and transmission lines
- Thermal power

Risk assessment
Specialized consulting services
Water and environment
- Dams and reservoirs
- Landfills biosolids
- Sanitary/storm sewers conveyance pumping stations
- Water resources planning management
- Water treatment and desalination plants
- Water transmission lines aqueducts
- Waste water planning and management

COMPETITORS

AECOM
Bechtel
Black & Veatch
CH2M HILL
Camp Dresser McKee
EA Engineering
Fluor
GDF SUEZ
Jacobs Engineering
KBR
Peter Kiewit Sons'
Severn Trent
Siemens Water Technologies
Tetra Tech
Veolia Environnement
WS Atkins
Zachry Inc.

HISTORICAL FINANCIALS

Company Type: Private

Income Statement

FYE: December 28

	REVENUE ($ mil.)	NET INCOME ($ mil.)	NET PROFIT MARGIN	EMPLOYEES
12/12	1,545	43	2.8%	7,000
12/05*	946	0	—	—
01/03	975	942	96.6%	—
12/01	774	19	2.6%	—
Annual Growth	6.5%	7.4%	—	—

*Fiscal year change

2012 Year-End Financials

Debt ratio: —
Return on equity: 2.80%
Cash ($ mil.): 96
Current ratio: 1.20
Long-term debt ($ mil.): —
Dividends
Yield: —
Payout: —
Market value ($ mil.): —

NATIONAL AUTOMOBILE DEALERS ASSOCIATION

The National Automobile Dealers Association (N.A.D.A.) has been around almost as long as there have been cars. Founded in 1917 N.A.D.A. represents more than 16000 new car and truck dealers in the US and abroad. Through its more than 32500 franchises N.A.D.A. offers a range of services including: government relations (lobbying of Congress education of dealers) legal and public affairs dealership operations and other courses through N.A.D.A University insurance and retirement benefits IT training and convention and exposition support. N.A.D.A. also publishes The N.A.D.A. Official Used Car Guide and AutoExec magazine. Membership is open to any dealer with a new car or truck sales and service franchise.

EXECUTIVES

Vp Conventions And Expositions, Stephen R Pitt
Vp Dealership Operations, John R Lyboldt
President, Phillip D. Brady
VP and CFO, Joseph L. Cowden
VP and and Chief Public Affairs Officer, David F. Hyatt
EVP and Chief Administration Officer, Bruce M. Kelleher
VP and CIO, Richard E. Malaise
Chairman American Truck Dealers, R. Kyle Treadway
Vice President Public Affairs, Jonathan Collegio
Vice Chairman, Jeff Carlson
Chairman, Bill Fox
Board Member, Jennifer Sorrell

LOCATIONS

HQ: NATIONAL AUTOMOBILE DEALERS ASSOCIATION
8400 WESTPARK DR STE 1, MC LEAN, VA 221023522
Phone: 7038217000
Web: WWW.NADAFRONTPAGE.COM

HISTORICAL FINANCIALS

Company Type: Private

Income Statement

FYE: December 31

	REVENUE ($ mil.)	NET INCOME ($ mil.)	NET PROFIT MARGIN	EMPLOYEES
12/12	105	19	18.9%	500
12/09	35	(0)	—	—
12/05	43	4	9.9%	—
12/02	59	0	—	—
Annual Growth	5.9%	—	—	—

2012 Year-End Financials

Debt ratio: —
Return on equity: 18.90%
Cash ($ mil.): 6
Current ratio: 0.30
Long-term debt ($ mil.): —
Dividends
Yield: —
Payout: —
Market value ($ mil.): —

NATIONAL EDUCATION ASSOCIATION OF THE UNITED STATES

The National Education Association (NEA) is dedicated to promoting the cause of public education and the teaching profession. The organization boasts a membership of 3.2 million elementary and secondary teachers support professionals administrators higher education faculty and student teachers. It operates in all US states through affiliates. The group's key issues include the No Child Left Behind Act professional pay education funding minority community outreach dropout prevention achievement gaps and other matters facing America's schools. Founded in 1857 the NEA also hosts Read Across America a one-day reading event held on Dr. Seuss' birthday.

Operations

In 1966 the NEA merged with the American Teachers Association. Today it serves as the nation's largest teachers union followed by the American Federation of Teachers with its more than 1.5 million members.

Among the magazines newsletters and journals it publishes are NEA Today This Active Life and The NEA Almanac of Higher Education. The group's web site provides links to its publications as well as to lesson plans articles on classroom management and instruction methods professional development resources and additional online tools.

As part of its focus the organization also puts on regional leadership conferences American Education Week and National Teacher Day. It also partners with other causes and groups to reach out to parents families communities businesses foundations education groups and children's advocates. Some of its partnerships include Democracy Day (with Rock the Vote) the MyMoneyAppUpChallenge Solar Decathlon 2010 Census Green Schools Civics Education and Mom Congress.

Geographic Reach

Based in Washington DC the NEA operates in all 50 states through affiliate organizations that altogether serve more than 14000 communities nationwide.

EXECUTIVES

President, Dennis Van Roekel
VP, Lily Eskelsen
Executive Director, John I. Wilson, age 67
Secretary and Treasurer, Rebecca Pringle

LOCATIONS

HQ: NATIONAL EDUCATION ASSOCIATION OF THE UNITED STATES
1201 16TH ST NW, WASHINGTON, DC 20036-3290
Phone: 202-833-4000
Web: WWW.NEA.ORG

PRODUCTS/OPERATIONS

Selected Key Issues

Achievement gaps
Dropout prevention
Education funding
Minority community outreach
No Child Left Behind Act
Professional pay

Selected Membership

Administrators
Elementary and secondary teachers Higher education faculty
Student teachers
Support professionals

HISTORICAL FINANCIALS

Company Type: Private

Income Statement FYE: August 31

	REVENUE ($ mil.)	NET INCOME ($ mil.)	NET PROFIT MARGIN	EMPLOYEES
08/11	376	3	0.9%	735
08/10*	376	16	4.3%	—
12/08	0	0	—	—
08/08	392	18	4.6%	—
Annual Growth	(1.4%)	(43.4%)	—	—

*Fiscal year change

2011 Year-End Financials

Debt ratio: —
Return on equity: 0.90%
Cash ($ mil.): 59
Current ratio: 2.20
Long-term debt ($ mil.): —
Dividends
Yield: —
Payout: —
Market value ($ mil.): —

NATIONAL FROZEN FOODS CORPORATION

EXECUTIVES

VP Sales, Robert E. (Bob) Ashmun
VP Operations, Ed Rosenbach
General Manager and VP Sales Rainier Food Products, Tony Miller

LOCATIONS

HQ: NATIONAL FROZEN FOODS CORPORATION
1600 FRVIEW AVE E STE 200, SEATTLE, WA 98102
Phone: 5419283306
Web: WWW.NFFC.COM

PRODUCTS/OPERATIONS

Selected Products

Beans (green Italian lima and wax)
Carrots (crinkle cut diced smooth sliced)
Peas
Squash
Sweet corn (on cob cut and cream style)
Vegetable purees

COMPETITORS

Allens
Birds Eye
Coloma Frozen Foods
Del Monte Foods
Dole Food
Faribault Foods
General Mills
Hanover Foods
Idaho Fresh-Pak
Mondelez International
NORPAC
Overhill Farms
Pictsweet
Sabroso
Seabrook Brothers
Seneca Foods
Smith Frozen Foods
Twin City Foods
Willow Wind Organic Farms

HISTORICAL FINANCIALS

Company Type: Private

Income Statement FYE: August 30

	REVENUE ($ mil.)	NET INCOME ($ mil.)	NET PROFIT MARGIN	EMPLOYEES
08/14	202	17	8.7%	1,009
08/13*	18	5	32.1%	—
04/12	197	13	6.9%	—
04/11	178	0	—	—
Annual Growth	4.4%	—	—	—

*Fiscal year change

2014 Year-End Financials

Debt ratio: —
Return on equity: 8.70%
Cash ($ mil.): 2
Current ratio: 0.70
Long-term debt ($ mil.): —
Dividends
Yield: —
Payout: —
Market value ($ mil.): —

NATIONAL GRAPE CO-OPERATIVE ASSOCIATION INC.

Well of course grape growers want to hang out in a bunch! The ‚Â more than 1090 ‚Âgrower/owner-members ‚Âof the National Grape Cooperative harvest Concord and Niagara grapes from almost 50000 acres of vineyards. The plucked ‚Âproduce ‚Âsupplies the coop's ‚Âwholly owned subsidiary Welch Foods. Welch Foods ‚Âmakes and sells fruit-based juices jams jellies and spreads ‚Âunder the Welch's and ‚ÂBama brands in the US and nearly 50 other countries. Offerings include fresh eating grapes distributed by C.H. Robinson Worldwide as well as dried fruit and frozen juice pops. ‚ÂThe grape ‚Âgrowers own vineyards in Pennsylvania Michigan New York Ohio Washington and Ontario Canada which produce ‚Âsome 300000 tons of grapes annually.

The entire business from growing to processing grapes is highly competitive and the difference between sales and cost of goods sold often so ‚Âslim that earning a profit is challenging. ‚ÂDespite the economic downturn and soaring commodity costs in 2011 Welch's ‚Âsustained less than a 10% decline in net income on a small slip in sales. The results reflect new value-priced product introductions coupled with an initiative started in 2009 to ‚Âslash costs through concentrating production and distribution. ‚Â Welch's initiative included adding a new bottle production facility to its plant in 2011 and ‚Âcutting its workforce by 17% in early 2010.

The coop also ‚Ârealized a ‚Âsmaller crop in 2011 in part due to a decline in family-farmer owners. ‚ÂThe 10% decrease in tons sold modestly reduced total net proceeds. Nonetheless net income on patron business grew ‚Â boosted by a sizeable ‚Âincrease in distributable proceeds per ton.

HISTORY

Looking for a steady supply of grapes for his processing plant in 1945 Russian immigrant Jack Kaplan convinced 900 grape growers to join the newly formed National Grape Cooperative. Also that year Welch Foods' parent company decided to spin off its purple fruit interests and Kaplan purchased a controlling interest. Welch's –a competitor at the time –had been started in 1869 when Dr. Thomas Welch a tee totaling dentist created an unfermented Concord grape wine to be used for nonalcoholic communions. The juice was coolly received at first but the advent of Prohibition helped push the company to the forefront of the fruit-drink industry.

While Kaplan had purchased his interest in Welch's with the intention of combining it with the National Grape Co-op it wasn't until the mid-1950s that the two could agree on the acquisition. Welch's product line grew throughout the 1960s and 1970s including the 1972 introduction of red grape and white grape juices. A glut of grapes depressed prices in the 1980s but the co-op rebounded by the 1990s.

In 1994 the co-op acquired jam and jelly maker BAMA Foods from Borden. Daniel Dillon became CEO of Welch's in 1995 and Fredrick Kalian was named president of the co-op the next year. Yakima Valley Grape Producers joined National Grape Co-op in 1997 adding new growers and more grapes to meet a growing demand spurred in part by newly discovered health benefits of purple and white grape juice. (Welch's helped fund the research.)

New products and increased advertising helped boost juice sales dramatically in 1998 and 1999. Fresh table grapes distributed by C.H. Robinson Worldwide were also introduced in 1999 and by 2000 were available nationwide. In 2001 the company announced it would be cutting up to 100 jobs –its first layoffs in more than two decades –due to slowing sales.

In 2003 the company introduced new variations of its products including single-serving juices (Welsh Squeezables). This along with increased marketing and new packaging have seen its sales growing during the last two years. Expansion in grocery channels and the introduction of low-calorie items and shrink-pack products led to further sales gains in 2004.

EXECUTIVES

President and CEO Welch Foods, David J. Lukiewski, age 58
President and Director, Joseph C. Falcone
Chief Legal Officer and Assistant Secretary, Vivian S. Y. Tseng
General Manager COO and Treasurer, Brent J. Roggie
Secretary and Assistant Treasurer, Timothy A. Buss
First VP and Director, Timothy E. Grow
Assistant Treasurer, Thomas A. Bockhorst
Assistant Secretary, Mathew A. Aufman
Third VP and Director, Jon B. Hinkelman
Second VP and Director, Anthony J. Falcone Jr.
Financial and Accounting Officer, Michael J. Perda
President and Director, Joseph C. Falcone
Director, Richard A. Boushey
Director, Douglas R. Forraht
Director, Randolph H. Graham
Director, Jerry A. Czebotar
First VP and Director, Timothy E. Grow
Director, Jon B. Hinkleman
Director, Marvin D. Vining
Director, Gary R. Youngs
Director, William G. (Bill) Barker III, age 53
Third VP and Director, Jon B. Hinkelman
Director, Dennis C. Vacco
Second VP and Director, Anthony J. Falcone Jr.
Director, Thomas G. Wilkinson
Director, Ned R. Totzke
Auditors: KPMGLLP

LOCATIONS

HQ: NATIONAL GRAPE CO-OPERATIVE ASSOCIATION INC.
2 S PORTAGE ST, WESTFIELD, NY 147871400
Phone: 7163265200
Web: WWW.WELCHS.COM

PRODUCTS/OPERATIONS

Selected Products

Food and snacks
- Dried fruit
- Fresh grapes
- Fruit 'N Yogurt
- Fruit snacks mixed
- Welch's frozen pops
- Welch's soda

Jams jellies and spreads
Juice
- 100% juices
- Concentrates

Essentials fruit blends
Fruit fizz sparkling juice beverage
Light lower calorie
Sparkling grape cocktails
Refrigerator cocktails

COMPETITORS

B&G Foods
Big Heart Pet Brands
Chiquita Brands
Coca-Cola
Constellation Brands
Cranberries Limited
Dole Food
Dr Pepper Snapple Group
Fresh Del Monte Produce
Goya
Hornell Brewing
IZZE
Mondelez International
Monster Beverage
NestlÃ© USA
Ocean Spray
PepsiCo
Procter & Gamble
Smucker
Snapple
Tropicana

HISTORICAL FINANCIALS

Company Type: Private

Income Statement FYE: August 31

	REVENUE ($ mil.)	NET INCOME ($ mil.)	NET PROFIT MARGIN	EMPLOYEES
08/13	608	65	10.7%	1,325
08/12	649	74	11.5%	—
08/11	640	74	11.6%	—
08/10	658	0	—	—
Annual Growth	(2.6%)	—	—	—

2013 Year-End Financials

Debt ratio: —
Return on equity: 10.70%
Cash ($ mil.): 5
Current ratio: 0.60
Long-term debt ($ mil.): —
Dividends
Yield: —
Payout: —
Market value ($ mil.): —

NATIONAL RIFLE ASSOCIATION OF AMERICA

The NRA believes in the right to bear arms. With more than 5 million members The National Rifle Association (NRA) is the staunch defender of Second Amendment rights. It's a major player in the political arena and stands firm in its resolve to protect the right to keep and bear arms. The NRA offers a variety of educational and gun safety programs and publishes magazines (America's 1st Freedom American Hunter Women's Outlook). It also caters to more than one million youth through its shooting sports events and affiliated programs with the likes of 4-H the Boy Scouts of America and others. It also sells NRA merchandise. Union army veterans William Church and George Wingate founded the NRA in 1871.

Operations

The Institute for Legislative Action (ILA) established in 1975 is the lobbying arm of the NRA. With offices in Fairfax and Washington DC the ILA has a staff of more than 80 with a team of full-time lobbyists defending Second Amendment issues on Capitol Hill in state legislatures and in local government bodies. The NRA also operates the National Firearms Museum in Fairfax Virginia.

The NRA has made a commitment to training education and marksmanship. Its education and training department is supported by more than 65000 certified instructors who offer lessons to some 750000 gun owners each year. Through NRA's law enforcement division training program the NRA offers certified and standardized firearm instructor training and has trained over 50000 law enforcement firearm instructors.

Strategy

The NRA's membership ranks topped a record 5 million in 2013 as efforts to pass gun-control legislation following multiple mass shootings –including the Newtown Connecticut and Colorado movie theater tragedies – swelled the organization's ranks. About 500000 new members joined in 2013.

EXECUTIVES

Secretary, Edward J. Land
EVP, Wayne LaPierre
First VP, Sandra (Sandy) Froman
President, John C. Sigler, age 68
Executive Director General Operations, Kayne Robinson, age 71
Chief Lobbyist and Executive Director NRA Institute for Legislative Action, Chris W. Cox
Director Corporate and Foundation Relations Office of Advancement, Nicole Capossela
Southern Regional Director, Al Hammond
Manager Women's Programs, Rosemary E. Herr
Director Law Enforcement Activities, Glen Hoyer
President The NRA Foundation, Allen D. Cors
Executive Director The NRA Foundation, Wayne Sheets
Director Strategic Giving Office of Advancement, Frank L. Cerutti

LOCATIONS

HQ: NATIONAL RIFLE ASSOCIATION OF AMERICA
11250 WAPLES MILL RD # 1, FAIRFAX, VA 220309400
Phone: 7032671000
Web: WWW.NRAILA.ORG

PRODUCTS/OPERATIONS

Selected Programs

Business Alliance & Clubs
NRA Sports
Competitions & Matches
Eddie Eagle GunSafe
Firearm Training
Hunter Services
Law Enforcement Services
Range Services
Women' s Programs
Friends of NRA Banquets
National Firearms Museum
NRA Headquarters Range
Gunsmithing Schools
NRA Recruiter
NRA Hunters Rights.
Youth
National Youth Shooting Sports Cooperative Program
Brownells/NRA Day Program
Brownells/NRA Outstanding Achievement Youth Award
Marksmanship Qualification Program
Youth Hunter Education Challenge
Brownells/NRA National Youth Shooting Sports Ambassador Program
Youth Education Summit
Resources & Information
Youth Wildlife Art Contest
Santioned Special Tournament
Junior Membership
InSights Magazine
Email List Signup
Youth Essay Contest
Special Offers
Volunteer State Coordinators
NRA' s Home Air Gun Program
Request for Eagle Scout Certificate
National Junior Shooting Camps

HISTORICAL FINANCIALS

Company Type: Private

Income Statement FYE: December 31

	REVENUE ($ mil.)	NET INCOME ($ mil.)	NET PROFIT MARGIN	EMPLOYEES
12/13	347	57	16.5%	500
12/09	237	1	0.5%	—
12/07	363	143	39.6%	—
12/06	758	0	—	—
Annual Growth	—	—	—	—

2013 Year-End Financials

Debt ratio: —
Return on equity: 16.50%
Cash ($ mil.): 18
Current ratio: 0.60
Long-term debt ($ mil.): —
Dividends
Yield: —
Payout: —
Market value ($ mil.): —

NATIONAL RURAL ELECTRIC COOPERATIVE ASSOCIATION

Would it shock you to learn that consumer-owned cooperatives provide electricity to more than 42 million people in the US? The National Rural Electric Cooperative Association (NRECA) is the cooperatives' voice in politics and policymaking. It publishes a monthly magazine and a weekly newspaper sponsors conferences and seminars and represents about 900 rural electric co-ops (from 47 states) in the US Congress and state legislatures. As the nation embraces investor-owned utilities NRECA has been lobbying hard for more moderate approaches to deregulation in order to protect consumers from potential monopolies. The association also provides power assistance and technical advice to developing nations.

Financial Performance

NRECA generated nearly $287 million in revenue in 2011 a 18% increase vs. 2010. Net income fell 51% over the same period. The $287 million in 2011 revenue included $27 million in membership dues $189 million in reimbursements $24 million from the member fee-for-service programs and $47 million from non-member fee-for-service programs.

EXECUTIVES

Director Media Relations, Patrick Lavigne
VP and Director, F. E. Wolski, age 63
Secretary Treasurer and Director, Michael J. Guidry, age 64
Media Representative, Tracy Warren
CEO, Jo Ann Emerson
Vice President of Operations, Dan Waddle
Director, Joe Bongiovanni
Director, Curtis Wynn
Director, Robert J. (Bob) Occhi, age 66
Director, Ronald Osterhout
Director, Gail F. Paine
Director, Ronald R. (Ron) Bergh, age 69
Director, Don R. McQuitty
Director, Perry E. Rubart
President and Director, Jack F. Wolfe Jr., age 69
VP and Director, F. E. Wolski, age 63
Secretary Treasurer and Director, Michael J. Guidry, age 64
Director, Anthony A. Anderson
Director, Martin Anderson

Director, Dean C. Belt
Director, Angus S. Hastings
Director, Mark Hofer
Director, Clarence M. Keller
Director, Gary Potter
Director, Lanny Rodgers
Director, Robert D. Kretzschmar
Director, Donald Link
Director, Ronald J. Schwartau
Director, Vernon N. Brinkley
Director, Phil Carson
Director, Raymond J. Cloud
Director, Mel Coleman
Director, Charles Dawsey
Director, Larry E. Elkins
Director, Dennis M. Esaki
Director, Roy Friedersdorf
Director, Edward (Ray) Garcia
Director, Thomas E. Madsen
Director, Thomas McQuiston
Director, Michael L. Miller
Director, Galen Mills
Director, Russell Nielsen
Director, Curtis Nolan
Director, Christian Nygaard
Director, Max W. Ott
Director, C. Brooks Sharp
Director, Jimmy D. Springs
Director, Ronald D. Springsteel
Director, M. LaDon (Don) Torgersen
Director, Guadalupe Vega
Director, Carl R. Widdowson
Director, Bryan Wolfe

LOCATIONS

HQ: NATIONAL RURAL ELECTRIC COOPERATIVE ASSOCIATION
4301 WILSON BLVD STE 1, ARLINGTON, VA 22203-1867
Phone: 703-907-5500

HISTORICAL FINANCIALS

Company Type: Private

Income Statement FYE: December 31

	REVENUE ($ mil.)	NET INCOME ($ mil.)	NET PROFIT MARGIN	EMPLOYEES
12/12	208	4	2.2%	885
12/08	162	0	0.1%	—
12/05	139	3	2.5%	—
12/05	974	0	—	—
Annual Growth	—	432.5%	—	—

2012 Year-End Financials

Debt ratio: —
Return on equity: 2.20%
Cash ($ mil.): 77
Current ratio: 1.90
Long-term debt ($ mil.): —
Dividends
Yield: —
Payout: —
Market value ($ mil.): —

NATIONAL UNIVERSITY

National University is the flagship school of the National University System. The institution offers more than 150 undergraduate and graduate degrees and teacher credential and certificate programs. A not-for-profit institution National University programs range across fields including business engineering education media and human services. The university enrolls 23000 students at multiple locations in California and Nevada; it also offers about 70 online degree programs. The school conducts research through the National University Community Research Institute (NUCRI). National University was founded in 1971.

Geographic Reach

National University operates through about 45 locations in California and Nevada including regional campuses in Bakersfield Costa Mesa Fresno Los Angeles Ontario Oxnard Redding Sacramento San Bernardino San Diego San Jose Stockton Twentynine Palms and Woodland Hills California as well as Henderson Nevada. It also has offices in Dallas and Houston Texas and it operates online information centers in Florida Georgia Virginia and Washington State (in addition to numerous online information locations in California). Some of the university's satellite centers are located on military bases.

Operations

National University consists of five schools: Education; Professional Studies; Business and Management; Health and Human Services and Engineering Technology and Media. It also includes the College of Letters and Sciences. The university employs more than 250 full-time faculty members.

The National University System is a group of affiliated universities to meet educational demands for modern times. It was formed in 2001 and includes affiliates John F. Kennedy University City University of Seattle Spectrum Pacific Learning and WestMed College as well as National University International and National University Virtual High School.

Strategy

To meet the rising needs of a growing population National University has been adding new locations. For instance during 2012 it added new online information centers in Arcadia and San Francisco California and in Seattle Washington. It also added a new university campus in Rancho Cordova California and it expanded its San Diego locations by adding a new facility to house programs for its School of Business and Management and School of Professional Studies.

National University strives to provide learning opportunities to a diverse student population. It is a leading issuer of master's degrees to minorities and women in California. It also serves a rising number of online students and is regularly adding new online courses to meet the needs of this audience.

Growing health care program demands prompted the university to add a Master of Healthcare Administration program at its Fresno campus in 2012. It also added bachelor's degree in allied health through a partnership with the San Mateo Community College District.

Auditors: KPMGLLP

LOCATIONS

HQ: NATIONAL UNIVERSITY
11255 N TORREY PINES RD, LA JOLLA, CA 92037-1011
Phone: 858-642-8000
Web: WWW.NU.EDU

PRODUCTS/OPERATIONS

Selected Schools and Colleges

College of Letters and Sciences
School of Business and Management
School of Education
School of Engineering Technology and Media
School of Health and Human Services
School of Professional Studies

HISTORICAL FINANCIALS

Company Type: Private

Income Statement FYE: June 30

	REVENUE ($ mil.)	NET INCOME ($ mil.)	NET PROFIT MARGIN	EMPLOYEES
06/11	203	25	12.4%	1,954
06/10	178	18	10.3%	—
06/09	165	5	3.1%	—
06/02	126	20	16.4%	—
Annual Growth	5.4%	2.2%	—	—

2011 Year-End Financials

Debt ratio: —
Return on equity: 12.40%
Cash ($ mil.): 38
Current ratio: —
Long-term debt ($ mil.): —
Dividends
Yield: —
Payout: —
Market value ($ mil.): —

NCH CORPORATION

HISTORY

Salesman Milton Levy founded National Disinfectant Co. in Dallas in 1919 to make disinfectants insecticides and soaps. The company's offerings grew in the 1930s to include Everbrite a top-selling industrial floor wax. Levy's sons Irvin Lester and Milton Jr. worked for the company as teenagers and took over its management after their father's death in 1946.

National Disinfectant expanded geographically in the 1950s and 1960s opening its first branch office in St. Louis in 1956. The company changed its name to National Chemsearch in 1960 to reflect its diversity. It also expanded into Europe and Latin America. National Chemsearch went public in 1965. Acquisitions boosted its product line to about 250 items by 1970. The company shortened its name to NCH in 1978.

NCH expanded its marketing to include catalog sales direct mail and telemarketing in 1986. It opened a South Korean plant in 1992. Troubled economies in Mexico and Venezuela hurt profits in 1994 and the next year NCH began work on a long-term business strategy that envisioned third-generation Levy family members moving into higher executive ranks.

Softened currency rates in Europe and Asia contributed to a decrease in profits for fiscal 1999. That year NCH focused on strengthening its customer relationships by boosting sales staff training and implementing an Internet-based corporate network.

In 2000 Irvin Levy became the company's chairman and NCH sold its electronic components business. The next year the company shut down its direct broadcast satellite equipment operations. In February 2002 the Levys took the company private by purchasing the 43% of the company that they didn't already own. The brothers originally offered a 20% premium to buy the shares but were greeted by lawsuits from shareholders who claimed they were taking advantage of a depressed market. The Levys settled the suits by upping the offer by $120 million.

EXECUTIVES

Chairman, Irvin L. Levy
Co-President and Director, Lester A. Levy Jr.
Co-President and Director, Robert M. Levy
Co-President and Director, Walter M. Levy
Co-President and Director, John I. Levy

Director Marketing Supply Line Direct, David Wilson
Director Product Development, Mike Benton
General Counsel, Rich Robinson
VP Research and Development, John Roheim
VP Sales, Tony Lewis
CEO NCH Europe, Charles Gile
CFO, Tom Hetzer
General Manager Supply Line Direct, Kent LeeMaster
Marketing Specialist Supply Line Direct, Andrea Berg
Co-President and Director, Robert M. Levy
Co-President and Director, Walter M. Levy
Co-President and Director, John I. Levy
Auditors: GrantThorntonLLP

LOCATIONS

HQ: NCH CORPORATION
2727 CHEMSEARCH BLVD, IRVING, TX 750626454
Phone: 9724380705
Web: WWW.US.CHEMSEARCH.COM

PRODUCTS/OPERATIONS

Selected Operations and Products

Chemical Specialties
- Cleaning chemicals
- Deodorizers
- Floor and carpet care products
- HVAC products
- Lubricants
- Oil production facility chemicals
- Paint
- Paint removers
- Water-treatment chemicals

Landmark Direct
- First-aid supplies
- Workplace signage and productivity products

Pet Care
Partsmaster Group
- Cutting tools
- Electrical products
- Fasteners
- Welding alloys

Plumbing Products Group
- Plumbing products for new construction
- Plumbing repair and replacement parts

Industrial and Institutional Maintenance
Industrial and commercial cleaning
Industrial Repair and maintenance
Drains Grease Traps and lift stations
Lubrication and coolants
Equipment and supplies
Parts washing
Grounds Care
Personal hygiene
Pet Care
Training pads
Stain and Odor Removers
Cleaners and Disinfectants
Allergy Relief and shed Control
Grooming products
Plumbing
Sinks
Faucets
Tub & Showers
Toilets
Drains
Specialty Industrial Supply
High Performance Cutting Tools
Welding
Abrasives
Compounds
Fasteners
Electrical and Automotive
Shop Supplies
Storage Hardware
Tools
Water Treatment Solutions
Boiler
Cooling Towers
Colsed Recirculation Systems
Biocides and Algaecides
Cleaner/Descalers
Equipment
Wastewater and Bio Remediation

COMPETITORS

Church & Dwight	H.B. Fuller
Cintas	Illinois Tool Works
Clariant	Pioneer Corporation
Danaher	Quaker Chemical
Detrex	Safety-Kleen
Ecolab	WD-40

HISTORICAL FINANCIALS

Company Type: Private

Income Statement

FYE: April 30

	REVENUE ($ mil.)	NET INCOME ($ mil.)	NET PROFIT MARGIN	EMPLOYEES
04/13	1,018	3	0.3%	8,500
04/12	1,045	6	0.6%	—
04/11	952	6	0.7%	—
04/10	885	0	—	—
Annual Growth	4.8%	—	—	—

2013 Year-End Financials

Debt ratio: —
Return on equity: 0.30%
Cash ($ mil.): 11
Current ratio: 1.30
Long-term debt ($ mil.): —

Dividends
Yield: —
Payout: —
Market value ($ mil.): —

NCH HEALTHCARE SYSTEM INC.

NCH Healthcare System provides a comprehensive range of health care services to residents in southwest Florida. The system includes two acute care hospitals (NCH Downtown Naples Hospital and NCH North Naples Hospital) with a combined 715-bed capacity and regional institutes which specialize in orthopedics and the treatment of cancer heart ailments and women's and children's health issues. NCH also operates an area network of outpatient and ambulatory care facilities that provide services ranging from diagnostics to rehabilitative care to surgery and emergency care.

Geographic Reach

NCH operates two hospitals and dozens of clinics and centers in Collier County primarily in Naples as well as surrounding communities in Collier and Lee counties including Bonita Immokalee and Marco Island.

Operations

Employing some 650 physicians NCH reports that it handles some 37000 inpatient admissions each year as well as 87000 emergency room visits 3000 births and 11000 surgical procedures. Its NCH Physician Group is a practice organization consisting of 90 doctors at 17 offices. The organization provides some $60 million in community care each year including charity medical services and community outreach programs.

NCH is a member of the Mayo Clinic Care Network which means that it benefits from care coordination and quality programs shared through a network of peers.

Financial Performance

After a 16% increase in 2011 NCH's revenues declined 2% to some $473 million in 2012 due to a decline net patient service revenue primarily attributed to a change in how the company accounts for self-paying customer revenue. Patient revenues account for more than 95% of revenues.

The organization's net income increased 223% to $23 million in 2012 due to asset sales and net gains following a 66% decrease in profits in 2011.

Strategy

In 2012 Mayo Clinic and NCH signed a collaboration deal whereby NCH became the first member of the Mayo Clinic Care Network in Florida and the Southeast region of the US. Among other things the deal gives NCH access to the expertise and resources of the much larger Mayo Clinic operations. The organization has formed collaborative care agreements with other area organizations to improve medical quality and costs in the region.

Other measures to improve care and resources include the expansion of the system's neonatal intensive care unit in 2012 to meet increased patient need. NCH has also enhanced stroke care and other specialist services in recent years.

NCH is streamlining its information technology systems to free up resources and focus on patient care operations. In 2010 the health network outsourced its medical records department (including billing and patient registration operations) to reduce internal hospital administrative functions. It outsourced its computer support department the previous year.

Company Background

In a move to focus on the provision of medical care in 2007 the company sold its DSI Laboratories subsidiary which provided medical reference and toxicology services to national laboratory services provider LabCorp.

EXECUTIVES

Chair, Mariann T. MacDonald, age 66
CEO President of the NCH, Alan S. Weiss
COO North Naples Hospital Campus, Gail A. Dolan
General Counsel and Chief of Staff, Kevin D. Cooper
Chief Information Officer, Helen Thompson
Secretary Treasurer and Trustee, Edwin Stedem
Chief Human Resources Officer, Brian Settle
Chief Operations Officer, Phillip Dutcher
CFO and Assistant Treasurer, Vicki Hale Orr
Chief Development Officer, Jim Martin
Chief Human Resources Officer, John McGirl
1st Vice Chair/Treasurer, Thomas Gazdic
2nd Vice Chair, Kay Gow
Chief Nursing Officer, Michele Thoman
Chief Medical Officer, Gary Parsons
Chief Administrative Officer NCH Physician Group, Zachary Bostock
Chief Strategy Officer, Mike Riley
Trustee, Jay H. Baker, age 79
President CEO and Trustee, Alan S. Weiss
Trustee, Carl E. Westman
Secretary Treasurer and Trustee, Edwin Stedem
Trustee, William Allyn
Trustee, Susan Dalton
1st Vice Chair/Treasurer, Thomas Gazdic
2nd Vice Chair, Kay Gow
Auditors: PricewaterhouseCoopersLLP

LOCATIONS

HQ: NCH HEALTHCARE SYSTEM INC.
350 7TH ST N, NAPLES, FL 34102-5754
Phone: 239-436-5000
Web: WWW.NCHMD.ORG

PRODUCTS/OPERATIONS

2012 Sales

	$ mil.	% of total
Net patient service revenues	457	97
Other	15	3
Total	473	100

Selected Subsidiaries and Facilities

Bonita Community Health Center
Collier Health Care Inc.
Community Home Services Inc.
Isabel Collier Read Healthpark
Marco Island Hospital Inc. (dba Marco Healthcare Center)

Naples Community Hospital Inc.
NCH Naples Downtown Hospital
NCH North Naples Hospital

Selected Services

Ancillary Services
Arts in Healing
Cardiac Services
Community Blood Center
da Vinci Surgical System
Diagnostic Services
Donating Blood
Heart Disease
Hospitals and Walk-In Centers
NCH Physician Group
Pediatric Services
Rehabilitation
Specialized Treatment Centers
Spiritual Care
Wellness and Nutrition
Women' s Services

COMPETITORS

Adventist Health System Sunbelt Healthcare
Baptist Health South Florida
Broward Health
HCA
Jackson Health System
Lakeland Regional Medical Center
Lee Memorial
Miami Children' s Hospital
Mount Sinai Medical Center of Florida
South Broward Hospital District
University of Miami Hospital

HISTORICAL FINANCIALS

Company Type: Private

Income Statement FYE: September 30

	REVENUE ($ mil.)	NET INCOME ($ mil.)	NET PROFIT MARGIN	EMPLOYEES
09/11	483	7	1.5%	3,500
09/08	456	25	5.6%	—
09/07	524	49	9.5%	—
09/06	475	35	7.5%	—
Annual Growth	0.3%	(27.2%)	—	—

2011 Year-End Financials

Debt ratio: —
Return on equity: 1.50%
Cash ($ mil.): 57
Current ratio: 2.10
Long-term debt ($ mil.): —
Dividends
Yield: —
Payout: —
Market value ($ mil.): —

NEIGHBORHOOD HEALTH PLAN INC

Neighborhood Health Plan (NHP) is a not-for-profit health plan provider that offers health insurance products and related services to more than 200000 members in Massachusetts. The organization is a leading provider of managed health care for members of MassHealth the state's Medicaid program for low-income and disabled residents. But it also provides commercial health plans for small businesses as well as low-cost and no-cost family and individual plans for people who qualify for subsidized health coverage under Massachusetts' 2006 health care reform law. NHP maintains a provider network of more than 2800 primary care physicians 400 specialists and dozens of hospitals. The company was founded in 1986.

EXECUTIVES

CEO, David Segal
Chief Medical Officer, Paul Mendis
CIO, Marilyn Daly
VP Operations, Katie Catlender
Interim CFO, Doug Thompson
Medical Director, Matthew Collins
Director Of Pharmacy, Peter Vargas
Vice President Of Clinical Operations, Deb Bonin
Vp Bus Dev, Reynold Spadoni
Vice President Provider Network, Kent Weiner
Vice President Of Facilities, Terry Rhymers
Vice President Of Operations, Krista O'Connor
Chairman, Matthew E. Fishman
Secretary, Debra Luckie, age 53
Board Member, John Fallon
Board Member, Zoila Feldman

LOCATIONS

HQ: NEIGHBORHOOD HEALTH PLAN INC
253 SUMMER ST FL 5, BOSTON, MA 02210-1120
Phone: 617-772-5500
Web: WWW.NHP.ORG

COMPETITORS

Aetna
Blue Cross and Blue Shield of Massachusetts
CIGNA
ConnectiCare
Fallon Community Health Plan
Harvard Pilgrim
Health New England
MVP Health Plan
Tufts Health Plan
UnitedHealth Group

HISTORICAL FINANCIALS

Company Type: Private

Income Statement FYE: December 31

	REVENUE ($ mil.)	NET INCOME ($ mil.)	NET PROFIT MARGIN	EMPLOYEES
12/08	855	27	3.2%	340
12/07	681	40	6.0%	—
12/06	1,779	0	—	—
Annual Growth	(30.7%)	64418.0%	—	—

2008 Year-End Financials

Debt ratio: —
Return on equity: 3.20%
Cash ($ mil.): 21
Current ratio: 0.30
Long-term debt ($ mil.): —
Dividends
Yield: —
Payout: —
Market value ($ mil.): —

NEIGHBORHOOD REINVESTMENT CORPORATION

Neighborhood Reinvestment Corporation (now dba NeighborWorks America) wants to be your neighbor. The not-for-profit organization supports more than 235 independent local organizations in suburban urban and rural communities across the country. Programs include building multi-family dwellings and helping low and middle income families with financing and insurance as well as job creation community facilities and economic development in rural areas. The organization also offers training for community leaders and would-be homeowners on community planning green building and financing among others. Established by Congress in 1978 NeighborWorks is funded by Congress private donations and corporate support.

Geographic Reach

NeighborWorks America operates a national office in Washgington DC and seven district offices in California Colorado Georgia. Massachusetts Missouri New York and Ohio.

Operations

NeighborWorks America ranked third among nonprofit builders of affordable homes in 2012 on the Builder 100 list and for the fourth year it was ranked among the top 100 of all home builders with 608 closings in 2012. To date the organization has leveraged more than $16 billion to invest in America's communities through its work in more than 4400 urban suburban and rural communities in all 50 states the District of Columbia and Puerto Rico.

Financial Performance

Congressional appropriations account for close to 90% of the nonprofit's revenue; while contributions generated around 10%. Major contributors and partners for NeighborWorks include Bank of America Ford Foundation Fannie Mae JPMorgan Chase Morgan Stanley and Federal Home Loan Bank of Dallas.

Strategy

NeighborWorks America's strategic plan for 2012 through 2016 includes employing and promoting green and sustainable building practices for the long-term benefit of the residents and communities in which it operates. The plan also establishes two specific outcomes: moving the NeighborWorks network to adopt comprehensive green strategies by designing at least two-thirds of the network as a NeighborWorks Green Organization; and further reducing the environmental impact of its operations and training practices.

EXECUTIVES

General Counsel and Secretary, Jeffrey T. Bryson
CFO, Michael L. Forster

LOCATIONS

HQ: NEIGHBORHOOD REINVESTMENT CORPORATION
999 N CAPITOL ST NE # 900, WASHINGTON, DC 20002-4684
Phone: 202-220-2300
Web: WWW.NW.ORG

HISTORICAL FINANCIALS

Company Type: Private

Income Statement FYE: September 30

	REVENUE ($ mil.)	NET INCOME ($ mil.)	NET PROFIT MARGIN	EMPLOYEES
09/10	312	2	0.8%	260
09/09*	359	7	2.0%	—
12/08	1	0	—	—
09/08	283	5	2.0%	—
Annual Growth	5.0%	(33.8%)	—	—

*Fiscal year change

2010 Year-End Financials

Debt ratio: —
Return on equity: 0.80%
Cash ($ mil.): 94
Current ratio: 1.30
Long-term debt ($ mil.): —
Dividends
Yield: —
Payout: —
Market value ($ mil.): —

NEMOURS FOUNDATION

Even if their offspring are fanatical about Finding Nemo parents of sick children may prefer finding Nemours. The Nemours Foundation operates the Nemours/Alfred I. duPont Hospital for Children in Wilmington Delaware; the Nemours Children's Hospital in Orlando Florida; and dozens of pediatric clinics in Delaware Florida New Jersey and Pennsylvania that treat acutely and chronically ill children. Specialties include orthopedics cardiology neurology and oncology. Nemours also has extensive research programs and it operates a clinic in Delaware that serves low-income elderly residents. The not-for-profit foundation was created in 1936 through the will of chemicals pioneer Alfred I. duPont.

Operations

Some of Nemours' facilities are operated in partnership with other health care providers. For example it runs pediatric programs with Bryn Mawr Hospital Lancaster General and Thomas Jefferson University Hospital in Pennsylvania as well as with AtlantiCare and Virtua Health in New Jersey.

Strategy

Nemours Foundation completed construction of a full-service children's hospital in Orlando Florida where it already operated a pediatric specialty clinic. The $400 million facility named Nemours Children's Hospital has 95 patient beds and emergency diagnostic specialty and outpatient units as well as educational and research centers. The foundation is also expanding the Nemours/Alfred I. duPont Hospital for Children in Delaware; the new patient tower is scheduled to open in 2014.

The Nemours Foundation has also invested in upgrading its information technology system. It uses a comprehensive electronic health record (EHR) system NemoursOne to connect all of its doctors and facilities with shared patient information. Some of the foundation's facilities participate in the state EHR network (Delaware Health Information Network).

EXECUTIVES

Chairman, John S. Lord, age 67
Executive Vice President Enterprise Services and Chief, Robert D. Bridges
SVP Hospital Operations; CEO Alfred I. duPont Hospital for Children, Thomas P. (Tom) Ferry
Vice President Human Resources, Theresa M. Young
President Chief Executive Officer, David J. Bailey, age 60
Vice Chairman, Richard T. (Dick) Christopher
Vice President Policy and Prevention, Debbie I. Chang
Vice President Corporate Services, Gina Altieri
Vice President Finance, Rodney McKendree
Vice President Service and Operational Excellence, Mariane Stefano
Vice President Quality and Patient Safety, Stephen T. Lawless
Executive Vice President, Roy Proujansky
VP Physician Practices Nemours Childrens Clinics Florida, R. Jay Cummings
VP and Chief Administrative Officer Nemours Childrens Clinics Florida, Jeffrey Green
Senior Vice President General Counsel, Steven R. Sparks
VP Physician Practices Delaware, Bernard J. Clark III
Vice President Chief Medical Officer, Lane Donnelly
Chief Medical Officer, Brent R. King
Vice President Physician Practices, Jay Cummings
Director, Brian P. Anderson, age 63
Director, Hugh M. Durden, age 71
Director, Toni Jennings, age 64
Vice Chairman, Richard T. (Dick) Christopher
Director, John F. (Jack) Porter III
Director, Leonard L. Berry
Director, Rosa B. Hakala
Director, Terri L. Kelly
Director, J. Michael McGinnis
Director, William T. (Tee) Thompson III

LOCATIONS

HQ: NEMOURS FOUNDATION
10140 CENTURION PKWY N, JACKSONVILLE, FL 32256-0532
Phone: 904-697-4100
Web: WWW.NEMOURS.ORG

COMPETITORS

All Children's Hospital
Baptist Health System
Children's Hospital Boston
Children's Hospital of Philadelphia
Children's Hospital of Pittsburgh
Children's National Medical Center
Children's Specialized Hospital
Christiana Care
Cincinnati Children's Hospital
Florida Hospital Waterman
HCA
Mayo Clinic Jacksonville
Miami Children's Hospital
Orlando Health
Shriners Hospitals For Children
St. Jude Children's Research Hospital
UF&Shands

HISTORICAL FINANCIALS

Company Type: Private

Income Statement FYE: December 31

	REVENUE ($ mil.)	NET INCOME ($ mil.)	NET PROFIT MARGIN	EMPLOYEES
12/08	160	(80)	—	4,400
12/07	635	53	8.5%	—
12/06	578	29	5.1%	—
12/05	546	48	8.9%	—
Annual Growth	(33.5%)	—	—	—

2008 Year-End Financials

Debt ratio: —
Return on equity: (-50.50%)
Cash ($ mil.): 164
Current ratio: 3.10
Long-term debt ($ mil.): —
Dividends
Yield: —
Payout: —
Market value ($ mil.): —

NEW HAMPSHIRE ELECTRIC COOPERATIVE INC

EXECUTIVES

President and CEO, Fred Anderson, age 58
VP Strategy and Government Relations, William Ray (Ray) Gosney Jr.
VP Power Supply and Access, Stephen E. (Steve) Kaminski
VP Public and Member Relations, Dena L. DeLucca
VP Operations, James (Jim) Bakas
Chairman, Earl Hansen
Treasurer and Director, David C. Talbot
Secretary and Director, Gail Paine
Assistant Treasurer and Director, Sharon L. Davis
Vice Chair, Jerry Hopkins
Corporate Counsel, Mark Dean
Treasurer and Director, David C. Talbot
Secretary and Director, Gail Paine
Vice Chair, Charles R. (Chuck) Braxton
Director, Sharon L. Davis
Director, Jerry Hopkins
Director, George (Chip) Kimball
Director, Georgie A. Thomas
Director, Warren Mackensen
Director, Ken Colburn
Director, Robert Johnson
Director, Bob Reals
Director, Kenneth Colburn
Auditors: BerryDunnMcNeil&Parker

LOCATIONS

HQ: NEW HAMPSHIRE ELECTRIC COOPERATIVE INC
579 TENNEY MOUNTAIN HWY, PLYMOUTH, NH 032643147
Phone: 6035368817
Web: WWW.NHEC.COM

HISTORICAL FINANCIALS

Company Type: Private

Income Statement FYE: December 31

	REVENUE ($ mil.)	NET INCOME ($ mil.)	NET PROFIT MARGIN	EMPLOYEES
12/13	125	6	5.2%	199
12/12	115	9	8.6%	—
12/11	124	12	10.2%	—
12/10	130	0	—	—
Annual Growth	(1.1%)	—	—	—

2013 Year-End Financials

Debt ratio: —
Return on equity: 5.20%
Cash ($ mil.): 2
Current ratio: 0.40
Long-term debt ($ mil.): —
Dividends
Yield: —
Payout: —
Market value ($ mil.): —

NEW HANOVER REGIONAL MEDICAL CENTER

Sometimes when you're sick you just have to hand over your health to a professional. Enter New Hanover Regional Medical Center (NHRMC). The integrated health system serves the Wilmington and Cape Fear area of North Carolina through its flagship 630-bed New Hanover Regional Medical Center the 130-bed Cape Fear Hospital and the 85-bed Pender Memorial Hospital. NHRMC also operates a rehabilitation center a behavioral health facility and a women's and children's hospital as well as home health hospice EMS transport physician practice and outpatient care clinic locations. The not-for-profit health network is affiliated with the UNC-Chapel Hill School of Medicine.

Geographic Reach

NHRMC's hospitals serve southeastern North Carolina. Its main campus is in Wilmington; the health network also operates the Cape Fear Hospital in Wilmington and the Pender Memorial Hospital in Burgaw.

Operations

NHRMC's medical staff includes more than 550 physicians and 750 active volunteers.

NHRMC is part of the Coastal Carolinas Health Alliance a cooperative of regional hospitals that use their combined buying size to negotiate lower prices for hospital equipment and supplies. The group also works together to increase community access to health care and promote continuing medical education amongst its peers.

Financial Analysis

NHRMC has seen revenue growth over the past few years including a 5% increase to some $667 million in 2012. The rise in revenues was primarily attributable to the expansion of the NHRMC physician network along with increased utilization of inpatient and outpatient services. Net income also increased in 2012 rising by more than 100% to some $36 million due to increased non-operating revenues.

NHRMC provided more than $140 million in charitable and uncompensated care during 2012 primarily to those who would not otherwise have access to healthcare.

Strategy

In 2013 NHRMC expanded its EMS transportation services by expanding its AirLink program. The medical center added a second helicopter to provide services in Onslow and Columbus counties. The move will help the organization reduce response times and improve critical care services.

In addition the medical center expanded outpatient care services in 2012 through the addition of a multi-specialty physician group (Hanover Medical Specialists) to its physician practice group.

Ownership

The medical network is governed by a board of trustees consisting of members appointed by the New Hanover County commissioners and representatives from the neighboring Pender County.

EXECUTIVES

Vice President Human Resources, Keith Strawn
Director Of Physical Therapy, Leslie Kesler
Medical Librarian, Donna Flake
President and CEO, Jack Barto
Executive Director of the NHRMC Foundation, Aline Lasseter
Vice President Of Legal Affairs, Lori Feezor
Vp Of Facilities Services, Thomas Walsh
Director Of Infection Control, Cheryl Schmitter
Director Of Surgery Services, Kathie Wheeler
Vice President Medical Affairs, Samuel S Spicer
Pharmd, Melissa M Blair
Nurse Manager Of Psych Unit, Karen Pleva
Director Of Respiratory Therapy, Kerry Lamb
Chairman, John D. (Jack) Fuller

LOCATIONS

HQ: NEW HANOVER REGIONAL MEDICAL CENTER
2131 S 17TH ST, WILMINGTON, NC 28401-7407
Phone: 910-343-7000
Web: WWW.NHRMC.ORG

PRODUCTS/OPERATIONS

Selected Locations

Behavioral Health Hospital (Wilmington North Carolina)
Betty H. Cameron Women' s and Children' s Hospital (Wilmington North Carolina)
Cape Fear Hospital (Wilmington North Carolina)
New Hanover Regional Medical Center (main campus; Wilmington North Carolina)
Pender Memorial Hospital (Burgaw North Carolina)
Rehabilitation Hospital (Wilmington North Carolina)

COMPETITORS

Blue Ridge HealthCare
Carolinas HealthCare System
Community Health Systems
Conway Medical Center
Grand Strand Regional Medical Center
High Point Regional Health System
Mission Hospitals
Novant Health
UNC Hospitals

HISTORICAL FINANCIALS

Company Type: Private

Income Statement

FYE: December 31

	REVENUE ($ mil.)	NET INCOME ($ mil.)	NET PROFIT MARGIN	EMPLOYEES
12/12*	204	12	6.1%	3,692
09/11	674	26	3.9%	—
06/10	528	19	3.6%	—
Annual Growth	(27.1%)	(13.1%)	—	—

*Fiscal year change

2012 Year-End Financials

Debt ratio: —
Return on equity: 6.10%
Cash ($ mil.): 25
Current ratio: 1.00
Long-term debt ($ mil.): —
Dividends
Yield: —
Payout: —
Market value ($ mil.): —

NEW JERSEY INSTITUTE OF TECHNOLOGY

A public research university New Jersey Institute of Technology (NJIT) offers about 100 undergraduate and graduate programs including about 20 doctoral programs in fields including architecture engineering computer science and liberal arts. The school also offers continuing education and distance courses. With some 500 full-time faculty members NJIT boasts a student-faulty ratio of 16:1. Its Albert Dorman Honors College provides students with individualized curricula and honors colloquia including travel and featured speakers. About 10000 students attend the NJIT which operates a single campus in Newark. NJIT was founded in 1881 as the Newark Technical School.

Operations

Newark's NJIT has some 7125 undergraduate and 2825 graduate students. Master's programs are offered across 56 specialties. The school also offers some 46 baccalaureate degree programs.

Strategy

Looking to provide additional capacity for students to reside on campus NJIT focuses on campus and area development. Through the efforts of three ongoing projects the university is working to enhance campus life for its students and increase its residential student numbers on campus by 600.

Financial Performance

Thanks to organic growth the university has logged revenue increases during the past three years. NJIT's revenue rose some 11% in 2011 vs. 2010 due to increases in tuition and fees and auxiliary enterprise revenues attributable to a boost in occupancy and residence hall charges and increases in federal state and other grants and contracts. Net income during the same reporting period increased by 61%. NJIT points to income from realized net gains on the sale of investments (partially offset by a decrease in interest and dividends) for the increases. Cash generated from tuition and fees and auxiliary enterprises contributed toward a cash flow bump of more than $20 million in 2011 vs. 2010.

EXECUTIVES

Chairperson, Kathleen Wielkopolski
SVP Administration and Treasurer, Henry A. Mauermeyer
Senior Vice President for Research and Development, Donald H. Sebastian
President, Joel S. Bloom
Vice President for Advancement, Charles R. Dees Jr.
VP Human Resources and Executive Director Compliance Training and Community Relations, Theodore T. Johnson
General Counsel and Secretary Board of Trustees, Holly Stern
Associate VP Enrollment Services and Dean of Admissions, Kathryn Kelly
Executive Director University Communications, Jean Llewellyn
Associate Provost for Information Services and Technology and CIO, David F. Ullman
University Registrar, Joseph F. Thompson
Executive Director Alumni Relations, Robert A. Boynton
President, Henry J. Ross
Co-Vice Chairperson, Vincent DeCaprio
Dean Newark College of Engineering, Sunil Saigal
Interim Provost; Dean College of Science and Liberal Arts, Fadi Deek
Dean College of Architecture and Design, Urs P. Gauchat
Dean School of Management, Pius J. Egbelu
Dean College of Computing Sciences, Narain Gehani
Executive Director Career Development Services, Gregory Mass
Interim VP Academic and Student Services, Jack Gentul
Director Financial Aid, Ivon Nunez
Director Institutional Research and Planning, Eugene P. Deess
Associate Vice President for Development, Jacquelynn Rhodes
Associate Vice President for Continuing & Distance Education, Gale Spak
Vice President of Human Resources, Kay Turner
Interim Dean Newark College of Engineering, Basil C. Baltzis
Dean Albert Dorman Honors College, Atam Dhawan
Interim Dean College of Computing Sciences, James Geller
SVP Administration Treasurer and Trustee, Henry A. Mauermeyer
General Counsel and Secretary Board of Trustees, Holly Stern
Co-Vice Chairperson, Vincent DeCaprio
Trustee, Stephen De Palma

LOCATIONS

HQ: NEW JERSEY INSTITUTE OF TECHNOLOGY
323 MARTIN LUTHER, NEWARK, NJ 07102
Phone: 973-596-3000
Web: WWW.NJIT.EDU

PRODUCTS/OPERATIONS

Selected Colleges

Newark College of Engineering
College of Architecture and Design
College of Science and Liberal Arts
School of Management
Albert Dorman Honors College
College of Computing Sciences

HISTORICAL FINANCIALS

Company Type: Private

Income Statement

FYE: June 30

	REVENUE ($ mil.)	NET INCOME ($ mil.)	NET PROFIT MARGIN	EMPLOYEES
06/12	197	0	0.3%	1,047
06/11	184	19	10.4%	—
06/09	162	(13)	—	—
06/08	149	(2)	—	—
Annual Growth	7.3%	—	—	—

2012 Year-End Financials

Debt ratio: —
Return on equity: 0.30%
Cash ($ mil.): 37
Current ratio: 0.80
Long-term debt ($ mil.): —
Dividends
Yield: —
Payout: —
Market value ($ mil.): —

NEW PRIME INC.

Check out this Prime number –more than 5800 remotely monitored temperature-controlled trailers. Specialized carrier New Prime (which does business simply as Prime) provides refrigerated flatbed and liquid bulk tanker trucking services throughout North America. The company operates in the US and Canada and serves Mexico through arrangements with other carriers. A subsidiary Prime Floral uses the parent company's refrigerated equipment and facilities to serve the flower industry. In addition to its freight-hauling operations Prime provides logistics services including freight brokerage.

Geographic Reach

The company serves customers in Canada Mexico and the US.

Operations

It operates through three divisions: Prime's liquid bulk fleet (Tanker Division) consists of 6800-gallon Walker Stainless MC407 trailers with air ride suspensions. The company's Refrigerated Division has a fleet of remotely monitored temperature-controlled trailers and serves businesses whose needs include transportation of fresh produce fresh cut floral produce pharmaceuticals fresh or frozen meats or any other dry or temperature controlled freight. Prime also has a Flatbed Division.

Sales and Marketing

Prime has hauled goods for such blue chip consumer goods makers as ConAgra Foods Kraft Foods and General Mills.

Strategy

Prime is shifting its strategy to align with customer preferences for shortening supply chain mileage and delivery time all of which is intended to offset lower consumer demand and volatile fuel costs.

It is also using technology to enhance its position as an industry leader in the safe cost-effective transport of temperature-sensitive goods. The company has embraced modern technology like the QUALCOMM satellite system which benefits shippers by providing continuous communication from initial dispatch to final delivery. This option helps to monitor load temperatures set points alarm conditions connect and disconnect times and uses the QUALCOMM link present in every Prime tractor to transfer this important data.

Prime Position Tracking enables the company to locate tractors in real-time within a 600 foot radius at all times. Prime Mapping and Routing provides detailed Rand McNally and PC*Miler directions to driver associates to ensure that loads get to their destination in the quickest safest and most efficient manner.

Company Background

Prime was founded in 1970 by Robert Low who continues to serve as Prime's president.

EXECUTIVES

President and CEO, Robert E. Low
Manager of Success Leasing Program, Fred Ege
Director of Logistics, Rick Gallagher
Director of Operations, Pat Leonard
Director of Flatbed and Tanker Operations, Jim Wilkins
VP Sales and Marketing, Steve Wutke
Director of Finance, Dean Hoedl
Director of Technology, Rodney Rader
Manager of Tanker Division, Brett Vonwiller

LOCATIONS

HQ: NEW PRIME INC.
2740 N MAYFAIR AVE, SPRINGFIELD, MO 65803-5084
Phone: 417-866-0001
Web: WWW.TRUCKJOB.COM

COMPETITORS

Boyd Bros. Transportation
C.H. Robinson Worldwide
C.R. England
Central Refrigerated Service
Comcar
Frozen Food Express
KLLM Transport Services
Marten Transport
Quality Distribution
Stevens Transport

HISTORICAL FINANCIALS

Company Type: Private

Income Statement FYE: March 29

	REVENUE ($ mil.)	NET INCOME ($ mil.)	NET PROFIT MARGIN	EMPLOYEES
03/13	1,164	70	6.0%	5,000
03/12	1,022	60	6.0%	—
03/10	941	47	5.0%	—
03/10	844	91	10.8%	—
Annual Growth	11.3%	(8.3%)	—	—

2013 Year-End Financials

Debt ratio: —
Return on equity: 6.00%
Cash ($ mil.): 0
Current ratio: 0.80
Long-term debt ($ mil.): —
Dividends
Yield: —
Payout: —
Market value ($ mil.): —

NEW YORK BLOOD CENTER INC.

New York Blood Center (NYBC) holds a very literal interpretation of the meaning of life. It is a not-for-profit blood distribution and research organization serving New York City and its environs in New York State and New Jersey as well as parts of Connecticut and Pennsylvania. As one of the largest blood centers in the US NYBC provides nearly 1 million blood components to some 200 hospitals each year. The center's facilities collect blood from more than 2000 donors each day. It also operates the nation's oldest and largest public cord blood bank. In addition its Kimball Research Institute includes more than a dozen research laboratories which study the prevention and treatment of blood-related illnesses.

Operations Areas of research in the Kimball Research Institute include virology molecular genetics cell biology and signaling viral immunology and infectious disease prevention. It has been responsible for the development and licensing of solvent and detergent technology used to deactivate the potency of viruses in blood and blood products (such as plasma and platelets used in transfusions). NYBC's clinical services division acts as an adjunct and resource to hospitals throughout its service areas by providing expertise in transfusion medicine as well as delivering more than 8500 specialized procedures each year. In addition the center maintains a bone marrow donor registry for the New York area provides hemophilia services to some 1500 patients and offers screening and education programs for cholesterol high blood pressure and cardiovascular disease.

EXECUTIVES

CIO, Michele Scaggiante
SVP and Chief Administrative Officer, Michael J. Monahan
SVP and COO, Elizabeth J. McQuail
VP and Director Lindsley F. Kimball Research Institute, Mohandas Narla
VP Customer Service, Robert Purvis
VP and Chief Medical Officer, Beth Shaz
Director National Cord Blood Program, Pablo Rubinstein
President Chief Executive Officer, Christopher D. Hillyer
Strategy and Corporate Planning Chief, Jeffrey Jacob
Head Xiaoling Xiong MD, Leszek Kotula
Head of the Viral Immunology Laboratory, Shibo Jiang
Head, Sara Lustigman
Vice President General Counsel Secretary, Jordana G. Schwartz
Senior Vice President Chief Financial Officer, Elizabeth C. Gibson

LOCATIONS

HQ: NEW YORK BLOOD CENTER INC.
310 E 67TH ST, NEW YORK, NY 10065-6273
Phone: 212-570-3010
Web: WWW.NYBC.ORG

COMPETITORS

Blood Systems Inc.
Daxor
HemaCare
Red Cross
SeraCare Life Sciences

HISTORICAL FINANCIALS

Company Type: Private

Income Statement FYE: March 31

	REVENUE ($ mil.)	NET INCOME ($ mil.)	NET PROFIT MARGIN	EMPLOYEES
03/12	335	0	0.1%	1,600
03/11	348	(11)	—	—
03/10	375	20	5.4%	—
03/09	329	(13)	—	—
Annual Growth	0.6%	—	—	—

2012 Year-End Financials

Debt ratio: —
Return on equity: 0.10%
Cash ($ mil.): 32
Current ratio: —
Long-term debt ($ mil.): —
Dividends
Yield: —
Payout: —
Market value ($ mil.): —

NEW YORK MEDICAL COLLEGE

It doesn't take a brain surgeon to figure out this school's specialty. New York Medical College (NYMC) confers advanced degrees to those preparing for careers in the medical and health professions. The institution's three divisions –the School of Medicine the School of Public Health and the Graduate School of Basic Medical Sciences –offer programs in more than 20 disciplines. NYMC has an enrollment of more than 1400 students who practice at nearby Westchester Medical Center and the Manhattan location of Saint Vincent Catholic Medical Centers. Founded in 1860 the medical college has been affiliated with the Archdiocese of New York since 1978. NYMC is part of Touro College.

Operations

The university manages more than $34 million for research and other sponsored programs in the areas of cardiovascular disease cancer kidney disease neurosciences and infectious diseases.

In addition to its 1400-plus students NYMC has 900 residents and fellows and nearly 3000 faculty members.

Financial Performance

NYMC logged flat revenue in 2011 with a push upward of 0.18% thank to an increase in tuition fees and housing net of tuition discount and private gifts and grants. Net income for the same reporting period rose sharply due to increases in non-operating activities income attributed to rising investment returns income from pension-related charges other than net periodic benefit cost acquisition contribution and acquisition related fair market value adjustments. NYMC also attributes the net income spike to an increase in temporarily restricted net assets and permanently restricted net assets and a decrease in total expenses.

Company Ownership

NYMC has been a wholly controlled subsidiary of Touro College a New York State not-for-profit education corporation since mid-2011.

EXECUTIVES

Chief Executive Officer, Karl P. Adler
Jr. Senior Vice President Chief Financial Officer, Stephen J. Piccolo Jr.
CIO, John C. Hammond
Vice President for Planning, William A. Steadman II
Provost and Dean School of Medicine, Ralph A. O'Connell
Dean Graduate School of Basic Medical Sciences, Francis L. Belloni
Vice Dean Westchester Medical Center, Renee Garrick
Vice Dean School of Public Health, James J. O'Brien
Vice President General Counsel, Waldemar A. (Tony) Comas
Chairman Department of Rehabilitation Medicine, Maria P. deAraujo
Dean School of Public Health, Robert W. Amler
Associate VP and Director Human Resources, Peter M. Brown
Associate Vice President Controller, George Nestler
Associate Provost and University Registrar, Judith A. Ehren
University Bursar, Diane Alexander
Chief Affiliation Officer, Howard Nelson
Director Web Communications, Kevin R. Cummings
Director Internal Audit, Redmond Jacobsen Jr.
Associate Director Information Services, Luis Montes
Associate General Counsel and Compliance Director, Dana H. Lee
University Budget Officer, Bonnie Gurran-Heindl
Director Security, William Allison
Vice Dean Medical Education, Martha S. Grayson
Vice Dean Clinical Affairs and Graduate Medical Education, Richard McCarrick
Senior Associate Dean Student Affairs, Gladys M. Ayala
Senior Associate Dean Fifth Pathway Program, Saverio S. Bentivegna
Senior Associate Dean, C. Gene Cayten
Senior Associate Dean NYMC Danbury Hospital, Pierre F. Saldinger
Senior Associate Dean and Medical Director Metropolitan Hospital Center, Richard K. Stone
Senior Associate Dean Westchester Medical Center, Paul K. Woolf
Director Advancement Services, Dee Demling
Director Research Information and Development, Lea Emmett
Director Development Communications and Donor Relations, Monica Maye
Senior Director Communications, Donna Moriarty
Director Purchasing, John Stein
Associate Director Information Services, Douglas Daly
Associate Director Human Resources, Theresa Gelchie
Associate Director Human Resources, Theresa Haviland
Associate Director Information Services, Chao-Chi Tien
Auditors: PricewaterhouseCoopersLLP

LOCATIONS

HQ: NEW YORK MEDICAL COLLEGE
40 SUNSHINE COTTAGE RD, VALHALLA, NY 10595-1524
Phone: 914-345-5853
Web: WWW.NYMC.EDU

PRODUCTS/OPERATIONS

Selected Schools

School of Health Sciences and Practice
School of Medicine
Graduate School of Basic Medical Sciences

Selected Departments

Anesthesiology
Biochemistry and Molecular Biology
Cell Biology and Anatomy
Dental Medicine
Dermatology
Emergency Medicine
Family and Community Medicine
Medicine
Microbiology and Immunology
Neurology
Obstetrics and Gynecology
Ophthalmology
Otolaryngology
Pathology
Pediatrics
Pharmacology
Physiology
Psychiatry and Behavioral Science
Radiation Medicine
Radiology
Rehabilitation Medicine
Surgery
Urology

HISTORICAL FINANCIALS

Company Type: Private

Income Statement

FYE: June 30

	REVENUE ($ mil.)	NET INCOME ($ mil.)	NET PROFIT MARGIN	EMPLOYEES
06/11	245	32	13.2%	1,300
06/10	215	(1)	—	—
Annual Growth	14.2%	—	—	—

2011 Year-End Financials

Debt ratio: —
Return on equity: 13.20%
Cash ($ mil.): 38
Current ratio: —
Long-term debt ($ mil.): —
Dividends
Yield: —
Payout: —
Market value ($ mil.): —

NEW YORK METHODIST HOSPITAL

New York Methodist Hospital is a not-for-profit acute-care teaching hospital serving Brooklyn residents. Established in 1881 as the Methodist Episcopal Hospital the facility has more than 650 licensed beds. It offers a full range of medical services including primary and emergency care as well as specialty services such as women's health cancer cardiovascular pediatric geriatric and behavioral health. The hospital also operates satellite clinics in surrounding areas. A member of New York-Presbyterian Healthcare System New York Methodist is a teaching hospital affiliated with Cornell University's Weill Medical College.

Geographic Reach

New York Methodist Hospital's main campus is in the Park Slope neighborhood of Brooklyn. It has several outpatient centers in other parts of Brooklyn as well.

Operations

New York Methodist Hospital handles about 40000 inpatient admissions and 100000 emergency department visits each year as well as 24000 surgeries and 5000 births. It also processes about 200000 laboratory sample processes annually.

New York Methodist Hospital includes specialty institutes in about 10 fields including pulmonary medicine cancer care and vascular health. In addition to providing inpatient care the organization operates some 10 primary and specialty outpatient centers. It also runs a number of graduate medical programs including programs affiliated with professional training schools in the areas of radiography medical technology radiation therapy and paramedics.

Strategy

To expand care for area residents New York Methodist is adding new specialist programs and equipment. For instance in 2012 the hospital added a robotic-assisted surgery program for bariatric procedures. It also opened a new wound care and hyperbaric oxygen therapy center for hard-to-heal wounds. In addition in 2013 the hospital moved its sleep disorder center into a new facility.

EXECUTIVES

President Chief Executive Officer, Mark J. Mundy, age 73
senior Vice President for finance, Edward Zaidberg, age 64
Executive Vice President for Medical Affairs, Stanley Sherbell
Chairman, John E. Carrington
SVP, Lauren Yedvab
VP, Colleen McManus
VP Communications and External Affairs, Lyn S. Hill
senior Vice President for nursing, Rebecca Flood
Assistant TreasurerTrustee and Board Member, Barbara Capozzi
Assistant Secretary and Trustee, Linda Malinskas
Assistant VP, Jennifer Donovan
Treasurer and Board Member, Robert Rodgers Jr.
VP, Richard Ortiz
VP Medical Affairs, Steven Silber
Vice Chairman, James Perkins
President Medical Board, Emil Baccash
Assistant TreasurerTrustee and Board Member, Barbara Capozzi
Assistant Secretary and Trustee, Linda Malinskas
Treasurer and Board Member, Robert Rodgers Jr.

Vice Chairman, James Perkins
Auditors: Ernst&YoungLLP

LOCATIONS

HQ: NEW YORK METHODIST HOSPITAL
506 6TH ST, BROOKLYN, NY 11215-3609
Phone: 718-780-3000
Web: WWW.NYM.ORG

COMPETITORS

Beth Israel Medical Center
Bronx-Lebanon Hospital
Brookdale University Hospital
Catholic Healthcare System
Kingsbrook Jewish Medical Center
Lutheran HealthCare
Maimonides Medical Center
New York City Health and Hospitals
North Shore-Long Island Jewish Health System
SUNY Downstate
Winthrop-University Hospital

HISTORICAL FINANCIALS

Company Type: Private

Income Statement FYE: December 31

	REVENUE ($ mil.)	NET INCOME ($ mil.)	NET PROFIT MARGIN	EMPLOYEES
12/09	516	4	0.9%	3,185
12/08	540	(37)	—	—
12/07	549	0	0.1%	—
12/06	515	24	4.7%	—
Annual Growth	0.1%	(42.4%)	—	—

2009 Year-End Financials

Debt ratio: —
Return on equity: 0.90%
Cash ($ mil.): 38
Current ratio: 0.60
Long-term debt ($ mil.): —
Dividends
Yield: —
Payout: —
Market value ($ mil.): —

NEW YORK POWER AUTHORITY

The hydropower generated by the mighty Niagara Falls is the real authority behind the New York Power Authority (NYPA). More than 70% of the power that NYPA produces is from hydropower resources. The company generates and transmits more than 20% of New York's electricity making it the largest state-owned public power provider in the US. It is also New York's only statewide electricity supplier. NYPA owns hydroelectric and fossil-fueled generating facilities (16 in total) that produce about 5700 MW of electricity and it operates more than 1400 circuit-miles of transmission lines.

Operations

The authority sells power to government agencies municipal systems rural cooperatives private companies private utilities (for resale) and neighboring states. Its clients include some of the largest electricity users in the US including the New York City government and the Metropolitan Transportation Authority. NYPA receives no state funds or tax credits. Instead it finances new projects through bond sales.

Financial Performance

In 2012 NYPA's revenues grew by 1% thanks to higher Southeastern New York governmental customer revenues resulting from increased third-party transmission (wheeling charges) and the full year of operation of a new clean natural gas-fueled power plant in Queens (the Astoria Energy II) partially offset by lower generation and a decrease in energy prices.

The company's net income declined by 26% due to lower non-operating revenues of $25 million and higher non-operating expenses of $72 million partially offset by an increase in operating income of $37 million.

Strategy

Following its shift from a regulated monopoly to a competitor in an open power market NYPA is aiming to grow by reducing the cost of the energy it provides and by developing electric transportation (such as electric cars) and other energy-efficiency projects including installing emergency power generators in metropolitan buildings. It is also working to improve the state's transmission grid increase its generating capacity and help support the state's directive to get 45% of its power from clean energy sources by 2015 (include 100 MW of power from solar arrays at buildings across the state). In 2012 NYPA was designated as the lead agency to reduce energy use at state facilities by 20% by 2020.

To improve its delivery of power is pursuing the development of a new cross-Hudson transmission line that will connect New York City customers to the PJM Interconnection power grid.

Ownership

NYPA is owned by the State of New York.

HISTORY

The Power Authority of the State of New York (aka New York Power Authority or NYPA) was established in 1931 by Gov. Franklin Roosevelt to gain public control of New York's hydropower resources. The utility's major power plants came on line with the opening of the St. Lawrence-Franklin D. Roosevelt Power Project (1958) and the Niagara Power Project (1961). The Blenheim-Gilboa Pumped Storage Power Project opened in 1973.

In the mid-1970s NYPA shifted to nuclear power when it opened the James A. FitzPatrick Nuclear Power Plant (1975) and the Indian Point 3 Nuclear Power Plant (1976). The company then opened gas- and oil-powered plants: the Charles Poletti Power Project (1977) and the Richard M. Flynn Power Plant (1994).

In 1998 the authority allocated low-cost electricity to five companies that planned to invest $104 million in business expansions in western New York. The company suffered a loss in 1999 in part from reduced hydro generation and a drop in investment earnings. In 2000 NYPA sold its two nuclear plants (1800 MW of capacity) to utility holding company Entergy for $967 million.

The company completed the installation of 11 gas-powered turbines at various locations in New York City and on Long Island in 2001; the program was initiated to prevent expected energy shortages that summer but it also helped maintain power in areas of the city during the September 11 terrorist attacks.

EXECUTIVES

Executive Vice President Chief Financial Officer, Donald A. Russak
Director Media Relations, Michael A. Saltzman
COO, Edward A. Welz
President Chief Executive Officer, Gil C. Quiniones
Senior Vice President Corporate Support Services, Joan Tursi
Senior Vice President Economic Development and Efficiency, James F. Pasquale
Vice President Environmental Justice Division, Sobeida Cruz
Senior Vice President Strategic Planning, Robert F. Lurie
Vice Chairman, Jonathan F. (Jon) Foster, age 52
Trustee, D. Patrick Curley
Trustee, Eugene L. Nicandri
Auditors: KPMGLLP

LOCATIONS

HQ: NEW YORK POWER AUTHORITY
123 MAIN ST STE 1600, WHITE PLAINS, NY 10601-3132
Phone: 914-681-6200
Web: WWW.NYPA.GOV

PRODUCTS/OPERATIONS

2012 Sales

Power sales	1,925	72
Transmission charges	150	6

Selected Operations

Transmission Control Facility
- Frederick R. Clark Energy Center (Oneida County)

Fossil-Fueled Plants
- Charles Poletti Power Project (New York City)
- Richard M. Flynn Power Plant (Suffolk County)
- PowerNow! Turbines (11 units in New York City and Long Island)

Hydropower Plants
- Blenheim-Gilboa Pumped Storage Power Project (Schoharie County)
- Niagara Power Project (Niagara County)
- St. Lawrence-Franklin D. Roosevelt Power Project (St. Lawrence County)

Small Hydropower Plants
- Ashokan Project (Ulster County)
- Crescent Plant (Albany and Saratoga Counties)
- Gregory B. Jarvis Plant (Oneida County)
- Kensico Project (Westchester County)
- Vischer Ferry Plant (Saratoga and Schenectady counties)

COMPETITORS

CH Energy
Con Edison
Dynegy
Enbridge
Entergy
Iberdrola USA
National Grid USA
Rochester Gas and Electric
TransCanada

HISTORICAL FINANCIALS

Company Type: Private

Income Statement FYE: December 31

	REVENUE ($ mil.)	NET INCOME ($ mil.)	NET PROFIT MARGIN	EMPLOYEES
12/12	2,673	175	6.5%	4,450
12/11	2,655	294	11.1%	
/ 0	0			
Annual Growth	—	—	—	—

2012 Year-End Financials

Debt ratio: —
Return on equity: 6.50%
Cash ($ mil.): 77
Current ratio: 0.10
Long-term debt ($ mil.): —
Dividends
Yield: —
Payout: —
Market value ($ mil.): —

NEW YORK SOCIETY FOR THE RELIEF OF THE RUPTURED & CRIPPLED

LOCATIONS

HQ: NEW YORK SOCIETY FOR THE RELIEF OF THE RUPTURED & CRIPPLED
535 E 70TH ST, NEW YORK, NY 100214823
Phone: 2126061000
Web: WWW.HSS.EDU

HISTORICAL FINANCIALS

Company Type: Private

Income Statement FYE: December 31

	REVENUE ($ mil.)	NET INCOME ($ mil.)	NET PROFIT MARGIN	EMPLOYEES
12/07	441	(21)	—	1,238
12/05	376	14	3.9%	—
12/04	330	15	4.7%	—
12/02	249	0	—	—
Annual Growth	12.1%	—	—	—

2007 Year-End Financials

Debt ratio: —
Return on equity: (-4.90%)
Cash ($ mil.): 11
Current ratio: 0.80
Long-term debt ($ mil.): —

Dividends
Yield: —
Payout: —
Market value ($ mil.): —

NEW YORK STATE CATHOLIC HEALTH PLAN INC

Fidelis Care hopes for always faithful health plan members. The New York State Catholic Health Plan which does business as Fidelis Care serves more than 900000 residents in some 60 counties across the state including the New York City area. Its provider network includes more than 50000 physicians hospitals and other health care professionals and facilities. Fidelis Care provides managed Medicaid Medicare and state-sponsored family and children's Health Plus plans as well as long-term care and behavioral health coverage. The church-sponsored plan was founded in 1993 by the bishops of New York's Roman Catholic dioceses and the Catholic Medical Center of Brooklyn and Queens.

Geographic Reach

Fidelis Care's regional offices are located in Rego Park Queens (Greater Metropolitan); Albany (Northeast); Syracuse (Central); and Buffalo (Western) with satellite offices in Poughkeepsie Rochester and Suffern.

Sales and Marketing

The health plan has expanded its membership by seeking new low-income patients who lack coverage. In addition to direct sales efforts Fidelis Care tries to maintain a presence at health centers frequented by its target audience partnering with neighborhood clinics to hold free health screenings and Health Plus enrollment information sessions.

Enroll NY a new website sponsored by not-for-profit organization Hudson Center for Health Equity & Quality is also connecting Fidelis Care and other Medicaid providers with potential customers. Beginning in 2013 Fidelis Care also sells through the New York State of Health insurance exchange marketplace.

Financial Performance

Fidelis Care reported gross revenues of $3.3 billion in 2012 up from $2.4 billion in 2011.

Strategy

Fidelis Care has grown by expanding rapidly into new counties in New York including a number of growth measures in the Medicare marketplace during 2012 and 2013. The health plan's recent activity includes completing construction of Fidelis Care's new operations center and offices in Getzville (Erie County) and the launch of its new provider portal (Provider Access Online). Other growth measures include a 2012 partnership with DentaQuest to promote dental checkups; it also launched a new member portal for members to access benefit information. In 2013 the company gained approval to be a qualified health plan provider on the official New York State of Health marketplace.

Fidelis Care regularly evaluates and broadens its plan offerings. Recent additions include its Fidelis Care at Home managed long-term care offering; the behavioral health and developmental disabilities coverage options; and its fully integrated dual advantage plans (for consumers with both Medicare and Medicaid coverage).

EXECUTIVES

President and CEO, Mark L. Lane
Chairman, Father Joseph M. Sullivan
EVP and COO, Father Patrick J. Frawley
Director Communications, Darla Shattenkirk

LOCATIONS

HQ: NEW YORK STATE CATHOLIC HEALTH PLAN INC
9525 QUEENS BLVD STE 8, REGO PARK, NY 11374-4510
Phone: 888-343-3547
Web: WWW.FIDELISCARE.COM

PRODUCTS/OPERATIONS

Selected Plans

Child Health Plus
Dual Advantage
Family Health Plus
Fidelis Care at Home (managed long-term care)
Medicaid Advantage Plus (managed long-term care)
Medicaid Managed Care
Medicare Advantage
New York State of Health

COMPETITORS

Aetna
Affinity Health
CIGNA
Capital District Physicians' Health Plan
EmblemHealth
Health Net
HealthPlus Amerigroup
Healthfirst
Healthplex
Humana
Independent Health
Lifetime Healthcare
MVP Health Plan
UnitedHealth Group
Vytra Healthcare
WellPoint
healthnow new york inc

HISTORICAL FINANCIALS

Company Type: Private

Income Statement FYE: December 31

	REVENUE ($ mil.)	NET INCOME ($ mil.)	NET PROFIT MARGIN	EMPLOYEES
12/11	2,413	76	3.2%	1,625
12/10	1,920	51	2.7%	—
12/08	1,435	27	1.9%	—
12/08	1,068	3	0.4%	—
Annual Growth	31.2%	170.7%	—	—

2011 Year-End Financials

Debt ratio: —
Return on equity: 3.20%
Cash ($ mil.): 275
Current ratio: 0.80
Long-term debt ($ mil.): —

Dividends
Yield: —
Payout: —
Market value ($ mil.): —

NEWARK BETH ISRAEL MEDICAL CENTER INC.

Part of the Saint Barnabas Health Care System Newark Beth Israel Medical Center is a 670-bed acute-care regional referral hospital. The facility serves residents of Newark and surrounding areas in northern New Jersey. The hospital offers services including primary diagnostic emergency surgical and rehabilitative care. It is home to specialized programs such as kidney transplantation cancer care dentistry sleep disorders geriatrics and women's health services. Newark Beth Israel Medical Center also houses the Children's Hospital of New Jersey and the Saint Barnabas Heart Center. The research and teaching hospital has a medical staff of more than 800 physicians.

Operations

Newark Beth Israel Medical Center along with sister hospital Saint Barnabas Medical Center has a teaching and research affiliation with the New Jersey Medical School (part of the University of Medicine and Dentistry of New Jersey). The hospital also has training programs with other regional schools.

Newark Beth Israel Medical Center handles about 25000 inpatient visits annually while the hospital's outpatient centers see some 300000 patients each year.

EXECUTIVES

Vice President Of Personnel, Zachary Lipner
Vp Medical Affairs, Carlo L Mainardi
Director Of Health Information, Mike Huston

LOCATIONS

HQ: NEWARK BETH ISRAEL MEDICAL CENTER INC.
201 LYONS AVE, NEWARK, NJ 07112-2027
Phone: 973-926-7000
Web: WWW.NEWARKBETHEM.COM

PRODUCTS/OPERATIONS

Selected Departments and Centers

Barnabas Health Heart Center
Center for Geriatric Health Care
Center for Women's Health
Children's Hospital of New Jersey
Cohen Comprehensive Cancer and Blood Disorder Center
Lung Center
Pacemaker and Defibrillator Center
Palliative Care Program
Regional Perinatal Center
Radiology
Robotic Surgery Center
Renal Transplantation
Sleep Disorders Center

COMPETITORS

AtlantiCare
Atlantic Health
Bergen Regional Medical
CentraState Healthcare System
Children' s Specialized Hospital
Chilton Medical Center
East Orange General Hospital
Englewood Hospital and Medical Center
Hackensack University Medical Center
JFK Health System
Meridian Health
Newton Medical Center
Robert Wood Johnson University Hospital
Robert Wood Johnson University Hospital at Rahway
St. Joseph' s Healthcare System
The Valley Hospital
Virtua Health
Winthrop-University Hospital

HISTORICAL FINANCIALS

Company Type: Private

Income Statement FYE: December 31

	REVENUE ($ mil.)	NET INCOME ($ mil.)	NET PROFIT MARGIN	EMPLOYEES
12/08*	438	(56)	—	3,000
06/05	441	0	—	—
12/03	387	(9)	—	—
12/02	45	1	3.9%	—
Annual Growth	45.8%	—	—	—

*Fiscal year change

2008 Year-End Financials

Debt ratio: —
Return on equity: (-12.90%)
Cash ($ mil.): 1
Current ratio: 0.40
Long-term debt ($ mil.): —
Dividends
Yield: —
Payout: —
Market value ($ mil.): —

NHS HUMAN SERVICES INC.

Northwestern Human Services (operating as NHS Human Services) exists to lend a helping hand to humans throughout the Northeast. The organization primarily offers a variety of behavioral health care services that include mental health and drug and alcohol rehabilitation mental retardation services juvenile justice autism special education foster care and elder care. The not-for-profit organization provides programs for nearly 40000 adults and children at more than 675 facilities in more than half a dozen eastern US states. NHS' programs are offered through its specialty care facilities mobile clinics and on an independent case management basis.

Operations

NHS has been working to develop programs for people with dual diagnoses and other issues involving multiple problems. The non-profit has also been expanding geographically.

Financial Performance

In 2013 NHS reported a slight dip on revenue as fewer people paid for its services. Services to those with intellectual and development disabilities still leads revenues contributing about 53%. Adult and children's services split the remainder about evenly. Despite the dip in revenue NHS continues to report positive net income and cash flow.

Strategy

In addition to expanding geographically and introducing new programs NHS has been updating its record keeping and going digital. Once the conversion to electronic health records is complete the organization will move to outsource its back office functions (payroll human resources and benefits) to reduce costs.

EXECUTIVES

Senior Corporate Director Communications, Richard Scott
Chairman and CEO, M. Joseph Rocks
CFO, Kevin McClure
EVP Eastern Region, Michael A. Barton
COO, Michael J. Breslin
Regional Vice President Western Region, Paul R. Beatrice
EVP Central & Western Regions, Carl E. Clark
Senior Vice President for Integrity and Quality, John M. Ciavardone
VP Children's Services, Karen Markle
Senior Vice President Eastern Region Corporate Dir. of I/DD Services, Terrence McNelis
EVP Corporate Administration, Leah Pason
Senior Vice President Facility Operations, John Scheck
Corporate Controller, Deanna Telese
Corporate Vice President of Financial Operations, Derrick Yacovelli
Corporate Director Real Estate Services, Robert Kotsur
VP Adult Behavioral Health Services, Cathy Murphy
Corporate Director of IT Services, Sean McCloat
Chief Information Officer, Christopher Rieder
Director, Stephen J. Carr
Director, John J. Egan Jr.
Director, Tami Fratis
Director, Richard H. Glanton
Director, Robert N. C. Nix III
Director, Gregory E. Smith
Director, Diane Sterthous
Director, Paul W. Tressler
Director, Kelly C. Wall
Director, Sean Bosken

LOCATIONS

HQ: NHS HUMAN SERVICES INC.
620 GERMANTOWN PIKE, LAFAYETTE HILL, PA 19444-1810
Phone: 610-260-4600
Web: WWW.NHSONLINE.ORG

PRODUCTS/OPERATIONS

2013 Sales

	$ mil.	% of total
Intellectual/Developmental Disabilities	259	53
Adult Behavioral Health	118	24
Children's	108	22
Other	6	1
Total	493	100

COMPETITORS

Albert Einstein Healthcare Network
Devereux Foundation
Diakon Lutheran Social Ministries
Excela Health
Genesis HealthCare System (Ohio)
Hazelden
HealthSouth
Providence Service
Select Medical
Watson Institute
YAI National Institute for People with Disabilitie

HISTORICAL FINANCIALS

Company Type: Private

Income Statement FYE: June 30

	REVENUE ($ mil.)	NET INCOME ($ mil.)	NET PROFIT MARGIN	EMPLOYEES
06/11	501	11	2.3%	6,500
06/10	28	0	2.3%	—
06/08	311	13	4.2%	—
06/07	288	8	3.0%	—
Annual Growth	14.8%	6.8%	—	—

2011 Year-End Financials

Debt ratio: —
Return on equity: 2.30%
Cash ($ mil.): 16
Current ratio: 1.30
Long-term debt ($ mil.): —
Dividends
Yield: —
Payout: —
Market value ($ mil.): —

NJVC LLC

LOCATIONS

HQ: NJVC LLC
14295 PARK MEADOW DR, CHANTILLY, VA 201512220
Phone: 7034299000
Web: WWW.NJVC.COM

HISTORICAL FINANCIALS

Company Type: Private

Income Statement FYE: September 30

	REVENUE ($ mil.)	NET INCOME ($ mil.)	NET PROFIT MARGIN	EMPLOYEES
09/13	443	17	3.9%	1,300
09/12	513	22	4.4%	—
09/11	542	44	8.1%	—
09/10	495	0	—	—
Annual Growth	(3.6%)	—	—	—

2013 Year-End Financials

Debt ratio: —
Return on equity: 3.90%
Cash ($ mil.): 0
Current ratio: 1.90
Long-term debt ($ mil.): —
Dividends
Yield: —
Payout: —
Market value ($ mil.): —

NOBLIS INC.

Noblis' noble pursuit is through its offering of science-related strategic and technology consulting services. The not-for-profit company which pledges to serve the public interest helps various government entities and other clients evaluate technology options and vendors as well as solve complex technical problems. Noblis provides strategic planning decision analysis and acquisition support services. The company addresses problems in areas such as criminal justice environment and energy health care homeland security public safety and transportation. Noblis has worked with such clients as the US Air Force Army Navy and Departments of Commerce and Defense.

Geographic Reach

Noblis has more than half a dozen offices located in Maryland Texas Virginia West Virginia and Washington DC.

Sales and Marketing

The company's product suite includes RASMAS a Web-based service allowing health care providers and suppliers to respond more efficiently to product recalls and AcquTrak an acquisitions support tool aimed at helping government entities reduce costs and schedule times.

Mergers and Acquisitions

In 2012 Noblis acquired ElanTech Systems a provider of government systems engineering program management and acquisition services to the intelligence community. The two companies made the deal because of the complementary strengths of their businesses; the acquisition expands Nobils' portfolio giving the firm a broader knowledge base and the ability to capitalize on emerging technology trends and bring innovative new capabilities to clients.

Company Background

The company was formed in 1996 as Mitretek Systems; it changed its name to Noblis in 2007.

EXECUTIVES

President Chief Executive Officer, Amr A. ElSawy
Director Transportation Systems Concepts and Planning, Steven (Steve) Zaidman
Director Center for Sustainability:Earth Energy and Climate, David L. Evans
Senior Vice President Chief Financial & Administrative Officer & Treasurer, Mark A. Simione
Corporate VP and CTO, H. Gilbert Miller
Corporate VP Corporate Mission Development, Robert J. Clerman
Vice President General Counsel Secretary, Sherry L. Rhodes
Director Transportation Systems, Daniel J. Brudnicki
Director Energy and Environmental Sustainability, Daniel J. Casagrande
Director Health Innovation, Diane Hartingh Price
Corporate Communications, Edna Davis
Vice President Business Development & Marketing, Pat Brosey
Director Human Resources and Organizational Development, Jean M. Cain
Vice President Enterprise Engineering and Environmental Solutions, Don Schaefer
Chief Scientist, Catherine M. Cotell
Director of Administration, Rick DuBois
Vice President of Security, Andrew Cohen
Vice President National Security and Intelligence, Drew Cohen
President CEO and Trustee, Amr A. ElSawy
Trustee, Ronald R. Blanck, age 72
Trustee, John E. McLaughlin

LOCATIONS

HQ: NOBLIS INC.
3150 FAIRVIEW PARK DR, FALLS CHURCH, VA 22042-4504
Phone: 703-610-2000
Web: WWW.ALERTS.RASMAS.NOBLIS.ORG

COMPETITORS

Accenture
Bain & Company
Boston Consulting
Deloitte Consulting
HP Enterprise Services
IBM
McKinsey & Company

HISTORICAL FINANCIALS

Company Type: Private

Income Statement FYE: September 30

	REVENUE ($ mil.)	NET INCOME ($ mil.)	NET PROFIT MARGIN	EMPLOYEES
09/12*	199	12	6.4%	804
10/11	151	4	3.0%	—
10/10	144	8	6.0%	—
10/09	145	(10)	—	—
Annual Growth	11.0%	—	—	—

*Fiscal year change

2012 Year-End Financials

Debt ratio: —
Return on equity: 6.40%
Cash ($ mil.): 1
Current ratio: 0.80
Long-term debt ($ mil.): —
Dividends
Yield: —
Payout: —
Market value ($ mil.): —

NORDIC PCL CONSTRUCTION INC.

LOCATIONS

HQ: NORDIC PCL CONSTRUCTION INC.
1099 ALAKEA ST STE 1560, HONOLULU, HI 968134500
Phone: 8085419101
Web: WWW.ENTERPRISES.PCL.COM

HISTORICAL FINANCIALS

Company Type: Private

Income Statement FYE: October 31

	REVENUE ($ mil.)	NET INCOME ($ mil.)	NET PROFIT MARGIN	EMPLOYEES
10/10	1,616	23	1.5%	150
10/09	1,467	6	0.4%	—
Annual Growth	10.2%	291.0%	—	—

2010 Year-End Financials

Debt ratio: —
Return on equity: 1.50%
Cash ($ mil.): 95
Current ratio: 0.90
Long-term debt ($ mil.): —
Dividends
Yield: —
Payout: —
Market value ($ mil.): —

NORKUS ENTERPRISES INC.

EXECUTIVES

President, Gerard K. (Gerry) Norkus, age 66
VP, Stephen J. Norkus
VP, Mark Norkus
Controller, Jane Lemonde
Auditors: Wiss&CompanyLLP

LOCATIONS

HQ: NORKUS ENTERPRISES INC.
505 RICHMOND AVE, POINT PLEASANT BEACH, NJ 087422552
Phone: 7328998485

COMPETITORS

Acme Markets
Costco Wholesale
Empire Merchants
Food Circus Super Markets
Pathmark Stores
Saker ShopRites
Wal-Mart
Weis Markets

HISTORICAL FINANCIALS

Company Type: Private

Income Statement FYE: April 25

	REVENUE ($ mil.)	NET INCOME ($ mil.)	NET PROFIT MARGIN	EMPLOYEES
04/09	157	0	0.4%	1,000
04/08	157	1	0.7%	—
04/07	153	0	0.6%	—
04/06	148	0	—	—
Annual Growth	2.0%	—	—	—

2009 Year-End Financials

Debt ratio: —
Return on equity: 0.40%
Cash ($ mil.): 0
Current ratio: 0.20
Long-term debt ($ mil.): —
Dividends
Yield: —
Payout: —
Market value ($ mil.): —

NORTH CAROLINA ELECTRIC MEMBERSHIP CORPORATION

It's a cooperative effort: North Carolina Electric Membership Corporation (NCEMC) generates and transmits electricity to the state's 26 electric cooperatives (more than 2.5 million people) in 93 of 100 North Carolina counties. The co-op owns more than 600 MW of generating capacity through four primarily natural gas peak load generators plus a 61.5% stake in Catawba Nuclear Station Unit 1 and a 31% stake in the Catawba Nuclear Station in South Carolina. It also buys power from Progress Energy American Electric Power and other for-profit utilities. NCEMC's member cooperatives serve more than 950000 metered businesses and homes in North Carolina. The wholesale co-op also operates an energy operations center.

NCEMC's cooperatives own operate and maintain more than 98000 miles of power lines primarily in rural areas of North Carolina. About 99% of co-op customers are residential (home owners and renters) and small businesses.

NCEMC members experienced an annual power delivery growth of 3.4% in the first decade of the 2000s and anticipated a 1.3% annual growth between 2012 and 2021.

To assist with local economic development projects NCEMC has teamed up with the USDA to give co-ops access to a $20 million federal rural development fund.

In August 2011 Hurricane Irene slammed into North Carolina causing serious disruption to the grid and cutting power to 152000 members. Despite major flood damage to some infrastructure power was restored to affected customers within a few days.

NCEMC (which was founded in 1949 with 17 co-op members) offers training programs engineering and construction management and power supply planning to member cooperatives.

EXECUTIVES

Director Corporate Communications, Jane Pritchard
SVP Legal Services; COO GreenCo Solutions, Robert B. (Bob) Schwentker
SVP EMC Technologies; COO North Carolina Association of Electric Cooperatives, Robert H. (Bob) Goodson
CEO, Joseph P. (Joe) Brannan
SVP and COO, Michael W. Burnette
President Board, Donald H. Spivey
Senior Communications Specialist, Kristie Aldridge
Vice President of Customer Services, Dan Allen
Vice President of Marketing, Brady Martin
Vice President of Member & Corporate Services, Dirk Burleson
Vice President Customer Service, Judy Gore
Vice President Member Services & Marketing, Marshall Cherry
VP of Sales & Economic Development, Tim Holder

Vice President Customer Services & Community Relations, Walter White
Auditors: GrantThorntonLLP

LOCATIONS

HQ: NORTH CAROLINA ELECTRIC MEMBERSHIP CORPORATION
3400 SUMNER BLVD, RALEIGH, NC 27616-2950
Phone: 919-872-0800
Web: WWW.NCEMCS.COM

PRODUCTS/OPERATIONS

Subsidiaries
North Carolina Association of Electric Cooperatives (NCAEC training programs)
The Tarheel Electric Membership Association Inc. (TEMA purchasing and materials supply)
North Carolina Cooperativ
Albemarle Electric Membership Corporatio
Blue Ridge Electric Membership Corporatio
Brunswick Electric Membership Corporatio
Cape Hatteras Electric Cooperativ
Carteret-Craven Electric Cooperativ
Central Electric Membership Corporatio
Edgecombe-Martin County Electric Membership Corporatio
EnergyUnited
Four County Electric Membership Corporatio
French Broad Electric Membership Corporatio
Halifax Electric Membership Corporatio
Haywood Electric Membership Corporatio
Jones-Onslow Electric Membership Corporatio
Lumbee River Electric Membership Corporatio
Pee Dee Electric Membership Corporatio
Piedmont Electric Membership Corporatio
Pitt & Greene Electric Membership Corporatio
Randolph Electric Membership Corporatio
Roanoke Electric Cooperativ
Rutherford Electric Membership Corporatio
South River Electric Membership Corporatio
Surry-Yadkin Electric Membership Corporatio
Tideland Electric Membership Corporatio
Tri-County Electric Membership Corporatio
Union Power Cooperativ
Wake Electric Membership Corporatio

COMPETITORS

AEP
Dominion Resources
Duke Energy
MEAG Power
Progress Energy
SCANA
Santee Cooper
TVA

HISTORICAL FINANCIALS

Company Type: Private

Income Statement FYE: December 31

	REVENUE ($ mil.)	NET INCOME ($ mil.)	NET PROFIT MARGIN	EMPLOYEES
12/11	1,012	17	1.7%	150
12/08	1,006	6	0.6%	—
12/07	942	2	0.3%	—
Annual Growth	1.8%	56.3%	—	—

2011 Year-End Financials

Debt ratio: —
Return on equity: 1.70%
Cash ($ mil.): 91
Current ratio: —
Long-term debt ($ mil.): —
Dividends
Yield: —
Payout: —
Market value ($ mil.): —

NORTH CENTRAL COOPERATIVE

LOCATIONS

HQ: NORTH CENTRAL COOPERATIVE
221 4TH AVE NW, CLARION, IA 505251035
Phone: 5155322881
Web: WWW.NCCOOP.COM

HISTORICAL FINANCIALS

Company Type: Private

Income Statement FYE: December 31

	REVENUE ($ mil.)	NET INCOME ($ mil.)	NET PROFIT MARGIN	EMPLOYEES
12/13	295	1	0.6%	96
12/12	300	3	1.1%	—
12/11	218	3	1.7%	—
12/10	140	0	—	—
Annual Growth	28.3%	—	—	—

2013 Year-End Financials

Debt ratio: —
Return on equity: 0.60%
Cash ($ mil.): 4
Current ratio: 0.30
Long-term debt ($ mil.): —
Dividends
Yield: —
Payout: —
Market value ($ mil.): —

NORTH CENTRAL COOPERATIVE INC

LOCATIONS

HQ: NORTH CENTRAL COOPERATIVE INC
2025 S WABASH ST, WABASH, IN 469924124
Phone: 2605639541
Web: WWW.NORTHCENTRALCOOP.COM

HISTORICAL FINANCIALS

Company Type: Private

Income Statement FYE: August 31

	REVENUE ($ mil.)	NET INCOME ($ mil.)	NET PROFIT MARGIN	EMPLOYEES
08/14	402	16	4.2%	280
08/13	426	19	4.6%	—
08/12	411	14	3.5%	—
08/11	322	0	—	—
Annual Growth	7.6%	—	—	—

2014 Year-End Financials

Debt ratio: —
Return on equity: 4.20%
Cash ($ mil.): 9
Current ratio: 1.30
Long-term debt ($ mil.): —
Dividends
Yield: —
Payout: —
Market value ($ mil.): —

NORTH CENTRAL FARMERS ELEVATOR

EXECUTIVES

Board President, Richard Osterday
Board Vice President, Larry Vetch
General Manager, Keith Hainy
Manager Grain Division, Mike Nickolas
Manager Petroleum Division, Troy Weig
Manager Farm Supply Division, Mike Geditz
Secretary and Treasurer, Quentin Larson
Controller, Joe Zikmund
Business Manager, Deanne Hoyle
Marketing Manager p, Matt Christopherson
Sales Manager p, Lane Mielke
Marketing Manager, Craig Haugaard
Director of Operations, David Dohman
Sales Manager p, Joel Vetter
Operations Manager, Mark Vogt

LOCATIONS

HQ: NORTH CENTRAL FARMERS ELEVATOR
12 5TH AVE, IPSWICH, SD 57451
Phone: 6054475803
Web: WWW.NCFE.COOP

COMPETITORS

ADM
CHS
Cargill
Dow AgroSciences
DuPont Agriculture & Nutrition
South Dakota Soybean Processors
South Dakota Wheat Growers

HISTORICAL FINANCIALS

Company Type: Private

Income Statement FYE: December 31

	REVENUE ($ mil.)	NET INCOME ($ mil.)	NET PROFIT MARGIN	EMPLOYEES
12/07	281	2	1.0%	200
12/06	135	(1)	—	—
12/05	1,140	0	0.0%	—
Annual Growth	(50.3%)	15571.1%	—	—

2007 Year-End Financials

Debt ratio: —
Return on equity: 1.00%
Cash ($ mil.): 8
Current ratio: 0.10
Long-term debt ($ mil.): —
Dividends
Yield: —
Payout: —
Market value ($ mil.): —

NORTH DAKOTA MILL & ELEVATOR ASSOCIATION INC

EXECUTIVES

President and General Manager, Vance Taylor
Controller and Financial Manager, Ed Barchenger
Logistics Manager, Mike Jones
Grain Manager, Jeff Bertsch
Production Manager, Chris Lemoine
Sales Manager, Steve Sannes
Quality Assurance Manager, Bob Sombke

LOCATIONS

HQ: NORTH DAKOTA MILL & ELEVATOR ASSOCIATION INC
1823 MILL RD, GRAND FORKS, ND 582031535
Phone: 7017957000

COMPETITORS

ADM
BakeMark
Bay State Milling
Bob' s Red Mill Natural Foods
Bunge Milling
C.H. Guenther & Son
CGC
CHS
Cargill
Chelsea Milling
Cooperative Elevator
General Mills
Gruma Corporation
Hodgson Mill
Horizon Milling
Italgrani
King Arthur Flour
Organic Milling
Seaboard
Smucker
Star of the West

HISTORICAL FINANCIALS

Company Type: Private

Income Statement FYE: June 30

	REVENUE ($ mil.)	NET INCOME ($ mil.)	NET PROFIT MARGIN	EMPLOYEES
06/14	256	9	3.6%	120
06/13	268	5	2.1%	—
06/12	262	3	1.4%	—
06/11	228	0	—	—
Annual Growth	3.9%	—	—	—

2014 Year-End Financials

Debt ratio: ——
Return on equity: 3.60%
Cash ($ mil.): 0
Current ratio: 1.10
Long-term debt ($ mil.): —
Dividends
Yield: —
Payout: —
Market value ($ mil.): —

NORTH GEORGIA ELECTRIC MEMBERSHIP FOUNDATION INC.

LOCATIONS

HQ: NORTH GEORGIA ELECTRIC MEMBERSHIP FOUNDATION INC.
1850 CLEVELAND HWY, DALTON, GA 307218315
Phone: 7062599441
Web: WWW.NGEMC.COM

HISTORICAL FINANCIALS

Company Type: Private

Income Statement FYE: June 30

	REVENUE ($ mil.)	NET INCOME ($ mil.)	NET PROFIT MARGIN	EMPLOYEES
06/13	237	8	3.5%	192
06/12	233	6	2.7%	—
06/11	243	4	1.8%	—
06/10	217	0	—	—
Annual Growth	2.9%	—	—	—

2013 Year-End Financials

Debt ratio: ——
Return on equity: 3.50%
Cash ($ mil.): 3
Current ratio: 1.20
Long-term debt ($ mil.): —
Dividends
Yield: —
Payout: —
Market value ($ mil.): —

NORTH KANSAS CITY SCHOOL DISTRICT NO. 74

LOCATIONS

HQ: NORTH KANSAS CITY SCHOOL DISTRICT NO. 74
2000 NE 46TH ST, KANSAS CITY, MO 641162042
Phone: 8164135000
Web: WWW.NKCSCHOOLS.ORG

HISTORICAL FINANCIALS

Company Type: Private

Income Statement FYE: June 30

	REVENUE ($ mil.)	NET INCOME ($ mil.)	NET PROFIT MARGIN	EMPLOYEES
06/14	221	9	4.2%	3,100
06/13	219	(9)	—	—
06/12	223	(5)	—	—
06/11	216	0	—	—
Annual Growth	0.7%	—	—	—

2014 Year-End Financials

Debt ratio: ——
Return on equity: 4.20%
Cash ($ mil.): 71
Current ratio: 1.60
Long-term debt ($ mil.): —
Dividends
Yield: —
Payout: —
Market value ($ mil.): —

NORTH MEMORIAL HEALTH CARE

North Memorial Health Care seeks victory over illness in the Twin Cities. Established in 1939 as Victory Hospital the health care network is home to North Memorial Medical Center a 520-bed hospital that includes a level I trauma center and the Humphrey Cancer Center. The hospital also operates specialty centers for cardiovascular care orthopedics pediatrics and women's health as well as an emergency vehicle fleet of more than 100 ambulances and helicopters. The adjacent outpatient center provides oncology radiation and imaging services. In addition North Memorial Health Care has a network of primary and specialty care clinics in the Twin Cities region and it provides home health and hospice services.

Geographic Reach

North Memorial Health Care's primary facility (North Memorial Medical Center) is located in Robbinsdale Minnesota. In partnership with Fairview Health Services the company operates the 130-bed Maple Grove Hospital in Maple Grove Minnesota. Its ambulance division serves the northwestern Twin Cities area as well other portions of Minnesota and Wisconsin.

Operations

As a regional trauma center North Memorial Medical Center must maintain a high level of technology resources and recruit skilled emergency room specialists. North Memorial's emergency fleet also adds to the facilities capabilities as it is one of the largest hospital-based ambulance services in the country with eight helicopters and about 100 ground ambulances. Outpatient facilities include rehabilitation centers sleep diagnostic labs family practice offices imaging centers and mental health facilities.

Strategy

The health network is expanding its facilities to improve services for area residents. In 2013 North Memorial opened the Plymouth City Center primary care clinic in Plymouth as well as a new heart and vascular institute in Buffalo and an urgent care center in Blaine.

EXECUTIVES

President and CEO, David W. Cress
VP Human Resources, David Abrams
VP and Chief Development Officer, Joseph G. Boston
VP Emergency and Trauma Services, Lisa H. Job
VP Emergency and Enterprise Operations, Mike Parrish
VP Development, Joe Boston
CEO, Loren (Larry) Taylor
President North Memorial Medical Center, Gayle Mattson
CEO Maple Grove Hospital, Andy Cochrane
Chief Medical Officer and President Physician Organization, J. Kevin Croston
VP Patient Care, Tracy Kirby
Chief Information Officer, Pat Taffe
VP Operations, Jeff Wicklander
VP Strategy and Business Development, Tiffany Zitzewitz
Chief Financial Officer, Pat Boran
Auditors: Deloitte&ToucheLLP

LOCATIONS

HQ: NORTH MEMORIAL HEALTH CARE
3300 OAKDALE AVE N, MINNEAPOLIS, MN 55422-2900
Phone: 763-520-5200
Web: WWW.NORTHMEMORIAL.COM

PRODUCTS/OPERATIONS

Selected Locations

Heart & Vascular Center - Maple Grove - Maple Grove Minnesota
Heart & Vascular Clinic Buffalo - Buffalo Minnesota
Heart & Vascular Clinic Monticello - Monticello Minnesota
Hope Chest Breast Center - Robbinsdale Minnesota
Humphrey Cancer Center - Robbinsdale Minnesota
Maple Grove Hospital - Maple Grove Minnesota
Maternal Fetal Medicine - Maple Grove - Maple Grove Minnesota
North Memorial Clinic Brooklyn Center - Brooklyn Center Minnesota
North Memorial Clinic Brooklyn Park - Brooklyn Park Minnesota
North Memorial Clinic Camden - Maple Grove - Maple Grove Minnesota
North Memorial Clinic Camden Minneapolis - Minneapolis Minnesota
North Memorial Clinic Camden Plymouth - Plymouth Minnesota
North Memorial Clinic Elk River - Elk River Minnesota
North Memorial Clinic Golden Valley - Golden Valley Minnesota
North Memorial Clinic Maple Grove - Maple Grove Minnesota
North Memorial Clinic Minnetonka - Minnetonka Minnesota
North Memorial Clinic Northeast - Minneapolis Minnesota
North Memorial Clinic Plymouth City Center - Plymouth Minnesota
North Memorial Clinic Silver Lake Clinic - St. Anthony - St. Anthony Minnesota
North Memorial Clinic Silver Lake Clinic Blaine Blaine Minnesota
North Memorial Medical Center - Robbinsdale Minnesota
North Memorial Urgent Care - Maple Grove - Maple Grove Minnesota
North Memorial Urgent Care Roseville - Roseville Minnesota
Outpatient Imaging Center - Robbinsdale Minnesota
Outpatient Psychiatric Clinic Robbinsdale Minnesota
Rehabilitation Services Robbinsdale Minnesota
Rehabilitation Services - Maple Grove Minnesota
Rehabilitation Services - Elk River Minnesota
Residential Hospice - Brooklyn Center Minnesota
Sleep Health Center - Maple Grove Minnesota
Sleep Health Center Robbinsdale Minnesota
Urgent Care - Blaine Minnesota

COMPETITORS

Allina Hospitals
Bethesda Hospital
Catholic Health Initiatives
CentraCare Health
Children' s Hospitals and Clinics of Minnesota
Fairview Health
First Care
HealthEast Care System
Mayo Clinic

Methodist Hospital (MN)
Park Nicollet Health Services
Regions Hospital
SCMC
St. John' s Hospital (Minnesota)
St. Luke' s Hospital (MN)
University of Minnesota Medical Center

HISTORICAL FINANCIALS

Company Type: Private

Income Statement FYE: December 31

	REVENUE ($ mil.)	NET INCOME ($ mil.)	NET PROFIT MARGIN	EMPLOYEES
12/12	565	(4)	—	5,180
12/09	605	(17)	—	—
12/05	544	8	1.5%	—
12/05	532	28	5.4%	—
Annual Growth	0.9%	—	—	—

2012 Year-End Financials

Debt ratio: ——
Return on equity: (-0.80%)
Cash ($ mil.): 10
Current ratio: 1.20
Long-term debt ($ mil.): —
Dividends
Yield: —
Payout: —
Market value ($ mil.): —

NORTH MISSISSIPPI HEALTH SERVICES INC.

North Mississippi Health Services (NMHS) isn't contained by its name: The health system reaches beyond its service territory in north Mississippi to provide health care to residents of northwestern Alabama and other areas of Mississippi. NMHS includes about half a dozen community hospitals including its flagship North Mississippi Medical Center in Tupelo. Combined the facilities have nearly 1000 beds designated for acute long term and nursing care. Specialty services include home health and long-term care inpatient and outpatient behavioral health and treatment centers for cancer and digestive disorders. NMHS also operates outpatient care and wellness clinics in the region.

Geographic Reach

In all NMHS serves two dozen counties across the two states. In addition to its main hospital in Tupelo NMHS operates health centers in communities including Eupora Iuka Pontotoc and West Point Mississippi and in Hamilton Alabama. It also manages a center in Calhoun City Mississippi. Its Baldwyn Nursing Facility is located in Baldwyn Mississippi.

Operations

During 2012 NMHS handled about 30000 inpatient visits as well as more than 140000 emergency room visits and some 365000 outpatient care visits. It also conducted about 25000 surgeries at its various facilities. Its outpatient centers include more than 30 primary and specialty care clinics in Mississippi and Alabama operated through the North Mississippi Medical Clinics division as well as more than half a dozen wellness centers.

Financial Performance

NMMC's revenues increased 2% to $852 million in 2012. Net income also rose 16% to some $33.5 million. The company's revenues have increased over the past five years due to organic growth measures; however net income has fluctuated due to variations in investment income and non-operating revenues.

EXECUTIVES

Vice President Human Resources, Rodger Brown
President and CEO, John R. Heer Jr.
CFO, Joe Reppert
VP Managed Care, Wally Davis
VP Facilities Management and Construction, Bruce Ridgway
VP and CIO, Tommy Bozeman
Vice Chairman, Robin McGraw
President North Mississippi Medical Center-Tupelo, Steve Altmiller
Chief Medical Officer, Mark Williams
Chief Strategy Officer, Ormella Cummings
VP Supply Chain, Mike Switzer
President North Mississippi Medical Center-Tupelo, Tim Moore
Chairman, Bobby Martin
President North Mississippi Medical Clinics, David Barber
President Health Care Foundation of North Mississippi, Dean Hancock
Vice President, Bruce Toppin

LOCATIONS

HQ: NORTH MISSISSIPPI HEALTH SERVICES INC.
830 S GLOSTER ST, TUPELO, MS 38801-4934
Phone: 662-377-3000
Web: WWW.NMHS.NET

Selected Locations

Baldwyn Nursing Facility (Baldwyn Mississippi)
Calhoun County Medical Clinic (managed facility; Calhoun Mississippi)
NMMC-Eupora (Eupora Mississippi)
NMMC-Hamilton (Hamilton Alabama)
NMMC-Iuka (Iuka Mississippi)
NMMC-Pontotoc (Pontotoc Mississippi)
NMMC-Tupelo (Tupelo Mississippi)
NMMC-West Point (West Point Mississippi)
North Mississippi Medical Clinics (NMMCI regional)

PRODUCTS/OPERATIONS

Selected Facilities and Services

Acute Stroke Unit
Advanced Wound Center and Hyperbarics
Bariatric Center
Behavioral Health Center
Breast Care Center
Cancer Center
Center for Digestive Health
Community Health
Critical Care Unit
CRNA Program
Diabetes Treatment Center
Emergency Services
Family Medicine Residency Center
Heart Institute
Home Health and Hospice
Hospitalists
Joint Replacement Center
Le Bonheur Specialty Clinics
Medical Imaging
North Mississippi Surgery Center
Outpatient Infusion
Pain Management Center
Pastoral Care
Physician Specialties
Radiology
Rehabilitation Services
Respiratory Therapy
Skilled Nursing Facility
Sleep Disorders Center
Surgical Services
Tupelo Wellness Center
Vein Center
Volunteer Services
Women' s Hospital
Women' s and Children Services

COMPETITORS

Baptist Memorial Health Care
Community Health Systems
Delta Regional Medical Center
Forrest General Hospital
HCA
Memorial Hospital at Gulfport
Methodist Healthcare
Natchez Regional Medical Center
North Mississippi Medical
Shelby County Health Care
Southwest Mississippi Regional Medical Center

HISTORICAL FINANCIALS

Company Type: Private

Income Statement FYE: September 30

	REVENUE ($ mil.)	NET INCOME ($ mil.)	NET PROFIT MARGIN	EMPLOYEES
09/12	852	(3)	—	6,000
09/11	834	(17)	—	—
09/10	788	40	5.1%	—
09/09	761	44	5.9%	—
Annual Growth	3.8%	—	—	—

2012 Year-End Financials

Debt ratio: ——
Return on equity: (-0.40%)
Cash ($ mil.): 106
Current ratio: 1.20
Long-term debt ($ mil.): —
Dividends
Yield: —
Payout: —
Market value ($ mil.): —

NORTH MISSISSIPPI MEDICAL CENTER INC.

At North Mississippi Medical Center you might get some Mississippi Mud ice cream after your tonsils are removed. The full-service 650-bed regional referral hospital in Tupelo Mississippi is part of the North Mississippi Health Services system an affiliation of hospitals and clinics serving northern Mississippi northwestern Alabama and parts of Tennessee. It's the largest private not-for-profit hospital in Mississippi and the largest non-metropolitan hospital in America. Specialty services at the medical center include cancer treatment women's health care cardiology and behavioral health care. The hospital also operates a skilled-nursing facility and home health and hospice organizations.

Geographic Reach

North Mississippi Medical Center serves more than 700000 people across 24 counties in north Mississippi northwestern Alabama and portions of Tennessee.

Operations

Besides being a Mississippi State Department of Health-designated Level II trauma center North Mississippi Medical Center offers more than 40 specialties as well as centers for excellence in cardiac surgery cardiology research neurology neurosurgery pulmonology rehabilitation cancer treatment chemical dependency and neonatal programs.

The medical center's Home Health Agency canvases 17 counties in north Mississippi and provides complex and extremely high-tech procedures that can be performed in the home setting. It also operates Baldwyn Nursing Facility.

Strategy

In 2012 North Mississippi Medical Center - Hamilton opened a new pulmonary rehabilitation unit. Also the medical center's Outpatient Rehabilitation Center in 2012 became the first outpatient rehabilitation center in Mississippi to offer Fiberoptic Endoscopic Evaluation of Swallowing (FEES) to assess swallowing function.

Awards and Recognition

North Mississippi Medical Center's hospitalist program has been recognized by The American Journal of Medicine for providing cost-effective care to patients in the hospital. The program begun in 1997 serves hospitalized patients who do not have a primary care physician or whose primary care physicians do not have hospital practices.

Ownership

North Mississippi Medical Center is part of North Mississippi Health Services.

EXECUTIVES

VP and CIO, Tommy Bozeman
VP and Legal Counsel, Bruce Toppin
President Chief Executive Officer, John R. Heer Jr.
Administrator Surgical Services North Mississippi Health Services, Michael (Mike) Denham
Chief Financial Officer, Joe Reppert
VP Managed Care, Wally Davis
Vice President, Bruce Ridgway
President, Steve Altmiller
Chief Medical Officer, Mark Williams
Vice President Human Resources, Rodger Brown
Vice President Community Hospitals, Tim Moore

LOCATIONS

HQ: NORTH MISSISSIPPI MEDICAL CENTER INC.
830 S GLOSTER ST, TUPELO, MS 38801-4934
Phone: 662-377-3000
Web: WWW.NMHS.NET

Selected Locations

Baldwyn Nursing Facility - Baldwyn Mississippi
NMMC - Eupora - Mississippi
NMMC - Hamilton - Alabama
NMMC - Iuka Mississippi
NMMC - Pontotoc Pontotoc Mississippi
NMMC - Tupelo Tupelo Mississippi
NMMC - West Point - West Point Mississippi

PRODUCTS/OPERATIONS

Selected Programs & Services

Acute Stroke Unit
Advanced Wound Center and Hyperbarics
Bariatric Center
Behavioral Health Center
Breast Care Center
Cancer Center
Center for Digestive Health
Community Health
Critical Care Unit
CRNA Program
Diabetes Treatment Center
Emergency Services
Family Medicine Residency Center
Gift & Floral Shop
Heart Institute
Home Health and Hospice
Hospitalists
Joint Replacement Center
Le Bonheur Specialty Clinics
Medical Imaging
North Mississippi Surgery Center
Outpatient Infusion
Pain Management Center
Pastoral Care
Physician Specialties
Radiology
Rehabilitation Services
Respiratory Therapy
Skilled Nursing Facility
Sleep Disorders Center
Surgical Services
Tupelo Wellness Center
Vein Center
Volunteer Services
West Bedtower Project
Women' s Hospital
Women' s and Children Services

COMPETITORS

Community Health Systems
Delta Regional Medical Center
Forrest General Hospital
HCA
Memorial Hospital at Gulfport
Natchez Regional Medical Center
Southwest Mississippi Regional Medical Center

HISTORICAL FINANCIALS

Company Type: Private

Income Statement FYE: September 30

	REVENUE ($ mil.)	NET INCOME ($ mil.)	NET PROFIT MARGIN	EMPLOYEES
09/12	620	(6)	—	6,000
09/11	614	4	0.8%	—
09/10	585	51	8.8%	—
09/09	559	54	9.8%	—
Annual Growth	3.5%	—	—	—

2012 Year-End Financials

Debt ratio: ——
Return on equity: (-1.00%)
Cash ($ mil.): 90
Current ratio: 1.10
Long-term debt ($ mil.): —

Dividends
Yield: —
Payout: —
Market value ($ mil.): —

NORTH PACIFIC PAPER CORPORATION

The old adage "all the news fit to print" might not be possible without North Pacific Paper Corporation (NORPAC). The company a joint venture between Weyerhaeuser and Nippon Paper produces newsprint for newspaper publishers and commercial printers. NORPAC manufactures a variety of different paper grades including standard and lightweight newsprint and super- and ultra-lightweight stocks especially for the Japanese market. The company produces more than 250000 tons of newsprint annually at its manufacturing facility in Longview Washington. Its products are sent via truck and train to customers in the western US or are shipped by boat to customers in Japan.

LOCATIONS

HQ: NORTH PACIFIC PAPER CORPORATION
3001 INDUSTRIAL WAY, LONGVIEW, WA 98632
Phone: 360-636-6400

PRODUCTS/OPERATIONS

Selected Products

Newsprint
- Lightweight
- Standard
- Super-lightweight

Printing and Publishing
- Norbite
- Norbrite Offset
- Norbrite Opaque
- Norbrite Plus

Other
- Groundwood forms
- Groundwood rotogravure
- Publication papers
- Super- and ultra-lightweight newsprint (for use in Japan)

COMPETITORS

Aylesford Newsprint
Boise Inc.
Brant Industries
Georgia-Pacific
Inland Empire Paper Company
International Paper
Norske Skog
Oji Holdings
Resolute Forest Products
SP Newsprint

HISTORICAL FINANCIALS

Company Type: Private

Income Statement FYE: December 31

	REVENUE ($ mil.)	NET INCOME ($ mil.)	NET PROFIT MARGIN	EMPLOYEES
12/08	534	22	4.2%	425
12/07	474	(3)	—	—
12/06	2,040	0	—	—
Annual Growth	—24921.7%		—	—

NORTH SHORE UNIVERSITY HOSPITAL

North Shore University Hospital (NSUH) knows you shouldn't have to leave the island for quality health care. The hospital has more than 800 beds devoted to adult and pediatric medicine rehabilitation stroke care women's health orthopedics urology wound healing dentistry and trauma emergency services among other areas. The Long Island hospital is home to specialist institutes for cancer care and cardiology. It also serves as a campus for the New York University School of Medicine the Hofstra North Shore-LIJ School of Medicine and other educational organizations. NSUH is part of the North Shore-Long Island Jewish Health System.

Geographic Reach

The hospital is located on the 60-acre Sandra Atlas Bass Campus. NSUH provides care to the Manhasset New York community on Long Island just outside of New York City's Queens borough. It also serves surrounding communities; its total service territory includes an area populated by about 7 million people in Long Island Manhattan Queens and Staten Island.

Operations

The not-for-profit hospital operates numerous satellite community health centers that provide primary surgery psychiatric dental and specialty care including the Schwartz Ambulatory Surgery Center. Its Stern Family Center for Extend Care and Rehabilitation has about 250 beds; NSUH also includes a Katz Women's Hospital (one of two in the system). The hospital provides comprehensive care in all health care specialties including organ transplant services. In addition the hospital operates mobile health vehicles and conducts educational and wellness programs for area residents.

NSUH has a staff of approximately 2700 specialist and subspecialist physicians. It handles about 50000 inpatient visits 84000 emergency room visits 20000 surgeries and 6000 births each year.

NSUH has medical health professional and nursing school affiliations with about 15 colleges and universities. Programs include residencies postgraduate training and fellowships.

Strategy

As part of a program to upgrade its medical equipment NSUH introduced a new diagnostic lab in 2013; the unit uses as 640-slice CT scanner to detect heart disease and heart attack risk. It also opened a video EEG (electroencephalogram) monitoring unit at its inpatient epilepsy wing during 2012.

EXECUTIVES

SVP Chief Administrative Officer and Chief of Staff, Gene Tangney

SVP and CFO North Shore-LIJ Health System, Robert S. (Bob) Shapiro
President North Shore-Long Island Jewish Health System, Ralph A. Nappi
Senior Vice President, Yosef Dlugacz
SVP North Shore-Long Island Jewish Health System Foundation, Cecelia T. Fullam
SVP and Chief Learning Officer, Kathleen Gallo
SVP Managed Care and Business Development, Howard B. Gold
Senior Vice President Strategy and Business Informatics, Jeffrey A. Kraut
EVP and COO North Shore-LIJ Health System, Mark J. Solazzo
SVP and Chief Nurse Executive, Maureen White
Regional Executive Director, Dennis Dowling
SVP and Chief Medical Officer, Lawrence G. Smith
SVP and General Counsel, Keith Thompson
Executive Director, Susan Somerville
SVP Academic Affairs and Chief Academic Officer North Shore-LIJ Health System, David L. Battinelli
SVP and Chief Development Officer North Shore-Long Island Jewish Health System Foundation, Kevin Dwyer
SVP and Chief Human Resources Officer, Joseph Cabral
Senior Vice President Chief Information Officer, John Bosco

LOCATIONS

HQ: NORTH SHORE UNIVERSITY HOSPITAL
300 COMMUNITY DR, MANHASSET, NY 11030-3816
Phone: 516-562-0100

PRODUCTS/OPERATIONS

Selected Centers and Services

Bariatric Services
Cancer Institute
Cardiovascular and Thoracic Services
Colorectal Surgery
Emergency Department / Trauma Services
Fertility and Reproductive Services
Geriatric and Palliative Medicine
Infectious Diseases / AIDS Research
Kidney Transplantation
Laparoendoscopic Single-Site Surgery
Military/Veterans Services
Minimally Invasive Robotic Surgery
Neuroscience
Obstetrics and Gynecology
Orthopaedics
Pain Management
Pediatric Services
Radiation Medicine
Travel Immunization
Urology Services
Wound Care

COMPETITORS

Brookhaven Memorial Hospital Medical Center
Catholic Health Services of Long Island
Catholic Healthcare System
Long Island College Hospital
Long Island Jewish Medical Center
Maimonides Medical Center
New York City Health and Hospitals
NewYork-Presbyterian Healthcare
Winthrop-University Hospital

HISTORICAL FINANCIALS

Company Type: Private

Income Statement FYE: December 31

	REVENUE ($ mil.)	NET INCOME ($ mil.)	NET PROFIT MARGIN	EMPLOYEES
12/08	1,184	(14)	—	30,000
12/02	930	42	4.6%	—
12/01	828	5	0.7%	—
12/00	769	21	2.8%	—
Annual Growth	5.5%	—	—	—

2008 Year-End Financials

Debt ratio: —
Return on equity: (-1.20%)
Cash ($ mil.): 388
Current ratio: 1.70
Long-term debt ($ mil.): —
Dividends
Yield: —
Payout: —
Market value ($ mil.): —

NORTHEASTERN SUPPLY INC.

EXECUTIVES

Chairman President and CEO, Steve Cook
VP Operations, Mike Combrooks
VP Purchasing, R.J. Kline
VP Residential Sales, Rick Tomaschefsky
VP Business Development, Steve Coppage
Manager Regional Sales, Don Bartsch
Regional Sales Manager, Bill Pritchett
Manager Regional Sales, Alan Cowan
Manager Regional Sales, Andy Kemp
Director Information Technology, Frank Collacchi
VP HVAC, Russ Everson
Commercial Plumbing Sales, Rick Yost
Controller, Bob Kahmer
Human Resources, Helene Headrick
Accounts Receivable, Lori Everson
Accounts Payable, Trina Wilson
Manager CDC, Norman Houck
Central Receiving, Richard Lazzara
Manager Commercial Plumbing Sales, Mike Tagliaferri
Human Resource Administrator, Martha Weaver
Director Inventory Management, Tony Gonclaves
Accounts Payable, Noel Blosser
Director of Information Technology, Matt Williams
Vice President Business Development, Mike Combrooks

LOCATIONS

HQ: NORTHEASTERN SUPPLY INC.
8323 PULASKI HWY, BALTIMORE, MD 212372941
Phone: 4105740010
Web: WWW.NORTHEASTERN.COM

2011 Locations

	No.
Maryland	16
Virginia	6
Pennsylvania	3
Delaware	3
West	1
Total	**29**

COMPETITORS

Ferguson Enterprises
HD Supply
Johnstone Supply
Lowe' s
Watsco
WinWholesale

HISTORICAL FINANCIALS

Company Type: Private

Income Statement FYE: December 31

	REVENUE ($ mil.)	NET INCOME ($ mil.)	NET PROFIT MARGIN	EMPLOYEES
12/12	111	2	2.1%	285
12/11	106	1	1.0%	—
12/09	100	2	2.6%	—
12/08	113	0	—	—
Annual Growth	(0.5%)	—	—	—

2012 Year-End Financials

Debt ratio: —
Return on equity: 2.10%
Cash ($ mil.): 2
Current ratio: 1.60
Long-term debt ($ mil.): —
Dividends
Yield: —
Payout: —
Market value ($ mil.): —

NORTHERN ILLINOIS UNIVERSITY FOUNDATION

LOCATIONS

HQ: NORTHERN ILLINOIS UNIVERSITY FOUNDATION
1425 W LINCOLN HWY, DEKALB, IL 601152828
Phone: 8157530282
Web: WWW.NIUFOUNDATION.ORG

HISTORICAL FINANCIALS

Company Type: Private

Income Statement FYE: June 30

	ASSETS ($ mil.)	NET INCOME ($ mil.)	INCOME AS % OF ASSETS	EMPLOYEES
06/09	73	3	5.0%	7
06/08	80	6	8.7%	—
06/07	83	9	10.9%	—
06/06	3	0	—	—
Annual Growth	173.2%	—	—	—

2009 Year-End Financials

Debt ratio: —
Return on equity: 21.60%
Cash ($ mil.): 2
Current ratio: —
Long-term debt ($ mil.): —
Dividends
Yield: —
Payout: —
Market value ($ mil.): —

NORTHERN VIRGINIA ELECTRIC COOPERATIVE

EXECUTIVES

Vice Chairman, J. Manley Garber
President, Stan C. Feuerberg
SVP Administration Substations and Telecommunications, Jim Moxley
VP Public Relations, Mike Curtis
VP and Corporate Counsel, Patrick Toulme
VP Business Development and Energy Services, Michael (Mike) Dailey
VP Electric Systems Operations, Allen Barbee
Chairman, Wade C. House
Assistant VP Customer Service, Diane Johnson
Secretary and Director, Michael E. Ragan
Treasurer and Director, Walter R. Grove
Public Relations, Priscilla Knight
Vice Chairman, J. Manley Garber
President, Stan C. Feuerberg
Secretary and Director, Michael E. Ragan
Treasurer and Director, Walter R. Grove
Director, James Chesley
Director, Cynthia Gilbride
Director, Ann Wheeler
Director, Harry Harris

Director, William Zilliott

LOCATIONS

HQ: NORTHERN VIRGINIA ELECTRIC COOPERATIVE
10323 LOMOND DR, MANASSAS, VA 201093113
Phone: 7033350500
Web: WWW.NOVEC.COM

Northern Virginia Electric Cooperative operates in rural areas in Clarke Fairfax Fauquier Loudoun Prince William and Stafford counties as well as in the Town of Clifton and the City of Manassas Park in northern Virginia.

PRODUCTS/OPERATIONS

Subsidiaries and Affiliates
NOVEC Energy Solutions (formerly America's Energy Alliance retail gas marketing)
NOVEC Solutions (formerly NOVASTAR energy products and services)

COMPETITORS

AEP
AGL Resources
Chesapeake Utilities
Constellation Energy Group
Delmarva Power
Dominion Resources
FirstEnergy
NiSource
Pepco Holdings
WGL Holdings

HISTORICAL FINANCIALS

Company Type: Private

Income Statement FYE: December 31

	REVENUE ($ mil.)	NET INCOME ($ mil.)	NET PROFIT MARGIN	EMPLOYEES
12/13	396	23	6.0%	275
12/09	419	50	12.2%	—
12/08	397	0	—	—
12/02	234	0	—	—
Annual Growth	4.9%	—	—	—

2013 Year-End Financials

Debt ratio: —
Return on equity: 6.00%
Cash ($ mil.): 54
Current ratio: 2.50
Long-term debt ($ mil.): —
Dividends
Yield: —
Payout: —
Market value ($ mil.): —

NORTHSHORE UNIVERSITY HEALTHSYSTEM

NorthShore University HealthSystem provides care to residents of Chicago's north side and its suburbs. The health system operates hospitals a home care organization and a Medical Group with hundreds of primary and specialty care physicians. With 360 beds the organization's flagship Evanston Hospital has teaching and research programs as well as capabilities for trauma cancer cardiology and women's health care. The system also includes Glenbrook Hospital (140 beds) while Highland Park Hospital (160 beds) and Skokie Hospital (200 beds). The health care system is affiliated with the University of Chicago Pritzker School of Medicine.

The company's health facility network has grown over the years through acquisitions. Some of NorthShore's notable buys include the Rush North Shore Medical Center in Skokie from the Rush System for Health for about $160 million. The hospital was renamed Skokie Hospital following the acquisition. The organization has also been working to expand its medical group to broaden its offering of specialized health care services. In 2009 NorthShore acquired the Chicago Institute of Neurosurgery and Neuroresearch adding 20 neurological physicians to its staff. The health system intends to make more acquisitions of that type until it's able to offer the community most major medical specialties.

NorthShore also widens its network and service offerings through organic growth. The health care provider regularly conducts expansion and remodeling projects at its facilities and has stepped up recruiting efforts to attract high-skill doctors. It has also been working to improve communication within its physician network by investing in information technology initiatives such as installing an electronic medical record (EMR) system and has committed to spending $1 billion in capital improvements over the next five years.

Fortunately for NorthShore it thrives in an area where the population is young and poverty is limited. While the health system receives a good amount of revenue from Medicare and Medicaid it also receives income from commercial insurance payers with a low level of charity care despite economic turmoil in the US. This patient mix coupled with increased hospital capacity and occupancy rates (more than 70%) has allowed the company to maintain revenue and income growth as well as plenty of cash on hand to fund its expansion initiatives.

Each of NorthShore's hospitals is known for a certain specialty. Evanston for example specializes in cancer and cardiac care; Glenbrook Hospital is known for advanced technology for the treatment of gastrointestinal disorders; Highland Park Hospital is the site of the first open hear surgery in the region; and Skokie Hospital is known for its expertise in cancer and cardiac care as well as orthopaedics.

EXECUTIVES

Secretary and Director, William (Bill) Wrigley Jr., age 50
President CEO and Director, Mark R. Neaman
Vice Chairman, A. Steven Crown
COO, Jeffrey H. Hillebrand, age 60
President NorthShore Medical Group, Joseph Golbus
President Evanston Hospital, Douglas M. Silverstein
President Skokie Hospital, Kristen Murtos
Chief Human Resources Officer, William R. (Bill) Luehrs
Chief Investment Officer, Thomas H. Hodges
Chief Nursing Officer, Nancy Semerdjian
CIO, Tom Smith
President Highland Park Hospital, Jesse Peterson Hall
Director Public Relations, James (Jim) Anthony
Chairman, Gregory K. Jones
Chairman Professional Staff and Director, Thomas C. Keeler
Chairman Department of Surgery and Director, Mark S. Talamonti
Executive Vice President Chief Financial Officer Treasurer, Gary E. Weiss
Chairman NorthShore University HealthSystem Foundation, John R. Walter
Chief Science Officer, Michael S. Caplan
President Glenbrook Hospital, Sean OGrady
Director, John R. Walter, age 66
Director, Harvey N. Medvin, age 78
Director, William L. Davis III, age 71
Director, Richard L. (Dick) Keyser, age 71
Secretary and Director, William (Bill) Wrigley Jr., age 50
President CEO and Director, Mark R. Neaman
Director, Samuel M. Mencoff, age 57
Director, William J. White
Director, Jonathan P. (Jon) Ward, age 60
Director, Lester B. Knight III, age 54
Vice Chairman, A. Steven Crown
Director, M. Jude Reyes, age 58
Director, Mary N. Dillon, age 53
Director, J. Mikesell (Mike) Thomas, age 62
Director, Connie K. Duckworth, age 60
Director, Percy L. Berger Sr.
Director, Janardan D. Khandekar
Chairman Professional Staff and Director, Thomas C. Keeler
Director, Susan B. Sentell
Chairman Department of Surgery and Director, Mark S. Talamonti
Director, Sonia Wang
Director, Ike Hong
Director, Andrew J. Mills
Director, Joseph Szokol

LOCATIONS

HQ: NORTHSHORE UNIVERSITY HEALTHSYSTEM
2650 RIDGE AVE, EVANSTON, IL 60201-1718
Phone: 847-570-5295
Web: WWW.ENH.ORG

PRODUCTS/OPERATIONS

Selected Hospitals

Evanston Hospital (Evanston Illinois)
Glenbrook Hospital (Glenview Illinois)
Highland Park Hospital (Highland Park Illinois)
NorthShore University HealthSystem Home and Hospice
NorthShore University HealthSystem Medical Group
NorthShore University HealthSystem Research Institute
Skokie Hospital (Skokie Illinois)

COMPETITORS

Advocate Health Care
Central DuPage Hospital
Children' s Hopsital of Chicago
KishHealth
Mercy Hospital and Medical Center
MetroSouth Medical
Northwest Community Healthcare
Northwestern Memorial HealthCare
Provena Health
Resurrection Health Care
Rockford Health System
Rush System for Health
Sherman Health Systems
University of Chicago Medical Center

HISTORICAL FINANCIALS

Company Type: Private

Income Statement FYE: September 30

	REVENUE ($ mil.)	NET INCOME ($ mil.)	NET PROFIT MARGIN	EMPLOYEES
09/09	1,085	(71)	—	9,000
09/08	26	0	0.4%	—
09/05	1,061	64	6.0%	—
09/04	1,015	44	4.3%	—
Annual Growth	1.3%	—	—	—

2009 Year-End Financials

Debt ratio: —
Return on equity: (-6.60%)
Cash ($ mil.): 24
Current ratio: 0.20
Long-term debt ($ mil.): —
Dividends
Yield: —
Payout: —
Market value ($ mil.): —

NORTHSIDE HOSPITAL INC.

Northside Hospital is no one-trick pony –it actually operates three hospitals serving Atlanta and surrounding areas. Also known as the Northside Healthcare Delivery System the Northside Hospital network includes some 820 licensed beds and more than 2200 physicians on multiple campuses with a host of outpatient health facilities including physician office parks and specialized cancer centers. All of Northside's hospitals are full-service acute care facilities that provide specialty care including cancer care surgery radiology and women's health. Northside Hospital opened in 1970.

Geographic Reach

Northside Hospital's three campuses are located in Atlanta Forsyth and Cherokee Georgia. It also operate about 40 outpatient clinics and physician practices are scattered across the northern Atlanta metropolitan area.

Operations

Northside Hospital handles about 700000 patient visits annually at its facilities. The organization's cancer treatment division partners with the Cancer Support Community of Atlanta to provide mental health social and educational services to cancer patients and survivors as well as family members and friends.

Strategy

Northside Hospital is conducting expansion and renovation efforts to meet the needs of area residents. It completed a $50 million expansion project at its Forsyth campus in 2012 that increased the facility's patient capacity by about 40% and added about 250 area jobs. Also in 2012 it opened a new outpatient surgery center (offering general orthopedic aesthetic and other specialties) near the Forsyth campus in the town of Cumming as well as a new outpatient medical imaging center in the nearby community of Buford.

Also in 2012 the hospital announced plans to construct a new four-story medical office building near the Cherokee campus in Woodstock Georgia.

EXECUTIVES

VP Administration and CEO Northside Hospital-Forsyth, Robert Putnam
CEO Northside Hospital-Cherokee, William (Billy) Hayes
Chair Department of Obstetrics and Gynecology, Ceana Nezhat
CEO Northside Hospital-Forsyth, Skip Putnam
Director Icu/coronary Care Unit, Amy Berryman
Vice President Planning And Real Estate, Doug Macdonald
Vice President Supply Chain Management, Carl Waller
Secretary, Jehan Norwood
Secretary, Terese Clonts

LOCATIONS

HQ: NORTHSIDE HOSPITAL INC.
1000 JOHNSON FY RD NE, ATLANTA, GA 30342-1611
Phone: 404-851-8000
Web: WWW.NORTHSIDE.COM

Selected locations

Alpharetta Medical Campus
Dunwoody Cancer Center
Imaging at Peachtree Dunwoody
Medlock Bridge Imaging
Meridian Park Plaza
Northside Hospital Doctors Center
Northside Hospital-Atlanta
Northside Hospital-Cherokee
Northside Hospital-Forsyth
Northside-Forsyth Outpatient Surgery Center
Northside Sugar Hill Imaging (Buford)
Pediatric Center at Northside/Alpharetta
Roswell Cancer Center
Townelake Medical Office/Riverstone Imaging

COMPETITORS

Children' s Healthcare of Atlanta
DeKalb Medical
Emory Healthcare
Grady Health System
Gwinnett Health System
Regency Hospital
Shepherd Center
Southern Regional Medical Center
SunLink Health Systems
The Fulton-DeKalb Hospital Authority
Northeast Georgia Health System
Piedmont Healthcare
WellStar Health System

HISTORICAL FINANCIALS

Company Type: Private

Income Statement

FYE: September 30

	REVENUE ($ mil.)	NET INCOME ($ mil.)	NET PROFIT MARGIN	EMPLOYEES
09/12	829	60	7.3%	8,000
09/09	1,002	8	0.8%	—
09/08	938	10	1.1%	—
Annual Growth	(3.1%)	56.4%	—	—

2012 Year-End Financials

Debt ratio: —
Return on equity: 7.30%
Cash ($ mil.): 121
Current ratio: 0.90
Long-term debt ($ mil.): —
Dividends
Yield: —
Payout: —
Market value ($ mil.): —

NORTHWEST DAIRY ASSOCIATION

Northwest Dairy Association (NDA) members milk a lot of cows. The dairy cooperative's 550-plus member/farmers ship 7.2 billion pounds of milk annually which is processed by the co-op's subsidiary Darigold and packaged and sold under the Darigold label. NDA produces fluid and cultured dairy products including milk butter cottage cheese sour cream and yogurt. It also makes bulk butter and cheese milk powder and whey products. The co-op caters to several sectors nationwide. Its customers include food retailers and wholesalers as well as foodservice and food-manufacturing companies. The association's membership spans half a dozen US states.

Geographic Reach

NDA members are located in Washington Oregon Idaho Montana California and Utah.

Operations

The cooperative's Darigold subsidiary which operates a dozen processing facilities across the Northwestern US sells nearly $2.5 billion in dairy products each year.

Sales and Marketing

Through Darigold NDA makes and markets a full line of dairy-based products for retail foodservice and commodity and specialty markets.

Mergers and Acquisitions

NDA added Country Classic Dairies to its operations in 2010. Its Montana-based operations churn out Darigold-branded products with help from its 30 member/farmers. Securing the Country Classics business added some 160 million pounds of milk a year (more than half of Montana's milk supply) to the co-op's total production. NDA and Country Classic's union was the culmination of the two businesses' longtime working relationship (at one time Country Classic used the Darigold name to market its products).

EXECUTIVES

Chairman, Jim Werkhoven
Treasurer, Adrian Boer
Treasurer, Sherman Polinder
President, James Wegner
VP, Steve Matzen
Auditors: KPMGLLP

LOCATIONS

HQ: NORTHWEST DAIRY ASSOCIATION
1130 RAINIER AVE S, SEATTLE, WA 98144-2842
Phone: 206-284-7220

PRODUCTS/OPERATIONS

Selected Products

Consumer
- Butter
- Buttermilk
- Cottage cheese
- Cream
- Half and half
- Milk
- Sour cream
- Whipping cream
- Yogurt

Ingredients
- Bleached sweet dry whey

Colored cheddar cheese
Cultured skim milk powder
Milk protein concentrate
Monterey Jack cheese
Nonfat dry milk
Salted sweet cream butter
Skim milk powder
Sweet cream buttermilk powder
Unsalted butter
Whey protein concentrate

COMPETITORS

Associated Milk Producers
Berkeley Farms
California Dairies Inc.
Dairy Farmers of America
Dean Foods
Humboldt Creamery
Land O' Lakes
Straus Family Creamery
Tillamook County Creamery Association

HISTORICAL FINANCIALS

Company Type: Private

Income Statement

FYE: March 31

	REVENUE ($ mil.)	NET INCOME ($ mil.)	NET PROFIT MARGIN	EMPLOYEES
03/08	2,207	87	4.0%	1,300
03/07	1,450	12	0.9%	—
03/04	1,297	(6)	—	—
03/03	1,140	2	0.2%	—
Annual Growth	14.1%	107.0%	—	—

2008 Year-End Financials

Debt ratio: —
Return on equity: 4.00%
Cash ($ mil.): 10
Current ratio: 0.90
Long-term debt ($ mil.): —
Dividends
Yield: —
Payout: —
Market value ($ mil.): —

NORTHWEST FARM CREDIT SERVICES ACA

Northwest Farm Credit Services is an agricultural lender that provides financial services to farmers ranchers agribusinesses commercial fishermen timber producers and rural home owners in Alaska Idaho Montana Oregon and Washington. The cooperatively-owned company has a network of around 50 branches and offers a broad range of flexible loan programs to meet the needs of people in the agriculture business. Farm Credit also provides leasing services appraisal services and life mortgage disability and crop insurance as well as legal advocacy and assistance to customers in need. The company is part of the Farm Credit System a network of lenders serving the US agriculture industry.

Congress created the Farm Credit System in 1916 to meet the financial needs of farmers ranchers and cooperatives who invest as well as borrow from the institutions within the system. All Farm Credit System members are regulated by the Farm Credit Administration.

EXECUTIVES

EVP Financial Services, Fred (Fred) DePell
EVP and General Counsel, Thomas (Tom) Tracy
EVP Corporate Administration and Secretary, Joan E. Haynes
EVP CFO and CIO, Tom Nakano
Chairman, Drew Eggers, $41,250 total compensation
SVP Agribusiness, Marnie Vandenberg
SVP Capital Markets, Jim D. Allen
Vice Chairman, Kevin Riel, $45,000 total compensation
Regional Vice President Services, Bill Conrad
Sr. Vice President - Insurance Services, Dean Benson
Vice President Industry Team Leader, Mark Dvarishkis
Regional Vice President Services, Tom Schmitt
Vice President Market Research and Development, Michael Stolp
Regional Vice President Services, Beau Reynolds
Director, Bruce Nelson
Director, Herb Karst
Vice Chairman, Kevin Riel
Director, Karen Schott
Director, Rick Barnes
Director, Jim Farmer
Director, Mark Gehring
Director, Shawn Walters
Auditors: PricewaterhouseCoopersLLP

LOCATIONS

HQ: NORTHWEST FARM CREDIT SERVICES ACA
1700 S ASSEMBLY ST # 102, SPOKANE, WA 99224-2116
Phone: 509-838-2429
Web: WWW.FARM-CREDIT.COM

PRODUCTS/OPERATIONS

Sales 2008

	$ mil.	% of total
$ in mil. % of total		
Interest income	438	88
Non interest income		
Patronage income	34	7
Loan and other fees	17	3
Other	7	2
Total	**497**	**100**

COMPETITORS

Bank of America
First Interstate
Idaho Independent Bank
KeyCorp
Northwest Bancorporation
U.S. Bancorp
Wells Fargo
Zions Bancorporation

HISTORICAL FINANCIALS

Company Type: Private

Income Statement FYE: December 31

	ASSETS ($ mil.)	NET INCOME ($ mil.)	INCOME AS % OF ASSETS	EMPLOYEES
12/11	8,696	159	1.8%	500
12/10	8,705	150	1.7%	—
12/09	8,579	106	1.2%	—
12/08	8,326	124	1.5%	—
Annual Growth	1.5%	8.6%	—	—

2011 Year-End Financials

Debt ratio: —
Return on equity: 38.90%
Cash ($ mil.): 62
Current ratio: —
Long-term debt ($ mil.): —
Dividends
Yield: —
Payout: —
Market value ($ mil.): —

NORTHWESTERN MEMORIAL HEALTHCARE

If you get blown over in the Windy City Northwestern Memorial HealthCare (NMHC) can get you upright again. Its primary facility Northwestern Memorial Hospital (NMH) is a teaching hospital serving residents of the Chicago area offering virtually every medical specialty. The hospital has more than 890 beds and is affiliated with Northwestern University's Feinberg School of Medicine. NMHC also operates the 200-bed Northwestern Lake Forest Hospital ambulatory surgery centers physicians' practices community clinics a home hospice program and health and wellness centers. Other subsidiaries of the NMHC health system include a philanthropic foundation an insurance company and a managed care contracts provider.

Operations

Other facilities operated by NMHC include Prentice Women's Hospital and Stone Institute of Psychiatry which are located on the NMH campus. The Prentice Women's Hospital offers services such as obstetrics gynecology breast and plastic surgery hematology/oncology and neonatal intensive care. In addition the Northwestern Lake Forest Hospital includes a health and fitness institute and a skilled nursing facility for seniors.

Founded in 1972 Northwestern Memorial Hospital and the Feinberg School of Medicine are heavily involved in medical research and conduct thousands of clinical research studies in a range of disciplines each year. NMHC employs some 1600 physicians who are also faculty members at the Feinberg School of Medicine.

Financial Analysis

NMHC experienced a 1% rise in revenues in 2012 to some $1.7 billion; the growth was attributed to increased earnings from patient services especially from higher reimbursements from Medicare and other third-party payers. However net income dropped by 58% to some $122 million due to decreased returns on investments.

Strategy

NMHC like many metropolitan health care providers is upgrading and expanding its facilities to meet the demands of a growing population. For instance the Prentice Women's Hospital increased the size of its neonatal intensive care unit in 2010. In addition in 2012 NMHC announced plans to open six new physician practice locations in the Chicago area.

EXECUTIVES

President and CEO, Dean M. Harrison
Executive Vice President Chief Financial Officer, Peter J. McCanna
Senior Associate Media Relations, Andrew Buchanan
Executive Vice President Northwestern Memorial, Dennis M. Murphy
Director Media Relations, Kris Lathan
Manager Media Relations, Jennifer Monasteri
SVP and General Counsel, Carol M. Lind
President, Stephen C. Falk
Senior Associate Media Relations, Kimberly Arndt
Chief of Staff, Gary Noskin
VP-Ops, Gary Fennessy

LOCATIONS

HQ: NORTHWESTERN MEMORIAL HEALTHCARE
251 E HURON ST STE 3-708, CHICAGO, IL 60611-2908
Phone: 312-926-2000
Web: WWW.NMH.ORG

PRODUCTS/OPERATIONS

Selected Operations

Northwestern Lake Forest Hospital
Northwestern Memorial Foundation
Northwestern Memorial Hospital
Northwestern Memorial Insurance Company
Northwestern Memorial Physicians Group

COMPETITORS

Advocate Health Care
Alexian Brothers Health System
Loyola University Health System
Mercy Hospital and Medical Center
NorthShore University HealthSystem
Resurrection Health Care
Rockford Health System
Rush System for Health
Sherman Health Systems
Sinai Health System
University of Chicago Medical Center

HISTORICAL FINANCIALS

Company Type: Private

Income Statement FYE: August 31

	ASSETS ($ mil.)	NET INCOME ($ mil.)	INCOME AS % OF ASSETS	EMPLOYEES
08/12	4,701	145	3.1%	6,000
08/11	42	1	4.5%	—
08/10	37	0	1.5%	—
08/09	33	(0)		—
Annual Growth	417.7%	—	—	—

2012 Year-End Financials

Debt ratio: —
Return on equity: 8.60%
Cash ($ mil.): 139
Current ratio: 0.80
Long-term debt ($ mil.): —
Dividends
Yield: —
Payout: —
Market value ($ mil.): —

NOVA SOUTHEASTERN UNIVERSITY INC.

Nova Southeastern University (NSU) gives a whole new meaning to "school of sharks." NSU whose mascot is the deep sea predator has an enrollment of more than 27000 students and offers a variety of undergraduate graduate and professional academic programs. NSU offers degrees in several medical disciplines (osteopathic medicine pharmacy optometry nursing) marine biology business law education and computer sciences. The not-for-profit independent school operates four campuses in the Miami-Fort Lauderdale area several health centers and an oceanographic center. Founded in 1964 Nova University merged with Southeastern University of the Health Sciences in 1994 to become Nova Southeastern University.

Operations

In addition to its undergraduate and graduate programs NSU also operates The University School a pre-K through 12th grade college preparatory day school that draws part of its staff from NSU's School of Education and Human services. The university's Mailman Segal Institute for Early Childhood Studies serves the local community with programming for parents and educators.

Geographic Reach

NSU is a distance education pioneer (it was the first US university to offer graduate programs online) offering classes on the Internet as well as at six regional centers in Florida and Puerto Rico.

Finance

Continuing a trend of earnings growth over the last five years from organic growth measures NSU reported a 4% rise in revenues in 2014 to some $640 million. The growth was attributed to increased tuition and fee income as well as revenues from auxiliary enterprises and government grants.

Strategy

As universities do NSU regularly invests in facility upgrades to meet the growing needs of its students. In 2014 it broke ground on the NSU Center for Collaborative Research (CCR) that will house an IBM supercomputer a tech incubator one of the state's largest wet labs and space for guest researchers. Other CCR facilities will include cancer and neuro-immune institutes an incubator for security businesses and an entire floor for the US Geological Survey which will partner with the university on research into Everglades restoration projects.

EXECUTIVES

Intrm Vp Information Tech, Greg Horne
Associate Vp Business Services, Marc M Crocquet
Chancellor Health Professions Division, Frederick Lippman
CEO President and Trustee, George L. Hanbury
VP Finance, W. David Heron
Dean Student Affairs, Brad Williams
Executive Director Alvin Sherman Library, Harriett MacDougall
Dean Shepard Broad Law Center, Athornia Steele
University Provost and EVP Academic Affairs, Frank DePiano
Dean University School, Jerome Chermak
Dean College of Health Care Sciences, Richard E. Davis
Dean Oceanographic Center, Richard E. Dodge
Dean Center for Psychological Studies, Karen Grosby
Dean College of Medical Sciences, Harold E. Laubach
Dean Mailman Segal Institute for Early Childhood Studies, Roni Leiderman
Dean College of Optometry, David S. Loshin
Dean College of Pharmacy, Andr Ã© Malav Ã©
Dean Farquhar College of Arts and Sciences, Don Rosenblum
Dean College of Osteopathic Medicine, Anthony J. Silvagni
Dean Fischler School of Education, H. Wells Singleton
Dean College of Dental Medicine, Robert A. Uchin
Dean Graduate School of Humanities and Social Sciences, Honggang Yang
EVP and COO, Jacqueline A. Travisano
CEO Health Clinics, Robert S. Oller
VP Information Technology and CIO, Tom West
Executive Assistant Vice President, Katharine Perren
Vp For Clinical Operations, Linda Smelser
Vp Institutional Advancement, Joe Pineta
Chair, Ronald G. Assaf
CEO President and Trustee, George L. Hanbury
Vice Chair, Barry J. Silverman
Auditors: Ernst&YoungLLP

LOCATIONS

HQ: NOVA SOUTHEASTERN UNIVERSITY INC.
3301 COLLEGE AVE, DAVIE, FL 333147796
Phone: 9542627300
Web: WWW.NSUNEWS.NOVA.EDU

PRODUCTS/OPERATIONS

2012 Revenues

	$ mil.	% of total
Tuition & fees	521	83
Government grants	37	6
Auxiliary operations	36	6
Contributions	14	2
Investment income	3	1
Other	17	2
Total	**630**	**100**

COMPETITORS

Florida Atlantic University
Florida International University
University of Florida

HISTORICAL FINANCIALS

Company Type: Private

Income Statement FYE: June 30

	REVENUE ($ mil.)	NET INCOME ($ mil.)	NET PROFIT MARGIN	EMPLOYEES
06/13	617	38	6.3%	2,500
06/12	689	48	7.1%	—
06/10	612	22	3.7%	—
06/09	595	0	—	—
Annual Growth	0.9%	—	—	—

2013 Year-End Financials

Debt ratio: ——
Return on equity: 6.30%
Cash ($ mil.): 63
Current ratio: 0.60
Long-term debt ($ mil.): —
Dividends
Yield: —
Payout: —
Market value ($ mil.): —

NOVELART MANUFACTURING COMPANY

LOCATIONS

HQ: NOVELART MANUFACTURING COMPANY
2121 SECTION RD, CINCINNATI, OH 452373509
Phone: 5133517700
Web: WWW.TOPICZINC.COM

HISTORICAL FINANCIALS

Company Type: Private

Income Statement FYE: September 30

	REVENUE ($ mil.)	NET INCOME ($ mil.)	NET PROFIT MARGIN	EMPLOYEES
09/14	359	0	—	160
09/13	330	0	—	—
09/12	309	0	—	—
09/11	284	0	—	—
Annual Growth	8.2%	—	—	—

2014 Year-End Financials

Debt ratio: ——
Return on equity: —
Cash ($ mil.): 0
Current ratio: 1.40
Long-term debt ($ mil.): —
Dividends
Yield: —
Payout: —
Market value ($ mil.): —

NYPRO INC.

Nypro is a real pro when it comes to injection molding. The company makes plastic parts used in devices that range from cell phones and electric razors to inkjet printer cartridges and personal computers. Nypro's three global units include Consumer & Electronics Packaging and Healthcare (medical devices such as single-use fluid and drug management components). Although custom-precision plastic-injection molding is Nypro's core business the company also offers assembly services to other manufacturers. Major customers include Dell Nokia and Procter & Gamble. Established in 1955 Nypro agreed to be acquired by electronics manufacturing services provider Jabil Circuit in early 2013.

Change of Company Type

In early 2013 electronics manufacturing services provider Jabil Circuit agreed to buy Nypro. Jabil is buying Nypro in order to expand its materials manufacturing operations into the healthcare market.

Geographic Reach

Nypro comprises more than 40 businesses throughout 15 countries in Asia/Pacific Europe and the US.

Financial Performance

Nypro generated $1.2 billion in total sales for its most recent fiscal year.

Strategy

One of the challenges Nypro has faced is getting its many business operations to work together smoothly. During the worldwide recession the company decentralized its operations by creating three global business units each with its own group president to focus on customers in Nypro's primary markets. The three units ensure a revenue balance in which no market accounts for more than 50%.

Nypro continues to push for an ever larger share of the medical plastics market. In early 2011 the company completed its purchase of Schlosser Medizintechnik a medical device manufacturer in Germany. Nypro has also bumped up its investment in new ventures and strategic companies — which tap new emerging markets –including New Ventures Group (NVG) and Radius Product Development Group as well as Nypro-branded NP Medical and Union Street Brand Packaging.

Company Background

In 1962 chairman Gordon Lankton joined Nypro (then known as Nylon Products Inc.) as general manager and co-owner. In 1969 he acquired the remainder of the company he didn't already own. In 1998 Lankton sold the firm to Nypro's employee stock ownership plan (ESOP).

EXECUTIVES

SVP and CFO, Greg G. Adams
President Nypro Healthcare, Boris Levin
President Nypro Packaging, Paul Kayser
President Nypro China, Simon Chiu
President and CEO, Theodore E. (Ted) Lapres
President Consumer and Electronics, Jim Sykes
Vp Latin America, Michael C Mackenty
Vice President Corporate Controller, Steve Ploof
Vice President Engineering Operations, Chuck Henry
Vice President Finance And Information Systems, Ed Philbin
Vp Human Resources And Organizational Development, Pat Davies
Vice President Manda, Jack McCabe
Vice President Of Quality And Regulatory Affairs, Eric Pettes
Vice President And General Manager Medical Device, Brian Highley

Vice President Corporate Human, Patricia Davies
Treas, Sergio A Cadavid
Chairman, Gordon B. Lankton
Board Member, Peter Benkiewicz
Auditors: PricewaterhouseCoopersLLP

LOCATIONS

HQ: NYPRO INC.
101 UNION ST, CLINTON, MA 01510-2935
Phone: 978-365-9721
Web: WWW.NYPRO.COM

PRODUCTS/OPERATIONS

Selected Markets

Consumer and Electronics
- Consumer/industrial
  - Adhesives
  - Electrical components
  - Fasteners
  - Fitness
  - Lawn and garden
  - Photography
  - Small and large appliances
  - Sporting goods
  - Storage
  - Tools
- Electronics/telecommunications
  - Assemblies and disposable cartridges
  - Consumer electronic products
  - Hard disk drive components
  - Laptop computer components and assemblies
  - Mechanical printer components
  - Mobile phones

Health care
- Collection containers
- Contact lenses
- Drug containers
- Drug syringes
- Inhalers
- Lancing devices
- Petri dishes
- Pipettes
- Surgical instruments
- Test tubes

Packaging
- Beverage containers
- Cosmetics
- Food storage
- Hair and personal care
- Kitchen and bath products

Selected Services

Assembly
Automation
Contract manufacturing
Decoration & finishing technologies
Injection molding
Mold design and fabrication
Product design and development
Program management

COMPETITORS

Berry Plastics
Blue Star Plastics
Deswell
Hoffer Plastics
MXL Industries
Omni Industries Holdings

HISTORICAL FINANCIALS

Company Type: Private

Income Statement FYE: June 30

	REVENUE ($ mil.)	NET INCOME ($ mil.)	NET PROFIT MARGIN	EMPLOYEES
06/12*	1,144	(6)	—	16,000
07/11	1,169	9	0.8%	—
07/10	1,234	29	2.4%	—
06/09	1,089	2	0.2%	—
Annual Growth	1.6%	—	—	—

*Fiscal year change

2012 Year-End Financials

Debt ratio: —
Return on equity: (-0.50%)
Cash ($ mil.): 44
Current ratio: 0.80
Long-term debt ($ mil.): —
Dividends
Yield: —
Payout: —
Market value ($ mil.): —

O"NEIL INDUSTRIES INC.

EXECUTIVES

Chairman, William E. O'Neil II
CEO, Richard J. Erickson
President Los Angeles, Brian G. Ramsay
President Denver, Todd Guthrie
Chairman Chicago, Michael J. (Mike) Faron
President Chicago, John A. Russell
President Tucson, John Hobbs
President Phoenix, Scott Dombrowski

LOCATIONS

HQ: O' ' NEIL INDUSTRIES INC.
1245 W WASHINGTON BLVD, CHICAGO, IL 606071929
Phone: 7732446003
Web: WWW.WEONEIL.COM

PRODUCTS/OPERATIONS

Selected Markets

Aerospace
Education
Green
Healthcare
Hospitality & Restaurants
Industrial
Infrastructure
Municipal
Office
Gaming & Recreation
Retail
Religious
Residential
Senior Living
Special Projects
Tribal

COMPETITORS

Bulley & Andrews
Clark Construction Group
Gilbane Building Company
Graycor
Leopardo
McShane Construction
Pepper Construction
Sundt
The Austin Company
Walsh Group

HISTORICAL FINANCIALS

Company Type: Private

Income Statement FYE: December 31

	REVENUE ($ mil.)	NET INCOME ($ mil.)	NET PROFIT MARGIN	EMPLOYEES
12/13	458	2	0.5%	400
12/12	458	2	0.5%	—
12/11	458	2	0.5%	—
12/10	0	0	—	—
Annual Growth	—	—	—	—

2013 Year-End Financials

Debt ratio: —
Return on equity: 0.50%
Cash ($ mil.): 31
Current ratio: 0.90
Long-term debt ($ mil.): —
Dividends
Yield: —
Payout: —
Market value ($ mil.): —

O'BRIEN & GERE LIMITED

O'Brien & Gere provides a range of engineering consulting and project management services throughout the US including wastewater management and water resources environmental compliance and remediation civil and facilities engineering and utility services. It also provides contract operations and maintenance. O'Brien & Gere serves municipal environmental manufacturing and federal clients. The company which employs hundreds of scientists engineers construction and other personnel operates nearly 30 offices in about a dozen states. Employee-owned O'Brien & Gere was formed by Earl O'Brien William Gere and Glenn Holmes as a water and wastewater engineering partnership in 1945.

Geographic Reach

The Syracuse New York-based firm has more than 25 branch offices in about a dozen states including Georgia Michigan New York Ohio Pennsylvania and Virginia.

Financial Performance

O'Brien & Gere reported $200 million in revenue in 2012. The company weathered the economic downturn rather well and enjoyed increases in its gross revenue in 2010 and 2011 ($170 million and $187 million respectively).

Strategy

The company is focused on making strategic investments in its energy environmental facilities and water programs. O'Brien & Gere also launched a new manufacturing and technology development facility. O'Brien & Gere plans to extend its core business and develop emerging markets in order to grow business. To that end in June 2013 the firm opened a new office in Utica New York as part of its strategic plan to expand services to clients across the Mohawk Valley and greater upstate New York regions.

Mergers and Acquisitions

The firm has made several acquisitions through the years in order to expand its geographic reach and grow its capabilities. In 2012 O'Brien & Gere acquired the remaining 55% of South Carolina-based architecture/engineering company Lindgergh & Associates.

EXECUTIVES

Vp, Gary A Angyal
Vp, Peter R Koval
Vp, Kevin B Bryant, age 63
Vp, Swiatoslav W Kaczmar
Vp, John E Kurtz
Vp, Robert F Patullo
CFO Treasurer and Director, Joseph M. McNulty
Chairman and CEO, James A. (Jim) Fox
Senior Vice President Industrial Business Unit Leader, Timothy J. Barry
Senior Vice President Environmental Business Unit Leader, Thomas A. Nowlan
President COO and Director, R. Leland (Lee) Davis
Senior Vice President Municipal Business Unit Leader, George B. Rest
Senior Vice President Federal Business Unit co-Leader, Richard R. Garcia
Senior Vice President Integrated Process Systems Business Unit Leader, Stephen C. Palin
Senior Vice President Federal Business Unit co-Leader, Jo Anne E. Walser
Senior Vice President, Terry Madden
Vp, Mark A Distler
Vp, Lawrence T Martin
Vp Human Resources, Miguel Cervantes

Vice President, Christopher Calkins
Vice President, Ron Harting
Vp, Darek Letkiewicz
Vice President, Larry Martin
Vice President, Larry Gallagher
Treas, Peter Johnson, age 75
CFO Treasurer and Director, Joseph M. McNulty
Chairman and CEO, James A. (Jim) Fox
President COO and Director, R. Leland (Lee) Davis

LOCATIONS

HQ: O' BRIEN & GERE LIMITED
333 W WASHINGTON ST # 400, SYRACUSE, NY 13202-5253
Phone: 315-437-6100
Web: WWW.OBG.COM

COMPETITORS

CH2M HILL
ENVIRON
Fluor
Jacobs Engineering
Parsons Corporation

HISTORICAL FINANCIALS

Company Type: Private

Income Statement FYE: December 31

	REVENUE ($ mil.)	NET INCOME ($ mil.)	NET PROFIT MARGIN	EMPLOYEES
12/11	187	2	1.5%	800
12/06	125	1	1.1%	—
12/00	123	(4)	—	—
12/99	132	(5)	—	—
Annual Growth	2.9%	—	—	—

2011 Year-End Financials

Debt ratio: —
Return on equity: 1.50%
Cash ($ mil.): 9
Current ratio: 0.90
Long-term debt ($ mil.): —
Dividends
Yield: —
Payout: —
Market value ($ mil.): —

O'NEIL INDUSTRIES INC.

A family of construction companies O'Neil Industries has also built W.E. O'Neil Construction Company and T.L. Roof & Associates. The employee-owned company operates in Arizona California Colorado and Illinois providing general contracting construction management design/build and structural concrete services for commercial projects in the US and Canada. O'Neil Industries has worked on corporate offices manufacturing and distribution facilities and mixed-use centers for clients in the education gaming health care hospitality and retail industries. The company also serves the residential and senior living sectors. Clients have included Boeing DePaul University and The Nature Conservancy.

Geographic Reach

While O'Neil Industries is primarily US-centric with a headquarters office in Chicago and five operating units in Illinois (Chicago) Arizona (Tucson and Phoenix) California (Los Angeles) and Colorado (Denver) the construction company also boasts a presence in Ontario Canada.

Operations

Recent projects in Arizona include America West Airlines Flight Training Facility (in Phoenix) Arizona Cancer Center (in Tucson) and Air Center Scottsdale's McClain Street Facility (Scottsdale). In El Segundo California O'Neil Industries completed the Aerospace A6 PODS project. The company transitioned its T.L. Roof & Associates business into its Tucson branch. Its O'Neil Construction Company unit serves as the company's concrete division.

Company Ownership

Founded in Chicago in 1925 by William O'Neil the O'Neil family still controls the company through chairman Bill O'Neil.

EXECUTIVES

Chairman, William E. O'Neil II
CEO, Richard J. Erickson
President Los Angeles, Brian G. Ramsay
President Denver, Todd Guthrie
Chairman Chicago, Michael J. (Mike) Faron
President Chicago, John A. Russell
President Tucson, John Hobbs
President Phoenix, Scott Dombrowski

LOCATIONS

HQ: O' NEIL INDUSTRIES INC.
1245 W WASHINGTON BLVD, CHICAGO, IL 60607-1929
Phone: 773-244-6003
Web: WWW.WEONEIL.COM

PRODUCTS/OPERATIONS

Selected Markets

Aerospace
Education
Green
Healthcare
Hospitality & Restaurants
Industrial
Infrastructure
Municipal
Office
Gaming & Recreation
Retail
Religious
Residential
Senior Living
Special Projects
Tribal

COMPETITORS

Bulley & Andrews
Clark Construction Group
Gilbane Building Company
Graycor
Leopardo
McShane Construction
Pepper Construction
Sundt
The Austin Company
Walsh Group

HISTORICAL FINANCIALS

Company Type: Private

Income Statement FYE: December 31

	REVENUE ($ mil.)	NET INCOME ($ mil.)	NET PROFIT MARGIN	EMPLOYEES
12/12	458	2	0.5%	400
12/11	458	2	0.5%	—
12/10	0	0	—	—
12/09	0	0	—	—
Annual Growth	—	—	—	—

2012 Year-End Financials

Debt ratio: —
Return on equity: 0.50%
Cash ($ mil.): 27
Current ratio: 0.90
Long-term debt ($ mil.): —
Dividends
Yield: —
Payout: —
Market value ($ mil.): —

O-AT-KA MILK PRODUCTS COOPERATIVE INCORPORATED

LOCATIONS

HQ: O-AT-KA MILK PRODUCTS COOPERATIVE INCORPORATED
700 ELLICOTT ST, BATAVIA, NY 140203744
Phone: 5853430536
Web: WWW.OATKAMILK.COM

HISTORICAL FINANCIALS

Company Type: Private

Income Statement FYE: December 31

	REVENUE ($ mil.)	NET INCOME ($ mil.)	NET PROFIT MARGIN	EMPLOYEES
12/13	296	8	2.9%	302
12/12	275	16	5.9%	—
12/11	274	12	4.6%	—
12/10	236	0	—	—
Annual Growth	7.8%	—	—	—

2013 Year-End Financials

Debt ratio: —
Return on equity: 2.90%
Cash ($ mil.): 12
Current ratio: 1.20
Long-term debt ($ mil.): —
Dividends
Yield: —
Payout: —
Market value ($ mil.): —

O. C. TANNER COMPANY

O.C. Tanner recognizes that it's nice to be appreciated. The company designs and helps implement employee recognition programs for customers around the world. Related services intended to help customers take full advantage of their investment in employee recognition include communication consulting research leadership training and social programs. The company which operates from offices in the US Canada and the UK has shipped awards to clients in about 150 countries. Over the years O.C. Tanner has counted numerous Fortune 100 companies among its clients.

Geographic Reach

O.C. Tanner serves global customers from its locations in Salt Lake City Utah (US); Burlington Ontario (Canada); and Loughton Essex (UK). Outside of the US its main markets are Australia Brazil Canada China Europe Hong Kong Japan India Mexico and Singapore.

Operations

In addition to its recognition programs Tanner provides ancillary products and services such as recognition publication and lecture series engagement studies and leadership recognition training. Tanner's roster of authors and speakers are available to give presentations on topics such as delivering appreciation strategies and the company hosts an annual Executive Recognition Summit where industry leaders come together to share insights into their companies' employee recognition practices.

Sales and Marketing

O.C. Tanner has served some 8500 businesses including about 35 Fortune 100 companies such as American Express Caterpillar Abbott Labs Chevron FedEx and Wells Fargo.

Strategy

O.C. Tanner seeks to cater its recognition programs to each client applying insights into the employees brands and cultures present within each customer's operations. Its packages include blends of recognition awards coaching communication solutions social tools and management assistance components and its services are available for smaller customers as well as multi-national corporations.

Company Background

Namesake Obert C. Tanner founded the company in 1927 by selling class rings and pins for school graduates.

Ownership

O.C. Tanner is owned by Obert's daughter and company chair Carolyn Tanner Irish.

EXECUTIVES

Vice President Supply Chain, Paul Terry
EVP Marketing, David Sturt
President O.C. Tanner International, John McVeigh
EVP Supply Chain and Production, Gary Peterson
SVP Finance, Scott Sperry
EVP Sales, Beth Thornton
President and CEO, Dave Petersen
SVP and CTO, Neil Nickolaisen
Vice President Sales & Business, Gail Bedke
Vice President Performance Recognition, Scott Jensen
Executive Vice President And Chief Technology Officer, Joel Dehlin
Svp Administration, Clark Campbell
Vice President Human Resources, Barbara O'Neil
Vice President Sales Business Dev, Tim Driscoll
Vice President Client Solutions, Kevin Salmon
General Counsel And Vice President, Brian Katz
Vice President Marketing And Channel Sales, Mario Micic
Vice President Sales Promotion, Ric Hammond
Executive Vice President Marketing, Cynthia Rodman
Sales Vp, Jane Rogers
Vice President General Manager, Reid Robison
Vice President Of Sales Northeast, Christine Kubert
Treasurer, Bob Anger
Chair, Carloyn Tanner Irish

LOCATIONS

HQ: O. C. TANNER COMPANY
1930 S STATE ST, SALT LAKE CITY, UT 841152383
Phone: 8014862430
Web: WWW.OCTANNER.COM

PRODUCTS/OPERATIONS

Selected Clients

Abbot
American Express
Bank of America
Caterpillar Inc.
Chevron Corporation
Comcast
ConocoPhillips
CVS
Dell
Dow Chemical
Express Scripts
FedEx
Freddie Mac
General Dynamics
HCA Corporate
Hess Corporation
Home Depot
Johnson Controls Inc.
JP Morgan Chase
Kraft Foods
The Kroger Co.
Marathon Petroleum
McKesson
Medco Health
Merck
Northrop Grumman
Raytheon
Safeway
State Farm Insurance
Sunoco Inc.
Sysco
Travelers
WellPoint
Wells Fargo

COMPETITORS

American Achievement
CA Short
ITAGroup
LoyaltyOne
Maritz Loyalty & Motivation
Pitney Bowes Marketing Solutions
TharpeRobbins

HISTORICAL FINANCIALS

Company Type: Private

Income Statement FYE: December 31

	REVENUE ($ mil.)	NET INCOME ($ mil.)	NET PROFIT MARGIN	EMPLOYEES
12/13	327	27	8.5%	1,700
12/12	316	19	6.3%	—
12/08	0	0	—	—
12/07	0	0	—	—
Annual Growth	—	—	—	—

O. C. TANNER MANUFACTURING

LOCATIONS

HQ: O. C. TANNER MANUFACTURING
1930 S STATE ST, SALT LAKE CITY, UT 841152311
Phone: 8014862430
Web: WWW.OCTANNER.COM

HISTORICAL FINANCIALS

Company Type: Private

Income Statement FYE: December 31

	REVENUE ($ mil.)	NET INCOME ($ mil.)	NET PROFIT MARGIN	EMPLOYEES
12/13	214	4	2.1%	1,100
12/12	210	3	1.8%	—
12/11	214	4	2.2%	—
12/10	0	0	—	—
Annual Growth	—	—	—	—

OAKLAND UNIVERSITY

Oakland University is the OU of the North. The Michigan public university serves a student base of more than 19500 offering about 130 baccalaureate degree programs and more than 100 graduate degree and certificate programs. It boasts a student-to-faculty ratio of 22-to-1. In addition to academic and specialty programs in areas ranging from business and technology to nursing and athletics its faculty members also coordinate hands-on research projects for graduate students. The main university campus spans some 1500 acres that house seven academic schools and colleges in Rochester Michigan. Oakland University also has satellite campuses in Macomb County and a law school in Auburn Hills.

Geographic Reach

Located in Rochester Michigan Oakland University's main campus comprises seven academic schools and colleges. The educational institution also operates a law school in Auburn Hills and satellite campuses in Macomb County.

Strategy

Oakland University works to expand and improve its programs and facilities to attract new students. In 2011 for instance it added two new bachelor's degree majors: one in creative writing and one in biomedical sciences. It also officially launched its graduate doctoral training program — the Beaumont School of Medicine. The university has also expanded its campus resources as it has increased enrollment levels during the past decade. It completed a new building in 2012 to house its nursing and health science schools and is working to construct a new engineering center.

Financial Performance

The university logged a 6% increase in revenue in fiscal 2012 as compared to 2011 due to rises in tuition revenue (net of scholarship allowances which was higher due to an enrollment increase). Indeed tuition rates increased by 7% in the fall of 2011 for undergraduates and graduates. Net income meanwhile also jumped by 9% during the same reporting period thanks to boosts in other revenue attributed to income from capital appropriation and increases in capital grants and gifts (partially offset by rising operating expense and declining non-operating revenues).

Sales and Marketing

The university advertises through several mediums such as television radio websites social networking sites billboards magazines newspapers and journals.

Company Background

Oakland University was founded in 1957 by Alfred and Matilda Wilson who donated $2 million and their 1500-acre estate to Michigan State University to start a new college in Oakland County. Named Michigan State University Oakland the college enrolled its first students in 1959. The school's name changed to Oakland University in 1963 and it became an autonomous institution in 1970.

EXECUTIVES

President, Gary D. Russi
Senior Vice President for Academic Affairs and Provost, Virindjer K. Moudgil
VP Legal Affairs General Counsel and Secretary, Victor A. Zambardi
VP Finance and Administration and Treasurer, John W. Beaghan
VP Government Relations, Rochelle A. Black
VP Student Affairs and Enroll Management, Mary Beth Snyder
Director University Communications and Marketing, Geoffrey C. Upward
CIO, Theresa M. (Terrie) Rowe
Assistant VP Human Resources, Ronald P. Watson
Assistant to the President, Karen S. Kukuk
Director Internal Audit, David Vartanian
Manager Employment, Gail A. Ryckman
Manager Labor and Employee Relations, Deborah K. Armstrong
Director Athletics, Tracy A. Huth
Chief Investment Officer, Jeffrey Phillips

Associate Vice President of Communications and Marketing, John Young

LOCATIONS

HQ: OAKLAND UNIVERSITY
2200 N SQUIRREL RD, ROCHESTER, MI 48309-4401
Phone: 248-370-2100
Web: WWW.OAKLAND.EDU

PRODUCTS/OPERATIONS

Selected Schools

Beaumont School of Medicine
College of Arts and Sciences
Cooley Law School
Macomb Campuses
School of Business Administration
School of Education and Human Services
School of Engineering and Computer Science
School of Health Sciences
School of Nursing

HISTORICAL FINANCIALS

Company Type: Private

Income Statement FYE: June 30

	REVENUE ($ mil.)	NET INCOME ($ mil.)	NET PROFIT MARGIN	EMPLOYEES
06/12	194	37	19.4%	2,650
06/10	172	27	15.9%	—
06/09	0	0	—	—
06/07	144	12	8.8%	—
Annual Growth	6.1%	24.3%	—	—

2012 Year-End Financials

Debt ratio: —
Return on equity: 19.40%
Cash ($ mil.): 37
Current ratio: 1.30
Long-term debt ($ mil.): —
Dividends
Yield: —
Payout: —
Market value ($ mil.): —

OAKWOOD HEALTHCARE INC.

Oakwood Healthcare stands proud as a regional health care provider in southeastern Michigan. It offers a range of health services to residents in more than 35 communities. At the center of the system are four hospitals with a total of more than 1200 beds: Oakwood Hospital & Medical Center a full-service teaching hospital; Oakwood Annapolis Hospital a community hospital; Oakwood Heritage Hospital a tertiary care hospital; and Oakwood Southshore Medical Center a community hospital. Founded in 1953 the system also includes community health and diagnostic facilities retirement and nursing communities rehabilitative care centers and specialty care centers for women children and seniors.

Geographic Reach

The health care network serves residents of Wayne County Michigan (including the Detroit metropolitan area) as well as the southeast Michigan towns of Canton Dearborn Monroe Taylor Trenton Wayne and Wyandotte.

Operations

Oakwood Healthcare has about 1300 physicians on its medical staff and handles about 56000 inpatient visits each year. Its emergency departments combined treat some 185000 patients annually. The system also provides home health care services.

Oakwood Healthcare's system is designed to care for patients from infancy to elderly. Health services for babies and their mothers include fetal diagnostics reproductive medicine and genetic counseling. On the other end of the spectrum Oakwood Healthcare provides senior services including independent living skilled nursing adult day care and palliative care among many other services.

The largest facility in Oakwood Healthcare Oakwood Hospital & Medical Center is a teaching affiliate of the Wayne State University School of Medicine. Areas of specialty care at the hospital include cardiology orthopedics neuroscience and oncology. In addition Oakwood Healthcare conducts research programs in partnership with Wayne State and other organizations including the University of Michigan.

Strategy

Oakwood Healthcare grows its inpatient and outpatient services on a regular basis to better serve area residents. For instance the organization completed a $31 million expansion and renovation project at Oakwood Heritage Hospital during 2012; the project added new surgical orthopedic and trauma rehabilitation centers. It also launched an extensive renovation and expansion project on the Oakwook Annapolis Hospital campus that year; construction efforts included the expansion of the emergency room and the addition of an inpatient hospice unit. In addition Oakwood Healthcare implemented the EPIC electronic health record (EHR) software system in 2012 to improve patient care coordination across its facilities.

One outpatient care area that Oakwood Healthcare has grown is its school-based clinic operations. In 2011 it opened one such clinic in Westland Michigan in partnership with the town's school district. In 2012 it enhanced women's health services at its diagnostic imaging center in Canton; it also opened a new wound care center in Dearborn during 2013.

EXECUTIVES

Hr Director & Vp, Paul Conway
SVP; Chief Medical Officer Oakwood Healthcare System, Malcolm Henoch
Division President Oakwood Southshore Medical Center, Edith Hughes
EVP Post Acute Operations, Douglas D. (Doug) Welday
Executive Vice President Physician Planning & Operations, Michael A. Geheb
President Oakwood Western Region, Eric Widner
Division President Post Acute Care, Elizabeth (Liz) Goch
President and CEO, Brian M. Connolly
Senior VP; Division President Oakwood Hospital and Medical Center, Kelly Smith
SVP and CIO, Paula F. Smith
COO, Greg Bock
SVP and CFO, John Keuten
Division President Oakwood Heritage Hospital, Lee Ann Odom
Senior Vice President, Maureen Dagostino
Ambulatory Services Director, Clinton Greenstone
Vice President, Tim Turner
Vice President, Stephanie Kearney
Vice President, Billy McCraight
Vice President Information Technology, Donald Smith
Senior Vice President Plant Manager, Jim Henoch
Vice President Operations, Patrick Smerecki
Vp Marketing, Kenneth Trester
Division President, Michael Gehab
Manager Treasury Services, Grace Patterson

LOCATIONS

HQ: OAKWOOD HEALTHCARE INC.
18101 OAKWOOD BLVD, DEARBORN, MI 48124-4089
Phone: 313-593-7000
Web: WWW.OAKWOOD.ORG

PRODUCTS/OPERATIONS

Selected Facilities

Lincoln/Jefferson-Barns Healthcare Centers (Westland Michigan)
Oakwood Annapolis Hospital (Wayne Michigan)
Oakwood Breast Care Centers (regional)
Oakwood Common Retirement Community (Dearborn Michigan)
Oakwood Healthcare Centers (regional)
Oakwood Heritage Hospital (Taylor Michigan)
Oakwood Hospital & Medical Center (Dearborn Michigan)
Oakwood Rehab & Skilled Nursing Center (Dearborn Michigan)
Oakwood Southshore Medical Center (Trenton Michigan)

COMPETITORS

Beaumont Health System
Chelsea Community Hospital
Children' s Hospital of Michigan
Crittenton Hospital
Detroit Medical Center
Garden City Hospital
Harper-Hutzel Hospital
Hayes Green Beach Memorial Hospital
McLaren Health Care
Mercy Health Partners Toledo
Mount Clemens Regional Medical Center
St. John Health
University of Michigan Health System

HISTORICAL FINANCIALS

Company Type: Private

Income Statement FYE: December 31

	REVENUE ($ mil.)	NET INCOME ($ mil.)	NET PROFIT MARGIN	EMPLOYEES
12/09	997	10	1.0%	9,200
12/02	744	(4)	—	—
12/01	666	(4)	—	—
12/00	658	(9)	—	—
Annual Growth	4.7%	—	—	—

2009 Year-End Financials

Debt ratio: —
Return on equity: 1.00%
Cash ($ mil.): 40
Current ratio: 0.30
Long-term debt ($ mil.): —
Dividends
Yield: —
Payout: —
Market value ($ mil.): —

OCEAN BEAUTY SEAFOODS LLC

EXECUTIVES

President and CEO, Mark Palmer
Manager National Retail Sales Fresh and Frozen, Kevin Palmer
VP Retail Sales Specialty Products, Ron Christianson
Regional Sales Manager Southwest Specialty Products, Danny Alva
National Sales Manager Shelf Stable Products, Larry Marlow
Regional Sales Manager West Coast Foodservice, Brian Hodgen
Distribution Astoria, Jim Matlock
Distribution Boise, Don Elder

Distribution Dallas, Ricardo Martinez
Distribution Helena, Todd Mee
Distribution Seattle, Frank Ragusa
Regional Sales Manager Northeast Specialty Products, David Govoni
VP Distribution, Jack Whitney

LOCATIONS

HQ: OCEAN BEAUTY SEAFOODS LLC
1100 W EWING ST, SEATTLE, WA 981191321
Phone: 2062856800
Web: WWW.OCEANBEAUTY.COM

PRODUCTS/OPERATIONS

Selected Brands

CircleSea
Commander
Deep Sea
Echo Falls
Icy Point
LASCCO
McGovern
Nathan' s
Neptune
Ocean Beauty
Ocean Bonita
Pillar Rock
Pink Beauty
Pirate
Port Clyde
RITE
Royal Alaska
Sea Choice
Searchlight
Sound Beauty
St. Andrews
Surf King
Three Star
Tribe

Selected Products

Imported finfish
- Mahi mahi
- Sea Bass
- Shark
- Swordfish
- Tuna

North Pacific finfish
- Cod
- Farm-raised
- Flounder
- Halibut
- Perch
- Pollock
- Rockfish
- Salmon
- Sole
- Sturgeon
- Whiting

Shellfish
- Coldwater shrimp meat
- Clams
- Crab
- Mussels
- Oysters
- Prawns

Other products
- Milt
- Pickled herring
- Roe
- Surimi

COMPETITORS

Alaska Sausage
Alaska Seafood company
Alaskan Leader Fisheries
Arrowac Fisheries
Banner Smoked Fish
Bumble Bee Foods
Chicken of the Sea
Gorton' s
High Liner Foods
Icelandic Group
Icicle Seafoods
Maruha Nichiro
Orca Bay Seafoods
Pacific Seafood Group
Peter Pan Seafoods
Princes Limited
Red Chamber Co.
Salmolux
Santa' s Smokehouse
Seafood Sales
StarKist
Trident Seafoods

HISTORICAL FINANCIALS

Company Type: Private

Income Statement FYE: December 28

	REVENUE ($ mil.)	NET INCOME ($ mil.)	NET PROFIT MARGIN	EMPLOYEES
12/13	425	11	2.6%	18,000
12/12	409	8	2.0%	—
12/11	431	7	1.6%	—
12/08	418	0	—	—
Annual Growth	0.3%	—	—	—

2013 Year-End Financials

Debt ratio: —
Return on equity: 2.60%
Cash ($ mil.): 3
Current ratio: 0.40
Long-term debt ($ mil.): —
Dividends
Yield: —
Payout: —
Market value ($ mil.): —

OCEAN DUKE CORPORATION

Ocean Duke maintains a regal demeanor in a fishy environment. The company is a seafood wholesaler offering a variety of frozen raw fish shrimp mollusks and crustaceans. Ocean Duke also sells breaded fish shrimp and squid. The company imports its products and serves foodservice food processing distribution and wholesale companies throughout the US.

LOCATIONS

HQ: OCEAN DUKE CORPORATION
3450 FUJITA ST, TORRANCE, CA 90505-4019
Phone: 310-326-3198

COMPETITORS

Arista Industries
Caspian Trading Company
Florida Fresh Seafood Corp.
Orca Bay Seafoods

HISTORICAL FINANCIALS

Company Type: Private

Income Statement FYE: March 31

	REVENUE ($ mil.)	NET INCOME ($ mil.)	NET PROFIT MARGIN	EMPLOYEES
03/11	158	2	1.4%	25
03/02	191	0	0.5%	—
03/01	196	1	0.5%	—
03/00	0	0	—	—
Annual Growth	—	—	—	—

2011 Year-End Financials

Debt ratio: —
Return on equity: 1.40%
Cash ($ mil.): 1
Current ratio: 0.50
Long-term debt ($ mil.): —
Dividends
Yield: —
Payout: —
Market value ($ mil.): —

OCLC ONLINE COMPUTER LIBRARY CENTER INCORPORATE

Working to reduce the cost of information OCLC Online Computer Library Center is a membership cooperative that provides access to the world's information. The group offers services and tools to some 72000 member libraries in about 170 countries. Services include computer-based cataloging preservation and library management. OCLC additionally facilitates interlibrary loan services administers the Dewey Decimal Classification system and operates the WorldCat database an online resource for finding library materials. OCLC was founded in 1967 by presidents of the colleges and universities in Ohio. OCLC which stands for Ohio College Library Center opened its first location in Ohio State's main library.

Geographic Reach

OCLC operates in about 170 countries across the Americas Asia Pacific Europe the Middle East and Africa. The organization generates some 77% of its revenue from the Americas. The remainder comes from outside the US.

Strategy

As part of its operations OCLC regularly maintains and enhances its existing services such as Connexion QuestionPoint CONTENTdm EZproxy and WorldCat through heavy investing activities. The company provides more than 5000 libraries in Africa Australia and Europe with integrated library management systems and works to release regular enhancements. The systems include Amlib Bibliotheca CBS LBS OLIB SunRise and TouchPoint.

OCLC also concentrates on expanding its capabilities with the addition of data centers. To this end it opened a new data center in Toronto in 212 as part of a plan to operate local and global systems at Webscale service levels. The Toronto location is OCLC's fifth globally and allows the group to deliver its namesake WorldShare Management Services to member libraries in Canada. Soon after OCLC opened additional data centers in London and in Sydney Australia. It already has a pair of primary operations data centers in the US. In 2013 another data center is scheduled to come online in Europe.

Mergers and Acquisitions

The organization expanded its operations in 2011 through the purchase of BOND a company that specializes in integrating systems for public libraries in German-speaking countries.

Financial Performance

OCLC logged a decrease of 1% in fiscal 2012 as compared to 2011 from $205.6 million to $203.5 million. Several factors contributed to the decline. The company sold the rights to license certain third-party databases that OCLC made available via FirstSearch it funded the translation of e-journals to an archive-only access service and it discontinued its Language Sets service. The company's business outside the US increased by $4.7 million in fiscal 2012 to $54.9 million reflecting the full-year revenue impact of the BOND acquisition in spring 2011.

Company Background

In 2010 the organization sold its NetLibrary division a provider of eBooks and audio books to database aggregator EBSCO Industries. The sale resulted in more than 60 job cuts. The previous year OCLC sold its Preservation Service Center which offered digitization retrospective conversion and cataloging services to libraries to Backstage Library Works a provider of microfilming and digital preservation services to libraries.

EXECUTIVES

Vice Chairman, David P. Lauer, age 71
President CEO and Director, Robert L. (Jay) Jordan
VP OCLC Research and Chief Strategist, Lorcan Dempsey
VP for the Americas and Global VP Marketing, Catherine K. (Cathy) De Rosa
VP and General Counsel, James T. (Jim) Houfek
Vice President Global and Regional Councils, George M. Needham
Executive Vice President Chief Financial Officer Treasurer, Rick J. Schwieterman
Managing Director OCLC Europe Middle East and Africa, Eric van Lubeek
Chairman, Larry Alford
Senior Public Relations Specialist The Americas Northern Africa the Middle East and Asia/Pacific, Bob Murphy
Marketing Coordinator Europe and Southern Africa, Gillian McLeod
VP OCLC Research Library Partnership, Jim Michalko
VP Business Development, William (Chip) Nilges
VP Human Resources, Tammi Spayde
VP Global Product Architecture, Michael A. (Mike) Teets
Vice President Global Engineering, Greg Zick
VP WorldCat and Metadata Services, Karen Calhoun
VP Library Services for the Americas, Bruce Crocco
Vice President Global Product Management, Robin Murray
VP Asia Pacific, Andrew H. Wang
VP OCLC Global Systems and Information Technology, Gene Oliver
President and CEO, Skip Prichard
Vice President Business Development, Chip Nilges
President Chief Executive Officer, Frederick G. Kilgour
Vice President General Counsel, Jim Houfek
Vice President Innovation, Mike Teets
Vice Chairman, David P. Lauer, age 71
Director, David P. Roselle, age 74
Director, Jane N. Ryland, age 69
President CEO and Director, Robert L. (Jay) Jordan
Director, Lizabeth A. (Betsy) Wilson
Director, Ralph K. Frasier
Director, Maggie Farrell
Director, Bruce Newell
Director, Anthony (Tony) Ferguson
Director, Kathleen R. T. Imhoff
Director, Sandra (Sandy) Yee

LOCATIONS

HQ: OCLC ONLINE COMPUTER LIBRARY CENTER INCORPORATE
6565 KILGOUR PL, DUBLIN, OH 43017-3395
Phone: 614-764-6000
Web: WWW.CONFERENCE-CENTER.OCLC.ORG

2012 Revenue

	% of total
Americas	77
Europe Middle East & Asia	19
	4
Total	**100**

PRODUCTS/OPERATIONS

2012 Revenue

	$ mil.	% of total
Products & services	200	99
Grants	1	1
Research library partner dues	0	-
Total	**203**	**100**

Selected Services

Cataloging and Metadata
Digital Collection Management
Discovery
Electronic Collection Management
Library Management
Resource Sharing

Selected Products

Connexion
CONTENTdm
Dewey Services
Digital Archive
FirstSearch
WorldCat

COMPETITORS

American Library
EBSCO
FactSet
Google
Informa
LexisNexis
ProQuest

HISTORICAL FINANCIALS

Company Type: Private

Income Statement

FYE: June 30

	REVENUE ($ mil.)	NET INCOME ($ mil.)	NET PROFIT MARGIN	EMPLOYEES
06/13	206	8	4.0%	1,227
06/12	203	(2)	—	—
06/10	205	30	14.6%	—
06/10	228	32	14.2%	—
Annual Growth	(3.2%)	(36.6%)	—	—

2013 Year-End Financials

Debt ratio: —
Return on equity: 4.00%
Cash ($ mil.): 127
Current ratio: 1.70
Long-term debt ($ mil.): —
Dividends
Yield: —
Payout: —
Market value ($ mil.): —

ODOM CORPORATION

The Odom Corporation wants you to drink up if you happen to be in the Pacific Northwest. The company distributes beer wine and spirits as well as sodas energy drinks and bottled waters from more than 500 domestic and foreign suppliers including Coca-Cola Diageo E. & J. Gallo MillerCoors and Pernod Ricard. The company serves retail customers throughout the northwestern US including those in Alaska Idaho Oregon and Washington. It also runs Odom-Southern Holdings a joint venture with Southern Wine and Spirits of America the #1 distributor of alcoholic beverages in the US. Milt Odom founded the company in 1933.

Since the mid-1990s Odom has largely expanded its operations through partnerships and more than 20 acquisitions. The company took a giant step forward in 2009 when it paired up with Miami-based Southern Wine and Spirits of America to form Odom-Southern Holdings. The partnership helped to expand Odom's wine and spirits distribution business in Alaska Idaho Montana Oregon Utah Washington and Wyoming. Following the joint venture's formation Odom-Southern Holdings acquired wine and spirits distribution rights for the state of Alaska from Alaska Distributors. In 2011 Odom-Southern Holdings acquired Washington-based wine wholesaler and distributor Cavatappi Distribuzione which sells wine from such countries as Australia France Italy and New Zealand.

In recent years Odom has upgraded its warehouse operations to boost efficiency and focus more on customer service. Its enhanced warehouse management system combines radio frequency technology and barcode scanning and has enabled the company to automate processes like inventory control order selection receiving shipping and returns processing. Such improvements are welcome at the high-volume distributor; Odom on average sells nearly 2 million cases of products monthly and processes some 4500 orders a day.

EXECUTIVES

V Pres, Jerry Dexter, age 64
National Sales Manager, Jeff Allen
Regional Sales Vice President On Premise, Amr Kora
Vice President, Ron Young
Adm Asst To Vice President Sales, Michele Breton
Vice President Of Western Washington And Oregon, Scott Cook
Vice Chairman Vice President, Bill Odom

LOCATIONS

HQ: ODOM CORPORATION
11400 SE 8TH ST STE 300, BELLEVUE, WA 98004-6409
Phone: 425-456-3535
Web: WWW.ODOMCORP.COM

PRODUCTS/OPERATIONS

Selected Brands

Beer
- Anchor Brewing
- Coors
- Fosters
- Green's
- Heineken
- Keystone
- Miller
- Pabst
- Red Stripe
- Samuel Adams
- Sierra Nevada

Energy Drinks
- Four Loko
- Full Throttle
- FUZE
- Honest Tea
- Nestea
- Rockstar
- V-8
- Viso
- VitaminWater

Sodas
- A&W
- Canada Dry
- Coca-Cola
- Crater Lake
- Dr. Pepper
- Fanta
- Fresca
- Sunkist
- Thomas Kemper
- Virgil's Rootbeer

Spirits
- Christian Brothers
- Finest Call
- O'maras
- Seagrams
- Smirnoff

Wine
- Arbor Crest
- Barefoot
- Barton & Guestier
- Concha y Toro
- Cupcake
- Franzia
- Newman's Own
- Purple Cowboy
- Red Bicyclette
- Sutter Home

COMPETITORS

Anheuser-Busch InBev
Columbia Distributing Company
Constellation Brands
Monster Beverage
Pepsi Amercias Beverages
PepsiCo

HISTORICAL FINANCIALS

Company Type: Private

Income Statement FYE: December 31

	REVENUE ($ mil.)	NET INCOME ($ mil.)	NET PROFIT MARGIN	EMPLOYEES
12/07	337	2	0.9%	1,500
12/06	304	1	0.6%	—
12/04	211	3	1.8%	—
12/03	151	2	1.6%	—
Annual Growth	22.1%	4.4%	—	—

2007 Year-End Financials

Debt ratio: —
Return on equity: 0.90%
Cash ($ mil.): 3
Current ratio: 0.70
Long-term debt ($ mil.): —
Dividends
Yield: —
Payout: —
Market value ($ mil.): —

OHIO STATE UNIVERSITY RESEARCH FOUNDATION

The Ohio State University Research Foundation was established in 1936 to function as a central agency for supporting research and development through grants management and information technology for Ohio State University one of the largest public universities in the US. The not-for-profit corporation provides administrative services for research programs including submitting support requests managing equipment and governmental and university compliance oversight. Ohio State University's total awards reached more than $37 million by July 2007 with some 330 awards.

EXECUTIVES

Senior Director Financial Services and Procurement, Jeffrey H. (Jeff) Kemper
President Board of Directors, Robert T. McGrath
Deputy Executive Director, Anne J.M. Moffat
Executive Director and Associate VP Research Administration, Robert A. Killoren

LOCATIONS

HQ: OHIO STATE UNIVERSITY RESEARCH FOUNDATION
1960 KENNY RD, COLUMBUS, OH 43210-1016
Phone: 614-688-8125
Web: WWW.OSU.EDU

HISTORICAL FINANCIALS

Company Type: Private

Income Statement FYE: June 30

	REVENUE ($ mil.)	NET INCOME ($ mil.)	NET PROFIT MARGIN	EMPLOYEES
06/12	499	0	0.1%	105
06/11	485	0	0.1%	—
06/09	437	0	0.2%	—
06/09	411	0	—	—
Annual Growth	6.6%	—	—	—

2012 Year-End Financials

Debt ratio: —
Return on equity: 0.10%
Cash ($ mil.): 48
Current ratio: 2.90
Long-term debt ($ mil.): —
Dividends
Yield: —
Payout: —
Market value ($ mil.): —

OHIOHEALTH CORPORATION

Operating throughout the central part of the state OhioHealth aims to keep Buckeyes healthy. The not-for-profit system runs eight acute care hospitals and is affiliated with another nine community hospitals and area health systems. All told OhioHealth has about 2000 staffed beds in and around Columbus. Additional facilities offer urgent care physical rehabilitation diagnostic imaging and sleep diagnostics services. Subsidiary HomeReach provides home health care and hospice care. Its WorkHealth program offers workers' compensation care management and occupational rehabilitation services. OhioHealth Group OhioHealth's joint venture with The Medical Group of Ohio operates the HealthReach PPO.

Operations

In addition to offering patient care OhioHealth also operates the The OhioHealth Research & Innovation Institute which coordinates research throughout the health system including conducting clinical trials of new drugs and medical devices. The system also operates The Center for Medical Education and Innovation a medical training facility that among other technologies offers human patient simulators on which medical professionals can practice new procedures in various clinical situations.

Strategy

The company is focused on expanding geographically and capitalizing on opportunities due to population growth in the area.

Company Background

The health system traces its roots back to 1892 when Protestant Hospital (now known as Riverside Methodist Hospital) opened. The system initially organized as U.S. Health Corporation in 1984 later took on the OhioHealth name in 1997.

EXECUTIVES

Vice President, Sean Huffman
COO, Michael W. (Mike) Louge
COO Riverside Methodist Hospital, Bruce Hagen
EVP and COO, Robert P. (Bob) Millen, age 61
President OhioHealth Riverside Methodist Hospital, Brian D. Jepson
Vice President Of Medical Education Quality And Patient Safety, Amy Knapke
Chief Medical Officer, Bruce Vanderhoff
SVP and CIO, Michael Krouse
SVP External Affairs; President OhioHealth Foundation, Karen Morrison
President Doctors Hospital, Mike Reichfield
President OhioHealth Physician Group, Hugh Thornhill
President OhioHealth Home Care, James P. Newbrough
President Hardin Memorial Hospital, Mark Seckinger
President MedCentral, Jean Halpin
President OhioHealth Grant Medical Center, Vinson M. Yates
Interim President Grant Medical Center, Michael Lawson
President Health, LaMar Wyse
Vice President Finance (Multiple Hospitals), Troy Hammett
Medical Director, Ngozi N Osuagwu
Pharm D, Michele Holley
Syst Vice President Marketing Comm, Margaret Shriver
Vp Govt Relation, Shawna Bosse
Vice President Ethics And Compliance, Colleen Shannon
Vice President Of Research, Belinda Dean
Vp Customer Experience, Mark Harris
Vice President, Keith Vesper
Director Of Surgery Services, Les Hood
Vice President Revenue Cycle, Jane Berkebile
System Vice President Of Managed Care, John Kontner
Vp & Corp Ctrllr, Craig Bjerke
Senior Vice President Finance, Steve Umland
System Vice President Laboratory, Marci Burchett
Vice President Customer Services, Alice O'Kane
System Vice President Of Security, Harry Trombitas
Vice President Operations, Albert Wright
Medical Director, Mark Vary
Chief Financial Officer Executive Vp, Michael Michaelson
Chief Operating Officer Executive Vp, Robert George
Vice President Applications, Robert Dop
Vice President, Steven Davies
Vice President Finance, Christine Colosky
Vice President Of Patient Care, Linda Pullins
Director Of Operating Room, Chris Rosenthal
System Vice President Internal Audit, Sarabeth Osman
Vice President, Robert Steggert
Nursing Director, Dianna Brown
Vice President Revenue Cycle, Lynn Weimer
Vice President Of Medical Affairs, Dean Colwell
Vice President Applications Systems, Charles Duran
Senior Vice President Business, Patrick Midkiff
Senior Vice President Market Development Officer, Joe Calvaruso
Nursing Services Director, Carolyn Puckett
Vice President Of Operations, Joe Hooper
Vice President Of Communications, Susan Merryman
Vice President Marketing, Scott Billman
Vice President Marketing, Laura McCoy
Medical Director, David Lee
Director Media Relations, Mark Hopkins
System Vice President Heart, Teresa Caulin Glaser
Director Of Infection Control, Kim Mc Carrel
Vice President Business Development, Denise Foley
Vice President Applications, Marci Kane
System Vice President Internal Audit, Sarabeth Lemoine
Vice President Of Finance, Steve Bush
Treasury Director, Jeffrey Alexander

LOCATIONS

HQ: OHIOHEALTH CORPORATION
180 E BROAD ST, COLUMBUS, OH 43215-3707
Phone: 614-544-4455
Web: WWW.OHIOHEALTH.COM

PRODUCTS/OPERATIONS

Selected Facilities

Owned
- Doctors Hospital (Columbus)
- Doctors Hospital Nelsonville (Nelsonville)
- Dublin Methodist Hospital (Dublin)
- Grady Memorial Hospital (Delaware)
- Grant Medical Center (Columbus)
- Hardin Memorial Hospital (Kenton)
- Marion General Hospital (Marion)
- Riverside Methodist Hospital (Columbus)

Affiliated
- Blanchard Valley Medical Center
- Galion Community Hospital (Galion)
- Genesis Healthcare System (Zanesville)
- Knox Community Hospital
- Morrow County Hospital (Mt. Gilead)
- Samaritan Regional Health System (Ashland)
- O'Bleness Memorial Hospital (Athens)
- Southern Ohio Medical Center (Portsmouth)

COMPETITORS

Adena Health System
Fairfield Medical Center
Licking Memorial Health Systems
Mercy Health (OH)
Mount Carmel Health
Nationwide Children' s Hospital
Regency Hospital
Select Medical

HISTORICAL FINANCIALS

Company Type: Private

Income Statement FYE: June 30

	REVENUE ($ mil.)	NET INCOME ($ mil.)	NET PROFIT MARGIN	EMPLOYEES
06/12	1,999	303	15.2%	15,000
06/11	2,328	412	17.7%	—
06/09	1,967	221	11.3%	—
06/09	1,794	0	—	—
Annual Growth	3.7%	—	—	—

2012 Year-End Financials

Debt ratio: —
Return on equity: 15.20%
Cash ($ mil.): 99
Current ratio: 0.30
Long-term debt ($ mil.): —
Dividends
Yield: —
Payout: —
Market value ($ mil.): —

OLD TIME POTTERY INC.

You won't find any dusty crocks or cracked pots at Old Time Pottery. The chain markets discounted closeout and overstock housewares silk flowers hanging baskets framed art linens rugs craft supplies seasonal merchandise and more. Its network of more than 30 stores spans some 10 states in the nation's South and Midwest. Old Time Pottery sources its inventory which the retailer displays in a warehouse-type setting from the canceled orders and excess stock of manufacturers. To its benefit the specialty retailer can accommodate lots of inventory as stores average about 2 acres in size. Founded in 1986 Old Time Pottery is controlled by the Peterson family.

Bankruptcy

Old Time Pottery exited Chapter 11 bankruptcy protection in August 2010 a year after its filing. Slipping store sales amid the recession contributed to the retailer's financial woes and it was forced into bankruptcy protection after failing to reach an agreement with its primary lender. To restructure itself the company shuttered seven underperforming locations and liquidated their merchandise. This move brought Old Time Pottery's store count down to about 30.

Strategy

With its bankruptcy behind it and the economy on the mend Old Time Pottery has had an eye on expanding. Since 2013 it has added two new stores in both Illinois and Florida and an additional store in Tennessee. It also shuttered a Old Time Pottery shop in North Carolina.

In 2014 the chain plans to continue to grow by opening new stores and adding jobs to its payroll.

It's also looking for ways to keep costs low. Old Time Pottery leverages the use of Electronic Data Interchange (EDI) to streamline its supply chain by identifying errors and discrepancies and communicating and correcting them. The effort works to reduce turnaround times and eliminate additional potential costs.

Geographic Reach

Tennessee-based Old Time Pottery boasts a network of stores that reach across Georgia Alabama Florida North Carolina Ohio Indiana Illinois South Carolina Missouri and Tennessee.

EXECUTIVES

CEO, Jack J. Peterson
VP, Sallie S. Peterson
President, Scott Peterson
CFO, Robert Sharp
Auditors: Ernst&YoungLLP

LOCATIONS

HQ: OLD TIME POTTERY INC.
480 RIVER ROCK BLVD, MURFREESBORO, TN 37128-4804
Phone: 615-890-6060
Web: WWW.OLDTIMEPOTTERYINDIANAPOLIS.COM

2013 Stores

	No.
Florida	9
Alabama	4
Indiana	3
North	2
Ohio	3
Tennessee	3
Illinois	3
Missouri	2
South	2
Georgia	1
Total	**32**

PRODUCTS/OPERATIONS

Selected Products

Floral
Home Decor
Housewares
Linens & Rugs

COMPETITORS

Bed Bath & Beyond
Big Lots
Cost Plus
Dollar General
Garden Ridge
Hancock Fabrics
Hobby Lobby
Jo-Ann Stores
Michaels Companies
Target Corporation
Tuesday Morning Corporation
Wal-Mart

HISTORICAL FINANCIALS

Company Type: Private

Income Statement FYE: December 31

	REVENUE ($ mil.)	NET INCOME ($ mil.)	NET PROFIT MARGIN	EMPLOYEES
12/12	154	7	5.0%	3,000
12/11	146	6	4.5%	—
12/06	208	1	0.5%	—
12/05	188	4	2.2%	—
Annual Growth	(2.8%)	9.5%	—	—

2012 Year-End Financials

Debt ratio: —
Return on equity: 5.00%
Cash ($ mil.): 6
Current ratio: 0.60
Long-term debt ($ mil.): —
Dividends
Yield: —
Payout: —
Market value ($ mil.): —

OLE' MEXICAN FOODS INC.

Its a wrap at Ole Mexican Foods. The company makes Mexican-American foods inducing tortillas and taco shells under brand names La Banderita La Centroamericana Ole and Verole. The company also produces salsa sour cream Mexican cheeses and sausages tostadas and tortilla chips among other items. Its customers include retail food outlets and foodservice operations. Headquartered in Norcross Georgia the company has nearly a dozen distribution centers across the US. It serves customers across the continental US and Alaska as well as in Puerto Rico.

Geographic Reach

Ole Mexican Foods has distribution centers in Arizona California Colorado Florida Illinois Kentucky North Carolina and Texas.

LOCATIONS

HQ: OLE' MEXICAN FOODS INC.
6585 CRESCENT DR, NORCROSS, GA 30071-2901
Phone: 770-582-9200
Web: WWW.OLEMEXICANFOODS.COM

PRODUCTS/OPERATIONS

Selected Brands and Products

Consumer
- La Banderita (corn tortillas flour tortillas tostadas cheese sausage)
- La Centroamericana (corn tortillas)
- Ole (corn tortillas flour tortillas tostadas cheese sausage pastry)
- Ole Mexican Foods (flour tortillas cheese yogurt)
- Verole (corn tortillas flour tortillas)
- Verole Quesos (cheese)

Foodservice
- Cheese
- Flavor wraps
- Flour tortillas
- Low-carb tortillas
- Tortilla chips
- White corn tortillas
- Yellow corn tortillas

COMPETITORS

Azteca Foods
Boar' s Head
Cacique Inc
Casa de Oro Foods
Cheesemakers Inc.
Chorizo De San Manuel
Don Miguel Mexican Foods
Goya
Gruma
Gruma Corporation
Grupo Bimbo
H&H Meat Products
La Tortilla Factory
Maseca
Patrick Cudahy
Roger Wood Foods
Rose Packing
Ruiz Mexican Foods
Tumaro' s Gourmet Tortillas

HISTORICAL FINANCIALS

Company Type: Private

Income Statement FYE: December 31

	REVENUE ($ mil.)	NET INCOME ($ mil.)	NET PROFIT MARGIN	EMPLOYEES
12/11	218	15	7.3%	500
12/03	65	5	9.0%	—
12/02	52	3	6.9%	—
12/01	50	4	9.0%	—
Annual Growth	15.7%	13.3%	—	—

2011 Year-End Financials

Debt ratio: —
Return on equity: 7.30%
Cash ($ mil.): 13
Current ratio: 2.30
Long-term debt ($ mil.): —
Dividends
Yield: —
Payout: —
Market value ($ mil.): —

OMNI CABLE CORPORATION

Omni Cable has it down to the wire. The company distributes electrical and electronic cables to wholesale customers in the US through 10 warehouses and distribution centers. Omni Cable also offers custom bundling coloring striping lashing twisting and imprinting of wires and cables. The employee-owned company was founded in 1977. Omni Cable has locations in Atlanta Boston Chicago Denver Houston Los Angeles Philadelphia St. Louis San Francisco and Tampa. It is expanding its facilities within the regions served and has relocated and upgraded its San Francisco branch to serve the Bay Area better.

EXECUTIVES

Branch Manager Georgia, Steve Sweat
EVP Sales and Marketing, Peter J. Comber
Regional Manager Rocky Mountains Division, Adam DiCola
Branch Manager West Chester, Chris Regan
VP St. Louis, Mark Serafino
EVP Sales Operations, Greg Donato

LOCATIONS

HQ: OMNI CABLE CORPORATION
2 HAGERTY BLVD, WEST CHESTER, PA 19382-7594
Phone: 610-701-0100
Web: WWW.OMNICABLE.COM

COMPETITORS

Gexpro
Premier Farnell
Sonepar USA

HISTORICAL FINANCIALS

Company Type: Private

Income Statement FYE: December 31

	REVENUE ($ mil.)	NET INCOME ($ mil.)	NET PROFIT MARGIN	EMPLOYEES
12/12	260	20	7.9%	235
12/11	256	0	—	—
12/10	202	12	5.9%	—
12/09	148	8	5.8%	—
Annual Growth	20.6%	33.5%	—	—

2012 Year-End Financials

Debt ratio: —
Return on equity: 7.90%
Cash ($ mil.): 24
Current ratio: 4.50
Long-term debt ($ mil.): —
Dividends
Yield: —
Payout: —
Market value ($ mil.): —

OPEN LINK FINANCIAL INC.

OpenLink Financial develops risk management trading portfolio management and operations processing software for more than 500 clients in the financial services commodities and energy industries. Its products sold worldwide link and automate front- and back-office applications for banks corporate treasury departments energy marketers and insurance companies. OpenLink also provides professional services (consulting maintenance support and training) as well as complementary niche products through subsidiaries such as dbcSMARTsoftware (software for agricultural commodities) and iRM (energy trade processing software). Founded in 1992 the company is owned by private equity firm Hellman & Friedman.

Geographic Reach In addition to US offices (New York City Houston) OpenLink has locations in key global trading centers such as Berlin Dubai London Moscow Sao Paulo Singapore Sydney Toronto and Vienna.

Financial Performance

Although privately held OpenLink reports revenues of more than $300 million.

Mergers and Acquisitions In 2012 OpenLink acquired software provider CubeLogic which allowed OpenLink to offer data extraction to enable enterprise-wide risk analysis. In 2011 OpenLink bought SolArc a specialist in commodity management applications particularly suited for traders of physical bulk commodities. The deal added clients and boosted OpenLink's expertise in supply chain management tools for such commodities as natural gas coal oil and agricultural products.

EXECUTIVES

Vice President Finance, Brian Rosengold
Svp Commodity And Energy Solutions, Jonathan Stochel
Senior Vice President Product Management, Phil Wang
Vice President Human Resources, Diane W Montaruli
Exec Vice President Cptl Markets, Gary Koche
CFO, David M. Obstler
EVP and CTO, Roger Burkhardt, age 51
EVP Strategic Advisor, Robert (Bob) Kalish
Managing Director America ‚Â's Financials and Corporations, John D'Aleo
EVP Product Management, Kenneth A. (Ken) Knowles
President and CEO, Mark N. Greene
SVP Global Support and Operations, Rich Grossi
Managing Director EMEA, Markus Seiser
Managing Director Americas Energy, Doug Wendler
EVP HR, ANDREW GOODMAN
Vice President Product Development, Mike Snow
Vice President Of Corporate Development, Henry Bonner
Vice President Corporate Technical Services, Chris Haase
Vice President Of Corporate Development, Garrick Hoadley
Vice President Customer Operations And Support, Daniel Roe
Vice President Technical Services North American Energy, Kenneth Hall
Senior Vice President Gas Products, Richard Couron
Vice President Global Sales Solutions, Michael Snayd
Vice President Of Solutions Marketing, Denise Teixeira
Vice President Of Sales, Brian Chan
Executive Vice President Field Ops, John Palmiero
Vice President Emea Asia Pacific, Ray Hall
Vice President Sales, Tim McCarthy
Vice President, Mark O'Toole
Executive Vice President Of Americas Energy, Douglas Wendler
Senior Vice President D, Richard Gold
Chairman, Robert B. (Brad) Henske
Vice Chairman, Kevin J. Hesselbirg
Treasurer, Claire Hughes
Auditors: Deloitte&ToucheLLP

LOCATIONS

HQ: OPEN LINK FINANCIAL INC.
1502 RXR PLZ FL 15, UNIONDALE, NY 11556-3810
Phone: 516-227-6600
Web: WWW.OLF.COM

PRODUCTS/OPERATIONS

Selected Services

Capital Markets Trading
- Derivatives Trading
- Commodities Trading
- Precious Metals Trading
- Base Metals Trading
- Back Office Solutions

Enterprise Credit Risk
Central Bank & Public Debt Management
Production Purchasing Forecasting & Margin Management
- Commodity Processing & Milling
- Raw Materials and Feedstock Procurement & Forecasting
- Margin Management on Finished Goods
- Fuel & Energy Procurement
- Airline Fuel Management

Supply Distribution & Trading
- Producer Services
- Midstream Management
- Crude Oil Refined Products & NGL' s Supply Management
- Rack Marketing
- Coal Supply Management & Trading
- Gas Supply Distribution & Trading including LNG
- Power Generation Transmission & Distribution
- Optimization & Planning
- Market Modeling
- Biofuels Production & Trading
- Agricultural Commodity Management

Treasury Management

COMPETITORS

Advent Software
Allegro Development
Charles River Systems
Enerwise Global
Integral Development
Oracle
SAP
SS&C
SunGard Energy Systems
SunGard Financial Systems
Trayport
Triple Point
Ventyx

HISTORICAL FINANCIALS

Company Type: Private

Income Statement FYE: December 31

	REVENUE ($ mil.)	NET INCOME ($ mil.)	NET PROFIT MARGIN	EMPLOYEES
12/08	183	17	9.4%	750
12/06	83	0	0.5%	—
12/05	880	0	—	—
Annual Growth	(40.7%)	8405.5%		

2008 Year-End Financials

Debt ratio: —
Return on equity: 9.40%
Cash ($ mil.): 49
Current ratio: 1.30
Long-term debt ($ mil.): —
Dividends
Yield: —
Payout: —
Market value ($ mil.): —

ORANGE COUNTY TRANSPORTATION AUTHORITY SCHOLARSHIP FOUNDATION IN

Public transportation in sunny Orange County California is overseen by the Orange County Transportation Authority (OCTA). The OCTA is the main provider of bus services in its 800-sq.-mi. territory which is home to more than 3 million people. In cooperation with the Southern California Regional Rail Authority the OCTA oversees Metrolink commuter rail service in Orange County. The agency also operates a 10-mile toll road and issues permits to taxi operators. Revenue from a half-cent local sales tax allows the agency to pay for road improvement and mass transit projects. The OCTA was formed in 1991 in a consolidation of seven transportation agencies.

EXECUTIVES

Director Motorist Services and Special Projects, Sue Zuhlke
Clerk of the Board, Wendy Knowles
Executive Director Finance and Administration, Ken Phipps
General Manager 91 Express Lanes and Treasurer, Kirk Avila
CIO, Bill Mao
Manager Accounting and Financial Reporting, Tom Wulf
Manager Financial Planning and Analysis, Andrew Oftelie
Director Contracts Administration and Materials Management, Virginia Abadessa
Manager Risk Management Human Resources, Al Gorski
Manager Training and Development, Julie Espy
Manager Metrolink Expansion, Dinah Minteer
Program Manager Construction, Charlie Guess
Executive Director Development, Kia Mortazavi
Executive Director External Affairs, Ellen S. Burton
Manager Marketing, Stella Lin
Manager Public Communications, Ted Nguyen
Chief Transit Police Services, Jim Rudy
General Manager Transit, Beth McCormick
Manager Service Planning and Customer Advocacy Transit, Scott Holmes
CEO, Will Kempton, age 68
Chairman, Jerry Amante
Vice Chair, Patricia (Pat) Bates
Executive Director Internal Audit, Kathleen O'Connell

Manager Labor and Employee Relations EEO, Sherry Bolander
Deputy CEO, Darrell Johnson
Program Manager Local Initiatives Rail, Jennifer Bergener
Program Manager SR-55 SR-57 SR-91 and Rail, Pradeep Gunaratne
Manager Human Resources, Lisa Arosteguy-Brown
Assistant to General Manager Transit, Erin Rogers
Executive Director Human Resources and Organizational Development, Patrick Gough
Manager Safety Human Resources, Angela Petrow
Section Manager General Services, Lori Parsel
Manager Contracts and Procurements, Carolina Coppolo
Project Manager Facilities Engineering Rail, Jim Kramer
Section Manager Metrolink Operations, Michael Litschi
Director Strategic Planning Development, Kurt Brotcke
Director Highway Project Delivery, Tom Bogard
Manager Planning and Analysis, Charlie Larwood
Section Manager Local and Capital Programs, Abbe McClenahan
Manager Regional Initiatives Development, Barry Engelberg
Program Manager I-5 and I-405 Development, Rose Casey
Section Manager Project Controls Development, Norbert Lippert
Manager Maintenance Transit, Tony Chavira
Manager Transit Program Management, Joeseph Vicente
Director, William J. (Bill) Dalton
Director, Bill Campbell
Director, Arthur C. (Art) Brown
Director, Carolyn V. Cavecche
Director, Richard T. Dixon
Director, Curt Pringle
Director, Miguel A. Pulido
Director, Gregory T. Winterbottom
Caltrans Director, Cindy Quon
Director, Peter Buffa
Vice Chair, Patricia (Pat) Bates
Director, Paul G. Glaab
Director, Allan Mansoor
Director, John Moorlach
Director, Don Hansen
Director, Janet Nguyen

LOCATIONS

HQ: ORANGE COUNTY TRANSPORTATION AUTHORITY SCHOLARSHIP FOUNDATION IN
550 S MAIN ST, ORANGE, CA 92868-4506
Phone: 714-560-6282
Web: WWW.OCTA.NET

HISTORICAL FINANCIALS

Company Type: Private

Income Statement FYE: June 30

	REVENUE ($ mil.)	NET INCOME ($ mil.)	NET PROFIT MARGIN	EMPLOYEES
06/12	609	23	3.8%	1,050
06/11	438	247	56.6%	—
06/10	421	(158)	—	—
06/07	602	(21)	—	—
Annual Growth	0.2%	—	—	—

OREGON HEALTH & SCIENCE UNIVERSITY MEDICAL GROUP

Oregon Health & Science University (OHSU) builds a bridge to medical education in the Beaver State. OHSU is the state's sole institution providing doctoral degrees in medicine dentistry and nursing. Its other two schools are science and engineering and in partnership with Oregon State University pharmacy. OHSU has about 2800 students. The university is also home to two hospitals (one a children's hospital) as well as specialty and primary care clinics research and interdisciplinary centers and community service programs. OHSU traces its roots to 1867 when members of the medical department at Willamette University began the first formal medical education program in Oregon.

Geographic Reach

OHSU's main campus includes about 40 buildings on 120 acres on Marquam Hill (overlooking downtown Portland). OHSU also operates two smaller research locations: The Schnitzer Campus in Portland and the West Campus in Hillsboro.

Operations

OHSU's medical school has a small student-teacher ratio at just 4:1. The organization is renowned for its research initiatives. It has about 3000 active research projects and produced about 120 inventions in 2012. OHSU receives about $350 million in research funding each year. The school engages in an array of multidisciplinary research projects including diseases of the central nervous system weight regulation cancer rare genetic disorders and infectious disease.

Much of the university's medical research is performed at or in concert with clinical care operations at the University Hospital the Doernbecher Children's Hospital and other family care and specialty centers. The medical centers care for some 250000 patients each year.

Researchers at OHSU's Stem Cell Center worked with the Oregon National Primate Research Center to pioneer the first successful cloned nonhuman primate embryonic stem cells. Such cells could help stem cell research gain acceptance as the human element that causes such controversy has been removed.

Financial Performance

OHSU reported a 5% increase in revenue to nearly $2 billion in 2012 due to higher net patient service revenues from higher patient volumes and complex procedures. Net income fell by 55% to $79 million due to higher operating expenses and lower state appropriations and investment returns. OHSU has an operating budget of some $2 billion.

Strategy

OHSU began construction of its collaborative life sciences building on the Schnitzer Campus in 2012. The building was scheduled to be completed in late 2013 and was built on land donated by the Schnitzer family in 2004. OHSU has purchased additional parcels of land in the area for future expansion efforts.

EXECUTIVES

VP and General Counsel, Amy M. Wayson
EVP and Executive Director OHSU Hospitals and Clinics, Peter F. Rapp
VP Research, Daniel M. Dorsa
President and Director, Joseph (Joe) Robertson Jr.
Dean School of Medicine, Mark Richardson
Chairman, Charles A. Wilhoite
Vice Chairman, Jay Waldron
Senior Vice President, Constance French
Vice President Finance and Administration, Lori Mueller
Vice President Pediatric Development, Mary Turina
Vice President Development, Sarah Panetta
President and Director, Joseph (Joe) Robertson Jr.
Vice Chairman, Jay Waldron
Director, Meredith Wilson
Director, R. Jon Yunker

LOCATIONS

HQ: OREGON HEALTH & SCIENCE UNIVERSITY MEDICAL GROUP
3181 SW SAM JACKSON PK RD, PORTLAND, OR 97239-3011
Phone: 503-494-8311
Web: WWW.OHSU.EDU

PRODUCTS/OPERATIONS

Selected schools

School of Dentistry
School of Medicine
School of Nursing
School of Pharmacy (with Oregon State University)
School of Science & Engineering

HISTORICAL FINANCIALS

Company Type: Private

Income Statement FYE: June 30

	REVENUE ($ mil.)	NET INCOME ($ mil.)	NET PROFIT MARGIN	EMPLOYEES
06/12	1,975	78	4.0%	14,000
06/06	1,257	140	11.2%	—
06/05	1,078	114	10.6%	—
06/04	1,078	114	10.6%	—
Annual Growth	7.9%	(4.6%)	—	—

2012 Year-End Financials

Debt ratio: ——
Return on equity: 4.00%
Cash ($ mil.): 209
Current ratio: 1.30
Long-term debt ($ mil.): —
Dividends
Yield: —
Payout: —
Market value ($ mil.): —

OREGON STATE UNIVERSITY

Oregon State University (OSU) offers about 200 undergraduate and more than 80 graduate degree programs at about a dozen colleges and schools including nationally recognized programs in engineering environmental sciences forestry and pharmacy. The university is also home to centers of marine science and gene research and biotechnology a wave research laboratory and the Linus Pauling Institute. It also offers professional certificate nondegree and extension programs as well as precollege programs for elementary and high school students. In addition to its main campus in Corvallis the university operates OSU-Cascades in Bend Oregon. OSU has an annual enrollment of more than 18000 students.

The university was founded as a private academy in 1858 the year before Oregon became a state. It was designated as the agricultural college of the state of Oregon ten years later.

EXECUTIVES

President, Edward J. (Ed) Ray
VP Finance and Administration, Mark McCambridge
EVP and Provost, Sabah Randhawa
Director for Community and Diversity, Terryl Ross
Faculty Senate President, Paul Doescher
Auditors: MossAdamsLLP

LOCATIONS

HQ: OREGON STATE UNIVERSITY
308 KERR ADM BLDG, CORVALLIS, OR 97331
Phone: 541-737-2198
Web: WWW.COAS.OREGONSTATE.EDU

PRODUCTS/OPERATIONS

Selected Colleges and Schools

College of Agricultural Sciences
College of Business
College of Education
College of Engineering
College of Forestry
College of Health and Human Services
College of Liberal Arts
College of Oceanic and Atmospheric Sciences
College of Pharmacy
College of Science
College of Veterinary Medicine
Graduate School
School of Electrical Engineering and Computer Science
University Honors College

HISTORICAL FINANCIALS

Company Type: Private

Income Statement FYE: June 30

	REVENUE ($ mil.)	NET INCOME ($ mil.)	NET PROFIT MARGIN	EMPLOYEES
06/12	354	(22)	—	8,188
06/05	78	26	34.3%	—
06/04	78	33	43.0%	—
06/03	377	5	1.5%	—
Annual Growth	(0.7%)	—	—	—

2012 Year-End Financials

Debt ratio: ——
Return on equity: (-6.40%)
Cash ($ mil.): 47
Current ratio: —
Long-term debt ($ mil.): —
Dividends
Yield: —
Payout: —
Market value ($ mil.): —

ORLANDO HEALTH INC.

It's not Disney World but for Floridians needing health care it is a prime destination. Orlando Health is a not-for-profit organization with a network of community and specialty hospitals with nearly 2300 beds in Central Florida. Its flagship facility the Orlando Regional Medical Center features a Level 1 trauma center and provides comprehensive acute care services in a range of specialties. Orlando Health also operates several community hospitals. Its specialty hospitals include the Arnold Palmer Hospital for Children and the Winnie Palmer Hospital for Women and Babies. It also operates the renowned M. D. Anderson Cancer Center Orlando (the first affiliate of Houston-based M. D. Anderson center).

Geographic Reach

Orlando Health operates throughout Orlando and in neighboring Clermont Longwood Ocoee and St. Cloud Florida.

Operations

In addition to the Orlando Regional Medical Center and three fully owned community hospitals the company operates two medical centers through partnerships. It holds a 50% stake in the South Lake Hospital and a 20% stake in the St. Cloud Regional Medical Center. It also operates physician practice associations and an emergency air transport service (Air Care).

Across its facilities Orlando Health has about 2000 affiliated physicians who provide a full spectrum of health care services. Areas of clinical excellence include heart and vascular care cancer care obstetrics and gynecology neonatology neurosciences surgery pediatric orthopedics and sports medicine. Annually Orlando Health serves more than 2 million residents of central Florida and 4500 international patients. The organization also provides between $250 and $300 million in community health programs each year.

As a statutory teaching hospital system Orlando Health also engages in medical training programs through affiliation agreements with the University of Central Florida College of Medicine and other institutions. Orlando Health offers a number of medical residency and fellowship programs; its seven residencies are offered to 250 participants and include programs in emergency medicine internal medicine OB-GYN orthopedic surgery pathology and pediatrics. The organization also conducts research studies and clinical trials through partnerships with educational and commercial organizations.

Strategy

Orlando Health is working to improve its operating model by improving the quality of patient outcomes; enhancing collaboration between physicians medical professionals hospitals research centers and other institutions; and increasing clinical integration of various disciplines to share resources and skills.

As an example of its collaborative and quality enhancement efforts Orlando Health is involved in the formation of a regional health information exchange to connect its electronic health record (EHR) systems with other Central Florida health providers and the public health department. The program aims to improve quality of care by eliminating redundant tests and other repeated efforts as well as by providing hospitals swift access to patient data.

Orlando Health is also focused on making improvements to its Orlando Regional Medical Center through a multi-year $297-million renovation project launched in 2012. The project which includes the addition of a new patient bed tower and a larger emergency department is expected to be completed in 2015. Other planned projects include the expansion of the neonatal intensive care unit (NICU) at Winnie Palmer Hospital for Women and Babies. In addition in 2012 Arnold Palmer Hospital added an outpatient rehabilitation center.

Mergers and Acquisitions

The health system expanded its network in 2012 by acquiring the 170-bed Health Central Hospital and its associated facilities in Ocoee Florida for $181 million. Orlando Health further expanded through the purchase of Physician Associates a professional practice organization in 2013.

EXECUTIVES

VP Finance Treasury and Accounting and CFO, Paul Goldstein
Vice President Human Resources, Nancy Dinon
Vice President Business Development, Karl Hodges
VP and CIO, Rick Schooler
SVP; President Arnold Palmer Medical Center Orlando Health Foundation and Arnold Palmer Medical Center Foundation, John Bozard
President CEO and Director, Sherrie Sitarik
Vice President Orlando, Clarence H. Brown III
Senior Vice President President Adult Hospitals Group, Shannon Elswick
President South Seminole Hospital, Steve Glazier
SVP Finance and Physician Services, Stephan J. Harr
Senior Vice President President Winnie Palmer Hospital for Women & Babies, Kathy Swanson
Manager Media Relations, Joe Brown
Treasurer and Director, Conrad Santiago
VP Revenue Management, Keith Eggert
Chief Academic Medical Officer, Jay Falk
VP Corporate Integrity, David Huddleson
SVP Strategy Innovation and Planning, Robert Miles
VP Patient Care and Chief Nursing Officer, Anne Peach
Director Public Affairs and Media Relations, Kena Lewis
SVP Legal Affairs, Mildred Beam
Vice President Operations, Myra Hancock
VP; Executive Director Orlando Health Foundation, Karen Jensen

VP; President Dr. P. Phillips Hospital, Mark A. Jones
VP and Chief Communications Officer, John Marzano
VP Development Arnold Palmer Medical Center Foundation, Chris Stowers
Manager Media Relations, Sabrina Childress
Manager Media Relations, Katie Dagenais
Secretary and Director, Sanford C. Shugart
Vice Chairman, Dianna Morgan
Corporate Director Compliance & Information Security, Steve Stallard
COO, Jessica Wertman
Chairman, Brian Besanceney
Vice President clinical integration, Jennifer Endicott
Chairman, Joan Meek
operations Manager Intensive Care Unit Progressive Care Unit, Kerry-Ann Farrow
Vice President American, Luanne Lumpkins
President CEO and Director, Sherrie Sitarik
Treasurer and Director, Conrad Santiago
Secretary and Director, Sanford C. Shugart
Director, Lennard D. Greenbaum
Director, Marilyn M. King
Director, Harvey Kobrin
Director, Rex V. McPherson II
Vice Chairman, Dianna Morgan
Chairman, Brian Besanceney

LOCATIONS

HQ: ORLANDO HEALTH INC.
1414 KUHL AVE, ORLANDO, FL 32806-2008
Phone: 321-843-7000
Web: WWW.GETINVOLVEDORLANDOHEALTH.COM

PRODUCTS/OPERATIONS

Selected Facilities

Arnold Palmer Hospital for Children (Orlando)
Dr. P. Phillips Hospital (formerly Orlando Regional Sand Lake Hospital Orlando)
Health Central Hospital (Ocoee)
Lucerne Pavilion (Orlando)
M. D. Anderson Cancer Center Orlando
Orlando Health Heart Institute
Orlando Health Rehabilitation Institute
Orlando Regional Medical Center
South Lake Hospital (50% affiliate Clermont)
South Seminole Hospital (Longwood)
St. Cloud Regional Medical Center (20% affiliate)
Winnie Palmer Hospital for Women & Babies (Orlando)

Selected Specialties

Cancer care (at M. D. Anderson Cancer Center Orlando)
Emergency and trauma care
Heart and vascular
Neurosciences
Oncology/hematology
Orthopedic and sports medicine
Surgery
Women' s services

Selected Services

Anesthesiology
Brain Injury Rehabilitation Center (BIRC)
Endocrinology (diabetes)
Endoscopy
Epilepsy care
Home health care
Infectious diseases
Internal medicine
Laboratory and pathology Services
Mammography
Memory Disorder Center
MRI
Multiple sclerosis treatment
Nephrology
Nuclear medicine
Ophthalmology
Otolaryngology (Ears Nose Throat)
Pain management
Patient and family counseling
Pediatric outpatient surgery
Pulmonary medicine
Radiology and diagnostic imaging
Rehabilitation and physical therapy

COMPETITORS

Adventist Health System Sunbelt Healthcare
All Children' s Hospital
Baptist Health South Florida
Baptist Health System
Catholic Health East
Community Health Systems
Florida Hospital Heartland
Florida Hospital Waterman
HCA
Health Central
Health First
Holmes Regional Medical Center
Mayo Clinic Jacksonville
Mount Sinai Medical Center of Florida
Munroe Regional Health System
Nemours Foundation
Ocala Regional Medical Center
Osceola Regional Medical Center
St. Vincent' s Health System
UF&Shands

HISTORICAL FINANCIALS

Company Type: Private

Income Statement

FYE: September 30

	REVENUE ($ mil.)	NET INCOME ($ mil.)	NET PROFIT MARGIN	EMPLOYEES
09/11	1,652	72	4.4%	10,000
09/10	1,700	91	5.4%	—
09/09	1,637	76	4.7%	—
09/08	1	(0)	—	—
Annual Growth	920.6%	—	—	—

2011 Year-End Financials

Debt ratio: —
Return on equity: 4.40%
Cash ($ mil.): 47
Current ratio: 1.10
Long-term debt ($ mil.): —
Dividends
Yield: —
Payout: —
Market value ($ mil.): —

OSC SPORTS INC.

Olympia Sports may not make you an Olympian but the company carries the gear to help you go for gold. The sporting goods retailer offers sports equipment fitness gear and apparel athletic shoes casual wear and sports accessories under such brands as Columbia Louisville Slugger Bauer PUMA Reebok and Teva. It sells merchandise through its website and via more than 225 banner stores across the Northeast and Mid-Atlantic states. In addition to its retail business the company oversees the private nonprofit Olympia Sports Foundation which runs a clothing bank and collaborates on projects with local charities and schools within its retail region. Founder and CEO Ed Manganello owns Olympia.

Geographic Reach

Based in Maine Olympia Sports operates sporting goods stores throughout the Northeast and the Mid-Atlantic states.

Operations

The regional retailer operates a website to sell its products to complement its portfolio of retail shops that serve those who reside in more than a dozen states.

Strategy

The company has been adding to its stores network in recent years. Olympia Sports has expanded into Maryland New York New Jersey Delaware Pennsylvania and Virginia.

Sales and Marketing

Besides its brick-and-mortar stores Olympia Sports sells name-brand sporting goods items through its website.

Company Ownership

Olympia Sports is owned by founder and CEO Ed Manganello.

EXECUTIVES

President of Olympia Sports, Ed Manganello
President, Dick Coffey
Training Coordinator, David Heath

LOCATIONS

HQ: OSC SPORTS INC.
5 BRADLEY DR, WESTBROOK, ME 04092-2013
Phone: 207-854-2794
Web: WWW.OLYMPIASPORTS.NET

2013 Stores

	No.
Massachusetts	63
New	53
Maine	29
New	21
Pennsylvania	20
Connecticut	14
Vermont	11
Rhode	5
Maryland	6
Virginia	5
New	2
Delaware	1
West	1
Total	**231**

PRODUCTS/OPERATIONS

Selected Brands

Adidas
Brooks
Champion
Columbia
Converse
Crocs
Easton
Etnies
Fathead
Life Is Good
Mizuno
Moving Comfort
New Balance
Nike
Oakley
Puma
Rawlings
Reebok
Saucony
SKLZ
Spalding
Teva

COMPETITORS

Dick' s Sporting Goods
Dunham' s
Eastern Mountain Sports
Finish Line
Foot Locker
Hat World
Kmart
L.L. Bean
Modell' s
REI
Sears
Sports Authority
Target Corporation
Wal-Mart

HISTORICAL FINANCIALS

Company Type: Private

Income Statement

FYE: September 30

	REVENUE ($ mil.)	NET INCOME ($ mil.)	NET PROFIT MARGIN	EMPLOYEES
09/11	183	9	5.2%	2,000
09/09	165	0	0.2%	—
09/08	191	4	2.3%	—
09/07	172	3	1.8%	—
Annual Growth	1.6%	32.5%	—	—

2011 Year-End Financials

Debt ratio: —
Return on equity: 5.20%
Cash ($ mil.): 0
Current ratio: 0.10
Long-term debt ($ mil.): —

Dividends
Yield: —
Payout: —
Market value ($ mil.): —

OSF HEALTHCARE SYSTEM

OSF Healthcare helps patients who are feeling oh-so-frail in northern Illinois and southwestern Michigan. OSF Healthcare system includes eight acute care hospitals and one long-term care facility that combined are home to about 1400 beds and offer a full spectrum of inpatient and outpatient medical and surgical services. The system's primary care physician network consists of about 650 physicians at more than 90 locations throughout its service area. Subsidiary OSF Home Care provides hospice home visit and equipment services and OSF Saint Francis provides ambulance pharmacy and health care management services. The not-for-profit system is a subsidiary of the Sisters of The Third Order of St. Francis.

Operations Along with its various acute care hospitals OSF Healthcare provides urgent care through its OSF PromptCare locations. PromptCare administers a range of services including labs MRI ultrasound and primary and specialty care.

Mergers and Acquisitions In 2012 OSF Healthcare got even bigger in Illinois after acquiring the 100-bed Ottawa Regional Hospital (ORH) which was renamed as OSF Saint Elizabeth Medical Center following the transaction. OSF Healthcare and the Ottawa hospital have collaborated on medical services and best practices for about a decade but by joining forces officially they believe that they can attract more physicians across all specialties and increase access to health care throughout the community. OSF Saint Elizabeth provides a range of specialty and general acute care including emergency surgery cardiology and thoracic care. It is also home to a physician group and several primary care clinics in Ottawa (which continued to operate as Ottawa Regional Medical Center for a transition period following the acquisition). OSF Healthcare had previously planned to acquire Rockford Health System's Rockford Memorial Hospital but after a challenge by the FTC due to competitive concerns the deal was called off.

EXECUTIVES

Chairperson, Sister Judith Ann Duvall
SVP and CFO, Daniel Baker
SVP Medical Services, Gerald J. McShane
SVP Marketing and Communications, James G. Farrell
SVP Strategic Effectiveness, R. Michael Gulley
SVP and Chief Nursing Officer, Susan Campbell
SVP Government Relations, Tara D. Canty
CEO, Kevin D. Schoeplein
SVP and CIO, James J. Mormann
SVP Supportive Care, Robert Sawicki
SVP Care Management, Ralph R. Velazquez
President of the United, Wyatt Earp
Auditors: KPMGLLP

LOCATIONS

HQ: OSF HEALTHCARE SYSTEM
800 NE GLEN OAK AVE, PEORIA, IL 61603-3200
Phone: 309-655-2850
Web: WWW.OSFHEALTHCARE.ORG

PRODUCTS/OPERATIONS

Selected Facilities

OSF Holy Family Medical Center (Monmouth IL)
OSF Saint Anthony Medical Center (Rockford IL)
OSF Saint Clare Home (Peoria Heights IL)
OSF Saint Elizabeth Medical Center (formerly Ottowa Regional Hospital Ottowa IL)
OSF Saint Francis Medical Center (Peoria IL)
OSF Saint James - John W. Albrecht Medical Center (Pontiac IL)
OSF St. Mary Medical Center (Galesburg IL)
OSF St. Francis Hospital (Escanaba MI)
OSF St. Joseph Medical Center (Bloomington IL)

COMPETITORS

Advocate BroMenn
Centegra Health System
Central DuPage Hospital
Covenant HealthCare
Genesis Health System
McDonough District Hospital
Memorial Health System
Northwestern Memorial HealthCare
Resurrection Health Care
Rush-Copley Medical Center
SwedishAmerican Health System
University of Chicago Medical Center
University of Michigan Health System
Wheaton Franciscan Services

HISTORICAL FINANCIALS

Company Type: Private

Income Statement FYE: September 30

	REVENUE ($ mil.)	NET INCOME ($ mil.)	NET PROFIT MARGIN	EMPLOYEES
09/08	1,477	26	1.8%	4,007
09/06	1,481	58	4.0%	—
Annual Growth	(0.1%)	(32.8%)	—	—

2008 Year-End Financials

Debt ratio: —
Return on equity: 1.80%
Cash ($ mil.): 110
Current ratio: 0.30
Long-term debt ($ mil.): —

Dividends
Yield: —
Payout: —
Market value ($ mil.): —

OTSUKA AMERICA INC

Otsuka America is the holding company for the US operations of Japan's Otsuka Pharmaceutical. Otsuka America oversees pharmaceutical research and development marketing and distribution of both prescription drugs and over-the-counter (OTC) medicines. The company's pharmaceutical subsidiaries include Otsuka America Pharmaceutical (prescription drug marketing) Otsuka Maryland Medicinal Laboratories (research) Cambridge Isotope Laboratories (chemical ingredients) and Pharmavite (nutritionals). To help wash down its pills Otsuka America also holds consumer beverage makers Crystal Geyser (bottled water) Ridge Vineyards (wine) and Soma Beverage Company (specialty bottled water).

Through its Otsuka America Pharmaceutical subsidiary Otsuka America markets its Japanese parent's pharmaceutical products in North America with a focus on neurology oncology cardiovascular and gastrointestinal therapeutics. Primary products include Pletal (marketed as Pletaal in Asia) for the treatment of peripheral arterial disease and Abilify (co-promoted with Bristol-Myers Squibb) used to treat schizophrenia and bipolar disorder. The company also sells some diagnostic tests and related equipment through its Meretek subsidiary.

Otsuka America has a full pipeline of drug candidates and seeks out potential products from other pharmaceutical companies. Research and development is conducted by subsidiaries Otsuka Maryland Medicinal Labs and Otsuka Pharmaceutical Development & Commercialization. Drug candidate Samsca (dehydration therapy) received FDA approval for US marketing in 2009. Aripiprazole and Tolvaptan treatments for schizophrenia and kidney disease respectively are next up in the pipeline.

Japanese parent Otsuka Pharmaceutical further expanded Otsuka America's portfolio by acquiring rights to IV Busulfex a bone marrow transplant therapy for oncology patients marketed in North America and other regions from PDL BioPharma for $200 million in 2008. Otsuka Pharmaceutical intends to further expand its North American operations in the fields of pharmaceuticals and diagnostics.

EXECUTIVES

SVP US Sales Otsuka America Pharmaceutical, Pamela Harris

LOCATIONS

HQ: OTSUKA AMERICA INC
1 EMBARCADERO CTR # 2020, SAN FRANCISCO, CA 94111-3750
Phone: 415-986-5300
Web: WWW.OTSUKA-AMERICA.COM

PRODUCTS/OPERATIONS

Selected Subsidiaries

Pharmaceuticals
- Cambridge Isotope Laboratories Inc.
- Otsuka America Pharmaceutical Inc.
- Otsuka Maryland Medicinal Laboratories Inc.
- Otsuka Pharmaceutical Development & Commercialization Inc.
- Pharmavite LLC

Beverages
- CG Roxane LLC
- Crystal Geyser Water Company
- Ridge Vineyards Inc.
- Soma Beverage Company LLC

COMPETITORS

Abbott Labs
Bayer AG
Bristol-Myers Squibb
Eli Lilly
GlaxoSmithKline
Johnson & Johnson
Merck
NBTY
NestlÃ©
Novartis
Pfizer
Sanofi-Aventis U.S
Takeda Pharmaceutical

HISTORICAL FINANCIALS

Company Type: Private

Income Statement FYE: December 31

	REVENUE ($ mil.)	NET INCOME ($ mil.)	NET PROFIT MARGIN	EMPLOYEES
12/07	2,755	51	1.9%	2,065
12/03	1,066	56	5.3%	—
12/02	612	153	25.0%	—
12/01	567	(56)	—	—
Annual Growth	30.1%	—	—	—

2007 Year-End Financials

Debt ratio: —
Return on equity: 1.90%
Cash ($ mil.): 99
Current ratio: 0.70
Long-term debt ($ mil.): —

Dividends
Yield: —
Payout: —
Market value ($ mil.): —

OTTER PRODUCTS LLC

Otter Products' products keep your precious electronic devices safe and dry. The company which goes by OtterBox makes about 170 models of cases for cell phones smart phones tablet computers and other portable electronics from Apple Dell Nokia Samsung Motorola and other manufacturers. It outsources production and sells its impact and water resistant Defender Reflex Commuter and Impact cases and watertight boxes at Best Buy Target and other retailers. OtterBox was formed in 1998 by CEO Curt Richardson and his wife Nancy. She came up with the name because otter skin is water repellant and otters are known for being playful and creative something the company works to incorporate into its culture.

Geographic Reach

OtterBox is located in Fort Collins Colorado. Its main international and EMEA office is located in Cork Ireland. The company opened OtterBox Hong Kong in 2011 and established distribution in 14 countries throughout the APAC region.

Strategy

In 2013 OtterBox expanded into the Vietnam retail market through distribution partner Petrosetco Distribution Joint Stock Company (PSD). Vietnam is a strategic market for OtterBox in Asia and presents significant opportunities as a result of the rapid growth of smartphone users within Vietnam.

Mergers and Acquisitions

In 2013 the company purchased San Diego-based TreeFrog Developments (dba LifeProof) for about $325 million. LifeProof makes complementary smartphone cases and accessories and Otter hopes the synergies and choices provided by the combined firm will drive its strategy of attracting and creating lifelong customers.

In 2012 OtterBox acquired Wrapsol and its family of premium protective film solutions for mobile devices.

EXECUTIVES

Founder Chairman, Curt Richardson
President CEO, Brian Thomas
PR Manager, Kristin Golliher
PR Specialist, Kelly Richardson
PR Coordinator Europe Middle East and Asia (EMEA), Rhona Cashman
Managing Director EMEA, Matt Clark

LOCATIONS

HQ: OTTER PRODUCTS LLC
209 S MELDRUM ST, FORT COLLINS, CO 80521-2603
Phone: 970-493-8446
Web: WWW.MEDIA.OTTERBOX.COM

COMPETITORS

Apple Inc.
Coach Inc.
Eagle Creek Travel Gear
Forward Industries
SKB Corporation
Skullcandy
Tamrac
Tandy Brands
Tenba
Tumi
ZAGG

HISTORICAL FINANCIALS

Company Type: Private

Income Statement FYE: December 31

	REVENUE ($ mil.)	NET INCOME ($ mil.)	NET PROFIT MARGIN	EMPLOYEES
12/11	347	104	30.1%	320
12/10	168	60	35.8%	—
12/09	48	15	31.7%	—
12/08	10	0	6.8%	—
Annual Growth	225.6%	434.2%	—	—

2011 Year-End Financials

Debt ratio: —
Return on equity: 30.10%
Cash ($ mil.): 0
Current ratio: 1.30
Long-term debt ($ mil.): —
Dividends
Yield: —
Payout: —
Market value ($ mil.): —

OUR LADY OF LOURDES MEDICAL CENTER INC

Our Lady of Lourdes Medical Center tends to the sick of southern New Jersey. The hospital is a general acute care facility with about 410 inpatient beds. In addition to general medical emergency and surgical care the hospital specializes in organ transplantation joint replacement rehabilitation dialysis treatment cardiac care and birthing care. The hospital also offers nursing and other medical training programs and it operates area clinics and provides community health and outreach services. Our Lady of Lourdes Medical Center part of Catholic Health East's Lourdes Health System is sponsored by the Franciscan Sisters of Allegany New York.

Operations

The medical center's specialty units include the New Jersey Heart Institute at Lourdes the Regional Perinatal Center and the Lourdes Rehabilitation Center as well as regional dialysis and organ transplant clinics. Besides offering primary and specialty care services in a variety of fields Our Lady of Lourdes Medical Center is a teaching and research facility through affiliations with area universities and health professional schools. It also operates its own nursing school.

Strategy

Our Lady of Lourdes Medical Center has undergone expansion efforts over the years to attract and retain customers in the region. In 2012 for instance it relocated and expanded its birthing center to include all-private rooms with improved family accommodations. It has also updated some of its medical equipment and energy systems including the addition of a new MRI imaging system during 2012 to improve patient comfort and diagnostic capabilities. Overall the Lourdes Health System has also expanded by opening new outpatient care centers in Camden and the greater Philadelphia metropolitan area.

The hospital also strives to expand services and resources for doctors and health professionals. In 2012 it enriched its educational programs by forming partnerships with the Immaculata University and Camden Community College to offer nursing bachelor's and master's degrees through its Our Lady of Lourdes School of Nursing.

EXECUTIVES

Chief Financial Officer, Michael J. Hammond
President CEO, Alexander J. (Alex) Hatala
CIO, Maureen Hetu
Vice President Planning and Development, Kimberly D. (Kim) Barnes
Vice President of Risk Management, Barbara A. Holfelner
Vice President Mission, Sister Helen Owens
Senior Vice President of Operations, Robert E. Ruggero
Vice President Medical Affairs, Alan Pope
General Counsel, Jennifer Schwartz
Director Marketing and Media Relations, Carol Lynn Daly
Vice President Operations, Joanne Gianndrea
Vice President Human Resources, Richard Kropp
Executive Vice President Chief Operating Officer, Mark Nessel
President of Education and Research, Audrey R. Jadczak

LOCATIONS

HQ: OUR LADY OF LOURDES MEDICAL CENTER INC
1600 HADDON AVE, CAMDEN, NJ 08103-3101
Phone: 856-757-3500
Web: WWW.LOURDESNURSINGSCHOOL.ORG

PRODUCTS/OPERATIONS

Selected Services
Bariatric Surgery
Cardiac Services
Community Outreach
Dialysis
Emergency Services
Joint Replacement Center
Organ Transplantation
Rehabilitation Center
Senior Services
Stroke
Women and Children' s Services

COMPETITORS

Abington Memorial Hospital
Albert Einstein Healthcare Network
Aria Health
Christiana Care
Fox Chase Cancer Center
Inspira Health Network
Jefferson Health System
Kennedy Health System
Mercy Health System
North Philadelphia Health System
TUHS
Tenet Healthcare
The Cooper Health System
University of Pennsylvania Health System
Virtua Health

HISTORICAL FINANCIALS

Company Type: Private

Income Statement FYE: December 31

	REVENUE ($ mil.)	NET INCOME ($ mil.)	NET PROFIT MARGIN	EMPLOYEES
12/12	271	30	11.1%	3,000
12/09	279	(21)	—	—
12/03	296	1	0.4%	—
12/03	243	21	8.9%	—
Annual Growth	1.2%	3.7%	—	—

2012 Year-End Financials

Debt ratio: —
Return on equity: 11.10%
Cash ($ mil.): 4
Current ratio: 1.20
Long-term debt ($ mil.): —
Dividends
Yield: —
Payout: —
Market value ($ mil.): —

OUR LADY OF LOURDES REGIONAL MEDICAL CENTER

Established in 1949 as part of the not-for-profit Franciscan Missionaries of Our Lady Health System Our Lady of Lourdes Regional Medical Center is a hospital that provides medical care in Louisiana. The facility with a medical staff of more than 450 physicians representing more than 50 specialties including cardiology neurology oncology rheumatology and respiratory services. The medical center also offers general family practice and pediatric care. Our Lady of Lourdes extends its reach outside the facility into the Acadiana community by offering primary care physicians' offices home health care programs and ocupational medicine.

EXECUTIVES

Director Information Systems, Nona Mire
Chairman, Henry C. Perret Jr.
Director Community Relations, Berch Stelly
CFO, Jeffrey D. (Jeff) Limbocker
Secretary and Director, Gerald Boudreaux
President Medical Staff and Director, Bryan LeBean
President and CEO, William F. (Bud) Barrow
Director, Richard G. (Gus) Zepernick Jr.
Director, William W. (Billy) Rucks IV, age 52
Director, Richard M. Dearman
Secretary and Director, Gerald Boudreaux
Vice Chairman, Ronald E. (Ron) Brumley
Director, Steve P. Landry
President Medical Staff and Director, Bryan LeBean
Director, Timothy J. (Tim) Lemoine
Director, Sister Magdalen O'Donovan
Director, John P. Schutte
Director, Richard K. Broussard
Director, Kemp Coreil
Director, Charles T. Goodson
Director, Jon Leleux
Director, Sister June Meyer
Director, R. Kevin Moody
Director, Kenneth L. Odinet
Director, Jerry Reaux
Auditors: KPMGLLP

LOCATIONS

HQ: OUR LADY OF LOURDES REGIONAL MEDICAL CENTER
4801 AMBSSDOR CFFERY PKWY, LAFAYETTE, LA 70508-6917
Phone: 337-470-2000
Web: WWW.LOURDESRMC.COM

COMPETITORS

BRGMC
CHRISTUS St. Frances Cabrini Hospital
General Health System
LHC Group
LSU System
Lafayette General Medical Center
Lane Regional Medical Center
Our Lady of the Lake RMC
River Parishes Hospital
Terrebonne General Medical Center
Woman' s Hospital

HISTORICAL FINANCIALS

Company Type: Private

Income Statement FYE: June 30

	REVENUE ($ mil.)	NET INCOME ($ mil.)	NET PROFIT MARGIN	EMPLOYEES
06/11	180	18	10.2%	1,700
06/10	162	(9)	—	—
06/09	142	(58)	—	—
06/08	163	(3)	—	—
Annual Growth	3.5%	—	—	—

2011 Year-End Financials

Debt ratio: —
Return on equity: 10.20%
Cash ($ mil.): 31
Current ratio: 0.90
Long-term debt ($ mil.): —
Dividends
Yield: —
Payout: —
Market value ($ mil.): —

OUR LADY OF THE LAKE HOSPITAL INC.

Our Lady of the Lake Regional Medical Center reaches out to Baton Rouge residents with a helping hand. Participating in teaching programs for LSU and Tulane medical schools the medical center has some 700 inpatient beds and includes emergency surgery general medical and specialty care centers for conditions including heart disease cancer orthopedics and ENT (ear nose and throat) disorders. Our Lady of the Lake also includes a Children's Hospital two nursing homes and an independent-living facility and it offers outpatient services at its main campus and at satellite facilities throughout the greater Baton Rouge area. Our Lady of the Lake was founded in 1923 by the Franciscan Missionaries of Our Lady.

As a major facility in the Baton Rouge area Our Lady of the Lake has been expanding its services in the region in recent years. In 2012 for instance the hospital constructed a freestanding emergency room facility in the suburban community of Livingston Louisiana. It is also building a new nine-story patient tower to the main hospital campus; the tower will house the heart and vascular center as well as an expanded ER and a new level 1 regional trauma center and will be completed in late 2013.

Our Lady of the Lake has also expanded its education programs. For instance it added a pediatric residency program in 2010. The hospital also moved to extend its relationship with LSU that year by agreeing to become the primary clinical site for the LSU medical school. The agreement came as LSU considered whether to build a replacement hospital for its aging teaching facility and coincides with the Our Lady of the Lake expansion projects. The partnership launched a new psychiatric residency program in 2012.

EXECUTIVES

Chief of Staff and Director, Walter L. Bringaze III
Vice Chief of Staff and Director, Daniel Butler
Chief of Staff and Director, Walter L. Bringaze III
Director, Donald H. Daigle
Auditors: KPMGLLP

LOCATIONS

HQ: OUR LADY OF THE LAKE HOSPITAL INC.
5000 HENNESSY BLVD, BATON ROUGE, LA 70808-4367
Phone: 225-765-7709
Web: WWW.OLOLCHILDRENS.COM

COMPETITORS

Ardent Health
Baton Rouge General
CHRISTUS St. Frances Cabrini Hospital
Dynacq Healthcare
General Health System
Lane Regional Medical Center
Our Lady of Lourdes
River Parishes Hospital
Woman' s Hospital

HISTORICAL FINANCIALS

Company Type: Private

Income Statement FYE: June 30

	REVENUE ($ mil.)	NET INCOME ($ mil.)	NET PROFIT MARGIN	EMPLOYEES
06/11	826	214	26.0%	1,800
06/10	614	12	2.0%	—
06/08*	6	1	18.4%	—
12/05	0	0	3.9%	—
Annual Growth	426.1%	668.8%	—	—

*Fiscal year change

2011 Year-End Financials

Debt ratio: —
Return on equity: 26.00%
Cash ($ mil.): 200
Current ratio: 2.90
Long-term debt ($ mil.): —
Dividends
Yield: —
Payout: —
Market value ($ mil.): —

OVERLAKE HOSPITAL MEDICAL CENTER

Over the lake and through the sound to Overlake Hospital Medical Center we go! The not-for-profit hospital provides health care services to residents of Bellevue Washington in the Puget Sound region. The nearly 350-bed facility provides comprehensive inpatient and outpatient services ranging from cancer care and surgery to specialized senior care. Overlake also operates a number of outpatient clinics providing primary care urgent care and specialty care such as weight loss surgery. The organization also provides patients with health and wellness programs addressing issues like women's and children's health.

Geographic Reach

Overlake provides health care services to residents of Bellevue Washington and the entire Puget Sound region. It operates clinics on its main campus in Bellevue as well as in Redmond and in Issaquah and on Mercer Island.

Operations

The medical center has more than 1000 physicians on staff and runs Centers of Excellence in cardiac care cancer care surgical services women's and infants' care and emergency and trauma care. The facility is home to a 24-hour urgent care clinic an anticoagulation clinic and a breast screening center. Overlake also operates numerous outpatient clinics providing primary care urgent care and specialty care.

In 2012 the hospital reported 20180 inpatient admissions; 315059 outpatient visits; 45286 health education visits; 13780 surgeries; and 3982 births.

Financial Performance

Overlake's revenues increased by 2% to $427 million in 2012 as the result of higher net patient revenues and contribution revenues partially offset by a loss on disposal of assets. Patients covered under commercial insurance and other negotiated contracts accounted for 66% of patient service revenues in 2012; Medicare patients 28%; and Medicaid patients 3%.

Net income declined in 2012 by 72% to $19 million due to an increase in expenses and a change in pension liability and net unrealized losses on investments.

Strategy

Increasing demand in the region has led the hospital to invest in expansions and equipment upgrades that include more emergency treatment capabilities and an on-campus helistop for trauma patients being airlifted to the area.

Along with its expansion and construction projects Overlake is investing in new technology to keep the health system in line with its competitors and to improve patient care. It is adding endoscopic video towers to its operating rooms to facilitate improved views of surgical procedures and is also moving to digitize all of its facilities with electronic health records.

In 2013 it opened the new $17.4 million David and Shelley Hovind Heart & Vascular center. The new 19200-square-foot facility bring's cardiac and vascular services together in one location.

In 2012 Overlake opened its new and expanded $3.6 million neonatal intensive care unit.

Overlake has also focused on adding new primary care clinics and expanding its physician network to serve patients in locations closer to where they live and work. In 2012 the Center continued to grow its network of clinics on the Eastside opening an Urgent Care Clinic at Overlake Medical Clinics Redmond at the Creekside Crossing Shopping Center.

Mergers and Acquisitions

Streamlining its operations in 2012 Overlake acquired Overlake Internal Medicine Associates Medical Oncology.

In late 2011 Overlake acquired Issaquah Medical Group and renamed it Overlake Medical Clinics Gilman. The acquisition expanded the company's network of primary care medical clinics on the east side of Puget Sound.

Company Background

Overlake founded in 1960 is led by CEO Craig Hendrickson a veteran health care executive.

EXECUTIVES

President CEO and Trustee, Craig L. Hendrickson
VP Finance and CFO, Gary McLaughlin
VP Professional Services, T.D. Sam Baxter
VP Human Resources, Lisa Brock
VP Patient Experience, Dianna Reely
VP Patient Care Services; Chief Nursing Officer, Julie Clayton
EVP and COO, David W. Schultz
VP Information Services and CIO, Jody Albright
VP System Change Management and Chief Compliance Officer, Richard Bryan
VP Strategy and Marketing, Caitlin Hillary Moulding
Director Medical Staff Services and Health Information Management, Marlene Tuttle
Chair, Cecily Hall
Chief Medical Officer and VP Network Development, Alan Ertle
VP Fund Development and Executive Director Overlake Hospital Foundation, Molly Stearns
Chief of Staff, J. Walter Smith
President Treasurer, Lynnette Anderson
Trustee, Janine Florence, age 65
President CEO and Trustee, Craig L. Hendrickson
Trustee, Douglas T. (Doug) Martin
Auditors: KPMGLLP

LOCATIONS

HQ: OVERLAKE HOSPITAL MEDICAL CENTER
1035 116TH AVE NE, BELLEVUE, WA 98004-4687
Phone: 425-688-5000
Web: WWW.OVERLAKEHOSPITAL.ORG

Selected Locations

Outpatient Rehabilitation Services
Outpatient Surgery (park in the West Garage; Outpatient Surgery is located on the first floor of the West Garage.)
Overlake Bellevue Campus and Overlake Medical Clinics Medical Tower
Overlake Medical Clinics Downtown Bellevue
Overlake Medical Clinics Issaquah
Overlake Medical Clinics Kirkland
Overlake Medical Clinics Redmond
Urgent Care Clinic in Issaquah
Urgent Care Clinic in Redmond

COMPETITORS

Catholic Health Initiatives
Franciscan Health System
Group Health Cooperative (Puget Sound)
Harrison Medical Center
MultiCare Health System
PeaceHealth
Providence Health & Services
Seattle Children' s Hospital
Swedish Health Services
University of Washington
Yakima Valley Memorial

HISTORICAL FINANCIALS

Company Type: Private

Income Statement FYE: June 30

	REVENUE ($ mil.)	NET INCOME ($ mil.)	NET PROFIT MARGIN	EMPLOYEES
06/13	422	40	9.5%	2,450
06/12	427	18	4.4%	—
06/10	417	68	16.3%	—
06/10	397	33	8.4%	—
Annual Growth	2.1%	6.4%	—	—

2013 Year-End Financials

Debt ratio: —
Return on equity: 9.50%
Cash ($ mil.): 15
Current ratio: 0.90
Long-term debt ($ mil.): —
Dividends
Yield: —
Payout: —
Market value ($ mil.): —

OZARKS ELECTRIC COOPERATIVE CORPORATION

Even people living up in the Ozark Mountains need power and Ozarks Electric Cooperative aims to deliver. The member-owned not-for-profit cooperative ,Âserves more than 62000 ,Âcustomers in about a dozen counties spread across northwest Arkansas and northeast Oklahoma. Its 350 miles of line reach industrial commercial residential and agricultural power users. ,ÂOzarks ,ÂElectric ,Âprovides its customers with energy audits and information on saving energy as well as energy efficient water heaters and surge protectors. It is a member of Touchstone Energy a national alliance of electric cooperatives in nearly 40 states. ,ÂThe coop ,Âwas formed in 1938.

EXECUTIVES

Vice President, Kay Wilkerson
Vice President Engineering Operations, Troy Scarbrough

LOCATIONS

HQ: OZARKS ELECTRIC COOPERATIVE CORPORATION
3641 W WEDINGTON DR, FAYETTEVILLE, AR 727045742
Phone: 4795212900
Web: WWW.OZARKSECC.COM

HISTORICAL FINANCIALS

Company Type: Private

Income Statement FYE: December 31

	REVENUE ($ mil.)	NET INCOME ($ mil.)	NET PROFIT MARGIN	EMPLOYEES
12/13	111	9	8.9%	190
12/12	111	9	8.9%	—
12/11	116	13	11.5%	—
12/10	111	0	—	—
Annual Growth	0.1%	—	—	—

2013 Year-End Financials

Debt ratio: —
Return on equity: 8.90%
Cash ($ mil.): 1
Current ratio: 0.40
Long-term debt ($ mil.): —
Dividends
Yield: —
Payout: —
Market value ($ mil.): —

PACE UNIVERSITY

If you want to keep pace with your peers chances are you'll need a higher education. Pace University offers certificate programs as well as undergraduate graduate and doctoral degrees through half a dozen schools: arts and sciences business computer science and information systems education law and nursing. Altogether the school is home to 100 undergraduate majors offering roughly 30 undergraduate and graduate degrees 50 master's programs and four doctoral programs. Nearly 13000 students attend the university's three New York campuses (Lower Manhattan Pleasantville-Briarcliff and White Plains). It has a student-faculty ratio of about 18:1.

Geographic Reach

Pace boasts campus locations in New York City and in Westchester County.

Operations

The school has an endowment of more than $100 million. Besides its three New York campuses the university also offers courses online and at a location in midtown Manhattan.

Financial Performance

The university logged a 3% increase in revenue in 2012 as compared to 2011 due to a boost in contributions as well as tuition and fees net government grants and contracts. Net income meanwhile dropped by 160% during the same reporting period thanks to rises in expenses and unrealized depreciation in fair value of derivative instruments in 2012 vs. appreciation in 2011.

Company Background

Pace was founded in 1906 by the brothers Homer and Charles Pace as a co-educational business school called Pace Institute. It wasn't until 42 years later under Robert Pace that it began its transformation into its current incarnation as a liberal arts and sciences college.

EXECUTIVES

Chairman, Aniello A. Bianco
Chief of Staff, Cindy Heilberger
President and Trustee, Stephen J. Friedman
EVP CFO and Treasurer, Toby R. Winer
VP Enrollment and Placement, Robina C. Schepp
SVP and Chief Administrative Officer, William (Bill) McGrath
VP Strategic Initiatives, Robert G. M. Keating
Dean for Students, Lisa Bardill Moscaritolo
Dean for Students, Marijo Russell-O'Grady
Dean College of Health Professions, Harriet R. Feldman
Dean School of Law, Michelle S. Simon
Dean Dyson College of Arts and Sciences, Nira Herrmann
EVP Academic Affairs and Provost, Uday Sukhatme
VP Information Technology and CIO, Thomas A. Hull
Dean Lubin School of Business, Neil S. Braun
Dean Seidenberg School of Computer Science and Information Systems, Amar Gupta
Dean School of Education, Andrea M. (Penny) Spencer
VP and Chief Marketing Officer, Frederica N. (Freddi) Wald

senior Vice President J.P. Morgan Chase & Co, Louis J. Amato
Trustee, Hal J. Upbin, age 74
Trustee, Marie J. Toulantis, age 60
Trustee, Ivan G. Seidenberg, age 66
Trustee, Richard F. (Rich) Zannino, age 53
Trustee, Carol Raphael, age 72
President and Trustee, Stephen J. Friedman
Trustee, Philip F. Bleser
Trustee, Mark M. Besca
Trustee, Donald L. Boudreau
Trustee, Christopher A. Edwards
Trustee, John A. Gerson
Trustee, Cynthia Greer Goldstein
Trustee, Barry M. Gosin
Trustee, Bridget-Anne Hampden
Trustee, James E. Healey
Trustee, Charles N. Jordan Jr.
Trustee, Harold O. Levy
Trustee, Suresh Munshani
Trustee, Michael O'Reilly
Trustee, Barbara Ann Porceddu
Trustee, Jack L. Salzman
Trustee, Prof Joseph F. Ryan
Trustee, Edward F. Murphy
Trustee, John T. O'Connor
Trustee, David J. Pecker
Trustee, Thomas J. Quinlan III
Trustee, Maria Fiorini Ramirez
Trustee, Jack J. Ribeiro
Trustee, Robert A. Rivero
Auditors: KPMGLLP

LOCATIONS

HQ: PACE UNIVERSITY
1 PACE PLZ, NEW YORK, NY 10038-1598
Phone: 212-346-1956
Web: WWW.LAW.PACE.EDU

PRODUCTS/OPERATIONS

Selected Colleges and Schools

Dyson College of Arts and Sciences
Lienhard School of Nursing
Lubin School of Business
School of Education
School of Law
Seidenberg School of Computer Science and Information Systems

HISTORICAL FINANCIALS

Company Type: Private

Income Statement FYE: June 30

	REVENUE ($ mil.)	NET INCOME ($ mil.)	NET PROFIT MARGIN	EMPLOYEES
06/13	326	20	6.2%	1,862
06/12	310	(15)	—	—
06/10	300	26	8.9%	—
06/10	274	(14)	—	—
Annual Growth	6.0%	—	—	—

2013 Year-End Financials

Debt ratio: —
Return on equity: 6.20%
Cash ($ mil.): 14
Current ratio: —
Long-term debt ($ mil.): —
Dividends
Yield: —
Payout: —
Market value ($ mil.): —

PACIFIC COAST PRODUCERS

Fruits seafood sauces and organic tomato puree rather than movies are the creative output of this particular group of Pacific Coast Producers. The cooperative markets the apricots grapes peaches pears and tomatoes grown by its approximately 165 California-based members. It turns the produce into private-label canned fruit sauces and juices and sells them to the retail and foodservice industries. Pacific Coast Producers typically serves retailers the likes of Albertson's Aldi Kroger Safeway SUPERVALU Whole Foods and Wal-Mart as well as the US Department of Agriculture. The company founded in 1971 operates three production sites and one distribution center in California.

Geographic Reach

From its base in Lodi California Pacific Coast Producers grows its fruits in California and sells them nationwide.

Strategy

The cooperative serves tomato processor Morning Star through a sales and marketing alliance it formed with the company in 2009. As part of the collaboration Pacific Coast Producers provides canned tomatoes to the retail and foodservice industries.

Sales and Marketing

Pacific Coast Producers sells the products it grows and processes to retailers and foodservice operators nationwide as well as to the US Department of Agriculture.

EXECUTIVES

President Chief Executive Officer, Daniel L. (Dan) Vincent
VP Information Systems, Peter C. Wtulich
Corporate Secretary, Kathi J. Shull
VP and General Counsel, Mona E. Shulman
VP Human Resources, Dick Ehrler
VP Retail Sales, Andrew K. Russick
VP Food Service Sales, Matt Strong
Controller and Assistant Treasurer, Stewart Easton
VP Operations, Daniel A. Sroufe
VP Field Operations, Steve Freeman
Manager Woodland Plant, Niraj Raj
Manager Lodi Plant, Michael VanGundy
Field Representative, Jerry Cordy
Manager Oroville Plant, Chris Ward
Field Representative, Rudy Lucero
Auditors: KPMGLLP

LOCATIONS

HQ: PACIFIC COAST PRODUCERS
631 N CLUFF AVE, LODI, CA 95240-0756
Phone: 209-367-8800
Web: WWW.PCOASTP.COM

PRODUCTS/OPERATIONS

Selected Products

Apricots
Catsup
Chili Sauces
Chunky Mixed Fruit
Concentrated Crushed Tomatoes
Diced Style Tomatoes
Extra Heavy Concentrated Crushed Round Tomato Puree
Formulated Pizza Sauces
Fruit Cocktail
Fruit for Salad
Fruit Mix
Ground Tomatoes
Marinara Sauces
Non-Formulated Pizza Sauce
Organic Tomatoes
Peaches
Pears
Random Cut / Strip Style Tomatoes
Seafood Sauces
Stewed Style Tomatoes
Tomato Juice
Whole Peeled Tomatoes

COMPETITORS

Allens
Campbell Soup
Cento
ConAgra
Del Monte Foods
Dole Food
Faribault Foods
General Mills
Glory Foods
Hain Celestial
Hanover Foods
Heinz
NORPAC
Pictsweet
Seneca Foods

HISTORICAL FINANCIALS

Company Type: Private

Income Statement FYE: May 31

	REVENUE ($ mil.)	NET INCOME ($ mil.)	NET PROFIT MARGIN	EMPLOYEES
05/13	534	18	3.5%	1,000
05/12	500	18	3.7%	—
05/10	498	17	3.4%	—
05/10	513	28	5.5%	—
Annual Growth	1.4%	(12.8%)	—	—

2013 Year-End Financials

Debt ratio: —
Return on equity: 3.50%
Cash ($ mil.): 1
Current ratio: 0.30
Long-term debt ($ mil.): —
Dividends
Yield: —
Payout: —
Market value ($ mil.): —

PACIFIC HIDE & FUR DEPOT

Pacific Steel & Recycling sells at one end of the steel mill and buys at the other. The company's Pacific Recycling unit supplies steel mills with scrap metal a key raw material. It operates ,Äabout 35 recycling centers in the northwestern US and Canada that also handle cardboard and scrap paper in addition to metals. The company's Pacific Steel unit buys steel products and resells them from steel service centers and distribution centers in the northwestern US. Pacific Steel's facilities handle items such as bar products and structurals flat-rolled products reinforcing bar and tubing and pipe. The company offers a variety of processing services.

Pacific Steel & Recycling also sells livestock equipment ,Ä(including gates feeders and fence wire) ornamental ironwork (handrails balusters and post tops) and trailer parts.

The company operates through several northwestern states in the US: Colorado Idaho Montana Nevada North Dakota South Dakota Utah Washington and Wyoming.

In 2012 the company acquired the assets of Canadian recycler Triple R Metals in Medicine Hat Alberta for an undisclosed amount. The acquisition was the first company outside of the US to be bought by Pacific Steel & Recycling. The metals recycling facility which has been in business for 10 years will operate under the name PHF Steel & Recycling.

The company has its roots in a fur-trading business that was founded in the 1880s.

EXECUTIVES

Vp-steel Ops, Ed Leppien
Vice President Business Development, Stuart Boylan
Vp-ops, Jeff Millhollin
V Pres, Ed Joyce
Vice President Scrap Operations, Pat Kons
Vice President Ferrous Processing And Trading, Ken Halko

LOCATIONS

HQ: PACIFIC HIDE & FUR DEPOT
5 RIVER DR S, GREAT FALLS, MT 594051872
Phone: 4067717222
Web: WWW.PACIFIC-STEEL.COM

COMPETITORS

Alaskan Copper
Reliance Steel
Ryerson

HISTORICAL FINANCIALS

Company Type: Private

Income Statement FYE: August 28

	REVENUE ($ mil.)	NET INCOME ($ mil.)	NET PROFIT MARGIN	EMPLOYEES
08/10	301	34	11.6%	780
08/08	241	2	1.2%	—
08/07	2,109	0	—	—
Annual Growth	(47.7%)	15604.6%	—	—

2010 Year-End Financials

Debt ratio: —
Return on equity: 11.60%
Cash ($ mil.): 38
Current ratio: 3.50
Long-term debt ($ mil.): —
Dividends
Yield: —
Payout: —
Market value ($ mil.): —

PALMETTO HEALTH

EXECUTIVES

CEO and Director, Charles D. (Chuck) Beaman Jr.
EVP and CFO, Paul Duane
SVP Human Resources, Willis (Trip) Gregory III
EVP and COO Palmetto Health Richland, Stan Hickson
EVP and COO Palmetto Health Baptist, Marty Bridges
COO Acute Care Services, James E. (Jim) Lathren
SVP and General Counsel, Howard P. West
SVP and Chief Medical Officer, James I. (Jim) Raymond
SVP Community Services, Vince Ford
Chair, William L. (Freedie) Freeman III
Treasurer and Director, Sara B. Fisher
President, John J. Singerling III
SVP and CIO, Michelle Edwards
SVP Ambulatory Services, Ellis M. (Mac) Knight
Vice Chair, James E. (Rick) Wheeler
SVP Marketing and Communications, Todd Miller
SVP Clinical Operations, Sarah Richter
Director, James A. Bennett
Director, William L. Cogdill Jr.
CEO and Director, Charles D. (Chuck) Beaman Jr.
Director, James C. Reynolds
Treasurer and Director, Sara B. Fisher
Director, Nathaniel Johnson (John) Stewart Jr.
Director, Robert H. Bunch
Vice Chair, James E. (Rick) Wheeler

LOCATIONS

HQ: PALMETTO HEALTH
1301 TAYLOR ST STE 8A, COLUMBIA, SC 292012955
Phone: 8032962100
Web: WWW.PALMETTOHEALTH.ORG

PRODUCTS/OPERATIONS

Selected Facilities – South Carolina

Palmetto Health Baptist Hospital Columbia
Palmetto Health Baptist Hospital Easley
Palmetto Health Children's Hospital (Columbia)
Palmetto Health Heart Hospital (Columbia)
Palmetto Health HomeCare
Palmetto Health Hospice
Palmetto Health Parkridge (Columbia)
Palmetto Health Physician Practices
Palmetto Health Richland (Columbia)
Specialty Centers
Bariatric Services/Weight Management Center
Breast Center
Cancer Centers
Carolina Stone Center
Da Vinci Robotic Surgery Center
Gamma Knife Center
Stroke Center
Total Joint Center
Trauma Center

COMPETITORS

AnMed Health
Beaufort Memorial Hospital
Bon Secours Health
CaroMont
Carolinas HealthCare System
Carolinas Hospital System
Community Health Systems
Doctors Hospital of Augusta
Georgetown Hospital System
Grand Strand Regional Medical Center
Greenville Hospital System
HCA
Health Management Associates
Laurens County Hospital
Lexington Medical Center
McLeod Health
Novant Health
Spartanburg Regional Healthcare System

HISTORICAL FINANCIALS

Company Type: Private

Income Statement FYE: September 30

	REVENUE ($ mil.)	NET INCOME ($ mil.)	NET PROFIT MARGIN	EMPLOYEES
09/08	1,188	0	—	10,200
09/07	1,131	41	3.6%	—
Annual Growth	5.0%	—	—	—

2008 Year-End Financials

Debt ratio: —
Return on equity: —
Cash ($ mil.): 8
Current ratio: 2.00
Long-term debt ($ mil.): —
Dividends
Yield: —
Payout: —
Market value ($ mil.): —

PALO ALTO MEDICAL FOUNDATION FOR HEALTH CARE RESEARCH AND EDUCAT

The Palo Alto Medical Foundation (PAMF) is a not-for-profit multi-specialty physicians group providing medical and outpatient care mostly in the San Francisco Bay Area. It operates through three divisions serving distinct geographical areas: the Palo Alto Medical Clinic and the Camino Medical Group serve Silicon Valley and the East Bay; and the Santa Cruz Medical Foundation operates farther south in and around Santa Cruz. An affiliate of Sutter Health the organization has some 1100 doctors covering dozens of medical specialties; its facilities also provide outpatient surgery diagnostic imaging and women's services. Additionally PAMF houses a Research Institute that performs medical research.

Geographic Reach

The Palo Alto Medical Foundation (PAMF) provides medical and outpatient care to the San Francisco Bay Area and Silicon Valley.

Operations

The medical foundation operates more than 50 medical centers including primary care clinics surgery hospitals urgent care centers and physical therapy and weight management clinics. Specialty care services include pediatrics neurology gynecology and oncology.

Strategy

In 2011 PAMF launched a Sutter application allowing patients to access their medical records on the go; the program is dubbed MyChart; the MyChart program was already available to patients via personal computers.

EXECUTIVES

Director Finance; Treasurer, Jane A. Risser
VP and Chief Innovation and Technology Officer, Paul C. Tang
CEO, Richard Slavin
President Santa Cruz Division, Larry D. deGhetaldi
EVP and Division President (Palo Alto), Francis A. Marzoni
VP Education Division, Janet Lederer
Secretary; VP Support Services and Project Development, David Jury
President Camino Division, Elizabeth Vilardo
VP Research Division, Harold S. Luft
Director, Jeff Gerard
President Mills-Peninsula Division, Brian C. Roach
COO, James Hereford
Division President (Alameda), Jimmy Hu
Associate Chief Medical Officer, Jesus Saucedo
Vice President Operations, Kathy Korbholz
Vice President Medical Management And Quality, Sharon Katz
Secretary; VP Support Services and Project Development, David Jury
Vice Chairman, Cary Hill
Chairman, Joseph Lacy

LOCATIONS

HQ: PALO ALTO MEDICAL FOUNDATION FOR HEALTH CARE RESEARCH AND EDUCAT
795 EL CAMINO REAL AMES B, PALO ALTO, CA 94301
Phone: 650-321-4121
Web: WWW.PAMF.ORG

Selected locations

ALAMEDA COUNTY
Castro Valley Primary Care Center
Castro Valley Women's Health Center
Dublin Center
Fremont Center
Livermore Center
SAN MATEO COUNTY
Menlo Park Surgical Hospital
Portola Valley Women's Health Center
Redwood City Center
Redwood City Women's Health Center
Redwood Shores Health Center
San Carlos Center Family Medicine
SANTA CLARA COUNTY
Gynecologic Oncology (Los Gatos)
Gynecologic Oncology (Mountain View)
Los Altos Center
Mountain View Center

Nephrology (Palo Alto)
Nephrology (San Jose)
OB/Gyn (Sunnyvale)
Palo Alto Center
Plastic Surgery
Santa Clara Center
Sleep Disorder Center
Sunnyvale Center
Currently closed and renovations being planned
SurgiCenter (Mountain View)
Vision Care Center
West Valley Center
SANTA CRUZ COUNTY
Main Clinic
Neurology
Neurosurgery
Physical Medicine & Rehabilitation
Scotts Valley
Watsonville
Westside Office

COMPETITORS

California Pacific Medical Center
Community Hospital of the Monterey Peninsula
Dignity Health
Good Samaritan Hospital (San Jose)
Healdsburg District Hospital
Hill Physicians Medical Group
John Muir Health
Marin General Hospital
Sandford Burnham Institute
Sequoia Healthcare District
Stanford Hospital and Clinics
UCSF Medical
ValleyCare Health System

HISTORICAL FINANCIALS

Company Type: Private

Income Statement FYE: December 31

	REVENUE ($ mil.)	NET INCOME ($ mil.)	NET PROFIT MARGIN	EMPLOYEES
12/11	1,434	3	0.2%	1,168
12/01	322	5	1.6%	—
/* 0	0		—	
Annual Growth	—	—	—	—

*Fiscal year change

2011 Year-End Financials

Debt ratio: —
Return on equity: 0.20%
Cash ($ mil.): 60
Current ratio: 1.10
Long-term debt ($ mil.): —
Dividends
Yield: —
Payout: —
Market value ($ mil.): —

PANORAMA CITY

LOCATIONS

HQ: PANORAMA CITY
1751 CIRCLE LN SE, LACEY, WA 985032570
Phone: 3604560111

HISTORICAL FINANCIALS

Company Type: Private

Income Statement FYE: July 31

	ASSETS ($ mil.)	NET INCOME ($ mil.)	INCOME AS % OF ASSETS	EMPLOYEES
07/13	171	4	2.5%	330
07/12	166	4	2.8%	—
07/11	160	4	2.6%	—
07/10	156	0	—	—
Annual Growth	3.1%	—	—	—

2013 Year-End Financials

Debt ratio: —
Return on equity: 10.40%
Cash ($ mil.): 4
Current ratio: 0.80
Long-term debt ($ mil.): —
Dividends
Yield: —
Payout: —
Market value ($ mil.): —

PAPER CONVERTING MACHINE COMPANY

EXECUTIVES

VP Sales and Marketing, Steve Kemp
Training Manager, Ann Charles
Training Manager, Mark Hansford

LOCATIONS

HQ: PAPER CONVERTING MACHINE COMPANY
2300 S ASHLAND AVE, GREEN BAY, WI 543045213
Phone: 9204945601
Web: WWW.PCMC.COM

PRODUCTS/OPERATIONS

Selected Products

Nonwoven converting
Printing
- Flexible packaging
- Labels and labeling
- Flexo
- Flexo and gravure
- Package printing
- Paper film and foil converting

Roll engraving
Tissue converting
- Accumulators
- Coaters
- Core machines
- Embossers
- Facial tissue machinery
- Laminators
- Printers
- Rewinders
- Saws
- Tail sealers
- Unwinds

Tissue packaging
- Tissue bundlers
- Tissue wrappers

COMPETITORS

Andritz AG
James Cropper
Norbord
Nordson
Polymer Group
Sandusky International
Voith
imagelinx

HISTORICAL FINANCIALS

Company Type: Private

Income Statement FYE: September 30

	REVENUE ($ mil.)	NET INCOME ($ mil.)	NET PROFIT MARGIN	EMPLOYEES
09/12	251	0	—	1,304
09/11	215	0	—	—
09/10	196	0	—	—
09/06	194	0	—	—
Annual Growth	4.4%	—	—	—

2012 Year-End Financials

Debt ratio: —
Return on equity: —
Cash ($ mil.): 5
Current ratio: 0.70
Long-term debt ($ mil.): —
Dividends
Yield: —
Payout: —
Market value ($ mil.): —

PARRISH TIRE COMPANY

LOCATIONS

HQ: PARRISH TIRE COMPANY
5130 INDIANA AVE, WINSTON SALEM, NC 271062822
Phone: 3367670202
Web: WWW.PARRISHTIRE.COM

HISTORICAL FINANCIALS

Company Type: Private

Income Statement FYE: December 31

	REVENUE ($ mil.)	NET INCOME ($ mil.)	NET PROFIT MARGIN	EMPLOYEES
12/12	298	2	0.8%	325
12/08	195	0	0.2%	—
12/03	125	0	0.3%	—
12/02	114	0	—	—
Annual Growth	10.1%	—	—	—

2012 Year-End Financials

Debt ratio: —
Return on equity: 0.80%
Cash ($ mil.): 0
Current ratio: 0.30
Long-term debt ($ mil.): —
Dividends
Yield: —
Payout: —
Market value ($ mil.): —

PASADENA HOSPITAL ASSOCIATION

No need to hunt for medical care if you're near Huntington Hospital. The not-for-profit Pasadena Hospital Association which does business as Huntington Hospital provides health care to residents of the San Gabriel Valley in Southern California. Founded in 1892 the hospital boasts some 625 beds and offers acute medical and surgical care and community services in a number of specialties including cardiology gastroenterology women's and children's health orthopedics and neurology. It engages in clinical cancer research (as well as diagnosis and treatment) through the Huntington Cancer Center. The hospital is also a teaching facility for the University of Southern California (USC) Keck School of Medicine.

Geographic Reach

Huntington Hospital serves the health care needs of those who reside in and around Southern California's San Gabriel Valley.

Operations

As part of its operations the California hospital runs The Stroke Center Heart and Vascular Center Huntington Hospital Cancer Center Regional Neonatal Intensive Care Unit Prenatal High Risk Unit and Pediatric Intensive Care Unit.

Strategy

Through its partnership with USC Huntington Hospital offers graduate medical education in areas such as general surgery and internal medicine. Its Huntington Cancer Center partners with area physicians (including some affiliated with USC and UCLA) and the City of Hope medical center to provide comprehensive oncology services and research potential new cancer treatments.

Huntington Hospital broke ground several years ago on an $80-million expansion effort to double the size of its emergency department. The project has included building a new portion that was completed in 2012. It is also renovating the existing emergency facility which is planned for completion by the end of 2013. The project to increase patient capacity up to 80000 and increase diagnostic facilities came in response to growing levels of ER visits.

Sales and Marketing

The medical center is working to upgrade its information technology systems including the addition of an electronic health record (EHR) system.

EXECUTIVES

President and CEO, Steven A. Ralph
EVP COO and CFO, Jim Noble
SVP External Affairs, Jane Haderlein
VP Administrative Services and Chief Human Resources Officer, Debra (Debbie) Ortega
SVP Hospital Operations, Bonnie Kass
VP Clinical Strategy and Physician Development, Bernadette Merlino
VP and CIO, Debra (Debbie) Tafoya
SVP Quality and Physician Services, Paula Verrette
Secretary Treasurer, James Shankwiler

LOCATIONS

HQ: PASADENA HOSPITAL ASSOCIATION
100 W CALIFORNIA BLVD, PASADENA, CA 91105-3010
Phone: 626-397-5000
Web: WWW.HUNTINGTONHOSPITAL.COM

PRODUCTS/OPERATIONS

Selected Services

Ambulatory Care/Dispensary
Angiography
Anticoagulation Clinic
Asthma Education and Management
Bariatric Surgery
Breast Cancer Program
Cardiac Catheterization Lab
Cardiac Electrophysiology (EP)
Cardiac Rehabilitation
Cardiac Screening and Diagnostics
Cardiothoracic Surgery
Community Outreach
CT Scanning (Type 2) Diabetes Prevention and Management
Epilepsy and Brain Mapping
Gastroenterology
Genetic Counseling
Geriatric Assessment Clinic
Gynecological Cancer Program
Heart and Vascular Services
Neurophysiology
Neuroradiology
Neurosciences
Neurosurgery
Obstetrics
Orthopedics
Ostomy Clinic
Pediatric Obesity Prevention
Prenatal High Risk Unit
Prostate Cancer Program
Radiation Oncology
Urology
Uterine Artery Embolization (UAE)

COMPETITORS

Adventist Health
Cedars-Sinai Medical Center
Citrus Valley Health Partners
Dignity Health
Glendale Adventist Medical Center
Kaiser Permanente
Los Angeles County Health Department
Memorial Health Services
St. Joseph Health System
Tenet Healthcare

HISTORICAL FINANCIALS

Company Type: Private

Income Statement FYE: December 31

	REVENUE ($ mil.)	NET INCOME ($ mil.)	NET PROFIT MARGIN	EMPLOYEES
12/09	491	89	18.2%	2,800
12/04	384	68	17.8%	—
12/02	309	(0)	—	—
12/01	257	3	1.2%	—
Annual Growth	8.4%	52.6%	—	—

2009 Year-End Financials

Debt ratio: —
Return on equity: 18.20%
Cash ($ mil.): 22
Current ratio: 1.40
Long-term debt ($ mil.): —
Dividends
Yield: —
Payout: —
Market value ($ mil.): —

PATTON BOGGS LLP

A Beltway insider Patton Boggs law firm specializes in public policy litigation and business law the latter of which is its largest practice area. The firm has continued to build its expertise in other practice areas including administrative and regulatory law food and drug health care employment intellectual property and real estate. Founded in 1962 Patton Boggs employs more than 600 lawyers and professionals. Patton Boggs hosts a weekly Internet radio program "Capital Thinking" that covers the intersection of public policy politics law and business.

Geographic Reach

Patton Boggs is based in Washington DC. The firm also has offices in Northern Virginia New Jersey New York Dallas Denver Anchorage and internationally in Qatar UAE Saudi Arabia. Patton Boggs maintains affiliations and relationships with other firms worldwide.

EXECUTIVES

Partner Washington D.C. and Co-Chairman Technology and Communications, Kevin J. Martin
Chairman, Thomas Hale Boggs Jr.
Director Professional Recruitment, Kara Reidy
Partner Washington D.C. and Co-Chairman Technology and Communications, Jennifer L. Richter
Vice Chairman, Donald V. Moorehead
Deputy Managing Partner, Charles P. (Charlie) Miller
Managing Partner Greater New York and New Jersey, James E. Tyrell Jr.
Managing Partner Northern Virginia, Douglas C. (Doug) Boggs
Managing Partner New Jersey, John McGahren
COO, Ralph E. Allen Jr.
Managing Partner Denver, Robert M. (Bob) Bearman
Managing Partner Anchorage, Walter T. Featherly
Senior Counsel Washington, Richard L. (Dick) Thompson
Founder of the firms, John F. Jonas
Director Public Relations and Communications, Elliott J. Frieder
Chairman CEO, Jamie Dimon
Owner, Fletcher Burlington
Vice President Broadcast Technology, Jay Adrick
President CEO, Lawrence B. Lindsey
Chairman of the Subcommittee on Commerce, Mary R-CA

LOCATIONS

HQ: PATTON BOGGS LLP
2550 M ST NW STE 200, WASHINGTON, DC 20037-1302
Phone: 202-457-6000
Web: WWW.PATTONBOGGS.COM

Selected Locations

Abu Dhabi United Arab Emirates
Anchorage Alaska
Dallas
Denver
Doha Qatar
McLean Virginia
Newark New Jersey
New York
Washington DC

PRODUCTS/OPERATIONS

Selected Areas of Practice

Administrative and regulatory
Antitrust competition policy and trade regulation
Appropriations
Bankruptcy and restructuring
Business
Construction projects infrastructure and finance
Consumer products
Corporate finance
Employee benefits executive compensation and ERISA
Employment law
Energy and natural resources
Environmental law
Estate planning and wealth preservation
Federal marketing
Food and drug
Government contracts
Health and safety law OSHA/ MSHA/ NIOSH
Health care
Homeland security defense and technology transfer
Housing
Immigration
Intellectual property
International practice
Litigation and dispute resolution
Mergers and acquisitions
Middle East and North Africa practice
Municipal representation
Native American affairs
Political law
Postal regulation
Public policy and lobbying
Real estate
Securities
Tax
Technology and communications
Trade and trade policy
Transportation and infrastructure

COMPETITORS

Arnold & Porter
Baker Donelson
Covington & Burling
Hogan Lovells
Pillsbury Winthrop
Shaw Pittman
Steptoe & Johnson
Venable LLP
Vinson & Elkins

HISTORICAL FINANCIALS

Company Type: Private

Income Statement FYE: December 31

	REVENUE ($ mil.)	NET INCOME ($ mil.)	NET PROFIT MARGIN	EMPLOYEES
12/12	326	130	40.0%	1,023
12/08	355	135	38.0%	—
12/07	310	139	45.1%	—
12/06	1,604	0	—	—
Annual Growth	—	347.1%	—	—

2012 Year-End Financials

Debt ratio: —
Return on equity: 40.00%
Cash ($ mil.): 39
Current ratio: 1.20
Long-term debt ($ mil.): —
Dividends
Yield: —
Payout: —
Market value ($ mil.): —

PAXTON MEDIA GROUP LLC

EXECUTIVES

Publisher and Editor The Paducah Sun, James F. (Jim) Paxton, age 58
Director Human Resources, Eric Rudolph
CFO, Richard E. Paxton
Marketing Manager, Kendra Mitchell
Operations Manager, Tom Maher
Executive Assistant, Janice Johnson
General Manager, Gary Adkisson
Executive Editor, Duke Conover
Advertising Director, Carolyn Raney
Vice President of.., Mark Sheppard
Human resources Director, Mike Park

LOCATIONS

HQ: PAXTON MEDIA GROUP LLC
201 S 4TH ST, PADUCAH, KY 420031524
Phone: 2703453152
Web: WWW.CADIZRECORD.COM

COMPETITORS

Cox Newspapers
Gannett
McClatchy Company
Media General
News & Record
Raycom Media
Sinclair Broadcast Group

HISTORICAL FINANCIALS

Company Type: Private

Income Statement FYE: December 28

	REVENUE ($ mil.)	NET INCOME ($ mil.)	NET PROFIT MARGIN	EMPLOYEES
12/08	188	0	—	2,000
12/06	204	0	—	—
12/05	0	0	—	—
12/03	0	0	—	—
Annual Growth	—	—	—	—

2008 Year-End Financials

Debt ratio: —
Return on equity: —
Cash ($ mil.): 0
Current ratio: 0.40
Long-term debt ($ mil.): —
Dividends
Yield: —
Payout: —
Market value ($ mil.): —

PCL CONSTRUCTION ENTERPRISES INC

PCL Construction Enterprises is the contractor to call on for commercial and civil construction concerns. The company serves as the parent to half a dozen US construction companies: PCL Construction Services PCL Civil Constructors PCL Construction PCL Industrial Services PCL Industrial Construction and Nordic PCL Construction. The companies serve as the operating entities for PCL one of Canada's largest general contracting groups. Having completed projects in nearly every US state PCL Construction Enterprises is active in the commercial institutional multi-family residential heavy industrial and civil construction sectors. PCL first entered the US construction market in 1975.

Geographic Reach

Denver-based PCL Construction Enterprises through its half a dozen operating units concentrates on commercial civil and industrial construction projects located in the US.

Its parent's work spans the US Canada the Caribbean and Australia.

Operations

PCL Construction Enterprises and its subsidiaries work on a variety of projects. PCL Construction Enterprises has completed bridges water and wastewater systems manufacturing plants office buildings and restaurants nationwide.

Like many construction companies PCL was hit by the economic recession. Backlogs were lacking and new projects became tougher to win due to an increase in competition. Contracts with water wastewater and renewable energy projects and universities have helped PCL Construction Enterprises through the downturn.

Sales and Marketing

PCL caters to customers in three primary sectors: commercial buildings civil infrastructure and heavy industrial construction. Clients have included the Alaska Railroad Corporation US Army Corps of Engineers Shaw Constructors and OUC-The Reliable One.

Its markets span big cities in Alaska Georgia California North Carolina Texas Colorado Hawaii Minnesota Florida Arizona and Washington.

EXECUTIVES

President US Buildings, Alfred E. (Al) Troppmann, age 65
President and COO, Peter E. Beaupre, age 64
Executive Vice President US Operations, Shaun P. Yancey, age 55
VP Finance, Michael J. (Mike) Kehoe
Director Corporate Development, Dale Kain
Vice President Corporate Finance, Gordon Stephenson
Vice President Risk Management, Hugh McLellan

LOCATIONS

HQ: PCL CONSTRUCTION ENTERPRISES INC
2000 S COLORADO BLVD 2-500, DENVER, CO 80222-7908
Phone: 303-365-6500
Web: WWW.ENTERPRISES.PCL.COM

PRODUCTS/OPERATIONS

Selected Operating Companies

Nordic PCL Construction Inc.
PCL Civil Constructors Inc.
PCL Construction Inc.
PCL Construction Services Inc.
PCL Industrial Construction Co.
PCL Industrial Services Inc.

COMPETITORS

Adolfson & Peterson Inc.
Andersen Construction
Brasfield & Gorrie
C.W. Driver
Dimeo Construction
FCI Constructors
Fluor
Gilbane Building Company
M. B. Kahn
Skanska USA Civil
Suffolk Construction
TIC Holdings
Torix General Contractors
Turner Corporation

HISTORICAL FINANCIALS

Company Type: Private

Income Statement FYE: October 31

	REVENUE ($ mil.)	NET INCOME ($ mil.)	NET PROFIT MARGIN	EMPLOYEES
10/11	1,689	8	0.5%	3,300
10/10	1,616	23	1.5%	—
10/09	2,182	52	2.4%	—
10/08	2,315	84	3.7%	—
Annual Growth	(10.0%)	(53.8%)	—	—

2011 Year-End Financials

Debt ratio: —
Return on equity: 0.50%
Cash ($ mil.): 127
Current ratio: 1.00
Long-term debt ($ mil.): —
Dividends
Yield: —
Payout: —
Market value ($ mil.): —

PDS TECH INC.

Need an IT pro to assist with your company's computer needs? PDS Tech wants to help. The company provides temporary technical industrial and general staffing services through more than 25 offices across the US with a concentration in Texas and on the East Coast. PDS Tech's specialties include aviation architecture engineering information technology administration and maritime staffing. Its PDS Engineering division handles engineering placement for the aerospace mechanical and structural engineering industries while the Information Services division offers technical consulting services in the IT and telecommunication industries. The company was founded in 1977 by aerospace engineer Art Janes.

EXECUTIVES

President and CEO, Arthur R. (Art) Janes
EVP CFO and General Counsel, Steven Cash Nickerson
Controller, Bryan Betzer

LOCATIONS

HQ: PDS TECH INC.
1925 W J CARPENTR FWY 5, IRVING, TX 75063
Phone: 214-647-9600
Web: WWW.PDSTECH.COM

PRODUCTS/OPERATIONS

PDS Operating Divisions
PDS Engineerin
PDS Aviation
PDS Information Services
PDS Maritime
PDS Profession
Offload Engineerin
Northwest Technical Services - Alaska

COMPETITORS

Adecco
Allegis Group
Butler America
CDI
COMFORCE
ManpowerGroup
On Assignment
SFN Group
StarTek
Volt Information

HISTORICAL FINANCIALS

Company Type: Private

Income Statement FYE: December 30

	REVENUE ($ mil.)	NET INCOME ($ mil.)	NET PROFIT MARGIN	EMPLOYEES
12/12	436	2	0.6%	10,000
12/11	397	5	1.3%	—
12/10	338	2	0.6%	—
12/09	344	0	0.1%	—
Annual Growth	8.2%	123.7%	—	—

2012 Year-End Financials

Debt ratio: —
Return on equity: 0.60%
Cash ($ mil.): 0
Current ratio: 3.70
Long-term debt ($ mil.): —

Dividends
Yield: —
Payout: —
Market value ($ mil.): —

PEACEHEALTH

PeaceHealth provides patients with a tranquil place to recover. Make that several tranquil places to recover. PeaceHealth serves residents in southeastern Alaska coastal regions of Washington and central portions of Oregon. Its medical centers include PeaceHealth Ketchikan Medical Center PeaceHealth St. Joseph Medical Center PeaceHealth St. John Medical Center Sacred Heart Medical Center (two campuses) Cottage Grove Community Hospital Peace Harbor Hospital PeaceHealth Peace Island Medical Center and PeaceHealth Southwest Medical Center. Other operations include physician practices community clinics hospices chemical dependency rehabilitation clinics and other outpatient facilities and services.

In 2012 PeaceHealth moved to equip its providers with genome mapping and molecular diagnostics tools and technologies by partnering with Seattle-based P4 Medicine Institute as its founding community health partner. (P4 refers to Predictive Preventive Personalized and Participatory medicine.) Using cutting-edge technologies its providers will be better able to predict disease and affect health outcomes in treating patients. P4 Medicine's consortium also includes as a partner Ohio State University Wexner Medical Center.

PeaceHealth and Southwest Washington Health System merged in early 2011 boosting PeaceHealth's hospital holdings from six to eight with the addition of the two-campus Southwest Washington Medical Center in Vancouver Washington.

Under terms of the affiliation Southwest Washington Health System became part of PeaceHealth allowing Southwest to benefit from its larger peer's medical and financial resources. The move allows both health systems to increase the scope of services they offer in Washington State where Southwest Washington Health System also operates clinics a medical group and a foundation through which it conducts fundraising efforts.

PeaceHealth was formed in 1923 by the Sisters of St. Joseph of Peace who opened the Little Flower Hospital in Ketchikan named after Saint Teresa. The Sisters of St. Joseph of Peace had previously opened St. Joseph Hospital in Bellingham in 1891.

EXECUTIVES

SVP Strategy Innovation and Development, Peter Adler
CEO and Chief Mission Officer Oregon West Network, John Hill
CEO and Chief Mission Officer Columbia Network, Joseph M. Kortum
Senior Vice President, John Haughom
SVP Legal Services, Stuart Hennessey
President and Chief Mission Officer, Alan Yordy
CEO PeaceHealth Medical Group, Howard Graman
CEO and Chief Mission Officer Northwest Network, Nancy Steiger
SVP and CFO, Kevin Walstrom
SVP Culture and People, Carol Aaron
CEO and Chief Mission Officer PeaceHealth St. John Medical Center, Josiah (Sy) Johnson
SVP Shared Services and VP Quality and Patient Safety, Elaine Dunda
Interim SVP Information Services, Tom Fricks
Vice President Human Resources, Craig Mills
Regional Vice President Hospital Operations, Tim Herrmann
Vice President Human Resources, Cindy Klein
Vice President of Services, Faye Lindquist
Vice President Operations PHMG, Henry Veldman
Chief Administrative Officer, Jim Barnhardt
Vice President of Quality, Marc Pierson
Vice President of Strategy, Nancy Tieman
Regional Vice President of Legal Affairs, Roger Saydack
Chief Operating Officer, Steve Omta
Vice President of Health, Chris Sprowl
Vice President Human Resources, Don Bourland
Vice President Medical Affairs, Sherry Catlin
SVP Knowledge and Information; CIO, Ryan D. Ball
Interim Vice President Culture & People, Althea Williams
President Foundation Board, Michael McNellis
Chief Development Officer, Sharon Thornton

LOCATIONS

HQ: PEACEHEALTH
1115 SE 164TH AVE, VANCOUVER, WA 98683-9324
Phone: 425-747-1711
Web: WWW.PEACEHEALTH.ORG/PAGES/SOUTHWEST-WASHINGTON-HEALTH

PRODUCTS/OPERATIONS

Selected Hospitals

PeaceHealth Ketchikan Medical Center (Ketchikan Alaska)
Cottage Grove Community Hospital (Cottage Grove Oregon)
Peace Harbor Hospital (Florence Oregon)
PeaceHealth Peace Island Medical Center (Friday Harbor Washington)
PeaceHealth Southwest Medical Center (Vancouver Washington)
PeaceHealth St. John Medical Center (Longview Washington)
PeaceHealth St. Joseph Medical Center (Bellingham Washington)
Sacred Heart Medical Center at RiverBend (Springfield Oregon)
Sacred Heart Medical Center University District (Eugene Oregon)

Other Operations

PeaceHealth Laboratories (locations throughout Oregon and Washington)
PeaceHealth Medical Group (operates in Alaska Oregon and Washington)

COMPETITORS

Alaska Native Tribal Health Consortium
Franciscan Health System
HCA
Harrison Medical Center
Immediate Care
MultiCare Health System
Overlake Hospital
Providence Health & Services
Seattle Children' s Hospital
South Peninsula Hospital
Swedish Health Services
Tenet Healthcare
Yakima Valley Memorial

HISTORICAL FINANCIALS

Company Type: Private

Income Statement FYE: June 30

	REVENUE ($ mil.)	NET INCOME ($ mil.)	NET PROFIT MARGIN	EMPLOYEES
06/09	1,372	(88)	—	6,690
06/06	1,048	103	9.8%	—
06/05	978	40	4.2%	—
06/04	885	50	5.7%	—
Annual Growth	9.2%	—	—	—

2009 Year-End Financials

Debt ratio: —
Return on equity: (-6.50%)
Cash ($ mil.): 145
Current ratio: 1.30
Long-term debt ($ mil.): —

Dividends
Yield: —
Payout: —
Market value ($ mil.): —

PENDLETON GRAIN GROWERS INC.

EXECUTIVES

Controller, Brian E. Wineland
Manager Human Resources, Jeannie Foster
Manager Agronomy, Joe McDonald
Manager Petroleum and Propane; Manager Service Center, Bryan Bailey
Manager Grain, Jon Sperl
Manager Pump and Irrigation, Reed Stewart
Division Manager Retail, Terry Potratz
Manager Feed and Seed Division and Pendleton Retail, James Cash
Director Advertising, Shannon Denton
President, Allen Waggoner
Manager Athena OR, Darlene Reinhart
Manager Hermiston OR, Doug Myers
Manager Island City OR, Rob Rea
Manager Milton-Freewater, Steve Irving
Credit Manager, Brenda Hunter
Sales Manager, Reed Stew
Vice Chairman, Paul Bracher

LOCATIONS

HQ: PENDLETON GRAIN GROWERS INC.
1000 SW DORION AVE, PENDLETON, OR 978011938
Phone: 5412767611
Web: WWW.PGGCOUNTRY.COM

COMPETITORS

ADM
Ag Processing Inc.
CHS
Cargill
GROWMARK

HISTORICAL FINANCIALS

Company Type: Private

Income Statement FYE: December 31

	REVENUE ($ mil.)	NET INCOME ($ mil.)	NET PROFIT MARGIN	EMPLOYEES
12/09	131	1	1.0%	180
12/08	128	1	0.9%	—
12/07	615	0	—	—
Annual Growth	—	11257.2%	—	—

2009 Year-End Financials

Debt ratio: —
Return on equity: 1.00%
Cash ($ mil.): 1
Current ratio: 0.30
Long-term debt ($ mil.): —

Dividends
Yield: —
Payout: —
Market value ($ mil.): —

PENNSYLVANIA HOSPITAL OF THE UNIVERSITY OF PENNSYLVANIA HEALTH S

Early to bed early to rise may have made Ben Franklin healthy wealthy and wise. But for those not so healthy he (along with Dr. Thomas Bond) found it wise to establish Pennsylvania Hospital the nation's first such institution. Chartered in 1751 the hospital is now a part of the University of Pennsylvania Health System (UPHS) and offers a comprehensive range of medical surgical and diagnostic services to the Philadelphia County area. Housing some 520 beds Pennsylvania Hospital offers specialized care in areas such as orthopedics vascular surgery neurosurgery and obstetrics; it is also a leading teaching hospital and a center for clinical research.

Operations

Pennsylvania Hospital has an average of about 29000 inpatient admissions per year including 5200 births as well as 115000 outpatient and emergency care visits. The medical center has more than 800 physicians on its medical staff. In addition to its extensive medical care services the company conducts medical training programs through its relationship with the University of Pennsylvania School of Medicine. Medical and clinical research programs are conducted with the school and with other research entities including government agencies. The hospital also collaborates with other UPHS entities including the Penn Presbyterian Medical Center and the Hospital of the University of Pennsylvania.

Strategy

To improve the quality of care in the region UPHS is expanding specialist programs at its facilities. In 2013 the organization expanded the orthopedic surgery program at Pennsylvania Hospital. The medical center is also enhancing services in fields including stroke care and women's health.

LOCATIONS

HQ: PENNSYLVANIA HOSPITAL OF THE UNIVERSITY OF PENNSYLVANIA HEALTH S
800 SPRUCE ST, PHILADELPHIA, PA 19107-6192
Phone: 215-829-3000
Web: WWW.PAHOSP.COM

PRODUCTS/OPERATIONS

Selected Centers

ALS Center
Birthing Suite
Center for Bloodless Medicine and Surgery
Crisis Response Center
CyberKnife
Diabetes Education Center
Joan Karnell Cancer Center
Pain Management Center
Parkinson' s Disease and Movement Disorders Center
Penn Comprehensive Neurosciences Center
Penn Orthopaedic Institute
Penn Center for Voice
Sports Medicine and Rehabilitation Center
Sleep Disorders Center
Vascular Center
Women' s Imaging Center

Selected Services

Behavioral health
Heart and vascular
Neonatology
Neurosurgery
Obstetrics (including high-risk maternal and fetal services)
Orthopedics
Otorhinolaryngology (ENT)
Urology
Vascular medicine/surgery

COMPETITORS

Abington Memorial Hospital
Albert Einstein Healthcare Network
Aria Health
Bryn Mawr Hospital
Catholic Health East
Children' s Hospital of Philadelphia
Crozer-Keystone Health System
Fox Chase Cancer Center
North Philadelphia Health System
TUHS
The Magee Memorial Hospital for Convalescents
Thomas Jefferson University Hospital

HISTORICAL FINANCIALS

Company Type: Private

Income Statement FYE: June 30

	REVENUE ($ mil.)	NET INCOME ($ mil.)	NET PROFIT MARGIN	EMPLOYEES
06/10	485	27	5.7%	2,200
06/09	453	0	—	—
06/09	0	0	—	—
Annual Growth	—	—	—	—

2010 Year-End Financials

Debt ratio: —
Return on equity: 5.70%
Cash ($ mil.): 77
Current ratio: 0.80
Long-term debt ($ mil.): —

Dividends
Yield: —
Payout: —
Market value ($ mil.): —

PEPPER CONSTRUCTION COMPANY

LOCATIONS

HQ: PEPPER CONSTRUCTION COMPANY
643 N ORLEANS ST, CHICAGO, IL 606543690
Phone: 3122664700
Web: WWW.PEPPERCONSTRUCTION.COM

HISTORICAL FINANCIALS

Company Type: Private

Income Statement FYE: September 30

	REVENUE ($ mil.)	NET INCOME ($ mil.)	NET PROFIT MARGIN	EMPLOYEES
09/12	673	12	1.9%	900
09/11	668	4	0.6%	—
09/10	503	4	0.9%	—
09/09	592	0	—	—
Annual Growth	4.4%	—	—	—

2012 Year-End Financials

Debt ratio: —
Return on equity: 1.90%
Cash ($ mil.): 25
Current ratio: 0.20
Long-term debt ($ mil.): —

Dividends
Yield: —
Payout: —
Market value ($ mil.): —

PEPPER CONSTRUCTION GROUP LLC

Pepper Construction Group ,Åspices up the construction business with a little of this and a pinch of that. ,ÂThe company provides general contracting and construction management services for commercial office education entertainment ,Â health care and institutional clients as well as waterworks projects. ,Â(Health care projects account for about 50% of Pepper's revenue.) Its ,Áclient list includes ,ÂUBS ,ÂNorthwestern University ,Â University of Notre Dame ,ÂTexas Heart Institute ,ÂLoyola University Medical Center ,Âand ,ÂNASA. Pepper Construction Group has divisions in Illinois Indiana Ohio and Texas. ,ÂStanley F. Pepper founded the company in Chicago in 1927. The group is owned by his family and employees of the firm.

Geographic Reach

Chicago-based Pepper Construction comprises four geographic divisions: Illinois; Indiana; Ohio; and Texas. Overall the company is active in about 20 states mostly in the central and northeastern states.

Operations

The company's Pepper Environmental Technologies unit ,Âprovides environmental services. Green building has become a large part of Pepper Construction's operations. Its Green Team of certified professionals have helped construct more than 2.9 million sq. ft. of eco-friendly space. The Green ,ÂTeam has built the ,ÂApple Computer flagship store ,Â HSBC ,Â Chicago North and ,ÂKohl's ,ÂChildren's Museum.

The firm's Pepper-Lawson Waterworks group ,Âconstructs water purification plants for municipal clients including Houston and Missouri City Texas.

EXECUTIVES

Svp And Cfo, Joel D Thomason
Evp And General Counsel, Thomas M O'Leary
Senior Vice President, Scott Higgins
Senior Vice President, Steve Slade
Vice President, Brad Benhart
Vice President Corporate Facilities, Malissa Jelley
Senior Vice President, Deborah Ebner
Vp Of Information Technology, Howie Piersma
Vice President Engineering Services, Kathline Caviston
Vice President, Michael Cowley
Vp Construction, Howard Olsen

LOCATIONS

HQ: PEPPER CONSTRUCTION GROUP LLC
643 N ORLEANS ST, CHICAGO, IL 606543690
Phone: 3122664703
Web: WWW.PEPPERCONSTRUCTION.COM

PRODUCTS/OPERATIONS

Selected Operations

Pepper Construction Group LLC (Chicago Illinois)
Pepper Construction Co. (Chicago Illinois)
Pepper Construction Co. of Indiana (Indianapolis Indiana)
Pepper Construction Co. of Ohio LLC (Dublin Ohio)
Pepper Environmental Technologies Inc. (Barrington Illinois)
Pepper-Lawson Construction LP (Houston Texas)
Pepper-Lawson Waterworks LLC (Houston Texas)

COMPETITORS

Barton Malow
Bovis Lend Lease
Bulley & Andrews
Graycor
M. A. Mortenson
McCarthy Building

C. G. Schmidt
Charles Pankow Builders
Clark Enterprises
Gilbane
Power Construction
Turner Corporation
Walbridge Aldinger
Walsh Group

HISTORICAL FINANCIALS

Company Type: Private

Income Statement FYE: September 30

	REVENUE ($ mil.)	NET INCOME ($ mil.)	NET PROFIT MARGIN	EMPLOYEES
09/11	911	15	1.7%	1,100
09/10	911	15	1.7%	—
Annual Growth	(0.0%)	(0.0%)	—	—

2011 Year-End Financials

Debt ratio: —
Return on equity: 1.70%
Cash ($ mil.): 1
Current ratio: 0.50
Long-term debt ($ mil.): —
Dividends
Yield: —
Payout: —
Market value ($ mil.): —

PEREZ TRADING COMPANY INC.

No matter how you say it paper or el papel Perez Trading has it. From its Miami warehouse the company distributes more than 15000 tons of paper and paperboard inventory including corrugated box equipment napkin paper printing paper and other printing and shipping equipment and supplies. Customers include commercial printers converters distributors and packaging manufacturers. Perez Trading imports and exports to nearly 30 countries encompassing the Caribbean Islands Central and South America Mexico ,Åand the US. Perez Trading has been family owned and operated since 1947.

EXECUTIVES

Chairman and CEO, John Perez
CFO, Carl A. Perez
VP Logistics, Jose Arenas
President, John D. Perez
Human Resources Manager, Alfred Parra
Paper Division Manager, Erick Bonilla
Converting Equipment Division Manager, Jose Rodriguez
Corrugated Box Equipment Division Manager, Jose Sanchez
Folding Carton Equipment Division Manager, Eladio Del Riego
Containerboard & Kraft Division Manager, Jose Sanchez
Printing Equipment & Supplies Division Manager, Noel Alcantara

LOCATIONS

HQ: PEREZ TRADING COMPANY INC.
3490 NW 125TH ST, MIAMI, FL 331672412
Phone: 3057690761
Web: WWW.PEREZTRADING.COM

COMPETITORS

Georgia-Pacific
Howard Smith Paper
International Paper
MeadWestvaco

HISTORICAL FINANCIALS

Company Type: Private

Income Statement FYE: December 31

	REVENUE ($ mil.)	NET INCOME ($ mil.)	NET PROFIT MARGIN	EMPLOYEES
12/13	526	16	3.2%	148
12/12	570	20	3.6%	—
12/11	532	18	3.5%	—
12/10	492	0	—	—
Annual Growth	2.3%	—	—	—

2013 Year-End Financials

Debt ratio: —
Return on equity: 3.20%
Cash ($ mil.): 0
Current ratio: 1.50
Long-term debt ($ mil.): —
Dividends
Yield: —
Payout: —
Market value ($ mil.): —

PET SUPERMARKET INC.

Pet Supermarket has it all for your furry and feathered friends. The company sells more than 10000 pet care products including food toys medicine and clothing through its website and more than 135 stores in a dozen states primarily Florida. Stores also offer vaccinations for dogs cats and ferrets and sell a variety of small animals such as hamsters guinea pigs rabbits and tropical fish. In addition Pet Supermarket works with area organizations to host adoptions and related events for cats and dogs. Like its pet superstore competitors customers can take their pets shopping with them. Founded in 1973 by Chuck West as Pet Circus the family-owned company became Pet Supermarket in 1986.

Geographic Reach

Based in Florida Pet Supermarket operates specialty stores along the Southeastern US.

Operations

Pet Supermarket sells pet care supplies through stores located primarily in Florida as well as in Tennessee Kentucky Georgia and North Carolina.

Sales and Marketing

The company carries popular brand names such as Nutro Pet Foods Hill's Science Diet Pet Foods Blue Buffalo Pet Foods Natural Balance Pet Foods Taste of the Wild Pet Foods Wellness Pet Food Purina Pro Plan Pet Food MidWest Homes for Pets Blue Ribbon Pet Products Nature's Valley Pet Products and Beefeaters Dog Treats.

Strategy

To strengthen its brand the retailer has rolled out e-commerce capabilities on its website. This helps to bring the Pet Supermarket name to customers who may not live near one of its retail stores. With its e-commerce operations in place the retailer is aggressively growing its store count in Florida where the bulk of its stores are located and throughout the Southeast. Stores typically measure between 7000 square feet and 11000 square feet. In 2013 Pet Supermarket expanded in North Carolina by adding a store in Greensboro between its Winston-Salem and Charlotte stores.

The company also has its eye on growth opportunities in other parts of the country and hopes to expand its existing base in the central and western US including in California Ohio Nevada and Wisconsin where it has a limited presence.

EXECUTIVES

Director Store Operations, Nina Love

LOCATIONS

HQ: PET SUPERMARKET INC.
1100 INTL PKWY STE 200, SUNRISE, FL 33323
Phone: 954-351-0834
Web: WWW.PETSUPERMARKET.COM

PRODUCTS/OPERATIONS

Selected Products

Bark control
Books
Bowls
Carriers
Collars
DVDs
Ear care
Eye care
Feeders
Flea control
Gates
Grooming
Housebreaking
Pet food
Pet toys
Ramps
Scratch posts
Stairs
Training
Treats

COMPETITORS

Drs. Foster & Smith
KV Vet
PETCO
PetCareRx
PetMed
PetSmart
Petland
Publix
United Pharmacal
Wal-Mart
Winn-Dixie

HISTORICAL FINANCIALS

Company Type: Private

Income Statement FYE: December 31

	REVENUE ($ mil.)	NET INCOME ($ mil.)	NET PROFIT MARGIN	EMPLOYEES
12/12	245	0	—	1,000
12/11	198	0	—	—
12/09	171	0	—	—
12/09	168	9	5.6%	—
Annual Growth	13.5%	—	—	—

2012 Year-End Financials

Debt ratio: —
Return on equity: —
Cash ($ mil.): 2
Current ratio: 0.40
Long-term debt ($ mil.): —
Dividends
Yield: —
Payout: —
Market value ($ mil.): —

PETERSBURG MOTOR COMPANY INC

LOCATIONS

HQ: PETERSBURG MOTOR COMPANY INC
100 MYERS DR, CHARLOTTESVILLE, VA 229011166
Phone: 4349511000
Web: WWW.COLONIALAUTOCENTER.COM

HISTORICAL FINANCIALS

Company Type: Private

Income Statement FYE: December 31

	REVENUE ($ mil.)	NET INCOME ($ mil.)	NET PROFIT MARGIN	EMPLOYEES
12/13	319	4	1.4%	388
12/12	269	3	1.3%	—
12/11	204	3	1.6%	—
12/09	129	0	—	—
Annual Growth	25.4%	—	—	—

2013 Year-End Financials

Debt ratio: ——
Return on equity: 1.40%
Cash ($ mil.): 7
Current ratio: 0.40
Long-term debt ($ mil.): —
Dividends
Yield: —
Payout: —
Market value ($ mil.): —

PETRO STAR INC.

Petro Star is an oil refining and fuel marketing shining star that brings heating fuel and energy (diesel gasoline and aviation and marine fuel)s to the citizens of the communities in the vast cold and lonely expanses of the US' largest state Alaska. It operates refineries at North Pole and Valdez and distributes fuels and lubricants throughout Interior Alaska Dutch Harbor Kodiak and Valdez. Started in 1984 by a group of petroleum industry veterans the company built its first refinery operations along the Trans-Alaska Pipeline at North Pole Alaska. Petro Star is a subsidiary of Arctic Slope Regional Corp..

The company has expanded through acquisitions including fuel distribution firm Sourdough Fuel (in 1986) as well as the 1991 purchase of Alaska Lube and Fuel (now Petro Star Lubricants). Kodiak Sales (in 1997) and North Pacific Fuel (in 1998).

In 2008 Petro Star secured a $158.7 million aviation fuel contract from the Defense Logistics Agency.

EXECUTIVES

VP Heating Fuel and Marine, Don Castle
VP Marketing Aviation Lubricants and Convenience Stores, Mark W. John
Director North Pacific Fuel Operations, Mark Hughes
Operations Manager Heating Fuel Lubricants and Marine Dutch Harbor, Norman Bautista
Operations Manager Kodiak, Terry Davis
General Manager Lubricants Anchorage, Shirley Merkley
General Manager Aviation Heating Fuel and Lubricants Fairbanks, Andy Cogan
General Manager, Jamie Olthoff
Manager Government Compliance and Safety, Lisa Lewis
Retail Operations Manager Fairbanks, Doug Richmond
Office Manager, Susan Moore
Director of Refinery Operations, John Meason
Marketing Manager of Sales, Nicole Stew

LOCATIONS

HQ: PETRO STAR INC.
3900 C ST STE 802, ANCHORAGE, AK 99503-5963
Phone: 907-339-6600

COMPETITORS

Exxon Mobil
Tesoro
Valero Energy

HISTORICAL FINANCIALS

Company Type: Private

Income Statement FYE: December 31

	REVENUE ($ mil.)	NET INCOME ($ mil.)	NET PROFIT MARGIN	EMPLOYEES
12/08	992	0	—	300
12/03	291	3	1.2%	—
12/02	267	1	0.7%	—
12/01	279	3	1.1%	—
Annual Growth	19.9%	—	—	—

2008 Year-End Financials

Debt ratio: —
Return on equity: —
Cash ($ mil.): 106
Current ratio: 1.50
Long-term debt ($ mil.): —
Dividends
Yield: —
Payout: —
Market value ($ mil.): —

PETROLEUM MARKETERS INCORPORATED

No fancy name for this company. It is what it says it is. Petroleum Marketers is a full-service petroleum company serving customers in Kentucky Maryland North Carolina Tennessee West Virginia and Virginia. The company's PM Terminals unit supplies gasoline diesel fuel motor oil and antifreeze to customers in its service area from eight bulk fuel storage facilities in Virginia. PMI Lubricants operates a fleet of bulk transport trucks while PM Transport offers for-hire tanker truckers for the transportation of petroleum products. The company also runs a chain of about 70 convenience stores/gas stations in Virginia under the banner Stop In Food Stores.

Geographic Reach

The company has convenience stores throughout Virginia and West Virginia. Petroleum Marketers' subsidiaries serve customers in Kentucky North Carolina Maryland Tennessee Virginia and West Virginia.

Some locations have fast food eateries in Virginia (run by its PM Foods division) including a number of Burger Kings and Arbys and one Subway located within or next door to Stop In Food Stores.

Operations

The company's major units include PM Foods PM Terminals (8 bulk storage facilities) PM Transport PMI Lubricants and Stop In Food Stores. Other units include PM Properties (real estate) and PMI Services Inc.

Ownership

The company is employee owned.

Company Background

In 2009 Petroleum Marketers launched an 85% ethanol/15% gas blend at its Albemarle County Shell station (the first E85 fuel blend in Central Virginia) as a prototype for use of the alternative fuel blend at other gas stations in the region.

Petroleum Marketers was founded in 1921. The company set up as PM Terminals in 1949.

EXECUTIVES

Chairman President and CEO, Ronald R. (Ron) Hare

LOCATIONS

HQ: PETROLEUM MARKETERS INCORPORATED
3000 OGDEN RD, ROANOKE, VA 24018-8857
Phone: 540-772-4900
Web: WWW.PETROLEUMMARKETERS.COM

PRODUCTS/OPERATIONS

Major Operating Units
PMI Lubricants
PM Foods
PM Terminals
PM Transport
Stop In Food Stores

COMPETITORS

Chevron
Cumberland Farms
Exxon Mobil
Gate Petroleum
Racetrac Petroleum
The Pantry

HISTORICAL FINANCIALS

Company Type: Private

Income Statement FYE: June 30

	REVENUE ($ mil.)	NET INCOME ($ mil.)	NET PROFIT MARGIN	EMPLOYEES
06/13	1,040	1	0.1%	1,500
06/12	1,081	1	0.2%	—
06/10	945	2	0.2%	—
06/10	797	4	0.6%	—
Annual Growth	9.3%	(37.4%)	—	—

2013 Year-End Financials

Debt ratio: ——
Return on equity: 0.10%
Cash ($ mil.): 9
Current ratio: 0.90
Long-term debt ($ mil.): —
Dividends
Yield: —
Payout: —
Market value ($ mil.): —

PETROLEUM TRADERS CORPORATION

EXECUTIVES

President, Michael B. Himes
VP, Vicki L. Himes
Operations Manager, Joe Jurczak
CFO, Linda Stephens
Distribution Manager, Rick Hauschild
Distribution Manager, Mayleen Brinker
Contract Sales Manager, Gayle Newton

LOCATIONS

HQ: PETROLEUM TRADERS CORPORATION
7120 POINTE INVERNESS WAY, FORT WAYNE, IN 468047928
Phone: 2604326622
Web: WWW.PETROLEUMTRADERS.COM

COMPETITORS

Petro Holdings
SMF Energy
Sun Coast Resources

HISTORICAL FINANCIALS

Company Type: Private

Income Statement FYE: June 30

	REVENUE ($ mil.)	NET INCOME ($ mil.)	NET PROFIT MARGIN	EMPLOYEES
06/14	2,670	14	0.6%	110
06/13	3,066	24	0.8%	—
06/12	2,796	13	0.5%	—
06/11	2,470	0	—	—
Annual Growth	2.6%	—	—	—

2014 Year-End Financials

Debt ratio: —
Return on equity: 0.60%
Cash ($ mil.): 9
Current ratio: 1.90
Long-term debt ($ mil.): —

Dividends
Yield: —
Payout: —
Market value ($ mil.): —

PHALCON LTD.

LOCATIONS

HQ: PHALCON LTD.
505 MAIN ST, FARMINGTON, CT 060322912
Phone: 8606779797
Web: WWW.PHALCONLTD.COM

HISTORICAL FINANCIALS

Company Type: Private

Income Statement FYE: December 31

	REVENUE ($ mil.)	NET INCOME ($ mil.)	NET PROFIT MARGIN	EMPLOYEES
12/13	279	21	7.6%	1,000
12/12	257	18	7.1%	—
12/11	214	13	6.2%	—
12/10	180	0	—	—
Annual Growth	15.7%	—	—	—

2013 Year-End Financials

Debt ratio: —
Return on equity: 7.60%
Cash ($ mil.): 50
Current ratio: 1.90
Long-term debt ($ mil.): —

Dividends
Yield: —
Payout: —
Market value ($ mil.): —

PHELPS MEMORIAL HOSPITAL ASSOCIATION

If you happen to spot the headless horseman in Sleepy Hollow it's possible he's on his way to Phelps Memorial Hospital for some medical treatment. The 240-bed hospital provides both physical and mental health care services to residents of Sleepy Hollow and Westchester County New York. Specialized services include cardiology emergency care orthopedics and psychiatry. It also includes a satellite location of the Memorial Sloan-Kettering Cancer Center and it provides geriatric health services through a partnership with Mount Sinai Hospital and operates a senior retirement community with Kendal Corporation. Phelps Memorial is one of four hospitals that make up the Stellaris Health Network.

Geographic Reach

Phelps Memorial is located on a 70-acre campus on the banks of the Hudson River in Sleepy Hollow. It serves surrounding areas of central Westchester County including Tarrytown.

Operations

Phelps Memorial Hospital handles some 27000 emergency room visits each year. Its maternity wing also managed more than 1000 birthing procedures and the hospital's counseling unit saw about 18000 patients. Other specialty divisions provide stroke care and home health and hospice services. The medical center operates family and specialty physician practices and mental health clinics in the region.

Through its affiliation with Mount Sinai Hospital (and therefore the Sinai Health System) Phelps Memorial's patients and physicians have access to specialized services from Mount Sinai Hospital. It also provides prenatal and high-risk pregnancy care in partnership with area providers Open Door Family Medical Centers and Westchester Medical Center. In 2012 the hospital became a teaching facility for family medicine and dental residency programs through an affiliation with New York Medical College.

The other hospitals in the Stellaris network are Lawrence Hospital Center Northern Westchester Hospital and White Plains Hospital Center. The medical centers operate independently but pool resources in areas including information technology procurement and best practices.

Financial Performance

In 2011 Phelps Memorial reported a financial surplus for the 20th year in a row. The not-for-profit company reinvests its profits into technology enhancements and capital improvements.

Strategy

The hospital's primary goals include enhancing the convenience of its services and increasing patient satisfaction. Towards that end Phelps Memorial restructured its west wing in 2011; the facility now houses its pre-surgical assessment pain management registration and outpatient laboratory departments. In 2013 it expanded services by launching new asthma treatment and lung nodule screening programs; it also opened a new family and diagnostic facility (Phelps at Croton) that year.

The Phelps Memorial Hospital has gone through other major renovations in recent years more than doubling its size with the addition of a new emergency department new offices more inpatient beds and an inpatient pediatrics unit.

EXECUTIVES

Vp Medical Staff, Saleem M Mir
Assistant Vp Behavioral Health And Nursing Services, Janet Goldberg
Assistant Vice President Quality And Case Management, William Reifer
President and CEO, Keith F. Safian
SVP Medical Affairs and Chief Medical Officer, Lawrence L. Faltz
VP Finance and CFO, Vincent DeSantis
VP Support Services, Kerry L. Pisano
Chief Nursing Officer, Mary McDermott
President Medical Staff, Franklin Zimmerman
Director Department of Anesthesiology, Paul Terracciano
Director Department of Emergency Medicine, Emil Nigro
Director Department of Family Medicine, Michael McCormick
Director Department of Medicine, Arthur Fass
Director Department of Obstetrics and Gynecology, Lawrence Mendelowitz
Director Department of Pathology, Stanley Oiseth
Director Department of Pediatrics, Margaret Stillman
Director Department of Psychiatry, L. Mark Russakoff
Director Department of Radiology, Robert Perelman
Director Department of Surgery, Richard Peress
Chief of Cardiology, Rajat Sanyal
Chief of Dermatology, Jeffrey Sturza
Chief of Dental and Oral Surgery, Michael C. Miller
Chief of Gastroenterology, Stephen K. Heier
Chief of General Surgery, Robert Raniolo
Chief of Infectious Diseases, Michael H. Miller
Chief of Nephrology, Louis Buzzeo
Chief of Neurology, Sanda Carniciu
Chief of Neurosurgery, John Robbins
Chief of Ophthalmology, Jean Tostanoski
Chief of Orthopedics, Gregg Cavaliere
Chief of Otolaryngology, Michael Bergstein
Chief of Plastic Surgery, Christian Guzman
Chief of Podiatry, John Cappa
Chief of Pulmonary Medicine, Gary Lehrman
Chief of Thoracic Surgery, Avraham Merav
Chief of Urology, Arno Housman
Chief of Vascular Surgery, Igor Laskowski
Assistant Vice President Facilities, William Liedy
Exec Secy To Sr Vice President Chief, Melanie Anderson
Director Of Surgery Services, Paula Keenan
Medical Director Physical Medicine And Rehabilita, Wei Liu
Chairman, Richard Sinni
Vice Chairman, Sean F. X. Dugan
Vice Chairman, Andrew Merryman

LOCATIONS

HQ: PHELPS MEMORIAL HOSPITAL ASSOCIATION
701 N BROADWAY, SLEEPY HOLLOW, NY 10591-1096
Phone: 914-366-3000
Web: WWW.PHELPSHOSPITAL.ORG

PRODUCTS/OPERATIONS

Selected Services

Alcohol & Substance Abuse Treatment
Behavioral Health
Blood Donor Services
Bone Densitometry
Cardiac Rehabilitation
Cardiovascular Laboratory
Cardiovascular Risk Assessment
Critical Care Unit
Decontamination Unit
Diabetes Adult
Diabetes Pediatric
Electroconvulsive Therapy
Emergency Services
Emergency Training Services
Endoscopy
Gastroenterology
Geriatrics
Hand Therapy
Health Management
Hearing (Audiology)
Hernia Center
Hip
Hospice
Hyperbaric Medicine
Incontinence
Infusion Center
Laboratory Services
Lung Nodule Center
Lymphedema
Mammography
Maternity
Memory Loss
Mental Health Services
MRI
Nutrition Counseling for Outpatients
Oncology Memorial Sloan-Kettering Cancer Center
Orthopedics
Ostomy Outpatient
Pain Center
Palliative Care
Pediatric Endocrinology
Pediatrics
Pharmacy
Physical Rehabilitation
Psychiatry
Pulmonology & Respiratory
Radiology

Respiratory Care
Respite
Senior Health & Internal Medicine
Sleep Disorders
Speech
Stroke Center
Swallowing Disorders

COMPETITORS

Bergen Regional Medical
Burke Rehabilitation Hospital
Englewood Hospital and Medical Center
Greenwich Hospital
Montefiore Medical
Nyack Hospital
The Valley Hospital
Valley Health System
Westchester Medical Center

HISTORICAL FINANCIALS

Company Type: Private

Income Statement FYE: December 31

	REVENUE ($ mil.)	NET INCOME ($ mil.)	NET PROFIT MARGIN	EMPLOYEES
12/09	182	5	3.2%	1,200
12/06	135	5	4.0%	—
12/05	129	5	4.4%	—
12/04	124	8	6.7%	—
Annual Growth	7.9%	(6.9%)	—	—

2009 Year-End Financials

Debt ratio: —
Return on equity: 3.20%
Cash ($ mil.): 13
Current ratio: 0.80
Long-term debt ($ mil.): —
Dividends
Yield: —
Payout: —
Market value ($ mil.): —

PHILLIPS AND JORDAN INCORPORATED

While some like to clear the air Phillips and Jordan (P&J) prefers to clear the land. Founded in 1952 as a small land clearing firm P&J is a general and specialty contractor that still provides land clearing services in addition to industrial commercial and residential site development and heavy civil construction on dams highways bridges railroads and waterways. P&J also performs reclamation landfill and disaster recovery services. The latter includes handling some of the nation's worst disaster cleanups including hurricanes floods toxic spills and land and rock slides. P&J operates about a dozen offices in eight states. The Phillips family owns and runs the company.

Geographic Reach

Knoxville Tennessee-based Phillips and Jordan has about a dozen offices in North Carolina and in California Florida North Dakota Tennessee and Wyoming.

Operations

Phillips and Jordan operates a fleet of more than 850 pieces of heavy and specialized equipment including excavators graders loaders tractors and trucks. The firm performs projects across the US.

True to its roots the company has built a reputation for taking on difficult land clearing jobs. With a fleet of specialized equipment P&J clears and grubs swamp forest mountain and agricultural land to make way for reservoirs pipelines power transmission lines railways and roadways. Clients come from both the public and private sectors.

Strategy

The booming oil and gas industry in Wyoming has drawn P&J to the state where in late 2013 it opened two rock pits in the Douglas area. The pits are managed from the firm's Douglas office. Also in 2013 P&J partnered with North Creek Energy to form a joint venture company Solar Jack LLC to market a system that offers oil and gas producers the opportunity to capture the regenerated energy from their pump jacks combined with solar energy to reduce energy consumption and costs. Previously the firm expanded its operations near Williston North Dakota opening an equipment maintenance shop and offices there in 2012.

EXECUTIVES

Vice President Human Resources, Jo Bullock
Vice President California Division, Randy Jordan
Vice President Oil Gas Group, Cecil Patterson
Vice President Safety & Risk Management, Steve D Thompson
Vice President, Dorinda A Futch
Assistant Vice President, David Edd
Sr Vp, Frank Wood
Asst Vice President, Mike Teem
Vice President Fl Heavy Div, Stanley Croy
Vice President Of Operations Mexico, Arturo Martinovich
Vice President Of Operations Mexico, Arturo Elrod
Vice President Human Resources, Jo Carpenter
Vice President, Page Riley
Vice President, Morgan Pierce
Vice President, Dale Joiner
Senior Vice President Secretary, Connie H Nichols, age 62

LOCATIONS

HQ: PHILLIPS AND JORDAN INCORPORATED
10201 PARKSIDE DR STE 300, KNOXVILLE, TN 379221983
Phone: 8656888342
Web: WWW.PANDJ.COM

PRODUCTS/OPERATIONS

Selected Services

Apartment site development
Disaster recovery
Heavy civil construction
Industrial and commercial site development
Land clearing
Landfill and liner design
Reclamation and mitigation
Subdivision site development

COMPETITORS

Boh Bros Construction
Clarkson Construction
Environmental Safety & Health
Hardaway Construction
McCarthy Building
Peter Kiewit Sons'
Rentenbach Constructors

HISTORICAL FINANCIALS

Company Type: Private

Income Statement FYE: December 31

	REVENUE ($ mil.)	NET INCOME ($ mil.)	NET PROFIT MARGIN	EMPLOYEES
12/13	215	4	2.1%	650
12/12	284	11	4.0%	—
12/11	356	12	3.4%	—
12/10	261	0	—	—
Annual Growth	(6.3%)	—	—	—

2013 Year-End Financials

Debt ratio: —
Return on equity: 2.10%
Cash ($ mil.): 13
Current ratio: 2.00
Long-term debt ($ mil.): —
Dividends
Yield: —
Payout: —
Market value ($ mil.): —

PHOENIX CHILDREN'S HOSPITAL INC.

Phoenix Children's Hospital (PCH) invests in the health of the next generation. Founded in 1983 the hospital provides a comprehensive range of medical services specifically for children and adolescents in the greater Phoenix area. The hospital has about 360 beds and provides care in a number of pediatric sub-specialties including childhood cancers hematology neuroscience heart disease trauma and orthopedics. In addition to a newborn intensive care unit (NICU) at its main campus PCH operates a second NICU on the campus of Banner Good Samaritan Regional Medical Center (a member of Banner Health).

Geographic Reach

PCH has several pediatric outpatient care centers in surrounding Phoenix suburbs.

Financial Performance

The hospital's revenue increased by 33% to $669 million in fiscal 2012 compared to fiscal 2011. Its net income was $28 million in fiscal 2012.

Strategy

To meet population growth levels in the region PCH is working to expand its medical center facilities. For instance in 2012 the hospital completed a multi-year $588 million construction project; the effort started in 2008 and increased the number of hospital beds from 350 to to 465. Capacity for specialties that include ICU operating rooms trauma care neurology sports medicine and pediatric research were also added in the new patient tower. The expansion efforts also allow PCH to accommodate patients from other areas of Arizona and surrounding states in the Southwest.

PCH added further to its research and educational operations by forming an affiliation with University of Arizona's College of Medicine in 2010. The two entities collaborate on research projects and physician training programs. PCH has additional clinical and non-clinical research collaborations with other institutions to make advances in pediatric care such as Mayo Clinic Translational Genomics Institute and the Children's Oncology Group.

EXECUTIVES

Chairman, Mark B. Bonsall
President and CEO, Robert L. Meyer
VP and Chief Medical Officer, Murray M. Pollack
Senior Vice President Human Resources, Thomas J. (Tom) Diederich
SVP and Chief Development Officer Foundation, Steven (Steve) Schnall
Chairman, David Cavazos
EVP Phoenix Children?s Medical Group and Surgeon-in-Chief, Dennis P. Lund
EVP Finance and CFO, Craig L. McKnight
EVP and COO, Betsy Kuzas
Vice Chairman, Jon Hulburd
Senior Vice President Legal Affairs and General Counsel, Carmen Neuberger
Physician-in-Chief, David Bank
SVP and Chief Information Officer, David Higginson
SVP Patient Care and Chief Nursing Officer, Pamela J. Carlson
Training Director, John L. Barton
Vice President Quality and Risk Management, Tamara Johnson
Vice President Planning Design and Construction, Dave Cottle
Vice President Finance, Dennis Bruns

Vice President Practice Operations for Phoenix Childrens Medical Group, Douglas Henson
Vice President Managed Care and Business Development, Ethel Hoffman
Vice President Network Development, Giff Loda
Chairman Senior Partner, Jacque J. Sokolov
General Partner, Ken Kendrick
Chairman of the Foundation Board, Larry Clemmensen
Vice President Revenue Cycle, Linda Flink
VP and Chief Medical Information Officer, Vinay Vaidya
SVP and Chief Administrative Officer Phoenix Children?s Medical Group, Roger Logan
SVP Business Development and Chief Strategy Officer, Robert Campbell
President Phoenix Children's Medical Staff, Jeffrey P. Morray
Chairman Phoenix Children's Hospital Foundation Board of Directors, Brian Swartz

LOCATIONS

HQ: PHOENIX CHILDREN' S HOSPITAL INC.
1919 E THOMAS RD, PHOENIX, AZ 85016-7710
Phone: 602-546-1000
Web: WWW.PHOENIXCHILDRENS.COM

COMPETITORS

Banner Health
Dignity Health
Flagstaff Medical Center
John C. Lincoln Health Network
Northern Arizona Healthcare
Scottsdale Healthcare
Shriners Hospitals For Children
University of Arizona Health Network

HISTORICAL FINANCIALS

Company Type: Private

Income Statement FYE: December 31

	REVENUE ($ mil.)	NET INCOME ($ mil.)	NET PROFIT MARGIN	EMPLOYEES
12/11	498	(5)	—	3,000
12/09	408	106	26.1%	—
12/06	424	(106)	—	—
12/06	1,086	0	—	—
Annual Growth	—	—	—	—

2011 Year-End Financials

Debt ratio: —
Return on equity: (-1.00%)
Cash ($ mil.): 61
Current ratio: 0.20
Long-term debt ($ mil.): —
Dividends
Yield: —
Payout: —
Market value ($ mil.): —

PIGGLY WIGGLY ALABAMA DISTRIBUTING CO. INC.

LOCATIONS

HQ: PIGGLY WIGGLY ALABAMA DISTRIBUTING CO. INC.
2400 J TERRELL WOOTEN DR, BESSEMER, AL 350202272
Phone: 2054812300
Web: WWW.PWADC.COM

HISTORICAL FINANCIALS

Company Type: Private

Income Statement FYE: July 27

	REVENUE ($ mil.)	NET INCOME ($ mil.)	NET PROFIT MARGIN	EMPLOYEES
07/12	733	0	0.1%	500
07/11	772	0	0.1%	—
07/10	837	0	0.0%	—
07/09	830	0	—	—
Annual Growth	(4.1%)	—	—	—

2012 Year-End Financials

Debt ratio: —
Return on equity: 0.10%
Cash ($ mil.): 6
Current ratio: 0.20
Long-term debt ($ mil.): —
Dividends
Yield: —
Payout: —
Market value ($ mil.): —

PIKEVILLE MEDICAL CENTER INC.

Taking a fall while hiking the rugged Appalachians might land you at Pikeville Medical Center (PMC). Serving patients in eastern Kentucky PMC has about 260 beds and provides a full range of inpatient outpatient and surgical services. Centers and departments within the hospital handle specialties such as diagnostic imaging echocardiogram neurosurgery cancer care and bariatric surgery. Employing 300 physicians PMC also operates a rehabilitation hospital a home health agency and outpatient family practice and specialty clinics as well as a physician residency program. PMC first opened on Christmas Day in 1924.

Strategy

Pikeville Medical Center is rapidly expanding its services and facilities to keep pace with the needs of area residents. It added new services in 2012 including pulmonary rehabilitation plastic surgery and orthopedic trauma. In addition the hospital launched a $130 million expansion project that will add an 11-story outpatient center (including physician practices and surgery suites) and a 10-story parking garage by 2014. Additional expansion efforts in recent years include opening new outpatient cancer diagnostic pain management and primary care clinics.

EXECUTIVES

VP; CEO Rehabilitation Services, Debbie Puckett
Center Chief Operating Officer, Juanita Deskins
VP and Assistant to the President and CEO, Cheryl Hickman
President CEO and Director, Walter E. May
COO, Jerry D. Johnson
Chief Medical Officer, William M. Johnson
Secretary, Joe D. Anderson
VP and Chief Nursing Officer, Debra Hampton
Chief of Staff and Director, Aaron Crum
President of the University of Pikeville, James Hurley
President CEO and Director, Walter E. May
Director, Ronald (Ron) Burchett
Director, Walter (Smokey) Blankenship
Director, T. T. Colley
Director, Dennis Halbert
Director, Judith Hinkle
Director, Jo Nell Robinson
Director, Mary Rado Simpson
Director, John Waddell
Chief of Staff and Director, Aaron Crum

LOCATIONS

HQ: PIKEVILLE MEDICAL CENTER INC.
911 BYPASS RD, PIKEVILLE, KY 41501-1689
Phone: 606-218-3500
Web: WWW.PIKEVILLEHOSPITAL.ORG

PRODUCTS/OPERATIONS

Selected Services

Bariatric Surgery
Breast Care Center
Critical Care
Diagnostics
Diabetes Education
Ear Nose & Throat (Otolaryngology)
Emergency
Endocrinology
Family Practice
Gastroenterology
Gynecology/Obstetrics
Family Practice Clinic
Heart Institute
Heart Failure/Coumadin Clinic
Home Health
Home Medical Equipment
Inpatient
Infectious Disease
Laboratory Services
Leonard Lawson Cancer Center
Neonatology
Nephrology
Neurosurgery
Ophthalmology
Other Patient Services
Orthopedic Surgery
Palliative Care
Pediatrics
Pharmacy
Plastic & Reconstructive Surgery
Pulmonary Clinic
Radiology
Rehabilitation
Residency Program
Rheumatology
Sleep
Urology
Women and Childrens' Services
Wound Care Center

COMPETITORS

Appalachian Regional Healthcare
Clinch Valley Medical Center
Community Health Systems
Highlands Health
Norton Community Hospital
Norton Healthcare
Russell County Medical Center
SunBridge Healthcare Corporation
University of Kentucky Chandler Hospital

HISTORICAL FINANCIALS

Company Type: Private

Income Statement FYE: September 30

	REVENUE ($ mil.)	NET INCOME ($ mil.)	NET PROFIT MARGIN	EMPLOYEES
09/09	267	27	10.2%	1,025
09/03	132	12	9.3%	—
09/02	127	13	10.4%	—
09/01	105	56	53.6%	—
Annual Growth	12.3%	(8.8%)	—	—

2009 Year-End Financials

Debt ratio: —
Return on equity: 10.20%
Cash ($ mil.): 78
Current ratio: 1.30
Long-term debt ($ mil.): —
Dividends
Yield: —
Payout: —
Market value ($ mil.): —

PILOT CORPORATION

Pilot offers a salve to those suffering from white-line fever. Its Pilot Flying J a joint venture between Pilot and CVC Capital Partners runs more than 650 travel centers that sell fuel and food across North America. Its truck stops feature restaurant chains such as Subway Pizza Hut and Taco Bell and offer hot showers. Pilot has fuel islands large enough to service several 18-wheelers. Pilot Truck Care Centers provide TLC (tender loving care) for big rigs while some 45 Pilot Food Marts (all in Tennessee) keep drivers fed. James Haslam II got Pilot off the ground in 1958 as a gas station that sold cigarettes and soft drinks; now his son CEO James Haslam III runs the firm. The Haslam family owns the company.

Operations

The combined network of more than 650 Pilot Travel Centers and Flying J travel plazas across North America serves more than 1.3 million customers each day. As a leading supplier of diesel fuel to the trucking industry Pilot Corp. supplies about 10% of the truck diesel fuel used in US.

Strategy

Travel centers are the company's focus; Pilot has built a nationwide network through organic growth and acquisitions. Continuing its nationwide expansion in June 2013 Pilot Flying J opened a new Pilot Travel Center in Canton Texas (its 662nd location overall in North America and 42nd location in Texas.)

In 2010 the company acquired the travel center business of rival Flying J and subsequently combined its former Pilot Travel Centers and Flying J as Pilot Flying J. Flying J which was in bankruptcy at the time of the takeover had more than 270 travel centers and fuel stops in some 40 US states and six Canadian provinces. CVC Capital Partners owns about 47% of Pilot Flying J. The private equity firm acquired its stake from Marathon Petroleum.

EXECUTIVES

Executive Vice President, Mark A Hazelwood
Vice President, Jim Alexander
Executive Vice President And Director Of Facility Revenue, Asa Hazelwood
Vice President Of Sales Western Region, Scott Wombold
Treas, David Clothier

LOCATIONS

HQ: PILOT CORPORATION
5508 LONAS DR, KNOXVILLE, TN 37909-3221
Phone: 865-588-7488
Web: WWW.PILOTFLYINGJ.COM

PRODUCTS/OPERATIONS

Selected Operations

Convenience stores (groceries gas and diesel and assorted merchandise)
Garages (truck repair and maintenance)
Travel centers (groceries showers gas and diesel restaurants and assorted merchandise)

COMPETITORS

7-Eleven
Chevron
Couche-Tard
Exxon Mobil
Love' s Country Stores
Motiva Enterprises
Royal Dutch Shell
Starbucks
Stuckey' s
TravelCenters of America
Wawa Inc.

HISTORICAL FINANCIALS

Company Type: Private

Income Statement — FYE: December 31

	REVENUE ($ mil.)	NET INCOME ($ mil.)	NET PROFIT MARGIN	EMPLOYEES
12/11	402	365	91.0%	13,000
12/10	415	373	89.9%	—
Annual Growth	(3.2%)	(2.0%)	—	—

2011 Year-End Financials

Debt ratio: —
Return on equity: 91.00%
Cash ($ mil.): 21
Current ratio: 2.50
Long-term debt ($ mil.): —
Dividends
Yield: —
Payout: —
Market value ($ mil.): —

PINNACLE HEALTH SYSTEM

PinnacleHealth helps central Pennsylvanians reach the peaks of wellness. PinnacleHealth System provides a continuum of care through its four hospitals that have a combined total of about 600 beds. Together Community General Hospital Harrisburg Hospital Polyclinic Hospital and the Helen M. Simpson Rehab Hospital provide general and specialty services in areas such as oncology cardiovascular medicine neurology mental health physical therapy women's health and orthopedics. PinnacleHealth is also home to a network of community health diagnostic ambulatory surgery and outpatient centers. Additionally the system administers home care and hospice care programs.

Geographic Reach

PinnacleHealth's main campus locations are located in Harrisburg Pennsylvania.

Operations

Altogether the system's facilities handle some 108000 emergency room visits and perform about 30000 surgeries and 4000 births each year. In addition PinnacleHealth is a teaching system offering residency programs in internal medicine general surgery pediatric surgery family practice podiatric surgery and orthopedic surgery. It offers fellowship programs in bariatric surgery maternal and fetal medicine toxicology and sports medicine.

Financial Performance

PinnacleHealth reported $825 million in annual revenue in 2012. About 50% of the organization's revenue comes from inpatient services while more than 40% is sourced to outpatient services.

Strategy

PinnacleHealth is conducting a major expansion project by building a new $100 million medical center in Hampden Township. The new West Shore campus will house a 110-bed acute care hospital with a full range of emergency general surgical and specialty health services as well as private patient rooms. The organization is also renovating and expanding its Harrisburg and Community campuses and it is upgrading medical equipment and information technology systems.

Company Background

PinnacleHealth traces its roots to 1873 the year when Harrisburg Hospital was founded.

EXECUTIVES

President and CEO, Roger Longenderfer
SVP Medical Affairs and Chief Medical Officer, Dana Kellis
SVP Community and Governmental Relations, Christopher P. Markley
VP Organizational Quality and Performance Improvement, Joan Silver

LOCATIONS

HQ: PINNACLE HEALTH SYSTEM
409 S 2ND ST STE 2B, HARRISBURG, PA 17104-1612
Phone: 717-231-8245
Web: WWW.PINNACLEHEALTH.ORG

PRODUCTS/OPERATIONS

Selected Facilities

Alex Grass Medical Sciences Building
Bloom Outpatient Center
Community General Osteopathic Hospital
Fredricksen Outpatient Center
Harrisburg Hospital
Helen M. Simpson Rehabilitation Hospital
Medical Sciences Pavilion
PinnacleHealth Women' s Outpatient Health Center
Polyclinic Campus
Women' s Inpatient Unit

Selected Services

Back and Spine Care
Cancer Care
Heart Vascular and Lung Care
Imaging (Radiology)
Orthopedics
Physical Therapy and Rehabilitation
Pregnancy and Childbirth
Primary Care
Surgery
Weight Loss and Bariatric Surgery

COMPETITORS

Altoona Regional
Ascension Health
Evangelical Community Hospital
Geisinger Health System
Guthrie Healthcare
Hanover Healthcare
HealthSouth
Hershey Medical Center
Holy Spirit
J. C. Blair Memorial Hospital
Lancaster General
Lewistown Hospital
Saint Vincent Health System
Select Medical
UPMC
WellSpan Health
York Hospital

HISTORICAL FINANCIALS

Company Type: Private

Income Statement — FYE: June 30

	REVENUE ($ mil.)	NET INCOME ($ mil.)	NET PROFIT MARGIN	EMPLOYEES
06/11	612	38	6.2%	4,837
06/09	0	(2)	—	—
06/08	578	(23)	—	—
06/07	486	32	6.8%	—
Annual Growth	5.9%	3.8%	—	—

2011 Year-End Financials

Debt ratio: —
Return on equity: 6.20%
Cash ($ mil.): 0
Current ratio: 0.50
Long-term debt ($ mil.): —
Dividends
Yield: —
Payout: —
Market value ($ mil.): —

PISTON AUTOMOTIVE L.L.C.

Surprisingly there are no pistons on the workbenches and pallets of Piston Automotive. Less surprisingly a former Detroit Pistons player Vinnie "the Microwave" Johnson leads it as chairman. Piston Automotive specializes in the supply of powertrain systems front-end and powertrain cooling systems chassis systems and interior systems for the automotive industry. The company was formed in 1995 by Johnson to serve major automotive makers and related OEM suppliers in the greater Detroit area. A year later Piston Automotive began suspension module assembly and sequencing operations.

Geographic Reach

Piston Automotive operates through two facilities in Michigan one in Missouri and another in Kentucky.

Strategy

The company's strategy for growth emphasizes joint ventures with major companies in the automobile sector. A major supplier for Ford Piston Automotive entered a joint venture with Valeo SA in 2012. The joint venture is called Detroit Thermal Systems LLC and will make air conditioning and heating components for Ford vehicles.

EXECUTIVES

Chairman and CEO, Vinnie Johnson
Executive Assistant, Vicki Richardson
CFO, Daniel Rose

LOCATIONS

HQ: PISTON AUTOMOTIVE L.L.C.
12723 TELEGRAPH RD STE 1, REDFORD, MI 48239-1489
Phone: 313-541-8689
Web: WWW.PISTONGROUP.COM

COMPETITORS

American Axle & Manufacturing
Dana Holding
Federal-Mogul
Honeywell International
Johnson Controls
Magna International
Meritor
Tower International
Visteon

HISTORICAL FINANCIALS

Company Type: Private

Income Statement FYE: December 31

	REVENUE ($ mil.)	NET INCOME ($ mil.)	NET PROFIT MARGIN	EMPLOYEES
12/11	473	10	2.1%	380
12/10	326	9	3.0%	—
12/09	0	0	—	—
12/08	162	0	0.0%	—
Annual Growth	42.9%	424.6%	—	—

2011 Year-End Financials

Debt ratio: —
Return on equity: 2.10%
Cash ($ mil.): 1
Current ratio: 0.90
Long-term debt ($ mil.): —
Dividends
Yield: —
Payout: —
Market value ($ mil.): —

PITT COUNTY MEMORIAL HOSPITAL INCORPORATED

Vidant Medical Center is an acute health services facility serving the vibrant community of Greenville North Carolina and surrounding areas. The 850-bed regional referral hospital's specialty divisions include Vidant Children's Hospital East Carolina Heart Institute a rehabilitation center and the outpatient Vidant SurgiCenter. Other services include oncology transplant women's health orthopedic behavioral care and home health and hospice care units. The medical center also serves as a teaching facility for East Carolina University's Brody School of Medicine. Vidant Medical Center (formerly Pitt County Memorial Hospital) is a member of University Health Systems of Eastern Carolina (dba Vidant Health).

Geographic Reach

Vidant Medical Center provides care to patients in a 29-county service territory in eastern North Carolina. It operates as a regional referral center for smaller community hospitals in the area taking on complex care cases in its specialized fields of medicine.

Operations

In addition to serving as a primary teaching facility for the Brody School of Medicine Vidant Medical Center provides clinical training for East Carolina University's allied health and nursing programs. About 2000 students complete clinical programs at the medical center and its affiliated Vidant Health facilities each year.

Financial Analysis

Revenues at Vidant Medical Center were some $935 million in 2011 up 3% from $907 million in 2010. Patient care revenues primarily from commercial and government health insurance reimbursements account for most of the hospital's annual earnings.

Strategy

To enhance its service offerings to area residents the Vidant Health organization regularly updates its facilities through capital improvement projects. In addition to basic equipment and infrastructure upgrades in 2011 the hospital completed phase one of an expansion project at the Vidant Medical Center that aims to improve the hospital's pediatric and cancer care capabilities.

To signify its mission to enhance the quality of life in its service territories in early 2012 University Health Systems of Eastern Carolina began operating as Vidant Health and the Pitt County Memorial Hospital was renamed as Vidant Memorial Hospital.

EXECUTIVES

President, Stephen J. Lawler
VP Human Resources, Tyree Walker
VP Operations, Thomas J. (Tom) Czaplijski
SVP, Van Smith
VP Support Services, Reggie Pearson
EVP, Bryan Floyd
SVP, Linda D. Hofler
SVP, Todd Hickey
SVP Medical Affairs, Paul Shackelford
VP Medical Affairs - Clincial Efficiency and Documentation, Tracy Eskra
VP Medical Affairs - Quality, Herbert Garrison

LOCATIONS

HQ: PITT COUNTY MEMORIAL HOSPITAL INCORPORATED
2100 STANTONSBURG RD, GREENVILLE, NC 27834-2832
Phone: 252-847-4100
Web: WWW.VIDANTHEALTH.COM

COMPETITORS

Adventist Health System Sunbelt Healthcare
Bon Secours Health
Carolinas HealthCare System
Duke University Health System
Greenville Hospital System
Novant Health
Sentara Healthcare
Tenet Healthcare
UNC Hospitals
Wake Forest University Baptist Medical Center

HISTORICAL FINANCIALS

Company Type: Private

Income Statement FYE: December 31

	REVENUE ($ mil.)	NET INCOME ($ mil.)	NET PROFIT MARGIN	EMPLOYEES
12/12*	395	19	4.8%	8,373
09/09	878	26	3.0%	—
09/08	796	42	5.3%	—
09/07	736	32	4.4%	—
Annual Growth	(11.7%)	(10.0%)	—	—

*Fiscal year change

2012 Year-End Financials

Debt ratio: —
Return on equity: 4.80%
Cash ($ mil.): 88
Current ratio: 1.40
Long-term debt ($ mil.): —
Dividends
Yield: —
Payout: —
Market value ($ mil.): —

PITT-OHIO EXPRESS LLC

Primarily a regional less-than-truckload (LTL) freight carrier Pitt Ohio operates a fleet of about 940 tractors and 3000 trailers. (LTL carriers consolidate freight from multiple shippers into a single truckload.) It maintains straight trucks and vans in its fleet. Pitt Ohio additionally provides truckload (TL) transportation through ECM Transport. It operates a network of about 20 terminals primarily in the Midwest and Mid-Atlantic US. Beyond freight hauling Pitt Ohio provides specialized logistics services for shippers. The family of Charles Hammel III owns Pitt Ohio which has grown from a business established by Hammel's grandfather in 1919.

Geographic Reach

Pitt Ohio is headquartered in Pittsburgh and operates across the Mid-Atlantic and Mid-West regions. It caters to Canada Mexico and other parts of the US through its affiliation with The Reliance Network.

Operations

Pitt Ohio is not historically a third-party logistics (3PL) provider but as the economy recovers the trend toward blending logistics and transportation is on the rise and the company recognizes that. What makes shippers seek a 3PL in the first place is usually for convenience. Given its experience through perhaps the worst recession in the trucking industry and its willingness to evolve Pitt Ohio is moving with the times and incorporating specialized logistics services for its dedicated accounts.

To extend its service throughout the US and Canada Pitt Ohio is part of The Reliance Network (TRNET) a group of regional LTL carriers. TRNET which serves all of North America includes Lakeville Motor Express Averitt Express Canadian Freightways/Epic Express DATS Trucking and Land Air Express. TRNET has the ability to bid jointly on LTL contracts as one entity. Alliances such as TRNET are important as freight companies search for ways to boost profitability and offset losses.

Financial Performance

Pitt Ohio has seen steady revenue growth since the Great Recession. Its total sales in 2012 were $388 million compared to the $346 million it generated in 2011.

Strategy

Probably one of the biggest reasons why Pitt Ohio weathered the Great Recession better than its competitors is because it took the time to diversify expand its services and reach and enter into partnerships with other regional carriers readying itself for when the economy recovers. Along with its expansion into the world of 3PL Pitt Ohio added Pitt Ohio Ground a small-package service in 2010.

To reach additional customers Pitt Ohio in 2012 enhanced its LTL Fast Track Product by offering national and international expedited services. Fast Track includes same-day delivery service next-day delivery service and second-day delivery service to all points in North America and several international destinations. The change was part of the company's effort to simplify its customers' process when expediting LTL freight.

Ownership

The family of Charles Hammel III owns Pitt Ohio which has grown from a business established by Hammel's grandfather in 1919.

Company Background

The company was originally known as Pitt Ohio Express referring to its travel between Pittsburgh and Ohio. When it began to offer more services than just freight hauling the company decided in 2010 to brand itself and adopt a new name –Pitt Ohio.

EXECUTIVES

President, Charles L. (Chuck) Hammel III
EVP and Chief Marketing Officer, Geoffrey (Geoff) Muessig
CFO and CIO, Scott R. Sullivan
COO, James P. (Jim) Fields
VP-Safety, Ron Uriah

LOCATIONS

HQ: PITT-OHIO EXPRESS LLC
15 27TH ST, PITTSBURGH, PA 15222-4729
Phone: 412-232-3015
Web: WWW.WORKS.PITTOHIO.COM

PRODUCTS/OPERATIONS

Selected Services

Ground transportation (small package shipping)
Less-than-truckload transportation
Supply chain services
- Distribution
- Fleet and asset management
- Management consulting
- Transportation

Truckload transportation

COMPETITORS

A. Duie Pyle Inc.
Estes Express
J.B. Hunt
Landstar System
New Penn Motor Express
Old Dominion Freight
Ryder System
Schneider National
UPS Freight
USF Holland
Ward Trucking

HISTORICAL FINANCIALS

Company Type: Private

Income Statement FYE: December 31

	REVENUE ($ mil.)	NET INCOME ($ mil.)	NET PROFIT MARGIN	EMPLOYEES
12/07	261	18	7.2%	3,000
12/06	243	24	10.1%	—
12/04	221	22	10.0%	—
12/02	205	65	32.1%	—
Annual Growth	5.0%	(22.2%)	—	—

2007 Year-End Financials

Debt ratio: —
Return on equity: 7.20%
Cash ($ mil.): 1
Current ratio: 1.30
Long-term debt ($ mil.): —
Dividends
Yield: —
Payout: —
Market value ($ mil.): —

PIZZAGALLI PROPERTIES LLC

LOCATIONS

HQ: PIZZAGALLI PROPERTIES LLC
346 SHELBURNE RD STE 601, BURLINGTON, VT 054014935
Phone: 8026606800
Web: WWW.PIZZAGALLIPROPERTIES.COM

HISTORICAL FINANCIALS

Company Type: Private

Income Statement FYE: December 31

	ASSETS ($ mil.)	NET INCOME ($ mil.)	INCOME AS % OF ASSETS	EMPLOYEES
12/11	78	4	5.8%	22
12/09	83	3	3.7%	—
12/07	94	4	5.3%	—
12/06	98	0	—	—
Annual Growth	(4.3%)	—	—	—

2011 Year-End Financials

Debt ratio: —
Return on equity: 24.50%
Cash ($ mil.): 1
Current ratio: 0.30
Long-term debt ($ mil.): —
Dividends
Yield: —
Payout: —
Market value ($ mil.): —

PJM INTERCONNECTION LLC

Interdependence is a given at PJM Interconnection which oversees a 62556-mile section of the North American power transmission grid that spans 13 northeastern and midwestern states and the District of Columbia. The regional transmission organization monitors and coordinates the movement of wholesale electricity in its service territory; its 816 members have a combined generating capacity of 185600 MW. Sanctioned by the Federal Energy Regulatory Commission PJM is charged with ensuring fair competition among power purchasers sellers and traders; it also is responsible for the reliable delivery of distributed electricity to 61 million consumers in its territory.

Geographic Reach

PJM coordinates the movement of wholesale electricity in all or parts of Delaware Illinois Indiana Kentucky Maryland Michigan New Jersey North Carolina Ohio Pennsylvania Tennessee Virginia West Virginia and the District of Columbia. Its total service area covers 21400 square miles.

Operations

In addition to overseeing and maintaining the generation and transmission reliability of the electric system the enterprise is also responsible for maintaining the integrity of the regional power grid as it accommodates new generating plants and other equipment such as substations and transmission lines. PJM also analyzes and forecasts the future power needs of the region and develops renewable energy resources as a way to expand power supply options and keep prices competitive.

In 2012 PJM reported that it had 1000 MW of solar power installed across its service area.

Financial Performance

The expansion of membership resulted in increased service and membership fees in 2012. This and higher FERC fees reimbursement helped to lift PJM's revenues by 12%. Despite higher FERC fee charges and increased costs for compensation outside services and depreciation and amortization the organization also posted a 12% rise in net income in 2012 thanks to its stronger revenue performance.

Strategy

To upgrade its infrastructure in 2013 PJM authorized $1.2 billion in improvements to its high-voltage electric transmission system that serves the Mid-Atlantic and all or parts of other states between the Mid-Atlantic and Chicago.

Growing its geographic coverage in 2012 PJM assumed operational control of the transmission systems of Duke Energy Ohio and Duke Energy Kentucky. In 2011 PJM integrated FirstEnergy's Ohio and Pennsylvania power utilities' transmission assets into its system.

Ownership

The organization is structured to secure independence and neutrality in its business operations. It has a two-tier committee structure consisting of 10-person Board of Managers (made up of individuals with no financial interests in PJM market participants) and a Members Committee which represents the interests of participating members. The structure is designed to secure that individual members have strong input on issues while protecting the neutrality of PJM's decision-making process.

PJM's members include power generation companies transmission owners electricity distributors power marketers and large industrial consumers.

Company Background

PJM was formed in 1927 when three utilities interconnected to share resources thus creating the world's first continuing power pool. In 1997 PJM became the first independent system operator.

In a move to improve the efficiency and reliability of its operations in 2010 PJM teamed up with Midwest ISO to coordinate the installation of synchrophasors to improve their operators' visibility of the grid. The upgrade is funded by the Department of Energy's $3.4 billion smart grid program. In 2010 the company also connected the system to more than 1500 MW of renewable power including more than 1030 MW of wind energy. That year it also formed a new subsidiary to provide an auction platform for trading solar renewable energy certificates.

EXECUTIVES

President CEO, W. Terry Boston
SVP Operations, Michael J. Kormos
VP Human Resources and Corporate Client Services, Nora C. Swimm
VP CFO and Treasurer, Suzanne Daugherty
Chairman, Howard Schneider
Vice Chairman, Lynn W. Eury
VP and General Counsel, Vincent P. Duane
Executive Vice President - Markets, Andrew L. Ott
Vice President - State & Member Services, Denise Foster
VP Information Technology Services, Thomas O'Brien
Director, Susan J. Riley, age 57
President CEO, W. Terry Boston
Director, William R. (Bill) Mayben
Director, Ake Almgren, age 68
Vice Chairman, Lynn W. Eury
Director, John M. Foster
Director, Jean D. Kinsey
Director, Richard T. Lahey Jr.
Auditors: PricewaterhouseCoopersLLP

LOCATIONS

HQ: PJM INTERCONNECTION LLC
955 JEFFERSON AVE, NORRISTOWN, PA 19403-2410
Phone: 610-666-8980
Web: WWW.PJMSETTLEMENT.COM

Operating Areas
Delaware
District of Columbia
Illinois
Indiana
Kentucky
Maryland
Michigan
New Jersey
North Carolina
Ohio
Pennsylvania
Tennessee
Virginia
West Virginia

HISTORICAL FINANCIALS

Company Type: Private

Income Statement FYE: December 31

	REVENUE ($ mil.)	NET INCOME ($ mil.)	NET PROFIT MARGIN	EMPLOYEES
12/12	324	0	0.3%	600
12/08	241	0	0.3%	—
12/06	274	0	0.2%	—
Annual Growth	2.8%	9.4%	—	—

2012 Year-End Financials

Debt ratio:
Return on equity: 0.30%
Cash ($ mil.): 1,119
Current ratio: 0.90
Long-term debt ($ mil.): —
Dividends
Yield: —
Payout: —
Market value ($ mil.): —

PLACID REFINING COMPANY LLC

A calm presence in the volatile oil and gas industry Placid Refining owns and operates the Port Allen refinery in Louisiana which converts crude oil into a number of petroleum products including diesel ethanol gasoline liquid petroleum gas jet fuel and fuel oils. Placid Refining's refinery has the capacity to process 80000 barrels of crude oil per day. The company is one of the largest employers and taxpayers in West Baton Rouge Parish. Placid Refining which is controlled by Petro-Hunt distribute fuels across a dozen states in the southeastern US from Texas to Virginia and is a major supplier of jet fuel to the US military.

Placid Refining's refinery (purchased in 1975) is strategically located on a 80-plus acre lot near the Mississippi River and about two miles from Interstate Highway 10 and about 10 minutes by car from downtown Baton Rouge.

To meet growing demand the Placid Refining invested $300 million in the late 2000s to expand the Port Allen refinery's throughput capacity from 55000 barrels per day to 80000 barrels per day. As part of this process in 2009 the company completed a 20000 barrels per day fluidized catalytic cracker gasoline hydrotreater.

In 2011 Placid Refining agreed to reduce the nitrogen oxide and sulfur dioxide emissions from its Port Allen refinery and agreed to pay $675000 to the State of Louisiana to settle previous emission violations.

EXECUTIVES

Manager Marketing and Distribution, Matt Pfister
Refinery Manager Port Allen, Joey Hagmann
Contracts Administrator and Media Relations, Candace M. Weber
Sales Manager, Joe Hankins
Community Relations, Ron Hancock
Credit Manager, Joy Hopkins

LOCATIONS

HQ: PLACID REFINING COMPANY LLC
1601 ELM ST STE 3400, DALLAS, TX 75201-7201
Phone: 214-880-8479

COMPETITORS

CITGO Refining and Chemicals
NuStar Energy
United Refining
Valero Energy

HISTORICAL FINANCIALS

Company Type: Private

Income Statement FYE: December 31

	REVENUE ($ mil.)	NET INCOME ($ mil.)	NET PROFIT MARGIN	EMPLOYEES
12/11	4,699	4	0.1%	200
12/10	3,686	39	1.1%	—
12/06	2,925	128	4.4%	—
12/04	1,429	37	2.6%	—
Annual Growth	18.5%	(27.1%)	—	—

2011 Year-End Financials

Debt ratio: —
Return on equity: 0.10%
Cash ($ mil.): 58
Current ratio: 0.80
Long-term debt ($ mil.): —
Dividends
Yield: —
Payout: —
Market value ($ mil.): —

PLAINS COTTON COOPERATIVE ASSOCIATION

EXECUTIVES

Corporate Secretary, John Johnson
VP Information Systems, Joe Tubb
VP Administration and Human Resources, Jim Taylor
VP Finance and Treasurer, Sam Hill
VP Fabric Sales and Product Development, Jack Mathews
President CEO, Wallace L. (Wally) Darneille
VP Marketing, Lonnie Winters
Vice Chairman, David Pearson
VP TELMARK, Stan Kirby
VP Grower Services, Dean Church
VP Textile Manufacturing, Bryan Gregory
Domestic Sales Manager, Chris Ford
Director Sales, Grady Martin
Export Sales Manager, Carlos Garcia
Chairman, Bob McGinnis
Vice President of Services, Greg Bell
V.P. of Warehouse Operations, Jay Cow
Auditors: RobinsonBurdetteMartin&CowanL.L.P.

LOCATIONS

HQ: PLAINS COTTON COOPERATIVE ASSOCIATION
3301 E 50TH ST, LUBBOCK, TX 794044331
Phone: 8067638011
Web: WWW.PCCA.COM

PRODUCTS/OPERATIONS

Selected Sales and Services

Apparel (finished jeans)
Buying cotton
Cotton gins
- Gin bookkeeping
- Gin patronage
- Marketing and invoicing
- Scale ticket software
- Support and training
- Technology solutions

Cotton producers
- Agent gins
- Cash marketing
- marketing contracts
- Pool marketing
- Textile division option

Textiles (denim fabric)
Warehousing

COMPETITORS

Alabama Farmers Cooperative
American Eagle Outfitters
Calcot
Calvin Klein
Dunavant Enterprises
Greenwood Mills
Guess?
International Cotton Marketing
J.G. Boswell Co.
Jordache Enterprises
L.L. Bean
Levi Strauss
OshKosh B' Gosh
Parkdale Mills
Ralph Lauren
Staplcotn
The Gap
Urban Outfitters
Wal-Mart
Weil Brothers Cotton
Wet Seal

HISTORICAL FINANCIALS

Company Type: Private

Income Statement FYE: June 30

	REVENUE ($ mil.)	NET INCOME ($ mil.)	NET PROFIT MARGIN	EMPLOYEES
06/14	947	(36)	—	800
06/13	1,080	10	1.0%	—
06/12	793	8	1.1%	—
06/11	1,835	0	—	—
Annual Growth	(19.8%)	—	—	—

2014 Year-End Financials

Debt ratio: —
Return on equity: (-3.90%)
Cash ($ mil.): 28
Current ratio: 0.80
Long-term debt ($ mil.): —
Dividends
Yield: —
Payout: —
Market value ($ mil.): —

PLANNED PARENTHOOD FEDERATION OF AMERICA INC.

He who fails to plan plans to fail could refer to parenting. No fear the Planned Parenthood Federation Of America provides sexual health information as well as reproductive healthcare through 800 affiliated health centers to more than 5 million people each year. PPFA also lobbies for reproductive rights and reproductive health issues and works to extend access to family planning services for all. The not-for-profit organization is supported by private and corporate donations and patient fees as well as government grants. Founded in 1916 by Margaret Sanger PPFA has grown to 84 affiliates in all 50 US states and the District of Columbia and is part of the International Planned Parenthood Federation.

Operations

PPFA's operations consist of: The Planned Parenthood Foundation which is tasked with raising funds and making grants to PPFA affiliates; Planned Parenthood Action Fund an advocate for informed individual choice in reproductive healthcare; and Voxent (formerly known as NGHN) a provider of technology support to some of PPFA's affiliates.

To help spread its mission PPFA pursues affiliate relationships currently counting 84 independent medical and related organizations and 120 outside (referred to as "ancillary") entities including four political action committees. PPFA affiliates provide expertise in the fields of medicine advocacy sexual health communications fundraising and law.

Geographic Reach

Geographically PPFA's offices in New York City and Washington DC head up its largely domestic program services created to support affiliates in defending reproductive rights of the women and families in the communities in which they are based. PPFA also operates three international offices which oversee programs advancing reproductive rights abroad.

Approximately 75% of the expenses incurred by PPFA are attributable to a number of program services. In the wake of higher revenues total program services increased 23%. Among the programs about half of all expenses are tied to grants and services driven by affiliates in the US. Less than 20% of expenses are associated with the field of family planning including domestic programs for advocacy medical services and education. Outlays for fundraising (which increased by one-third over 2010) and management and general administration represented some 16% and 9% respectively of total expenses in 2011.

Strategy

PPFA's strategy for growth rests on providing community-based heathcare with a focus on access to reproductive services. To this end it is taking steps to improve the Planned Parenthood outreach to Latino communities. PPFA also supports Green Choices an information initiative to promote a healthier and greener environment. Another key area is the PPFA Board of Advocates a volunteer membership of more than 400 leaders in the arts and entertainment field. Members participate in PPFA events and public service announcements as well as blog posts give their name to fundraising efforts and lobby elected officials.

Financial Performance

In fiscal 2012 (ends June) PPFA's revenue decreased by 15% as compared to 2011 due to a decrease in both Contribution & Grants and Other Revenue. PPFA posted revenue of $172.5 million in fiscal 2012 most of which were from the Contribution & Grants accounting about 98% of the revenue of which major donors foundations and corporations and direct response were the highest contributors accounting for about 50% and 30% of Contribution & Grants respectively. Approximately 77% of the expenses incurred by PPFA are attributable to a number of program services. Among the programs about half of all expenses are tied to grants and services driven by affiliates in the US. About 27% of expenses are associated with the field of family planning including domestic programs for advocacy medical services and education. Outlays for fundraising and management & general administration represented some 15% and 8% respectively of total expenses in 2012.

EXECUTIVES

President and CEO, Cecile Richards
EVP and COO, Lisa David
EVP and Chief Experience Officer, Dawn Laguens
VP Global Programs, Latanya Mapp Frett
CIO, Tom Subak
CFO, Wallace D ,ÅSouza
VP Education, Leslie Kantor
Senior Vice President Compliance, Leslie Pargament
Vice President For Public Policy, Melissa Reed
Vice President Information Technology, Lee Tury
Vice President Communications, Eric Ferrero
Vice President Of Public Affairs, Amelia Auner
Vice President Of Information, Fabio Castano
Vice President Of Education, Haydee Morales
Vice President For Programming, Jamal Peterkin
Vice President Medical Affairs, Vanessa Cullins
Vice President Of Education And Training, Jen Slonaker
Vice President Of Public Affairs, Traci Perry
Clinic Director, Angela Martinez
Vice President Finance, Diahnn Barrera
Vice President Human Resource, Brenda Blaisdell
Vice President, Carla Goldstein
Vice President Engineering, Linda Kostka
Vice President Of Medical Records, Lu Arendt
Vice President Client Services, Julie Rabinovitz
Vice President Human Resources, Carole Williams
Vice President Administration Chief, Mary Grinnell
Vice President, Bruce Tisch
Vice President For Education, Michael McGee
Vice President, Dana Singiser
Vice President Of Public Affairs And Government Relations, Yvonne Gutierrez
Chairman, Alexis McGill Johnson
Auditors: KPMGLLP

LOCATIONS

HQ: PLANNED PARENTHOOD FEDERATION OF AMERICA INC.
434 W 33RD ST FL 12, NEW YORK, NY 10001-2600
Phone: 212-541-7800
Web: WWW.PLANNEDPARENTHOODACTION.ORG

PRODUCTS/OPERATIONS

HISTORICAL FINANCIALS

Company Type: Private

Income Statement FYE: June 30

	REVENUE ($ mil.)	NET INCOME ($ mil.)	NET PROFIT MARGIN	EMPLOYEES
06/12	159	34	21.4%	210
06/11	184	87	47.6%	—
06/10	85	5	6.6%	—
06/09	106	21	20.5%	—
Annual Growth	14.5%	16.1%	—	—

2012 Year-End Financials

Debt ratio: ——
Return on equity: 21.40%
Cash ($ mil.): 23
Current ratio: 0.40
Long-term debt ($ mil.): —
Dividends
Yield: —
Payout: —
Market value ($ mil.): —

POMP''S TIRE SERVICE INC..

EXECUTIVES

President, James Wochinske
Company Controller, Dick Martin
Retail Manager, William (Bill) Sutter

LOCATIONS

HQ: POMP' ' S TIRE SERVICE INC..
1123 CEDAR ST, GREEN BAY, WI 543014703
Phone: 9204358301
Web: WWW.POMPSTIRE.COM

PRODUCTS/OPERATIONS

Selected Brands

Bandag
Bridgestone
Firestone
General
Goodrich
Goodyear
Kelly
Michelin
Yokohama

COMPETITORS

Bauer Built
Discount Tire
Pep Boys
Sears
TBC
TCI Tire Centers

HISTORICAL FINANCIALS

Company Type: Private

Income Statement FYE: December 31

	REVENUE ($ mil.)	NET INCOME ($ mil.)	NET PROFIT MARGIN	EMPLOYEES
12/12	427	15	3.5%	1,200
12/11	398	12	3.2%	—
12/10	342	11	3.2%	—
12/09	284	0	—	—
Annual Growth	14.5%	—	—	—

2012 Year-End Financials

Debt ratio: ——
Return on equity: 3.50%
Cash ($ mil.): 0
Current ratio: 0.70
Long-term debt ($ mil.): —
Dividends
Yield: —
Payout: —
Market value ($ mil.): —

PONDEROSA HOMES II INC.

LOCATIONS

HQ: PONDEROSA HOMES II INC.
6130 STONERIDGE MALL RD # 185, PLEASANTON, CA 945883279
Phone: 9254608900
Web: WWW.PONDEROSAHOMES.COM

HISTORICAL FINANCIALS

Company Type: Private

Income Statement FYE: December 31

	ASSETS ($ mil.)	NET INCOME ($ mil.)	INCOME AS % OF ASSETS	EMPLOYEES
12/13	90	9	10.0%	30
12/06	163	20	12.8%	—
12/05	170	32	19.2%	—
12/04	0	0	—	—
Annual Growth	70.6%	—	—	—

2013 Year-End Financials

Debt ratio: ——
Return on equity: 11.50%
Cash ($ mil.): 13
Current ratio: 0.60
Long-term debt ($ mil.): —
Dividends
Yield: —
Payout: —
Market value ($ mil.): —

PORT OF HOUSTON AUTHORITY

EXECUTIVES

Manager Environmental Affairs, Aston A. Hinds
Executive Director, Alec G. Dreyer, age 52
Managing Director, Wade M. Battles
Manager Management Information Systems, Eddie Fuller
Chairman, James T. (Jim) Edmonds
Associate General Counsel, Thomas Schroeter
Director Small Business Development, Gilda Ramirez
Director Trade Development, John P. Horan
Manager Human Resources, Melanie Sherman
Manager Training and Development, Carolyn Ashley
Manager Purchasing, Curtis Rose
Director Public Affairs, Argentina James
General Counsel, Erik A. Eriksson
Director Operations, Jimmy M. Jamison
Assistant General Counsel, Margot Campbell
Assistant General Counsel, Linda Henry
Director Planning and Environment, Charlie Jenkins
Director Business Development Port of Houston Authority International, Rainer P. Lilienthal
Manager Trade Development Customer Services, Robert Morgan Jr.
Manager Trade Development Special Projects, Rodney Petrie
Manager Trade Development Turning Basin Terminals, Ricardo J. Arias
Manager Foreign Trade Zone, Jack Beasley
Director Administration, Jim Eldridge
Director Facilities, James Jackson
Chief Engineer, Steve DeWolf
Manager Real Estate, Brenda McDonald
Manager Maintenance, James Hare
Manager Office Services, Adrian Price
Manager Marine, Ruben Arredondo
Manager Turning Basin Terminals, Walt Kleczkowski
Assistant Manager Turning Basin Terminals, Angus Hanes
Operations Supervisor Turning Basin Terminals, Jo Anna Dahl
Operations Supervisor Turning Basin Terminals, Michael Schubert
Manager Community Relations, Grace Moolchan
Manager Barbours Cut Container Terminals, Roger Guenther
Manager Market Development, Brian T. Reeves
Controller, Steve Hackbarth
Manager Channel Development, Lloyd Saunders
General Manager Trade Development, Ricky W. Kunz
Manager Eastern Trade Development, Keith Miceli
Manager Communications, Lisa A. Whitlock
Manager Cruise Line Sales Marketing and Operations, Kay Adams
Manager Port Security and Emergency Operations, William H. Crews
Assistant General Counsel, Elizabeth Bernel
Interim Police Chief, Gilbert Thompson
Manager Trade Development Container Terminals, James Nash
Commissioner, Kase L. Lawal
Commissioner, Janiece M. Longoria, age 57
Commissioner, Steve Phelps
Commissioner, James W. (Jim) Fonteno Jr.
Commissioner, Jimmy A. Burke
Commissioner, Elyse Lanier
Auditors: Deloitte&ToucheLLP

LOCATIONS

HQ: PORT OF HOUSTON AUTHORITY
111 EAST LOOP N, HOUSTON, TX 770294326
Phone: 7136702400
Web: WWW.PORTOFHOUSTON.COM

COMPETITORS

Alabama State Docks
Port of Corpus Christi
The Port of New Orleans

HISTORICAL FINANCIALS

Company Type: Private

Income Statement FYE: December 31

	REVENUE ($ mil.)	NET INCOME ($ mil.)	NET PROFIT MARGIN	EMPLOYEES
12/13	233	67	29.0%	595
12/12	225	54	24.1%	—
12/11	206	33	16.0%	—
12/10	186	0	—	—
Annual Growth	7.8%	—	—	—

PORT OF PORTLAND

LOCATIONS

HQ: PORT OF PORTLAND
7200 NE AIRPORT WAY, PORTLAND, OR 972181016
Phone: 5039447000
Web: WWW.PORTOFPORTLAND.COM

HISTORICAL FINANCIALS

Company Type: Private

Income Statement FYE: June 30

	REVENUE ($ mil.)	NET INCOME ($ mil.)	NET PROFIT MARGIN	EMPLOYEES
06/14	251	23	9.3%	785
06/13	237	23	10.0%	—
06/12	234	43	18.6%	—
06/11	236	0	—	—
Annual Growth	2.2%	—	—	—

2014 Year-End Financials

Debt ratio: —
Return on equity: 9.30%
Cash ($ mil.): 264
Current ratio: 2.90
Long-term debt ($ mil.): —

Dividends
Yield: —
Payout: —
Market value ($ mil.): —

PORTAGE INC.

Portage Environmental helps carry the load for customers needing environmental engineering services. The firm's offerings include environmental remediation process and project engineering and decontamination and decommissioning services. Portage Environmental counts US government agencies (such as the Department of Defense and the Department of Energy) and Native American tribes among its clients and has conducted projects in 20 US states as well as in Afghanistan Guam Iraq Japan Kuwait Qatar and South Korea. The firm operates from some two dozen offices throughout the US. President and CEO Michael Spry helped found Portage Environmental in 1992.

EXECUTIVES

Vp Business Development, Harry Fugate

LOCATIONS

HQ: PORTAGE INC.
1075 S UTAH AVE STE 200, IDAHO FALLS, ID 83402-3320
Phone: 208-528-6608
Web: WWW.PORTAGEINC.COM

COMPETITORS

AMEC Earth & Environmental
GZA GeoEnvironmental
TRC Companies

HISTORICAL FINANCIALS

Company Type: Private

Income Statement FYE: December 31

	REVENUE ($ mil.)	NET INCOME ($ mil.)	NET PROFIT MARGIN	EMPLOYEES
12/10	245	6	2.6%	300
12/06	33	1	5.7%	—
12/05	29	1	6.4%	—
12/04	24	0	1.1%	—
Annual Growth	46.4%	68.4%	—	—

2010 Year-End Financials

Debt ratio: —
Return on equity: 2.60%
Cash ($ mil.): 5
Current ratio: 2.20
Long-term debt ($ mil.): —

Dividends
Yield: —
Payout: —
Market value ($ mil.): —

POWDER RIVER ENERGY CORPORATION

LOCATIONS

HQ: POWDER RIVER ENERGY CORPORATION
221 MAIN ST, SUNDANCE, WY 82729
Phone: 3072833531
Web: WWW.PRECORP.COOP

HISTORICAL FINANCIALS

Company Type: Private

Income Statement FYE: December 31

	REVENUE ($ mil.)	NET INCOME ($ mil.)	NET PROFIT MARGIN	EMPLOYEES
12/13	204	4	2.2%	269
12/10	165	6	4.1%	—
12/09	166	15	9.6%	—
12/08	759	0	—	—
Annual Growth	(23.1%)	—	—	—

2013 Year-End Financials

Debt ratio: —
Return on equity: 2.20%
Cash ($ mil.): 27
Current ratio: 2.20
Long-term debt ($ mil.): —

Dividends
Yield: —
Payout: —
Market value ($ mil.): —

POWELL ELECTRONICS INC.

Powell Electronics distributes switches sensors connectors relays and other electronic components. The company stocks more than 100000 parts from such manufacturers as 3M Amphenol AVX Emerson Network Power EnerSys Honeywell ITT RF Industries Winchester Electronics and TE Connectivity. It also manufactures custom assemblies and offers several services including bar coding special packaging materials management and wire cutting. Powell Electronics was founded in 1946 by the late Harold Powell who started selling components from his garage after World War II. His family continues to own the company.

Geographic Reach

Powell Electronics has more than 10 branches in nine states: Alabama California Florida Illinois Massachusetts New Jersey North Carolina Texas and Washington. The company also has one each in China and the Netherlands to serve the Asia/Pacific and Western Europe regions.

Sales and Marketing

The company supplies many industries particularly companies that serve key market sectors such as military aerospace telecommunications transportation medical imaging and instrumentation and the US government.

Strategy

Though Powell Electronics primarily targets the aerospace and defense communications government medical imaging and transportation markets the company is looking for manufacturers of alternative energy and commercial aviation products to spur growth.

EXECUTIVES

VP Marketing, Ernie Schilling Jr.
CEO, Ernie Schilling
SVP and CFO, Robert (Bob) Carroll
VP Midwest Division, Albert (Al) Fiorillo
VP Western Region, Bob Williams
VP Florida Region Caribbean Central and South America, Trevor R. McGain
Director Information Technology and Controller, Bob Oldrati

LOCATIONS

HQ: POWELL ELECTRONICS INC.
200 COMMODORE DR, SWEDESBORO, NJ 080851270
Phone: 8562418000
Web: WWW.POWELL.COM

COMPETITORS

Allied Electronics
Arrow Electronics
Avnet Electronics Marketing
Carlton-Bates
Digi-Key
Millennia Group
Minarik
N.F. Smith

HISTORICAL FINANCIALS

Company Type: Private

Income Statement — FYE: December 31

	REVENUE ($ mil.)	NET INCOME ($ mil.)	NET PROFIT MARGIN	EMPLOYEES
12/12	108	3	3.5%	205
12/11	109	3	3.3%	—
12/10*	98	3	3.7%	—
03/10	22	0	—	—
Annual Growth	69.2%	—	—	—

*Fiscal year change

2012 Year-End Financials

Debt ratio: —
Return on equity: 3.50%
Cash ($ mil.): 4
Current ratio: 2.40
Long-term debt ($ mil.): —
Dividends
Yield: —
Payout: —
Market value ($ mil.): —

POWER CONSTRUCTION COMPANY LLC

The Midwest is the best for Power Construction Company a general contractor operating in the Chicago area for nearly 90 years. The company provides customers with preconstruction planning construction management and design/build services. It serves several markets such as health care education hotel and corporate projects. Power Construction is engaged in new building construction as well as buildouts expansions and renovations. More than 90% of the firm's business comes from repeat customers which have included Astellas Pharma US Federal Express and Walgreen. Jerome Goldstein founded the company which is still owned by management in 1926.

Geographic Reach

Based in Schaumburg Illinois Power Construction serves the greater Chicago area.

Strategy

The construction company is the largest builder that works exclusively in its region. By limiting the scope of its business to the Chicago and its surrounding communities Power Construction is able to provide clients with hands-on leadership and management of its projects. It's objective is to "understand the expectations of clients architects and subcontractors then work hard to exceed those expectations." It uses project management tools to collaborate electronically on many of its projects. This enables project participants to access and enter data in real time.

Power Construction favors the private sector and independent not-for-profits including hospitals and schools. It built a 360000-sq.-ft hospital for Centegra Health System in Huntley Illinois as well as the five-story Bienen School of Music on the campus of Northwestern University that spans some 163000 sq. ft.

As part of its strategy its focuses on five clients types. These clients need comprehensive services and tend to have more complex projects. To this end Power Construction primarily serves healthcare education corporate developer and hospitality clients.

While the company is primarily focused on serving its repeat customers it continues to seek key prospects for new business.

Sales and Marketing

About 90% of Power Construction's projects are awarded from repeat clients. As part of the way it markets itself the company boasts that it has never been involved in litigation for performance matters with any client architect or subcontractor. Past customers have included Federal Express Walgreen and Astellas Pharma US.

Financial Performance

The company generates some $600 million in revenue annually.

Company Ownership

Power Construction is management-owned.

EXECUTIVES

Chairman, Alvin L. (Al) Gorman
VP Business Development, Gary Schreiber
VP, Jeff Geier
Auditors: PricewaterhouseCoopers

LOCATIONS

HQ: POWER CONSTRUCTION COMPANY LLC
2360 PALMER DR, SCHAUMBURG, IL 60173-3824
Phone: 847-925-1300
Web: WWW.POWERCONSTRUCTION.NET

PRODUCTS/OPERATIONS

Selected Clients

Corporate
Education
Fine restaurant
Healthcare
Hospitality
Lab/R&D
Retail

Selected Services

Preconstruction planning
Construction management
General contracting
Design/build

Selected Projects

Corporate
- Abbott Labs/J45
- Calamos Investments Financial Center
- Leo Burnett Corporate Interiors
- O' Hare Mail Processing Center
- Panduit Headquarters

Developer
- 201 W. Madison Parking Facility
- Bannockburn Corporate Center
- ParkView Condominiums
- Yorktown Center and The Shops at Butterfield

Education
- British School of Chicago
- Gordon Center for Integrative Science
- Stritch School of Medicine

Health care
- Alexian Medical Office Building
- Cardinal Bernardin Cancer Center
- Campus improvements at Resurrection Medical Center

Hospitality
- CityGate Centre Grand Hotel
- Hugo' s Frog Bar & Fish House - Naperville
- The Mather
- Weinberg Community for Senior Living

COMPETITORS

Bovis Lend Lease
Bulley & Andrews
Flintco
Foster Wheeler
Graycor
James McHugh
Leopardo
McCarthy Building
O' Neil Industries
Pepper Construction
Peter Kiewit Sons'
Superior Construction
Turner Corporation
Walsh Group

HISTORICAL FINANCIALS

Company Type: Private

Income Statement — FYE: December 31

	REVENUE ($ mil.)	NET INCOME ($ mil.)	NET PROFIT MARGIN	EMPLOYEES
12/11	259	9	3.8%	185
12/10	259	9	3.8%	—
12/09	0	0	—	—
12/08	29	0	—	—
Annual Growth	106.6%	—	—	—

2011 Year-End Financials

Debt ratio: —
Return on equity: 3.80%
Cash ($ mil.): 57
Current ratio: 1.10
Long-term debt ($ mil.): —
Dividends
Yield: —
Payout: —
Market value ($ mil.): —

POWERSOUTH ENERGY COOPERATIVE

EXECUTIVES

President and CEO, Gary L. Smith
VP External Affairs, Horace Horn
VP and CFO, Ferrell Walton
VP Power Delivery, Larry Avery
COO, Damon Morgan
Vice President of PowerSouth&rsquo, Beth Woodard
Director Economic Development, Seth Hammett
VP and CFO, Rick Kyle
Manager Corporate Communications, Mark Ingram
President Chairman of the PowerSouth Board of Trustees, Ronald Jones
Director Power Production, David Powell
Director Power Supply, Ron Graham
Auditors: Deloitte&ToucheLLP

LOCATIONS

HQ: POWERSOUTH ENERGY COOPERATIVE
2027 E THREE NOTCH ST, ANDALUSIA, AL 364212427
Phone: 3342222571
Web: WWW.POWERSOUTH.COM

PRODUCTS/OPERATIONS

View Archived What Charts | Edit

2012 Sales

Electric		
Municipalities	7	
Other	1	
Total	**0**	**100**

HISTORICAL FINANCIALS

Company Type: Private

Income Statement FYE: December 31

	REVENUE ($ mil.)	NET INCOME ($ mil.)	NET PROFIT MARGIN	EMPLOYEES
12/13	609	25	4.1%	600
12/12	591	26	4.5%	—
12/11	640	28	4.4%	—
12/10	673	0	—	—
Annual Growth	(3.3%)	—	—	—

2013 Year-End Financials

Debt ratio: ——
Return on equity: 4.10%
Cash ($ mil.): 16
Current ratio: 0.10
Long-term debt ($ mil.): —
Dividends
Yield: —
Payout: —
Market value ($ mil.): —

PRAIRIE FARMS DAIRY INC.

EXECUTIVES

Director Information Services, Mark Harris
CEO, Fletcher Gourley

LOCATIONS

HQ: PRAIRIE FARMS DAIRY INC.
1100 BROADWAY, CARLINVILLE, IL 626261183
Phone: 2178542547
Web: WWW.PRAIRIEFARMS.COM

Selected Areas of Distribution

Arkansas
Illinois
Indiana
Iowa
Kansas
Kentucky
Michigan
Mississippi
Missouri
Nebraska
Ohio
Oklahoma
Tennessee

PRODUCTS/OPERATIONS

Branded Partners
Belfonte Ice Cream & Dairy Foods Company
Coleman Dairy
Hiland Dairy Foods Company
Hiland-Roberts Ice Cream Company
Ice Cream Specialtie
LuVel Dairy Products
Madison Farms Butter
Muller-Pinehurst Dairy
Roberts Dairy Company
Southern Belle Dairy
Swiss Valley Farms
Turner Dairy

Selected Products

Butter
Cultured dairy products
- Cottage cheese (regular low fat and fat-free; small and large curd)
- Dips
- Sour cream
- Yogurt (regular low fat and fat-free)

Fluid milk products
- Buttermilk
- Cream
- Egg nog (seasonal)
- Milk (regular low fat and fat-free)
- Flavored milk

Frozen desserts
- Frozen yogurt
- Ice cream (regular low fat and fat-free)
- Novelties
- Sherbet

Juices drinks and iced tea

COMPETITORS

Associated Milk Producers
Dairy Farmers of America
Darigold Inc.
Dean Foods
Dreyer' s
Farmland Dairies
Foremost Farms
Friendly' s Ice Cream
HP Hood
Land O' Lakes
Quality Chekd
Rockview Dairies
Wells' Dairy

HISTORICAL FINANCIALS

Company Type: Private

Income Statement FYE: September 30

	REVENUE ($ mil.)	NET INCOME ($ mil.)	NET PROFIT MARGIN	EMPLOYEES
09/14	1,878	(5)	—	1,965
09/13	1,721	14	0.8%	—
09/12	1,649	38	2.4%	—
09/11	1,607	0	—	—
Annual Growth	5.3%	—	—	—

2014 Year-End Financials

Debt ratio: —
Return on equity: (-0.30%)
Cash ($ mil.): 10
Current ratio: 0.90
Long-term debt ($ mil.): —
Dividends
Yield: —
Payout: —
Market value ($ mil.): —

PREMIER AG CO-OP INC.

EXECUTIVES

CEO, Harold Cooper
Board President, Kenny Bense
Board Vice President, James Geis
Manager Energy and Petroleum, Mike Carson
Controller, Mike Lafferty
Manager Grain Elevators and Grain Merchandising, Gary Fischer
Manager Agronomy, Mark Canary
Manager Country Mart, Ron Loveland
Manager Franklin Crops, Burk Admire
Manager St. Paul Crops and Greenberg Crops, Mike Schwering
Manager Trafalgar Crops, Mike Sisson
Grain Administrator, Jane Smith

LOCATIONS

HQ: PREMIER AG CO-OP INC.
785 S MARR RD, COLUMBUS, IN 472017490
Phone: 8123799501
Web: WWW.PREMIERAG.COM

COMPETITORS

ADM
AGRI Industries
Andersons
CHS
Cargill
Farmers Cooperative Company
Farmers Cooperative Society
Heartland Co-op
Orscheln Farm and Home
West Central Co-op

HISTORICAL FINANCIALS

Company Type: Private

Income Statement FYE: July 31

	REVENUE ($ mil.)	NET INCOME ($ mil.)	NET PROFIT MARGIN	EMPLOYEES
07/14	139	4	3.5%	100
07/13	141	4	3.2%	—
07/12	159	3	2.2%	—
07/11	142	0	—	—
Annual Growth	(0.7%)	—	—	—

2014 Year-End Financials

Debt ratio: —
Return on equity: 3.50%
Cash ($ mil.): 2
Current ratio: 1.80
Long-term debt ($ mil.): —
Dividends
Yield: —
Payout: —
Market value ($ mil.): —

PREMIER HEALTHCARE SOLUTIONS INC.

Collective buying power is the premise behind Premier. The group purchasing organization (GPO) is an alliance of more than 2900 US hospitals and some 100000 other health care sites. Owned by a group of about 180 not-for-profit hospitals it works to negotiate lower-cost contracts for medical supplies by contracting with hundreds of suppliers nationally for everything from pacemakers and catheters to furniture and food service equipment. Premier serves facilities of all sizes from the smallest rural hospital to huge academic medical centers and its group purchasing power represents more than $40 billion each year. In

2013 the company rode the rising IPO tide and went public raising $760 million.

IPO

Premier premiered on the stock exchange in September 2013. The $760 million take was well in excess of the $648 to $746 million it anticipated. The holding company will use the proceeds to buy additional shares of its general partner Premier GP and for general corporate purposes including working capital and possible acquisitions.

Operations In addition to hospitals the company also consists of 400000 physicians and offers insurance and risk management services (Premier Insurance Management Services) as well as programs to help hospitals improve performance in a variety of areas such as supply chain and energy usage.

Additionally Premier houses one of the largest clinical and financial databases in the US with information on more than 130 million patient discharges. Web-based applications allow hospitals to compare their performance with that of their peers track the results of institutional changes they've implemented and share best practices for patient care. The data warehouse is also used by the FDA to track drug use and the Centers for Medicare & Medicaid Services (CMS) to analyze future changes to its payment system.

Geographic Reach

The company has offices in Charlotte North Carolina and Washington DC. Its purchasing members are located throughout the US.

Sales and Marketing

Premier has about 300 contracts with small women minority and veteran-owned businesses through its diverse suppliers program. The company has collaboration with Centers for Medicare & Medicaid Services the Institute for Healthcare Improvement (IHI) and other public and private entities.

Financial Performance

Premier's total annual revenue increased by 13% in fiscal 2013 (year-end June) compared to 2012 due to growth in its segments.

The supply chain services segment net revenue grew from $591 million in 2012 to $664 million in 2013 representing net revenue growth of 12% which was attributed to increase in net administrative fees revenue.

Premier's profits increased by 87% in 2013 compared to 2012 due to the increase in gross revenue while its cash flow increased by $163 million due to cash provided by investing activities and proceeds from the sale of marketable securities.

Strategy Premier has championed and is embracing a unique item coding system that allows for improved tracking of medical products including medical devices in order to reduce costs associated with redundant ordering and lost or stolen equipment. The group has also developed a similar quality tracking system that has been picked up by CMS and a division of the UK's National Health Service.

EXECUTIVES

President Chief Executive Officer and Director, Susan D. DeVore, age 55, $970,071 total compensation
President Premier Insurance Management Services PHSI, Robert L. Dowdy
Chief Medical Officer, Richard Bankowitz
Senior Vice President of Premier Performance Partners, R. Wesley (Wes) Champion, age 48
Senior Vice President of Healthcare Informatics, Keith J. Figlioli
Senior Vice President and Chief Financial Officer, Craig S. McKasson, age 47, $495,853 total compensation
President and chief mission officer, Alan R. Yordy
Chief Operating Officer, Michael J. (Mike) Alkire, age 51, $785,447 total compensation
President of Supply Chain Services, Durral R. Gilbert, age 48
Senior Vice President Member Field Services, Andy Brailo
Vp Sales, Dan Schuman
Vice Chair of the Board, Charles E. Hart, age 64
President Chief Executive Officer and Director, Susan D. DeVore, age 55
Chair of the Board, Richard J. (Rich) Statuto, age 57
Asst Treas, Lisa Stein

LOCATIONS

HQ: PREMIER HEALTHCARE SOLUTIONS INC.
13034 BALNTYN CORP PL, CHARLOTTE, NC 28277-1498
Phone: 704-357-0022
Web: WWW.PREMIERINC.COM

PRODUCTS/OPERATIONS

Selected operations

COMPETITORS

0
Aetna
Allscripts
CVS
Deloitte & Touche
Express Scripts
Global Healthcare Exchange
HealthTrust
MedAssets
Medline Industries
Novation
Owens & Minor
PSS World Medical
UnitedHealth Group

HISTORICAL FINANCIALS

Company Type: Private

Income Statement FYE: June 30

	REVENUE ($ mil.)	NET INCOME ($ mil.)	NET PROFIT MARGIN	EMPLOYEES
06/12	768	327	42.6%	1,260
06/11	679	311	45.8%	—
06/10	0	0	—	—
06/09	538	291	54.2%	—
Annual Growth	12.6%	3.9%	—	—

2012 Year-End Financials

Debt ratio: —
Return on equity: 42.60%
Cash ($ mil.): 140
Current ratio: 1.80
Long-term debt ($ mil.): —
Dividends
Yield: —
Payout: —
Market value ($ mil.): —

PREMIER WEST COMPANIES LLC

LOCATIONS

HQ: PREMIER WEST COMPANIES LLC
501 W MAIN ST, MOUNT HOREB, WI 535721903
Phone: 6082510199
Web: WWW.PREMIERCOOPERATIVE.COM

HISTORICAL FINANCIALS

Company Type: Private

Income Statement FYE: September 30

	REVENUE ($ mil.)	NET INCOME ($ mil.)	NET PROFIT MARGIN	EMPLOYEES
09/14	222	10	4.7%	55
09/13	201	10	5.0%	—
09/12	170	8	4.9%	—
09/11	127	0	—	—
Annual Growth	20.4%	—	—	—

2014 Year-End Financials

Debt ratio: —
Return on equity: 4.70%
Cash ($ mil.): 8
Current ratio: 0.60
Long-term debt ($ mil.): —
Dividends
Yield: —
Payout: —
Market value ($ mil.): —

PRESIDENT & TRUSTEES OF WILLIAMS COLLEGE

EXECUTIVES

VP Operations, Stephen P. Klass
Interim President, William G. (Bill) Wagner
Director Communications for Alumni Relations and Development, Robert H. White
Controller, Susan S. Hogan
CTO, Dinny S. Taylor
Director Financial Aid, Paul J. Boyer
Director Admission, Richard L. Nesbitt
Director Career Counseling, John H. Noble
College Librarian, David M. Pilachowski
Registrar and Associate Dean, Charles R. Toomajian
VP Strategic Planning and Institutional Diversity, Michael E. Reed
Provost and Treasurer, William J. Lenhart
Director Alumni Relations, Brooks Foehl
Chief Investment Officer, Collette Chilton
Associate VP Facilities, D. Prideaux-Brune

LOCATIONS

HQ: PRESIDENT & TRUSTEES OF WILLIAMS COLLEGE
880 MN ST HOPKS HL FL 1, WILLIAMSTOWN, MA 01267
Phone: 4135974412
Web: WWW.WILLIAMS.EDU

HISTORICAL FINANCIALS

Company Type: Private

Income Statement FYE: June 30

	REVENUE ($ mil.)	NET INCOME ($ mil.)	NET PROFIT MARGIN	EMPLOYEES
06/11	149	245	163.6%	950
06/10	146	92	62.9%	—
Annual Growth	2.1%	165.3%	—	—

2011 Year-End Financials

Debt ratio: —
Return on equity: 163.60%
Cash ($ mil.): 14
Current ratio: —
Long-term debt ($ mil.): —
Dividends
Yield: —
Payout: —
Market value ($ mil.): —

PRESIDENT AND BOARD OF TRUSTEES OF SANTA CLARA COLLEGE

Santa Clara University wants its students to achieve clarity. The Jesuit Catholic school offers degrees in more than 40 disciplines. Its variety of graduate programs include business engineering law pastoral ministries counseling psychology and education. With more than 8800 students Santa Clara University boasts a student/faculty ratio of 12:1 and support from a $688 million endowment. Notable alumni include Oakland mayor and former governor of California Jerry Brown soccer player Brandi Chastain Cirrus Logic chairman Michael Hackworth and winemaker Sam Sebastiani. Santa Clara University was founded in 1851 making it California's oldest higher-education institution.

Geographic Reach

Santa Clara University serves undergraduate and graduate students in California's Silicon Valley.

Operations

The educational institution is recognized as the having the fourth-highest graduation rate among all US master's universities. Its budget reached $378 million in 2013.

EXECUTIVES

Chairman, Robert J. (Bob) Finocchio Jr., age 61
VP University Relations, James (Jim) Purcell
VP Administration and Finance, Robert Warren
Senior Vice Provost, Don Dodson
Vice Provost Undergraduate Education, Helen E. Moritz
Vice Provost Planning and Administration, Charles Erekson
Associate VP Finance, Harry Fong
Dean College of Arts and Sciences, W. Atom Yee
Dean Leavey School of Business, Barry Posner
Associate Vice Provost for Enrollment Management and Dean Undergraduate Admission, Sandra Hayes
Chief Investment Officer, John Kerrigan
Executive Director Markkula Center for Applied Ethics, Kirk O. Hanson
Manager Student Administration Technical Group Information Technology, John Price
Manager Student Administration Systems Management, Robert Boyd
Director Media Relations, Deepa Arora
Director Mission Church, Charles (Charlie) White
Director Counseling and Psychological Services, Larry A. Wolfe
Director Facilities Maintenance and Operations, Jeffrey (Jeff) Charles
Director Budget Office, Dennis Roberts
Associate Director Human Resources, Ingrid C. Williams
Vice Chair, Margaret M. (Peggy) Bradshaw
Executive Director Ignatian Center for Jesuit Education, Father Kevin P. Quinn
Trustee, Robert W. (Bob) Peters
Provost and VP Academic Affairs, Dennis Jacobs
President, Father Michael E. Engh, age 64
Director Campus Ministry, John Robert Treacy
Dean School of Law, Lisa Kloppenberg
Chancellor, Father William Rewak
CIO, Ronald Danielson
Dean Leavey School of Business, S. Andrew Starbird
Dean School of Education and Counseling Psychology, Nicholas Ladany
Dean School of Engineering, M. Godfrey Mungal
Dean Jesuit School of Theology, Father Thomas J. Massaro
Trustee, William S. Carter
Trustee, David C. Drummond, age 50
Trustee, Regis P. McKenna
Trustee, Donald L. (Don) Lucas, age 84
Vice Chair, Margaret M. (Peggy) Bradshaw
Trustee, Father Gerald T. Cobb
Trustee, Robert W. (Bob) Peters
Trustee, Margaret M. (Peggy) Bradbury
Trustee, Richard M. Moley
Trustee, Robert H. Smith
Trustee, John A. Sobrato

LOCATIONS

HQ: PRESIDENT AND BOARD OF TRUSTEES OF SANTA CLARA COLLEGE
500 EL CAMINO REAL, SANTA CLARA, CA 95050-4345
Phone: 408-554-4000
Web: WWW.SCU.EDU

PRODUCTS/OPERATIONS

Degrees Offered
Undergraduate Degrees
Bachelor of Arts
Bachelor of Science
Bachelor of Science in Commerce
Graduate Degrees
Business (MBA EMBA MSIS)
Counseling Psychology (M.A.)
Education (M.A.)
Engineering (M.S. Ph.D.)
Law (J.D. LL.M.)
Pastoral Ministries (M.A.)

HISTORICAL FINANCIALS

Company Type: Private

Income Statement FYE: June 30

	REVENUE ($ mil.)	NET INCOME ($ mil.)	NET PROFIT MARGIN	EMPLOYEES
06/12	312	(38)	—	1,431
06/11	351	24	6.9%	—
06/05	341	33	9.7%	—
06/05	0	0	—	—
Annual Growth	—	—	—	—

2012 Year-End Financials

Debt ratio: ——
Return on equity: (-12.30%)
Cash ($ mil.): 95
Current ratio: —
Long-term debt ($ mil.): —
Dividends
Yield: —
Payout: —
Market value ($ mil.): —

PRESIDENT AND FELLOWS OF MIDDLEBURY COLLEGE

EXECUTIVES

Chair, Marna C. Whittington, age 66
President, Ronald D. Liebowitz
VP Finance and Treasurer, Patrick J. Norton
Associate VP Human Resources and Organizational Development, Drew Macan
Provost and EVP, Alison Byerly
Dean of Curriculum and Faculty Development, Robert (Bob) Cluss
Dean Environmental Affairs, Nan Jenks-Jay
VP College Advancement, James R. Keyes
Dean of Faculty, James (Maggie) Ralph
SVP and Chief Philanthropic Advisor, Michael D. Schoenfeld
Dean of Admissions, Gregory B. Buckles
VP Administration, Timothy Spears
Athletics Director, Erin Quinn
CIO, Michael Roy
Dean of College, Shirley M. Collado
Dean of Faculty, Andrea H. Lloyd
Dean of Students, Katy Smith-Abbott

LOCATIONS

HQ: PRESIDENT AND FELLOWS OF MIDDLEBURY COLLEGE
38 COLLEGE ST, MIDDLEBURY, VT 05753
Phone: 8024435000
Web: WWW.MIDDLEBURY.EDU

Selected Locations

Center for the Comparative Study of Race and Ethnicity
Chellis House
Middlebury College Snow Bowl
Ralph Myhre Golf Course
Rikert Nordic Center
Rohatyn Center for International Affairs
Scott Center for Spiritual & Religious Life

HISTORICAL FINANCIALS

Company Type: Private

Income Statement FYE: June 30

	REVENUE ($ mil.)	NET INCOME ($ mil.)	NET PROFIT MARGIN	EMPLOYEES
06/13	260	113	43.4%	1,000
06/12	233	(24)	—	—
06/08	278	50	18.3%	—
06/06	181	0	—	—
Annual Growth	5.3%	—	—	—

2013 Year-End Financials

Debt ratio: ——
Return on equity: 43.40%
Cash ($ mil.): 29
Current ratio: —
Long-term debt ($ mil.): —
Dividends
Yield: —
Payout: —
Market value ($ mil.): —

PRESSURE VESSEL SERVICE INC.

LOCATIONS

HQ: PRESSURE VESSEL SERVICE INC.
10900 HARPER AVE, DETROIT, MI 482133364
Phone: 3139211200
Web: WWW.PVSCHEMICALS.COM

HISTORICAL FINANCIALS

Company Type: Private

Income Statement FYE: December 31

	REVENUE ($ mil.)	NET INCOME ($ mil.)	NET PROFIT MARGIN	EMPLOYEES
12/13	549	12	2.3%	800
12/12	566	21	3.8%	—
12/11	461	12	2.6%	—
12/10	356	0	—	—
Annual Growth	15.5%	—	—	—

PRIDGEON & CLAY INC.

A moving target not a sitting duck Pridgeon & Clay (P&C) takes on all rivals within the metal forming industry. An independent manufacturer and supplier of stamped and fine blanked components the family-owned company designs and produces an array of parts for auto assembly plants across the US. Its lineup includes steering column lock nuts brackets for headlights to engines control arms flanges exhaust parts and muffler shields. Stamping equipment runs from fine blanking presses to high tonnage and progressive presses. P&C also makes blanks for equipment in other industries. The company touts hand assembly spot welding and tapping services along with a global sales force.

Geographic ReachP&C has more than 100 stamping presses. Its operations are supplemented by PC NAVA a Mexico-based joint venture between P&C and NAVA Hermanos S.A. P&C also runs five manufacturing facilities in the US (Grand Rapids; and Franklin Indiana) Mexico Germany Hungary and a joint venture in Poland as well as engineering and sales branches in North America Germany and China.

Operations

Normal 0 false false false EN-US X-NONE X-NONE

/* Style Definitions */ table.MsoNormalTable {mso-style-name:"Table Normal"; mso-tstyle-rowband-size:0; mso-tstyle-colband-size:0; mso-style-noshow:yes; mso-style-priority:99; mso-style-parent:""; mso-padding-alt:0in 5.4pt 0in 5.4pt; mso-para-margin-top:0in; mso-para-margin-right:0in; mso-para-margin-bottom:10.0pt; mso-para-margin-left:0in; line-height:115%; mso-pagination:widow-orphan; font-size:11.0pt; font-family:"Calibri""sans-serif"; mso-ascii-font-family:Calibri; mso-ascii-theme-font:minor-latin; mso-hansi-font-family:Calibri; mso-hansi-theme-font:minor-latin;}The company's Advanced Engineering Lab is an American Association for Laboratory Accreditation accredited independent testing facility.

Sales and Marketing

Serving both OEM and Tier 1 manufacturers the company provides services to a large variety of industries including agriculture automobiles and heavy trucks fuel cells and batteries hardware and appliances marine craft medical supply motorcycles and solar and wind energy.

Strategy

Outlasting the automotive industry's melt down and even the bankruptcies of a couple of its major customers P&C has reached out for new markets. The company is investing in research and development of stamped components for customers in commercial hardware and wind power industries. P&C is also branching out into medical supply.

Company Background

P&C was founded in 1948 by John Pridgeon and Don Clay.

EXECUTIVES

Vice President Operations, Bill McKibben
Vice President, Pam Frost
President and COO, Michael J. Alcala
Vice President And General Manager China Operations, Lou Kocsondy
Vice President Of International Operations, Rick Martin
Vice President Manufacturing, Darrin Baldinelli
Member Of The Board, Don Huizenga

LOCATIONS

HQ: PRIDGEON & CLAY INC.
50 COTTAGE GROVE ST SW, GRAND RAPIDS, MI 495071685
Phone: 6162415675
Web: WWW.PRIDGEONANDCLAY.COM

PRODUCTS/OPERATIONS

Selected Products

Axle Components
Brake Components
Chassis Frame and Body
Class 8 Truck Parts
Cones
Exhaust Components
Flanges
Non Automotive Parts
Transmission Components

Selected Services

Advanced Engineering and Design
Assembly
De-burring
Deep Drawn Stamping
Distribution Center
Fine Blanking
In-die Sensoring and Welding
Package and Distribution
Progressive Die Stamping
Prototyping
Resistance Welding
Riveting
Robotic MIG Welding
Studding
Tool Design and Build
Transfer Press Stamping
Truck Fleet
Wide Variety of Secondary Services

COMPETITORS

Batesville Tool & Die
Defiance Metal Products
Exact Tool
Hannibal Industries
Martinrea International
Mid-South Industries
Ohio Stamping and Machine LLC
Precision Resource
Steel Technologies
Talan Products

HISTORICAL FINANCIALS

Company Type: Private

Income Statement FYE: December 31

	REVENUE ($ mil.)	NET INCOME ($ mil.)	NET PROFIT MARGIN	EMPLOYEES
12/13	287	7	2.5%	600
12/12	294	1	0.4%	—
12/11	267	5	1.9%	—
12/10	220	0	—	—
Annual Growth	9.3%	—	—	—

2013 Year-End Financials

Debt ratio: —
Return on equity: 2.50%
Cash ($ mil.): 1
Current ratio: 1.40
Long-term debt ($ mil.): —
Dividends
Yield: —
Payout: —
Market value ($ mil.): —

PRIMEX INTERNATIONAL TRADING CORP

Primex International Trading is a leading exporter and international trader that specializes in dried fruits and nuts. Through affiliate offices located around the world the company ships such products as almonds hazelnuts and pecans as well as apricots figs and raisins. Primex also has its own pistachio orchards and a processing plant in California. The company was founded in 1989 by Ali Amin whose family has been involved in producing pistachios for four generations. It first started planting pistachio orchards in 1990. In 2008 the company shipped about 30 million pounds of pistachios and more than 40 million pounds of almonds.

EXECUTIVES

Vice President Of Sales, William Green

LOCATIONS

HQ: PRIMEX INTERNATIONAL TRADING CORP
5777 W CENTURY BLVD # 1485, LOS ANGELES, CA 90045-5600
Phone: 310-568-8855
Web: WWW.PRIMEX-USA.COM

COMPETITORS

BALSU USA
Big Heart Pet Brands
Blue Diamond Growers
Diamond Foods
Dole Food
Golden Peanut and Tree Nuts
Green Valley Pecan
John Sanfilippo & Son
ML Macadamia Orchards
McCall Farms
Meridian Nut Growers
Santa Clara Nut Co.
Sun World International
SunWest Foods
Texoma Peanut
Tropical Nut & Fruit
Young Pecan

HISTORICAL FINANCIALS

Company Type: Private

Income Statement FYE: December 31

	REVENUE ($ mil.)	NET INCOME ($ mil.)	NET PROFIT MARGIN	EMPLOYEES
12/11	262	1	0.7%	31
12/01	57	0	0.3%	—
12/00	47	0	0.5%	—
12/99	836	0	—	
Annual Growth	—	153.4%	—	—

2011 Year-End Financials

Debt ratio: —
Return on equity: 0.70%
Cash ($ mil.): 3
Current ratio: 1.00
Long-term debt ($ mil.): —
Dividends
Yield: —
Payout: —
Market value ($ mil.): —

PRODUCERS RICE MILL INC.

EXECUTIVES

President Chief Executive Officer, Keith Glover
Senior Vice President Rice Sales, Marvin (Butch) Baden
VP Finance and Administration, Kent Lockwood
VP Operations, Kenny Dryden
VP Marketing Consumer Products, Gary Reifeiss
Assistant VP Finance and Administration, Mary Ratcliff
Director Human Resources, Karen Bagley
Traffic Manager, Jason Earney
Director Marketing Foodservice and Retail, Christy Kalder
Sales Manager Food Service National Accounts, Mike Cullen
Credit Supervisor, Vicki Baker
Accounting Supervisor, Michele Adamson
Chairman, Gary Sebree

Vice Chairman and VP, Jerry Hoskyn
Supervisor Customer Service, Ashley Parker
Assistant VP Rice Sales and Co-Products, Jason Chastain
General Sales Manager Food Service, Steve Nicholas
Retail Sales Manager, Tony Richmond
Secretary, Ashley Eagle
Executive Assistant President CEO, Lana Flowers
Safety Director, David Hodges
MIS Director, Annette Henderson
Sales Service Manager, Denise Henley
Secretary, Sandy Crosby

LOCATIONS

HQ: PRODUCERS RICE MILL INC.
518 E HARRISON ST, STUTTGART, AR 721603700
Phone: 8706724420
Web: WWW.PRODUCERSRICE.COM

COMPETITORS

ADM
American Rice
CHS
Cargill
Cereal Byproducts
Farmers Rice Milling
Farmers' Rice Cooperative
Goya
Mars Incorporated
Mondelez International
PepsiCo
RiceX
Riceland Foods
Specialty Rice

HISTORICAL FINANCIALS

Company Type: Private

Income Statement FYE: July 31

	REVENUE ($ mil.)	NET INCOME ($ mil.)	NET PROFIT MARGIN	EMPLOYEES
07/14	546	327	59.9%	730
07/13	568	368	64.8%	—
07/12	478	302	63.3%	—
07/11	499	0	—	—
Annual Growth	3.0%	—	—	—

2014 Year-End Financials

Debt ratio: —
Return on equity: 59.90%
Cash ($ mil.): 1
Current ratio: 0.90
Long-term debt ($ mil.): —
Dividends
Yield: —
Payout: —
Market value ($ mil.): —

PRODUCTION TOOL SUPPLY

Production Tool Supply totes the tools of the trade –and it distributes them to customers worldwide. With nine showrooms in Michigan and Ohio the company (PTS) distributes brand-name discount industrial tools and machinery. It markets approximately 235000 products through a 1700-page catalog on the Internet and through independent distributors. Products include cutting tools carbide tools abrasives measuring tools clamps and vises power tools tool safety products and power machinery by blue chip OEMs such as Bosch Porter-Cable and Sandvik. D. Dan Kahn founded PTS in 1951 to serve small factories and shops in the Detroit area. The Kahn family still controls the company.

Geographic Reach

The company has store locations in Grand Rapids Jackson Lansing Madison Heights Novi Redford Roseville Michigan; and Cleveland. It has more than 400000 sq. ft. of manufacturing space.

Sales and Marketing

Products are sold under such brand names as Brands A-9 Accu-Lube Accurate Acer Acu-Rite Eagle Eagle-Rock Ecco Tool Co Inc Edge Z-Drive Zebra Skimmers.

EXECUTIVES

CFO, Michael Brenner

LOCATIONS

HQ: PRODUCTION TOOL SUPPLY
8655 E 8 MILE RD, WARREN, MI 48089-4030
Phone: 586-755-2200

PRODUCTS/OPERATIONS

Selected Products

Abrasives
- Abrasives
- Diamond tools
- Grinding-wheel dressers
- Wire brushes

Cutting Tools
- Countersinks and counterbores
- Drills
- Reamers
- Saw blades
- Taps and dies
- Threading tools and accessories

Fluids
- Adhesives/sealants
- Cleaning/lubricants
- Machining fluids/applicators
- Marking/paint

Hand Tools
- Cutting
- Edge deburring
- Electrical tools
- Fastening
- Fastener drive tools
- Hand files
- Marking labeling etching
- Pliers/cutters
- Plumbing tools
- Pullers/heaters
- Scribers and tweezers
- Striking tools

Machinery
- Bandsaws
- CNC machinery
- Cut-off saws
- Drill presses
- Lathes
- Milling machines
- Sandblasters

Material handling
- Furniture
- Handling equipment
- Storage

Measuring Tools
- Comparators/magnifiers
- Gages
- Indicators
- Precision tools
- Service plates
- SPC equipment

MRO/Safety Tools
- Brushes
- Cabinets
- Extension cords
- Fans
- Gloves
- Lamps and lights
- Vacuums

Power Tools
- Air tools
- Electric power tools
- Marking and etching tools

Work-Holding Tools
- Boring heads
- Chucks
- Collet fixtures
- Magnetic chucks
- Quick-change tooling
- Tapping heads
- Vises

COMPETITORS

AIS Construction Equipment
Carbide Tool Services
Carlson Systems
DXP Enterprises
Fastenal
Industrial Distribution Group
J. O. Galloup
MSC Industrial Direct
Michigan Tractor
Total Plastics
W.W. Grainger
Wurth Group

HISTORICAL FINANCIALS

Company Type: Private

Income Statement FYE: October 31

	REVENUE ($ mil.)	NET INCOME ($ mil.)	NET PROFIT MARGIN	EMPLOYEES
10/11	168	23	14.0%	357
10/10	129	14	11.6%	—
10/09	117	10	9.2%	—
10/08	181	27	15.4%	—
Annual Growth	(2.6%)	(5.6%)	—	—

2011 Year-End Financials

Debt ratio: —
Return on equity: 14.00%
Cash ($ mil.): 16
Current ratio: 4.40
Long-term debt ($ mil.): —
Dividends
Yield: —
Payout: —
Market value ($ mil.): —

PROTESTANT MEMORIAL MEDICAL CENTER INC.

With about 315 beds Memorial Hospital has plenty of space to take care of Prairie Staters. The Bellevue Illinois-based hospital is owned and operated by Protestant Memorial Medical Center a community-based not-for-profit organization. Memorial Hospital provides general medical surgical and emergency care as well as pediatric home health and cardiovascular care. Specialty services include treatment for sleep disorders and women's health. The hospital also operates Memorial Convalescent Center a nearly 110-bed skilled nursing facility and the Belleville Health and Sports Center which provides fitness facilities to promote community health. The hospital first opened its doors in 1958.

Operations

Other operations include diagnostic centers in O'Fallon Illinois and an off-campus physical therapy center in east Belleville. Also Memorial Hospital collaborates with the Southern Illinois University School of Medicine for certain research programs and services. In 2009 Memorial Hospital joined the Memory and Aging Network at the school of medicine to become a designated Alzheimer's Disease Primary Provider Site. The program includes a network of about 35 provider sites that collect data on the frequency type and progression of dementia.

Strategy

Memorial Hospital plans to build a $118 million new satellite hospital in nearby Shiloh called Memorial Hospital - East. The new facility will include 94 beds private patient rooms surgical suites a cardiac catheterization lab as well as an intensive care unit and an obstetrics unit. The hospital is expected to open in 2016. When the new hospital opens hospital officials expect the main campus in Belleville to reduce its capacity and convert all patient rooms to single occupancy.

EXECUTIVES

VP Finance, Joe Lanius

VP Human Resources, Ed French
Director Hospital/Community Relations, Anne Thomure
President CEO, Mark J. Turner
VP Medical Affairs, William Casperson
VP Medical Staff Services, James B. Davis

LOCATIONS

HQ: PROTESTANT MEMORIAL MEDICAL CENTER INC.
4500 MEMORIAL DR, BELLEVILLE, IL 62226-5360
Phone: 618-233-7750
Web: WWW.MEMHOSP.COM

COMPETITORS

Ascension Health
BJC HealthCare
Barnes-Jewish Hospital
Christian Hospital
RehabCare
St. Anthony' s Medical Center

HISTORICAL FINANCIALS

Company Type: Private

Income Statement FYE: December 31

	REVENUE ($ mil.)	NET INCOME ($ mil.)	NET PROFIT MARGIN	EMPLOYEES
12/12	263	15	6.0%	2,344
12/11	259	9	3.7%	—
12/09	248	7	3.2%	—
12/08	235	(24)	—	—
Annual Growth	2.8%	—	—	—

2012 Year-End Financials

Debt ratio: ——
Return on equity: 6.00%
Cash ($ mil.): 17
Current ratio: 2.50
Long-term debt ($ mil.): —
Dividends
Yield: —
Payout: —
Market value ($ mil.): —

PROVIDENCE COLLEGE

Students don't need divine intervention to get into Providence College they just need good grades and an interest in liberal arts. The Catholic institution of higher education offers undergraduate and graduate degrees at its four schools: Arts and Sciences Business Continuing Education and Professional Studies. It offers degrees in about 50 academic disciplines including biology business education marketing politics and psychology. It has a student-to-faculty ratio of 12:1 with students primarily coming from New England and the Midwest and Mid-Atlantic regions. Providence College was founded in 1917 by the Dominican Friars of the Province of St. Joseph and the Diocese of Providence.

EXECUTIVES

Assoc Vp Human Resources, Kathleen Alvino
Vp For Academic Affairs, Hugh F Lena
Asst Vp Alumni Relations, Robert Ferreira
Assoc Vp/asst Treasurer, Jacqueline White
Assoc Vp Development, Lisa Bousquet
Asst Vp Business Services, Warren Gray
Executive Vice President, Hugh Frazier
Vice President Class, Katie Tripp
Assistant To Assistant Vice President For Student Affairs Dean Of Students, Susan McCauley
Asst To President/exec Vp, Ann M Molak
Assistant Vice President Capital Projects Facilities Planning, Rapoza Mark
Exec Vp/treasurer, Kenneth Sicard
Executive Board Member, Paige Nossek

LOCATIONS

HQ: PROVIDENCE COLLEGE
1 CUNNINGHAM SQ, PROVIDENCE, RI 02918-0001
Phone: 401-865-1000
Web: WWW.SUPPORT.PROVIDENCE.EDU

HISTORICAL FINANCIALS

Company Type: Private

Income Statement FYE: June 30

	REVENUE ($ mil.)	NET INCOME ($ mil.)	NET PROFIT MARGIN	EMPLOYEES
06/11	216	24	11.2%	800
06/10	145	24	16.5%	—
06/09	142	(15)	—	—
06/08	139	11	8.6%	—
Annual Growth	15.9%	26.7%	—	—

2011 Year-End Financials

Debt ratio: ——
Return on equity: 11.20%
Cash ($ mil.): 38
Current ratio: —
Long-term debt ($ mil.): —
Dividends
Yield: —
Payout: —
Market value ($ mil.): —

PROVIDENCE HOSPITAL

Providence Hospital and Medical Centers provides health care in the Motor City and surrounding areas. The main Providence Hospital is a 365-bed teaching facility that has been recognized for its cardiology program and clinical expertise in behavioral medicine. It offers a variety of other services ranging from cancer treatment and neurosurgery to orthopedics and women's health. The network also includes dozens of affiliated general practice and specialty health clinics. The not-for-profit medical center founded in 1845 as St. Vincent's Hospital in Detroit by the Daughters of Charity is part of Catholic health ministry St. John Health (itself a subsidiary of Ascension Health).

Operations

As part of its health care system Providence Hospital and Medical Centers operates a host of hospitals and medical centers across the metropolitan Detroit area. They include Providence Southfield and four namesake Providence Medical Center locations in Farmington Hills Livonia Dearborn Heights and South Lyon. Across its system the medical facilities employ some 1500 physicians and enlist the help of about 300 active volunteers.

EXECUTIVES

VP Operations Acute Services and Chief Nursing Officer, Kathy Ryan

LOCATIONS

HQ: PROVIDENCE HOSPITAL
16001 W 9 MILE RD, SOUTHFIELD, MI 48075-4803
Phone: 248-424-3000
Web: WWW.REALMEDICINE.ORG/PROVIDENCE/

PRODUCTS/OPERATIONS

Selected Primary Services

Cancer clinical trials
Cardiac rehabilitation
Childbirth
Congenital heart disease clinic
Emergency
Oncology
Orthopedics
Senior services
Surgery
Women's health

COMPETITORS

Beaumont Health System
Crittenton Hospital
Detroit Medical Center
Henry Ford Health System
McLaren Health Care
Oakwood Healthcare
Trinity Health (Novi)
University of Michigan Health System

HISTORICAL FINANCIALS

Company Type: Private

Income Statement FYE: June 30

	REVENUE ($ mil.)	NET INCOME ($ mil.)	NET PROFIT MARGIN	EMPLOYEES
06/11	706	27	3.9%	4,700
06/10	593	1	0.3%	—
06/09*	532	(53)	—	—
12/08	0	0	—	—
Annual Growth	101319.4%	—	—	—

*Fiscal year change

2011 Year-End Financials

Debt ratio: ——
Return on equity: 3.90%
Cash ($ mil.): 26
Current ratio: 2.20
Long-term debt ($ mil.): —
Dividends
Yield: —
Payout: —
Market value ($ mil.): —

PROVIDENCE HOSPITAL

Providence Hospital is a pillar in the health care community of Washington DC. The oldest continuously operating hospital in our nation's capitol the 410-bed facility provides a full spectrum of services from behavioral health to women's services. It also administers programs for sleep disorders geriatric care and palliative care in addition to its comprehensive medical and surgical services. Providence Hospital's affiliates include the adjacent Carroll Manor Nursing and Rehabilitation Center a 250-bed facility for long-term and rehabilitative care as well as several outpatient family behavioral and occupational health clinics in the region. Providence Hospital is part of the Ascension Health network.

Operations

The main hospital and rehab facility includes the OB/GYN Center for Life a pharmacy and a wellness center. In addition area facilities operated by the hospital include the Seton House behavioral health center several Senior Wellness centers the Fort Lincoln Family Medicine Center (which serves Colmar Manor Maryland) and the Perry Family Health Center.

Company Background

Chartered by President Abraham Lincoln in 1861 Providence Hospital is the longest continuously operating hospital in the US capital.

EXECUTIVES

SVP Business Development Marketing PR and Government Relations, Karol Marciano
SVP Planning Project Integration and Risk Management, Deborah Morrison
VP Mission Integration, Matt Lukasiak
CIO, Alan Wyman
Vice Chair, Sister Mary Bader
Chairman, William J. Cox
President and CEO, Amy Freeman
SVP and CFO, Rick Talento
VP Human Resources, Matt Lasecki
Senior Vice President Operations, James Rohrbaugh
SVP Medical Affairs, Raymond Cox

Chief of Clinical Excellence and Program Director of Graduate Medical Education, Kamlajit Sethi
SVP Behavioral Health and Support Services, Vicki Shockey
Vice President Physician Enterprise, Fahad Tahir
Vice President Administrator Carroll Manor, Tina Sandri
President CEO, Nicholas Simmonds
Auditors: DeloitteTaxLLP

LOCATIONS

HQ: PROVIDENCE HOSPITAL
1150 VARNUM ST NE, WASHINGTON, DC 20017-2104
Phone: 202-269-7000
Web: WWW.PROVHOSP.ORG

Selected Facilities

Carroll Manor Nursing And Rehabilitation Center (Washington DC)
Congress Heights Senior Wellness Center (Washington DC)
Model Cities Senior Wellness Center (Washington DC)
Hattie Holmes Senior Wellness Center (Washington DC)
Fort Lincoln Family Medicine Center (Colmar Manor Maryland)
Perry Family Health Center (Washington DC)
Police and Fire Clinic (Washington DC)
Seton House (Washington DC; behavioral health services)
Wellington Pharmacy (Washington DC)
Wellness Institute (Washington DC)

COMPETITORS

Adventist HealthCare
Children' s National Medical Center
Dimensions Healthcare
Doctors Community Hospital
Fauquier Hospital
HSC Pediatric Center
MedStar Health
Sibley Memorial Hospital
Suburban Hospital

HISTORICAL FINANCIALS

Company Type: Private

Income Statement

FYE: June 30

	REVENUE ($ mil.)	NET INCOME ($ mil.)	NET PROFIT MARGIN	EMPLOYEES
06/11	229	8	3.8%	2,517
06/10	235	8	3.5%	—
06/09	230	(13)	—	—
06/08	19	(3)	—	—
Annual Growth	125.8%	—	—	—

2011 Year-End Financials

Debt ratio: —
Return on equity: 3.80%
Cash ($ mil.): 15
Current ratio: 1.30
Long-term debt ($ mil.): —
Dividends
Yield: —
Payout: —
Market value ($ mil.): —

PRUDENTIAL OVERALL SUPPLY INC.

EXECUTIVES

Chairman, J. Daniel (Dan) Clark
VP Sales and Marketing, Jerry Martin
CFO, John Thompson
Auditors: KPMGPeatMarwickLLP

LOCATIONS

HQ: PRUDENTIAL OVERALL SUPPLY INC.
16901 ASTON, IRVINE, CA 926064829
Phone: 9492504855
Web: WWW.PRUDENTIALUNIFORMS.COM

Selected Markets

Arizona
California
Colorado
Massachusetts
Nevada
New Mexico
Texas
Virginia

COMPETITORS

ARAMARK
Alsco
Ameripride Services
Angelica Corporation
Aramark Uniform and Career Apparel
Cintas
G&K Services
Mission Linen Supply

HISTORICAL FINANCIALS

Company Type: Private

Income Statement

FYE: December 31

	REVENUE ($ mil.)	NET INCOME ($ mil.)	NET PROFIT MARGIN	EMPLOYEES
12/12	145	4	3.4%	1,457
12/11	141	4	3.1%	—
12/10	139	1	0.9%	—
12/08	0	0	—	—
Annual Growth	—	—	—	—

2012 Year-End Financials

Debt ratio: —
Return on equity: 3.40%
Cash ($ mil.): 8
Current ratio: 1.50
Long-term debt ($ mil.): —
Dividends
Yield: —
Payout: —
Market value ($ mil.): —

PSCU INCORPORATED

Credit unions turn to PSCU to provide key services. One of the nation's largest credit union service organizations PSCU (short for Payment Systems for Credit Unions) provides credit debit ATM and prepaid card servicing as well as electronic banking bill payment risk management specialized marketing and contact center services to credit unions across the US. The not-for-profit cooperative serves more than 1500 institutions nationwide which combined represent more than 15 million cardholder accounts and one million online bill payment subscribers.

Geographic Reach

PSCU operates four Contact Centers covering three major US regions: the Eastern US with one center located in St. Petersburg Florida; the Western US with one center in Phoenix Arizona; and the Midwest with two centers in Detroit Michigan.

Operations

The centers perform new member enrollment automated lending collections cardholder support cross-selling and customer service.

Financial Performance

The company's revenues grew by 7% in 2011 due to a rise in transaction volume and a growth in product servicing. Total cardholders and subscribers increased to 15 million in 2011 up from 14.3 million reflective of gains in all key payments channels of Debit Credit and Bill Payments.

PSCU remained profitable throughout the economic downturn as credit union enrollments swelled nationwide in part due to consumers' dissatisfaction with large banks.

Strategy

The company's strategy is focused on Member Owner Payments Revenue Optimization to empower clients to outperform the marketplace in member acquisition and engagement.

To grow its membership in 2012 PSCU launched Mobile Bill Pay capabilities for PayLynx Bill Pay users.

Ownership

PSCU is owned by more than 680 member credit unions.

Company Background

PSCU was formed in 1977 by leaders from Pinellas County Teachers Credit Union and the federal credit unions of GTE Publix Employees Suncoast Schools and Railroad and Industrial.

EXECUTIVES

Senior Vice President Chief Risk Officer, Steve Ruwe
Chairman, Craig Esrael
Vice Chairman, Mike Valentine
Executive Vice President, Steve Salzer
EVP, Charles E. (Chuck) Fagan III
President and CEO, Michael J. (Mike) Kelly
EVP Credit Debit Prepaid eCommerce Contact Center and Information Technology, Tom Gandre
EVP Credit Union Experience, Fredda McDonald
EVP Human Resources, Lynn Heckler
Executive Vice President & Chief Financial Officer, Brian Caldarelli
Senior Vice President & Chief Sales Officer, James Guild
Senior Vice President & Chief Marketing Officer, Dan Csont

LOCATIONS

HQ: PSCU INCORPORATED
560 CARILLON PKWY, SAINT PETERSBURG, FL 33716-1294
Phone: 727-572-8822
Web: WWW.PSCUFS.COM

PRODUCTS/OPERATIONS

Selected Services

Advisors Plus
Credit Solutions
Debit Solutions
eCommerce Solutions
EMV
Prepaid Solutions
Risk Management Solutions
Total Member Care
Technology Tools
PSCU Partnerships/Sponsorships
Credit Union Cherry Blossom Run
Credit Union Student Choice
Filene Research Institute
Financial Service Center Cooperatives (FSCC)
Ongoing Operations
The Colonial Williamsburg Foundation

COMPETITORS

CUSO Financial Services
Southwest Corporate FCU
U.S. Central
Western Bridge

HISTORICAL FINANCIALS

Company Type: Private

Income Statement

FYE: December 31

	REVENUE ($ mil.)	NET INCOME ($ mil.)	NET PROFIT MARGIN	EMPLOYEES
12/12	377	38	10.2%	1,400
12/11	425	29	6.9%	—
12/10	662	284	43.0%	—
Annual Growth	(24.5%)	(63.2%)	—	—

2012 Year-End Financials

Debt ratio: —
Return on equity: 10.20%
Cash ($ mil.): 121
Current ratio: 0.80
Long-term debt ($ mil.): —

Dividends
Yield: —
Payout: —
Market value ($ mil.): —

PUBLIC BROADCASTING SERVICE

You might say these shows get a lot of public support. Public Broadcasting Service (PBS) is a non-profit organization that provides educational and public interest programming to more than 350 member public TV stations in the US. In addition to such programs as NOVA "This Old House" and Downton Abbey it provides related services such as distribution fundraising support and technology development. PBS gets its revenue from underwriting membership dues federal funding (including grants from the not-for-profit Corporation for Public Broadcasting) royalties license fees and product sales. The organization was founded in 1969 to provide cultural and educational programming.

Geographic Reach

PBS reaches about 120 million people through television and nearly 28 million people online each month.

Operations

PBS operates through more than 350 member public TV stations across the US.

Financial Performance

PBS saw is revenue decrease by almost 17% during fiscal year 2011 as compared to 2010.

Strategy

While PBS –and its federal funding –regularly finds itself caught in the crossfire between liberal and conservative political groups supporters of the non-profit trumpet the benefits of publicly-funded television programming created to serve groups often overlooked by commercial broadcasters.

PBS' children's programming and news shows such as Frontline and PBS NewsHour (formerly The NewsHour with Jim Lehrer) are often touted as examples of how public broadcasting can fill voids left by the major networks.

The organization has also been looking to capitalize on new distribution channels to get its programming to the public. PBS sells its programs on DVD and through Apple's iTunes store. It has also ramped up its online video efforts.

EXECUTIVES

SVP and CFO, Barbara L. Landes
COO, Michael D. Jones
SVP PBS Ventures, Andrew L. Russell
General Manager Children's Programming; SVP Marketing and Communications, Lesli Rotenberg
SVP and Chief TV Programming Executive, John F. Wilson
SVP General Counsel and Corporate Secretary, Katherine Lauderdale
VP Strategy and Ventures, Loren Mayor
SVP Station Services, Joyce Herring
President CEO and Director, Paula A. Kerger
SVP Interactive, Jason Seiken
Chair, Geoffrey Sands
Vice Chairman, Allen Weatherly
CTO, John McCoskey
SVP Education, Robert M. Lippincott
Associate General Counsel and Assistant Corporate Secretary, Mary L. Plantamura
SVP Development, Brian J. Reddington
Chairman CEO, Allan Landon
Director, Fred Berens, age 71
Director, Ernest W. Bromley, age 62
Director, Donna A. Tanoue, age 59
Director, James R. Pagliarini
Vice Chair, Jennifer Lawson
President CEO and Director, Paula A. Kerger
Director, Sharon Percy Rockefeller
Director, John S. Domaschko
Director, M. Howard Jacobson
Director, Peter Morrill
Director, Thomas K. Williams
Director, DeAnne Hamilton
Vice Chairman, Allen Weatherly
Director, Peter Frid
Director, Ruby Calvert
Director, Paula Castadio
Director, Malcolm Brett
Director, Jon Abbott
Director, Molly Corbett Broad
Director, Jack Galmiche
Director, Charles T. Hagel
Director, Helen Hernandez
Director, Larry Irving
Director, John King
Director, Leo Soong
Director, Lloyd Wright
Auditors: BDOUSALLP

LOCATIONS

HQ: PUBLIC BROADCASTING SERVICE
2100 CRYSTAL DR STE 100, ARLINGTON, VA 22202-3784
Phone: 703-739-5000
Web: WWW.PBS.ORG

PRODUCTS/OPERATIONS

Selected Programming

Antiques Roadshow
Austin City Limits
Barney
Downton Abbey
Frontline
Juila Child: Lessons with Master Chefs
Live from Lincoln Center
Masterpiece Theatre
Mister Rogers' Neighborhood
MotorWeek
Mystery!
Nature
NOVA
NOW
P.O.V.
PBS NewsHour
Reading Rainbow
Sesame Street
Teletubbies
This Old House
Victory Garden
Washington Week
ZOOM

COMPETITORS

ABC Cable Networks
ABC Inc.
AMC Networks
BBC Worldwide
CBS
Current Media
Discovery Communications
HBO
MTV Networks
NBC
Scripps Networks
Turner Broadcasting

HISTORICAL FINANCIALS

Company Type: Private

Income Statement FYE: June 30

	REVENUE ($ mil.)	NET INCOME ($ mil.)	NET PROFIT MARGIN	EMPLOYEES
06/11	475	(28)	—	507
06/10	505	28	5.6%	—
06/09	502	(80)	—	—
06/08	4	1	35.6%	—
Annual Growth	358.2%	—	—	—

2011 Year-End Financials

Debt ratio: —
Return on equity: (-6.00%)
Cash ($ mil.): 29
Current ratio: 1.30
Long-term debt ($ mil.): —

Dividends
Yield: —
Payout: —
Market value ($ mil.): —

PUBLIC HEALTH SOLUTIONS

Public Heath Solutions (formerly Medical and Health Research Association of New York City) is here to help. Public Health Solutions (PHS) is a not-for-profit organization that works with the NYC Department of Health to create and administer projects aimed at providing better healthcare to the city's low-income at-risk population. It helps about 200000 people a year with studies like the Human Papillomavirus Screening Project and others looking at disease awareness and prevention in minority groups. Services include women's and children's health HIV/AIDS health care smoking cessation counseling and access to health care. The organization was founded in 1957 to conduct health research projects.

EXECUTIVES

Administrative Assistant, Sonya Williamson
Office Manager, Jennifer Banos
Board Member, David Harris

LOCATIONS

HQ: PUBLIC HEALTH SOLUTIONS
40 WORTH ST FL 5, NEW YORK, NY 10013-2955
Phone: 646-619-6400
Web: WWW.HEALTHSOLUTIONS.ORG

HISTORICAL FINANCIALS

Company Type: Private

Income Statement FYE: December 31

	REVENUE ($ mil.)	NET INCOME ($ mil.)	NET PROFIT MARGIN	EMPLOYEES
12/07	225	7	3.3%	650
12/06	214	(2)	—	—
12/05	1,130	0	0.0%	—
Annual Growth	(55.3%)	2019.1%	—	—

2007 Year-End Financials

Debt ratio: —
Return on equity: 3.30%
Cash ($ mil.): 20
Current ratio: 0.30
Long-term debt ($ mil.): —

Dividends
Yield: —
Payout: —
Market value ($ mil.): —

PUBLIC HOSPITAL DISTRICT

LOCATIONS

HQ: PUBLIC HOSPITAL DISTRICT
1415 E KINCAID ST, MOUNT VERNON, WA 982744126
Phone: 3604244111
Web: WWW.CASCADESKAGITHEALTH.ORG

HISTORICAL FINANCIALS

Company Type: Private

Income Statement FYE: December 31

	REVENUE ($ mil.)	NET INCOME ($ mil.)	NET PROFIT MARGIN	EMPLOYEES
12/11	216	4	2.3%	1,072
12/10*	186	0	0.4%	—
06/10	612	0	—	—
Annual Growth	—	9529.9%	—	—

*Fiscal year change

2011 Year-End Financials

Debt ratio: —
Return on equity: 2.30%
Cash ($ mil.): 1
Current ratio: 1.60
Long-term debt ($ mil.): —
Dividends
Yield: —
Payout: —
Market value ($ mil.): —

PUBLIC UTILITIES BOARD

This PUB has no beer. Brownsville Public Utilities Board (Brownsville PUB) is a municipally-owned utility company providing electric water and wastewater services to residential and commercial customers in Brownsville Texas. Brownsville PUB serves 46000 with electric service and 47000 with water and wastewater service. The utility's two water treatment plants have the capacity to provide 40 million gallons of treated water per day. It gets its water supply from the Rio Grande. The utility's wastewater system has 174 lift stations and two treatment plants.

Brownsville PUB is challenged to keep pace with explosive population growth in Brownsville (2.5% a year since 2000). In 2012 its major growth initiatives included bringing water to a colonias (undeveloped but populated rural community) on the edge of Brownsville a seawater desalination plant a filtration project and sewer overflow remediation.

Customer growth and higher power water and wastewater demand lifted the utility's revenues by more than 8% in 2011 while the robust revenues and lower fuel costs (due to low natural gas prices) and a drop in depreciation and other costs helped the company to report a 52% jump in operating income for the year.

The utility got it start in 1907 after local residents voted for the issuance of bonds to build electric and water plants and construct a utility system.

In the 1960s Brownsville citizens narrowly defeated a bid by electrical provider Central Power & Light Co. to buy the Brownsville utility. Following this the city set up Brownsville PUB as a municipally owned utility giving customers control over the management of their utility.

EXECUTIVES

CEO General Manager and Director, John S. Bruciak
Director Environmental Services, Albert Gomez
Director Water and Wastewater Engineering Operations, Genoveva G. Gomez
Director Communications and Administrative Services, Lucila Cano Hernandez
Director Transmission and Distribution, James McCann
Assistant General Manager Chief Operating Officer, Fernando Saenz
Director Purchasing, Diane Solitaire
Manager Customer Service, Susan Walker
Chief Financial Officer, Leandro G. Garcia
Human Resources Manager, Emilia Guerra
Account Manager, Ana I. Lozano
Chairman, David S. Morales
CEO General Manager and Director, John S. Bruciak

LOCATIONS

HQ: PUBLIC UTILITIES BOARD
1425 ROBINHOOD ST, BROWNSVILLE, TX 78521-4230
Phone: 956-983-6100
Web: WWW.BROWNSVILLE-PUB.COM

PRODUCTS/OPERATIONS

2011 Sales

	% of total
Electric	74
Water	13
Wastewater	13
Total	**100**

HISTORICAL FINANCIALS

Company Type: Private

Income Statement FYE: September 30

	REVENUE ($ mil.)	NET INCOME ($ mil.)	NET PROFIT MARGIN	EMPLOYEES
09/09	163	10	6.3%	482
09/08	209	34	16.6%	—
09/06	421	0	—	—
Annual Growth	—	2707.7%	—	—

2009 Year-End Financials

Debt ratio: —
Return on equity: 6.30%
Cash ($ mil.): 10
Current ratio: 0.70
Long-term debt ($ mil.): —
Dividends
Yield: —
Payout: —
Market value ($ mil.): —

PUGET SOUND BLOOD CENTER & PROGRAM

Residents of the Emerald City can go here to give red. Puget Sound Blood Center (PSBC) is a not-for-profit blood and tissue bank serving more than 70 hospitals and clinics in and around Seattle. The blood center collects and processes donated blood through about a dozen donation centers and several mobile units; it also registers bone marrow donors provides testing and training services to patients with hemophilia and collects cord blood for use in stem cell transplantation. Its PSBC Research Institute conducts research on improving transfusion and transplantation medicine. PSBC was formed in 1944.

Geographic Reach

PSBC serves health care facilities in 14 counties in western Washington plus the nearby San Juan Islands. The company also has cord blood bank partnerships with hospitals across Washington and in Oregon and Hawaii.

Operations

PSBC funds its activities including its research efforts by charging services fees to clients as well as through research grants research partnerships and philanthropic donations. It also sells blood derivatives and related products (such as plasma).

Research programs focus on improving transfusion and transplantation medicine for patients with ailments including leukemia cancer serious injuries and burns.

Financial Analysis

PSBC reported revenues of $151 million in 2012. The company's earnings reflected a little more than 1% increase over revenues in 2011.

Strategy

Growth in its service territory and customer base as well as the increasingly complex blood testing needs of its clients has led PSBC to expand its facilities in recent years. For instance in 2011 it opened a new blood lab dedicated to pediatric transfusion services. It also completed construction of a new facility for its research institute that year.

At the same time PSBC is also selling off some operations to focus on core services. In 2012 it agreed to sell its Northwest Tissue Services unit which conducts human tissue donation and processing to LifeNet Health. It also agreed to sell its donor testing unit which performs blood testing for external clients such as other blood banks to Creative Testing Solutions (CTS); PSBC will retain an equity stake in CTS through the deal.

EXECUTIVES

EVP Finance, Robert J. Gleason
EVP Marketing and Community Relations, Maria E. Geyer
EVP Blood Services Laboratories, Sandy Linauts
Press Contact, Michael Young
President Chief Executive Officer, James P. AuBuchon
Vice Chair, Alan W. Schulkin
EVP Quality and Organizational Effectiveness, Lynn Craig
EVP Medical Division, Thomas H. Price
EVP Human Resources, Sally Sullivan
Chief Medical Officer for PSBC and medical director for the centralized transfusion service and the immunohematology reference laboratory, Theresa Nester
Chief Operating Officer, David C. Fennell
Trustee, Robert C. Wallace
Trustee, Barbara C. Sherland
Trustee, Colleen Ferris
Trustee, A. Kent Fisher
Trustee, Leslie Giblett
Trustee, John B. Hayhurst
Trustee, Steve Hix
Trustee, Toni Hoffman
Trustee, Susan J. Naficy
Trustee, Steve Nicholes
Trustee, Marnie Roozen
Trustee, Jon Summers
Trustee, Mirtha Vaca-Wilkens

LOCATIONS

HQ: PUGET SOUND BLOOD CENTER & PROGRAM
921 TERRY AVE, SEATTLE, WA 98104-1239
Phone: 206-292-6500
Web: WWW.PSBC.ORG

Selected Washington Service Counties

Clallam
Clark
Cowlitz
Grays Harbor
Jefferson

King
Kitsap
Lewis
Mason
Pierce
San Juan Islands
Skagit
Snohomish
Thurston
Whatcom

PRODUCTS/OPERATIONS

Selected Services

Blood Services
Clinical Services
Clinical Trial Support
Cord Blood Program
Research Institute
Specialty Diagnostics Laboratories
  Genomics Testing Laboratory
  Hemostasis Reference Laboratory
  Immunogenetics/HLA Laboratory
  Platelet Immunology Laboratory
Transfusion Medicine
  Compatibility Testing Laboratory
  Donor Testing/Virology Laboratory
  Red Cell Reference Laboratory

COMPETITORS

Blood Systems Inc.
CSL Plasma
Daxor
Haemonetics
HemaCare
Red Cross
SeraCare Life Sciences

HISTORICAL FINANCIALS

Company Type: Private

Income Statement FYE: June 30

	REVENUE ($ mil.)	NET INCOME ($ mil.)	NET PROFIT MARGIN	EMPLOYEES
06/13	152	(2)	—	750
06/12	150	(1)	—	—
06/10	164	9	6.0%	—
06/10	149	1	0.8%	—
Annual Growth	0.5%	—	—	—

2013 Year-End Financials

Debt ratio: —
Return on equity: (-1.60%)
Cash ($ mil.): 3
Current ratio: 1.20
Long-term debt ($ mil.): —
Dividends
Yield: —
Payout: —
Market value ($ mil.): —

PYCO INDUSTRIES INC.

EXECUTIVES

President, Gail Kring
VP Finance, Tony Morton
Director Information Technology, Jeff Tucker
SVP Marketing, Robert Lacy
VP Oil Trading and Packaged Oil, Ronnie Gilbert
Manager Marketing and Transportation, Kelly Jack
Mid-South Division Manager, John Stewart
Controller Mid-South Division, Kathy Garrett
Traffic and Sales Mid-South Division, Willie Willis
Chairman, Thomas W. Horsford
Oil Administrator and Logistics, Lisa Buxton
Sales Manager, Seth Terrell

LOCATIONS

HQ: PYCO INDUSTRIES INC.
2901 AVENUE A, LUBBOCK, TX 794042231
Phone: 8067473434
Web: WWW.PYCOINDUSTRIESINC.COM

PRODUCTS/OPERATIONS

Selected Products

Hulls
  Feed for cattle
  Furfural
  Oil well drilling mud
Linters
  Cellulose esters and ethers
  Cellulose nitrate
  Felts
  Films
  Food casings
  Medical grade cotton
  Paper
  Yarns
Meal
  Feed
  Fertilizer
Oil
  Fatty acids
  Glycerine
  Refined
Whole seed
  Feed for cattle

COMPETITORS

ADM
Cargill

HISTORICAL FINANCIALS

Company Type: Private

Income Statement FYE: September 30

	REVENUE ($ mil.)	NET INCOME ($ mil.)	NET PROFIT MARGIN	EMPLOYEES
09/14	184	22	12.4%	160
09/13	176	18	10.6%	—
09/12	196	11	5.8%	—
09/06	234	0	—	—
Annual Growth	(2.9%)	—	—	—

2014 Year-End Financials

Debt ratio: —
Return on equity: 12.40%
Cash ($ mil.): 34
Current ratio: 1.20
Long-term debt ($ mil.): —
Dividends
Yield: —
Payout: —
Market value ($ mil.): —

QUAKER VALLEY FOODS INC.

Quaker Valley Foods (QVF) is known by friends high and low for its take-out fresh and frozen staples. The food distributor makes daily deliveries of meat and other provisions to foodservice customers across the Northeast US. QVF a member of the UNIPRO Foodservice coop offers beef pork poultry frozen seafood imported meats (mutton and goat) cheeses salads and other items from its Philadelphia warehouse. Customers range from wholesalers and jobbers to independent retail and wholesale groceries and major supermarket chains. Its vendors include Hormel Swift Packerland Carolina Turkey Tyson Alpine Lace and Land O' Lakes. QVF was started by two brothers-in-law in 1975 and is led by its founders' sons.

EXECUTIVES

President, Wayne Hudis
VP Operations, Kenneth Fleekop

LOCATIONS

HQ: QUAKER VALLEY FOODS INC.
2701 RED LION RD, PHILADELPHIA, PA 19114-1019
Phone: 215-992-0900
Web: WWW.QUAKERVALLEYFOODS.COM

PRODUCTS/OPERATIONS

Selected Products

Beef
Deli and provisions
Goats
Lamb
Mutton imported
Pork
Poultry
Seafood frozen

COMPETITORS

Associated Wholesale Grocers
C&S Wholesale
Feesers
McLane
Meadowbrook Meat Company
Nash-Finch
Performance Food
SUPERVALU
Schiff s
Sysco
US Foods
Vista Food Exchange

HISTORICAL FINANCIALS

Company Type: Private

Income Statement FYE: December 29

	REVENUE ($ mil.)	NET INCOME ($ mil.)	NET PROFIT MARGIN	EMPLOYEES
12/12	290	5	1.8%	145
12/11*	195	0	0.2%	—
01/11	177	0	0.2%	—
01/10	160	0	0.4%	—
Annual Growth	21.8%	104.6%	—	—

*Fiscal year change

2012 Year-End Financials

Debt ratio: —
Return on equity: 1.80%
Cash ($ mil.): 1
Current ratio: 0.60
Long-term debt ($ mil.): —
Dividends
Yield: —
Payout: —
Market value ($ mil.): —

QUALITY OIL COMPANY LLC

With more services than your average oil company Quality Oil helps its customers get fueled up cooled off and well rested. And they can smoke if they want to. The company distributes fuel oil and propane to customers in the Winston-Salem area of North Carolina. Quality Oil provides air conditioning and heating equipment service operates 47 convenience stores (Quality Marts) and about 20 service stations and owns hotels in five southern states. In addition the company operates 60 Quality Plus locations at which drivers can buy cigarettes at discount prices. The company also provides Right-a-Way oil change services at many of its gas stations.

Geographic Reach

Quality Oil owns and operates four Hampton Inns two Hampton Inn & Suites and one Homewood Suites in the Carolinas Florida Georgia and Virginia. Affiliate Reliable Tank Line LLC transports petroleum products and provides fleet fueling services at 10 locations in North Carolina northern South Carolina eastern Virginia and eastern Tennessee. Quality Oil Heating-Cooling has assets throughout North Carolina and parts of South Carolina Virginia Florida and Tennessee and serves Forsyth County Stokes County Davie County Davidson County Yadkin County Rowan County and Iredell County.

Operations

In addition the company's real estate unit (Quality Oil Real Estate) operates a diverse portfolio of retail and hotel sites industrial units residential subdivision developments and a shopping center. Quality Marts and Quality Plus also provide heating and cooling and fleet fueling services.

Sales and Marketing

The company markets Shell oil products.

Strategy

To sharpen its competitive edge in 2013 Quality Oil created a new department –Retail Technology –to maintain PDI Pricebook and POS Systems and test and implement future technological developments.

To increase operational efficiency in 2012 Quality Oil installed Professional Datasolutions Inc. (PDI) scanning software at all of its retail outlets.

Mergers and Acquisitions

To complement its existing oil and propane business in 2012 Quality Oil acquired regional gas station and convenience store operator Horn Oil Co. in Mocksville North Carolina.

Company Background

Expanding its store network in 2011 the company opened Quality Mart locations #46 and #47 in Kernersville and Morrisville.

Quality Oil was founded in 1929 by Joe Glenn and Bert Bennett as a Shell oil products distributor and is still owned and operated by descendants of the founders.

EXECUTIVES

President, Graham Bennett
SVP Convenience Store Operations, Tim Lowman
SVP Gasoline Sales, Andy Sayles
Vice President - Shell Stations, Danny Brown
SVP Construction, Ernie Rhymer
Vice President Retail Technology, Harry Alexander
SVP Information Technology, Carol Holt
SVP Hotel Division, Rob Hill
SVP Human Resources, Tracy Harmon
VP Business Transformation, David Bohanon
SVP Reliable Tank Line, Buddy Jenkins
SVP Finance, Don McIver
Warehouse and Shell Products, Eric Riley
Fuel Buying and Wholesale, Josh McClure
Marketing Coordinator, Michael Robb
Operations Manager, Robb Cranston
Vice President Real Estate, Daniel Dinsbeer

LOCATIONS

HQ: QUALITY OIL COMPANY LLC
1540 SILAS CREEK PKWY, WINSTON SALEM, NC 27127-3705
Phone: 336-722-3441
Web: WWW.QUALITYOILNC.COM

PRODUCTS/OPERATIONS

Selected Brands

Hampton Inn
Quality Heating and Air Conditioning
Quality Mart
Quality Oil Appliance Sales and Service
Quality Oil Commercial Heating and On-Site Fueling
Quality Oil Fuel Oil
Quality Oil Gas Logs and Heaters
Quality Oil Propane
Quality Plus
Reliable Tank Line
Shell Oil products

Selected Mergers and Acquisitions

2012
Horn Oil Co. (Mocksville North Carolina; gas station and convenience store operator)

COMPETITORS

A.T. Williams
Cumberland Farms
E-Z Mart Stores
Hyatt
Marriott
Racetrac Petroleum
WilcoHess

HISTORICAL FINANCIALS

Company Type: Private

Income Statement FYE: December 31

	REVENUE ($ mil.)	NET INCOME ($ mil.)	NET PROFIT MARGIN	EMPLOYEES
12/09	634	11	1.9%	1,000
12/08	806	27	3.4%	—
12/07	619	10	1.8%	—
12/06	542	15	2.8%	—
Annual Growth	5.4%	(8.1%)	—	—

2009 Year-End Financials

Debt ratio: —
Return on equity: 1.90%
Cash ($ mil.): 11
Current ratio: 0.70
Long-term debt ($ mil.): —
Dividends
Yield: —
Payout: —
Market value ($ mil.): —

QUEEN OF THE VALLEY MEDICAL CENTER

The Queen of the Valley Medical Center reigns over the whole of Napa Valley. The 190-bed hospital provides acute and tertiary care to the residents of California's Napa County. It operates a level III trauma center and provides emergency surgery and wound care services as well as specialty family work health nutritional and rehabilitation services. "The Queen" as it is known colloquially operates regional cancer orthopedic women's and heart centers as well as the Napa Valley Imaging Center and the Napa Valley Women's Healthcare Center. Queen of the Valley Medical Center is part of St. Joseph Health.

Current expansion efforts at Queen of the Valley Medical Center include construction of a $30 million three-story diagnostic and surgical pavilion. The new center will add high-tech surgical suites and diagnostic laboratory and imaging facilities as well as private ICU rooms. The hospital is also developing a new neuroscience center.

The medical center was founded in 1958 by the Sisters of St. Joseph of Orange. It expanded its facilities a number of times over the years. For instance in 2006 the hospital added a wellness center and a unit dedicated to maternal and infant care. These expansion efforts prompted a name change from Queen of the Valley Hospital to Queen of the Valley Medical Center in 2007 to reflect the facility's expanded offerings and its emphasis on not just medical care but also community-based outreach and prevention services.

EXECUTIVES

Director Of Pharmacy, Diane Heine
Vice President Of Human Resources, Robert Eisen
Vice President, Richard P Green
Vice President Finance Chief Financial, Keith Miller
Vice President Mission Integration, Marian Schubert

LOCATIONS

HQ: QUEEN OF THE VALLEY MEDICAL CENTER
1000 TRANCAS ST, NAPA, CA 94558-2906
Phone: 707-251-1761
Web: WWW.STJHS.ORG

COMPETITORS

Adventist Health
Community Hospital of the Monterey Peninsula
Dignity Health
HCA
John Muir Health
Providence Health & Services
Stanford Hospital and Clinics
Sutter Health
Tenet Healthcare
UCSF Medical
Western Medical Center - Santa Ana

HISTORICAL FINANCIALS

Company Type: Private

Income Statement FYE: June 30

	REVENUE ($ mil.)	NET INCOME ($ mil.)	NET PROFIT MARGIN	EMPLOYEES
06/10	276	25	9.1%	1,070
06/09	242	(5)	—	—
06/09	333	0	—	—
Annual Growth	(16.8%)	358461443%	—	—

2010 Year-End Financials

Debt ratio: —
Return on equity: 9.10%
Cash ($ mil.): 95
Current ratio: 1.50
Long-term debt ($ mil.): —
Dividends
Yield: —
Payout: —
Market value ($ mil.): —

QUINNIPIAC UNIVERSITY

At Quinnipiac University the first thing you may have to learn is how to pronounce it (for the record it's KWIN-uh-pe-ack). The private university offers a variety of liberal arts undergraduate programs as well as graduate programs in selected professional fields (business education health sciences communications and law) to some 8500 students. It often appears on lists of top colleges including those published by U.S. News & World Report. The university which is known to political junkies and others for its polling operation includes eight schools and colleges across three Connecticut campuses (Mount Carmel York Hill and North Haven).

Company Background Originally named the Connecticut College of Commerce the school was founded in 1929 by Samuel W. Tator as a small business college awarding associate's degrees. The college changed its name in 1951 to Quinnipiac College commemorating the early Indian settlers who made their home in and around the New Haven Connecticut harbor area.

EXECUTIVES

Vice Chairman, Carlton L. Highsmith, age 61
President and Trustee, John L. Lahey, age 68
SVP Finance, Patrick J. Healy, age 70
Vice President for public affairs, Lynn M. Bushnell
VP and Dean of Students, Manuel Carreiro
VP and Dean of Admissions, Joan Isaac Mohr
Chairman, Terry W. Goodwin

Dean Academic Services and Research Support, Linda K. Broker
Director Admissions, Carla May Knowlton
Director Admissions for Transfer and Part-Time Students, Mary E. Wargo
Director Arnold Bernhard Library, Charles M. Getchell
Director Athletics and Recreation, John J. McDonald
senior Vice President for academic and student affairs, Mark A. Thompson
Associate Dean School of Business, Charles M. Brooks
Dean School of Communications, David Donnelly
Vice President for development and alumni affairs, Donald J. Weinbach
Associate VP Development and Alumni Affairs, Dianna Pategas
Associate VP Facilities Administration, Joseph D. Rubertone
Associate Director Facilities, Keith Woodward
Director Administrative Services, John J. Meriano
Director Human Resources, Anna M. Spragg
Senior Director Financial Aid, Dominic R. Yoia
Senior Associate Director Financial Aid, Laurie Folsom
Director Graduate Admissions, Scott Farber
Director Marketing Communications for Admissions, Louise M. Howe
Director Graduate Financial Aid, Heather Hamilton
Director Student Health Services, Katheryn B. Macaione
VP CIO and CTO, Richard C. Ferguson
Dean School of Law, Brad Saxton
Director Learning Center, Andrew Delohery
Dean College of Arts and Sciences, Johannes D. (Hans) Bergmann
Registrar, Dorothy M. Lauria
Director Residential Life, Cindy Long Porter
Chief of Security and Safety, John R. Twining
Dean Academic Technology, John Paton
Bursar, Valerie Carbone
Controller, Daniel Johnson
Interim Dean School of Health Sciences, Edward R. O'Connor
Dean Division of Education, Cynthia K. Dubea
Managing Director, David M. Darst
Vice President for human resources, Ronald Mason
VP CIO and CTO, Fred Tarca
Dean School of Communications, Lee Kamlet
Dean School of Education, Kevin Basmadjian
Vice President executive associate to the president, Jean Husted
Trustee, William G. Spears, age 75
Trustee, William C. (Bill) Weldon, age 64
Vice Chairman, Carlton L. Highsmith, age 61
President and Trustee, John L. Lahey, age 68
Trustee, David R. Nelson
Trustee, William L. (Bill) Ayers Jr.
Trustee, Frederick J. Mancheski
Vice Chairman, Murray Lender
Secretary and Trustee, Robert J. Hauser Jr.
Trustee, Alexander Alexiades
Trustee, John R. Antonino
Trustee, Anthony J. Baudanza
Trustee, Patrick Baumgarten
Trustee, Donald P. Calcagnini
Trustee, Albert Canosa
Trustee, Peter R. DeGeorge
Trustee, Gabriel Ferrucci
Trustee, Dennis P. Flanagan
Trustee, Mary-Jane Foster, age 62
Trustee, Hugh F. Keefe
Trustee, Richard G. Kelley
Trustee, Marcus R. McCraven
Trustee, John F. Meuser
Trustee, Paula Moynahan
Trustee, Donald L. Perlroth
Trustee, Jonathan M. Reeves
Trustee, Arthur H. Rice
Trustee, Edward L. Scalone
Auditors: Deloitte&ToucheLLP

LOCATIONS

HQ: QUINNIPIAC UNIVERSITY
275 MOUNT CARMEL AVE, HAMDEN, CT 06518-1908
Phone: 203-582-8200
Web: WWW.QUINNIPIACBOBCATS.COM

HISTORICAL FINANCIALS

Company Type: Private

Income Statement FYE: June 30

	REVENUE ($ mil.)	NET INCOME ($ mil.)	NET PROFIT MARGIN	EMPLOYEES
06/11	349	68	19.5%	900
06/10	290	45	15.6%	—
06/09	235	(0)	—	—
06/08	3	1	38.5%	—
Annual Growth	385.8%	287.2%	—	—

2011 Year-End Financials

Debt ratio: —
Return on equity: 19.50%
Cash ($ mil.): 7
Current ratio: —
Long-term debt ($ mil.): —
Dividends
Yield: —
Payout: —
Market value ($ mil.): —

R. E. MICHEL COMPANY

Blowing hot and cold is good for R.E. Michel. The company is one of the nation's largest wholesale distributors of heating air-conditioning and refrigeration (HVAC-R) equipment parts and supplies. The family-owned and operated firm offers more than 16000 items through about 2 sales offices located across the Southern Mid-Atlantic and Northeastern regions of the country. R.E. Michel ships more than 20000 items each day from its 900000-sq.-ft. distribution center in Maryland. Its Exclusive Supplier Partnership (ESP) program offers customers inventory control advertising and marketing support. R.E. Michel was founded in 1935 as a supplier to the home heating oil burner industry.

Geographic Reach

The HVAC wholesaler maintains a handful of offices to cater to customers located in the Southern US as well as in the Mid-Atlantic and Northeastern regions. Most recently opened offices reside in Ohio California Virginia Florida South Carolina Arizona and Tennessee.

Sales and Marketing

R.E. Michel uses up to 50 trailers to ship its more than 10000 items each day. To this end the company also ships more than 3200 items via the United Parcel Service each week. As part of its business it publishes a 1300 page catalog that includes 20000 catalog line items.

EXECUTIVES

President, Butch Michel
Vice President Of Fin Human Resources, Holly Porter

LOCATIONS

HQ: R. E. MICHEL COMPANY
1 RE MICHEL DR, GLEN BURNIE, MD 210606408
Phone: 4107604000
Web: WWW.REMICHEL.COM

PRODUCTS/OPERATIONS

Selected Products and Services

Air conditioning & heating
Indoor air quality
Boilers
Water heating equipment
Hydronic & steam systems
Valves
Pipe & fittings
Fuel oil systems
Gas systems
Chemicals
Refrigeration equipment & supplies
Controls
Electrical supplies
Motors
Air handling products
Venting products
Duct registers & grilles
Tools & test instruments
O.E.M. Parts

COMPETITORS

Emco Corporation
Ferguson Enterprises
Gensco
HD Supply
Lowe' s
MSC Industrial Direct
W.W. Grainger
WinWholesale

HISTORICAL FINANCIALS

Company Type: Private

Income Statement FYE: December 31

	REVENUE ($ mil.)	NET INCOME ($ mil.)	NET PROFIT MARGIN	EMPLOYEES
12/13	685	31	4.6%	1,674
12/12	611	3	0.6%	—
12/11	606	8	1.4%	—
12/10	593	0	—	—
Annual Growth	4.9%	—	—	—

2013 Year-End Financials

Debt ratio: —
Return on equity: 4.60%
Cash ($ mil.): 0
Current ratio: 0.60
Long-term debt ($ mil.): —
Dividends
Yield: —
Payout: —
Market value ($ mil.): —

R. L. JORDAN OIL COMPANY OF NORTH CAROLINA INC.

EXECUTIVES

President, Dan Durbin
Director of HR, Deanna Williamson

LOCATIONS

HQ: R. L. JORDAN OIL COMPANY OF NORTH CAROLINA INC.
1451 FERNWOOD GLENDALE RD, SPARTANBURG, SC 293073044
Phone: 8645852784
Web: WWW.RLJOC.COM

2012 Stores

	No.
South	41
North	13
Total	**54**

COMPETITORS

7-Eleven
Colonial Group
Cumberland Farms
Exxon Mobil
McDonald' s
Mountain Empire Oil
Quiznos
Racetrac Petroleum
Spinx
The Pantry

HISTORICAL FINANCIALS

Company Type: Private

Income Statement FYE: September 30

	REVENUE ($ mil.)	NET INCOME ($ mil.)	NET PROFIT MARGIN	EMPLOYEES
09/07	278	(0)	—	900
09/06	270	(1)	—	—
09/05	1,428	0	—	—
Annual Growth	—	—	—	—

2007 Year-End Financials

Debt ratio: —
Return on equity: (-0.10%)
Cash ($ mil.): 4
Current ratio: 0.60
Long-term debt ($ mil.): —

Dividends
Yield: —
Payout: —
Market value ($ mil.): —

R.S. HUGHES COMPANY INC.

R.S. Hughes distributes the stuff that holds the world together –duct tape that is –plus a lot more. Established in 1954 the employee-owned company maintains some 45 warehouse locations in the US and Mexico. It ,Â supplies adhesives (epoxies aerosols hot glues silicones) electrical specialties (tubing terminals films tape and barriers) safety products (glasses ear plugs masks) tapes (masking foam vinyl cloth foil duct joining) and abrasives (roll disc brush wheel belt and air tools). R.S. Hughes also distributes labels and signs (printable labels and tags safety signs) and aerosols and coatings (WD-40 paints lubricants oils cleaners).

EXECUTIVES

V Pres, Joseph Vargas, age 58

LOCATIONS

HQ: R.S. HUGHES COMPANY INC.
1162 SONORA CT, SUNNYVALE, CA 940865378
Phone: 4087393211
Web: WWW.RSHUGHES.COM

PRODUCTS/OPERATIONS

Selected Products

Adhesives
Abrasive power tools
Aerosol paints and lubricants
Coatings
Labels
Printers
Sealants
Tapes

COMPETITORS

DXP Enterprises
HD Supply
Industrial Distribution Group
Plymouth Rubber
W.W. Grainger

HISTORICAL FINANCIALS

Company Type: Private

Income Statement FYE: September 28

	REVENUE ($ mil.)	NET INCOME ($ mil.)	NET PROFIT MARGIN	EMPLOYEES
09/14	302	15	5.1%	460
09/13	281	15	5.5%	—
09/12*	253	15	6.2%	—
10/11	231	0	—	—
Annual Growth	9.2%	—	—	—

*Fiscal year change

2014 Year-End Financials

Debt ratio: —
Return on equity: 5.10%
Cash ($ mil.): 10
Current ratio: 2.70
Long-term debt ($ mil.): —

Dividends
Yield: —
Payout: —
Market value ($ mil.): —

RADY CHILDREN'S HOSPITAL-SAN DIEGO

Rady Children's Hospital-San Diego handles the big injuries of pint-sized patients. Serving as the region's only pediatric trauma center the nonprofit hospital boasts more than 460 beds. As part of its services Rady Children's Hospital-San Diego offers comprehensive pediatric care including surgical services convalescent care a neonatal intensive care unit and orthopedic services. Across its service area the hospital also operates about 25 satellite centers that provide such primary and specialized care services as physical therapy and hearing diagnostics. Rady Children's Hospital a teaching hospital affiliated with the University of California San Diego Medical School was founded in 1954.

Geographic Reach

Rady Children's Hospital serves as the pediatric medical center that caters to the California region of San Diego Imperial and southern Riverside counties. It provides care to more than 82% of the region's children.

Operations

Rady Children's operates its own 36-bed emergency department –The Sam S. and Rose Stein Emergency Care Center –that each day sees up to 300 patients. It is the only regional emergency center solely dedicated and equipped to care for children. The hospital also operates California's only pediatric skilled nursing facility –The Helen Bernardy Center –to provide 24-hour care to disabled and medically fragile children in a homelike environment.

For treating non-life-or-limb-threatening injuries and illnesses the hospital operates neighborhood urgent care centers in Escondido La Mesa Oceanside and San Diego.

Through its medical school affiliation Rady Children's engages in about 260 research studies and 170 clinical trials in all pediatric specialties. It collaborates with University of California San Diego the Sanford-Burnham Medical Research Institute The Scripps Research Institute the Salk Institute for Biological Studies and St. Jude Children's Research Hospital. Specialized research facilities on campus include the Autism Discovery Institute the Blair L. Sadler Center for Quality and the Child and Adolescent Services Research Center.

The hospital operates a LEED-certified Acute Care Pavilion which holds a neonatal intensive care unit the Peckham Center for Cancer and Blood Disorders and the Warren Family Surgical Center. It serves those suffering from eating disorders through its inpatient center (opened in 2011) to allow for intensive psychiatric therapy for patients with anorexia and bulimia and to aid families with home care.

Company Background

By Hospitals & Health Networks magazine Rady Children's Hospital was recognized in 2012 as one of the most wired hospitals in the nation. The hospital was recognized in U.S. News & World Report's 2011 ranking of the top 50 children's hospitals in 10 specialty areas. These included orthopedics urology neonatology diabetes and endocrinology and cancer. The hospital ranked in the top 25 in these specialties but also achieved rankings in the remaining categories: pulmonology nephrology cardiology and heart surgery gastroenterology and neurology and neurosurgery.

EXECUTIVES

Chairman, David F. Hale, age 65
SVP and CFO, Roger G. Roux
SVP and COO, Margareta E. (Meg) Norton
President and CEO, Kathleen A. Sellick
Vice President Human Resources, Mamoon Syed
Chief Medical Officer, Donald Kearns
VP and CIO, Albert Oriol
VP and Chief Nursing Executive, Mary Fagan
Vice President Government Affairs, Barbara Ryan
Senior Vice President, Irvin A. Kaufman
Auditors: Deloitte&ToucheLLP

LOCATIONS

HQ: RADY CHILDREN' S HOSPITAL-SAN DIEGO
3020 CHILDRENS WAY, SAN DIEGO, CA 92123-4223
Phone: 858-576-1700
Web: WWW.HELPSDKIDS.ORG

Selected Satellite Locations

Chula Vista
El Centro
Encinitas
Escondido
La Jolla
La Mesa
Murrieta
Oceanside
San Diego
Solana Beach

PRODUCTS/OPERATIONS

Selected Services

Allergy/Immunology
Attention Deficit Hyperactivity Disorder
Audiology/Hearing
Autism Discovery Institute
Behavioral Health
Brachial Plexus Clinic
Cancer & Blood Disorders
Cardiology
Cardiovascular Surgery
Celiac Disease Clinic
Center for Healthier Communities
Cerebral Palsy Center
Chadwick Center For Children & Families
Child & Adolescent Psychiatry Services (CAPS)
Child & Adolescent Services Research Center (CASRC)
Child Life Services
Children's Care Connection (C3)
Children's Hospital Emergency Transport (CHET)
Cleft Palate Clinic
Craniofacial Disorders
Critical Care
Cystic Fibrosis Center
Dental Surgery
Dermatology
Developmental Evaluation Clinic
Developmental-Behavioral Pediatrics
Developmental Screening & Enhancement Program (DSEP)
Developmental Services
Down Syndrome Center
Eating Disorders/

Medical-Behavioral Disorders Unit
Emergency Medicine
Endocrinology/Diabetes
Fatty Liver Clinic
Feeding Team
Gastroenterology Hepatology & Nutrition
Genetics/Dysmorphology
Heart Institute
Helen Bernardy Center for Medically Fragile Children
Hematology/Oncology
HomeCare
Hospice
Infectious Diseases
Kawasaki Disease Clinic
Kidney/Liver Tranplant Program
Kidney Disease
Laboratory Services/Pathology
Liver Disease
Liver Transplant
Muscle Disease Clinic
Metabolic Medicine
Neonatology
Nephrology
Neurology
Neurosurgery
Newborn Screening Program
Nutrition Clinic
Occupational Therapy
Ophthalmology
Orthopedics
Otolaryngology/ENT
Pain Services
Palliative Care
Pediatric Surgery
Pediatrics & Hospital Medicine
Pharmacy Services
Physical Therapy
Prader-Willi Syndrome Clinic
Psychiatry
Pulmonary/Respiratory Medicine
Radiology
Rehabilitation Medicine
Rheumatology
Sleep Center
Speech/Language Pathology
Spiritual Care
Sports Medicine
Surgery
Toddler School (Alexa's PLAYC)
Trauma Center
Urgent Care
Urology
Weight & Wellness Center

COMPETITORS

All Children' s Hospital
Children' s Health System
Children' s Hospital & Research Center at Oakland
Children' s Hospital of Orange County
Children' s Hospital of Philadelphia
Children' s Hospital of Richmond
Children' s Specialized Hospital
Childrens Hospital Los Angeles
Cook Children' s Health Care System
Dell Children' s Medical Center
Nationwide Children' s Hospital
Palomar Health
Scripps health
Seattle Children' s Hospital
Sharp HealthCare
Shriners Hospitals For Children
St. Jude Children' s Research Hospital
Sutter Health
Tri-City Healthcare District
UCSD Medical
UCSF Medical

HISTORICAL FINANCIALS

Company Type: Private

Income Statement

FYE: June 30

	REVENUE ($ mil.)	NET INCOME ($ mil.)	NET PROFIT MARGIN	EMPLOYEES
06/11	756	96	12.7%	2,313
06/10	619	42	6.9%	—
06/09	490	(56)	—	—
06/08	511	69	13.7%	—
Annual Growth	14.0%	11.2%	—	—

2011 Year-End Financials

Debt ratio: —	
Return on equity: 12.70%	Dividends
Cash ($ mil.): 47	Yield: —
Current ratio: 0.70	Payout: —
Long-term debt ($ mil.): —	Market value ($ mil.): —

RALEY"S

Raley's has to stock plenty of fresh fruit and great wines —it sells to the people that produce them. The company operates about 130 supermarkets and superstores in California and Nevada. In addition to about 80 flagship Raley's Superstores the company operates about 20 Bel Air Markets (in the Sacramento area) Nob Hill Foods (an upscale Bay Area chain with more than 20 locations) and nearly 10 discount warehouse stores under the Food Source banner in Northern California and Nevada. Raley's stores typically offer groceries natural foods and liquor as well as instore pharmacies. Founded during the Depression by Thomas Porter Raley the company is owned by Tom's daughter Joyce Raley Teel.

Operations

In addition to supermarkets Raley's operates about a dozen Aisle 1 full-service fuel stations in Northern California and Nevada.

Raley's three smaller chains serve different markets. Bel Air Markets are located in the greater Sacramento area. Nob Hill Foods stores are located along the Central Coast region of California and in the Bay Area. Food Source stores caters to customers in Hayward California the Sacramento area and northern Nevada.

Financial Performance

The privately-owned company rang up an estimated $3.2 billion in sales in fiscal 2013 (ended June) compared with $3.1 billion the prior year.

Strategy

The company's store count is trending down as it struggles to compete. Indeed Raley's shuttered about a half a dozen stores in 2012. Raley's is being squeezed between non-traditional grocery operators such as Wal-Mart and WinCo Foods on the low end and more upscale chains like Whole Foods and grocery-giant Safeway. In a bid to cut costs the company has trimmed its executive ranks and cut health care coverage for retired hourly employees. The cost cutting has fueled speculation about Raley's future and led to strike threats by its unionized work force. The retailer has been closing conventional Raley's stores and in some cases converting them to its discount Food Source banner. The growing discount warehouse format caters to economically-stressed and value-seeking shoppers a growing niche in California and Nevada. Still the grocery chain's attempts to market itself as a value retailer haven't resonated with customers who increasingly are shopping elsewhere. Also Raley's has struggled to expand beyond its core market in California. It has a relatively small footprint in Nevada and exited New Mexico five years ago with the sale of its stores there to Albertsons.

EXECUTIVES

Vice President Information Technology, Jeffrey D Szczesny
President and CEO, Michael J. Teel
SVP Store Operations, Kevin Konkel
SVP Sales Merchandising Marketing and Advertising, Kevin Curry
VP and Interim CFO, Ken Mueller
CIO, Mike O'Dell
Pharmacy Manager, Eric Hazard, age 57
Pharmacy Manager, Sheldon H Teranishi
Pharmacist Manager, Donald S Lew
Pharmacy Manager, Chona Sabistina
Pharmacy Manager, Irene White
Pharmacy Manager, Kim Haney
Pharmacy Manager, Donna Gilreath
Pharmacy Manager, Karen Ratcliff
Pharmacy Manager, Rich Dyba
Senior Web Designer And Vice President West Coast Sales, Jack Metcalf
Vice President, Tyler Lang
Vice President A, Debra Martin
Vice President Purchasings, Rich Wardwell
Vice President Information Systems, Nancy Keprta
Vice President, Debra Cullifer
Vice President Of Marketing, Christine McGlasson
Vice President Real Estate, Linda Kelly
Pharmacy Manager, Dennis Higa
Vice President, Frank Sciarrotta
Vice President Finance, Jeff Cummings
Vice President, Elaine Barr
Rph, Jyothi Somireddy
Vice President, Dennis Ferguson
Vice President Of Coporate, Terry Tremelling
Pharmacist Manager, Christine Pham
Vp, Barry Bounds
Vp Pharmacy Wellness, Lee Worthy
Vice President Distribution And Logistics, Roger Bresnahan
Vice President Marketing And Consumer Relationships, David Palmer
Pharmacy Manager, Rose Barnes
Vice President, Cathy Reay
Vice President, Carol Saltzman
Executive Vice President, Tom Kees
Vice President Design, Ken Moffet
Pharmacy Manager, Cheryl Oneto
Vice President Of Sales And Marketing, Steve Hanratty
Pharmacy Manager, George Polhemus
Pharmacy Manager, Lee Young
Pharmacy Manager, Cindy Fong
Sr Vp, Bob Abel
Senior Vice President And Chief Information Officer, Gary Baumgartner
Vice President Real Estate, Kent Hagerty
Co-Chairman, James E. (Jim) Teel
Co-Chairman and Owner, Joyce Raley Teel, age 79
Treasurer, Rob Kiehlmeier
Treasurer, Lisa Johnson

LOCATIONS

HQ: RALEY' ' S
500 W CAPITOL AVE, WEST SACRAMENTO, CA 956052696
Phone: 9163733333
Web: WWW.RALEYS.COM

2013 Stores

	No.
California	124
Northern	16
Total	**140**

PRODUCTS/OPERATIONS

2013 Stores

	No.
Supermarkets	
Raley's	78
Nob	22
Bel	20
Food	8
Aisle 1 fuel	12
Total	**140**

COMPETITORS

Andronico' s Market
Costco Wholesale
Food 4 Less Holdings
Grocery Outlet
Kroger
Lunardi' s Super Market
Ralphs Grocery
Safeway
Save Mart
Trader Joe' s
Wal-Mart
Whole Foods
WinCo Foods

HISTORICAL FINANCIALS

Company Type: Private

Income Statement FYE: June 29

	REVENUE ($ mil.)	NET INCOME ($ mil.)	NET PROFIT MARGIN	EMPLOYEES
06/13	3,054	(8)	—	14,000
06/12	3,162	(1)	—	—
06/10	3,064	0	—	—
06/09	0	0	—	—
Annual Growth	—	—	—	—

2013 Year-End Financials

Debt ratio: —
Return on equity: (-0.30%)
Cash ($ mil.): 21
Current ratio: 0.30
Long-term debt ($ mil.): —
Dividends
Yield: —
Payout: —
Market value ($ mil.): —

RAPID CITY REGIONAL HOSPITAL INC.

Mt. Rushmore sightseers bikers and locals alike can seek medical care at Rapid City Regional Hospital. The medical facility is a general and psychiatric hospital with some 330 acute care beds and 50 psychiatric beds located in the Black Hills region of western South Dakota. In addition to emergency and acute care the not-for-profit hospital also offers a behavioral health center a rehabilitation facility a cancer care institute and women's and children's departments. Rapid City Regional Hospital which was established in 1973 is part of Regional Health a network of regional hospitals medical clinics and senior care centers.

Operations

In addition to Rapid City Regional Hospital the Regional Health group includes the Custer Regional Lead-Deadwood Regional Spearfish Regional and Sturgis Regional hospitals. It also operates area clinics and doctors' offices including a family medicine clinic that manages a physician residency program as well as retirement communities and nursing homes. Altogether Regional Health has a total of about 40 facilities in South Dakota's Black Hills region.

EXECUTIVES

President CEO, Charles E. Hart, age 64
CEO, Timothy H. Sughrue
VP Medical Affairs, Robert Allen Jr.
Chief Medical Officer, James Keegan
Chairman, Sharon I. Lee
VP Operations, Suzanne Koehler
VP Patient Care, Rita Haxton
VP Ancillary Services, Allan Berreth
Executive Vice President and Chief Administrative Officer, Joseph Sluka
VP Medical Affairs, David L. Klocke
VP Professional Services, Paul Clemments
Vice Chairman, Dennis Popp

LOCATIONS

HQ: RAPID CITY REGIONAL HOSPITAL INC.
353 FAIRMONT BLVD, RAPID CITY, SD 57701-7393
Phone: 605-719-1000
Web: WWW.REGIONALHEALTH.COM

PRODUCTS/OPERATIONS

Selected Services

Bariatrics and Weight Management
Behavioral Health
Bones Muscles and Joints
Brain and Spine
Cancer Care
Clinics (Primary and Speciality)
Diabetes
Heart and Vascular Care
Home Care
Home Medical Equipment
Hospice Care
Hospitalist
Hyperbaric Oxygen Therapy
Infusion Services
Intensive Care
Laboratory Services
Labor and Delivery
Lactation Services
Medical Imaging
Digital Mammography
Neonatal Care
Neurology
Nutrition Services
Pain Management
Pediatrics
Physical Therapy and Rehabilitation
Regional Health Research
Senior Care
Sepsis
Sports Medicine
Stroke Care
Telemedicine
Wound Care

COMPETITORS

Avera Health
Mayo Clinic
Sanford Health-MeritCare
St. Alexius Medical Center
St. Mary' s Healthcare

HISTORICAL FINANCIALS

Company Type: Private

Income Statement FYE: June 30

	REVENUE ($ mil.)	NET INCOME ($ mil.)	NET PROFIT MARGIN	EMPLOYEES
06/12	443	46	10.6%	4,200
06/11	142	39	27.6%	—
06/10	409	65	16.0%	—
06/09	381	42	11.0%	—
Annual Growth	5.1%	3.7%	—	—

2012 Year-End Financials

Debt ratio: —
Return on equity: 10.60%
Cash ($ mil.): 7
Current ratio: —
Long-term debt ($ mil.): —
Dividends
Yield: —
Payout: —
Market value ($ mil.): —

RAPIDES PARISH SCHOOL DISTRICT

LOCATIONS

HQ: RAPIDES PARISH SCHOOL DISTRICT
619 6TH ST, ALEXANDRIA, LA 713018150
Phone: 3184870888
Web: WWW.RPSB.US

HISTORICAL FINANCIALS

Company Type: Private

Income Statement FYE: June 30

	REVENUE ($ mil.)	NET INCOME ($ mil.)	NET PROFIT MARGIN	EMPLOYEES
06/14	241	12	5.0%	3,400
06/13	234	(2)	—	—
06/12	234	5	2.5%	—
06/11	232	0	—	—
Annual Growth	1.2%	—	—	—

2014 Year-End Financials

Debt ratio: —
Return on equity: 5.00%
Cash ($ mil.): 83
Current ratio: —
Long-term debt ($ mil.): —
Dividends
Yield: —
Payout: —
Market value ($ mil.): —

RAPPAHANNOCK ELECTRIC COOPERATIVE

Like the river it's named after the Rappahannock Electric Cooperative (REC) keeps the power running smoothly. The consumer-owned cooperative provides electricity to homes businesses and industries in parts of 22 counties from the Blue Ridge Mountains to the mouth of the Rappahannock River in eastern Virginia. REC supplies power to more than 157000 members over more than 16000 miles of power line. REC offers surge protection internet services and home security plans to entice customers as competition from other suppliers arrives. Once rural in nature the cooperative's territory has seen large pockets of suburban growth.

Geographic Reach

The company serve members in 22 Virginia counties: Albemarle Caroline Clarke Culpeper Essex Fauquier Frederick Goochland Greene Hanover King and Queen King William Louisa Madison Orange Page Rappahannock Rockingham Shenandoah Spotsylvania Stafford and Warren.

Sales and Marketing

REC's largest customer is Bear Island Paper Company the second largest power consumer in the state of Virginia. Other major customers include DuPont GE Kings Dominion Amusement Park and Merillat Industries.

Financial Performance

In 2012 the company reported revenues of $405.6 million (1% down on 2011). Residential customers accounted for more than half of the REC's total sales in 2012.

Strategy

REC is also pursuing ways to help its customers to become more energy efficient to help them save money and to help the cooperative trim its power capacity growth plans. Supported by a $16 million federal green energy grant the company has replaced customers' older meters with smart (automated efficient) ones.

In 2012 REC and Old Dominion Electric Cooperative offered a pilot energy efficiency program (energy retrofits) for REC's members in Albemarle Louisa Greene Madison and Orange counties.

Company Background

REC was formed when the Virginia Electric Cooperative in Bowling Green and the Northern Piedmont Electric Cooperative in Culpeper merged in 1980.

Dramatically growing its business in 2010 the company and fellow co-op Shenandoah Valley Electric Cooperatives acquired Potomac Edison (Allegheny Energy's electric distribution operations in Virginia) for about $340 million. The expansion increased REC's coverage from 16 counties to 22 and its customer base by about 50%.

EXECUTIVES

Vice President Engineering, Robert Ellis
President and CEO, Kent D. Farmer
VP Engineering and Operations, Timothy C. Martin
Vice President Customer Service, David Koogler
Vice Chairman, Linda R. Gray
Chairman, Darlene H. Carpenter

LOCATIONS

HQ: RAPPAHANNOCK ELECTRIC COOPERATIVE
247 INDUSTRIAL CT, FREDERICKSBURG, VA 224082443
Phone: 5408988500
Web: WWW.MYREC.COOP

PRODUCTS/OPERATIONS

2012 Sales

Residential	60	
Small commercial	8	
Total	**0**	**100**

COMPETITORS

Dominion Virginia Power
Pepco Energy Services
WGL Holdings

HISTORICAL FINANCIALS

Company Type: Private

Income Statement FYE: December 31

	REVENUE ($ mil.)	NET INCOME ($ mil.)	NET PROFIT MARGIN	EMPLOYEES
12/13	400	15	3.8%	423
12/12	4	16	352.0%	—
12/11	410	17	4.2%	—
12/10	352	0	—	—
Annual Growth	4.3%	—	—	—

2013 Year-End Financials

Debt ratio: —
Return on equity: 3.80%
Cash ($ mil.): 7
Current ratio: 0.10
Long-term debt ($ mil.): —
Dividends
Yield: —
Payout: —
Market value ($ mil.): —

RARITAN BAY MEDICAL CENTER.

Health care is not rare at Raritan Bay Medical Center (RBMC). The not-for-profit center operates two hospitals in central New Jersey: Its Perth Amboy campus has about 390 beds and its Old Bridge campus has more than 110 beds. RBMC provides acute care and emergency services as well as ambulatory care through its outpatient clinics. Its Perth Amboy location provides specialized care in fields including women's and children's health. RBMC is affiliated with the University of Medicine and Dentistry of New Jersey - Robert Wood Johnson Medical School as well as the Cancer Institute of New Jersey.

Geographic Reach

RBMC serves residents of Monmouth and Middlesex counties in New Jersey.

Operations

With more than 600 physicians on its staff RBMC offers a broad range of services including general medical surgical emergency and critical care. It also provides diagnostic imaging and lab services as well as specialist units for cardiac stroke wound healing bariatric pulmonary sleep medicine rehabilitation and behavioral health care services.

Strategy

To expand its services in the region in 2013 RBMC launched construction efforts on a new medical office building at the Perth Amboy campus. The program is part of the health network's ongoing growth and renewal project. It also opened a new family practice office in 2013.

To help fuel efforts to increase efficiencies and improve quality and cost structures the RBMC organization announced that it entered talks to partner with hospital management group Prospect Medical Holdings in 2013.

Company Background

The Perth Amboy hospital opened its doors in 1902 with 12 beds and a six-member medical staff; the nursing school opened in 1903.

EXECUTIVES

President CEO and Assistant Secretary, Michael R. D'Agnes
VP Operations Old Bridge Campus, Leonard K. Dunikoski
Director Department of Psychiatry, Arunesh K. Mishra
SVP Patient Care Services and Chief Nursing Officer, Joan Harewood

LOCATIONS

HQ: RARITAN BAY MEDICAL CENTER.
530 NEW BRUNSWICK AVE, PERTH AMBOY, NJ 08861-3685
Phone: 732-442-3700
Web: WWW.RBMC.ORG

PRODUCTS/OPERATIONS

Selected Centers and Services

Bay Family Medicine
Bay Obstetrics and Gynecology
Behavioral Health
Cardiology Diagnostic and Treatment Center
CareOne at Raritan Bay Medical Center
Center for Balance
Center for Sleep Medicine
Center for Women
Center for Wound Healing
Diagnostic Radiology
Dr. Sam Gordon Berkow Maternity Pavilion
Emergency Medical Services
Human Motion Institute
Infectious Diseases and Immunology
Institute for Weight Loss
Integrative Medicine
Laboratory Services
Medical Pavilion at Woodbridge
Pediatrics
Physical Medicine and Rehabilitation
Pulmonary Rehabilitation
Renal Dialysis
Same Day Surgery
Stroke Center

COMPETITORS

Atlantic Health
Barnabas Health
Beth Israel Medical Center
Catholic Healthcare System
CentraState Healthcare System
Children' s Specialized Hospital
East Orange General Hospital
Hackensack University Medical Center
JFK Health System
Jersey City Medical Center
Maimonides Medical Center
Memorial Sloan-Kettering
Newark Beth Israel Medical Center
Robert Wood Johnson University Hospital
Robert Wood Johnson University Hospital at Rahway
Saint Peter' s University Hospital
St. Joseph' s Healthcare System
Staten Island University Hospital
The Valley Hospital
Trinitas Regional Medical Center
Valley Health System

HISTORICAL FINANCIALS

Company Type: Private

Income Statement FYE: December 31

	REVENUE ($ mil.)	NET INCOME ($ mil.)	NET PROFIT MARGIN	EMPLOYEES
12/08	228	(6)	—	1,970
12/06	232	3	1.5%	—
12/05	230	(2)	—	—
12/04	240	240	99.7%	—
Annual Growth	(1.3%)	—	—	—

2008 Year-End Financials

Debt ratio: —
Return on equity: (-3.00%)
Cash ($ mil.): 0
Current ratio: 0.50
Long-term debt ($ mil.): —
Dividends
Yield: —
Payout: —
Market value ($ mil.): —

RAYBURN COUNTRY ELECTRIC COOPERATIVE INC

This is indeed Sam Rayburn country. Rayburn Country Electric Cooperative (Rayburn Electric) operates in the old stomping grounds of the legendary Texas politician and former speaker of the US House of Representatives. Rayburn Electric is a power generation and transmission organization that supplies wholesale power to five rural distribution cooperatives operating in 16 counties in north central and northeastern Texas. The five distribution cooperatives (Fannin County Electric Coop FEC Electric Coop Grayson-Collin Electric Coop Lamar County Electric Coop and Trinity Valley Electric Coop) collectively own the company. In 2010 it acquired a 25% stake in a Texas power plant from Calpine for $215 million.

EXECUTIVES

Executive Vice President, David Naylor

LOCATIONS

HQ: RAYBURN COUNTRY ELECTRIC COOPERATIVE INC
980 SIDS RD, ROCKWALL, TX 75032-6512
Phone: 972-771-1336
Web: WWW.RAYBURNELECTRIC.COM

COMPETITORS

Bluebonnet Electric
TMPA
Brazos Electric

HISTORICAL FINANCIALS

Company Type: Private

Income Statement FYE: December 31

	REVENUE ($ mil.)	NET INCOME ($ mil.)	NET PROFIT MARGIN	EMPLOYEES
12/11	316	0	—	8
12/10	238	1	0.7%	—
12/08	238	1	0.6%	—
12/08	272	0	—	—
Annual Growth	5.1%	—	—	—

2011 Year-End Financials

Debt ratio: ——
Return on equity: —
Cash ($ mil.): 19
Current ratio: 0.10
Long-term debt ($ mil.): —

Dividends
Yield: —
Payout: —
Market value ($ mil.): —

RAYMOURS FURNITURE COMPANY INC.

EXECUTIVES

CEO, Neil Goldberg
SVP Marketing, Lisa King

LOCATIONS

HQ: RAYMOURS FURNITURE COMPANY INC.
7248 MORGAN RD, LIVERPOOL, NY 130904535
Phone: 3154532500
Web: WWW.RAYMOURFLANIGAN.COM

PRODUCTS/OPERATIONS

Selected Products

Accents
Area Rugs
Bedrooms
Dining Rooms
Entertainment
Home Decor
Home Office
Living Rooms
Mattresses
Youth Bedrooms

Selected Brands

Berkline
Bernhardt
Broyhill
Cindy Crawford Home
Kathy Ireland Home
La-Z-Boy
Natuzzi
Rowe
Sealy
Stanley Furniture
Stearns & Foster
Tempur-Pedic

COMPETITORS

ABC Home Furnishings
American Signature
Bassett Furniture
Bob' s Discount Furniture Bob' s Discount Furnitu
Crawford Furniture
Dillard' s
Ethan Allen
Euromarket Designs
IKEA
Jennifer Convertibles
La-Z-Boy
Room & Board
Rooms To Go
Williams-Sonoma

HISTORICAL FINANCIALS

Company Type: Private

Income Statement FYE: December 29

	REVENUE ($ mil.)	NET INCOME ($ mil.)	NET PROFIT MARGIN	EMPLOYEES
12/07	881	30	3.4%	4,400
12/06	780	23	3.0%	—
12/05	46	0	—	—
Annual Growth	—46328.7%		—	—

2007 Year-End Financials

Debt ratio: ——
Return on equity: 3.40%
Cash ($ mil.): 0
Current ratio: 0.20
Long-term debt ($ mil.): —

Dividends
Yield: —
Payout: —
Market value ($ mil.): —

RDO EQUIPMENT CO

RDO Equipment has built a business herding Deere in a big way. The company sells and rents new and used trucks and heavy equipment to customers in the agriculture and construction industries. As the largest independent dealer of John Deere equipment RDO Equipment operates 60-plus locations in 10 states. Of these 10 locations are dedicated Vermeer dealerships while its RDO Truck Centers offer heavy-duty Volvo GMC Isuzu and Mack trucks. RDO Integrated Controls is the company's acquisitive positioning division. RDO also supplies lawn and garden equipment and provides maintenance and repair services and replacement parts. Chairman Ronald Offutt founded the family owned and operated company in 1968.

Geographic Reach

North Dakota-based RDO Equipment has stores in Arizona California Minnesota Montana North Dakota Oregon South Dakota Texas and Washington. Outside the US the company operates through partnerships in Australia Mexico Russia and Ukraine.

Strategy

RDO has grown its network of dealerships and menu of services primarily through acquisitions. The company's positioning division —RDO Integrated Controls —has been busy during the past couple years inking deals to expand its territory as a top dealer of Topcon-branded positioning products. In fall 2014 the company plans to open a new store in McKinney Texas adding to the half a dozen locations it already operates in the state. The McKinney location will offer sales parts services and rental of John Deere heavy construction equipment.

Mergers and Acquisitions

In March 2013 RDO Integrated Controls added South Dakota to the map of territories where it provides Topcon-branded construction supplies with the purchase of the Topcon Survey Contract for the state of South Dakota from Mathison's Co. The deal extended RDO's reach in the Dakotas Minnesota Montana and Wyoming. Also in November 2013 RDO acquired Water Tech Ag Supply a California-based company that provides agricultural irrigation systems. The company has half a dozen locations in California and one in Yuma Arizona.

In 2012 RDO Integrated Controls acquired Topcon California a California and Hawaii dealer for Topcon Construction positioning products that operates stores in Sacramento and Tustin California. Buying Topcon California extends the division's reach to a total of eight states: Arizona California Hawaii Minnesota Montana North Dakota South Dakota and Wyoming. The company's purchase of Laser Control in 2011 gave RDO Equipment's positioning unit a presence in Minnesota and the Dakotas.

EXECUTIVES

SVP Special Projects, Larry E. Scott
Director HR, Ryan Johnson
Precision Product Manager, Brian Verkuehlen
VP Organizational Development, Gean Zimmerman
Sales Manager, Brian Lohse
Service Manager, Andrew Polley
Non-Executive Chairman of the Board, Eddy Hartenstein
Interim Chief Executive Officer; Director, James Meyer
Executive Vice President; Chief Administrative Officer, Dara Altman
Sales Manager, Craig Kleindl
Chief Financial Officer; Executive Vice President, David Frear
Sales Manager, Todd Koenigs
President; Chief Content Officer, Scott Greenstein
Executive Vice President; General Counsel; Secretary, Patrick Donnelly
Sales Manager, Nic Miller
Sales Manager, Michael Wollschlager
Chief Executive Officer; Director, Mel Karmazin
Vice President Midwest Construction, Lon Kindseth
Vice President of Southwest Construction, Dennis Howard
Vice President of RDO Integrated Controls, Kelly Gress
Executive Vice President with responsibility for the company&rsquo, Ryan Offutt
Independent Director, Jack Shaw
Independent Director, James Mooney
Independent Director, Carl Vogel
Independent Director, Vanessa Wittman
Independent Director, Lawrence Gilberti
Independent Director, Leon Black
Auditors: PricewaterhouseCoopersLLP

LOCATIONS

HQ: RDO EQUIPMENT CO
700 7TH ST S, FARGO, ND 58103-2704
Phone: 701-239-8700
Web: WWW.RDOEQUIPMENT.COM

2012 Locations

	No.
California	12
Minnesota	11
North	9
Arizona	7
Texas	6
South	5
Oregon	4
Montana	3
Washington	2
Total	**59**

PRODUCTS/OPERATIONS

Selected Brands

Hitachi
John Deete
Sakai
Topcon
Vermeer
Wirtgen

Selected Products

Balers
Chippers

Combines
Dozers
Drills
Excavators
Planters
Scrapers
Tractors
Trenchers
Wheel loaders

COMPETITORS

Briggs Equipment	Komatsu America
Hertz	Mustang CAT
Home Depot	Scott Equipment

HISTORICAL FINANCIALS

Company Type: Private

Income Statement FYE: January 31

	REVENUE ($ mil.)	NET INCOME ($ mil.)	NET PROFIT MARGIN	EMPLOYEES
01/13	1,650	82	5.0%	1,500
01/12	1,251	63	5.1%	—
01/11	1,000	26	2.7%	—
01/10	870	18	2.1%	—
Annual Growth	23.8%	64.4%	—	—

2013 Year-End Financials

Debt ratio: —	
Return on equity: 5.00%	Dividends
Cash ($ mil.): 1	Yield: —
Current ratio: 0.10	Payout: —
Long-term debt ($ mil.): —	Market value ($ mil.): —

READING HOSPITAL

No it's not a square on the game of Monopoly but The Reading Hospital and Medical Center does treat patients in Berks County Pennsylvania and the surrounding area. Operating as Reading Health System the not-for-profit 735-bed medical center provides acute care and rehabilitation programs as well as behavioral and occupational health services. Specialty units include cancer cardiovascular weight management diabetes orthopedic trauma (level II) and women's health centers. In addition to the main hospital the Reading Health System includes Reading Health Rehabilitation Hospital and medical centers in nearby communities as well as laboratory imaging and outpatient centers throughout its region.

Geographic Reach

Reading Health System's main hospital campus is located on a 22 building campus on 36 acres in West Reading Pennsylvania.

Operations

Altogether Reading Health System operates more than 60 locations with roughly 800 combined beds including primary and specialty care centers operated by Reading Health Physician Partners Reading Health Medical Services and the Quick Care and Urgent Care organizations. It employs some 1000 physicians and serve a population of more than 750000 residents. The Reading Health System served about 130000 emergency room patients during 2012; it also handled 30000 inpatient discharges and 19000 surgeries.

More than 90% of the company's revenues come from patient care services while residential (rehabilitation) and other services account for the rest. Each year Reading Health System provides more than $200 million in community benefits including outreach and charity care efforts.

Financial Performance

Reading Health System reported revenues of $923 million in 2012 up from $880 million in 2011. Profits declined to $13 million in 2012 however compared to net income of $47 million in 2011.

Strategy

Like most other hospitals Reading Health System sees its fair share of uninsured or underinsured patients seeking care at the ER for problems that are often not emergencies which can put a strain on hospital finances. Reading works to divert these patients to its Quick Care and Urgent Care Centers to help reduce some of that burden. The organization is also working to increase the size of its primary care network.

Within the main hospital Reading Health System is working to add new specialists such as interventional neuroradiologists and pediatric hospitalists as well as physicians who specialize in cardiac revascularization and robotic surgery procedures. It is also working to modernize technologies build new facilities and expand partnerships with area health care organizations. For instance in 2012 the system opened an outpatient center in Mohnton and a women's health center in Berkshire Heights; it also renovated its hospital emergency department that year.

In 2013 Reading Health System implemented its Reading HealthConnect electronic health record (EHR) system. In addition the network broke ground on a $354 million expansion at the main West Reading hospital campus. The facility will include new surgery and emergency treatment capacity and will add 150 private patient rooms; the project also includes conversion of existing rooms to private status.

In late 2012 The Reading Hospital and Medical Center announced its new operating name Reading Health System. The company rebranded to reflect its growing presence in the region.

Mergers and Acquisitions

The organization also occasionally grows by purchasing other medical care providers. In 2012 for instance Reading Health System purchased the Surgical Institute of Reading.

Company Background

The Reading Hospital and Medical Center was founded in 1868 as The Reading Dispensary.

EXECUTIVES

VP and Chief Nursing Officer, Donna Weber
VP, Margaret M. Bligh
SVP Business Development and Planning, Richard Mable
VP, Carl Seidl
Assistant VP Quality Management, Debra Levengood
Director Communication Services, Wendie Waschitsch
CEO, Clint Matthews
Chairman, C. Thomas Work
Chair Department of Obstetrics and Gynecology and Director, A. George Neubert
Chair Department of Medicine and Director, Cecilia M. Smith
COO, Therese Sucher
VP Trauma and Surgical Services, James Demetriades
VP Support Services, Paul Toburen
VP Finance, Dan Cochran
SVP and and Chief Medical Officer, M. Joseph Grennan Jr.
President Medical Staff and Director, Brent J. Wagner
VP and CFO, Richard W. Jones
Chief Compliance Officer, Kathleen Wetzel
Director, Jay S. Sidhu, age 62
Director, Bruce P. Bengtson
Director, Barbara Arner
Director, Theodore W. Auman
Director, J. Marc Aynardi
Director, Elizabeth Ehrlich
Director, Bernard Fromm
Director, Robert J. Gibble
Director, Victor Hammel
Director, Samuel A. McCullough
Director, Terrence J. McGlinn
Director, Marlin Miller Jr.
Chair Department of Obstetrics and Gynecology and Director, A. George Neubert
Director, Richard M. Palmer Jr.
Director, G. David Reynolds Jr.
Director, David H. Roland
Director, Thomas P. Handwerk
Director, John Roland
Director, Elizabeth B. Rothermel
Director, Julia H. Klein
Director, Sidney D. Kline Jr.
Director, Chris G. Kraras
Director, Edward T. Lentz
Chair Department of Medicine and Director, Cecilia M. Smith
Director, James R. Stoudt
Director, David L. Thun
Director, Mary Ellen Batman
President Medical Staff and Director, Brent J. Wagner

LOCATIONS

HQ: READING HOSPITAL
6TH AND SPRUCE ST, READING, PA 19611-1428
Phone: 484-628-8000
Web: WWW.READINGHOSPITAL.ORG

Selected Pennsylvania Operations

The Reading Health Dispensary (Reading)
The Reading Hospital (West Reading)
Reading Health Medical Services
Reading Health Medical Services at Muhlenberg (Reading)
Reading Health Medical Services at Northern Berks (Hamburg)
Reading Health Medical Services at Spring Ridge (Wyomissing)
Reading Health Medical Services at Wyomissing (Wyomissing)
Reading Health Medical Services at Wyomissing Plaza (Reading)
Reading Health Physicians
Reading Health Rehabilitation Hospital (Wyomissing)
QuickCare Centers (regional)
Urgent Care Centers (regional)

Selected Services

Audiology
Behavioral Health Services
Behavioral Medicine Pain Management
Center for Public Health
Chaplaincy Services
Chest Pain Center
Cleft Palate Clinic
Cochlear Implant Program
da Vinci Surgical System
Diabetes Center
Emergency Services
Epilepsy Monitoring Unit
Family Risk Assessment Program (FRAP)
HelpLine
Hospitalist Program
Infusion Center
Interventional Radiology
Laboratory Services
Library Services
Mammography Services
Nutrition Services
Occupational Health Services
Occupational Therapy
Pain Management
Palliative Care Program
Pediatrics - St' Chris Care
PET/CT Imaging
Physical Therapy
QuickCare -Reading Health Physician Network
Radiology Services
Rehabilitation Services
Respiratory Care
Senior Assessment Program

Sleep Center
Social Service
Speech and Hearing Center
Stroke Center
The Reading Hospital Home Care
Tobacco-Free Wellness Program
Travel Immunization Service
Women' s Health Services
Wound Healing and Hyperbaric Medicine Center

COMPETITORS

Ascension Health
Doylestown Hospital
Jefferson Health System
Lancaster General
Lehigh Valley Health Network
Moses Taylor Hospital
Sacred Heart Hospital of Allentown
St. Luke' s University Health Network
Universal Health Services
University of Pennsylvania Health System
Wyoming Valley Health Care System

HISTORICAL FINANCIALS

Company Type: Private

Income Statement FYE: June 30

	REVENUE ($ mil.)	NET INCOME ($ mil.)	NET PROFIT MARGIN	EMPLOYEES
06/12	811	78	9.7%	5,500
06/09	675	42	6.2%	—
06/06	640	50	7.8%	—
06/06	488	0	—	—
Annual Growth	—	593.3%	—	—

2012 Year-End Financials

Debt ratio: —
Return on equity: 9.70%
Cash ($ mil.): 188
Current ratio: 2.80
Long-term debt ($ mil.): —
Dividends
Yield: —
Payout: —
Market value ($ mil.): —

REC SOLAR INC.

REC Solar is helping its customers to say "So long!" to fossil fuel-buring power dependence. The company designs and installs solar electric systems for residential small commercial government and utilty customers in six states –Arizona California Colorado Hawaii New Jersey and Oregon. Its systems range from simple rooftop panel displays for residential customers to industrial solar electric systems for Costco. REC Solar uses solar panels manufactured by Kyocera Mitsubishi Sanyo and Sharp and components by Satcon SMA Solar Technology and Xantrex.

Geographic Reach

REC Solar serves customers in Arizona California Colorado Hawaii New Jersey and Oregon.

Strategy

The company is focused on making solar power affordable and simple and specializes in residential business government and utility projects offering a local presence in all major solar markets in the US. Since its founding in 1997 REC Solar has installed more than 8000 systems nationwide (with more than 100 MW of total capacity).

In 2012 REC Solar established itself as one of the top solar companies in Florida's emerging solar market with work on five installations at IKEA and Department of Veteran's Affairs Medical Center locations totaling almost 5 MW. All told REC Solar has installed solar panels at 13 IKEA locations across the US.

Ownership

Investment group Mainstream Energy owns both REC Solar and AEE Solar.

EXECUTIVES

CEO, Paul Winnowski
VP and General Manager Regional Business, Ethan Miller
CFO, Betsy Wallace
VP and General Manager Commercial Business, Dave Morosoli

LOCATIONS

HQ: REC SOLAR INC.
775 FIERO LN STE 200, SAN LUIS OBISPO, CA 93401-7904
Phone: 805-528-9705
Web: WWW.RECSOLAR.COM

PRODUCTS/OPERATIONS

Utility Services
Development
Co-development support
Engineering and design
Financing Option
Construction
Project Management
Procurement and logistics
Full turnkey installati
Operation
On-going service and support
Full Operations and maintenance service
System monitoring
Business/Government Services
Development
Feasibility
Engineering and design
Financing and Incentives
Construction
Project Management
Sourcing and Procuremen
Installation
Operation
Operations and Maintenanc
System monitoring
Solar marketing and PR

COMPETITORS

Conergy Inc.
Entech Solar
Real Goods Solar
SolarCraft Services
Sun Edison
Westinghouse Solar

HISTORICAL FINANCIALS

Company Type: Private

Income Statement FYE: December 31

	REVENUE ($ mil.)	NET INCOME ($ mil.)	NET PROFIT MARGIN	EMPLOYEES
12/08*	155	(3)	—	350
04/06	5	1	24.8%	—
Annual Growth	200.5%	—	—	—

*Fiscal year change

2008 Year-End Financials

Debt ratio: —
Return on equity: (-2.20%)
Cash ($ mil.): 11
Current ratio: 1.00
Long-term debt ($ mil.): —
Dividends
Yield: —
Payout: —
Market value ($ mil.): —

REGIONS HOSPITAL FOUNDATION

If you live around the Twin Cities Regions Hospital can help with your medical needs. The not-for-profit hospital has more than 450 beds and provides acute medical and emergency care services as well as specialty programs in areas including behavioral health rehabilitation burn care cancer cardiovascular orthopedic pediatrics and women's care. Regions Hospital is one of a handful of level I trauma centers in Minnesota and is also a teaching and residency center for the University of Minnesota Medical School. Regions Hospital is part of HealthPartners which operates a network of medical centers and a health plan in the Twin Cities area.

Geographic Reach

Regions Hospital serves the St. Paul Minnesota metropolitan area as well as patients from other areas across Minnesota and in western Wisconsin. It also sees visitors from other Midwest states.

Operations

In 2012 Regions Hospital operated at a 78% occupancy rate with some 25000 inpatient visits. It also handled 78000 emergency center visits 13000 surgeries and some 2500 births. It has about 650 physicians on its staff plus another 800 affiliated doctors who are members of the HealthPartners Medical Group physician practice organization.

The hospital provided some $56 million in community benefits during 2012 including charity care and outreach programs.

Strategy

The hospital has expanded its facilities in recent years to meet the demands of a growing Twin Cities population and address certain underserved community health needs. For instance in 2012 Regions Hospital completed construction of a new $36 million eight-story inpatient mental health center with about 100 beds designed to replace its aging mental health facility. In addition in 2009 the hospital wrapped up a $180 million expansion and renovation project that gave it a new 10-story patient tower with 20 new operating rooms more than 35 private patient beds and shell space for further expansion in the future.

In addition the hospital looks to enhance services through new equipment and procedural offerings as well as through partnerships with other area providers.

Ownership

Parent HealthPartners is a not-for-profit cooperative organization. Other HealthPartners facilities include Lakeview Hospital (Stillwater Minnesota) Hudson Hospital (Hudson Wisconsin) and Westfields Hospital (New Richmond Wisconsin). It also operates health clinics and urgent care centers in the area.

In 2013 HealthPartners merged with another Twin Cities hospital operator Park Nicollet Health Services. The combined organization continues to operate under the HealthPartners name. The merger created the second-largest hospital group in Minnesota giving the combined organization a broader operational base through which it aims to provide high-quality accountable care in the region. The organization's operations are gradually being combined following the transaction. Regions Hospital will become part of a new hospital division Park Nicollet HealthPartners Care Group.

Company Background

Established in 1872 Regions Hospital became part of the HealthPartners network in 1993.

EXECUTIVES

President CEO, Brock D. Nelson, age 63
CFO, Heidi Conrad
Vice President Patient Care Services, Christine Boese

LOCATIONS

HQ: REGIONS HOSPITAL FOUNDATION
640 JACKSON ST, SAINT PAUL, MN 55101-2595
Phone: 651-254-3456
Web: WWW.REGIONSHOSPITAL.COM

PRODUCTS/OPERATIONS

Selected Specialties and Divisions

Behavioral Health
Birth Center
Breast Health Center
Burn Center
Cancer Care Center
Center for Dementia and Alzheimer' s Care
Digestive Care Center
Emergency Center
Heart Center
Level I Trauma Center
Level I Pediatric Trauma Center
Neurosciences
Orthopedics
Palliative Care Unit
Rehabilitation Institute
Spine Center
Stroke Center
Surgery Center

COMPETITORS

Abbott Northwestern Hospital
Allina Hospitals
Amery Regional Medical Center
Bethesda Hospital
Catholic Health Initiatives
CentraCare Health
Children' s Hospitals and Clinics of Minnesota
Fairview Health
Gillette Children' s
HealthEast Care System
Mayo Clinic
Methodist Hospital (MN)
North Memorial Health Care
Olmsted Medical
Park Nicollet Health Services
Paynesville Area Healthcare System

HISTORICAL FINANCIALS

Company Type: Private

Income Statement FYE: December 31

	REVENUE ($ mil.)	NET INCOME ($ mil.)	NET PROFIT MARGIN	EMPLOYEES
12/12	581	36	6.3%	3,000
12/06	413	4	1.0%	—
12/05	430	12	2.8%	—
12/04	7	0	0.0%	—
Annual Growth	71.3%	320.5%	—	—

2012 Year-End Financials

Debt ratio: —
Return on equity: 6.30%
Cash ($ mil.): 64
Current ratio: 1.70
Long-term debt ($ mil.): —
Dividends
Yield: —
Payout: —
Market value ($ mil.): —

RENFRO CORPORATION

For those who tend to misplace their socks Renfro can foot the bill. The company designs and manufacturers hundreds of styles of socks and legwear products and markets them in North America through department stores specialty stores and e-commerce sites. Renfro's products are sold under several brands including Carhartt Fruit of the Loom Dr. Scholl's Copper Sole Polo Work King and Wrangler among others. The company also sells its owns brands K. Bell and Hot Sox. The clothing company's customers include well-known retailers such as Costco Kmart J.C. Penney Target and Wal-Mart.

Geographic Reach

North Carolina-based Renfro makes and distributes socks from its facilities in five US states Canada Mexico India Pakistan and China. It operates sales offices throughout North America Europe and Asia.

Operations

Renfro specializes in developing making and marketing socks under its own brands including K. Bell and Hot Sox and via private label for others. It licenses Fruit of the Loom Dr. Scholl's Ralph Lauren Cooper Sole Wrangler and Carhartt.

Sales and Marketing

The clothing company serves some of the world's biggest retailer including Wal-Mart Kmart Macy's Costco J.C. Penney Sears and Target among others.

Strategy

With the fashionable return of Sperry Top-Siders to wardrobes the company is expanding beyond its iconic loafers to a number of items including socks. Renfro will be making men's and women's socks under the Sperry brand. This comes on top of recent editions from Richlu (Canadian brands Tough Ducks and Work King under license) and Fruit of the Loom (Renfro purchased Fruit of the Loom maker DeSoto Mills).

In 2014 Renfro signed a licensing agreement with New Balance Athletic Shoe to design manufacture and market new lines of New Balance socks as well as manufacture the brand's current lines.

Company Background

The company was founded in 1921.

EXECUTIVES

Vice President, Gary Goins
Vice President Information Technology, Bruce Stonestreet
Sr V Pres, Charlie M Nichols, age 55
Sr V Pres, Susan C Bevard, age 50
CEO and President, Andrew L. Kilby
Vice President Manufacturing, Norman Smith
Vice President Of International Marketing, Peter Worcester
Vice President Of Sales, Dan Harrison
The Vice President Of Sales, Doug Lindner
Senior Vice President Merchandising, Jay Robinson
Vice President Marketing Merchandising, John Hoskins
Vice President Corporate Marketing, Stonie Stone
National Account Manager, Lennie Averna
Vice President Planning, Doug Brackney
Vice President International Sourcing, Harold Amos
Vice President Engineering, Carrol Epting

LOCATIONS

HQ: RENFRO CORPORATION
661 LINVILLE RD, MOUNT AIRY, NC 270303101
Phone: 3367198000
Web: WWW.RENFRO.COM

PRODUCTS/OPERATIONS

Selected Brands

Carhartt
Copper Sole
Dr. Scholl' s
Fruit of The Loom
Hot Sox
K. Bell
Polo
Ralph Lauren/Lauren
Spalding
Sperry
Wrangler

COMPETITORS

Gildan Activewear
Hanesbrands
Jockey International
MAST
Russell Brands
The Gap
Triumph Apparel
Under Armour
VF Corporation

HISTORICAL FINANCIALS

Company Type: Private

Income Statement FYE: January 29

	REVENUE ($ mil.)	NET INCOME ($ mil.)	NET PROFIT MARGIN	EMPLOYEES
01/11	390	9	2.5%	5,000
01/10	375	11	3.1%	—
01/08	593	0	0.0%	—
Annual Growth	(13.1%)	2454.2%	—	—

2011 Year-End Financials

Debt ratio: —
Return on equity: 2.50%
Cash ($ mil.): 9
Current ratio: 1.20
Long-term debt ($ mil.): —
Dividends
Yield: —
Payout: —
Market value ($ mil.): —

REPLACEMENT PARTS INC.

Replacement Parts works Bumper to Bumper. The company's subsidiary Crow-Burlingame operates about 160 stores under the Bumper To Bumper banner in Arkansas Louisiana Mississippi Missouri Oklahoma and Texas. Replacement Parts also distributes auto parts through three Parts Warehouses in Arkansas Louisiana and Oklahoma. The company was founded in 1919 by grocer J.G. Burlingame and candy salesman William Robert Crow grandfather of president Fletcher Lord Jr. The duo first entered the auto business by purchasing new cars in St. Louis and driving them around Little Rock to attract buyers. Employees own about 15% of the company through its stock ownership program.

Auditors: BKDLLP

LOCATIONS

HQ: REPLACEMENT PARTS INC.
1901 E ROOSEVELT RD, LITTLE ROCK, AR 72206-2533
Phone: 501-375-1215
Web: WWW.REPLACEMENTPARTS.COM

COMPETITORS

Advance Auto Parts
AutoZone
CARQUEST
CSK Auto
Discount Tire
General Parts
Genuine Parts
Goodyear Tire & Rubber
O' Reilly Automotive
Pep Boys
Sears
Wal-Mart

HISTORICAL FINANCIALS

Company Type: Private

Income Statement FYE: December 31

	REVENUE ($ mil.)	NET INCOME ($ mil.)	NET PROFIT MARGIN	EMPLOYEES
12/07	187	3	1.7%	1,115
12/06	179	5	2.8%	—
12/04	149	2	1.9%	—
12/03	137	1	0.9%	—
Annual Growth	8.0%	24.7%	—	—

2007 Year-End Financials

Debt ratio: —
Return on equity: 1.70%
Cash ($ mil.): 0
Current ratio: 0.80
Long-term debt ($ mil.): —
Dividends
Yield: —
Payout: —
Market value ($ mil.): —

REPUBLIC MORTGAGE HOME LOANS LLC

LOCATIONS

HQ: REPUBLIC MORTGAGE HOME LOANS LLC
5241 S STATE ST STE 2, MURRAY, UT 841074848
Phone: 8012889400
Web: WWW.REPUBLICMORTGAGE.COM

HISTORICAL FINANCIALS

Company Type: Private

Income Statement FYE: December 31

	ASSETS ($ mil.)	NET INCOME ($ mil.)	INCOME AS % OF ASSETS	EMPLOYEES
12/13	71	3	5.2%	368
12/09	94	8	8.6%	—
12/07	92	(5)	—	—
12/06	0	0	—	—
Annual Growth	90.9%	—	—	—

2013 Year-End Financials

Debt ratio: —
Return on equity: 6.90%
Cash ($ mil.): 18
Current ratio: 0.40
Long-term debt ($ mil.): —
Dividends
Yield: —
Payout: —
Market value ($ mil.): —

RESEARCH TRIANGLE INSTITUTE INC

The scientists at Research Triangle Institute address the problems of a sphere (the planet). Operating mainly under its trade name RTI International (RTI) the not-for-profit enterprise conducts research in such areas as advanced technologies environmental resources and medicine. It provides such services as certification and materials testing as well as software used in laboratories and research projects. Serving the US federal government other governments nonprofits and for-profit companies RTI offers analytical perspectives on public policy and has more than 3740 researchers working in offices around the world.

Geographic Reach

RTI serves clients in more than 75 countries. It has eight US offices and offices in China El Salvador India Indonesia Kenya Spain Sweden the UAE and the UK.

Operations

The company offers analytical perspectives on public policy. Its staff members represent more than 80 nationalities and speak nearly 90 languages enabling RTI to communicate and collaborate effectively with peer researchers clients and stakeholders around the world.

Sales and Marketing

The organization works with clients in government industry academia and public service. RTI's main clients are the Department of Health and Human Services and the US Agency for International Development. RTI's private sector clients have included 3M Chevron Cisco Systems GE and Sanofi-Aventis.

Financial Performance

During fiscal 2013 RTI reported revenue totaling $783 million. The institute reinvests its net income in programs facilities and new capabilities.

EXECUTIVES

Vice President Of Legal Affairs, Lisa Gilliland
Senior Vice President Operations, Lon Maggart
Vice President Governance Economic Dev, Philip B Schwehm
EVP and COO, James J. (Jim) Gibson
EVP RTI Health Solutions, Allen W. Mangel
President and CEO, E. Wayne Holden
EVP International Development Group, Aaron S. Williams
EVP Social Statistical and Environmental Sciences, Timothy J. (Tim) Gabel
EVP and CFO, Michael H. (Mike) Kaelin
Chair Fellow Program and Distinguished Fellow Early Childhood Development, Don Bailey
Vice President Behavioral Health Research Division, Gary A Zarkin
Vice President Of Communications Information And Marketing, Karen Lauterbach
Executive Vp, Franklin Gram
Sr V Pres, G E Story
Vice President Assistant General Counsel Ip And Licensing, Dean Woodward
Vice President Human Resources, Walter Goodlett
Vice President Marketing, Susana Gutthann
Vice President Federal Healthcare Optimization And Strategic Solutions, Lynn Sclavounos
Vice President Hlth Socl Plcy Rsrch Div, Janet Mitchell
Senior Vice President Social, Richard Kulka
Vice President Of Research Triangle Park, Lyn Olson
Vice President And Chief Information, Marykay Wells
Vice President Engineering And Information Technology, David Myers
Executive Vice President, Michael Witt
Unit Vice President Of Finance, Luis Crouch
Vice President Corporate Communications, Chris Davis
Vice President Of The Health Sciences, John Heinrich
Vice President Marketing, Maria Vazquez Gragg
Senior Vice President Research Dev, Satinder Sehti
Vice President Technology Development, Eric Vigan
Vice President Science Integration, Bernadette Marriott
Vice President Of Research Triangle Park, Sabrena Mervin-blake
Vice President Stat Srvy Computing, Donald Camburn
Vice President Education Studies, John Riccobono
Vice President Statistics And Epidemiology, Sally Morton
Vice President Of Special Programs, Alvin Cruze
Vice President, Kati Copley Merriman
Vice President Of Operations, Lynn Soby
Vice President Health Promotion Research Vice President Of Health Promotion Research, W Evans
Vice President, Isabel Devtech
Vice President Corporate Dev Strat Pln, Tasha Jennings
Vice President Finance, Francis Neary
Vice President Patient Reported, Sheri Fehnel
Vice President, Michael Phillips
Vice President Finance International, Sherrill Speers
Senior Vice President Of Research, Ronald Johnson
Vice President Treasurer And Chief Ris, E Sax
Hr Director & Vp, Sanne Bellemans
Vice President Compensation And Benef, Kristen Vosburgh
Senior Vice President, Edward Story
Vice President Epidemiology Sciences Division, Roy Whitmore
Vice President Of Health Social And Economics Research, Allen Miedema
Vice President Us Health Economics, Stephanie Earnshaw
Vice President International Education, Melinda Taylor
Vice President Of Finance, Chris Simmons
Vice President Partn For Genomics, Judith Lessler
Executive Vice President, Rick Witt
Senior Vice President Finance Group, Christopher Danzi
Vice President Information Technology, Mohammed Anwauhaq
Senior Vice President Secy Chief Lgl, Scott Merrell
Vice President Marketing, Kelvin Butz
Int Vice President Genomics, Joseph Pratt
Vice President Contracts, Mary Reiss
Executive Assistant To The Vp, Cindy Dieffenbach
Vice President And Chief Medical Offic, Bradford Walters
Cvpp Chief Of Party, Sonia Silva
Vice President Corporate Affairs, Sally Johnson
Vice President Federal Healthcare Optimization And Strategic Solutions, Chuck Thompson
Vice President Of Electronics And Systems, James Clary
Vice President For Business Marketing And Communications, Lonna Milburn
Top Computer Executive (Cio Vice President Or Director Of Mis Or It Etc), David Roseberry
Senior Vice President Chief Legal, Pedro Leon
Vp Business Development Gcc, Derek Farwagi
Exec Vp Operations, Robert Befus
Vice President Social Statistical Environmental Sciences Human Resources Rti International, Alisa Miller
Vice President, Kati Copleymerriman
Vp Research Services, Howard Speizer
Vice President Business Strategy, Nicole Barnes
Vp Of Finance International Development, Laurens Albada
Vice President Information Technology, Jeff Lowe
Sr Vp, Craig Hill
Vp Finance And Operations International, Karen Posner
Vice President Organizational, Tony Gambill
Vp Finance, Richard Brewer
Vice President Environmental Sciences, Terrence Pierson
Vice President Health Promotion, W Evans
Vice President Of Facilities, Denny Naugle
Senior Vice President Science, Satinder Sethi
Sr Vice President Gen Counsel Corp Secy, Greg Story
Vice President Pharmacoepidemiology And Risk Mngmt, Elizabeth Andrews
Executive Vice President, E Holden
Senior Vice President General Counsel And Corporate Secretary, G Story
Vice President, Jim Haidt
Vice President And Assistant General, Chris Buchholtz
Vice President Internal Audit, Frank Gram
Vice President Information Technology, F Carroll
Vice Chairman, Peter M. Scott
Chairman, William M. Moore
Treasurer, Rick Sisson
Board Member, J Gilligan
Board Member, T Nagle
Member Board Of Directors, Ina Wallace
Board Member, P Wynn
Board Member, P Rizzo
Treasurer Of Research Triangle Park, Satish Barnela
Board Member, W Little
Board Member, J Siedow
Treasurer, Edward Lilly
Board Member, M Broad

Honorary Member, Robert Bodo
Board Member, P Scott
Board Member, W Moore
Board Member, P Lange
Board Member, T Darden

LOCATIONS

HQ: RESEARCH TRIANGLE INSTITUTE INC
3040 CORNWALLIS RD, DURHAM, NC 277090128
Phone: 9195416000
Web: WWW.RTI.ORG

PRODUCTS/OPERATIONS

Selected Research Areas

Advanced technology research and development
Drug discovery and development
Economic and social
Education and training
Energy
Environmental
Health
International development
Laboratory and chemistry
Statistics
Survey

COMPETITORS

Argonne National Laboratory
Battelle Memorial
QSS Group
Sandford Burnham Institute
Urban Institute

HISTORICAL FINANCIALS

Company Type: Private

Income Statement FYE: September 30

	REVENUE ($ mil.)	NET INCOME ($ mil.)	NET PROFIT MARGIN	EMPLOYEES
09/13	782	37	4.8%	2,680
09/12	733	11	1.6%	—
09/11	777	24	3.1%	—
09/10	758	0	—	—
Annual Growth	1.0%	—	—	—

2013 Year-End Financials

Debt ratio: —
Return on equity: 4.80%
Cash ($ mil.): 78
Current ratio: 0.80
Long-term debt ($ mil.): —
Dividends
Yield: —
Payout: —
Market value ($ mil.): —

RESTAURANT SUPPLY CHAIN SOLUTIONS LLC

LOCATIONS

HQ: RESTAURANT SUPPLY CHAIN SOLUTIONS LLC
950 BRECKENRIDGE LN # 300, LOUISVILLE, KY 402074674
Phone: 5028965900
Web: WWW.UFPC.COM

HISTORICAL FINANCIALS

Company Type: Private

Income Statement FYE: December 31

	REVENUE ($ mil.)	NET INCOME ($ mil.)	NET PROFIT MARGIN	EMPLOYEES
12/12	238	10	4.6%	205
12/11	145	11	7.8%	—
12/10	116	10	8.7%	—
12/09	200	0	—	—
Annual Growth	5.9%	—	—	—

2012 Year-End Financials

Debt ratio: —
Return on equity: 4.60%
Cash ($ mil.): 13
Current ratio: 1.00
Long-term debt ($ mil.): —
Dividends
Yield: —
Payout: —
Market value ($ mil.): —

REX HEALTHCARE INC.

EXECUTIVES

President, David W. Strong
VP Ambulatory Services, Tom Williams
VP Support Services, Chad T. Lefteris
VP Marketing Public Relations Community Relations and Government Affairs, Lisa Schiller
SVP CFO and Interim CIO, Bernadette Spong
SVP Patient Services and Chief Nursing Officer, Mary Lou Powell
Vice President Re, Sylvia Hackett
COO, Steve Burriss
SVP Heart and Vascular Services UNC Health Care System, R. Erick Hawkins
VP Surgical Services, Jane Byrd
VP Rex Physician Services and Executive Operations Director University of North Carolina Physician Network, Bob Ricker
CIO, Novlet Bradshaw
General Counsel, Don Esposito
VP Post Acute Services UNC Health Care System, Tamie Stanton
VP Medical Affairs Chief Medical Officer and Chief Medical Information Officer, Linda Butler
Executive Director, Amy Daniels
Treasurer of Wake County Interact Board, Carolina Scout
Chairman, A. Dale Jenkins

LOCATIONS

HQ: REX HEALTHCARE INC.
4420 LAKE BOONE TRL, RALEIGH, NC 276077505
Phone: 9197843100
Web: WWW.REXHEALTH.COM

PRODUCTS/OPERATIONS

Selected Specialty Services

Oncology
Heart and vascular
Surgical Services: Bariatric Heartburn and GI
Orthopedic Neuro and Spine
Rehabilitation
Emergency and Urgent Care
Women's Services
Wound Healing

COMPETITORS

Carolinas HealthCare System
Cone Health
Cumberland County Hospital System
Danville Regional Medical Center
Duke University Health System
FirstHealth of the Carolinas
Morehead Memorial Hospital
Novant Health
Vidant Health
Wake Forest University Baptist Medical Center
WakeMed

HISTORICAL FINANCIALS

Company Type: Private

Income Statement FYE: June 30

	REVENUE ($ mil.)	NET INCOME ($ mil.)	NET PROFIT MARGIN	EMPLOYEES
06/13	731	8	1.2%	5,500
06/12	719	34	4.8%	—
06/11	628	69	11.0%	—
06/10	571	0	—	—
Annual Growth	8.6%	—	—	—

2013 Year-End Financials

Debt ratio: —
Return on equity: 1.20%
Cash ($ mil.): 74
Current ratio: 1.30
Long-term debt ($ mil.): —
Dividends
Yield: —
Payout: —
Market value ($ mil.): —

RICELAND FOODS INC.

EXECUTIVES

VP-Commodity Ops, Scott Gower
VP-Mktg, Terry Harris
Director Marketing Food Ingredients, Dan Meins
Manager Grain Terminal West Memphis (AR), David Hunt
District Manager Brinkley (AR), Opal Derrick
Director New Madrid (MO) Operations, Ed Williams
District Manager Gillett and Dumas (AR), David Curtis
District Manager Newport and Tuckerman (AR), Alvin Mullins
District Manager Jonesboro (AR), Freddie Gahr
Sales Manager - Private Label, Kevin McGilton

LOCATIONS

HQ: RICELAND FOODS INC.
2120 S PARK AVE, STUTTGART, AR 721606822
Phone: 8706735500
Web: WWW.RICELAND.COM

PRODUCTS/OPERATIONS

Selected Products

Consumer
- Saffron Yellow Rice Mix
- Rice N Easy Mix Wild Rice
- Long Grain & Wild Mix Rice N Easy Mix
- Broccoli & Cheese Rice N Easy Mix
- Spanish Rice Mix Rice N Easy Mix
- Chicken Rice Mix Rice N Easy Mix
- Long Grain Rice Riceland Extra Long Grain Rice
- Riceland GOLD Perfected Rice
- Riceland Jasmine Rice
- Riceland Natural Brown Rice
- Riceland Plump & Tender Medium Grain Rice

Food Service
- Oil
- Rice

Food Ingredients
- Long grain milled rice
- Long grain brown rice
- Medium grain milled rice
- Parboiled rice
- Broken grains

COMPETITORS

AarhusKarlshamn
Goya

American Rice	JFC International
CHS	Lotus Foods
Cereal Byproducts	Louis Dreyfus Group
Connell Company	Producers Rice Mill
Ebro Foods	Riviana Foods
Farmers Rice Milling	Specialty Rice
Farmers' Rice Cooperative	

HISTORICAL FINANCIALS

Company Type: Private

Income Statement FYE: July 31

	REVENUE ($ mil.)	NET INCOME ($ mil.)	NET PROFIT MARGIN	EMPLOYEES
07/14	1,148	2	0.2%	1,646
07/13	1,314	58	4.4%	—
07/12	1,159	1	0.1%	—
07/11	1,107	0	—	—
Annual Growth	1.2%	—	—	—

2014 Year-End Financials

Debt ratio: —
Return on equity: 0.20%
Cash ($ mil.): 5
Current ratio: 1.20
Long-term debt ($ mil.): —

Dividends
Yield: —
Payout: —
Market value ($ mil.): —

RICH PRODUCTS CORPORATION

Starting in 1945 with "the miracle cream from the soya bean" Rich Products has grown from a niche maker of soy-based whipped toppings and frozen desserts to a global US frozen foods maker. The family-owned business has developed other products such as toppings and icings and Coffee Rich (nondairy coffee creamer). It has expanded its product line to include frozen bakery and pizza doughs and ingredients for the food service and in-store bakery markets plus appetizers baked goods seafood meatballs and barbecue meat. Rich Products markets more than 2000 frozen food items that are sold in more than 110 countries; it has kitchens and bakeries around the world including about 50 locations on six continents.

Geographic Reach

Rich Products has operations in 20 countries worldwide including the US and Canada Argentina Australia Brazil China India Korea Mexico Russia South Africa Turkey United Arab Emirates the UK and Vietnam. Altogether the company sells its products in 112 countries.

Operations

Rich Products offers a variety of food items including topping and icings breads and rolls finished desserts pizza doughs bakery products appetizers and snacks BBQ meatballs and pasta and gluten-free and all-natural products.

Beyond food the Rich family through Rich's Entertainment Group owns the Buffalo Bisons the Jamestown Jammers and the Northwest Arkansas Naturals minor league baseball teams. It also owns and operates a number of catering operations and restaurants in New York and Florida through its Be Our Guest group. In addition the family owns a corporate and leisure travel management and event-planning business called The Travel Team; Roar Logistics which offers truck and rail shipping solutions; and the Palm Beach National Gold & Country Club.

Financial Performance

Rich Products boasts $3.3 billion in annual sales and more than 9000 employees worldwide.

Strategy

While the company has developed a history in the states Rich Products has focused on expanding globally in recent years primarily in the Asia/Pacific region. It operates in Australia through its 2011 purchase of wholesale bakery manufacturer VSE International which boasts a portfolio of 800 products. Selling off a logistics operation a couple years ago has helped Rich Products fuel its global growth. To expand its frozen food bakery and food service businesses in China and throughout Asia the company sold its KangXin Logistics unit to China Merchants Americold Logistics in 2010 in a deal worth a hefty $90 million.

The company is also expanding in emerging markets in western Asia. In 2012 the company formed Rich's Turkey to serve that country's more than 75 million people. Turkey will also serve as a base from which to reach potential customers in Iran Iraq Syria Bulgaria and Azerbaijan.

Closer to home in late 2012 the company acquired a pair of food companies: family-owned Goglanian Bakeries Inc.; and f'real foods of Orinda California. The Goglanian Bakeries purchase expands Rich's pizza business while f'real foods serves up milkshakes smoothies and frozen coffee beverages to convenience stores. Concurrently Rich's entered into a joint venture –called Twin Star Bakery –with business partner The Stolbun Group. Twin Star operates a desserts manufacturing plant near Houston.

As part of its strategy Rich Products works to keep up with popular food trends such as gluten-free products as it jockeys for market share in the baked goods category. As early as 2010 the company began offering gluten-free items such as Parisian cakes. It has also made several acquisitions to round out its portfolio and get a foot in Canada's door. Rich Products acquired Celebration Foods maker and distributor of frozen desserts and ice cream cakes to satisfy its long-term growth strategy and to fill out its frozen dessert portfolio. The deal included the Celebration business its manufacturing facilities corporate operations research and development direct-store-distribution (DSD) system and a licensing agreement for Carvel-branded ice cream cakes sold in certain distribution channels. Also the company's Canadian division –Rich Products of Canada Ltd. –acquired Dorgel Ltd. & Elistan Foods a leading manufacturer and marketer of frozen desserts and ice cream cakes in Canada. The 2012 purchase marks Rich's entry into the branded retail market in Canada.

Spending some $11 million the company's expanding its food manufacturing facility in Georgia by 40% to grow its capacity by 30%.

EXECUTIVES

Vp Procurement And Inventory Planning Consumer Brands Division, Gary Bunn
Evp And Chief Administrative Officer, Maureen O Hurley
Vice President Finance, Mary Kiener
Vp Marketing Foodservice Division North American Business Group, Dinsh Guzdar
Vp Marketing, Lou Lesemann
Vp International Human Resources, Judy Campbell
President and CEO, William G. (Bill) Gisel, age 61
EVP Global Business Development and Director, Kevin R. Malchoff
Vice Chairman; President Rich's Entertainment Group, Melinda R. (Mindy) Rich, age 57
Executive VP Chief Financial Officer, James R. (Jim) Deuschle
Executive VP Chief Operating Officer, Richard M. Ferranti
V Pres Finance, Dave Carere
Vice President Of National Account Sales, Paul Rich
Vp Marketing Consumer Brands Division, Jamie McKeon
Svp Finance North American Business Group, Georgia Dachille
Vice President Communications, Dwight Gram
Vice President Engineering, Tim Falken
Vice President Finance And Business Development, David Faturos
Vice President Distribution, Mike Welker
Vice President Marketing, Nick Stambula
Senior Vice President Finance International, Elizabeth Lansing
Senior Vice President Of Operations, Dave Konst
Vice President Marketing, Deborah Andrews
Vice President Information Technology, Kevin Ridlon
Vice President Of Salesbakery Products, John Wellenzohn
Vice President, Marty Hurley
Executive Vice President, Edward Moore
National Account Manager, Melanie Roberts
National Sales Manager, William Leslie
Svp And Cio, Paul Klein
National Account Manager, Brian Hilsenrath
Vp Customer Development Consumer Brands Division, Craig Entwistle
Vice President Operations And Engineering, Richard Dorsett
President and CEO, William G. (Bill) Gisel, age 61
EVP Global Business Development and Director, Kevin R. Malchoff
Vice Chairman; President Rich's Entertainment Group, Melinda R. (Mindy) Rich, age 57
Chairman, Robert E. (Bob) Rich

LOCATIONS

HQ: RICH PRODUCTS CORPORATION
1 ROBERT RICH WAY, BUFFALO, NY 142131701
Phone: 7168788422
Web: WWW.RICHS.COM

PRODUCTS/OPERATIONS

Selected Product Categories

Appetizers & snacks
Bakery products
BBQ
Breads & rolls
Cakes & desserts
Cooking creams
Gluten-free & all-natural
Meatballs & pasta
Pizza
Shrimp & seafood
Syrups & soaked cakes
Toppings & icings

Selected Consumer Brands

Byron's BBQ
Casa
Farm Rich
French Meadow Bakery
Mother' s Kitchen
Rich' s
SeaPak

COMPETITORS

BakeMark	Gorton' s
Campbell Soup	Heinz
Canada Bread Company	Hom/Ade Foods
ConAgra	Kraft Foods Group Inc.
Dawn Food Products	NestlÃ©
Dean Foods	Pinnacle Foods
General Mills	Schwan' s
Gonnella Baking	Windsor Foods

HISTORICAL FINANCIALS

Company Type: Private

Income Statement FYE: December 31

	REVENUE ($ mil.)	NET INCOME ($ mil.)	NET PROFIT MARGIN	EMPLOYEES
12/12	2,858	0	—	8,400
12/11	2,736	0	—	—
12/10	2,465	0	—	—
Annual Growth	7.7%	—	—	—

RIGGINS INC.

LOCATIONS

HQ: RIGGINS INC.
3938 S MAIN RD, VINELAND, NJ 083607743
Phone: 8568257600
Web: WWW.RIGGINSOIL.COM

HISTORICAL FINANCIALS

Company Type: Private

Income Statement FYE: December 31

	REVENUE ($ mil.)	NET INCOME ($ mil.)	NET PROFIT MARGIN	EMPLOYEES
12/13	456	0	0.0%	105
12/12	491	0	0.0%	—
12/11	471	0	0.0%	—
12/10	327	0	—	—
Annual Growth	11.7%	—	—	—

2013 Year-End Financials

Debt ratio: —
Return on equity: —
Cash ($ mil.): 1
Current ratio: 1.00
Long-term debt ($ mil.): —
Dividends
Yield: —
Payout: —
Market value ($ mil.): —

RIP GRIFFIN TRUCK SERVICE CENTER INC.

EXECUTIVES

President, Mark Griffin

LOCATIONS

HQ: RIP GRIFFIN TRUCK SERVICE CENTER INC.
4710 4TH ST, LUBBOCK, TX 794164900
Phone: 8067958785
Web: WWW.RIPGRIFFIN.COM

COMPETITORS

Allsup' s
Chevron
E-Z Mart Stores
Love' s Country Stores
Pilot Corporation
Racetrac Petroleum
Stuckey' s
Valero Energy

HISTORICAL FINANCIALS

Company Type: Private

Income Statement FYE: December 31

	ASSETS ($ mil.)	NET INCOME ($ mil.)	INCOME AS % OF ASSETS	EMPLOYEES
12/13	126	3	2.6%	88
12/12	122	4	3.4%	—
12/11	119	3	2.6%	—
12/10	114	0	—	—
Annual Growth	3.4%	—	—	—

2013 Year-End Financials

Debt ratio: —
Return on equity: 1.50%
Cash ($ mil.): 11
Current ratio: 0.90
Long-term debt ($ mil.): —
Dividends
Yield: —
Payout: —
Market value ($ mil.): —

RITZVILLE WAREHOUSE CO.

LOCATIONS

HQ: RITZVILLE WAREHOUSE CO.
201 E 1ST AVE, RITZVILLE, WA 991692393
Phone: 5096590130
Web: WWW.RITZWHSE.COM

HISTORICAL FINANCIALS

Company Type: Private

Income Statement FYE: April 30

	REVENUE ($ mil.)	NET INCOME ($ mil.)	NET PROFIT MARGIN	EMPLOYEES
04/13	242	3	1.6%	65
04/12	254	5	2.3%	—
04/11	223	6	2.8%	—
04/10	117	0	—	—
Annual Growth	27.5%	—	—	—

2013 Year-End Financials

Debt ratio: —
Return on equity: 1.60%
Cash ($ mil.): 1
Current ratio: 0.40
Long-term debt ($ mil.): —
Dividends
Yield: —
Payout: —
Market value ($ mil.): —

RIVER VALLEY COOPERATIVE

LOCATIONS

HQ: RIVER VALLEY COOPERATIVE
102 S MAIN ST, WALCOTT, IA 527737761
Phone: 5632846223
Web: WWW.RIVERVALLEYCOOP.COM

HISTORICAL FINANCIALS

Company Type: Private

Income Statement FYE: June 30

	REVENUE ($ mil.)	NET INCOME ($ mil.)	NET PROFIT MARGIN	EMPLOYEES
06/09	410	8	2.1%	84
06/08	276	5	1.8%	—
06/07	1,159	0	—	—
Annual Growth	—29738.0%		—	—

2009 Year-End Financials

Debt ratio: —
Return on equity: 2.10%
Cash ($ mil.): 0
Current ratio: 0.40
Long-term debt ($ mil.): —
Dividends
Yield: —
Payout: —
Market value ($ mil.): —

RIVERSIDE HEALTHCARE ASSOCIATION INC.

Extra! Extra! Read all about it! Residents of Newport News (and about a dozen other cities in Eastern Virginia) Turn to Riverside Health for Medical Care. The not-for-profit health care provider administers general emergency and specialty medical services from five hospitals Riverside Regional Medical Center Riverside Walter Reed Hospital Riverside Tappahannock Hospital and Riverside Shore Memorial Hospital and Riverside Doctors Hospital as well as a psychiatric hospital a physical rehabilitation facility and retirement communities. Riverside also operates physician offices and medical training facilities. Specialty centers provide home and hospice care cancer treatment and dialysis.

Geographic Reach

It serves Eastern Virginia including cities of Gloucester Hampton Newport News Poquoson Richmond Tappahannock West Point Williamsburg and Yorktown; Eastern Shore Area of Virginia; Counties of Essex Gloucester Isle of Wight James City King and Queen King William Lancaster Mathews Middlesex New Kent Northumberland Richmond and Surry.

Operations

Combined Riverside's hospitals (including rehabilitation and psychiatric) are home to nearly 1000 beds. Its major hospitals include Riverside Regional Medical Center (450-bed flagship hospital); Riverside Walter Reed Hospital (67-bed acute care facility); Riverside Tappahannock Hospital (67-bed serving the Northern Neck rural area); Riverside Shore Memorial Hospital (143-bed facility); and Riverside Doctors' Hospital Williamsburg (40 private rooms). It also operates specialty medical facilities including a psychiatric hospital a physical rehabilitation facility and retirement communities.

Strategy

To keep up with demand Riverside Health has been upgrading its older facilities and building new ones.

In 2013 the company opened a new hospital the Doctors Hospital in Williamsburg. The 40 room hospital provides acute and emergency care as well as specialty services including cardiology neurology and pulmonary care.

That year Riverside broke ground on the new Riverside Shore Memorial Hospital in Onley which is expected to be completed in late 2015. It will have 57 private inpatient rooms with the ability to add 12 more in the future.In 2012 Riverside Walter Reed Hospital opened a new intensive care unit.

It is also investing in technology physician expertise and patient services. In 2013 Riverside Shore Medical Center at Metompkin converted to digital mammography equipment offering patients a superior diagnostic tool to film mammograms.

Company Background

The original charter for Riverside dates back to 1915 when the company began as one hospital founded by the community. In 1962 the hospital was relocated to the present site in central Newport News.

EXECUTIVES

President and Chief Executive Officer, William B. Downey
Senior Vice President Acute Care Division and Administrator Riverside Regional Medical Center, Patrick R. (Pat) Parcells
Executive Vice President and Chief Medical Officer; Director, Barry L. Gross
Executive Vice President and Chief Operating Officer, Wade D. Broughman
Senior Vice President and Medical Director, James E. Lesnick
Senior Vice President Lifelong Health and Aging Related Services, Michael Martin
Senior Vice President and Chief Financial Officer, W. William (Bill) Austin Jr.
Senior Vice President and Chief Nursing Officer, Terris Kennedy
Senior Vice President and Chief Information Officer, John T. Stanley

LOCATIONS

HQ: RIVERSIDE HEALTHCARE ASSOCIATION INC.
701 TOWN CENTER DR # 1000, NEWPORT NEWS, VA 23606-4283
Phone: 757-534-7000
Web: WWW.RIVERSIDE-ONLINE.COM

Selected Facilities – Virginia

HOSPITALS
Riverside Behavioral Health Center (Hampton)
Riverside Doctors' Hospital (Williamsburg)
Riverside Regional Medical Center (Newport News)
Riverside Rehabilitation Institute (Williamsburg)
Riverside Tappahannock Hospital (Tappahannock)
Riverside Shore Memorial Hospital (Nassawadox)
Riverside Walter Reed Hospital (Gloucester)
RETIREMENT COMMUNITIES
Patriots Colony (Williamsburg)
Sanders (Gloucester)
Warwick Forest (Newport News)
SURGERY CENTERS
Doctors Surgery Center (Williamsburg)
Peninsula Surgery Center (Newport News)
Riverside Hampton Surgery Center (Hampton)

COMPETITORS

Alleghany Regional Hospital
Bon Secours Health
Carilion Clinic
Centra Health Inc.
Children' s Hospital of The King' s Daughters
Franklin Hospital Corp.
Novant Health
Sentara Healthcare
Wake Forest University Baptist Medical Center

HISTORICAL FINANCIALS

Company Type: Private

Income Statement FYE: December 31

	REVENUE ($ mil.)	NET INCOME ($ mil.)	NET PROFIT MARGIN	EMPLOYEES
12/12	948	41	4.4%	8,000
12/11	952	(25)	—	—
12/09	872	7	0.8%	—
12/09	788	46	5.9%	—
Annual Growth	6.3%	(3.4%)	—	—

2012 Year-End Financials

Debt ratio: —
Return on equity: 4.40%
Cash ($ mil.): 53
Current ratio: 1.20
Long-term debt ($ mil.): —
Dividends
Yield: —
Payout: —
Market value ($ mil.): —

RIVERSIDE HOSPITAL INC.

Riverside Hospital operates as Riverside Regional Medical Center a 570-bed acute-care facility that serves the residents of Newport News Virginia. Founded in 1916 the hospital moved to its current 72-acre campus in 1963 providing more than 30 medical specialties including cancer treatment cardiology birthing and diagnostic imaging. It specializes in cardiovascular and neurological surgeries and provides radiosurgery (radiation surgery) through a partnership with the University of Virginia Health System. Its emergency department is a Level II Trauma Center that treats some 57000 patients each year. Riverside Hospital is part of the Riverside Health System.

Geographic Reach

Riverside Hospital serves the health care needs of those who reside in and around Newport News Virginia.

Operations

As part of its operations Riverside Hospital operates a heart center neonatal center 18-bed neonatal intensive care unit cancer care center and radiosurgery center through a partnership with Chesapeake Regional and the University of Virginia Health System. Riverside Hospital works to prevent diagnose and treat diseases of the stomach intestines esophagus pancreas gall bladder liver and biliary tract through its Peninsula Gastroenterology & Riverside Endoscopy Center.

EXECUTIVES

VP Medical Affairs, Christopher Stolle
SVP and Administrator, Patrick R. (Pat) Parcells
Secretary and Treasurer Medical Staff, Kendall C. Jones
VP Ambulatory Services, Susan McAndrews
VP Patient Care Services; Chief Nursing Officer and Service Line Administrator Women's Health Services, Gwen Hartzog
VP Operations, Michael (Mike) Doucette
Service Line Chief Women's Health Services, Jeffrey Henke
Director Facilities Engineering, Dave Pone
Director Information Systems, Dennis Loftus
Service Line Chief Surgical Service Line, Marshall Cross
Service Line Chief Neurosciences Service Line, Tom Reagan
Service Line Administrator Oncology Service Line, Carrie Schmidt
Service Line Chief Oncology Service Line, Mark Ellis
Vice President Va International Terminals, Regina P. Brayboy
Senior Vice President Riverside, Michael Martin
Senior Vice President Chief Information Officer CIO, John T. Stanley
Senior Vice President and Chief Nursing Officer CNO, Terris Kennedy
Vice President, Scott Stabler
Chairman, Gordon L. Gentry
Senior Vice President Riverside, Rondra J. Matthews

LOCATIONS

HQ: RIVERSIDE HOSPITAL INC.
500 J CLYDE MORRIS BLVD, NEWPORT NEWS, VA 23601-1929
Phone: 757-594-2000
Web: WWW.RIVERSIDEONLINE.COM

PRODUCTS/OPERATIONS

Selected Services

Diagnostic Services
Cardiac testing
CT
Digital mammography
Electrocardiography
Magnetic resonance imaging
Nuclear medicine
PET
Ultrasound
Nutrition Services
Radiosurgery Center
Leksell Gamma Knife Synergy S Radiosurgery
Gastroenterology Procedures
Colonoscopy and polypectomy
Flexible sigmoidoscopy
Upper endoscopic exams and therapy
Endoscopic retrograde cholangiopancreatography (ERCP)
Percutaneous endoscopic gastrostomy (PEG)
Capsule/Cam (M2A) study of the small intestine
Esophageal dilation
Esophageal and anal manometry
BRAVO pH study of the esophagus
Pulmonary Rehabilitation
Surgical Services

COMPETITORS

Alleghany Regional Hospital
Bon Secours Health
Carilion Clinic
Centra Health Inc.
Children' s Hospital of The King' s Daughters
Franklin Hospital Corp.
Novant Health
Sentara Healthcare
Wake Forest University Baptist Medical Center

HISTORICAL FINANCIALS

Company Type: Private

Income Statement FYE: December 31

	REVENUE ($ mil.)	NET INCOME ($ mil.)	NET PROFIT MARGIN	EMPLOYEES
12/12	479	70	14.7%	3,500
12/11	466	36	7.8%	—
12/09	429	20	4.9%	—
12/09	413	15	3.8%	—
Annual Growth	5.0%	65.2%	—	—

2012 Year-End Financials

Debt ratio: —
Return on equity: 14.70%
Cash ($ mil.): 214
Current ratio: 5.40
Long-term debt ($ mil.): —
Dividends
Yield: —
Payout: —
Market value ($ mil.): —

ROBERT WOOD JOHNSON UNIVERSITY HOSPITAL

LOCATIONS

HQ: ROBERT WOOD JOHNSON UNIVERSITY HOSPITAL
1 ROBERT WOOD JOHNSON PL, NEW BRUNSWICK, NJ 089011928
Phone: 7328283000
Web: WWW.RWJUH.EDU

PRODUCTS/OPERATIONS

Selected Services

Bariatric Surgery
Bloodless Surgery
Cardiothoracic Surgery
Colorectal Surgery
Comprehensive Sleep Disorders Center
Diabetes
Digestive Disorders
Emergency Department
Executive Health Program
Heart Transplantation
Injury Prevention
Kidney and Pancreas Transplantation
Lab Services (blood work and blood collection)
Level 1 Trauma Center
Neurosciences
- Clinical Neurosciences Center
- Deep Brain Stimulation for Movement Disorders
- Laser Ablation for Brain Tumor Treatment
- Neurosurgery
- New Jersey Brain Aneurysm & AVM Program
- Parkinson' s Disease Information and Referral Center
- Stroke Center
- The Gamma Knife Center: Advanced Treatment for Brain and Spine

New Jersey Pain Institute at RWJUH
Orthopedic Surgery
Outpatient Radiology: University Radiology at Robert Wood Johnson
Palliative Care Program
Pastoral Care
Pelvic Floor and Incontinence Program
Physical and Occupational Therapy
Prostate Cancer Surgery
Radiation Oncology
- Gynecologic Brachytherapy
- Prostate Brachytherapy
- TomoTherapy
- Total Skin Electron Beam Therapy

Radiology (including CT MRI and ultrasound)
Speech and Hearing Program
The Center for Wound Healing
The Limb Preservation Program
Therapeutic Apheresis
Thoracic Surgery
Vascular Surgery

HISTORICAL FINANCIALS

Company Type: Private

Income Statement FYE: December 31

	REVENUE ($ mil.)	NET INCOME ($ mil.)	NET PROFIT MARGIN	EMPLOYEES
12/14	1,043	83	8.0%	4,674
12/13	833	108	13.0%	—
12/12*	823	83	10.2%	—
09/12	622	0	—	—
Annual Growth	29.4%	—	—	—

*Fiscal year change

ROBERTS & DYBDAHL INC.

Roberts & Dybdahl can't sell you a house but it can sell you some important pieces. The company is a wholesale distributor of lumber lumber products and building materials to customers in Illinois Indiana Iowa Kansas Nebraska and Wisconsin. Products include treated lumber boards shingles siding studs trusses joists and engineered wood products. Roberts & Dybdahl operates about 10 distribution centers and some half a dozen on-site truss manufacturing facilities able to custom build roof and floor trusses to customer specifications. The company was founded as Carroll Wholesale in 1955 by Howard Roberts and Hub Dybdahl.

EXECUTIVES

Director Purchasing, Cyndee Johnson
Manager Regional Trading Lumber Kansas, Brandon Alles
Regional Trading Manager Lumber Iowa, Alan Shearer
Regional Sales Manager Lumber Wisconsin, William (Bill) Johnson
Regional Trading Manager Lumber Illinois, Jim Jones
Assistant Regional Trading Manager Lumber Illinois, John Rich
Regional Trading Manager Lumber Illinois, Kerry Russell

LOCATIONS

HQ: ROBERTS & DYBDAHL INC.
5034 GRAND RIDGE DR, WEST DES MOINES, IA 50265-5754
Phone: 515-283-7100
Web: WWW.ROBERTSDYBDAHL.COM

2009 Locations

	No.
Iowa	3
Illinois	2
Indiana	1
Kansas	1
Nebraska	1
Wisconsin	1
Total	9

COMPETITORS

84 Lumber
Babcock Lumber
Builders FirstSource
Edward Hines Lumber
HD Supply
Huttig Building Products
International Paper
Weekes Forest Products

HISTORICAL FINANCIALS

Company Type: Private

Income Statement FYE: December 31

	REVENUE ($ mil.)	NET INCOME ($ mil.)	NET PROFIT MARGIN	EMPLOYEES
12/12	220	1	0.7%	238
12/11	181	0	0.5%	—
12/10	187	1	0.8%	—
12/09	160	(1)	—	—
Annual Growth	11.2%	—	—	—

2012 Year-End Financials

Debt ratio: —
Return on equity: 0.70%
Cash ($ mil.): 2
Current ratio: 2.20
Long-term debt ($ mil.): —
Dividends
Yield: —
Payout: —
Market value ($ mil.): —

ROBERTS DAIRY COMPANY LLC

Holy cow! Roberts Dairy Foods is a leading producer of fluid cultured and frozen dairy products. It offers milk yogurt sour cream cottage cheese and other dairy products. A division of Hiland Dairy the firm operates production plants in Omaha and Kansas City and 10 distribution centers located in the Midwest. The company markets its products under the Roberts and Hiland-Dairy brands; it also provides private-label services and school milk. Through a joint venture named Hiland-Roberts the company makes ice cream products from a facility in Norfolk Nebraska. Founded as a milk route by J.R. Roberts in 1906 Roberts Dairy Foods serves retail food and food service customers throughout the Midwest.

Geographic Reach

Roberts Dairy Foods has two production plants and 10 distribution centers in Nebraska Iowa Kansas and Missouri. Roberts Dairy serves a region that includes Nebraska Iowa Missouri Kansas and parts of Colorado Illinois and South Dakota.

Strategy

In 2011 the company changed its name from Roberts Dairy to Roberts Dairy Foods to reflect its expansion beyond milk. It also adopted a new logo that year to emphasize the freshness of its products. Non-dairy products include juices lemonade fruit punches and teas. Other specialty markets for the company include kosher and gluten-free products.

EXECUTIVES

President, Jeff Powell
Manager Corporate Marketing, Al Streeter
General Manager Sales Kansas City, Jon Bebermeyer

LOCATIONS

HQ: ROBERTS DAIRY COMPANY LLC
2901 CUMING ST, OMAHA, NE 68131-2108
Phone: 402-344-4321
Web: WWW.ROBERTSDAIRYEFCU.ORG

PRODUCTS/OPERATIONS

Selected Products

Butter
Cottage cheese
Cream
Dips
Egg nog
Half-and-half
Ice cream
Juice & lemonade
Milk
Sour cream
Yogurt

COMPETITORS

Associated Milk Producers
Dairy Farmers of America
Dean Foods
Land O' Lakes
Organic Valley
Sunkist
Swiss Valley Farms
Tree Top
Tropicana
Welch' s

HISTORICAL FINANCIALS

Company Type: Private

Income Statement FYE: September 30

	REVENUE ($ mil.)	NET INCOME ($ mil.)	NET PROFIT MARGIN	EMPLOYEES
09/08	359	0	0.2%	320
09/07	319	2	0.7%	—
09/06	591	0	—	—
Annual Growth	—	8220.6%	—	—

2008 Year-End Financials

Debt ratio: —
Return on equity: 0.20%
Cash ($ mil.): 3
Current ratio: 0.10
Long-term debt ($ mil.): —
Dividends
Yield: —
Payout: —
Market value ($ mil.): —

ROBINSON OIL CORPORATION

Like Hamlet's Denmark something's rotten in the state of Robinson Oil. The company owns and operates Rotten Robbie a regional brand of independent gas stations that caters to consumer and commercial motorists. The chain consists of some 35 stops in Northern California mainly around the San Francisco Bay Area. Some stops are kiosks; about half are larger with Mrs. Robbie's Markets a food store and several offer commercial fleet fueling services affiliated with Pacific Pride and other cardlock networks. Diesel is available at all locations and at certain stores kerosene propane and biodiesel. Founded in the 1930s as a private-label fuel retailer Robinson Oil is a fourth-generation family-owned business.

Robinson Oil purchases products refined by one of five San Francisco Bay Area refineries: Chevron Conoco-Phillips Shell Tesoro and Valero. Most of the crude oil originates in California or Alaska.

Robinson Oil's growth strategy is based upon selling high volumes of fuel at a competitive price. When gas is abundant it is able to target car and truck drivers with prices considerably lower than major service stations. The strategy however is impacted by volatile fuel costs attributable to the capacity of state refineries known to fall short of demand coupled with the limited number of refineries elsewhere that make California's special reformulated blend. In August 2012 a fire at the state's Chevron refinery the largest in Northern California cut production to about 60% choking gas supplies and sending up prices at the pump. The event forced stations to battle over both supplies and the price for a fill-up.

Robinson Oil co-founder the late Herb Richards in 1948 pioneered the self-service gas station (and selling gas for less than other stations) against a backlash of concern over the safety in drivers pumping their own gas. Richards created the Rotten Robbie banner in 1973 intending that customers would not assume the worse and remember the best about his stations. He also boosted the company's presence by giving away a Cadillac every few weeks and offering free merchandise stamps to collect and redeem for discounts on groceries.

LOCATIONS

HQ: ROBINSON OIL CORPORATION
955 MARTIN AVE, SANTA CLARA, CA 95050-2608
Phone: 408-327-4300
Web: WWW.ROBINSONOILCORP.COM

PRODUCTS/OPERATIONS

Selected Products

BioDiesel
Commercial fleet fueling
- CFN (Commercial Fueling Network)
- FleetWide Corp.
- Pacific Pride (PacPride)

Convenience store
Diesel
Kerosene
Lotto
Propane
- Blue Rhino
- Bulk

COMPETITORS

7-Eleven
Chevron
Couche-Tard
Flyers Energy

HISTORICAL FINANCIALS

Company Type: Private

Income Statement FYE: December 31

	REVENUE ($ mil.)	NET INCOME ($ mil.)	NET PROFIT MARGIN	EMPLOYEES
12/12	464	10	2.3%	250
12/09	292	8	2.8%	—
12/08	409	12	3.0%	—
12/07	1,025	0	0.0%	—
Annual Growth	(14.7%)	827.0%	—	—

2012 Year-End Financials

Debt ratio: —
Return on equity: 2.30%
Cash ($ mil.): 9
Current ratio: 0.90
Long-term debt ($ mil.): —
Dividends
Yield: —
Payout: —
Market value ($ mil.): —

ROCHESTER INSTITUTE OF TECHNOLOGY (INC)

The Rochester Institute of Technology (RIT) is a privately-endowed university with nine colleges focused on providing career-oriented education to about 18000 students. The school which ,Âhas ,Âa student-faculty ratio of about 14:1 ,Âoffers more than 90 bachelor's degree programs ,Âin art and design business engineering science and ,Âhotel management. RIT also confers master's and doctorate degrees. ,ÂThe university's ,ÂNational Technical Institute for the Deaf is the first and largest technological college for learners who suffer from hearing loss. RIT which traces its roots back to 1829 counts among its alumni the CEOs of Kodak and The Associated Press.

Operations

Spanning some 1300 acres in Rochester New York RIT's campus ,Âserves 15000 undergraduate and 2900 graduate students with help from its faculty and staff of more than 4000. Approximately 1300 deaf and hard-of-hearing students live study and work alongside hearing students on the RIT campus. Tuition runs nearly $33000 for general students and more than $12000 for deaf and hard-of-hearing students.

RIT ,Â operates a campus in Dubai's Silicon ,ÂOasis a government owned high tech complex. ,Â The campus ,Â serves the university's ,Âgoal of growing its reputation worldwide and expanding international opportunities for students. RIT Dubai offers undergraduate and graduate degree programs in ,Âengineering business information technology and leadership.

Financial Performance

RIT logged a 4% revenue rise in 2012 as compared to 2011 due to an increase in tuition and fees net of scholarships and sales and services of auxiliaries and private contributions. Meanwhile net income decreased by 84% during the same reporting period attributable to increased operating expenses and loss from investment returns and other non-operating activities. As a result of cash provided by operating activities RIT's cash outflow dropped $7.8 million in 2012 vs. 2011.

Sales and Marketing

The university sources its students globally from all 50 US states and from more than 100 countries.

EXECUTIVES

SVP Finance and Administration, James H. Watters
Dean Kate Gleason College of Engineering, Harvey Palmer
President, William W. (Bill) Destler
Dean College of Applied Science and Technology, H. Fred Walker
SVP Academic Affairs and Provost, Jeremy A. Haefner
Assistant VP and CIO, Jeanne Casares
Dean Sounders College of Business, DT Ogilvie
Dean B. Thomas Golisano College of Computing and Information Siences, Andrew Sears
Dean College of Health Sciences and Technology, Daniel B. Ornt
Dean College of Imaging Arts & Sciences, Lorraine Justice
Dean College of Liberal Arts, James J. Winebrake
Dean College of Science, Sophia Maggelakis
President and Dean National Technical Institute for the Deaf, Gerard J. Buckley
Executive Assistant President, Barry Culhane
Assoc Vp Government Relations, Deborah Stendardi
Vp Of Development/alumni, Lisa Cauda
Assistant To Senior Vice President, Edward Lincoln
Secretary, David Lawlor
Board Member, Mary Matchett

LOCATIONS

HQ: ROCHESTER INSTITUTE OF TECHNOLOGY (INC)
1 LOMB MEMORIAL DR, ROCHESTER, NY 146235698
Phone: 5854752411
Web: WWW.RIT.EDU

PRODUCTS/OPERATIONS

Selected Colleges

College of Applied Science and Technology
- School of Engineering Technology
- School of International Hospitality and Service Innovation

E. Philip Saunders College of Business
B. Thomas Golisano College of Computing and Information Sciences
Kate Gleason College of Engineering
College of Health Sciences and Technology
College of Imaging Arts and Sciences
- School for American Crafts
- School of Art
- School of Design
- School of Film and Animation
- School of Media Sciences
- School of Photographic Arts and Sciences

College of Liberal Arts
National Technical Institute for the Deaf
College of Science

Selected Graduate & Undergraduate Programs

Accounting
Applied Networking & Systems Administration

Applied Statistics
Biochemistry
Business
Civil Engineering Technology
Clinical Chemistry
Computer Integrated Machining Technology
Computer Science
Digital Imaging & Publishing Technology
Electrical/Mechanical Engineering Technology
Environmental Science
Finance
Glass & Glass Sculpture
Health Systems Administration
Healthcare Billing & Coding Technology
Imaging Arts: Photography
Industrial & Systems Engineering
Instruction Technology
Management
Medical Illustration
Metals/Jewelry Design
Ophthalmic Optical Finishing Technology
Print Media
Psychology
Service Leadership and Innovation
Voice Communication
Woodworking and Furniture Design

HISTORICAL FINANCIALS

Company Type: Private

Income Statement FYE: June 30

	REVENUE ($ mil.)	NET INCOME ($ mil.)	NET PROFIT MARGIN	EMPLOYEES
06/13	504	52	10.4%	2,400
06/12	490	16	3.4%	—
06/06	370	45	12.2%	—
06/05	350	0	—	—
Annual Growth	4.6%	—	—	—

2013 Year-End Financials

Debt ratio: —
Return on equity: 10.40%
Cash ($ mil.): 67
Current ratio: —
Long-term debt ($ mil.): —
Dividends
Yield: —
Payout: —
Market value ($ mil.): —

ROCKINGHAM MEMORIAL HOSPITAL INC

Rockingham Memorial Hospital (RMH) won't rock you to sleep but you may sleep better knowing the acute care medical center is close by. The hospital serves residents in Virginia's Shenandoah Valley offering some 240 beds. In addition to emergency services and general surgeries and care procedures RMH offers specialized services including cardiovascular care cancer treatment sleep disorder diagnosis behavioral health care medical imaging orthopedic procedures obstetrics and rehabilitation as well as home health hospice and wellness services. RMH founded in 1912 is part of the Sentara Healthcare system.

Geographic Reach

RMH is located in Harrisonburg Virginia and serves residents in seven surrounding counties.

Operations

RMH handles about 16000 inpatient visits and 190000 outpatient visits per year as well as some 2000 births and 19000 surgeries. Its emergency room handles about 70000 patients annually while the RMH Cancer Center conducts about 14000 treatment procedures.

Strategy

RMH completed construction of a brand new hospital to replace its existing facility in mid-2010. The organization raised funds for the construction of its new facility through the sale of the previous hospital building to James Madison University as well as through private donations staff donations bond sales. The new hospital included an expanded emergency room and all private-patient rooms and helped RMH improve on technology quality of care and patient convenience.

Ownership

RMH became part of regional health system Sentara Healthcare in 2011 when its parent organization RMH Healthcare was acquired by Sentara.

EXECUTIVES

Associate Director Public Relations and Communications, Debra (Deb) Thompson
SVP Clinical Effectiveness and Chief Medical Officer, Dale Carroll
VP Acute Care Services and Chief Nursing Executive, Donna Hahn
Auditors: S.B.Hoover&CompanyL.L.P.

LOCATIONS

HQ: ROCKINGHAM MEMORIAL HOSPITAL INC
2010 HEALTH CAMPUS DR, HARRISONBURG, VA 22801-3293
Phone: 540-433-4100
Web: WWW.RMHONLINE.COM

PRODUCTS/OPERATIONS

Selected Services

Bariatric Surgery
Behavioral Health
Blood Donor Center
Business Office
Center for Sleep Medicine
Chaplain Services
Childcare Connection
Community Health
East Rockingham Health Center
Emergency Department
Family Birthplace
Gifts & Floral
Grief and Loss Services
Hahn Cancer Center
Healthsource
Heart and Vascular Center
Home Care Services
Hospice
Hospitalists
Image Recovery Center
Imaging Services
Joint Services
Laboratory Services
Lifeline
Luray Health Center
Mount Jackson Health Center
New Market Health Center
Occupational Health Center
Orthopedics and Sports Medicine
Palliative Care
Pharmacy
Physician Billing
Pulmonary Services
Rehab Services
Security
Senior Advantage
South Main Health Center
Surgical Services
Valley Behavioral Medicine
Virginia Funkhouser Health Sciences Library
Volunteer Services
Wellness Center
Women's Center

COMPETITORS

Carilion Clinic
Centra Health Inc.
HCA Capital Division
Loudoun Healthcare
MedStar Health
University of Virginia Health System
Valley Health
Virginia Hospital & Healthcare

HISTORICAL FINANCIALS

Company Type: Private

Income Statement FYE: December 31

	REVENUE ($ mil.)	NET INCOME ($ mil.)	NET PROFIT MARGIN	EMPLOYEES
12/08	264	10	3.8%	1,892
12/06	229	18	7.8%	—
12/05	214	5	2.5%	—
12/04	188	14	7.6%	—
Annual Growth	8.9%	(8.2%)	—	—

2008 Year-End Financials

Debt ratio: —
Return on equity: 3.80%
Cash ($ mil.): 55
Current ratio: 1.00
Long-term debt ($ mil.): —
Dividends
Yield: —
Payout: —
Market value ($ mil.): —

ROCKVIEW DAIRIES INC.

LOCATIONS

HQ: ROCKVIEW DAIRIES INC.
7011 STEWART AND GRAY RD, DOWNEY, CA 902414347
Phone: 5629275511
Web: WWW.ROCKVIEWFARMS.COM

PRODUCTS/OPERATIONS

Selected Products

Butter
Buttermilk
Cottage cheese
Cream
Half & half
Milk
Juice
Sour cream
Yogurt

COMPETITORS

Aurora Organic Dairy
California Dairies Inc.
Dairy Farmers of America
Dean Foods
Farmland Dairies
Foster Dairy Farms
Friendship Dairies
Garelick Farms
Kemps LLC
Land O' Lakes
Oberweis Dairy
Organic Valley
Roberts Dairy
Springfield Creamery
Stonyfield Farm
Turkey Hill Dairy

HISTORICAL FINANCIALS

Company Type: Private

Income Statement FYE: March 31

	REVENUE ($ mil.)	NET INCOME ($ mil.)	NET PROFIT MARGIN	EMPLOYEES
03/08	333	8	2.4%	250
03/07	265	3	1.5%	—
03/06	2,112	0	—	—
Annual Growth	—13235.1%		—	—

2008 Year-End Financials

Debt ratio: —
Return on equity: 2.40%
Cash ($ mil.): 3
Current ratio: 0.90
Long-term debt ($ mil.): —
Dividends
Yield: —
Payout: —
Market value ($ mil.): —

ROGER WILLIAMS MEDICAL CENTER

Roger Williams Medical Center (RWMC) established in 1878 is a community-owned hospital that offers medical and emergency care specialty surgery and diagnostic facilities. Other services provided by the longtime medical facility include subacute care orthopedics and sleep disorder therapy. RWMC also operates a home health agency and provides health care services at a nursing home through an affiliation with Elmhurst Extended Care. With more than 150 beds RWMC operates a cancer care specialty center that also conducts academic research in cancer treatment. Roger Williams is a teaching hospital affiliated with Boston University's School of Medicine.

Operations

RWMC and nearby St. Joseph Health Services operate an affiliation under the name Charter Care Health Partners to bolster the financial health of each of the not-for-profit hospitals. They cut costs by merging certain operations including some administrative duties and clinical services. The alliance comprises two acute-care hospitals and several specialty care centers.

EXECUTIVES

Corporate Compliance Officer, George Curtis
President, Kenneth H. (Ken) Belcher, age 58
Treasurer, Addy Kane
VP and Administrator Elmhurst Extended Care, Richard Gamache
VP Patient Care Services and Chief Nursing Officer, Joanne Dooley
President Medical Staff, Michael Bonitati
Secretary, Gary R. Pannone
Vice Chairman, Donald C. McQueen
Director Cancer Center and Chief of Surgical Oncology, N. Joseph Espat
Chairman, Sheri L. Smith
CFO, Michael E. Conklin Jr.
VP and CIO, Susan Cerrone Abely
Vice Chairman, Rev Kenneth Sicard
Auditors: PricewaterhouseCoopersLLP

LOCATIONS

HQ: ROGER WILLIAMS MEDICAL CENTER
825 CHALKSTONE AVE, PROVIDENCE, RI 02908-4728
Phone: 401-456-2000
Web: WWW.RWMC.ORG

PRODUCTS/OPERATIONS

Selected Services

Allergy/Immunology
Anesthesiology
Cardiology
Critical Care Unit
Emergency Services
Endocrinology
Infectious Diseases
Nephrology
Neurology
Occupational & Environmental Medicine
Ophthalmology
Otolaryngology
Pathology Laboratory
Podiatry
Primary Care
Psychiatry
Pulmonary Function Testing
Rehabilitation
Rheumatology
Substance Addiction
Urology
Women's Health

Selected Affiliations

CharterCare
Our Lady of Fatima Hospital
Elmhurst Extended Care

COMPETITORS

Baystate Health
Care New England
Lifespan Corporation
Memorial Hospital of Rhode Island
Partners HealthCare
Southcoast Health
Sturdy Memorial

HISTORICAL FINANCIALS

Company Type: Private

Income Statement FYE: September 30

	REVENUE ($ mil.)	NET INCOME ($ mil.)	NET PROFIT MARGIN	EMPLOYEES
09/09	185	(2)	—	1,500
09/08	173	(4)	—	—
09/07	1,814	0	—	—
Annual Growth	—	—	—	—

2009 Year-End Financials

Debt ratio: —
Return on equity: (-1.30%)
Cash ($ mil.): 15
Current ratio: 0.90
Long-term debt ($ mil.): —
Dividends
Yield: —
Payout: —
Market value ($ mil.): —

ROLLINS COLLEGE

Students get rolling at Rollins College. The school ,Äis a liberal arts college with an enrollment of some 3200 undergraduate students seeking associate bachelor and master's degrees. Rollins' core arts and sciences and professional studies ,Äprograms offer about 30 majors. ,ÄIn addition ,Äits Crummer Graduate School of Business offers an MBA program and its Hamilton Holt School provides undergraduate and graduate evening degree and outreach programs ,Äin 10 major fields. The college has 200 ,Äfaculty members and ,Äa student-to-teacher ratio of 10:1. Rollins was founded in 1885 by New England Congregationalists and is the oldest college in Florida. It is named for Chicago businessman and philanthropist Alonzo Rollins.

Sales and Marketing

Rollins spent some $892000 on advertising during fiscal 2012.

Financial Performance

Rollins increased revenues by 6% to $105 million ,Äin 2012 due to higher net tuition and student fee income as well as private grants and endowment releases. Net income declined to a loss of $27 million however due to increased operating expenses and lower endowment and investment income levels. Cash flow rose as the college borrowed nearly $30 million in higher educational bonds to fund renovation and expansion efforts.

Strategy

Construction and renovation efforts include expansion and improvement efforts on two existing academic buildings and the construction of two new residential halls as well as several infrastructure improvement projects.

To expand its educational programs Rollins launched an undergraduate college of professional studies in 2011. The new school division will focus on business management communications educational and legal studies. Three ,Äacademic programs from the ,Äarts and sciences college –communication education and international business ,Ä–were transferred to the new professional studies college. In addition the Rollins MBA division added a new executive MBA program featuring Saturday classes.

EXECUTIVES

Asst Vp Human Res/risk Mgmt, Maria Martinez
Vp Finance/treasurer, Jeffrey G Eisenbarth
Asst Vp Of Public Relations, Ann Marie Varga
President, Grant Cornwell

LOCATIONS

HQ: ROLLINS COLLEGE
1000 HOLT AVE 2715, WINTER PARK, FL 327894409
Phone: 4076462000
Web: WWW.ROLLINS.EDU

PRODUCTS/OPERATIONS

Selected Programs

Evening Undergraduate and Graduate Programs
Hamilton Holt School
Full-Time Undergraduate Programs
The College of Arts and Sciences
The College of Professional Studies
MBA Programs
Crummer Graduate School of Business

HISTORICAL FINANCIALS

Company Type: Private

Income Statement FYE: May 31

	REVENUE ($ mil.)	NET INCOME ($ mil.)	NET PROFIT MARGIN	EMPLOYEES
05/14	122	17	14.3%	645
05/13	154	2	1.4%	—
05/12	105	(27)	—	—
05/11	99	0	—	—
Annual Growth	7.3%	—	—	—

2014 Year-End Financials

Debt ratio: —
Return on equity: 14.30%
Cash ($ mil.): 4
Current ratio: —
Long-term debt ($ mil.): —
Dividends
Yield: —
Payout: —
Market value ($ mil.): —

RONILE INC.

Ronile can spin a yarn –a textile one that is. The company manufactures custom-dyed accent yarns including twisted space-dyed air-ply and heatset yarns. Ronile's slew of finished yarn goods include nylon polyester acrylic and other wool fibers which are marketed to carpet rug home furnishings craft and automotive markets. Ronile also operates through subsidiary Bacova Guild Ltd. a manufacturer and supplier of printed accent rugs room-size rugs and bath ensembles to US retail chains and Gulistan a division supplying broadloom carpet. Employee-owned the company is led by its founder's son Phillip Essig.

Ronile was founded in 1984 as a yarn spinning company by Abe and Elinor Essig. The company's name derives from "Elinor" spelled backward.

EXECUTIVES

Vp Of Finance, Elinor Essig, age 76

LOCATIONS

HQ: RONILE INC.
701 ORCHARD AVE, ROCKY MOUNT, VA 24151-1848
Phone: 540-483-0261
Web: WWW.RONILE.COM

COMPETITORS

Beaulieu of America
Interface Inc.
Mohawk Industries
Shaw Industries

HISTORICAL FINANCIALS

Company Type: Private

Income Statement FYE: June 30

	REVENUE ($ mil.)	NET INCOME ($ mil.)	NET PROFIT MARGIN	EMPLOYEES
06/07*	232	0	—	1,383
07/06	245	0	—	—
07/05	597	0	0.0%	—
Annual Growth	(37.6%)	—	—	—

*Fiscal year change

2007 Year-End Financials

Debt ratio: —
Return on equity: —
Cash ($ mil.): 0
Current ratio: 1.00
Long-term debt ($ mil.): —
Dividends
Yield: —
Payout: —
Market value ($ mil.): —

ROOFING WHOLESALE CO. INC.

Business at Roofing Wholesale doesn't have to be complicated but it should be over your head. Roofing Wholesale Company (RWC) distributes residential and commercial roofing stone flooring and stucco to contractors builders and do-it-yourself home owners through ten locations in Arizona California Nevada and New Mexico. It also operates an online store. Products include asphalt shingles cedar shakes and shingles clay tiles fasteners marble floors and slate roofs. John Lisherness father of current president Harley Lisherness founded the family-owned company in 1958.

EXECUTIVES

Vp Operations, Michael O'Day
Vice President Human Resources, Mike Nelson

LOCATIONS

HQ: ROOFING WHOLESALE CO. INC.
1918 W GRANT ST, PHOENIX, AZ 850095991
Phone: 6022583794
Web: WWW.RWC.ORG

COMPETITORS

Acoustical Material Services
BMC
BMD
HD Supply
Pacific Coast Building Products

HISTORICAL FINANCIALS

Company Type: Private

Income Statement FYE: December 31

	REVENUE ($ mil.)	NET INCOME ($ mil.)	NET PROFIT MARGIN	EMPLOYEES
12/13	106	4	4.5%	225
12/12	105	7	7.0%	—
12/11	128	11	9.3%	—
12/10	95	0	—	—
Annual Growth	3.9%	—	—	—

2013 Year-End Financials

Debt ratio: —
Return on equity: 4.50%
Cash ($ mil.): 9
Current ratio: 1.50
Long-term debt ($ mil.): —
Dividends
Yield: —
Payout: —
Market value ($ mil.): —

ROSE INTERNATIONAL INC.

Rose International keep its customers' tech gardens in bloom. The company provides outsourced IT services including database performance optimization application development and project management to businesses and government agencies in the US. Other services include vendor management payroll processing training and staffing and call center operations. Rose —its name is an acronym for "reliable open systems engineering"—serves customers in such industries as financial services energy technology telecommunications and health care. Its software development activities are overseen in Missouri and in India by subsidiary Rose I.T. Solutions.

Geographic Reach

Rose International has about 20 offices located nationwide and one in New Delhi India.

Sales and Marketing

In addition to commercial clients the company targets public sector agencies. Government clients have included the US Air Force Army and Navy the State of Missouri and the USDA. Rose International has sales and service partnerships with such IT vendors as IBM Microsoft and Cisco Systems.

Ownership

Established in 1993 as Rose Imaging the company is owned by founder Himanshu Bhatia.

EXECUTIVES

VP Midwestern Region, Hans de Bruijn
CEO, Himanshu (Sue) Bhatia, age 52
President, Gulab Bhatia
Executive Vice President, Eric Token
VP-Contingent Workforce Svcs, Phil Black
VP State and Local Government Division, John Truesdell
VP Finance, Larry Crane
VP Western Region, Harish Vakharia
Associate Director Marketing and Business Development, Jonnie Gray
Marketing Manager, Lori Buehler
Auditors: BrownSmithWallaceLLC

LOCATIONS

HQ: ROSE INTERNATIONAL INC.
16401 SWINGLEY RIDGE RD, CHESTERFIELD, MO 63017-0757
Phone: 636-532-3126
Web: WWW.ROSEINT.COM

PRODUCTS/OPERATIONS

Selected Services

Application Development
Database Performance Optimization Practice
Operations Maintenance and Support
Project Management and PMI Training
Workforce Solutions

Selected Industries Served

Energy
Entertainment
Financial
Government Agencies
Healthcare
Retail and Consumer
Technology and Telecommunication

COMPETITORS

Accenture
Affiliated Computer Services
Analysts International
Computer Sciences Corp.
HP Enterprise Group
HP Enterprise Services
IBM Global Services
Infosys
Leidos
Maryville Data Systems
S2 Tech
Tata Consultancy
Unisys
World Wide Technology

HISTORICAL FINANCIALS

Company Type: Private

Income Statement FYE: December 31

	REVENUE ($ mil.)	NET INCOME ($ mil.)	NET PROFIT MARGIN	EMPLOYEES
12/12	357	11	3.2%	6,000
12/11	357	13	3.8%	—
12/10	228	9	4.0%	—
12/09	161	5	3.5%	—
Annual Growth	30.5%	27.4%	—	—

2012 Year-End Financials

Debt ratio: —
Return on equity: 3.20%
Cash ($ mil.): 1
Current ratio: 3.00
Long-term debt ($ mil.): —
Dividends
Yield: —
Payout: —
Market value ($ mil.): —

ROSEN HOTELS AND RESORTS INC.

Want to make your Florida stay a little rosy? Rosen Hotels & Resorts owns and operates seven hotels in Orlando collectively totaling more than 6300 rooms and suites. Its properties are located near major area attractions such as Disney World (from Walt Disney Parks) and Universal Studios Orlando (from Universal Parks & Resorts). Its portfolio consists of hotels such as the Rosen Plaza Hotel and Rosen Inn. Three of its hotels are home to major Orlando convention centers: Rosen Plaza Rosen Centre and Rosen Shingle Creek. In addition subsidiary Millennium Technology Group manages computer systems for its hotels. The family-owned Rosen Hotels & Resorts was founded by president Harris Rosen in 1974.

Geographic Reach

The company is Florida's largest independent hotel chain.

Company Background

Harris Rosen a former manager at Hilton and executive at Disney has made a name for himself as a prominent Orlando businessman. Among his notable achievements are providing employees with healthcare via onsite clinics and the donation of a site to the University of Central Florida for the Rosen College of Hospitality Management.

EXECUTIVES

CFO, Frank A. Santos
President and COO, Harris Rosen
Director Planning and Development, Garritt Toohey
Director Operations, Derek Baum
Director Human Resources, Jonni Kimberly
Director Purchasing, Scott Farrow
Director Information Technology, Jim Bina
VP Engineering and Facilities Management, Daniel Gutierrez

Associate Director Human Resources, Dorea Mays
Manager Risk, Ashley Bacot
Administrator Medical Center, Kenneth Aldridge Jr.
Corporate Controller, Randall Rickmann
VP Sales and Marketing, Leslie Menichini
Director of IT, Mike Lewis

LOCATIONS

HQ: ROSEN HOTELS AND RESORTS INC.
9840 INTERNATIONAL DR, ORLANDO, FL 32819-8111
Phone: 407-996-1706
Web: WWW.ROSENHOTELSANDRESORTS.COM

PRODUCTS/OPERATIONS

Selected Properties

Rosen Shingle Creek
Rosen Centre Hotel
Rozen Plaza Hotel
Clarion Inn Lake Buena Vista
Rosen Inn at Pointe Orlando
Rosen Inn
Quality Inn International

COMPETITORS

Central Florida Investments Inc.
Disney Parks & Resorts
Larry Blumberg and Associates
Marriott Vacations
Orange Lake Country Club
Peabody Management
Starwood Hotels & Resorts
Wyndham Vacation

HISTORICAL FINANCIALS

Company Type: Private

Income Statement FYE: January 31

	REVENUE ($ mil.)	NET INCOME ($ mil.)	NET PROFIT MARGIN	EMPLOYEES
01/13	268	76	28.5%	3,420
01/12	8	0	—	—
01/11	8	0	—	—
01/10	8	0	—	—
Annual Growth	218.4%	—	—	—

2013 Year-End Financials

Debt ratio: ——
Return on equity: 28.50%
Cash ($ mil.): 5
Current ratio: 0.90
Long-term debt ($ mil.): —
Dividends
Yield: —
Payout: —
Market value ($ mil.): —

ROTH STAFFING COMPANIES L.P.

Roth Staffing Companies L.P. offers temporary and temp-to-hire staffing and permanent placement services through its specialized business lines. Ultimate Staffing Services specializes in administrative customer service clerical manufacturing & production positions. Ledgent Finance & Accounting focuses on accounting and finance professionals while Ledgent Technology & Engineering concentrates on professionals in those fields. Adams & Martin Group recruits legal professionals. In addition One Squared Managed Solutions provides managed staffing program (MSP) and vendor management system (VMS) services. Founded in 1994 by CEO Ben Roth the company serves clients in some 20 states and Washington DC through more than 100 branches and a number of on-premise locations.

Operations

In addition to staffing Roth Staffing Companies L.P. offers executive search services recruitment process outsourcing 1099 (independent contractor) management and payroll services.

EXECUTIVES

Founder and CEO, Ben Roth
EVP, Pam Sexauer
President and COO, Adam Roth
SVP Professional Services, Julie Hagan Porter
VP Accounting and Finance, Pauline Francis
SVP, Kristi Kennedy-Lahiff
VP Sales, Susan Ahrens
SVP and General Counsel, Jennifer Jech Simonson
SVP, Robert Hankin
VP, Colleen Hooker
Sr. VP of Professional Services, Julie Hagan
Sr. Vice President General Counsel, Jennifer Simonson
Regional Vice President, Mary Boland
VP Ledgent Technology, Brett Roth

LOCATIONS

HQ: ROTH STAFFING COMPANIES L.P.
333 CITY BLVD W STE 100, ORANGE, CA 92868-2952
Phone: 714-939-8600
Web: WWW.ADAMSMARTINGROUP.COM

COMPETITORS

Adecco
Allegis Group
Kelly Services
Kforce
ManpowerGroup
On Assignment
Randstad Holding
Robert Half
SFN Group
TrueBlue
Volt Information

HISTORICAL FINANCIALS

Company Type: Private

Income Statement FYE: December 31

	REVENUE ($ mil.)	NET INCOME ($ mil.)	NET PROFIT MARGIN	EMPLOYEES
12/11	244	0	—	500
12/10	202	0	—	—
12/09	214	0	—	—
12/08	214	0	—	—
Annual Growth	4.5%	—	—	—

2011 Year-End Financials

Debt ratio: ——
Return on equity: —
Cash ($ mil.): 0
Current ratio: 2.80
Long-term debt ($ mil.): —
Dividends
Yield: —
Payout: —
Market value ($ mil.): —

ROTTERDAM VENTURES INC.

LOCATIONS

HQ: ROTTERDAM VENTURES INC.
695 ROTTERDAM INDL PARK, SCHENECTADY, NY 12306
Phone: 5183560419
Web: WWW.GALESI.COM

HISTORICAL FINANCIALS

Company Type: Private

Income Statement FYE: November 30

	ASSETS ($ mil.)	NET INCOME ($ mil.)	INCOME AS % OF ASSETS	EMPLOYEES
11/10	520	10	2.1%	150
11/07	544	17	3.2%	—
11/06	176	0	0.0%	—
Annual Growth	31.1%	1500.6%	—	—

2010 Year-End Financials

Debt ratio: ——
Return on equity: 23.00%
Cash ($ mil.): 34
Current ratio: 6.50
Long-term debt ($ mil.): —
Dividends
Yield: —
Payout: —
Market value ($ mil.): —

RUMSEY ELECTRIC COMPANY

EXECUTIVES

President Chief Executive Officer, Gerald M. (Jerry) Lihota, age 66
Executive Vice President Chief Financial Officer, Scott M. Cutler, age 63
VP Construction Sales, Jack Graham
VP Operations and Logistics, Larry Haggerty
VP Utility Sales Mid-Atlantic, Chip Jones
VP Relay and Power Systems, Steven Cabibbo
Supervisor Credit and Collections, Ted Blucas
Manager Business Development Greater Philadelphia and DE, Fred Capanna
Manager Business Development Greater Philadephia DE, Shawn Huber
Purchasing Manager, Jim Napuda
SVP, Paul Esterheld
Manager Automation, Doug Metz
GSS Administrator Automation Training Service Warranty and Repairs PA and NJ, Barbara Dever
GSS Administrator Automation Training Service Warranty and Repairs Lehigh Valley South Jersey, Nitza Colon
Lighting Specialist PA and NJ, Jon Morris
Lighting Specialist DE and MD, Chris Lewandowski
Switchgear Specialist PA and NJ, Chip Vandevere
Switchgear Specialist PA and NJ, Mike Karlson
Switchgear Specialist DE and MD, Steve McPhee
Manager Warehouse, Bill Johnson
Manager Information Technology, Matt Prior
Director Human Resources, Ned Clopton
Director Marketing, Jill Michener
QualityTraining and Technology, Jim Poach
General Manager Lighting Systems, Ralph Giorondo

LOCATIONS

HQ: RUMSEY ELECTRIC COMPANY
15 COLWELL LN, CONSHOHOCKEN, PA 194281878
Phone: 6108329000
Web: WWW.RUMSEY.COM

PRODUCTS/OPERATIONS

Selected Products

Automation and controls
Ballasts
Control panel components
Enclosures
Energy saving components
Fixtures
Lamps

Lighting
Lighting controls
Lighting services
Mechanical components
Metering
Power distribution
Process components
Protection and control products
Relay and power systems
Safety and supply parts
Switchgear
Tools
Transformers

COMPETITORS

Anixter International
Billows Electric Supply
Colonial Electric Supply
Consolidated Electrical
Fromm Electric
Gexpro
Graybar Electric
Rexel Inc.
United Electric Supply
WESCO International

HISTORICAL FINANCIALS

Company Type: Private

Income Statement FYE: December 31

	REVENUE ($ mil.)	NET INCOME ($ mil.)	NET PROFIT MARGIN	EMPLOYEES
12/13	225	9	4.1%	284
12/12	197	10	5.4%	—
12/11	196	2	1.0%	—
12/10	187	0		
Annual Growth	6.4%	—	—	—

2013 Year-End Financials

Debt ratio: —
Return on equity: 4.10%
Cash ($ mil.): 14
Current ratio: 2.20
Long-term debt ($ mil.): —
Dividends
Yield: —
Payout: —
Market value ($ mil.): —

RUSSELL & SMITH FORD INC.

LOCATIONS

HQ: RUSSELL & SMITH FORD INC.
3440 SOUTH LOOP W, HOUSTON, TX 770255296
Phone: 7136634111
Web: WWW.RSFORD.COM

HISTORICAL FINANCIALS

Company Type: Private

Income Statement FYE: May 31

	REVENUE ($ mil.)	NET INCOME ($ mil.)	NET PROFIT MARGIN	EMPLOYEES
05/14	304	4	1.5%	310
05/13	265	3	1.3%	—
05/12	222	2	0.9%	—
05/11	194	0	—	—
Annual Growth	16.1%	—	—	—

2014 Year-End Financials

Debt ratio: —
Return on equity: 1.50%
Cash ($ mil.): 7
Current ratio: 0.20
Long-term debt ($ mil.): —
Dividends
Yield: —
Payout: —
Market value ($ mil.): —

RUSSELL SIGLER INC.

Russell Sigler has built a business providing a rather cool service in a hot region. Through about 30 offices located primarily in California and Arizona (but also in Idaho Nevada New Mexico and Texas) the company provides commercial and residential air conditioning contractors with equipment parts supplies and technical support. Its brands include Carrier Bryant and Payne. Russell Sigler has distributed Carrier products for more than 60 years. As part of its business the company also operates a residential and commercial distribution joint venture with industry giant Carrier. Russell Sigler owns a 60% stake while Carrier holds 40%.

Geographic Reach

Based in Tolleson Arizona Russell Sigler has branch locations in Arizona California Idaho Nevada New Mexico and Texas.

Sales and Marketing

Russell Sigler provides its products to retail stores and to dealers.

LOCATIONS

HQ: RUSSELL SIGLER INC.
9702 W TONTO ST, TOLLESON, AZ 85353-9703
Phone: 623-388-5100
Web: WWW.SIGLERPARTSCENTER.COM

Selected Locations

California
Arizona
Texas
Idaho
New Mexico
Nevada

COMPETITORS

Chas Roberts Air Conditioning
Ferguson Enterprises
Gustave A. Larson Company
HD Supply
Johnstone Supply
US Airconditioning Distributors
Watsco
WinWholesale

HISTORICAL FINANCIALS

Company Type: Private

Income Statement FYE: December 31

	REVENUE ($ mil.)	NET INCOME ($ mil.)	NET PROFIT MARGIN	EMPLOYEES
12/11	440	(3)	—	550
12/09	140	(0)	—	—
12/08	176	1	0.8%	—
12/06	224	3	1.7%	—
Annual Growth	14.4%	—	—	—

2011 Year-End Financials

Debt ratio: —
Return on equity: (-0.90%)
Cash ($ mil.): 0
Current ratio: 0.40
Long-term debt ($ mil.): —
Dividends
Yield: —
Payout: —
Market value ($ mil.): —

RUTHERFORD ELECTRIC MEMBERSHIP CORPORATION

EXECUTIVES

Interim General Manager, Joseph H. Joplin
VP Member and Corporate Services, S. Dick Burleson
VP Engineering, Jeffrey C. Brittain
VP District Operations, Randy C. Ward
Member Services Representative Rutherford-Polk District, Gordon L. McDaniel
Member Services Representative Burke-McDowell District, Tommy W. Chapman
Member Services Representative Lincoln-Gaston District, Jonathan W. Pitman
Purchasing Agent, David R. Beam
President Board of Directors, Joesph N. Quinn
VP Board of Directors, Harold R. Oates
Secretary and Director, Paul G. Dalton
Treasurer and Director, David W. McGimsey
Assistant Secretary and Director, H. Frank Queen
Manager Operations, Colon L. Saunders
VP Board of Directors, Harold R. Oates
Secretary and Director, Paul G. Dalton
Treasurer and Director, David W. McGimsey
Assistant Secretary and Director, H. Frank Queen

LOCATIONS

HQ: RUTHERFORD ELECTRIC MEMBERSHIP CORPORATION
186 HUDLOW RD, FOREST CITY, NC 280432575
Phone: 7042451621
Web: WWW.CAROLINAENERGIES.COM

HISTORICAL FINANCIALS

Company Type: Private

Income Statement FYE: December 31

	REVENUE ($ mil.)	NET INCOME ($ mil.)	NET PROFIT MARGIN	EMPLOYEES
12/09	118	10	8.8%	178
12/05	110	7	6.4%	
12/04	94	0	0.3%	
12/01	78	0	—	—
Annual Growth	5.3%	—	—	—

2009 Year-End Financials

Debt ratio: —
Return on equity: 8.80%
Cash ($ mil.): 13
Current ratio: 0.10
Long-term debt ($ mil.): —
Dividends
Yield: —
Payout: —
Market value ($ mil.): —

RUTLAND HOSPITAL INC.

For those seeking health care in the New England region Rutland Regional Medical Center (RRMC) just might be the destination for you. Part of Rutland Regional Health Services it runs a hospital that boasts about 190 beds and serves patients in Vermont and eastern New York. RRMC offers about 40 medical specialties including cancer care diabetes treatment and total joint replacement. The acute-care facility also has centers dedicated to cardiac rehabilitation and women's health. To meet growing community medical needs RRMC also operates a prostate care unit and a 30-bed psychiatric unit. Along with a range of specialty care options RRMC administers primary care and emergency medical transport.

Geographic Reach

RRMC serves communities in Rutland County and surrounding portions of southern and central Vermont as well as eastern New York. It operates about 25 locations in Rutland Vermont as well as single facilities in towns including East Dorset Killington and Poultney Vermont.

Operations

Established in 1896 RRMC gets nearly half of its patient income from Medicare accounts about 20% from Blue Cross and Blue Shield contracts and the balance from a mix of commercial managed care contracts Medicaid and self-pay patients. The facility provides about $6 million in charity care each year.

The hospital employs 200 physicians and handles some 7000 inpatient 34000 emergency room and 190000 outpatient visits per year as well as 4500 surgeries and 400 births. Affiliated facilities in the Rutland Regional Health Services network include an orthopedic clinic a sports medicine center a health plan and a health foundation as well as two long-term care centers.

Financial Performance

RRMC increased revenues 8% to $197 million in 2012. It also reported a profit that year of $10.9 million (after a net loss of $2.7 million in 2011) due to higher revenues.

Strategy

To expand services in the region RRMC is expanding into new markets and entering into collaborations with other area providers. It also increases specialist offerings; in 2012 for instance RRMC added a wing with six private patient rooms for inpatient psychiatric care. In 2013 it also announced plans to open an outpatient center for addiction recovery.

The hospital in 2011 upgraded its information systems through a 20-month $10 million initiative to install an electronic health record (EHR) system that now manages the clinical administrative human resources and financial aspects of RRMC's daily operations. What helped to fund its IT initiatives was RRMC's decision to shutter its 12-unit inpatient rehabilitation facility which was completed in late 2012. The move is expected to save the hospital some $3 million annually. The hospital took other restructuring measures to shore up its finances in 2012 due to a budget gap created by state caps on expenses.

To further improve efficiencies and reduce medical spending RRMC is participating in Vermont's Blueprint for Health program which seeks to coordinate care between various medical providers. For instance through the program the hospital is helping to implement a care management infrastructure for patients with chronic diseases.

EXECUTIVES

President, Thomas W. Huebner
CFO, Edward Ogorzalek
Chair, Jessica L. Anderson
Vice Chair, Michael Dick
President Medical Staff, Daniel M. Foley
Auditors: BKDLLP

LOCATIONS

HQ: RUTLAND HOSPITAL INC.
160 ALLEN ST, RUTLAND, VT 05701-4595
Phone: 802-775-7111
Web: WWW.RRMC.ORG

PRODUCTS/OPERATIONS

Selected Services

Acute care
Cancer
Cardiology
Diagnostic imaging
ENT and audiology
Laboratory
Orthopedics
Preventative care
Surgery
Women' s health

COMPETITORS

Ellis Hospital
Fletcher Allen Health Care
New England Alliance for Health
Southwestern Vermont Health Care
Springfield Hospital

HISTORICAL FINANCIALS

Company Type: Private

Income Statement FYE: September 30

	REVENUE ($ mil.)	NET INCOME ($ mil.)	NET PROFIT MARGIN	EMPLOYEES
09/11	189	(4)	—	1,350
09/10	181	(1)	—	—
09/09	172	(18)	—	—
09/08	163	(8)	—	—
Annual Growth	5.0%	—	—	—

2011 Year-End Financials

Debt ratio: —
Return on equity: (-2.50%)
Cash ($ mil.): 10
Current ratio: —
Long-term debt ($ mil.): —
Dividends
Yield: —
Payout: —
Market value ($ mil.): —

RYAN LLC

The professionals at Ryan aren't too concerned when clients notice their SALT-y language. One of the US's largest state and local tax (SALT) consulting firms Ryan provides tax advice preparation and planning for major corporations and other businesses. It also offers advice on federal and international tax issues. The firm specializes in audit defense dispute resolution strategic planning tax process efficiencies and tax recovery. Founded in 1991 in Texas Ryan serves customers through some 60 offices in more than 20 states as well as in Canada and Europe. Ryan traces its roots to a certified public accounting firm co-founded by CEO G. Brint Ryan in 1991. It bought a portion of Thomson Reuters in 2013.

Geographic Reach

Dallas-based Ryan has about 60 offices across the US and in 40 countries including Amsterdam Australia Canada India Singapore and the UK. The firm is active in Latin America through its partnership with Godoy & Hoyos Abogados.

Strategy

The company often looks to form partnerships with other companies to broaden the scope of its services and geographic reach. To this end Ryan in 2013 formed a strategic alliance with Colombia-based Godoy & Hoyos Abogados to support the expansion of its international tax practice in Latin America. Previously the firm partnered with real estate giant Jones Lang LaSalle in 2010 to provide property tax services to commercial real estate clients. It has also teamed with recovery audit specialist PRG-Schultz International; US Tax Advantage which provides international tax services to US and foreign-based companies; and Associated Consultants an administrator of hiring tax credits.

Mergers and Acquisitions

Ryan has grown by adding new practices and making acquisitions. In 2013 the company purchased the Thomson Reuters Property Tax Services business adding 600 property tax and unclaimed property professionals. The move makes Ryan the largest global provider of property tax services and North America's largest indirect tax practice. As part of the agreement Ryan will operate a Center for Tax Excellence in India staffed by some 145 professionals. The center serves as a foundation for building Ryan's business in South Asia and extends the reach of its indirect tax practice to China's emerging markets.

In mid-2012 Ryan acquired The TAARP Group LLP the leading tax and penalty review firm in the US. The move added specialized federal income tax expertise and a number of Fortune 500 firms to Ryan's client roster. Other recent moves by Ryan to expand is business both geographically and by specialty include the launch of new groups devoted to fraud and forensic recovery and tax accounting risk services (2010) its entry into Canada by purchasing sales tax recovery firm Robert Brakel & Associates (2010) and the opening of a London office (2008).

Ryan spun off its tax software products including CertiSoft STS and Workflow in 2009 as an independent company called Second Decimal. The move has allowed it to focus its core tax services.

EXECUTIVES

EVP and Chief of Staff, Delta Emerson
Chief Executive Officer, G. Brint Ryan, age 50
Principal in Charge Houston, Mark W. Bennett
Principal in Charge Los Angeles, Richard V. Carlson
Principal, Randy W. Donald
Principal, Ginny Buckner Kissling
Principal in Charge New York, Jeremiah T. Lynch
Jr. Executive Vice President Chairman, Gerry L. Ridgely Jr.
Principal in Charge Austin, Eric L. Stein
VP and Principal, Richard H. Thompson
VP and Principal, James M. Trester
Principal, Korey Kim
Principal in Charge Chicago, James (Jim) Kranjc
Principal, Trisha C. Fortune
Principal in Charge Pittsburgh, Helen Lemmon
Principal, William Samuels
Senior Vice President and Chief Financial, David English, age 45
Principal, Richard D. (Rich) Fosburg
SVP Chief Legal Officer Secretary and Principal, Gregory S. (Greg) Weiss
Principal in Charge Atlanta, Douglas J. (Doug) DeRito
Principal, Mark W. Eidman
Principal, Bruce Gibson
Principal, Stephen J. Allen
Principal, Karey W. Barton
Principal, Tony Chavez
Principal, Damon N. Chronis
Principal, Julie Chronis
Principal, Jim Crandall
Principal, Neil Fett
Principal, Leslie S. Hahn
Principal, Dena J. Hall
Principal, Noel E. Hall Jr.
Principal, Michael Henry
Principal in Charge St. Louis, Randy Hilger
Principal, Nigel Hoyle
Principal, Dennis J. Kolumber Jr.
Principal, Luke G. Krieger
EVP and Vice Chairman Global Corporate Development, Brendan F. Moore
Principal, Mark L. Nachbar

Principal, Dave Naney
Principal, Greg Odell
Principal in Charge Columbus Detroit and Lansing, John M. Polizzi
Principal, Kevin S. Powell
Principal, Gerard Quinlan
Principal, Lester C. Rhodes
Managing Principal Canadian Operations, Garry Round
EVP Chief Strategy Officer and Principal, Jon C. Sweet
Senior Vice President Chief Marketing Officer, James R. Aubele
Senior Vice President Chief Information Officer, Blake K. Holman
SVP and Chief Real Estate Officer, Robert M. Wertz
VP Operations, Brooke A. Keene
Principal in Charge Boston, Janet L. Askenburg
Senior Vice President Operations and Business Planning, Joe Mileti
Senior Vice President of Strategic Operations, Jon Stover
Vice President of Training, Kathy Weaver
Senior Vice President of Talent Acquisition, MaryKay Manning
Vice President of Legal, Richard Nearhood

LOCATIONS

HQ: RYAN LLC
13155 NOEL RD STE 100, DALLAS, TX 75240-5050
Phone: 972-934-0022
Web: WWW.RYAN.COM

Selected Locations

Atlanta
Austin TX
Baton Rouge LA
Boston
Calgary AB
Charlotte NC
Chicago
Cleveland
Columbus
Dallas
Denver
Detroit
Downers Grove IL
El Paso TX
Ft. Lauderdale FL
Houston
Indianapolis
Jacksonville FL
Kansas City KS
Lansing MI
London
Los Angeles
Lubbock TX
Minneapolis
Montreal
Nashville TN
New Orleans
New York
Philadelphia
Pittsburgh
Providence RI
Sacramento CA
Salt Lake City
San Antonio
San Francisco
San Jose CA
Seattle
St. Louis
Tampa
Toronto
Washington DC

PRODUCTS/OPERATIONS

Selected Services

Alternative compliance procedures
Audit representation
Audit sampling analysis and evaluation
Captive insurance
Strategic planning
Tax compliance outsourcing
Tax refunds
Tax research
Tax systems implementation
Utility exemption studies
Voluntary disclosure and registration
Strategic alliances

Selected Industries Served

Business services
Construction
Financial services
Food services
Health care and pharmaceuticals
Manufacturing
Retail
Telecommunications
Transportation
Utilities

COMPETITORS

CliftonLarsonAllen
Management Insights
Moss Adams LLP
Peisner Johnson & Company
SALT Group
SC&H Group
UHY Advisors TX

HISTORICAL FINANCIALS

Company Type: Private

Income Statement FYE: December 31

	REVENUE ($ mil.)	NET INCOME ($ mil.)	NET PROFIT MARGIN	EMPLOYEES
12/12	241	9	4.1%	1,595
12/11	225	25	11.2%	—
12/09	212	24	11.6%	—
12/09	190	26	13.7%	—
Annual Growth	8.3%	(27.6%)	—	—

2012 Year-End Financials

Debt ratio: —
Return on equity: 4.10%
Cash ($ mil.): 1
Current ratio: 0.70
Long-term debt ($ mil.): —
Dividends
Yield: —
Payout: —
Market value ($ mil.): —

SACRED HEART HOSPITAL INC.

Sacred Heart Hospital is a more than 300-bed medical center that serves the western Wisconsin region. Specialized services include cardiology orthopedics cancer care behavioral health care imaging pediatrics and emergency medicine. Founded in 1889 by the Hospital Sisters of the Third Order of St. Francis the medical center is part of the Hospital Sisters Health System.

EXECUTIVES

CEO and Board President, Stephen (Steve) Ronstrom
Director Human Resources, Robert (Bob) Hassemer
CFO, Patricia Hitel
Chief of Staff, Greg C. Heiler
Director Development, Ann Kaiser
Chair, Robert (Bob) Krause
Vice Chair, Jeff Halloin
COO, Faye Deich
Chief Nursing Officer, Amy Dwyer
Regional Director Marketing Communications, Becky Swanson
CEO and Board President, Stephen (Steve) Ronstrom
Director, Sister Marybeth Culnan
Vice Chair, Jeff Halloin
Director, James Docksey
Director, Julie Furst-Bowe
Director, Thomas J. (Jake) Leinenkugel
Director and Board Secretary, Chris Longbella
Director, Thomas Peller
Director, Sister Janice Schneider

LOCATIONS

HQ: SACRED HEART HOSPITAL INC.
900 W CLAIREMONT AVE, EAU CLAIRE, WI 54701-5105
Phone: 715-839-4121
Web: WWW.URLDELETED:SACREDHEARTEAUCLAIRE.ORG

COMPETITORS

Abbott Northwestern Hospital
Allina Hospitals
Amery Regional Medical Center
Aspirus
Bethesda Hospital
Children' s Hospitals and Clinics of Minnesota
Fairview Health
Franciscan Skemp Healthcare
Gundersen Lutheran
HealthEast Care System
Luther Midelfort
Methodist Hospital (MN)
North Memorial Health Care
Tomah Memorial Hospital

HISTORICAL FINANCIALS

Company Type: Private

Income Statement FYE: June 30

	REVENUE ($ mil.)	NET INCOME ($ mil.)	NET PROFIT MARGIN	EMPLOYEES
06/08	174	22	12.7%	1,000
06/05	144	19	13.4%	—
06/03	1,258	0	—	—
Annual Growth	—	1072.1%	—	

2008 Year-End Financials

Debt ratio: —
Return on equity: 12.70%
Cash ($ mil.): 3
Current ratio: 0.30
Long-term debt ($ mil.): —
Dividends
Yield: —
Payout: —
Market value ($ mil.): —

SADDLEBACK MEMORIAL MEDICAL CENTER

Saddleback Memorial Medical Center part of Memorial Health Services serves the residents of southern Orange County in California. With some 325 beds the not-for-profit medical center provides general medical and surgical services as well as specialty care in areas such as cancer heart disease and physical rehabilitation. It operates two campuses one in Laguna Hills and one in San Clemente. The medical center also features several facilities for women's health including the Saddleback Women's Hospital and the MemorialCare Breast Center. In addition Saddleback Memorial provides home health care and hospice services.

Operations

Saddleback Memorial Center sees about 17000 inpatients each year. It also handles some 50000 emergency room visits and 8500 inpatient and outpatient surgeries.

The main hospital campus –Saddleback Memorial-Laguna Hills –is home to the Saddleback

Women's Hospital and the MemorialCare Cancer Institute while both the Laguna Hills and San Clemente locations house MemorialCare Breast Center and Memorial Heart and Vascular Institute sites. The Saddleback Memorial-San Clemente campus offers additional specialty services such as weight-loss surgery and infusion therapy. Saddleback Memorial Medical Center is recognized in its industry for its care services in areas including endocrinology (diabetes) gastroenterology and orthopedics.

Strategy

As part of parent MHS' efforts to provide quality care and reduce medical expenses in the California health care market Saddleback Memorial has installed electronic health record (EHR) systems at its facilities. The Laguna Hills was one of the first centers to install the system in 2006 and the San Clemente campus applied the technology in 2011.

MHS has also expanded the Saddleback Memorial's resources to attract new patients. For instance in 2010 it acquired a new outpatient imaging center in San Clemente and in 2012 it formed an affiliation with Orange County physicians' organization Greater Newport Physicians (giving the Saddleback Memorial greater access to general and specialty doctors).

To improve hospital care in 2012 Saddleback Memorial upgraded its robotic surgery system (to the da Vinci Si system) to provide advanced minimally invasive surgery services to its patients. The medical center also has improved its reconstruction and grafting surgery systems in recent years.

EXECUTIVES

CEO, Steve Geidt
Administrator, Liz Bear
CFO, John Bishop
Director Human Resources, Ron Salzberg

LOCATIONS

HQ: SADDLEBACK MEMORIAL MEDICAL CENTER
24451 HEALTH CENTER DR, LAGUNA HILLS, CA 92653-3689
Phone: 949-837-4500
Web: WWW.MEMORIALCARE.ORG

COMPETITORS

Children' s Hospital of Orange County
Hoag Memorial Hospital
Kaiser Permanente
Southwest Healthcare
St. Joseph Hospital of Orange
Tenet Healthcare
UC Irvine Medical Center
Western Medical Center - Santa Ana

HISTORICAL FINANCIALS

Company Type: Private

Income Statement FYE: June 30

	REVENUE ($ mil.)	NET INCOME ($ mil.)	NET PROFIT MARGIN	EMPLOYEES
06/08	364	32	8.8%	1,209
06/01	170	4	2.5%	—
06/99	2,141	0	0.0%	—
Annual Growth	2.0%	(11.9%)	—	—

2008 Year-End Financials

Debt ratio: —
Return on equity: 8.80%
Cash ($ mil.): 0
Current ratio: 0.60
Long-term debt ($ mil.): —
Dividends
Yield: —
Payout: —
Market value ($ mil.): —

SAINT AGNES MEDICAL CENTER

Protecting and caring for the vulnerable Saint Agnes continues to ward off death for the patients at Saint Agnes Medical Center. The medical center provides healthcare to Valley residents of Fresno California through a 436-bed acute care hospital. Along with general surgery the hospital offers a variety of services including asthma management bariatric surgery (for which it has scored state-wide accolades) cardiac rehabilitation hospice care and home care. The facility also has centers dedicated to cancer child development and women's health. The hospital is part of Trinity Health the fourth-largest health care system in the US.

Geographic Reach

Saint Agnes Medical Center provides care to residents of the Fresno California area (Fresno and Madera counties).

Operations

Saint Agnes Medical Center is a 436-bed medical campus that has more than 2600 staff members. In 2012 the center had almost 25700 admissions and more than 25970 out-patient visits.

Financial Performance

In 2013 the center had operating revenues of $433.8 million.

Strategy

Saint Agnes Medical Center has launched a new state-of-the-art Electronic Medical Record (EMR) system. The new EMR system replaced paper medical records and streamlined patient care. In 2013 Saint Agnes became the first medical center in greater Fresno to receive American College of Radiology accreditations in Breast MRI and Nuclear Medicine (through 2014).

Ownership

Saint Agnes Medical Center owned by Trinity Health.

Company Background

The hospital system was established in 1929 by nine Holy Cross Sisters.

Saint Agnes Medical Center sponsors a number of community outreach programs throughout the Valley including adult day care senior activity programs health care clinics for the uninsured and services for poor and homeless women.

EXECUTIVES

COO, Mark T. Bateman
President and CEO, Nancy Hollingsworth
Chief Medical Officer, Stephen Soldo
Chairman, Michael Martinez
CFO, Phil Robinson
Chief Nursing Officer, Debi Pasley
President Chief Executive Officer, Jim Leonard
Executive Vice President COO, Rick OConnell
Trustee, Phillip Sanchez
Trustee, William Owen
Trustee, William Hadcock
Trustee, Lee Jay Kolligian
Trustee, Dianne Nury

LOCATIONS

HQ: SAINT AGNES MEDICAL CENTER
1303 E HERNDON AVE, FRESNO, CA 93720-3309
Phone: 559-450-3000
Web: WWW.SAMC.COM

PRODUCTS/OPERATIONS

Selected Programs and Services

Cancer Services
Emergency Services
Endoscopy
Heart & Vascular
Home Health Care
Hospice
Imaging Services
Laboratory Services
Neuroscience
Occupational Health Center
Orthopaedics
Surgery
Palliative Care
Pulmonary Rehabilitation
Women' s Services
Wound Care Hyperbaric Medicine and Amputation Prevention

Selected Facilities

Breast Center
Cancer Center
The California Eye Institute at Saint Agnes
Child Development Center
Home Health and Hospice
Medical Library
Occupational Health Center
Outpatient Surgery North
Satellite Labs
Wound Care Hyperbaric Medicine and Amputation Prevention

COMPETITORS

Community Medical Centers
Dignity Health
HCA
Kaiser Permanente
Memorial Hospitals Association
Northern Inyo Hospital
Tenet Healthcare

HISTORICAL FINANCIALS

Company Type: Private

Income Statement FYE: June 30

	REVENUE ($ mil.)	NET INCOME ($ mil.)	NET PROFIT MARGIN	EMPLOYEES
06/11	487	6	1.2%	2,400
06/10	438	8	1.8%	—
06/09	394	(52)	—	—
06/08	420	24	5.8%	—
Annual Growth	5.1%	(37.2%)	—	—

2011 Year-End Financials

Debt ratio: —
Return on equity: 1.20%
Cash ($ mil.): 0
Current ratio: 0.40
Long-term debt ($ mil.): —
Dividends
Yield: —
Payout: —
Market value ($ mil.): —

SAINT ALPHONSUS REGIONAL MEDICAL CENTER INC.

Saint Alphonsus Regional Medical Center makes medical care its primary mission. The hospital part of Trinity Health provides Boise Idaho and the surrounding region with general acute and specialized health care services. The medical center has some 380 beds and includes a trauma center an orthopedic spinal care unit an air transport service and a home health and hospice division. It also operates a secondary campus the 150-bed Saint Alphonsus Medical Center - Nampa and it provides general practice and specialty health services through the Saint Alphonsus Medical Group physician practice organization and through outpatient care clinics. The Sisters of the Holy Cross founded the hospital in 1894.

Geographic Reach

Saint Alphonsus Regional Medical Center serves a territory that includes portions of southwestern Idaho northern Nevada and eastern Oregon.

Operations

Saint Alphonsus Regional Medical Center provides outpatient services through the 70 affiliated physician practices that make up the Saint Alphonsus Medical Group. It also operates the Saint Alphonsus Health Plaza which provides urgent care and outpatient surgery laboratory rehabilitation and primary care services.

Strategy

Saint Alphonsus Regional Medical Center expands its facilities to improve medical care in its service territory. It recently added a new Center for Advanced Healing a nine-story patient tower that includes surgery and intensive care units. It is also working to upgrade its medical equipment and communication systems.

EXECUTIVES

Medical Director Physician Relations, Rick Turner
Chairman, George H. Juetten, age 66
President CEO and Trustee, Sally E. Jeffcoat
CEO Saint Alphonsus Medical Center Nampa Idaho - Saint Alphonsus Health System, Karl Keeler
COO, Rodney Reider
VP System Philanthropy Marketing/Communications and Advocacy Saint Alphonsus Health System, Linda Payne Smith
Director Communications Saint Alphonsus Health System, Kristen Micheletti
Director Marketing Saint Alphonsus Health System, Sarah Berg
President CEO and Trustee, Sally E. Jeffcoat
Trustee, Shauna Williams

LOCATIONS

HQ: SAINT ALPHONSUS REGIONAL MEDICAL CENTER INC.
1055 N CURTIS RD, BOISE, ID 83706-1309
Phone: 208-367-2121
Web: WWW.SAINTALPHONSUS.ORG

COMPETITORS

Ascension Health
HCA
Intermountain Health Care
St. Luke's Health System

HISTORICAL FINANCIALS

Company Type: Private

Income Statement FYE: June 30

	REVENUE ($ mil.)	NET INCOME ($ mil.)	NET PROFIT MARGIN	EMPLOYEES
06/10	449	13	3.1%	3,500
06/09	428	(8)	—	—
06/09	0	0	—	—
Annual Growth	—83909.3%	—	—	—

2010 Year-End Financials

Debt ratio: —
Return on equity: 3.10%
Cash ($ mil.): 9
Current ratio: 0.30
Long-term debt ($ mil.): —
Dividends
Yield: —
Payout: —
Market value ($ mil.): —

SAINT ELIZABETH MEDICAL CENTER INC.

It doesn't have much to do with the Holy Trinity except for the fact that St. Elizabeth Medical Center (operating as St. Elizabeth Healthcare) does business in a trinity of states. The system provides health care services to residents in Kentucky Ohio and West Virginia. St. Elizabeth Healthcare's programs include stroke and cardiac care hospice services and neurosurgery. The system is home to six hospitals with about 1200 beds and dozens of primary care offices. St. Elizabeth Healthcare was formed through a merger between St. Elizabeth Medical and nearby St. Luke Hospitals. The organization has one board of directors and one management structure and is sponsored by the Catholic Diocese of Covington.

St. Elizabeth Healthcare owned and operated ambulance services company TransCare of Kentucky until 2010 when it agreed to sell the provider of emergency and non-emergency ambulance services in Northern Kentucky to Rural/Metro Corporation one of the nation's largest of ambulance and private fire protection services. St. Elizabeth Healthcare made the sale to expand ambulance services in Northern Kentucky.

St. Elizabeth's opened The Regional Diabetes Center at its Covington campus. With this expansion St. Elizabeth has more endocrinologists in one center than nearly anywhere else in the eastern US that specializes in diabetes management and other endocrine disorders.

Also in 2010 the health system began development of a Neonatal Intensive Care Unit (NICU) at St. Elizabeth Edgewood. The hospital completed the first phase of a major renovation of the OB and NICU space to provide higher levels of neonatal care with about 20 newly-built private NICU beds and post-partum rooms that were upgraded and expanded.

2010 was a busy year for St. Elizabeth which also formed the St. Elizabeth Physicians group by merging with Summit Medical Group and Patient-First. St. Elizabeth Physicians is home to roughly 160 physicians and mid-level providers and nearly 1000 total employees.

The St. Elizabeth Business Health Division offers health care services to employers and their employees to try to cut down on lost production due to sick days. The division focuses on wellness and prevention as well as personalized exercise plans drug screening and injury/care prevention.

EXECUTIVES

President and Trustee, Joseph W. Gross
Chair, Thomas C. Colvin
EVP and COO, John S. Dubis
Treasurer, Garren Colvin
Secretary, Barbara L. Krohman
Director Public Relations and Marketing Communications, Sandra Sims
CIO, Alex Rodriguez
Chairman, Barry Wendt
Treasurer, Nathan VanLaningham
President and Trustee, Joseph W. Gross
Trustee, John S. Domaschko
Trustee, Michael A. Conner
Trustee, Barry L. Dick
Trustee, Michael J. Gibbons
Trustee, George S. Hall
Trustee, Shirley Howard
Trustee, Ralph F. Huller
Trustee, Bari Joslyn
Trustee, Fred A. Macke Jr.
Trustee, Rt. Hon. Gary W. Moore
Trustee, Heidi C. Murley
Trustee, Ted Robinson
Trustee, Paul A. Sartori
Trustee, Jo Ann Simpson
Trustee, Joan Wurtenberger
Auditors: Ernst&YoungLLP

LOCATIONS

HQ: SAINT ELIZABETH MEDICAL CENTER INC.
1 MEDICAL VILLAGE DR, EDGEWOOD, KY 41017-3403
Phone: 859-301-2000
Web: WWW.SAINTE.PPS-INC.COM

Selected locations

St. Elizabeth Covington (Covington Kentucky)
St. Elizabeth Edgewood (Edgewood Kentucky)
St. Elizabeth Grant (Williamstown Kentucky)
St. Elizabeth Ft. Thomas (St. Thomas Kentucky)
St. Elizabeth Florence (Florence Kentucky)
St. Elizabeth Falmouth (Falmouth Kentucky)

COMPETITORS

Adventist Health System
Bethesda North
Catholic Health Initiatives
Catholic Health Partners
Christ Hospital
Cincinnati Children's Hospital
Deaconess Associations
HCA
Kettering Health Network
Mount Carmel Health
OhioHealth
Regency Hospital
Tenet Healthcare
TriHealth
UC Health
Universal Health Services

HISTORICAL FINANCIALS

Company Type: Private

Income Statement FYE: December 31

	REVENUE ($ mil.)	NET INCOME ($ mil.)	NET PROFIT MARGIN	EMPLOYEES
12/08	623	(32)	—	6,227
12/06	483	49	10.2%	—
12/05	520	0	0.0%	—
Annual Growth	6.2%	—	—	—

2008 Year-End Financials

Debt ratio: —
Return on equity: (-5.20%)
Cash ($ mil.): 53
Current ratio: 1.10
Long-term debt ($ mil.): —
Dividends
Yield: —
Payout: —
Market value ($ mil.): —

SAINT FRANCIS HOSPITAL AND MEDICAL CENTER

Saint Francis takes care of the hearts of Hartford Connecticut. The Saint Francis Hospital and Medical Center also known as Saint Francis Care is a regional medical center with some 620 beds. The hospital specializes in cardiology oncology neurology orthopedics and women's and children's health services. It also offers behavioral health weight management trauma care and injury rehabilitation programs. Saint Francis serves as a teaching hospital affiliated with the University of Connecticut Schools of Medicine and Dentistry. It also operates the nearby Mount Sinai Rehabilitation Hospital a 60-bed facility that provides brain trauma sports medicine and orthopedic care.

Operations

Saint Francis' on-campus specialty centers include the Hoffman Heart Institute which specializes in open-heart surgeries and catheterization procedures and the Saint Francis/Mount Sinai Regional Cancer Center. In addition to its main campuses (Saint Francis and Mount Sinai Rehabilitation) Saint Francis operates health clinics and medical offices in about a dozen surrounding communities. The medical center also operates specialty clinics such as radiology and imaging centers and it maintains a medical laboratory in a joint venture with nearby Bristol Hospital.

Financial Performance

During fiscal 2012 and fiscal 2011 approximately 40% respectively of net patient service revenue was received under the Medicare program; about 15% under the Medicaid program; and almost 20% came from from Blue Cross. The hospital's net loss decreased by 65% in fiscal 2012 compared to the previous year due to net gain on investments and increased income from gifts contributions and donations.

Strategy

Saint Francis has initiated a number of internal cost-reduction efforts to keep its operations and finances healthy. It is also improving its internal information management systems to increase efficiencies at its facilities.

As a sign of economic troubles and health care reform changes in the US market Saint Francis is exploring affiliations with other regional hospitals to improve care and control medical costs. As example: in 2012 Saint Francis established an affiliation with nearby Johnson Memorial Medical Center. It is also involved in efforts by the Connecticut legislature to form a UConn Health Network with the University of Connecticut Health Center and other area providers.

Company Background

Established in 1897 Saint Francis began an affiliation with Mount Sinai Hospital in 1990 and merged with it in 1995. Mount Sinai Hospital originally founded in 1923 was then converted from an acute care center into the Mount Sinai Rehabilitation Hospital.

EXECUTIVES

President and CEO, Christopher M. (Chris) Dadlez
Chief Medical Officer and SVP Medical Affairs, Rolf W. Knoll
SVP Patient Care Services and Chief Nursing Officer, Kathleen M. (Kate) Roche
VP Facilities Support Services and Construction, Robert J. (Bob) Falaguerra
EVP and Chief Physician Executive, Arthur W. DeTore
President and CEO Saint Francis HealthCare Partners Inc., Jess Kupec
VP and CIO, Linda Shanley
SVP; Chief Development Officer; President Saint Francis Foundation, E. Merritt Donough
SVP and CFO, John N. Giamalis
Senior Vp Of Planning, Christopher Hartley
Director Of Radiology Services, Leonard Quartararo
Director Icu/coronary Care Unit, Loraine Mc Cafferty
Sr Vice President Chief Innovation Ofc, Gregory Makoul
Sr Vp Of Marketing Services, James Schepker
Radiology Director, Kathleen Smith
Vice President Human Resources, Dawn L Bryant
Vp Of Finance, David Bittner
Vice President Mission Integration, Stephen T Surprenant
Vice President Finance, Nancy Vincent
Rph, Asmita Bhuva
Director Of Infection Control, David Neville
Vice President Of Mission Integration, Judith Carey
Director Of Physical Therapy, Maura Murray
Senior Vice President Of Operations, Ronald Lapensee
Secretary, Beverly Hudson
Vice Chairman Surgery Dir, Laurie Loiacono
Secretary, Pauline Devino

LOCATIONS

HQ: SAINT FRANCIS HOSPITAL AND MEDICAL CENTER
114 WOODLAND ST, HARTFORD, CT 06105-1208
Phone: 860-714-4000
Web: WWW.STFRANCISCARE.ORG

COMPETITORS

Backus
Bristol Hospital
Connecticut Children' s Medical Center
Griffin Health
Hartford Health Care
Hospital of Central Connecticut
Lawrence & Memorial Hospital
MidState Medical Center
Stamford Health
University of Connecticut Health Center
Yale New Haven Health System

HISTORICAL FINANCIALS

Company Type: Private

Income Statement FYE: September 30

	REVENUE ($ mil.)	NET INCOME ($ mil.)	NET PROFIT MARGIN	EMPLOYEES
09/11	674	(53)	—	3,270
09/10	651	(10)	—	—
09/09	638	(16)	—	—
09/08	616	(72)	—	—
Annual Growth	3.1%	—	—	—

2011 Year-End Financials

Debt ratio: —
Return on equity: (-7.90%)
Cash ($ mil.): 111
Current ratio: 2.00
Long-term debt ($ mil.): —
Dividends
Yield: —
Payout: —
Market value ($ mil.): —

SAINT JOSEPH'S UNIVERSITY

Saint Joseph's University (SJU) provides higher education from its campus on the outskirts of Philadelphia. The Jesuit Catholic university has more than 300 full-time faculty members and an enrollment of about 9000 students. It offers 50 undergraduate majors and 40 graduate and professional study areas including an Ed.D. in Educational Leadership. About 650 undergraduate students attend its College of Professional and Liberal Studies the remainder attend the College of Arts and Sciences and the Haub School of Business. SJU also conducts study abroad honors service and faith learning and other special study programs. SJU was founded in 1851 by the Society of Jesus.

Operations

SJU's academic centers include the Arrupe Center for Business Ethics the Catholic Bioethics Institute the Kinney Center for Autism Education and the Richard Johnson Institute for Anti-Violence. Such centers support SJU's commitment to provide specialized learning programs through community engagement.

Financial Performance

SJU had a budget of some $212 million for fiscal 2013. The university's endowment funds totaled about $170 million as of mid-2012. Undergraduate tuition runs at about $38000 per year.

EXECUTIVES

Associate Vp Marketing And Communications, Joe Lunardi
Asst Vp Alumni Relations, Thomas M Monagham
Asst Vp Govt Relations, Wadell Ridley

LOCATIONS

HQ: SAINT JOSEPH' S UNIVERSITY
5600 CITY AVE, PHILADELPHIA, PA 19131-1376
Phone: 610-660-1000
Web: WWW.SJUHAWKS.COM

PRODUCTS/OPERATIONS

Selected Schools and Colleges

College of Arts and Sciences
College of Professional and Liberal Studies
Haub School of Business

HISTORICAL FINANCIALS

Company Type: Private

Income Statement FYE: May 31

	REVENUE ($ mil.)	NET INCOME ($ mil.)	NET PROFIT MARGIN	EMPLOYEES
05/12	275	(4)	—	1,138
05/11	267	9	3.6%	—
05/09	246	18	7.5%	—
05/09	248	0	—	—
Annual Growth	3.5%	—	—	

2012 Year-End Financials

Debt ratio: —
Return on equity: (-1.60%)
Cash ($ mil.): 58
Current ratio: —
Long-term debt ($ mil.): —
Dividends
Yield: —
Payout: —
Market value ($ mil.): —

SAINT LOUIS UNIVERSITY

This university gives students a SLU of opportunities. Saint Louis University (SLU) is a Jesuit Catholic school offering about 100 undergraduate 70 graduate and a host of professional degree programs through about a dozen schools and colleges including a school of medicine and a campus in Madrid Spain. Most programs require core classes in philosophy and theology. SLU has an enrollment of about 9000 undergraduate and 5000 graduate and professional students. Its student-teacher ratio is 12:1. Saint Louis University was founded in 1818 by Reverend Louis William Du Bourg Catholic Bishop of Louisiana.

Geographic Reach

SLU's students hail from all 50 states and about 70 foreign countries. In addition to its main campus in St. Louis Missouri the university operates a campus in Madrid Spain.

Operations

In addition to its extensive educational programs SLU's students and staff are involved in a number of research projects in areas including cancer molecular biology cardiovascular disease biodefense and neurology and aging.

SLU also operates primary and specialty medical care clinics (some through its SLU Physicians organization) on its medical school campus. The medical campus also includes the SLU Hospital which is owned by Tenet Healthcare but which serves as a primary teaching facility for the university.

Financial Performance

SLU is supported by an endowment of some $880 million as of mid-2011. About two-thirds of the university's revenues come from educational activities (including student tuition and fees) while another third comes from patient care at the medical center campus. It also receives about $62 million in research funding from external partners including government agencies (like the National Institutes of Health) and private foundations.

Strategy

In 2011 SLU completed the construction of its new Health Sciences Education Union building; the center includes an auditorium and medical simulation labs. The university also opened its new Hotel Ignacio a Midtown boutique hotel designed to enhance the neighborhood where its main campus is located.

In addition to expanding its physical facilities the university grows or rearranges its academic departments to meet the needs of students in a changing society and economy. In 2012 it established a College for Public Health and Social Justice combining its previous schools of public health and social work to increase the focus on social justice. It also upgraded its neurosurgery division to an independent department in 2011 due to strong growth in the program. SLU also occasionally partners with other area universities on special degree programs.

To expand its research programs SLU established a cancer education prevention and research center for minority patient groups in late 2012.

Mergers and Acquisitions

SLU added about 20 acres to its campus in 2011 by purchasing several properties to expand its medical center campus. It also acquired a building to expand its Madrid campus.

EXECUTIVES

President, Rev Lawrence H. Biondi, age 76
VP Secretary and General Counsel, William R. Kauffman
VP Advancement and University Relations, Jeff Fowler
Dean Doisy College of Health Sciences, Charlotte B. Royeen
Interim VP Academic Affairs, Ellen F. Harshman
Dean Graduate School and Dean College of Arts and Sciences, Donald G. (Don) Brennan
Dean School of Law, Jeffrey E. Lewis
Interim Dean School of Public Health, Homer Schmitz
VP Facilities Management and Civic Affairs, Kathleen T. Brady
VP Student Development, Kent Porterfield
Manager Research Compliance, Mary Christine McMahon
Registrar and Ombudsperson, John H. Jaffry
Director Marketing and Communications Publications, Laura A. Geiser
Manager Public Safety, Jacqueline A. Jackson
Director Payroll Services, Marsha D. McBride
Accounting Manager, Karen M. Wamhoff
Associate Director Student Financial Services Medical School, Sandra B. (Sandy) Pritt
Director Controller, Gregory K. (Greg) Haney
Treasurer and Chief Investment Officer, Gary L. Whitworth
Assistant VP Business Services, Janice D. Crawford
Director Grounds, Jeffrey R. (Jeff) Macko
Network Architect, Bradley S. (Brad) Frischkorn
Senior Project Manager Electronic Health Records, James E. Hooper Jr.
Vice Chairman, Thomas H. Brouster Sr.
VP Academic Affiars, Manoj Patankar
VP Human Resources, Kenneth Fleischmann
Chairman, John K. Pruellage, age 74
Director University Relations, Clayton Berry
Senior Media Specialist, Jeanette Grider
Director Audit Services, Elizabeth Winchester
Information Security Auditor, Anthony Petralia
Director Office of University Compliance, Kathleen Merlo
Director Office of Diversity and Affirmative Action, Jennifer Scheessele
Risk Management Administrator, Tracy Merton
Administrator Safety and Emergency Preparedness, Sam Simon
Director Department of Public Safety, Michael Lauer
Director Office of Environmental Safety and Services, Mark Haenchen
VP Medical Affairs and Dean School of Medicine, Philip O. Alderson
VP Research, Raymond Tait
Assistant to the President, Bridget Fletcher
Dean School of Nursing, Teri A. Murray
Dean College of Philosophy and Letters, Michael Barber
Interim Dean School for Professional Studies, Jennifer Giancola
Assistant VP University Libraries, Gail M. Staines
Interim VP and CFO, David Heimburger
Interim VP and CIO, Keith Hacke
President and Trustee, Rev Lawrence H. Biondi, age 75
Vice Chairman, Thomas H. Brouster Sr.

LOCATIONS

HQ: SAINT LOUIS UNIVERSITY
221 N GRAND BLVD, SAINT LOUIS, MO 63103-2097
Phone: 314-977-2222
Web: WWW.CONCENTRA.COM

PRODUCTS/OPERATIONS

Colleges Schools and Degree Granting Centers
Advanced Dental Education Center for (CADE)
Arts and Sciences College of
Business John Cook School of
Education and Public Service College of
Engineering Aviation and Technology Parks College of
Health Care Ethics Albert Gnaegi Center for
Health Sciences Doisy College of
Law School of
Madrid Spain Campus
Medicine School of
Nursing School of
Outcomes Research Center for (SLUCOR)
Philosophy and Letters College of
Professional Studies School for
Public Health School of
Social Work School of

HISTORICAL FINANCIALS

Company Type: Private

Income Statement FYE: June 30

	REVENUE ($ mil.)	NET INCOME ($ mil.)	NET PROFIT MARGIN	EMPLOYEES
06/11	829	64	7.8%	7,500
06/10	750	28	3.8%	—
06/09	697	0	—	—
06/08	633	(54)	—	—
Annual Growth	9.4%	—	—	—

2011 Year-End Financials

Debt ratio: —
Return on equity: 7.80%
Cash ($ mil.): 115
Current ratio: —
Long-term debt ($ mil.): —
Dividends
Yield: —
Payout: —
Market value ($ mil.): —

SAINT MARY'S HOSPITAL INC.

LOCATIONS

HQ: SAINT MARY' ' S HOSPITAL INC.
56 FRANKLIN ST STE 1, WATERBURY, CT 067061281
Phone: 2037096000
Web: WWW.STMH.ORG

HISTORICAL FINANCIALS

Company Type: Private

Income Statement FYE: September 30

	REVENUE ($ mil.)	NET INCOME ($ mil.)	NET PROFIT MARGIN	EMPLOYEES
09/13	239	18	7.7%	1,520
09/12	225	15	6.7%	—
Annual Growth	6.1%	22.6%	—	—

2013 Year-End Financials

Debt ratio: —
Return on equity: 7.70%
Cash ($ mil.): 28
Current ratio: 1.30
Long-term debt ($ mil.): —
Dividends
Yield: —
Payout: —
Market value ($ mil.): —

SAINT TAMMANY PARISH HOSPITAL SERVICE DISTRICT 1

St. Tammany Parish Hospital serves communities in St. Tammany Parish and Washington Parish along the northern shores of Lake Ponchartrain in eastern Louisiana. The not-for-profit hospital has about 240 beds and offers acute care diagnostic rehabilitation and community wellness services. It also includes centers and clinics specializing in surgery breast care cardiology and sleep disorders. In addition St. Tammany Parish Hospital operates a home health and hospice agency an outpatient services center and a primary care physicians' office. The company's facilities are served by doctors in St. Tammany Physicians Network.

Geographic Reach

The hospital serves patients in St. Tammany Parish and Washington Parish in southeastern Louisiana.

Financial Performance

More than half of St. Tammany Parish Hospital's billable revenues in 2012 came from insurance companies; Medicare makes up one third while Medicaid and self-pay patients account for about 10% of sales.

Strategy

In response to growing demand for primary care on the North Shore of Lake Ponchartrain in 2013 the hospital broke ground on a $21 million project that will expand the emergency department to treat more mental health-related emergencies.

Company Background

The hospital opened its doors in 1954.

EXECUTIVES

President CEO, Patti Ellish
SVP and COO, Sharon A. Toups

SVP and Chief Medical Officer, Robert Capitelli
SVP and Chief Nursing Officer, Kerry Milton
Sr. VP Chief Financial Officer, Tim C. Lessing

LOCATIONS

HQ: SAINT TAMMANY PARISH HOSPITAL SERVICE DISTRICT 1
1202 S TYLER ST, COVINGTON, LA 70433-2330
Phone: 985-898-4000
Web: WWW.STPH.ORG

PRODUCTS/OPERATIONS

Selected Services and Facilities

Adult Rehabilitation
Adult Rehabilitation Outpatient
Adult Weight Management
Angiography
Breast Center
Bronchoscopy
Cardiac Care (Heart)
Cardiac Cath Lab
Cardiac Rehab Outpatient
Cardiac Rehabilitation
Cardiology
Cardiology Non-Invasive
Center for Wound Care and Hyperbaric Medicine
Colonoscopy
Community Wellness Center
Coumadin Clinic
Covington Surgery Center
Critical Care
CT Scan
Diabetes Education Program
Diagnostic X-ray
EGD (Esophagogastroduodenoscopy)
Embolizations Emergency Services
Endoscopic Retrograde Cholangioancreatography
Endoscopy
ERCP
Esophageal Motility Studies
Family Medical Clinic Franklinton
Fluoroscopy
Gynecologic Surgery
Hospital Medicine
Hospitalist
Hyperbaric Medicine
Intensive Care Unit (ICU)
Interventional Radiology
Kyphoplasty
Labor & Delivery Suite
Lymphedema Management
Mammography
Mary Bird Perkins Cancer Center
MaternalChild Services
Medical Nutrition Therapy
Medical Surgical Nursing Care
MRI
Neonatal Intensive Care Unit
Nephrostograms
New Family Center
Nuclear Medicine
Occupational Therapy
Oncology Nursing Care
Outpatient Pavilion
Pacemaker Clinic
Parenting Center
Pediatric Care
Pediatric Rehabilitation Outpatient
Pediatric Unit
Physical Therapy
Post-Operative Care
Pre-Operative Care
Primary Care Physicians
Prostate Cancer
Prostatectomy
Pulmonary Rehab
Radio Frequency Ablation
Radiology/Imaging
Respiratory Services
Rehabilitation Services
Robotic Surgery
Sigmodoscopy
Sleep Disorders Center
Speech Therapy
St. Tammany Physician's Network Covington
St. Tammany Physician's Network Mandeville
St. Tammany Physician's Network Masonville
Surgery Inpatient
Surgery Outpatient
Ultrasound
Urologic Surgery
Vertebroplasty
Wellness Works
Women's Health
Wound Care

COMPETITORS

Ascension Health
Baton Rouge General
Dynacq Healthcare
General Health System
HCA
MedCath
Medical Properties Trust
Our Lady of the Lake RMC
Regency Hospital
River Parishes Hospital
West Jefferson Medical Center
Woman' s Hospital

HISTORICAL FINANCIALS

Company Type: Private

Income Statement FYE: December 31

	REVENUE ($ mil.)	NET INCOME ($ mil.)	NET PROFIT MARGIN	EMPLOYEES
12/12	225	13	6.1%	1,520
12/11	223	16	7.6%	—
12/09	200	8	4.2%	—
12/08	1	0	—	—
Annual Growth	270.6%	—	—	—

2012 Year-End Financials

Debt ratio: —
Return on equity: 6.10%
Cash ($ mil.): 44
Current ratio: 2.50
Long-term debt ($ mil.): —
Dividends
Yield: —
Payout: —
Market value ($ mil.): —

SAINT THOMAS HOSPITAL

LOCATIONS

HQ: SAINT THOMAS HOSPITAL
4220 HARDING PIKE, NASHVILLE, TN 372052095
Phone: 6152225976

HISTORICAL FINANCIALS

Company Type: Private

Income Statement FYE: June 30

	REVENUE ($ mil.)	NET INCOME ($ mil.)	NET PROFIT MARGIN	EMPLOYEES
06/11	493	60	12.2%	99
06/10	455	60	13.3%	—
Annual Growth	8.4%	(0.2%)	—	—

2011 Year-End Financials

Debt ratio: —
Return on equity: 12.20%
Cash ($ mil.): 35
Current ratio: 2.10
Long-term debt ($ mil.): —
Dividends
Yield: —
Payout: —
Market value ($ mil.): —

SALEM HOSPITAL

Salem Hospital serves the health care needs of residents in and around Oregon's Willamette Valley. The acute care hospital has about 455 beds and a medical staff of more than 440 physicians in more than 45 specialty areas. These include oncology joint replacement obstetrics diabetes weight loss and mental health among others. The not-for-profit hospital provides a range of services from emergency and critical care to rehabilitation and community wellness programs. Its Center for Outpatient Medicine provides cancer care outpatient surgery and imaging services and has a sleep disorders center. Salem Hospital is part of Salem Health which also includes West Valley Hospital and Willamette Health Partners.

The hospital also has a Family Birth Center which offers family-health education services and neo-natal intensive-care services. Additionally it provides space to community support services to benefit families.

As with many health care institutions in this age of reform Salem Hospital is working hard to improve patient experience and the quality of health care it provides while reducing the cost of care and eliminating waste within its systems. In 2012 parent Salem Health reported a 16% reduction in inpatient volumes at Salem Hospital during the period from October 2011 through January 2012. This reduction is key to its decision to reduce its budget over the next year by 30%. Some of the measures it will be taking include improving clinical documentation to ensure payments are received standardizing care processes improving scheduling of surgeries leaving 30 open positions unfilled and cutting another 30 positions.

Inspired by Toyota's lean production processes the hospital entered into a five-year contract with John Black and Associates in 2010 to begin what it projects to be a transformation that will be accomplished incrementally over the next 20 years. Its goal is to improve care using a holistic patient-centered approach and reduce waste in terms of waits inventory and other day-to-day processes.

Salem Hospital set a goal of becoming a Magnet hospital in 2003 and accomplished the feat in 2010. (Only 6% of hospitals in the US have achieved Magnet status.) Magnet certification is awarded to hospitals that meet a set of criteria that measures the quality and strength of their nursing staffs as set by the American Nurses' Credentialing Center an affiliate of the American Nurses Association. Criteria includes patient outcomes job satisfaction and low turnover. In 2009 the hospital opened a new patient tower. The next year it sold its money-losing home care department to LHC Group as a way of cutting operating costs. Salem Hospital operates under the guidance of a 15-member volunteer Board of Trustees.

LOCATIONS

HQ: SALEM HOSPITAL
890 OAK ST SE, SALEM, OR 97301-3905
Phone: 503-561-5200
Web: WWW.SALEMHEALTH.ORG

PRODUCTS/OPERATIONS

Selected Services

Bariatrics
Cancer
Diabetes
Gynecology
Heart
Joint replacement
Neurosciences
Obstetrics
Orthopedics
Pain management
Psychiatric medicine
Psychology
Rehabilitation
Spine
Sleep
Stroke
Weight-loss surgery

COMPETITORS

Adventist Health
Asante Health System
Kadlec Regional Medical Center
Kaiser Foundation Hospitals
Legacy Emanuel Hospital and Health Center
Legacy Health System
Oregon Health & Science University
PeaceHealth Southwest Medical Center
Providence Health & Services

HISTORICAL FINANCIALS

Company Type: Private

Income Statement FYE: September 30

	REVENUE ($ mil.)	NET INCOME ($ mil.)	NET PROFIT MARGIN	EMPLOYEES
09/09	493	20	4.2%	3,400
09/08	2	(1)	—	—
09/04	321	22	7.1%	—
09/03	278	11	4.3%	—
Annual Growth	10.0%	9.7%	—	—

2009 Year-End Financials

Debt ratio: —
Return on equity: 4.20%
Cash ($ mil.): 3
Current ratio: —
Long-term debt ($ mil.): —
Dividends
Yield: —
Payout: —
Market value ($ mil.): —

SAM LEVIN INC.

EXECUTIVES

President and CEO, Robert Levin

LOCATIONS

HQ: SAM LEVIN INC.
301 FITZ HENRY RD, SMITHTON, PA 154798715
Phone: 7248722055
Web: WWW.LEVINFURNITURE.COM

2009 Stores

	No.
Ohio	7
Pennsylvania	7
Total	**14**

COMPETITORS

Ashley Furniture
Bassett Furniture
Havertys
J. C. Penney
Macy' s
Rooms To Go

HISTORICAL FINANCIALS

Company Type: Private

Income Statement FYE: December 31

	REVENUE ($ mil.)	NET INCOME ($ mil.)	NET PROFIT MARGIN	EMPLOYEES
12/13	188	7	3.8%	400
12/12	187	7	4.1%	—
12/11	170	11	6.8%	—
12/10	145	0	—	—
Annual Growth	8.8%	—	—	—

2013 Year-End Financials

Debt ratio: —
Return on equity: 3.80%
Cash ($ mil.): 13
Current ratio: 0.60
Long-term debt ($ mil.): —
Dividends
Yield: —
Payout: —
Market value ($ mil.): —

SAM SWOPE AUTO GROUP LLC

EXECUTIVES

Executive Vice President and Chief Financial, Michael (Mike) Sanderson
Chairman of the Board, Patricia (Patti) Swope
Owner, Dodge Sprinter

LOCATIONS

HQ: SAM SWOPE AUTO GROUP LLC
10 SWOPE AUTOCENTER DR, LOUISVILLE, KY 402991806
Phone: 8122828285
Web:
WWW.SAMSWOPEAUTOGROUP.WISEBUYINGMALL.C
OM

COMPETITORS

AutoNation
Jeff Wyler Automotive
Martin Management Group
Penske Automotive Group
Sonic Automotive

HISTORICAL FINANCIALS

Company Type: Private

Income Statement FYE: December 31

	REVENUE ($ mil.)	NET INCOME ($ mil.)	NET PROFIT MARGIN	EMPLOYEES
12/07	444	59	13.4%	900
12/06	434	57	13.2%	—
12/05	1,598	0	0.0%	—
Annual Growth	(47.2%)	66206.2%	—	—

2007 Year-End Financials

Debt ratio: —
Return on equity: 13.40%
Cash ($ mil.): 12
Current ratio: 0.50
Long-term debt ($ mil.): —
Dividends
Yield: —
Payout: —
Market value ($ mil.): —

SAMARITAN''S PURSE

LOCATIONS

HQ: SAMARITAN' ' S PURSE
801 BAMBOO RD, BOONE, NC 286078721
Phone: 8282621980
Web: WWW.SAMARITANSPURSE.COM

HISTORICAL FINANCIALS

Company Type: Private

Income Statement FYE: December 31

	REVENUE ($ mil.)	NET INCOME ($ mil.)	NET PROFIT MARGIN	EMPLOYEES
12/13	473	59	12.5%	525
12/12	389	(35)	—	—
12/11	388	38	9.8%	—
12/08	313	0	—	—
Annual Growth	8.6%	—	—	—

2013 Year-End Financials

Debt ratio: —
Return on equity: 12.50%
Cash ($ mil.): 53
Current ratio: 2.20
Long-term debt ($ mil.): —
Dividends
Yield: —
Payout: —
Market value ($ mil.): —

SAMPSON-BLADEN OIL COMPANY INCORPORATED

LOCATIONS

HQ: SAMPSON-BLADEN OIL COMPANY INCORPORATED
520A E RAILROAD ST, CLINTON, NC 283284304
Phone: 9105924177
Web: WWW.SBOIL.COM

HISTORICAL FINANCIALS

Company Type: Private

Income Statement FYE: October 31

	REVENUE ($ mil.)	NET INCOME ($ mil.)	NET PROFIT MARGIN	EMPLOYEES
10/09	308	(0)	—	280
10/08	449	7	1.7%	—
10/07	1,996	0		
Annual Growth	—	—	—	

2009 Year-End Financials

Debt ratio: —
Return on equity: (-0.20%)
Cash ($ mil.): 11
Current ratio: 0.80
Long-term debt ($ mil.): —
Dividends
Yield: —
Payout: —
Market value ($ mil.): —

SAN DIEGO UNIFIED PORT DISTRICT

EXECUTIVES

Executive Vice President Administration, Karen G. Porteous
EVP, Dan E. Wilkens
President and CEO, Wayne K. Darbeau
Director Communications and Community Services, Irene McCormack
Director General Services, Pedro Cruz
Vice President Strategy & Business Development, Brandy J. Christian
Director Financial Services, Janice Erickson
Senior Director Facilities and Chief Engineer, Charles T. Heinrichs
Chief Harbor Police, Kirk Sanfilippo
Director Purchasing, Garnet (Dave) Thompson
Director Public Art, Catherine Sass
Director Audit Risk Management and Safety, Vilma Sevilla
Director Contracts and Quality Assurance, Gerald H. Wold
Director Information Technology, Adolfo Segura
Port Attorney, Duane E. Bennett
Vice Chairman, Scott H. Peters
Chairman, Ann Moore
Vice Chairman, Bob Nelson
EVP Operations, Randa Coniglio
CFO and Treasurer, Jeff McEntee
Chief Financial Officer, Robert DeAngelis
Commissioner, Robert J. (Rocky) Spane
Commissioner, Stephen P. Cushman
Commissioner, Sylvia C. Rios
Commissioner, Michael B. Bixler

Vice Chairman, Scott H. Peters
Vice Chairman, Bob Nelson
Auditors: KPMG

LOCATIONS

HQ: SAN DIEGO UNIFIED PORT DISTRICT
3165 PACIFIC HWY, SAN DIEGO, CA 921011128
Phone: 6196866200
Web: WWW.PORTOFSANDIEGO.ORG

COMPETITORS

Port of Long Beach
Port of Los Angeles
Port of Seattle

HISTORICAL FINANCIALS

Company Type: Private

Income Statement FYE: June 30

	ASSETS ($ mil.)	NET INCOME ($ mil.)	INCOME AS % OF ASSETS	EMPLOYEES
06/14	692	8	1.2%	604
06/13	677	(4)	—	—
06/12	682	(8)	—	—
06/11	683	0	—	—
Annual Growth	0.4%	—	—	—

2014 Year-End Financials

Debt ratio: —
Return on equity: 5.70%
Cash ($ mil.): 49
Current ratio: 1.70
Long-term debt ($ mil.): —
Dividends
Yield: —
Payout: —
Market value ($ mil.): —

SAN JOAQUIN REFINING CO. INC.

The late Buck Owens is not the only natural resource to come from Bakersfield. California's San Joaquin Valley serves as the backdrop for Bakersfield-based independent refiner San Joaquin Refining which refines locally produced heavy crude oil. The majority of its crude oil is derived from Kern County. San Joaquin Refining's refined products are used in the development of adhesives asphalt electrical insulation lubricants paints plastics printing inks rubber roofing materials and other items. The company also owns more than 90 storage tanks capable of storing 800000 barrels of crude oil.

San Joaquin Refining is located in Kern County which is not only the largest oil-producing county in the San Joaquin Valley but is also the largest oil-producing county in California. The county produces about 600000 barrels of crude oil per day or 8% of total US production and about 1% of the world's output.

The company was founded in 1969.

EXECUTIVES

Vp Supply And Distribution, Mark Del Papa

LOCATIONS

HQ: SAN JOAQUIN REFINING CO. INC.
3129 STANDARD ST, BAKERSFIELD, CA 93308-6242
Phone: 661-327-4257
Web: WWW.SJR.COM

COMPETITORS

Big West Oil
Catlettsburg Refining
El Dorado Refinery
Navajo Refining Company
Paramount Petroleum
Shell Martinez Refinery

HISTORICAL FINANCIALS

Company Type: Private

Income Statement FYE: December 31

	REVENUE ($ mil.)	NET INCOME ($ mil.)	NET PROFIT MARGIN	EMPLOYEES
12/11	567	25	4.5%	20
12/06	371	26	7.1%	—
12/05	288	16	5.7%	—
12/04	215	3	1.6%	—
Annual Growth	14.9%	33.5%	—	—

SAN JUAN REGIONAL MEDICAL CENTER INC.

LOCATIONS

HQ: SAN JUAN REGIONAL MEDICAL CENTER INC.
801 W MAPLE ST, FARMINGTON, NM 874015630
Phone: 5056092000
Web: WWW.SANJUANREGIONAL.COM

HISTORICAL FINANCIALS

Company Type: Private

Income Statement FYE: June 30

	REVENUE ($ mil.)	NET INCOME ($ mil.)	NET PROFIT MARGIN	EMPLOYEES
06/13	250	6	2.5%	1,700
06/12	246	6	2.5%	—
06/11	278	13	5.0%	—
06/10	259	0	—	—
Annual Growth	(1.2%)	—	—	—

2013 Year-End Financials

Debt ratio: —
Return on equity: 2.50%
Cash ($ mil.): 30
Current ratio: 0.70
Long-term debt ($ mil.): —
Dividends
Yield: —
Payout: —
Market value ($ mil.): —

SANFORD-BURNHAM MEDICAL RESEARCH INSTITUTE

EXECUTIVES

CEO, John C. Reed, age 55
Senior Vice President External Relations, Ann Carollo
Senior Director Business Development, Leslie Molony
President, Kristina Vuori
Vice President Drug Discovery and Development, Michael J. Jackson
Executive Vice President Chief Administrative Officer Chief Financial Officer Treasurer, Gary F. Raisl
Communications Manager, Heather Buschman
Vice President Government Relations, Elizabeth Gianini
Vice President Communications, Deborah Robison
Vice President Administration, Cyril Doucet
Interim Senior Vice President External Relations, Blair Blum

LOCATIONS

HQ: SANFORD-BURNHAM MEDICAL RESEARCH INSTITUTE
10901 N TORREY PINES RD, LA JOLLA, CA 920371005
Phone: 8587955000
Web: WWW.SANFORDBURNHAM.ORG

PRODUCTS/OPERATIONS

Selected Research Centers

Del E. Webb Neuroscience Aging and Stem Cell Research Center
Diabetes and Obesity Research Center
Infectious and Inflammatory Disease Center
NCI Cancer Center
Sanford Children's Health Research Center

COMPETITORS

Howard Hughes Medical Institute
Jackson Laboratory
Memorial Sloan-Kettering
Stowers Institute For Medical Research
The Palo Alto Medical Foundation
Whitehead Institute for Biomedical Research

HISTORICAL FINANCIALS

Company Type: Private

Income Statement FYE: June 30

	REVENUE ($ mil.)	NET INCOME ($ mil.)	NET PROFIT MARGIN	EMPLOYEES
06/14	153	16	10.8%	1,157
06/13	152	7	5.1%	—
06/12	162	0	0.5%	—
06/11	163	0	—	—
Annual Growth	(1.9%)	—	—	—

2014 Year-End Financials

Debt ratio: —
Return on equity: 10.80%
Cash ($ mil.): 29
Current ratio: 0.30
Long-term debt ($ mil.): —
Dividends
Yield: —
Payout: —
Market value ($ mil.): —

SAPP BROS. INC.

Need air in those 18 wheels? Sapp Bros Travel Centers (formerly Sapp Bros Truck Stops) has the usual air gas food but also offers human conveniences such such as laundry rooms mailbox rentals private showers and TV lounges. The company operates a chain of some 15 truck stops –readily identifiable by the giant red-and-white coffeepot logo –along interstate highways from Utah to Pennsylvania; with a concentration in Nebraska. Half of the locations also operate service centers offering oil changes new tires and safety checks. Its sister company Sapp Bros Petroleum distributes fuels and lubricants to more than 200 retailers. The firm is run by CEO Bill Sapp one of the four founding Sapp brothers.

Geographic Reach

Omaha-based Sapp Bros. has travel centers in eight states: Nebraska Iowa Utah Colorado Wyoming Kansas Illinois and Pennsylvania.

Strategy

To raise its profile and rev up its business Sapp Bros. in 2013 joined the roster of VP Racing Fuels's retail brand partners. The benefits of the affiliation include association with an attractive retail image competitive credit card rates and the ability to source unbranded fuel for its travel centers.

EXECUTIVES

CFO Secretary and Treasurer, Allen Marsh
President, Don Quinn

LOCATIONS

HQ: SAPP BROS. INC.
9915 S 148TH ST, OMAHA, NE 68138-3876
Phone: 402-895-7038
Web: WWW.SAPPBROSTRUCKSTOPS.COM

2012 Locations

	No.
Nebraska	8
Iowa	2
Colorado	1
Illinois	1
Kansas	1
Pennsylvania	1
Utah	1
Wyoming	1
Total	16

COMPETITORS

Exxon Mobil
Love' s Country Stores
Pilot Flying J
Stuckey' s
TravelCenters of America

HISTORICAL FINANCIALS

Company Type: Private

Income Statement FYE: September 30

	REVENUE ($ mil.)	NET INCOME ($ mil.)	NET PROFIT MARGIN	EMPLOYEES
09/12	1,677	13	0.8%	1,115
09/11	1,271	14	1.2%	—
09/10	718	9	1.3%	—
09/09	485	9	2.0%	—
Annual Growth	51.1%	11.7%	—	—

2012 Year-End Financials

Debt ratio: —
Return on equity: 0.80%
Cash ($ mil.): 6
Current ratio: 1.00
Long-term debt ($ mil.): —
Dividends
Yield: —
Payout: —
Market value ($ mil.): —

SAPP BROS. PETROLEUM INC.

There have been few poor saps in this family since the Sapp brothers made a go of their petroleum products business. Sapp Bros Petroleum distributes petroleum products such as fuels lubricants propane antifreeze absorbents additives and equipment through more than 10 locations in Nebraska and western Iowa. It has a sideline selling used computer parts such as modems processors and keyboards. The regional fuel distributor was founded by the four Sapp brothers in 1980 and is run by CEO Bill Sapp who also runs sister company Sapp Bros Truck Stops.

EXECUTIVES

CFO, Allen Marsh
General Manager Fuel and Propane, Darrell Henson
General Manager Lubricant Products, Ken Broz
General Manager Trucks and Retail Propane, Chriz Klotz
Fuel and Propane Sales, Eric Ziph
Lubricant Sales, Ron Kritenbrink
Lubricant Sales, Brian Swearingen
Lubricant Sales, Josh Broz
Lubricant Sales, Todd Bell
General Manager, Bill Young
President, Keith Crandall
Office Manager, Jeannea Sybesma

LOCATIONS

HQ: SAPP BROS. PETROLEUM INC.
9915 S 148TH ST STE 2, OMAHA, NE 68138-3876
Phone: 402-895-2202
Web: WWW.SAPPBROSPETRO.COM

COMPETITORS

Exxon Mobil
Shell Oil Products

HISTORICAL FINANCIALS

Company Type: Private

Income Statement FYE: October 31

	REVENUE ($ mil.)	NET INCOME ($ mil.)	NET PROFIT MARGIN	EMPLOYEES
10/09	563	5	1.0%	285
10/08	922	3	0.3%	—
10/07	1,566	0	—	—
Annual Growth	—19890.6%			—

2009 Year-End Financials

Debt ratio: —
Return on equity: 1.00%
Cash ($ mil.): 2
Current ratio: 1.10
Long-term debt ($ mil.): —
Dividends
Yield: —
Payout: —
Market value ($ mil.): —

SARAH BUSH LINCOLN HEALTH CENTER

With the moniker of the Illinois' favorite son's stepmother (Sarah Bush Lincoln) who wouldn't want to go to this health center? And apparently the locals agree since Sarah Bush Lincoln Health Center (SBLHC) has a market share of about 44% in its seven-county service area in east central Illinois and an inpatient market share for Coles County of nearly 80%. SBLHC has 128 beds and provides a wide range of health care services including emergency medicine behavioral health care surgical services and cancer treatment. The center also offers support groups and continuing education classes.

Geographic Reach

The regional hospital is centrally located in East Central Illinois' Coles County and serves seven counties.

Operations

The health center has expanded its behavioral health services by joining forces with the Coles County Mental Health Center (now Life Links) and the Human Resources Center of Edgar and Clark to create the Regional Behavioral Health Network an organization that expands access to mental health care for people in crisis. Together the three firms respond to about 3000 crises inquires for behavioral health services annually. The collaborative effort is partially funded by grants.

SBLHC has also expanded its Lincolnland Home Care and Hospice services to cover nearly two dozen counties.

Strategy

To enhance care and convenience to people who are hospitalized SBLHC introduced a Hospitalist program in 2011. Jospitalists are more available throughout the day to talk with patients and their family members follow up on test results answer nurses' questions and respond quickly to issues that may arise.

As part of an ongoing expansion drive SBLHC opened a second medical office building at its main campus in 2011. The two-story clinic allows Orthopedics and Sports Medicine room to expand to accommodate the needs of the community. Physical and Occupational Therapy services are also housed in the new facility. The therapy area includes three therapy gyms a therapy pool locker room and a massage room. Lincolnland Home Care and Hospice Human Resources Employee and Organizational Development and Health Occupations occupy the building's second floor.

To better accommodate the community and keep up with changing technology and healthcare needs SBLHC also launched a $48 million expansion and renovation project in 2011. The three-year plan calls for the renovation and expansion of the Emergency Room surgical suites and the laboratory and the conversion of some units to private patient rooms.

Company Background

SBLHC opened its doors in 1977. It was named after President Abraham Lincoln's stepmother Sarah Bush Lincoln.

EXECUTIVES

President and CEO, Gary L. Barnett
CFO, Craig Sheagren
President and CEO, Timothy Ols
VP Operations, Dennis Pluard
VP Medical Affairs, James Hildebrandt
VP Patient Care Services, Mary Lou Wild
Chairman, Scott Lensink

LOCATIONS

HQ: SARAH BUSH LINCOLN HEALTH CENTER
1000 HEALTH CENTER DR, MATTOON, IL 61938-9261
Phone: 217-258-2525
Web: WWW.SARAHBUSH.ORG

PRODUCTS/OPERATIONS

Selected Programs/Services

Advanced Wound Center
Audiology
Center for Interventional Pain
Emergency Department
EMS
Gastroenterology
Heart Center
Hospitalist Program
Laboratory
Lifeline
Lincolnland Hospice
Lincolnland Home Care
Orthopedics and Sports Medicine
Outpatient Surgery Center
Patient Care
Physical Medicine & Rehabilitation
Psychiatry and Counseling
Radiology
Regional Cancer Center
Women and Children's Center

COMPETITORS

Carle Hospital
Crawford Memorial Hospital
Decatur Memorial Hospital
Hospital Sisters Health System
Iroquois Memorial Hospital
Memorial Health System (Colorado)
Memorial Medical Center
St. John' s Hospital (Illinois)

HISTORICAL FINANCIALS

Company Type: Private

Income Statement FYE: June 30

	REVENUE ($ mil.)	NET INCOME ($ mil.)	NET PROFIT MARGIN	EMPLOYEES
06/12	200	18	9.0%	1,543
06/11	195	14	7.2%	—
06/08	132	(6)	—	—
06/08	0	(0)	—	—
Annual Growth	290.2%	—	—	—

2012 Year-End Financials

Debt ratio: —
Return on equity: 9.00%
Cash ($ mil.): 89
Current ratio: 1.60
Long-term debt ($ mil.): —
Dividends
Yield: —
Payout: —
Market value ($ mil.): —

SARGENT ELECTRIC COMPANY

EXECUTIVES

COO, Gary W. Groom
President and CEO, Stephan H. (Steve) Dake
CFO, Elizabeth A. (Beth) Lawrence
CEO Sargent Safety Services, Gregory A. (Greg) Woodworth
SVP Operations, Richard S. (Dick) Rectenwald
General Manager Northwest Indiana, Thomas (Tom) Frame
General Manager Terre Haute, Charles E. (Chuck) Wheat
General Manager Commercial, Mark Staudt
General Manager Industrial, Jim Voss

LOCATIONS

HQ: SARGENT ELECTRIC COMPANY
2767 LIBERTY AVE, PITTSBURGH, PA 152224703
Phone: 4123388480
Web: WWW.SARGENT.COM

COMPETITORS

EMCOR
Fisk Electric
Integrated Electrical Services
Limbach Facility Services
MYR Group
Miller Electric
Miller Electric Co

HISTORICAL FINANCIALS

Company Type: Private

Income Statement FYE: December 31

	REVENUE ($ mil.)	NET INCOME ($ mil.)	NET PROFIT MARGIN	EMPLOYEES
12/13	187	10	5.5%	400
12/11	89	0	0.4%	—
12/10	79	0	0.8%	—
12/09	107	0	—	—
Annual Growth	14.9%	—	—	—

2013 Year-End Financials

Debt ratio: —
Return on equity: 5.50%
Cash ($ mil.): 0
Current ratio: 1.70
Long-term debt ($ mil.): —
Dividends
Yield: —
Payout: —
Market value ($ mil.): —

SATTERFIELD AND PONTIKES CONSTRUCTION INC.

Satterfield & Pontikes Construction (S&P) provides general contracting consultation and construction management services primarily in the Gulf Coast region of Texas and Louisiana. The company often works on buildings for the commercial retail industrial educational entertainment and recreational sectors. High profile projects include the Texas A&M University Health Science Center and the expansion of the World War II Museum in New Orleans. S&P specializes in concrete work and early-stage site work as well as 3-D modeling and virtual design. The company was founded in 1989 and is headed by majority owner and CEO George Pontikes.

S&P works from offices in Houston Dallas/Fort Worth New Orleans San Antonio and Austin.

The firm has looked outside of the Gulf Region for work. In 2011 it was chosen by Delta Air Lines to work on the $1.2 billion expansion of a terminal and the demolition of another at JFK International airport in New York.

EXECUTIVES

President CEO, George A. Pontikes Jr.
Vice President, John Marshall
Executive Vice President, Laura Pontikes
Dallas and Ft. Worth Business Unit, George West
Vice President Houston, Kenneth Smith
Chief Financial Officer, Anjy Salinas
Vice President San Antonio, Brad Shearer
Executive Vice President, Charles T. Fote
Senior Vice President, Frank M. Roetzel
Senior Vice President Dallas/Fort Worth/San Antonio/New Orleans, Jason D. Haralson
Auditors: Melton&MeltonLLP

LOCATIONS

HQ: SATTERFIELD AND PONTIKES CONSTRUCTION INC.
11000 EQUITY DR STE 100, HOUSTON, TX 77041-8235
Phone: 713-996-1300
Web: WWW.SATPON.COM

PRODUCTS/OPERATIONS

Selected Services

Building information modeling
Construction
Construction management
Design build
Development
Green building
Practical Project Delivery

COMPETITORS

Balfour Construction
C.F. Jordan
Falkenberg Construction
Skanska USA Building
Spawglass Holding
Turner Corporation

HISTORICAL FINANCIALS

Company Type: Private

Income Statement FYE: December 31

	REVENUE ($ mil.)	NET INCOME ($ mil.)	NET PROFIT MARGIN	EMPLOYEES
12/12	377	(8)	—	300
12/11	388	0	0.1%	—
12/09	445	8	1.9%	—
12/09	482	11	2.3%	—
Annual Growth	(7.8%)	—	—	—

2012 Year-End Financials

Debt ratio: —
Return on equity: (-2.30%)
Cash ($ mil.): 27
Current ratio: 1.00
Long-term debt ($ mil.): —
Dividends
Yield: —
Payout: —
Market value ($ mil.): —

SAVE THE CHILDREN FEDERATION INC.

Save the Children helps poor and malnourished children in about 15 US states and about 120 countries focusing on such areas as health and nutrition economic development education child protection and the HIV/AIDS epidemic. The humanitarian organization also participates in international disaster relief efforts for children and their families. It spends about 90% of its budget on program services with the rest going toward administration and fundraising. Save the Children was founded in 1932 inspired by the international children's rights movement begun in the UK in 1919 by Eglantyne Jebb founder of the British Save the Children Fund. It is a member of the International Save the Children Alliance.

Geographic Reach

Save the Children operates programs in nearly 120 countries including the US. It is made up of 29 member organizations worldwide.

Financial Performance

The global aid organization's revenue declined by 3.5% in 2012 versus 2011 due largely to a 12% decline in private gifts grants and contributions which account for nearly half of its total revenue. Save the Children directed 89% of its expenses to programs which benefit children and allow the humanitarian organization to keep private costs (includes fundraising and management and general) at about 10% is one of the best ratios for nonprofit organizations.

EXECUTIVES

Chairperson, Anne M. Mulcahy, age 62
SVP and Managing Director U.S. Programs, Mark Shriver
President CEO and Trustee, Carolyn S. Miles, age 52
Vice President International Programs, Diana K. Myers
Vice Chairman, Mark V. Mactas
Vice Chairperson, Cokie Roberts
Corporate Secretary, Andrea Williamson-Hughes
VP Strategic Operations, Tom Krift
Director Office of Stakeholder Accountability and Senior Advisor to the President, Dick Staufenberger
VP Resource Development, Barbara Erickson
VP Finance and CFO, Rick Trowbridge
VP Policy and Humanitarian Response, Michael Klosson

VP Marketing and Communications, Susan Ridge
VP U.S. Programs, Kathy Spangler
President, Rick Stoner
Vice President Human Resources, Mona Lau
Vice President General Counsel, Gretchen Wagner
Executive Vice President & Chief Operating Officer, Carlos Carrazana
Vice President Resource Development, Robert Thompson
Trustee, Susan L. Decker, age 51
Trustee, Joseph (Joe) Mandato, age 70
Trustee, Pernille Spiers-Lopez
Trustee, Andrea L. Rich, age 70
Trustee, Thomas S. Murphy
President CEO and Trustee, Carolyn S. Miles, age 52
Trustee, Charlotte M. Guyman
Trustee, Bill Haber
Vice Chairman, Mark V. Mactas
Trustee, Heath B. McLendon
Trustee, Henry S. Miller
Trustee, Bradley C. Palmer
Trustee and Chairman Save the Children International, Charles R. Perrin
Vice Chairperson, Cokie Roberts
Trustee, Randall S. Eisenberg
Trustee, David J. Mastrocola
Trustee, Sunil Sani

LOCATIONS

HQ: SAVE THE CHILDREN FEDERATION INC.
54 WILTON RD, WESTPORT, CT 06880-3131
Phone: 203-221-4000
Web: WWW.SAVETHECHILDREN.ORG

2012 Expenditures

% of total	
Asia	43
Africa	34
Latin America	9
Middle East	7
US	7
Total	**100**

Selected Countries of Operation

Australia
Brazil
Canada
Denmark
Dominican Republic
Fiji
Finland
Germany
Guatemala
Honduras
Hong Kong
Iceland
India
Italy
Japan
Jordan
Korea
Lithuania
Mexico
Netherlands
New Zealand
Norway
Romania
South Africa
Spain
Swaziland
Sweden
Switzerland
United Kingdom
United States

PRODUCTS/OPERATIONS

2012 Revenue

	$ mil.	% of total
Private gifts grants & contracts	286	48
US government grants & contracts	174	29
Commodities & ocean freight	72	12
Child sponsorship	48	8
Other	15	3
Total	**597**	**100**

HISTORICAL FINANCIALS

Company Type: Private

Income Statement

FYE: September 30

	REVENUE ($ mil.)	NET INCOME ($ mil.)	NET PROFIT MARGIN	EMPLOYEES
09/07	356	9	2.8%	3,000
09/06	332	20	6.3%	—
09/05	1,710	0	0.0%	—
Annual Growth	(54.4%)	2354.7%	—	—

2007 Year-End Financials

Debt ratio: —
Return on equity: 2.80%
Cash ($ mil.): 63
Current ratio: 0.80
Long-term debt ($ mil.): —
Dividends
Yield: —
Payout: —
Market value ($ mil.): —

SAWNEE ELECTRIC MEMBERSHIP CORPORATION

Sawnee Electric Membership Corporation (Sawnee EMC) wasn't around on the night the lights went out in Georgia but it plans to make sure they stay on. The electric distribution cooperative serves about 152000 ,Âresidential commercial and industrial meters in a seven-county area of northern ,ÂGeorgia comprised of Cherokee Dawson Forsyth Fulton Gwinnett Hall and Lumpkin counties. Residential customers in the area (which includes the sprawling ,ÂAtlanta suburbs) account for two-thirds of electricity usage. While small and medium users must get their electricity from Sawnee potential customers with loads exceeding 900 kilowatts can shop around. Sawnee EMC distributes electricity over 9970 miles of power line.

The cooperative provides ,Âits members with the option of gas service through a partnership with Coweta-Fayette EMC Natural Gas a subsidiary of fellow Georgia-based power co-op Coweta-Fayette EMC. In 2010 it had 16000 Sawnee EMC customers participating in this arrangement.

As part of its commitment to green energy Sawnee EMC has also teamed up with Green-e Energy a leading national renewable energy certification and verification program to offer certified renewable power to Sawnee EMC members. It is encouraging its members to conserve energy and help keep down costs offering home energy audits installing Smart meters and encouraging the use of ,Âenergy-efficient light bulbs.

In 2010 Sawnee EMC reported a jump in revenues and operating income thanks to a growth in its membership and higher energy use due to a hotter-than-usual summer.

The company was founded as the Forsyth County Electric Membership Corporation in 1938 as part of the Roosevelt government's national rural electrification drive. It was renamed for local landmark ,ÂSawnee ,ÂMountain ,Âin 1950.

EXECUTIVES

V Pres- Office Services, Bill Parsons
Vp, Larry Kohn
Vice President Operations, Chet Blackstock
Vice President, Jack Hylton
Vice President Of Engineering, Greg Farr
Treasurer, Lamar V Sexton

LOCATIONS

HQ: SAWNEE ELECTRIC MEMBERSHIP CORPORATION
543 ATLANTA RD, CUMMING, GA 300402701
Phone: 7708872363
Web: WWW.SAWNEE.COM

PRODUCTS/OPERATIONS

2011 Power Customers

% of total	
Residential	90
Commercial &	10
Total	**100**

COMPETITORS

Cobb EMC
Georgia Power
Jackson Electric Membership

HISTORICAL FINANCIALS

Company Type: Private

Income Statement

FYE: December 31

	REVENUE ($ mil.)	NET INCOME ($ mil.)	NET PROFIT MARGIN	EMPLOYEES
12/13	335	0	—	300
12/12	325	0	—	—
12/08	0	(0)	—	—
12/03	201	0	—	—
Annual Growth	5.2%	—	—	—

2013 Year-End Financials

Debt ratio: —
Return on equity: —
Cash ($ mil.): 23
Current ratio: 1.10
Long-term debt ($ mil.): —
Dividends
Yield: —
Payout: —
Market value ($ mil.): —

SCHEWEL FURNITURE COMPANY INCORPORATED

Schewel Furniture Company operates about 50 retail furniture and bedding stores in Virginia West Virginia and North Carolina. In addition to home furnishings the chain sells appliances electronics carpeting and related accessories. Typical store units average 18000 sq. ft. and primarily target the lower- and middle-income markets. Newer stores are larger in the 40000-55000 square foot range. Customers can also browse furniture collections and other items available at Schewel stores through the company's Web site. The family-run company now in its fourth generation of management got its start in 1897 when Elias Schewel began selling small furniture pieces out of his horse-drawn wagon.

EXECUTIVES

V Pres, Wes Moreland, age 67
Treas-controller, William S Sprinkle, age 67

LOCATIONS

HQ: SCHEWEL FURNITURE COMPANY INCORPORATED
1031 MAIN ST, LYNCHBURG, VA 245041800
Phone: 4348452326
Web: WWW.SCHEWELS.COM

COMPETITORS

Ashley Furniture
Grand Home Furnishings

Bassett Furniture
Flooring America
Furnitureland South
Havertys
Rooms To Go
Rowe Fine Furniture

HISTORICAL FINANCIALS

Company Type: Private

Income Statement FYE: March 31

	REVENUE ($ mil.)	NET INCOME ($ mil.)	NET PROFIT MARGIN	EMPLOYEES
03/14	121	4	3.7%	850
03/13	121	6	5.3%	—
03/12	117	3	3.3%	—
03/11	111	0	—	—
Annual Growth	3.0%	—	—	—

2014 Year-End Financials

Debt ratio: —
Return on equity: 3.70%
Cash ($ mil.): 8
Current ratio: 1.50
Long-term debt ($ mil.): —

Dividends
Yield: —
Payout: —
Market value ($ mil.): —

SCHUMACHER ELECTRIC CORPORATION

EXECUTIVES

Chairman and CEO, Donald A. (Don) Schumacher
MIS Director, Bob Gorny
CFO, Daniel Frano
CTO, Chris Hadsall

LOCATIONS

HQ: SCHUMACHER ELECTRIC CORPORATION
801 E BUSINESS CENTER DR, MOUNT PROSPECT, IL 600562179
Phone: 8473851600
Web: WWW.BATTERYCHARGERS.COM

PRODUCTS/OPERATIONS

Selected Products

Battery chargers
- Deep cycle chargers
- Farm and ranch chargers
- Gel cell chargers
- Hand-held continuous charge chargers
- Hand-held continuous charge with engine start
- Jump starter and DC power sources
- Maintainer/slow/trickle chargers
- Wheel-style starters/chargers

Transformers
- Audio
- Ferro-resonant
- Power
- Inductors

Welding equipment and accessories
- Abrasives and wire wheels
- ARC welders
- Gas welding rods
- MIG welders
- Plasma cutters
- Torch outfits
- Welding electrodes
- Welding tools

COMPETITORS

AMETEK
Airgas
Charles Industries
ENGlobal
EnerSys
Gexpro
Havells Sylvania
Honda
Lincoln Electric
Metalcraft
OSRAM
SL Industries
Snap-on
Valley National Gases

HISTORICAL FINANCIALS

Company Type: Private

Income Statement FYE: December 31

	REVENUE ($ mil.)	NET INCOME ($ mil.)	NET PROFIT MARGIN	EMPLOYEES
12/13	142	2	2.1%	125
12/03	85	0	—	—
12/02	0	0	—	—
12/01	0	0	—	—
Annual Growth	—	—	—	—

2013 Year-End Financials

Debt ratio: —
Return on equity: 2.10%
Cash ($ mil.): 6
Current ratio: 2.10
Long-term debt ($ mil.): —

Dividends
Yield: —
Payout: —
Market value ($ mil.): —

SCIENTIFIC RESEARCH CORP

Scientific Research Corporation (SRC) doesn't limit its services to the laboratory. The government contractor provides a wide variety of engineering and research services including consulting systems engineering project management network design hardware and software development prototyping testing and evaluation systems integration and training. Its expertise encompasses communications and intelligence systems electronic warfare simulation and instrumentation systems. In some cases SRC works as a subcontractor for larger companies such as Booz Allen. SRC's clients include the US government and military state agencies and private sector businesses.

Operations The company's integrated systems and solutions division specializes in software development network engineering systems automation digital signal processing production engineering and logistical support services for intelligence systems. It also provides other IT and wireless network support services. SRC's simulation test and instrumentation division offers products and engineering services to support surveillance radar and instrumentation systems. It also develops sensor systems and provides interoperability testing services for military weapons systems. The company's communications networks and electronics unit provides research and development systems integration design deployment and support services for military and commercial communications and network systems.

Geographic Reach SRC operates from about 15 offices located mainly in the southern and eastern US; it also has a few facilities in the Southwest and in California.

EXECUTIVES

CEO, Michael L. (Mike) Watt, age 52
CFO and Secretary, Thomas L. Papst
Senior Vice President, Larrie Judd
Vice President, Todd Marek
Executive Vice President For Operations, Tim Washington
Vice President Human Resources, Sandra Holtzclaw

LOCATIONS

HQ: SCIENTIFIC RESEARCH CORP
2300 WINDY RIDGE PKWY SE 400S, ATLANTA, GA 30339-5665
Phone: 770-859-9161
Web: WWW.SCIRES.COM

COMPETITORS

Boeing
CACI International
Computer Sciences Corp.
HP Enterprise Services
Leidos
Lockheed Martin
Long Wave
ManTech
Northrop Grumman
QinetiQ
Raytheon
Research Triangle Institute
SRA International
Serco Inc.

HISTORICAL FINANCIALS

Company Type: Private

Income Statement FYE: December 31

	REVENUE ($ mil.)	NET INCOME ($ mil.)	NET PROFIT MARGIN	EMPLOYEES
12/12	360	26	7.3%	1,006
12/11	326	21	6.7%	—
12/10	322	22	6.9%	—
12/08	226	13	6.0%	—
Annual Growth	12.2%	17.7%	—	—

2012 Year-End Financials

Debt ratio: —
Return on equity: 7.30%
Cash ($ mil.): 34
Current ratio: 1.50
Long-term debt ($ mil.): —

Dividends
Yield: —
Payout: —
Market value ($ mil.): —

SCOTT & WHITE HEALTH PLAN

The Scott & White Health Plan (SWHP) works to keep its members Safe & Well. The not-for-profit company provides health insurance plans and related services to more than 200000 members across some 50 counties in and around Central Texas. Owned by the Scott & White network of hospitals and clinics SWHP has employer-sponsored plans (including HMO PPO and consumer choice options) as well as several choices for individuals and families. It also offers COBRA state-administered continuation plans the Young Texan Health Plan for children Medicare and dental and vision benefits. The company began offering its services in 1982. Owner Scott & White is exploring a merger with Baylor Health Care System.

In late 2012 the boards of Scott & White and Baylor Health Care System signed an agreement of their intent to merge to form a $7.7 billion organization called Baylor Scott & White Health. The combined organization will be the largest not-for-profit health system in Texas with 42 hospitals more than 350 patient care sites more than 4000 active physicians 34000 employees and the Scott & White Health Plan.

EXECUTIVES

CEO, Allan Einboden
Associate Executive Director Sales and Marketing Operations, Lee Green

LOCATIONS

HQ: SCOTT & WHITE HEALTH PLAN
1206 WEST CAMPUS DR, TEMPLE, TX 76502-7124
Phone: 254-298-3000
Web: WWW.SWHP.ORG

PRODUCTS/OPERATIONS

Selected Products
Employer plans
Individual and family plans
Medicare plans
Vital Care programs

COMPETITORS

Aetna
Blue Cross and Blue Shield of Texas
CIGNA
Centene
Humana
Mercy Health Plans
Texas Health Resources
USHEALTH Group
UnitedHealth Group

HISTORICAL FINANCIALS

Company Type: Private

Income Statement FYE: December 31

	REVENUE ($ mil.)	NET INCOME ($ mil.)	NET PROFIT MARGIN	EMPLOYEES
12/09	660	13	2.0%	426
12/08	621	(4)	—	—
12/07	586	8	1.4%	—
12/06	557	3	0.7%	—
Annual Growth	5.8%	54.1%	—	—

2009 Year-End Financials

Debt ratio: —
Return on equity: 2.00%
Cash ($ mil.): 8
Current ratio: 1.40
Long-term debt ($ mil.): —
Dividends
Yield: —
Payout: —
Market value ($ mil.): —

SCOTT & WHITE MEMORIAL HOSPITAL

Scott & White Healthcare serves the health care needs of Central Texas. The not-for-profit health care organization is a multi-specialty physician-led system with a dozen hospital sites and more than 60 regional clinics; it also has affiliate entities throughout the area. The network has more than 1700 licensed beds and 900 associated doctors. Scott & White's flagship campus in Temple with about 640 beds includes a children's hospital a long-term acute care hospital and a mental health clinic. It also owns health maintenance organization Scott & White Health Plan and is a teaching affiliate of Texas A&M University. Founded in the 1890s Scott & White has agreed to merge with Baylor Health Care System.

Change in Company Type

In late 2012 the boards of Scott & White Healthcare and Baylor Health Care System signed an agreement of their intent to merge to form a $7.7 billion organization called Baylor Scott & White Health. The combined organization will be the largest not-for-profit health system in Texas with 42 hospitals more than 350 patient care sites more than 4000 active physicians 34000 employees and the Scott & White Health Plan. A definitive agreement is expected in 2013.

Strategy

Scott & White has adopted a strategy to enhance its presence as a managed care network and attract more complex cases through greater market share and broader integrated delivery systems. To that end it is expanding its hospital and clinic operations. Fiscal 2011 revenues for the network increased from the previous year by about 8% due to its acquisitions.

Scott & White has been steadily expanding its geographic range throughout Central Texas both through acquisitions and by building new facilities in rapidly growing communities. Its hospitals are located in Brenham Llano Round Rock Taylor Temple and Waco with two more being constructed in College Station (scheduled to open in 2013 with more than 140 beds) and Marble Falls (construction started in late 2011). Acquisitions have included the purchase of the King's Daughters Hospital in Temple in 2009. Following the purchase Scott & White converted the hospital into a 64-bed facility to house the Scott & White Children's Hospital which is located on the Scott & White Hospital - Temple campus which also houses the only Level I Trauma Center between Austin and Dallas.

Scott & White expanded further by acquiring the 25-bed Johns Community Hospital in Taylor in 2010 (fiscal 2011). It also formed a partnership with the 60-bed Trinity Medical Center in Brenham that year. The hospitals now operate as Scott & White Hospital - Taylor and Scott & White Hospital - Brenham. In January 2011 Scott & White purchased Llano County Hospital Authority dba Llano Memorial Healthcare System and renamed the entity Scott & White Hospital - Llano.

In late 2011 Scott & White broke ground on the Wayne & Eileen Hurd Regional Medical Center - Scott & White a hospital that will have 72 beds and 12 ICU beds in Marble Falls Texas. The 200000-sq.-ft. hospital will be constructed in phases and when completed will also include a specialty physician clinic and a surgical and diagnostic center.

EXECUTIVES

President Scott & White, Alfred B. Knight
CEO Scott & White Health Plan, Allan Einboden
President and CEO, Robert W. Pryor, age 63
Medical Director, Kathleen A Jones
Medical Director, Christopher D Spradley
Vice President Of Claims, Brenda Lee
Associate Vice President Health System, Susan Watson
Director Of Nursing, Sherry Perry
Vice President Sales And Marketing, Lee Green
Assoc Vice President Rco, Alice Cantu
Vp Of Quality Improvement, Terry Long
Director Physician Recruitment, Stephanie Hobson
Director Of Physical Therapy, Scott Snell
Associate Vice President Information, Tom Maden
Associate Vice President Information Technology Audit, Tom Tharp
Vice President Information Technology Service Management, Jay Yellott
Vice President Learning & Training, Don Cauthen
Vice President, Martin Prince
Vice President Facilities And Constructon, Scott Liles
Vice President Quality And Patient, Terry Greetis
Vice President Medical Delivery, Maria Rasalan
Vice President Information Technology, Jay Hamilton
Vice President For Development, Brian Quiroz
Vice President Information Systems, Mike Maguire
Vice President Medicare Programs, Mitch Brodsky
Vice President, Charley Gomez
Clinic Manager, Eduardo Lara
Associate Vice President Systems, Margaret Patel
Associate Vice President Finance, Travis Smith
Auditors: Ernst&YoungLLP

LOCATIONS

HQ: SCOTT & WHITE MEMORIAL HOSPITAL
2401 S 31ST ST, TEMPLE, TX 76508-0001
Phone: 254-724-2111
Web: WWW.CAREERS.SW.ORG

PRODUCTS/OPERATIONS

2011 Revenues

	$ mil.	% of total
Patient services & premiums	1,996	96
Other	91	4
Total	2,088	100

Selected Texas Facilities
Children's Hospital at Scott & White - Temple
Scott & White Hospital - Brenham
Scott & White Hospital - College Station (scheduled to open in 2013)
Scott & White Hospital - Llano
Scott & White Hospital - Round Rock
Scott & White Hospital -Taylor
Scott & White Hospital -Temple
Temple Continuing Care Hospital
Waco Hillcrest Baptist Medical Center
Wayne & Eileen Hurd Regional Medical Center - Scott & White (under construction in 2012)

Selected Centers and Institutes
Bone and Joint Institute
Cancer Institute
Cosmetic Surgery Center
Eye Institute
Heart and Vascular Institute
Neuroscience Institute
Sleep Institute
Women's Health Services

COMPETITORS

Baylor Health
Community Health Systems
Cook Children' s Health Care System
Dell Children' s Medical Center
HCSC
Hill Country
Seton Healthcare Network
Shriners Hospitals For Children
St. David' s Health Care
St. David' s Round Rock Medical Center
Texas Children' s Hospital

HISTORICAL FINANCIALS

Company Type: Private

Income Statement FYE: August 31

	REVENUE ($ mil.)	NET INCOME ($ mil.)	NET PROFIT MARGIN	EMPLOYEES
08/11	1,446	91	6.3%	8,000
08/10	902	41	4.6%	—
08/09	814	0	0.0%	—
08/06	804	0	—	—
Annual Growth	12.5%	—	—	—

2011 Year-End Financials

Debt ratio: —
Return on equity: 6.30%
Cash ($ mil.): 84
Current ratio: 1.50
Long-term debt ($ mil.): —
Dividends
Yield: —
Payout: —
Market value ($ mil.): —

SCOTT EQUIPMENT COMPANY L.L.C.

Scott Equipment Company sells and rents construction and farm equipment through some 25 locations located in the South and Midwest. The company also offers parts and service financing and insurance. Scott Equipment is part of the Scott family of companies which also includes Scott Toyota Lift (material handling) Scott Irrigation (pivot irrigation systems) and Scott Truck (sales leasing and service). The company's beginnings date back to 1939 when Tom Scott founded Scott Truck & Tractor. It is operated by descendants of the founder. Scott Equipment has shut down several agricultural stores (Scott Tractor) to focus on its Construction Equipment division.

EXECUTIVES

President, Scott Cummins

LOCATIONS

HQ: SCOTT EQUIPMENT COMPANY L.L.C.
1002 HWY 165 BY PASS, MONROE, LA 71203
Phone: 318-387-4160
Web: WWW.SCOTTCOMPANIES.COM

COMPETITORS

Briggs Equipment
Deere
H&E Equipment
J. A. Riggs Tractor
Komatsu America
Mustang CAT
Rain Bird Corporation
Van Keppel

HISTORICAL FINANCIALS

Company Type: Private

Income Statement FYE: December 31

	REVENUE ($ mil.)	NET INCOME ($ mil.)	NET PROFIT MARGIN	EMPLOYEES
12/08	317	12	4.0%	525
12/07	323	17	5.5%	—
12/06	299	6	2.1%	—
12/05	265	3	1.3%	—
Annual Growth	6.1%	56.8%	—	—

2008 Year-End Financials

Debt ratio: —
Return on equity: 4.00%
Cash ($ mil.): 0
Current ratio: 0.20
Long-term debt ($ mil.): —

Dividends
Yield: —
Payout: —
Market value ($ mil.): —

SCOTTSDALE HEALTHCARE CORP.

Scottsdale Healthcare Corp. a not-for-profit organization serves the health care needs of central Arizona residents. Its operations include three acute care hospitals that combined boast some 835 beds. Scottsdale Healthcare also operates other campuses that offer physician offices a cancer center home health and other health care services. It conducts clinical research through the Scottsdale Healthcare Research Institute. The group's Essential Touch Wellness Center and Boutique provides spa-like stress-reduction therapies. With a staff of some 1400 physicians the company offers more than 50 medical specialties. Scottsdale Healthcare was established in 1962 as City Hospital of Scottsdale.

Geographic Reach

Scottsdale Healthcare serves central Arizona specifically in an around the entire Northeast Valley as well as the area north of Loop 101.

Strategy

Since 2012 the health care network has been expanding into Northeast Phoenix to deepen its relationships with community physicians and diversify beyond its three-hospital Scottsdale campuses. To this end it plans to open new Scottsdale Healthcare Primary Care physician offices in 2013 –one each in Phoenix and Tempe –to join existing locations in Arcadia Scottsdale and Grayhawk.

What makes Scottsdale Healthcare stand out is its military training program the only one of its kind in the country. Its Readiness Skill Sustainment Training Program gives National Guard Air Force Reserve and nearby Air Force base personnel 12 days of training in treating trauma burns and other wounds they might encounter when deployed in a war zone. Participants also work in intensive care ride along with EMS personnel and get orthopedics and operating room practice. It has since expanded the program to include a $1.6-million military trauma training center which serves military medical personnel with classroom and simulation training and trains civilian paramedics and firefighters.

The organization performs clinical research through the Scottsdale Healthcare Research Institute. Through the institute the organization conducts clinical trials in a range of disciplines including cancer and other complex diseases.

EXECUTIVES

Chairman, Steven M. (Steve) Wheeler, age 66
VP and CIO, James R. (Jim) Cramer
President and CEO, Thomas J. (Tom) Sadvary
SVP Medical Affairs, James F. Burke
SVP and Chief Clinical Officer, Peggy J. Reiley
Senior Vice President Chief Talent Officer, Carol Henderson
EVP Healthcare Operations, Gary E. Baker
Senior Vice President General Counsel, Alan B. Kelly
President Scottsdale, John N. Ferree Jr.
Senior Vice President Chief Financial Officer, Todd LaPorte
VP Operations Osborn Campus, Vikki Noyes
VP and Administrator Thompson Peak Hospital, Kim Post
Vice President Research, Mark Slater
Vice President Finance, Brian Steines
Vice Chairman, Brad A. Gazaway
VP Marketing and Business Development, Dave Barber
Chief Medical Officer; VP Physician Alignment, Richard Silver
Vice President and Chief Nurse Executive, Kathi Zarubi
Vice President Clinical Service Lines Business Development, Dean Thomas
Senior Vice President and Chief Clinical Officer, Joanne Clavelle
Vice President Integrated Delivery Network, Lois Uniat

LOCATIONS

HQ: SCOTTSDALE HEALTHCARE CORP.
7400 E OSBORN RD, SCOTTSDALE, AZ 85251-6403
Phone: 480-882-6186

PRODUCTS/OPERATIONS

Selected Services

Bariatric Weight Loss Surgery
Cancer Care
Community Health
Corporate Health
Diabetes Management
Diagnostic Imaging Services
Digestive Health
Emergency Services
Heart & Vascular
Home Health Services
Infusion & Treatment Services
Minimally Invasive Surgery
Neurosciences
Nutrition Services
Orthopedic Services
Outpatient Therapy Services
Pediatrics
Sleep Disorders Center
Trauma Center
Wound Management
Urgent Care Plus
Urology Services

COMPETITORS

Banner Health
Community Health Systems
Dignity Health
Flagstaff Medical Center
Iasis Healthcare
John C. Lincoln Health Network
Mayo Clinic
Phoenix Children' s Hospital
St. Joseph Health System
Sun Health
Universal Health Services
University of Arizona Health Network
Vanguard Health Systems
Yuma Regional Medical Center

HISTORICAL FINANCIALS

Company Type: Private

Income Statement FYE: September 30

	REVENUE ($ mil.)	NET INCOME ($ mil.)	NET PROFIT MARGIN	EMPLOYEES
09/09	808	11	1.5%	6,500
09/07	748	67	9.0%	—
09/07	0	0	—	—
Annual Growth	—	—	—	—

2009 Year-End Financials

Debt ratio: —
Return on equity: 1.50%
Cash ($ mil.): 55
Current ratio: 1.30
Long-term debt ($ mil.): —

Dividends
Yield: —
Payout: —
Market value ($ mil.): —

SCRIPPS HEALTH

Scripps Health houses many a script-writing physician in its hospitals. The not-for-profit health system serves the San Diego area through four acute-care hospitals on five campuses. Altogether the health system is home to 1400 inpatient beds and a network of outpatient clinics. The system also offers home health care and operates community outreach programs. Its hospitals along with more than 20 outpatient Scripps Clinic and Scripps Coastal Medical Center locations employ more than 2600 affiliated general practice and specialty physicians. The Scripps Health Foundation raises philanthropic funds for Scripps Health is affiliated with biomedical research center The Scripps Research Institute.

The health network's facilities include the 700-bed Scripps Mercy Hospital which has a main campus in San Diego and a satellite campus in Chula Vista as well as Scripps Green Hospital (173 beds in La Jolla) Scripps Memorial Hospital Encinitas (160 beds) and Scripps Memorial Hospital La Jolla (310 beds). Scripps Health is also the official health care provider for the San Diego Padres baseball team.

Each year the not-for-profit Scripps Health organization brings in more than $2 billion in annual revenues. Its reported earnings were more than $2.4 billion in 2011 primarily sourced to patient service revenues. The company also brings in some funds from government grants commercial research partnerships and charitable donations. Scripps Health provides some $320 million in unreimbursed and charity care services each year as well.

As a major provider in the larger San Diego area Scripps Health is constantly evaluating its scope of services to meet ever-increasing demand for health care. The company is building several outpatient clinics including cancer treatment and cardiac care centers. It is also expanding and upgrading its hospitals; for instance the La Jolla hospital is adding a $456 million 170-bed cardiovascular institute (scheduled to open in 2015) and the Encinitas center is undergoing a $94 million expansion project (scheduled for completion in 2014) that includes the addition of a new ER and critical care wing.

The health system's overall strategy is to remain on the cutting edge of technology in order to treat patients more effectively therefore reporting better patient outcomes (making itself eligible for certain government incentives). It also aims to make itself the destination of choice for patients (both locally and globally) for heart cancer care and other types of specialty care.

In addition Scripps Health has launched an initiative to increase the number of clinical trials conducted at its facilities in partnership with pharmaceutical and medical device companies. While Scripps Health continues to grow the company keeps an eye on its bottom line continuing to evaluate its budget on a regular basis to reduce expenses when necessary.

HISTORY

Scripps Health was founded by Ellen Browning Scripps in 1924 when the Scripps Memorial Hospital and Scripps Metabolic Clinic opened in La Jolla.

The network grew through the opening of Scripps Green Hospital in 1977 and the Scripps Memorial Hospital Encinitas campus was added through the purchase of San Dieguito Hospital the following year.

Scripps Mercy Hospital which was first established in 1890 in San Diego joined the Scripps network in 1995.

The Scripps Health system expanded once again when it acquired the Scripps Mercy Hospital Chula Vista campus in 2004.

EXECUTIVES

Chief Executive; SVP Scripps Green Hospital, Robin B. Brown
Chief Executive SVP Scripps Memorial Hospital La Jolla, Gary G. Fybel
SVP and Chief Executive Scripps Mercy Hospital and Scripps Memorial Hospital Chula Vista, Tom Gammiere
CFO and Treasurer, Richard K. Rothberger
Chief Executive; SVP Scripps Memorial Hospital Encinitas, Carl J. Etter
President and CEO, Christopher D. Van Gorder
Corporate Senior Vice President Chief Medical Officer, James LaBelle
Chief Executive; SVP Scripps Medical Foundation, Shiraz M. Fagan
Vice President, Joseph Traube
Vice President Medical Services Regional Sites, Peter D Aldrich
Corporate Vice President Legal, Lawrence Kline
Director Of Radiology, William Marshall
Vp Digital Ad Sales Technology, Sandy Sexton
Pharmacy Manager Ambulatory Services, Vyvy Vo
Vp Finance, Melissa Studds
Vice President Chief Nurse And Operations, Cindy Steckel
Vice Chair, Maureen A. Stapleton
Vice Chairman, Robert Tjosvold
Cnsl, Myralinn Beaver Scofield
Treasurer, Richard McKeown
Auditors: Ernst&YoungLLP

LOCATIONS

HQ: SCRIPPS HEALTH
4275 CAMPUS POINT CT, SAN DIEGO, CA 92121-1513
Phone: 858-678-7000
Web: WWW.SCRIPPS.ORG

Selected California Facilities

Scripps Clinic (outpatient centers)
Scripps Coastal Medical Center (outpatient centers formerly Scripps Mercy Medical Group)
Scripps Green Hospital (La Jolla)
Scripps Memorial Hospital Encinitas
Scripps Memorial Hospital La Jolla
Scripps Mercy Hospital (San Diego)
Scripps Mercy Hospital Chula Vista

PRODUCTS/OPERATIONS

2011 Sales

Patient service (net)	2,144	87
Net assets released	14	1
Total	**2,451**	**100**

COMPETITORS

Adventist Health
Cedars-Sinai Medical Center
Community Health Systems
Dignity Health
Good Samaritan Hospital (IN)
Grossmont Hospital
HCA
Los Angeles County Health Department
Mayo Clinic
Palomar Health
Paradise Valley Hospital
Prospect Medical
Providence Saint Joseph Medical Center
Rady Children' s Hospital
Sharp HealthCare
St. Joseph Health System
Tenet Healthcare
Tri-City Healthcare District
UCSD Medical

HISTORICAL FINANCIALS

Company Type: Private

Income Statement

FYE: September 30

	REVENUE ($ mil.)	NET INCOME ($ mil.)	NET PROFIT MARGIN	EMPLOYEES
09/08	1,953	18	0.9%	11,000
09/07	1,781	223	12.6%	—
Annual Growth	9.7%	(91.7%)	—	—

2008 Year-End Financials

Debt ratio: —
Return on equity: 0.90%
Cash ($ mil.): 249
Current ratio: 1.50
Long-term debt ($ mil.): —
Dividends
Yield: —
Payout: —
Market value ($ mil.): —

SEALASKA CORPORATION

Sealaska Corporation is a native-owned investment firm active in natural resources manufacturing services and gaming. The holding company owns land in southeastern Alaska home to the Tlingit Haida and Tsimshian peoples. Sealaska core holdings include Sealaska Timber Corporation Alaska Coastal Aggregates Sealaska Constructors Sealaska Environmental Services and Colorado-based information technology services provider Managed Business Solutions. Sealaska's subsidiaries operate throughout North America and around the world. Its companies often win government contracts for construction environmental and engineering projects.

Sealaska owns about 290000 acres of timberland as well as the minerals rights to construction-grade aggregates on more than 565000 acres. The company also invests in stocks bonds and private equity.

The corporation has experienced a steady increase in its total revenues over the years (although there was a slight decline in 2008 due to the economic recession). Business diversity helped Sealaska weather the recession. Profits have been spotty as the corporation deals with market uncertainty and possible budget cuts in the federal government.

About 60% of Sealaska's revenues come from its services segment which includes subsidiary Sealaksa Environmental Services Sealaksa Constructors Synergy Systems and Managed Business Solutions. The services division expanded in 2010 with the acquisition of 70% of Flordia-based Security Alliance which provides guard and private investigation services.

More than 25% of Sealaska's revenues are earned from manufacturing activities. The manufacturing arm consists mainly of injection-molded plastics maker Nypro Kanaak which is a joint venture with Massachusetts-based Nypro. The division grew its revenue by 30% in 2011 after landing two major clients (Clorox and SC Johnson). Kraft also is another major client. In 2011 Sealaska shut down its mechanical parts manufacturer Olympic Fabrication.

Sealaska's natural resources division has experienced revenue growth over the years driven mostly by its timber operations. Demand in Asia and favorable prices have helped the timber segment maintain strong harvests. The company has worked to maintain sustainability and drive growth in that sector. Sealaska continues to seek custody of additional tribal lands in order to gain access to timber and is working on a Congressional bill that wound grant the tribes ownership to more land in southeast Alaska.

Sealaska's Alaska Coastal Aggregates subsidiary also is experiencing growth. The company supplies aggregate material for state and federal projects Alaska Coastal Aggregates is growing its cement and sand operations in southeast Alaska and developing a supply line to mines in the region.

The corporation is also looking to expand its reach on a global level. Its Sealaska Global Logistics arm ships freight internationally. In 2011 Sealaska Global Logistics entered the Asian market by establishing operations there. The logistics division also is looking the establish positions in emerging markets in Europe Mexico and South Africa.

Subsidiary Haa Aani (meaning "our land")was established in 2009 as a way to promote the culture social and economic viability of Southeast Alaska. Haa Aani has assisted tribal members with their efforts to establish businesses such as a new oyster farms in southeastern Alaska. Haa Aani also promotes renewable energy initiatives such as a biomass heating system for commercial buildings. In 2012 Haa Aani launched a non-profit community development financial institution in order to provide financing and promote economic development.

Sealaska's also is developing a gaming casino and resort in Cloverdale California. The corporation through its End-to-End Enterprises subsidiary is partners with the Pomo Indians of California on the project.

Sealaska is the largest of 13 corporations formed under the Alaska Native Claims Settlement Act (ANCSA) of 1971 which promised some 44 million acres of land to Alaska natives. The company is owned by some 21000 tribal member shareholders.

EXECUTIVES

EVP, Richard P. (Rick) Harris, $240,000 total compensation
President and CEO, Chris E. McNeil Jr., $350,000 total compensation
COO, Samuel (Sam) Landol, $250,000 total compensation
Manager Information Systems, Robert (Rob) Johnson
Director Corporate Communications, Todd P. Antioquia
Chairman, Albert M. Kookesh, age 65
Vice Chair, Rosita F. Worl, age 76
VP and CFO, Doug Morris
Director Business Development Sealaska Timber Corporation (STC), Ed Davis
Manager Shareholder Records, Ella D. Bennett
VP Corporate Secretary and VP Human Resources, Nicole D. Hallingstad
Manager Human Resources, Kenneth L. (Ken) Southerland
President & CEO Haa Aani LLC, Russell A. Dick
Corporate Counsel, E. Budd Simpson
Chief Investment Officer and Treasurer, Anthony Mallott
VP and General Counsel, Jaeleen Kookesh Araujo
Assistant to the President and CEO, Katherine Eldemar
Operations Controller, Nathan McCowan
Internal Auditor, Mark Shirley
Headquarters Controller, Vicki Soboleff
Manager Natural Resources, Ron Wolfe
Manager Records, Linda Wynne
President and CEO Sealaska Timber Corporation (STC), Wade Zammit
General Manager Nypro Kanaak Alabama, Kenneth Fair
President and CEO Sealaska Environmental Services, Derik Frederiksen
COO Sealaska Environmental Services, Neil Hart
General Manager Alaska Coastal Aggregates, Dean McDonald
President and CEO Managed Business Solutions, Richard Noe, $293,119 total compensation
General Manager Nypro Kanaak Guadalajara, Julio Oropeza
President and General Manager Synergy Systems and Olympic Fabrication, Damon Pistulka
Director Sales and Marketing Nypro Kanaak, Ed Rivera
General Manager, Bob Wysocki
President and CEO Managed Business Solutions (MBS) and MBS Systems, Jon Duncan
COO, Terry Downes
COO Sealaska Environmental Services, Lewis Ivers
Director, Byron I. Mallott, age 71
Director, Patrick M. Anderson, age 60
Director, Clarence Jackson Sr., age 79
Director, Jacqueline L. (Jackie) Johnson Pata, age 58
Director, Edward K. Thomas, age 72
Vice Chair, Rosita F. Worl, age 76
Director, Joseph G. Nelson, age 43
Director, Sidney Edenshaw, age 50
Director, J. Tate London, age 52
Director, Jodi Mitchell, age 50
Director, William (Bill) Thomas, age 66
Director, Barbara Cadiente-Nelson, age 60
Auditors: KPMGLLP

LOCATIONS

HQ: SEALASKA CORPORATION
1 SEALASKA PLZ STE 400, JUNEAU, AK 99801-1276
Phone: 907-586-1512
Web: WWW.SEALASKA.COM

PRODUCTS/OPERATIONS

2011 Sales

	$ mil.	% of total
Services	145	55
Manufacturing	72	28
Natural resources	45	17
Investments	(3.9)	-
Gaming	0	-
Corporate & other	0	-
Total	**259**	**100**

Selected Subsidiaries

Alaska Coastal Aggregates
Managed Business Solutions (majority owned)
Nypro Kanaak (joint venture)
Sealaska Constructors LLC
Sealaska Environmental Services
Sealaska Timber Corporation
Security Alliance

COMPETITORS

Plum Creek Timber
Tembec
West Fraser Timber
chugach alaska

HISTORICAL FINANCIALS

Company Type: Private

Income Statement FYE: December 31

	REVENUE ($ mil.)	NET INCOME ($ mil.)	NET PROFIT MARGIN	EMPLOYEES
12/12	311	13	4.3%	1,400
12/11	259	8	3.2%	—
12/10	223	17	7.8%	—
12/09	0	0	11.8%	—
Annual Growth	1057.4%	726.1%	—	—

2012 Year-End Financials

Debt ratio: —
Return on equity: 4.30%
Cash ($ mil.): 34
Current ratio: 0.50
Long-term debt ($ mil.): —
Dividends
Yield: —
Payout: —
Market value ($ mil.): —

SEATTLE MORTGAGE COMPANY

LOCATIONS

HQ: SEATTLE MORTGAGE COMPANY
600 UNIVERSITY ST # 1850, SEATTLE, WA 981011176
Phone: 2062811500
Web: WWW.SEATTLEMORTGAGE.COM

HISTORICAL FINANCIALS

Company Type: Private

Income Statement FYE: December 31

	ASSETS ($ mil.)	NET INCOME ($ mil.)	INCOME AS % OF ASSETS	EMPLOYEES
12/09	590	(33)	—	400
12/08	665	(19)	—	—
12/07	613	(106)	—	—
Annual Growth	(1.9%)	—	—	—

2009 Year-End Financials

Debt ratio: —
Return on equity: (-156.60%)
Cash ($ mil.): 53
Current ratio: —
Long-term debt ($ mil.): —
Dividends
Yield: —
Payout: —
Market value ($ mil.): —

SEATTLE UNIVERSITY

Seattle University isn't very big but as one of 28 Jesuit universities in the US it is part of a Roman Catholic teaching legacy that spans the country and the world. With an enrollment of about 7500 students the school offers 64 undergraduate more than 35 graduate degree programs and 28 certificate programs through its eight schools (College of Arts and Sciences Albers School of Business and Economics College of Education School of Law Matteo Ricci College College of Nursing College of Science and Engineering and School of Theology and Ministry).

Operations

In 2012 Seattle University had 4589 undergraduate students and 1933 graduate students. Some 40% of the first year students were from Washington State and some 7% of all students were from outside the US.

The average class size is 19 and the faculty-to-student ratio is 1 to 13.

Financial Performance

In 2012 the university reported a 10% decrease in revenues due to a drop in investment income a loss incurred in net realized and unrealized losses on investments and a change in value of interest rate swap agreements.

Its net income declined by 90% in 2012 due to a decrease in revenues and an increase in expenses attributed largely to higher costs for instruction academic support and auxiliary enterprises.

Strategy

Growing its portfolio of degree programs in 2012 Seattle University's Albers School of Business and Economics added the Bridge MBA to its family of graduate degrees.

Company Background

Seattle University was founded in 1891 by two Jesuit priests.

EXECUTIVES

President, Father Stephen V. Sundborg
EVP, Timothy P. Leary
VP University Advancement, Mary Kay McFadden
Provost, Isiaah Crawford
Interim VP Finance, James Adolphson
VP Human Resources and University Services, Jerry Huffman
VP Student Development, Jacob Diaz
VP and University Counsel, Mary S. Peterson
VP University Planning and Vice Provost, Robert J. Dullea
CFO and Vice President for Finance and Business Affairs, Connie Kanter
Auditors: KPMGLLP

LOCATIONS

HQ: SEATTLE UNIVERSITY
901 12TH AVE, SEATTLE, WA 98122-4411
Phone: 206-296-6150
Web: WWW.SEATTLEU.EDU

PRODUCTS/OPERATIONS

Schools and Colleges
Albers School of Business and Economics
College of Arts and Sciences
College of Education
College of Nursing
College of Science and Engineerin
Matteo Ricci College
School of Law
School of Theology and Ministry

COMPETITORS

University of Washington
Washington State University
Western Washington University

HISTORICAL FINANCIALS

Company Type: Private

Income Statement FYE: June 30

	REVENUE ($ mil.)	NET INCOME ($ mil.)	NET PROFIT MARGIN	EMPLOYEES
06/10	236	11	4.9%	1,100
06/09	236	0	—	—
06/09	0	0	—	—
Annual Growth	—70296.4%		—	—

2010 Year-End Financials

Debt ratio: —
Return on equity: 4.90%
Cash ($ mil.): 50
Current ratio: —
Long-term debt ($ mil.): —
Dividends
Yield: —
Payout: —
Market value ($ mil.): —

SECURITIES INVESTOR PROTECTION CORPORATION

Securities Investor Protection Corporation (SIPC) is an industry-financed insurance plan that protects clients of most broker-dealers registered with the US Securities and Exchange Commission (SEC). SIPC insures customers' securities (up to $500000 per account) against losses due to the financial failure of brokerage firms. Losses caused by fluctuations in market value are not protected. The not-for-profit membership corporation was mandated by the Securities Investor Protection Act and has more than 6000 members. Its board is appointed by the US president the treasury secretary and the Federal Reserve Board. Assessments from members and investments in government securities provide money for the SIPC Fund.

While SIPC will replace missing cash and hard securities (stocks and bonds) it doesn't protect less tangible investments such as commodity futures or investment contracts. Nor does it insure against fraud.

As investment firms imploded throughout 2008 SIPC shifted into high gear to process more than 900000 claims from customers and creditors of Lehman Brothers and more than 15000 claims from investors in Bernard L. Madoff Investment Securities. By late 2009 SIPC was looking at potential payouts of $534 million to former Madoff investors —greater than the sum total of its payouts since it was created in 1970.

During 2011 the firm disagreed with the SEC's efforts to make it pay customers of fraudster R. Allen Stanford. SIPC contends that while Stanford Group was a member of SIPC the defrauded customers didn't lose their money in a failed brokerage.

EXECUTIVES

President and CEO, Stephen P. Harbeck
Chairman, Orlan M. Johnson
Director, William H. Heyman, age 65
Vice Chairman, Todd S. Farha, age 44
Director, David J. Stockton
Director, William S. (Bill) Jasien
Director, Mark S. Shelton
Director, David G. Mason
Auditors: GrantThorntonLLP

LOCATIONS

HQ: SECURITIES INVESTOR PROTECTION CORPORATION
805 15TH ST NW STE 800, WASHINGTON, DC 20005-2207
Phone: 202-371-8300
Web: WWW.SIPC.ORG

HISTORICAL FINANCIALS

Company Type: Private

Income Statement FYE: December 31

	ASSETS ($ mil.)	NET INCOME ($ mil.)	INCOME AS % OF ASSETS	EMPLOYEES
12/12	1,912	512	26.8%	35
12/11	1,606	131	8.2%	—
12/09	1,382	(271)	—	—
12/09	1,307	80	6.2%	—
Annual Growth	13.5%	85.1%		

2012 Year-End Financials

Debt ratio: —
Return on equity: 113.20%
Cash ($ mil.): 31
Current ratio: —
Long-term debt ($ mil.): —
Dividends
Yield: —
Payout: —
Market value ($ mil.): —

SECURITY FINANCE CORPORATION OF SPARTANBURG

Folks looking for a little financial security just might turn to Security Finance Corporation of Spartanburg. Founded in 1955 the consumer loan company provides personal loans typically ranging from $100 to $600 (some states however allow loan amounts as high as $3000). Customers can also turn to Security Finance for credit reports and tax preparation services. The company operates approximately 800 offices in about 15 states that are marketed under the Security Finance Sunbelt Credit and PFS banner names. A subsidiary of Security Group the financial institution also has locations operating as Security Financial Services in North Carolina and Longhorn Finance in Texas.

Geographic Reach

From its headquarters in South Carolina Security Finance boasts offices in about 15 states across the US.

Strategy

Security Finance exited Colorado in 2010 after the state's attorney general general office filed a compliant that the company had been refinancing some consumer loans more than three times a year (the limit under Colorado law). The company agreed to repay acquisition fees that it had charged the customers for refinancing the loans.

Company Ownership

Security Finance is a subsidiary of Security Group Inc.

Auditors: Deloitte&ToucheLLP

LOCATIONS

HQ: SECURITY FINANCE CORPORATION OF SPARTANBURG
181 SECURITY PL, SPARTANBURG, SC 29307-5450
Phone: 864-582-8193
Web: WWW.SECURITY-FINANCE.COM

Selected Locations

Alabama
Florida
Georgia
Idaho
Illinois
Louisiana
Missouri
Nevada
New Mexico
North Carolina
Oklahoma
South Carolina
Tennessee
Texas
Utah
Wisconsin

PRODUCTS/OPERATIONS

Selected Banners

Longhorn Finance (Texas)
PFS
Security Finance
Security Financial Services (North Carolina)
Sunbelt Credit

COMPETITORS

1st Franklin Financial
ACE Cash Express
Advance America
Bank of America
Capital One
Cash America
Cash Plus
Community Choice Financial
DFC Global
EZCORP
First Cash Financial Services
GE Capital
OneMain Financial
Springleaf
Value Financial Services
World Acceptance

HISTORICAL FINANCIALS

Company Type: Private

Income Statement FYE: December 31

	ASSETS ($ mil.)	NET INCOME ($ mil.)	INCOME AS % OF ASSETS	EMPLOYEES
12/12	461	53	11.6%	2,500
12/11	322	42	13.1%	—
12/10	495	41	8.4%	—
12/09	432	30	7.1%	—
Annual Growth	2.1%	20.4%	—	—

2012 Year-End Financials

Debt ratio: —
Return on equity: 13.60%
Cash ($ mil.): 8
Current ratio: —
Long-term debt ($ mil.): —
Dividends
Yield: —
Payout: —
Market value ($ mil.): —

SECURITY HEALTH PLAN OF WISCONSIN INC.

Security Health Plan of Wisconsin provides health insurance coverage and related services to some 200000 members in more than 35 Wisconsin counties. Its managed network of providers includes more than 4000 physicians 40 hospitals and health care facilities as well as 55000 pharmacies across the US. Security Health Plan provides policies for groups and individuals. Its products include HMO coverage plans and supplemental Medicare plans as well as prescription drug and equipment coverage disease management programs and administration services for self-funded plans. Established in 1986 the company is the managed healthcare arm of Marshfield Clinic which operates medical practices across the state.

Geographic Reach

Headquartered in the town of Marshfield Security Health Plan serves the counties of Adams Ashland Barron Bayfield Burnett Chippewa Clark Columbia Dane Douglas Dunn Eau Claire Forest Iron Jackson Juneau Langlade Lincoln Marathon Marquette Monroe Oneida Pepin Portage Price Rusk Sauk Sawyer Shawano Taylor Trempealeau Vilas Washburn Waupaca Waushara and Wood.

Operations

Since it is affiliated with a medical care provider Security Health Plan's coverage decisions are directly impacted by the practicing physician. The company's provider network consists of independent physician locations and parent Marshfield Clinic's more than 50 locations in Wisconsin.

In addition to HMO plans the firm's comprehensive medical coverage plans include POS (point of service) and high-deductable offerings. Security Health Plan offers health care reimbursement accounts through third-party provider agreements with Employee Benefits Corporation and Diversified Benefits Services. In addition the company provides community education and wellness programs.

Sales and Marketing

Security Health Plan serves individuals families and small to large employer groups.

Strategy

Originally started in 1986 as an offshoot of the Greater Marshfield Community Health Plan Security Health Plan's service territory has grown over the years. For instance in 2012 the company extended its Advocare Medicare Advantage plan offering into several new counties. Security Health Plan also regularly adds primary care and specialty providers to its network to provide a broader range of accessible care services to its members as well as to strengthen its operations in underserved regions. The company is also looking to enhance its IT systems to allow for greater information access communication methods and collaboration among its providers and members.

EXECUTIVES

Director Utilization Management (Medical) Efficiency Analysis, Lawrence McFarlane
Chief Administrative Officer, Steven (Steve) Youso
Director Disease Management Quality Incentives and Outcomes Improvement, Michele L. Bachhuber
Director Behavioral Health Utilization Case Management and Pharmacy Management, Edward J. Krall
Director Health Services, Jane Wolf
President, Karl J. Ulrich
Chief Medical Officer, Russel J. (Russ) Kuzel
Director Technology Assessment Wellness, Andrea Hillerud
Chief Marketing Officer at Security, John Kelly

LOCATIONS

HQ: SECURITY HEALTH PLAN OF WISCONSIN INC.
1515 N SAINT JOSEPH AVE, MARSHFIELD, WI 54449-1343
Phone: 715-387-5621
Web: WWW.SECURITYHEALTH.ORG

COMPETITORS

Aetna
Blue Cross Blue Shield of Wisconsin
CIGNA
Centene
Dean Health Plan
Group Health Cooperative
Gundersen Lutheran
Humana
UnitedHealth Group
Unity Health Plans Insurance
WEA Trust
Wisconsin Physicians Service Insurance Corporation

HISTORICAL FINANCIALS

Company Type: Private

Income Statement FYE: December 31

	REVENUE ($ mil.)	NET INCOME ($ mil.)	NET PROFIT MARGIN	EMPLOYEES
12/09	814	27	3.4%	1,006
12/05	385	0	—	—
12/04	369	17	4.7%	—
12/02	285	7	2.6%	—
Annual Growth	16.1%	20.9%	—	—

2009 Year-End Financials

Debt ratio: —
Return on equity: 3.40%
Cash ($ mil.): 38
Current ratio: 0.70
Long-term debt ($ mil.): —
Dividends
Yield: —
Payout: —
Market value ($ mil.): —

SELECT ENERGY SERVICES LLC

LOCATIONS

HQ: SELECT ENERGY SERVICES LLC
1820 N INTERSTATE 35, GAINESVILLE, TX 762402179
Phone: 9406681818
Web: WWW.SELECTENERGYSERVICES.COM

HISTORICAL FINANCIALS

Company Type: Private

Income Statement FYE: December 31

	REVENUE ($ mil.)	NET INCOME ($ mil.)	NET PROFIT MARGIN	EMPLOYEES
12/10	502	55	11.0%	3,700
12/09	115	11	10.4%	—
Annual Growth	336.8%	364.4%	—	—

2010 Year-End Financials

Debt ratio: —
Return on equity: 11.00%
Cash ($ mil.): 22
Current ratio: 1.40
Long-term debt ($ mil.): —
Dividends
Yield: —
Payout: —
Market value ($ mil.): —

SELLEN CONSTRUCTION CO. INC.

LOCATIONS

HQ: SELLEN CONSTRUCTION CO. INC.
227 WESTLAKE AVE N, SEATTLE, WA 981095217
Phone: 2066827770
Web: WWW.SELLEN.COM

HISTORICAL FINANCIALS

Company Type: Private

Income Statement FYE: December 31

	REVENUE ($ mil.)	NET INCOME ($ mil.)	NET PROFIT MARGIN	EMPLOYEES
12/12	396	4	1.0%	600
12/11	426	9	2.3%	—
12/10	600	17	2.9%	—
12/09	478	0	—	—
Annual Growth	(6.1%)	—	—	—

2012 Year-End Financials

Debt ratio: —
Return on equity: 1.00%
Cash ($ mil.): 32
Current ratio: 1.20
Long-term debt ($ mil.): —
Dividends
Yield: —
Payout: —
Market value ($ mil.): —

SEMINOLE ELECTRIC COOPERATIVE INC.

This Seminole is not only a native Floridian but it has also provided electricity in the state since 1948. Seminole Electric Cooperative generates and transmits electricity for 10 member distribution cooperatives that serve 1.7 million residential and business customers (858972 meters in 2012) in 45 Florida counties. Seminole Electric has more than 2120 MW of primarily coal-fired generating capacity. The cooperative also buys electricity from other utilities and independent power producers and it owns 400 miles of transmission lines. Some 90% of its power load uses the transmission systems of other utilities through long-term contracts.

Geographic Reach

The company serves customers in 45 counties in northeast south central and southeast Florida.

Operations

Seminole Electric's primary resources include the 1300 MW Seminole Generating Station and the 810 MW Richard J. Midulla Generating Station. The coop's renewable energy resources include waste-to-energy facilities landfill gas-to-energy facilities and a biomass facility. It also buys power as needed on the market.

Seminole Electric has more than 400 miles of transmission line.

Financial Performance

The coop's revenues dropped by 5% in 2012 due to lower overall sales. Members' revenues declined due to lower rates and as well as a reduction in member energy requirements in fiscal 2012. Non-Members' revenues decreased primarily due to a lower volumes sold.Seminole Electric's net margin dropped by 56% in 2012 due to lower revenues and increased asset impairment charges (stemming from unrecovered investment in the Crystal River 3 nuclear unit) slightly offset by the lower decrease rate of total operating expenses.

Strategy

As part of Florida's push to get more power generation from renewable sources in 2011 Seminole Electric boosted its portfolio of purchased green energy to more than 140 MW (including 113 MW from waste-to-energy facilities). The company generated 5.5% of its revenues from power sales from renewable sources in 2011 making Seminole Electric one of the largest green energy providers in Florida. In 2012 it was also making major environmental improvements to its coal-fired Seminole Generating Station.

Company Background
Seminole Electric was formed in 1948 to aggregate the power demands of its members and is governed by a board of trustees representing the 10 member utilities. The cooperative built its first power plant in the 1970s.

EXECUTIVES

Vice President Of Administration, Al Garcia
Director Project Engineering, James R. Frauen
VP Commercial and Portfolio Management, Mark T. Sherman
CFO, Jo Ann Fuller
CEO and General Manager, Lisa Johnson
Director Information Systems, Steven W Saunders
Director Transmission, Mark Churilla
Vice President Technical Services, Michael Opalinski
Vice Chair, W. F. Hart
Chair, Malcolm Page
Auditors: PricewaterhouseCoopersLLP

LOCATIONS

HQ: SEMINOLE ELECTRIC COOPERATIVE INC.
16313 N DALE MABRY HWY, TAMPA, FL 33618-1427
Phone: 813-963-0994
Web: WWW.SEMINOLE-ELECTRIC.COM

PRODUCTS/OPERATIONS

2012 Sales

Members	97
Other	1

2012 Retail Sales

% of total	
Residential	68
Commercial/Industrial	31
Other	1
Total	**100**

Members
Central Florida Cooperativ
Clay Cooperativ
Glades Cooperativ
Lee County Cooperativ
Peace River Cooperativ
Sumter Cooperativ
Suwannee Valley Cooperativ
Talquin Cooperativ
Tri-County Cooperativ
Withlacoochee River Cooperativ

COMPETITORS

-0.4	JEA
Duke Energy	NextEra Energy
Florida Power & Light	Progress Energy
Florida Public Utilities	Southern Company
	TECO Energy

HISTORICAL FINANCIALS

Company Type: Private

Income Statement FYE: June 30

	REVENUE ($ mil.)	NET INCOME ($ mil.)	NET PROFIT MARGIN	EMPLOYEES
06/13*	1,230	3	0.2%	528
12/12	1,222	11	1.0%	—
09/12	1,208	10	0.8%	—
12/11	1,291	27	2.1%	—
Annual Growth	(4.7%)	(88.8%)	—	—

*Fiscal year change

2013 Year-End Financials

Debt ratio: —
Return on equity: 0.20%
Cash ($ mil.): 53
Current ratio: 0.20
Long-term debt ($ mil.): —
Dividends
Yield: —
Payout: —
Market value ($ mil.): —

SENTARA HEALTHCARE

Sentara Healthcare is not-for-profit organization that operates a network of hospitals and other health facilities primarily in the coastal Hampton Roads area of southeastern Virginia. The system includes 10 acute care hospitals housing a total of some 2400 beds. One of its hospitals Sentara Norfolk includes a dedicated cardiac hospital with more than 100 beds. In addition to its acute care facilities Sentara Healthcare operates several outpatient care facilities as well as nursing homes rehab centers medical practices imaging centers and home health agencies. Its Optima Health unit provides HMO PPO and other health insurance products to about 440000 Virginians.

Geographic Reach
Sentara Healthcare is the region's largest integrated health care provider serving more than 2 million residents. Its facilities serve customers throughout southeastern and northern Virginia as well as in northeastern North Carolina. It operates in the Virginia cities of Alleghany Charlottesville Hampton Roads Harrisonburg Richmond and Roanoke. In North Carolina Sentara has a presence in Currituck and Elizabeth City.

Operations
Across the Sentara Healthcare system the organization boasts a medical staff of about 3680. The medical system's multi-specialty physicians group the Sentara Medical Group has more than 380 primary care and specialty physicians. Its Sentara Senior Services unit operates about 10 nursing and assisted living centers.

The health care group also runs 160-bed Sentara Princess Anne Hospital an acute care facility located on the Princess Anne outpatient campus in Virginia Beach. Opened in mid-2011 it operates through a 70%-owned joint venture with Bon Secours Health System. The $145 million facility encompasses five stories and offers comprehensive surgical procedures intensive care advanced cardiac care and a maternity center.

Strategy
While it is already one of the largest health care organizations in the state Sentara Healthcare continues to grow through acquisitions construction (both expansions and new buildings) and mergers. In 2011 Sentara bought Martha Jefferson Hospital (aka Martha Jefferson Health Services) adding a 175-bed acute care facility and a network of primary and specialty care clinics in central Virginia. In 2010 acquired RMH Healthcare which operates 238-bed Rockingham Memorial Hospital in Harrisonburg Virginia as well as a wellness center and physicians group. In 2009 the company expanded its home health services by acquiring Bath Community House Home Health and Hospice of the Highlands renaming it Sentara Highlands Home Health. It also purchased the 180-bed Potomac Hospital (now operating as Sentara Potomac Hospital) in Woodbridge through a merger transaction.

Company Background
Sentara Healthcare was founded in 1888 as Norfolk's 25-bed Retreat for the Sick.

EXECUTIVES

Vp Of Human Resources, Michael Taylor
President and COO, Howard P. Kern
SVP and CIO, Bertram S. (Bert) Reese
CEO, David L. Bernd
SVP and CFO, Robert A. (Rob) Broerman
VP and President Martha Jefferson Hospital, James E. Haden
President Healthcare Performance Improvement (HPI), Gary R. Yates
SVP and President Sentara Health Plans, Michael M. Dudley
President Sentara Leigh Hospital, Terrie Edwards
President Sentara CarePlex Hospital, Debra A. Flores
President Sentara Virginia Beach General Hospital, Elwood B. (Bernie) Boone
Chief Nursing Officer, Genemarie McGee
SVP and Chief Medical Officer, Terry Gilliland
President Sentara Williamsburg Regional Medical Center, David J. Masterson
President Sentara Norfolk General Hospital, Kurt Hofelich
President Sentara Life Care Corporation, Bruce Robertson
President Sentara Princess Anne Hospital, Thomas Thames
Vp Of Recruitment, Patricia Evans
Vice President Finance, Leo Deleon
Vice President Of Corporate Finance, Vikki Lorenz
Vice President Coporate Strategy, Grace Hines
Vice President Managed Care Contracting, Lance Torcom
Senioe Vice President, Ken Krakaur
Corporate Vice President Southside, Michael Fache
Medical Director, Scott James
Senior Vice President Clinical Effectiveness Chief Marketing Officer, Dale Carroll
Vp Of Quality Assurance, Fred Schrever
Chairman, Bob Fort
Vice Chairman, Henry (Sandy) Harris

LOCATIONS

HQ: SENTARA HEALTHCARE
6015 POPLAR HALL DR, NORFOLK, VA 23502-3819
Phone: 757-455-7000
Web: WWW.SENTARA.COM

PRODUCTS/OPERATIONS

Mergers and Acquisitio
FY2011
Martha Jefferson Hospital
FY2010
RMH Healthcare (Rockingham Memorial Hospital wellness center and physicians group)
FY2009
Bath Community House Home Health and Hospice of the Highlands
Potomac Hospital

Selected Hospitals

Charlottesville
- Martha Jefferson Hospital
- MJH Outpatient Care Center
- Health Services at Proffit Road
- Health Services at Spring Creek
- Sentara Home Care Services
- Optima Health

Hampton Roads
- Sentara CarePlex Hospital
- Sentara Heart Hospital
- Sentara Leigh Hospital
- Sentara Norfolk General Hospital
- Sentara Obici Hospital
- Sentara Princess Anne Hospital
- Sentara Virginia Beach General Hospital
- Sentara Williamsburg Regional Medical Center
- Orthopaedic Hospital at Sentara CarePlex
- Sentara Northern Virginia Medical Center
- Martha Jefferson Hospital
- RMH Healthcare

Harrisonburg
- RMH Healthcare
- Optima Health

Northern Virginia
- Sentara Northern Virginia Medical Center
- Sentara Lake Ridge
- Sentara Medical Group physicians
- Sentara Home Care Services
- Sentara Heart and Vascular Center
- Optima Health

Selected Services

Cancer
Cardiac (Heart)
Digestive (Colorectal)
Home Care

Imaging
Maternity
Neurosciences
Rehabilitation
Seniors
Thoracic
Transplant
Trauma/Emergency Services
Urology
Vascular
Weight Loss Surgery
Women's

COMPETITORS

Aetna
Anthem Health Plans of Virginia
Bon Secours Health
CIGNA
Carilion Clinic
Centra Health Inc.
Children' s Hospital of The King' s Daughters
Franklin Hospital Corp.
HCA Capital Division
Humana
Inova
Kaiser Foundation Health Plan of the Mid-Atlantic
Norton Community Hospital
Novant Health
Riverside Health System (Virginia)
Twin County Regional Healthcare
UnitedHealth Group
Wake Forest University Baptist Medical Center

HISTORICAL FINANCIALS

Company Type: Private

Income Statement FYE: December 31

	REVENUE ($ mil.)	NET INCOME ($ mil.)	NET PROFIT MARGIN	EMPLOYEES
12/12	4,068	307	7.6%	22,000
12/11	3,930	103	2.6%	—
12/10	3,385	316	9.4%	—
12/09	2,945	347	11.8%	—
Annual Growth	11.4%	(3.9%)	—	—

2012 Year-End Financials

Debt ratio: —
Return on equity: 7.60%
Cash ($ mil.): 857
Current ratio: 1.00
Long-term debt ($ mil.): —
Dividends
Yield: —
Payout: —
Market value ($ mil.): —

SERVCO PACIFIC INC.

LOCATIONS

HQ: SERVCO PACIFIC INC.
2850 PUKOLOA ST STE 300, HONOLULU, HI 968194475
Phone: 8085641300
Web: WWW.SERVCO.COM

PRODUCTS/OPERATIONS

Selected Operations

Automotive
- Rex Tire and Supply
- Scion Dealers of Hawaii
- Subaru Dealers of Hawaii
- Suzuki Dealers of Hawaii
- Servco Australia
- Servco Chevy
- Servco Lexus
- Servco Truck & Commercial
- Toyota Dealers of Hawaii

Servco Home and Appliance Distribution
Servco Insurance Services
Servco Raynor Overhead Doors
Servco School and Office Furniture

HISTORICAL FINANCIALS

Company Type: Private

Income Statement FYE: June 30

	REVENUE ($ mil.)	NET INCOME ($ mil.)	NET PROFIT MARGIN	EMPLOYEES
06/13*	1,094	20	1.9%	925
12/12	923	15	1.7%	—
/ 0	0	—	—	
Annual Growth	—	—	—	—

*Fiscal year change

2013 Year-End Financials

Debt ratio: —
Return on equity: 1.90%
Cash ($ mil.): 16
Current ratio: 0.30
Long-term debt ($ mil.): —
Dividends
Yield: —
Payout: —
Market value ($ mil.): —

SES HOLDINGS LLC

LOCATIONS

HQ: SES HOLDINGS LLC
114 E FORELINE ST, GAINESVILLE, TX 762403320
Phone: 9406680251
Web: WWW.SES-HOLDINGS.COM

HISTORICAL FINANCIALS

Company Type: Private

Income Statement FYE: December 31

	ASSETS ($ mil.)	NET INCOME ($ mil.)	INCOME AS % OF ASSETS	EMPLOYEES
12/13	892	(32)	—	4,200
12/12	941	2	0.3%	—
12/11	1,019	131	12.9%	—
12/10	617	0	—	—
Annual Growth	13.1%	—	—	—

2013 Year-End Financials

Debt ratio: —
Return on equity: (-3.90%)
Cash ($ mil.): 35
Current ratio: 2.00
Long-term debt ($ mil.): —
Dividends
Yield: —
Payout: —
Market value ($ mil.): —

SETON HALL UNIVERSITY

Seton Hall University is a Catholic institution with an enrollment of approximately 10000 students. The university offers about 150 undergraduate and graduate degree programs as well as more than a dozen doctoral programs at eight colleges and schools including the Whitehead School of Diplomacy and International Relations Stillman School of Business and Immaculate Conception Seminary School of Theology. It also offers degree and certificate programs online. With a history dating back to 1856 Seton Hall University was named after Mother Elizabeth Ann Seton the first American-born saint (and an aunt of school founder Bishop James Roosevelt Bayley).

EXECUTIVES

VP University Advancement, Joseph G. Sandman
Vice President for Administration at Seton Hall University, Dennis J. Garbini
CFO, Stephen A. Graham
VP and General Counsel, Catherine A. Kiernan
VP; Interim Dean Whitehead School of Diplomacy and International Relations, Rev Paul A. Holmes
VP Student Affairs and Enrollment Services, Laura Wankel
Controller, John Passaro
EVP Administration, Paula Marie Buley
EVP and Provost, Larry A. Robinson
Director Athletics and Recreational, Joe Quinlan Jr.
Chairman, Rev John J. Myers
Vice Chairman, Father James M. Cafone
Dean School of Theology, Robert Coleman
Executive Vice President for Operations Catholic, Phillip Frese
Dean W. Paul Stillman School of Business, Karen Boroff
Dean College of Education and Human Services, Joseph DePierro
Director Seton World Wide, Philip DiSalvio
Dean Freshman Studies and Special Academic Programs, Tracy Gottlieb
Dean College of Nursing, Phyllis Shanley Hansell
Dean School of Law, Patrick E. Hobbs
Dean College of Arts and Sciences, Joseph Marbach
Dean University Libraries, Joseph F. McGinn
DeanWhitehead School of Diplomacy and International Relations, John K. Menzies
Dean School of Health and Medical Sciences, Brian B. Shulman
CIO, Stephen Landry
Human Resources and Information Technology Administrator, Jane Hudson
Manager Training and Development Human Resources, Therese Chidiac
President Adelante, Julieta Caraballo
President Black Student Union, Kevaan Walton
President Interfraternity Council, Michael Kurlander
President International Students Association, Morella Mirabal
President Martin Luther King Scholars, Lauren Jackson
President Multicultural Greek Council, Charee Marquez
President Panhellenic Council, Nicole Fopeano
President Senior Class Council, Elizabeth Rathbun
President Student Activities Board, Richard Evans
President Student Government Association, Michael McLaughlin
President, A. Gabriel Esteban
Vice President, Jillian Winkler
Associate Vice President, Greg Tobin
Art Director, Elyse Carter
Account Manager, Christine Aromando
Department Secretary, Andrea Davis
Senior Director Integrated Marketing, Linda Karten
Vice-President, Laura Toledo
CFO, Richard Mandelbaum
Vice President for Development, Alma Amendola
Dean College of Arts and Sciences, Michael Zavada
Dean School of Diplomacy and International Relations, Andrea Bartoli
Dean College of Education and Human Services, Grace M. May
Dean of Students, Karen Van Norman
Dean Stillman School of Business, Joyce Strawser
Dean University Libraries, John E. Buschman
Dean Continuing and Professional Studies, Nancy Low-Hogan
Vice President for enrollment management on, Alyssa McCloud
Vice President for university advancement, David J. Bohan
President The, Gerald P. Buccino

President Loras College, James E. Collins
Trustee, Patricia A. Cahill
Trustee, Patrick M. Murray, age 72
Vice Chairman, Father James M. Cafone
Trustee, Pamela M. Swartzberg
Trustee, Rev Arthur J. Serratelli
Trustee, Kurt T. Borowsky
Rector and Dean Immaculate Conception Seminary/School of Theology and Trustee, Robert Coleman
Trustee, John Doran
Trustee, Phillip Frese
Trustee, Joseph P. LaSala
Trustee, Joseph R. Reilly
Trustee, John J. Schimpf
Trustee, Bruce Tomason
Trustee, Robert Wister

LOCATIONS

HQ: SETON HALL UNIVERSITY
400 S ORANGE AVE, SOUTH ORANGE, NJ 07079-2697
Phone: 973-761-9000
Web: WWW.MATH.SHU.EDU

PRODUCTS/OPERATIONS

Selected Schools & Colleges

College of Arts and Sciences
College of Education and Human Services
College of Nursing
Immaculate Conception Seminary School of Theology
School of Health and Medical Sciences
School of Law
Stillman School of Business
Whitehead School of Diplomacy & International Relations

HISTORICAL FINANCIALS

Company Type: Private

Income Statement FYE: June 30

	REVENUE ($ mil.)	NET INCOME ($ mil.)	NET PROFIT MARGIN	EMPLOYEES
06/12	256	(0)	—	2,700
06/11	256	39	15.4%	—
06/10	335	4	1.5%	—
06/09	232	(29)	—	—
Annual Growth	3.3%	—	—	—

2012 Year-End Financials

Debt ratio: —
Return on equity: (-0.10%)
Cash ($ mil.): 38
Current ratio: —
Long-term debt ($ mil.): —
Dividends
Yield: —
Payout: —
Market value ($ mil.): —

SEYFARTH SHAW LLP

Every day is labor day at law firm Seyfarth Shaw which specializes in handling employment-related matters for its clients. The firm divides its numerous practices into four main areas: business services employee benefits labor and employment and litigation. Overall Seyfarth Shaw has about 800 attorneys in 14 offices –ten spread throughout the US plus four international outposts. Seyfarth Shaw draws clients from industries such as financial services life sciences and telecommunications. Henry Seyfarth Lee Shaw and Owen Fairweather founded the firm in 1945.

Geographic Reach

The firm maintains offices in Atlanta Boston Chicago Houston London Los Angeles Melbourne New York Sacramento San Francisco Shanghai Sydney and Washington DC. It extends its offerings through alliances with other firms in leading business centers around the world.

Sales and Marketing

Seyfarth's clients have included more than 300 companies from the FORTUNE 500.

Strategy

The firm has been expanding its real estate practice.

EXECUTIVES

Chairman Intellectual Property Practice Group, Brian L. Michaelis
Office Managing Partner Chicago, David J. Rowland
National Chairman Real Estate Department, Paul P. Mattingly
National Chairman Seyfarth's Labor & Employment Department, Lisa J. Damon
Managing Partner San Francisco, Nick C. Geannacopulos
Chairman National Wage and Hour Litigation Practice Group, Richard L. Alfred
Managing Partner and the Chairman Houston, Mark W. Coffin
Managing Partner, Russell B. Swapp
Chairman Asia Pacific Transactional Practice, Craig Carracher
CIO, Andrew D. Jurczyk
Managing Director, Philippe Weiss
Senior Legal Project Manager, Jenny L. Lee
CEO SeyfarthLean Consulting, Robert Saccone
Vice President Research Director, Athena Goehl
Legal Secretary, Kristine Kramer
Legal Secretary, Carol Alaniz
Legal Secretary, Denise Little
Legal Secretary, Beverly Maxwell
Legal Secretary, Sherry Loving
Legal Secretary, Maria Torigian
Legal Secretary, Melissa Witmer
Legal Secretary, Nancy Davilla
Senior Vice President, Ronald Swanstrom
Legal Secretary, Ellen Ferebee
Legal Secretary, Antoinette Riebling
Legal Secretary, June Daniel
Secretary, Regina Hohmann
Secretary, Kathy Rubenzer
Secretary, Inah Lee
Secretary, Laura Thixton
Secretary, Rebecca Garner
Secretary, Rose Clayton
Secretary, Cherilyn Heath
Secretary, Yolanda Vasquez
Secretary, Christine McNeil
Secretary, Gloria Lovett
Secretary, Karla Villalobos Roque
Secretary, Valerie Norris
Secretary, Kirk Krilla
Secretary, Jean Murray
Secretary, Sue McNatt
Secretary, Kathy McCarthy
Secretary, Jennie Nishida
Secretary, Karin Emery
Secretary, Kathy Truesdale
Secretary, Robin Banks
Secretary, Kim Hovey
Secretary, James Aguilera
Secretary, Linda Milbourn
Secretary, Jolynn Simon
Secretary, Geraldine Lofaso
Secretary, Eva Salazar
Secretary, Ann Pleasant
Secretary, Rebecca Ortega
Secretary, Charles Jaffee
Secretary, Sandra Prado
Secretary, Sandra Martinez
Secretary, Maria Palanca
Secretary, Kelley Lehr
Secretary, Maria Torres
Secretary, Darlene Romero
Secretary, Sallye Thornton
Secretary, Margaret Brueck
Secretary, Jodi Snyder
Secretary, Patricia Thurman
Secretary, Lynne Mateja
Secretary, Laura Henderson
Secretary, Melanie Alexander
Secretary, Eloisa Flores
Secretary, Seema White
Secretary, Sandra McMillan
Secretary, Deborah Hodgson
Secretary, Jennifer Woods
Secretary, Carla Bryant
Secretary, Nancy Hull
Secretary, Joanne Penta
Secretary, Theresa Ponds
Secretary, Kathy Olson
Secretary, Maridith Winter
Secretary, Fern Jenkins
Secretary, Karen Shepardson

LOCATIONS

HQ: SEYFARTH SHAW LLP
131 S DEARBORN ST # 2400, CHICAGO, IL 60603-5863
Phone: 312-460-5000
Web: WWW.SEYFARTH.COM

PRODUCTS/OPERATIONS

Selected Practice Areas

Bankruptcy workouts and business reorganization
Commercial class action defense
Commercial litigation
Construction
Corporate
E-discovery
Employee benefits and executive compensation
Environmental safety and toxic torts
Government contracts
Intellectual property
International
Labor and employment
Product liability
Real estate
Securities and financial litigation
Tax
Trade secrets computer fraud and non-competes

Selected Industries Served

Financial services
Health care
Hospitality
Insurance
Life sciences: pharmaceuticals biotechnology and medical devices
Media
Professional services
Retail
Technology
Telecommunications
Trusts and estates

COMPETITORS

Baker & McKenzie
Baker Botts
Hinshaw & Culbertson
Jones Day
Kirkland & Ellis
Littler Mendelson
Mayer Brown
McDermott Will & Emery
Ogletree Deakins
Paul Hastings
Proskauer Rose
Sidley Austin
Skadden Arps
Winston & Strawn

HISTORICAL FINANCIALS

Company Type: Private

Income Statement FYE: December 31

	REVENUE ($ mil.)	NET INCOME ($ mil.)	NET PROFIT MARGIN	EMPLOYEES
12/08	462	146	31.7%	1,608
12/07	431	141	32.9%	—
12/06	385	136	35.3%	—
12/05	332	124	37.4%	—
Annual Growth	11.7%	5.8%	—	—

2008 Year-End Financials

Debt ratio: —
Return on equity: 31.70%
Cash ($ mil.): 41
Current ratio: 3.30
Long-term debt ($ mil.): —
Dividends
Yield: —
Payout: —
Market value ($ mil.): —

SGT INC.

Like its acronym name suggests SGT (aka Stinger Ghaffarian Technologies) is used to taking military orders; in this case very specific technical ones. An engineering services firm SGT provides aerospace engineering project management IT systems development and related services to NASA the US Navy the US Air Force and other primarily military-related government entities through contracts. The company also offers science-related services such as earth climate and planetary modeling and analysis. SGT's facilities are located near airfields and other military facilities.

Geographic Reach

SGT operates a more than dozen offices including in Houston Cleveland and Los Angeles White Sands (New Mexico) and Wallops Island (Virginia).

Strategy

In 2013 the company formed a new subsidiary Houston-based engineering products subsidiary Intuitive Machines Inc. The partnership leverages synergies between control systems motor control robotics advanced manufacturing mechanics electronics software computational analysis sensing and other core competencies to address significant challenges across a range of industries.

In 2011 SGT opened an office in El Segundo California to support activities at the nearby Air Force Space and Missile Systems Center.

Company Background

SGT was founded in 1994 by Harold Stinger and CEO Kam Ghaffarian.

EXECUTIVES

VP Business Development, Charlie Goorevich
Chairman, Harold Stinger
President CEO, Kam Ghaffarian
CFO, Joe Morway
SVP NASA Business Unit, Dave Wolt
SVP Civil Business Unit, Andy Endal
VP Business Operations, Matt Yetman
VP Quality, Brian Bolger
VP Corporate Communications, Shelley Johnson
Marketing Manager, Marianne Dailey
Senior Vice President Civil Business Unit, Christine Matthews
VP-SIs, Ron Marinzel
Senior Vice President National Security Programs, Wayne Friedman

LOCATIONS

HQ: SGT INC.
7701 GREENBELT RD STE 400, GREENBELT, MD 20770-6521
Phone: 301-614-8600
Web: WWW.SGT-INC.COM

COMPETITORS

Ball Aerospace
CACI International
CDI Government Services
Digital Fusion
Lockheed Martin Space Systems
QSS Group
Raytheon IIS
Sierra Nevada Corp
Techshot
United Space Alliance

HISTORICAL FINANCIALS

Company Type: Private

Income Statement

FYE: September 30

	REVENUE ($ mil.)	NET INCOME ($ mil.)	NET PROFIT MARGIN	EMPLOYEES
09/08	292	8	2.8%	1,500
09/06	112	2	2.4%	—
09/05	80	1	2.2%	—
09/04	26	0	0.0%	—
Annual Growth	81.6%	1179.6%	—	—

2008 Year-End Financials

Debt ratio: —
Return on equity: 2.80%
Cash ($ mil.): 0
Current ratio: 1.20
Long-term debt ($ mil.): —
Dividends
Yield: —
Payout: —
Market value ($ mil.): —

SHAMROCK FOODS COMPANY

You might say Shamrock Foods is milking the food service business for all it's worth. Distribution business Shamrock Foods ranks in the top 10 US food services companies while its Shamrock Farms unit represents one of the largest dairy operators in the southwestern US. The company's distribution operations supply food and related products to food service operators in 10 states in the Intermountain region through a handful of distribution centers. Shamrock Farms home to more than 10000 cows produces and offers a full line of dairy products including fluid milk half and half and ice cream. Founded in 1922 as a mom-and-pop dairy Shamrock Foods is still owned and operated by the founding McClelland family.

Geographic Reach

The Phoenix-based company's distribution area spans Arizona California Colorado Kansas New Mexico Nevada Nebraska Texas Utah and Wyoming. It supplies its customers from distribution centers in Denver Phoenix and Albuquerque.

Operations

Shamrock Foods carries some 16000 food service products including fresh produce dry groceries frozen foods ethnic specialties meat seafood and beverages along with Shamrock Farms' dairy products. It also carries cleaning and paper products and other supplies and equipment. Its customers include restaurants fast-food outlet schools hospitals and institutions in 10 states.

Strategy

Looking to extend its reach eastward Shamrock Foods in 2013 broke ground on a $50 million manufacturing facility in Virginia where it will process milk and other dairy products.

The company works to develop new products and maintains relationships with other businesses to keep its products in front of customers. Shamrock Farms sells Rockin' Refuel a protein-fortified chocolate milk that the company says helps rebuild and repair muscles after exercise. In addition to its Shamrock-branded dairy products the dairy company offers private-label services and is the milk supplier for all US Subway sandwich shops.

EXECUTIVES

President Shamrock Farms Company, Norman McClelland
SVP CFO Secretary and Treasurer, F. Phillips (Phil) Giltner III
President, Kent McClelland
VP & CIO, Rob Baxter

LOCATIONS

HQ: SHAMROCK FOODS COMPANY
3900 E CAMELBACK RD # 300, PHOENIX, AZ 85018-2614
Phone: 602-477-2500
Web: WWW.SHAMROCKFARMS.NET

PRODUCTS/OPERATIONS

Selected Products

Beverages
Center of the plate
Dairy
Cleaning supplies
Dry goods and groceries
Frozen foods
Mexican foods
Pacific rim foods
Paper and disposable products
Produce
Specialty produce
Seafood
Supplies and equipment

Selected Brands

Aspen Gold
Brickfire Bakery
Chef Mark
Emerald Valley Ranch
Gold Canyon
Katy' s Kitchen
Lotus Garden
Prairie Creek
Pro Clean
Proware
Shamrock Farms
Silverbrook
Southern Pearl
Villa Frizzoni

COMPETITORS

Blue Bell
C&S Wholesale
California Dairies Inc.
Dairy Farmers of America
Dean Foods
Land O' Lakes
McLane
Meadowbrook Meat Company
Nash-Finch
Performance Food Services Group of America
Stonyfield Farm
Sysco
US Foods
United Dairymen of Arizona
Wells' Dairy

HISTORICAL FINANCIALS

Company Type: Private

Income Statement

FYE: September 30

	REVENUE ($ mil.)	NET INCOME ($ mil.)	NET PROFIT MARGIN	EMPLOYEES
09/12	1,353	0	—	2,600
09/11	1,353	0	—	—
09/10	1,808	0	—	—
09/09	1,353	0	—	—
Annual Growth	(0.0%)	—	—	—

2012 Year-End Financials

Debt ratio: —
Return on equity: —
Cash ($ mil.): 15
Current ratio: 0.70
Long-term debt ($ mil.): —
Dividends
Yield: —
Payout: —
Market value ($ mil.): —

SHANDS JACKSONVILLE MEDICAL CENTER INC.

Close to the shifting sands of the northern Florida coast Shands Jacksonville Medical Center (doing business as UF Health Jacksonville) offers a range of services to the 19 counties it serves in Florida and southern Georgia. The 695-bed hospital includes a cardiovascular center Level III neonatal intensive care unit and a Level I trauma center. It also operates primary and specialty clinics in the Jacksonville area. Founded in 1870 as the Duval Hospital and Asylum UF Health Jacksonville started the first cancer program in Florida in 1948. The medical center is affiliated with the University of Florida and is the largest of seven hospitals in the Shands HealthCare family.

Geographic Reach

UF Health Jacksonville's facilities are located in Jacksonville Florida and surrounding areas of northeastern Florida and southeastern Georgia.

Operations

UF Health Jacksonville operates about 40 outpatient care centers. Overall its facilities handle some 34000 inpatient visits and 600000 outpatient visits per year. The hospital's affiliation with the University of Florida (UF) includes collaborative treatment and research programs in areas including cancer cardiovascular neurology orthopedic and pediatric care.

Strategy

UF Health Jacksonville has plans to build a second campus on the north side of Jacksonville to meet the needs of a growing community. It's also exploring ways to increase clinical efficiencies such as implementing an electronic health record (EHR) system (with help from federal stimulus funding); it also is looking to maximize funding opportunities for its research programs.

In 2010 in the midst of economic challenges parent Shands HealthCare aligned UF Health Jacksonville's administration more closely with its other academic hospital Shands at the University of Florida in Gainesville. The sister hospitals continue to operate independently but benefit from a shared academic and research focus; the hospitals are working together to increase operational efficiency and flexibility within the system.

EXECUTIVES

CFO, Michael E. Gleason
CEO, Russell E. Armistead Jr.
SVP Hospital Operations, Greg Miller
Vice President of Human Resources, Lesli Ward
VP Primary Care Services, Rita James
Chief Medical Information Officer, Joseph J. Tepas III
SVP Chief Medical Officer and Chief Quality Officer, David J. Vukich
VP and Chief Nursing Officer, Patrice Jones
VP Specialty Care Services, Barbara Vernoski
Vice President of Government Affairs, Penny Thompson
President UF, David S. Guzick
Chief Administrative Officer, Mark Anderson

LOCATIONS

HQ: SHANDS JACKSONVILLE MEDICAL CENTER INC.
655 W 8TH ST, JACKSONVILLE, FL 32209-6511
Phone: 904-244-5576
Web: WWW.RAINBOW.JAX.UFL.EDU

PRODUCTS/OPERATIONS

Selected Services

Cancer services
Cardiovascular services
Neuroscience services
Orthopaedic services
Pediatrics
Poison Center
Trauma and critical care services
Women and families

COMPETITORS

Baptist Health System
Bay Medical Center
Brooks Rehabilitation
Florida Hospital Tampa Bay Division
Mayo Clinic Jacksonville
Nemours Foundation
North Florida Regional Medical Center
Ocala Regional Medical Center
Orange Park Medical
Orlando Health
Palms West Hospital
St. Vincent' s Health System

HISTORICAL FINANCIALS

Company Type: Private

Income Statement FYE: June 30

	REVENUE ($ mil.)	NET INCOME ($ mil.)	NET PROFIT MARGIN	EMPLOYEES
06/10	592	19	3.2%	3,000
06/09	591	7	1.2%	—
06/09	1,174	0	—	—
Annual Growth	—	5738109.0%	—	—

2010 Year-End Financials

Debt ratio: —
Return on equity: 3.20%
Cash ($ mil.): 58
Current ratio: 1.30
Long-term debt ($ mil.): —
Dividends
Yield: —
Payout: —
Market value ($ mil.): —

SHARI'S MANAGEMENT CORPORATION

This Shari keeps the kitchen open all day and all night. Shari's Management Corporation owns and operates more than 100 Shari's family restaurants in six states (primarily in the Northwest) that serve breakfast lunch and dinner 24 hours a day. The chain of eateries offers standard American fare such as pancakes and eggs sandwiches and burgers and beef chicken and pasta dishes as well as a selection of appetizers and desserts through a menu of about 120 items. The company is owned by a group of private investors led by Circle Peak Management. Ron and Sharon (Shari) Berquist opened the first Shari's in Hermiston Oregon in 1978.

Geographic Reach

The chain's 100 locations are located throughout California Idaho Nebraska Oregon Washington and Wyoming.

Operations

In a given year Shari's pours over 50000 cups of coffee serves 4000 dozen eggs grills a mile of sausage links and toasts nearly 50000 slices of bread.

Strategy

Shari's Management has continued to expand slowly with funding from its private equity investors. As it grows outside of its core market the company faces the challenge of creating a brand identity in a segment crowded with national chains such as Denny's and IHOP (owned by DineEquity). Shari's expanded into the San Francisco market in 2009 when it purchased and converted four Bakers Square locations from troubled VICORP Restaurants.

EXECUTIVES

President and CEO, Bruce MacDiarmid
SVP Menu Development, Kevin Bechtel
VP IT and Facilities, Tom Matson
Secretary, Ray Damron
VP Marketing, Michael Kiriazis

LOCATIONS

HQ: SHARI' S MANAGEMENT CORPORATION
9400 SW GEMINI DR, BEAVERTON, OR 97008-7105
Phone: 503-605-4299

Selected Locations

California
Idaho
Nebraska
Oregon
Washington
Wyoming

COMPETITORS

Brinker
Carlson Restaurants
Catalina Restaurant Group
Darden
Denny' s
DineEquity
Elmer' s Restaurants
Golden Corral
McMenamins
OSI Restaurant Partners
Panera Bread
Perkins & Marie Callender' s
Red Robin
Ruby Tuesday
The Holland Inc.

HISTORICAL FINANCIALS

Company Type: Private

Income Statement FYE: January 2

	REVENUE ($ mil.)	NET INCOME ($ mil.)	NET PROFIT MARGIN	EMPLOYEES
01/08	170	1	0.9%	4,000
01/07	165	40	24.3%	—
Annual Growth	3.0%	(96.2%)	—	—

2008 Year-End Financials

Debt ratio: —
Return on equity: 0.90%
Cash ($ mil.): 1
Current ratio: 0.10
Long-term debt ($ mil.): —
Dividends
Yield: —
Payout: —
Market value ($ mil.): —

SHARON REGIONAL HEALTH SYSTEM INC.

Ready to show some mercy to the ill in Mercer County is Sharon Regional Health System (SRHS) serving residents throughout northwestern Pennsylvania and northeastern Ohio. The not-for-profit hospital has some 240 beds and operates a network of nearly 20 outpatient clinics. Specialty services include behavioral health care cancer treatment home health and hospice care women's health services rehabilitation and speech and occupational therapy. As one of the region's primary health care providers SRHS has had to work to keep up with patient demand by opening a new $2 million diagnostic and imaging clinic expanding existing facilities and adding new care programs such as its Cancer Genetics Program.

EXECUTIVES

Vp-hr, John Davidson
CIO, Donna Walters

President and CEO, John R. (Jack) Janoso
Board Member and President Medical Staff, George Garrow
Chief Medical Information Officer, Robert Morgenstern
VP Patient Care Services and Chief Nursing Officer, Lisa Bertolasio
Director Of Radiology Services, Joann Esposito
Board Member, Cloyd E Brenneman
Chairman, Robert C. Jazwinski
Board Member and President Medical Staff, George Garrow
Board Member, Mary Ann Odem

LOCATIONS

HQ: SHARON REGIONAL HEALTH SYSTEM INC.
740 E STATE ST, SHARON, PA 16146-3328
Phone: 724-983-5864
Web: WWW.SHARONREGIONAL.COM

PRODUCTS/OPERATIONS

Selected Medical Services

Advanced Wound Recovery Center
Behavioral Health Services
Breast Care Center
Cancer Care Center
Center for Digestive Diseases
Corporate Health Services
Diabetes Center
Diagnostic and Imaging Center
Ear Nose Throat and Hearing Center
Emergency Care Center
Foundation
Heart and Vascular Institute
Home Health Agency
Hospice / Palliative Care
Hubbard Diagnostic and Specialty Center
Inpatient Rehab Unit
Interventional Pain Management Center
Medical Imaging
Neshannock Diagnostic and Specialty Center
Outpatient Rehabilitation Services
Pediatric Rehabilitation
Physician Recruitment
Rehabilitation Services
School of Nursing
School of Radiography
Sleep Medicine Center
Sports Medicine Services
Surgical Services
Travel Clinic
Therapeutic Pool
Transitional Care Unit
Volunteer Office
Women's Center
Wound Recovery Center

Selected Community Locations

Brookfield Family Medicine Center (Brookfield Ohio)
Greenville Behavioral Health Services (Greenville Pennsylvania)
Hubbard Diagnostic & Specialty Center (Hubbard Ohio)
Mercer Family Medicine (Mercer Pennsylvania)

COMPETITORS

Butler Health System
Heritage Valley Health
Robinson Memorial Hospital
Titusville
UPMC

HISTORICAL FINANCIALS

Company Type: Private

Income Statement FYE: June 30

	REVENUE ($ mil.)	NET INCOME ($ mil.)	NET PROFIT MARGIN	EMPLOYEES
06/12	165	0	0.2%	1,850
06/11	184	8	4.5%	—
06/10	174	(6)	—	—
06/09	172	(5)	—	—
Annual Growth	(1.5%)	—	—	—

2012 Year-End Financials

Debt ratio: —
Return on equity: 0.20%
Cash ($ mil.): 6
Current ratio: 0.90
Long-term debt ($ mil.): —
Dividends
Yield: —
Payout: —
Market value ($ mil.): —

SHARP MEMORIAL HOSPITAL

EXECUTIVES

Executive Vice President Hospital Operations, Daniel L. (Dan) Gross
Senior Vice President Chief Executive Officer, Tim Smith
CFO, Kevin Thompson
Chief Nursing Officer, Jennifer Jacoby
VP Clinic Services, Janie Kramer
Senior Vice President of Business Development, Alison J. Fleury
Senior Vice President of Marketing and Communications, James H. Nuckols
Senior Vice President Chief Information Officer, William A. Spooner

LOCATIONS

HQ: SHARP MEMORIAL HOSPITAL
7901 FROST ST, SAN DIEGO, CA 921232701
Phone: 8589393636
Web: WWW.SHARP.COM

COMPETITORS

Adventist Health
Grossmont Hospital
Palomar Health
Rady Children' s Hospital
Scripps health
Tenet Healthcare
Tri-City Healthcare District
UCSD Medical

HISTORICAL FINANCIALS

Company Type: Private

Income Statement FYE: September 30

	REVENUE ($ mil.)	NET INCOME ($ mil.)	NET PROFIT MARGIN	EMPLOYEES
09/13	992	183	18.5%	3,500
09/12	965	194	20.2%	—
09/09	734	49	6.7%	—
09/08	670	0	—	—
Annual Growth	8.2%	—	—	—

2013 Year-End Financials

Debt ratio: —
Return on equity: 18.50%
Cash ($ mil.): 1
Current ratio: 1.50
Long-term debt ($ mil.): —
Dividends
Yield: —
Payout: —
Market value ($ mil.): —

SHAWMUT WOODWORKING & SUPPLY INC.

Shawmut Woodworking & Supply which does business as Shawmut Design and Construction provides beginning-to-end construction services from preconstruction planning to post-construction quality assurance checks. Shawmut Woodworking & Supply has experience building retail hotel gaming spa sports restaurant education banking healthcare and life science facilities. The construction firm also handles corporate interiors and high-end residential construction. It boasts expertise in cultural and historical preservation projects. Founded in 1982 by Jim Ansara the employee-owned company serves clients nationwide and operates in a handful of states.

Geographic Reach

Shawmut Woodworking & Supply maintains a headquarters office in Boston as well as offices in New York; Los Angeles; Las Vegas; Providence Rhode Island; New Haven Connecticut; and West Springfield Massachusetts.

Strategy

To extend the reach of its operations Shawmut Woodworking & Supply in 2013 added new offices on both US coasts. It added an office in Los Angeles and another in West Springfield Massachusetts.

The company continues to build its reputation for constructing high-end retail stores in New York and beyond. Projects have included boutiques for Gucci Chanel and Juicy Couture. It's working on Boston's $115-million Dudley Municipal Building with an anticipated completion of January 2015.

Sales and Marketing

Shawmut Woodworking & Supply's clients include Harvard University Massachusetts Institute of Technology Babson College Bank of America Accenture Mercantile Bank Cisco Systems the Nantucket Whaling Museum Harry Winston Hard Rock Cafe and Ruth's Hospitality Group.

Company Ownership

Shawmut Woodworking & Supply is a 100% employee-owned company.

EXECUTIVES

CEO, Thomas Goemaat
VP Purchasing, Gary Bergeron
President, William (Bill) Hughes
VP Field Operations, Paul E. Doherty
VP Retail, Les Hiscoe
Chief Marketing Officer, Brian Stys
Vice President of Field Operations, Michael C. Sanchez
Chief Financial Officer, Roger C. Tougas
Vice President, Ron Simoneau
Vice President People Strategies, Susan Ehrlich
Executive Vice President Stadium Development and Finance New York Jets, Thad Sheely
Vice President, Tony Miliote
Vice President of Retail & Gaming, William Pisani
Director of Marketing, Michael Potter
Vice President of Administration and Student Life, Roy Schifilliti

LOCATIONS

HQ: SHAWMUT WOODWORKING & SUPPLY INC.
560 HARRISON AVE STE 200, BOSTON, MA 02118-2632
Phone: 617-622-7000
Web: WWW.SHAWMUT.COM

PRODUCTS/OPERATIONS

Selected Markets

Academic
Commercial
Corporate interiors
Cultural and historic
Gaming
Healthcare and science
Restaurants
Retail
Spas and healthclubs
Sports venues

Selected Services

Services
- Pre-Construction
- Master planning services
- Master project scheduling
- Lease review
- Value engineering
- Feasibility studies
- Green design services
- Drawing reviews
- Facilities audits and campus assessments
- Collaborative approach with architect/design team
- Comprehensive conceptual estimating
- BIM and virtual construction
- In-house M/E/P expertise
- Bid packages
- Constructability reviews
- Due diligence and site surveys
- Pre-qualification of subcontractors
- Management of permitting and approvals
- Development of specific phasing schedules and delivery methods
- Open book subcontractor bidding
- Logistics planning
- National purchasing power

Construction
- Master project scheduling
- Weekly project team meetings
- Sites monitored by a Safety Manager
- Zero-tolerance safety program
- BIM and virtual construction services
- LEED documentation certification and green building techniques
- Permitting services
- Design/build services
- Communication with surrounding community
- Coordination of owner-supplied items and vendors
- Procurement solutions
- Schedule and budget controls
- 24-hour/7 days-a-week emergency services
- Specialized services for program clients
- Indoor air quality management
- Construction and demolition waste recycling
- Customized waterproofing details

Post-Construction
- Commissioning and close-out services
- O&M manuals and training
- Project services division
- 1-year warranty walkthrough

COMPETITORS

Andrew Velez Construction
BBL Construction Services
Barr & Barr
Conti Enterprises
E.W. Howell
Skanska USA Building
Structure Tone
Turner Corporation
URS

HISTORICAL FINANCIALS

Company Type: Private

Income Statement FYE: November 30

	REVENUE ($ mil.)	NET INCOME ($ mil.)	NET PROFIT MARGIN	EMPLOYEES
11/12	680	4	0.6%	711
11/11	662	3	0.6%	—
11/09*	618	(21)	—	—
12/05	440	3	0.7%	—
Annual Growth	6.4%	4.4%	—	—

*Fiscal year change

2012 Year-End Financials

Debt ratio: —
Return on equity: 0.60%
Cash ($ mil.): 75
Current ratio: 1.10
Long-term debt ($ mil.): —
Dividends
Yield: —
Payout: —
Market value ($ mil.): —

SHAWNEE MISSION MEDICAL CENTER INC

Shawnee Mission Medical Center (SMMC) cares for Kansas City residents primarily on the Kansas-side. The health care facility located in the city's southwest suburbs has some 500 inpatient beds. It also offers outpatient surgery and other health services in areas such as pediatrics rehabilitation oncology and radiology. The medical center's emergency department receives some 50000 visits each year. SMMC also operates satellite facilities including the Shawnee Mission Outpatient Pavilion in nearby Lenexa which offers emergency and outpatient diagnostic general practice and surgical care. SMMC is part of Adventist Health System.

Geographic Reach

SMMC is located on a more than 50-acre campus in Shawnee Mission (near Kansas City) in Johnson County Kansas and serves the surrounding area. The main hospital campus includes a free-standing surgery center six physician practice buildings a child-care center for associates and a community health center.

Operations

SMMC handles some 20000 inpatient admissions each year as well as some 200000 outpatient visits. Its staff includes about 700 physicians who specialize in about 50 fields of medicine. Specialist care centers include a Chest Pain Emergency Center and the Center for Women's Health. The hospital also provides primary and specialty care through the Shawnee Mission Physicians Group including after-hours clinical care and cardiology and reproductive medicine services.

Strategy

The SMMC organization looks at community needs to determine where it should grow. In 2103 the hospital opened a $44 million new birthing center to meet the growing need for obstetric services in the Kansas City area. The expansion effort tripled the size of the medical center's labor and delivery and postpartum rooms allowing it to accommodate up to 5000 births annually and added a level III neonatal intensive care unit.

Company Background

SMMC is part of a network of more than 500 health care facilities sponsored by the Seventh-day Adventist Church.

EXECUTIVES

Senior Vice President, Robin Harrold
President and CEO, Ken Bacon
SVP and COO, Trevor Wright
Executive Vice-President Chief Financial Officer, Jack Wagner
VP and Chief Nursing Officer, Sheri Hawkins
Chief Medical Officer, Larry Botts
Auditors: Ernst&YoungLLP

LOCATIONS

HQ: SHAWNEE MISSION MEDICAL CENTER INC
9100 W 74TH ST, SHAWNEE MISSION, KS 66204-4004
Phone: 913-676-2000
Web: WWW.SHAWNEEMISSION.ORG

PRODUCTS/OPERATIONS

Selected Centers and Services

Bariatric Surgery
Behavioral Health
Britain Center (Cancer)
Center for Pain Medicine
CorporateCare
Diabetes
Emergency Services
Express Care
GI Services
Hand Specialty Center
HEALTHaware
Heart and Vascular Center
Home Health Care
Maternity
Holistic Care
Men' s Health Program
Neurology
Nutrition and Weight Loss
Orthopedics
Plastic Surgery
Radiology
Rehabilitation Services
Reproductive Medicine
Robotic Surgery
Sleep Disorders Center
SM Outpatient Pavilion
SportsCare
Support Groups
Surgical Services
TherapyPlus
Transfer Center Urgent Care
Weight Loss Surgery
Women' s Health
Wound Care Center

COMPETITORS

Ascension Health
Children' s Mercy Hospital
CoxHealth
HCA
Heartland Health
Mercy Health
Saint Luke' s Health System
Sisters of Charity of Leavenworth
Stormont-Vail HealthCare
Truman Medical Centers
University of Kansas Medical Center
Via Christi Health System

HISTORICAL FINANCIALS

Company Type: Private

Income Statement FYE: December 31

	REVENUE ($ mil.)	NET INCOME ($ mil.)	NET PROFIT MARGIN	EMPLOYEES
12/12	343	30	9.0%	1,850
12/09	358	24	6.7%	—
12/08	304	19	6.4%	—
Annual Growth	3.0%	12.1%	—	—

2012 Year-End Financials

Debt ratio: —
Return on equity: 9.00%
Cash ($ mil.): 236
Current ratio: 4.60
Long-term debt ($ mil.): —
Dividends
Yield: —
Payout: —
Market value ($ mil.): —

SHELBY COUNTY BOARD OF EDUCATION

LOCATIONS

HQ: SHELBY COUNTY BOARD OF EDUCATION
160 S HOLLYWOOD ST, MEMPHIS, TN 381124801
Phone: 9013212500
Web: WWW.SCSK12.ORG

HISTORICAL FINANCIALS

Company Type: Private

Income Statement FYE: June 30

	REVENUE ($ mil.)	NET INCOME ($ mil.)	NET PROFIT MARGIN	EMPLOYEES
06/13	391	(10)	—	4,800
06/12	422	(13)	—	—
06/11	414	(24)	—	—
06/10	395	0	—	—
Annual Growth	(0.3%)	—	—	—

2013 Year-End Financials

Debt ratio: —
Return on equity: (-2.80%)
Cash ($ mil.): 35
Current ratio: —
Long-term debt ($ mil.): —
Dividends
Yield: —
Payout: —
Market value ($ mil.): —

SHENANDOAH VALLEY ELECTRIC COOPERATIVE INC

LOCATIONS

HQ: SHENANDOAH VALLEY ELECTRIC COOPERATIVE INC
147 DINKEL AVE, MOUNT CRAWFORD, VA 228412358
Phone: 5404342200
Web: WWW.SVEC.COOP

HISTORICAL FINANCIALS

Company Type: Private

Income Statement FYE: December 31

	REVENUE ($ mil.)	NET INCOME ($ mil.)	NET PROFIT MARGIN	EMPLOYEES
12/13	212	11	5.2%	221
12/12	213	15	7.1%	—
12/11	216	18	8.4%	—
12/10	163	0	—	—
Annual Growth	9.1%	—	—	—

2013 Year-End Financials

Debt ratio: —
Return on equity: 5.20%
Cash ($ mil.): 6
Current ratio: 0.20
Long-term debt ($ mil.): —
Dividends
Yield: —
Payout: —
Market value ($ mil.): —

SHEPHERD CENTER INC.

Here to shepherd those with catastrophic injuries back to good health is Shepherd Center. The not-for-profit hospital specializes in medical treatment research and rehabilitation for people with spinal cord and brain injuries as well as patients with neuromuscular disorders (such as spina bifida) and chronic pain. Shepherd Hospital boasts more than 150 beds including a 10-bed intensive care unit. Of its patients who have suffered injuries about 60% have been in car accidents. Founded in 1975 by James Shepherd (who was paralyzed in a bodysurfing accident) and his family the hospital conducts neurological and neuromuscular research through its Virginia C. Crawford Research Institute.

Operations

Aside from its primary Shepherd Hospital Shepherd Center operates the Shepherd Pain Institute and the Andrew C. Carlos Multiple Sclerosis Institute.

It's ranked by U.S. News & World Report magazine as one of the top 10 rehabilitation hospitals in the nation. Shepherd Center employs more than 1400 people. Seeing some 6600 people on an outpatient basis each year the center admits more than 960 patients to its inpatient programs and another 570 to its programs for day patients.

Geographic Reach

Based in Atlanta Shepherd Center serves not only its home state of Georgia but the entire nation as one of the leading rehabilitation hospitals in the US.

EXECUTIVES

Medical Director Emeritus and Board Member, David F. Apple Jr.
Chairman, James H. Shepherd Jr.
President CEO, Gary R. Ulicny
VP Facility Services, Wilma Bunch
CFO, Stephen B. Holleman
Director Public Relations, Larry Bowie
VP Research and Technology and CIO, Michael L. Jones
Medical Director and Board member, Donald P. Leslie
VP Development and Executive Director Shepherd Center Foundation, Scott H. Sikes
Administrative Assistant, Teri Grimes
Medical Director Emeritus and Board Member, David F. Apple Jr.
President CEO and Board Member, Gary R. Ulicny
Board Member and Secretary, Stephen B. Goot
Medical Director and Board member, Donald P. Leslie
Board Member and VP, Emory A. Schwall
Board Member and Recording Secretary, Alana Shepherd
Board Member, Bernie Marcus
Board Member, Charles T. Nunnally III
Board Member, James D. Thompson

LOCATIONS

HQ: SHEPHERD CENTER INC.
2020 PEACHTREE RD NW, ATLANTA, GA 30309-1465
Phone: 404-352-2020
Web: WWW.SHEPHERD.ORG

PRODUCTS/OPERATIONS

Selected Facilities

Andrew C. Carlos Multiple Sclerosis Institute
Shepherd Hospital
Shepherd Pain Institute

COMPETITORS

DeKalb Medical
Emory Healthcare
Grady Health System
Northside Hospital
Piedmont Healthcare
Regency Hospital
Saint Joseph' s Health System
Southern Regional Medical Center
WellStar Health System

HISTORICAL FINANCIALS

Company Type: Private

Income Statement FYE: March 31

	REVENUE ($ mil.)	NET INCOME ($ mil.)	NET PROFIT MARGIN	EMPLOYEES
03/13	168	23	13.9%	800
03/12	159	23	14.8%	—
03/10	134	16	12.4%	—
03/10	127	33	26.2%	—
Annual Growth	9.8%	(11.2%)	—	—

2013 Year-End Financials

Debt ratio: —
Return on equity: 13.90%
Cash ($ mil.): 15
Current ratio: 3.00
Long-term debt ($ mil.): —
Dividends
Yield: —
Payout: —
Market value ($ mil.): —

SHEPHERD ELECTRIC COMPANY INCORPORATED

For well over a hundred years Shepherd Electric has steered customers through a range of electrical needs. The company supplies a variety of electrical products to wholesale and retail customers primarily to the commercial construction market but it also serves government entities industrial firms and OEMs. Shepherd Electric carries products from major manufacturers such as 3M Brady Eaton Hadco Fluke General Electric and Thomas & Betts among many others. The company was founded in 1892 by Ernest Fluharty and Henry Shepherd. Shepherd Electric is owned by the Vogel family which has had a controlling interest in the company since 1931.

Shepherd Electric operates from four locations in the Baltimore and Washington DC area. Some of the lighting and switchgear projects that the company has been involved with include working with the US Chamber of Commerce Johns Hopkins Cancer Center University of Maryland Medical System and The Baltimore Museum of Art.

EXECUTIVES

CEO, Charles C. Vogel III, age 84
President, Stuart L. Vogel, age 58
VP and General Manager, Jim Shearer

LOCATIONS

HQ: SHEPHERD ELECTRIC COMPANY INCORPORATED
7401 PULASKI HWY, BALTIMORE, MD 21237-2542
Phone: 410-866-6000
Web: WWW.SHEPHERDELEC.COM

COMPETITORS

Billows Electric Supply
Colonial Electric Supply
Consolidated Electrical
Dominion Electric Supply
Fromm Electric
Gexpro
Graybar Electric
Rumsey Electric
United Electric Supply
W.W. Grainger
WESCO International

HISTORICAL FINANCIALS

Company Type: Private

Income Statement FYE: December 31

	REVENUE ($ mil.)	NET INCOME ($ mil.)	NET PROFIT MARGIN	EMPLOYEES
12/12	183	5	3.0%	185
12/11	163	2	1.8%	—
12/09	151	2	1.8%	—
12/09	164	2	1.3%	—
Annual Growth	3.7%	37.9%	—	—

2012 Year-End Financials

Debt ratio: ——
Return on equity: 3.00%
Cash ($ mil.): 5
Current ratio: 1.90
Long-term debt ($ mil.): —

Dividends
Yield: —
Payout: —
Market value ($ mil.): —

SHI INTERNATIONAL CORP.

Businesses that need more than boxes of hardware and software can call SHI International. The company distributes scores of computer hardware and software products from suppliers such as Adobe Cisco HP Microsoft and McAfee. It resells PCs networking products data storage systems printers software and keyboards among other items. SHI offers a range of professional services including software licensing asset management managed desktop services systems integration and vocational training. The company serves corporate government and health care customers from nearly 30 offices across the US Canada the UK Germany France and Hong Kong. SHI was founded in 1989 by chairman Koguan Leo.

Geographic Reach

Based in Somerset New Jersey SHI has a global reach through its 28 offices located across the US Canada the UK Germany France and Hong Kong. In the US the company operates primarily in Texas and California but also in Arizona Colorado Florida Georgia Illinois Indiana Kansas Massachusetts Michigan Minnesota Missouri New Jersey New York Pennsylvania Virginia and Washington. Specifically its cloud briefing center is housed in New York City and its corporate call center runs from Austin Texas. The company's 420000-sq.-ft. headquarters operates beside its 140000-sq.-ft. Integration Center in Somerset New Jersey.

Operations

SHI serves several sectors and verticals. The company specializes in software and hardware procurement deployment planning configuration data center optimization IT asset management and cloud computing as well as custom IT solutions.

Strategy

The company has transformed itself from a $1 million regional reseller of software to a more than $4 billion global provider of information technology products and services. To this end SHI has invested some $20 million in a new data center that provides cloud services specifically what the company terms infrastructure-as-a-service (IaaS). The data center is one of six in the US that houses virtual machines for IT professionals to provide services such as application deployment disaster recovery software-as-a-service (SaaS). It also offers on-demand burst computing services where customers use the additional bandwidth to handle peaks in demand. HP Networking provides the network infrastructure for the data center which became operational in 2011.

SHI's professional services unit already provides some cloud services and data center consulting. SHI sees IaaS as a logical extension of the software asset management (SAM) service it already provides. Under the SAM program SHI handles software deployment licensing compliance and inventories across a business.

SHI partners with Omaha Nebraska-based information security software specialist Solutionary to manage data security services using its ActiveGuard software product to block computer network security breaches as data center security is one of the biggest concerns for businesses in a cloud computing environment.

Sales and Marketing

The company has a 99% annual customer retention rate.

Awards and Recognition

SHI is the largest minority and women-owned Business Enterprise (MWBE) in the US. The company's ranked 18th on CRN's 2012 Solution Provider 500 list of the largest IT solution providers in North America.

EXECUTIVES

President and CEO, Thai Lee, age 57
VP Finance and Corporate Secretary, Paul Ng
VP and General Manager, Hal Jagger
Chief Technology Officer, Richard (Rich) Taggart
Vice President, Celeste Lee
Vp Sales & Marketing, Jeremy Hourrier
Vice President Internal Audit And Finance Operations, Kevin Boyles
Chairman, Koguan Leo

LOCATIONS

HQ: SHI INTERNATIONAL CORP.
290 DAVIDSON AVE, SOMERSET, NJ 08873-4145
Phone: 732-764-8888
Web: WWW.SHI.COM

PRODUCTS/OPERATIONS

Selected Products

Accessories
Peripherals
Hardware
Memory
Software

Selected Services

Cloud services
Computer vocational training services
Data center services
Events
Hardware services
Networking
POLARIS Software asset management
Storage
Strategic consulting
Webinars

COMPETITORS

ASI Computer Technologies
Agilysys
Arrow Electronics
Avnet
CDW
CompuCom
Computacenter
Ingram Micro
Insight Enterprises
PC Mall
Softchoice
Tech Data

HISTORICAL FINANCIALS

Company Type: Private

Income Statement FYE: December 31

	REVENUE ($ mil.)	NET INCOME ($ mil.)	NET PROFIT MARGIN	EMPLOYEES
12/12	4,389	61	1.4%	2,200
12/11	3,757	35	1.0%	
12/08	0	0		
Annual Growth	—	—	—	—

2012 Year-End Financials

Debt ratio: ——
Return on equity: 1.40%
Cash ($ mil.): 87
Current ratio: 1.10
Long-term debt ($ mil.): —

Dividends
Yield: —
Payout: —
Market value ($ mil.): —

SHO-ME POWER ELECTRIC COOPERATIVE

LOCATIONS

HQ: SHO-ME POWER ELECTRIC COOPERATIVE
301 W JACKSON ST, MARSHFIELD, MO 657062128
Phone: 4178592615
Web: WWW.SHOMEPOWER.COM

HISTORICAL FINANCIALS

Company Type: Private

Income Statement FYE: December 31

	REVENUE ($ mil.)	NET INCOME ($ mil.)	NET PROFIT MARGIN	EMPLOYEES
12/13	204	6	3.3%	125
12/12	209	13	6.2%	—
12/11	208	8	3.9%	—
12/09	211	0	—	—
Annual Growth	(0.8%)	—	—	—

2013 Year-End Financials

Debt ratio: ——
Return on equity: 3.30%
Cash ($ mil.): 0
Current ratio: —
Long-term debt ($ mil.): —

Dividends
Yield: —
Payout: —
Market value ($ mil.): —

SHORE MEMORIAL HOSPITAL

You might be able to get a room with a view of the ocean at Shore Memorial Hospital. Operating as Shore Medical Center the facility is a not-for-profit community hospital with some 300 beds. It offers acute care services and more than 35 specialized care programs including oncology cardiology neurology obstetrics and orthopedic care. Shore Medical Center is affiliated with The University of Pennsylvania Health System and The Children's Hospital of Philadelphia. In addition to the hospital Shore Medical Center operates community-based health and fitness centers.

Geographic Reach

Shore Medical Center is located in Somers Point New Jersey which is located about 60 miles southeast of downtown Philadelphia.

Operations

Shore Medical Center has some 370 physicians on its staff which handles some 11000 inpatient visits per year. The hospital also manages some 6000 surgeries 1000 births and 47000 emergency room visits per year. Inpatient services account for about half of annual operating revenues while outpatient and emergency services each account for between 15% and 20% of sales.

As part of its affiliation with The University of Pennsylvania Health System Shore Medical Center has access to larger neuroscience and cardiovascular care programs among other specialties. It partners with the Children's Hospital of Philadelphia to provide pediatric services.

Financial Performance

Shore Medical Center reported $212 million in operating revenues for 2012.

Strategy

To expand its services for children and infants in 2013 Shore Medical Center formed a partnership with Onsite Neonatal Partners. Through the collaboration Onsite will provide staff for Shore Medical Center's 24-hour neonatal and pediatric care divisions.

In the realm of medical education Shore Medical Center strengthened its position by teaming up with Drexel University's College of Medicine to provide clinical education programs beginning in 2012. Through the partnership Drexel students will be able to conduct one-month rotations at the hospital in about 10 medical fields.

Shore Memorial Hospital adopted the Shore Medical Center brand after it completed a $125 million expansion project in 2011. The project included a new surgical pavilion that expanded its cardiovascular surgery and endoscopy centers as well as other specialist departments and diagnostic exam and laboratory units. Expansion efforts also included the opening of a new pediatric care center. The change in branding reflects the facility's broader service offerings and its connections to other health providers in the region.

EXECUTIVES

VP Finance and CFO, James T. Foley
VP Medical Affairs, Peter R. Jungblut, age 46
President CEO, Ron Johnson
VP Human Resources, Alan L. Beatty
Executive Director Shore Memorial Health Foundation, William D. Elliott
VP Nursing and Chief Nursing Officer, Joan T. Gavin
Chairman, Gerald L. Corcoran
Chairman-Elect, Jay Gillian
Secretary and Assistant Treasurer, Fernando Delasotta
Treasurer and Assistant Secretary, Robert J. Bray
Secretary Treasurer, Sandy Tzaferos
Vice President Chief Development Officer, Thomas J. Mundell
Chairman-Elect, Jay Gillian
Trustee, Robert J. Beach
Trustee, David Beyel
Trustee, Charles Bisciegla
Trustee, Louis P. DeScioli
Trustee, Joseph DiOrio
Trustee, Arthur T. Ford III
Trustee, Carol L. Gaffney
Trustee, Thomas H. Heist IV
Trustee, Richard H. Kabat
Trustee, Gary G. Schaffer
Trustee, David A. Spitalnick
Trustee, Richard L. Traa

LOCATIONS

HQ: SHORE MEMORIAL HOSPITAL
100 MEDICAL CENTER WAY, SOMERS POINT, NJ 08244-2389
Phone: 609-653-3800
Web: WWW.SHOREMEDICALCENTER.ORG

PRODUCTS/OPERATIONS

2012 Operating Revenues

	% of total
Inpatient	50
Outpatient	19
Emergency	15
Same day	6
Dialysis	4
Observation	2
Other	4
Total	**100**

COMPETITORS

AtlantiCare
Capital Health System
Christiana Care
Crozer-Keystone Health System
Doylestown Hospital
Inspira Health Network
Jefferson Health System
Kennedy Health System
Princeton HealthCare
The Cooper Health System
Virtua Health

HISTORICAL FINANCIALS

Company Type: Private

Income Statement FYE: December 31

	REVENUE ($ mil.)	NET INCOME ($ mil.)	NET PROFIT MARGIN	EMPLOYEES
12/12	202	(3)	—	1,600
12/09	202	5	2.6%	—
12/07	180	(7)	—	—
12/07	183	(5)	—	—
Annual Growth	2.0%	—	—	—

2012 Year-End Financials

Debt ratio: —
Return on equity: (-1.70%)
Cash ($ mil.): 0
Current ratio: 0.50
Long-term debt ($ mil.): —
Dividends
Yield: —
Payout: —
Market value ($ mil.): —

SHRINERS HOSPITALS FOR CHILDREN

The Shriners' red fez and mini-scooter parades are the goofy side to their very serious support of the Shriners Hospitals For Children. The system operates nearly two dozen hospitals throughout North America. The majority of its hospitals specialize in orthopedic conditions; others specialize in treating serious burn injuries spinal cord injuries and cleft lips and palates. Founded by the fellowship Shriners International the hospitals are supported by a multitude of fundraising events arranged by the organization's 340000 members. As a result Shriners Hospitals is able to treat children regardless of their families' ability to pay.

Geographic Reach

Shriners Hospitals' 22 facilities are located in the US Canada and Mexico.

Operations

Along with providing medical surgical and rehabilitative services and social educational and transitional services the organization conducts research to advance treatments for such disorders as bone disease pediatric burn nutrition and brittle bone disease.

Shriners Hospitals provides residency education and postgraduate fellowship opportunities to medical students and physicians looking to specialize in pediatric training. The hospitals have affiliations with more than 60 medical teaching facilities worldwide.

Financial Performance

Shriners Hospitals is largely supported by philanthropic donations.

Company Background

Shriners Hospitals For Children was founded by Shriners International in 1922.

EXECUTIVES

EVP, John McCabe
President and CEO; Chairman Board of Trustees, Douglas E. Maxwell
VP Hospital Operations, Eugene R. D'Amore
Chief Medical Officer, Kenneth Guidera
VP Finance and Accounting, Sharon Russell
Radiology Medical Director, Scott Dorfman
Vp Communications And Development, Marlena Lagina-kleine
Director Of Health Information, Teresa Brugger
Director Of Radiology, Susan Wagy
Radiology Medical Director, Kathleen A Murray
Vice President Human Resource, Susan Porth
Vice President Engineering, Norm Johnson
V P Marketing, Michelle Orsinger
V P Marketing, Ron Jansen
Interim Sr Vice President Human Resrcs, Kris Johnson
Executive Vice President, Mike Uhl
System Vice President Of Revenue Cycle, Scot Fache
Director Of Pharmacy, Roy Saylors
Vice President Of Revenue Cycle, Scott R Laubisch
Vice President Hospital Operations, Joseph Melchiorre
Aultman Human Resources Vice President, Amy Suarez
Vice President Of Engineering, Kent Southworth
Medical Librarian, Lynda Vanwagoner
Nursing Director, Gerald Harris
Vice President And Chief Information, Eugene Mayfield
Vice President, Dan Draper
Director Of Nursing, Robert Lusk
Director Of Pharmacy, Judy Peterson
Chairman, John A. Cinotto
First Vice President Board of Directors, Dale W. Stauss

LOCATIONS

HQ: SHRINERS HOSPITALS FOR CHILDREN
2900 N ROCKY POINT DR, TAMPA, FL 33607-1460
Phone: 813-281-0300
Web: WWW.SUPPORT.SHRINERSHOSPITALS.ORG

COMPETITORS

Akron Children's Hospital

All Children's Hospital
Children's Health System
Children's Healthcare of Atlanta
Children's Hopsital of Chicago
Children's Hospital & Medical Center
Children's Hospital & Research Center at Oakland
Children's Hospital Boston
Children's Hospital and Health System
Children's Hospital of Michigan
Children's Hospital of Orange County
Children's Hospital of Philadelphia
Children's Hospital of Pittsburgh
Children's Hospital of Richmond
Children's Hospital of The King's Daughters
Children's Hospitals and Clinics of Minnesota
Children's Medical Center of Dallas
Children's Mercy Hospital

Children' s National Medical Center
Children' s Specialized Hospital
Childrens Hospital Los Angeles
Cincinnati Children' s Hospital
Cook Children' s Health Care System
Dell Children' s Medical Center
East Tennessee Children' s Hospital
Miami Children' s Hospital
Nationwide Children' s Hospital
Rady Children' s Hospital
Seattle Children' s Hospital
St. Jude Children' s Research Hospital
Texas Children' s Hospital
Women & Children' s Hospital

HISTORICAL FINANCIALS

Company Type: Private

Income Statement FYE: December 31

	REVENUE ($ mil.)	NET INCOME ($ mil.)	NET PROFIT MARGIN	EMPLOYEES
12/09	285	(300)	—	6,100
12/08	0	0	98.5%	—
12/06	616	636	103.3%	—
12/05	583	278	47.7%	—
Annual Growth	(16.4%)	—	—	—

2009 Year-End Financials

Debt ratio: —
Return on equity: (-105.50%)
Cash ($ mil.): 6
Current ratio: —
Long-term debt ($ mil.): —
Dividends
Yield: —
Payout: —
Market value ($ mil.): —

SILVER CROSS HOSPITAL AND MEDICAL CENTERS

Silver Cross Hospital and Medical Centers serve the Illinois counties of Will Grundy and Cook through its main hospital campus and nine satellite facilities throughout the area. Its services include cardiovascular care women's health rehabilitation and behavioral health care. Outpatient facilities provide primary and specialty care services including medical imaging and dialysis. The hospital's name comes from the emblem (the Maltese Cross) of the Christian organization that founded the not-for-profit hospital the International Order of The King's Daughters and Sons.

Geographic Reach

Silver Cross Hospital and Medical Centers serves patients in Cook Grundy and Will counties in Illinois.

Strategy

In 2012 the hospital opened a replacement facility in New Lenox to house its main hospital and to keep pace with population growth in its service territory. The $400 million Silver Cross Hospital facility has about 290 private patient rooms and will be located.

The new 70-acre New Lenox campus also includes two medical offices buildings and the University of Chicago Medicine Comprehesive Cancer Center.

Silver Cross Hospital and Medical Centers also collaborates with the Rehabilitation Institute of Chicago to provide outpatient rehabilitation services at four of the health system's locations.

Company Background

Silver Cross Hospital admitted its first patient in Joliet Illinois in 1895.

EXECUTIVES

President and CEO, Paul Pawlak
SVP Finance and CFO, William Brownlow
Vice President Human Resources, Mark Jepson
Senior Vice President Business Development, Ruth Colby
Director Community Relations and Marketing, Tracy Simons
Administrative Director Cardiology and Diagnostic Imaging Services, Marybeth Antone
Vice President, David Schlappy
EVP and COO, Mary Bakken
Vice President Patient Care Services, Peggy Gricus
VP Operations, Geoff Tryon
Senior Vice President Finance Chief Financial Officer, John Krepps
Chief of Staff, Umesh Sharma
Administrative Director Emergency Services, Brandt Fick
VP Foundation, Larry Johnson
VP and CIO, Kevin Lane
Vice President Managed Care, Wayne Aardsma
Chairman, James Roolf
First Vice Chairman, Douglas Hutchison Jr.
Second Vice Chairman, Mark Stofan
Vice President Operations, Geoffrey Tryon
First Vice Chairman, Douglas Hutchison Jr.
Second Vice Chairman, Mark Stofan

LOCATIONS

HQ: SILVER CROSS HOSPITAL AND MEDICAL CENTERS
1200 MAPLE RD, JOLIET, IL 60432-1439
Phone: 815-740-1100
Web: WWW.SILVERCROSS.ORG

PRODUCTS/OPERATIONS

Selected Departments/Facilities

Behavioral Health/Chemical Dependency
Birthing Center
Cancer Center
Cardiology
Center for Women's Health
Colon Cancer Screening
Diagnostic Imaging
Diabetes
Dialysis
Encore Shop
Emergency Department
Free-Standing Emergency Care Center
Home Health Care
Incontinence & Pelvic Floor Disorders
Interventional Radiology
Joint Replacement Education
Intensive Care
Outpatient Infusion Center
Pediatric Services
Pet Therapy
Prostate Health
Pulmonary Program
Rehabilitation - RIC
Surgery - Same Day
Surgery - Using the da Vinci Robot
Senior Advantage
Silver Cross Emergency Medical Services System
Sleep Disorders Center
Weight Loss Surgery
Wound Healing & Treatment Center

Selected Services

Behavioral health care
Birthing services
Cancer care
Cardiovascular care/Cath Lab
Cardiopulmonary Rehabilitation
Chemical Dependency Services
Chemo and Radiation
Colon cancer screening/Colonoscopies
Da Vinci Robotic Surgery
Diabetes management
Diagnostic testing and imaging (ultrasound x-ray MRI PET/CT scan etc.)
Dialysis
Dietary Counseling
Emergency care
Health educational programs and screenings
Home health care
Hospitalists
Infusion Therapy (chemotherapy etc.)
Incontinence Care
Intensive care
Laboratory testing
Lifeline Emergency Personal Response Service
Mammography
Medical/Surgical inpatient care
Neonatal care
Neurology/Neurosurgery
Obstetrical/gynecological care
Orthopedic care
Pain management
Pastoral care
Pediatric care
Pulmonary care
Rehabilitation (physical speech occupational)
Senior Advantage Program
Sleep Disorders Carre
Support Groups
Stroke care
Surgery (outpatient & inpatient)
Weight Loss Surgery
Women's Health
Wound care

COMPETITORS

Adventist Health System Sunbelt Healthcare
Advocate Health Care
Covenant Ministries
Elmhurst Memorial Healthcare
Mercy Hospital and Medical Center
Northwestern Memorial HealthCare
Provena Health
Resurrection Health Care
Sinai Health System
St. Bernard Hospital and Health Care Center
University of Chicago Medical Center

HISTORICAL FINANCIALS

Company Type: Private

Income Statement FYE: September 30

	REVENUE ($ mil.)	NET INCOME ($ mil.)	NET PROFIT MARGIN	EMPLOYEES
09/08	244	21	8.6%	1,700
09/06*	187	13	7.3%	—
12/05	601	0	0.0%	—
Annual Growth	(25.9%)	988.3%	—	—

*Fiscal year change

2008 Year-End Financials

Debt ratio: —
Return on equity: 8.60%
Cash ($ mil.): 34
Current ratio: 0.40
Long-term debt ($ mil.): —
Dividends
Yield: —
Payout: —
Market value ($ mil.): —

SINAI HOSPITAL OF BALTIMORE INC

Sinai Hospital of Baltimore part of the LifeBridge Health network provides medical care in northwestern Baltimore. The 470-bed hospital is a not-for-profit medical center that includes such facilities as a heart center a children's hospital a cancer institute and a rehab center. Other specialties include orthopedics neurology and women's care. Medical students from Johns Hopkins University and the University of Maryland do some of their training at the hospital. Sinai Hospital of Baltimore was founded in 1866 as the Hebrew Hospital and Asylum and became a subsidiary of LifeBridge when it merged with other area providers in 1998.

Operations

The Sinai Hospital of Baltimore handles about 26000 inpatient admissions and some 75000 emergency room visits per year. It also conducts about 20000 inpatient and outpatient surgeries annually.

The medical center conducts a number of education and training programs including residencies and fellowships for about 400 medical students each year. It is a designated training site for the Johns Hopkins University's ambulatory and internal medicine clerkships.

Strategy

Sinai Hospital of Baltimore has completed several expansion efforts in recent years. In 2012 it opened a new dedicated inpatient hospice unit as well as a new center for geriatric surgery. In addition the 20-bed Friedman Neurological Rehabilitation Center was completed that year.

EXECUTIVES

Vice President, Barbara Epke
Director Of Surgery Services, Neal Naff
Director Of Physical Therapy, Ellen Zerbst
Auditors: PricewaterhouseCoopersLLP

LOCATIONS

HQ: SINAI HOSPITAL OF BALTIMORE INC
2401 W BELVEDERE AVE, BALTIMORE, MD 21215-5270
Phone: 410-601-5678
Web: WWW.SINAI-BALT.COM

PRODUCTS/OPERATIONS

Selected Centers

Alvin & Lois Lapidus Cancer Institute at LifeBridge Health
Center for Joint Preservation and Replacement
Children's Hospital at Sinai
ER-7 Emergency Center
Heart Center at Sinai
International Center for Limb Lengthening
Krieger Eye Institute
Louis and Phyllis Friedman Neurological Rehabilitation Center
Rubin Institute for Advanced Orthopedics
Sandra and Malcolm Berman Brain & Spine Institute
Sinai Rehabilitation Center
The Spine Center at Sinai

Selected Services

Allergy and Immunology
Anesthesia
Cardiology
Cancer/Medical Oncology
Dermatology
Dialysis
Emergency Medicine
Endocrinology and Metabolism
Family Medicine
Gastroenterology
General Internal Medicine
Geriatric Medicine
Infectious Diseases
Nephrology (kidneys)
Pulmonary and Critical Care Medicine
Rheumatology (joints tendons)
Neurology
Neurosurgery
Obstetrics and Gynecology
Ophthalmology (eye care)
Oral and Maxillofacial Surgery and Dentistry
Orthopedic Surgery
Otolaryngology (ear nose & throat)
Pathology
Pediatrics
Pharmacy
Physical Medicine and Rehabilitation
Psychiatry
Radiation Oncology
Radiology
Surgery
Urology

COMPETITORS

Anne Arundel Medical Center
Ascension Health
Bon Secours Health
Franklin Square Hospital Center
GBMC
Johns Hopkins Health System
MedStar Health
Meritus Health
University of Maryland Medical System

HISTORICAL FINANCIALS

Company Type: Private

Income Statement FYE: June 30

	REVENUE ($ mil.)	NET INCOME ($ mil.)	NET PROFIT MARGIN	EMPLOYEES
06/12	711	23	3.3%	1,403
06/11	691	36	5.3%	—
06/10	665	14	2.1%	—
06/09	577	(3)	—	—
Annual Growth	7.2%	—	—	—

2012 Year-End Financials

Debt ratio: —
Return on equity: 3.30%
Cash ($ mil.): 92
Current ratio: 1.20
Long-term debt ($ mil.): —
Dividends
Yield: —
Payout: —
Market value ($ mil.): —

SINGER EQUIPMENT COMPANY INC.

LOCATIONS

HQ: SINGER EQUIPMENT COMPANY INC.
150 S TWIN VALLEY RD, ELVERSON, PA 195209387
Phone: 6103876400
Web: WWW.SINGEREQUIPMENT.COM

HISTORICAL FINANCIALS

Company Type: Private

Income Statement FYE: December 29

	REVENUE ($ mil.)	NET INCOME ($ mil.)	NET PROFIT MARGIN	EMPLOYEES
12/12	223	3	1.7%	240
12/05	98	1	1.3%	—
Annual Growth	12.5%	17.2%	—	—

2012 Year-End Financials

Debt ratio: —
Return on equity: 1.70%
Cash ($ mil.): 2
Current ratio: 1.50
Long-term debt ($ mil.): —
Dividends
Yield: —
Payout: —
Market value ($ mil.): —

SKIDMORE COLLEGE

Skidmore College offers more than 40 degree programs including majors in both traditional liberal arts disciplines and pre-professional areas. The private college grants bachelor's and master's degrees in the sciences humanities social sciences business education social work and the arts. Skidmore enrolls about 2400 students from the US and some 40 other countries and boasts a student-faculty ratio of about 9 to 1. It was founded by Lucy Skidmore Scribner in 1903 as the Young Women's Industrial Club of Saratoga.

EXECUTIVES

Vice President For Advancement, Michael T Casey
Senior Vice President And Chief Information Officer, Dan Green

LOCATIONS

HQ: SKIDMORE COLLEGE
815 N BROADWAY, SARATOGA SPRINGS, NY 128661698
Phone: 5185805000
Web: WWW.SKIDMORE.EDU

HISTORICAL FINANCIALS

Company Type: Private

Income Statement FYE: May 31

	REVENUE ($ mil.)	NET INCOME ($ mil.)	NET PROFIT MARGIN	EMPLOYEES
05/13	140	32	23.4%	720
05/12	137	(23)	—	—
05/11	135	33	24.6%	—
05/10	134	0	—	—
Annual Growth	1.4%	—	—	—

2013 Year-End Financials

Debt ratio: —
Return on equity: 23.40%
Cash ($ mil.): 16
Current ratio: —
Long-term debt ($ mil.): —
Dividends
Yield: —
Payout: —
Market value ($ mil.): —

SLOAN IMPLEMENT COMPANY INC.

There's no slowin' down at Sloan Implement. The company provides the tools of trade for farmers in Illinois. Headquartered in Assumption Illinois Sloan is an authorized dealer of John Deere equipment and new and used parts. Founded in 1931 the company sells and services new and used Deere equipment including combines tractors manure spreaders tillers earth moving and lawn machinery and grain-handling equipment at five locations in Wisconsin and at 11 locations in Illinois; it also ships products nationwide and to international customers.

EXECUTIVES

President, Jim Steck
Parts Manager, Dustin Duduit
Manager Service, Chuck Standley
Store Manager Atwood (IL), Craig Wynne
Store Manager Carlinville (IL), Greg McCallum
Store Manager Effingham (IL), Larry Probst
Store Manager Taylorville (IL), Rod Carls
Store Manager Shelbyville (IL), Gary Patterson
Store Manager Virden (IL), Roger Spires
Service Manager, Bill Winstead
Office Manager, Chris McMahan
Service Manager Trucking, Shawn Jordan

LOCATIONS

HQ: SLOAN IMPLEMENT COMPANY INC.
120 N BUSINESS 51, ASSUMPTION, IL 62510-1120
Phone: 217-226-4411
Web: WWW.SLOANS.COM

COMPETITORS

Evergreen FS
Southern FS
Two Rivers FS

HISTORICAL FINANCIALS

Company Type: Private

Income Statement FYE: December 31

	REVENUE ($ mil.)	NET INCOME ($ mil.)	NET PROFIT MARGIN	EMPLOYEES
12/07	217	9	4.3%	350
12/06	146	4	3.0%	—
12/05	150	5	3.4%	—
12/04	159	4	2.9%	—
Annual Growth	10.8%	27.2%	—	—

2007 Year-End Financials

Debt ratio: —
Return on equity: 4.30%
Cash ($ mil.): 0
Current ratio: 0.10
Long-term debt ($ mil.): —
Dividends
Yield: —
Payout: —
Market value ($ mil.): —

SMO INCORPORATED

LOCATIONS

HQ: SMO INCORPORATED
6355 CRAIN HWY, LA PLATA, MD 206464267
Phone: 3019323600
Web: WWW.WILLSGROUP.COM

HISTORICAL FINANCIALS

Company Type: Private

Income Statement FYE: September 30

	REVENUE ($ mil.)	NET INCOME ($ mil.)	NET PROFIT MARGIN	EMPLOYEES
09/10	496	6	1.3%	25
09/09	395	8	2.1%	—
09/06	0	0	—	—
09/05	0	0	—	—
Annual Growth	—	—	—	—

2010 Year-End Financials

Debt ratio: —
Return on equity: 1.30%
Cash ($ mil.): 6
Current ratio: 1.00
Long-term debt ($ mil.): —
Dividends
Yield: —
Payout: —
Market value ($ mil.): —

SNAPPING SHOALS ELECTRIC TRUST INC.

EXECUTIVES

President and CEO, Randall G. Meadows
VP Energy Services, Terry Clark
VP Engineering Services, Brad Thomas
VP Line Services, Charles Woodward
VP Corporate Services, Randy Shaw
Manager Engineering, Melvin Allen
Manager MIS, Louise Blackman
Manager Member Services, Randy Price
Manager Human Resources, Margie Rowe
Manager Economic Development, Danny Stone
Manager Consumer Services, Dennis Thompson
Executive Assistant, Cathy Dyer
Chairman, James I. White
Vice Chairman, Olin Bonner
Secretary Treasurer and Director, Anthony Norton
Assistant Secretary Assistant Treasurer and Director, Joseph Sharp
Secretary Treasurer, Brenda Mason
Accounting Supervisor, Katie Johnston
President CEO of Snapping Shoals EMC, Brad Thomas
Assistant Secretary Treasurer, Walter Johnson
Vice Chairman, Olin Bonner
Secretary Treasurer and Director, Anthony Norton
Assistant Secretary Assistant Treasurer and Director, Joseph Sharp
Director, Ruby Woods
Director, Brenda Mason
Director, D. L. (Pete) Knox
Director, Jarnett W. Wigington
Director, James Sockwell
Director, Lewis Washington

LOCATIONS

HQ: SNAPPING SHOALS ELECTRIC TRUST INC.
14750 BROWN BRIDGE RD, COVINGTON, GA 300164113
Phone: 7707863484
Web: WWW.CO.HENRY.GA.US

HISTORICAL FINANCIALS

Company Type: Private

Income Statement FYE: December 31

	REVENUE ($ mil.)	NET INCOME ($ mil.)	NET PROFIT MARGIN	EMPLOYEES
12/12	170	2	1.2%	270
12/11	176	2	1.6%	—
12/10	186	4	2.4%	—
12/09	179	0	—	—
Annual Growth	(1.8%)	—	—	—

2012 Year-End Financials

Debt ratio: —
Return on equity: 1.20%
Cash ($ mil.): 2
Current ratio: 0.50
Long-term debt ($ mil.): —
Dividends
Yield: —
Payout: —
Market value ($ mil.): —

SOMERSET MEDICAL CENTER

Serving central New Jersey Somerset Medical Center provides a variety of health care services including cancer care women's health cardiology and surgical and rehabilitative services. Founded in 1899 the hospital has 355 beds as well as a medical and dental staff of approximately 650 members. The medical center is affiliated with the University of Medicine and Dentistry of New Jersey - Robert Wood Johnson Medical School campus. It also provides clinical research services in affiliation with The Cancer Institute of New Jersey. Somerset Medical Center agreed to merge with Robert Wood Johnson University Hospital in 2013.

Change in Company Type

The merger will create a 965-bed medical organization with multiple campuses including locations in New Brunswick and Somerville. The transaction is designed to enhance the organizations' abilities to offer a wide range of care to patients.

Geographic Reach

Somerset Medical Center serves central New Jersey residents in communities including Bridgewater Dunellen Flemington Hillsborough Princeton Raritan Somerset Somerville and Warren.

Operations

The medical center is designated as a primary stroke center and is nationally recognized as a leader in orthopedic surgery. Somerset is also one of nine hospitals that serve as a Medical Coordination Center to coordinate health care resources in the event of a disaster in the Central West region.

In addition to medical services Somerset Medical Center offers residency programs in fields including obstetrics and psychiatry through its partnership with the Robert Wood Johnson Medical School. It also operates outpatient clinics in surrounding areas.

Financial Performance

In fiscal 2011 Somerset Medical Center reported some $255 million in revenue a 3% increase over 2011 results due to higher net patient revenues and lower provisions for bad debts (unpaid medical bills). The company reported a net loss both years due to investment losses and pension liability adjustments among other factors though 2012 showed some improvement.

Strategy

To accommodate its growing number of patients Somerset Medical Center has completed a major expansion and renovation project that included constructing the Steeplechase Cancer Center to combine all its outpatient cancer services. It has also expanded in fields including emergency medicine surgery gastroenterology and sleep diagnostics.

Another area of focus for Somerset Medical Center is patient safety including technology upgrades to its clinical computer systems to monitor medical events and help reduce the risk of medication errors. Other patient safety initiatives include a falls-prevention program enhanced infection prevention efforts and a rapid response team.

Mergers and Acquisitions

The medical center also occasionally grows its network through acquisitions. In late 2011 for instance Somerset Medical Center purchased stakes in three physical therapy practices for some $2.3 million to expand its services in Somerville and surrounding communities.

EXECUTIVES

VP Information Technology Services and Planning and CIO, David P. Dyer
President Somerset Medical Center Foundation, Paul Huegel
VP Marketing Public Relations and Community Services, Victoria A. Allen
SVP Operations, Glenn McCreesh
Chairman, James Heston

LOCATIONS

HQ: SOMERSET MEDICAL CENTER
110 REHILL AVE, SOMERVILLE, NJ 08876-2598
Phone: 908-685-2200
Web: WWW.SMCFOUNDATION.COM

PRODUCTS/OPERATIONS

Selected Services

Bariatric Surgery
Behavioral Health
Blood Donation
Cancer Center
Cardiac Care
Cardiac Catheterization
Cardiac Pavilion/ Telemetry Unit
Common CT Procedures
Common Diagnostic Procedures
Common Interventional Procedures
Common MRI Procedures

Common Nuclear Procedures
Common Ultrasound Procedures
Critical Care Services
Diabetes Center
Emergency Department Services
Emergency Medical Services
Home Phlebotomy Services
Joint Replacement
Laboratory Services
Maternity
Minimally Invasive Sinus Surgery Program
Neuroscience
Orthopedic Services
Orthopedic Surgery
Osteoarthritis Services
Outpatient Services
Pediatric Hospitalist Program
Pediatric Same Day Surgery
Pediatric Services
Pediatric Surgery
PET/CT Scanning
Radiology
Rehabilitation
Respiratory Care
Robotic Surgery
Same Day Center
Senior Services
Speakers Bureau
Sports Medicine & Rehab
Sunshine Suite
Testing Services
The Baby Suites
Therapeutic Hypothermia
Urgent Care Center at Hillsborough
Vascular Disease
Vascular Tests

COMPETITORS

Atlantic Health
Barnabas Health
Bergen Regional Medical
Capital Health System
CentraState Healthcare System
JFK Health System
JFK Medical Center
Princeton HealthCare
Raritan Bay Medical Center
Robert Wood Johnson University Hospital
Saint Peter' s University Hospital
St. Joseph' s Healthcare System

HISTORICAL FINANCIALS

Company Type: Private

Income Statement FYE: December 31

	REVENUE ($ mil.)	NET INCOME ($ mil.)	NET PROFIT MARGIN	EMPLOYEES
12/12	245	(1)	—	1,743
12/11	260	(4)	—	—
12/08	260	(1)	—	—
12/08	240	0	0.4%	—
Annual Growth	0.5%	—	—	—

2012 Year-End Financials

Debt ratio: —
Return on equity: (-0.50%)
Cash ($ mil.): 7
Current ratio: 0.90
Long-term debt ($ mil.): —
Dividends
Yield: —
Payout: —
Market value ($ mil.): —

SOMERSET TIRE SERVICE INC.

Somerset Tire Service (STS) operates about 145 tire and auto centers throughout New Jersey New York and Pennsylvania. The company primarily sells tires auto parts batteries and accessories under such top brand names as Bridgestone Firestone Michelin Toyo Pirelli Goodyear Yokohama and Continental. Operating under the banner STS Tire & Auto Centers the company's locations feature a window between the store and service bays so customers can watch the work being done on their cars. STS has grown by acquiring other regional tire and service centers with hopes of saturating the Northeast before moving outside its home region. Founded in 1958 the company is employee-owned.

Geographic Reach

Based in New Jersey STS operates more than 80 of its stores in its home state as well as 30 stores each in New York and Pennsylvania. The company is the largest independent tire and automotive service company in the Northeast.

Operations

To support its distribution business STS in 2010 began operations at a 200000-sq.-ft. warehouse in Bridgewater Township New Jersey which today represents its largest location and boasts 20 loading docks as well as the capability to store 350000 tires. The facility serves the company's retail stores and wholesale customers on the East Coast.

Strategy

In recent years STS has concentrated on expanding its retail footprint with an ultimate goal of reaching a network that numbers some 150 stores. In 2014 the firm opened a location in Whiting New Jersey. Previous expansion efforts include opening about 25 stores in its tri-state market of New York New Jersey and Pennsylvania in 2012. It opened another handful of stores in 2013.

Company Background

STS is recognized for its environmental commitment due to events that occurred many years ago. The company began work on a warehouse facility in 2005 having owned the land on which the facility was built since 1971. It had not started construction until decades later because the land was classified as "brownfield" (for high arsenic levels) and required substantial cleanup to be usable. (STS did not know the extent of the pollution at the time of purchase.) The cleanup efforts were substantial.

EXECUTIVES

V P Retail Oprs, Kevin B Traier, age 59
V P Wholesale Oprs, Mark S Reiner, age 58
Vice President Marketing, Patrick Schulte
Vice President, Ted Haase
Vice President Of Information Technology, Mike Cardali
Vice President Sales, Abdoul Pierce
Vice President And General Counsel, Michael Matejek
Auditors: WithumSmith+Brown

LOCATIONS

HQ: SOMERSET TIRE SERVICE INC.
1 STS DR BLDG STE 1, BRIDGEWATER, NJ 08807
Phone: 7323568500
Web: WWW.STSTIRE.COM

2014 Stores

	No.
New	83
New	30
Pennsylvania	30
Total	143

PRODUCTS/OPERATIONS

Selected Services

Battery
Brakes
Engines
General maintenance
Seasonal service
Shocks
Struts
Tire services

Selected Brands

Bridgestone
Continental
Firestone
Goodyear
Michelin
Pirelli
Toyo Tires
Yokohama

COMPETITORS

Advance Auto Parts
AutoZone
Bridgestone Retail Operations
CARQUEST
Goodyear Tire & Rubber
Monro Muffler Brake
Pep Boys
Precision Auto
Sears
Wal-Mart

HISTORICAL FINANCIALS

Company Type: Private

Income Statement FYE: December 31

	REVENUE ($ mil.)	NET INCOME ($ mil.)	NET PROFIT MARGIN	EMPLOYEES
12/13	214	9	4.6%	800
12/12	203	7	3.8%	—
12/11	201	8	4.3%	—
12/10	189	0	—	—
Annual Growth	4.4%	—	—	—

2013 Year-End Financials

Debt ratio: —
Return on equity: 4.60%
Cash ($ mil.): 2
Current ratio: 0.30
Long-term debt ($ mil.): —
Dividends
Yield: —
Payout: —
Market value ($ mil.): —

SONORA QUEST LABORATORIES LLC.

LOCATIONS

HQ: SONORA QUEST LABORATORIES LLC.
1255 W WASHINGTON ST, TEMPE, AZ 852811210
Phone: 6026855000
Web: WWW.SONORAQUEST.COM

HISTORICAL FINANCIALS

Company Type: Private

Income Statement FYE: December 31

	REVENUE ($ mil.)	NET INCOME ($ mil.)	NET PROFIT MARGIN	EMPLOYEES
12/08	232	48	20.8%	1,200
12/07	205	42	20.9%	—
12/06	200	43	21.9%	—
12/05	183	0	—	—
Annual Growth	8.2%	—	—	—

2008 Year-End Financials

Debt ratio: —
Return on equity: 20.80%
Cash ($ mil.): 7
Current ratio: 1.90
Long-term debt ($ mil.): —
Dividends
Yield: —
Payout: —
Market value ($ mil.): —

SOUTH DAKOTA STATE UNIVERSITY

South Dakota State University (SDSU) is big on education in the Mount Rushmore State. The college offers undergraduate graduate and pre-professional programs to some 13000 students. Academic offerings include agriculture engineering and pharmacy courses. Its SDSU Sioux Falls Program targets non-traditional students (such as students with jobs and families) by providing evening and weekend classes. Notable SDSU alumni include former US Senator Tom Daschle and professional football players Adam Timmerman and Adam Vinatieri. SDSU a public school governed by the South Dakota Board of Regents was founded as a land grant college in 1881.

Geographic Reach

The university's main campus is located in Brookings South Dakota. SDSU's four attendance centers (where select courses are offered) are located in Pierre Rapid City Sioux Falls and Watertown. It also has eight extension offices across the state.

Operations

SDSU students can choose from more than 180 areas of study including about 70 undergraduate majors 30 master's degree programs 15 doctoral degrees and 10 certificates. Its classes are organized under colleges of agriculture and biological sciences; arts and sciences; education and human sciences; nursing; pharmacy; and engineering. The university also operates a university college a graduate school and an honors college.

SDSU receives grants and contracts to help fund research programs in fields including agriculture engineering geospatial data environmental science energy human health and pharmaceutical studies. Agricultural research is a core field of exploration for university students primarily through the school's South Dakota Agricultural Experiment Station.

With a student-to-faculty ratio of about 19:1 SDSU operates with an annual budget of $299 million.

Financial Performance

The university's operating revenue was reported at some $199 million in fiscal 2012 an increase of 4% over fiscal 2011 due to higher tuition fees and state support as well as other sources of income. Increase in net assets declined 44% to $17.7 million on higher expenses from supplies and contractual services as well as the lack of certain federal appropriations.

Strategy

SDSU's core operating goals are to provide quality academic programs through environment innovative staff and engaged students; offer support for research creativity and scholarship through facilities services and infrastructure; and to create beneficial partnerships with government community and global organizations to enhance academic opportunities.

Program and facility enhancements include the establishment of a new center for Agribusiness and Food Systems Management in 2013. It also opened several new residence halls that year. Projects under construction include new learning and research spaces for the engineering and architecture departments.

EXECUTIVES

EVP Administration, Michael (Mike) Reger
VP Academic Affairs and Provost, Carol J. Peterson
Vice President for Research and Dean of Graduate School, Kevin D. Kephart
Grants Administrator, Jacqueline Nelson
Director Human Resources, David Hanson
President CEO, Dick McComish
Vice President for Academic Affairs, Laurie Nichols

LOCATIONS

HQ: SOUTH DAKOTA STATE UNIVERSITY
2201 ADMINISTRATION LANE, BROOKINGS, SD 57007-0001
Phone: 605-688-6101
Web: WWW.BHSU.EDU

PRODUCTS/OPERATIONS

Select Colleges

College of Agriculture & Biological Sciences
College of Arts & Sciences
College of Education & Human Sciences
College of Nursing
College of Pharmacy
Graduate School
Jerome J. Lohr College of Engineering
University College
Van D. & Barbara B. Fishback Honors College

HISTORICAL FINANCIALS

Company Type: Private

Income Statement

FYE: June 30

	REVENUE ($ mil.)	NET INCOME ($ mil.)	NET PROFIT MARGIN	EMPLOYEES
06/12	198	17	8.9%	2,000
06/11	190	31	16.5%	—
06/07	134	6	4.9%	—
06/07	123	9	7.4%	—
Annual Growth	10.0%	14.2%	—	—

2012 Year-End Financials

Debt ratio: —
Return on equity: 8.90%
Cash ($ mil.): 67
Current ratio: 2.70
Long-term debt ($ mil.): —
Dividends
Yield: —
Payout: —
Market value ($ mil.): —

SOUTH DAKOTA WHEAT GROWERS ASSOCIATION

EXECUTIVES

Senior Vice President Agronomy and Corporate Marketing, Steve Briggs
Chief Executive Officer, Dale Locken
Senior Vice President Grain, Roger Krueger
VP Operartions, Roger Price
Vice President Human Resources and Organizational Development, Judy Stulken
Senior Vice President Operations, Chris Pearson
Chief Financial Officer, Blake Bomesberger

LOCATIONS

HQ: SOUTH DAKOTA WHEAT GROWERS ASSOCIATION
908 LAMONT ST S, ABERDEEN, SD 574015515
Phone: 6052255500
Web: WWW.WHEATGROWERS.COM

Selected Counties of Operation

North Dakota
- Dickey
- LaMoure
- Stutsman

South Dakota
- Aurora
- Beadle
- Brown
- Brule
- Clark
- Corson
- Day
- Edmunds
- Faulk
- Hand
- Hyde
- Jerauld
- Lyman
- Marshall
- Sanborn
- Spink

PRODUCTS/OPERATIONS

2011 Sales

	$ mil.	% of total
% of total		
Grain		54
Agronomy & related		38
Retail sales &		8
Total		100

COMPETITORS

ADM
CHS
Cargill
Country Pride
North Central Farmers Elevator
Northern Growers

HISTORICAL FINANCIALS

Company Type: Private

Income Statement

FYE: July 31

	REVENUE ($ mil.)	NET INCOME ($ mil.)	NET PROFIT MARGIN	EMPLOYEES
07/14	1,498	20	1.4%	638
07/13	1,847	20	1.1%	—
07/12	1,667	16	1.0%	—
07/10	1,020	0	—	—
Annual Growth	10.1%	—	—	—

2014 Year-End Financials

Debt ratio: —
Return on equity: 1.40%
Cash ($ mil.): 143
Current ratio: 0.60
Long-term debt ($ mil.): —
Dividends
Yield: —
Payout: —
Market value ($ mil.): —

SOUTH TEXAS ELECTRIC COOPERATIVE INC.

LOCATIONS

HQ: SOUTH TEXAS ELECTRIC COOPERATIVE INC.
2849 FM 447, NURSERY, TX 77976
Phone: 3615756491
Web: WWW.STEC.ORG

HISTORICAL FINANCIALS

Company Type: Private

Income Statement

FYE: December 31

	REVENUE ($ mil.)	NET INCOME ($ mil.)	NET PROFIT MARGIN	EMPLOYEES
12/13	359	19	5.3%	145
12/12	320	23	7.4%	—
12/11	320	21	6.8%	—
12/10	328	0	—	—
Annual Growth	3.0%	—	—	—

2013 Year-End Financials

Debt ratio: —
Return on equity: 5.30%
Cash ($ mil.): 69
Current ratio: 0.50
Long-term debt ($ mil.): —
Dividends
Yield: —
Payout: —
Market value ($ mil.): —

SOUTHCO DISTRIBUTING COMPANY

EXECUTIVES

General Manager, Buddy Davis
VP and CFO, Chris Wise
Executive Vice President of Sales, Mel Fairchild
Corporate Programs Director, Wendy Whitfield
President of Southco, Sherwin Herring, age 62
President, Sonny Wooten
Credit Manager, Jimmy Shelton
Operations Manager, Scott Barry
Executive Vice President Ext, April Garver, age 36
Transportation Director, Max Stevens
Foodservice Director, Steve Broadwell
Controller, Nichole Hill
Business Development Manager, Craig Smith
Purchasing and Inventory Control Director, Scott Andraka
Human Resources Director, Gerald Jones
Food Service Director Institutional Division and Key Accounts Manager Sales, Gregg Curtis
Development Manager Ext, Paul Lucas
Accounts Manager - Sales, Benny Randall
Business Manager, Bobby Wiggins
Service Manager Ext, Donnie Stiles
Service Manager Ext, Ray Flowers
Service Manager Supervisor Ext, Sammy Crocker
Service Manager Ext, Tim Weaver
Service Manager Ext, Jerry Cannon
Service Manager Ext, Lorry Cummings

LOCATIONS

HQ: SOUTHCO DISTRIBUTING COMPANY
2201 S JOHN ST, GOLDSBORO, NC 275307163
Phone: 9197358012
Web: WWW.SOUTHCODISTRIBUTING.COM

COMPETITORS

Core-Mark
Eby-Brown
Hot Stuff Foods
Marketfare Foods
McLane
Performance Food
Perky' s Pizza
Pizza Pro
Sysco
US Foods

HISTORICAL FINANCIALS

Company Type: Private

Income Statement FYE: December 28

	REVENUE ($ mil.)	NET INCOME ($ mil.)	NET PROFIT MARGIN	EMPLOYEES
12/12	397	2	0.7%	225
12/06	253	1	0.4%	—
12/05	0	0	—	—
12/00	203	0	—	—
Annual Growth	5.7%	—	—	—

2012 Year-End Financials

Debt ratio: —
Return on equity: 0.70%
Cash ($ mil.): 0
Current ratio: 1.00
Long-term debt ($ mil.): —
Dividends
Yield: —
Payout: —
Market value ($ mil.): —

SOUTHERN ILLINOIS HEALTHCARE ENTERPRISES INC

Southern Illinois Healthcare a nonprofit health care system operates the flagship 140-bed tertiary-care Memorial Hospital of Carbondale as well as Herrin Hospital (with 114 beds) and St. Joseph Memorial Hospital (with 25 beds). The hospitals serve residents of a 16-county region across southern Illinois. The nearly 280-bed system provides services such as birthing cardiac cancer and emergency care as well as surgery and rehabilitation. Its cardiac care is offered through an affiliation with the Prairie Heart Institute at St. John's Hospital in Springfield Illinois. The medical school at Southern Illinois University conducts its Family Practice Residency Program at Memorial Hospital of Carbondale.

Operations

Across its health system Southern Illinois Healthcare employs more than 3000 people. Physicians at its primary hospital Memorial Hospital of Carbondale represent nearly 40 medical specialties. It maintains the only dedicated pediatric unit in the region as well as the largest birthing center with Level II Plus Special Care Nursery.

EXECUTIVES

VP; Administrator St. Joseph Memorial Hospital, John Brothers
President and CEO, Rex Budde
VP; Administrator St. Joseph Memorial Hospital, Scott Seaborn
VP and General Counsel, Bill Sherwood
VP; Administrator Ambulatory and Physician Services, Phil Schaefer
VP Human Resources, Pam Henderson
VP Innovation Technology, David Holland
VP; Administrator Memorial Hospital of Carbondale, Bart Millstead
VP CFO and Treasurer, Mike Kasser
VP; Administrator Herrin Hospital and Miners Memorial Health Center, Terence Farrell
VP and Chief Nursing Officer, Julie Firman
Chairman, Steven Sabens
Vice Chairman, W. Eugene Basanta
VP and Chief Medical Officer, James Miller
President Founder, Kathleen Fralish
President Emeritus John, Bob Mees

LOCATIONS

HQ: SOUTHERN ILLINOIS HEALTHCARE ENTERPRISES INC
1239 E MAIN ST, CARBONDALE, IL 62901-3114
Phone: 618-457-5200
Web: WWW.SIH.NET

PRODUCTS/OPERATIONS

Selected Facilities

Herrin Hospital
Memorial Hospital of Carbondale
St. Joseph Memorial Hospital

Selected Services

Birthing Center
Cancer
Senior Renewal
Heart
Infusion Therapy
Neurosciences
Occupational Health
Pediatrics
Rehabilitation
Robotic-assisted Surgery
Sleep Medicine
Stroke
Surgical Services
Weight Loss Surgery
Wound Healing

COMPETITORS

Community Health Systems
Heartland Health
Memorial Hospital (Illinois)
Saint Francis Medical Center
St. John' s Hospital (Illinois)

HISTORICAL FINANCIALS

Company Type: Private

Income Statement FYE: March 31

	REVENUE ($ mil.)	NET INCOME ($ mil.)	NET PROFIT MARGIN	EMPLOYEES
03/13	440	47	10.7%	1,600
03/12	385	6	1.7%	—
03/11	394	52	13.2%	—
Annual Growth	5.6%	(4.9%)	—	—

2013 Year-End Financials

Debt ratio: —
Return on equity: 10.70%
Cash ($ mil.): 5
Current ratio: 1.40
Long-term debt ($ mil.): —
Dividends
Yield: —
Payout: —
Market value ($ mil.): —

SOUTHERN ILLINOIS POWER CO-OPERATIVE

LOCATIONS

HQ: SOUTHERN ILLINOIS POWER CO-OPERATIVE
11543 LAKE OF EGYPT RD, MARION, IL 629598500
Phone: 6189641448
Web: WWW.SIPOWER.ORG

HISTORICAL FINANCIALS

Company Type: Private

Income Statement FYE: December 31

	REVENUE ($ mil.)	NET INCOME ($ mil.)	NET PROFIT MARGIN	EMPLOYEES
12/13	204	4	2.4%	125
12/10	154	4	2.8%	—
12/09	157	2	1.4%	—
12/08	1,630	0	—	—
Annual Growth	(34.0%)	—	—	—

2013 Year-End Financials

Debt ratio: —
Return on equity: 2.40%
Cash ($ mil.): 2
Current ratio: 0.60
Long-term debt ($ mil.): —
Dividends
Yield: —
Payout: —
Market value ($ mil.): —

SOUTHERN METHODIST UNIVERSITY INC

What do former first lady Laura Bush actress Kathy Bates and NFL Hall-of-Famer Doak Walker have in common? They're all graduates of Southern Methodist University (SMU). Founded in 1911 by what is now The United Methodist Church SMU is a nonsectarian private institution offering undergraduate graduate and professional degrees in arts business engineering humanities law science and theology through seven schools. It's ,Âone of a handful of schools nationwide to offer an academic major in human rights. ,ÂSome 11000 students attend the university which has a student-faculty ratio of 11:1. About 85% of the 700-member full-time faculty hold the doctorate or highest degree in their fields.

Geographic Reach

SMU is housed in more than 75 buildings. The Texas university operates through a main campus located in University Park within Dallas County. Also in Texas it maintains property ,Âin ,ÂDallas (19 acres) Highland Park (2 acres) and Plano (25 acres). In Taos New Mexico SMU holds 423 acres.

Operations

The university offers more than 120 undergraduate degrees and about 130 graduate degrees through seven schools. ,ÂSMU also offers more than two dozen doctorates. Most of the ,Âits degrees are conferred in the humanities and sciences and business.

Sales and Marketing

SMU's enrollment includes ,Âinternational students from 90 countries. The largest numbers of students in descending order are from India China Saudi Arabia Mexico Korea Taiwan (Province of China) Guatemala Thailand Iran and Canada.

Financial Performance

Endowment gifts from donors reached $14.9 million in 2012. The private university's revenue decreased by 9% in 2012 as compared to 2011 due to dips in tuition and fees net realized and unrealized gains grants and contracts. Net income also decreased by 44% during the same reporting period. Revenue declines and increases in program expenses contributed to the net income woes.

EXECUTIVES

V Pres, Patricia Lasalle
Assoc Vp Research/dean Grad St, James E Quick
Department Chair, John Ubelaker
Assoc Vp/exec Dir Pub Affairs, Patti Lasalle
Treas, Michael A Condon
Treasurer, Maxim Rabinovich
Secretary Treasurer, William Bridge

LOCATIONS

HQ: SOUTHERN METHODIST UNIVERSITY INC
6425 BOAZ LN, DALLAS, TX 75205
Phone: 2147682000
Web: WWW.SMU.EDU

PRODUCTS/OPERATIONS

Selected Schools and Divisions

Annette Caldwell Simmons School of Education and Human Development
Bobby B. Lyle School of Engineering
Cox School of Business
Dedman College of Humanities and Sciences
Dedman School of Law
Meadows School of the Arts
Perkins School of Theology

HISTORICAL FINANCIALS

Company Type: Private

Income Statement FYE: May 31

	REVENUE ($ mil.)	NET INCOME ($ mil.)	NET PROFIT MARGIN	EMPLOYEES
05/13	563	115	20.5%	2,200
05/11	602	58	9.6%	—
05/09	236	(171)	—	—
Annual Growth	24.3%	—	—	—

2013 Year-End Financials

Debt ratio: ——
Return on equity: 20.50%
Cash ($ mil.): 290
Current ratio: —
Long-term debt ($ mil.): —
Dividends
Yield: —
Payout: —
Market value ($ mil.): —

SOUTHERN MINNESOTA BEET SUGAR COOPERATIVE

Southern Minnesota Beet Sugar Cooperative (SMBSC) offers a sweet deal to its approximately 585 member/farmers. The co-op slices about 3 million tons of Minnesota-grown sugar beets annually. Converted products include baker's sugar and fruit sugar as well as molasses beet pulp pellets and shreds and raffinate (liquid from desugaring molasses). The co-op also provides member services such as seed agronomy research farm support products and workers' compensation insurance. SMBSC's refined and liquid sugars are marketed through Cargill Sweeteners; the by-products (dried beet pulp and beet molasses for use in cattle feed) are marketed by Midwest Agri-Commodities in North American and Europe.

Operations

The beet sugar processor's operations consist of a main factory with an annual processing capacity of about 3 million tons of harvested sugar beets. The factory campus comprises settling ponds water-holding lagoons receiving strips off-site receiving stations and 1100 acres of land some of which is planted with grass and irrigated with waste water from the ponds and treatment plant. In addition the co-op has several silos to hold bulk granulated sugar a warehouse to store industrial-size bags of sugar and more than a dozen thick-juice storage tanks. Campus expansions since the factory's start in 1975 have included a molasses desugarization facility increases to processing capacity and new equipment.

The co-op has grown both through investments in added capacity to attract new member/farmers and acquisitions. Acquired in 2005 subsidiary Spreckels Sugar Company operates a beet sugar factory in Brawley California. Sugar produced under the Spreckels Sugar brand is sold to markets in the western US. Based in Sheridan Wyoming SMBSC's Holly Seed a former subsidiary of Imperial Sugar also acquired in 2005 develops beet seed varieties to increase sucrose content and yields. Holly Seed partners with SESVanderHave to supply seeds adapted to growing sugar beets worldwide.

EXECUTIVES

President, Kelvin P. Thompsen

LOCATIONS

HQ: SOUTHERN MINNESOTA BEET SUGAR COOPERATIVE
83550 COUNTY ROAD 21, RENVILLE, MN 56284
Phone: 320-329-8305
Web: WWW.SMBSC.COM

PRODUCTS/OPERATIONS

Selected Products

Ag liming material
Baker's sugar
Beet pulp pellets
Beet pulp shreds
Fruit sugar
Granulated sugar
Liquid sucrose
Liquid sugar
Molasses
Raffinates
Refined sugar

COMPETITORS

Amalgamated Sugar
American Crystal Sugar
C&H Sugar
Connell Company
Florida Crystals
Imperial Sugar
King Ranch
M. A. Patout
Michigan Sugar Company
Minn-Dak Co-op
Sterling Sugars
Sugar Cane Growers Cooperative of Florida
Sugar Foods
U.S. Sugar
United Sugars
Western Sugar Cooperative

HISTORICAL FINANCIALS

Company Type: Private

Income Statement FYE: August 31

	REVENUE ($ mil.)	NET INCOME ($ mil.)	NET PROFIT MARGIN	EMPLOYEES
08/12	474	196	41.3%	610
08/11	509	214	42.2%	—
08/10	439	154	35.2%	—
08/08	380	120	31.7%	—
Annual Growth	5.7%	12.9%	—	—

2012 Year-End Financials

Debt ratio: ——
Return on equity: 41.30%
Cash ($ mil.): 1
Current ratio: 0.40
Long-term debt ($ mil.): —
Dividends
Yield: —
Payout: —
Market value ($ mil.): —

SOUTHERN NEW HAMPSHIRE MEDICAL CENTER

Southern New Hampshire Medical Center (SNHMC) provides medical care for the residents of the Nashua New Hampshire area and surrounding region. The two-campus hospital which has about 190 beds and is part of the Southern New Hampshire Health System offers centers for cancer treatment diabetes education fertility and childbirth obesity sleep disorders trauma and other programs. Outpatient and rehabilitation services are offered through several clinic locations. SNHMC is also affiliated with physician practice organization Foundation Medical Partners and it is a teaching facility for the Dartmouth Medical School.

Geographic Reach

SNHMC's main campus is located in the heart of downtown Nashua New Hampshire and serves patients in the Greater Nashua area.

Operations

The Medical Center has a medical staff of more than 500 primary and specialty care providers from Foundation Medical Partners Dartmouth-Hitchcock Nashua and local independent practices.

Strategy

SNHMC is expanding its network of medical facilities to keep pace wth demand. In 2012 Foundation Medical Partners opened Southern New Hampshire Health System at Pelham. In 2011 SNHMC opened Hudson and Merrimack locations to meet the growing needs of the greater Nashua community.

Company Background

The company was founded as an 8-bed emergency hospital in 1893

EXECUTIVES

President and CEO, Thomas E. (Tom) Wilhelmsen Jr.
VP Planning and Communications, Scott R. Westover
SVP; President and COO Foundation Medical Partners, Susan M. DeSocio
VP Medical Affairs and Chief Medical Officer, Stephanie Wolf-Rosenblum
VP Patient Care Services and Chief Nursing Officer, Colette D. Tilton
VP Clinical and Support Services, Richard T. Duguay III
Vice President for Compliance, Barbara J. Richards
Chief of Staff, Sean W. Fitzpatrick
Chairperson, John M. Mercier
Chairman Leadership Steering Committee, George Rooney
SVP and CFO, Michael S. Rose
VP Information Technology and Chief Medical Information Officer, Andrew Watt
VP Emergency Medicine and Medical Director Emergency Department, Joseph Leahy

LOCATIONS

HQ: SOUTHERN NEW HAMPSHIRE MEDICAL CENTER
8 PROSPECT ST, NASHUA, NH 03060-3925
Phone: 603-577-2000
Web: WWW.SNHHS.ORG

PRODUCTS/OPERATIONS

Selected Medical Services

Aesthetics
Allergy and Immunology
Anesthesia and Pain Management
Arthritis
Asthma
Audiology (Hearing Evaluations for Children)
Auditory Brainstem Response
Clinical Trials and Open Protocols
Ear Nose and Throat
Endocrinology
Family Practice
Genetic Counseling
Geriatric Medicine and Services
Hematology
Hospice Care
Hospitalist Program
Internal Medicine
Kidney Care
Maternity
Nephrology
Neurology
Neurosurgery
Nutrition
Pathology
Plastic Surgery
Podiatry
Pulmonary Medicine
Psychiatry
Pulmonary Rehab Program
Renal Dialysis
Rheumatology
Sleep Center
Sports Medicine
Stroke
Urology
Vascular Services
Specialty Medical Services
Behavioral Health
Cancer Care
Diabetes Care
Digestive Health
Dermatology
Emergency Department
Heart Care
Immediate Care
Laboratory Services
Orthopedics
Pediatric Services
Radiology Services
Rehabilitation Services
Spine and Brain Care
Surgical Services
Women's Services

COMPETITORS

Catholic Medical Center
Concord Hospital
Elliot Health System
Exeter Health Resources
Frisbie Memorial Hospital
Steward Health Care

HISTORICAL FINANCIALS

Company Type: Private

Income Statement FYE: September 30

	REVENUE ($ mil.)	NET INCOME ($ mil.)	NET PROFIT MARGIN	EMPLOYEES
09/12	194	16	8.3%	1,200
09/11	274	(4)	—	—
09/10	214	7	3.7%	—
09/09	197	0	—	—
Annual Growth	(0.5%)	—	—	—

2012 Year-End Financials

Debt ratio: —
Return on equity: 8.30%
Cash ($ mil.): 52
Current ratio: 1.80
Long-term debt ($ mil.): —
Dividends
Yield: —
Payout: —
Market value ($ mil.): —

SOUTHERN PIPE & SUPPLY COMPANY INC.

Southern Pipe and Supply Co. sells pipes and anything that connects to them. Serving everyone from contractors and homeowners to commercial real estate property owners Southern Pipe sells plumbing heating and air-conditioning supplies through more than 90 stores located throughout seven southeastern states. The company operates a central distribution center and a handful of Southern Bath & Kitchen showrooms that feature various products for homeowners. Southern Pipe's vendors include dozens of supply companies and manufacturers such as MOEN Kohler and Amana Heating and Air Conditioning. Southern Pipe and Supply Co. was founded in 1938.

Geographic Reach

Mississippi-based Southern Pipe and Supply Co. operates about 25 locations in Mississippi and about 65 others across Alabama Arkansas Florida Georgia Louisiana and Tennessee.

Sales and Marketing

As part of its business Southern Pipe and Supply Co. serves as a distributor for some of the industry's most well-known names such as Kohler Delta Elkay Pfister Rheem Watts Zurn Lennox and Ridgid.

Operations

The company's Central Distribution Center which averages some 70000 transactions monthly boasts an error rate of less than 1% on orders shipped to its branches. For its designated more than 900 critical-service items the center has reached a near perfect fill rate of 99.7%.

EXECUTIVES

Hr Director & Vp, Ernst Prost
Chairman, Marty Davidson

LOCATIONS

HQ: SOUTHERN PIPE & SUPPLY COMPANY INC.
4330 HIGHWAY 39 N, MERIDIAN, MS 393011082
Phone: 6016932911
Web: WWW.SOUTHERNPIPE.COM

Selected Locations

	No.
Mississippi	26
Alabama	17
Louisiana	16
Georgia	14
Arkansas	10
Florida	4
Tennessee	3
Total	90

PRODUCTS/OPERATIONS

Selected Products

Heating & cooling equipment
Kitchen & bath fixtures
Plumbing
Residential & commercial pipe valves & fittings
Tools & safety equipment
Water metering fire hydrants & fittings
Waterworks

COMPETITORS

Baker Distributing
Ferguson Enterprises
HD Supply
Lowe' s
Stuart C. Irby
WinWholesale
Wolverine Tube

HISTORICAL FINANCIALS

Company Type: Private

Income Statement FYE: December 31

	REVENUE ($ mil.)	NET INCOME ($ mil.)	NET PROFIT MARGIN	EMPLOYEES
12/10	284	6	2.1%	767
12/09	261	3	1.3%	—
12/00	1,879	0	—	—
Annual Growth	—	231.4%	—	—

2010 Year-End Financials

Debt ratio: —
Return on equity: 2.10%
Cash ($ mil.): 5
Current ratio: 1.40
Long-term debt ($ mil.): —
Dividends
Yield: —
Payout: —
Market value ($ mil.): —

SOUTHERN REGIONAL HEALTH SYSTEM INC.

Southern Regional Health System operates the Southern Regional Medical Center (SRMC) in a southern suburb of Atlanta. With more than 330 beds this hospital offers patients cardiac monitoring diagnostic imaging occupational and speech rehabilitation and an abundance of other services. Other facilities include the Women's Life Center which provides women's and newborn healthcare and a 30-bed long-term acute care hospital. The system's Spivey Station campus in Jonesboro includes a women's imaging center and surgery center. SRMC was established in 1971 to provide health care to residents of Clayton County and the surrounding areas.

Geographic Reach

SRMC serves patients in the Georgia counties of Clayton County Fulton Henry DeKalb Fayette among a few others.

Operations

SRMC owns the Advanced Primary Stroke Center and the Georgia Orthopedic Institute. It performs minimally-invasive robotic surgeries with the da Vinci Surgical System and a variety of rehabilitation services. In 2012 SRMC delivered 2975 babies and had 80035 emergency department visits.

Financial Performance

SRMC saw its net revenue decrease by 8% in 2012 over 2011 due to a sizable decrease in revenue from patient care. As a result it suffered a net loss of more than $13 million for 2012.

EXECUTIVES

VP-Patient Care Svcs, Maria Kulma
President and CEO, James E. (Jim) Crissey
Chief Medical Officer, Willie Cochran Jr.
President and CEO, Stephen W. Mahan
SVP and CFO, Steven Lee Boles Jr.
EVP and COO, John R. McLain
SVP and Chief Nursing Officer, Janis M. Darnaby
Vice President of Finance and Accounting at Southern Regional, Gina Dickson
Vice President of Human Resources, Stacey J. Hancock

LOCATIONS

HQ: SOUTHERN REGIONAL HEALTH SYSTEM INC.
11 UPPER RIVERDALE RD SW, RIVERDALE, GA 30274-2615
Phone: 770-991-8000
Web: WWW.SOUTHERNREGIONAL.ORG

PRODUCTS/OPERATIONS

Selected Medical Services and Specialties

Georgia Orthopedic Joint Replacement
Heart and Vascular
Imaging
Surgery
Weight Management
Women's Health

COMPETITORS

DeKalb Medical
Emory Healthcare
Grady Health System
Piedmont Healthcare
Shepherd Center
SunLink Health Systems
West Georgia Health System

HISTORICAL FINANCIALS

Company Type: Private

Income Statement FYE: June 30

	REVENUE ($ mil.)	NET INCOME ($ mil.)	NET PROFIT MARGIN	EMPLOYEES
06/11	264	(3)	—	2,315
06/10	258	(10)	—	—
06/09	266	(30)	—	—
06/08	262	(5)	—	—
Annual Growth	0.2%	—	—	—

2011 Year-End Financials

Debt ratio: ——
Return on equity: (-1.20%)
Cash ($ mil.): 5
Current ratio: 0.60
Long-term debt ($ mil.): —
Dividends
Yield: —
Payout: —
Market value ($ mil.): —

SOUTHERN VALLEY CO-OP.

LOCATIONS

HQ: SOUTHERN VALLEY CO-OP.
721 W HUMPHREY, LAKE CRYSTAL, MN 56055
Phone: 5077266455
Web: WWW.CRYSTALVALLEY.COOP

HISTORICAL FINANCIALS

Company Type: Private

Income Statement FYE: August 31

	REVENUE ($ mil.)	NET INCOME ($ mil.)	NET PROFIT MARGIN	EMPLOYEES
08/08	222	7	3.3%	165
08/07	162	3	2.2%	—
08/06	80	4	5.5%	—
08/05	81	0	—	—
Annual Growth	39.9%	—	—	—

2008 Year-End Financials

Debt ratio: ——
Return on equity: 3.30%
Cash ($ mil.): 6
Current ratio: 0.20
Long-term debt ($ mil.): —
Dividends
Yield: —
Payout: —
Market value ($ mil.): —

SOUTHLAND INDUSTRIES

Southland Industries designs builds and maintains a variety of mechanical systems for facilities around North America. The employee-owned mechanical engineering firm provides design construction fabrication and maintenance of plumbing process piping fire protection HVAC and controls and automation systems. Southland Industries' clients are in the health care life sciences hospitality industrial education government and telecommunication sectors. Projects include the renovation of the Pentagon following the terrorist attacks of September 11 and the M Resort in Las Vegas. Founded in 1949 Southland Industries has about a half-dozen offices in California Maryland Nevada Virginia and Baltimore.

Financial Performance

Southland Industries' fiscal 2011 (ends September) revenue total $407 million vs. about $435 million the previous year. The firm's revenues have followed a downward path since their peak of $471 million in fiscal 2008.

EXECUTIVES

CEO, Andrew A. Fimiano
Chief Business Development Officer, Joseph G. Cvetas
CFO, Jon Spallino
COO, Chuck Allen
Chief Design Officer, Peter Pobjoy
Northern California Division Leader, Rick Blazier
Mid-Atlantic Division Leader, Mike Miller
CEO, Ted Lynch
Southern California Division Leader, Christopher Taylor
Southwest Division Leader, Nicolas Sfeir
Auditors: Deloitte&ToucheLLP

LOCATIONS

HQ: SOUTHLAND INDUSTRIES
7390 LINCOLN WAY, GARDEN GROVE, CA 92841-1427
Phone: 714-901-5800
Web: WWW.SOUTHLANDINDUSTRIES.COM

PRODUCTS/OPERATIONS

Selected Services

Controls and automation
Energy analysis
Fire protection
HVAC
Planning and development
Plumbing
Process piping
Project management
Maintenance
Repair and retrofit

COMPETITORS

ACCO
Atlas Comfort Systems
Comfort Systems USA
EMCOR
Kinetics
Limbach Facility Services
University Mechanical & Engineering

HISTORICAL FINANCIALS

Company Type: Private

Income Statement FYE: September 30

	REVENUE ($ mil.)	NET INCOME ($ mil.)	NET PROFIT MARGIN	EMPLOYEES
09/11	407	61	15.0%	1,900
09/08	471	44	9.4%	—
09/07	363	28	7.8%	—
09/06	280	8	3.2%	—
Annual Growth	7.7%	47.0%	—	—

2011 Year-End Financials

Debt ratio: ——
Return on equity: 15.00%
Cash ($ mil.): 25
Current ratio: 0.80
Long-term debt ($ mil.): —
Dividends
Yield: —
Payout: —
Market value ($ mil.): —

SOUTHWEST CATHOLIC HEALTH NETWORK CORPORATION

Southwest Catholic Health Network (SCHN) which does business as Mercy Care Plan is a not-for-profit provider of managed health care services in Arizona. The Mercy Care Plan provides these services under a contract with the Arizona Health Care Cost Containment System the state of Arizona's Medicaid program. The plan provides health coverage and prescription drug benefits to some 300000 members. The company founded in 1985 is affiliated with St. Joseph's Hospital & Medical Center (which is part of Catholic Healthcare West) Dignity Health and Carondelet Health Network. The plan is administered by health care management firm Schaller Anderson.

Geographic Reach

SCHN serves the Arizona counties of Maricopa Pima Graham Greenlee and Cochise providing covered services to enrolled members.

Sales and Marketing

As part of its business SCHN provides patients with prescriptions through retail pharmacies mail order pharmacies home infusion pharmacies long-term care pharmacies and Indian Health Service/Tribal/Urban Indian Health Program (I/T/U) pharmacies.

Financial Performance

SCHN logged a 10% decline in revenue in 2012 as compared to 2011. The provider points to a decrease in capitation premiums delivery/HIV AIDS supplement reinsurance and third-party recoveries for the double-digit drop. During the same reporting period SCHN posted a $7.5 million net loss thanks to revenue decreases paired with increases in investment fees and unrealized losses on investments incurred by the company during 2012.

Operations

SCHN provides coverage to families children the elderly and the developmentally disabled. In addition to traditional HMO coverage the company also offers disease management and preventative health care services.

Along with the Centers for Medicare & Medicaid Services (CMS) SCHN provides qualified members with medical and prescription drug benefits. Its Mercy Care Long Term Care (MCLTC) offers services to those covered by the AHCCCS Arizona Long Term Care System (ALTCS) which accounts for 22% of revenue.

The Division of Developmental Disabilities Long Term Care serves members who are enrolled through the Arizona Department of Economic Security/Division of Development Disabilities (DES/DDD) which generates approximately 2% of SCHN's revenue. Through a contract with the DES/DDD the company provides medical care to qualified members.

EXECUTIVES

Chief Operating Officer for Mercy Care Plan, Mark Fisher
Chief Financial Officer, Chuck Sowers
Vice President of Medicare Products Mercy Care Plan, Matt Cowley
Vice President Strategy and Development, Christi Lundeen
Chief Operating Officer, Lorry Bottrill
Chief Medical Officer, Charlton Wilson

LOCATIONS

HQ: SOUTHWEST CATHOLIC HEALTH NETWORK CORPORATION
4350 E COTTON CENTER BLVD, PHOENIX, AZ 85040-8852
Phone: 602-230-9921
Web: WWW.MERCYCAREPLAN.COM

PRODUCTS/OPERATIONS

2012 Revenue

% of total	
Acute	57
DES/DDD	2
HCG	1
ALTCS	22
Medicare	18
Total	**100**

COMPETITORS

Aetna
Blue Cross Blue Shield of Arizona
CIGNA HealthCare of Arizona
Health Net
UnitedHealth Group
Vanguard Health Systems

HISTORICAL FINANCIALS

Company Type: Private

Income Statement FYE: June 30

	REVENUE ($ mil.)	NET INCOME ($ mil.)	NET PROFIT MARGIN	EMPLOYEES
06/11	1,939	58	3.0%	500
06/10	1,904	49	2.6%	—
06/09	1,814	0	—	—
06/08	1,816	32	1.8%	—
Annual Growth	2.2%	22.0%	—	—

2011 Year-End Financials

Debt ratio: —
Return on equity: 3.00%
Cash ($ mil.): 181
Current ratio: 1.10
Long-term debt ($ mil.): —
Dividends
Yield: —
Payout: —
Market value ($ mil.): —

SOUTHWEST LOUISIANA ELECTRIC MEMBERSHIP CORPORATION

EXECUTIVES

General Manager and CEO, J. U. Gajan
Director Marketing and Communications, George Fawcett
Director Engineering, Jim Laque
CFO, Gary Smith
Director Operations, Glenn Tamporello
Dispatch Supervisor, Merlin Alleman
Auditors: BriscoeBurke&GrigsbyLLP

LOCATIONS

HQ: SOUTHWEST LOUISIANA ELECTRIC MEMBERSHIP CORPORATION
3420 NE EVANGELINE TRWY, LAFAYETTE, LA 705072554
Phone: 3378965384
Web: WWW.SLEMCO.COM

HISTORICAL FINANCIALS

Company Type: Private

Income Statement FYE: December 31

	REVENUE ($ mil.)	NET INCOME ($ mil.)	NET PROFIT MARGIN	EMPLOYEES
12/13	198	(0)	—	270
12/08	161	9	5.7%	—
12/07	152	10	6.9%	—
12/06	1,743	0	—	—
Annual Growth	—	—	—	—

2013 Year-End Financials

Debt ratio: —
Return on equity: (-0.10%)
Cash ($ mil.): 15
Current ratio: 1.50
Long-term debt ($ mil.): —
Dividends
Yield: —
Payout: —
Market value ($ mil.): —

SOUTHWEST RESEARCH INSTITUTE INC

EXECUTIVES

VP Geosciences and Engineering, Wesley C. Patrick
VP Space Science and Engineering, James L. Burch
VP Chemistry and Chemical Engineering, Michael G. MacNaughton
VP Aerospace Electronics and Information Technology, Richard D. Somers
VP Finance CFO and Secretary, Beth Ann Rafferty
EVP and Director, Walter D. Downing
President and Director, J. Dan Bates, age 70
VP Fuels and Lubricants Research, Lee J. Grant
VP Legal and Patent Office and General Counsel, John W. McLeod
Treasurer and Assistant Secretary, Jack S. Fernandi
VP Special Programs, Katharine C. Golas
VP Signal Exploitation and Geolocation, William G. Guion
VP Applied Physics, Edward D. (Ed) Moore
VP Institute Environmental Safety and Quality Systems, Amos E. Holt
Chairman, John C. Korbell
Vice Chairman, Philip J. Pfeiffer, age 66
VP Applied Power, Bob Keys
VP Automation and Data Systems, Susan B. Crumrine
VP Engine Emissions and Vehicle Research, Bruce B. Bykowski
VP Mechanical Engineering, Danny M. Deffenbaugh
Director, Ricardo Romo
Director, Roger R. Hemminghaus, age 76
Director, H. Bartell Zachry Jr.
EVP and Director, Walter D. Downing
President and Director, J. Dan Bates, age 70
Director, Eugene L. Ames Jr.
Director, Milton B. Lee
Director, Mary Ann Rankin
Director, Wayne S. Alexander
Director, A. Baker Duncan
Director, Richard W. Calvert
Director, John B. Roberts
Director, Curtis Vaughan Jr.
Director, Richard B. Curtin
Vice Chairman, Philip J. Pfeiffer, age 66

LOCATIONS

HQ: SOUTHWEST RESEARCH INSTITUTE INC
6220 CULEBRA RD, SAN ANTONIO, TX 782385100
Phone: 2106845111
Web: WWW.SWRI.ORG.CN

PRODUCTS/OPERATIONS

Selected Technical Divisions

Aerospace Electronics and Information Technology
Applied Physics
Applied Power
Automation and Data Systems
Chemistry and Chemical Engineering
Engine Emissions and Vehicle Research
Fuels and Lubricants Research
Geosciences and Engineering
Mechanical Engineering
Signal Exploitation and Geolocation
Space Science and Engineering
Training Simulation and Performance Improvement

COMPETITORS

Argonne National Laboratory
Battelle Memorial
Berkeley Lab
Brookhaven Lab
Lawrence Livermore Lab
QinetiQ
Southern Research Institute

HISTORICAL FINANCIALS

Company Type: Private

Income Statement FYE: September 26

	REVENUE ($ mil.)	NET INCOME ($ mil.)	NET PROFIT MARGIN	EMPLOYEES
09/14	548	7	1.4%	2,973
09/13	569	29	5.2%	—
09/12	584	36	6.2%	—
09/11	581	0	—	—
Annual Growth	(1.9%)	—	—	—

2014 Year-End Financials

Debt ratio: —
Return on equity: 1.40%
Cash ($ mil.): 21
Current ratio: 0.20
Long-term debt ($ mil.): —
Dividends
Yield: —
Payout: —
Market value ($ mil.): —

SPAW GLASS CONSTRUCTION CORPORATION

You don't need a spyglass to notice general contractor SpawGlass Construction Corp.'s projects. The buildings include the Cynthia Woods Mitchell Pavillion the Cockrell Butterfly Center and Wortham IMAX Theatre. SpawGlass provides design/build and preconstruction services to its clients for projects that range from office buildings special events facilities and dormitories to retail institutional and health care facilities. The company founded in 1953 is an employee-owned subsidiary of SpawGlass Holding LP which also owns general builder SpawGlass Contractors.

EXECUTIVES

Vp Corporate Business Development, Joel Stone
Vp Finance And Administration, Bobby Friedel
Senior Vice President, Jack Mulligan
Vice President, Lloyd Nakayama
Division President, Ron Taylor
Sec-treas, Dan Hinson

LOCATIONS

HQ: SPAW GLASS CONSTRUCTION CORPORATION
13800 WEST RD, HOUSTON, TX 77041-1114
Phone: 281-970-5300
Web: WWW.SPAWGLASS.COM

COMPETITORS

Austin Commercial	Harvey Builders
C.F. Jordan	N.C. Sturgeon
Clay Development & Construction	Tellepsen Builders
	W.S. Bellows

HISTORICAL FINANCIALS

Company Type: Private

Income Statement FYE: December 31

	REVENUE ($ mil.)	NET INCOME ($ mil.)	NET PROFIT MARGIN	EMPLOYEES
12/10	150	10	7.0%	220
12/05	241	2	1.1%	—
12/04	259	2	1.0%	—
12/03	226	1	0.6%	—
Annual Growth	(5.6%)	33.9%	—	—

SPAW GLASS HOLDING L.P.

Deep in the heart of Texas SpawGlass Holding is busy providing general building and construction management services for commercial and institutional projects through its SpawGlass Construction and SpawGlass Contractors subsidiaries. The group also offers design/build delivery and tenant finish-out services. Among its landmark projects is the interior restoration of the Texas State Capitol. It also worked on the NASA Shuttle Flight Training Facility near Houston and the University of Texas Health Science Center at San Antonio. Louis Spaw and Frank Glass formed SpawGlass in 1953. The company now employee-owned has offices in Austin Houston San Antonio and the Rio Grande Valley in Texas.

EXECUTIVES

SVP Senior Living and Campus Housing, John English
VP Human Resources, Laurie Dralle
VP Estimating, Doug Worrell

LOCATIONS

HQ: SPAW GLASS HOLDING L.P.
9331 CORPORATE DR, SELMA, TX 78154-1250
Phone: 210-651-9000
Web: WWW.SPAWGLASS.COM

COMPETITORS

Beck Group	Structure Tone Southwest
Cadence McShane	Tellepsen Builders
Harvey Builders	Turner Corporation
Linbeck	W.S. Bellows
Manhattan Construction	
Satterfield & Pontikes	

HISTORICAL FINANCIALS

Company Type: Private

Income Statement FYE: December 31

	REVENUE ($ mil.)	NET INCOME ($ mil.)	NET PROFIT MARGIN	EMPLOYEES
12/09	460	8	1.9%	450
12/07	336	5	1.8%	—
12/06	1,121	0	—	—
Annual Growth	—	4051.4%	—	—

2009 Year-End Financials

Debt ratio: —
Return on equity: 1.90%
Cash ($ mil.): 41
Current ratio: 1.00
Long-term debt ($ mil.): —
Dividends
Yield: —
Payout: —
Market value ($ mil.): —

SPECTRUM HEALTH SYSTEM

Offering more health services than colors in the rainbow Spectrum Health is a regional health system that serves western Michigan. The not-for-profit network operates nearly 10 hospitals that boast more than 1900 beds. Its health system provides a variety of services from general surgery to specialized cancer care. Besides its Spectrum Health Medical Group and West Michigan Heart Spectrum Health also operates Priority Health a health plan with 600000 members. Spectrum Health also runs more than 180 service sites which include urgent care centers primary care physician offices community clinics rehabilitation and other outpatient facilities and continuing care residences and services for the elderly.

Operations

Spectrum Health's other hospitals include Blodgett Hospital Butterworth Hospital Kelsey Hospital Reed City Hospital and United Hospital. Blodgett Hospital expanded in 2010 with a new patient care addition consisting of 285 private rooms new and renovated nursing units and renovated public spaces.

Spectrum Health conducts hundreds of research studies each year through its Institutional Review Board. The organization has more than 300 physicians involved in research as investigators and at least 6000 patients enrolled in heart and cancer clinical studies.

Mergers and Acquisitions

The company has expanded its health network in recent years through acquisitions. Spectrum Health acquired Gerber Memorial Health Services which operates a 60-bed hospital near the company's service area in 2010; the facility now operates as Spectrum Health Gerber Memorial.

Strategy

The health system regularly expands its footprint. In 2011 Spectrum Health opened a new 14-story building for its Helen DeVos Children's Hospital. The health network is also focused on expanding its health plan operations which account for about half of annual revenue. To this end Priority Health has added about 100000 customers in recent years by offering plans in eight new counties in northern Michigan and by adding the Bronson Healthcare provider network in southwestern Michigan.

Company Background

Spectrum Health was formed through the 1997 merger of Blodgett Hospital and Butterworth Hospital. Kent Community Hospital joined the organization in 1999 and the United Memorial Health System (Kelsey Hospital and United Hospital) became a member in 2003.

HISTORY

.

EXECUTIVES

EVP and Chief Medical Officer, John MacKeigan
President and CEO, Richard C. (Rick) Breon
SVP and CIO, Patrick O'Hare
Chief Nursing Officer, Shawn M. Ulreich
Manager Media Relations, Bruce Rossman
SVP and Chief Quality Officer, John J. Byrnes
EVP Spectrum Health Delivery System, Matthew G. (Matt) Van Vranken
EVP and Chief Strategy Officer, John Mosley
President Blodgett Hospital, James (Jim) Wilson, age 58
President Helen DeVos Children's Hospital, Robert H. (Bob) Connors
President Spectrum Health Medical Group, James M. Tucci
President Spectrum Health Grand Rapids, Kevin Splaine
Director Public Relations, Carrie Manders
Manager Media Relations, Susan Krieger
VP Facilities, Jonathan Flyte
Director eServices, Janelle Logan
SVP Community Relations, Steven R. Heacock
SVP and Chief Human Resource Officer, Roger E. Jansen
Auditors: Ernst&YoungLLP

LOCATIONS

HQ: SPECTRUM HEALTH SYSTEM
100 MICHIGAN ST NE, GRAND RAPIDS, MI 49503-2560
Phone: 616-391-1774
Web: WWW.SHMG.ORG

PRODUCTS/OPERATIONS

Selected Services

Cancer
Continuing care
Digestive disease
Heart & vascular
Neurosciences
Orthopedics
Outpatient
Pediatric
Rehabilitation
Transplant
Women's health

Selected Operations

Helen DeVos Children's Hospital
Priority Health
Spectrum Health Blodgett Hospital
Spectrum Health Butterworth Hospital
Spectrum Health Continuing Care
Spectrum Health Kent Community Campus
Spectrum Health Gerber Memorial Hospital
Spectrum Health Reed City Hospital
Spectrum Health Special Care Hospital
Spectrum Health United Memorial
Kelsey Hospital
United Hospital

COMPETITORS

Ascension Health
Blue Cross Blue Shield of Michigan
Borgess Health
Bronson Battle Creek
Bronson Health Care
CareSource
Covenant HealthCare
Great Lakes Health Plan
Hayes Green Beach Memorial Hospital
Health Alliance Plan of Michigan
HealthPlus of Michigan
McLaren Bay
McLaren Health Care
Mercy Health Hackley
Munson Healthcare
OmniCare Health Plan
Sheridan Community Hospital
Total Health Care
Zeeland Community Hospital

HISTORICAL FINANCIALS

Company Type: Private

Income Statement FYE: June 30

	REVENUE ($ mil.)	NET INCOME ($ mil.)	NET PROFIT MARGIN	EMPLOYEES
06/11	3,667	247	6.7%	16,996
06/10	1,446	142	9.9%	—
06/09	1,266	0	—	—
06/08	13	1	13.2%	—
Annual Growth	550.9%	421.0%	—	—

2011 Year-End Financials

Debt ratio: —
Return on equity: 6.70%
Cash ($ mil.): 164
Current ratio: 0.50
Long-term debt ($ mil.): —
Dividends
Yield: —
Payout: —
Market value ($ mil.): —

SPF ENERGY INC.

LOCATIONS

HQ: SPF ENERGY INC.
100 27TH ST NE, MINOT, ND 587035164
Phone: 7018521194
Web: WWW.SPFENERGY.COM

COMPETITORS

BP
Redwood Coast Petroleum
Wilson Oil

HISTORICAL FINANCIALS

Company Type: Private

Income Statement FYE: December 31

	REVENUE ($ mil.)	NET INCOME ($ mil.)	NET PROFIT MARGIN	EMPLOYEES
12/14	1,026	16	1.6%	300
12/13	1,012	8	0.9%	—
12/12	1,062	5	0.5%	—
12/11	1,078	0	—	—
Annual Growth	(1.6%)	—	—	—

2014 Year-End Financials

Debt ratio: —
Return on equity: 1.60%
Cash ($ mil.): 12
Current ratio: 1.80
Long-term debt ($ mil.): —
Dividends
Yield: —
Payout: —
Market value ($ mil.): —

SRI INTERNATIONAL

HISTORY

In the 1920s Stanford University professor Robert Swain envisioned a research center devoted to chemistry physics and biology. Swain received support from university president Ray Lyman and alumnus Herbert Hoover but the Great Depression and WWII postponed the venture.

Finally in 1946 the Stanford Research Institute was formed in conjunction with the university. That year the David Sarnoff Research Center invented the color TV tube under the wing of RCA Laboratories.

During Stanford Research's early years it worked on such projects as logistics for Disneyland magnetic ink for character recognition and strategies for combating air pollution. The think tank was the focus of student protests in the 1960s because of its defense work. In 1969 Stanford Research Institute was one of four nodes on the first computer network the ARPANET. It became fully independent in 1970 as SRI International.

During the 1960s and 1970s SRI won large contracts from the US Department of Defense for research in such areas as radar speech recognition and noise cancellation technologies. It got a tremendous boost in 1987 when longtime client General Electric gave SRI the Sarnoff Research Center (as a tax write-off) plus $250 million in business along with $65.2 million in cash.

In 1993 SRI founded Pangene to commercialize gene cloning and analysis technology. The next year it founded GeneTrace to develop genetics-related products for biomedical research and Nuance Communications to commercialize speech-recognition products. Intuitive Surgical which develops minimally invasive surgical technologies was formed in 1995.

SRI developed two key components for use in an improved mail sorting program which the US Postal Service announced in 1997 it would use to save millions in processing costs. The David Sarnoff Research Center changed its name to Sarnoff Corporation that year.

In 1998 SRI and the National Science Foundation teamed to develop innovative science and math teaching programs. The following year SRI began working with network equipment leader Cisco Systems and the US Army to develop a voice and multimedia communications system for the military. In 2001 SRI partnered with SPEEDCOM Wireless to co-develop wireless technology.

In order to complement its biosciences division SRI bought Quality Clinical Labs (QCL) a few years later. QCL was a California-based clinical pathology analysis center specializing in clinical hematology and chemistry evaluations.

SRI's former subsidiary the Sarnoff Corporation fully integrated into SRI's operations during 2011.

EXECUTIVES

VP Information and Computing Sciences Division, William Mark
VP Human Resources, Jean E. (Jeanie) Tooker
SVP and CFO, Thomas J. Furst
President CEO and Board Member, Curtis R. Carlson
Vice President Corporate and Marketing Communications, Alice R. Resnick
VP Legal and Business Affairs and General Counsel, Richard Abramson
VP Biosciences Division, Walter H. Moos, age 59
VP Engineering and Systems Division, John W. Prausa
Co-Director Center for Technology in Learning, Barbara Means
VP Ventures, Norman D. Winarsky
VP Engineering R&D Division, Scott Seaton
VP Strategic Business Initiatives, Stephen J. (Steve) Ciesinski
Executive Director Education Division, Patrick Shields
Director Analytical Chemistry Department, Helen Parish
Director Cancer Biology Program, Keith Laderoute
VP Physical Sciences Division, Eric Pearson
Director Marine Technology Program, Larry Langebrake
Director Formulations Research and Development Biosciences Division, Gita Shankar
VP Products and Services Division, Mark A. Clifton
Vice President General Manager Government Business Development, Jerry Harrison
Program Manager Software Engineering Program, Mark Johnson
Co-Director Center for Technology in Learning, Jeremy Roschelle
Director Center for Health Sciences, Gary Swan
VP Education Division, Denise Glyn Borders
Chief Scientist, Ronald E. Pelrine
Board Member, Philip J. (Phil) Quigley, age 70
Board Member, Richard B. Brewer, age 62
Board Member, Mariann Byerwalter, age 53
President CEO and Board Member, Curtis R. Carlson
Board Member, Henry Kressel, age 79
Board Member, Leslie F. Kenne, age 65
Chairman, Adm. Vernon E. (Vern) Clark, age 68
Board Member, Charles A. Holloway
Board Member, John J. Young Jr.

LOCATIONS

HQ: SRI INTERNATIONAL
333 RAVENSWOOD AVE, MENLO PARK, CA 940253493
Phone: 6508592000
Web: WWW.SRI.COM

PRODUCTS/OPERATIONS

Selected Research Areas

Automation and robotics
Automotive and commercial equipment technologies
Chemistry materials and applied physics
Communications
Defense and intelligence
Homeland defense and national security
Information science and software development
Medical devices
Product engineering
Pharmaceutical services
Policy
Sensors and measurement systems

COMPETITORS

Aerospace Corporation
Battelle Memorial
Bayer Corp.
CACI International
Charles Stark Draper Laboratory
DaVinci Institute
DuPont
MIT
MITRE
PAREXEL
Quintiles Transnational
RAND Corporation
Research Triangle Institute
SwRI
University of California
Wellcome Trust
Westat

HISTORICAL FINANCIALS

Company Type: Private

Income Statement FYE: December 28

	REVENUE ($ mil.)	NET INCOME ($ mil.)	NET PROFIT MARGIN	EMPLOYEES
12/13	547	(5)	—	2,437
12/12	560	(5)	—	—
12/11	585	14	2.5%	—
12/10	502	0	—	—
Annual Growth	2.9%	—	—	—

2013 Year-End Financials

Debt ratio: —
Return on equity: (-1.00%)
Cash ($ mil.): 26
Current ratio: 1.30
Long-term debt ($ mil.): —
Dividends
Yield: —
Payout: —
Market value ($ mil.): —

ST BARNABAS MEDICAL CENTER INC

Part of the Saint Barnabas Health Care System Saint Barnabas Medical Center is a 600-bed acute-care hospital that provides a full range of health services to residents of Livingston New Jersey and surrounding areas. The not-for-profit medical center provides general inpatient and outpatient care programs as well as burn and perinatal care. It also houses units specializing in organ transplant stroke care cardiac surgery and comprehensive cancer treatment. Its Institute for Reproductive Medicine and Science provides assisted reproductive technology services. Saint Barnabas Medical Center treats some 35000 inpatients and more than 85000 emergency-room patients each year.

Operations In combination with its satellite Saint Barnabas Ambulatory Care Center the medical center serves about 300000 outpatients per year. Saint Barnabas Medical Center is also a teaching affiliate of several regional schools including the University of Medicine and Dentistry of New Jersey and Drexel University College of Medicine.

Company Background New Jersey's first hospital Saint Barnabas Medical Center was founded in 1865 in a private home.

EXECUTIVES

President and CEO, Ronald J. Del Mauro

LOCATIONS

HQ: ST BARNABAS MEDICAL CENTER INC
94 OLD SHORT HILLS RD # 1, LIVINGSTON, NJ 07039-5668
Phone: 973-322-5000
Web: WWW.NJBURNCENTER.COM

COMPETITORS

Atlantic Health
Children' s Specialized Hospital
Chilton Medical Center
East Orange General Hospital
Hackensack University Medical Center
JFK Health System
JFK Medical Center
Meridian Health
Newark Beth Israel Medical Center
Raritan Bay Medical Center
Robert Wood Johnson University Hospital
Robert Wood Johnson University Hospital at Rahway
Saint Peter' s University Hospital
St. Joseph' s Healthcare System
Trinitas Regional Medical Center
Virtua Health

HISTORICAL FINANCIALS

Company Type: Private

Income Statement FYE: December 31

	REVENUE ($ mil.)	NET INCOME ($ mil.)	NET PROFIT MARGIN	EMPLOYEES
12/12	652	74	11.5%	479
12/08	510	(4)	—	—
12/03	438	9	2.1%	—
12/03	1,550	0	0.0%	—
Annual Growth	(9.2%)	275.4%	—	—

2012 Year-End Financials

Debt ratio: —
Return on equity: 11.50%
Cash ($ mil.): 0
Current ratio: 0.30
Long-term debt ($ mil.): —
Dividends
Yield: —
Payout: —
Market value ($ mil.): —

ST DAVID ROUND ROCK MEDICAL CENTER

St. David's Round Rock Medical Center serves the growing Williamson County community located in Central Texas. The facility includes an acute care hospital with approximately 175 beds a heart center a women's center and an outpatient surgery center. Other services include respiratory therapy vascular lab work orthopedics and intermediate care. ‚ÂThe medical center is part of St. David's HealthCare Partnership a joint venture between St. David's Health Care System and HCA. The hospital's size was almost doubled through expansion construction ‚Âin 2006.

EXECUTIVES

Director Of Infection Control, Lauri Davidson
Director Of Physical Therapy, Dana Keesey
Operating Room Director, Kathleen Bradshaw
V P Marketing, Lisa Berryhill
Vice President Marketing, Charles Tawater
Vice President Of Engineering, Danny Reid
Director Of Radiology, Tom Wilson

LOCATIONS

HQ: ST DAVID ROUND ROCK MEDICAL CENTER
2400 ROUND ROCK AVE, ROUND ROCK, TX 786814004
Phone: 5123411000
Web: WWW.STDAVIDSFOUNDATION.ORG

COMPETITORS

Dell Children' s Medical Center
HealthSouth
Kaiser Foundation Health Plan
Scott & White
Seton Healthcare Network
Tenet Healthcare

HISTORICAL FINANCIALS

Company Type: Private

Income Statement FYE: February 28

	REVENUE ($ mil.)	NET INCOME ($ mil.)	NET PROFIT MARGIN	EMPLOYEES
02/13*	131	19	15.2%	610
12/05	40	36	90.2%	
Annual Growth	18.5%	(8.1%)	—	

*Fiscal year change

2013 Year-End Financials

Debt ratio: —
Return on equity: 15.20%
Cash ($ mil.): 0
Current ratio: 2.30
Long-term debt ($ mil.): —
Dividends
Yield: —
Payout: —
Market value ($ mil.): —

ST FRANCIS HOSPITAL

Sure St. Francis Hospital can handle your gall bladder and sinus difficulties but it's really on top of your heart problems. The hospital's Heart Center –New York State's only specially designated cardiac center –provides surgical diagnostic and treatment services. The 365-bed St. Francis Hospital also has centers for ENT (ear nose and throat) orthopedic vascular prostate cancer gastrointestinal and general surgery services. As part of Catholic Health Services of Long Island St. Francis opened its doors in 1954 to children and adults. It was originally established as St. Francis Hospital and Sanatorium for Cardiac Children in 1936.

Geographic Reach

St. Francis Hospital is located in Roslyn New York. In addition it has satellite New York locations in Greenvale (DeMatteis Center for Cardiac Research and Education) West Islip (South Bay Cardiovascular Center) and Hicksville (Bishop McHugh Health Center) as well as administrative offices in Port Washington.

Operations

St. Francis Hospital's Heart Center performs about 8000 cardiac catheterizations 3000 coronary angioplasties and about 1500 open-heart operations every year. The center's DeMatteis Center for Cardiac Research and Education works to develop improved techniques for heart disease diagnosis including conducting clinical trials through partnerships with device and equipment makers and provides patient education and fitness programs.

Strategy

St. Francis Hospital has expanded in recent years to keep up with growing patient demand. It opened the Bishop McHugh Health Center to provide outpatient primary care services for uninsured and underinsured patients in 2012.

The hospital completed its largest expansion project to date in 2009 with the construction of the $190 million Nancy and Frederick DeMatteis Pavilion; the project increased the hospital's clinical space by about 40% and added 85 beds.

EXECUTIVES

President CEO, Alan D. Guerci
Senior Vice President Chief Financial Officer, William C. Armstrong
VP Legal Affairs, Patricia J. Hajnosz
Senior Vice President Patient Care and Chief Nursing Officer, Ann Cella
Vice President Development and Public Affairs, Sherry Friedman
VP Human Resources, Miles H. Kucker
EVP and Chief Administrative Officer, Akram Boutros
SVP and COO, Ruth Hennessey
VP Buildings and Grounds, James Proce
VP Finance, William M. Rennie
Senior Vice President Medical Affairs and Medical Director, Jack Soterakis
Vice President Human Resources, Barbara Fierro
Vice President Ambulatory Services, Patricia E. Daye
Vice President Facilities, George Huryn
President of the Professional Staff, Newell Robinson
Auditors: KPMGLLP

LOCATIONS

HQ: ST FRANCIS HOSPITAL
100 PORT WASHINGTON BLVD, ROSLYN, NY 11576-1353
Phone: 516-562-6000
Web: WWW.STFRANCISHEARTCENTER.COM

PRODUCTS/OPERATIONS

Selected Services

Anesthesiology
Breast Surgery
Cardiology
Cardiothoracic Surgery
Diabetes Care Center
Emergency Medicine
Gastroenterology
General Surgery
Hematology/Oncology
Nephrology
Neurology
Orthopedic Surgery
Otolaryngology
Podiatry
Psychiatry
Pulmonary Medicine
Radiology
Rehabilitation
Urology
Vascular Services
Women's Center

COMPETITORS

Bronx-Lebanon Hospital
Brookhaven Memorial Hospital Medical Center
Calvary Hospital
Catholic Health Services of Long Island
Continuum Health Partners
Franklin Hospital
Huntington Hospital
Long Beach Medical Center
Long Island Jewish Medical Center
Mather Memorial Hospital
MediSys Health Network
Memorial Sloan-Kettering
New York City Health and Hospitals
NewYork-Presbyterian Healthcare
North Shore University Hospital
North Shore-Long Island Jewish Health System
NuHealth

HISTORICAL FINANCIALS

Company Type: Private

Income Statement FYE: December 31

	REVENUE ($ mil.)	NET INCOME ($ mil.)	NET PROFIT MARGIN	EMPLOYEES
12/08	385	28	7.4%	2,184
12/04	366	47	12.9%	—
12/02	828	0	—	—
Annual Growth	—	606.6%	—	—

2008 Year-End Financials

Debt ratio: —
Return on equity: 7.40%
Cash ($ mil.): 117
Current ratio: 2.20
Long-term debt ($ mil.): —
Dividends
Yield: —
Payout: —
Market value ($ mil.): —

ST JOHN'S UNIVERSITY NEW YORK

No university is an island but one of St. John's campuses is on Manhattan Island. A private co-educational Roman Catholic school St. John's University offers undergraduate and graduate programs in more than 100 majors through five colleges a law school and a distance learning program. St. John's has more than 20000 students at five campuses (Queens Staten Island and Manhattan in New York City one in Oakdale New York and one graduate center in Rome). The school has a 17-to-1 student-faculty ratio. More than 80% of its graduates reside in the New York region including notable alumni such as former New York governors Hugh Carey and Mario Cuomo. The school was founded in 1870 by the Vincentian Community.

EXECUTIVES

President, Rev Donald J. Harrington, age 68
VP Institutional Advancement, Adrian Kerrigan
VP Student Affairs, Kathryn T. Hutchinson
Vice Chairman, Rev Michael J. Carroll
Dean College of Professional Studies, Kathleen V. MacDonald
Director Alumni Relations, William G. Schaeffer
Director Athletics, Chris P. Monasch
Director Purchasing, Jeffrey L. Weiss
Manager Facilities Services, Darren J. Deans
Associate VP Academic Support Services, Nancy S. Kaplan
Director Human Resource Services, Cynthia F. Simpson
Director University Staffing and Employment Development, Joan C. Vivian
Director Employee Benefits, Maria Conti
Manager Telecommunications and Technology Projects, Roy Ippolito
Manager Network Initiatives, Stanley R. Jurgielewicz
Director Staten Island Library, Mark Meng
Head of Reference Services Rittenberg Law Library, Barbara Traub
Executive Director Development and Alumni Relations, George Richardson
Director Budget Services, Edward Kling
Registrar, Janet M. Keogan
Assistant VP Media Relations, Dominic Scianna
VP and Secretary, Dorothy E. Habben
VP and CIO, Joseph J. Tufano
SVP and Chief of Staff Office of the President, Robert D. Wile
EVP and COO, Martha K. Hirst
EVP Mission and Student Services, James J. Maher
VP for Enrollement Management, Beth M. Evans
VP and University Secretary, Dorthy E. Habben
SVP Human Resources and Strategic Planning, Mary T. Harper Hagan
Provost, Robert A. Mangione
VP Business Affairs and CFO, Sharon Hewitt Watkins
Chairman, Peter P. D?Angelo
Dean College of Liberal Arts and Sciences, Jeffrey Fagen
Dean University Libraries, Theresa Maylone
Dean School of Education, Jerrold Ross
VP Marketing and Communications, Hallie G. Sammartino
Dean Peter J. Tobin College of Business, Victoria Shoaf
Dean School of Law, Michael A. Simons
Acting Dean College of Pharmacy and Health Sciences, S. William Zito
Auditors: KPMGLLP

LOCATIONS

HQ: ST JOHN' S UNIVERSITY NEW YORK
8000 UTOPIA PKWY, JAMAICA, NY 11439-9000
Phone: 718-990-6161
Web: WWW.STJOHNS.EDU

PRODUCTS/OPERATIONS

Selected Colleges and Schools

College of Pharmacy and Allied Health Professions
College of Professional Studies
The Peter J. Tobin College of Business
St. John's College of Liberal Arts and Sciences
St. John's Distance Learning
The School of Education
School of Law

HISTORICAL FINANCIALS

Company Type: Private

Income Statement FYE: May 31

	REVENUE ($ mil.)	NET INCOME ($ mil.)	NET PROFIT MARGIN	EMPLOYEES
05/13	473	64	13.5%	3,310
05/12	471	2	0.6%	—
05/10	450	82	18.4%	—
05/10	440	1	0.4%	—
Annual Growth	2.4%	220.4%	—	—

2013 Year-End Financials

Debt ratio: —
Return on equity: 13.50%
Cash ($ mil.): 7
Current ratio: —
Long-term debt ($ mil.): —
Dividends
Yield: —
Payout: —
Market value ($ mil.): —

ST JOHNS HOSPITAL SISTERS OF THE THIRD ORDER OF ST FRANCIS

Truck-struck Homer Simpson might use his last gasp trying to blurt out "St. John's Hospital of the Hospital Sisters of the Third Order of St. Francis-Springfield" to his ambulance driver but he might be better off using the hospital's more common name St. John's. D'oh! The 430-bed St. John's Hospital serves residents of central and southern Illinois with general and specialized health care services. The teaching hospital affiliated with Southern Illinois University's School of Medicine has centers devoted to women and children's health trauma cardiac care cancer orthopedics and neurology. It also operates area health clinics. St. John's Hospital is part of the Hospital Sisters Health System.

Founded in 1875 the facility has grown to boast about 700 physicians from more than 30 specialties. In addition to educating medical students through Southern Illinois University's School of Medicine St. Johns also supports those working on careers in nursing through its own nursing school St. John's College. It also offers courses in pharmacy pathology respiratory therapy and electroneurodiagnostics (brain disorder diagnostics) professions.

St. John's and its parent organization are sponsored by the Hospital Sisters of the Third Order of St. Francis a Catholic health ministry organization that operates about a dozen hospital systems in Illinois and Wisconsin. The Third Order of St. Francis refers to secular men and women who follow the teachings and lifestyle of St. Francis of Assisi.

Medicare and Medicaid patients account for about two-thirds of the hospital's payer mix with private insurance and self-pay customers making up the rest. St. John's also provides some charity care to low-income patients.

In 2012 the company formed a collaboration agreement with Boyd Healthcare which operates the nearby Boyd Memorial Hospital. The two companies plan to work together to increase access to primary and specialty care including remote telemedicine resources in the region. The health care providers have partnered on similar projects in previous years; such partnerships become increasingly important as the US health care landscape shifts towards an accountable care model where providers must coordinate patient care across area facilities.

Other strategic initiatives at the hospital include increasing doctor and nurse retention rates growing nursing school enrollment rates and increasing patient satisfaction scores. Part of its efforts to reach more patients has led St. John's to open new outpatient health centers in areas near the main hospital facility. The hospital has also renovated its main buildings including the revamp of its day surgery and intermediate care departments during 2010. It also launched a $161 million master plan to upgrade other portions of the hospital in 2011 including the renovation of several floors within the patient tower and the demolition of several smaller buildings that will be replaced by a five-story surgery wing.

EXECUTIVES

President CEO and Director, Robert P. (Bob) Ritz, age 52

LOCATIONS

HQ: ST JOHNS HOSPITAL SISTERS OF THE THIRD ORDER OF ST FRANCIS
800 E CARPENTER ST, SPRINGFIELD, IL 62769-0002
Phone: 217-544-6464
Web: WWW.STJOHNSCOLLEGESPRINGFIELD.EDU

COMPETITORS

Advocate Health Care
Blessing Hospital
Community Health Systems
Decatur Memorial Hospital
Good Samaritan Hospital (IN)
HCA
Memorial Health System
Memorial Hospital (Illinois)
Southern Illinois Healthcare
St. Elizabeth Healthcare
Tenet Healthcare
UC Health

HISTORICAL FINANCIALS

Company Type: Private

Income Statement FYE: June 30

	REVENUE ($ mil.)	NET INCOME ($ mil.)	NET PROFIT MARGIN	EMPLOYEES
06/08	393	(8)	—	3,000
06/05	387	50	13.1%	—
06/04	1,737	0	—	—
Annual Growth	—	—	—	—

2008 Year-End Financials

Debt ratio: —
Return on equity: (-2.20%)
Cash ($ mil.): 0
Current ratio: 0.20
Long-term debt ($ mil.): —
Dividends
Yield: —
Payout: —
Market value ($ mil.): —

ST LAWRENCE UNIVERSITY

St. Lawrence University is a four-year liberal arts college that also offers graduate degrees in education. The university has an enrollment of more than 2500 students as well as 200 faculty members and a student-to-teacher ratio of 12:1. Major fields of study include biology computer science economics history psychology foreign language and religious studies. Actors Kirk Douglas and Viggo Mortensen and ‚Â US Senator ‚Â Susan Collins ‚Âare among the school's alumni. Founded in 1856 by members of the Universalist Church (now Unitarian Universalist) St. Lawrence is the oldest continuously coeducational institution of higher learning in New York State.

Geographic Reach

St. Lawrence ‚Â is located in Canton New York. ‚ÂThe school is named ‚Âthe river in upstate New York that separates the US and Canada. Students at St. Lawrence hail from across the US and about 45 international countries.

Operations

St. Lawrence provides degrees including Bachelor of Arts Bachelor of Science and Master of Education as well as a Certificate of Advanced Studies in Education Administration.

In addition to its core fields of study St. Lawrence has special programs in partnership with other institutions. For instance it conducts a collaborative MBA program with Clarkson University and Union College and a rural medicine program with SUNY Upstate. It also offers a nursing program in collaboration with NYU and semester study programs with institutions in Nashville; Washington DC; upstate New York; and New York City as well as in the Adirondacks.

Financial Performance

St. Lawrence University reported a 1% increase in revenue in 2012 to some $112 million ‚Âdue to higher income from tuition fees room and board (which total about $56000 per student per year) as well as auxiliary activities and private gifts. Net income dropped into the red ‚Âin 2012 due to investment losses.

Strategy

To enhance student resources on campus St. Lawrence announced plans to build a new residence hall in 2012. The new building will house 150 students and will be completed in 2014.

EXECUTIVES

V Pres Fin, Katheryn Mullaney, age 63
Intrm Vp Univ Advancement, Thomas Pynchon
Assoc Vp Relations, Lisa M Cania
Vp/dean Of Academic Affairs, Valerie D Lehr
Vp/dean Admiss/fin Aid, Jeffrey Rickey
Vp University Advancement, Laura Ellis
Vp For Communications, Tom Evelyn
Vice President And Dean Division Of Student Life And Co Curricular Education, Joseph Tolliver

LOCATIONS

HQ: ST LAWRENCE UNIVERSITY
23 ROMODA DR, CANTON, NY 136171501
Phone: 3152295011
Web: WWW.ALUMNI.STLAWU.EDU

HISTORICAL FINANCIALS

Company Type: Private

Income Statement FYE: June 30

	REVENUE ($ mil.)	NET INCOME ($ mil.)	NET PROFIT MARGIN	EMPLOYEES
06/14	117	36	31.5%	650
06/13	112	19	17.4%	—
06/12	112	(13)	—	—
06/11	110	0	—	—
Annual Growth	1.9%	—	—	—

2014 Year-End Financials

Debt ratio: —
Return on equity: 31.50%
Cash ($ mil.): 9
Current ratio: —
Long-term debt ($ mil.): —
Dividends
Yield: —
Payout: —
Market value ($ mil.): —

ST PATRICK HOSPITAL CORPORATION

Feeling a little green? St. Patrick Hospital and Health Sciences Center is here to help. The not-for-profit hospital boasts some 250 beds (both acute-care and transitional) and serves nearly 20 counties in and around Missoula Montana. Its specialty services include cancer treatment surgery and occupational health. As part of its services the center provides Life Flight air transport to critically ill or injured patients. The hospital provides outpatient primary and specialty care through a host of affiliated physician practices and clinics throughout the area. St. Patrick Hospital and Health Sciences Center was founded in 1873 by the Sisters of Providence and is part of Providence Health & Services.

Geographic Reach

St. Patrick Hospital and Health Sciences Center serves those who reside in Missoula Montana and the surrounding counties which generate 95% of its patient volume.

Operations

The center's facility which opened in 1984 admitted more than 7900 patients in 2011 and logged more than 37900 days of patient care. Its physician offices and outpatient services are located adjacent to the hospital. They comprise the Western Montana Clinic the Montana Neuroscience Institute the Montana Cancer Center and the International Heart Institute. Outpatient services provided by St. Patrick Hospital and Health Sciences Center include physical occupational speech diabetic and cardiac rehabilitation.

EXECUTIVES

Chief Nursing Officer, Joyce Dombrouski
President CEO and Director, Jeff D. Fee
Chief Operations and Strategy Officer, Mark Wakai
COO, Craig Aasved
Vice President of Mission Leadership, Mike Cox
CFO, Kirk Bodlovic
Chief Physician Executive, Jorge Reyno
Owner President CEO, Jim Caras
President CEO and Director, Jeff D. Fee
Director, Meg Eddy
Director, Anne Guest
Director, Michael Snyder

LOCATIONS

HQ: ST PATRICK HOSPITAL CORPORATION
500 W BROADWAY ST, MISSOULA, MT 59802-4008
Phone: 406-543-7271
Web: WWW.SAINTPATRICK.ORG

PRODUCTS/OPERATIONS

Selected Services

Cardiology
Cancer Center
Diabetes Care Center
Diagnostic Imaging
Emergency Department
First STEP
Joint Replacement
Laboratory
Life Flight
Neurobehavioral Medicine
Neurology
Broadway Pharmacy
Rehabilitation
Sleep Center
Stroke Center
Surgery

COMPETITORS

Billings Clinic
Glendive Medical Center
St. Alexius Medical Center
St. James Healthcare
Wyoming Medical Center

HISTORICAL FINANCIALS

Company Type: Private

Income Statement FYE: December 31

	REVENUE ($ mil.)	NET INCOME ($ mil.)	NET PROFIT MARGIN	EMPLOYEES
12/12	227	37	16.6%	1,460
12/05	191	8	4.3%	—
12/04	163	6	3.8%	—
12/02	1,361	0	0.0%	—
Annual Growth	(16.4%)	212.6%	—	—

2012 Year-End Financials

Debt ratio: —
Return on equity: 16.60%
Cash ($ mil.): 1
Current ratio: 1.60
Long-term debt ($ mil.): —
Dividends
Yield: —
Payout: —
Market value ($ mil.): —

ST PETER'S UNIVERSITY HOSPITAL

Serving the central portions of the Garden State Saint Peter's University Hospital has about 480 beds. The facility is sponsored by the Roman Catholic Diocese of Metuchen New Jersey and provides patients with a staff of more than 900 physicians and dentists. Saint Peter's also offers one of the country's largest Neonatal Intensive Care Units minimally invasive surgical (MIS) procedures and specialized cancer diabetes and geriatric care. In affiliation with the Children's Hospital of Philadelphia Saint Peter's provides cardiac care for infants and children. The teaching hospital established in 1907 is also affiliated with the Drexel University College of Medicine.

Geographic Reach

Saint Peter's University Hospital serves the residents of central New Jersey from its New Brunswick campus.

Operations

As part of the Saint Peter's Healthcare System the non-profit acute care facility performs some 30000 inpatient treatments and more than 200000 outpatient procedures each year. It also delivers some 6100 newborns annually and is a state-designated children's hospital and regional perinatal center. Supported by 2800 healthcare professionals Saint Peter's University Hospital serves as a regional specialist in geriatrics oncology orthopedics women's services and ambulatory care. It offers both adults and children cancer care services including inpatient care and outpatient radiation and infusion.

Strategy

In 2013 Saint Peter's University Hospital which is nationally recognized for its perinatal care opened a redesigned and expanded perinatal center that houses both maternal-fetal medicine and antenatal testing services. Some 500 low-birthweight babies are delivered at the hospital each year. The facility also logs more than 2200 high-risk obstetrics clinic visits each year.

It also sponsors residency programs in obstetrics and gynecology pediatrics and internal medicine as a regional medical campus of Drexel University College of Medicine. The medical institution also sponsors a residency program in orthopedic surgery in affiliation with the University of Medicine and Dentistry of New Jersey-Robert Wood Johnson Medical School. It has agreements with Rutgers University and Kean University to enhance its educational programs.

Awards and Recognition

Additionally Saint Peter's University Hospital is recognized as a magnet hospital for nursing excellence by the American Nurses Credentialing Center it has won the Beacon Award for Critical Care Excellence in Nursing and is recognized by the American Diabetes Association in every area of diabetes education.

EXECUTIVES

Director Marketing and Media Relations, Michelle Lazzarotti
Chairman, Bipin Patel
Chairman, John A. Carlson

LOCATIONS

HQ: ST PETER' S UNIVERSITY HOSPITAL
254 EASTON AVE, NEW BRUNSWICK, NJ 08901-1766
Phone: 732-745-8600
Web: WWW.SAINTPETERSHCS.COM

PRODUCTS/OPERATIONS

Selected Services

Adult services
Cancer care
Diagnostic technology
Hearth health
Maternity
Movement sports & rehabilitation
Neonatal Intensive Care (NICU)
Nutrition & weight management
Outreach
Patient education
Pediatric & adolescent
Surgery
Women' s health

COMPETITORS

Catholic Health East
CentraState Healthcare System
JFK Medical Center
Princeton HealthCare
Raritan Bay Medical Center
Robert Wood Johnson University Hospital
Robert Wood Johnson University Hospital at Rahway
Saint Barnabas Medical
Somerset Medical Center

HISTORICAL FINANCIALS

Company Type: Private

Income Statement FYE: December 31

	REVENUE ($ mil.)	NET INCOME ($ mil.)	NET PROFIT MARGIN	EMPLOYEES
12/08	391	(34)	—	2,475
12/06	392	4	1.0%	—
12/05	373	4	1.1%	—
12/04	351	5	1.7%	—
Annual Growth	2.7%	—	—	—

2008 Year-End Financials

Debt ratio: —
Return on equity: (-8.80%)
Cash ($ mil.): 0
Current ratio: 0.90
Long-term debt ($ mil.): —
Dividends
Yield: —
Payout: —
Market value ($ mil.): —

ST. ALEXIUS MEDICAL CENTER

Established in 1885 St. Alexius Medical Center has been serving the health care needs of those who reside in the Dakotas and Montana longer than any other area hospital. The medical facility with more than 300 beds caters to central and western North Dakota and parts of South Dakota and Montana. Specialty services include cancer care trauma care geriatrics orthopedics and rehabilitation. As part of its operations the longtime hospital also owns and manages a handful of smaller regional hospitals and community clinics. St. Alexius Medical Center is part of the PrimeCare health group along with the Mid Dakota Cancer Treatment & Research Center The Bone & Joint Center and other medical providers.

Operations

St. Alexius Medical Center owns and operates hospitals and clinics in North Dakota (in Garrison and Turtle Lake) and manages the hospitals and clinics owned by Mobridge Regional Hospital in Mobridge South Dakota. Also part of its operations St. Alexius Medical Center owns and operates specialty and primary care clinics in Minot North Dakota and a primary care clinic in Mandan North Dakota.

Company Ownership

A Roman Catholic organization St. Alexius Medical Center is sponsored by the Sisters of St. Benedict of the Annunciation Monastery located in Bismarck North Dakota. The medical facility follows the Ethical and Religious Directives for Catholic Health Care Services as promulgated by the United States Conference of Catholic Bishops.

EXECUTIVES

President and CEO, Gary P. Miller

Vice President Material & Facility Resources, Frank Kilzer
VP Medical Affairs, Shiraz Hyder
VP and Chief Nursing Officer, Rosanne Schmidt
Chair, John Castleberry
Vice President Mission Effectiveness, Mariah Dietz
Vice President Physician Services & Outreach, Kurt Waldbillig
VP Accounting and Finance, Susan Sisk
Vice President Corporate Compliance & Patient Advocacy, Amy Hornbacher

LOCATIONS

HQ: ST. ALEXIUS MEDICAL CENTER
900 E BROADWAY AVE, BISMARCK, ND 58501-4520
Phone: 701-530-7000
Web: WWW.ST.ALEXIUS.ORG

PRODUCTS/OPERATIONS

Selected Services

Acceleration
Arthritis Clinic
Balance and Dizziness Center
Behavioral and Mental Health
Cardiac Rehabilitation
Clinical Research Services
Community Health
Community Pharmacy
Deep Brain Stimulation
Dialysis
EAP
Emergency & Trauma
Family Practice Clinic
Geriatrics (Older Adults)
Heart and Vascular Center
Home Care and Hospice
Human Performance Center
Kidney Dialysis
Mandan Clinic
Minot Medical Clinic
Neonatology Clinic
Nephrology Clinic
Neurology
Neuroscience
Neurosurgery
Occupational Health and Wellness
Occupational Therapy - Outpatient
Orthopedics
Pediatric Cardiology Clinic
Pediatric Neurology Clinic
Physical Medicine & Rehabilitation
Physical Therapy - Outpatient
Radiology Services
Rehabilitation Unit - Inpatient
Spine Center
Stroke Center
Surgical Services
Telemedicine and Videoconferencing Services
Therapy at HPC
Urology Clinic
Women's Health

COMPETITORS

Altru Health
Avera Health
Billings Clinic
Catholic Health Initiatives
Sanford Health-MeritCare

HISTORICAL FINANCIALS

Company Type: Private

Income Statement FYE: June 30

	REVENUE ($ mil.)	NET INCOME ($ mil.)	NET PROFIT MARGIN	EMPLOYEES
06/12	294	11	3.7%	1,947
06/11	275	12	4.6%	—
06/10	243	6	2.6%	—
06/09	243	6	2.6%	—
Annual Growth	6.6%	20.3%	—	—

2012 Year-End Financials

Debt ratio: —
Return on equity: 3.70%
Cash ($ mil.): 33
Current ratio: 1.50
Long-term debt ($ mil.): —
Dividends
Yield: —
Payout: —
Market value ($ mil.): —

ST. ANTHONY'S HOSPITAL INC.

Saint or not if you need medical care in St. Petersburg Florida St. Anthony's Hospital has you covered. The facility offers a full array of health care services including emergency medicine surgery cancer treatment and heart care as well as services in fields including neurology orthopedics and metabolic care. The 400-bed hospital also provides outpatient services through several ambulatory surgery rehabilitation and imaging centers. St. Anthony's Hospital is a member of the BayCare Health System and as such provides home health and occupational health services through agencies affiliated with that system.

Operations

St. Anthony's Hospital includes a number of specialty centers including extensive cardiovascular care centers including one of the first cardiac catheterization labs in Pinellas County. With an eye for innovative technologies the medical center has also added robotic surgery systems and digital mammography equipment. It also provides surgical specialties in areas including bariatrics joint replacement colorectal care and ENT (ear nose and throat) procedures.

The hospital is also involved with a number of outreach programs to the community including the Faith Community Nursing program and the Pinellas Care Clinic which specializes in providing outpatient medical care to adults with HIV.

Strategy

St. Anthony's Hospital completed construction of a new patient care tower in 2012; the expansion includes a new emergency room. In addition the hospital conducted a total of some $30 million in facility improvements in previous years including new heart and breast care centers.

Company Background

St. Anthony's Hospital was founded in 1931 when the Sisters of the Third Order of St. Francis of Allegany purchased the ailing Faith Hospital.

EXECUTIVES

President, William (Bill) Ulbricht
VP Medical Affairs, James McClintic
VP Operations, Ron Colaguori
VP Mission, Mary McNally
Director Of Him, Jim Bacon
Pharmacy Manager, Charlie Guestella
Medical Director, Andrea Woods

LOCATIONS

HQ: ST. ANTHONY' S HOSPITAL INC.
1200 7TH AVE N, SAINT PETERSBURG, FL 33705-1388
Phone: 727-825-1100
Web: WWW.STANTHONYSFOUNDATION.ORG

Selected facilities

St. Anthony's Outpatient Center - Carillon
St. Anthony's Outpatient Center - St. Petersburg
St. Anthony's Outpatient Imaging Centers
St. Anthony's Physician's Surgery Center
St. Anthony's Resource Center
Susan Sheppard McGillicuddy Breast Center
Carillon Surgery Center

PRODUCTS/OPERATIONS

Selected services

Behavioral Health
Bariatrics
Breast Center
BayCare HomeCare
Cancer Care
Center for Intestinal Continence
Center for Joint Replacement
Center for Robotic Surgery
Emergency Services
Faith Community Nursing
Heart - Cardiac Care
Laboratory Services
Imaging Services
Neuroscience
Orthopedics
Palliative Care
Minimally Invasive Skull Base Institute
Respiratory Services
Sleep Disorders Center
Stroke
Surgical Services
Vascular Services
Wound Healing Center

COMPETITORS

All Children' s Hospital
Bayfront Health
Florida Hospital Tampa Bay Division
H. Lee Moffitt Cancer Center & Research Institute
Manatee Memorial Hospital
Northside Hospital and Heart Institute
Shriners Hospitals For Children
St. Joseph' s Women' s Hospital
St. Joseph' s-Baptist Health Care
Tampa General Hospital

HISTORICAL FINANCIALS

Company Type: Private

Income Statement FYE: December 31

	REVENUE ($ mil.)	NET INCOME ($ mil.)	NET PROFIT MARGIN	EMPLOYEES
12/09	181	6	3.8%	1,076
12/08	159	(12)	—	—
12/06	150	(4)	—	—
12/03	111	1	1.7%	—
Annual Growth	8.5%	24.2%	—	—

2009 Year-End Financials

Debt ratio: —
Return on equity: 3.80%
Cash ($ mil.): 0
Current ratio: —
Long-term debt ($ mil.): —
Dividends
Yield: —
Payout: —
Market value ($ mil.): —

ST. ANTHONY'S MEDICAL CENTER

St. Anthony's Medical Center applies its skills to medical cases in the Midwest. The hospital serves residents in the areas surrounding St. Louis Missouri as well as portions of southwestern Illinois. With about 770 beds and more than 800 affiliated physicians the hospital provides a comprehensive offering including inpatient and outpatient medical surgical diagnostic and behavioral health care. The hospital also operates a level 2 trauma center cancer and chest pain units and a pediatric emergency center as well as several urgent care facilities. It also offers home health hospice laboratory and pharmacy services. St. Anthony's Medical Center was founded in 1900 by the Franciscan Sisters of Germany.

Geographic Reach

St. Anthony's Medical Center is one of the largest hospitals in the St. Louis metropolitan area. It serves a population base of more than 900000 people in ten counties in Missouri and Illinois. It also operates four urgent care centers in surrounding communities of Arnold Big Bend Fenton and Lemay.

Operations

St. Anthony's Medical Center's ER is staffed by an independently-owned group of emergency physicians –in this case Emergency Physicians of St. Louis –who contract to provide services to the hospital. The physician-group model of employment aims to improve patient flow and reduce waiting times at the ER.

Strategy

St. Anthony's Medical Center completed a $90 million four-year redesign and expansion project in 2010 with the opening of its endovascular laboratory center which combined together catheterization radiology and electrophysiology units. Earlier phases included a new heart and surgical pavilion. To bring more cardiac physicians into the mix the medical center partnered with a physician practice association The Heart Specialty Associates in 2011.

To enhance patient convenience St. Anthony's Medical Center opened a new retail pharmacy in the lobby of its Medical Plaza building adjacent to the main hospital building.

EXECUTIVES

Chairman, David M. Sindelar, age 56
EVP Corporate Finance, John McGuire
Director St. Anthony's Hospice, Edward L. Burns
President and CEO, Thomas H. Rockers
VP Human Resources, Ann Bollone
EVP and COO, Robert Thames
VP Marketing and Communications, Tess Niehaus
President Medical Staff, Robert Beckman
President Chief Executive Officer of St, James E. Gardner
President of St. Anthony?s Physician Organization (SAPO) Office of the President, Christopher Bowe President

LOCATIONS

HQ: ST. ANTHONY' S MEDICAL CENTER
10010 KENNERLY RD, SAINT LOUIS, MO 63128-2106
Phone: 314-525-1000
Web: WWW.STANTHONYSMEDCENTER.COM

PRODUCTS/OPERATIONS

Selected Services

Acute Rehabilitation
Audiology/Hearing
Behavioral Health
Breast Center
Cancer Care Center
Diabetes Education
Emergency/Trauma
Heart Specialty Center
Home Care
Hospice Field Program
Hyland Behavioral Health
Long-term Acute Care
Neuroscience and Stroke
Occupational Medicine
Oncology
Orthopedics
Ostomy Clinic
Outpatient Imaging
Pediatric Services
Physical Therapy
Pregnancy and Birth
Pharmacy
Pulmonary
Radiology/Imaging Centers
Rehabilitation (cardiac and acute)
Senior Services
Sleep Disorder Center
Social Services (Care Management)
Speech Therapy
Sports & Therapy
Stroke
Surgery
Urgent Care Centers
Urological Gynecology
Vestibular Rehab
Weight Management
Women's Medical/Surgical Unit
Wound Treatment

COMPETITORS

Ascension Health
BJC HealthCare
Barnes-Jewish Hospital
Christian Hospital
CoxHealth
HCA
Memorial Hospital (Illinois)
Mercy Health
Mercy Hospital St. Louis
RehabCare
SSM Health Care
Saint Francis Medical Center
St. John' s Health System
St. Luke' s Hospital (MO)
Tenet Healthcare

HISTORICAL FINANCIALS

Company Type: Private

Income Statement FYE: June 30

	REVENUE ($ mil.)	NET INCOME ($ mil.)	NET PROFIT MARGIN	EMPLOYEES
06/12	467	(29)	—	3,900
06/11	473	53	11.3%	—
06/10	439	(10)	—	—
06/09	427	(4)	—	—
Annual Growth	3.0%	—	—	—

2012 Year-End Financials

Debt ratio: —
Return on equity: (-6.40%)
Cash ($ mil.): 2
Current ratio: 1.10
Long-term debt ($ mil.): —
Dividends
Yield: —
Payout: —
Market value ($ mil.): —

ST. JOHN HEALTH SYSTEM INC.

St. John Health System aims to bring health into the lives of the ill. The not-for-profit system provides health care services to residents of Tulsa and surrounding areas in northeastern Oklahoma and southern Kansas. In addition to flagship facility St. John Medical Center it owns or manages eight other community hospitals as well as urgent care and long-term care facilities. St. John Health System provides primary and specialty medical care through OMNI Medical Group and offers health insurance through CommunityCare health plan. Established in 1926 by the Sisters of the Sorrowful Mother the health system is part of Marian Health.

Operations

Facilities owned managed or sponsored by St. John Health System include hospitals Oklahoma State University Medical Center St. John Sapulpa St. John Owasso St. John Broken Arrow Pawhuska City Hospital Sedan City Hospital Nowata Hospital and Jane Phillips Medical Center. The company's senior living facilities include Franciscan Villa Frances Streitel Villa Heartsworth House and Rosewood Terrace.

Strategy

St. John Health System will periodically add services to its offerings to meet community demand. In early 2011 St. John Health opened the St. John Weight Management Institute to offer its patients weight loss options including bariatric surgery. The health system's newest hospital St. John Broken Arrow near Tulsa was constructed in 2009.

In 2012 Marian Health entered talks with another Catholic health system operator Ascension Health over the possibility of merging St. John Health System and other Marian organizations into the Ascension organization.

EXECUTIVES

COO, David Pynn
President and CEO, Sister M. Therese Gottschalk
President St. John Medical Center Foundation, Richard Boone
VP Medical Affairs, William Allred
CFO, Lex Anderson
CIO, Mike Reeves
VP Mission Services, Ann Meuser
Coordinator Media Relations, Cora Scott
Chairman, R. J. Sullivan Jr.
Media Relations, Joy McGill
CEO St. John Medical Center, Charles Anderson

LOCATIONS

HQ: ST. JOHN HEALTH SYSTEM INC.
1923 S UTICA AVE, TULSA, OK 74104-6520
Phone: 918-744-2180
Web: WWW.SJHEALTHSYSTEM.COM

PRODUCTS/OPERATIONS

Selected Facilities and Operations – Oklahoma

CommunityCare (health plan)
Jane Phillips Medical Center (Bartlesville)
Nowata Hospital
Oklahoma State University Medical Center (managed facility in Tulsa)
OMNI Medical Group (physicians group)
Pawhuska City Hospital
Regional Medical Laboratory (clinical lab testing)
Sedan City Hospital
St. John Broken Arrow Hospital
St. John Medical Center (Tulsa)
St. John Owasso Hospital
St. John Physicians
St. John Sapulpa Hospital

COMPETITORS

Ardent Health Services
CIGNA
Catholic Health Initiatives
Community Health Systems
Deaconess Health Care
HCA
Hillcrest Medical Center
INTEGRIS Health
Kindred Healthcare
Marian Health System
Norman Regional Health
Presbyterian Healthcare Services
SSM Health Care
Saint Francis Health System
UnitedHealth Group
WellPoint

HISTORICAL FINANCIALS

Company Type: Private

Income Statement FYE: September 30

	ASSETS ($ mil.)	NET INCOME ($ mil.)	INCOME AS % OF ASSETS	EMPLOYEES
09/12	1,413	74	5.3%	4,011
09/11	1,155	17	1.5%	—
09/10	1,132	41	3.7%	—
09/09	1,116	(9)	—	—
Annual Growth	8.2%	—	—	—

2012 Year-End Financials

Debt ratio: —
Return on equity: 7.70%
Cash ($ mil.): 83
Current ratio: 1.90
Long-term debt ($ mil.): —
Dividends
Yield: —
Payout: —
Market value ($ mil.): —

ST. JOHN''S UNIVERSITY

LOCATIONS

HQ: ST. JOHN' ' S UNIVERSITY
8000 UTOPIA PKWY, JAMAICA, NY 114399000
Phone: 7189902000
Web: WWW.STJOHNS.EDU

HISTORICAL FINANCIALS

Company Type: Private

Income Statement FYE: May 31

	REVENUE ($ mil.)	NET INCOME ($ mil.)	NET PROFIT MARGIN	EMPLOYEES
05/13	473	64	13.5%	—
05/12	652	30	4.7%	—
Annual Growth	(27.4%)	107.4%	—	—

2013 Year-End Financials

Debt ratio: —
Return on equity: 13.50%
Cash ($ mil.): 7
Current ratio: —
Long-term debt ($ mil.): —
Dividends
Yield: —
Payout: —
Market value ($ mil.): —

ST. JOSEPH HEALTH SYSTEM

St. Joseph Health System has earned a medal for decades by caring for patients on the West Coast and more recently the South Plains. The health care network operates 14 acute care hospitals three home health agencies a half-dozen urgent care centers and other health care delivery organizations throughout California and in eastern New Mexico and West Texas. In its primary market of California the health system has some 2900 beds at 10 hospitals. Its Covenant Health System unit operates in Texas and New Mexico with about 1200 beds in its network of some 50 primary care facilities.

Geographic Reach

The network operates 14 acute care hospitals three home health agencies a half-dozen urgent care centers and other health care delivery organizations throughout California and in eastern New Mexico and West Texas.

Financial Analysis

St. Joseph Health System brought in $4.22 billion in revenue during fiscal 2011.

Strategy

Already one of the largest health systems on the West Coast St. Joseph continues to grow thanks principally to its proficient fundraising.

The system invests regularly in network and facility expansion efforts. In 2013 it formed an affiliation with Hoag Memorial Hospital Presbyterian which operates two hospitals in Orange County. The Hoag operations are being combined with five of St. Joseph's area hospitals to form a new network called Covenant Health Network. The affiliated facilities will provide comprehensive care in the region while retaining their respective identities and religious affiliations.

In 2011 the system spent $125 million to open a new tower on St. Jude Medical Center in Fullerton California.

That same year St. Joseph Health System invested in technology like the Computerized Provider order Entry (CPOE) which enhances patient care and safety by utilizing evidence-based order sets eliminating transcription errors reducing wait times and providing decisions support directly to providers. CPOE adoption was 67% across ministries including St Jude Medical Center Mission Hospital in Mission Viejo and Laguna Beach Santa Rosa Memorial Hospital and Queen of Valley Medical center.

Company Background

St. Joseph Health System traces its roots back to 1920 when St. Joseph Hospital in Eureka California was first established. The health care system was officially organized in 1982 as it expanded and took on additional health care facilities. The system is a ministry of The Sisters of St. Joseph of Orange which itself was organized in 1912.

EXECUTIVES

Exec Vp Of Wellness & Health, Elliot B Sternberg
Senior Vice President, Susan Whitaker
Vp Advocacy And Government Relations, Ron Diluigi
Sr Vp Ministry Integrity, Margaret Hambleton
Vp Workforce Planning And Diversity, Ryan Faulkner
Vp Contracting, Rick Ingram
Vice President And General Counsel, Jim Watson
Radiology Medical Director, Daniel Weissberg, age 73
President and CEO Redwood Memorial Hospital and St. Joseph Hospital Eureka, Joe Mark
EVP Mission Integration, Marian Schubert
EVP West Texas and Southern New Mexico, Richard H. Parks
EVP Strategic Services, Annette M. Walker
EVP Northern California Region, Kevin Klockenga
Chief Financial Officer, Jo Escasa-Haigh
Assistant Vice President Information, Bill Lazarus
Vice President Communications, Tim Ottinger
Senior Vice President Chief Med Quality Officer, Nancy Pratt
Vice President, James Frey
Assistant Vice President, Kevin Murphy
Senior Vice President, Jennifer Perry
Assistant Vice President Information Services, James Reid
Vp Finance, Jim McManus
Vice President Talent And Oe, Kate Wilhelm
Vice President Education Group Impl, Judy Danforth
Vice President Of Leadership Institute And Governance Support, Jeff Thies
Vice President Of Marketing And Public Affairs, Druann Copping
Vice President, Jeri Williams
Vice President And Chief Information, Ray Thorpe
Senior Vice President Operations, Toni Small
Vice President, Johnny Cox
Vice President Quality And Medical Affairs, Mark Montgomery
Vice President, Doreen Dyda
Vice President Of Revenue Cycle Management, Kristen Merkh
Vice President Chief Compliance Officer, Kim Lansford
Medical Records Director, Sandy Barber
Vice President And General Counsel, Tara Cowell
Vice President Sales, Trudy Hutton
Vice President Infrastructure, Jim Horn
Vice President Finance, Edward Wong
Assistant Vice President Of Org Development And Training, Ann John
Senior Vice President Of Information, Molly Gouge
Assistant Vice President Strategic Services Of Oange, Melinda Bowles
Vice President And Program Manager, Judy Rhodes
Director Of Utilization Review, Pat Atallah
Vice President Sponsorship South Division, Sistermarian Schubert
Vice President Quality And Ambulatory Services, Liz Ruiz
Vp Of Human Resources, Rodney Cates
Senior Vice President Human Resources, Cindra Syverson
Senior Vice President And Chief, Jeff Flocken
Vp Quality Chief Medical Officer, G Mark
Regional Vice President Revenue Cycle Technology, Sheryl Klaja
Vice President Clinical Support Services, Ricardo Diaz
Vice President Community Outreach, Maya Dunne
Vice President Shared Operations Revenue Cycle Se, Debbie Salas
Vice President, Barbara Cox
Assistant Vice President, Ronald Scott
Assistant Vice President Information Technology Pr, Gregory Hoff
Vice President, Julianne Holt
Vice President, Rhonda Fitzgerald
Vice President Administrator Chief Oper, Cory Rayyes
Vice President Investments And Cash Management, Lisa Laird
Vice President, Janet Mortenson
Pharmd, Sharon Lee
Senior Vice President Professional Groups Division, Deborah Knight
Jd Cfre Vice President Gift Planning, Amanda J Ferrari
Assistant Vice President Executive Architect, Wesley Okamoto
Vice President Foundation, Winnie Johnson
Vice President Chief Marketing Officer Sjh And Rmh, Scott Sageman
Vpma, James Kyle
Vice President Of Ambulatory Solutions And Strategy, Kevin Manemann
Vice Chair Publications Assistant Vice President And Corporate Counsel St Joseph Health System, Daniel Glassman
Assistant Vice President Knowledge Management, Ginny Ripslinger
Director Physician Recruitment, Jacque Kaster
Vice President Treas Director, David Henigson
Vice President Of Nursing, Kathy Peoples
Senior Vice President Cmio, Michael Do
Vice President Mission Integration, Joshua Allee
Vice President Human Resources Shared Services, Janet Okimoto
Vice President Performance Improvement, Mary Vincent
Respiratory Therapy Director, Mary Lazos
Vice President Information Technology, Charles Fennell
Regional Vice President Human Resources, Robert Eisen
Director Of Physical Therapy, Renne Blackwell
Vice President Of Human Resources, Mike Costa
Director Physician Recruitment, Regina Fuller
Vice President For Scientific, Ronald Smith
Respiratory Therapy Director, Todd Teasdale
Vice President Information Technology, Scott Scbula
Chief Info Ofc Vice President Or Dir, John Liversidge
Vice President Sales, Liz Gallegos Toledo
Vice President Of Patient And Nursing Services, Linda F Johnson
Vice Present And Chief Financial, Andy Rybolt
Senior Vice President Enterprise, Charles Zewdie

Vice President Ministry Information Technology Ser, David Humphries
Medical Records Director, Marilyn Buchanan
Director Of Medical Records, Daniel Pothen
Vp Associate General Counsel, James Kelly
Vice President Performance Improvement, Catherine Camenga
Senior Vice President, David Zembik
Respiratory Therapy Director, Brad Blevins
Vp Finance, J Golan
Vice President And Cso, Samuel Pierrelouis
Hr Director & Vp, Mary Rogers
Vp Finance, J Marc
Vice President Mission Integration, John Perring-mulligan
Senior Vice President Of Finance, Joann Haigh
Vice President Operations, Kelly Linden
Vice President Business Development, Ann Orders
Vice President, Marysol Cacciata
Chairman, Walter W. (Bill) Noce
Vp Finance And Treasurer, Garrett Kop
Secretary, Jo Tabor
Member Board Of Directors, Keith Marton
Secretary Treasurer, Leon Faris
Secretary, Denise Blanchard
Board Member, Ruth Seigle
Secretary, Dana Gray
Secretary, Barb Smythe

LOCATIONS

HQ: ST. JOSEPH HEALTH SYSTEM
3345 MICHELSON DR STE 100, IRVINE, CA 92612-0693
Phone: 949-381-4000
Web: WWW.STJHS.ORG

Selected Operations

Northern California
- Petaluma Valley Hospital
- Queen of the Valley Medical Center (Napa)
- Redwood Memorial Hospital (Fortuna)
- St. Joseph Home Care Network (Sonoma)
- St. Joseph Hospital (Eureka)
- Santa Rosa Memorial Hospital

Southern California
- Mission Hospital (Mission Viejo)
- Mission Hospital Laguna Beach
- St. Joseph Hospital (Orange)
- St. Jude Medical Center (Fullerton)
- St. Mary Medical Center (Apple Valley)

West Texas/Eastern New Mexico
- Covenant Health System
  - Artesia General Hospital (New Mexico)
  - Covenant Hospital Levelland (Texas)
  - Covenant Hospital Plainview (Texas)
  - Covenant Medical Center (Lubbock TX)
  - Nor-Lea General Hospital (Lovington NM)
  - Roosevelt General Hospital (Portales NM)

COMPETITORS

Adventist Health
Arrowhead Medical Center
Banner Health
Catholic Health Initiatives
Cedars-Sinai Medical Center
Citrus Valley Health Partners
City of Hope
Dignity Health
HCA
Loma Linda University Medical Center
Los Angeles County Health Department
Memorial Health Services
Pasadena Hospital Association
Prospect Medical
Scripps health
Sutter Health
Tenet Healthcare
Western Medical Center - Santa Ana

HISTORICAL FINANCIALS

Company Type: Private

Income Statement FYE: June 30

	REVENUE ($ mil.)	NET INCOME ($ mil.)	NET PROFIT MARGIN	EMPLOYEES
06/11	4,223	348	8.3%	21,500
06/10	4,268	268	6.3%	—
06/08	3,943	53	1.3%	—
06/07	3,668	302	8.2%	—
Annual Growth	3.6%	3.6%	—	—

2011 Year-End Financials

Debt ratio: —
Return on equity: 8.30%
Cash ($ mil.): 250
Current ratio: 0.90
Long-term debt ($ mil.): —
Dividends
Yield: —
Payout: —
Market value ($ mil.): —

ST. JOSEPH HOSPITAL OF ORANGE

If you're feeling green or blue in Orange County St. Joseph Hospital of Orange is there to help get back to feeling pink and rosy. The California hospital provides general medical and surgical services as well as specialty care such as women's health mental health services oncology cardiology and physical rehabilitation. Part of the St. Joseph Health System the hospital provides primary care and specialty outpatient services through a network of affiliated physician practices. It also operates low-income and mobile clinics. Founded in 1929 by the Sisters of St. Joseph of Orange the hospital has about 525 beds and a medical staff of some 1000.

Geographic Reach

St. Joseph Hospital serves Orange County California and the greater Los Angeles metropolitan area.

Operations

In addition to physician group affiliates St. Joseph Hospital Affiliated Physicians and St. Joseph Heritage Medical Group the hospital also partners with the Childrens Hospital of Orange County to help expand pediatric care throughout the region.

Strategy

St. Joseph Hospital has been working to expand its community outreach programs related to cancer through a number of projects including offering improved access to clinical trials; providing better overall access to cancer care; and implementing measures to garner support for the implementation of cancer electronic health records. St. Joseph Hospital is using stimulus money and about a $3 million award from the National Cancer Institute Community Cancer Centers Program to help fund its various projects.

EXECUTIVES

Vice President Mission Integration, Linda Simon
President and CEO, Larry Ainsworth
Chief Financial Officer, Tina Mycroft
Vice President Foundation, Chanda Parrett
Executive Vice President Chief Operating Officer, Jeremy Zoch
Vice President Patient Care Services and Chief Nursing Officer, Katie Skelton
President Chief Executive Officer, Steven C. Moreau
Auditors: Ernst&YoungLLP

LOCATIONS

HQ: ST. JOSEPH HOSPITAL OF ORANGE
1100 W STEWART DR, ORANGE, CA 92868-3891
Phone: 714-771-8000
Web: WWW.SJO.ORG

COMPETITORS

Anaheim Regional Medical Center
Children' s Hospital of Orange County
Citrus Valley Health Partners
Hoag Memorial Hospital
Kaiser Permanente
Memorial Health Services
Pasadena Hospital Association
Providence Health & Services
Southwest Healthcare
Sutter Health
Tenet Healthcare
Torrance Memorial Medical Center
Trinity Health (Novi)
UC Irvine Medical Center
Western Medical Center - Santa Ana

HISTORICAL FINANCIALS

Company Type: Private

Income Statement FYE: June 30

	REVENUE ($ mil.)	NET INCOME ($ mil.)	NET PROFIT MARGIN	EMPLOYEES
06/12	645	23	3.6%	3,300
06/11	661	32	4.9%	—
06/09	638	26	4.2%	—
06/09	509	(14)	—	—
Annual Growth	8.2%	—	—	—

2012 Year-End Financials

Debt ratio: —
Return on equity: 3.60%
Cash ($ mil.): 77
Current ratio: 0.30
Long-term debt ($ mil.): —
Dividends
Yield: —
Payout: —
Market value ($ mil.): —

ST. JOSEPH REGIONAL HEALTH CENTER

LOCATIONS

HQ: ST. JOSEPH REGIONAL HEALTH CENTER
2801 FRANCISCAN DR, BRYAN, TX 778022544
Phone: 9797763777
Web: WWW.ST-JOSEPH.ORG

HISTORICAL FINANCIALS

Company Type: Private

Income Statement FYE: December 31

	REVENUE ($ mil.)	NET INCOME ($ mil.)	NET PROFIT MARGIN	EMPLOYEES
12/13	293	37	12.9%	1,200
12/12	272	30	11.1%	—
12/08	274	(12)	—	—
12/05	0	0	—	—
Annual Growth	—	—	—	—

2013 Year-End Financials

Debt ratio: —
Return on equity: 12.90%
Cash ($ mil.): 10
Current ratio: 0.20
Long-term debt ($ mil.): —
Dividends
Yield: —
Payout: —
Market value ($ mil.): —

ST. JOSEPH'S HOSPITAL HEALTH CENTER

With about 430 inpatient beds St. Joseph's Hospital Health Center serves the residents of 16 central New York counties. The not-for-profit hospital system provides general emergency and surgical care as well as specialty services in areas such as obstetrics cardiology dialysis and wound care. In addition to its inpatient facilities the organization operates a home health agency a nursing school medical and dental residency programs and several outpatient care centers. Its Franciscan Companies affiliate offers some ancillary services including the provision of medical supplies home health equipment and senior services. St. Joseph's Hospital Health Center was founded in 1869.

Geographic Reach

St. Joseph's Hospital Health Center's service territory includes the New York counties of Broome Cayuga Chenango Cortland Delaware Herkimer Jefferson Lewis Madison Oneida Onondaga Oswego Otsego St. Lawrence Tioga and Tompkins.

Operations

With a total of some 800 physicians St. Joseph's Hospital Health Center admits some 25000 inpatients each year. It also handles some 70000 emergency room visits and about 640000 outpatient visits annually. The hospital provides about $22 million in charity and community care each year as well.

Strategy

St. Joseph's Hospital Health Center is conducting a massive $220 million expansion program at its main campus. The first phase opened in 2011 and includes a larger emergency room facility with chest pain and psychiatric units. The hospital broke ground on the second phase of the project in 2012. The program will add a new patient tower surgery facilities a sterilization center and an intensive care unit.

Mergers and Acquisitions

In late 2010 St. Joseph's Hospital Health Center boosted its physician network significantly by acquiring North Medical a physician practice organization that operates five practices: Family Physicians Urgent Care Orthopedics & Rehabilitation The Women's Place and Living Proof Longevity Centre. Its practices are home to about 80 physicians and mid-level practitioners.

EXECUTIVES

VP Information Management and CIO, Charles J. Fennell
VP Development, Douglas G. Smith
President, Kathryn H. Ruscitto
Chairperson, George Deptula
SVP and COO, Mary W. Brown
VP Clinical and Educational Services and Chief Nursing Officer, AnneMarie Czyz
Interim VP Financial Services and CFO, David G. Hardy
SVP Physician Enterprise, Fred Letourneau
SVP System Development and Ambulatory Care Leadership, Mark E. Murphy
President Franciscan Management Services Inc., Frank L. Smith Jr.

LOCATIONS

HQ: ST. JOSEPH' S HOSPITAL HEALTH CENTER
301 PROSPECT AVE, SYRACUSE, NY 13203-1899
Phone: 315-448-5111
Web: WWW.SJHSYR.ORG

PRODUCTS/OPERATIONS

Selected Services

Centers of Excellence
- Cardiac Services
- The Center for Orthopedic and Spine Care
- Vascular Services
- Women and Children' s Services
- Wound Care
- Home Care
- Dialysis
- Bariatric (Weight Loss) Services

Other Services and Centers
- Aesthetic Services
- Behavioral Health
- da Vinci Robotic Surgery
- Emergency Services
- Imaging
- Infusion (CPEPCNY)
- Interventional Radiology
- Medical Equipment
- Obstetric Services
- Palliative Care
- Pharmacy
- Physical Medicine & Rehabilitation
- Pulmonary Services
- Sleep Laboratory
- Social Adult Day Care
- Surgical Services
- Urology Services

Outpatient Services
- Dental Services
- Family Medicine Center
- Obstetrics and Gynecology
- Pediatric Office
- Physician Health
- Primary Care
- Westside Family Health Center

COMPETITORS

Catholic Health System
Ellis Hospital
Kaleida Health
Lifetime Health
Oneida Healthcare Center
SUNY Upstate Medical University
United Health Services Hospitals
Unity Health System
Upstate University Hospital at Community General

HISTORICAL FINANCIALS

Company Type: Private

Income Statement FYE: December 31

	REVENUE ($ mil.)	NET INCOME ($ mil.)	NET PROFIT MARGIN	EMPLOYEES
12/09	436	5	1.2%	3,300
12/08	399	6	1.6%	—
12/05	363	11	3.2%	—
12/98	221	2	1.3%	—
Annual Growth	6.4%	6.0%	—	—

2009 Year-End Financials

Debt ratio: —
Return on equity: 1.20%
Cash ($ mil.): 5
Current ratio: 0.50
Long-term debt ($ mil.): —
Dividends
Yield: —
Payout: —
Market value ($ mil.): —

ST. JUDE CHILDREN'S RESEARCH HOSPITAL INC.

St. Jude Children's Research Hospital studies and treats catastrophic diseases in children especially pediatric cancers. The hospital which only has about 80 beds annually treats more than 5900 children most of whom are treated on an outpatient basis as part of its research efforts into finding cures and more effective treatments. The hospital not only helps children with their health it also helps their parents: It pays all expenses that not covered by insurance and doesn't require payment from patients without insurance. St. Jude Children's Research Hospital was founded in 1962.

Geographic Reach

St. Jude Children's Research Hospital is located in Memphis Tennessee. The facility has affiliations with six other US hospitals in Alabama Illinois Louisiana Missouri and Tennessee. It shares its research findings with scientific and medical organizations worldwide.

Operations

St. Jude Children's Research Hospital has a 2.5-million-sq.-ft. campus for its research clinical and administrative operations. It is the only pediatric cancer center to be designated as a Comprehensive Cancer Center by the National Cancer Institute.

While it is best known for its research in pediatric cancers St. Jude Children's Research Hospital also treats children with genetic immune defects and pediatric AIDS and it has one of the largest pediatric sickle cell programs in the US.

As part of the organization's education mission it provides about 350 postdoctoral fellowships to those doctors who seek to specialize in pediatric medicine. St. Jude Children's Research Hospital is affiliated with the University of Tennessee Health Sciences Center at Memphis. Along with offering fellowships it serves as the training site for medical students and residents learning a variety of disciplines.

Financial Analysis

The hospital's revenues increased 20% to $1.26 billion in fiscal 2011 compared to the $1.05 billion it claimed in fiscal 2010. Public contributions cover most of St. Jude Children's Research Hospital operating costs of $1.8 million a day.

Strategy

Throughout the year St. Jude Children's Research Hospital coordinates events to raise funds and awareness - from golf tournaments and triathlons to radiothons and telethons. Corporate supporters include Kmart which raised almost $7 million for St. Jude Children's Research Hospital through its annual "Thanks and" "Giving?" campaign in 2010.

Company Background

Entertainer Danny Thomas founded St. Jude in 1962; Thomas also founded the fundraising organization for the hospital the American Lebanese Syrian Associated Charities (ALSAC).

EXECUTIVES

SVP and CFO, Michael (Mike) Canarios
CEO and Director, William E. Evans
SVP Support Operations and Human Resources, Mary Anna Quinn
EVP Deputy Director and Scientific Director, James Downing
SVP and Chief Legal Officer, Clinton D. Hermes

SVP Patient Care Services and Chief Nursing Officer, Pam Dotson
EVP and Clinical Director, Joseph Laver
SVP and CIO, Clayton Naeve
Chair Biostatistics, James Boyett
Co-Chair Oncology, Amar Gajjar
Chair Immunology, Doug Green
Chair Genetics, Gerard Grosveld
Chair Chemical Biology and Therapeutics, Kip Guy
Chair Biochemistry, James Ihle
Chair Radiological Sciences, Larry Kun
Chair Developmental Neurobiology, James Morgan
Chair Oncology, Ching-Hon Pui
Chair Pharmaceutical Sciences, Mary Relling
Director International Outreach Program, Raul Ribeiro
Chair Epidemiology and Cancer Control, Les Robison
Chair Tumor Cell Biology, Charles Sherr
Chair Infectious Diseases, Elaine Tuomanen
Chair Structural Biology, Stephen White
Chair Surgery, Andrew Davidoff
EVP; Director Comprehensive Cancer Center, Richard J. Gilbertson
SVP Public Relations, Kimberly Ovitt
Chair Pathology, David Ellison
Chair Psychology, Sean Phipps
CAO, Alberto Broniscer

LOCATIONS

HQ: ST. JUDE CHILDREN' S RESEARCH HOSPITAL INC.
262 DANNY THOMAS PL, MEMPHIS, TN 38105-3678
Phone: 901-595-3300
Web: WWW.STJUDE.ORG

PRODUCTS/OPERATIONS

US Affiliate Clinics
Children's Hospital of Illinois (OSF Healthcare System) University of Illinois College of Medicine at Peoria
Feist-Weiller Cancer Center LSU Health Sciences Center (Shreveport Louisiana)
Huntsville Hospital (Huntsville Alabama)
Johnson City Medical Center East Tennessee State University
Our Lady of the Lake Regional Medical Center (Baton Rouge Louisiana)
St. John's Health System (Springfield Missouri)

Selected International Outreach Partner Sites

American University of Beirut/Children's Cancer Center of Lebanon (Beirut Lebanon)
Beijing Children's Hospital (Beijing)
Davao Medical Center (Philippines)
Hospital 20 Aout 1953 (Casablanca Morocco)
Hospital Benjamin Bloom (San Salvador El Salvador)
Hospital Civil de Guadalajara (Guadalajara Mexico)
Hospital de Especialidades Pediatricas (Maracaibo Venezuela)
Hospital de la Sociedad de Lucha Contra el Cancer Nucleo de Quito (Quito Ecuador)
Hospital de Ninos Baca Ortiz (Quito Ecuador)
Hospital de Ninos J.M. de los Rios (Caracas Venezuela)
Hospital d'Enfants (Rabat Morocco)
Hospital Escuela Materno Infantil (Tegucigalpa Honduras)
Hospital Luis Calvo Mackenna (Santiago Chile)
Hospital Nacional de Ninos (San Jose Costa Rica)
Hospital Pediatrico de Sinaloa (Culiacan Mexico)
King Hussein Cancer Center (Amman Jordan)
Our Lady's Hospital for Sick Children (Dublin Ireland)
Shanghai Children's Medical Center (Shanghai)
Unidad de Oncologia Pediatrica Instituto Materno Infantil de Pernambuco; Centro
de Hematologia e Oncologia Pediatrica (Recife) - Brazil
Unidad Nacional de Oncologia Pediatrica (Guatemala City Guatemala)

COMPETITORS

Ascension Health
Baptist Memorial Health Care
Catholic Health Partners
Children' s Medical Center of Dallas
Children' s National Medical Center
Cincinnati Children' s Hospital
City of Hope
Damon Runyon Cancer Research
Dana-Farber
Fox Chase Cancer Center
H. Lee Moffitt Cancer Center & Research Institute
HCA
Health Management Associates
LifePoint Hospitals
MD Anderson Cancer Center
Memorial Sloan-Kettering
Methodist Healthcare
Nationwide Children' s Hospital
Roswell Park Cancer Institute
Shelby County Health Care
Shriners Hospitals For Children
Tenet Healthcare
UT Medical Group

HISTORICAL FINANCIALS

Company Type: Private

Income Statement FYE: June 30

	REVENUE ($ mil.)	NET INCOME ($ mil.)	NET PROFIT MARGIN	EMPLOYEES
06/12	638	3	0.5%	2,500
06/11	573	(26)	—	—
06/09	589	(5)	—	—
06/09	551	0	—	—
Annual Growth	5.0%	—	—	—

2012 Year-End Financials

Debt ratio: —
Return on equity: 0.50%
Cash ($ mil.): 10
Current ratio: 0.30
Long-term debt ($ mil.): —
Dividends
Yield: —
Payout: —
Market value ($ mil.): —

ST. JUDE HOSPITAL

St. Jude Medical Center gets sickly Southern Californians on their feet again. The faith-based not-for-profit acute care facility with some 385 beds serves the residents of Orange County. The medical center provides an onsite cancer center (the Virginia K. Crosson Cancer Center) and a heart institute that offers cardiac surgeries and rehabilitation programs. It also provides inpatient and outpatient physical rehabilitation services and a variety of community outreach programs. Established by the Sisters of St. Joseph of Orange religious order in the 1950s St. Jude Medical Center is part of the St. Joseph Health System.

Geographic Reach

St. Jude serves residents in communities in California's Orange County including Brea Buena Park Fullerton La Habra Placentia and Yorba Linda.

Operations

Beyond the medical center's campus St. Jude operates its Heritage Medical Group with outpatient locations throughout its region. The medical group includes specialists in plastic surgery rheumatology and gastroenterology. Altogether St. Jude employs some 700 physicians. It handles more than 17000 inpatient admissions each year as well as 13000 surgeries 2000 births and 54000 emergency room visits.

The organization spends some $47 million in community benefits including outreach and charity care. Its mobile and fixed-site community clinics offer medical dental and preventative care services for low-income residents.

Strategy

St. Jude is expanding its facilities through the construction of a new $312 million patient tower schedule to open in late 2014. The Northwest Tower will feature private patient rooms as well as enhanced surgical and data management capabilities. Other improvement measures include technology upgrades such as a new neurovascular surgical system added in 2012.

In October 2011 St. Jude Medical Center closed its 12-bed pediatric unit and redirected patients younger than 16 to nearby Children's Hospital of Orange County. St. Jude's NICU (neonatal intensive care unit) remains open and the hospital continues to provide emergency and outpatient services to children.

EXECUTIVES

President CEO, Lee Penrose
EVP and COO, Doreen Dann
VP Medical Affairs, Joseph Lawton
VP Healthy Communities, Barry Ross
VP Resource Development, Susan Smith

LOCATIONS

HQ: ST. JUDE HOSPITAL
101 E VALENCIA MESA DR, FULLERTON, CA 92835-3875
Phone: 714-871-3280
Web: WWW.STJUDEMEDICALCENTER.ORG

COMPETITORS

Anaheim Regional Medical Center
Children' s Hospital of Orange County
Hoag Memorial Hospital
Memorial Health Services
UC Irvine Medical Center
Western Medical Center - Santa Ana

HISTORICAL FINANCIALS

Company Type: Private

Income Statement FYE: June 30

	REVENUE ($ mil.)	NET INCOME ($ mil.)	NET PROFIT MARGIN	EMPLOYEES
06/11	496	56	11.4%	2,600
06/10	492	61	12.4%	—
06/09	412	0	—	—
06/08	419	40	9.7%	—
Annual Growth	5.8%	11.5%	—	—

2011 Year-End Financials

Debt ratio: —
Return on equity: 11.40%
Cash ($ mil.): 93
Current ratio: 3.30
Long-term debt ($ mil.): —
Dividends
Yield: —
Payout: —
Market value ($ mil.): —

ST. LUKE'S HEALTH NETWORK INC.

St. Luke's University Hospital (formerly St. Luke's Hospital - Bethlehem Campus) serves residents of Pennsylvania's Lehigh Valley with primary specialty and emergency care services. The not-for-profit teaching hospital has about 480 acute-care beds. Its medical specialties include trauma oncology cardiology orthopedics neurology open-heart surgery radiology and robotic surgery. The medical center also operates outpatient surgery centers and general physician care clinics and it operates home health and community wellness programs. St. Luke's University Hospital was founded in 1872 and is part of the St. Luke's University Health Network.

LOCATIONS

HQ: ST. LUKE' S HEALTH NETWORK INC.
801 OSTRUM ST, BETHLEHEM, PA 18015-1000
Phone: 610-954-4000
Web: WWW.BETHLEHEM.SLHN.ORG

PRODUCTS/OPERATIONS

Selected Services

Cancer Center
Children's health
Diagnostic and Treatment Centers
Emergency
Heart Center
Neuroscience
Orthopaedics
Radiology/Imaging
Regional Breast Center (Center Valley)
Urgent Care Centers
Women's Imaging & Health Centers

COMPETITORS

Ascension Health
Evangelical Community Hospital
Lehigh Valley Health Network
Moses Taylor Hospital
Reading Hospital and Medical Center
Sacred Heart Hospital of Allentown
Wyoming Valley Health Care System

HISTORICAL FINANCIALS

Company Type: Private

Income Statement FYE: June 30

	REVENUE ($ mil.)	NET INCOME ($ mil.)	NET PROFIT MARGIN	EMPLOYEES
06/11	682	38	5.6%	2,958
06/10	670	23	3.4%	—
Annual Growth	1.9%	67.2%	—	—

2011 Year-End Financials

Debt ratio: ——
Return on equity: 5.60%
Cash ($ mil.): 74
Current ratio: 1.10
Long-term debt ($ mil.): —
Dividends
Yield: —
Payout: —
Market value ($ mil.): —

ST. LUKE'S HOSPITAL OF DULUTH

St. Luke's cares for colds cancers and other conditions in the chilly northern US. St. Luke's Hospital provides a variety of health care services to patients in northeastern Minnesota northwestern Wisconsin and parts of Michigan. The medical center has some 270 beds and a staff of about 370 physicians. Services include cardiology emergency medicine pediatrics oncology rehabilitation and vascular surgery. In addition to acute care services the organization offers primary and specialty health care services through a network of outpatient clinics.

Geographic Reach

St. Luke's serves a 17-county region in three states —encompassing northeastern Minnesota northwestern Wisconsin and the western Upper Peninsula of Michigan –through its acute care hospital in Duluth Minnesota and about 40 outpatient clinics providing primary and specialty care services.

Operations

St. Luke's handles about 10600 inpatient visits per year as well as 900 births 10000 surgeries and 70000 emergency room or urgent care visits. Its emergency room serves as a regional trauma center. St. Luke's also sees about 485000 patients annually at its primary and specialty care clinics. Its outpatient service divisions include Q Care (express medical clinic) St. Luke's Orthopedics and St. Luke's Infusion Therapy Clinic. The hospital conducts medical studies through a partnership with the Whiteside Institute for Clinical Research; it also has collaborative care relationships with the Pavilion Surgery Center and the Lake View Memorial Hospital.

Financial Performance

St. Luke's reported $697 million in patient services revenue in 2011. After contractual deductions and other obligations total revenues were reported at about $317 million.

Strategy

To expand its services for area residents in 2012 St. Luke's completed construction of a new medical office building which is located adjacent to the main hospital facilities and will include centers for sports medicine pediatrics neurosurgery and plastic surgery. Also that year St. Luke's opened its da Vinci Si surgical system suite which allows surgeons to conduct minimally invasive surgical procedures using the robotic system. In addition in 2011 the hospital formed a new maternal child health department to improve its birthing services; the new unit provides labor and delivery nursery and pediatric services.

Company Background

St. Luke's Hospital was founded in 1881. What was established as a typhoid response clinic became the city of Duluth's first hospital.

EXECUTIVES

President ; Sandra Barkley, John Strange
VP Clinics, Sandra Barkley
VP Finance and CFO, James (Jim) Wuellner
VP Support Services, Ron Franzen
VP Network Development and Chief Nursing Officer, Jo Ann Hoag
VP Medical Affairs and Medical Director, Gary Peterson
VP and CEO Lakeview Memorial Hospital, Brian Carlson
Marketing Specialist, Mary Greene
Chief of Staff, Ann Rock
Founder, Joseph Pilates
Treasurer, Melinda Machones

LOCATIONS

HQ: ST. LUKE' S HOSPITAL OF DULUTH
915 E 1ST ST, DULUTH, MN 55805-2193
Phone: 218-726-5555
Web: WWW.SLHDULUTH.COM

Selected Services Centers and Affiliates

Birthing Center
Breast Center
Cardiac Care
Cancer Care
Diagnostic Imaging
Emergency Care
Family Medicine
Laboratory Services
Lake View Pharmacy
Lake View Memorial Hospital
Northland Pharmacy
Pavilion Outpatient Surgery Center
Physical Rehabilitation Services
Sleep Center
St. Luke' s Center for Diagnostic Imaging
St. Luke' s Foundation
Surgery
Urgent Care
Whiteside Institute for Clinical Research

COMPETITORS

Allina Hospitals
CentraCare Health
First Care
Gillette Children' s
North Memorial Health Care
Sanford Bemidji
Spectrum Health
Howard Young Health Care

HISTORICAL FINANCIALS

Company Type: Private

Income Statement FYE: December 31

	REVENUE ($ mil.)	NET INCOME ($ mil.)	NET PROFIT MARGIN	EMPLOYEES
12/09	307	8	2.6%	2,200
12/08	276	1	0.6%	—
12/06	264	1	0.4%	—
12/05	244	1	0.6%	—
Annual Growth	5.9%	56.0%	—	—

2009 Year-End Financials

Debt ratio: ——
Return on equity: 2.60%
Cash ($ mil.): 13
Current ratio: —
Long-term debt ($ mil.): —
Dividends
Yield: —
Payout: —
Market value ($ mil.): —

ST. MARY MEDICAL CENTER INC.

LOCATIONS

HQ: ST. MARY MEDICAL CENTER INC.
1500 S LAKE PARK AVE, HOBART, IN 463426699
Phone: 2199420551
Web: WWW.COMHS.ORG

HISTORICAL FINANCIALS

Company Type: Private

Income Statement FYE: June 30

	REVENUE ($ mil.)	NET INCOME ($ mil.)	NET PROFIT MARGIN	EMPLOYEES
06/13	215	17	8.2%	800
06/10	189	14	7.7%	—
06/09	163	0	—	—
06/08	1,004	0	—	—
Annual Growth	(26.5%)	—	—	—

2013 Year-End Financials

Debt ratio: ——
Return on equity: 8.20%
Cash ($ mil.): 4
Current ratio: 1.90
Long-term debt ($ mil.): —
Dividends
Yield: —
Payout: —
Market value ($ mil.): —

ST. MARY'S HEALTH CARE SYSTEM INC.

St. Mary's Health Care System cares for the residents of northeast Georgia. Its primary facility St. Mary's Hospital has almost 200 acute-care beds. From health and wellness programs to women's and children's services the hospital also has centers dedicated to outpatient rehabilitation home health and long-term care. Specialty services include neurology cardiovascular care orthopedics and gastroenterology. It also operates the 25-bed St. Mary's Good Samaritan Hospital and a retirement village. The organization is sponsored by the

Sisters of Mercy of the Americas St. Mary's Health Care System is a member of the Catholic Health East family of hospitals.

Operations

St. Mary's Health Care System includes St. Mary's Hospital St. Mary's Good Samaritan Hospital Highland Hills Village retirement community and Center for Alzheimer's and Dementia Care and provides regional home health care and hospice services.

St. Mary's Hospital is the only hospital in the region to achieve The Joint Commission Gold Seal of Approval certification in advanced primary stroke heart failure care and total knee replacement.

Strategy

Expanding its services and geographic coverage in 2012 St. Mary's Health Care System acquired St. Mary's Good Samaritan Hospital a not-for-profit 25-bed Critical Access Hospital serving greater Greene County and the Lake Oconee communities of Georgia.

It also brought Athens Internal Medicine Associates (a medical practice in Athens) into its health system in 2011.

Ownership

St. Mary's Health Care System is a member of the Catholic Health East family of hospitals.

Company Background

St. Mary's Health Care System traces its roots to the founding of St. Mary's Hospital in 1906 and has been the official health care provider for the University of Georgia Athletic Association since 1999.

EXECUTIVES

Vp Of Human Resources, Jeff English
Director Patient Care/nursing, Nina Evans
Director Of Radiology, Charles Smith
Nursing Director, Darlene Morocco

LOCATIONS

HQ: ST. MARY' S HEALTH CARE SYSTEM INC.
1230 BAXTER ST, ATHENS, GA 30606-3712
Phone: 706-389-3000
Web: WWW.STMARYSATHENS.COM

COMPETITORS

Athens Regional Medical Center
DeKalb Medical
Emory Healthcare
Gwinnett Health System
Northeast Georgia Health System
Northside Hospital
Piedmont Healthcare
Regency Hospital
WellStar Health System
West Georgia Health System

HISTORICAL FINANCIALS

Company Type: Private

Income Statement FYE: December 31

	REVENUE ($ mil.)	NET INCOME ($ mil.)	NET PROFIT MARGIN	EMPLOYEES
12/12	161	29	18.5%	1,350
12/09	173	11	6.6%	—
Annual Growth	(2.3%)	37.7%	—	—

2012 Year-End Financials

Debt ratio: —
Return on equity: 18.50%
Cash ($ mil.): 28
Current ratio: 1.60
Long-term debt ($ mil.): —
Dividends
Yield: —
Payout: —
Market value ($ mil.): —

ST. MARY'S MEDICAL CENTER

Nobody wants to get sick but if you're ailing in West Virginia St. Mary's Medical Center wants you to know you are in good hands. The not-for-profit 395-bed medical facility serves patients in areas such as cardiac emergency neuroscience and cancer treatment. The largest health care facility in the tri-state region St. Mary's Medical Center is also a teaching facility affiliated with Joan C. Edwards Marshall University School of Medicine. St. Mary's Home Health Services administers care for patients in a six county area in Ohio and West Virginia. Services include IV therapy and occupational and physical therapy. St. Mary's Medical Cener was founded in 1924.

EXECUTIVES

Director Physician Recruitment, Mary-anne Brown
Director Of Him, Cheryl Willis
Vp Oncology Services, Vera Rose
Vp Support Services Planning And Development, Tim Parnell
Director Of Radiology Services, Fred Kirby
Vp Schools Of Nursing And Health Professionals, Shelia Kyle
Vp Of Medical Affairs, Lee Taylor
Director Of Nursing, Sharon Alexander
Director Icu/coronary Care Unit, Samantha Ash
Director Of Respiratory Therapy, Kevin Queen
Respiratory Therapy Director, Greg Blake
Vice President, Chris Trotter
Contract Anls Vice President Purchasing, Lavona Turvey
Board Of Directors, Kathy Tygart

LOCATIONS

HQ: ST. MARY' S MEDICAL CENTER
2900 1ST AVE, HUNTINGTON, WV 25702-1241
Phone: 304-526-1234
Web: WWW.STMARYS.ORG

PRODUCTS/OPERATIONS

Selected Services

Breast Center
Behavioral health
Emergency care
Home health care
Intensive care
Interventional radiology
Joslin Diabetes Center Affiliate
Maternity care
Occupational Health Center
Pain Relief Center
Pastoral care
Pharmacy
Regional Heart Institute
Regional Cancer Center
Regional Neuroscience Center
Regional Orthopedic Center
Regional Sleep Center
Regional Spine Center
Regional Stroke Center
Regional Orthopedic Center
Regional Wound Center
Rehabilitation
Skilled Nursing Care
Support groups
Weight Loss Surgery Center

COMPETITORS

Adena Health System
CAMC Health
Clinch Valley Medical Center
Fairfield Medical Center
Highlands Health
Pikeville Medical Center

HISTORICAL FINANCIALS

Company Type: Private

Income Statement FYE: September 30

	REVENUE ($ mil.)	NET INCOME ($ mil.)	NET PROFIT MARGIN	EMPLOYEES
09/09	341	1	0.5%	2,000
09/07	289	1	0.6%	—
09/04	245	6	2.8%	—
09/03	217	0	—	—
Annual Growth	7.8%	—	—	—

2009 Year-End Financials

Debt ratio: —
Return on equity: 0.50%
Cash ($ mil.): 8
Current ratio: 0.80
Long-term debt ($ mil.): —
Dividends
Yield: —
Payout: —
Market value ($ mil.): —

STANDARD ELECTRIC COMPANY

EXECUTIVES

President, Laverne N. (Vern) Weber, age 75
Marketing Manager, Jeff Marner
Sales Manager Southern Regional, Dan Shimkos
Sales Manager, John Wisniewski
Sales Manager Northern Regional, Tim Schell
Sales Manager Grand Rapids Area, Dave LaGosh
Sales Manager U.P. Electric and Wittock, Mike Horton
Quality Manager, Ron Simpson
Vice President, Bill Gray

LOCATIONS

HQ: STANDARD ELECTRIC COMPANY
2650 TRAUTNER DR, SAGINAW, MI 486049599
Phone: 9894972100
Web: WWW.STANDARDELECTRICCO.COM

COMPETITORS

Kendall Electric
McNaughton-McKay
Medler Electric
Utility Supply and Construction
Werner Electric Supply

HISTORICAL FINANCIALS

Company Type: Private

Income Statement FYE: February 28

	REVENUE ($ mil.)	NET INCOME ($ mil.)	NET PROFIT MARGIN	EMPLOYEES
02/14	159	1	1.1%	250
02/13	152	1	1.0%	—
02/12	155	1	1.1%	—
02/11	132	0	—	—
Annual Growth	6.5%	—	—	—

2014 Year-End Financials

Debt ratio: —
Return on equity: 1.10%
Cash ($ mil.): 0
Current ratio: 0.80
Long-term debt ($ mil.): —
Dividends
Yield: —
Payout: —
Market value ($ mil.): —

STANLEY STEEMER INTERNATIONAL INC.

EXECUTIVES

Chairman and CEO, Wesley C. Bates
CFO, Mark Bunner
EVP, Phillip P. Ryser
VP Human Resources, Eric Smith
Director MIS, Dale Bevins

LOCATIONS

HQ: STANLEY STEEMER INTERNATIONAL INC.
5800 INNOVATION DR, DUBLIN, OH 430163271
Phone: 6147642007
Web: WWW.STANLEYSTEEMER.COM

PRODUCTS/OPERATIONS

Selected Products

Gonzo Pet Hair Lifter
Handi Brush
Pet-Mess Solution Kit
Stanley Steemer Door Mat
Stanley Steemer Hardwood Floor Cleaner Kit
Stanley Steemer Neutral Tile & Grout Cleaner
Stanley Steemer Odor Out Plus
Stanley Steemer Red Wine Remover
Stanley Steemer Spot Remover

Selected Services

Residential Cleaning
- Carpet Cleaning
- Furniture Cleaning
- Tile & Grout Cleaning
- Hardwood Floor Services
- Air Duct Cleaning
- Water Damage Restoration
- Area Rug Cleaning
- Autos Boats & RVs
- Insurance Services

Commercial Cleaning
- Carpet Cleaning
- Furniture Cleaning
- Tile & Grout Cleaning
- Hardwood Floor Services
- Air Duct Cleaning
- Water Damage Repair
- National Accounts

COMPETITORS

Dwyer Group
Maid to Perfection
Molly Maid
ServiceMaster
The BMS Enterprises

HISTORICAL FINANCIALS

Company Type: Private

Income Statement FYE: December 31

	REVENUE ($ mil.)	NET INCOME ($ mil.)	NET PROFIT MARGIN	EMPLOYEES
12/13	199	18	9.2%	2,000
12/12	192	10	5.5%	—
12/11	191	11	6.3%	—
12/10	186	0	—	—
Annual Growth	2.3%	—	—	—

2013 Year-End Financials

Debt ratio: —
Return on equity: 9.20%
Cash ($ mil.): 26
Current ratio: 1.20
Long-term debt ($ mil.): —
Dividends
Yield: —
Payout: —
Market value ($ mil.): —

STAR OF THE WEST MILLING COMPANY

EXECUTIVES

President, Art Loeffler
Vice President Flour Milling Division, Mike Fassezke
VP Edible Bean Marketing, Joe Cramer
Controller, Eric Bushey
Director Information Technology, Jim Koski
VP Grain Marketing, Gary Kaufman
VP Elevator Division, Jim Howe
Human Resources, Tim Brooks
Plant Manager, Mark Kern
Manager Maintenance, Frank Frysh
Manager Customer Service Flour Department, Janice Weiss
Director Safety, Wayne Bauer
Office Manager, Anne Stesny
Technical Director, Laurie Murphy
Head, Keith Weber
Operations Manager, Joe Ignash

LOCATIONS

HQ: STAR OF THE WEST MILLING COMPANY
121 E TUSCOLA ST, FRANKENMUTH, MI 487341731
Phone: 3306732941
Web: WWW.STAROFTHEWEST.COM

PRODUCTS/OPERATIONS

Selected Products

Beans
- Black beans
- Cranberry beans
- Dark red kidney beans
- Great northern beans
- Light red kidney beans
- Navy beans (pea beans)
- Pink beans
- Pinto beans
- Small reds
- Small white beans
- Yelloweye beans

Flour
- Cardinal flour
- Cracked wheat
- Crushed wheat
- Heavy bran flakes
- Heritage Brand All Purpose
- Light bran
- Patriot whole wheat flour
- Peerless flour
- Perfection pretzel flour
- Soft wheat flour and specialty products
- Special soft white wheat cake flour

Grain
- Corn
- Soybeans
- Wheat

Plant food

COMPETITORS

Bay State Milling
Bunge Milling
C.H. Guenther & Son
CGC
Chippewa Valley Bean
DeBruce Grain
Horizon Milling
Italgrani
Kelley Bean
North Dakota Mill
Seaboard
US Soy
Washington Quality Foods

HISTORICAL FINANCIALS

Company Type: Private

Income Statement FYE: December 31

	REVENUE ($ mil.)	NET INCOME ($ mil.)	NET PROFIT MARGIN	EMPLOYEES
12/13	416	15	3.7%	239
12/12	444	17	3.9%	—
12/11	394	15	4.0%	—
12/10	294	0	—	—
Annual Growth	12.3%	—	—	—

2013 Year-End Financials

Debt ratio: —
Return on equity: 3.70%
Cash ($ mil.): 43
Current ratio: 1.40
Long-term debt ($ mil.): —
Dividends
Yield: —
Payout: —
Market value ($ mil.): —

STATIC CONTROL COMPONENTS INC.

Static Control Components (SCC) isn't stuck on static cling. The company that made a name for itself by selling anti-static products has made an even greater impression by selling parts for rebuilt toner cartridges. Its Imaging Division which sells parts to recycle used printer cartridges has captured more than half of the world market. SCC also makes electrical testing tools. In 2006 Static Control Components sold its SCC Products affiliate to 3M. President and CEO Ed Swartz founded Static Control Components in 1987; the company is owned and operated by his family.

Static Control Components (SCC) sells its products worldwide through its website company offices as well authorized distributors. The company maintains some 20 manufacturing locations.

Rival Lexmark International sued SCC claiming its components and software for Lexmark toner cartridges violated both general copyright law and the federal Digital Millennium Copyright Act of 1998. Static Control ultimately prevailed in the federal appellate courts.

EXECUTIVES

Vice President Sales, Bryan Bonacum
Executive Vice President, Dale Lewis
Vice President Sales Latin America And Distributor Markets, Juan Bonell

LOCATIONS

HQ: STATIC CONTROL COMPONENTS INC.
3010 LEE AVE, SANFORD, NC 27332-6210
Phone: 919-774-3808
Web: WWW.SCC-INC.COM

COMPETITORS

Canon
Clover Technologies
Hewlett-Packard
Illinois Tool Works
Lexmark
Wazana Brothers

HISTORICAL FINANCIALS

Company Type: Private

Income Statement FYE: December 31

	REVENUE ($ mil.)	NET INCOME ($ mil.)	NET PROFIT MARGIN	EMPLOYEES
12/11	191	7	4.1%	1,200
12/04	264	0	—	—
12/03	245	5	2.2%	—
12/02	238	3	1.5%	—
Annual Growth	(2.4%)	8.8%	—	—

2011 Year-End Financials

Debt ratio: —
Return on equity: 4.10%
Cash ($ mil.): 0
Current ratio: 1.20
Long-term debt ($ mil.): —
Dividends
Yield: —
Payout: —
Market value ($ mil.): —

STAVIS SEAFOODS INC.

LOCATIONS

HQ: STAVIS SEAFOODS INC.
212 NORTHERN AVE STE 305, BOSTON, MA 022102088
Phone: 6174826349
Web: WWW.STAVIS.COM

HISTORICAL FINANCIALS

Company Type: Private

Income Statement FYE: December 28

	REVENUE ($ mil.)	NET INCOME ($ mil.)	NET PROFIT MARGIN	EMPLOYEES
12/13	203	0	0.4%	120
12/07	164	0	0.4%	—
12/06	0	0	—	—
12/05	154	0	—	—
Annual Growth	3.6%	—	—	—

STEINER ELECTRIC COMPANY

Steiner Electric electrifies Chicago by distributing electrical products and providing related supplies and services through locations in northern Illinois and northwest Indiana. Besides such standard electrical supplies as ballasts and fasteners the company's products include industrial supplies automation products motors and drives lighting products generators and bar code devices. Services include energy audits turnkey project management motor repair and electric vehicle charging. Customers purchase Steiner Electric's products for commercial construction residential and industrial applications. The founding Steiner family owns the firm.

Geographic Reach

The company has facilities in Loves Park St. Charles Gurnee Chicago Tinley Park and Crystal Lake (all in Illinois) and in Hobart Indiana.

Operations

Steiner Electric's Data Collection Group installs and supports bar code scanners radio-frequency identification (RFID) readers and wireless networks. Its Automation Products and Information Systems Group provides technology from Siemens and other vendors that track factory production data.

Sales and Marketing

The company serves contractor education enterprise fiber optic government healthcare industrial/commercial and residential markets.

Mergers and Acquisitions

In 2011 Steiner Electric acquired Illinois-based Inland Cutting Products and the Industrial Sling integrated them into its Crown Industrial Supply Division. The Inland acquisition helps Steiner Electric service supply contracts through its Supplier Partnership Group which helps customers in tool crib management and the supply of maintenance repair and operations products for an entire manufacturing plant.

Company Background

Steiner Electric was formed in 1916 by George S. Steiner.

LOCATIONS

HQ: STEINER ELECTRIC COMPANY
1250 TOUHY AVE, ELK GROVE VILLAGE, IL 60007-4985
Phone: 847-228-0400
Web: WWW.STEINER-ELECTRIC.COM

PRODUCTS/OPERATIONS

Selected Products

Automation products
- Industrial computers
- Motion control
- Pneumatics
- SCADA software
- Sensors
- Vision systems

Barcode products
- Barcode labels
- Printers
- Scanners
- Vehicle mounted computers

Electrical supplies
- Ballasts
- Cables
- Fasteners
- Fittings
- Heaters
- Lamps
- Lighting
- Motors
- Safety switches
- Tools
- Transformers
- Wires

Industrial supplies
- Indexable tooling
- Machine tool accessories
- Precision instruments
- Safety equipment
- Tapes

Generators
Lighting
Motors
Unlimited power supply

COMPETITORS

Consolidated Electrical
Graybar Electric
McNaughton-McKay
Revere Electric
Rexel
Springfield Electric
Turtle & Hughes
WESCO International

HISTORICAL FINANCIALS

Company Type: Private

Income Statement FYE: December 31

	REVENUE ($ mil.)	NET INCOME ($ mil.)	NET PROFIT MARGIN	EMPLOYEES
12/12	230	0	—	500
12/11	181	0	—	—
12/09	181	0	—	—
12/09	0	0	—	—
Annual Growth	—	—	—	—

2012 Year-End Financials

Debt ratio: —
Return on equity: —
Cash ($ mil.): 1
Current ratio: 1.10
Long-term debt ($ mil.): —
Dividends
Yield: —
Payout: —
Market value ($ mil.): —

STEPHEN GOULD CORPORATION

Others can worry about what's inside –Stephen Gould Corporation concentrates on the package. The company provides a full range of packaging-related design and printing services for customers worldwide. Its products include gift packaging point-of-purchase displays product merchandising and retail and industrial packaging. Stephen Gould Corporation also provides graphic design and package-engineering services as well as assembly and fulfillment. The company was originally founded in 1939 by Stephen Gould David Golden and Leonard Beckerman.

Geographic Reach

Stephen Gould Corporation operates from about 40 facilities; branches are located primarily in the US (more than 20 states) but also in China Ireland Malaysia and Mexico.

EXECUTIVES

Vice President Business Development, Bob Challinor
V P Business Development, Wiley Ehrke
Vice President Engineering, Douglas Williams
Vice President Chief Security Officer, Julie Racine
Vp Sales, Ted Vitas

LOCATIONS

HQ: STEPHEN GOULD CORPORATION
35 S JEFFERSON RD, WHIPPANY, NJ 079811043
Phone: 9734281510
Web: WWW.STEPHENGOULD.COM

PRODUCTS/OPERATIONS

Selected Products and Services

Products
- Aerospace reusable cases
- Corrugated containers
- Gift packaging
- Industrial packaging
- Point of sale packaging
- Protective packaging

Services
- Creative services
- Logistics & facilities
- Package design & engineering

COMPETITORS

Consolidated Carqueville
Focus Packaging &
Gibraltar Packaging
Metro Packaging and Imaging

Display group	R.R. Donnelley
Fort Dearborn	WS Packaging Group

HISTORICAL FINANCIALS

Company Type: Private

Income Statement FYE: December 31

	REVENUE ($ mil.)	NET INCOME ($ mil.)	NET PROFIT MARGIN	EMPLOYEES
12/13	526	3	0.7%	325
12/12	526	3	0.7%	—
12/11	519	4	0.8%	—
12/10	500	0	—	—
Annual Growth	1.7%	—	—	—

2013 Year-End Financials

Debt ratio: —
Return on equity: 0.70%
Cash ($ mil.): 9
Current ratio: 1.50
Long-term debt ($ mil.): —
Dividends
Yield: —
Payout: —
Market value ($ mil.): —

STEPHENSON WHOLESALE COMPANY INC.

Buying a candy bar and a box of nails is made easier thanks to Stephenson Wholesale. Operating through subsidiaries Indian National Wholesale Company and GLC Marketing the company is a leading supplier of food and non-food goods to convenience stores and other retail outlets in Oklahoma and Texas. It also distributes goods to snack bars concessions operators and tribal smoke shops. The family-owned company was founded in 1953 by Ralphen Cross.

EXECUTIVES

VP Administration, Dawn Laxson

LOCATIONS

HQ: STEPHENSON WHOLESALE COMPANY INC.
230 S 22ND AVE, DURANT, OK 74701-5646
Phone: 580-920-0125
Web: WWW.INWSUPPLY.COM

COMPETITORS

Associated Wholesale Grocers	GSC Enterprises
C&S Wholesale	H. T. Hackney
Core-Mark	McLane
Eby-Brown	Nash-Finch

HISTORICAL FINANCIALS

Company Type: Private

Income Statement FYE: December 31

	REVENUE ($ mil.)	NET INCOME ($ mil.)	NET PROFIT MARGIN	EMPLOYEES
12/12	395	2	0.8%	315
12/11	404	3	0.9%	—
12/10	401	2	0.7%	—
12/09	380	2	0.6%	—
Annual Growth	1.3%	11.7%	—	—

2012 Year-End Financials

Debt ratio: —
Return on equity: 0.80%
Cash ($ mil.): 4
Current ratio: 1.40
Long-term debt ($ mil.): —
Dividends
Yield: —
Payout: —
Market value ($ mil.): —

STEUART INVESTMENT COMPANY

LOCATIONS

HQ: STEUART INVESTMENT COMPANY
5454 WSCNSIN AVE STE 1600, CHEVY CHASE, MD 20815
Phone: 3019512700

HISTORICAL FINANCIALS

Company Type: Private

Income Statement FYE: December 31

	ASSETS ($ mil.)	NET INCOME ($ mil.)	INCOME AS % OF ASSETS	EMPLOYEES
12/10	445	(11)	—	60
12/09	118	7	6.1%	—
12/08	325	0	0.0%	—
Annual Growth	16.9%	—	—	—

2010 Year-End Financials

Debt ratio: —
Return on equity: (-11.50%)
Cash ($ mil.): 9
Current ratio: 0.60
Long-term debt ($ mil.): —
Dividends
Yield: —
Payout: —
Market value ($ mil.): —

STEVENS INSTITUTE OF TECHNOLOGY (INC)

Even before the advent of the internal combustion engine Stevens Institute of Technology was educating students in science technology and engineering. Founded in 1870 through an endowment from engineer Edwin Stevens the university offers undergraduate master's and doctoral degrees in engineering science humanities computer science and technology management. About 2500 undergraduates are enrolled and the school has some 3500 graduate students. Stevens Institute teams up with corporate and military institutions to provide students with hands-on research experience; Stevens Technologies a for-profit subsidiary of the school licenses and sells the technological fruits of these partnerships.

Operations

Stevens Institute has about 400 faculty members and a student-to-teacher ratio of 7:1 for undergrads and 10:1 for graduate students. It offers about 30 undergraduate 45 master's and 20 Ph.D. degree programs as well as 122 graduate certificates.

The university includes three national research centers of excellence and its annual research budget is about $27 million. Research programs are conducted in fields including medicine energy finance defense and STEM (science technology engineering and mathematics) fields. Stevens Institute collaborates with the University of Southern California on the Systems Engineering Research Center (SERC) which develops and tests complex defense systems for the Department of Defense. The center is located on the Stevens Institute campus.

In addition to Stevens Technologies Stevens Institute has for profit operations through its real estate investment subsidiary Ravenswood Corporation. It also owns Castle Point Holdings which provides a corporate interface between Stevens and startup companies.

Financial Performance

Stevens Institute reported a 5% rise in revenues to $183 million in 2012 due to higher tuition and fees (which account for about two-thirds of earnings) as well as contributions and auxiliary enterprise income. Net income decreased 75% to $2.7 million however due to higher operating expenses and lower returns on investments.

Strategy

Stevens Institute forms partnerships with other universities and commercial and government entities to expand both its educational and research programs. In 2012 it partnered with Seton Hall University to offer a joint legal degree with Hackensack University Medical Center to conduct biomedical clinical education programs and with mPhase Technologies on battery technology research projects.

The university also widens its offerings through organic measures. For instance in 2012 it launched a new graduate program in enterprise project management and opened a new financial teaching and research facility (the Hanlon Financial Systems Lab).

EXECUTIVES

Chairman, Lawrence T. (Larry) Babbio Jr., age 70
VP Human Resources and Secretary, Mark L. Samolewicz
Vice President Chief Administrative Officer, Maureen P. Weatherall
Associate VP Information Technology and Administrative Computing, Eric Rosenberg
VP University Research and Enterprise Development, Helena S. Wisniewski, age 64
VP Facilities and Community Relations, Henry P. Dobbelaar Jr.
Executive Assistant to the President and Assistant Secretary, Diana Colombo
Controller and Assistant Treasurer, Michael D'Onofrio
Executive Director Office Alumni, Anita Lang
Director Athletics, Russell Rogers
Dean Residence Life, Trina Ballantyne
Director Special Functions, Barbara Migliori
Dean University Admissions, Daniel G. Gallagher
Director International Admissions and Honors Programs, Edwina W. Fleming
Director Physical Plant, Kenneth Goldklang
Manager Campus Bookstore, Teresa Tridente
VP Research Enterprise, Joseph (Joe) Mitola
VP Finance Treasurer and CFO, Randy L. Greene
VP and Provost, George P. Korfiatis
Vice President for Advancement Chief Administrative Officer, Fred Regan
Professor & Dean Academic Administration, Prof Siva Thangam
Head Library Acquisitions and Collection Development, Scott Smith
Director Assessment & Academic Communications, Christine del Rosario
Executive Director Web Campus, Robert Ubell
Director Procurement, Doris Schultz
President, Nariman Farvardin
Program Director for an Open House to learn more about the EMTM program and its extension to the MBA in Technology Management degree, Murrae Bowden

Service Center Administrative Assistant, Carol Condello
Service Center Manager, Celia Llano
Administrative Assistant, Lisa Golizio
Assistant Director of Communications, Amy Meckeler
Associate Director of Admissions, Benjamin Laster
Office Manager, Cathy McGuire
Director Admissions & Information Systems, Laura Grieme-Meinecke
Director of Financial Aid, Shawn ONeill
Assistant Director of Financial Aid, Steven Schaber
Administrative Assistant, Suny Henning
Trustee, Richard R. (Rick) Roscitt
Trustee, Richard F. Spanier, age 74
Trustee, Edward C. Eichhorn
Trustee, John J. LoPorto, age 78
Trustee, Thomas A. (Tom) Corcoran, age 70
Trustee, Philip P. Crowley
Trustee, Virginia P. Ruesterholz, age 52
Trustee, Edward G. Amoroso
Trustee, Stephen T. Boswell
Trustee, David J. Farber
Trustee, Angie M. Hankins
Trustee, Barrett Hazeltine
Trustee, Katherine C. Hegmann
Trustee, Edwin J. Hess
Trustee, George W. Johnston
Trustee, James M. Walsh
Trustee, Cardinal Warde
Trustee, Jerald M. Wigdortz
Trustee, Harold P. Wilmerding
Trustee, Martin C. Fliesler
Trustee, Robert J. Hoar
Trustee, Juan P. Jaime
Trustee, Richard S. Magee
Auditors: GrantThorntonLLP

LOCATIONS

HQ: STEVENS INSTITUTE OF TECHNOLOGY (INC)
1 CASTLE POINT TER, HOBOKEN, NJ 07030-5906
Phone: 201-216-5000
Web: WWW.DC.STEVENS.EDU

PRODUCTS/OPERATIONS

Selected Schools and Colleges

Charles V. Schaefer Jr. School of Engineering and Science
College of Arts and Letters
School of Systems and Enterprises
Wesley J. Howe School of Technology Management

HISTORICAL FINANCIALS

Company Type: Private

Income Statement FYE: June 30

	REVENUE ($ mil.)	NET INCOME ($ mil.)	NET PROFIT MARGIN	EMPLOYEES
06/11	215	2	1.0%	500
06/10	211	8	4.0%	—
06/08	168	(1)	—	—
06/07	129	24	18.6%	—
Annual Growth	13.6%	(45.6%)	—	—

2011 Year-End Financials

Debt ratio: —
Return on equity: 1.00%
Cash ($ mil.): 20
Current ratio: —
Long-term debt ($ mil.): —
Dividends
Yield: —
Payout: —
Market value ($ mil.): —

STEVENS TRANSPORT INC.

Staying cool is a must for Stevens Transport. An irregular-route refrigerated truckload carrier (or reefer) Stevens hauls temperature-controlled cargo throughout the US covering the 48 contiguous states. Through alliances Stevens also covers every province in Canada and every state in Mexico. The company operates a fleet of about 2000 Kenworth and Peterbuilt tractors and 3500 Thermo King refrigerated trailers from a network of more than a dozen service centers. Partnerships with railroads allow Stevens to arrange intermodal transport of temperature-controlled cargo. The company also provides third-party logistics services. Stevens Transport was founded in 1980.

Geographic Reach

Stevens Transport maintains its operations across Canada Mexico and the US through its partnerships with BNSF Norfolk Southern CSX and Union Pacific. It has 13 logistics offices located in Canada and throughout the US.

Operations

The company owns 49% of B2B Transport which provides an array of transportation related services to large mid-sized and small companies throughout North America.

Sales and Marketing

Stevens has provided refrigerated shipping services for such big names as General Mills Kraft Foods M&M Mars Procter & Gamble and Wal-Mart.

Strategy

Even in a US economy ripe with unpredictable fuel costs and a decline in consumer confidence one thing has always worked in Stevens' favor: people will always need their food. The company has managed to maintain a steady growth rate by keeping costs down updating the technology of its trucking equipment and maintaining an efficient operating structure. Along these lines in 2012 it implemented new mobile computing platforms across its fleet of tractors to enhance its customer services and optimize productivity.

EXECUTIVES

President, Clay M. Aaron
EVP, Michael Richey
VP Logistic Sales, Daniel Bell
Vice Chairman, Todd S. Aaron
Vice President Risk Management, William Tallent
VP Secretary and Treasurer, Bob Nelson
Chairman and CEO, Steven L. Aaron
VP Operations, Smokey Adams
Vice President Driver Resources and Administration, Angela A. Horowitz
Vice Chairman, Todd S. Aaron
VP Administration Secretary Treasurer and Director, Bob Nelson

LOCATIONS

HQ: STEVENS TRANSPORT INC.
9757 MILITARY PKWY, DALLAS, TX 75227-4805
Phone: 972-216-9000
Web: WWW.STEVENSTRANSPORT.COM

PRODUCTS/OPERATIONS

Selected Services

Intermodal
International
Logistics
Truckload

COMPETITORS

C.R. England
Central Refrigerated Service
Comcar
Covenant Transportation
Frozen Food Express
Henderson Trucking
Jim Palmer Trucking
KLLM Transport Services
Marten Transport
Navajo Shippers
Prime Inc.
Southern Refrigerated Transport
TransAm Trucking
Watkins Associated Industries
Willis Shaw Express

HISTORICAL FINANCIALS

Company Type: Private

Income Statement FYE: December 31

	REVENUE ($ mil.)	NET INCOME ($ mil.)	NET PROFIT MARGIN	EMPLOYEES
12/12	607	85	14.0%	2,100
12/11	566	76	13.5%	—
12/08	0	0	—	—
12/07	492	67	13.6%	—
Annual Growth	4.3%	4.9%	—	—

2012 Year-End Financials

Debt ratio: —
Return on equity: 14.00%
Cash ($ mil.): 66
Current ratio: 2.30
Long-term debt ($ mil.): —
Dividends
Yield: —
Payout: —
Market value ($ mil.): —

STEWARD HEALTH CARE SYSTEM LLC

Steward Health Care System wants to be a steward of good health. With a total of 2100 beds Steward Health operates 11 hospitals including Carney Hospital Good Samaritan Medical Center Holy Family Hospital Norwood Hospital St. Elizabeth's Medical Center and Saint Anne's Hospital. Several of the hospitals are affiliated with Boston-area medical schools. The company is a top health care provider in New England; its territory ranges from Rhode Island to eastern Massachusetts and southern New Hampshire. In addition to hospitals Steward Health also includes a physician practice organization an outpatient clinic network and a home care and hospice agency. Steward is owned by Cerberus Capital Management.

Operations

Other operations include Por Cristo a charitable organization providing services in Ecuador and Laboure College a medical school that confers bachelor's degrees in nursing.

Mergers and Acquisitions

Acquisitions in 2011 and 2012 included five Massachusetts hospitals: Merrimack Valley Hospital (120 beds) Nashoba Valley Medical Center (60 beds formerly part of Essent Healthcare) Morton Hospital (150 beds) Quincy Medical Center (200 beds) and New England Sinai Hospital (210 post-acute care beds).

Company Background

The company changed its name from Caritas Christi to Steward Health after being acquired by Cerberus Capital Management in 2010; it had previously been operated by the Catholic Archdiocese of Boston. The acquisition by Cerberus was worth some $895 million and provided operational funding and capital for hospital improvement projects; it also helped pay down debt obligations. As a result of the transaction Steward Health became a for-profit corporation; however a stipulation of the deal mandated that the health system's hospitals retain their pastoral and charitable care policies. The sale to Cerberus was not the first attempt by the Archdiocese of Boston to sell the ailing Caritas Christi system which had been suffering from financial troubles for several years prior to the deal.

EXECUTIVES

Senior Vice President Chief Marketing Officer, Brian Carty, age 64
Chief Human Resources Officer, Stuart Grief
COO, Joshua S. Putter
President - Steward, Mark Girard
Chairman and CEO, Ralph de la Torre
EVP and General Counsel, Joseph Maher Jr.
EVP Corporate Strategy and Management, Mark Rich
SVP, Sister Marie Puleo
Executive Vice President, Robert E. (Bob) Guyon Jr.
Senior Vice President Chief Medical Officer, Justine M. Carr
Chief Financial Officer, James R. Renna
President - Steward Medical Group, Michael G. Callum
VP and Chief Compliance Officer, Karen Murray
Director Media Relations, Christopher Murphy
Chief Information Officer, Drexel DeFord
Vice President of Services, Carole A. Billington
Vice President Medical Affairs, Harvey Kowaloff
President, Craig A. Jesiolowski
Director Information Systems, Jennifer Marrandette
Vice President of Business Development, John A. Jurczyk
Director Human Resources, Lisa Berry
General Counsel, Lisa Gray
Vice President Finance, Michael Bushell
Vice President, Susan B. Oldrid
Director Marketing & Planning, Wendy R. Bauer
Vice President Operations, William Fleming
Vice President of Finance, Kevin Kilday
VP-Decision Svcs & Integrations, Michael O'Reilly
Vice President of Medical Affairs, Paul Allen
Vice President of Finance, Jeffrey P. Dion

LOCATIONS

HQ: STEWARD HEALTH CARE SYSTEM LLC
500 BOYLSTON ST FL 5, BOSTON, MA 02116-3791
Phone: 617-419-4700
Web: WWW.STEWARD.ORG

Selected Hospitals – Massachusetts

Carney Hospital (Dorchester)
Good Samaritan Medical Center (Brockton)
Holy Family Hospital (Methuen)
Merrimack Valley Hospital (Haverhill acquired in 2011)
Morton Hospital (Taunton acquired in 2011)
Nashoba Valley Medical Center (Ayer acquired in 2011)
New England Sinai Hospital (Stoughton acquired in 2012)
Norwood Hospital (Norwood)
Quincy Medical Center (Quincy acquired in 2011)
Saint Anne's Hospital (Fall River)
St. Elizabeth's Medical Center (Brighton)

COMPETITORS

Berkshire Health Systems
Boston Medical Center
Cambridge Health Alliance
Cape Cod Healthcare
Care New England
CareGroup
Children' s Hospital Boston
Emerson Hospital
Hallmark Health
Lahey Health System
Massachusetts General Hospital
New England Alliance for Health
Northeast Health System
Partners HealthCare
Southcoast Hospitals Group
Southern New Hampshire Medical Center
Winchester Healthcare

HISTORICAL FINANCIALS

Company Type: Private

Income Statement — FYE: September 30

	REVENUE ($ mil.)	NET INCOME ($ mil.)	NET PROFIT MARGIN	EMPLOYEES
09/07	1,240	30	2.5%	12,000
09/06	1,220	47	3.9%	—
Annual Growth	1.7%	(35.9%)	—	—

2007 Year-End Financials

Debt ratio: —
Return on equity: 2.50%
Cash ($ mil.): 73
Current ratio: 0.80
Long-term debt ($ mil.): —
Dividends
Yield: —
Payout: —
Market value ($ mil.): —

STEWART BUILDERS INC.

Concrete is the key to Stewart Builders' success in the construction industry. Stewart Builders through main subsidiaries Keystone Concrete Placement and Keystone Structural Concrete provides concrete construction services for commercial industrial and institutional facilities as well as for residential markets primarily serving working on projects in the Lone Star State. Other subsidiaries do site work and construct basements. President Don Stewart and his sons founded the firm in 1993. The company has operations in Austin Georgetown Houston and San Antonio Texas.

EXECUTIVES

VP, D. Craig Stewart
VP New Business Development Estimating and Project Management, Mark A. Stewart
Senior Estimator and Project Manager, Rodney J. Horn
Owner, Baker Hughes

LOCATIONS

HQ: STEWART BUILDERS INC.
16575 VILLAGE DR, JERSEY VILLAGE, TX 77040-1124
Phone: 713-983-8002
Web: WWW.KEYSTONECONCRETE.COM

COMPETITORS

American Pan & Engineering
Baker Concrete
Ceco Concrete
KHS&S
United Forming
Western Construction

HISTORICAL FINANCIALS

Company Type: Private

Income Statement — FYE: December 31

	REVENUE ($ mil.)	NET INCOME ($ mil.)	NET PROFIT MARGIN	EMPLOYEES
12/12	206	5	2.4%	1,400
12/10	144	0	—	—
12/09	169	0	—	—
12/08	265	0	—	—
Annual Growth	(6.1%)	—	—	—

2012 Year-End Financials

Debt ratio: —
Return on equity: 2.40%
Cash ($ mil.): 6
Current ratio: 1.60
Long-term debt ($ mil.): —
Dividends
Yield: —
Payout: —
Market value ($ mil.): —

STEWART'S SHOPS CORP.

I scream you scream we all scream for Stewart's ice cream —especially if we live in upstate New York or Vermont home to some 330 Stewart's Shops. The chain of convenience stores sells more than 3000 products across 30-plus counties. They include dairy items groceries food to go (soup sandwiches hot entrees) beer coffee gasoline and of course ice cream. In addition to its retail business the company owns about 100 rental properties including banks hair salons and apartments near its stores. Stewart's Shops formerly known as Stewart's Ice Cream Company was established in 1945. The founding Dake family owns about two-thirds of the company; employee compensation plans own the rest.

Geographic Reach

Based in New York Stewart's Shops operates a chain of convenience stores across upstate New York and in Vermont.

Operations

The convenience store chain which spans New York and Vermont offers consumers milk ice creams coffee to-go foods beer gasoline and groceries. As part of its business Stewart's Shops also acquires and develops (preferably adjacent) properties the likes of shops banks hair salons and apartments that it then leases or sells.

Stewart's Shops makes its own dairy products including its own ice cream in more than 50 flavors that are hand-dipped and packaged. Recognized for its quality products the company relies on a group of about 45 farmers in New York to supply its milk.

The vertically-integrated company which makes about 75% of the items it sells also offers private-label goods and national brands in its stores. Its private-label brands extend far beyond dairy products to include soda chips bread and juices.

Sales and Marketing

Stewart's Shops serves consumers through its New York and Vermont shops; two-thirds of its stores sell gas.

Strategy

The convenience store operator regularly extends its reach. In 2014 it's focused on Syracuse New York following several store openings in 2013 in Keeseville Herkimer Rotterdam and Heuvelton New York. The latter shops boast an expanded cooler walk-in beer cave and seating.

The company is also investing in environmentally friendly facilities. In 2013 for instance it had 2400 solar panels installed at its manufacturing and distribution center. Stewart's Shops anticipates that the effort will save nearly $40000 a year in energy costs at the plant after about a 5-year period.

It enlisted the help of Paragon Software in 2014 to automate the planning of daily and seasonal deliveries. In turn Stewart's Shops aims to lower mileage reduce fuel usage and improve truckload efficiencies.

EXECUTIVES

President, Gary C. Dake, age 54
VP Plant Operations, Jim Norton
Senior Vice President Of Information Technology Operations, Dave Caruso
Chairman, William (Bill) Dake, age 76

LOCATIONS

HQ: STEWART' S SHOPS CORP.
2907 ROUTE 9, BALLSTON SPA, NY 12020
Phone: 5185811201
Web: WWW.STEWARTSSHOPS.COM

PRODUCTS/OPERATIONS

Selected Products

Ice Cream
Coffee
Food to go
Gasoline
Milk

COMPETITORS

7-Eleven
Ahold U.S.A.
Ben & Jerry' s
Carvel
Cumberland Farms
Exxon Mobil
Friendly' s Ice Cream
Golub
Hannaford Bros.
Kroger
McDonald' s
Pathmark Stores
Sunoco
TravelCenters of America

HISTORICAL FINANCIALS

Company Type: Private

Income Statement FYE: December 29

	REVENUE ($ mil.)	NET INCOME ($ mil.)	NET PROFIT MARGIN	EMPLOYEES
12/13	1,577	73	4.7%	3,800
12/12*	1,528	64	4.2%	—
01/11	1,296	53	4.2%	—
01/10	1,187	0	—	—
Annual Growth	7.3%	—	—	—

*Fiscal year change

2013 Year-End Financials

Debt ratio: —
Return on equity: 4.70%
Cash ($ mil.): 34
Current ratio: 0.60
Long-term debt ($ mil.): —
Dividends
Yield: —
Payout: —
Market value ($ mil.): —

STG INC.

STG provides technical TLC to government agencies. Serving the US Defense Department and about 50 other federal agencies the company provides information technology services such as project management application development network implementation security systems support and IT systems integration. It also offers data security assessment and compliance reporting services as well as foreign language translation and transcription. In addition to the DOD STG counts the US departments of State and Agriculture among its clients as well as Fortune 100 companies. Internationally the company has worked with NATO the Korea Airports Authority and other overseas agencies. STG was founded in 1986 by Simon Lee.

Operations

STG serves as a prime contractor on a number of government programs. Its key areas of specialty are enterprise network operations cyber security financial services systems engineering and integration software engineering and linguistics and intelligence software development.

Financial Performance

According to a 2013 Washington Technology ranking revenue earned by STG in 2013 from prime contracts with defense and civilian customers was up about $10 million (to $225 million) between 2012 and 2013. Unlike previous years revenue from prime contracts with non-government customers exceeded government contracts during that period.

EXECUTIVES

Chairman and CEO, Simon S. Lee
President, Paul A. Fernandes
Chief Operating Officer, Thomas P. (Tom) Anderson
Senior Vice President Defense Sector, Glenn W. Davis Jr.
Chief Financial Officer, Patrick G. Attilio
Senior Vice President Financial Services Practice, Paul G. Hudecek
Senior Vice President Civil Agencies Sector, Mark A Jendzejec
Senior Vice President of Business Development, Michael J. King
Chief Technology Officer Vice President, Richard J. Parkington
Chief Technology Officer and Senior Vice President, Bill B. Perlowitz

LOCATIONS

HQ: STG INC.
12011 SUNSET HILLS RD, RESTON, VA 20190-5918
Phone: 703-691-2480
Web: WWW.STGINC.COM

PRODUCTS/OPERATIONS

COMPETITORS

Accenture
BAE Systems Inc.
Booz Allen
CACI International
Computer Sciences Corp.
General Dynamics Information Technology
HP Enterprise Group
HP Enterprise Services
IBM Global Services
Jacobs Engineering
Leidos
Lockheed Martin Information Systems
ManTech
Northrop Grumman
Raytheon
SRA International
Unisys

HISTORICAL FINANCIALS

Company Type: Private

Income Statement FYE: December 31

	REVENUE ($ mil.)	NET INCOME ($ mil.)	NET PROFIT MARGIN	EMPLOYEES
12/12	212	5	2.8%	1,350
12/11	261	20	7.7%	—
12/10	233	16	7.1%	—
12/09	214	19	9.0%	—
Annual Growth	(0.2%)	(32.6%)	—	—

2012 Year-End Financials

Debt ratio: —
Return on equity: 2.80%
Cash ($ mil.): 1
Current ratio: 1.30
Long-term debt ($ mil.): —
Dividends
Yield: —
Payout: —
Market value ($ mil.): —

STILES CORPORATION

Stiles Corporation is a full-service commercial real estate development and investment firm. It provides architectural design and construction realty services and property management. The firm operates primarily throughout the southeastern US with a special interest in Florida. The company's Capital Group unit offers asset management and arranges financing for development projects. Since 1951 when the company was founded Stiles has built more than 37 million sq. ft. of office industrial retail and mixed use properties. The firm's completed projects include Fort Lauderdale's Las Olas City Centre and Trump International Tower as well as the PGA Financial Plaza at MacArthur Center in Palm Beach Gardens.

Geographic Reach

Stiles Corporation operates throughout Florida with an extended reach throughout the Southeastern US.

Operations

In addition to its headquarters in Fort Lauderdale Stiles maintains offices in the Florida cities of Miami Tampa Fort Myers and Orlando. It has a presence in Charlotte North Carolina as well.

Since 1984 Stiles has leased more than 3.5 million sq. ft. of real estate across Florida. The company serves as the asset management team for a portfolio of more than $1.3 billion including nearly $400 million in equity. The portfolio consists of 4.5 million sq. ft. in combined office retail and industrial buildings as well as more than 1300 acres of land.

Strategy

Stiles Corporation's primary strategy is to secure development projects for new commercial real estate projects as well as acquire properties in Florida's major metropolitan areas such as Miami-Dade Broward Palm Beach Tampa Bay Greater Orlando and Jacksonville. As a way to stretch its business Stiles Corporation in 2012 partnered with Levine Properties based in Charlotte North Carolina through a strategic alliance to develop real estate in the Carolinas. The joint venture is focused on developing grocery-anchored commercial and residential projects.

With the downturn in the real estate industry Stiles Corporation has been diversifying its portfolio. The company has acquired properties (especially office buildings and shopping centers) in Miami as well as other parts of Florida. It has also concentrated on offering third-party services such as leasing property management and construction as these areas provide it with reliable fee-based income.

The company also focuses on environmentally-friendly design and construction. It built Miami's first Leadership in Energy and Environmental Design (LEED) certified office building and has committed that all of its new buildings will be environmentally friendly.

Sales and Marketing

The company has been working to remake its image as a one-stop development firm by launching a new branding scheme aimed at emphasizing all of its services (not just general contracting and developing). Stiles Corporation clients include IBM FedEX Bank of America Nokia UBA and Auto Nation.

EXECUTIVES

Chairman and CEO, Terry W. Stiles
President, Douglas P. (Doug) Eagon
COO, Stephen R. (Steve) Palmer
President Real Estate Investments, Robert (Bob) Breslau
President Real Estate Strategic Services, Denny O'Shea
President Stiles Construction, Timothy (Tim) Moore
President Stiles Architectural Group, Jeff Peal
President Stiles Property Management, Chris Rotolo
CFO, Robert Esposito
EVP, Kenneth (Ken) Stiles

President Development and Asset Services, David Siegel
Chairman Chief Executive Officer, Mike Jackson
Chief Investment Officer, Rocco Ferrera
President Stiles Realty, Paul Marko
Vice President Financial Services, David Channon
President Residential Group, Jay Jacobson
President North Carolina, Scott MacLaren

LOCATIONS

HQ: STILES CORPORATION
301 E LAS OLAS BLVD, FORT LAUDERDALE, FL 33301-2295
Phone: 954-627-9150
Web: WWW.STILES.COM

PRODUCTS/OPERATIONS

Selected Services

Build
- Architecture
- Construction
- Tenant improvements

Invest
- Development services
- Financial services
- New development & acquisitions

Manage
- Asset management
- Leasing & brokerage
- Property management

Selected Divisions and Departments

Stiles Acquisitions
Stiles Architecture Group
Stiles Asset Management & Finance
Stiles Capital Group
Stiles Construction Co.
Stiles Development Co.
Stiles Leasing & Brokerage
Stiles Property Management
Stiles Real Estate Investment Services
Stiles Realty Co.
Stiles Tenant Improvement

COMPETITORS

Benderson Development
Carter
DYL Group
Echelon Development
Flagler Development
St. Joe
The Haskell Company
Tishman Construction

HISTORICAL FINANCIALS

Company Type: Private

Income Statement FYE: December 31

	REVENUE ($ mil.)	NET INCOME ($ mil.)	NET PROFIT MARGIN	EMPLOYEES
12/12	170	3	1.9%	284
12/11	89	(3)	—	—
12/10	84	9	11.1%	—
12/09	123	0	0.0%	—
Annual Growth	11.2%	598.6%	—	—

2012 Year-End Financials

Debt ratio: —
Return on equity: 1.90%
Cash ($ mil.): 15
Current ratio: 1.50
Long-term debt ($ mil.): —
Dividends
Yield: —
Payout: —
Market value ($ mil.): —

STM INDUSTRIES INC.

LOCATIONS

HQ: STM INDUSTRIES INC.
1985 TATE BLVD SE STE 2, HICKORY, NC 286021433
Phone: 8283222700
Web: WWW.SHURTAPE.COM

HISTORICAL FINANCIALS

Company Type: Private

Income Statement FYE: January 1

	REVENUE ($ mil.)	NET INCOME ($ mil.)	NET PROFIT MARGIN	EMPLOYEES
01/11	374	20	5.4%	1,125
01/10*	374	20	5.4%	—
12/08	1,090	0	—	—
Annual Growth	—23064.0%	—	—	—

*Fiscal year change

2011 Year-End Financials

Debt ratio: —
Return on equity: 5.40%
Cash ($ mil.): 2
Current ratio: 1.30
Long-term debt ($ mil.): —
Dividends
Yield: —
Payout: —
Market value ($ mil.): —

STORMONT-VAIL HEALTH CARE INC

Stormont-Vail HealthCare helps to take care of the health of residents in northeastern Kansas. Its facilities include the 590-bed Stormont-Vail Regional Health Center an emergency and trauma center an outpatient surgery center and a network of community clinics located throughout the 12-county region. Its Cotton-O'Neil centers treat heart disease cancer skin problems and digestive system ailments as well as various clinics and ExpressCare locations. Specialized services include behavioral health obstetrics orthopedics and physical and occupational rehabilitation.

Geographic Reach

Stormont-Vail HealthCare serves a 12-county area in northeast Kansas.

Strategy

The health system pursues strategic partnerships and organic growth to keep up with demand.

The system has partnerships with the School of Nursing Century Health Solutions Kansas Rehabilitation Hospital and LifeStar of Kansas.

In 2012 DaVita Health Care acquired Kansas Dialysis Services (jointly owned by affiliates of St. Francis Health Center and Stormont-Vail HealthCare). The unit provides outpatient inpatient and home dialysis care to 350 patients in the four Kansas cities. DaVita will continue to have a working relationship with both organizations.

In 2011 Stormont-Vail HealthCare added pediatric critical care services to provide care to infants in the neonatal intensive care unit.

Company Background

The first hospital to serve residents in northeastern Kansas (Christ's Hospital where Stormont-Vail Regional Health Center is located today) opened in 1884. Stormont-Vail HealthCare was formed with the merger of Stormont-Vail Regional Health Center and Cotton-O'Neil Clinic in 1995. PediatricCare joined the system in 1996.

EXECUTIVES

President and CEO, Maynard F. Oliverius
Director Marketing, Nancy Burkhardt
CFO, Vernon Long
SVP and Chief Medical Officer, Kent Palmberg
President Director Stormont-Vail Foundation, Don Schepker
Corporate Accounting, Ken Stone
Director Surgery, Robert Wehmeyer
Auditors: McGladreyLLP

LOCATIONS

HQ: STORMONT-VAIL HEALTH CARE INC
1500 SW 10TH AVE, TOPEKA, KS 66604-1301
Phone: 785-354-6000
Web: WWW.STORMONTVAIL.ORG

PRODUCTS/OPERATIONS

Facilities
Behavioral Health Services at Stormont-Vail West
Cotton-O'Neil Clinic
Cotton-O'Neil Digestive Health Center
Cotton-O'Neil Heart Center
Diabetes and Endocrinology Center
PediatricCare
Stormont-Vail Cancer Center
Stormont-Vail Regional Health Center
Stormont-Vail Single Day Surgery
Stormont-Vail WorkCare

COMPETITORS

Hays Medical Center
Shawnee Mission Medical Center
Sisters of Charity of Leavenworth
University of Kansas Medical Center
Via Christi Health System

HISTORICAL FINANCIALS

Company Type: Private

Income Statement FYE: September 30

	REVENUE ($ mil.)	NET INCOME ($ mil.)	NET PROFIT MARGIN	EMPLOYEES
09/09	430	2	0.7%	3,000
09/08	416	18	4.3%	—
09/06	335	15	4.5%	—
09/05	314	12	3.9%	—
Annual Growth	8.2%	(30.1%)	—	—

2009 Year-End Financials

Debt ratio: —
Return on equity: 0.70%
Cash ($ mil.): 72
Current ratio: 0.70
Long-term debt ($ mil.): —
Dividends
Yield: —
Payout: —
Market value ($ mil.): —

STRACK AND VAN TIL SUPER MARKET INC

EXECUTIVES

VP Operations, Jeff Strack

LOCATIONS

HQ: STRACK AND VAN TIL SUPER MARKET INC
9632 CLINE AVE, HIGHLAND, IN 463223094
Phone: 2199247588
Web: WWW.STRACKANDVANTIL.COM

PRODUCTS/OPERATIONS

2013 Stores

	No.
Strack & Van	20
Ultra	16
Town & Country Food	2
Total	**38**

COMPETITORS

ALDI
Dominick' s
Jewel Osco
Kmart
Meijer
Roundy' s
Target Corporation
Trader Joe' s
Wal-Mart
Whole Foods

HISTORICAL FINANCIALS

Company Type: Private

Income Statement FYE: August 1

	REVENUE ($ mil.)	NET INCOME ($ mil.)	NET PROFIT MARGIN	EMPLOYEES
08/10	961	15	1.7%	2,300
08/09	995	13	1.4%	—
Annual Growth	(3.4%)	16.1%	—	—

2010 Year-End Financials

Debt ratio: —
Return on equity: 1.70%
Cash ($ mil.): 10
Current ratio: 0.20
Long-term debt ($ mil.): —
Dividends
Yield: —
Payout: —
Market value ($ mil.): —

STRIKE LLC

Strike Construction aims to strike it rich by constructing installing and testing pipelines for the oil and gas industry. The family-owned contracting firm builds and repairs onshore pipelines and meter stations for customers such as Kinder Morgan SandRidge Energy and TransCanada. It also performs state-mandated integrity tests to ensure pipeline safety and offers remediation services in case a pipe should require repairs. Subsidiary Pickett Systems designs and installs flow measurement systems for onshore and offshore use. Strike Construction is licensed to work in about 30 states but the bulk of its business is concentrated in oil-rich Texas and along the Gulf Coast.

Operations

Strike Construction provides services in a range of sectors of the oil gas utility and power industries through five business units: Pickett Systems Strike Testing Strike Industrial Strike Instrumentation & Electrical and Strike Oilfield.

EXECUTIVES

CEO, Steve Pate
EVP, Kacey Smart
EVP, Jarvie Arnold
EVP, Jason Heckt
EVP, Kevin Pate
CFO, Douglas Jones
President and COO, A. Cole Pate
Vice President, James Helfer

LOCATIONS

HQ: STRIKE LLC
831 CROSSBRIDGE DR, SPRING, TX 77373-3501
Phone: 281-362-9708

COMPETITORS

B. L. Harbert
Bechtel
Fluor
Holloman
Southwest Gas
TIC Holdings
Technip USA
Tellepsen Builders
Willbros
Zachry Inc.

HISTORICAL FINANCIALS

Company Type: Private

Income Statement FYE: December 31

	REVENUE ($ mil.)	NET INCOME ($ mil.)	NET PROFIT MARGIN	EMPLOYEES
12/12	545	47	8.6%	1,000
12/10	192	7	4.1%	—
12/08	114	7	6.8%	—
12/07	58	3	5.7%	—
Annual Growth	56.5%	69.8%	—	—

2012 Year-End Financials

Debt ratio: —
Return on equity: 8.60%
Cash ($ mil.): 0
Current ratio: 1.50
Long-term debt ($ mil.): —
Dividends
Yield: —
Payout: —
Market value ($ mil.): —

STURDY MEMORIAL HOSPITAL INC.

Sturdy Memorial Hospital has been a stalwart provider of health care to southeast Massachusetts and Rhode Island since 1913. In addition to comprehensive medical surgical and emergency care the hospital offers cardiac and pulmonary rehabilitation women's health services diagnostic imaging and a center devoted to treating multiple sclerosis patients. It also operates pain management cancer and wound care centers. The hospital is engaged in ongoing expansion projects including the construction of a two story outpatient facility which will feature a four unit endoscopy suite; an infusion therapy center; and ambulatory offices. The not-for-profit hospital employs more than 150 physicians.

EXECUTIVES

President and CEO, Linda J. Shyavitz
Treasurer and CFO, Joseph Casey
Chief Ambulatory Care and Emergency Medicine, Brian Kelly
VP Clinical Services, Robin Morris
VP Patient Services, Marita Prater
Director Of Radiology Services, Nancy Moynihan
Director Icu/coronary Care Unit, Polly Keister
Dir Of Maternal Health Programs, Paula Boothman
Director Of Medical Records, Mary Barry
Occupational Therapy Director, Chris Quinn
Physical Therapy Director, Keri Dickinson
Chairman, Timothy O ,ÂNeill

LOCATIONS

HQ: STURDY MEMORIAL HOSPITAL INC.
211 PARK ST, ATTLEBORO, MA 02703-3137
Phone: 508-222-5200
Web: WWW.STURDYMEMORIAL.ORG

PRODUCTS/OPERATIONS

Selected Services

Allergy
Anesthesiology
Dentistry
Dermatology
Endocrinology
Gastroenterology
Hematology
Nephrology
Neurology
Neurosurgery
Ophthalmology
Orthopedics
Otolaryngology
Pathology
Urology

COMPETITORS

Care New England
Caritas Norwood Hospital
Kent Hospital
Lifespan Corporation
Memorial Hospital of Rhode Island
Milford Regional Medical Center
Southcoast Health

HISTORICAL FINANCIALS

Company Type: Private

Income Statement FYE: September 30

	REVENUE ($ mil.)	NET INCOME ($ mil.)	NET PROFIT MARGIN	EMPLOYEES
09/12	164	30	18.4%	1,100
09/11	155	(7)	—	—
09/10	158	17	11.2%	—
09/09	153	(10)	—	—
Annual Growth	2.3%	—	—	—

2012 Year-End Financials

Debt ratio: —
Return on equity: 18.40%
Cash ($ mil.): 9
Current ratio: 1.00
Long-term debt ($ mil.): —
Dividends
Yield: —
Payout: —
Market value ($ mil.): —

SUBURBAN HOSPITAL INC

Don't let the name fool you this hospital isn't just for big city expatriates. Suburban Hospital a member of the Johns Hopkins Medicine network is an acute-care medical-surgical hospital with about 235 beds that provides all major medical services except obstetrics to the residents of Montgomery County in Maryland. Specialized services include behavioral health cardiology cancer care home care and pediatrics. Founded in 1943 Suburban Hospital serves as the regional trauma center for the county and is equipped with a helipad. Other services include a center for sleep disorders 24-hour stroke team diagnostic pathology and radiology departments and a range of inpatient and outpatient programs.

Geographic Reach

Suburban Hospital is located in Bethesda Maryland. The facility primarily serves residents of Maryland's Montgomery County and the surrounding area.

Operations

Suburban Hospital has 233 beds more than 1000 medical staff and more than 500 nursing staff. The community-based not-for-profit hospital is an acute-care medical-surgical hospital featuring all major services except obstetrics. The hospital's admissions total more than 14000 annually.

The facility's major services include a comprehensive cancer and radiation oncology center NIH Heart Center at Suburban Hospital a designated Primary Stroke Center and senior care programs.

Suburban Hospital's other services include the NIH-Suburban MRI Center a center for sleep disorders and state-of-the-art diagnostic pathology and radiology departments.

Strategy

Suburban Hospital is in the midst of a $230 million upgrade and expansion at its existing campus that will create more private rooms larger operating rooms additional physician offices and improved access to the trauma center.

Suburban Hospital has formed joint ventures or affiliations with The National Institutes of Health NRH/Suburban Regional Rehab Potomac Home Health Care and Potomac Home Support (with Sibley Memorial Hospital) and Johns Hopkins Community Physicians among others.

EXECUTIVES

Senior Vice President, Leslie Weber

President and Trustee, Brian A. Gragnolati
SVP and CFO, Marty Basso
EVP and COO, Jacqueline (Jacky) Schultz, age 57
VP Information Systems and CIO, Christopher T. Timbers
President, Gene E. Green
Chief Nursing Officer and Senior Director of Nursing, Barbara Jordan
President Suburban Hospital Auxiliary, Dale Midlam
Director Of Patient Relations, Ruth Dalgetty
Medical Director, Anthony Caputy
Medical Director Behavioral Health Services, Harry Gill
Medical Director Respiratory Care, Steven Kariya
Pharmacy Manager, Karen Michaels
President and Trustee, Brian A. Gragnolati
Chairman, Christopher J. Doherty, age 54
Treasurer, Merle Postal

LOCATIONS

HQ: SUBURBAN HOSPITAL INC
8600 OLD GEORGETOWN RD, BETHESDA, MD 20814-1497
Phone: 301-896-3100
Web: WWW.SUBURBANHOSPITAL.ORG

COMPETITORS

Adventist HealthCare
Children' s National Medical Center
Chindex International
Dimensions Healthcare
Doctors Community Hospital
Georgetown University Hospital
Inova Alexandria Hospital
MedStar Health
Providence Hospital (Washington DC)

HISTORICAL FINANCIALS

Company Type: Private

Income Statement FYE: June 30

	REVENUE ($ mil.)	NET INCOME ($ mil.)	NET PROFIT MARGIN	EMPLOYEES
06/12	263	(2)	—	1,550
06/11	256	32	12.8%	—
06/10	240	15	6.4%	—
06/09	243	(5)	—	—
Annual Growth	2.7%	—	—	—

2012 Year-End Financials

Debt ratio: —
Return on equity: (-1.00%)
Cash ($ mil.): 12
Current ratio: 0.40
Long-term debt ($ mil.): —
Dividends
Yield: —
Payout: —
Market value ($ mil.): —

SUDDATH VAN LINES INC

LOCATIONS

HQ: SUDDATH VAN LINES INC
815 S MAIN ST STE 400, JACKSONVILLE, FL 322078157
Phone: 9043907100
Web: WWW.SUDDATH.COM

HISTORICAL FINANCIALS

Company Type: Private

Income Statement FYE: December 31

	REVENUE ($ mil.)	NET INCOME ($ mil.)	NET PROFIT MARGIN	EMPLOYEES
12/09	211	8	3.8%	1,800
12/08	237	8	3.6%	—
12/07	1,813	0	—	—
Annual Growth	—27492.3%		—	—

2009 Year-End Financials

Debt ratio: —
Return on equity: 3.80%
Cash ($ mil.): 0
Current ratio: 1.30
Long-term debt ($ mil.): —
Dividends
Yield: —
Payout: —
Market value ($ mil.): —

SUFFOLK CONSTRUCTION COMPANY INC.

Suffolk Construction Company provides construction services from top to bottom. The company kicks off the building process with pre-construction services and follows through with design/build general contracting and construction management. As part of its business Suffolk Construction builds for both the public and private sectors including military automotive education health care retail and assisted living clients across the US. The firm is owned by president and CEO John Fish whose family has been in construction for four generations. Suffolk was founded in 1982 and operates in the Northeast Mid-Atlantic Southeast and West Coast regions.

Strategy

Suffolk Construction serves several sectors to keep the company thriving even in challenging times. The firm extended its reach into the growing health care sector by launching National Healthcare Group which specializes in building health care projects nationwide.

Before the company breaks ground at a job site it uses technologies such as virtual models and Building Information Modeling (BIM) to build projects virtually. The practice minimizes risk lessens design conflicts and issues and lowers costs for Suffolk Construction clients.

Mergers and Acquisitions

Already a successful builder in the New England area Suffolk Construction has been working to expand nationally through acquisitions. In 2009 it bought Massachusetts-based William A. Berry & Son creating Suffolk's Berry Division which specializes in health care and biomedical projects. Suffolk Construction also acquired The Dietze Construction Group based in Ashburn Virginia in 2010. The deal strengthened Suffolk's position in the Mid-Atlantic region and expanded its ability to serve the government health care education science/technology and commercial sectors. Giving the company a boost in the West Suffolk Construction acquired Southern California-based ROEL Construction in 2011.

Sales and Marketing

Suffolk Construction serves the health care industry. The company also relies on winning work from federal and local governments. To this end Suffolk has built for the Army Corps of Engineers the US Marine Corps and US Navy.

Geographic Reach

The Boston-based construction firm operates nationwide across the Northeast Mid-Atlantic Southeast and West Coast regions.

Company Ownership

Suffolk Construction is owned and operated by the Fish family.

EXECUTIVES

Chairman and Chief Executive Officer, John F. Fish
President West Region, Andrew J. (Andy) Ball
Executive Vice President and Chief Financial Officer, Michael (Mike) Azarela
President and General Manager Northeast Region, Mark L. DiNapoli
President & General Manager Southeast Region, Rex B. Kirby
General Manager San Diego, Wayne Hickey
EVP Operations, Jeffrey A. Gouveia Jr.
Chief Operating Officer San Francisco Office, Michael (Mike) DiNapoli
Executive Vice President Work Acquisition Northeast Region, Peter Welsh
Chief Marketing Officer and Chief People Officer, Kimberly Steimle
President Healthcare/Science and Technology & Chief Innovation Officer, Peter Campot
Vice President and Chief Information Officer, Corren Collura
Executive Vice President & General Manager Mid-Atlantic Region, Stephen Skinner
Vice President & Chief Operating Officer Commercial Education and Government Northeast Region, Angus Leary
Executive Vice President of National Business Development, Christopher Woods
Auditors: McGladreyLLP

LOCATIONS

HQ: SUFFOLK CONSTRUCTION COMPANY INC.
65 ALLERTON ST, BOSTON, MA 02119-2923
Phone: 617-445-3500
Web: WWW.SUFFOLKCONSTRUCTION.COM

PRODUCTS/OPERATIONS

Selected Services

Building information modeling
Construction management
Design/build
General contracting
Preconstruction
Sustainable building

COMPETITORS

Balfour Construction
Bovis Lend Lease
Clark Enterprises
DooleyMack
Kraus-Anderson
McCarthy Building
Pepper Construction
Swinerton
Turner Corporation
Tutor Perini
Walsh Group
Whiting-Turner

HISTORICAL FINANCIALS

Company Type: Private

Income Statement FYE: August 31

	REVENUE ($ mil.)	NET INCOME ($ mil.)	NET PROFIT MARGIN	EMPLOYEES
08/12	1,349	0	—	1,150
08/11	1,290	0	—	—
08/10	1,257	0	—	—
08/09	1,257	0	—	—
Annual Growth	2.4%	—	—	—

SUFFOLK UNIVERSITY

Suffolk University provides a well-rounded education around the Athens of America and abroad. From its main campus in Boston and its satellite and branch campuses across Massachusetts as well as through study abroad programs the university provides undergraduate and graduate degrees in more than 70 areas of study through the College of Arts and Sciences Sawyer Business School and Suffolk Law School. It also runs about 25 institutes and research centers. More than 9000 students attend the private university which has a 12:1 student-to-faculty ratio and offers courses taught by about 900 faculty members. The university was founded in 1906 as the Suffolk School of Law.

Geographic Reach

Suffolk University's main campus consists of 16 buildings on Beacon Hill and in downtown Boston; the university also operates a branch campus in Madrid Spain as well as offers degree programs at two satellite sites in Massachusetts (Cape Cod Community College and the MBA-North facility in Lawrence). Students from all 50 states and more than 100 countries around the globe attend the university.

Financial Performance

Suffolk University reported a 2% increase in revenues to some $237 million in 2012 due to higher tuition and fee income and endowment-sourced funding. Net income decreased 66% however to about $12 million due to lower investment returns.

Strategy

Suffolk University is enhancing student opportunities especially for international learning opportunities such as seminars study tours and service-learning and study abroad programs. It is also working to expand its interdisciplinary study programs such as entrepreneurship public policy and intellectual property. Other strategic initiatives include renovating and enhancing campus facilities and increasing career opportunities for graduates. Suffolk University is also working to increase budget transparency and to diversify its revenue sources.

EXECUTIVES

Dean Sawyer Business School, William J. O'Neill Jr., age 72
President, David J. Sargent
VP and Treasurer, Francis X. Flannery
VP Enrollment and International Programs, Marguerite J. Dennis
Chair, Nicholas A. Macaronis
Director Athletics, James (Jim) Nelson
VP External Affairs, John A. Nucci
Director Suffolk University Political Research Center, David Paleologos
Vice Chair, Carol Sawyer Parks
Dean College of Arts and Sciences, Kenneth S. Greenberg
VP Student Affairs, Nancy Stoll
Registrar and Assistant VP Enrollment, Mary M. Lally
Registrar Law School, Lorraine D. Cove
Senior Marketing and Public Relations Strategist, Mariellen Norris
Vice President of Marketing and Communications, Greg Gatlin, age 48
Provost, Barry Brown
VP Academics, Janice C. Griffith
Acting VP Advancement, Andrew Thompson
Dean Law School, Alfred C. Aman Jr.
Vice President for Finance and Treasurer, Danielle Manning
President Archbishop, Dennis M. Duggan
President CEO, John L. Brooks
Senior Vice President for Advancement, Stephen Morin
Auditors: KPMGLLP

LOCATIONS

HQ: SUFFOLK UNIVERSITY
8 ASHBURTON PL, BOSTON, MA 02108-2770
Phone: 617-573-8000
Web: WWW.LAW.SUFFOLK.EDU

PRODUCTS/OPERATIONS

Selected Colleges Schools Institutes and Research Centers

Colleges and Schools
- College of Arts and Sciences
- Sawyer Business School
- Suffolk Law School

Institutes and Research Centers
- Beacon Hill Institute
- Center for Advanced Legal Studies
- Center for Crime & Justice Policy Research
- Center for Entrepreneurship
- Center for Global Business Ethics and Law
- Center for Global Enterprise
- Center for Innovation & Change Leadership
- Center for Restorative Justice
- Center for Teaching Excellence
- Center for Women' s Health and Human Rights
- Friedman Field Station
- Institute for Executive Education and Lifelong Learning
- Institute for Public Service
- John Joseph Moakley Archive and Institute
- Juvenile Justice Center
- Knowledge Globalization Institute
- Macaronis Institute for Trial and Appellate Advocacy
- McDonnell International Business Institute
- Moakley Center for Public Management
- Moakley Institute on Public Policy and Political Leadership
- Poetry Center
- Political Research Center
- Rappaport Center for Law and Public Service
- Rosenberg Institute for East Asian Studies
- Sagan Energy Research Laboratory

HISTORICAL FINANCIALS

Company Type: Private

Income Statement FYE: June 30

	REVENUE ($ mil.)	NET INCOME ($ mil.)	NET PROFIT MARGIN	EMPLOYEES
06/11	298	5	1.8%	800
06/10	282	4	1.7%	—
06/09	275	20	7.3%	—
06/08	205	(12)	—	—
Annual Growth	13.2%	—	—	—

2011 Year-End Financials

Debt ratio: —
Return on equity: 1.80%
Cash ($ mil.): 0
Current ratio: —
Long-term debt ($ mil.): —
Dividends
Yield: —
Payout: —
Market value ($ mil.): —

SUMMA HEALTH SYSTEM

Acute care hospitals plus a network of outpatient and primary care clinics plus a health care plan yields the sum of Summa Health System. The not-for-profit system serves the residents of the greater Akron Ohio area through five acute care hospitals and a whole slew of other health care sites. It also has an affiliation and management agreement with the nearby Robinson Memorial Hospital. Together its hospitals are home to more than 2000 beds. In addition to general medical and surgical care Summa's key services include cardiac stroke behavioral health cancer care emergency services and women's health.

Geographic Reach

Summa is expanding its services through locations in the Ohio counties of Summit Portage and Medina.

Operations

Summa's medical facilities include Summa Akron City Hospital Summa St. Thomas Hospital Summa Western Reserve Hospital Summa Barberton Hospital Summa Wadsworth-Rittman Hospital Summa affiliate Robinson Memorial Hospital and joint venture Crystal Clinic Orthopaedic Center. In addition outpatient care is extended throughout the area through a network of community health centers. Summa also operates home health and hospice organizations. Altogether Summa serves about 1 million patients each year.

The system's health care plan called SummaCare offers HMO PPO and POS (point of service) health insurance products to employer groups individuals and Medicare recipients in northern Ohio. It also administers health plans for self-funded groups through its Apex Benefit Services unit. SummaCare covers about 230000 members. Its services are accepted at 50 hospitals and about 7000 providers.

Several of Summa's facilities are teaching hospitals and as such support the education of the organization's physicians and health care professionals. For instance Summa Western Reserve Hospital provides osteopathic medicine training programs through an affiliation with Ohio University. Akron City Hospital and St. Thomas Hospital are teaching affiliates of the Northeastern Ohio Universities College of Medicine and offer about 15 accredited residency training programs.

The health system invests about $10 million each year in research support for many areas including cardiology cancer and geriatrics. It is a founding member of Akron's Austen BioInnovation Institute. Major research programs are supported by grants from institutions such as the National Institutes of Health and the Department of Defense. Summa also spends more than $100 million on community care programs each year.

Financial Performance

Summa reported revenues of about $1.6 billion in 2012. The organization estimates that it makes a $2.8 billion business impact on the Ohio economy as well as a $99 million impact on the state government's revenue.

Strategy

Summa has conducted growth efforts in recent years to expand its presence and service offerings in the region through organic growth efforts and partnership formations. For instance the organization opened a new Summa Rehab Hospital through a partnership with Vibra; the $25 million facility consists of a 70000-sq. ft. freestanding medical building. The Summa network also invested in expanding new emergency care clinics in Green and Medina and it consolidated its home health and hospice organizations to improve profitability.

Also in 2012 Summa formed a joint management services organization with two affiliated physician organizations: Community Health Care and Pioneer Physicians Network. Together the organizations aim to streamline clinical processes.

In 2013 Summa also entered talks to form a partnership with hospital group Catholic Health Partners (CHP). The strategic partnership would give CHP a minority stake in the Summa network. Through the deal Summa hopes to expand its strategic initiatives and strengthen its finances.

Summa invests heavily in the latest technology continually seeking out the latest treatment options for some of today's most serious medical conditions.

Company Background

The company was formed in 1989 through the merger of Akron City Hospital and St. Thomas Hospital.

EXECUTIVES

President and CEO, Thomas J. Strauss
President Summa Hospitals, Robert Harrigan
VP Legal Services, William A. Powel III
VP Medical Affairs, Dale P. Murphy
President Robinson Memorial Hospital, Stephen Colecchi
Chief Medical Officer, Erik Steele
VP Human Resources, Kyle J. Klawitter
VP Planning and Corporate Support, Patrice Lange
Chief Medical Information Officer, Charles E. Ross
SVP Medical Education and Chief Academic Officer, Joseph Zarconi
VP Service Lines and Ancillary Services, Unhee Kim
President SummaCare, Martin P. Hauser
Public Relations Director, Mike Bernstein
SVP and Chief Nursing Officer, Lanie Ward
VP and Chief Medical and Quality Officer, Michael Hillman
President Summa Barberton Hospital and Summa Wadsworth-Rittman Hospital, Thomas DeBord
SVP and CFO, Brian Derrick
CEO Summa Western Reserve Hospital, Robert Kent
President Summa Physicians Inc., Gus Kious
COO Summa Foundation, Steven Schmidt
President and Chief Development Officer Summa Foundation, Phylis Ferrara
President and CEO Crystal Clinic Orthopaedic Center, Ronald Suntken
Chairman, Norman Wells Jr.
President Summa Hospitals, Thomas Malone
Auditors: Ernst&YoungLLP

LOCATIONS

HQ: SUMMA HEALTH SYSTEM
95 ARCH ST STE G50, AKRON, OH 44304-1477
Phone: 330-375-3000
Web: WWW.SUMMAHEALTH.ORG

PRODUCTS/OPERATIONS

2012 Payers

	% of total
Medicare	47
Commercial/Managed	31
Medicaid	15
Self-pay	7
Total	**100**

Selected Ohio Facilities

Hospitals
- Akron City Hospital (Akron)
- Barberton Hospital (Barberton)
- Cuyahoga Falls General Hospital (aka Western Reserve Hospital Cuyahoga Falls)
- Robinson Memorial Hospital (affiliate Ravenna)
- St. Thomas Hospital (Akron)
- Wadsworth-Rittman Hospital (Wadsworth)

Other facilities
- Crystal Clinic Orthopaedic Center (Akron)
- Natatorium Rehabilitation and Wellness Center (Cuyahoga Falls)
- Summa Health Center at Cuyahoga Falls (Cuyahoga Falls)
- Summa Health Center at Green (Uniontown)
- Summa Health Center at Lake Medina
- Summa Health Center at Western Reserve (Hudson)
- Summa Health Center at White Pond/Park West (Akron)
- Summa Rehabilitation Services at White Pond (Akron)
- Summa Wellness Institute at Western Reserve (Hudson)
- Specialty Surgery Center (Akron)

COMPETITORS

Akron Children' s Hospital
Akron General Health System
Aultman Health Foundation
Humana Health Plan of Ohio
Kaiser Foundation Health Plan of Ohio
Lake Health
Medical Mutual
Mercy Medical Center (OH)
Parma Community General Hospital
Regency Hospital
The Cleveland Clinic
Trinity Health System
United Healthcare of Ohio
University Hospitals Health System

HISTORICAL FINANCIALS

Company Type: Private

Income Statement FYE: December 31

	REVENUE ($ mil.)	NET INCOME ($ mil.)	NET PROFIT MARGIN	EMPLOYEES
12/09	168	6	3.8%	7,406
12/08	1,264	(75)	—	—
12/07	940	71	7.6%	—
12/06	797	61	7.7%	—
Annual Growth	(40.4%)	(52.8%)	—	—

2009 Year-End Financials

Debt ratio: —
Return on equity: 3.80%
Cash ($ mil.): 28
Current ratio: —
Long-term debt ($ mil.): —
Dividends
Yield: —
Payout: —
Market value ($ mil.): —

SUMMIT ELECTRIC SUPPLY CO. INC

SUMMIT continues its ascent. SUMMIT Electric Supply founded in 1977 by the father-and-son team of Victor Jury Sr. and Victor Jr. (president and CEO) distributes goods from manufacturers such as Dialight Eaton Fluke and Thomas & Betts. Products include cable conduits switches fuses lamps light fixtures instruments and safety equipment. The company offers in-house marine cable braiding for offshore oil and gas customers. SUMMIT also sells to electrical contractors government agencies construction firms and public utilities. It has some 20 branches located in New Mexico Arizona Louisiana and Texas and a service center in Dubai. The Jury family continues to own a controlling interest in SUMMIT.

Geographic Reach

SUMMIT has locations in about 20 markets across Arizona Louisiana New Mexico and Texas. It also has a marine division based in New Orleans a Latin American sales office and a service center in Dubai UAE.

Financial Performance

SUMMIT's sales have rebounded from the drubbing they took during the global economic downturn when electrical wholesalers were hit hard as construction slowed and businesses cut back on expansion plans. Indeed SUMMIT's 2012 sales exceeded their pre-recession high. The $385 million in sales the electrical wholesaler rang up in 2012 was a 7% increase vs. the prior year. Strength in the MRO (maintenance repair and overhaul) and energy markets have buoyed sales. The company is also benefitting from its aggressive expansion in such growth markets as Latin America and the Middle East.

Strategy

In 2010 SUMMIT announced plans to expand its presence in the Middle East by opening a full-service branch in Dubai and actively developing a customer base across the region. The company initially opened a sales office in Dubai a region that has seen a boom in construction projects in 2007. SUMMIT is also actively working to expand sales in Latin America where it is focused on industrial construction projects in oil gas and mining across the region.

EXECUTIVES

Vice President Asset Management, Drew Ott
President and CEO, Victor R. Jury Jr.
Senior Vice President Business Development, Joe Chesky
VP Marketing, Sheila Hernandez
Service Center Leader Albuquerque, Wiley Shaw
Regional VP Southwest, Scott Cogan
Service Center Leader Farmington, Kenneth King
Service Center Leader Corpus Christi, Ted Mendoza
Service Center Leader Fort Worth, Richard Efurd
Service Center Leader Gonzales, W. Damain Kerek
VP Operations, Cole Harrison
Service Center Leader La Porte, Mike Mares
Marine Division Director, Ed Dowey
Chief Financial Officer Vice President Finance, Russ Hiller
Vice President Associate Resources and General Counsel, Dan Long
VP Information Technologies, David Wascom
Regional VP Gulf Coast, Dan Ferrari
Service Center Leader Phoenix, Craig Rusk
Service Center Leader San Antonio, Allen O'Dell
Service Center Leader Austin, Matt Darling
Service Center Leader Clute, Steve Lincoln
Service Center Leader Dallas, Michael (Mike) Kizer
Service Center Leader El Paso, Chris Gallegos
Service Center Leader Houston, Rodney Ilseng
Director EP&C Sales, Ralph Mouret
Operations Manager, Buddy Morin

LOCATIONS

HQ: SUMMIT ELECTRIC SUPPLY CO. INC
2900 STANFORD DR NE, ALBUQUERQUE, NM 87107-1814
Phone: 505-346-2900
Web: WWW.SUMMIT.COM

PRODUCTS/OPERATIONS

Selected Products

Ballasts
Box hangers
Brackets
Cable
Chemicals
Conduit
Drills
Enclosures
Fasteners
Fuses and fuse kits
Gaskets
Gloves
Goggles
Hand tools
Installation tools
Junction boxes
Lamps (HID and incandescent)
Light fixtures
Lubricants
Outlet boxes
PVC pipe
Power tools
Raceway
Receptacles
Safety equipment
Saws
Screws
Switches
Terminals
Test equipment
Transformers

Uninterruptible power supplies
Wire
Wire guards

COMPETITORS

Border States Electric	Kirby Risk
Consolidated Electrical	Rexel Inc.
Crescent Electric Supply	Sonepar USA
Graybar Electric	Stuart C. Irby
Hisco	W.W. Grainger
	WESCO International

HISTORICAL FINANCIALS

Company Type: Private

Income Statement FYE: December 31

	REVENUE ($ mil.)	NET INCOME ($ mil.)	NET PROFIT MARGIN	EMPLOYEES
12/12	384	10	2.6%	497
12/11	358	7	2.1%	—
12/06	301	7	2.6%	—
12/06	337	5	1.6%	—
Annual Growth	2.2%	10.6%	—	—

2012 Year-End Financials

Debt ratio: —
Return on equity: 2.60%
Cash ($ mil.): 0
Current ratio: 1.20
Long-term debt ($ mil.): —
Dividends
Yield: —
Payout: —
Market value ($ mil.): —

SUMMIT MATERIALS LLC

LOCATIONS

HQ: SUMMIT MATERIALS LLC
1550 WYNKOOP ST FL 3, DENVER, CO 802021130
Phone: 3038930012
Web: WWW.SUMMIT-MATERIALS.COM

HISTORICAL FINANCIALS

Company Type: Private

Income Statement FYE: December 27

	REVENUE ($ mil.)	NET INCOME ($ mil.)	NET PROFIT MARGIN	EMPLOYEES
12/14	1,204	(6)	—	3,300
12/13	916	(103)	—	—
Annual Growth	31.4%	—	—	—

2014 Year-End Financials

Debt ratio: —
Return on equity: (-0.50%)
Cash ($ mil.): 13
Current ratio: 0.70
Long-term debt ($ mil.): —
Dividends
Yield: —
Payout: —
Market value ($ mil.): —

SUN COAST RESOURCES INC.

Breaking the glass ceiling with large containers of Texas tea woman-owned Sun Coast Resources buys refined oil and sells it to more than 10000 third-party customers such airlines and construction educational energy industrial and retail companies in about 40 states. The company has an extensive truck fleet (more than 1000 vehicles) and delivers gasoline and diesel fuels marine and aviation fuels and lubricants. It also provides oilfield transportation and services onsite and fleet fueling petroleum tanks and generator fueling services. In 2013 the Houston Chronicle ranked Sun Coast as the 8th largest private company based in Houston.

Geographic Reach

Sun Coast owns and operates 18 offices in Arkansas New Mexico Mississippi Oklahoma Texas and Louisiana. It also has more than of 350000 sq. ft. of office and warehouse space in nine facilities in Texas. It markets its products in 40 US states. Sun Coast also provides equipment and services in fast-growing shale plays including the Eagle Ford Eagle Ford Bryan Permian Haynesville Cline Woodford and Marcellus.

Operations

Sun Coast carries a full line of Chevron oils and lubricants and is one of Chevron's largest lubricant distributors in the US. Other Sun Coast services include additive packages bulk storage and warehousing a computerized fleet tracking system and customized schedule and deliveries. The company has 1.5 million gallons of bulk fuel storage more than 10000 fuel and lubricant tanks including skid tanks aviation certified tanks emergency ISO tanks and others. Its truck fleet includes bobtails lowboys lube trucks pick-ups roll-backs and vacuum trucks. Its transport trucks are capable of hauling 7500 gallons of diesel fuel and 8600 gallons of gasoline. Its bobtails are used for orders of less than 4500 gallons. Sun Coast's lubricant trucks are capable of hauling 2000 gallons of bulk lubricants as well as drums totes and other packaged products.

The company's products include aviation gasoline (avgas) gasoline jet fuel kerosene marine diesel ultra-low sulfur diesel fuel and Chevron Conoco Mystik Phillips 66 and TOTAL lubrication products. It also offers services card lock service filtration and fluid purification fleet fueling and mobile on-site fueling spill response and other services.

Sun Coast's crude/condensate segment serves more than 300 well sites and numerous gathering facilities and transports more 37000 barrels per day (more than 10 million barrels a year).

Sales and Marketing

Sun Coast provides fuel supply services and related equipment to communication companies delivery services firms government entities utilities and other fleet operators.

Financial Performance

Buoyed by higher oil prices and the rapid growth of company assets in 2013 Sun Coast's revenues rose to $2 billion up from $1.94 billion in 2012.

Strategy

The company pursues a strategy of organic growth supplemented by complementary acquisitions in its core geographic markets.

Mergers and Acquisitions

It expanded into Louisiana in 2012 with the purchase of St. Martin Oil and Gas which operated a small fleet of fuel transportation trucks from two bulk storage facilities in St. Martinville and Denham Springs.

Further expanding its portfolio in 2012 the company acquired assets from bankrupt SMF Energy including its wholly owned affiliate H&W Petroleum Co. Properties included more than 100 fuel trucks and support vehicles previously used by SMF's mobile refueling operations outside of Texas and about 100 fuel and chemical transportation and support vehicles from H&W its Lufkin blending facility and fuel storage tanks across Texas.

That year Sun Coast further expanded its branded and unbranded fuel and lubricant distribution business by buying Houston-based ADA Resources.

Company Background

In 2011 the company bought the commercial fuel and disaster response businesses of Cypress Texas-based Roy Moffitt Customized Fueling.

Sun Coast was founded in 1985 by president and CEO Kathy Lehne with $2000 in start-up capital.

EXECUTIVES

Founder President CEO of Sun Coast Resources, Kathy Lehne
VP Sales and Marketing, Kyle Lehne
Director IT, Bryan Frazier
Senior Managing Director Trading, Steve Boyd
Director Safety, Stratton Williams
senior Vice President field operations, Tom Bittenbender
CFO, Sheila Kahanek
Director Operations, Larry Bothmann
Director of Marketing, Miranda Fuller
Auditors: Melton&MeltonLLP

LOCATIONS

HQ: SUN COAST RESOURCES INC.
6405 CAVALCADE ST BLDG 1, HOUSTON, TX 77026-4315
Phone: 713-844-9600
Web: WWW.SUNCOASTRESOURCES.COM

PRODUCTS/OPERATIONS

Selected Products

Petroleum Products
- Aviation gasoline
- High sulfur diesel fuel
- Jet fuel
- Kerosene
- Lubricants
- Marine fuels
- Mid-grade fuel
- Low sulfur diesel fuel
- Premium low sulfur diesel fuel
- Premium unleaded gasoline
- Unleaded gasoline

Oils and Lubricants
- Automatic transmission fluid
- Chain oils
- Food-grade oils
- Fuel Additives
- Gear oils
- Greases
- Heat transfer oils
- Hydraulic oils
- Metal-working oils
- Motor oils
- Refrigeration oils
- Solvents and chemicals

Selected Mergers and Acquisitions

2012
St. Martin Oil and Gas (Louisiana; fuel transportation and storage)
SMF Energy (fuel trucks and support vehicles)
ADA Resources (Houston Texas; branded and unbranded fuel and lubricant distribution)
2011
Roy Moffitt Customized Fueling (Cypress Texas; Commercial fuel and disaster response businesses)

COMPETITORS

George Warren	Martin Resource Management
Global Partners	Mercury Air Group
Gulf Oil	SMF Energy
J.A.M. Distributing	

HISTORICAL FINANCIALS

Company Type: Private

Income Statement FYE: December 31

	REVENUE ($ mil.)	NET INCOME ($ mil.)	NET PROFIT MARGIN	EMPLOYEES
12/07	1,064	2	0.3%	1,649
12/06	864	7	0.8%	—
12/05	867	13	1.6%	—
12/04	697	3	0.4%	—
Annual Growth	15.1%	(2.7%)	—	—

2007 Year-End Financials

Debt ratio: —
Return on equity: 0.30%
Cash ($ mil.): 0
Current ratio: 3.10
Long-term debt ($ mil.): —
Dividends
Yield: —
Payout: —
Market value ($ mil.): —

SUN-MAID GROWERS OF CALIFORNIA

The Sun-Maid's basket runneth over. Sun-Maid Growers is the producer of Sun-Maid Raisins. Packaged in the familiar red boxes with the smiling red-sunbonneted maid Lorraine Collett Petersen offering her basket laden with grapes the brand is seen in just about every food store in the US. In addition to offering every toddler's (and moms of toddlers) favorite little-red-boxed snack the grower-owned cooperative manufactures industrial and food service products and exports to more than 50 countries. The company's other dried fruits include pitted prunes currants apricots cranberries figs dates apples fruit bits and tropical fruit mixtures. Founded in 1912 the coop is owned by 750 family farmers.

Geographic Reach

Headquartered in Kingsburg California Sun-Maid's facilities are located in California's Central Valley –the world's largest raisin producing area –where vineyards belonging to some 750 family farmers span approximately 50000 acres.

Operations

Sun-Maid whose growers harvest some 200 million pounds of grapes every year also licenses its brand for products including raisin bread raisin muffins and raisin cookie mix as well as chocolate- and vanilla yogurt-covered raisins. Retail products make up about half of the co-op's sales; ingredient products comprise the rest.

Sales and Marketing

In 2013 Sun-Maid Growers hired San Francisco-based Baker Street Advertising as its agency of record. The agency's responsibilities for the brand include marketing strategy research and creative development for advertising and communications across all media channels including broadcast print online social media and event marketing.

EXECUTIVES

Vice President, Rick Bruno
Vice President Operations, James Henderson, age 71
Vp Domestic Sales, Joe Tamble
Vice President Sales, Michael Cassidy

LOCATIONS

HQ: SUN-MAID GROWERS OF CALIFORNIA
13525 S BETHEL AVE, KINGSBURG, CA 936319212
Phone: 5598976235
Web: WWW.SUNMAID.COM

PRODUCTS/OPERATIONS

Selected Products

Bakery
- Oatmeal raisin cookie mix
- Raisin bread
- Raisin muffins

Dried apples
Dried California apricots
Dried Calimyrna figs
Dried chopped dates
Dried cranberries
Dried fruit bits
Dried golden raisins and cherries
Dried Mediterranean apricots
Dried mission figs
Dried mixed fruit
Dried pitted dates
Dried pitted plums
Dried tropical trio
Raisins
- Baking raisins
- Chocolate yogurt-covered raisins
- Chocolate-covered raisins
- Golden raisins
- Jumbo raisins
- Vanilla yogurt-covered raisins
- Zante currents

COMPETITORS

Cherry Central Cooperative Inc.
Dole Food
Encore Fruit Marketing
Florida Food Products Inc
Fresh Del Monte Produce
General Mills
Gold Harbor
Golden West Nuts
Graceland Fruit
Kendall Frozen Fruits
Lion Raisins
Meridian Nut Growers
Multiple Organics
National Raisin
Pinnacle Foods
Riviana Foods
Shoreline Fruit
SunOpta
Sunview Vineyards
Tree Top
Tropical Nut & Fruit
United Natural
Valley Fig Growers
Waymouth Farms
Welch' s

HISTORICAL FINANCIALS

Company Type: Private

Income Statement FYE: July 31

	REVENUE ($ mil.)	NET INCOME ($ mil.)	NET PROFIT MARGIN	EMPLOYEES
07/14	389	11	3.0%	800
07/13	360	15	4.3%	—
07/12	360	8	2.3%	—
07/11	352	0	—	—
Annual Growth	3.4%	—	—	—

2014 Year-End Financials

Debt ratio: —
Return on equity: 3.00%
Cash ($ mil.): 0
Current ratio: 0.30
Long-term debt ($ mil.): —
Dividends
Yield: —
Payout: —
Market value ($ mil.): —

SUNFLOWER ELECTRIC POWER CORPORATION

Rural Kansans bloom under the light provided by Sunflower Electric Power an electricity generation and transmission cooperative. The utility has interests in six fossil-fueled generation facilities (600 MW of capacity) and operates a more-than-1150-mile transmission system with 76 substations. Sunflower Electric Power provides electricity to its owners six member distribution cooperatives which collectively have more than 51000 customers in western Kansas; it also indirectly serves a further 10000 meters as wholesale power suppliers to regional cities and towns.

Expanding its geographic coverage in 2007 Sunflower Electric Power purchased the Kansas electric properties of Aquila. In 2009 the Kansas Corporation Commission approved ITC Great Plains' plan to build a 345 kV transmission line extending 89 miles between Spearville and Hays. In addition to increasing power supply to Sunflower Electric Power's customers in Western Kansas the new line offers infrastructure support for the development of wind farms in the region a growth industry in the area.

Sunflower Electric Power was organized in 1957 to provide reliable long-term power supply to its six member distribution cooperatives at the lowest possible costs.

EXECUTIVES

President and CEO, L. Earl Watkins Jr.
EVP, Sid Severson
Vice Chairman, Larry M. Evans
Chairman, Loren Ochs
Executive Manager Financial Services and Treasurer, Jayne Clarke
VP General Counsel and Secretary, Mark Calcara
VP Member Services and External Affairs, Clare Gustin
Senior Manager Information Systems, Jerry Herman
Manager Regulatory Relations, Tom Hestermann
VP Administration, Jana Horsfall
Executive Manager Engineering and Energy Services, Bob Johnson
Senior Manager Special Projects, Steve Miller
Senior Manager Power Production, Steve Moss
SVP and COO, Kyle Nelson
VP Transmission Policy and Engineering, Noman L. Williams
Executive Manager Compliance and Corporate Security, Keith Overland
VP and CFO, Davis Rooney
VP Transmission Policy, Steve Ferry
Executive Manager Transmission, Mark Helm
Manager Coal Resources, Dave Chaney
Manager Culture and Leadership Development, Carol Haberman
Senior Manager Power Supply, Corey Linville
Manager System Operations, Allan George
Manager Supply Chain, Gary Ratts
Manager Power Production Engineering and Environment, Paul Reynolds
Manager Maintenance, Steve Ricard
Manager Contracts and Billing Systems, Ken Roberts
Manager Gas Resources, Derek Seacat
Manager Transmission Engineering, Clarence Suppes
Manager Human Resources, Tom Zerfas
VP and CIO, Bill Branch
Director, Charles Ayers, age 69
Vice Chairman, Larry M. Evans
Director, Neil Norman
Director, David Schneider
Director, Paul Seib Jr.
Director, Earl Steffens
Director, Perry E. Rubart
Director, David Jesse
Director, Robert Johnson
Director, Allan Miller
Director, Terry Janson
Auditors: KPMGLLP

LOCATIONS

HQ: SUNFLOWER ELECTRIC POWER CORPORATION
301 W 13TH ST, HAYS, KS 67601-3087
Phone: 785-628-2845
Web: WWW.SUNFLOWER.NET

PRODUCTS/OPERATIONS

Sales

	$ mil.	% of total
Member power sales	115	59
Nonmember power sales	33	17
Revenue from affiliates	24	12
Other	22	12
Total	**195**	**100**

COMPETITORS

AES
Constellation Energy Group
GenOnEnergy

HISTORICAL FINANCIALS

Company Type: Private

Income Statement FYE: December 31

	REVENUE ($ mil.)	NET INCOME ($ mil.)	NET PROFIT MARGIN	EMPLOYEES
12/11	233	31	13.7%	215
12/10	213	21	10.2%	—
12/09	195	16	8.2%	—
12/08	232	13	5.9%	—
Annual Growth	0.1%	32.5%	—	—

2011 Year-End Financials

Debt ratio: —
Return on equity: 13.70%
Cash ($ mil.): 22
Current ratio: 0.80
Long-term debt ($ mil.): —
Dividends
Yield: —
Payout: —
Market value ($ mil.): —

SUNKIST GROWERS INC.

HISTORY

Sunkist Growers was founded in the early 1890s as the Pachappa Orange Growers a group of California citrus farmers determined to control the sale of their fruit. Success attracted new members and in 1893 the Southern California Fruit Exchange was born. The name "Sunkissed" was coined by an ad copywriter in 1908 and it was soon reworked into "Sunkist" and registered as a trademark becoming the first brand name for a fresh produce item. Eventually the co-op renamed itself after its popular brand: It became Sunkist Growers in 1952. Sunkist began licensing its trademark to other companies in the early 1950s.

As early as 1916 efforts to increase citrus consumption included designing and marketing glass citrus juicers and encouraging homemakers to "Drink an Orange." The co-op also promoted the practice of putting lemon slices in tea or water and funded early research on the health benefits of vitamins (vitamin C in particular). In 1925 tissue wrappers gave way to stamping the Sunkist name directly on each piece of fruit.

Although Sunkist pioneered bottled orange juice in 1933 its juice marketing efforts were never as successful as those of its Florida competitors. Florida oranges are drippy and dowdy and thus better suited for juicing. Capitalizing on this aspect Florida growers dominated the market for fresh and frozen juice.

In 1937 Congress created a system of citrus shipment quotas and limits (known as "marketing orders") that ultimately proved most beneficial to large citrus cooperatives. By the early 1990s the marketing order system was under political attack and in 1992 the Justice Department filed civil prosecution against Sunkist alleging that the co-op had reaped unfair extra profits by surpassing its lemon shipment limits. In 1994 after much legal wrangling the quotas were abolished and the Justice Department dropped its case against Sunkist.

Inconveniently warm weather and increasing competition from imported citrus marked the harvests of 1996. That year the co-op had trouble maintaining discipline among its members; some undercut Sunkist price levels while others flooded the market to sell their fruit at the higher early market prices creating a supply surplus. Also that year the co-op relinquished the marketing of all Sunkist juices in North America to Florida-based Lykes Bros. in a licensing agreement.

The co-op agreed in 1998 to distribute grapefruit from Florida's Tuxedo Fruit providing Sunkist with a winter grapefruit supply and increasing its year-round consumer a-peel. Also in 1998 Russell Hanlin Sunkist president and CEO since 1978 was succeeded by Vince Lupinacci. Lupinacci who had held positions with Pepsi and Six Flags became the first person from outside the citrus business to hold Sunkist's top post.

In 1998 the company sold 90 million cartons of fresh citrus –the greatest volume in its history –despite increased competition from imported Latin American South African and Spanish crops a damaging California freeze and the ill effects of El Ni?o. The next year production was almost halved because of adverse weather.

Lupinacci resigned in 2000 citing personal and family reasons. Chairman emeritus James Mast then took the helm as acting president. Although the company grew its market through exports to China in 2000 its profits were squeezed that year by increasing foreign competition a citrus glut and lessened demand. In mid-2001 Jeff Gargiulo replaced Mast as Sunkist's president and CEO.

In 2003 Sunkist formed a joint venture with strawberry shipper Coastal Berry Co. to market strawberries under the Sunkist label year-round. (Coastal Berry's president and CEO John Gargiulo and Sunkist's former president and CEO Jeff Gargiulo are brothers.) Also that year Sunkist began offering pre-cut bagged fruit to retail customers and restaurants in order to keep up with a changing market and consumer demand.

In retrospect 2006 was an eventful year for Sunkist. The co-op's largest producer and 16-year-member Paramount Citrus Association left the organization. In addition chairman and CEO David Krause stepped down and president Jeff Gargiulo left the company. Krause was replaced as chairman by Nicholas Bozick president of produce grower/packer Richard Bagdasarian Inc. Sunkist veteran and former president of Fruit Growers Supply Company Timothy Lindgren was appointed president and CEO. And citing expense as the determining factor the co-op discontinued marketing berries (strawberries blueberries and raspberries) in 2006. Lindgren retired in 2008; he was replaced by EVP Russ Hanlin.

LOCATIONS

HQ: SUNKIST GROWERS INC.
14130 RIVERSIDE DR, SHERMAN OAKS, CA 914232392
Phone: 8189864800
Web: WWW.SUNKIST.COM

PRODUCTS/OPERATIONS

Selected Products

- Fresh fruit
  - Grapefruit
    - Melo Golds
    - Oro Blancos
    - Pummelos
    - Sweeties
    - Texas Rio Star
    - Western
  - Lemons
    - Eurkea/Lisbon
    - Meyer
  - Limes
    - Key
    - Persian
  - Mandarins
    - Clementine
    - Honey
    - Royal
    - Satsuma
    - Shasta Gold
  - W. Murcott
  - Oranges
    - Cara Cara
    - Moro
    - Navel
    - Valencia
  - Tangelos
    - Minneola
    - Orlando
  - Tangerines
    - Dancy
    - Fairchild
    - Pixie
- Packaged fruit
  - Beverage concentrates
  - Carbonated beverages (under license)
  - Chilled fruit jellies (under license)
  - Fruit juice
  - Fruit juice drinks
  - Fruit snacks (under license)
  - Powdered fruit drinks
  - Vitamins (under license)

HISTORICAL FINANCIALS

Company Type: Private

Income Statement FYE: October 31

	REVENUE ($ mil.)	NET INCOME ($ mil.)	NET PROFIT MARGIN	EMPLOYEES
10/14	1,234	6	0.5%	500
10/13	1,046	33	3.2%	—
10/12*	1,003	6	0.6%	—
12/09	0	0	—	—
Annual Growth	—	—	—	—

*Fiscal year change

2014 Year-End Financials

Debt ratio: —
Return on equity: 0.50%
Cash ($ mil.): 2
Current ratio: 1.10
Long-term debt ($ mil.): —
Dividends
Yield: —
Payout: —
Market value ($ mil.): —

SUNSWEET GROWERS INC.

EXECUTIVES

Chairman, Gary S. Thiara
Vice Chairman, Tim D. Smith
VP-Strategic Bus Processes, Harold Upton
Chief Executive Officer, Arthur Driscoll II
VP Global Marketing and Sales, Dane L. Lance
Vice President Manufacturing, Gene Dodson
Vice President Chief Financial Officer, Ana Klein
Vice President Member Services & Dryers, Melvin Ward
Vice President Global Sales & Marketing, Brad Schuler
Vice Chairman, Tim D. Smith
Director, J. Michael Billiou III
Director, Joe Turkovich
Director, Brendon Flynn
Director, Ren L. Fairbanks

Director, Robert (Bob) Kolberg
Director, John Rehermann
Director, Hans F. Smith
Director, Phillip Filter
Director, Robert Amarel Jr.
Auditors: KPMGLLP

LOCATIONS

HQ: SUNSWEET GROWERS INC.
901 N WALTON AVE, YUBA CITY, CA 959939370
Phone: 5306745010
Web: WWW.SUNSWEET.COM

PRODUCTS/OPERATIONS

Selected Products and Brands

Juices
- Amazing Prune Light
- Juicers
- PlumSmart
- PlumSmart Light
- Prune Juice
- Prune Juice with Pulp

Prunes
- 60 CALORIE PACKS
- Amazins
- BITE SIZE PRUNES
- D' NOIR PRUNES
- ESSENCE
- Lighter Bake
- PREMIUM PRUNES
- WHOLE PRUNES

Specialty Fruits
- Antioxidant Blend
- Berry Blend
- Blueberries
- Cherries
- Cranberries
- Dates
- Jumbo Red Raisins
- Mediterranean Apricots
- Philippine Mangos
- Philippine Pineapple
- PlumSweets

COMPETITORS

Cherry Central Cooperative Inc.
Chiquita Brands
Del Monte Foods
Dole Food
Fresh Del Monte Produce
Graceland Fruit
Maui Land & Pineapple
Meridian Nut Growers
Naturipe Farms
Ocean Spray
Pro-Fac
Seneca Foods
Shoreline Fruit
Stewart & Jasper Orchards
Sunkist
Tropical Nut & Fruit
Valley Fig Growers
Waymouth Farms

HISTORICAL FINANCIALS

Company Type: Private

Income Statement

FYE: July 31

	REVENUE ($ mil.)	NET INCOME ($ mil.)	NET PROFIT MARGIN	EMPLOYEES
07/14	261	81	31.3%	700
07/13	266	71	26.7%	—
07/12	281	64	22.8%	—
07/11	245	0	—	—
Annual Growth	2.1%	—	—	—

2014 Year-End Financials

Debt ratio: —
Return on equity: 31.30%
Cash ($ mil.): 7
Current ratio: 0.40
Long-term debt ($ mil.): —
Dividends
Yield: —
Payout: —
Market value ($ mil.): —

SUPERIOR BULK LOGISTICS INC.

Superior Bulk Logistics through subsidiaries Superior Carriers and Carry Transit hauls liquid and dry bulk cargo including both chemical and food-grade products. Overall the trucking units of Superior Bulk Logistics operate a fleet of some 980 tractors and 1765 trailers. The company's SuperFlo unit provides transloading services —the transfer of cargo between railcars and trucks. Superior Bulk Logistics' Sanicare Wash Systems unit cleans tank truck trailers and other bulk containers used for food products. Superior Bulk Logistics offers service between Mexico and the US and Canada through a partnership with Transpormex a division of Grupo Dexel.

Geographic Reach

Stationed in Illinois Superior Bulk Logistics delivers more than 8 billion pounds or products and provides its services in the US Canada and Mexico.

Operations

The company's subsidiaries include Superior Carriers SuperFlo and Carry Transit.

EXECUTIVES

Chairman, Richard T. (Dick) Lewis
President and COO Superior Carriers, William J. (Bill) O'Donell
SVP and Chief Marketing Officer, Gary W. Watt
VP Administration and Assistant Secretary, William R. (Bill) Lavery
VP Information Services, Ronald B. (Ron) Bauman
VP Quality Assurance, Kenneth J. (Ken) Sevcik
Director Marketing, Craig L. Johnson
President and CEO; CEO Superior Carriers, Len F. Fletcher
VP Operations Carry Transit, Bill Kennedy
President Carry Transit, Jim Blackmon
VP Business Development Carry Transit, Joe Nolan
VP Finance and Treasurer, Tim McCann
EVP Sales, Wes Stone

LOCATIONS

HQ: SUPERIOR BULK LOGISTICS INC.
711 JORIE BLVD STE 101N, OAK BROOK, IL 60523-2285
Phone: 630-573-2555
Web: WWW.SUPERIORBULKLOGISTICS.COM

COMPETITORS

A&R Logistics
Bulkmatic
Groendyke Transport
Kenan Advantage Group
Quality Distribution
Ruan Transportation Management Systems
Schneider National
Trimac

HISTORICAL FINANCIALS

Company Type: Private

Income Statement

FYE: December 31

	REVENUE ($ mil.)	NET INCOME ($ mil.)	NET PROFIT MARGIN	EMPLOYEES
12/09	188	2	1.1%	1,160
12/07	234	7	3.1%	—
12/07	457	0	0.0%	—
Annual Growth	(35.9%)	6582.3%	—	—

2009 Year-End Financials

Debt ratio: —
Return on equity: 1.10%
Cash ($ mil.): 1
Current ratio: 0.50
Long-term debt ($ mil.): —
Dividends
Yield: —
Payout: —
Market value ($ mil.): —

SUPERIOR OIL COMPANY INC.

Despite the name Superior Oil actually distributes industrial products and provides chemical and waste services. Superior's solvents and chemicals division supplies manufacturers of paints and coatings pharmaceuticals fabricated metal products and adhesives. The fiberglass and resins unit sells to clients that make products ranging from parts for recreational vehicles to bathtubs and showers. Superior Oil also provides blending solvent reclamation and hazardous waste removal services. The company has nine stocking facilities and a fleet of trucks trailers and tankers. The company is owned by members of its management team.

EXECUTIVES

Sales Manager Nashville Tennessee Sales Distribution Center, Wade Childress
Sales Manager Springfield Missouri Sales Distribution Center, Bob Worthy
Sales Manager Louisville Kentucky Sales Distribution Center, Scott Bridges
Sales Manager Cincinnati Ohio Sales Distribution Center, Ken Smith
Solvents Sales Manager Elkhart Indiana Sales Distribution Center, Wayne Dixon

LOCATIONS

HQ: SUPERIOR OIL COMPANY INC.
1402 N CAPITOL AVE # 100, INDIANAPOLIS, IN 46202-2374
Phone: 317-781-4400
Web: WWW.SUPERIOROIL.COM

PRODUCTS/OPERATIONS

Selected Products and Services

Acetate esters
Alcohols
Aliphatic naphthas
Aromatic hydrocarbons
Caustic soda
Chelating agents
Compliance management
Equipment programs
Glycol ethers
Glycols
Heat exchange fluids
Ketones
Lacquer thinners
Paint strippers
Plasticizers
Professional waste services
Recycling programs
Regulatory services
Silicones
Technical support
Terpenes
Transportation

COMPETITORS

Aceto
Brenntag North America
HallStar
Harcros Chemicals
ICC Chemical
Univar USA
Wego Chemical & Mineral

HISTORICAL FINANCIALS

Company Type: Private

Income Statement FYE: December 31

	REVENUE ($ mil.)	NET INCOME ($ mil.)	NET PROFIT MARGIN	EMPLOYEES
12/12	202	0	—	250
12/11	191	0	—	—
12/10	167	0	—	—
12/09	132	0	—	—
Annual Growth	15.3%	—	—	—

2012 Year-End Financials

Debt ratio: —
Return on equity: —
Cash ($ mil.): 1
Current ratio: 1.20
Long-term debt ($ mil.): —
Dividends
Yield: —
Payout: —
Market value ($ mil.): —

SUTTER GOULD MEDICAL FOUNDATION

LOCATIONS

HQ: SUTTER GOULD MEDICAL FOUNDATION
1700 MCHENRY AVE STE 60B, MODESTO, CA 953504333
Phone: 2095264500
Web: WWW.SUTTERGOULD.ORG

HISTORICAL FINANCIALS

Company Type: Private

Income Statement FYE: December 31

	REVENUE ($ mil.)	NET INCOME ($ mil.)	NET PROFIT MARGIN	EMPLOYEES
12/11	305	(8)	—	4
12/09	288	(7)	—	—
Annual Growth	2.8%	—	—	—

2011 Year-End Financials

Debt ratio: —
Return on equity: (-2.60%)
Cash ($ mil.): 23
Current ratio: 1.00
Long-term debt ($ mil.): —
Dividends
Yield: —
Payout: —
Market value ($ mil.): —

SUTTER WEST BAY HOSPITALS

Sutter West Bay Hospitals (doing business as California Pacific Medical Center or CPMC) is a health care complex located in the heart of hospital-heavy San Francisco. The private not-for-profit center's four area campuses (California Davies Pacific and St. Luke's) offer acute and specialty care including obstetrics and gynecology cardiovascular services pediatrics neurosciences orthopedics and organ transplantation. With more than 1300 beds between its campuses the center also conducts professional education and biomedical clinical and behavioral research. CPMC is part of the West Bay Region division of the Sutter Health hospital system.

Geographic Reach

CPMC serves patients from San Francisco Marin San Mateo Oakland Berkeley Palo Alto Santa Rosa San Jose. and the Bay Area.

Operations

CPMC's Sutter Health West Bay Region also includes Novato Community Hospital Sutter Lakeside Hospital and Sutter Medical Center of Santa Rosa. In addition to acute medical services CPMC also provides outpatient services at clinics in the San Francisco area operates home health and hospice organizations and conducts health education and charity care programs.

In 2011 CPMC's Research Institute conducted more than 200 clinical trials including studies on aging cancers epilepsy diabetes cardiovascular disease osteoporosis organ transplantation and more. That year CPMC's Kidney and Pancreas Transplant Program performed the first ever single-hospital five-way kidney swap transplant in California. CPMC's Joint Replacement Center is one of the leading joint replacement centers in the Bay Area performing roughly 1200 hip knee shoulder and elbow procedures per year. It has 1859 CPMC Medical Staff (including St. Luke's) and 109 medical residents and fellows.

That year the healthcare system reported about 619400 outpatient visits and 30300 inpatient cases.

Strategy

In order to meet California's seismic construction standards CPMC plans to renovate or rebuild most of its hospital campuses which are among the oldest medical centers in the San Francisco area. Its $2.5 billion reorganization plan includes the construction of a new 550-bed Cathedral Hill Campus that will include a full acute care hospital plus specialized women's and children's departments. CPMC also plans to rebuild and downsize the St. Luke's campus and convert the Pacific and California campuses into ambulatory care clinics. Reconstruction efforts at the Davies campus will include a new patient pavilion and a new Davies Neurosciences Institute for expanded neurological care. Major construction projects began in 2011 and will extend through 2015.

In 2010 the company sold its outpatient kidney dialysis operations to DaVita to focus on core operations.

Ownership

CPMC is part of the West Bay Region division of the Sutter Health hospital system.

Company Background

In 2007 parent Sutter Health merged St. Luke's Hospital into California Pacific to help keep the ailing St. Luke's afloat; St. Luke's provides care to many of San Francisco's low-income patients. CPMC had announced plans to turn St. Luke's into an outpatient facility in 2007; however the company rescinded those plans after San Franciscans objected to the proposal.

EXECUTIVES

Vice President Nursing & Chief Nursing Officer, Diana Karner
Executive Vice President & CEO North Bay Hospitals, Grant Davies
VP Academic Affairs, Warren Browner
Controller, Henry Yu
VP Information Technology and CIO, Craig Vercruysse
President CPMCFoundation & Region Vice President Philanthropy, Mark Kimbell
Region Chief Information Officer, Anne Barr
Chief Medical Executive, Vernon Giang
Radiology Director, James J Wille
Director Of Medical Records, Michelle Torres
Radiology Director, Phil Revetta
Vice President Supply Chain Services, Dennis Maher
Supervisor Of Medical Records, Flormeline David
Director Of Him, Jane Schulze
Senior Vice President Marketing And Public Relations, Sarah Grover
Director Of Radiology, Cheryl Halcovich
Director Of Medical Records, Lisa Haux
Medical Librarian, Heidi Mortensen
Medical Director, Carolyn Tague
Regional Chief Financial Officer And Vice President, Jeff Sprague

LOCATIONS

HQ: SUTTER WEST BAY HOSPITALS
633 FOLSOM ST FL 7, SAN FRANCISCO, CA 94107-3618
Phone: 415-563-4321
Web: WWW.CPMC.ORG

PRODUCTS/OPERATIONS

Selected Hospitals

California Campus (aka Children's Hospital of San Francisco)
Davies Campus (aka Davies Medical Center or Franklin Hospital)
Pacific Campus (aka Presbyterian Medical Center)
St. Luke's Campus (aka St. Luke's Hospital)

COMPETITORS

Children' s Hospital & Research Center at Oakland
Dignity Health
HCA
John Muir Health
St. Joseph Health System
Stanford Hospital and Clinics
Tenet Healthcare
UCSF Medical
ValleyCare Health System

HISTORICAL FINANCIALS

Company Type: Private

Income Statement FYE: December 31

	REVENUE ($ mil.)	NET INCOME ($ mil.)	NET PROFIT MARGIN	EMPLOYEES
12/11	1,616	67	4.1%	3,597
12/09	1,245	159	12.8%	—
12/08	830	168	20.3%	—
12/04	801	138	17.3%	—
Annual Growth	10.5%	(9.9%)	—	—

2011 Year-End Financials

Debt ratio: —
Return on equity: 4.10%
Cash ($ mil.): 76
Current ratio: 0.90
Long-term debt ($ mil.): —
Dividends
Yield: —
Payout: —
Market value ($ mil.): —

SWEDISH HEALTH SERVICES

Swedish Health Services hopes that the Swedish reputation for good health is transferred to its patients in the Pacific Northwest. The largest nonprofit health provider in the greater Seattle area Swedish Health operates five acute care hospitals. It also runs two ambulatory care centers and the Swedish Medical Group physician practice organization which has about 100 primary and specialty care offices in the greater Puget Sound region. Swedish is affiliated with Providence Health & Services a Catholic not-for-profit organization with about 30 hospitals in five states.

Geographic Reach

Swedish Health has three hospital locations in Seattle as well as hospitals in Edmonds and Issaquah Washington. Its ambulatory centers (with emergency and specialty facilities) are located in Redmond and Everett Washington.

Operations

Swedish Health has 2800 physicians and its hospitals are home to about 1500 beds. The network's facilities see about 50000 inpatients per year as well as 130000 emergency room visits 7000 births and 50000 surgeries. Swedish Health operates numerous institutes across its campuses including its Cancer Institute Heart and Vascular Institute Neuroscience Institute and Orthopedic Institute. Other medical specialties include transplants pediatrics and women's health.

Swedish Health also conducts clinical research programs with as many as 700 trials being conducted at one time making it one of the largest clinical trial sites in the US. The network's research programs are supported by government and commercial partners.

The network spends some $36 million on charity care (medical care for uninsured patients) each year.

Strategy

The company grows both organically and through partnerships. Swedish Health formed its affiliation with Providence Health & Services in 2012. Through the affiliation Swedish Health combined with Providence's Washington facilities under a new not-for-profit holding company. The two health systems retain their independent identities but share clinical and IT resources to work towards reducing medical costs and increasing the quality of care in the region.

Also in 2012 Swedish Health's Swedish Neuroscience Institute Acute TeleStroke Program formed partnerships with Walla Walla General Hospital and Whidbey General Hospital to bolster stroke support services at the two smaller hospitals.

The company completed construction and opened its fifth acute-care hospital in 2011. The facility is located in Issaquah (a Seattle metropolitan-area community) where Swedish Health already operated an emergency and specialty center. The new hospital campus includes emergency services primary care outpatient centers and imaging units.

Swedish Health expanded its First Hill campus in Seattle with the addition of an endoscopy center for minimally invasive surgical procedures (primarily for digestive and respiratory ailments) in 2012. Also that year it opened a new cerebrovascular center for neurological testing at the Cherry Hill campus in Seattle.

To balance the costs of growth Swedish Health occasionally exits underperforming businesses. In 2012 for instance the company ceased operations of its Swedish Visiting Nurse Services program which provide home health care hospice and therapy services. The unit had incurred continuous losses since 2009.

Company Background

Not-for-profit Swedish Health began in 1910 as a single hospital with 24 beds.

EXECUTIVES

Interim Chief Executive Swedish, Marcel Loh
VP External Affairs, Dan Dixon
VP Human Resources, Joanne I. Suffis
Chief Medical Officer, John H. Vassall II
SVP Seattle COO, Rayburn S. Lewis
VP Development and Executive Director Foundation, Don Theophilus
Manager Media Relations, Ed Boyle
Chief Administrative Officer Swedish/First Hill, Mike Carter
CEO Swedish/Edmonds, David E. Jaffee
CEO Issaquah ACCs, Chuck Salmon
SVP Physician Services; Chief Medical Officer Swedish Medical Group, Ralph Pascualy
CIO, Tom Wood
Chief Nursing Officer, June Altaras
Executive Director Swedish Medical Group, Bryan Mueller
SVP and COO Seattle, Todd Strumwasser
CFO, Dan Harris
Vice President Performance Improvement and Strategic Development, Heidi Aylsworth

LOCATIONS

HQ: SWEDISH HEALTH SERVICES
747 BROADWAY, SEATTLE, WA 98122-4379
Phone: 206-386-6000
Web: WWW.SWEDISH.ORG

PRODUCTS/OPERATIONS

Selected Washington Facilities

Ballard Campus (Seattle)
Cherry Hill Campus (Seattle)
Edmonds Campus (Edmonds)
First Hill Campus (Seattle)
Issaquah Campus (Issaquah)
Mill Creek Campus (ambulatory center in Everett)
Redmond Campus (ambulatory center in Redmond)

Selected Institutes and Services

Cancer Institute
Emergency Services
Heart and Vascular Institute
Neuroscience Institute
Orthopedic Institute
Pediatric Specialty Care
Primary Care
Pregnancy and Childbirth
Surgical Services
Transplant Program
Women' s Health

COMPETITORS

Franciscan Health System
Harrison Medical Center
Kaiser Permanente
MultiCare Health System
Overlake Hospital
PeaceHealth
Providence Health & Services
Seattle Children' s Hospital
University of Washington
Wenatchee Valley Medical Center
Yakima Valley Memorial

HISTORICAL FINANCIALS

Company Type: Private

Income Statement FYE: December 31

	REVENUE ($ mil.)	NET INCOME ($ mil.)	NET PROFIT MARGIN	EMPLOYEES
12/07	1,153	78	6.8%	6,916
12/06	1,087	56	5.2%	—
Annual Growth	6.1%	40.5%	—	—

2007 Year-End Financials

Debt ratio: —
Return on equity: 6.80%
Cash ($ mil.): 43
Current ratio: 1.40
Long-term debt ($ mil.): —
Dividends
Yield: —
Payout: —
Market value ($ mil.): —

SWINERTON BUILDERS

EXECUTIVES

SVP and Southern California Regional Manager, Gary J. Rafferty
SVP and Division Manager, Frank Foellmer
VP and Division Manager, Steve Johnson
President, Michael (Mike) Re
VP and San Diego Division Manager, Don Adair
SVP and General Manager Northern California, Eric Foster
VP and Denver Division Manager, Kevin L. Ott
Operations Manager San Francisco, Bill Krill
Business Development Los Angeles, Cheryl Johnson
Operations Manager Los Angeles Special Projects Group, Kim Grant
VP Southern California, Chris Day
VP and Division Manager, Dave Callis
Corporate Marketing Director, Meggie Doscher

LOCATIONS

HQ: SWINERTON BUILDERS
260 TOWNSEND ST, SAN FRANCISCO, CA 941071719
Phone: 4154212980
Web: WWW.SWINERTON.COM

PRODUCTS/OPERATIONS

Selected Services

BIM/VD&C
Corporate Services
Critical Facilities
General Contracting
Government Construction
Management & Consulting
Preconstruction
Renewable Energy
Sustainable Construction/LEED

COMPETITORS

Andersen Construction
Charles Pankow Builders
Clark Builders Group
Cordoba
DPR Construction
Devcon Construction
Gilbane Building Company
Hathaway Dinwiddie Construction
Hensel Phelps Construction
J.F. Shea
Jaynes Companies
Kitchell
Torix General Contractors
Turner Corporation
W. L. Butler
Webcor Builders
Whiting-Turner

HISTORICAL FINANCIALS

Company Type: Private

Income Statement FYE: December 31

	REVENUE ($ mil.)	NET INCOME ($ mil.)	NET PROFIT MARGIN	EMPLOYEES
12/13	1,674	4	0.3%	900
12/12	1,429	6	0.4%	—
12/11	948	0	—	—
12/10	796	0	—	—
Annual Growth	28.1%	—	—	—

2013 Year-End Financials

Debt ratio: —
Return on equity: 0.30%
Cash ($ mil.): 28
Current ratio: 0.10
Long-term debt ($ mil.): —
Dividends
Yield: —
Payout: —
Market value ($ mil.): —

SWINERTON INCORPORATED

Swinerton is building up the West just as it helped rebuild San Francisco after the 1906 earthquake. The construction group builds commercial industrial and government facilities including resorts subsidized housing public schools soundstages hospitals and airport terminals. Through its subsidiaries (including Swinerton Builders) Swinerton offers general contracting and design/build services as well as construction and program management. It also provides property management for conventional subsidized and assisted living residences. The employee-owned company traces its roots to 1888. Swinerton offices are located throughout California in Colorado Hawaii Texas Oregon and Washington.

Swinerton takes environmental stewardship to heart and has a special renewable energy division focused on solar and wind projects. As one of the top waste-reducing companies in California Swinerton employs green building construction and design practices to conserve resources reduce waste and create healthier environments. The company's own headquarters building in San Francisco received Gold LEED-EB (Leadership in Energy & Environmental Design for Existing Buildings) –a top certification from the U.S. Green Building Council. Swinerton also built the LEED platinum rated NASA Ames Research Center Sustainability Base the greenest government building in history.

In addition to a focus on sustainable design and renewable energy projects Swinerton established a division to handle government construction projects. The division delivers large-scale complex design and construction services for government agencies. Through the division Swinerton has worked on federal courthouses and administrative buildings training centers VA hospitals and military housing projects.

EXECUTIVES

VP San Diego, Christopher Day
National Marketing Director, Mark Gudenas
President, Jeffrey C. (Jeff) Hoopes
President Harbison-Mahony-Higgins Builders (HMH), David Higgins Jr.
President of Swinerton Property Services, Sue Twitchel
Marketing Manager Swinerton Builders, Will Cannell
Business Development Representative Lyda Swinerton Builders, Leland Rocchio
VP and Hawaii Division Manager Swinerton Builders, George Ehara
SVP and Division Manager Swinerton Builders Washington, Andy Holden
VP Community Relations, Charles (Rick) Moore
Auditors: PricewaterhouseCoopers

LOCATIONS

HQ: SWINERTON INCORPORATED
260 TOWNSEND ST, SAN FRANCISCO, CA 94107-1719
Phone: 303-418-5304
Web: WWW.SWINERTON.COM

PRODUCTS/OPERATIONS

Selected Companies and Divisions

Cameron Swinerton
Harbison-Mahony-Higgins Builders Inc. (HMH general contracting)
Swinerton Builders (general contracting)
Swinerton Government Services
Swinerton Management & Consulting (property assessment)
Swinerton Property Services (property management)
William P. Young Construction (engineering and civil construction)

COMPETITORS

A.G. Spanos
Bechtel
Beck Group
Bovis Lend Lease
Charles Pankow Builders
Cordoba
DPR Construction
Devcon Construction
Gilbane
Hathaway Dinwiddie Construction
Hensel Phelps Construction
J.F. Shea
JCM Partners
Kitchell
Menas Realty
Rudolph & Sletten
Skanska USA Building
Sundt
Turner Corporation
Tutor-Saliba
Webcor Builders
Western National Group
Whiting-Turner

HISTORICAL FINANCIALS

Company Type: Private

Income Statement FYE: December 31

	REVENUE ($ mil.)	NET INCOME ($ mil.)	NET PROFIT MARGIN	EMPLOYEES
12/12	1,506	0	—	900
12/11	1,080	0	—	—
12/10	981	0	—	—
12/09	1,215	0	—	—
Annual Growth	7.4%	—	—	—

2012 Year-End Financials

Debt ratio: —
Return on equity: —
Cash ($ mil.): 92
Current ratio: 0.20
Long-term debt ($ mil.): —
Dividends
Yield: —
Payout: —
Market value ($ mil.): —

SYRACUSE UNIVERSITY

Syracuse University is a serious school with a silly mascot. While it wasn't until 1995 that Otto the Orange was officially adopted as the school's mascot Syracuse's tradition of quality higher education ‚Ädates back to 1870. The school enrolls more than 21000 undergraduate and graduate students and has ‚Äsome 1000 ‚Äfull-time faculty members on its campus in ‚Äcentral New York State. It offers about 500 degree programs in areas such as communications computer science engineering psychology art mathematics music and information. Notable alumni include Dick Clark Ted Koppel Joyce Carol Oats Joe Biden and Aaron Sorkin.

Geographic Reach

Syracuse's student ‚Äpopulation includes residents of all 50 US states and international students from about 125 countries. In addition to its main campus in central New York State the university also has satellite ‚Äcampuses in New York City Los Angeles and Washington DC. ‚ÄIt also has an extensive study abroad program with some 40% of its student body enrolling in curriculum programs in ‚Äcountries including Chile China France Italy Spain ‚ÄTurkey and the UK.

Operations

Syracuse's degree programs are organized under 13 schools in the fields of architecture arts and sciences education engineering and computer science graduate studies sports information law management public affairs communication visual and performing arts and continuing education.

Several of the colleges have research centers in areas such as ‚Äaccounting pop culture investment biomaterials health engineering energy technology business management and public affairs. Overall the university has sponsored programs in research teaching and other areas with a total of about $80 million in funding much of which comes from the federal and state governments.

Financial Performance

Syracuse reported a 3% decrease in revenues to $819 million in 2012 due to lower gains on investment transactions (slightly offset by higher tuition and fees). ‚ÄHowever net income in 2012 ‚Ädipped into the red ‚Ädue to investment losses increased expenses and interest rate swap ‚Äand currency forward agreements.

Student tuition and fees are the largest component of university revenues accounting for about 55% of earnings. ‚ÄSyracuse charges ‚Äfull-time undergraduate tuition of some $38000 per year. Auxiliary enterprises including ‚Ä room board bookstore sales and parking fees account for about a quarter of annual revenues.

Syracuse has a total endowment worth ‚Äsome $940 million as of mid-2012.

Company Background

Syracuse is an education corporation that operates under the direction of an independent board of trustees under the New York Not-for-Profit Corporation Law. The university was granted a charter by the state of New York in 1870.

EXECUTIVES

Interim Vice Chancellor and Provost, Elizabeth D. Liddy
Interim CIO and VP Information Technology and Services, Samuel Scozzafava
Chancellor and President, Kent Syverud
Treas, William F Patrick

LOCATIONS

HQ: SYRACUSE UNIVERSITY
900 S CROUSE AVE STE 620, SYRACUSE, NY 132440001
Phone: 3154431870
Web: WWW.SYR.EDU

PRODUCTS/OPERATIONS

Selected Academic Units

College of Arts and Sciences
College of Law
College of Visual and Performing Arts
University College
David B. Falk College of Sports and Human Dynamics
Graduate School
L.C. Smith College of Engineering and Computer Science
Martin J. Whitman School of Management
Maxwell School of Citizenship and Public Affairs
School of Architecture
School of Education
School of Information Studies
S.I. Newhouse School of Public Communications

HISTORICAL FINANCIALS

Company Type: Private

Income Statement FYE: June 30

	REVENUE ($ mil.)	NET INCOME ($ mil.)	NET PROFIT MARGIN	EMPLOYEES
06/13	869	136	15.7%	4,350
06/12	818	(73)	—	—
06/11	839	145	17.3%	—
06/10	978	0	—	—
Annual Growth	(3.9%)	—	—	—

2013 Year-End Financials

Debt ratio: —
Return on equity: 15.70%
Cash ($ mil.): 138
Current ratio: 0.80
Long-term debt ($ mil.): —
Dividends
Yield: —
Payout: —
Market value ($ mil.): —

TALLAHASSEE MEMORIAL HEALTHCARE INC.

Tallahassee Memorial HealthCare (TMH) aims to take the hassle out of health care. The community health system serves residents of Florida's state capital and its surrounding communities. The system is anchored by Tallahassee Memorial Hospital a not-for-profit facility with more than 770 beds and 550-plus physicians on staff who represent some 50 different specialties. Founded in 1948 TMH provides general medical and surgical care as well as specialty care in areas such as oncology rehabilitation women's and children's health obesity and diabetes. TMH also has a trauma center offers a family practice residency program and provides primary medical care through a handful of regional clinics.

Operations

TMH is Florida's eighth-largest hospital boasting more than 24000 inpatient admissions per year. As part of its operations TMH has a 60-bed psychiatric hospital and offers adult day care and home health care services. It operates the only Level II trauma center in the region which benefits from newly added telemedicine equipment that includes videoconferencing. Trauma centers are specially trained and equipped to handle severe injuries and all such patients in the area are routed to trauma certified facilities. To expand its capabilities TMH opened the Tallahassee Memorial Emergency Center - Northeast in mid-2013 and broke ground in 2013 on a new surgery and adult intensive care facility that's anticipated to cost as much as $175 million.

The system partners with the H. Lee Moffitt Cancer Center & Research Institute in Tampa to allow cancer patients to participate in clinical trials and other experimental and research opportunities.

The system offers a range of cardiovascular services from diagnostic procedures to open-heart surgery a designated acute brain and spinal cord injury center and a 110000-sq.-ft. childbirth facility –the region's only Level Three Neonatal Intensive Care Unit.

Geographic Reach

TMH serves some 16 counties across North Florida and South Georgia.

Strategy

The medical facility operates the Tallahassee Memorial Transition Center created in partnership with Capital Health Plan and Florida State University College of Medicine. The center was designed to improve wellness through new approaches and collaborative research. Looking to position itself as a regional center for healthcare Tallahassee Memorial has plans to roll out more new services and add physicians.

EXECUTIVES

President CEO and Director, G. Mark O'Bryant
Vice President Chief Financial Officer, William (Bill) Giudice
VP and Chief Nursing Officer, Barbara MacArthur
VP and Chief Communications Officer, Warren Jones
Vice President Chief Operating Officer, Jason Moore
Administrator Regional Development, Geri Forbes
VP and CIO, Don Lindsey
VP and Chief Improvement and Planning Officer, Cynthia Blair
VP and Chief Human Resource Officer, Steve Adriaanse
President CEO, Paula Fortunas
Chief Medical Officer, Dean Watson
Administrator Behavioral Health Center, Carl Mahler
Administrator Emergency Medicine Services, Freda Lyon
Director Premier Health and Fitness Center, Len Harvey
Administrator Orthopedic and Neurological Services, Judy Greenwald
Administrator Surgery Services, David Thompson
Administrator Women and Children?s Services, Kathy Walecko

LOCATIONS

HQ: TALLAHASSEE MEMORIAL HEALTHCARE INC.
1300 MICCOSUKEE RD, TALLAHASSEE, FL 32308-5054
Phone: 850-431-1155
Web: WWW.TMH.ORG

PRODUCTS/OPERATIONS

Selected Services

Behavioral Health Center
Rehabilitation Center
Cancer Center
Bixler Emergency Center
Heart & Vascular Center
Diabetes Center
Orthopedic Center
NeuroScience Center
Surgical Services
Women' s Pavilion
Home Health Care
Clinical Genetics Center
Bariatric Center
Chronic Pain Management
Lipid Center

COMPETITORS

Adventist Health System Sunbelt Healthcare
Baptist Health System
Bay Medical Center
H. Lee Moffitt Cancer Center & Research Institute
HCA
Jackson County Hospital of Florida
Munroe Regional Health System
Sacred Heart Health System
UF&Shands

HISTORICAL FINANCIALS

Company Type: Private

Income Statement FYE: September 30

	REVENUE ($ mil.)	NET INCOME ($ mil.)	NET PROFIT MARGIN	EMPLOYEES
09/12	479	40	8.4%	6,430
09/09	435	24	5.7%	—
09/06	411	21	5.3%	—
09/06	363	62	17.3%	—
Annual Growth	4.7%	(7.2%)	—	—

2012 Year-End Financials

Debt ratio: —
Return on equity: 8.40%
Cash ($ mil.): 157
Current ratio: 2.70
Long-term debt ($ mil.): —

Dividends
Yield: —
Payout: —
Market value ($ mil.): —

TAUBER OIL COMPANY

EXECUTIVES

VP Credit Finance, Stephen E. Hamlin
Owner and Principal, David W. Tauber, age 64
Owner and Principal, Richard E. Tauber
Controller, Joseph E. Sassin
VP Intermediate and Heavy Feedstocks, Kevin A. Wilson
VP Tauber Petrochemical, J. Scott Podsednik
VP Tauber Petrochemical, Robert D. Mackenzie
VP Operations Tauber Petrochemical, Steven C. Starcke
Credit Manager, Lisa K. Simon
Operations Manager Blending Components, Dave Swayne
Operations Manager, Steven M. Elliott
VP Transportation and Marketing Blending Components and Carbon Black Feedstocks, Jan Hicks
VP International Marketing Carbon Black Feedstocks, Kavan J. Mehta
Vice President Supply & Marketing, Jeff Bryant
Operations Manager Natural Gas Liquids, Carolyn Boudreaux
Operations Manager Intermediate & Heavy Feedstocks, Dack Franks
Operations Manager Tauber Petrochemical Co., Audry O'Toole
Operations Manager Tauber Petrochemical Co, Michael Price
VP Public Relations, Connie Kubiak
VP Natural Gas Liquids, Brad Kerby
VP Blending Components, Ed Naspinski
VP Natural Gas & Emissions, Earl Thomas
VP Natural Gas & Emissions, Neal Stockham
Vice President, Audry OToole
Vice President, Julee Briscoe

LOCATIONS

HQ: TAUBER OIL COMPANY
55 WAUGH DR STE 700, HOUSTON, TX 770075837
Phone: 7138698700
Web: WWW.TAUBEROIL.COM

PRODUCTS/OPERATIONS

Selected Products:

Natural Gas Liquids
- Butane
- Ethane
- Isobutane
- Propane

Petrochemicals
- Benzene
- Methanol
- MTBE
- Styrene monomer
- Toluene
- Xylene

Refined
- Aviation jet fuel
- Kerosene
- Low sulfur diesel
- No. 2 fuel oil

COMPETITORS

Exxon Mobil
George Warren
Global Partners
Tesoro
Valero Energy

HISTORICAL FINANCIALS

Company Type: Private

Income Statement FYE: December 31

	REVENUE ($ mil.)	NET INCOME ($ mil.)	NET PROFIT MARGIN	EMPLOYEES
12/13	4,769	16	0.3%	135
12/12	5,088	21	0.4%	—
12/11	4,427	7	0.2%	—
12/10	3,155	0	—	—
Annual Growth	14.8%	—	—	—

2013 Year-End Financials

Debt ratio: —
Return on equity: 0.30%
Cash ($ mil.): 26
Current ratio: 0.70
Long-term debt ($ mil.): —
Dividends
Yield: —
Payout: —
Market value ($ mil.): —

TEAM INDUSTRIES INC.

It takes a team TEAM Industries to make the drivetrains that and other vehicles parts. The Ricke family owned company designs tests manufacturers and assembles powertrain transmissions drivetrains gear sets and chassis components for snowmobile all-terrain vehicle lawn mowers and other vehicles through partnerships with CNH Ford Honda Ingersoll-Rand Kawasaki Textron Yamaha and other OEMs. TEAM maintains half a dozen facilities throughout Minnesota and North Carolina; its manufacturing capabilities run from ductile iron and shaft machining to aluminum die-casting and gear/spline making. The company also offers engineering R&D and testing services.

Geographic Reach

TEAM operates six manufacturing facilities five in Minnesota (Audubon Bagley Cambridge Detroit Lakes and Park Rapids) and one in North Carolina (Andrews) with more than 850000 sq. ft. of total manufacturing space.

Operations

The company sells its products through six locations: TEAM Andrews acts as its precision machining gear manufacturing and metallurgical lab; TEAM Audubon specializes in gear cutting and heat treating; TEAM Bagley is its corporate headquarters; TEAM Detroit Lakes has expertise in aluminum die casting; TEAM Park Rapids works with CNC (computer numerical control) machining and loctite (a brand of adhesives) impregnation casting; and Motek-TEAM Industries is another metallurgical lab with a focus on induction hardening.

Ownership

TEAM is owned by its founding family the Rickes.

Company Background

The company was established in 1967 as Motek Engineering and Manufacturing by Don and Bea Ricke.

EXECUTIVES

President and CEO, David Ricke

LOCATIONS

HQ: TEAM INDUSTRIES INC.
105 PARK AVE NW, BAGLEY, MN 56621-9558
Phone: 218-694-3550
Web: WWW.TEAM-IND.COM

PRODUCTS/OPERATIONS

Selected Products

Axle assemblies and housings (spiral straight bevel or hypoid gearing)
Continuously variable transmissions (10-200 horsepower & up to 10000 rpm)
Differentials (with a variety of traction control mechanisms)
Gear sets
Transaxles (for a variety of electric or gas powered vehicles)
Transmissions and gear boxes (using parallel axis gears crossed axis gears worm sets planetary)
Wet brake assemblies

Selected Market Applications

Agricultural
All-terrain vehicles
Alternative on-road vehicles
Automotive
Golf carts
Lawn & garden
Marine
Motorcycles
Off-highway construction & others
Personal watercraft
Snowmobiles
Turf care
Utility vehicles

COMPETITORS

American Axle & Manufacturing
Arctic Cat
BorgWarner
Dana Holding
Federal-Mogul
GKN
Lippert Components
Magna International
Meritor
Polaris Industries
Visteon

HISTORICAL FINANCIALS

Company Type: Private

Income Statement FYE: September 29

	REVENUE ($ mil.)	NET INCOME ($ mil.)	NET PROFIT MARGIN	EMPLOYEES
09/12	288	25	8.8%	1,100
09/11	251	22	9.1%	—
09/10	193	10	5.2%	—
09/09	165	(8)	—	—
Annual Growth	20.5%	—	—	—

2012 Year-End Financials

Debt ratio: —
Return on equity: 8.80%
Cash ($ mil.): 10
Current ratio: 0.90
Long-term debt ($ mil.): —
Dividends
Yield: —
Payout: —
Market value ($ mil.): —

TEAMSTER BENEFIT TRUST

LOCATIONS

HQ: TEAMSTER BENEFIT TRUST
39420 LIBERTY ST STE 260, FREMONT, CA 945382297
Phone: 5107964676
Web: WWW.TEAMSTERSBENEFITTRUST.COM

HISTORICAL FINANCIALS

Company Type: Private

Income Statement FYE: September 30

	REVENUE ($ mil.)	NET INCOME ($ mil.)	NET PROFIT MARGIN	EMPLOYEES
09/10	219	(0)	—	3
09/09	223	10	4.7%	—
Annual Growth	(1.5%)	—	—	—

2010 Year-End Financials

Debt ratio: —
Return on equity: (-0.20%)
Cash ($ mil.): 1
Current ratio: 0.60
Long-term debt ($ mil.): —
Dividends
Yield: —
Payout: —
Market value ($ mil.): —

TEKSYSTEMS INC.

TEKsystems a subsidiary of staffing giant Allegis provides IT consulting and staffing services from locations in North America and Europe. Considered one of the nation's largest IT staffing firms the company places more than 70000 technical professionals each week who work in a variety of fields including biotechnology telecommunications and construction and engineering. TEKsystems has some 90 offices serving more than 5500 clients. In addition the company runs the thingamajob.com website which is an online job board for technical staff. Spinning off of fellow Allegis unit Aerotek TEKsystems was formed in 1994 to focus on the IT needs of clients.

Like all players in the staffing industry TEKsystems and its parent were affected by the negative effects stemming from the 2008 and 2009 recession. Bitten by the decline in demand for workers for some of its key industries –banking and finance accounting human resources and sales and marketing among others –Allegis cut 10% of its workforce in 2009.

EXECUTIVES

President, Keith Bozeman
CFO, Jay Alvather
VP Global Services and National Sales, Greg DeLuca
VP Organizational Development, Matt Hannigan
VP, Garrett Haycock
Director of Business Operations, Andy Lovelace
Director of Business Operations, Chris Decker
Director of Business Operations, Chris Thune
Director of Business Operations, Mike Greenstreet
Director of Business Operations, Shawn Reynolds

LOCATIONS

HQ: TEKSYSTEMS INC.
7437 RACE RD, HANOVER, MD 21076-1112
Phone: 410-579-3000
Web: WWW.TEKSYSTEMS.COM

PRODUCTS/OPERATIONS

Selected Services

Component services
Staffing services
Team services
Workforce management services

Selected Markets Served

Communications
Information technology
Financial services
Government

COMPETITORS

Acro Service
Adecco
CDI
CorSource Technology Group
Info Technologies
Kelly Services
ManpowerGroup
Prosum
Robert Half
SFN Group

HISTORICAL FINANCIALS

Company Type: Private

Income Statement FYE: December 31

	REVENUE ($ mil.)	NET INCOME ($ mil.)	NET PROFIT MARGIN	EMPLOYEES
12/12	3,319	328	9.9%	2,900
12/11	2,987	195	6.5%	—
12/09	2,632	186	7.1%	—
12/09	2,242	219	9.8%	—
Annual Growth	14.0%	14.4%	—	—

2012 Year-End Financials

Debt ratio: ——
Return on equity: 9.90%
Cash ($ mil.): 24
Current ratio: 2.90
Long-term debt ($ mil.): —
Dividends
Yield: —
Payout: —
Market value ($ mil.): —

TEMPLE UNIVERSITY HEALTH SYSTEM INC.

EXECUTIVES

VP and COO, Robert E. Pezzoli
VP Human Resources, Robert Birnbrauer
VP and CFO, Robert H. Lux
VP and CIO, Arthur Papacostas
VP Communications and External Affairs, David Newell
CEO and Executive Director Jeanes Hospital, Linda Grass
CEO and Executive Director Northeastern Hospital, John Buckley
Executive Director Temple University Hospital - Episcopal Campus, Kathleen Barron
CEO Temple Physicians, Eric Mankin
Director Public Relations, Rebecca Harmon
Chief Counsel, Beth Koob
Manager Internal Communications, Steve Bates
Coordinator Public Relations, Thomas Mitchell
VP and Chief Medical Officer, Calvin B. Johnson

LOCATIONS

HQ: TEMPLE UNIVERSITY HEALTH SYSTEM INC.
2450 W HUNTING PARK AVE, PHILADELPHIA, PA 191291302
Phone: 2157070900
Web: WWW.TEMPLE.EDU

PRODUCTS/OPERATIONS

Selected Facilities

Esther Boyer Pavilion (outpatient pediatric care)
Jeanes Hospital
Temple University Hospital
Temple University Hospital (TUH) Episcopal Campus

COMPETITORS

Albert Einstein Healthcare Network
Aria Health
Children' s Hospital of Philadelphia
Community Health Systems
Crozer-Keystone Health System
Doylestown Hospital
Jefferson Health System
Mercy Health System
North Philadelphia Health System
Northwestern Human Services
Our Lady of Lourdes Medical Center
Pennsylvania Hospital
The Magee Memorial Hospital for Convalescents
Thomas Jefferson University Hospital
University of Pennsylvania Health System

HISTORICAL FINANCIALS

Company Type: Private

Income Statement FYE: June 30

	REVENUE ($ mil.)	NET INCOME ($ mil.)	NET PROFIT MARGIN	EMPLOYEES
06/13	1,355	107	7.9%	7,573
06/12	1,004	(48)	—	—
06/11	994	45	4.6%	—
06/09	0	0	—	—
Annual Growth	888.5%	—	—	—

2013 Year-End Financials

Debt ratio: ——
Return on equity: 7.90%
Cash ($ mil.): 110
Current ratio: 1.10
Long-term debt ($ mil.): —
Dividends
Yield: —
Payout: —
Market value ($ mil.): —

TEMPLE UNIVERSITY-OF THE COMMONWEALTH SYSTEM OF HIGHER EDUCATION

Where better to worship a good education than at Temple University? Part of Pennsylvania's Commonwealth System of Higher Education Temple has nine different campuses in the Philadelphia area as well as in Tokyo and Rome and educational programs in China Greece France Israel and the UK. More than 36000 students are enrolled in Temple's 320 academic programs. Temple's Health Sciences Center includes Temple University Hospital and schools that teach medicine and dentistry. The system has a student-teacher ratio of about 15:1. Dr. Russell Conwell founded Temple University in 1884; it was incorporated as Temple University in 1907.

Geographic Reach

Temple Univeristy operates nine distinct campuses. Seven are in and around Philadelphia. Farther afield Temple has campuses in Tokyo and Rome.

Operations

Temple's campus in suburban Ambler Pennsylvania offers programs in community and regional planning horticulture and landscape architecture. Together all of its campuses offer a combined total of about 140 bachelor's 125 master's 60 doctoral and nearly 10 professional degrees. Students can obtain professional degrees in dentistry law medicine pharmacy and podiatric medicine among others.

Financial Performance

Temple's revenue increased 2% in 2012 vs. 2011 driven by increasing tuition fees and patient care activities at the Temple's Health Sciences Center. Net income fell by 58% over the same period due to higher educational and general expenses among other factors.

EXECUTIVES

Chairman, Patrick J. (Pat) O'Connor
President, Ann Weaver Hart, age 66
VP Computing Financial Services and CIO, Timothy C. O'Rourke
Associate VP and Controller, Frank P. Annunziato
Director Purchasing, Theresa (Terry) Burt
SVP University Counsel and Secretary, George E. Moore
SVP Institutional Advancement, David Unruh
SVP Government Community and Public Affairs, Kenneth (Ken) Lawrence Jr.
SEVP Health Affairs; Dean and CEO School of Medicine, Larry R. Kaiser
VP Student Affairs, Theresa A. Powell
VP Human Resources, Deborah Hartnett
Director Communications, Ray Betzner
Vice Chair, Anthony J. Scirica
President, Richard M. (Dick) Englert
EVP Financial Affairs CFO and Treasurer, Anthony Wagner
Associate VP Human Resources, Harry A. Young
Senior Vice Provost Research and Graduate Education, Kenneth (Ken) Blank
Senior Vice Provost Enrollment Management, William N. Black
Senior Vice Provost International Affairs and Dean College of Science and Technology, Hai-Lung Dai
Senior Vice Provost Undergraduate Studies, Peter Jones
Vice Provost Academic Affairs and Assessment, Jodi Levine Laufgraben
Senior Vice Provost Faculty Development and Faculty Affairs, Diane Maleson
Vice Provost University College, Vicki Lewis McGarvey
Dean Boyer College of Music and Dance; Interim Dean Tyler School of Art; Vice Provost Arts, Robert T. Stroker
Senior Vice Provost Strategic Initiatives and Communications, Betsy Leebron Tutelman
Administrative Assistant, Bobbi Shedrick
Director - Human Resources, Joanne Zeas
Director - Human Resources, Lisa M. Stepp
President TUP T, Joseph J. Thoder
VP CFO and Treasurer, Ken Kaiser
Trustee, Jon A. Boscia, age 61
Trustee, Mitchell L. Morgan, age 59
Trustee, Joseph W. (Chip) Marshall III, age 61
President, Ann Weaver Hart, age 66
Trustee, William H. Cosby Jr.
Trustee, Frank Baldino Jr.
Trustee, Joan H. Ballots
Trustee, Leonard Barrack
Trustee, Theodore Z. Davis
Trustee, Nelson A. Diaz
Trustee, Ronald R. Donatucci
Trustee, Judith A. Felgoise
Trustee, Lewis F. Gould Jr.
Trustee, Lon R. Greenberg
Trustee, Lacy H. Hunt
Trustee, Ulrick P. Joseph
Trustee, Lewis Katz
Trustee, Adrian R. King Jr.
Trustee, Susanna E. Lachs
Trustee, Patrick V. Larkin
Trustee, Solomon C. Luo
Trustee, Scott Mazo
Trustee, Theodore A. McKee
Trustee, Christopher W. McNichol
Trustee, J. William Mills
Trustee, Daniel H. Polett
Trustee, Milton L. Rock
Trustee, Robert A. Rovner
Trustee, Jane Scaccetti
Vice Chair, Anthony J. Scirica

Trustee, Michael J. Stack III
Trustee, James S. White
Trustee, Michael P. Williams
Auditors: Deloitte&ToucheLLP

LOCATIONS

HQ: TEMPLE UNIVERSITY-OF THE COMMONWEALTH SYSTEM OF HIGHER EDUCATION
1801 N BROAD ST, PHILADELPHIA, PA 19122-6003
Phone: 215-204-1380
Web: WWW.WRTI.ORG

Selected Campuses

Philadelphia
- Ambler
- Center City
- Fort Washington
- Harrisburg
- Main
- Podiatric Medicine
  - Health Sciences Center

International
- Japan
- Rome Italy

HISTORICAL FINANCIALS

Company Type: Private

Income Statement

FYE: June 30

	REVENUE ($ mil.)	NET INCOME ($ mil.)	NET PROFIT MARGIN	EMPLOYEES
06/12	2,254	(37)	—	9,061
06/08	2,034	228	11.2%	—
06/07	1,902	118	6.2%	—
06/06	1,837	(1)	—	—
Annual Growth	3.5%	—	—	—

2012 Year-End Financials

Debt ratio: —
Return on equity: (-1.70%)
Cash ($ mil.): 237
Current ratio: 0.40
Long-term debt ($ mil.): —
Dividends
Yield: —
Payout: —
Market value ($ mil.): —

TENASKA FRONTIER PARTNERS LTD

LOCATIONS

HQ: TENASKA FRONTIER PARTNERS LTD
1044 N 115TH ST STE 400, OMAHA, NE 681544410
Phone: 4026919500
Web: WWW.TENASKA.COM

HISTORICAL FINANCIALS

Company Type: Private

Income Statement

FYE: December 31

	REVENUE ($ mil.)	NET INCOME ($ mil.)	NET PROFIT MARGIN	EMPLOYEES
12/11	219	0	—	28
12/10	198	0	—	—
12/08	411	0	—	—
12/07	332	0	—	—
Annual Growth	(9.9%)	—	—	—

2011 Year-End Financials

Debt ratio: —
Return on equity: —
Cash ($ mil.): 13
Current ratio: 0.70
Long-term debt ($ mil.): —
Dividends
Yield: —
Payout: —
Market value ($ mil.): —

TERRACON CONSULTANTS INC.

Employee-owned Terracon Consultants provides geotechnical environmental construction material evaluation pavement engineering and construction management and facilities engineering services. One of the nation's top design firms the company serves the agriculture energy telecommunications commercial development and transportation sectors as well as government clients. Founded in Iowa in 1965 Terracon began as a joint venture between Shive Hall and Hattery (civil consulting) Soil Testing Services (geotechnical testing) and Gerald Olson P.E. (the company's founder and a project engineer). The company now has more than 130 offices in some 40 states.

Geographic Reach

Kansas-based Terracon has operations throughout the US Canada Cuba and Mexico.

Strategy

Acquisitive Terracon is expanding its menu of services and geographic footprint via acquisitons of regional companies across the US.

Mergers and Acquisitions

Terracon has expanded its geotechnical environmental engineering and testing capabilities with a string of recent purchases. In 2012 it acquired California-based Earthtec Inc. a provider of geotechnical environmental special inspection and other services to clients in Northern California. Also in 2012 it purchased Utah-based IHI Environmental a provider of industrial hygiene occupational safety and environmental consulting services to public and private sector clients across the western US. Previously Terracon bought Colorado firm Geotechnical Engineering Group boosting its presence in the West; and Stafford Consulting Engineers a building envelope system specialist with a presence in the Southeast. Also that year Terracon acquired Dressler Consulting Engineers a building forensics engineering firm based in Kansas and Nodarse & Associates a Florida-based environmental geotechnical and construction materials engineering firm.

Ownership

Terracon is owned by its employees. The firm was ranked 51st on the Employee Ownership 100 the list of the top 100 largest majority employee-owned companies in the US in 2012.

EXECUTIVES

President and CEO, David Gaboury
CFO, Roger R. Herting
Senior Vice President, Kevin Langwell
Principal and Office Manager Lincoln Nebraska, Brad Levich
Principal and Office Manager Conroe Texas, Mark McClintock
Principal and Marketing and Communications Manager Olathe Kansas, Vanessa Zambo
EVP and Director, Dan Israel
Office Manager, Cale Wilson
executive Vice President Chief Administrative Officer for Terracon, Gayle Packer

LOCATIONS

HQ: TERRACON CONSULTANTS INC.
18001 W 106TH ST STE 300, OLATHE, KS 66061-6447
Phone: 913-599-6886
Web: WWW.TERRACON.COM

PRODUCTS/OPERATIONS

Selected Services

Construction Materials
- Construction quality control and quality assurance programs
- Deep foundation nondestructive testing
- Design and review of concrete grout and asphaltic concrete mixes
- Field and lab testing and analysis
- Forensic investigation and evaluation
- On-site observation and monitoring
- Special inspections

Geotechnical
- Subsurface exploration and testing
- Foundation analysis and design
- Soil stabilization
- Groundwater control
- Pavement design

Environmental
- Site assessment
- Industrial hygiene and occupational safety
- Regulatory compliance
- Solid waste planning and design

Construction Materials
- Quality control
- Testing
- Design and review of concrete
- Pavement engineering and construction management

Facilities
- Roof/waterproofing consulting
- Foundation/structural consulting
- Life cycle cost analysis
- Peer reviews
- Seismic risk assessments
- Construction administration

COMPETITORS

AECOM
Fluor
HNTB Companies
Jacobs Engineering
KBR
URS

HISTORICAL FINANCIALS

Company Type: Private

Income Statement

FYE: December 31

	REVENUE ($ mil.)	NET INCOME ($ mil.)	NET PROFIT MARGIN	EMPLOYEES
12/12	380	10	2.7%	2,753
12/11	353	8	2.5%	—
12/10	319	6	2.0%	—
12/09	294	7	2.4%	—
Annual Growth	8.9%	14.0%	—	—

2012 Year-End Financials

Debt ratio: —
Return on equity: 2.70%
Cash ($ mil.): 5
Current ratio: 1.00
Long-term debt ($ mil.): —
Dividends
Yield: —
Payout: —
Market value ($ mil.): —

TEXAS A & M RESEARCH FOUNDATION INC

Established in 1944 the Texas A&M Research Foundation provides administrative services and support for scientific and technical research primarily within The Texas A&M University System. Its Program Development Department helps university faculty locate and approach potential sponsors and funding opportunities.The organization also provides accounting and financing support as well as grant and contract negotiations. The foundation supports a number of projects and initiatives from the Center for Advancement and Study of Early Texas Art to vaccine research at the university system's college of medicine. It is a private not-for-profit organization.

EXECUTIVES

SVP and CFO, Linda F. Woodman, age 66
Assistant VP Management Information Systems, Tye Rougas
Assistant VP Human Resources and Risk Management, Adam T. Davidson
Associate VP General Counsel and Corporate Secretary, Steve R. Garrett
Interim President CEO COO and VP, Leo Paterra
Associate VP Pre Award, Jane Zuber
Associate VP IODP, Lynne M. Schulze
Associate VP IODP, Bill Lancaster
Chairman, H. Jarrell Gibbs

LOCATIONS

HQ: TEXAS A & M RESEARCH FOUNDATION INC
400 HARVEY MTCHL PKWY 3, COLLEGE STATION, TX 77845-4375
Phone: 979-845-8600
Web: WWW.IODP.TAMU.EDU

HISTORICAL FINANCIALS

Company Type: Private

Income Statement FYE: August 31

	REVENUE ($ mil.)	NET INCOME ($ mil.)	NET PROFIT MARGIN	EMPLOYEES
08/12	195	(1)	—	483
08/11	202	3	1.6%	—
08/09	194	2	1.5%	—
08/09	192	1	0.8%	—
Annual Growth	0.5%	—	—	—

2012 Year-End Financials

Debt ratio: —
Return on equity: (-1.00%)
Cash ($ mil.): 26
Current ratio: 1.60
Long-term debt ($ mil.): —
Dividends
Yield: —
Payout: —
Market value ($ mil.): —

TEXAS CHILDREN'S HOSPITAL

Parents in the Lone Star State can rest easy knowing Texas Children's Hospital has the doctors and facilities to diagnose and treat sick children. The hospital is the flagship facility of Texas Children's Hospital Integrated Delivery System. Founded in 1954 the hospital provides full-service medical care for children conducts extensive research and trains pediatric medical professionals. The Houston-area hospital part of the Texas Medical Center complex has clinical facilities for every ailment ranging from psychological troubles to surgery and physical rehabilitation as well as specialized heart cancer and neurological care. It is the primary pediatric training facility for the Baylor College of Medicine.

Operations

Texas Children's Hospital's staff includes more than 1500 primary physicians and other medical specialists as well as some 6000 nurses. The hospital has satellite facilities in and around Houston and it operates the Texas Children's Pediatric Associates primary care network of more than 150 physicians. The company also runs the Texas Children's Health Plan which offers Medicaid and Texas CHIP (Children's Health Insurance Plan) programs.

Texas Children's International coordinates care for sick children who come to Texas Children's Hospital from abroad. The international segment also sends out medical teams to care for critically ill children throughout Latin America the Middle East Europe Africa and Asia. For instance it has established a number of AIDS clinics in African countries.

Financial Analysis

Though most of its revenues come from patient care fees Texas Children's Hospital relies heavily on donations and federal funding to supplement its operations. For instance the hospital and Baylor College of Medicine represent one of the most active and well-funded pediatric research programs in the US with more than 800 basic research and clinical studies backed by $100 million in annual grants.

Strategy

In 2010 the hospital completed a $1.5 billion expansion effort. Called Vision 2010 the expansion extended neurological maternity and research capacity as well as upgraded equipment. As a result the hospital opened the Duncan Neurological Research Institute dedicated to researching brain disorders. The expansion program also included the building of a new suburban community hospital Texas Children's Hospital West Campus which opened in 2011.

EXECUTIVES

President and CEO, Mark A. Wallace, age 61
Physician-in-Chief, Mark W. Kline
Obstetrician/Gynecologist-in-Chief, Dale Brown
Surgeon-in-Chief, Charles D. Fraser
CFO, Benjamin (Ben) Melson
Media Contact, Carol Wittman
Media Contact, Christy Brunton
Obstetrician/Gynecologist-in-Chief, Michael A. Belfort

LOCATIONS

HQ: TEXAS CHILDREN' S HOSPITAL
6621 FANNIN ST, HOUSTON, TX 77030-2399
Phone: 832-824-1000
Web: WWW.BCM.EDU

COMPETITORS

Baylor Health
CHRISTUS Health
Children' s Hospital of Philadelphia
Children' s Medical Center of Dallas
Cook Children' s Health Care System
Dell Children' s Medical Center
Mayo Clinic
Memorial Hermann Healthcare
Methodist Hospital System
Shriners Hospitals For Children
St. Jude Children' s Research Hospital
St. Luke' s Episcopal Hospital
Tenet Healthcare

HISTORICAL FINANCIALS

Company Type: Private

Income Statement FYE: September 30

	REVENUE ($ mil.)	NET INCOME ($ mil.)	NET PROFIT MARGIN	EMPLOYEES
09/09	1,001	43	4.3%	6,000
09/06*	768	103	13.5%	—
12/05	856	168	19.7%	—
09/05	898	72	8.1%	—
Annual Growth	2.7%	(12.1%)	—	—

*Fiscal year change

2009 Year-End Financials

Debt ratio: —
Return on equity: 4.30%
Cash ($ mil.): 37
Current ratio: 0.10
Long-term debt ($ mil.): —
Dividends
Yield: —
Payout: —
Market value ($ mil.): —

TEXAS CHRISTIAN UNIVERSITY INC

Home of the Horned Frogs (the school mascot) Texas Christian University (TCU) offers bachelor's master's and doctorate degrees in more than 200 fields of study. More than 10000 undergraduate and graduate students attend the university's nine colleges and schools. TCU has about 550 full-time faculty members and a student-to-faculty ratio of 13:1. Brothers Addison and Randolph Clark established the school in 1873 as Addran Male and Female College (the school changed its name to Texas Christian University in 1902). TCU is affiliated with the Disciples of Christ a Protestant denomination.

Geographic Reach

TCU's campus takes up about 280 acres about five miles from downtown Fort Worth.

Operations

The TCU academic programs are organized under nine schools in fields including liberal arts communication education fine arts science and engineering nursing and health and business.

Tuition fees room and board cost about $45000 per year.

Strategy

TCU is investing in facility upgrades and enhancement efforts as part of its strategic plan entitled Academy of Tomorrow. Over the past few years the school has invested in academic administrative recreational and residence facilities. In 2012 it began construction on a new commons building on the eastern end of its campus. TCU also expands its academic programs; in 2013 it added new master's degrees in social work and criminal justice and criminology.

EXECUTIVES

Chancellor, Victor J. Boschini Jr.
Vice Chancellor Government Affairs, Larry D. Lauer
Vice Chancellor Student Affairs, Kathy Cavins-Tull
Vice Chancellor Academic Affairs and Provost, R. Nowell Donovan
Vice Chancellor Finance and Administration, Brian G. Gutierrez
Manager Human Resources and Benefits Coordinator, Tracy Thompson
Chief Investment Officer, James R. Hille
Vice Chancellor University Advancement, Donald J. Whelan Jr.
Dean Mary Couts Burnett Library, June Koelker
CTO, Bryan Lucas
Chief of Staff, Karen Baker
Dean Harris College of Nursing and Health Sciences, Paulette Burns
Dean AddRan College of Liberal Arts, F. Andrew Schoolmaster
Dean Neeley School of Business, O. Homer Erekson
Dean College of Communication, David Whillock
Dean College of Fine Arts, Scott A. Sullivan
Vice Chancellor Marketing and Communication, Tracy Syler-Jones
Chairman, Clarence Scharbauer III
Vice Chairman, Mark L. Johnson
Dean College of Science and Engineering, Philip S. Hartman
Dean Brite Divinity School, Joretta Marshall

LOCATIONS

HQ: TEXAS CHRISTIAN UNIVERSITY INC
2800 S UNIVERSITY DR, FORT WORTH, TX 76129-0002
Phone: 817-257-7000
Web: WWW.TCU.EDU

PRODUCTS/OPERATIONS

Selected Colleges and Schools

AddRan College of Liberal Arts
College of Communication
College of Education
College of Fine Arts
College of Science and Engineering
Harris College of Nursing and Health Sciences
John V. Roach Honors College
Neeley School of Business
Relationship with Brite Divinity School

HISTORICAL FINANCIALS

Company Type: Private

Income Statement FYE: May 31

	REVENUE ($ mil.)	NET INCOME ($ mil.)	NET PROFIT MARGIN	EMPLOYEES
05/12	441	(4)	—	3,400
05/09	263	0	—	—
05/05	216	8	3.8%	—
Annual Growth	10.7%	—	—	—

2012 Year-End Financials

Debt ratio: —
Return on equity: (-0.90%)
Cash ($ mil.): 50
Current ratio: —
Long-term debt ($ mil.): —
Dividends
Yield: —
Payout: —
Market value ($ mil.): —

TEXAS GUARANTEED STUDENT LOAN CORPORATION

TG may sound like a college fraternity but it's more about tuition and books than togas and beer. Texas Guaranteed Student Loan Corporation commonly known as TG was formed by the Texas legislature in 1979 to administer the Federal Family Education Loan Program (FFELP) in the Lone Star State. However the FFELP was eliminated in 2010 and private borrowers can no longer originate government-sponsored student loans which are now provided exclusively through the US Department of Education. TG continues to service and provide support for the approximately $26 billion worth of loans in its existing portfolio. TG is a public not-for-profit corporation that receives no state funding.

Financial Performance

TG is comprised of two funds: the Operating Fund which is the property of TG and the Federal Fund considered the property of the US government. In fiscal 2012 (ended September) TG's total revenue increased by 17% to $134.3 million versus $115.2 million in fiscal 2011. Of that revenue from the Operating Fund accounted for 88% of the total with the Federal Fund representing the rest. Total assets in fiscal 2012 were $832.1 million versus $828.6 million the prior year.

EXECUTIVES

Director Center for Financial Aid Policy in Community Colleges, Donna G. Smith
SVP Finance and Administration and CFO, James Patterson
President and CEO, Sue McMillin
SVP Information Technology, Lloyd Dodge
Assistant VP Human Resources and Organizational Development, Mary Negrete
VP Operations, Rinn Harper
VP Customer Relations, Kim Alexander
VP Collections, Phillip Cervin
VP Policy and Compliance, Carol Lindsey
Assistant VP Strategic Planning and Development, Kara Thompson
Vice Chair, Yvonne Batts
Secretary and Director, F. H. (Skip) Landis
SVP Legal and Regulatory Affairs General Counsel and Chief Ethics Officer, Deanne Varner
Assistant VP TG Ombudsman, Luanne Dodge
VP Student and Institutional Success, Jacob Fraire
Assistant VP Congressional and Legislative Relations, George Torres
VP Marketing and Product Management, John Zanot
Chair, Ivan A. Andarza
Assistant VP and Portfolio Manager, Cal Abbott
Assistant VP Corporate Services, John Sutton
Assistant VP and Controller, Mark Zarsky
Assistant VP Default Recovery Services, Susan High
Assistant VP Relationship Management and Consulting, Kevin Struckhoff
Assistant VP Customer Training and Event Management, Vickie Tanner
Assistant VP Enterprise Project Management Office, Jim Zimmerman
Assistant VP Research and Analytical Services, Jeff Webster
Assistant VP Default Prevention, Shelia Dunlap
Assistant VP Claims, Ron Stroud
Assistant VP Customer Support and Reporting, Sam Wilson
Assistant VP Program Review, Nancy Wilson
Assistant VP Compliance Administrative Operations, James Wingard
Assistant VP Enterprise Architect, Bud Loveall
Director of Financial Literacy Operations, Sharon Cabeen
Director, Dora Ann Verde
Vice Chair, Yvonne Batts
Secretary and Director, F. H. (Skip) Landis
Director, Connie S. Sitterly
Director, Phil W. Worley
Director, Michael J. Savoie
Director, Richard M. Rhodes
Director, Steven Tays
Director, Welcome W. Wilson Jr.
Auditors: KPMGLLP

LOCATIONS

HQ: TEXAS GUARANTEED STUDENT LOAN CORPORATION
301 SUNDANCE PKWY, ROUND ROCK, TX 78681-8004
Phone: 512-219-5700
Web: WWW.TGSLC.ORG

PRODUCTS/OPERATIONS

2012 Revenue

	$ mil.	% of total
Operating fund	118	88
Federal fund	15	12
Total	**134**	**100**

COMPETITORS

Brazos Higher Education Service Corp.
Nelnet
Sallie Mae

HISTORICAL FINANCIALS

Company Type: Private

Income Statement FYE: September 30

	ASSETS ($ mil.)	NET INCOME ($ mil.)	INCOME AS % OF ASSETS	EMPLOYEES
09/08	783	(64)	—	600
09/05	520	60	11.6%	—
09/04	459	60	13.2%	—
09/03	407	57	14.0%	—
Annual Growth	13.9%	—	—	—

2008 Year-End Financials

Debt ratio: —
Return on equity: (-29.10%)
Cash ($ mil.): 23
Current ratio: —
Long-term debt ($ mil.): —
Dividends
Yield: —
Payout: —
Market value ($ mil.): —

TEXAS HEALTH HARRIS METHODIST HOSPITAL FORT WORTH

Harris Methodist Fort Worth Hospital is the largest and busiest hospital in Fort Worth. It is a private not-for-profit 730-bed tertiary care hospital serving the residents of Tarrant County and nearby communities in Texas. Harris Methodist provides both inpatient and outpatient care through its main medical center and on-site health clinics. Specialized services include emergency medicine trauma care orthopedics occupational health women's health oncology and rehabilitation. Its Harris Methodist Heart Center has about 100 beds. The hospital which opened its doors in 1930 is the flagship facility of the Texas Health Resources hospitals system.

Operations

Harris Methodist also known as Texas Health Harris Methodist Hospital Fort Worth serves as a regional referral center. The hospital employs a medical staff of about 800 physicians.

Sales and Marketing

To promote its services to area residents Harris Methodist uses a range of marketing avenues including print television online radio and outdoor advertising.

Strategy

To meet the growing needs of Fort Worth area residents in 2012 Harris Methodist launched a $58 million construction project to add a new emergency care center adjacent to the medical center campus. The 75000-sq. ft. center scheduled for completion in 2014 will increase the hospital's emergency room capacity from about 60 beds to 90 beds. A sky bridge will connect the new emergency care center to the main hospital.

Mergers and Acquisitions

To further expand outpatient services in 2012 Harris Methodist acquired the Clear Fork Surgery Center (now named Texas Health Outpatient Surgery Center Fort Worth). The ambulatory surgery center is located on the Harris Methodist hospital campus and was previously operated through a venture with Symbion and a group of physicians. The center performs about 10000 procedures per year.

EXECUTIVES

VP Operations, Lillie M. Biggins

Chief Medical Officer, Joseph S. (Joe) Prosser
Chief Nursing Officer, Elaine Nelson
Director Of Radiology Services, John Tauscher
Medical Librarian, Scarlett Burchfield
Director Of Physical Therapy, Karen Mallet
Hr Director & Vp, Margaret Nolan
Medical Records Director, Turkashia Scott
Secretary, Erik Pahl

LOCATIONS

HQ: TEXAS HEALTH HARRIS METHODIST HOSPITAL FORT WORTH
1301 PENNSYLVANIA AVE, FORT WORTH, TX 76104-2122
Phone: 817-250-2000
Web: WWW.TEXASHEALTH.ORG

PRODUCTS/OPERATIONS

Selected Centers and Services

Breast Center
Breastfeeding Resource Center
Business Health Services
Cancer
Complementary or Alternative Medicine
Diabetes
Emergency Trauma Services
Executive Health Program
Fitness Center
Heart and Vascular
Gastroenterology
Home Health
Hospitalist Program
Imaging
Infertility
Mobile Health Unit
Neurosciences
Occupational Health
Orthopedics
Outpatient Physical Therapy
Respiratory
Weight Loss
Texas Health Physician Offices Saginaw
Palliative Care
Rehabilitation
Sports Medicine
Primary Stroke Center
Surgery
Texas Health Physician Offices Keller
Vascular and Interventional Radiology
Women and Infants
Wound Care

COMPETITORS

Baylor University Medical Center
Cook Children' s Health Care System
HCA
HealthSouth
JPS Health Network
Parkland Health & Hospital System
Tenet Healthcare
The Methodist Health System

HISTORICAL FINANCIALS

Company Type: Private

Income Statement FYE: December 31

	REVENUE ($ mil.)	NET INCOME ($ mil.)	NET PROFIT MARGIN	EMPLOYEES
12/11	656	44	6.7%	3,500
12/06	548	36	6.7%	—
12/05	501	56	11.3%	—
12/04	469	35	7.6%	—
Annual Growth	4.9%	3.0%	—	—

TEXAS STATE UNIVERSITY-SAN MARCOS

Texas State University-San Marcos is saddled up and ready to rope some graduates. The school has more than 34000 students pursuing degrees in about 100 undergraduate programs nearly 90 graduate programs and a dozen doctoral programs. Comprising eight colleges as well as a graduate school Texas State is the largest school in the Texas State University system which includes Angelo State University Lamar University Sam Houston State University and Sul Ross State University. It also offers bachelor's and graduate-level courses at a campus in Round Rock.

Geographic Reach

Texas State's main campus in the Central Texas community of San Marcos consists of some 460 acres. The university also operates some 5000 acres of recreational and instruction properties in the area.

Strategy

As Texas State is ranked among the top US colleges for awarding degrees to bachelor's degrees to Hispanic students the university targets a portion of its marketing efforts towards minority students. About 35% of its student body is composed of ethnic minorities. Texas State also enrolls student through international efforts.

To accommodate its growing student base Texas State has been expanding its campus facilities. For instance it opened a new undergraduate academic center in 2012.

Company Background

The former Southwest Texas State University (the name was changed in 2003) was originally a teacher's college founded by the state legislature in 1903.

EXECUTIVES

VP Finance and Support Services, William A. (Bill) Nance
President, Denise M. Trauth
VP Student Affairs, Joanne Smith
Treasurer, Valarie Van Vlack
Provost and VP Academic Affairs, Gene Bourgeois
VP University Advancement, Barbara Breier
Associate Vice President Technology Resources T, Mark Hughes
Associate Vice President University Library, Joan Heath
Vice President for Information Technology, Don Volz
Vice President Information Technology, Van Wyatt
Associate Vice President Instructional Technologies Support T, Milt Nielsen

LOCATIONS

HQ: TEXAS STATE UNIVERSITY-SAN MARCOS
601 UNIVERSITY DR, SAN MARCOS, TX 78666-4684
Phone: 512-245-2111
Web: WWW.TXSTATE.EDU

PRODUCTS/OPERATIONS

Schools and Colleges
College of Applied Arts
College of Education
College of Fine Arts and Communicat
College of Health Profession
College of Liberal Arts
College of Science
The Graduate College
McCoy College of Business Administra
University College (general studies)

HISTORICAL FINANCIALS

Company Type: Private

Income Statement FYE: August 31

	REVENUE ($ mil.)	NET INCOME ($ mil.)	NET PROFIT MARGIN	EMPLOYEES
08/12	330	19	5.8%	3,156
08/11	313	95	30.5%	—
08/09	279	66	23.7%	—
08/09	279	66	23.7%	—
Annual Growth	5.7%	(33.9%)	—	—

2012 Year-End Financials

Debt ratio: —
Return on equity: 5.80%
Cash ($ mil.): 243
Current ratio: 1.30
Long-term debt ($ mil.): —
Dividends
Yield: —
Payout: —
Market value ($ mil.): —

THE AEROSPACE CORPORATION

EXECUTIVES

VP CFO and Treasurer, Ellen M. Beatty
President CEO and Trustee, Wanda M. Austin
Vice President Space Launch Operations, Ray F. Johnson
SVP Engineering and Technology Group, Rami R. Razouk
SVP Operations and Support Group, Jerry M. (Mike) Drennan
Principal Director Strategic Planning, M. H. Goodman
VP Civil and Commercial Operations, Gary P. Pulliam
SVP Systems Planning Engineering and Quality, Rand H. Fisher
Senior Vice President Public Policy and Corporate Affairs, Michael Montelongo, age 58
SVP Space Systems Group, David J. Gorney
Chairman, Peter B. Teets
VP and CIO, William C. (Willie) Krenz
SVP National Systems Group, Manuel De Ponte
Vice President National Systems Group, Bernard W. Chau
VP Strategic Space Operations, Catherine J. Steele
Senior Vice President General Counsel Secretary, Malissia R. Clinton
Vice President Technology and Laboratory Operations, Sherrie L. Zacharius
Principal Director Corporate Communications Directorate, S. K. Steele
Acting Principal Director Finance Directorate Assistant CFO and Assistant Treasurer, E. M. Beatty
Vice Chairman, Gen. Thomas S. Moorman Jr.
General Manager MILSATCOM Division, W. H. Goodman
Director External Communications, Pamela V. (Pam) Keeton
Vice President Space Program Operations, Wayne H. Goodman
Vice President Program Assessments, Howard J. (Mitch) Mitchell
Executive Vice President of Operations, Tina W. Jonas
Vice President Civil and Commercial Operations, Randy Kendall
Vice President General Manager of the Space Systems Division, David M. DiCarlo
President ? Achievement Award was, Patrick Mak

Trustee, Rufus A. Fulton Jr., age 72
Trustee, Vincent Vitto, age 73
Trustee, Gen. Howell M. Estes III
Trustee, Barbara M. Barrett, age 62
Trustee, Robert S. (Bob) Walker
President CEO and Trustee, Wanda M. Austin
Trustee, Michael Montelongo, age 58
Trustee, Nelson F. Gibbs
Trustee, M. Elisabeth Pate-Cornell
Trustee, Sally K. Ride
Trustee, K. Anne Street
Trustee, John E. McLaughlin
Trustee, Jeffrey H. Smith
Vice Chairman, Gen. Thomas S. Moorman Jr.
Auditors: Deloitte&ToucheLLP

LOCATIONS

HQ: THE AEROSPACE CORPORATION
2310 E EL SEGUNDO BLVD, EL SEGUNDO, CA 902454609
Phone: 3103365000
Web: WWW.AEROSPACE.ORG

COMPETITORS

AKKA Technologies
QinetiQ
Orbital Research

HISTORICAL FINANCIALS

Company Type: Private

Income Statement FYE: September 30

	REVENUE ($ mil.)	NET INCOME ($ mil.)	NET PROFIT MARGIN	EMPLOYEES
09/14	881	5	0.6%	3,920
09/13	868	0	0.0%	—
09/12	903	4	0.5%	—
09/11	939	0	—	—
Annual Growth	(2.1%)	—	—	—

2014 Year-End Financials

Debt ratio: —
Return on equity: 0.60%
Cash ($ mil.): 14
Current ratio: 0.20
Long-term debt ($ mil.): —
Dividends
Yield: —
Payout: —
Market value ($ mil.): —

THE AMALGAMATED SUGAR COMPANY LLC

LOCATIONS

HQ: THE AMALGAMATED SUGAR COMPANY LLC
1951 S SATURN WAY STE 100, BOISE, ID 837092924
Phone: 2086582243
Web: WWW.AMALGAMATEDSUGAR.COM

PRODUCTS/OPERATIONS

Selected Products

Bakers' special sugar
Brown sugar
Dark brown sugar
Extra-fine granulated sugar
Fine granulated sugar
Gel gran granulated sugar
Industrial coarse sugar
Powdered sugar 10x and 12x
Sugar packets
Sugar standards
Type 50 medium invert sugar
Type O liquid sucrose (66.5 brix)
Type O liquid sucrose (67.5 brix)

COMPETITORS

Alico Inc.
American Crystal Sugar
Associated British Foods
C&H Sugar
Cosun
Cumberland Packing
Eurosugar
Florida Crystals
Imperial Sugar
Ingredion
M. A. Patout
Merisant
Michigan Sugar Company
Minn-Dak Co-op
Nippon Beet Sugar
Nordzucker
NutraSweet
SMBSC
Sterling Sugars
Sudzucker
Sugar Cane Growers Cooperative of Florida
U.S. Sugar
Western Sugar Cooperative

HISTORICAL FINANCIALS

Company Type: Private

Income Statement FYE: December 31

	REVENUE ($ mil.)	NET INCOME ($ mil.)	NET PROFIT MARGIN	EMPLOYEES
12/13	953	62	6.6%	1,500
12/12	907	14	1.6%	—
12/11	886	46	5.3%	—
12/10	841	0	—	—
Annual Growth	4.2%	—	—	—

2013 Year-End Financials

Debt ratio: —
Return on equity: 6.60%
Cash ($ mil.): 1
Current ratio: 0.10
Long-term debt ($ mil.): —
Dividends
Yield: —
Payout: —
Market value ($ mil.): —

THE ASSOCIATED PRESS

HISTORY

The Associated Press traces its roots to 1846 when New York Sun publisher Moses Yale Beach agreed to share news arriving by telegraph about the Mexican-American War with four other New York newspapers. The cooperative news gathering effort was later established as the AP which began selling wire reports to other papers and started creating regional associations. Adapting to changing technologies and public interests AP began covering sports financial and public interest stories in the 1920s and was selling news reports to radio stations in the 1940s. Advancements during WWII included using transatlantic cable and radio-teletype circuits to deliver news and photos.

In the late 1960s AP and Dow Jones introduced services to improve business and financial reporting. AP improved photo delivery reception and storage in the 1970s with the advent of Laserphoto and the Electronic Darkroom. It began transmitting news by satellite and offering color photographs to newspapers in the 1980s. In 1985 Louis Boccardi took over the job as president and CEO of AP.

AP adjusted to the media-heavy culture of the 1990s by launching the APTV international news video service and the All News Radio network in 1994. It then moved onto the Internet with The WIRE in 1996 and began offering online access to its Photo Archive in 1997. It bought Worldwide Television News in 1998 combining it with APTV to form AP Television News Limited (APTN). The following year it purchased the radio news contracts of UPI after the rival organization announced it was getting out of broadcast news.

In 2000 AP created an Internet division AP Digital to focus on marketing news to online providers. The cooperative continued its Internet focus the following year launching AP Online en Espa?ol (news for Spanish-language websites) and AP Entertainment Online (multimedia entertainment news for websites). Also that year AP bought the Newspaper Industry Communication Center from the Newspaper Association of America.

In 2002 the company launched an expanded editorial partnership with Dow Jones Newswires increasing the amount of financial news distributed on AP wires. Later that year it acquired Capitolwire a provider of state government news. Boccardi stepped down as CEO in 2003 handing the reins to former USA TODAY publisher Tom Curley.

AP relocated in 2004 from Rockefeller Plaza (its home for 65 years) to a new headquarters on the west side of Manhattan that features a 105000-sq.-ft. newsroom and serves as a central hub of digital news streams.

The organization moved to strengthen its sports information coverage in 2005 merging its AP MegaSports operation with News Corporation's STATS Inc. to form STATS LLC a 50-50 joint venture that provides sports-related information content and statistical analysis.

The following year AP launched The Online Video Network (OVN) service to provide news video to AP member and customer websites. The co-op responded to the harsh economy by cutting costs in 2008 with consolidation of its print broadcast and digital sales and marketing units. It continued its cost-cutting efforts in 2009 when it cut some 90 jobs instituted a hiring freeze and bought out about 100 employees.

EXECUTIVES

President and CEO, Thomas (Tom) Curley, age 65
Chairman, Mary E. Junck, age 66
President & CEO, Gary B. Pruitt, age 56
SVP Business Development and Partner Relations Europe Middle East Africa and Asia, Daisy Veerasingham
SVP and Executive Editor, Kathleen Carroll
Manager Media Relations, Jack Stokes
Director International News, Sandy MacIntyre
VP and Director Human Resources, Jessica Bruce, age 48
SVP Digital Strategy and Products, James M. (Jim) Kennedy
VP and Director Marketing and Corporate Communications, Ellen Hale
Senior Managing Editor US News, Michael (Mike) Oreskes, age 59
Vice Chairman, Jon K. Rust
SVP and CIO, Lorraine Cichowski
SVP Sales for the Americas, Sue A. Cross, age 53
Senior Managing Director International News, John Daniszewski, age 60
Director US Broadcast News, Kevin Roach
General Manager Mobile and Emerging Products AP Digital, Jeff Litvack
VP U.S. Newspaper Market, Kate Lee Butler
Manager Social Networks and News Engagement, Lauren McCullough
Director Media Relations, Paul Colford
VP Business Operations, Nigel Baker
Manager Stylebook, Colleen Newvine
Deputy Standards Editor, David Minthorn
Standards Editor, Thomas Kent
Editor South Region, Lisa Marie Pane
Editor Asia Pacific, Brian Carovillano

News Editor Central Region, David Scott, age 37
News Editor West Region, Traci Carl, age 41
Director East-Central Europe, Ian Phillips, age 43
SVP and CFO, Ken Dale
VP AP Images, Fernando Ferre
Director, Dunia A. Shive, age 53
Director, Samuel (Sam) Zell, age 72
President and CEO News Licensing Group, David Westin
Director, Gary B. Pruitt, age 56
Director, H. Graham Woodlief Jr., age 68
Director, Paul C. Tash
Director, Michael E. Reed
Director, Steven R. Swartz, age 51
Director, Boisfeuillet (Bo) Jones Jr.
Director, Craig A. Dubow, age 59
Director, David R. Lord, age 65
Director, Charles V. Pittman
Director, David M. Paxton, age 57
Director, Donna J. Barrett
Director, R. Jack Fishman
Director, R. John Mitchell
Director, Steven O. Newhouse
Director, Elizabeth (Betsy) Brenner, age 59
Director, Jon K. Rust
Auditors: Ernst&YoungLLP

LOCATIONS

HQ: THE ASSOCIATED PRESS
450 W 33RD ST FL 16, NEW YORK, NY 100012626
Phone: 2126211500
Web: WWW.AP.ORG

PRODUCTS/OPERATIONS

Selected Products and Services

AP Digital News (Internet and wireless news delivery)
AP Images (photo services)
AP Mobile (mobile applications)
APTN (AP Television News international television news service)
ENPS (electronic news production system)
Online Video Network (video content distribution)

COMPETITORS

Agence France-Presse
Bloomberg L.P.
Business Wire
Comtex News
Corbis
Dow Jones
E. W. Scripps
Gannett
Getty Images
GlobeNewswire
Marketwire
New York Times
PR Newswire
Reuters
Tribune Company
UPI

HISTORICAL FINANCIALS

Company Type: Private

Income Statement

FYE: December 31

	REVENUE ($ mil.)	NET INCOME ($ mil.)	NET PROFIT MARGIN	EMPLOYEES
12/13	595	3	0.5%	3,533
12/12	622	(25)	—	—
12/11	627	(193)	—	—
12/10	630	0	—	—
Annual Growth	(1.9%)	—	—	—

2013 Year-End Financials

Debt ratio: —
Return on equity: 0.50%
Cash ($ mil.): 14
Current ratio: 0.60
Long-term debt ($ mil.): —
Dividends
Yield: —
Payout: —
Market value ($ mil.): —

THE BANK OF CANTON

LOCATIONS

HQ: THE BANK OF CANTON
490 TURNPIKE ST, CANTON, MA 020212704
Phone: 7818281690

HISTORICAL FINANCIALS

Company Type: Private

Income Statement

FYE: December 31

	ASSETS ($ mil.)	NET INCOME ($ mil.)	INCOME AS % OF ASSETS	EMPLOYEES
12/13	624	2	0.3%	122
12/08	839	1	0.2%	—
12/06	823	5	0.6%	—
12/05	0	0	—	—
Annual Growth	—	—	—	—

2013 Year-End Financials

Debt ratio: —
Return on equity: 7.20%
Cash ($ mil.): 27
Current ratio: —
Long-term debt ($ mil.): —
Dividends
Yield: —
Payout: —
Market value ($ mil.): —

THE BIG TEN CONFERENCE INC

LOCATIONS

HQ: THE BIG TEN CONFERENCE INC
1500 HIGGINS RD, PARK RIDGE, IL 600685735
Phone: 8476961010

HISTORICAL FINANCIALS

Company Type: Private

Income Statement

FYE: June 30

	REVENUE ($ mil.)	NET INCOME ($ mil.)	NET PROFIT MARGIN	EMPLOYEES
06/13	318	5	1.9%	25
06/11	265	(0)	—	—
06/10	232	(4)	—	—
06/09	221	0	—	—
Annual Growth	9.4%	—	—	—

2013 Year-End Financials

Debt ratio: —
Return on equity: —
Cash ($ mil.): 35
Current ratio: 1.90
Long-term debt ($ mil.): —
Dividends
Yield: —
Payout: —
Market value ($ mil.): —

THE BRANCH GROUP INC

EXECUTIVES

CEO, James C. (Jim) Harrison IV
VP Human Resources, Terry Keffer
Treasurer, Melanie Wheeler
Corporate Safety Director, Danny Minnix
Controller, Matt Wise
President Branch Highways Inc., J. William Karbach
President Branch and Associates Inc., Stephen B. Aud
President R.E. Daffan Inc., Lawrence B. Dickenson
President E. V. Williams Inc., Thomas L. Partridge
President G. J. Hopkins Inc., Elwyn M. Clifton

LOCATIONS

HQ: THE BRANCH GROUP INC
442 RUTHERFORD AVE NE, ROANOKE, VA 240162116
Phone: 5409821678
Web: WWW.BRANCHGROUP.COM

PRODUCTS/OPERATIONS

Selected Subsidiaries

Branch & Associates Inc. (builder construction services)
Branch Highways Inc. (highway bridge airport infrastructure and site development)
E.V. Williams Inc. (highway site development and concrete paving construction servives)
G.J. Hopkins Inc. (mechanical and electrical construction services)
R. Edward Daffan (construction and architectural services)

COMPETITORS

Bechtel
English Construction Company
Fluor
K3 Construction
KBS
S. W. Rodgers
Tesoro Corporation
Turner Corporation
Washington Division
Whiting-Turner

HISTORICAL FINANCIALS

Company Type: Private

Income Statement

FYE: December 31

	REVENUE ($ mil.)	NET INCOME ($ mil.)	NET PROFIT MARGIN	EMPLOYEES
12/13	326	0	—	800
12/12	271	0	—	—
12/11	238	0	—	—
12/10	228	0	—	—
Annual Growth	12.7%	—	—	—

2013 Year-End Financials

Debt ratio: —
Return on equity: —
Cash ($ mil.): 43
Current ratio: 0.80
Long-term debt ($ mil.): —
Dividends
Yield: —
Payout: —
Market value ($ mil.): —

THE BROTHER'S BROTHER FOUNDATION

He ain't heavy he's my brother's brother. The lyrics aren't quite right but the sentiment is the same. The not-for-profit Brother's Brother Foundation (BBF) provides emergency and nonemergency medical supplies textbooks food shoes and other humanitarian supplies to people in some 120 countries using a combination of gifts from the general public corporations and the US government. BBF is a gift-in-kind charity meaning the bulk of the donations are goods rather than money. The organization was established in 1958 by the renowned anesthesiologist Robert Hingson as Brother's Keeper but later changed its name.

Hingson invented the jet inoculation gun used to provide 1000 inoculations per hour.

EXECUTIVES

President, Luke L. Hingson
VP Development, Karen H. Dempsey
Medical Director, Chip Lambert
Educational Program Coordinator, Carol Taylor
VP Finance, William P. (Bill) Davis

LOCATIONS

HQ: THE BROTHER' S BROTHER FOUNDATION
1200 GALVESTON AVE, PITTSBURGH, PA 15233-1604
Phone: 412-321-3160
Web: WWW.BROTHERSBROTHER.ORG

HISTORICAL FINANCIALS

Company Type: Private

Income Statement FYE: December 31

	REVENUE ($ mil.)	NET INCOME ($ mil.)	NET PROFIT MARGIN	EMPLOYEES
12/11	242	7	3.0%	12
12/10	273	(0)	—	—
12/08	268	1	0.4%	—
12/08	1,084	(1)	—	—
Annual Growth	(39.3%)	—	—	—

2011 Year-End Financials

Debt ratio: —
Return on equity: 3.00%
Cash ($ mil.): 2
Current ratio: 20.50
Long-term debt ($ mil.): —
Dividends
Yield: —
Payout: —
Market value ($ mil.): —

THE CARTER-JONES LUMBER COMPANY

EXECUTIVES

President Carter Lumber Company, Neil C. Sackett
SVP COO and CFO, Jeffrey S. (Jeff) Donley

LOCATIONS

HQ: THE CARTER-JONES LUMBER COMPANY
601 TALLMADGE RD, KENT, OH 442407331
Phone: 3306736100
Web: WWW.CARTERLUMBER.COM

PRODUCTS/OPERATIONS

Selected Subsidiaries

Carter-Jones Lumber Company
Griggs Lumber
Holmes Lumber
Kempsville Building Materials
Kight Home Center

COMPETITORS

84 Lumber
ABC Supply
BlueLinx
Guardian Building Products Distribution
HD Supply
Lowe' s
Menard
Pro-Build
Stock Building Supply
Weekes Forest Products

HISTORICAL FINANCIALS

Company Type: Private

Income Statement FYE: December 31

	REVENUE ($ mil.)	NET INCOME ($ mil.)	NET PROFIT MARGIN	EMPLOYEES
12/10	334	(4)	—	1,575
12/09	314	(4)		
12/08	2,083	0	—	—
Annual Growth	—	—	—	—

2010 Year-End Financials

Debt ratio: —
Return on equity: (-1.40%)
Cash ($ mil.): 2
Current ratio: —
Long-term debt ($ mil.): —
Dividends
Yield: —
Payout: —
Market value ($ mil.): —

THE CATHOLIC UNIVERSITY OF AMERICA

The Catholic University of America (CUA) established in 1887 by US bishops has an enrollment of more than 7000 students from all 50 states and nearly 100 countries. With graduate and undergraduate programs in 13 colleges CUA offers degrees in such fields as architecture and planning arts and sciences engineering music and nursing; it's expanding into business and economics. CUA is the only US university with ecclesiastical faculties granting canonical degrees in canon law philosophy and theology. Some 80% of undergraduates and nearly 60% of graduate students are Catholic. The University's Theological College prepares men for the priesthood serving dioceses nationwide.

Geographic Reach

The university's 193-acre campus is located north of Capitol Hill in Washington D.C. The campus comprises more than a dozen schools and nearly two dozen research facilities.

Operations

As part of its operations CUA offers its students several areas of study. It boasts schools in architecture and planning arts and sciences business and economics canon law engineering law library and information sciences music nursing philosophy professional studies social services and theology and religious studies. Its architecture program is the largest in the D.C. area and the legal clinic at its Columbus School of Law is rated among the top 12 in the nation.

The university which has a student-faculty ratio is 9:1 grants undergraduate degrees in 72 programs master's degrees in 103 programs and doctoral or terminal degrees in 66 programs.

Financial Performance

CUA's revenue rose by 2% in 2012 as compared to 2011 due to an increase in net tuition and fees thanks to growth in enrollment tuition rates and auxiliary revenue. Net income for the same reporting period declined by 90% attributable to rising operating expenses and a declines in investment return in excess of amounts designated for current operations.

Strategy

To cater to those who have requested an increased focus on business education CUA in 2013 is building a School of Business and Economics. Instead of focusing on theories the school will offer students an education model based on Catholic social doctrine and the natural law.

Sales and Marketing

CUA sources its students from all 50 states and nearly 100 countries.

EXECUTIVES

Executive Director Campus Planning and Information Technology and CIO, Ziaeddin Mafaher
Associate VP and General Counsel, Craig W. Parker
Associate VP Public Affairs, Victor A. Nakas
VP Student Life, Susan D. Pervi
VP University Relations and Chief of Staff, Frank G. Persico
Executive Director Facilities Operations, Carl A. Petchik
Director Campus Ministry and University Chaplain, Rev Robert Schlageter
VP University Development, Robert M. Sullivan
VP Enrollment Management, W. Michael Hendricks
Director Human Resources, Barbara Coughlin
Director Career Services, Alan P. Goodman
Associate Provost for Research and Director Technology Transfer, Ralph Albano
Head of Acquisitions Libraries, Kathern Miraglia
Head of Collection Management Libraries, Zofia Dunian
Head of Electronic Services Libraries, Shanyun Zhang
Director Office of Alumni Relations, Marion M. Gosney
Director Athletics, Michael S. (Mike) Allen
Executive Director University Development, Michael Catell
Director Planned Giving, Michael Green
Assistant VP Development, Amy Wilson
Dean Columbus School of Law, Veryl V. Miles
President, John H. Garvey, age 66
Chancellor, Donald W. Wuerl
Vice Chair Board of Trustees, David A. Donohoe
Associate VP and Chief Human Resources Officer, Christine Peterson
Provost, James F. Brennan
VP Finance and Treasurer, Cathy Wood
Assistant VP University Relations for University Events, Suzanne McCarthy
Director Library Administration, Stephen J. Connaghan
Associate Provost University Libraries, Kimberly B. Kelley
Head of Cataloging Libraries, Chiyono Sata
Head of Information Processing Libraries, Kristen Fredericksen
Controller, Sheri Hardison
Director Grants and Contracts, Susan Warshawsky
University Registrar, Adriana Farella
Director Academic Technology Services, Bill Lantry
Director Information Systems and Services, Jim Gallamo
Director Information Technology, Betsy Ramsey
Director Institutional Research and Assessment, Brian Johnston
Director Annual Giving, Mark Roberts
Director Donor Relations, David S. McMullen
Assistant VP Global Education, Tanith Fowler Corsi
Associate VP Academic Planning, Sara Thompson
Chairman Board of Trustees, Rev Allen H. Vigneron
Auditors: PricewaterhouseCoopersLLP

LOCATIONS

HQ: THE CATHOLIC UNIVERSITY OF AMERICA
620 MICHIGAN AVE NE, WASHINGTON, DC 20064-0002
Phone: 202-319-5000
Web: WWW.CUA.EDU/CONTACT-US.CFM

PRODUCTS/OPERATIONS

Selected Schools

Benjamin T. Rome School of Music
Columbus School of Law
Metropolitan School of Professional Studies
National Catholic School of Social Service
School of Architecture and Planning
School of Arts and Sciences
School of Business and Economics
School of Canon Law
School of Engineering
School of Library and Information Science
School of Nursing
School of Philosophy
School of Theology and Religious Studies

HISTORICAL FINANCIALS

Company Type: Private

Income Statement FYE: April 30

	REVENUE ($ mil.)	NET INCOME ($ mil.)	NET PROFIT MARGIN	EMPLOYEES
04/12	227	4	1.9%	4,239
04/09	0	0	—	—
04/06	167	24	14.6%	—
04/05	198	4	2.2%	—
Annual Growth	2.0%	(0.2%)	—	—

2012 Year-End Financials

Debt ratio: —
Return on equity: 1.90%
Cash ($ mil.): 51
Current ratio: —
Long-term debt ($ mil.): —
Dividends
Yield: —
Payout: —
Market value ($ mil.): —

THE CHILDREN'S HOSPITAL CORPORATION

Children's Hospital Boston is an elder in the world of pediatric care. The 400-bed hospital offers acute health care and specialty services for children from birth to age 21. The medical center is also Harvard Medical School's main teaching hospital for children's health care and it is the world's largest pediatric research center. Its John F. Enders Pediatric Research facility provides research for the treatment of childhood diseases. Specialty services include cardiovascular surgery digestive care neurology oncology ophthalmology orthopedics transplants blood diseases and fetal care. The not-for-profit hospital was founded in 1869.

Operations

Children's Hospital Boston handles about 25000 inpatient visits per year as well as 27000 surgeries and 160000 radiological exams. Its specialized clinical programs handle about 560000 appointments annually. The hospital is considered a safety-net hospital and as such is one of the largest providers of medical care to low-income children in the state. About 30% of the hospital's patients are either uninsured or have health care coverage through public assistance.

In addition to its educational and research partnerships with Harvard the medical center collaborates with other universities as well as drugmakers medical equipment firms and research institutes. Altogether it has some 1100 scientists at its research centers including the Enders Pediatric Research Laboratories and the Karp Family Research Laboratories. Children's Hospital Boston receives some $225 million in research funding per year.

Along with the main hospital the system operates a handful of primary and specialty care centers throughout the Boston area. It also provides services collaborative pediatric care at about a dozen area hospitals including Good Samaritan Medical Center in Brockton and Holy Family Hospital in Methuen. It also operates a cancer clinic within the main Children's Hospital Boston facilities through a partnership with the Dana Farber Cancer Institute.

Strategy

Due to increasing economic troubles and health reform measures in the US Children's Hospital Boston has been working to cut costs. Through its efficiency and operational restructuring efforts the medical center reduced expenses by some $60 million in 2010.

Despite the cost-control efforts the main Children's Hospital Boston campus is undergoing expansion and renovation efforts as part of a 10-year expansion plan.

One way to increase research funding is to increase external partnerships. Children's Hospital Boston formed a research collaboration with diagnostic and lab supply firm Life Technologies in 2012 to develop new gene sequencing workflows. In 2013 the two companies expanded their relationship by forming Claritas Genomics; the venture will develop new genetic and genomic-based diagnostic tests.

EXECUTIVES

Chief Innovation Officer, Naomi Fried
CEO and Trustee, James Mandell
President COO and Trustee, Sandra L. Fenwick, age 63
SVP and CFO, David Kirshner
CFO, Doug Vanderslice
VP Real Estate Planning and Development, Charles Weinstein
VP Public Affairs and Marketing, Michelle Davis
SVP and CIO, Daniel Nigrin
VP Research Administration, Carleen Brunelli
Executive Chair Children's Hospital Trust, Janet (Jan) Cady
VP Child Advocacy, M. Laurie Cammisa
VP and Chief Administrative Officer Children's Hospital Boston at Waltham, Steven Gordon
VP Human Resources, Inez Stewart
SVP Chief Safety and Quality Officer, Kathy Jenkins
VP Ambulatory Care and Network Services, Mark Marcantano
SVP and General Counsel, Stuart Novick
SVP Patient Care Operations Chief Nursing Officer and Trustee, Eileen Sporing
SVP Network Development and Strategic Partnerships, Wendy E. Warring
VP Support Services, Henry Tomasuolo
Surgeon-in-Chief and Trustee, James Kasser
SVP and Chief Administrative Officer, Dick Argys
Physician-in-Chief, Gary R. Fleisher
Chair, Stephen R. Karp
Anesthesiologist-in-Chief, Paul R. Hickey
Executive Director Satellite Clinical Operations, Julee Bolg
President Children's Hospital Trust, Lynn Susman
SVP and Chief Marketing and Communications Officer, Margaret Coughlin
VP Government Relations, Josh Greenberg
Chief Investment Officer, Phil Rotner
Executive Director Satellite Administrative Operations, Jane Venti
Trustee, Ralph C. Martin II
CEO and Trustee, James Mandell
Trustee, William L. Boyan
President COO and Trustee, Sandra L. Fenwick, age 63
SVP Patient Care Operations Chief Nursing Officer and Trustee, Eileen Sporing
Surgeon-in-Chief and Trustee, James Kasser
Trustee, Douglas A. Berthiaume
Trustee, Steven Fishman
Trustee, Harvey Lodish
Trustee, George W. Phillips
Trustee, Robert A. Smith
Trustee, Robert E. (Bob) Smyth
Trustee, Alison Taunton-Rigby
Trustee, Ann Thornburg
Trustee, Marc B. Wolpow
Trustee, Gregory Young
Auditors: Ernst&YoungLLP

LOCATIONS

HQ: THE CHILDREN' S HOSPITAL CORPORATION
300 LONGWOOD AVE, BOSTON, MA 02115-5737
Phone: 617-355-6000
Web: WWW.GIVING.CHILDRENSHOSPITAL.ORG

PRODUCTS/OPERATIONS

Selected Services

Major centers
- Brain Center
- Cancer and Blood Diseases Center
- Heart Center
- Orthopedic Center
- Transplant Center

Other Services
- Airway breathing and lungs
- Allergies and asthma
- Anatomy and function
- Bone joint and muscle
- Brain and nervous system
- Cancer and blood disorders
- Common childhood health topics and conditions
- Craniofacial anomalies
- Diet and nutrition
- Digestive metabolic and renal disorders
- Ears nose and throat
- Emergency medicine and trauma
- Eyes and vision
- Genetic disorders and birth defects
- Heart blood and circulation
- International patient care
- Medical tests
- Newborns
- Psychiatric (mental) conditions
- Reproductive and urinary conditions
- Skin and vascular
- Viruses and infections

COMPETITORS

Baystate Medical Center
Beth Israel Deaconess Medical Center
Boston Medical Center
Cambridge Health Alliance
Cape Cod Hospital
CareGroup
Children' s Hospital of Philadelphia
Dana-Farber
Nemours Foundation
Newton-Wellesley Hospital
Northeast Health System
Partners HealthCare
Shriners Hospitals For Children
Steward Health Care
Sturdy Memorial

HISTORICAL FINANCIALS

Company Type: Private

Income Statement FYE: September 30

	REVENUE ($ mil.)	NET INCOME ($ mil.)	NET PROFIT MARGIN	EMPLOYEES
09/09*	1,348	94	7.0%	8,000
06/05	4	0	13.0%	—
09/03	695	69	9.9%	—
09/02	624	21	3.5%	—
Annual Growth	11.6%	23.5%	—	—

*Fiscal year change

2009 Year-End Financials

Debt ratio: —
Return on equity: 7.00%
Cash ($ mil.): 0
Current ratio: 0.20
Long-term debt ($ mil.): —
Dividends
Yield: —
Payout: —
Market value ($ mil.): —

THE CHILDRENS HOSPITAL LOS ANGELES

Childrens Hospital Los Angeles (CHLA) is dedicated to treating the youngest critical care patients in the region. The more than 600-bed hospital specializes in treating seriously ill and injured children from its neonatal intensive care unit to its pediatric organ transplant center. CHLA's pediatric specialists also provide care at its ambulatory care center in Arcadia and through about 40 off-site practice sites. The hospital's pediatric specialties include cancer kidney failure and cystic fibrosis care. CHLA serves more than 97000 children every year. It is one of only 12 children's hospitals in the nation (and the only one in California) ranked in all 10 pediatric specialties by U.S. News & World Report.

Operations

The CHLA medical staff includes about 600 physicians most of which are members of the CHLA Medical Group. Its emergency department treats almost 66000 patients and the hospital admits some 11000 children annually. Nearly 50% of its patients are under the age of four. CHLA is also the only freestanding Level 1 Pediatric Trauma Center in LA County approved by the Committee on Trauma of the American College of Surgeons and among only 5% of US hospitals to be designated as a Magnet Hospital by the American Nurses Credentialing Center.

It is also a teaching hospital through its affiliation with the Keck School of Medicine of the University of Southern California and is home to the Saban Research Institute which conducts biomedical research into pediatric diseases. CHLA's training programs include 575 medical students 85 full-time residents three chief residents and 98 fellows.

Strategy

CHLA is expanding its facilities to keep up with demand. Inititatives in 2011 included the opening of an outpatient services center in Arcadia to serve the San Gabriel Valley early in the year. The big news however was the completion of the hospital's $636 million 460000-sq.-ft. building –dubbed the Marion and John E. Anderson Pavilion in honor of the longtime supporters –to replace its existing inpatient building. The new facility expanded capacity in CHLA's critical care intensive care emergency room and transplant units and boosted its licensed bed count to about 350 beds.

Also that year CHLA and the University of Southern California created a new Center for Technology and Innovation in Pediatrics to develop pediatric medical devices through shared programs and resources and address and eliminate barriers to commercialization of these products which lag behind the development of adult devices by as much as 10 years. Additionally CHLA and NanoSmart Pharmaceuticals partnered to develop and evaluate NanoSmart's tumor-targeting platform that utilizes human autoimmune antibodies to fight pediatric cancer.

Company Background

Although it sometimes operates as Children's Hospital Los Angeles the absent apostrophe in the legal Childrens Hospital of Los Angeles name is no accident. The intentional spelling honors the original incorporation documents filed in 1901 when the institution was founded as Childrens Hospital Society of Los Angeles.

EXECUTIVES

President CEO of Childrens Hospital Los Angeles, Richard D. (Rich) Cordova
SVP Finance and CFO, DiemLan (Lannie) Tonnu
Senior Vice President Chief Financial Officer, Claudia Looney
VP and Chief Human Resources Officer, Hugo Santos, age 63
VP and CIO, Marty W. Miller
VP Chief of Surgery and Trustee, Henri R. Ford
VP Patient Care Services and Chief Nursing Officer and Trustee, Mary Dee Hacker
VP Government Business and Community Relations, Gail L. Margolis
Co-Chair, Theodore R. Samuels
Co-Chair, Cathy Siegel Weiss
Senior Vice President, Rodney B. Hanners
SVP and General Counsel, Lawrence L. Foust
VP Ancillary and Support Services, Keith M. Hobbs
Vice President Human Resources, DeAnn Marshall
President CEO, Best Place
Vice President of Patient Care Services and Chief Nursing Officer, Mary Hacker
Vice President Access Ambulatory and Network Operations, Smitha Ravipudi
Trustee, Peggy Tsiang Cherng, age 66
Trustee, Enrique (Rick) Hernandez Jr., age 58
Trustee, Paul Schaeffer, age 65
President CEO and Trustee, Richard D. (Rich) Cordova
Trustee, Brian E. Henderson
Trustee, Maria Contreras-Sweet
Director, Stuart E. Siegel
Trustee, Elizabeth Lowe
VP Chief of Surgery and Trustee, Henri R. Ford
VP Patient Care Services and Chief Nursing Officer and Trustee, Mary Dee Hacker
Trustee, Marion Anderson
Trustee, Brooke Anderson
Trustee, CeCe Baise
Trustee, June Banta
Trustee, Otis Booth III
Trustee, Patricia A. Brown
Trustee, Margaret D. Eberhardt
Trustee, Richard Farman
Trustee, Giselle Fernandez-Farrand
Trustee, Lynda Boone Fetter
Trustee, Peggy Galbraith
Trustee, Herbert Gelfand
Trustee, Ronald E. Gother
Trustee, Mary Hart
Trustee, Marcia Wilson Hobbs
Trustee, Linda Joyce Hodge
Trustee, James Hunt
Trustee, William H. Hurt
Trustee, Francine Kaufman
Trustee, Carol Mancino
Trustee, Gregory S. Martin
Trustee, Bonnie McClure
Trustee, Alex Simpson
Trustee, Caryll Sprague Mingst
Trustee, Mary Adams O'Connell
Trustee, John D. (Jack) Pettker
Trustee, J. Kristoffer Popovich
Trustee, Ronald Preissman
Trustee, Dayle Roath
Trustee, Cheryl Saban
Co-Chair, Theodore R. Samuels
Trustee, Scott Sanford
Trustee, Victoria Simms
Trustee, Suzan Smigel
Trustee, Russell K. Snow Jr.
Trustee, Joyce Bogart Trabulus
Trustee, Esther Wachtell
Co-Chair, Cathy Siegel Weiss
Trustee, Michael R. Whalen
Trustee, Robert Adler
Trustee, Alex Chaves Sr.
Trustee, Martha N. Corbett
Trustee, John Delfino
Trustee, Gloria Holden
Trustee, Susan H. Mallory
Trustee, Alex Meneses
Trustee, Alan Purwin
Trustee, Kathy Luppen Rose
Trustee, Monica Rosenthal
Trustee, James Terrile
Trustee, Alyce Williamson
Trustee, Alan J. Wilson
Trustee, Jeffrey Worthe
Trustee, Dick Zeigler

LOCATIONS

HQ: THE CHILDRENS HOSPITAL LOS ANGELES
4650 W SUNSET BLVD, LOS ANGELES, CA 90027-6062
Phone: 323-660-2450
Web: WWW.CHLA.ORG

COMPETITORS

Cedars-Sinai Medical Center
Children' s Hospital of Chicago
Children' s Hospital & Research Center at Oakland
Children' s Hospital Boston
Children' s Hospital of Orange County
Children' s Hospital of Philadelphia
Children' s National Medical Center
Cincinnati Children' s Hospital
Cook Children' s Health Care System
Dignity Health
Good Samaritan Hospital (Los Angeles)
Hollywood Presbyterian Medical Center
Los Angeles County Health Department
Nationwide Children' s Hospital
Shriners Hospitals For Children

HISTORICAL FINANCIALS

Company Type: Private

Income Statement FYE: June 30

	REVENUE ($ mil.)	NET INCOME ($ mil.)	NET PROFIT MARGIN	EMPLOYEES
06/10	564	(34)	—	3,000
06/09	405	(94)	—	—
06/08	589	20	3.5%	—
06/05	457	(24)	—	—
Annual Growth	4.3%	—	—	—

2010 Year-End Financials

Debt ratio: —
Return on equity: (-6.10%)
Cash ($ mil.): 4
Current ratio: 0.10
Long-term debt ($ mil.): —
Dividends
Yield: —
Payout: —
Market value ($ mil.): —

THE CHRISTIAN BROADCASTING NETWORK INC

Standards & Practices probably won't find much wrong with these TV programs. The Christian Broadcasting Network (CBN) is one of the leading producers of religious television programming in the country offering news and entertainment shows with a spiritual message. Its centerpiece is The 700 Club a daily show featuring a mix of news and commentary interviews feature stories and Christian ministry co-hosted by CBN founder Pat Robertson. The company's programs are syndicated to broadcast and cable TV outlets that reach audiences around the world. CBN generates most of its revenue through ministry donations.

Geographic ReachCBN programs have aired in 108 languages (from Mandarin to Spanish and from Turkish to Welsh) in 218 different countries and territories. It currently broadcasts in 139 countries with programs and content translated into 62 languages. The company has offices in Africa Asia Europe the Middle East North America (Canada and US) and Russia and the Commonwealth of Independent States.OperationsCBN has a broad portfolio of ministries and services.This portfolio includes The 700 Club & Prayer Center. CBN's The 700 Club program brings a magazine-style mix of news interviews testimonies and insights from Christian leaders. CBN's Prayer Center provides prayer as well as biblical guidance and resources to callers. The 700 Club Interactive is a show designed for viewer interaction and uses a chat community Skype live phone calls and social networking. CBN is launching a massive media campaign to promote the Bible under the brand Superbook. Orphan's Promise ministers to the physical spiritual and educational needs of orphaned and vulnerable children.CBN's Operation Blessing International's core programs include disaster relief medical aid hunger relief orphan care water wells and community development. CBN.com offers streaming video teaching; in-depth discipleship courses; Online Bible; CBN Radio; Bible teachings; my.CBN.com a social network; and free downloads of videos widgets and articles.

Financial PerformanceThe company's revenue increased to $542 million during fiscal 2013 a 11% increased from previous year's $487 million. The spike was largely due to increases in revenue from Gifts in kind by 24% to $245 million in fiscal 2013 compared to $197 million in fiscal 2012 and additional investment gain and other revenues.

EXECUTIVES

Vice President Marketing, John Turver
President and COO, Michael D. Little
CEO, Gordon Robertson
Vice President, Randy E Morell
Worldreach Vice President, Ben Edwards
Associate Medical Director, Thomas Pearson
Vice President, Edie Wasserberg
Executive Secretary To The Vice President, Jo-ann Boyd
Chairman, M. G. (Pat) Robertson, age 84
President and COO, Michael D. Little

LOCATIONS

HQ: THE CHRISTIAN BROADCASTING NETWORK INC
977 CENTERVILLE TPKE, VIRGINIA BEACH, VA 234631001
Phone: 7572263030
Web: WWW.CBN.COM

COMPETITORS

Eden Communications
Guideposts
Integrity Media
Salem Communications
Thomas Nelson
Trinity Broadcasting
Zondervan

HISTORICAL FINANCIALS

Company Type: Private

Income Statement FYE: March 31

	REVENUE ($ mil.)	NET INCOME ($ mil.)	NET PROFIT MARGIN	EMPLOYEES
03/11	285	6	2.4%	941
03/10	283	8	3.0%	—
03/09	2,135	0	0.0%	—
Annual Growth	(63.5%)	1932.4%	—	—

2011 Year-End Financials

Debt ratio: —
Return on equity: 2.40%
Cash ($ mil.): 18
Current ratio: 0.60
Long-term debt ($ mil.): —
Dividends
Yield: —
Payout: —
Market value ($ mil.): —

THE CITY OF LANSING BY ITS BOARD OF WATER AND LIGHT

Letting off a little steam is a good thing for Lansing Board of Water and Light which provides electricity to 96000 residential commercial and industrial customers and water to about 55000 customers in Lansing Michigan. The city-owned utility also produces and distributes steam to 250 customers along 14 miles of steam line. Lansing Board of Water and Light can chill out too. Its chilled water system delivers up to 10000 tons of chilled water capacity to 14 customers to cool the interior of buildings in the downtown area. Lansing Board of Water and Light is the largest municipally owned utility in the state. It is also a major employer in the Lansing area.

In 2007 Lansing Board of Water and Light became the first utility in Michigan to adopt a Renewable Portfolio Standard - setting specific goals for acquiring renewable energy. By law all Michigan utilities must get 10% of their energy from renewable sources by 2015. In 2008 the utility broke ground on the largest largest solar cell array in Michigan in downtown Lansing.

Lansing Board of Water and Light was founded in 1885 when the citizens of Lansing approved a $100000 bond issue to establish a water system to provide the town with drinking water and fire protection. The utility added electricity to its services in 1892 and steam heat in 1919.

EXECUTIVES

Vice Chairman, Sandra Zerkle
Corporate Secretary, Rhonda Jones
CFO, Susan Devon
Executive Director Water Operations and Special Projects, Dick Peffley
Executive Director Strategic Planning and Development, George Stojic
Executive Director Electric Operations, Doug Wood
Director Governmental and Public Relations, Calvin Jones
Director Internal Audit, Susan Pifer
General Manager, J. Peter Lark
Manager Electric System Integrity, Alan Carroll
Director Human Resources, Terri L. Singleton
Energy Efficiency Specialist, Aileen Gow
General Counsel, Brandie Ekren
Manager Finance and Planning, William (Bill) Aldrich
Director Communications, Mark Nixon
Chairman, Frank B. Lain
Marketing Manager, Sue Warren
Vice Chairman, Sandra Zerkle
Director, Julee M. Rodocker
Director, Robert W. Cochran
Director, Peter W. Kramer
Director, Tony DeLuca
Auditors: Plante&MoranPLLC

LOCATIONS

HQ: THE CITY OF LANSING BY ITS BOARD OF WATER AND LIGHT
1232 HACO DR, LANSING, MI 48912-1610
Phone: 517-702-6000
Web: WWW.LBWL.COM

HISTORICAL FINANCIALS

Company Type: Private

Income Statement FYE: June 30

	REVENUE ($ mil.)	NET INCOME ($ mil.)	NET PROFIT MARGIN	EMPLOYEES
06/12	320	22	7.1%	740
06/11	306	7	2.5%	—
06/10	18	17	97.3%	—
Annual Growth	317.5%	12.6%	—	—

2012 Year-End Financials

Debt ratio: —
Return on equity: 7.10%
Cash ($ mil.): 45
Current ratio: 1.30
Long-term debt ($ mil.): —
Dividends
Yield: —
Payout: —
Market value ($ mil.): —

THE COMMUNITY HOSPITAL GROUP INC

JFK Medical Center plays a central role in health care in central New Jersey. The medical center is an acute care facility with some 500 beds and 950 physicians providing emergency surgical trauma and other inpatient services. The hospital includes the JFK New Jersey Neuroscience Institute which treats stroke and other neurological conditions and the JFK Johnson Rehabilitation Institute which treats traumatic injuries. JFK Medical Center also offers diagnostic imaging cancer care senior and hospice care and family practice services. It is also a teaching hospital affiliated with several area universities. The hospital is part of the JFK Health System.

Strategy

To expand its capacity for emergency services JFK Medical Center launched construction of a new ER pavilion in 2013. The project includes the addition of a three-story structure above the existing ER facilities. To keep pace with cutting-edge medical technologies the hospital has also made recent investments in upgrades to its diagnostic imaging cardiac catheterization and wound healing equipment.

EXECUTIVES

Director Public Relations and Marketing Solaris Health System, Steven Weiss
President Medical Staff, Matthew Smith
CFO Solaris Health System, Richard Smith

LOCATIONS

HQ: THE COMMUNITY HOSPITAL GROUP INC
98 JAMES ST STE 400, EDISON, NJ 08820-3902
Phone: 732-321-7000
Web: WWW.NJNEURO.ORG

PRODUCTS/OPERATIONS

Selected Centers and Affiliates

Adult Medical Day Program
Haven Hospice
JFK at Home
JFK Dental Clinic
JFK Family Medicine Center
JFK Hartwyck Nursing Convalescent and Rehabilitation Centers
JFK Johnson Rehabilitation Institute (JRI)
JFK Mediplex Surgery Center
JFK New Jersey Neuroscience Institute
JFK Medical Center Muhlenberg Campus/JFK-Muhlenberg Snyder Schools
Whispering Knoll Assisted Living

COMPETITORS

Ball Memorial Hospital
Barnabas Health
Bergen Regional Medical
Capital Health System
CentraState Healthcare System
Henry County Memorial Hospital
Monmouth Medical Center
Newton Medical Center
Princeton HealthCare
Robert Wood Johnson University Hospital
Saint Peter' s University Hospital
St. Joseph' s Healthcare System

HISTORICAL FINANCIALS

Company Type: Private

Income Statement

FYE: December 31

	REVENUE ($ mil.)	NET INCOME ($ mil.)	NET PROFIT MARGIN	EMPLOYEES
12/12	427	15	3.6%	3,000
12/10	427	(17)	—	—
12/09	423	(37)	—	—
12/06	322	7	2.5%	—
Annual Growth	4.8%	11.5%	—	—

2012 Year-End Financials

Debt ratio: —
Return on equity: 3.60%
Cash ($ mil.): 33
Current ratio: 1.30
Long-term debt ($ mil.): —
Dividends
Yield: —
Payout: —
Market value ($ mil.): —

THE COMMUNITY PRESERVATION CORPORATION

LOCATIONS

HQ: THE COMMUNITY PRESERVATION CORPORATION
28 E 28TH ST FL 9, NEW YORK, NY 100167943
Phone: 2128695300
Web: WWW.COMMUNITYP.COM

HISTORICAL FINANCIALS

Company Type: Private

Income Statement

FYE: June 30

	ASSETS ($ mil.)	NET INCOME ($ mil.)	INCOME AS % OF ASSETS	EMPLOYEES
06/13	804	(6)	—	170
06/10	1,486	1	0.1%	—
06/09	1,502	0	—	—
Annual Growth	(14.4%)	—	—	—

2013 Year-End Financials

Debt ratio: —
Return on equity: (-16.70%)
Cash ($ mil.): 234
Current ratio: 1.20
Long-term debt ($ mil.): —
Dividends
Yield: —
Payout: —
Market value ($ mil.): —

THE CONSERVATION FUND A NONPROFIT CORPORATION

The Conservation Fund was green before green was cool. The nonprofit organization is well known for negotiating deals to protect environmentally sensitive lands. It will typically purchase property financed through a revolving land fund federal and state grants and contributions from various sources and sell it back to local groups to manage. It also invests in small businesses that show a sustainable use of natural resources as well as works with communities and other not-for-profits to plan for growth and conservation. Since its founding in 1985 the Fund and its partners have protected more than 7 million acres of wildlife habitat and watersheds working landscapes and open-spaces in all 50 US states.

Partnerships are fundament to the nonprofit organization which has no membership no environmental agenda and no charitable endowment. Government partners include such agencies as the Bureau of Land Management the National Park Service the US Fish & Wildlife Service and the USDA Forest Service. The Fund counts more than 1700 local land trusts as part of its community partnerships. Some of the Funds' foundation partners are the Richard King Mellon Foundation Gordon and Betty Moore Foundation Charles Stewart Mott Foundation McKnight Foundation Richard and Rhoda Goldman Fund and Robert W. Woodruff Foundation.

During 2011 the Fund supported protection of a diversity of regions. Among many its work focused on the Appalachian Trail Vermont; wildlife refuges in Maryland and Georgia national parks in Pennsylvania and South Dakota; a scout ranch in Colorado and forests in California Arizona and Texas.

Financially support and revenue generated by the Fund jumped more than 40% in 2011 over the prior year led by a 500% increase in state and federal grants. Its main revenue engine is a revolving fund which is used to acquire high priority land and hold it until the partner can buy it back. Moneys repaid are returned to the fund for the next land deal. Conservation land transactions account for roughly 40% of all proceeds raised of which more than 95% is applied to conservation programs with less than 1% going toward general and administration expenses –a point of pride for the Fund.

The Fund's mission has gained momentum as it demonstrates the considerable return on investment from conservation programs. To this end its New Forest Fund has made strides in conserving working forests coupled with sustained economic growth. The Conservation Fund further points to the use of taxpayer money to support national parks which reportedly provide a four-fold economic benefit through tourism sportsmen and outdoor recreation private sector spending and job creation.

EXECUTIVES

President and CEO, Lawrence A. Selzer
EVP and General Counsel, Richard L. Erdmann
SVP and CFO, David K. Phillips Jr.
Chairman, J. Rutherford Seydel II
SVP Western Region, Sydney S. Macy
Real Estate Department Manager, Margaret A. (Meg) McCants
Vice Chairman, R. Michael Leonard
President Metropolis Strategies, George A. Ranney Jr.
VP Southeast Region, Rex R. Boner
VP and Florida Director, Elizabeth B. Dowdle
VP Northwest Region, Mark W. Elsbree
VP and Director Freshwater Institute, Joseph A. Hankins
VP Sustainable Programs, Erik J. Meyers
VP Regional Counsel and Assistant Secretary, Jodi R. O'Day
Assistant Secretary, Beth Ann Burns
Assistant Secretary and Deputy General Counsel, Paul F. Hurt
Real Estate Legal Manager, G. Jean Pompa
Vice President Public Affairs, Kay Kelly Arnold
VP Marketing and Communications, Kathryn S. Brown
CIO, Wendy Sams-Richardson
Director Fundraising, Alisa Borland
Manager Human Resources and Administration, Joyce Ferrell
Director Government Relations, Christy Plumer
Manager Media Relations, Ann Simonelli
Vice President of Sustainable Programs and Director of The Conservation Fund ?s Conservation Leadership Network, Kris Hoellen
President, Marten R. Jenkins
Operations Manager, Trevor Cutsinger
Director of Operations, Scott Tsukuda
Operations Manager, Carrie Gombos
Vice President of Real Estate for the Midwest, Tom Duffus
Vice President of Conservation Ventures at the Fund, Evan Smith
Vice President Director of the Resourceful Communities Program, Mikki Sager
President Chief Executive Officer of the Fund, Larry Selzer
Executive Vice President CB Richard Ellis, Jay F. Wagley
Director, B. Francis Saul III, age 51
Director, Dennis H. Reilley, age 60
Director, David N. (Dave) Weidman, age 57
Director, James M. (Jim) Whitehurst, age 45
Director, Charles R. Jordan
Director, Sylvia A. Earle
Director, Stephen A. Elbert, age 65
Director, Norman L. Christensen Jr.
Vice Chairman, R. Michael Leonard
Director, Georgina A. Moreno
Director, George A. Ranney Jr.
Director, Kay Kelly Arnold
Director, Truman T. Semans Sr.
Director, Kenneth Olden
Director, Gray N. Thornton
Auditors: CBIZMHMLLC

LOCATIONS

HQ: THE CONSERVATION FUND A NONPROFIT CORPORATION
1655 FORT MYER DR # 1300, ARLINGTON, VA 22209-3113
Phone: 703-525-6300
Web: WWW.CONSERVATIONFUND.ORG

PRODUCTS/OPERATIONS

2011 Use of funds

	$ mil.	% of total
Conservation programs	191	97
General & administrative	3	2
Fundraising	1	1
Total	**196**	**100**

2011 Sources of Funds

	$ mil.	% of total
Revenue		
Conservation land transactions	105	43
State & federal grants	58	24
Mitigation/carbon/timber	8	4
Investment & other program income	7	3
Contract income	4	2
Contributions		
Foundation contributions	23	9
Gifts of land	15	7
Individual contributions	10	4
Corporate contributions	7	3
Other contributions	2	1
Total	**244**	**100**

HISTORICAL FINANCIALS

Company Type: Private

Income Statement FYE: December 31

	REVENUE ($ mil.)	NET INCOME ($ mil.)	NET PROFIT MARGIN	EMPLOYEES
12/12	179	41	23.3%	95
12/09	186	31	17.0%	—
12/04	68	28	42.0%	—
12/04	68	28	42.0%	—
Annual Growth	12.8%	4.8%	—	—

2012 Year-End Financials

Debt ratio: —
Return on equity: 23.30%
Cash ($ mil.): 137
Current ratio: 2.00
Long-term debt ($ mil.): —
Dividends
Yield: —
Payout: —
Market value ($ mil.): —

THE CORPORATION OF GONZAGA UNIVERSITY

Gonzaga University is a private liberal arts institution providing instruction to more than 7800 undergraduate graduate doctoral and law students. The school offers about 75 undergraduate majors two dozen master's degree programs and two leadership study doc at its six colleges and schools. The university offers a juris doctorate degree at its School of Law. The Roman Catholic university is run by the Society of Jesus –the Jesuits –and is named after a sixteenth-century Italian Jesuit Aloysius Gonzaga the patron saint of youth. The university was founded in 1887 as a men's college.

Geographic Reach

The university's main 130-acre campus in Spokane Washington contains more than 100 buildings and is located near the Spokane River about half a mile from downtown. In addition Gonzaga University has a campus in Florence Italy where Aloysius Gonzaga lived as a student.

Operations

Gonzaga University has more than 400 faculty members and a student-to-faculty ratio of 11:1. Areas of study include business education law politics arts engineering and science. It also enrolls students in a number of internship research and community outreach programs.

Financial Performance

Gonzaga University reported operating revenue of $257 million for fiscal 2012. Most of the university's revenues come from student tuition and fees; other sources of income include auxiliary enterprises endowment income and government grants and contracts. The university is supported by endowment funds totaling some $148 million.

Strategy

In 2013 the university launched a construction project to add a $60 million 170000-sq. ft. University Center to the Gonzaga campus. It also built a new $6 million tennis and golf center.

Gonzaga also adds new educational programs to enhance services for students. For instance it launched a new nursing doctorate program in 2013.

EXECUTIVES

Chancellor, Father Bernard J. Coughlin
VP Finance, Charles J. Murphy
VP University Relations, Margot J. Stanfield
VP Student Life, Sue D. Weitz
Corporate Counsel, Michael Casey
VP Mission, Father Patrick Lee
President, Thayne M. McCulloh
University VP, Harry H. Sladich
President Council, Young Alumni
Associate Director Operations, Brian Kenny
Department Secretary, Jamie Kelp
Executive Vice President, Earl F. Martin

LOCATIONS

HQ: THE CORPORATION OF GONZAGA UNIVERSITY
502 E BOONE AVE, SPOKANE, WA 99258-1774
Phone: 509-328-4220
Web: WWW.GONZAGA.EDU

PRODUCTS/OPERATIONS

Selected Schools and Colleges

College of Arts and Sciences
School of Business Administration
School of Education
School of Engineering
School of Law
School of Professional Studies

2012 Revenues

	% of total
Tuition & fees	80
Auxiliary enterprises	11
Net assets released from restriction	3
Unrestricted contributions	1
Organized activities	1
Government grants & contracts	1
Other	3
Total	100

HISTORICAL FINANCIALS

Company Type: Private

Income Statement FYE: May 31

	REVENUE ($ mil.)	NET INCOME ($ mil.)	NET PROFIT MARGIN	EMPLOYEES
05/12	194	12	6.4%	650
05/11	186	36	19.8%	—
05/09	177	24	13.8%	—
05/09	165	(39)	—	—
Annual Growth	5.6%	—	—	—

2012 Year-End Financials

Debt ratio: —
Return on equity: 6.40%
Cash ($ mil.): 57
Current ratio: —
Long-term debt ($ mil.): —
Dividends
Yield: —
Payout: —
Market value ($ mil.): —

THE CORPORATION OF MERCER UNIVERSITY

Mercer University covers a lot of Georgia with one campus in Macon another in Atlanta and a third in Savannah. The main campus in Macon includes the Walter F. George School of Law (one of the nation's oldest law schools) while The Cecil B. Day Graduate and Professional campus in Atlanta includes schools of theology pharmacy and nursing. Savannah is home to a new four-year M.D. program at the Mercer School of Medicine at Memorial University Medical Center. The university which has a total enrollment of more than 8300 students also has educational centers in Douglas County Henry County and Eastman. Mercer was founded in 1833 by Jesse Mercer a prominent Georgia Baptist.

EXECUTIVES

President, William D. Underwood
Senior Vice President for Marketing Communications & Chief of Staff, Larry D. Brumley
Administrative Assistant to SVP Marketing Communications, Debra Leahy
Administrative Assistant to President, Vonne Sheffield
Provost, Wallace L. Daniel

LOCATIONS

HQ: THE CORPORATION OF MERCER UNIVERSITY
1400 COLEMAN AVE, MACON, GA 31207-0001
Phone: 478-301-2700
Web: WWW.MERCER.EDU

COMPETITORS

Baylor University
Benedict College
Clark Atlanta University
Georgia Southern University
Interdenominational Theological Center
Kennesaw State University
Morris College
Spelman College
University of Mobile
University of West Georgia

HISTORICAL FINANCIALS

Company Type: Private

Income Statement FYE: June 30

	REVENUE ($ mil.)	NET INCOME ($ mil.)	NET PROFIT MARGIN	EMPLOYEES
06/11	270	8	3.0%	1,658
06/10	255	0	0.2%	—
06/09	235	0	—	—
06/08	263	40	15.3%	—
Annual Growth	0.8%	(41.6%)	—	—

2011 Year-End Financials

Debt ratio: —
Return on equity: 3.00%
Cash ($ mil.): 28
Current ratio: —
Long-term debt ($ mil.): —
Dividends
Yield: —
Payout: —
Market value ($ mil.): —

THE DAVID AND LUCILE PACKARD FOUNDATION

One of the wealthiest philanthropic organizations in the US The David and Lucile Packard Foundation primarily provides grants to not-for-profit entities operating in three areas: conservation and science; children families and communities; and population. The foundation has approximately $6.2 billion in assets and in 2006 awarded nearly $225 million in national and international grants with an extra focus on Northern California's Monterey San Mateo Santa Clara and Santa Cruz counties. The late David Packard (cofounder of Hewlett-Packard) and his wife the late Lucile Salter Packard created the foundation in 1964. Their children now run the organization.

EXECUTIVES

Director Organizational Effectiveness, Stephanie McAuliffe
VP and CFO, George A. Vera, age 66
Vice Chairman, Julie E. Packard
Vice Chairman, Nancy Packard Burnett
Chairman, Susan Packard Orr
President and CEO, Carol S. Larson, age 52
Director Children Families and Communities, Lois Salisbury
VP and Director Communications, Chris DeCardy
Senior Program Manager Population, Sono Aibe
Director Conservation and Science, Walter Reid
Chief Investment Officer, John H. Moehling
Director Program-Related Investments, Mary Anne Rodgers
Director Local Grantmaking, Irene Wong
Director Evaluation, Gale Berkowitz
Director Population, Musimbi Kanyoro
Controller, Kenneth (Ken) Tsuboi
Director Operations and Technology, Matthew D. (Matt) Sharp
Vice President Chief Financial Officer, Craig Neyman
Vice Chairman, Julie E. Packard
Vice Chairman, Nancy Packard Burnett
President and CEO, Carol S. Larson, age 52
Auditors: Deloitte&ToucheLLP

LOCATIONS

HQ: THE DAVID AND LUCILE PACKARD FOUNDATION
300 2ND ST, LOS ALTOS, CA 94022-3694
Phone: 650-948-7658
Web: WWW.PACKARD.ORG

HISTORICAL FINANCIALS

Company Type: Private

Income Statement FYE: December 31

	REVENUE ($ mil.)	NET INCOME ($ mil.)	NET PROFIT MARGIN	EMPLOYEES
12/10	701	412	58.8%	85
12/09	398	74	18.8%	—
12/06	809	587	72.6%	—
12/05	0	0	69.6%	—
Annual Growth	302.5%	289.2%	—	—

2010 Year-End Financials

Debt ratio: —
Return on equity: 58.80%
Cash ($ mil.): 213
Current ratio: 1.60
Long-term debt ($ mil.): —
Dividends
Yield: —
Payout: —
Market value ($ mil.): —

THE DELONG CO INC

LOCATIONS

HQ: THE DELONG CO INC
513 FRONT ST, CLINTON, WI 53525
Phone: 6086762255
Web: WWW.DELONGCOMPANY.COM

HISTORICAL FINANCIALS

Company Type: Private

Income Statement FYE: September 30

	REVENUE ($ mil.)	NET INCOME ($ mil.)	NET PROFIT MARGIN	EMPLOYEES
09/14	1,306	19	1.5%	250
09/13	1,326	25	1.9%	—
09/12	0	22	—	—
09/11	995	0	—	—
Annual Growth	9.5%	—	—	—

2014 Year-End Financials

Debt ratio: —
Return on equity: 1.50%
Cash ($ mil.): 16
Current ratio: 0.90
Long-term debt ($ mil.): —
Dividends
Yield: —
Payout: —
Market value ($ mil.): —

THE DOUGLAS STEWART COMPANY INC

LOCATIONS

HQ: THE DOUGLAS STEWART COMPANY INC
2402 ADVANCE RD, MADISON, WI 537186737
Phone: 6082211155
Web: WWW.DSTEWART.COM

HISTORICAL FINANCIALS

Company Type: Private

Income Statement FYE: March 31

	REVENUE ($ mil.)	NET INCOME ($ mil.)	NET PROFIT MARGIN	EMPLOYEES
03/11	286	6	2.4%	164
03/10	267	8	3.3%	—
03/09	1,389	0	—	—
Annual Growth	(54.6%)	53432.0%	—	—

2011 Year-End Financials

Debt ratio: —
Return on equity: 2.40%
Cash ($ mil.): 7
Current ratio: 1.20
Long-term debt ($ mil.): —
Dividends
Yield: —
Payout: —
Market value ($ mil.): —

THE DREES COMPANY

The Drees Company is a big homebuilder in Cincinnati and one of the nation's top private builders. Drees targets first-time and move-up buyers with homes that are priced from about $100000 to more than $1 million. Drees also builds condominiums townhomes and patio homes. Its homes portfolio ranges from its former Zaring Premier Homes luxury division to the company's more financially accessible and modest Marquis Homes division. Drees is active in Florida Indiana Kentucky Maryland North Carolina Ohio Tennessee Texas Virginia and Washington DC. The family-owned firm was founded in 1928.

OperationsIn addition to home building architecture energy efficiency upgrades and design services Drees also provides new construction financing solutions through its subsidiary and mortgage lending business First Equity Mortgage which has closed more than $1 billion in loans.Geographic ReachHeadquartered in Fort Mitchell Kentucky Drees operates across nearly 10 states in cities including Cincinnati and Cleveland Ohio; Indianapolis; Nashville; Raleigh North Carolina; Jacksonville Florida; Austin Houston and Dallas Texas; and the Greater Washington DC area.Sales and MarketingIn recent years Drees has concentrated on the fast-growing "move up" segment market targeting home buyers looking to upgrade into larger houses.In 2012 Drees converted its longtime Zaring Premier Homes luxury brand name to its flagship Drees Homes brand. While the move required rebranding in the greater Cincinnati area Drees is banking on its brand reputation and recognition. It also allowed the residential homebuilder to consolidate its advertising sales and marketing efforts. Financial PerformanceWhile full details of the private company could not be found Drees' CEO David Drees announced in July 2013 that he expected the company to reach $629 million in revenue by April 1 2014. Looking further back Drees had revenues as high as $1.2 billion in 2006 which slid dramatically following the financial crisis to $490 million in revenue in 2010. To its benefit Texas markets –specifically Austin and Dallas –remained active throughout the recession. Drees was also helped by entering the recession with a relatively low debt load of $364 million. By March 2013 Drees had sold land to generate cash flow and reduced its debt to $125 million. StrategyRanked among the top 25 largest national homebuilders by BUILDER Magazine Drees has been steadily expanding over the past few years to capitalize on an improving housing market. In recent years Drees has concentrated on the fast-growing and lucrative "move up" segment of the homebuyer's market targeting home owners that are looking to upgrade to larger houses with higher-end amenities. In late 2014 the company landed a $100 million contract to build 237 homes in three Cincinnati-based residential communities with the average house priced between $307000 and $360000. In September 2014 the company entered its first ever foray into the Houston Texas market with plans to price its houses there for more than $300000 –prime pricing to lure these "move up" buyers.Company BackgroundA family-operated enterprise since its founding by immigrant Theodore Drees in 1928 the company is run by the third generation of the Drees family.

EXECUTIVES

President and CEO, David Drees, age 54
Treasurer, Lawrence G. (Larry) Herbst
Division President, David Hausfeld
Vice President Architecture, William T Spears
Vice President Operations, Jack Herbstreit
Vice President Of Architecture, Jeffrey Turner
Vice President National Purchasing, Justin Metz
Regional Vp Of Production Process, John Heeter

LOCATIONS

HQ: THE DREES COMPANY
211 GRANDVIEW DR STE 300, FORT MITCHELL, KY 410172790
Phone: 8595784200
Web: WWW.DREESHOMES.COM

Selected Locations

Florida
Jacksonville
Indiana
Indianapolis
Kentucky
Fort Mitchell
North Carolina
Raleigh
Ohio
Cincinnati
Cleveland
Dayton
Tennessee
Nashville
Texas
Austin
Dallas
Washington DC

COMPETITORS

D.R. Horton
Fischer Homes
KB Home
Lennar
M/I Homes
PulteGroup
The Ryland Group

HISTORICAL FINANCIALS

Company Type: Private

Income Statement FYE: March 31

	REVENUE ($ mil.)	NET INCOME ($ mil.)	NET PROFIT MARGIN	EMPLOYEES
03/14	683	35	5.3%	850
03/13	584	19	3.3%	—
03/12	548	14	2.6%	—
03/11	536	0	—	—
Annual Growth	8.4%	—	—	—

2014 Year-End Financials

Debt ratio: —
Return on equity: 5.30%
Cash ($ mil.): 5
Current ratio: —
Long-term debt ($ mil.): —
Dividends
Yield: —
Payout: —
Market value ($ mil.): —

THE FIRST DISTRICT ASSOCIATION

LOCATIONS

HQ: THE FIRST DISTRICT ASSOCIATION
101 S SWIFT AVE, LITCHFIELD, MN 553552800
Phone: 3206933236
Web: WWW.FIRSTDISTRICT.COM

HISTORICAL FINANCIALS

Company Type: Private

Income Statement FYE: September 30

	REVENUE ($ mil.)	NET INCOME ($ mil.)	NET PROFIT MARGIN	EMPLOYEES
09/14	745	27	3.7%	150
09/13	627	16	2.6%	—
09/12	523	18	3.6%	—
09/11	476	0	—	—
Annual Growth	16.1%	—	—	—

THE FISHEL COMPANY

The Fishel Company reels in revenue by laying out lines. The company (also known as Team Fishel) provides consulting engineering construction management and maintenance services for electric and gas utility and communications infrastructure projects. The aerial and underground utility contractor designs and builds distribution networks for telecommunications cable and broadband television gas transmission and distribution and electric utilities throughout the US. It also counts municipalities state and federal agencies universities commercial building owners financial services companies health care proiders and residential real estate developers among its clients.

Geographic Reach

The Fishel Company is licensed to do business in some two dozen states. It operates from about 25 offices located in Arkansas Arizona California Florida Georgia Kentucky Nevada New Mexico Ohio Oklahoma Pennsylvania Tennessee Texas and Virginia.

Ownership

Kenneth Fishel founded the firm in 1936 as an underground contractor for telephone companies. It is owned by his daughter chairman Diane Fishel Keeler and family.

EXECUTIVES

President CEO, John E. Phillips
VP and CFO, Paul R. Riewe
VP Western Region, William E. (Bill) Pauley
Chairman, Diane Fishel Keeler
VP and CIO, Ken E. Katz
Vice President, Vance Mauldin
Vice President, Scott Homberger

LOCATIONS

HQ: THE FISHEL COMPANY
1366 DUBLIN RD, COLUMBUS, OH 43215-1093
Phone: 614-274-8100
Web: WWW.TEAMFISHEL.COM

PRODUCTS/OPERATIONS

Selected Services

Emergency restoration repair & maintenance
Fiber overbuilds
GPS survey
Network installation
Permitting
Project management
Right of way
Site Design
Utility construction

Selected Markets

Commercial industrial advanced logistics
Electric Distribution & Transmission
Financial & health care
Gas distribution & transmission pipeline
Telecom & broadband cable
Wireless backhaul

COMPETITORS

Dycom
EMCOR
Integrated Electrical Services
MDU Construction Services
MYR Group
MasTec
Pike Electric Corporation
Quanta Services

HISTORICAL FINANCIALS

Company Type: Private

Income Statement FYE: December 31

	REVENUE ($ mil.)	NET INCOME ($ mil.)	NET PROFIT MARGIN	EMPLOYEES
12/12	281	(2)	—	1,400
12/11	174	7	4.5%	—
12/09	162	1	1.1%	—
12/08	182	1	0.6%	—
Annual Growth	11.4%	—	—	—

2012 Year-End Financials

Debt ratio: —
Return on equity: (-0.70%)
Cash ($ mil.): 1
Current ratio: 0.80
Long-term debt ($ mil.): —
Dividends
Yield: —
Payout: —
Market value ($ mil.): —

THE G W VAN KEPPEL COMPANY

If you ask The G. W. Van Keppel Co. being stuck in the middle isn't half bad. The company touts its role as a middle man matching original equipment manufacturers with operators of their heavy duty workhorses. Founded in 1926 it has grown to distribute a slew of construction aggregate and material handling equipment under blue chip brands including Volvo Hyster and Champion Motor Graders. The company also offers repair and maintenance services rental equipment and aftermarket parts for its equipment. G. W. Van Keppel is led by its founder's third generation chairman and president Bill Walker.

Geographic Reach

The company operates through 15 locations crossing Arkansas Iowa Kansas Oklahoma Missouri Wisconsin and Texas.

Operations

G. W. Van Keppel operates through the divisions of Bobcat of Springfield Construction Equipment Material Handling Peerless Conveyor Quarry Supplies and Trench Safety.

Sales and Marketing

The company sells its products through dealers and sales representatives in the US. It targets the aggregate construction mining and material handling markets.

EXECUTIVES

Executive Vice President, Kevin Kientz, age 61

LOCATIONS

HQ: THE G W VAN KEPPEL COMPANY
1801 N 9TH ST, KANSAS CITY, KS 661012023
Phone: 9132814800
Web: WWW.VANKEPPEL.COM

COMPETITORS

Briggs Equipment
DXP Enterprises
Duncan Industrial Solutions
HOLT Texas
J. A. Riggs Tractor
John Henry Foster
Maxim Crane Works
Rocky Duron & Associates
Victor L. Phillips
Warren CAT

HISTORICAL FINANCIALS

Company Type: Private

Income Statement FYE: November 30

	REVENUE ($ mil.)	NET INCOME ($ mil.)	NET PROFIT MARGIN	EMPLOYEES
11/07	163	1	0.8%	200
11/05	139	20	14.8%	—
11/04	115	2	2.1%	—
11/02	106	0	—	—
Annual Growth	9.0%	—	—	—

2007 Year-End Financials

Debt ratio: —
Return on equity: 0.80%
Cash ($ mil.): 1
Current ratio: 0.30
Long-term debt ($ mil.): —
Dividends
Yield: —
Payout: —
Market value ($ mil.): —

THE GARDEN CITY CO-OP INC

LOCATIONS

HQ: THE GARDEN CITY CO-OP INC
106 N 6TH ST, GARDEN CITY, KS 678465545
Phone: 6202756161
Web: WWW.GCCOOP.COM

HISTORICAL FINANCIALS

Company Type: Private

Income Statement FYE: August 31

	REVENUE ($ mil.)	NET INCOME ($ mil.)	NET PROFIT MARGIN	EMPLOYEES
08/08	425	13	3.2%	23
08/07	237	5	2.4%	—
08/06	0	0	—	—
Annual Growth	—	—	—	—

2008 Year-End Financials

Debt ratio: —
Return on equity: 3.20%
Cash ($ mil.): 0
Current ratio: 0.20
Long-term debt ($ mil.): —
Dividends
Yield: —
Payout: —
Market value ($ mil.): —

THE GEORGE J FALTER COMPANY

Auditors: CliftonGundersonLLP

LOCATIONS

HQ: THE GEORGE J FALTER COMPANY
3501 BENSON AVE, BALTIMORE, MD 212271098
Phone: 4106463641
Web: WWW.FALTERFUNDRAISING.COM

COMPETITORS

Atlantic Dominion
C&S Wholesale
Century Distributors
Core-Mark
Eby-Brown
H. T. Hackney
McLane
Nash-Finch

HISTORICAL FINANCIALS

Company Type: Private

Income Statement FYE: December 31

	REVENUE ($ mil.)	NET INCOME ($ mil.)	NET PROFIT MARGIN	EMPLOYEES
12/09	188	0	0.3%	130
12/08*	181	0	0.4%	—
06/07	1,295	0	—	—
Annual Growth	—	4433.1%	—	—

*Fiscal year change

2009 Year-End Financials

Debt ratio: —
Return on equity: 0.30%
Cash ($ mil.): 1
Current ratio: 0.80
Long-term debt ($ mil.): —
Dividends
Yield: —
Payout: —
Market value ($ mil.): —

THE GOLUB CORPORATION

EXECUTIVES

Chairman, Neil M. Golub, age 77
President and CEO, Jerel T. (Jerry) Golub, age 56
VP-HR, Margaret Davenport
VP Public Relations and Consumer Services, Mona J. Golub, age 50
VP Floral Operations, Jon Strom
SVP Administration, David Golub, age 53
Director In-Store Marketing Programs, Jane N. Golub
VP Supply Chain Integration, Thomas (Tom) Bird
VP Produce & Floral Merchandising, Rick Reed

LOCATIONS

HQ: THE GOLUB CORPORATION
461 NOTT ST, SCHENECTADY, NY 123081812
Phone: 5183555000
Web: WWW.PRICECHOPPER.COM

2013 Stores

	No.
New	81
Massachusetts	16
Vermont	15
Connecticut	8
Pennsylvania	8
New	4
Total	132

COMPETITORS

7-Eleven
A&P
ALDI
BJ' s Wholesale Club
Big Y Foods
CVS Caremark
Costco Wholesale
Cumberland Farms
DeMoulas Super Markets
Gerrity' s
Hannaford Bros.
Shaw' s
Stewart' s Shops
Stop & Shop
TOPS Markets
Target Corporation
Wal-Mart
Wegmans

HISTORICAL FINANCIALS

Company Type: Private

Income Statement FYE: April 27

	REVENUE ($ mil.)	NET INCOME ($ mil.)	NET PROFIT MARGIN	EMPLOYEES
04/14	3,472	18	0.5%	21,741
04/13	3,484	24	0.7%	—
04/12	3,627	37	1.0%	—
04/11	3,459	0	—	—
Annual Growth	0.1%	—	—	—

2014 Year-End Financials

Debt ratio: —
Return on equity: 0.50%
Cash ($ mil.): 24
Current ratio: 0.30
Long-term debt ($ mil.): —
Dividends
Yield: —
Payout: —
Market value ($ mil.): —

THE GOOD SAMARITAN HOSPITAL OF MD INC

Good Samaritan Hospital of Maryland provides emergency care and promotes good health in the Baltimore area. The 300-bed hospital operating as MedStar Good Samaritan provides acute medical and specialty services including rehabilitation (50-bed ward) transitional care (30-bed sub-acute ward) orthopedics cancer care cardiology dialysis and women's health as well as serving as a community teaching facility. The hospital founded in 1968 also operates nursing and assisted-living facilities for the elderly and it provides educational seminars diagnostic screening and preventative medical care through its Good Health Center. MedStar Good Samaritan of Maryland is part of the MedStar Health system.

Operations MedStar Good Samaritan has about 370 physicians on its medical staff. It serves about 16000 inpatients and handles some 140000 outpatient visits per year. The hospital's primary specialty centers include spine arthritis and joint replacement clinics.

Financial Performance

MedStar Good Samaritan reported some $327 million in net operating revenues in fiscal 2011. It also had assets of $177 million and stated community benefits (including outreach and charity care) at some $30 million.

Strategy

The hospital is working to provide an increasing variety of specialty services to patients in the Baltimore area. As such in 2012 MedStar Good Samaritan added a wound healing center for the treatment of chronic wounds. The hospital also expanded its community service provisions that year when it expanded its infant and toddler daycare center.

EXECUTIVES

Chairman Department of Medicine, Dana Frank
VP Medical Affairs, Martin L. Binstock
VP Finance, Deana L. Stout
Vice President Operations, Thomas J. Senker
Director Marketing and Communications, Kris Roeder
President, Jeffrey A. Matton
VP Human Resources, Laura E. O'Donnell
VP Patient Care Services Chief Nursing Officer, Shirley Roth
VP Strategic Planning and Business Development, Jennifer Weiss Wilkerson

Media Relations Manager, Debbie Bangledorf
VP Development, Geannine Darby
Chairman Department of Surgery, Dale Buchbinder
President of Medical Staff, Howard Freeland
Chief of Anesthesiology, Michael Sendak
Chairman Emergency Medicine, Kevin Scruggs
Chief of Radiology, Allen Weksberg
Chairman Department of Pathology, Moira Larsen
Chairman Deptartment of Physical Medicine and Rehabilitation, Kenneth Silver
Chairman, Anthony Read
Vice Chairman, Wilmot C. Ball Jr.
Assistant VP Information Services, Janet Decker
Vice President Human Resources, Laura ODonnell
Vice President Strategic Planning and Business Development, Jennifer Weiss Wilkerson ACHE
Director, Herbert Friedman
Director, Kenneth A. Samet, age 56
Vice Chairman, Wilmot C. Ball Jr.
Director, Charles L. Bauermann
Director, Kay G. Bee
Director, Sheldon M. Glusman
Director, W. Kenneth Gue
Director, Davis M. Hahn
Director, Rev Lawrence M. Johnson
Director, Jayne H. McGeehan
Director, Earl Richardon
Director, T. Edgie Russell
Director, James K. Smolev
Director, Jeremy P. Weiner
Auditors: PricewaterhouseCoopersLLP

LOCATIONS

HQ: THE GOOD SAMARITAN HOSPITAL OF MD INC
5601 LOCH RAVEN BLVD, BALTIMORE, MD 21239-2945
Phone: 443-444-3780
Web: WWW.GOODSAM-MD.ORG

PRODUCTS/OPERATIONS

Selected Services and Divisions

Belvedere Green (senior living)
Burn Reconstruction Center
Cancer Care/Oncology
Cardiology/Heart Care
Diabetes/Endocrinology
Diagnostic Imaging
Ear Nose and Throat
Emergency Services
Gastroenterology
Good Health Center
Kidney Care/Nephrology
MedStar Good Samaritan Nursing Center (senior living)
MedStar Pharmacy
Orthopedics
Pain Management
Pediatrics
Physical Therapy
Plastic Surgery
Primary Care Center
Pulmonary Services
Rehabilitation Services
Renal Dialysis
Rheumatology [Rheumatoid Arthritis/Sjgren's Syndrome]
Senior Living
Sleep Center
Sports Medicine
Stroke Rehabilitation
Surgical Services
Transitional Care
Urology
Vascular Services
Weight Management Good Weighs
Women's Health
Woodbourne Woods (senior living)
Wound Healing Center

COMPETITORS

Adventist HealthCare
Anne Arundel Medical Center
Ascension Health
Bon Secours Health
Inova
Johns Hopkins Health System
Levindale Hospital
Novant Health
Catholic Health East
Children' s National Medical Center
Christiana Care
Civista Health
GBMC
Sentara Healthcare
University of Maryland Medical System
Valley Health
Virginia Hospital Center

HISTORICAL FINANCIALS

Company Type: Private

Income Statement FYE: June 30

	REVENUE ($ mil.)	NET INCOME ($ mil.)	NET PROFIT MARGIN	EMPLOYEES
06/12	320	(1)	—	2,146
06/11	331	14	4.2%	—
06/10	322	10	3.2%	—
06/09	314	0	—	—
Annual Growth	0.6%	—	—	—

THE HITE COMPANY

EXECUTIVES

President, T. Scott Lawhead
Director Operations, Rick Gavin
Manager Purchasing, Andy Miller
Director Showroom Operations, Jackie Robertson
Regional Sales Manager East, Tim Arnold
Regional Sales Manager West, John Brady

LOCATIONS

HQ: THE HITE COMPANY
3101 BEALE AVE, ALTOONA, PA 166011509
Phone: 8149446121
Web: WWW.HITELIGHTING.COM

PRODUCTS/OPERATIONS

Selected Products

Automation and control
Data communications
Electrical supplies
Heating and ventilations
Lamps and lighting
Power quality
Professional audio/video
Surveillance/security

COMPETITORS

Graybar Electric
Rexel Inc.
W.W. Grainger

HISTORICAL FINANCIALS

Company Type: Private

Income Statement FYE: December 31

	REVENUE ($ mil.)	NET INCOME ($ mil.)	NET PROFIT MARGIN	EMPLOYEES
12/12	126	0	—	230
12/11	96	0	—	—
12/10	96	0	—	—
12/09	96	0	—	—
Annual Growth	9.7%	—	—	—

2012 Year-End Financials

Debt ratio: —
Return on equity: —
Cash ($ mil.): 0
Current ratio: 0.80
Long-term debt ($ mil.): —
Dividends
Yield: —
Payout: —
Market value ($ mil.): —

THE INGALLS MEMORIAL HOSPITAL

Founded by Chicago-area industrialist Frederick Ingalls in 1923 Ingalls Memorial Hospital still serves Chicago's south suburbs. With more than 560 beds the main hospital offers a variety of acute and tertiary health care services including cancer treatment cardiovascular care orthopedic surgery rehabilitation services neurosurgery women's health and other clinical services. It also includes specialty centers in areas such as sleep therapy and addiction treatment. Ingalls Memorial Hospital also acts as a health system operating outpatient offices and clinics and providing home health and hospice services in the area.

Geographic Reach

Ingalls Memorial Hospital's main campus encompasses some 22 acres in the south suburbs of Chicago. Its family and urgent care centers are located in Calumet City Flossmoor Matteson and Tinley Park. The system also includes rehabilitation centers in Calumet City and South Holland; a wellness center in Homewood; and a cancer and surgery center in Tinley Park.

Operations

Ingalls Memorial Hospital employs 450 physicians who specialize in 30 fields. The medical center sees about 18000 inpatient admissions per year. It also handles about 1100 births and more than 47000 emergency department visits annually.

In addition to the hospital the health system includes a handful of family care centers and several urgent care and surgery clinics as well as outpatient rehabilitation wellness and cancer support centers. Ingalls Health System also operates home health and hospice agencies and it provides community health screenings and other outreach programs.

Strategy To improve primary care services Ingalls Memorial Hospital has conducted expansion and renovation efforts at several of its family clinic locations in recent years. It is also growing its range of advanced cancer treatment offerings; its infusion center was the first Chicago-area cancer center to administer a new prostate cancer drug Provinge in 2012.

EXECUTIVES

Nursing Director, Jill Zaki
Vp Of Corp Affairs Svs, Gdiane Jacoby
Director Icu/coronary Care Unit, Paul Zielske
Director Of Home Healthcare, Sondra Enger
Vp Chief Information Officer, Michael Devore
Rph, Martha Jelski
Vice President For Revenue Management, John Czech
Vice President Patient Care Service, Christine Rosner
Rph, Anna Niedzwiecki
Medical Director, Amjad Akhtar
Interim Vice President And Cno, Marian Purdue
Director Of Nursing, Shirley Corbett
Vice President, Rick Zehr
Assistant Vice President Investment, Eric Steuer
Interim Associate Vice President Of Financial Services, Siva Schulman
Chief Information Officer And Vice President Infor, David Hoddes
Director Of Radiology, Gagan Ahuja
Rph, Charlotte Clark
Vice President Development Fnd, Joseph Moser
Nursing Services Director, Kathy Mikols
Board Member, Richard King

Board Member, Samuel Cutrara
Board Member, Lyndell Beckham
Board Of Directors, Nathaniel Sutton

LOCATIONS

HQ: THE INGALLS MEMORIAL HOSPITAL
1 INGALLS DR, HARVEY, IL 60426-3558
Phone: 708-333-2300
Web: WWW.INGALLS.ORG

PRODUCTS/OPERATIONS

Selected Services

Advanced Orthopedic Institute
- Joint Center
- Spine Center
- Sports Medicine
- Rehabilitative Services

Behavioral Health
- Inpatient Adult Care
- Addictions
- Adolescent
- Depression Risk

Cancer Care
- Newly Diagnosed
- Research
- Technology and Treatments

Heart and Vascular
- Diabetes
- Heart Care Center
- Leg Veins
- Stroke

Home Care and Hospice
- Palliative Care

Interventional Radiology
- Interventional Oncology
- Uterine Fibroids
- Vein Clinic

Irwin Retina Center
- Clinical Research
- Diabetic Retinopathy
- Macular Degeneration

Neurosciences
- Stroke
- Concussion Program
- Sleep Centers

Occupational Health
- Employer Resource Center
- Worksite Wellness and Prevention

Outpatient Services
- Advanced Imaging
- Pharmacy
- Same Day Surgery
- Urgent Aid

Rehabilitation Services
- Acute Care
- Day Rehabilitation
- Home Care
- Inpatient Rehabilitation
- Outpatient Rehabilitation

Wellness
- Complementary Medicine
- Nutrition and Weight Management

Women's Services
- Breast Center
- Maternity Unit
- Osteoporosis
- Uterine Fibroids

Additional Services
- Complementary Medicine
- Dermatology
- Diabetes
- Dialysis
- Ear/Nose/Throat
- Gastroenterology
- Occupational Health
- Ophthalmology
- Pain Management
- Pediatrics
- Rheumatology
- Therapies
- Urinary Incontinence
- Weight Management
- Wound Care

COMPETITORS

Advocate Health Care
Alexian Brothers Health System
Loyola University Health System
MetroSouth Medical
Mount Sinai Hospital
NorthShore University HealthSystem
Rush System for Health
Saint Margaret Mercy Healthcare
St. Bernard Hospital and Health Care Center
Vanguard MacNeal Hospital
WellGroup HealthPartners

HISTORICAL FINANCIALS

Company Type: Private

Income Statement FYE: September 30

	REVENUE ($ mil.)	NET INCOME ($ mil.)	NET PROFIT MARGIN	EMPLOYEES
09/12	293	36	12.6%	2,296
09/09	267	(15)	—	—
09/07	270	(39)	—	—
09/07	264	24	9.2%	—
Annual Growth	2.1%	8.8%	—	—

2012 Year-End Financials

Debt ratio: —	
Return on equity: 12.60%	Dividends
Cash ($ mil.): 3	Yield: —
Current ratio: 0.90	Payout: —
Long-term debt ($ mil.): —	Market value ($ mil.): —

THE INSTITUTE OF ELECTRICAL AND ELECTRONICS ENGINEERS INCORPORAT

A leading technology-related professional group The Institute of Electrical and Electronics Engineers (IEEE) has almost 416000 members including 100000-plus students in 160 countries. The IEEE provides technical and professional information to members on topics such as aerospace systems biomedical engineering computers consumer electronics electric power and telecommunications. It sponsors more than 1300 annual conferences and publishes a variety of technical literature including journals magazines and conference proceedings. The IEEE was formed in 1964 in a combination of the American Institute of Electrical Engineers (founded in 1884) and the Institute of Radio Engineers (founded in 1912).

Geographic Reach

Nearly 50% of IEEE members are in the US. China India and the Pacific Rim countries account for nearly a quarter of its membership followed by Europe the Middle East and Africa with 18%. Latin America and Canada are each home to about 4% of IEEE members.

Financial Analysis

The IEEE's 2011 revenue fell by more than 2% vs. 2010 to $383.8 million from about $393 million. Total expenses exceeded revenue in 2011. Total assets declined over the same period: from $438.4 million in 2010 to $436.2 million last year. The decrease was primarily due to an investment loss offset by an increase in capitalized equipment related to IEEE Business Platform.

Strategy

The institute caters to engineers from a wide range of specialties —from aerospace and electronic systems to ultrasonics and frequency control –with nearly 40 different types of society memberships. The organization's membership grew despite the recent downturn in the global economy and continues to increase during the recovery. Among the IEEE more than one-fifth of its members are under the age of 30 and men outnumber women 9:1.

EXECUTIVES

General Counsel and Chief Compliance Officer, Eileen M. Lach, age 63
President CEO, Moshe Kam
President and CEO, Peter W. Staecker
Executive Director, E. James (Jim) Prendergast
Managing Director IEEE-USA, Chris Brantley
Staff Executive Human Resources, Elizabeth (Betsy) Davis
Staff Executive Publications, Anthony Durniak
Managing Director Educational Activities, Doug Gorham
Managing Director Member and Geographic Activities, Cecelia Jankowski
Staff Executive Corporate Strategy, Matt Loeb
Chief Marketing Officer, Patrick D. Mahoney
Staff Executive Information Technology and Chief Information Officer, Alexander Pasik
CFO, Thomas Siegert
Managing Director Technical Activities, Mary Ward-Callan
Corporate Sales Manager, Emily Csernica
Corporate Account Manager East, James Boruch
Account Manager, Michael Petro
Account Manager, Wendy McCarville
Account Manager East, Joe Vaitkus
Account Manager Central, Barry Holquist
Corporate Account Manager West, Molly Faust
President Principal Engineer, Bruno Lequesne
President IEEE Power Electronics Society PELS, Dushan Boroyevich
President IEEE Product Safety Engineering Society PSES, Elya Joffe
President IEEE Power and Energy Society PES, Noel Schulz
President IEEE-USA, Russell Lefevre
President-Elect and Director, Peter W. Staecker
Executive Director, E. James (Jim) Prendergast
Auditors: Ernst&YoungLLP

LOCATIONS

HQ: THE INSTITUTE OF ELECTRICAL AND ELECTRONICS ENGINEERS INCORPORAT
3 PARK AVE FL 17, NEW YORK, NY 10016-5902
Phone: 732-981-0060
Web: WWW.IEEE.ORG

2011 Members

	% of total
US	50
India China & Pacific	24
Europe Middle East &	18
Canada	4
Latin	4
Total	**100**

PRODUCTS/OPERATIONS

Selected IEEE Societies

Aerospace and Electronic Systems
Antennas and Propagation
Broadcast Technology
Circuits and Systems
Communications
Computational Intelligence
Electromagnetic Compatibility
Geoscience and Remote Sensing

HISTORICAL FINANCIALS

Company Type: Private

Income Statement FYE: December 31

	REVENUE ($ mil.)	NET INCOME ($ mil.)	NET PROFIT MARGIN	EMPLOYEES
12/11	383	(16)		1,068
12/09	338	18	5.5%	—
12/08	0	0	—	—
12/06	330	40	12.3%	—
Annual Growth	3.0%	—	—	—

2011 Year-End Financials

Debt ratio: —
Return on equity: (-4.40%)
Cash ($ mil.): 12
Current ratio: 0.20
Long-term debt ($ mil.): —
Dividends
Yield: —
Payout: —
Market value ($ mil.): —

THE JACKSON LABORATORY

The Jackson Laboratory was into genetics before genetics was cool. Founded in 1929 the not-for-profit organization is a leading researcher of human diseases their causes and their potential cures. Much of its research into mammalian genetics is focused on mice which share a similar genetic makeup to humans. In addition to its own research in areas such as cancer immunology and metabolic disease the organization maintains colonies of mice and supplies them under the brand name JAX to other laboratories around the globe. Additionally The Jackson Laboratory offers educational programs –including internships workshops and predoctoral programs –for both current and future scientists.

Geographic Reach

The company has locations in Sacramento California; Farmington Connecticut; and Bar Harbor Maine.

Financial Performance

The Jackson Laboratory receives operating revenue from public sector support in the form of federal grants private sector support in the form of private foundation grants philanthropic contributions and resource revenue in the form of cost and fees collected for JAX Mice & Services its service for supplying mice models used for research. The organization's operating revenue increased by 12% in 2011 over 2010 due to a 8% spike in government support and a 14% uptick in revenue from JAX Mice & Services.

Strategy

The Jackson Laboratory in 2012 finished its purchase of the former Lowe's building in Ellsworth Maine following a strategy of Ellsworth expansion and also launched a $27 million expansion of its JAX West facility in Sacramento.

EXECUTIVES

Treasurer, Daniel R. (Dan) Tishman, age 58
Secretary, William Rudolf
Director Scientific Program Development, Barbara J. Tennent
Executive Vice President Chief Operating Officer, Charles E. (Chuck) Hewett
Director Laboratory Animal Health Services, Peggy J. Danneman
Director Education Office, Jon Geiger
Vice President for Research, Robert Braun
Director Genetic Resources and Senior Research Scientist, Leah Rae Donahue
VP Advancement and External Relations, Michael E. Hyde
Chief Financial Officer, Linda Jensen
Senior Director Scientific Services, Valerie Scott
President and CEO, Edison Liu
Chairman, Leo A. Holt
Communications Director Business hours, Barry Teater
Vice President for Development and Communications, Kristen Rozansky
Vice President for External Affairs and Strategic Partnerships, Michael E. Hyde

LOCATIONS

HQ: THE JACKSON LABORATORY
600 MAIN ST, BAR HARBOR, ME 04609-1500
Phone: 207-288-6000
Web: WWW.LIBRARY.JAX.ORG

COMPETITORS

Caliper Life Sciences
Charles River Laboratories
Deltagen
Harlan Laboratories
Howard Hughes Medical Institute
Taconic Farms
Whitehead Institute for Biomedical Research

HISTORICAL FINANCIALS

Company Type: Private

Income Statement FYE: May 31

	REVENUE ($ mil.)	NET INCOME ($ mil.)	NET PROFIT MARGIN	EMPLOYEES
05/10	200	29	14.9%	1,300
05/09	166	(25)	—	—
05/09	143	0	—	—
Annual Growth	—181630.1%		—	—

2010 Year-End Financials

Debt ratio: —
Return on equity: 14.90%
Cash ($ mil.): 74
Current ratio: 0.70
Long-term debt ($ mil.): —
Dividends
Yield: —
Payout: —
Market value ($ mil.): —

THE JEFFERSON COUNTY ASSISTED HOUSING CORPORATION

LOCATIONS

HQ: THE JEFFERSON COUNTY ASSISTED HOUSING CORPORATION
500 OFFICE PARK DR # 300, MOUNTAIN BRK, AL 352232437
Phone: 2054452800

HISTORICAL FINANCIALS

Company Type: Private

Income Statement FYE: December 31

	REVENUE ($ mil.)	NET INCOME ($ mil.)	NET PROFIT MARGIN	EMPLOYEES
12/09	407	6	1.7%	83
12/08	17	8	47.8%	—
12/07	14	8	56.2%	—
12/05	22	0	—	—
Annual Growth	106.9%	—	—	—

2009 Year-End Financials

Debt ratio: —
Return on equity: 1.70%
Cash ($ mil.): 23
Current ratio: —
Long-term debt ($ mil.): —
Dividends
Yield: —
Payout: —
Market value ($ mil.): —

THE JERRY BROWN CO INC

LOCATIONS

HQ: THE JERRY BROWN CO INC
2690 PRAIRIE RD, EUGENE, OR 974029747
Phone: 5419982300
Web: WWW.JBCO.COM

HISTORICAL FINANCIALS

Company Type: Private

Income Statement FYE: December 31

	REVENUE ($ mil.)	NET INCOME ($ mil.)	NET PROFIT MARGIN	EMPLOYEES
12/10	379	2	0.6%	60
12/09	316	2	0.7%	—
12/08	1,532	0	—	—
Annual Growth	(50.3%)	24239.9%	—	—

2010 Year-End Financials

Debt ratio: —
Return on equity: 0.60%
Cash ($ mil.): 2
Current ratio: 1.00
Long-term debt ($ mil.): —
Dividends
Yield: —
Payout: —
Market value ($ mil.): —

THE JUDGE GROUP INC

If your business requires staffing technology consulting or training services The Judge Group will be predisposed to render a verdict in your favor. The company offers temporary and permanent employee placement services in a wide variety of service and manufacturing sectors but specializes in technology staffing. The company's technology consulting services address such areas as enterprise content management and strategy. It also offers training for IT-related and other professional functions through its Berkeley division. Martin Judge founded the company in 1970.

Geographic Reach

The Judge Group operates from a network of more than 25 offices throughout the US and has locations in Asia and Canada.

Strategy

The company's growth strategy revolves around the opening of offices in select markets and by entering alliances with other human resources services firms. In 2011 it launched offices in Houston Milwaukee and Phoenix. The following year it established an office in the important metropolitan area of Baltimore. In 2013 it opened its newest office in Ottawa Ontario.

The Judge Group has also expanded its international reach by launching Judge China a firm which provides clients with consulting expertise for accessing markets in the most populous country in the world through offices in Beijing and Shanghai.

The Judge Group launched its newest division Veterans in Professional Careers (VIP Careers) in 2013. The new division's strategy is to reduce the unemployment rate of military veterans wounded warriors and military spouses by providing consulting staffing and training services.

EXECUTIVES

Chief Operating Officer, Katy A. Wiercinski
President Judge Inc., Richard T. Furlano, age 63
Chief Financial Officer, Robert G. Alessandrini, $137,308 total compensation
CEO, Martin E. Judge Jr., $588,665 total compensation
President Judge Executive Search, Stephen D. Green
President, Gary R. Morris
CIO, Kenneth F. Krieger
President North America, Brian T. Anderson
EVP, Dennis F. Judge Jr.
President Berkeley Training, Peter Pedone
President Judge Unified Communications, James D. Miner
Global Managing Director, Scott O. Wilson
Director National Recruiting Center, Frank Santoro
Vice President Strategic Account Mgmt, Brian P. Propp
EVP Sales, Michael Tedesco
President Judge Consulting, Edward Carmody
President Human Capital Management Solutions, Sanjay M. Shah

LOCATIONS

HQ: THE JUDGE GROUP INC
300 CONSHOHOCKEN STATE RD # 300, CONSHOHOCKEN, PA 19428-3801
Phone: 610-667-7700
Web: WWW.JUDGE.COM

PRODUCTS/OPERATIONS

Selected Services

Corporate training
- Custom content development
- Information technology training
- Professional development
- Project staffing and logistics

Enterprise-wide staffing
- Financial services
- Food/beverage
- Government
- Health care
- Insurance
- Manufacturing
- Pharmaceutical
- Retail/supermarkets
- Technology
- Utilities/telecom
- Wholesale distribution

Technology consulting
- Application design and development
- Audio visual design and implementation
- E-discovery and compliance
- Enterprise content management
- Research validation and compliance
- SAP implementation services
- Technology strategy and architecture

COMPETITORS

Accenture	Kenexa
Adecco	Kforce
Aquent	ManpowerGroup
Butler America	NTT Data
CDI	RCM Technologies
IBM Global Services	Taleo
Kelly Services	Unisys

HISTORICAL FINANCIALS

Company Type: Private

Income Statement FYE: September 30

	REVENUE ($ mil.)	NET INCOME ($ mil.)	NET PROFIT MARGIN	EMPLOYEES
09/12	251	2	1.2%	570
09/11	222	2	1.2%	—
09/08	188	2	1.5%	—
09/07	166	3	2.1%	—
Annual Growth	8.6%	(3.4%)	—	—

2012 Year-End Financials

Debt ratio: —
Return on equity: 1.20%
Cash ($ mil.): 1
Current ratio: 2.40
Long-term debt ($ mil.): —
Dividends
Yield: —
Payout: —
Market value ($ mil.): —

THE KLEINFELDER GROUP INC

The Kleinfelder Group isn't afraid to get its hands dirty. Since its start as a materials testing lab in 1961 the company has expanded to become one of the largest engineering consulting and design groups in the US. Kleinfelder's operating subsidiaries offer soils and materials testing geotechnical engineering construction management and environmental services. With about 50 domestic offices and locations in Australia and Guam the group targets the energy transportation water commercial/industrial government and education markets; projects run the gamut from building underground parking garages to establishing wind farms. Jim Kleinfelder who retired in 1993 founded the employee-owned company.

Geographic Reach

Kleinfelder has operations in the US and Calgary Canada. It opened offices in Australia and Guam in 2010.

Strategy

Kleinfelder is expanding at home and abroad though organic growth and frequent acquisitions of environmental services firms. It entered Canada in 2012 with an office in Calgary and continued its expansion in Australia (begun in 2010) with a pair of acquisitions there.

In 2011 the firm introduced a program to certify greenhouse gas emissions to help clients remain compliant in clean air regulations. Two years earlier it launched a nuclear services division to serve the uranium mining and milling power generation and spent-fuel storage sectors.

Mergers and Acquisitions

In 2012 Kleinfelder acquired two Australian environmental services firms: Ecobiological Group and Alliance Environmental Engineering and Consulting Pty Ltd.. The twin purchases strengthen Kleinfelder's position in the retail petroleum assessment and remediation market there and help the company grow its multinational client list throughout Australia and the Asia-Pacific Region.

Closer to home Kleinfelder in 2013 purchased Simon Wong Engineering (SWE) a San Diego-based firm providing project management structural and bridge engineering services construction management and inspection services and public relations support to the transportation and water markets in California to strengthen its resources to serve its global clients. The SWE purchase followed two domestic acquisitions: Omni Environmental in Princeton New Jersey and Houston-based Corrigan Consulting in 2012. In 2011 it purchased InSite Environmental in Stockton California.

Ownership

The Kleinfelder Group is owned by its employees.

EXECUTIVES

SVP Sales and Marketing, Larry Peterson
Chief Strategy Officer, Kevin E. Pottmeyer
President Chief Executive Officer, William C. (Bill) Siegel
VP Corporate Marketing and Communications, Terry Reynolds
Chief Financial Officer, John M. Pilkington
SVP and Manager Energy Division, Michael Kesler
VP and General Counsel, Chuck Alpert
Chief Information Officer, Linda Lannen
Chief Legal Officer, Charles S. Alpert

LOCATIONS

HQ: THE KLEINFELDER GROUP INC
5015 SHOREHAM PL, SAN DIEGO, CA 92122-5926
Phone: 858-320-2000
Web: WWW.KLEINFELDER.COM

PRODUCTS/OPERATIONS

Selected Acquisitions

2013
- Simon Wong Engineering (San Diego CA; project management)

2012
- Alliance Environmental Engineering & Consulting Pty Ltd. (St. Kilda Victoria Australia; environmental engineering)
- Ecobiological Group (New South Wales Australia; ecological and brushfire consultancy)
- Omni Environmental (Princeton NJ; environmental consulting)
- Corrigan Consulting Inc. (Houston TX; environmental and professional engineering services)

Selected Services

Architecture
Chemical data management
Construction testing
Dewatering and infiltration
Due diligence
Ecological risk
Engineering geology
Environmental and process engineering design
Geotechnical engineering
GIS

Hydraulics
Hydrogeology
Materials laboratory testing
Numerical earthquake engineering
Pavement engineering
Regulatory compliance
Retaining walls
Risk assessment
Site development
Solid waste
Seismic earthquake engineering
Structural engineering
Tunneling and deep foundation engineering
Water/wastewater engineering

COMPETITORS

AECOM
ATC Associates
CH2M HILL
Cadmus Group
Dudek
Geocon Group
HNTB Companies
Holguin Fahan & Associates
Jacobs Engineering
LCS Constructors
Leighton Group
Ninyo & Moore
Precision Assessment Technology
Professional Service Industries
RECON Environmental
SCS Tracer Environmental
URS
USA Environmental
Willdan Geotechnical

HISTORICAL FINANCIALS

Company Type: Private

Income Statement FYE: March 31

	REVENUE ($ mil.)	NET INCOME ($ mil.)	NET PROFIT MARGIN	EMPLOYEES
03/13	224	1	0.5%	1,522
03/12	216	5	2.5%	—
03/10	222	8	3.7%	—
03/10	221	7	3.2%	—
Annual Growth	0.4%	(47.9%)	—	—

2013 Year-End Financials

Debt ratio: —
Return on equity: 0.50%
Cash ($ mil.): 6
Current ratio: 1.10
Long-term debt ($ mil.): —
Dividends
Yield: —
Payout: —
Market value ($ mil.): —

THE LANE CONSTRUCTION CORPORATION

EXECUTIVES

EVP and CFO, James M. Ferrell
President and CEO, Robert E. (Bob) Alger
EVP Administration and Secretary, Donald P. Dobbs
EVP and Chief Development Officer, Michael M. Cote
EVP and COO, Kirk D. Junco
VP CIO Treasurer and Assistant Secretary, Vincent J. Caiola
Director Taxes Assistant Secretary and Assistant Treasurer, Ann M. Falsey
EVP and General Counsel, Jay S. Cruickshank
EVP Operations, David F. Benton
VP Human Resources, Kristy L. Blackman
Regional VP Southeast Region, James O. Hughes
Regional VP Northeast Region, Scott A. Leach
VP Pursuits Design-Build and JV Bid-Build Projects, David J. Rankin
Vice President Chief Marketing Officer, Michael L. Johnson
Assistant Vice President Engineering, Thomas R. Larson
Assistant Vice President Controller, Mark J. Tomkalski
VP Pursuits P3 and Alternative Financing Projects, Joseph P. Lark
Regional VP Mid-Atlantic Region, Mark A. Schiller
Regional VP Mid-South Region, Michael R. Hindt
Regional VP South Central Region, Lawrence G. Hurley

LOCATIONS

HQ: THE LANE CONSTRUCTION CORPORATION
90 FIELDSTONE CT, CHESHIRE, CT 064101212
Phone: 2032353351
Web: WWW.LANECONSTRUCT.COM

PRODUCTS/OPERATIONS

Selected Projects
Airports
Bridges
Design-Build
Federal
Heavy Civil
Highways
Public Private Partnerships
Plants & Paving
Rail
Specialty Paving

Selected Divisions
Civil Wall Solutions
Cold River Materials Prestress of the Carolinas
Senate Asphalt
Sunquip
Sunrise Materials
Virginia Paving Company
Virginia Sun & Lighting Company
Wardwell
White Bros.

COMPETITORS

Angelo Iafrate
Austin Industries
Balfour Beatty Inc
Bechtel
Clark Enterprises
Granite Construction
J.F. White Contracting
MBC Holding
Peter Kiewit Sons'
Sargent Corp
Skanska USA Civil
The Middlesex Corporation
Turner Corporation
Tutor-Saliba
Vecellio & Grogan
Walsh Group

HISTORICAL FINANCIALS

Company Type: Private

Income Statement FYE: December 31

	REVENUE ($ mil.)	NET INCOME ($ mil.)	NET PROFIT MARGIN	EMPLOYEES
12/13	1,091	(22)	—	3,500
12/12	1,229	26	2.2%	—
12/11	1,002	20	2.0%	—
12/09	848	0	—	—
Annual Growth	6.5%	—	—	—

2013 Year-End Financials

Debt ratio: —
Return on equity: (-2.10%)
Cash ($ mil.): 15
Current ratio: 0.90
Long-term debt ($ mil.): —
Dividends
Yield: —
Payout: —
Market value ($ mil.): —

THE MARY IMOGENE BASSETT HOSPITAL

LOCATIONS

HQ: THE MARY IMOGENE BASSETT HOSPITAL
1 ATWELL RD, COOPERSTOWN, NY 133261394
Phone: 6075473456
Web: WWW.BASSETT.ORG

HISTORICAL FINANCIALS

Company Type: Private

Income Statement FYE: December 31

	REVENUE ($ mil.)	NET INCOME ($ mil.)	NET PROFIT MARGIN	EMPLOYEES
12/09	366	1	0.5%	3,200
12/08	336	8	2.6%	
12/07	312	(2)	—	—
12/06	301	0	—	—
Annual Growth	6.7%	—	—	—

2009 Year-End Financials

Debt ratio: —
Return on equity: 0.50%
Cash ($ mil.): 12
Current ratio: 0.60
Long-term debt ($ mil.): —
Dividends
Yield: —
Payout: —
Market value ($ mil.): —

THE MEMORIAL HOSPITAL

The Memorial Hospital known as Memorial Hospital of Rhode Island brings a reminder of good health to the residents of the Blackstone Valley which encompasses parts of southern Massachusetts and northern Rhode Island. Founded in 1901 the not-for-profit hospital has some 300 beds and offers general medical and surgical care as well as specialty services in areas such as oncology cardiovascular care orthopedics rehabilitation women's health and home health care. It is also a teaching institution for Brown University's Warren Alpert Medical School. Through a handful of satellite clinics located throughout its service area Memorial Hospital of Rhode Island provides primary and preventive care.

Memorial Hospital of Rhode Island has an affiliation with the Brigham and Women's Hospital in Boston through which the facilities collaborate on emergency medicine services and quality improvement initiatives. The hospitals expanded the agreement to cover cardiovascular care in 2011.

Memorial Hospital of Rhode Island reported some $164 million in total patient revenues in 2011 down slightly from about $167 million in 2010.

EXECUTIVES

Vp Environmental And Support Services, Thomas L Ross
Vp Strategic Planning And Business Development, Thomas J Gough
President and COO, Edward Schottland
CFO, Paul Beaudoin
Chief Nursing Officer, Elizabeth Jordan
Vp Of Professional Practice, Judy V Tilburg
Auditors: Deloitte&ToucheLLP

LOCATIONS

HQ: THE MEMORIAL HOSPITAL
111 BREWSTER ST, PAWTUCKET, RI 02860-4474
Phone: 401-729-2000
Web: WWW.IMRESIDENTS-MHRI.ORG

COMPETITORS

Baystate Health
Day Kimball Hospital
Lifespan Corporation
Partners HealthCare
Roger Williams Medical Center
Southcoast Health
Sturdy Memorial
Yale New Haven Health System

HISTORICAL FINANCIALS

Company Type: Private

Income Statement FYE: September 30

	REVENUE ($ mil.)	NET INCOME ($ mil.)	NET PROFIT MARGIN	EMPLOYEES
09/11	181	(4)	—	1,400
09/10	182	(1)	—	—
09/09	171	(6)	—	—
09/08	175	(1)	—	—
Annual Growth	1.0%	—	—	—

2011 Year-End Financials

Debt ratio: —
Return on equity: (-2.80%)
Cash ($ mil.): 0
Current ratio: 1.60
Long-term debt ($ mil.): —
Dividends
Yield: —
Payout: —
Market value ($ mil.): —

THE MERCHANTS COMPANY

EXECUTIVES

President and CEO, Andrew B. (Andy) Mercier
VP and CFO, Jarrod Gray
Director Sales Mississippi, Ralph Brown
Director Sales Alabama, Bill Truxal
Business Development Manager, Mark McDonald

LOCATIONS

HQ: THE MERCHANTS COMPANY
1100 EDWARDS ST, HATTIESBURG, MS 394015511
Phone: 6013532461
Web: WWW.THEMERCHANTSCOMPANY.COM

COMPETITORS

Ben E. Keith
Cheney Brothers
MAINES
McLane Foodservice
Meadowbrook Meat Company
Performance Food
Quirch Foods
Reinhart FoodService
Services Group of America
Sysco
US Foods

HISTORICAL FINANCIALS

Company Type: Private

Income Statement FYE: September 30

	REVENUE ($ mil.)	NET INCOME ($ mil.)	NET PROFIT MARGIN	EMPLOYEES
09/11	489	2	0.5%	500
09/10	441	5	1.2%	—
09/08	2,033	0	—	—
Annual Growth	— 2341.1%		—	—

2011 Year-End Financials

Debt ratio: —
Return on equity: 0.50%
Cash ($ mil.): 0
Current ratio: 1.00
Long-term debt ($ mil.): —
Dividends
Yield: —
Payout: —
Market value ($ mil.): —

THE METHODIST HOSPITAL

Methodist Hospital provides care for Houstonians. The not-for-profit organization also known as Methodist Hospital System owns and operates several Houston-area medical centers including Methodist Hospital in Houston's Texas Medical Center complex and the suburban San Jacinto Methodist Methodist Sugar Land Methodist West Houston and Methodist Willowbrook hospitals. The system's flagship Methodist Hospital has 950 beds and is known for innovations in urology and neurosurgery among other specialties. The system also manages the Methodist Hospital Physician Organization.

Geographic Reach

The hospital system consists of five acute-care locations in the Houston Texas metropolitan area. The network added its fifth hospital in late 2010 when it completed construction of a new 200 bed community hospital on Houston's west side named Methodist West Houston Hospital.

Through its Methodist International unit the system serves international patients and provides consulting services worldwide.

Operations

The Methodist Hospital System's five hospitals together have about 1700 beds.

In addition the health system operates the Methodist Hospital Research Institute which conducts medical and clinical research. The research organization is based at the main Methodist Hospital location and works in partnership with the hospital's physicians to improve treatments for medical conditions. Construction of a new larger 12-story building to house the Research Institute was completed and opened in 2010.

The hospital has educational and research affiliations with Cornell University's Weil Cornell Medical College the New York-Presbyterian Hospital University of Houston Rice University Baylor College of Medicine and other organizations.

Strategy

To widen its capacity for medical care Methodist Hospital completed construction of a new 26-story Methodist Outpatient Center in mid-2010; the center is located near the flagship Methodist Hospital in Houston's Texas Medical Center complex.

The company also completed major expansion projects at its Sugar Land and Willowbrook hospitals in 2009 and 2010 more than doubling the capacity at both facilities. Other projects have included a new imaging and women's diagnostic center in the Houston's Upper Kirby neighborhood which opened in 2009.

EXECUTIVES

Assistant Secretary, Robert K. Moses Jr., age 72
Chairman Neurology Methodist Hospital Neurological Institute, Stanley H. Appel
SVP and Chief Nursing Executive The Methodist Hospital, Ann Scanlon McGinity
President and CEO The Methodist Hospital System, Marc L. Boom
Director Public Relations, Stefanie Asin
SVP Human Resources, Lauren Rykert
CEO Methodist Sugar Land Hospital, Chris Siebenaler
Chairman, Ewing Werlein Jr.
VP Operations The Methodist Hospital, Karin Larson-Pollock
Chairman of Neurosurgery and Director Methodist Neurological Institute, Robert Grossman
EVP The Methodist Hospital, Roberta Schwartz
Director Eddy Scurlock Stroke Center Methodist Neurological Institute, David Chiu
President-elect Medical Staff, Wade Rosenberg
Secretary, D. Gibson Walton
Assistant Secretary, Emily A. Crosswell
Treasurer, Carlton E. Baucum
CEO San Jacinto Methodist Hospital, Donna Gares
Director Research Institute, Michael W. (Mike) Lieberman
VP Human Resources, Carole Hackett
VP Operations, Vicki Brownewell
VP Operations, Katherine Walsh
VP Operations, Bryan Croft
VP Operations, Clare Rose
VP Operations, Stephen Spielman
VP Operations, David Bernard
VP Research Institute, Ed Jones
CEO Methodist Willowbrook Hospital, Beryl Ramsey
CEO Research Institute, Mauro Ferrari
President Medical Staff, Victor Fainstein
CEO Methodist West Houston Hospital, Wayne Voss
Operations Manager, Alex C. Varkey
Chief Financial Officer Vice President, Keith Barber
Chairman of the Board, Lawrence Reilly
Vice President and Chief Nursing Officer, Sheila Fata
Director, Morrie K. Abramson
Director, John F. Bookout III, age 60
Director, Lawrence W. (Larry) Kellner, age 55
Director, Gary W. Edwards
Assistant Secretary, Robert K. Moses Jr., age 72
Director, Gregory V. (Greg) Nelson
Chairman, Ewing Werlein Jr.
President-elect Medical Staff, Wade Rosenberg
Secretary, D. Gibson Walton
Assistant Secretary, Emily A. Crosswell
Treasurer, Carlton E. Baucum
Director, W. Earl Bledsoe
Director, Mary A. Daffin
Director, Connie M. Dyer
Director, James A. Elkins III
Director, Rev Richard W. Goodrich
Director, Robert E. Jackson
Director, Vidal G. Martinez
Director, Thomas J. Pace III
Director, Janice Riggle Huie
Director, Pliny C. Smith
Director, Joseph C. (Rusty) Walter III
Director, Elizabeth B. Wareing
Director, Stephen P. Wende
Director, Sandra Gayle Wright

LOCATIONS

HQ: THE METHODIST HOSPITAL
6565 FANNIN ST, HOUSTON, TX 77030-2707
Phone: 713-790-3311
Web: WWW.METHODISTHEALTHCAREERS.COM

PRODUCTS/OPERATIONS

Selected Houston-Area Hospitals

Methodist Hospital - Texas Medical Center (Houston)
Methodist Sugar Land Hospital
Methodist Willowbrook Hospital (Houston)
Methodist West Houston Hospital (Houston)
San Jacinto Methodist Hospital (Baytown)

COMPETITORS

CHRISTUS Health
Dynacq Healthcare
HCA
Johns Hopkins Medicine
MD Anderson Cancer Center
Mayo Clinic
Memorial Hermann Healthcare
St. Luke' s Episcopal Health System
Tenet Healthcare
Texas Children' s Hospital
Texas Health Resources
Tomball Regional
Universal Health Services

HISTORICAL FINANCIALS

Company Type: Private

Income Statement

FYE: December 31

	REVENUE ($ mil.)	NET INCOME ($ mil.)	NET PROFIT MARGIN	EMPLOYEES
12/12	2,331	386	16.6%	14,000
12/11	2,284	101	4.4%	—
12/10	2,115	354	16.8%	—
12/09	2,086	655	31.4%	—
Annual Growth	3.8%	(16.1%)	—	—

2012 Year-End Financials

Debt ratio: —
Return on equity: 16.60%
Cash ($ mil.): 55
Current ratio: 0.20
Long-term debt ($ mil.): —
Dividends
Yield: —
Payout: —
Market value ($ mil.): —

THE METHODIST HOSPITALS INC

The Methodist Hospitals Inc. is a not-for-profit community-based health care system that provides medical care to Indiana residents. More than 560 physicians representing some 60 specialties serve its two campus hospitals which have a combined total of about 530 beds. The system provides care for a range of specialized areas from neurology and neurosurgery oncology and home health and hospice to rehabilitation and orthopedics. The emergency department treats more than 59000 patients a year. The system also provides screenings charitable care and community education programs. The Methodist Hospitals established in 1923 reinvests all of its profits to improve patient care.

Methodist's main service areas include Lake and Porter counties extending west to the border east to LaPorte and south to Lowell. Its two campuses are the Northlake Campus in Gary and the Southlake Campus in Merrillville. The two campuses which are 14 miles apart are both full-service facilities. In 2010 both campuses received major investments to replace all patient room furnishings. That year Methodist Hospitals invested more than $36 million in technology equipment and patient programs.

The system also operates the Midlake Campus an outpatient facility with physician offices and other services in Gary. Midlake's Rehab Center has provided outpatient rehabilitation services since 2003.

To better serve it patients and secure its growth Methodist Hospitals is implementing patient-centered initiatives. These range from investing in new treatments technologies and safety programs to seeking out best-in-class physicians and hiring nurses and support staff who are highly qualified and caring.

Methodist Hospitals has also embarked on making improvements to its facilities as a result of a financial turnaround that began in 2009. It has earmarked $18 million for capital projects at both campuses. These include: a newly completed multispecialty navigational operating room suite (for almost $2 million) renovation of the Northlake campus lobby renovation of the emergency department at the Southlake campus (about $8 million) and beautification projects.

Additionally in 2012 Methodist Hospitals opened a new 14- bed inpatient Geriatric Behavioral Health Services unit at its Northlake campus.

EXECUTIVES

Chair, Charles D. Brooks Jr.
President Medical Staff, Adolphus Anekwe
President and CEO, Ian E. McFadden
Manager Marketing and Corporate Communications, Evelyn Morrison
VP Operations, Tony Jones
CFO, Loren Chandler
Marketing and Corporate Communications, Amber Raza
Director of Facilities and Environmental Services, Tom Burnett
Vice President Medical Affairs, Michael Davenport
Vice President Marketing and Human Resources, Alex Horvath
Vice President, Denise C. Dillard
Executive Director of Services, Rachel A. Gajos
Vice President Operations, Wright Alcorn
Vice President Physician Integration, James M. Kirchner
Director, Bruce W. Bergland
Director, Benjamin T. Luna
Director, Scott T. Ribordy
Director, Patsy Allan
Director, John R. Barney
Director, Okechi N. Nwabara
Director, Douge Barthelemy
Director, Hilbert L. Bradley
Director, Bruce L. Dahltorp
Director, William B. Davis
Director, F. Ritchey Eibel
Director, Glenn C. Hannah
Director, Rev H.S. Malone
Director, I.J. Roberts
Director, Rev David A. Schrader
Director, F.C. Richardson

LOCATIONS

HQ: THE METHODIST HOSPITALS INC
600 GRANT ST, GARY, IN 46402-6001
Phone: 219-886-4000
Web: WWW.METHODISTHOSPITALS.ORG

PRODUCTS/OPERATIONS

Selected Services

Behavioral health sciences
Bloodless medicine (surgery without blood transfusions)
Cardiovascular
- Cardiopulmonary rehabilitation

Diabetes Center
Emergency/trauma services
Home health
Maternity
NeuroScience Institute
- Gamma Knife (non-invasive brain surgery)
- Multiple Sclerosis Center
- Spine Care Center
- Stroke Center

Oncology Institute
Orthopedic services
Outpatient
Rehabilitation
Surgical weight loss/ bariatric services
Women's services
- Advanced obstetrical services

Wound Center

Selected Affiliations

American Cancer Society
American Heart Association
American Lung Association
Anthem Coronary Service Network
Edgewater Systems for Balanced Living
Gary Career Center
Gary Southshore Railcats
Indiana State Medical Association
Indiana University Northwest Campus
- Medical School
- Radiological Tech Program
- Respiratory Program
- School of Nursing

International Association for Healthcare Security and Safety
Ivy Technical Vocational School
Lakeshore Kids Immunization Fair
March of Dimes
Multiple Sclerosis Society
National Alliance for Mentally Ill (NAMI)
Purdue University Calumet Campus
- School of Nursing

Purdue University North Central Campus
- School of Nursing

Valparaiso University
- School of Nursing

Rosalind Franklin University

HISTORICAL FINANCIALS

Company Type: Private

Income Statement

FYE: December 31

	REVENUE ($ mil.)	NET INCOME ($ mil.)	NET PROFIT MARGIN	EMPLOYEES
12/09	291	5	2.0%	3,260
12/04	310	9	3.2%	—
12/03	298	7	2.5%	—
12/02	267	(9)	—	—
Annual Growth	1.3%	—	—	—

2009 Year-End Financials

Debt ratio: —
Return on equity: 2.00%
Cash ($ mil.): 51
Current ratio: 0.80
Long-term debt ($ mil.): —
Dividends
Yield: —
Payout: —
Market value ($ mil.): —

THE METROHEALTH SYSTEM

Helping Cleveland's metropolitan citizens stay healthy (and healing them when they aren't) is what MetroHealth System is all about. At the center of the system is MetroHealth Medical Center an acute care hospital that serves as a teaching affiliate for Case Western Reserve University. The hospital's services include oncology behavioral health vascular care orthopedics burn care and pediatrics. The system also operates outpatient clinics Greater Cleveland as well as long-term care facilities a regional rehabilitative clinic and a medical helicopter program. MetroHealth is owned by Ohio's Cuyahoga County.

Geographic Reach

The MetroHealth is one of the largest most comprehensive health care providers in Northeast Ohio serving the medical needs of the Greater Cleveland area.

Operations

More than 400 primary care and specialty care physicians practice within MetroHealth. On an annual basis MetroHealth Medical Center provides care to more than 28000 inpatients and delivers 2900 newborns. More than 900000 visits are recorded in the medical center's outpatient centers. The system affiliates with Akron Children's Hospital to expand access to pediatric care throughout the region. Through the partnership Akron Children's provides specialty care at MetroHealth's main campus in the areas of pediatric cardiology gastroenterology cancer and blood disorders and critical care. The MetroHealth affiliation is Akron Children's fourth location in Cuyahoga County.

Financial Performance

MetroHealth's revenue was $742 million in fiscal 2012 which was an increase of about 2% compared to the previous fiscal period.

Strategy

As emergency rooms continue to burst at the seams more hospitals are finding ways to divert non-emergent patients to more appropriate care settings. MetroHealth has done that with its MetroExpressCare unit for residents who need to see a doctor and would probably otherwise end up at the emergency room. The family medicine physicians who see patients at MetroExpressCare are also available to establish longer-term relationships with patients coming to MetroHealth for the first time. If the physician determines that it's a more serious problem the patient can be referred to MetroHealth's emergency department.

Having options such as MetroExpressCare available is especially important to MetroHealth because it is its region's safety net hospital. As such it receives the lion's share of uninsured patients many of whom end up in the ER because ERs are required to see all patients regardless of their ability to pay under the Emergency Medical Treatment and Active Labor Act. Being able to provide a less expensive option to those patients decreases MetroHealth's bad debt (or unpaid patient bills) and helps reduce crowding at its ER.

Ownership

MetroHealth is owned by Ohio's Cuyahoga County.

Background

The MetroHealth has been serving the medical needs of the Greater Cleveland community since 1837. It has been a major affiliate of Case Western Reserve University since 1914.

EXECUTIVES

President and CEO, John A. Brennan
Vice President Foundation and System Philanthropy, Kate Brown
VP and Chief Accounting Officer, Geoffrey Himes
VP Human Resources, Debbie Warman
Assistant Operations Director, Sara Laskey

LOCATIONS

HQ: THE METROHEALTH SYSTEM
2500 METROHEALTH DR, CLEVELAND, OH 44109-1900
Phone: 216-778-7800
Web: WWW.METROHEALTH.ORG

Selected locations

J. Glen Smith Health Center (In partnership with the City of Cleveland Cleveland)
MetroHealth Asia Town Health Center (Cleveland)
MetroHealth Beachwood Health Center (Beachwood Ohio)
MetroHealth Broadway Health Center (Cleveland)
MetroHealth Brooklyn Health Center (Cleveland)
MetroHealth Buckeye Health Center (Cleveland)
MetroHealth Center for Sleep Medicine South Campus (Independence Ohio)
MetroHealth Center for Sleep Medicine West Campus (Westlake Ohio)
MetroHealth Lakewood Health Center (Lakewood)
MetroHealth Lee-Harvard Health Center (Cleveland)
MetroHealth Medical Center Main Campus (Cleveland)
MetroHealth Old Brooklyn Campus (Cleveland)
MetroHealth Pepper Pike Health Center (Pepper Pike Ohio)
MetroHealth Premier Health Center (Westlake Ohio)
MetroHealth Rehabilitation Institute of Ohio (Cleveland)
MetroHealth Strongsville Health Center (Strongsville Ohio)
MetroHealth West 150th Health and Surgery Center (Cleveland)
MetroHealth Westlake Health Center (Westlake)
MetroHealth West Park Health Center (Cleveland)
The Elisabeth Severance Prentiss Center for Skilled Nursing Care at MetroHealth (Cleveland)
Thomas F. McCafferty Health Center (In partnership with the City of Cleveland Cleveland)

PRODUCTS/OPERATIONS

MetroHealth System Departments and Services
Aamoth Family Pediatric Wellness Center
Adolescent Clinic (Teen Health)
Advanced Gynecology (Center for Advanced Gynecology
Advantage (MetroHealth Advantage)
Allergy & Immunology Clinic
Allergy Services (Department of Ear Nose & Throat)
Amigas Unidas Program
Anesthesiology
Art Therapy
Arthritis Center (Rheumatol
Audiology
Bariatric Surgery (Weight Loss Surgery Program)
Behavioral Health (Child and Teen Mental Health Services)
Birth Control Procedures
Birthing Services
Bone Health and Surgery (Orthopaed
BREAST Program (Community Breast Cancer Outreach)
Burn Care Center
Cancer Care Center
Cardiology Cardiovascular (Heart & Vascular Center)
Center for Advanced Gynecology
Center for Behavioral Health (Child and Teen Mental Health Services)
Centers for Community Health
Center for Sleep Medicine
Cerebrovascular
Childbirth Education
Child Life and Education
Children's Health (Pediatric
Children's Health Specialtie
Closing the Gap (MetroHealth Buckeye Health Center)
Comprehensive Care Program (Services for Children with Special Needs)
Concussion Clinic
Cosmetic Dermatolog
Dentistry and Oral Health
Dermatology
Diabetes Self-Management Program
Digital Mammogram
Ear Nose and Throat (ENT/Otola
Emergency Medicine/Emergency Department
Endocrinology
Endoscopy Suite (Gastroent
ExpressCare (MetroExpr
Family Medicine Clinic at MetroHealth Medical Center
Fertility Services
Freedom From Smoking
Gastroenterology and Endoscopy Suite
Genetics Clinic
Geriatrics (Senior Health & Wellness Center)
Gynecology
Gynecology Advanced (Center for Advanced Gynecology
Gynecologic Oncology
Hand Center
Heart & Vascular Center
Hematology and Oncology (Cancer Care Center)
High-Risk Pregnancy Services
Hospital Medicine
Immunology (Allergy & Immunology Clinic)
Infectious Disease
Infertility Clinic
Infusion Therapy (Allergy & Immunology Clinic)
Internal Medicine Clinic at MetroHealth Medical Center
Internal Medicine and Pediatrics (Med-PEDS)
Kids' Health (Pediatric
Kids' Korner Free Daycare Service at MetroHealth Medical Center
Latina Clinic: English | En espa?ol
LGBT Pride Clinic (At Thomas F. McCafferty Health Center Health Center)
Life Flight (Metro Life Flight)
Long-Term/Skilled Nursing Care
Maternal-Fetal Medicine (High-Risk Pregnancy Services)
Medicine (Department of Medicine)
Mental Health (Psychiatr
Metro Life Flight
MetroHealth Advantage
MetroExpressCare
MetroHealth Rehabilitation Institute of Ohio
MetroHealth Select Health Plan
MetroHealth Simulation Center
Mi MetroHealth Mi Comunidad
MyChart
Neonatology Neonatal Intensive Care Unit (NICU)
Nephrology
Neurology
Neurosciences
Northeast Ohio Chapter of the National Spinal Cord Injury Association (NSCIA)
Northeast Ohio Regional Spinal Cord Injury System (NORSCIS)
Nose Ear and Throat (ENT Otolaryngo
Nursing
Nutrition
Obstetrics
Obstetrics and Gynecology
Occupational Medicine
Oncology (Cancer Care Center)
Opthalmologic (Eye) Surgery
Oral Health (Dentistry
Oral and Maxillofacial Surgery
Orthopaedics
Osteopathic Medicine
Otolaryngology (Ear Nose and Throat)
Pain Management
Palliative Care
Pastoral Care
Pathology
Pediatrics
Permanent Birth Control Procedures
Pharmacy
Pregnancy Resources
Pride Clinic (At Thomas F. McCafferty Health Center Health Center)
Psychiatry (Behavioral/Mental Health)
Pulmonary and Critical Care
Quality Indicators
Radiology
Rehab Rehabilitation Services (MetroHealth Rehabilitation Institute of Ohio)
Reiki
Reproductive Endocrinology and Infertility Clinic
Rheumatology (Arthritis Center)

Select Health Plan

Senior Health and Wellness Center
Simulation Center
Skeletal (Orthopaedics)
Skilled Nursing/Long-Term Care
Sleep Medicine Sleep Studies
Spanish-language Information
Special Needs Services for Children (Comprehensive Care)
Spine Center
Stroke Stroke & Cerebrovascular Center
Surgery
Throat (Otolaryngology ENT)
Teen Health
Trauma Burns and Critical Care
Travel Clinic
Urgent Care (MetroExpressCare
Urology
Vascular Health and Surgery (Heart & Vascular Center
Weight Loss Surgery Program (Bariatric Surgery)
X-ray (Radiology)

COMPETITORS

AdCare
Catholic Health Initiatives
Cincinnati Children's Hospital
Community Health Systems
Kettering Health Network
Lake Health
MedCath
OhioHealth
Premier Health Partners
Robinson Memorial Hospital
The Cleveland Clinic
University Hospitals Health System

HISTORICAL FINANCIALS

Company Type: Private

Income Statement

FYE: December 31

	REVENUE ($ mil.)	NET INCOME ($ mil.)	NET PROFIT MARGIN	EMPLOYEES
12/09	673	58	8.7%	6,000
12/08	642	(3)	—	—
12/07	1,941	0	0.0%	—
Annual Growth	(41.1%)	36722.0%	—	—

2009 Year-End Financials

Debt ratio: ——
Return on equity: 8.70%
Cash ($ mil.): 2
Current ratio: 0.60
Long-term debt ($ mil.): —

Dividends
Yield: —
Payout: —
Market value ($ mil.): —

THE METROPOLITAN MUSEUM OF ART

You won't find too much about a certain New York baseball team at this Met. One of the world's premier cultural institutions The Metropolitan Museum of Art (also known as "the Met") acquires and exhibits artwork from around the world. Its collection of more than 2 million pieces ranges from the prehistoric era to the present day. In addition to hosting exhibits the Met loans artwork to other museums publishes books and catalogs and develops educational programs. It also displays art online. The City of New York owns the museum's 2 million-sq.-ft. complex which is located on the east side of Central Park; the museum itself owns its art collection. The Met was founded in 1870.

Highlights from the collection at the Met's Main Building on Fifth Avenue include American and European paintings and Egyptian and Islamic art. The institution's holdings also include The Cloisters museum and gardens located in Fort Tryon Park in Upper Manhattan. The Cloisters is devoted to the art and architecture of medieval Europe.

During the fiscal year 2011 some 5.6 million people visited the Met including The Cloisters museum and gardens. That number is the highest recorded in 40 years and was more than 400000 greater than in fiscal year 2010. In addition museum membership reached a record-breaking 139800 in 2011. In particular visitors were drawn to special exhibitions in 2011 including the popular Alexander McQueen: Savage Beauty a retrospective on the British fashion designer who died in 2010.

Also in 2011 the Met launched a redesign of its website. New features include gallery overviews an interactive floor plan and suggested itineraries for planning museum visits. The site had not been thoroughly updated since 2011 and the redesign was three years in the making.

EXECUTIVES

Secretary and General Counsel, Sharon H. Cott
SVP External Affairs, Harold Holzer
Chairman, James R. (Jamie) Houghton, age 77
President, Emily K. Rafferty
VP Construction, J. Nicholas Cameron
VP Development and Membership, Nina Diefenbach
VP Facilities Management, Philip T. Venturino
Frederick P. and Sandra P. Rose Associate Director Education, Kent Lydecker
Associate Director Administration, Doralynn Pines
SVP CFO and Treasurer, Olena Paslawsky
VP Human Resources, Debra A. McDowell
Chief Investment Officer, Suzanne E. Brenner
Director and CEO, Thomas P. Campbell, age 50
Assistant Secretary and General Manager, Grace Brady
Associate Director Exhibitions and Director International Affairs Geneva Office, Mahrukh Tarapor
VP Communications, Elyse Topalian
Vice Chairman, Annette de la Renta
Vice Chairman, S. Parker Gilbert

LOCATIONS

HQ: THE METROPOLITAN MUSEUM OF ART
1000 5TH AVE FRNT, NEW YORK, NY 10028-0198
Phone: 212-879-5500
Web: WWW.METMUSEUM.ORG

PRODUCTS/OPERATIONS

Selected Curatorial Departments

American Decorative Arts
Ancient Near Eastern Art
Arts of Africa Oceania and the Americas
Asian Art
Costume Institute
Drawings and Prints
Egyptian Art
European Paintings
Greek and Roman Art
Islamic Art
Medieval Art
Modern Art
Musical Instruments
Photographs

COMPETITORS

American Museum of Natural History
Brooklyn Museum
Museum of the City of New York
Smithsonian

HISTORICAL FINANCIALS

Company Type: Private

Income Statement FYE: June 30

	REVENUE ($ mil.)	NET INCOME ($ mil.)	NET PROFIT MARGIN	EMPLOYEES
06/13	326	290	88.9%	2,372
06/12	314	(193)	—	—
06/10	470	124	26.5%	—
06/10	292	3	1.3%	—
Annual Growth	3.7%	328.7%	—	—

2013 Year-End Financials

Debt ratio: —
Return on equity: 88.90%
Cash ($ mil.): 1
Current ratio: —
Long-term debt ($ mil.): —
Dividends
Yield: —
Payout: —
Market value ($ mil.): —

THE MIDDLE TENNESSEE ELECTRIC MEMBERSHIP CORPORATION

EXECUTIVES

Chairman, Gordon Bone
President, Frank Jennings
VP Engineering, Tom Suggs
VP Marketing and Communications, Chris Jones
VP Operations, Jeff Gill
Vice President of Operations, John Florida
VP Human Resources and Corporate Services, Shannon Kaprive
VP Finance, Bernie Steen
Manager Franklin District, Dan Florida
Manager Lebanon District, Ken Throneberry
Manager Murfreesboro and Woodbury Districts, Ron Washington
Vice Chairman, Will Jordan
Vice President of Engineering, Dan Dement
Vice President of Information Systems, Gray Bateman
Vice President of District Services, Brad Gibson
Director, Steve Seger
Director, Gloria O'Steen
Director, Bill Giddens
Director, David Lee
Director, Mike Woods
Vice Chairman, Will Jordan
Director, Luther Lenning
Director, Dan Smith
Director, Jim Mills

LOCATIONS

HQ: THE MIDDLE TENNESSEE ELECTRIC MEMBERSHIP CORPORATION
555 NEW SALEM HWY, MURFREESBORO, TN 371293390
Phone: 6158909762
Web: WWW.MTEMC.COM

HISTORICAL FINANCIALS

Company Type: Private

Income Statement FYE: June 30

	REVENUE ($ mil.)	NET INCOME ($ mil.)	NET PROFIT MARGIN	EMPLOYEES
06/13	524	27	5.3%	375
06/12	510	19	3.8%	—
06/11	525	31	6.0%	—
Annual Growth	(0.0%)	(5.9%)	—	—

2013 Year-End Financials

Debt ratio: —
Return on equity: 5.30%
Cash ($ mil.): 58
Current ratio: 1.40
Long-term debt ($ mil.): —
Dividends
Yield: —
Payout: —
Market value ($ mil.): —

THE MITRE CORPORATION

EXECUTIVES

Deputy CFO, Mark W. Kontos
SVP and COO, David H. Lehman
VP General Counsel and Corporate Secretary, Sol Glasner
VP and Chief Human Resources Officer, Lisa R. Bender
President CEO and Trustee, Alfred Grasso
Corporate Chief Engineer and MITRE Fellow, Louis S. Metzger
SVP and General Manager Center for Integrated Intelligence Systems, Robert F. Nesbit
Chairman, James R. Schlesinger, age 86
Director SVP and General Manager Center for Advanced Aviation System Development and FAA Federally Funded Research and Development Center, Agam N. Sinha
Senior Vice President General Manager Center for National Security, Raymond Haller
VP Joint and Service Programs, Stephen D. Huffman
Vice Chairman, Charles S. Robb, age 75
SVP Programs and Technology -Center for Connected Government, Richard J. Byrne
Senior Vice President Chief Security Officer, Gary J. Gagnon
SVP and General Manager Center for Connected Government Director Homeland Security Systems Engineering and Development Institute DHS FFRDC, Jason F. Providakes
Executive Director Corporate Communications and Public Affairs, Catherine L. Crawford
Manager Media Corporate Citizenship and Branding, Jennifer J. Shearman
VP and Director Center for Enterprise Modernization, James E. (Jim) Cook
Media Relations, Karina H. Wright
VP and CIO, Joel Jacobs
Senior Vice President, Peter Sherlock
Vice President Chief Human Resources Officer, Karen Quinn-Quintin
VP and CTO, Mark T Maybury

VP Programs and Technology, Gregory K Crawford
senior Vice President General Manager of the Washington Command, DoD FFRDCs
Vice President Programs and Technology, Greg Crawford
Trustee, Nicholas M. (Nick) Donofrio, age 68
Trustee, Martin C. Faga, age 73
President CEO and Trustee, Alfred Grasso
Trustee, John J. Hamre, age 63
Trustee, William B. Mitchell, age 78
Trustee, Cleve L. Killingsworth Jr., age 62
Trustee, Cathy E. Minehan, age 65
Trustee, Victor A. DeMarines, age 77
Trustee, Adm. Edmund P. (Ed) Giambastiani Jr., age 65
Trustee, Jane C. Garvey, age 70
Trustee, John P. Stenbit, age 73
Trustee, Elizabeth J. Keefer
Trustee, Gen. Montgomery C. Meigs
Trustee, Gen. Ronald R. (Ron) Fogleman
Trustee, Donald M. Kerr
Trustee, William Happer Jr.
Vice Chairman, Charles S. Robb, age 75

LOCATIONS

HQ: THE MITRE CORPORATION
202 BURLINGTON RD, BEDFORD, MA 017301420
Phone: 7812712000
Web: WWW.MITRE.ORG

PRODUCTS/OPERATIONS

Selected Practice Areas

Acquisition and systems analysis
Aviation systems safety and security
Command and control
Cybersecurity
Emerging technologies
Enterprise systems engineering
Global networking
Healthcare transformation
Homeland security
Information Technology
Intelligence surveillance and reconnaissance
Large-scale enterprise transformation
Systems engineering

COMPETITORS

Altarum
Battelle Memorial
Berkeley Lab
ComGlobal Systems
EDSI
General Atomics
Institute for Defense Analyses
Leidos
QinetiQ
SITA
SRI International
Sandia National Laboratories
SwRI
The Scripps Research Institute
Wyle Information Systems

HISTORICAL FINANCIALS

Company Type: Private

Income Statement FYE: October 5

	REVENUE ($ mil.)	NET INCOME ($ mil.)	NET PROFIT MARGIN	EMPLOYEES
10/08	1,234	22	1.8%	7,000
10/07	1,113	23	2.1%	—
Annual Growth	10.9%	(4.6%)	—	—

2008 Year-End Financials

Debt ratio: —
Return on equity: 1.80%
Cash ($ mil.): 36
Current ratio: 0.80
Long-term debt ($ mil.): —
Dividends
Yield: —
Payout: —
Market value ($ mil.): —

THE NEW HAMPSHIRE CHARITABLE FOUNDATION

LOCATIONS

HQ: THE NEW HAMPSHIRE CHARITABLE FOUNDATION
37 PLEASANT ST, CONCORD, NH 033014005
Phone: 6032256641
Web: WWW.NHCF.ORG

HISTORICAL FINANCIALS

Company Type: Private

Income Statement FYE: December 31

	ASSETS ($ mil.)	NET INCOME ($ mil.)	INCOME AS % OF ASSETS	EMPLOYEES
12/09	425	(5)	—	36
12/99	220	30	13.7%	—
12/98	190	20	10.9%	—
Annual Growth	7.6%	—	—	—

2009 Year-End Financials

Debt ratio: —
Return on equity: (-19.20%)
Cash ($ mil.): 45
Current ratio: —
Long-term debt ($ mil.): —
Dividends
Yield: —
Payout: —
Market value ($ mil.): —

THE NEW LIBERTY HOSPITAL DISTRICT OF CLAY COUNTY MISSOURI

New Liberty Hospital District which operates as Liberty Hospital hopes to liberate health care patients in northwestern Missouri. The facility is a 250-bed acute care hospital that serves communities located north of Kansas City. Founded in 1974 Liberty Hospital offers general and specialty health care services including trauma care obstetrics cancer care diagnostics surgical services vascular and cardiac medicine (including open-heart surgery) rehabilitation and pediatrics. The not-for-profit medical facility has about 300 physicians on staff and also operates a skilled nursing facility and offers home health and hospice services.

Strategy

Liberty Hospital is expanding its facilities to improve services in the region. In 2011 for instance the medical center opened a new $15 million heart and vascular center that expands its capacity for open-heart surgeries and catheterization procedures. It also relocated its wound clinic to a larger facility that year.

In 2012 Liberty Hospital opened its new 40-room outpatient center (Liberty Clinic) that includes laboratory and diagnostic facilities. The medical center also acquired a family practice location in the nearby community of Kearney (now known as the Kearney Clinic) that year.

Liberty Hospital is also conducting programs to improve its medical equipment including the installation of an upgraded da Vinci robotic surgery system in 2011.

Ownership

Liberty Hospital is a political subdivision district hospital organized under the Revised Statues of Missouri (Chapter 206). It is governed by board of trustees consisting of six publicly elected members.

EXECUTIVES

Secretary, Tom Jones
Treasurer, James (Jim) Streu
VP Board of Trustees, Bill Riggs
Administrator, Joseph W. (Joe) Crossett
Assistant Administrator Finance, Erin Parde
Director Public Relations and Marketing, Matt Smithmier

LOCATIONS

HQ: THE NEW LIBERTY HOSPITAL DISTRICT OF CLAY COUNTY MISSOURI
2525 GLENN HENDREN DR, LIBERTY, MO 64068-9625
Phone: 816-781-7200
Web: WWW.LIBERTYHOSPITAL.ORG

PRODUCTS/OPERATIONS

Selected Services

Breast Center
Cancer Center
Diagnostic Imaging
Emergency and Trauma
Gastroenterology
Heart and Vascular Center
Home Health
Hospice
Hyperbaric Medicine
Intensive Care
Interventional Radiology
Lung Cancer Clinic
Maternity
Neurology
Orthopedics
Pain Management
Palliative Care
Pediatrics
Pulmonary
Rehabilitation
Robotic Surgery
Sleep Lab
Surgery
WorkHealth Solutions
Wound Clinic

COMPETITORS

Ascension Health
Children' s Mercy Hospital
Mercy Health
Saint Luke' s Health System
Sisters of Charity of Leavenworth
Truman Medical Centers
University of Kansas Medical Center
Via Christi Health System

HISTORICAL FINANCIALS

Company Type: Private

Income Statement FYE: June 30

	REVENUE ($ mil.)	NET INCOME ($ mil.)	NET PROFIT MARGIN	EMPLOYEES
06/08	157	17	11.0%	1,700
06/05	122	13	11.2%	—
06/04	2,010	0	0.0%	—
Annual Growth	(47.1%)	1690.1%	—	—

2008 Year-End Financials

Debt ratio: —
Return on equity: 11.00%
Cash ($ mil.): 9
Current ratio: 0.70
Long-term debt ($ mil.): —
Dividends
Yield: —
Payout: —
Market value ($ mil.): —

THE NEW SCHOOL

When James Lipton asks you what your favorite swear word is you know you've made it. The New School's drama department (formerly called The Actor's Studio) was made famous by the cable show Inside the Actors Studio which features Lipton interviewing movie and television stars. The school offers degrees in theater for playwriting directing and acting and has taught "Method" acting to grads such as Marlon Brando and Robert De Niro. It is also home to Parsons The New School for Design and has schools devoted to general studies liberal arts social research management and urban policy and music. More than 10500 traditional students and 5600 continuing education students are enrolled at The New School.

Operations

The New School offers more than 90 degree and diploma programs and majors to a population of undergraduate and graduate students who come from all 50 states and more than 100 foreign countries (about one-quarter of its students hail from international locations). It boasts small class sizes and a student-teacher ratio of about 10:1.

The New School for Public Engagement is the university's founding division and is composed of five schools: Milano School of International Affairs Management and Urban Policy; School of Language Learning and Teaching; School of Media Studies; School of Undergraduate Studies; and School of Writing. It has since added six divisions: Drama Jazz Lang Mannes Parsons and Social Research.

Financial Performance

The New School's 2011 revenue grew by more than 5% vs. 2010. Net income increased 13% over the same period.

Strategy

Parsons' new academic center in Paris is slated to open in fall 2013. The Paris site will offer students a program that addresses the global nature of contemporary art and design practice and reflects Europe's culture and philosophy.

The New School was founded in 1919 by a group of university professors and intellectuals in New York City as place for students wanting to explore their creativity and engage in deep thought while studying liberal arts. Dozens of years later The New School has gained a reputation for its unconventional teaching methods as well as for being the home of many world-renowned institutes including the think tank The World Policy Institute. It also hosts the annual National Book Awards which has helped establish the careers of some of the country's most recognized authors including Richard Powers and Jonathan Franzen.

Auditors: KPMGLLP

LOCATIONS

HQ: THE NEW SCHOOL
66 W 12TH ST, NEW YORK, NY 10011-8871
Phone: 212-229-5600
Web: WWW.NEWSCHOOL.EDU

PRODUCTS/OPERATIONS

Selected Schools

Eugene Lang College The New School for Liberal Arts
Mannes College The New School for Music
Milano The New School for Management and Urban Policy
The New School for Drama
The New School for General Studies
The New School for Jazz and Contemporary Music
The New School for Public Engagement
The New School for Social Research
Parsons The New School for Design

HISTORICAL FINANCIALS

Company Type: Private

Income Statement FYE: June 30

	REVENUE ($ mil.)	NET INCOME ($ mil.)	NET PROFIT MARGIN	EMPLOYEES
06/12	317	(3)	—	855
06/11	305	35	11.8%	—
06/10	288	31	11.0%	—
06/09	271	(32)	—	—
Annual Growth	5.2%	—	—	—

2012 Year-End Financials

Debt ratio: ——
Return on equity: (-1.10%)
Cash ($ mil.): 9
Current ratio: —
Long-term debt ($ mil.): —
Dividends
Yield: —
Payout: —
Market value ($ mil.): —

THE NEW YORK AND PRESBYTERIAN HOSPITAL

The New York and Presbyterian Hospital is a learned institution: The hospital is affiliated with both the Columbia University College of Physicians & Surgeons and the Weill Cornell Medical College of Cornell University. Known as NewYork-Presbyterian Hospital the organization comprises two major medical centers Columbia University Medical Center and Weill Cornell Medical Center which conduct educational and research programs in partnership with the universities. The two facilities combined have about 2600 beds and offer specialized programs for burns digestive diseases pediatrics women's health and other conditions. NewYork-Presbyterian Hospital is part of the NewYork-Presbyterian Healthcare System.

Geographic Reach

In addition to its flagship campuses NewYork-Presbyterian/Columbia and NewYork-Presbyterian/Weill Cornell NewYork-Presbyterian Hospital operates two small community hospitals in Manhattan –the Allen Hospital and the Lower Manhattan Hospital –and an inpatient mental health facility (the Westchester Division). The broader NewYork-Presbyterian Healthcare System operates facilities in other areas of New York as well as in New Jersey and Connecticut. The NewYork-Presbyterian Hospital/Columbia campus houses the Morgan Stanley Children's Hospital as well as other specialist units.

Operations

Altogether the NewYork-Presbyterian Hospital campuses handle some 2 million patient visits each year (both on an inpatient and outpatient basis) including inpatient admissions and more than 215000 emergency room visits and about 13000 births. The facilities employ a total of more than 6000 physicians including residents and fellows. NewYork-Presbyterian Hospital provides more than $80 million in charity and community care services each year.

Sales and Marketing

Medicare and Medicaid recipients account for about 60% of NewYork-Presbyterian Hospital's patients. Commercial managed care organizations and insurance firms as well as self-pay customers account for the rest.

Financial Performance

NewYork-Presbyterian Hospital reported $3.9 billion in revenue in 2012 up from some $3.7 billion in 2011.

Strategy

NewYork-Presbyterian Hospital expands its facilities through regular construction programs. For instance in 2013 it announced plans to build a new ambulatory care center on York Ave. Also that year the medical center opened an autism and brain development center on the Westchester campus; launched a center for precision medicine (individualized medical treatments) at the Weill Cornell campus; and entered into a collaboration with the New York City Department of Education (along with Microsoft and City University of New York) to establish a technical education and career school for high school and early college students.

Past expansion efforts include a new $50 million children's emergency department at the Morgan Stanley facility in 2011 a cardiovascular care wing added to the Columbia campus in 2010 and the launch of myNYP an electronic personal health record system in 2009.

Mergers and Acquisitions

The NewYork-Presbyterian/Lower Manhattan Hospital was added to the organization in 2013. The 180-bed community hospital extended NewYork-Presbyterian Hospital's patient reach in Manhattan; Lower Manhattan Hospital previously operated as New York Downtown Hospital.

Company Background

NewYork-Presbyterian Hospital was formed through the 1998 merger of the New York Hospital (founded in 1771) and the Presbyterian Hospital (founded in 1868). New York Hospital was known for advancing care in areas including women's health and surgery while the Presbyterian Hospital was known for its pediatric division and its cancer center.

EXECUTIVES

Vp Strategy And Financial Planning, David Alge
Vp Facilities Development, Donna A Barbaro
Svp And Coo Newyork-presbyterian/milstein, Andria Castellanos
Vice President Of Marketing Svs, David A Feinberg
Vp And Deputy General Counsel, Anita R Golbey
Vp Public Affairs And Chief Public Affairs Officer, Myrna A Manners
Svp Ambulatory Care And Patient Centered Care Services, Jaclyn A Mucaria
Vp Insurance Nyp Healthcare System, Eric R Vorenkamp
Vp And Medical Director Behavioral Health Nyp/weill Cornell, Phillip J Wilner
Svp Facilities Development And Real Estate, Louis F Reuter
Vp Patient Care Services Newyork-presbyterian/weill Cornell, Suzanne Boyle
Vp Revenue Cycle Operations, Paul J Dunphey
Vp Patient Care Services Newyork-presbyterian/columbia, Georgia J Persky
Vp Quality And Patient Safety, Karen Scott Collins
SVP and CIO, Aurelia G. Boyer
EVP CFO and Treasurer, Phyllis R. Lantos
CEO, Steven J. (Steve) Corwin
SVP and COO NewYork-Presbyterian/Columbia, Robert E. Kelly
SVP Finance and Assistant Treasurer, Mark E. Larmore
Chief Nursing Officer; VP Patient Services NewYork-Presbyterian/Columbia, Wilhelmina Manzano
VP Medical Affairs, Laura L. Forese
VP Medical Affairs and Associate Chief Medical Officer, Richard S. Liebowitz
Vp Clinical Business Development Nyp Healthcare System, Richard H Gemming
Vp Claims And Litigation Management, Brian J Noonan

Vp And Chief Of Staff To The Ceo And President; Chief Communications Officer, Jolie Singer
Vp Perioperative Services Newyork-presbyterian/weill Cornell, Beryl Muniz
Director Of Nursing, Laurie Walsh
Vice President Dio Bklyn The Brooklyn Hospital C, Benson Yeh
Vice President Cqo Dept Chr Bklyn, Vasantha K Kondamudi
Department Head Physician Services Newyork Presb, Diane Vazquez
Vice President Fac Prac Bklyn, Karen L Milano
Operations Vice President, Elizabeth Vega
Vice President Womens Aux Ny, Susan B Leder
Senior Vice President, Fritz Reuter
Medical Director, Neal E Flomenbaum
Vice President Real Estate, Cohen Martin
Chairman Board of Trustees, John J. Mack, age 70
EVP CFO and Treasurer, Phyllis R. Lantos
SVP Finance and Assistant Treasurer, Mark E. Larmore
Secretary, Mary P Wong
Secretary Medical Service Newyork Presbyterian H, Sandra Cardenas-arroya

LOCATIONS

HQ: THE NEW YORK AND PRESBYTERIAN HOSPITAL
525 E 68TH ST, NEW YORK, NY 100654870
Phone: 2127465454
Web: WWW.NYP.ORG

PRODUCTS/OPERATIONS

2012 Patient Mix

Commercial	38	
Medicaid	28	
Total	**0**	**100**

COMPETITORS

Ascension Health
Beth Israel Medical Center
Bronx-Lebanon Hospital
Catholic Healthcare System
Continuum Health Partners
Lenox Hill Hospital
Lutheran HealthCare
Maimonides Medical Center
MediSys Health Network
Memorial Sloan-Kettering
Montefiore Medical
New York City Health and Hospitals
North Shore-Long Island Jewish Health System
Winthrop-University Hospital
Yale New Haven Health System

HISTORICAL FINANCIALS

Company Type: Private

Income Statement FYE: December 31

	REVENUE ($ mil.)	NET INCOME ($ mil.)	NET PROFIT MARGIN	EMPLOYEES
12/13	4,264	595	14.0%	15,078
12/06	2,833	171	6.1%	—
12/04	2,427	56	2.3%	—
Annual Growth	6.5%	29.9%	—	—

2013 Year-End Financials

Debt ratio: ——
Return on equity: 14.00%
Cash ($ mil.): 152
Current ratio: 0.90
Long-term debt ($ mil.): —
Dividends
Yield: —
Payout: —
Market value ($ mil.): —

THE NEW YORK INDEPENDENT SYSTEM OPERATOR INC

Keeping the lights on in Times Square is only part of the job description of the New York Independent System Operator (New York ISO). The company which replaced the New York Power Pool manages and monitors wholesale activities on the state's transmission grid which consists of more than 11000 miles of high-voltage lines. The New York ISO is charged with providing fair access to the state's competitive wholesale power market while ensuring the reliable efficient and safe delivery of power to New York's 19.5 million residents. New York ISO had 37900 MW of generating capacity in 2013. The not-for-profit company is governed by a 10-person board of directors.

Geographic Reach

New York ISO administers the wholesale power market for New York State. It is responsible for the New York Control Area a part of the Eastern Interconnection interconnected power systems that cover most of the eastern US and Canada.

Sales and Marketing

New York ISO serves about 360 market participants.

Financial Performance

The ISO's revenue increased by 6% in 2012 due to higher revenues from grants planning studies fees and services partially offset by lower Rate Schedule 1 tariff charge revenues.The company's grant revenue of $15.3 million came from a 50% reimbursement received from Department of Energy for one of its projects that was being monitored by New York ISO. Planning studies revenues were offset by the corresponding study expenses.

Strategy

New York ISO's strategy includes adding new green power sources and improving plant efficiency to meet clean air regulations. Since 2000 the company has added more than 8600 MW of new power generation including renewable power generation (hydro and wind). In 2012 it had 1414 MW of wind generation in operation with plans for adding a further 4000 MW from renewable energy sources.

The company's 2012-2016 strategic plan calls for it to integrate gas operations and renewable power resources and expand wholesale electricity markets in addition to implementing Smart Grid technology to enhance its core mission of providing power reliably across its transmission system.

With an eye towards using more natural gas as a power plant fuel in 2012 the company formed a working group to improve coordination between its market participants natural gas utilities pipelines and other industry players.

In a move to further increase operational efficiency and lower the costs of electric transmission congestion management in 2013 New York ISO and fellow ISO PJM Interconnection began jointly managing transmission limits that occur near the boundaries between their regions.

Company Background

In 2009 New York ISO was granted $37.8 million by the Department of Energy to support the reliability of the bulk electricity grid in New York and develop a Smart Grid infrastructure. This was supplemented in 2010 with a federal $76 million Smart Grid Investment Grant to enable the construction of a statewide Phasor Measurement Network to enhance New York ISO's ability to detect system vulnerabilities and avoid blackouts.

The company has it origins in the Northeast Blackout of 1965 following which New York's eight largest electric utilities joined to create the New York Power Pool in order to reduce the likelihood of another major power interruption. New York ISO was formed in 1998 as part of the ongoing restructuring of New York State's electric power industry.

EXECUTIVES

COO, Richard (Rick) Gonzales
President Chief Executive Officer, Stephen G. Whitley
VP System and Resource Planning, Henry Chao
Senior Communications and Media Relations Specialist, Kenneth Klapp
Director, Robert A. Hiney
Director, Erland E. (Erkie) Kailbourne, age 72
Director, Alfred F. (Al) Boschulte, age 72
Director, Michael Bemis
Director, Thomas F. Ryan Jr., age 73
Director, Ave M. Bie
President Chief Executive Officer, Stephen G. Whitley
Auditors: KPMGLLP

LOCATIONS

HQ: THE NEW YORK INDEPENDENT SYSTEM OPERATOR INC
10 KREY BLVD, RENSSELAER, NY 12144-9681
Phone: 518-356-6000
Web: WWW.NYISO.COM

HISTORICAL FINANCIALS

Company Type: Private

Income Statement FYE: December 31

	REVENUE ($ mil.)	NET INCOME ($ mil.)	NET PROFIT MARGIN	EMPLOYEES
12/11	154	0	—	500
12/10	149	0	—	—
12/08	139	0	—	—
12/08	144	0	—	—
Annual Growth	2.2%	—	—	—

2011 Year-End Financials

Debt ratio: ——
Return on equity: —
Cash ($ mil.): 390
Current ratio: —
Long-term debt ($ mil.): —
Dividends
Yield: —
Payout: —
Market value ($ mil.): —

THE NEWTRON GROUP L L C

Some contractors bomb but The Newtron Group keeps on ticking. Through subsidiaries The Newtron Group offers a variety of industrial electrical and other specialty construction and contracting services nationwide. Services include instrumentation and control systems installation and maintenance; fiber optic installation and testing; industrial pipe and panel fabrication; aviation services; and electrical heat tracing. Newtron serves clients in such industries as refining power generation mining pharmaceuticals and semiconductors. Subsidiaries include electrical contractor Triad Electric and Controls and fiber optics firm Com-Net Services. The Newtron Group has offices in California Louisiana and Texas.

EXECUTIVES

VP Marketing, Duff Schempf
President, Glen Redd

LOCATIONS

HQ: THE NEWTRON GROUP L L C
8183 W EL CAJON DR, BATON ROUGE, LA 70815-8093
Phone: 225-927-8921
Web: WWW.THENEWTRONGROUP.COM

PRODUCTS/OPERATIONS

Selected Subsidiaries

Com-Net Services Inc. (fiber optics)
Executive Aviation Inc. (hangar space fuel supplies)
Newtron Inc. (electrical and instrumentation)
Newtron Heat Trace (industrial heat tracing)
Newtron Mechanical (industrial mechanics)
Triad Electric and Controls Inc. (electrical and instrumentation)
Triad Control Systems Inc. (control panel fabrication)

Selected Industries

Cement
Electronics
Food processing
Gas transmission
Metals and mining
Petrochemical
Pharmaceuticals
Power generation
Pulp and paper
Refining
Semiconductors
Waste treatment

COMPETITORS

EMCOR
Fisk Electric
Industrial Specialty Contractors
Jelec
MMR Group
Motor City Electric
Pike Corporation

HISTORICAL FINANCIALS

Company Type: Private

Income Statement FYE: June 30

	REVENUE ($ mil.)	NET INCOME ($ mil.)	NET PROFIT MARGIN	EMPLOYEES
06/13	443	0	—	2,000
06/12	296	2	0.7%	—
06/10	311	3	1.0%	—
06/10	362	5	1.5%	—
Annual Growth	7.0%	—	—	—

2013 Year-End Financials

Debt ratio: —
Return on equity: —
Cash ($ mil.): 11
Current ratio: 0.20
Long-term debt ($ mil.): —
Dividends
Yield: —
Payout: —
Market value ($ mil.): —

THE NORTH CAROLINA MUTUAL WHOLESALE DRUG COMPANY

LOCATIONS

HQ: THE NORTH CAROLINA MUTUAL WHOLESALE DRUG COMPANY
816 ELLIS RD, DURHAM, NC 277036019
Phone: 9195962151
Web: WWW.MUTUALDRUGCOMPANY.COM

HISTORICAL FINANCIALS

Company Type: Private

Income Statement FYE: March 31

	REVENUE ($ mil.)	NET INCOME ($ mil.)	NET PROFIT MARGIN	EMPLOYEES
03/10	1,035	0	0.0%	160
03/09	1,024	0	0.1%	—
Annual Growth	1.1%	(68.7%)	—	—

2010 Year-End Financials

Debt ratio: —
Return on equity: —
Cash ($ mil.): 53
Current ratio: 0.90
Long-term debt ($ mil.): —
Dividends
Yield: —
Payout: —
Market value ($ mil.): —

THE NORTH HIGHLAND COMPANY

The North Highland Company hopes its consulting services help its business clients chart a course toward improved operations. The company provides management and technology consulting services through more than 20 offices in 10 US states mainly in the southeastern US and more than 30 offices overseas. Its services cover areas such as business strategy supply chain management marketing and customer service business process improvement and technology management. The company's partners include Big Insight Sourcing Group The Difference and True Bridge Resources.

Geographic Reach

North Highland has US offices in Atlanta Boston Charlotte Dallas Denver Houston Jacksonville Los Angeles Minneapolis Nashville New York Orlando Philadelphia Richmond Sacramento San Antonio San Francisco St. Louis Tallahassee Tampa Trenton and Washington DC. It has more than 30 offices outside of the US. The company has grown organically over the years by opening offices in carefully chosen markets. In 2012 the company opened its first office in Boston and an office in St. Louis to expand its market penetration.

Strategy

North Highland's consultants typically work for clients in their home areas rather than traveling to engagements. The company believes that working locally gives it an edge in understanding clients' needs and in hiring qualified consultants who prefer to avoid the travel generally associated with the profession.

In 2012 the company launched Enfathom a new business intelligence and analytics solutions division created to help clients organize and analyze their data to produce meaningful actionable insights.

Mergers and Acquisitions

North Highland also looks to acquisitions and partnerships as a means for growth and penetrating other markets. In 2011 it bought Minneapolis-based Insight Solutions Group a consulting firm catering to a wide array of industry sectors. The year before it purchased a majority interest in Chinese consulting firm HBC Consulting.

In 2011 the company announced GENEX Partners as a new member company and consulting partner within Highland Worldwide. The partnership further extends North Highland's global reach in Japan.

Ownership

Chairman Dave Peterson helped found the employee-owned company in 1992.

Company Background

The North Highland name comes from the street address of the company's first office in Atlanta.

EXECUTIVES

Group Vice President For Florida Washington Dc And St Louis, Linda Ferrone
CEO, Dan Reardon
CFO, Kirk Hancock
Co-President, David Deiters
President North Highland Division, Alex Bombeck
EVP, Michael Lee
CFO, David D. Cathcart, age 40
VP Information Systems, Roger Hardgrove
Vice President And Local Office Leader, Kathy Battistoni
Vice President, Tara Stotland
Vp & Corporate Controller, Christy Thomas
Vice President, Colin Gunter
Vice President Atlanta, Andy Mayfield
Vice President And Office Leader New York, Ken Nowack
Vice President Operations, Sheila Mullins
Vice President Of Charlotte Office, Keith Anthony
Vice President, Matt Beyer
Vice President, Chris Wilhelmi
Vice President, Daniel Durham
Vice President, Dan Fukushima
Vice President, Carrie Nelson
Vice President Product Management, David Aguiar
Chief Financial Officer Services Lead Vice President, Katie Downs
Vice President Seattle Market Leader, Bob Colleran
Vice President, Jim Neal
Vice President Market Lead Chicago, Jose Martinez
Vice President, Margie Kluska
Executive Vice President Denver, Bruce Siegel
Vice President, Suresh Gupta
Vice President And Wealth Management, Jill Jacques
Vice President, Paul Patterson
Vice President Local Office Lead, Marty Brennan
Vice President, Beth Hayes
Vice President, Andy Moose
Vice President, Vijay Desai
Vice President, Craig Sanders
Vice President And Office Lead Dallas Ft Worth, Jim Schwalbe
Vice President Cross Market Services, David Conner
Chairman, Michael W. (Mike) Trapp, age 75
Board Member, Jennifer Merritt

LOCATIONS

HQ: THE NORTH HIGHLAND COMPANY
3333 PIEDMONT RD NE, ATLANTA, GA 30305-1811
Phone: 404-233-1015
Web: WWW.NORTHHIGHLAND.COM

PRODUCTS/OPERATIONS

Selected Practice Areas

Application integration
Business process improvement
Change management
Customer relationship management
Data management
Disaster recovery
Financial reporting and budgeting
Human resources strategy
Internet/intranet design
IT strategy
Lean manufacturing
Marketing strategy
Mergers and acquisitions integration
Organizational effectiveness
Risk management
Six Sigma
Supply chain assessment

COMPETITORS

A.T. Kearney
Bain & Company
Booz Allen
Boston Consulting
Deloitte Consulting
McKinsey & Company
PA Consulting

HISTORICAL FINANCIALS

Company Type: Private

Income Statement FYE: December 31

	REVENUE ($ mil.)	NET INCOME ($ mil.)	NET PROFIT MARGIN	EMPLOYEES
12/08	170	8	4.7%	800
12/05	87	2	2.7%	—
12/04	59	57	96.4%	—
12/03	47	1	3.1%	—
Annual Growth	29.0%	40.2%	—	—

2008 Year-End Financials

Debt ratio: —
Return on equity: 4.70%
Cash ($ mil.): 8
Current ratio: 1.50
Long-term debt ($ mil.): —
Dividends
Yield: —
Payout: —
Market value ($ mil.): —

THE OLTMANS CONSTRUCTION CO

EXECUTIVES

Chairman and CEO, Joseph O. (Joe) Oltmans II
VP Special Projects, Charles Roy
VP Project Management, Jim Woodside
Auditors: KPMGLLP

LOCATIONS

HQ: THE OLTMANS CONSTRUCTION CO
10005 MISSION MILL RD, WHITTIER, CA 906011739
Phone: 5629089578
Web: WWW.OLTMANS.COM

COMPETITORS

Bernards Brothers
DPR Construction
Duke Construction
KPRS Construction
Menemsha Development
Moorefield Construction
Ryan Companies US
Swinerton
Webcor Builders

HISTORICAL FINANCIALS

Company Type: Private

Income Statement FYE: March 31

	REVENUE ($ mil.)	NET INCOME ($ mil.)	NET PROFIT MARGIN	EMPLOYEES
03/08	326	5	1.6%	409
03/07	315	4	1.3%	—
03/06	317	3	1.1%	—
03/05	242	0	—	—
Annual Growth	10.4%	—	—	—

2008 Year-End Financials

Debt ratio: —
Return on equity: 1.60%
Cash ($ mil.): 18
Current ratio: 0.80
Long-term debt ($ mil.): —
Dividends
Yield: —
Payout: —
Market value ($ mil.): —

THE PARADIES SHOPS LLC

For the frequent flyer this is retail paradise. The Paradies Shops operates more than 550 shops in more than 75 airports hotels and aquariums throughout the US and Canada. It serves more than a half billion passengers annually with retail sites that include bookstores gift shops jewelry stores ladies accessory shops newsstands sunglass stores and western stores among others. Paradies Shops is also the exclusive licensee of Brooks Brothers CNBC PGA Tour and the New York Times. The firm operates several hotel properties and the retail program for the Georgia Aquarium in Atlanta. The company was founded by the Paradies family in 1960. In 2010 it sold a majority stake to Freeman Spogli & Co.

Geographic Reach

The Atlanta-based company operates stores at more than 75 locations including 17 of the top 25 airports in the US.

Strategy

Airport retail has experienced rapid growth in recent years as terminals become more akin to shopping malls with a captive audience. Flight delays and more stringent security requirements have increased waiting times for passengers many of whom turn to shopping for relief from the boredom. The Paradise Shops tailors its merchandise to regional tastes selling sports-related merchandise at its ACC (Atlantic Coast Conference) Shops in the Raleigh-Durham International Airport or Texas-themed goods and apparel at the Dallas-Fort Worth International Airport for example.

Ownership

Following the sale to the private equity firm the Paradies family retained a significant stake in the airport retailer and CEO Gregg Paradies continued to run the business.

EXECUTIVES

VP Merchandising, Jeffrey R. (Jeff) Brown, age 54
Chairman, Dick Dickson
President Chief Executive Officer, Gregg Paradies
Chief Operating Officer, Lou Bottino
Vice Chairman, James N. (Jim) Paradies
Regional VP, Rick Lillie
Vice President Business Development, Bruce Feuer
Senior Vice President Chief Administrative Officer, Don Marek
Regional Vice President, Charlene Yde
Regional VP, Patrick Wallace
VP Training and Customer Service, Jill Paradies
Chief Financial Officer, Kevin Smith
General Manager, Lisa Loera
Vice President General Counsel, Karen Leach
Vice President Food and Beverage, Leslie Christon
Vice President Chief Information Officer, Tony Dudek
Senior Vice President Strategic Planning and Business Development, John Cugasi
Senior Vice President Chief Merchandising Officer, Karen Johnston

LOCATIONS

HQ: THE PARADIES SHOPS LLC
2849 PACES FERRY RD SE # 400, ATLANTA, GA 30339-6201
Phone: 404-344-7905
Web: WWW.THEPARADIESSHOPS.COM

PRODUCTS/OPERATIONS

Selected Brands

ACC Shops
Bass Pro Shops
Big 12 conference
Big Ten Conference
Brighton Collectibles
Brooks Brothers
CNBC News
Details
Drugs & More
Dylan' s Candy Bar
Explore!
Harley-Davidson
Hometown Faborites
KidZoo
Marketplace
PGA Tour Shops
The New York Times Bookstore
Retail Court
SPANX
TravelMart
Vera Bradley

COMPETITORS

Barnes & Noble
DFS Group
Hudson Group
Puente Concessions
SkyMall

HISTORICAL FINANCIALS

Company Type: Private

Income Statement FYE: June 30

	REVENUE ($ mil.)	NET INCOME ($ mil.)	NET PROFIT MARGIN	EMPLOYEES
06/07	372	13	3.7%	4,000
06/03	248	0	—	—
06/02	223	0	—	—
Annual Growth	10.8%	—	—	—

2007 Year-End Financials

Debt ratio: —
Return on equity: 3.70%
Cash ($ mil.): 12
Current ratio: 0.60
Long-term debt ($ mil.): —
Dividends
Yield: —
Payout: —
Market value ($ mil.): —

THE PLAZA GROUP INC

The Plaza Group (TPG) is an international distributor of petrochemical solvents and chemical intermediates. Established in 1994 TPG is the exclusive marketer of some products from companies such as Shell Oil and Frontier Oil. The company markets to FORTUNE 500 companies major international enterprises direct consumers and chemical distributors. Its products are used in the production of resins coatings and adhesives. TPG partners with global suppliers (like SABIC Innovative Plastics Total Petrochemicals and Alon) in Asia Australia Europe and the Americas. The company is owned by president Randy Velarde.

EXECUTIVES

VP, Wilfred J. (Wilf) Kimball
President, Randy E. Velarde
VP, Vicki Velarde
Director Business and Sales East and West Coasts and Europe, Steve Willett
Controller, Robert (Bob) Imm
Administrative Assistant, Mary Esquivel
Sales Manager Domestic and Mexican Sales, Jose Flores
Manager Customer Service, Teresa Hitt
VP Plastics, Giuseppe Maniscalco, age 64
Sales Director, Venere Vitiello
Controller, Ray Heinen
Commercial Manager, Erika Bernhardt
Customer Service, Michael S. Moyers

LOCATIONS

HQ: THE PLAZA GROUP INC
10375 RICHMOND AVE # 1620, HOUSTON, TX 77042-4292
Phone: 713-266-1059
Web: WWW.THEPLAZAGRP.COM

COMPETITORS

Cole Chemical
ICC Chemical
Sinochem

HISTORICAL FINANCIALS

Company Type: Private

Income Statement FYE: December 31

	REVENUE ($ mil.)	NET INCOME ($ mil.)	NET PROFIT MARGIN	EMPLOYEES
12/12	288	3	1.2%	18
12/11	271	4	1.6%	—
12/04	198	2	1.2%	—
12/04	129	4	3.5%	—
Annual Growth	10.5%	(3.4%)	—	—

2012 Year-End Financials

Debt ratio: —
Return on equity: 1.20%
Cash ($ mil.): 0
Current ratio: 1.10
Long-term debt ($ mil.): —
Dividends
Yield: —
Payout: —
Market value ($ mil.): —

THE PRIDDY FOUNDATION

LOCATIONS

HQ: THE PRIDDY FOUNDATION
807 8TH ST STE 1010, WICHITA FALLS, TX 763013310
Phone: 9407238720
Web: WWW.PRIDDYFDN.ORG

HISTORICAL FINANCIALS

Company Type: Private

Income Statement FYE: December 31

	REVENUE ($ mil.)	NET INCOME ($ mil.)	NET PROFIT MARGIN	EMPLOYEES
12/13	8,791	3	0.0%	4
12/12	3	(4)	—	—
12/10	32	27	86.7%	—
12/09	0	0	—	—
Annual Growth	—	—	—	—

2013 Year-End Financials

Debt ratio: —
Return on equity: —
Cash ($ mil.): 14
Current ratio: —
Long-term debt ($ mil.): —
Dividends
Yield: —
Payout: —
Market value ($ mil.): —

THE PRINCIPIA CORPORATION

LOCATIONS

HQ: THE PRINCIPIA CORPORATION
13201 CLAYTON RD, SAINT LOUIS, MO 631311002
Phone: 3144342100
Web: WWW.COMMUNITY.PRINCIPIA.EDU

HISTORICAL FINANCIALS

Company Type: Private

Income Statement FYE: June 30

	REVENUE ($ mil.)	NET INCOME ($ mil.)	NET PROFIT MARGIN	EMPLOYEES
06/14	266	82	30.8%	600
06/13	226	39	17.5%	—
06/12	138	(37)	—	—
06/11	222	0	—	—
Annual Growth	6.1%	—	—	—

2014 Year-End Financials

Debt ratio: —
Return on equity: 30.80%
Cash ($ mil.): 4
Current ratio: —
Long-term debt ($ mil.): —
Dividends
Yield: —
Payout: —
Market value ($ mil.): —

THE RESEARCH FOUNDATION OF STATE UNIVERSITY OF NEW YORK

EXECUTIVES

President, John J. O'Connor
SVP Finance and Treasurer, Bonny G. Boice
VP Information Services and CIO, Gerard P. Drahos
VP Investment and Debt, Frank J. Gabriel
VP Philanthropy and Alumni Affairs, Michael F. Luck
VP Technology Transfer, M. Guven Yalcintas
VP Corporate Communications, Catherine J. Kaszluga
VP Administration and Human Resources and Secretary, Lynn D. Manning
VP Internal Audit and Management Advisory Services, Frank Zuraf
Vice Chairman, George B. Stefano
SVP Research, James A. Weyhenmeyer
General Counsel, Christopher J. Hanifin
VP Sponsored Programs Operations, Roberta Teliska
Chairman, John B. Clark
Director, Robert L. Ecklin, age 74
Director, Louis R. Tomson
Director, George M. Philip, age 65
Director, John B. Simpson
Vice Chairman, George B. Stefano
Director, Raymond W. Cross
Director, Shirley S. Kenny
Director, Bahgat G. Sammakia
Director, Paul W. Kutey, age 53
Director, John B. Fitzgibbons
Director, John C. LaRosa
Director, Myron J. Mitchell
Director, Risa I. Palm
Director, Steven J. Scheinman
Auditors: PricewaterhouseCoopersLLP

LOCATIONS

HQ: THE RESEARCH FOUNDATION OF STATE UNIVERSITY OF NEW YORK
35 STATE ST, ALBANY, NY 122072826
Phone: 5184347000

PRODUCTS/OPERATIONS

2011 Revenues

	% of total
Federal grants &	58
Private grants &	18
State grants &	17
Investments	2
Inventions &	1
Local grants &	1
Gifts capital gifts &	1
Other	2
Total	100

HISTORICAL FINANCIALS

Company Type: Private

Income Statement FYE: June 30

	REVENUE ($ mil.)	NET INCOME ($ mil.)	NET PROFIT MARGIN	EMPLOYEES
06/13	1,079	42	3.9%	8,000
06/12	1,114	12	1.2%	—
06/09	985	(71)	—	—
06/08	9	0	—	—
Annual Growth	159.5%	—	—	—

2013 Year-End Financials

Debt ratio: —
Return on equity: 3.90%
Cash ($ mil.): 0
Current ratio: 0.70
Long-term debt ($ mil.): —
Dividends
Yield: —
Payout: —
Market value ($ mil.): —

THE ROCKEFELLER UNIVERSITY

Rockefeller University sniffs out solid scientific evidence. The university is a leading US research institution and scientific graduate school providing training in biomedical and physical science fields such as biochemistry structural biology immunology neuroscience and human genetics. The university is centered around more than 70 research laboratories and a hospital and it runs M.D.-Ph.D. programs in conjunction with the Memorial Sloan-Kettering Cancer Center and the Weill Medical College at Cornell University. Rockefeller University's research is funded by entities such as the National Institutes of Health and the Howard Hughes Medical Institute as well as private gifts and endowments.

Operations

Rockefeller University maintains a small enrollment with only about 170 Ph.D. students and 25 M.D.-Ph.D. students. It also has some 200 research and clinical scientists on campus 350 postdoctoral researchers and 1000 clinicians technicians support staff and administrators.

The university doesn't charge tuition but instead relies on investment income research grants and contracts and private grants and gifts to fund its operations. To promote collaboration and innovation the university maintains an open structure with no formal departments. It also provides its Ph.D. students with amenities such as scholarships subsidized housing and annual research budgets to encourage independent study and creativity.

Financial Performance

Rockefeller University reported a 68% decline in revenues to some $157 million in 2012 due to reduced government grants and contracts investment losses and depreciation of derivative instruments; these elements were partially offset by an increase in private grants and gifts. The university also posted a net income loss in 2012 due to lower revenues and increased research and academic expenses. Rockefeller's earnings and profits tend to fluctuate from year to year due to the variability of its income sources.

Strategy

Rockefeller completed a $380 million renovation and construction program in 2010. The project included modernization of historical laboratory buildings and the construction of a new five-story Collaborative Research Center.

Company Background

The school has been a university since 1955 although it was originally founded by John D. Rockefeller in 1901 as The Rockefeller Institute for Medical Research. The Rockefeller University Hospital the first research-focused medical center in the US opened in 1910.

EXECUTIVES

Vp Finance And Treasure, James H Lapple
Vice President Human Resources, Virginia Huffman
President, Marc Tessier-Lavigne, age 54
VP Academic Affairs, Michael W. Young
VP University Strategy and Research Operations, Timothy P. O ,ÂConnor
Executive Vice President Acting, Fred Bohen
Vice Chairman, Henry R. Kravis, age 70
Vice Chairman, Richard E. Salomon, age 72
Chairman, Russell L. Carson
Vice Chairman, Marnie S. Pillsbury
Auditors: KPMGLLP

LOCATIONS

HQ: THE ROCKEFELLER UNIVERSITY
1230 YORK AVE, NEW YORK, NY 10065-6399
Phone: 212-327-8078
Web: WWW.ROCKEFELLER.EDU

HISTORICAL FINANCIALS

Company Type: Private

Income Statement FYE: June 30

	REVENUE ($ mil.)	NET INCOME ($ mil.)	NET PROFIT MARGIN	EMPLOYEES
06/11	424	107	25.4%	1,700
06/06	413	271	65.5%	—
06/05	413	271	65.5%	—
06/04	285	61	21.4%	—
Annual Growth	5.8%	8.4%	—	—

2011 Year-End Financials

Debt ratio: —
Return on equity: 25.40%
Cash ($ mil.): 154
Current ratio: 0.20
Long-term debt ($ mil.): —
Dividends
Yield: —
Payout: —
Market value ($ mil.): —

THE RUDOLPH/LIBBE COMPANIES INC

The corporate model of a conglomerate composed of independent unrelated businesses is not for The Rudolph/Libbe Companies. The group of companies can build or oversee real estate projects (general contractor Rudolph/Libbe Inc.); perform mechanical electrical and structural work (GEM Industrial); and then represent those properties in the market (RLWest Properties). Operating in the Ohio/Michigan corridor the group provides site selection design/build and construction management. Its portfolio includes industrial retail municipal residential educational health care and mixed-use projects. Fritz and Phil Rudolph and their cousin Allan Libbe founded flagship subsidiary Rudolph/Libbe Inc. in 1955.

The Rudolph/Libbe Companies also has a partnership with Winter Construction. The contracting partnership Winter RLG specializes in industrial construction for the automotive food processing industrial manufacturing power generation and distribution industries. Clients have included Campbell Soup FedEx and Alcoa.

In 2009 Rudolph/Libbe's real estate development division merged with another Ohio-based firm Park West Management & Development. The resulting RLWest Properties offers property management build-to-suit for lease or purchase and land sites for sale in Ohio.

EXECUTIVES

President; CEO Rudolph/Libbe Inc., William D. (Bill) Rudolph
President Rudolph/Libbe Properties, Stephen Welly
EVP Rudolph/Libbe Inc., Scott W. Libbe
Auditors: Ernst&YoungLLP

LOCATIONS

HQ: THE RUDOLPH/LIBBE COMPANIES INC
6494 LATCHA RD, WALBRIDGE, OH 43465-9788
Phone: 419-241-5000
Web: WWW.RUDOLPHLIBBE.COM

COMPETITORS

Albert M. Higley
Atlas Industrial Holdings
Danis
Messer Construction
Ruhlin
Skanska USA Building

HISTORICAL FINANCIALS

Company Type: Private

Income Statement FYE: December 31

	REVENUE ($ mil.)	NET INCOME ($ mil.)	NET PROFIT MARGIN	EMPLOYEES
12/12	375	13	3.6%	600
12/11	472	13	2.8%	—
12/10	237	1	0.6%	—
12/09	230	2	1.2%	—
Annual Growth	17.7%	69.2%	—	—

2012 Year-End Financials

Debt ratio: —
Return on equity: 3.60%
Cash ($ mil.): 14
Current ratio: 0.20
Long-term debt ($ mil.): —
Dividends
Yield: —
Payout: —
Market value ($ mil.): —

THE SAVANNAH COLLEGE OF ART AND DESIGN INC

With more than 11000 students Savannah College of Art and Design (SCAD) is one of the largest art and design schools in the US. It has undergraduate degrees in arts and fine arts as well as master's degrees in a range of subjects. The institution includes nine schools offering courses of study in fields such as architecture interior and graphic design fashion film and television painting dance and art history. The school also offers certificates in digital publishing digital publishing management historic preservation interactive design and typeface design.

Geographic Reach

SCAD has campuses in Atlanta and Savannah Georgia as well as in Hong Kong and Lacoste France. Students at the college hail from all 50 US states and more than 100 international countries.

Operations

Annual tuition runs at about $30000. The institution employs about 700 full- and part-time faculty members.

The school's most popular majors include animation fashion graphic design illustration and photography. In addition to regular coursework SCAD provides online distance education courses.

Company Background

The school was founded in 1978 and has taken an active role in restoring architectural landmarks in Savannah.

EXECUTIVES

COO, Brian Murphy
President and cofounder of the Savannah College of Art and Design, Paula S. Wallace

LOCATIONS

HQ: THE SAVANNAH COLLEGE OF ART AND DESIGN INC
342 BULL ST, SAVANNAH, GA 31401-4518
Phone: 912-525-5000
Web: WWW.SCAD.EDU

PRODUCTS/OPERATIONS

Degrees Offered
Bachelor of Arts (B.A.)
Bachelor of Fine Arts (B.F.A.)
Master of Architecture (M.Arch.)
Master of Arts (M.A.)
Master of Fine Arts (M.F.A.)
Master of Urban Design (M.U.D.)
Master of Arts in Teaching Art (M.A.)

Selected Schools

School of Building Arts
School of Communication Arts
School of Design
School of Digital Media
School of Entertainment Arts
School of Fashion
School of Fine Arts
School of Foundation Studies
School of Liberal Arts

HISTORICAL FINANCIALS

Company Type: Private

Income Statement FYE: June 30

	REVENUE ($ mil.)	NET INCOME ($ mil.)	NET PROFIT MARGIN	EMPLOYEES
06/10	314	10	3.2%	1,200
06/09	283	21	7.7%	—
06/09	0	0	—	—
Annual Growth	—10763307.5%		—	—

2010 Year-End Financials

Debt ratio: —
Return on equity: 3.20%
Cash ($ mil.): 5
Current ratio: —
Long-term debt ($ mil.): —
Dividends
Yield: —
Payout: —
Market value ($ mil.): —

THE SCOULAR COMPANY

The Scoular Company's business is a grind — and that's a good thing. The company is best known for buying selling storing handling and transporting agricultural products (mainly grains) worldwide. It deals in the mainstays of farming — corn hay millet rice sorghum soybeans and wheat —and gets them where they need to go. It transports these products via rail truck barge and seagoing container vessels. Scoular's other divisions offer fishmeal products for farm-animal pet and aquaculture feeds; ingredients for food manufacturers; renewable fuels; and truck freight brokering. It has customers in Asia Africa the Americas and Europe. George Scoular founded the business in Nebraska in 1892.

Geographic Reach

Scoular has operations in some 20 US states as well as in Canada and Mexico. The company has about a dozen merchandising offices and some 60 grain-handling facilities in North America with a storage capacity topping 120 million bushels. Scoular handles some 335 million bushels of grain a year.

Sales and Marketing

Scoular serves customers in the aquaculture flour milling food processing and manufacturing grain production industrial ag processing livestock feeding and manufacturing pet food manufacturing and renewable fuels sectors. Its services include bagging blending cleaning containerizing organic certifying packaging sorting sourcing and storage. It also offers risk management as well as transportation and logistics services.

Financial Performance

The Scoular Company's sales totaled $6.1 billion in 2012.

Strategy

The company is actively expanding its grain handling capacity. Scoular in 2012 acquired a grain-handling facility in Atlanta Nebraska as well as two grain facilities in Weiser Idaho. In 2011 the company formed a joint venture with Johnson Grain to own and manage two grain elevators and a loading facility in Illinois. Later that year Scoular acquired two grain elevators in Kansas from Ada Grain; during 2011 the facilities received operational upgrades (such as faster equipment and new scales) to speed up the unloading process. Scoular has also pumped up its holdings in the renewable energy market acquiring a 55 million-gallon ethanol plant and nearly 2 million-bushel train facility in Kansas in early 2011. Additionally Scoular is a minority investor in other ethanol production facilities.

Ownership

One of the US's largest private companies Scoular is owned by its employees.

EXECUTIVES

Vice President Overland Park Kansas, George V. Schieber
Sr. Vice President Omaha Nebraska, John M. Heck
Vice Chairman, Marshall E. Faith
CEO, Charles (Chuck) Elsea
COO, Robert (Bob) Ludington
Sr. Vice President Minneapolis Minnesota, Joan C. Maclin
Chairman and President, David M. Faith
VP Finance and Treasurer, Roger L. Barber
Sr. Vice President Salina Kansas, Curt Engel
Vice President Overland Park Kansas, Steve Dunn
Sr. Vice President Minneapolis Minnesota, John Messerich
Sr. Vice President Overland Park Kansas, Jim Konz
Vice President Omaha Nebraska, Omer Sagheer
Vice President Minneapolis Minnesota, Kurt Peterson

LOCATIONS

HQ: THE SCOULAR COMPANY
2027 DODGE ST STE 200, OMAHA, NE 68102-1229
Phone: 402-342-3500
Web: WWW.SCOULAR.COM

PRODUCTS/OPERATIONS

Selected Customer Industries Products and Services

Aquaculture (feed ingredients)
- Animal fats
- Animal proteins
- Fish oil
- Fishmeal
- Grain byproducts
- Vegetable fats
- Vegetable proteins

Flour milling (buying selling storing and shipping)
- Durum
- Hard red spring
- Hard red winter
- Soft red winter

Food manufacturing and processing (conventional organic and functional ingredients blending packaging co-packing)
- Ingredients
  - ProteinsDairyPeaPotatoRiceSoy
  - Specialty floursSoy
  - StarchesPeaPotatoRiceTapioca
  - Textured proteinsSoy

Grain production (marketing buying storing handling and shipping programs)
- Corn
- Hay
- Millet
- Rice
- Sorghum
- Soybeans
- Wheat

Industrial ag processing (feedstock supply byproduct marketing and crush risk management)
- Products
  - Citrus pulp
  - Distillers grains
  - Hominy feed
  - Wheat mill feeds
  - Whole cottonseed

Identity-preserved grain
- Corn
- Soybeans
- Wheat
- White corn

Livestock feeding and feed manufacturing (grain and feed ingredient sourcing risk management)
- Grains and oilseeds
  - Barley
  - Canola
  - Corn
  - Field peas
  - Flax
  - Lentils
  - Rye
  - Soybeans
  - Wheat
- Other
  - Canola meal
  - Citrus pulp
  - Distillers grains
  - Hominy feed
  - Wheat mill feed
  - Whole cottonseed

Pet food manufacturing (ingredients)
- Products
  - Fats
  - Flours
  - Gravy dust mix
  - Proteins
  - Starches
  - Yellow corn
- Sourcing and solutions
  - Animal oils
  - Animal proteins
  - Fish oil
  - Fishmeal
  - Frozen fish
  - Fruits
  - Grain products
  - Pea protein fiber flour and starch
  - Pomaces
  - Specialty starches flours
  - Variety meats
  - Vegetable oils
  - Vegetable proteins
  - Vegetables

Transportation
- Container and vessel (freight forwarding logistics and documentation in more than 50 countries)
- Rail truck and barge (logistics for shipping agricultural products in North America)

COMPETITORS

ADM
Andersons
Bartlett and Company
Bunge Limited
CHS
Cargill
DeBruce Grain
Excel Maritime Carriers
Louis Dreyfus Group
Syntroleum
TBS International
TORM

HISTORICAL FINANCIALS

Company Type: Private

Income Statement FYE: May 31

	REVENUE ($ mil.)	NET INCOME ($ mil.)	NET PROFIT MARGIN	EMPLOYEES
05/13	211	27	12.9%	800
05/12	211	27	13.1%	—
05/10	203	26	12.9%	—
05/10	172	22	13.0%	—
Annual Growth	7.0%	6.7%	—	—

2013 Year-End Financials

Debt ratio: —
Return on equity: 12.90%
Cash ($ mil.): 9
Current ratio: 0.60
Long-term debt ($ mil.): —
Dividends
Yield: —
Payout: —
Market value ($ mil.): —

THE SCRIPPS RESEARCH INSTITUTE

The Scripps Research Institute (TSRI) is a not-for profit organization that performs basic biomedical research in molecular and cellular biology chemistry immunology neuroscience disease and vaccine development. TSRI receives the majority of its funding from federal agencies such as the National Institutes of Health. TRSI opened a second facility in Florida in 2009. Its staff includes more than 2900 scientists and lab technicians and the organization traces its history back to 1924 when philanthropist Ellen Browning Scripps founded Scripps Metabolic Clinic.

Geographic Reach

TRSI is located on campuses in La Jolla California and Jupiter Florida.

Financial Performance

TSRI reported revenue of $393.3 million in 2011. That figure was down slightly from the $406.3 million the organization claimed in revenue for 2010.

TSRI receives the majority of its funding from the National Institutes of Health. Other contributors include the American Cancer Society the American Heart Association the Cystic Fibrosis Foundation the Leukemia & Lymphoma Society and the Juvenile Diabetes Association.

EXECUTIVES

SVP and CFO, Donna J. Weston
Chief Business Counsel Assistant Secretary and Trustee, Thomas E. Northrup
Vice President Research Services, Emily Holmes
VP Scientific Operations Scripps Florida, Harry W. Orf
Vice President Office of Sponsored Programs, Kaye Wynne
Dean Faculty, Gerald F. Joyce
Dean Graduate and Postgraduate Studies, James R. (Jamie) Williamson
VP Office of Philanthropy Florida, William Melton
Vice President Business Development, Scott Forrest
VP Business Development, W. Mark Crowell
Executive Director Science Communication, Floyd E. Bloom
Vice President Facilities Services, Pete Herold
Associate Dean Graduate Studies, William R. Roush
Acting SVP of Operations, Cary E. Thomas
Senior Managing Director, Gary N. Coburn
President The Skaggs Institute for Research, Claudia S. Luttrell
Vice President Human Resources, Cindy Scott-Lunau
Associate Vice President, Alex Bruner
Executive Assistant, Madeline Fenner
Executive Vice President Chief Financial Officer, Fredric G. Reynolds
Senior Vice President External Affairs, David Blinder
Senior Director Florida Operations, Dawn Johnson
Executive Vice President Amgen, Dennis M. Fenton
Executive Vice President Chief Scientific Officer, Peter K. Vogt
Chairman of the Board of Trustees, Richard A. Gephardt
President The Scripps Research Institute, Michael A. Marletta
President AT&T Florida, Marshall M. Criser
President and CEO, Michael A. Marletta
Trustee, J. Gary Burkhead
Trustee, Amin J. Khoury, age 75
Trustee, Phillip Frost
Trustee, A. Brent Eastman
Trustee, John J. Moores, age 70
Trustee, George H. Conrades, age 75
Trustee, Paul L. Herrling, age 67
Trustee, Thomas E. Dewey Jr., age 81
Trustee, Richard J. Elkus Jr., age 79
Trustee, Thomas H. (Tom) Insley, age 63
Chief Business Counsel Assistant Secretary and Trustee, Thomas E. Northrup
Trustee, Warren Beatty
Trustee, Gerald Cohn
Trustee, J. Michael Cook
Trustee, Alexander W. Dreyfoos
Trustee, Marjorie Fink
Trustee, Louis L. Gonda
Trustee, Lawrence C. Horowitz
Trustee, Ralph J. Shapiro
Trustee, Mark S. Skaggs
Trustee, Andrew Viterbi
Auditors: Deloitte&ToucheLLP

LOCATIONS

HQ: THE SCRIPPS RESEARCH INSTITUTE
10550 N TORREY PINES RD, LA JOLLA, CA 92037-1000
Phone: 858-784-1000
Web: WWW.SCRIPPS.EDU

COMPETITORS

Argonne National Laboratory
Battelle Memorial
Berkeley Lab
Brookhaven Lab
Lawrence Livermore Lab
Life Technologies Corporation
MITRE
Quintiles Transnational
SRI International
SwRI

HISTORICAL FINANCIALS

Company Type: Private

Income Statement FYE: September 30

	REVENUE ($ mil.)	NET INCOME ($ mil.)	NET PROFIT MARGIN	EMPLOYEES
09/09	375	(18)	—	99
09/08	464	137	29.7%	—
09/05	387	63	16.3%	—
09/04	326	39	12.2%	—
Annual Growth	2.8%	—	—	—

2009 Year-End Financials

Debt ratio: —
Return on equity: (-5.00%)
Cash ($ mil.): 28
Current ratio: 0.40
Long-term debt ($ mil.): —
Dividends
Yield: —
Payout: —
Market value ($ mil.): —

THE SHEPHERD GOOD HOSPITAL INC

LOCATIONS

HQ: THE SHEPHERD GOOD HOSPITAL INC
700 E MARSHALL AVE, LONGVIEW, TX 756015572
Phone: 9033152000
Web: WWW.GSMC.ORG

PRODUCTS/OPERATIONS

Selected Locations

Good Shepherd Medical Center Longview
Good Shepherd Medical Center Linden
Good Shepherd Medical Center Marshall
Good Shepherd Family Health Center Longview
Good Shepherd Family Health Center Gladewater
Good Shepherd Family Health Center Gilmer
Good Shepherd Family Health Center Henderson
Good Shepherd Glenn Garrett Clinic Hughes Springs
Good Shepherd Glenn Garrett Clinic Jefferson
Good Shepherd Family Health Center Kilgore
Good Shepherd Glenn-Garrett Clinic Linden
Good Shepherd Family Health Center White Oak
Good Shepherd Family Health Center Gilmer
Good Shepherd Family Health Center Henderson
Good Shepherd Glenn Garrett Clinic Hughes Springs
Good Shepherd Glenn Garrett Clinic Jefferson
Good Shepherd Family Health Center Kilgore
Good Shepherd Glenn-Garrett Clinic Linden
Good Shepherd Family Health Center White Oak

HISTORICAL FINANCIALS

Company Type: Private

Income Statement FYE: September 30

	REVENUE ($ mil.)	NET INCOME ($ mil.)	NET PROFIT MARGIN	EMPLOYEES
09/13	270	2	0.9%	2,200
09/12*	282	(11)	—	—
03/12	24	1	5.1%	—
09/11	267	0	—	—
Annual Growth	0.5%	—	—	—

*Fiscal year change

2013 Year-End Financials

Debt ratio: —
Return on equity: 0.90%
Cash ($ mil.): 9
Current ratio: 1.60
Long-term debt ($ mil.): —
Dividends
Yield: —
Payout: —
Market value ($ mil.): —

THE SUSAN G KOMEN BREAST CANCER FOUNDATION INC

Susan G. Komen For the Cure is dedicated to fighting breast cancer through education research screening and treatment programs. One of its well known fundraisers is an annual 5-K road race called the Komen Race for the Cure. The organization also operates a national help line and a website. Founded in 1982 by Nancy Brinker the organization is named in the memory of Brinker's sister Susan who died of breast cancer in 1980 at age 36. Brinker a breast cancer survivor herself promised her sister she would do everything she could to end breast cancer. Since its founding Komen for the Cure has invested more than $2.2 billion including more than $750 million to research in combating breast cancer.

Financial Performance

The organization's total net public support and revenue declined 9% in 2012 vs. 2011 to about $399 million from $439 million. Komen's change in net assets fell 82% over the same period. The drop off in support and revenue resulted from declining contributions sponsorships and race entry fees as well as contributed goods and services partially offset by increasing interest and dividends and gains on investments.

EXECUTIVES

Chairperson, Alexine C. Jackson
VP Strategic Relationships, Susan Carter Johns
Vice President Human Resources, Katie Rohlman
EVP and Chief Marketing Officer, Katrina McGhee
VP Survivorship and Outcomes, Diana Rowden
General Counsel, Jonathan Blum
Founder Chief Executive Officer, Nancy G. Brinker
Chief Financial Officer, Mark E. Nadolny
President, Elizabeth (Liz) Thompson
Senior Advisor Washington DC, Mike Williams
VP Information Technology, David Dawson
VP Research Evaluation and Scientific Programs, Chandini Portteus
VP Business Development and Partnerships, Margo Lucero
VP Development, Julie Teer
VP Global Networks, Nancy Macgregor
Director New Business Development, Larry Lundy
Vice President Marketing, Dorothy Jones

Senior Vice President Affiliate Network, Carol Corcoran
Vice President Human Resources, Katie Merrell
President Merck Vaccines, Julie L. Gerberding
President International Prevention Research Institute, Peter Boyle
President CEO, Tom Gentile
Director, Brenda J. Lauderback, age 65
Director, Linda Custard
Director, Connie O'Neill
Director, Dorothy S. Paterson
CEO and Director, Nancy G. Brinker
Director, John D. Raffaelli
Director, Eric Brinker
Director, Linda Law

LOCATIONS

HQ: THE SUSAN G KOMEN BREAST CANCER FOUNDATION INC
5005 LYNDON B JOHNSON FWY # 250, DALLAS, TX 75244-6100
Phone: 972-855-1600
Web: WWW.KOMEN.ORG

HISTORICAL FINANCIALS

Company Type: Private

Income Statement FYE: March 31

	REVENUE ($ mil.)	NET INCOME ($ mil.)	NET PROFIT MARGIN	EMPLOYEES
03/12	197	8	4.4%	260
03/09	159	3	2.2%	—
03/07	307	38	12.5%	—
03/06	1,463	0	—	—
Annual Growth	—	184.7%	—	—

2012 Year-End Financials

Debt ratio: ——
Return on equity: 4.40%
Cash ($ mil.): 56
Current ratio: 0.30
Long-term debt ($ mil.): —
Dividends
Yield: —
Payout: —
Market value ($ mil.): —

THE TOLEDO HOSPITAL

One of the region's largest acute-care facilities The Toledo Hospital provides medical care to the residents of northwestern Ohio and southeastern Michigan. Boasting some 800 beds the facility offers several specialties and services including the Jobst Vascular Center which provides cardiac and vascular services in conjunction with The University of Michigan. The Toledo Hospital which shares a medical complex with the Toledo Children's Hospital also operates trauma emergency outpatient arthritis sleep disorder and women's health centers. The Toledo Hospital is a member of Toledo-based ProMedica Health System a mission-based not-for-profit healthcare organization formed in 1986.

Geographic Reach

The Toledo Hospital serves the residents of a 27-county area consisting of northwest Ohio and southeast Michigan.

Operations

The health care facility has expanded its footprint in Toledo in recent years. Besides its primary hospital it operates a stroke unit the Jobst Vascular Center a medical complex with the Toledo Children's Hospital and centers devoted to trauma emergencies arthritis sleep disorders and women's health. The Toledo Hospital and the Toledo Children's Hospital operate the Renaissance a 10-story medical complex that has enabled the pair to expand capacity with private rooms intensive and intermediate care units and pediatric hematology and oncology services.

Strategy

To address the needs of area residents The Toledo Hospital in late 2012 rolled out a program that makes a cardiologist available 24 hours a day seven days a week. It's the only hospital in the region to provide this service. In early 2012 the hospital opened a 20-bed stroke unit and a new 15-bed neuro intensive care unit on a newly developed floor of its Renaissance tower.

EXECUTIVES

Director Jobst Vascular Center, Anthony J. Comerota
Director Media Relations ProMedica Health System, Tedra White
President, Kevin Webb

LOCATIONS

HQ: THE TOLEDO HOSPITAL
2142 N COVE BLVD, TOLEDO, OH 43606-3896
Phone: 419-291-4000
Web: WWW.PROMEDICA.ORG

PRODUCTS/OPERATIONS

Selected Services

Arthritis and Osteoporosis Center
Bariatric Surgery
Behavioral Health and Psychiatric Services
Breast Care Center
Cancer Care
Critical Care
Diabetes
Dialysis
Emergency Services
Endoscopy Services
Fertility Services
Heart Care
Hemophilia Outpatient Clinic
Hyperbaric Medicine
Laboratory Services
Lactation Services
Maternal Fetal Medicine
Mom & Me Boutique
Neurology
Neurophysiology
OccuHealth
Orthopaedics
Outpatient Surgery
Palliative Care
Radiology / Imaging Services
Rehabilitation Services
Respiratory Care
Sleep Medicine
Surgical Services
Trauma Services
Urology / Nephrology
Vascular Services
Women' s Services

COMPETITORS

Chelsea Community Hospital
Firelands Regional Health System
Mercy Health Partners Toledo
Oakwood Healthcare
Sylvania Franciscan Health
Tenet Healthcare
Trinity Health (Novi)
University of Toledo Medical Center
University of Michigan Health System

HISTORICAL FINANCIALS

Company Type: Private

Income Statement FYE: December 31

	REVENUE ($ mil.)	NET INCOME ($ mil.)	NET PROFIT MARGIN	EMPLOYEES
12/09	635	19	3.0%	5,586
12/08	548	33	6.1%	—
12/05	518	28	5.5%	—
12/04	23	16	71.9%	—
Annual Growth	93.6%	2.7%	—	—

2009 Year-End Financials

Debt ratio: ——
Return on equity: 3.00%
Cash ($ mil.): 30
Current ratio: 0.20
Long-term debt ($ mil.): —
Dividends
Yield: —
Payout: —
Market value ($ mil.): —

THE TRUSTEES OF MOUNT HOLYOKE COLLEGE

Mount Holyoke College was the first of the Seven Sisters –the female equivalent of the predominantly male Ivy League. The nation's oldest continuing institution of higher learning for women Mount Holyoke offers nearly 50 departmental and interdisciplinary majors to about 2300 female students. Mount Holyoke is part of the Five College Consortium which also includes Amherst Hampshire Smith and the University of Massachusetts. (Mount Holyoke students can take classes at any of these schools.) Notable alumnae include poet Emily Dickinson and Tony- and Pulitzer Prize-winning playwright Wendy Wasserstein.

Geographic Reach

The college has students from 46 US states and almost 80 countries.

Operations

The independent residential liberal arts college for women has a student-to-faculty ratio of 10:1 and charges $41270 in annual tuition and $12140 for room and board.

Financial Performance

The college reported a marginal 1% increase in revenues in 2012 as the result of higher tuition and fees. It also receives revenues from contributions grants and contracts and returns from its endowment of $591 million.Mount Holyoke saw a net loss in 2012 due to higher operating expenses and a loss from non-operating activities (attributed to loss in endowment investment return in 2012 compared to a gain in 2011).

Company Background

Mount Holyoke was founded in 1837 by chemist and educator Mary Lyon.

EXECUTIVES

Director Information Technology, Donna Baron
Dean of Students, Liz Braun
Dean of Studies, Joseph D. Cohen
President emerita American Film Institute, Jean Firstenberg

LOCATIONS

HQ: THE TRUSTEES OF MOUNT HOLYOKE COLLEGE
50 COLLEGE ST, SOUTH HADLEY, MA 01075-1448
Phone: 413-538-2000
Web: WWW.ATHLETICS.MTHOLYOKE.EDU

COMPETITORS

Amherst College
Bryn Mawr
Hollins University
Scripps College
Smith College
University of Massachusetts
Vassar College
Wellesley College

HISTORICAL FINANCIALS

Company Type: Private

Income Statement FYE: June 30

	REVENUE ($ mil.)	NET INCOME ($ mil.)	NET PROFIT MARGIN	EMPLOYEES
06/10	156	(16)	—	1,000
06/09	136	(31)	—	—
06/09	0	0	—	—
Annual Growth	—	—	—	—

2010 Year-End Financials

Debt ratio: —
Return on equity: (-10.40%)
Cash ($ mil.): 6
Current ratio: —
Long-term debt ($ mil.): —
Dividends
Yield: —
Payout: —
Market value ($ mil.): —

THE TRUSTEES OF THE SMITH COLLEGE

Girl Power abounds at Smith. The nation's largest liberal arts college for women Smith College provides 1000 courses in some 50 academic areas including the arts humanities languages sciences and social sciences. It enrolls nearly 2900 undergraduate students and employs about 300 professors. Annually nearly half of Smith juniors study abroad. Founded in 1871 by Sophia Smith (who left funds in her will to create a women's college) and her minister John Greene the school also offers graduate degrees in areas such as education social work and fine arts. Smith's notable alumna include chef Julia Child author and political commentator Molly Ivins and feminist icon Gloria Steinem.

EXECUTIVES

President, Carol T. Christ, age 69
VP Finance and Administration, Ruth Constantine
VP Advancement, Patricia Jackson
Dean of Admission, Deb Shaver
CIO, David Gregory
Provost and Dean of Faculty, Marilyn R. Schuster
President they hired, Clark Seelye
Vice President for Public Affairs and Strategic Initiatives, Laurie Fenlason

LOCATIONS

HQ: THE TRUSTEES OF THE SMITH COLLEGE
1 CHAPIN WAY, NORTHAMPTON, MA 01063-6302
Phone: 413-585-2700
Web: WWW.SMITH.EDU

HISTORICAL FINANCIALS

Company Type: Private

Income Statement FYE: June 30

	REVENUE ($ mil.)	NET INCOME ($ mil.)	NET PROFIT MARGIN	EMPLOYEES
06/12	218	(37)	—	1,300
06/11*	206	221	107.4%	—
12/08	0	0	—	—
06/07	0	0	—	—
Annual Growth	—	—	—	—

*Fiscal year change

2012 Year-End Financials

Debt ratio: —
Return on equity: (-17.20%)
Cash ($ mil.): 32
Current ratio: —
Long-term debt ($ mil.): —
Dividends
Yield: —
Payout: —
Market value ($ mil.): —

THE UCLA FOUNDATION

Helping to make La-La Land a little more erudite The UCLA Foundation raises manages and disperses funds to help support the tripartite education research and service mission of UCLA. With more than $1 billion in assets the organization funds the aforementioned purposes as well as campus improvements and special programs. About half of the foundation's gifts received are provided by foundations; corporations and alumni each account for some 15% of gifts. The UCLA Progress Fund predecessor of the foundation was established in 1945 by the school's alumni association.

EXECUTIVES

Evp, Rhea Turteltaub
Auditors: PricewaterhouseCoopersLLP

LOCATIONS

HQ: THE UCLA FOUNDATION
10920 WILSHIRE BLVD # 200, LOS ANGELES, CA 90024-6502
Phone: 310-794-3193
Web: WWW.UCLAFOUNDATION.ORG

HISTORICAL FINANCIALS

Company Type: Private

Income Statement FYE: June 30

	ASSETS ($ mil.)	NET INCOME ($ mil.)	INCOME AS % OF ASSETS	EMPLOYEES
06/11	2,022	447	22.1%	317
06/10	1,555	157	10.1%	—
06/09	1,308	(37)	—	—
06/00	849	0	—	—
Annual Growth	8.2%	—	—	—

2011 Year-End Financials

Debt ratio: —
Return on equity: 127.30%
Cash ($ mil.): 1
Current ratio: —
Long-term debt ($ mil.): —
Dividends
Yield: —
Payout: —
Market value ($ mil.): —

THE UNION MEMORIAL HOSPITAL

Not quite for time immemorial but MedStar Union Memorial Hospital (formerly Union Memorial Hospital) has been caring for patients for a long time (since 1839). The Baltimore-area facility is a specialty acute-care hospital with 250 beds and more than 620 physicians. Areas of clinical research and expertise include cardiac care orthopedics and sports medicine. In addition it offers a range of inpatient and outpatient services including diabetes and endocrine center eye surgery center general surgery oncology and thoracic and vascular surgery. MedStar Union Memorial offers post-graduate programs orthopedic surgery residencies and hand surgery fellowships. The company is a part of MedStar Health.

Operations

MedStar Union Memorial offers a full array of diagnostic medical surgical and rehabilitative services. The hospital provides graduate medical education through residency programs and fellowship programs. MedStar Union Memorial offers 19 postgraduate first year positions in medicine; a surgical training program; and an orthopedic surgical program. MedStar's Online Clinical Library provides access both onsite and offsite to electronic resources for drug information evidence-based medicine point of care full-test textbooks and more the 400 full-text journals.

Strategy

To emphasize it parent's brand as part of its future growth strategy Union Memorial Hospital changed its name to MedStar Union Memorial Hospital in 2012.

Ownership

The company is a part of MedStar Health.

Company Background

As Union Memorial the company celebrated its sesquicentennial anniversary in 2004. The hospital has been repeatedly recognized as among "America's Best Hospitals" by U.S. News & World Report. It's also considered one of the top 100 hospitals for intensive care and cardiovascular services.

EXECUTIVES

VP Finance, Joseph B. Smith
President, Bradley S. Chambers
VP Medical Affairs, Stuart B. Bell
VP Patient Care Services, Sharon Bottcher
VP Orthopedics Anesthesiology and Surgery, Steve Koenigsberg
Vice President Cardiovascular Services, Cheryl Lunnen
Assistant VP Information Technology, Mike W. Dailey
Vice President MedStar Sports Medicine, Lew Lyon
VP Operations, Neil MacDonald
VP Human Resources, Holly Phipps Adams
Chairman, Mark T. Jensen
Vice-Chair, Ebben D. Finney III
Assistant Secretary, Linda Heath
Manager Media Relations, Debra Schindler
VP Philanthropy, Michael C. Cather
Assistant Vice President Medical Affairs, Rohit Gulati
Assistant Vice President Marketing & Communications, Jo Anna Shuba
President and Director, Bradley S. Chambers
Vice-Chair, Ebben D. Finney III
Director, Derrick A. Adams
Director, Philip C. Buescher

Director, Timothy D. A. Chriss
Director, Leslie Matthews
Director, George W. Moran
Director, Thomas B. O'Neill
Director, Michael Randolph
Director, Kenneth A. Samet, age 56
Director, Peter Sloane
Director, David N. Willis
Director, Christopher G. Wunder

LOCATIONS

HQ: THE UNION MEMORIAL HOSPITAL
201 E UNIVERSITY PKWY, BALTIMORE, MD 21218-2891
Phone: 410-554-2865
Web: WWW.UNIONMEMORIAL.ORG

PRODUCTS/OPERATIONS

Selected Facilities

Arnold Palmer SportsHealth Center
The Curtis National Hand Center
The Harry and Jeanette Weinberg Heart Institute
Union Memorial Orthopaedics and Sports Medicine
Vascular Institute

COMPETITORS

Anne Arundel Medical Center
Johns Hopkins Health System
LifeBridge Health
St. Agnes HealthCare
University of Maryland Medical System

HISTORICAL FINANCIALS

Company Type: Private

Income Statement FYE: June 30

	REVENUE ($ mil.)	NET INCOME ($ mil.)	NET PROFIT MARGIN	EMPLOYEES
06/12	418	(2)	—	2,400
06/11	428	17	4.1%	—
06/09	438	0	—	—
06/08	424	28	6.7%	—
Annual Growth	(0.4%)	—	—	—

THE UNIVERSITY OF ARIZONA MEDICAL CENTER

The University of Arizona Health Network (UAHN) heals Arizonans and trains Wildcats. University of Arizona Medical Center (UMC) is the primary teaching hospital for the University of Arizona (UA) and offers medical treatment research and education services. The not-for-profit medical center has some 480 beds and provides cancer cardiology geriatric respiratory transplant and dialysis care as well as general practice and home health services. The hospital is located at the Arizona Health Sciences Center which is home to the UA medical schools the Arizona Cancer Center the Sarver Heart Center and the Steele Children's Research Center. The network also includes the Diamond Children's Hospital. The University of Arizona Health Network was formed in 2010 when University Physicians Hospital merged with University Medical Center.

Geographic Reach

UAHN serves patients in Tucson Arizona and surrounding areas.

Strategy

In 2010 the hospital and University Physicians Healthcare (UPH a physicians' practice organization) integrated their administrative operations into one organization which was named University of Arizona Health Network in 2011.

The University of Arizona Health Network works in partnership with the University of Arizona College of Medicine and was created to facilitate better coordination integration and promotion of clinical activities to support the College of Medicine's education research and patient-care goals.

The hospital has undergone extensive expansion efforts including a new six-story patient tower adding about 200 patient beds. The first phase of the tower which included new emergency trauma and intensive care centers was completed in 2009. The second and final stage which included the addition of the 120-bed Diamond Children's Medical Center was completed in 2010.

Company Background

UAHN was formed in 2010.

EXECUTIVES

Dean UA College of Medicine, Steven Goldschmid
Vice President Chief Information Officer, Shirley Gabriel
President and CEO, Michael Waldrum
SVP and CEO Hospital Division, Karen D. Mlawsky
VP and CFO, Misty Hansen
President UMC Foundation and UPH Foundation, Kent Rollins
SVP and CEO Health Plans, James Stover
Chief Medical Officer Quality & Safety University & South Campuses, Andreas Theodorou
Chief Medical Officer South Campus, John Kettelle
Vice President Learning & Training, Eskild Petterson
Respiratory Therapy Director, Cheryl Hamilton
Pharm D, Jennifer Sinnard
Vp, Judy A Dye
Chairman, Steven W. Lynn
Board Member, Jamie Matanovich
Board Member, Judy Ginac
Auditors: RSMMcGladreyInc.

LOCATIONS

HQ: THE UNIVERSITY OF ARIZONA MEDICAL CENTER
1501 N CAMPBELL AVE, TUCSON, AZ 85724-0001
Phone: 520-694-0111
Web: WWW.UPH.ORG

COMPETITORS

Banner Health
John C. Lincoln Health Network
Northern Arizona Healthcare
Phoenix Children' s Hospital
Scottsdale Healthcare
Sun Health
Yuma Regional Medical Center

HISTORICAL FINANCIALS

Company Type: Private

Income Statement FYE: June 30

	REVENUE ($ mil.)	NET INCOME ($ mil.)	NET PROFIT MARGIN	EMPLOYEES
06/09	541	0	—	3,000
06/08	512	27	5.3%	—
06/05	708	0	0.0%	—
Annual Growth	(6.5%)	—	—	—

2009 Year-End Financials

Debt ratio: —
Return on equity: —
Cash ($ mil.): 3
Current ratio: —
Long-term debt ($ mil.): —
Dividends
Yield: —
Payout: —
Market value ($ mil.): —

THE UNIVERSITY OF CHICAGO MEDICAL CENTER

It may have received its official dedication on Halloween but The University of Chicago Medical Center (UCMC) works hard to make visiting the hospital a little less spooky. UCMC is a complex of facilities located on The University of Chicago campus that include the acute care Bernard A. Mitchell Hospital the Comer Children's Hospital a women's health and maternity facility and an outpatient care center. Established in 1927 (and dedicated on Halloween of that year) the complex includes the affiliated University of Chicago Pritzker School of Medicine and forms the clinical arm of The University of Chicago Division of Biological Sciences. UCMC houses about 550 beds.

Geographic Reach

UCMC is located in Hyde Park on the south side of Chicago. Its main medical campus includes the Center for Care and Discovery Comer Children's Hospital Bernard A. Mitchell Hospital Chicago Lying-in Hospital and Duchossois Center for Advanced Medicine. UCMC also manages a network of area physicians and specialty clinics located in Chicago and its suburbs as well as in northwestern Indiana.

Operations

Its Bernard A. Mitchell Hospital includes helicopter transportation operations emergency level-one pediatric trauma services and regional burn and peri-natal units. The roughly 155-bed Comer Children's Hospital offers disease care education and research as well as expanded newborn intensive care services.

UCMC sees some 23000 inpatients and 75000 emergency room visits per year. The hospital is one of the largest providers of uncompensated care in Illinois providing millions of dollars in charity care every year.

As part of the university's Biological Sciences division UCMC operates medical research centers focused on cancer immunology diabetes cardiology and neurology. The cancer center is especially intent on discovering improved treatment and prevention measures using gene and protein-based treatments. The Gwen and Jules Knapp Center for Biomedical Discovery works on discovery programs for a variety of medical conditions including diabetes cancer and pediatrics.

Financial Performance

UCMC experienced a 9% increase in sales to some $1.3 billion in 2012 due to higher net patient service revenues. However the medical center reported a net income loss of some $35.6 million that year due to higher operating expenses from salary wage and benefit increases as well as supply costs physician service expenses other expenses and declined investment returns.

Strategy

UCMC is widening its service offerings through facility construction efforts. It completed a 1.2 million sq. ft. medical research and patient-centered care hospital pavilion on its main campus (named the Center for Care and Discovery) in 2012; the new facility opened its doors to 145 patients the following year.

Also in 2012 UCMC launched a new brand identity that encompasses the academic medical institution's operations: University of Chicago Medicine.

Company Background

First Lady Michelle Obama served as VP for community and external affairs at UCMC; she resigned from her post in early 2009 when she made the move to the White House.

EXECUTIVES

Vice Chair, Thomas A. Reynolds III, age 62
President, Sharon O'Keefe
EVP Medical Affairs and Dean Division of the Biological Sciences and Pritzker School of Medicine; Trustee, Kenneth S. Polonsky
EVP Corporate Strategy and Public Affairs, Susan S. Sher
Vice Chair, Frank M. Clark
Chairman, Rodney L. (Rod) Goldstein
EVP Strategic Affiliations; Associate Dean for Community-Based Research, Eric E. Whitaker
Director Medical Center Communications, John Easton
COO and Associate Dean, Carolyn S. Wilson
VP and Chief Human Resources Officer, Larry A. Callahan
VP and Chief Pharmacy Officer, David Hicks
VP Risk Management Patient Safety and Compliance, Krista Curell
Secretary and Chief of Staff to the Dean, Jennifer A. Hill
Treasurer, Ann M. McColgan
VP Finance, Richard B. Miller
VP and General Counsel, John Satalic
CFO, James M. Watson
Assistant Director of Media and Social Media, Lorna Wong
Trustee, John Bucksbaum, age 57
Trustee, Craig J. Duchossois
Trustee, James S. (Jim) Frank
Trustee, James S. Crown, age 60
Vice Chair, Thomas A. Reynolds III, age 62
Trustee, Paula Wolff
Trustee, Stanford J. Goldblatt
EVP Medical Affairs and Dean Division of the Biological Sciences and Pritzker School of Medicine; Trustee, Kenneth S. Polonsky
Trustee, Paul F. Anderson
Trustee, Robert H. Bergman
Trustee, Ellen Block
Trustee, Kevin J. Brown
Vice Chair, Frank M. Clark
Trustee, Christopher J. Murphy III
Trustee, Brien M. O'Brien
Trustee, James Reynolds Jr.
Trustee, Michael Tang
Trustee, Terry L. Van Der Aa
Trustee, Kelly R. Welsh
Trustee, Robert J. Zimmer
Trustee, Andrew M. Alper
Trustee, Stephanie Comer
Trustee, Melody Spann-Cooper
Trustee, Thomas F. Rosenbaum
Trustee, Gordon Segal
Trustee, Benjamin Shapiro

LOCATIONS

HQ: THE UNIVERSITY OF CHICAGO MEDICAL CENTER
5841 S MARYLAND AVE MC6098, CHICAGO, IL 60637-1447
Phone: 773-702-1000
Web: WWW.UCHOSPITALS.EDU

PRODUCTS/OPERATIONS

Selected Services

Cancer
Endocrinology
Gastroenterology
Geriatrics
Heart
Kidney disease
Neurosciences
Orthopaedics
Respiratory disease
Surgery
Transplantation
Women's services

Selected Facilities

Bernard A. Mitchell Hospital
Center for Care and Discovery
Chicago Lying-in Hospital (Maternity and Women's Hospital)
Comer Children's Hospital
Duchossois Center for Advanced Medicine (outpatient care and diagnostics)
Gwen and Jules Knapp Center for Biomedical Discovery
LaRabida Children's Hospital (affiliated facility)
Mercy Hospital (affiliated facility)
University of Chicago Pritzker School of Medicine
Weiss Memorial Hospital (affiliated facility)

COMPETITORS

Advocate Health Care
Alexian Brothers Health System
Covenant Ministries
Elmhurst Memorial Healthcare
Loyola University Health System
Mercy Hospital and Medical Center
NorthShore University HealthSystem
Northwest Community Healthcare
Northwestern Memorial HealthCare
Resurrection Health Care
Rush System for Health
Silver Cross Hospital
Sinai Health System
St. Bernard Hospital and Health Care Center

HISTORICAL FINANCIALS

Company Type: Private

Income Statement FYE: June 30

	REVENUE ($ mil.)	NET INCOME ($ mil.)	NET PROFIT MARGIN	EMPLOYEES
06/09	1,294	(190)	—	5,000
06/08	1,286	38	3.0%	—
06/07	1,092	234	21.5%	—
06/06	861	98	11.5%	—
Annual Growth	14.5%	—	—	—

2009 Year-End Financials

Debt ratio: —
Return on equity: (-14.70%)
Cash ($ mil.): 100
Current ratio: 0.90
Long-term debt ($ mil.): —
Dividends
Yield: —
Payout: —
Market value ($ mil.): —

THE UNIVERSITY OF DAYTON

More than 10000 students make the University of Dayton one of the nation's largest Catholic universities and the largest private university in Ohio. The institution offers some 70 majors. Students are recruited on a national basis and from foreign countries. The student population approximates 7300 undergraduate and 3000 graduate students. It has student and faculty ratio of 15:1 and charges tuition and fees of $33400 per annum. Well-known alumni include the late author and columnist Erma Bombeck and Super Bowl-winning NFL coaches Jon Gruden and Chuck Noll.

Geographic Reach

The university's students are primarily from Ohio and nine other Midwestern and Eastern US states.

Financial Performance

In 2012 the university saw a 4% increase in revenues due to higher student tuition and fees. Net income decreased by 120% in 2012 thanks to an increase in expenditures a decline in investment gains in the deficit of amounts designated for current operations a loss in the change in the net unrealized loss on interest rate swap agreements and a change in postretirement benefit obligations.

Company Background

The University of Dayton was founded in 1850 by the Society of Mary (the Marianists).

EXECUTIVES

Chair, Allen M. Hill, age 68
President, Daniel J. Curran
VP Research and Executive Director UDRI, Mickey V. McCabe
Associate Provost and CIO, Thomas D. (Tom) Skill
Dean University Libraries, Kathleen M. Webb
VP Finance and Administrative Services, Thomas E. Burkhardt
Dean College of Arts and Science, Paul Benson
VP Human Resources, Joyce M. Carter
Vice President for Enrollment Management and Marketing, Sundar Kumarasamy
Interim VP University Advancement, Dave Harper
Provost, Joseph Saliba
VP Student Development, William Fischer
VP and Director Athletics, Tim Wabler
VP Mission and Rector, James F. Fitz
Department Secretary, Gina Newlin
Assistant Director of Operations and Graduate Student Services, Diane Helmick
Associate Director of Media Relations, Shawn Robinson
Secretary, Denise Quillen
Assistant Director Media Relations, Cameron Fullam
Trustee, Catherine V. Babington, age 61
Trustee, Allen M. Hill, age 67
Trustee, David P. Yeager
Trustee, Richard H. Finan, age 78
President Secretary and Trustee, Daniel J. Curran
Trustee, Robert J. (Bob) Froehlich
Trustee, H. John (Jack) Proud
Vice Chair, Stephen M. Glodek
Trustee, Edward M. Brink
Trustee, William J. Campbell
Trustee, Rev Thomas A. Cardone
Trustee, Annette Casella
Trustee, Margaret A. Cavanaugh
Trustee, Steven D. Cobb
Trustee, Rev James F. Fitz
Trustee, David P. Fitzgerald
Trustee, Frank P. Geraci
Executive Director International Center for Marianist Formation and Trustee, Thomas F. Giardino
Trustee, Francisco T. Gonzalez
Trustee, Darlene Gutmann
Trustee, John Haley
Trustee, George Hanley
Trustee, Susan Kettering
Trustee, Peter Luongo
Rector and Trustee, Rev Paul M. Marshall
Trustee, Richard Pfleger
Trustee, John Riazzi
Trustee, Kurtis (Kurt) Sanford
Trustee, Katharine Schipper
Trustee, Westina Matthews Shatteen
Trustee, Rev Ralph A. Siefert
Trustee, Sister Francis Marie Thrailkill
Trustee, Andrew F. Veres
Trustee, Rev Daryl Ward
Trustee, David C. Winch

LOCATIONS

HQ: THE UNIVERSITY OF DAYTON
300 COLLEGE PARK AVE, DAYTON, OH 45469-0002
Phone: 937-229-1000
Web: WWW.DINING.UDAYTON.EDU

HISTORICAL FINANCIALS

Company Type: Private

Income Statement FYE: June 30

	REVENUE ($ mil.)	NET INCOME ($ mil.)	NET PROFIT MARGIN	EMPLOYEES
06/13	444	96	21.7%	4,500
06/12	418	(21)	—	—
06/10	402	104	26.1%	—
06/10	396	54	13.7%	—
Annual Growth	3.8%	21.2%	—	—

2013 Year-End Financials

Debt ratio: —
Return on equity: 21.70%
Cash ($ mil.): 28
Current ratio: —
Long-term debt ($ mil.): —

Dividends
Yield: —
Payout: —
Market value ($ mil.): —

THE UNIVERSITY OF HARTFORD

While its roots date back to 1877 The University of Hartford wasn't officially chartered until 1957 with the merger of the Hartford Art School the Hartt School of Music and Hillyer College. The modern-day university still has a strong arts and music programs and its Museum of American Political Life is home to what has been called the country's largest private collection of political memorabilia. University of Hartford which operates three campuses in West Hartford has about 7000 students enrolled in more than 80 undergraduate and 30 graduate programs including business nursing and engineering.

Geographic Reach

The University of Hartford's students hail from about 45 states and 50 international countries.

Operations

The University of Hartford consists of seven schools and colleges that offer programs in fields including arts architecture sciences business education nursing health engineering and technology. It employs 350 faculty members and has a student-to-faculty ratio of 13:1.

In addition to higher education the university operates two magnet schools (elementary and high school) on its campus as well as a community service center that coordinates volunteer opportunities for students staff and alumni members. In addition University of Hartford runs engineering design business development and professional development programs that work in partnerships with area businesses.

Hartford alumni include Broadway musical director Timothy Stella actress Marin Ireland and TV writer Kent McCray as well as a number of business entrepreneurs in medical scientific and technology fields.

Strategy

University of Hartford is improving its campus by investing in infrastructure enhancements. It is also working to improve its academic community through faculty recruitment and student recruitment efforts as well as through the development of interdisciplinary mission-centered and transformational learning programs.

EXECUTIVES

President, Walter Harrison
VP Student Affairs and Dean Students, J. Lee Peters
Human Resources Manager, Jen Conley
Associate VP and Treasurer, Thomas J. Perra
Dean Undergraduate Studies, Guy C. Colarulli
Dean Admission, Richard A. Zeiser
VP Finance and Administration, Arosha Jayawickrema
Director Media Relations, David (Dave) Isgur
Executive Director Information Technology Services and CIO, George Brophy
VP Institutional Advancement, Christine Pina
Director Career Services, John Kniering
VP University Relations, John J. Carson, age 70
VP General Counsel and Secretary, Thomas Dorer
Dean Faculty Development, H. Frederick Sweitzer
Vice Chairman, Roger R. Klene
Provost, Sharon L. Vasquez
Secretary, Anna Frazao
Assistant Director of Electronic & Social Media, Meagan Fazio
Chairman, Lucille M. Nickerson
Vice Chairman, Dominic Fulco III
Dean Hartford Art School, Nancy Stuart
Dean Barney School of Business, Martin (Marty) Roth
Dean The Hartt School, Aaron A. Flagg
Dean Hillyer College, David H. Goldenberg
Dean College of Engineering Technology and Architecture, Louis Manzione
Dean College of Education Nursing and Health Professions, Ralph Mueller
Dean College of Arts and Sciences, Joseph C. Voelker
Director Data Center Services, Richard LaFlamme
Vice Chairman, Roger R. Klene
Vice Chairman, Dominic Fulco III

LOCATIONS

HQ: THE UNIVERSITY OF HARTFORD
200 BLOOMFIELD AVE, WEST HARTFORD, CT 06117-1599
Phone: 860-768-4393
Web: WWW.ADMISSION.HARTFORD.EDU

PRODUCTS/OPERATIONS

Selected Schools and Colleges

Barney School of Business
College of Arts and Sciences
College of Education Nursing and Health Professions
College of Engineering Technology and Architecture
Hartford Art School
The Hartt School
Hillyer College

HISTORICAL FINANCIALS

Company Type: Private

Income Statement FYE: June 30

	REVENUE ($ mil.)	NET INCOME ($ mil.)	NET PROFIT MARGIN	EMPLOYEES
06/13	170	21	12.7%	950
06/12	165	(10)	—	—
06/10	165	19	11.6%	—
06/10	159	2	1.8%	—
Annual Growth	2.3%	97.2%	—	—

2013 Year-End Financials

Debt ratio: —
Return on equity: 12.70%
Cash ($ mil.): 28
Current ratio: —
Long-term debt ($ mil.): —

Dividends
Yield: —
Payout: —
Market value ($ mil.): —

THE UNIVERSITY OF TULSA

If you're "Living on Tulsa Time" and looking for an education then the home of the Golden Hurricanes is the place to be. The University of Tulsa is a private university affiliated with the Presbyterian Church (USA) with an enrollment of more than 4000 students. The school offers nearly 60 undergraduate and more than 30 graduate programs including ten doctoral degree programs at colleges of arts and sciences business and engineering and natural sciences. The University of Tulsa was founded in Muskogee in 1882 as the Presbyterian School for Indian Girls and was chartered as Henry Kendall College in 1894. The school moved to Tulsa in 1907 and became The University of Tulsa in 1920.

EXECUTIVES

President, Steadman Upham
VP Academic Affairs and Provost, Roger Nathaniel Blais
EVP and Treasurer, Kevan C. Buck
Dean College of Engineering and Natural Sciences, Steven J. Bellovich
Dean Research and Graduate Studies, Janet A. Haggerty
VP Information Services and CIO, Dale A. Schoenefeld
Chair Management and Marketing, Ralph W. Jackson
Dean College of Engineering & Natural Sciences, James R. Sorem Jr.

LOCATIONS

HQ: THE UNIVERSITY OF TULSA
800 TUCKER DR, TULSA, OK 74104-9700
Phone: 918-631-2000
Web: WWW.BIO.UTULSA.EDU

HISTORICAL FINANCIALS

Company Type: Private

Income Statement FYE: June 30

	REVENUE ($ mil.)	NET INCOME ($ mil.)	NET PROFIT MARGIN	EMPLOYEES
06/12	173	(23)	—	1,033
06/11	180	134	74.7%	—
06/10	163	74	45.8%	—
06/09	154	(197)	—	—
Annual Growth	4.1%	—	—	—

2012 Year-End Financials

Debt ratio: —
Return on equity: (-13.40%)
Cash ($ mil.): 30
Current ratio: 0.90
Long-term debt ($ mil.): —

Dividends
Yield: —
Payout: —
Market value ($ mil.): —

THE VALLEY HOSPITAL INC

The Valley Hospital is second to none when it comes to its Same-Day Service program. More than one-third of the company's annual patients experience its longstanding continuum of one-day service; fully half the surgeries performed are same-day. The not-for-profit hospital is a 450-bed facility providing general and emergency services to residents of New Jersey's Bergen County. The hospital belongs to the Valley Health System which also includes subsidiaries Valley Home Care and Valley Health Medical Group and is an affiliate member of NewYork-Presbyterian Healthcare. The Valley Hospital New Jersey's second busiest has more than 1000 physicians on its medical staff.

Operations

The Valley Hospital is well known for its cardiology cancer maternity and neonatal care programs (including its neonatal ICU). Its emergency department treats more than 74000 patients each year.

EXECUTIVES

SVP and CFO, Richard (Rich) Keenan
Vp Of Strategic Planning, Gail Callandrillo
Director Of Infection Control, Andrea Aluisi
Vp Of Medical Affairs, Mitchell A Rubinstein

LOCATIONS

HQ: THE VALLEY HOSPITAL INC
223 N VAN DIEN AVE, RIDGEWOOD, NJ 07450-2736
Phone: 201-447-8000
Web: WWW.VALLEYHEALTH.COM

COMPETITORS

Barnabas Health
Bergen Regional Medical
Englewood Hospital and Medical Center
Hackensack University Medical Center
Jersey City Medical Center
Meridian Health
Newton Medical Center
Raritan Bay Medical Center
Robert Wood Johnson University Hospital at Rahway

HISTORICAL FINANCIALS

Company Type: Private

Income Statement FYE: December 31

	REVENUE ($ mil.)	NET INCOME ($ mil.)	NET PROFIT MARGIN	EMPLOYEES
12/09	587	44	7.6%	2,900
12/08	531	33	6.4%	—
12/06	446	28	6.3%	—
12/05	419	54	12.9%	—
Annual Growth	8.8%	(4.8%)	—	—

2009 Year-End Financials

Debt ratio: —
Return on equity: 7.60%
Cash ($ mil.): 0
Current ratio: 0.30
Long-term debt ($ mil.): —
Dividends
Yield: —
Payout: —
Market value ($ mil.): —

THE WALDINGER CORPORATION

The Waldinger Corporation may actually do most of its work before the walls are even up. The company is an electrical mechanical and sheet metal contractor that primarily serves US customers across the Midwest and Southeast. Through its work in more than 40 states Waldinger designs fabricates installs and maintains HVAC refrigeration electrical plumbing and piping for commercial institutional and industrial clients. Waldinger also operates a division devoted to the food service industry. The company has offices in Iowa Kansas Missouri and Nebraska. Austrian tinsmith Harry Waldinger founded the company as Capital City Tin Shop in 1906.

Geographic Reach

From its headquarters in Des Moines Iowa Waldinger caters to clients nationwide through its offices in the Midwestern states of Iowa Kansas Missouri and Nebraska.

Operations

Waldinger has worked on projects throughout most of the US covering more than 40 states. Its projects portfolio includes a handful of nuclear power plants ethanol plants the Houston Astrodome the Louisiana Superdome and Cape Kennedy's Vehicle Assembly Building.

For commercial clients Waldinger works on corporate headquarters data centers office buildings and retail outlets. Industrial projects typically include alternative energy manufacturing water and waste water. Projects in the research and education sector include laboratories universities and schools and residence halls. Waldinger also serves the healthcare market through projects for hospitals and clinics and assisted living facilities as well as for arenas and casinos as part of the sports and entertainment market.

EXECUTIVES

CEO, Jack F. Krantz

LOCATIONS

HQ: THE WALDINGER CORPORATION
2601 BELL AVE, DES MOINES, IA 50321-1189
Phone: 515-284-1911
Web: WWW.WALDINGER.COM

PRODUCTS/OPERATIONS

Selected Sectors

Commercial
Healthcare
Hospitality
Industrial
Research and education
Sports and entertainment

COMPETITORS

ACCO
Duke Construction
EMCOR
F.A. Wilhelm
Fluor
Limbach Facility Services
Market & Johnson
MasTec
Siemens AG
Yates Companies

HISTORICAL FINANCIALS

Company Type: Private

Income Statement FYE: December 31

	REVENUE ($ mil.)	NET INCOME ($ mil.)	NET PROFIT MARGIN	EMPLOYEES
12/12	186	0	—	900
12/11	160	0	—	—
12/10	155	0	—	—
12/09	174	0	—	—
Annual Growth	2.3%	—	—	—

2012 Year-End Financials

Debt ratio: —
Return on equity: —
Cash ($ mil.): 20
Current ratio: 1.60
Long-term debt ($ mil.): —
Dividends
Yield: —
Payout: —
Market value ($ mil.): —

THE WALSH GROUP LTD

The Walsh Group erects walls halls malls and more. Operating through Walsh Construction Archer Western Contractors and R&L Brosamer the family owned group provides design/build general contracting and construction services for industrial public and commercial projects. Walsh provides complete project management services from demolition and planning to general contracting and finance. The company is involved in the construction of bridges highways water treatment facilities airports hotels convention centers correctional facilities and commercial industrial and residential buildings; it also renovates and restores buildings.

Geographic Reach

Walsh Construction is based in Chicago and has experience building civil and transportation projects throughout North America. Archer Western is headquartered in Atlanta and has seven regional offices. Beyond the continental US the Walsh Group has operations in Canada as well as in Hawaii Alaska and Puerto Rico.

Operations

In 2012 Walsh was listed in Engineering News-Record's Top Contractors list as the largest water and desalination plant builder the second largest domestic heavy contractor in the US the second largest hydroplant builder and the second largest bridge builder.

Strategy

Walsh's geographic diversity and its wide range of project experience helped it remain successful through the economic recession. Federal contracts also helped Walsh survive at a time when private-sector building and construction was down. The health care water and waste water sectors have remained strong markets for the company's construction services.

In 2011 Walsh was awarded its first overseas embassy project a $200 million contract to build the New American Embassy at Oslo Norway.

In 2010 Walsh made its first ever acquisition. It bought California-based R&L Brosamer which specializes in heavy highway and other transportation projects. R&L Brosamer often works on projects for Bay Area Rapid Transit California Department of Transportation and Los Angeles World Airports. The deal helped Walsh strengthen its presence in California and bordering states.

Ownership

The founding Walsh family owns the firm.

Company Background

The Walsh Group has invested more than $450 Million in capital equipment and regularly employs over 5000 engineers and skilled trade professionals.

The company was founded in 1898 by Matthew Myles Walsh.

EXECUTIVES

Co-Chairman and CEO, Matthew M. (Matt) Walsh
Co-Chairman, Daniel J. Walsh
President Building Division, Michael Whelan
Contact Aviation Facilities Walsh Construction, Vince Piscopo
SVP, Dave Marchiori
Contact Education Walsh Construction, John Hamilton
Contact Data Centers Walsh Construction, Sam Bahou
Contact Federal Building Walsh Construction, Stu Bryant
Contact Healthcare Walsh Construction, Keith Kovach

Contact Senior Living Walsh Construction, Eric Larsen
Contact WTP and WWTP Archer Western Contractors, Jeff Dunifon
President Heavy Civil Division, Don Gillis
CFO, Tim Gerken
VP Heavy/Civil Division, Daniel Walsh Jr.
VP Corporate Equipment, Michael Gibbons
VP Building Division, Matthew Walsh IV
President Walsh Construction, Sean Walsh

LOCATIONS

HQ: THE WALSH GROUP LTD
929 W ADAMS ST, CHICAGO, IL 60607-3021
Phone: 312-563-5400
Web: WWW.WALSHGROUP.COM

PRODUCTS/OPERATIONS

Projects
Airports
Athletic facilities
Bridges
Conference centers
Correctional facilities
Data centers
Educational facilities
Entertainment
Government
Health care
High rise residentia
Highways and bridges
Hotels
Interiors
Laboratories
Parking garages
Renovations
Retail centers
Senior housing
Treatment plants
Warehouse and distributi

COMPETITORS

Bechtel
Black & Veatch
Bovis Lend Lease
Brasfield & Gorrie
C. G. Schmidt
CH2M HILL
Flatiron Construction
Fluor
Granite Construction
Hunt Companies
Hunt Construction
Jacobs Engineering
James McHugh
Lane Construction
MWH Global
McCarthy Building
Peter Kiewit Sons'
Skanska
TIC Holdings
Turner Corporation
Vecellio & Grogan

HISTORICAL FINANCIALS

Company Type: Private

Income Statement FYE: December 31

	REVENUE ($ mil.)	NET INCOME ($ mil.)	NET PROFIT MARGIN	EMPLOYEES
12/11	3,617	124	3.4%	5,000
12/10	3,462	186	5.4%	—
12/09	3,316	191	5.8%	—
12/08	3,534	203	5.8%	—
Annual Growth	0.8%	(15.1%)	—	—

2011 Year-End Financials

Debt ratio: —
Return on equity: 3.40%
Cash ($ mil.): 183
Current ratio: 1.00
Long-term debt ($ mil.): —
Dividends
Yield: —
Payout: —
Market value ($ mil.): —

THE WASHINGTON AND LEE UNIVERSITY

One of the oldest colleges in the country Washington and Lee University (W&L) was founded in 1749 and is named after George Washington (who bequeathed the school its first major endowment) and Confederate general Robert E. Lee (a former president of the institution). The highly ranked liberal arts school in Lexington Virginia is attended by more than 2300 students who take courses in about 40 major areas including public policy politics international studies physics and biochemistry. The university has more than 200 faculty and a student-to-faculty ratio of 9:1. Former US Supreme Court Justice and W&L alumni Lewis F. Powell donated his personal and professional papers to the university's prestigious law school.

Geographic Reach

W&L enrolls students from nearly all US states as well as about 50 foreign countries.

Operations

The W&L School of Law is one of the smallest law schools in the US to receive national recognition. It has its own dean and faculty and educates about 400 students.

Under the leadership of Robert E. Lee (1865-1870) the school became the first in the US to offer studies in business and journalism. Today W&L offers the only fully accredited journalism program and business school among the top-tier US liberal arts schools.

Financial Performance

W&L increased revenues by 4% to $131 million in 2012 due to increases in income from tuition and fees endowment returns and auxiliary enterprises. Tuition accounts for a majority of revenues and falls at about $44000 per year. Net income fell 79% however to $46 million due to increased expenses and investment return losses.

Strategy

W&L is currently working to expand its international study programs to include subjects in fields such as Latin American Middle Eastern and East Asian studies. It is also expanding its law commerce governance and women's studies programs as well as its freshman seminar series to provide a broader range of services to students. The university is also working to enroll more needs-based and minority students as well as to recruit top-quality faculty members and conduct campus enhancement projects.

EXECUTIVES

VP University Advancement, Dennis W. Cross
Provost, June R. Aprille
General Counsel, Leanne M. Shank
VP Finance and Treasurer, Steven G. McAllister
University Librarian, Merrily Taylor
President, Kenneth P. (Ken) Ruscio
Dean College, Howard Dobin
Executive Director Alumni Office, Waller T. (Beau) Dudley
Executive Director Communications and Public Affairs, Jeffery G. Hanna
CTO, Richard Peterson
Executive Director Human Resources, Amy D. Barnes
University Registrar, D. Scott Dittman
Dean Undergraduate Admissions and Financial Aid, William M. Hartog
Provost, Robert A. (Bob) Strong
CTO/CIO, Dave Saacke
Dean School of Law, Nora V. Demleitner
Dean Williams School of Commerce Economics and Politics, Larry C. Peppers
Interim Dean of The College, Suzanne P. Keen

LOCATIONS

HQ: THE WASHINGTON AND LEE UNIVERSITY
204 W WASHINGTON ST, LEXINGTON, VA 24450-2554
Phone: 540-458-8400
Web: WWW.WLU.EDU

HISTORICAL FINANCIALS

Company Type: Private

Income Statement FYE: June 30

	REVENUE ($ mil.)	NET INCOME ($ mil.)	NET PROFIT MARGIN	EMPLOYEES
06/12	254	81	32.0%	700
06/11	173	13	7.8%	—
06/09	163	3	2.0%	—
06/09	182	0	—	—
Annual Growth	11.7%	—	—	—

2012 Year-End Financials

Debt ratio: —
Return on equity: 32.00%
Cash ($ mil.): 6
Current ratio: —
Long-term debt ($ mil.): —
Dividends
Yield: —
Payout: —
Market value ($ mil.): —

THE WASHINGTON UNIVERSITY

Washington University in St. Louis (WUSTL) is the gateway to higher education for more than 13000 students. Founded in 1853 the independent university offers 90 bachelor's master's and doctoral degrees and has about 3400 faculty members. It offers approximately 1500 courses in fields such as arts and sciences business design and visual arts engineering law medicine and social work. WUSTL which has multiple campuses in and near the city of St. Louis also offers associate degree and continuing education programs. The affiliated Washington University Medical Center is an acute-care hospital that also provides educational training and research services.

In addition to the main 170-acre Danforth Campus in St. Louis WUSTL's facilities include the nearby 165-acre Medical Campus (housing the School of Medicine and the hospital facilities). WUSTL also operates three smaller satellite academic campuses and music research and art centers in the greater St. Louis area.

The Medical Campus conducts extensive collaborative studies between students faculty and hospital staff as well as external institutions. Areas of research include genome sequencing of cancer patients and children's developmental studies. The 2000-acre Tyson Research Center outside the city is a biological field station that conducts environmental studies and research activities including renewable energy and sustainability programs some of which is coordinated with outside groups.

In 2011 WUSTL reported nearly $2.3 billion in revenues an increase of 5% over the previous year due to increased income from its patient care operations research grants and tuition segments. Nonoperational activities including interest on endowment investments and charitable gifts gave WUSTL's bottom line a boost in 2011 as well.

The university has an endowment of some $5.4 billion.

WUSTL has made efforts to extend its collaborations with third parties which can help bring in academic and research funds. For instance in 2011 it formed a business school partnership with the Brookings Institution in Washington DC to offer courses on government and corporate policymaking and leadership development. In addition the university has worked to attract more government research grants in recent years. It is also upgrading some classroom and student facilities as well as hiring more experienced teachers and medical staff members to maintain its tuition auxiliary enterprise (lodging and vending) health services and research income expectations.

EXECUTIVES

Head Nurse, Barbara Faszl
Auditors: PricewaterhouseCoopersLLP

LOCATIONS

HQ: THE WASHINGTON UNIVERSITY
1 BROOKINGS DR, SAINT LOUIS, MO 63130-4899
Phone: 314-935-5000
Web: WWW.WUSTL.EDU

PRODUCTS/OPERATIONS

Selected Schools and Colleges

College of Arts & Sciences
Graduate School of Arts & Sciences
University College and Summer School (Arts & Sciences)
George Warren Brown School of Social Work
Sam Fox School of Design & Visual Arts
School of Engineering & Applied Science
School of Law
School of Medicine
Olin Business School

HISTORICAL FINANCIALS

Company Type: Private

Income Statement

FYE: June 30

	REVENUE ($ mil.)	NET INCOME ($ mil.)	NET PROFIT MARGIN	EMPLOYEES
06/13	2,393	557	23.3%	9,600
06/12	2,307	(49)	—	—
06/10	2,245	989	44.1%	—
06/10	2,129	682	32.0%	—
Annual Growth	4.0%	(6.5%)	—	—

2013 Year-End Financials

Debt ratio: —
Return on equity: 23.30%
Cash ($ mil.): 198
Current ratio: —
Long-term debt ($ mil.): —
Dividends
Yield: —
Payout: —
Market value ($ mil.): —

THE WATERBURY HOSPITAL

EXECUTIVES

President and CEO, John H. Tobin
VP Human Resources, Kathy Mulston
Chairman Board of Trustees, David W. Griffin
Chief of Staff, Dave Pizzuto
Engineering and Facilities, Steve Jalowiec
Auditors: Ernst&YoungLLP

LOCATIONS

HQ: THE WATERBURY HOSPITAL
64 ROBBINS ST, WATERBURY, CT 067082600
Phone: 2035736000
Web: WWW.WATERBURYHOSPITAL.ORG

PRODUCTS/OPERATIONS

Selected Medical Services

Advanced Care Services
Auxiliary
Behavioral Health
Emergency Department
Family Birthing Center
Health Center Library
Laboratory Services
Orthopedic Services
Reed Cardiology
Sleep Lab
Specialty Programs & Services
The Hospitalist Program
The Stroke Center
Waterbury Hospital Pharmacy Program

COMPETITORS

Baystate Medical Center
Bridgeport Hospital
Bristol Hospital
Connecticut Children' s Medical Center
Greenwich Hospital
Griffin Health
Hartford Health Care
Hospital of Central Connecticut
Mather Memorial Hospital
MidState Medical Center
New Milford Hospital
Peconic Bay Medical Center
Saint Francis Hospital
Westchester Medical Center
Western Connecticut Health Network
Yale New Haven Health System

HISTORICAL FINANCIALS

Company Type: Private

Income Statement

FYE: September 30

	REVENUE ($ mil.)	NET INCOME ($ mil.)	NET PROFIT MARGIN	EMPLOYEES
09/13	207	(2)	—	1,625
09/09	251	(2)	—	—
09/08	237	(7)	—	—
Annual Growth	(2.7%)	—	—	—

2013 Year-End Financials

Debt ratio: —
Return on equity: (-1.10%)
Cash ($ mil.): 23
Current ratio: 1.60
Long-term debt ($ mil.): —
Dividends
Yield: —
Payout: —
Market value ($ mil.): —

THE WHITING-TURNER CONTRACTING COMPANY

Whiting-Turner Contracting provides construction management general contracting and design/build services primarily for large commercial institutional and infrastructure projects conducted across the US. A key player in retail construction the employee-owned company also undertakes such projects as biotech cleanrooms theme parks historical restorations senior living residences educational facilities stadiums and corporate headquarters. Clients past and present include the US military AT&T General Motors and Texas A&M University. Whiting-Turner Contracting operates some 30 locations nationwide.

Geographic Reach

The company has offices in California Colorado Connecticut Delaware Florida Georgia Maryland Massachusetts Missouri Nevada New Jersey New York North Carolina Ohio Pennsylvania Texas Virginia and Washington DC.

Operations

Whiting-Turner Contracting's project portfolio includes the Joseph B. Whitehead Building at Emory University Vanderbilt Hall at Yale University projects at Universal Studios theme park and a vaccine facility at Chesapeake Biological Laboratories. Projects in the firm's hometown of Baltimore have included the city's convention center and the football stadium for the Baltimore Ravens Normal 0 false false false EN-US X-NONE X-NONE /* Style Definitions */ table.MsoNormalTable {mso-style-name:"Table Normal"; mso-tstyle-rowband-size:0; mso-tstyle-colband-size:0; mso-style-noshow:yes; mso-style-priority:99; mso-style-parent:""; mso-padding-alt:0in 5.4pt 0in 5.4pt; mso-para-margin-top:0in; mso-para-margin-right:0in; mso-para-margin-bottom:10.0pt; mso-para-margin-left:0in; line-height:115%; mso-pagination:widow-orphan; font-size:11.0pt; font-family:"Calibri""sans-serif"; mso-ascii-font-family:Calibri; mso-ascii-theme-font:minor-latin; mso-hansi-font-family:Calibri; mso-hansi-theme-font:minor-latin;}. More recent projects include the Horseshoe Casino Cleveland University of Maryland Baltimore County (UMBC) Performing Arts & Humanities Naval Facilities Engineering Command (NAVFAC) Jacksonville Sentara Princess Anne Hospital Norwalk Community College Texas A&M University at Galveston Mary Moody Northen Student Center renovation Opry Mills the College of Business & Economics Vinson Hall Parking Garage a Coastal Studies Institute facility a Blue Diamond Growers building and a USPS Call Center.

Strategy

The company prefers to grow organically instead of making many acquisitions. It has been steadily expanding by opening new offices in places such as California Texas and Virginia.

In 2013 Whiting-Turner Contracting was awarded a $38.6 million contract for energy efficiency improvements at Marine Corps Base Camp Lejeune North Carolina. That year it was also awarded a $10.5 million project for an armory at Marine Corps Air Station Cherry Point in the same state.

In 2012 The Jackson Laboratory selected of Whiting-Turner Contracting to manage the design development phase of Institute for Genomic Medicine in Farmington Connecticut. The new facility on a 17-acres site will open in 2014.

Company Background

G.W.C. Whiting and LeBaron Turner classmates at MIT founded the company in 1909 to build sewer lines.

EXECUTIVES

VP Richmond, Dani Niccolucci
SVP Allentown, Jack DaSilva
Division VP Fort Lauderdale, Robert (Rob) Mitchell
Division VP Delaware and Maryland, James (Jim) Martini
SVP District of Columbia, Richard L. Vogel
Exec V Pres, Stephen P Duffy, age 77
Vp Marketing, David Boucher
Hr Director & Vp, Edward Spaulding
Division VP Pleasanton, Troy Caldwell
SVP Irvine, Len Cannatelli
SVP Baltimore, Gino J. Gemignani
Division VP Dallas, Espen S. Brooks
VP Bridgewater, Chris Martinson

SVP Atlanta, Keith Douglas
SVP Connecticut, Daniel (Dan) Bauer
VP Boston, Kevin Shields
Regional Manager Las Vegas, Paul Schmitt
Division VP Chantilly, Kempton C. Haile
VP Tampa, Brent A. Voyles
Senior Project Manager (Denver), Mark Faul
VP San Diego, Steven Likins
VP Orlando, Robert Minutoli
Division VP Raleigh, Chris Carlson
VP White Plains, David Brickley
VP San Antonio, Daryl Steinbeck
VP Norfolk, John Berotti
Senior Project Manager Sacramento, Jack Stackalis
VP Cleveland, Jeff Maeder
Regional Manager Kansas City, Adam Eshelbrenner
Regional Manager Charlotte, Chris Woods
Regional Manager Houston, Michael Browning
President and CEO, Timothy J. Regan, age 58
Vice President, John Giovannone
Sr V Pres, Garrett W Hall, age 69
Senior Vice President, Christine Zavodny
Vice President, Kevin Seicke
Vice President, Ted Border
Vice President, Steve Lambertson
Vice President, Sam Abutaleb
Vice President, Larry Garland
Vice President, J Breig
Vice President, Tony Moag
Secretary, Willie McFarlin

LOCATIONS

HQ: THE WHITING-TURNER CONTRACTING COMPANY
300 E JOPPA RD STE 800, BALTIMORE, MD 212863047
Phone: 4108211100
Web: WWW.WHITING-TURNER.COM

Selected Locations

Maryland - Baltimore (Headquarters)
California - Irvine
California - Los Angeles
California - Pleasanton
California - Sacramento
California - San Diego
Colorado - Denver
Connecticut - New Haven
Delaware - Newark
District of Columbia
Florida - Ft. Lauderdale
Florida - Orlando
Florida - Tampa
Georgia - Atlanta
Maryland - Cambridge
Massachusetts - Boston
Missouri - Kansas City
Nevada - Las Vegas
New Jersey - Bridgewater
New York - White Plains
North Carolina - Charlotte
North Carolina - Raleigh
Ohio - Cleveland
Pennsylvania - Allentown
Texas - Dallas
Texas - Houston
Texas - San Antonio
Virginia - Chantilly
Virginia - Norfolk
Virginia - Richmond

PRODUCTS/OPERATIONS

Selected Services

Construction management
  Agency
  At-risk
Design/build
General contracting
Preconstruction

Selected Markets

Biotechnology and pharmaceutical
Cleanroom and high-technology
Education
Entertainment
Federal/military
Food/beverage distribution
Health care
Historical restoration
Industrial and manufacturing
Interiors
Life sciences
Lodging and hospitality
Mission critical facilities
Mixed use
Offices and headquarters
Parking garages
Restaurants
Retail
Senior living
Sports
Sustainable
Technology
  Microelectronics
  Nano
Theme parks
Utilities
Warehouse and distribution

COMPETITORS

Barton Malow
Bechtel
Bovis Lend Lease
Choate Construction
Clark Construction Group
DPR Construction
Fisher Development
Fluor
Gilbane
Hensel Phelps Construction
Hoffman Corporation
J.E. Dunn Construction Group
Jacobs Engineering
Kitchell
McCarthy Building
Peter Kiewit Sons'
Skanska
Suffolk Construction
Swinerton
Turner Corporation
Tutor Perini
Weitz

HISTORICAL FINANCIALS

Company Type: Private

Income Statement FYE: December 31

	REVENUE ($ mil.)	NET INCOME ($ mil.)	NET PROFIT MARGIN	EMPLOYEES
12/12	3,781	56	1.5%	1,839
12/11	3,897	57	1.5%	—
Annual Growth	(3.0%)	(1.9%)	—	—

2012 Year-End Financials

Debt ratio: —
Return on equity: 1.50%
Cash ($ mil.): 53
Current ratio: 0.70
Long-term debt ($ mil.): —
Dividends
Yield: —
Payout: —
Market value ($ mil.): —

THE WICHITA STATE UNIVERSITY

You are still in Kansas if you attend Wichita State University (WSU). The state-supported school enrolls more than 15000 students with more than 85% hailing from Kansas. Along with its main campus WSU provides classes at four additional campuses. The school offers 70 undergraduate degrees in more than 200 subjects. Its Graduate School offers more than 40 master's programs a dozen doctoral degree programs an educational specialist program and more than 20 graduate certificate programs as well as research opportunities. WSU colleges include business education engineering fine arts health professions and liberal arts and sciences. The school was founded in 1895 as a Congregational institution.

Geographic Reach

Besides its 330-acre main campus in Wichita Kansas WSU counts four other campuses that serve its traditional and non-traditional student body.

Operations

WSU offers undergraduate and graduate degrees from half a dozen colleges including Fairmount College of Liberal Arts and Sciences W. Frank Barton School of Business College of Education College of Engineering College of Fine Arts and College of Health Professions.

Enrolling students from 110 countries WSU employs some 450 full-time faculty members (75% of which hold the highest degrees in their field) and boasts a student/faculty ratio of 20:1.

The main campus is also home to a roughly 150 student organizations that cover a wide range of topics –from academics and multicultural interests to politics and special interests and more. The school also hosts 15 NCAA Division I teams and a wide range of intramurals and club teams.

WSU is the only urban-serving research institution in Kansas. WSU and Via Christi Health formed a joint venture in 2008 and founded The Center of Innovation for Biomaterials in Orthopaedic Research (CIBOR). The venture was restructured in 2012 to move CIBOR to the National Institute for Aviation Research (NIAR) on the university campus. CIBOR is managed by NIAR but remains a joint venture of WSU and Via Christi Health. Located on the WSU campus NIAR operates nearly 20 cutting-edge laboratories. It has partnered with Cisco Systems to provide one of the nation's best advanced-networking research centers.

Financial Performance

WSU logged a 2% increase in revenue in fiscal 2012 as compared to 2011 due to a jump in tuition and fee revenue having raised its tuition rates and seen changes in enrollment. The school also attributes the revenue boost to increases in state and local contracts and grants and sales and services of educational activities. Net income during the same reporting period dropped by 49% due to declines in non-operating revenues from dips in state appropriations and other revenues as the result of gifts for capital projects. Rising operating expenses attributed to the increase in expenses related to WSU's mission of instruction research and public service also conspired to keep net income down.

EXECUTIVES

Compensation Manager, Michael (Mike) Turner
President and CEO Wichita State University Foundation, Elizabeth H. King
VP and General Counsel, Ted D. Ayres
Director Athletics, Eric L. Sexton, age 49
CIO, Ravi Pendse
Executive Director Computing and Telecommunications Services, Gary L. Ott
Associate Director Human Resources, Rhonda Cantrell
Director Human Resources, Frankie Brown
Assistant Director of Human Resources, Connie Landreth
Director News and Media Relations, Joe Kleinsasser
Associate Director Financial Operations, Teresa Moore
Senior Internal Auditor, Terry Coltrain
Director Physical Plant, Woodrow DePontier
Chief of University Police, Paul Dotson
Manager Central Services, Ellen Abbey
Interim Provost, Keith H. Pickus
VP Administration and Finance, Mary Herrin
Executive Director Government Relations, Andrew Schlapp
President, John W. Bardo

LOCATIONS

HQ: THE WICHITA STATE UNIVERSITY
1845 FAIRMOUNT ST, WICHITA, KS 67260-0001
Phone: 316-978-3040
Web: WWW.FOUNDATION.WICHITA.EDU

Selected Campuses

Main
Wichita Kansas
Satellite
Eugene M. Hughes Metropolitan Complex Wichita Kansas
WSU Downtown Center Wichita Kansas
WSU South Campus Derby Wichita
WSU West Campus Wichita Kansas

PRODUCTS/OPERATIONS

Selected Colleges and Schools

College of Education
College of Engineering
College of Fine Arts
College of Health Professions
Fairmount College of Liberal Arts and Sciences
Graduate School
W. Frank Barton School of Business

HISTORICAL FINANCIALS

Company Type: Private

Income Statement FYE: June 30

	REVENUE ($ mil.)	NET INCOME ($ mil.)	NET PROFIT MARGIN	EMPLOYEES
06/12	184	10	5.8%	3,395
06/11	182	20	11.3%	—
06/10	166	14	8.5%	—
06/09	147	11	7.7%	—
Annual Growth	7.9%	(1.8%)	—	—

2012 Year-End Financials

Debt ratio: —
Return on equity: 5.80%
Cash ($ mil.): 127
Current ratio: 3.00
Long-term debt ($ mil.): —
Dividends
Yield: —
Payout: —
Market value ($ mil.): —

THE WILLAMETTE VALLEY COMPANY

LOCATIONS

HQ: THE WILLAMETTE VALLEY COMPANY
1075 ARROWSMITH ST, EUGENE, OR 974029121
Phone: 5414849621
Web: WWW.WILVACO.COM

COMPETITORS

Benjamin Moore
Insl-X
Vista Paint

HISTORICAL FINANCIALS

Company Type: Private

Income Statement FYE: December 31

	REVENUE ($ mil.)	NET INCOME ($ mil.)	NET PROFIT MARGIN	EMPLOYEES
12/13	142	0	—	260
12/12*	126	0	—	—
03/11	104	0	—	—
03/10	0	0	—	—
Annual Growth	—	—	—	—

*Fiscal year change

2013 Year-End Financials

Debt ratio: —
Return on equity: —
Cash ($ mil.): 7
Current ratio: 1.80
Long-term debt ($ mil.): —
Dividends
Yield: —
Payout: —
Market value ($ mil.): —

THE WILLIAM PATERSON UNIVERSITY OF NEW JERSEY

William Paterson University has evolved into a fully accredited liberal-arts university. William Paterson which has more than 1000 full-time faculty members enrolls about 11500 undergraduate and graduate students and offers more than offers 45 undergraduate 22 masters one doctoral and three post-baccalaureate certificate programs through five colleges. The university has a 370-acre campus with some 40 major buildings and other facilities including the David and Lorraine Cheng Library which boasts more than 350000 bound volumes. Tuition and fees in 2012 were $11694 for full-time students who were New Jersey residents and $19094 for non-residents. William Paterson is accredited by the Middle States Association of Colleges and Secondary Schools.

Geographic Reach

In addition to its primary campus in Wayne New Jersey William Paterson also offers satellite programs at Mercer County Community College in West Windsor.

Operations

The university's five colleges are Arts and Communication Cotsakos College of Business Education Humanities and Social Sciences and Science and Health. William Paterson has a student to faculty ratio is 16:1 and offers more than 250 degree and non-degree programs. The university offers pre-professional programs in engineering law medicine (which includes dentistry optometry podiatry and veterinary science) pharmacy physical therapy and speech-language pathology.

The school's library provides access to more than 21000 titles online and more than 3000 titles in print and microform format.

Financial Performance

William Paterson reported a 5% increase in revenues in 2012 due to a rise in net student revenues federal grants and contracts state local and other grants and contracts as well as auxiliary enterprises.Its net income dropped by 33% in 2012 thanks to an increase in operating expenses and a drop in non-operating revenues attributed to cut in State of New Jersey appropriations and an increase in interest on capital asset-related debt. William Paterson saw an increase in revenues from 2010 through 2012 due to organic growth. The drop in net income over that same time period was due to an increase in expenses and a decline in non-operating revenues.

Company Background

William Paterson was founded in 1855 as a normal school (teacher's college) for the city of Paterson New Jersey

The university is named after statesman and patriot William Paterson (1745-1806). Paterson was New Jersey's first attorney general attendee at the 1787 Constitutional Convention in Philadelphia member of the first US Senate governor of New Jersey and chosen by George Washington as an associate justice of the US Supreme Court.

EXECUTIVES

Vice Chair, William J. (Will) Pesce, age 63
President Vice President for institutional advancement, Arnold Speert
VP Administration and Finance, Stephen Bolyai
VP Institutional Advancement, Sandra Deller
Provost and SVP Academic Affairs, Edward Weil
VP Student Development, John Martone
Associate Provost, Steve Hahn
Associate VP and Dean Graduate Studies and Research and Associate Professor Educational Leadership, Nina Jemmott
Associate VP Enrollment Management, William Anderson
Associate VP Administration, Timothy W. Fanning
Associate Vice President Marketing and Public Relations, Stuart Goldstein
Chief of Staff to the President and Board of Trustees, Marc Schaeffer
Executive Assistant to the Provost and SVP Academic Affairs and Associate Professor of Education, Robert Seal
Associate VP Capital Planning Design and Construction, Robert Bennett
Dean Christos M. Cotsakos College of Business and Professor of Economics Finance and Global Business, Sam Basu
Dean College of the Humanities and Social Sciences and Professor of History, Isabel Tirado
Dean College of Science and Health and Professor of Nursing, Sandra DeYoung
Executive Director for Continuing and Professional Education, Bernadette Tiernan
Associate VP and Dean of Student Development, Glen Sherman
Associate VP Campus Life, Roland Watts
Associate Dean College of Education and Associate Professor of Secondary and Middle School Education, Dorothy Feola
Associate Dean College of the Humanities and Social Sciences, Kara Rabbitt
Associate Dean College of Science and Health and Professor of Chemistry, Jean Fuller-Stanley
Secretary, Michael L. Jackson
Chair, Vincent J. Mazzola
Media Relations, Mary Beth Zeman
Associate VP for Human Resources, John Polding
Interim Associate Dean Christos M. Cotsakos College of Business and Associate Professor of Economics and Finance, Rajiv Kashyap
Interim Associate Dean College of the Arts and Communication and Professor of Art, Imafidon Olaye
Dean College of the Arts and Communication and Professor of Music, Raymond Torres-Santos
Interim Dean College of Education and Professor of Education, Ana Maria Schuhmann
Executive Assistant, Sina Brehmer-Songer
Administrative Assistant, Jane Oeler
Assistant Director Alumni Relations and Communications, Sharon Ryan
Finance Operations Manager, Yvette Villanueva
Administrative Assistant, Madeline Garcia
Vice Chair, William J. (Will) Pesce, age 63
Trustee, Linda A. Niro, age 59
President Vice President for institutional advancement, Arnold Speert
Trustee, Stephen (Steve) Adzima
Trustee, Frederick L. Gruel
Trustee, Henry J. Pruitt Jr.
Trustee, Robert H. Taylor
Trustee, Jennifer Bauer
Trustee, Robert Guarasci
Trustee, Anna Marie Mascolo

LOCATIONS

HQ: THE WILLIAM PATERSON UNIVERSITY OF NEW JERSEY
300 POMPTON RD, WAYNE, NJ 07470-2103
Phone: 973-720-2000
Web: WWW.WW2.WPUNJ.EDU

PRODUCTS/OPERATIONS

2012 Revenues

% of total	
Student	73
Federal grants &	14
State local & other grants &	10
Auxiliary	3
Total	**100**

Selected Academic Programs

Accounting
Anthropology
Art
Biology
Chemistry
Communication
Computer Science
Economics
English
Environmental Science
Geography
History
Languages and Culture
Mathematics
Music
Nursing
Philosophy
Political Science
Psychology
Colleges
Arts and Communication
Cotsakos College of Business
Education
Humanities and Social Sciences
Science and Health

HISTORICAL FINANCIALS

Company Type: Private

Income Statement FYE: June 30

	REVENUE ($ mil.)	NET INCOME ($ mil.)	NET PROFIT MARGIN	EMPLOYEES
06/12	158	8	5.5%	1,300
06/09	0	0	—	—
06/08	118	17	15.1%	—
06/07	109	19	18.2%	—
Annual Growth	7.7%	(15.2%)	—	—

2012 Year-End Financials

Debt ratio: ——
Return on equity: 5.50%
Cash ($ mil.): 115
Current ratio: 4.10
Long-term debt ($ mil.): —
Dividends
Yield: —
Payout: —
Market value ($ mil.): —

THE WILLS GROUP INC

The Wills Group willingly delivers petroleum products and related products and services to its customer base in southern Maryland and adjacent areas. The family-owned company operates four business subsidiaries: Dash-In Convenience Stores (with 35 locations including 18 franchises); DMO (provider of propane heating oil and HVAC equipment); and Southern Maryland Oil (SMO) and SMO Motor Fuels (distribution of diesel gasoline and kerosene products). More than 90% of SMO's gasoline products are Shell-branded fuels. The Wills Group supplies more than 300 dealer-operated gas stations in Delaware southern Maryland and Washington DC.

Operations

The Wills Group divides its business into four operations: Dash-In Convenience Stores (serving the Maryland; Delaware; and Tidewater Virgina regions); DMO (propane heating oil and HVAC equipment maker); and Southern Maryland Oil (SMO) and SMO Motor Fuels (distribution of diesel gasoline and kerosene products).

Company Background

The company was founded in 1926 by Jim Wills and Harold Swann. In 1942 The Wills Group was the first principal fuel supplier to the newly built Patuxent Naval Air Station. In 1972 the company developed the first branded self-service station in Maryland. In 2012 Lock Wills was serving as the president of The Wills Group.

EXECUTIVES

President, Lock Wills
Executive Vice President Retail Marketing, Mel L. Strine
VP Human Resources, Stephen Niven

LOCATIONS

HQ: THE WILLS GROUP INC
6355 CRAIN HWY, LA PLATA, MD 20646-4267
Phone: 301-932-3600
Web: WWW.WILLSGROUP.COM

COMPETITORS

Dixie Gas & Oil
Petroleum Marketers
Quarles Petroleum
SMF Energy
Weis Markets
Woodfin Oil

HISTORICAL FINANCIALS

Company Type: Private

Income Statement FYE: September 30

	REVENUE ($ mil.)	NET INCOME ($ mil.)	NET PROFIT MARGIN	EMPLOYEES
09/12	1,039	15	1.5%	280
09/11	1,052	17	1.7%	—
09/10	768	13	1.7%	—
09/09	614	11	1.9%	—
Annual Growth	19.1%	10.5%	—	—

2012 Year-End Financials

Debt ratio: ——
Return on equity: 1.50%
Cash ($ mil.): 20
Current ratio: 0.80
Long-term debt ($ mil.): —
Dividends
Yield: —
Payout: —
Market value ($ mil.): —

THIRTEEN

You might say this broadcaster has some public appeal for New Yorkers. Educational Broadcasting Corporation (EBC) operates two public broadcasting stations serving the New York City area. Its flagship Thirteen/WNET the highest-rated public TV station in the US offers a wealth of locally produced content focused on the Big Apple as well as programming supplied by the Public Broadcasting Service (PBS). Thirteen/WNET is also a major producer of shows for PBS that are distributed to other public TV stations. Thirteen/WNET began broadcasting in 1962.

Geographic Reach

In addition to Thirteen/WNET the non-profit corporation operates WLIW21 which serves audiences on Long Island.

Operations

EBC Thirteen/WNET also operates several digital channels and on-demand video services.

Strategy

Thirteen/WNET has been restructuring operations and making reductions in staff to cut costs. EBC has also beefed up its fundraising efforts.

EXECUTIVES

Vice President Personnel, Carmen D Rienzo
Vp Media Operations And Cio, Kenneth Devine
Vp National Productions, Stephen Segaller
Vice President Marketing, Katherine Schultheis
Vice President And Director Corporate Communications, Stella Giammasi
V Pres Human Resources, Charlene Shapiro
Vice President, Deborah Macfarlane
Chairman Emeritus, Henry R Kravis, age 71

LOCATIONS

HQ: THIRTEEN
825 8TH AVE FL 14, NEW YORK, NY 100197435
Phone: 2125602000
Web: WWW.WNET.ORG

COMPETITORS

A&E Networks
ABC Inc.
CBS Corp
Discovery Communications
ION Media Networks
NBC
Scripps Networks
Turner Broadcasting
Univision

HISTORICAL FINANCIALS

Company Type: Private

Income Statement FYE: June 30

	REVENUE ($ mil.)	NET INCOME ($ mil.)	NET PROFIT MARGIN	EMPLOYEES
06/12	105	13	12.9%	400
06/11	105	12	11.6%	—
06/10	127	10	7.9%	—
06/09	146	0	—	—
Annual Growth	(10.4%)	—	—	—

2012 Year-End Financials

Debt ratio: ——
Return on equity: 12.90%
Cash ($ mil.): 1
Current ratio: 0.40
Long-term debt ($ mil.): —
Dividends
Yield: —
Payout: —
Market value ($ mil.): —

THOMAS JEFFERSON UNIVERSITY

Thomas Jefferson University declares its graduates to be masters of health advancement. Its Jefferson Medical College boasts departments and clinics in surgery and specialized areas including obstetrics neurology and psychiatry. The Graduate Studies department offers programs in public health and biomedical studies. The university's College of Health Professions has programs in nursing pharmacy bioscience technologies and counseling. With about 2600 students the university tests or treats 25000 inpatients and more than 300000 outpatients each year. Philadelphia-based Thomas Jefferson University was founded as Jefferson Medical College in 1824. It has granted more than 30000 medical degrees.

Strategy

The university aims to remain at the forefront of medical research. Public and private funding of Jefferson research exceeds $64 million annually. In

2012 Thomas Jefferson University partnered with the Japanese Association for the Development of Community Medicine and the Noguchi Medical Research Institute to establish the Japan Center for Health Professions Education and Research at Jefferson. The pilot project which extends through 2014 will share health personnel for clinical education and research across the three entities. It also entered into a research collaboration with Nanobiotix a company that is developing novel cancer nanotherapeutics. The 2012 alliance is meant to accelerate the development of the company's lead compound NBTXR3 in the US.

Thomas Jefferson University is also adding to its campus. In 2012 it opened a new facility at 901 Walnut St. The Jefferson Health Professions Academic Building now houses the university's schools of nursing pharmacy health professions and population health. It is also home to the departments of occupational and physical therapy radiologic sciences and the Jefferson Clinical Neuroscience Center.

Financial Performance

Thomas Jefferson University logged a 5% increase in revenue in 2012 as compared to 2011 primarily due to an increase in net patient service revenue less provision for bad debts and tuition and fees. During the same reporting period net income decreased by 155% thanks to rising operating expenses due to non-operating changes in unrestricted net assets as well as from defined benefit plan net actuarial. Cash flow meanwhile rose by $11 million as the university used less cash in its investing activities in 2012 over 2011.

EXECUTIVES

VP Finance and CFO, Richard J. Schmid
VP Research, Steven E. McKenzie
VP and University Counsel, Cristina G. Cavalieri
SVP Development, Frederick E. Ruccius
Interim President, Richard C. Gozon, age 75
SVP Academic Affairs, Michael J. Vergare
VP Facilities Management, Ronald Bowlan
CIO, Doug Herrick
SVP and Dean Jefferson Medical College, Richard J. Tykocinski
President Emeritus, Donna Brennan
Vice President of Career Development PhD, Nathan Fried
Trustee, Gerard H. (Jerry) Sweeney, age 57
Trustee, Douglas J. MacMaster Jr., age 83
Trustee, David R. Binswanger
Trustee, Jack Farber
Trustee, Lawrence Smith
Trustee, Kenneth H. Boone
Trustee, Jeffrey P. Orleans
Trustee, Kenneth A. Graham
Trustee, Joseph J. McLaughlin
Trustee, Charles G. Kopp
Auditors: PricewaterhouseCoopersLLP

LOCATIONS

HQ: THOMAS JEFFERSON UNIVERSITY
1020 WALNUT ST STE 1, PHILADELPHIA, PA 19107-5567
Phone: 215-955-6000
Web: WWW.JEFFERSON.EDU

PRODUCTS/OPERATIONS

Selected Research Centers and Institutes

Center for Translational Medicine
Daniel Baugh Institute
Delaware Health Science Alliance
Farber Institute for Neuroscience
Jefferson Coordinating Center for Clinical Research
Jefferson Vaccine Center
Kimmel Cancer Center

Selected Colleges and Schools

Jefferson Medical College
Jefferson Graduate School of Biomedical Sciences
Jefferson School of Health Professions
Jefferson School of Nursing
Jefferson School of Pharmacy
Jefferson School of Population Health

HISTORICAL FINANCIALS

Company Type: Private

Income Statement FYE: June 30

	REVENUE ($ mil.)	NET INCOME ($ mil.)	NET PROFIT MARGIN	EMPLOYEES
06/12	731	(38)	—	4,000
06/11	714	70	9.9%	—
06/10	661	3	0.5%	—
06/08	380	35	9.2%	—
Annual Growth	17.7%	—	—	—

2012 Year-End Financials

Debt ratio: —
Return on equity: (-5.30%)
Cash ($ mil.): 68
Current ratio: —
Long-term debt ($ mil.): —
Dividends
Yield: —
Payout: —
Market value ($ mil.): —

THOMAS JEFFERSON UNIVERSITY HOSPITALS INC.

Named after the "Man of the People" Thomas Jefferson University Hospital serves the people of the Keystone State with a medical staff of more than 1100 and some 970 beds. Part of the Jefferson Health System the hospital provides acute tertiary and specialty medical care. Aside from the main campus it operates through a Center City Campus Methodist Hospital Jefferson Voorhees and Jefferson Hospital for Neuroscience. The hospital also administers cardiac care at the Jefferson Heart Institute which provides everything from minimally invasive surgical procedures to heart transplants. It is also the teaching hospital for Thomas Jefferson University. Thomas Jefferson University Hospital was founded in 1825.

Geographic Reach

Through a handful of locations Thomas Jefferson University Hospital provides health care services to the residents of Philadelphia and the Delaware Valley. It shares a 13-acre campus with Thomas Jefferson University.

Operations

As part of its operations Thomas Jefferson University Hospital offers several premier programs to its patients as well as 35 different specialties. The hospital performed Delaware Valley's first liver transplant and designated a kidney transplant center for live and deceased donor transplants. In addition to transplantation the hospital provides surgical services heart and vascular digestive diseases and bones and joints in addition to its Kimmel Cancer Canter and Jefferson Hospital for Neuroscience. In fiscal year 2012 the health system logged more than 485000 outpatient visits.

EXECUTIVES

President, David P. McQuaid
VP and CIO, Stephen Tranquillo
SVP and CFO, Neil G. Lubarsky
SVP and Chief Medical Officer, Geno Merli
COO, Richard Webster
Auditors: PricewaterhouseCoopersLLP

LOCATIONS

HQ: THOMAS JEFFERSON UNIVERSITY HOSPITALS INC.
111 S 11TH ST, PHILADELPHIA, PA 19107-4824
Phone: 215-955-5806
Web: WWW.NEMOURS.ORG

PRODUCTS/OPERATIONS

Selected Services

Cancer
Diabetes & Endocrinology
Ear Nose & Throat
Gastroenterology
Geriatrics
Gynecology
Nephrology
Orthopedics
Pulmonology
Rehabilitation
Urology

Selected University Locations

Jefferson at the Navy Yard
Jefferson Medical College
Jefferson College of Graduate Studies
Jefferson Radiology
Jefferson School of Health Professions
Jefferson School of Nursing
Jefferson School of Pharmacy
Jefferson School of Population Health
Jefferson Voorhees

COMPETITORS

Albert Einstein Healthcare Network
Bryn Mawr Hospital
Catholic Health East
Community Health Systems
Doylestown Hospital
Main Line Health
Mercy Health System
North Philadelphia Health System
Our Lady of Lourdes Medical Center
Pennsylvania Hospital
TUHS
Universal Health Services
University of Pennsylvania Health System

HISTORICAL FINANCIALS

Company Type: Private

Income Statement FYE: June 30

	REVENUE ($ mil.)	NET INCOME ($ mil.)	NET PROFIT MARGIN	EMPLOYEES
06/10	1,250	49	4.0%	4,701
06/09	0	0	—	—
06/09	0	0	—	—
Annual Growth	—	—	—	—

2010 Year-End Financials

Debt ratio: —
Return on equity: 4.00%
Cash ($ mil.): 206
Current ratio: —
Long-term debt ($ mil.): —
Dividends
Yield: —
Payout: —
Market value ($ mil.): —

THUNDERBIRD SHERM"S MARKET INC

LOCATIONS

HQ: THUNDERBIRD SHERM' ' S MARKET INC
730 S GRAPE ST, MEDFORD, OR 975013628
Phone: 5418570850
Web: WWW.SHERMSMARKETS.COM

HISTORICAL FINANCIALS

Company Type: Private

Income Statement FYE: October 31

	REVENUE ($ mil.)	NET INCOME ($ mil.)	NET PROFIT MARGIN	EMPLOYEES
10/12	210	8	4.1%	650
10/11	206	7	3.6%	—
10/10	204	8	4.2%	—
10/09	205	0	—	—
Annual Growth	0.9%	—	—	—

2012 Year-End Financials

Debt ratio: ——
Return on equity: 4.10%
Cash ($ mil.): 6
Current ratio: 1.00
Long-term debt ($ mil.): —
Dividends
Yield: —
Payout: —
Market value ($ mil.): —

TIFFIN MOTOR HOMES INC.

At Tiffin Motorhomes the family that stays together makes recreational vehicles together. The family-owned manufacturer builds a line of luxury recreational vehicles (RVs) including the Allegro Allegro Bus Phaeton and Zephyr models. RVs span 35 to 44 feet in length and offer amenities from washers and dryers to garden tubs to side-by-side refrigerators. Construction pluses feature thick glass windows added storage and reinforced steel crossbracing. Tiffin's vehicles are sold by dealers across the US and Canada. Spotlighting its nameplates the company owns the Allegro Club an organization of local US chapters that promotes race car rallies and RV events. Robert Tiffin founded the company in 1972.

A weak economy tight consumer credit markets and mounting fuel prices have combined to wipe out an estimated 50% of shipments by the Class A motor home builder. Since 2008 Tiffin has cut its workforce in half from its high in 2005 and slashed production by about 70% to four models a day from its former glory of 13. The belt-tightening fell on the heels of expanding the operations of its subsidiary Waterway Inc. Waterway manufactures the side and roof panels of Tiffin's motor homes.

EXECUTIVES

General Manager, Tim Tiffin
Manager Research and Development, Van Tiffin
Quality and Assistant Plant Manager, Lex Tiffin
Media Relations, Stephanie Umfress

LOCATIONS

HQ: TIFFIN MOTOR HOMES INC.
105 2ND ST NW, RED BAY, AL 35582-3859
Phone: 256-356-8661
Web: WWW.TIFFINMOTORHOMES.COM

COMPETITORS

Airstream
Forest River
Gulf Stream Coach
Jayco Inc.
Keystone RV
Monaco RV
Motor Coach Industries
Newmar Corporation
Rexhall Industries
Thor Industries
Winnebago

HISTORICAL FINANCIALS

Company Type: Private

Income Statement FYE: February 28

	REVENUE ($ mil.)	NET INCOME ($ mil.)	NET PROFIT MARGIN	EMPLOYEES
02/07	419	24	5.9%	545
02/05	286	(0)	—	—
02/04	1,280	0	—	—
Annual Growth	(31.1%)	28998.8%	—	—

2007 Year-End Financials

Debt ratio: ——
Return on equity: 5.90%
Cash ($ mil.): 10
Current ratio: 0.70
Long-term debt ($ mil.): —
Dividends
Yield: —
Payout: —
Market value ($ mil.): —

TNEMEC COMPANY INC.

EXECUTIVES

Chairman, Albert C. Bean Jr.
EVP, Chase Bean
VP Marketing, Mark Thomas
President CEO, Pete Cortelyou
VP Technical and Regulatory Affairs, Joe Davis
VP Sales, Terry Wallace
VP Research and Development, Remi Briand
Electronic Marketing Manager, Jessi Bixler

LOCATIONS

HQ: TNEMEC COMPANY INC.
6800 CORPORATE DR, KANSAS CITY, MO 641201372
Phone: 8164833400
Web: WWW.TNEMEC.COM

COMPETITORS

American Air Liquide
Ashland Inc.
Cohesant
Insl-X
PPG Industries
RPM International
Structural Group

HISTORICAL FINANCIALS

Company Type: Private

Income Statement FYE: December 31

	REVENUE ($ mil.)	NET INCOME ($ mil.)	NET PROFIT MARGIN	EMPLOYEES
12/13	123	5	4.6%	265
12/12	128	6	4.8%	—
12/11	124	4	3.7%	—
12/10	115	0	—	—
Annual Growth	2.2%	—	—	—

2013 Year-End Financials

Debt ratio: —
Return on equity: 4.60%
Cash ($ mil.): 4
Current ratio: 1.20
Long-term debt ($ mil.): —
Dividends
Yield: —
Payout: —
Market value ($ mil.): —

TOM LANGE COMPANY INC.

Tom Lange Company wants you to eat your veggies. One of the largest purchasers and distributors of fresh fruits and vegetables in the US Tom Lange supplies its comestibles to clients in the retail wholesale and food service trades. The company also provides third party logistics services specializing in truckload freight movement. The company was founded in 1960 as a three-man operation in St. Louis Missouri Tom Lange has grown to encompass 35 offices in the US and Canada. Produce subsidiaries include Seven Seas M&M Marketing and Seven Seas Fruit.

EXECUTIVES

Vice President Of Sales, Eric Hoffmann
Senior Vice President, Bruce Rubin
Vice President Of Sales, Gregg Biada

LOCATIONS

HQ: TOM LANGE COMPANY INC.
755 APPLE ORCHARD RD, SPRINGFIELD, IL 62703-5914
Phone: 217-786-3300
Web: WWW.TOMLANGE.COM

COMPETITORS

A. Duda & Sons
Caito Foods Service
Coast Citrus Distributors
Cristina Foods
FreshPoint
Get Fresh Produce
The Oppenheimer Group
Wilson Farms

HISTORICAL FINANCIALS

Company Type: Private

Income Statement FYE: August 31

	REVENUE ($ mil.)	NET INCOME ($ mil.)	NET PROFIT MARGIN	EMPLOYEES
08/12	414	0	0.1%	110
08/11	445	1	0.4%	—
08/07	407	3	0.8%	—
08/07	0	0	—	—
Annual Growth	—	—	—	—

2012 Year-End Financials

Debt ratio: ——
Return on equity: 0.10%
Cash ($ mil.): 10
Current ratio: 1.40
Long-term debt ($ mil.): —
Dividends
Yield: —
Payout: —
Market value ($ mil.): —

TORRANCE MEMORIAL MEDICAL CENTER

Back in 1925 Jared Sydney Torrance founded Torrance Memorial Medical Center in the southern

California town that also bears his name. The not-for-profit medical center now includes 400 beds surgical suites clinical and diagnostic labs and specialist centers for cancer metabolic heart and other conditions. It is one of three burn centers in Los Angeles. Torrance Memorial Medical Center reaches beyond its walls and into the community with hospice care and home health care. The hospital also provides nursing residency programs and it offers staffing support services to physicians offices in the area.

Geographic Reach

Torrance Memorial serves residents of communities in the South Bay Peninsula and Harbor areas within the Los Angeles metropolitan area.

Operations

Torrance Memorial has about 1000 physicians on its medical staff. It is also supported by a volunteer organization with about 900 members.

The hospital provides more than $50 million in community benefits each year including subsidized care for Medicare and Medicaid patients and charity care for uninsured patients. Other programs include community outreach efforts including parenting and wellness classes.

Strategy

In order to accommodate the medical needs of a growing population the hospital is building a new 400000 sq. ft. $450 million patient tower featuring new medical technologies increased capacity and a modernized design. The seven-story tower will have more than 250 private rooms and about 20 surgical and interventional treatment rooms. The tower meets the hospital's needs for a growing customer base as a number of other area hospitals have closed in recent years. It is expected to open in late 2015. About $200 million of the construction costs is being procured through fundraising efforts.

Company Background

Founded by Jared Torrance and his wife Helena in 1925 Torrance Memorial acquired the smaller Riviera Community Hospital in 1967. The medical center moved to its current location in 1971.

EXECUTIVES

President and CEO, Craig Leach
VP Human Resources, Lois Michael
SVP Patient Services, Peggy Berwald
Vice President Finance, Bill Larson
Vice President Information Technology, Bernadette Reid
Vice President Information Technology, Heather Shay
CAO, Christine Curtis

LOCATIONS

HQ: TORRANCE MEMORIAL MEDICAL CENTER
3330 LOMITA BLVD, TORRANCE, CA 90505-5002
Phone: 310-325-9110

PRODUCTS/OPERATIONS

Selected Centers and Services

Bariatric Surgery Program
Blood Donor Center
Breast Diagnostic Center
Burn Center
Cancer Institute
Cardiovascular Institute
Chemical Dependency
Diabetes
Eating Disorders Program
Emergency Care
Endoscopy Center and GI Lab
Home Health
Hospice
Laboratory Testing (includes Outpatient Lab)
Maternal Child Health Services
Nuclear Medicine
Orthopedics
Palliative Care
Pediatrics
Pharmacy
Radiation Oncology
Radiology
Rehabilitation
Sleep Disorders Center
Stroke Center
Surgical Services
Transitional Care Unit
Urgent Care
Wound Center

COMPETITORS

Brotman Medical Center
Cedars-Sinai Medical Center
Childrens Hospital Los Angeles
Dignity Health
Good Samaritan Hospital (Los Angeles)
HCA
Hollywood Presbyterian Medical Center
Kaiser Permanente
Long Beach Memorial
Los Angeles County Health Department
Providence Health System Southern California
Sisters of Charity of Leavenworth
Tenet Healthcare
Universal Health Services
White Memorial Medical Center

HISTORICAL FINANCIALS

Company Type: Private

Income Statement FYE: September 30

	REVENUE ($ mil.)	NET INCOME ($ mil.)	NET PROFIT MARGIN	EMPLOYEES
09/13*	351	13	4.0%	3,500
06/13	239	11	4.6%	—
12/12	460	37	8.2%	—
09/12	354	31	8.9%	—
Annual Growth	(0.8%)	(55.9%)	—	—

*Fiscal year change

2013 Year-End Financials

Debt ratio: —
Return on equity: 4.00%
Cash ($ mil.): 14
Current ratio: 0.40
Long-term debt ($ mil.): —
Dividends
Yield: —
Payout: —
Market value ($ mil.): —

TOTAL QUALITY LOGISTICS INC.

Total Quality Logistics sets a high standard for moving merchandise. The third-party logistics (non-asset based) provider specializes in arranging freight transportation using reefers (refrigerated trucks) vans and flatbeds —moving in excess of 500000 loads each year. The trucking brokerage company serves more than 7000 clients across the US Canada and Mexico ranging from small businesses to Fortune 500 organizations. Founded in 1997 by company president Ken Oaks Total Quality Logistics (TQL) has contracts with carriers that include single owner operators and large fleets. Customers have included Kroger Dole Food and Laura's Lean Beef.

Geographic Reach

TQL largely caters to customers in the Greater Cincinnati Area where it has nearly five offices. It has about 25 satellite locations located in Chicago; Cleveland; Charlotte North Carolina; Charleston South Carolina; Detroit; Indianapolis; Denver; Columbus Ohio; Houston; Lexington Kentucky; Louisville; Nashville Tennessee; Orlando Florida; Dayton Ohio; Erlanger Kentucky; Pittsburgh; Tampa; and Austin Texas.

Operations

The company began as a produce shipper —not a popular item for most brokers because it is perishable —and expanded into flatbed shipments and other dry freight. As a non-asset-based business TQL does not own trucks or warehouses nor does it employ drivers. Rather it arranges for independent carrier companies and owner/operators to transport its customers' freight; TQL manages the shipment while it is on the road. Additionally the company has no expensive overhead and is not limited by fleet size equipment or shipping routes allowing more flexibility for its customers.

Sales and Marketing

The company serves more than 10000 customers and 50000 carriers across North America to move more than 800000 loads each year. Customers include Dole Food Wholesalers and Kroger.

Financial Performance

TOL posted $1.6 billion in annual sales for 2013 up from the $1.4 billion it posted the previous year. With no expense overhead to bog down its balance sheet the company has enjoyed three straight years of sizable growth.

Strategy

TQL grows its business by gradually launching additional locations and sales offices in key cities across the country. In 2013 it expanded its sales office in Charlotte North Carolina and moved its operations in Lexington Kentucky to a larger space. Also that year TQL launched a new sales office in Orlando Florida. In 2012 the company opened new offices in the key metropolitan areas of Cleveland Detroit and Pittsburgh. In 2014 it announced plans to launch a new office in Nashville Tennessee.

EXECUTIVES

President, Kenneth Oaks
EVP, Kerry Byrne

LOCATIONS

HQ: TOTAL QUALITY LOGISTICS INC.
4289 IVY POINTE BLVD, CINCINNATI, OH 45245-0002
Phone: 513-831-2600
Web: WWW.TQL.COM

COMPETITORS

Alliance Shippers
C.H. Robinson Worldwide
Echo Global
Greatwide Logistics
MIQ Logistics
Menlo Worldwide
Pacer International
Roadrunner Transportation Systems
Ryder System
Schneider Logistics
Transplace
UPS Supply Chain Solutions

HISTORICAL FINANCIALS

Company Type: Private

Income Statement FYE: December 30

	REVENUE ($ mil.)	NET INCOME ($ mil.)	NET PROFIT MARGIN	EMPLOYEES
12/12	1,387	0	—	2,150
12/11	1,046	0	—	—
12/08	762	0	—	—
Annual Growth	16.2%	—	—	—

TOURO COLLEGE

Touro College is a Jewish university (the largest private Jewish-based educational institution in the US) and has sister institutions in France Germany Israel and Russia and branches in California Florida and Nevada. Some 19000 (Jewish and non-Jewish) students are enrolled in its 32 schools on 25 campuses which offer associate bachelor's and master's degrees in business education and law as well as professional degrees in osteopathic medicine pharmacy law and other fields. Touro also oversees the operations of New York Medical College. The institution claims some 75000 alumni.

Operations

Touro has more than 2200 full-time and about 1380 part-time faculty members.

The school has an annual operating budget of $460 million.

Strategy

The school is looking to expand its academic programs and research footprint.

Company Background

Dr. Bernard Lander a social behavior and Jewish studies scholar founded Touro College in 1971 to teach Jewish and secular subjects. The college is named after Judah and Isaac Touro who founded the Touro Synagogue in 1790.

Lander an orthodox rabbi died in 2010. He was one of the longest-serving college presidents in the country. Senior provost and medical doctor Alan Kadish was selected to replace Lander.

Under Lander's leadership Touro College grew quickly from a small school with 35 students to a multi-campus college with thousands of students. Touro continues to expand. It assumed control of New York Medical College in mid-2010. The Catholic-led medical school remains an independent institution. Some at the New York Medical College opposed the merger citing a well-publicized cash-for-grades scandal. In 2009 Touro's former director of admissions was found guilty of tampering with student transcripts and selling degrees. He was sentenced to two to eight years in prison. Nevertheless the deal went through and now New York Medical College is a member of the Touro College and University System.

EXECUTIVES

Data Manager, Michael J. Lee
Director Communications, Barbara Franklin
Senior Provost and CEO Global e-Learning Programs, Bernard J. Luskin
Chairman, Mark Hasten
President C.E.O, Alan Kadish
Executive Assistant, Annalene Antonio

LOCATIONS

HQ: TOURO COLLEGE
27 W 23RD ST FL 5, NEW YORK, NY 10010-4282
Phone: 212-463-0400
Web: WWW.TOURO.EDU

HISTORICAL FINANCIALS

Company Type: Private

Income Statement FYE: June 30

	REVENUE ($ mil.)	NET INCOME ($ mil.)	NET PROFIT MARGIN	EMPLOYEES
06/11	203	(9)	—	4,600
06/10	277	15	5.7%	—
06/09	145	0	—	—
06/08	0	0	—	—
Annual Growth	—	—	—	—

2011 Year-End Financials

Debt ratio: —
Return on equity: (-4.50%)
Cash ($ mil.): 12
Current ratio: —
Long-term debt ($ mil.): —
Dividends
Yield: —
Payout: —
Market value ($ mil.): —

TOWNSHIP HIGH SCHOOL DISTRICT 211 FOUNDATION

Township High School District 211 is the largest high school district in Illinois with some 12500 students attending its five high schools (grades 9 to 12) –James B. Conant William Fremd Hoffman Estates Palatine and Schaumburg –and two special education academies. The district's student-teacher ratio is nearly 14-to-1 and serves several suburban communities 25 miles northwest of Chicago. The school district started as one school (Palatine High School) in the Palatine-Schaumburg Township area in 1875 with the first graduating class in 1877.

Geographic Reach

Township High School District 211 serves the northwest suburbs of Chicago including the the communities of Hoffman Estates Inverness Palatine and Schaumburg as well as parts of Arlington Heights Elk Grove Village Hanover Park Rolling Meadows Roselle Streamwood and South Barrington.

Financial Performance

The school district reported revenue of nearly $240 million in 2012 nearly 85% of it coming from local property taxes.

HISTORY

All five district schools have been named among the top schools in the nation.

EXECUTIVES

Superintendent of Schools, Nancy N. Robb
Associate Superintendent for Instruction, Jeffery A. Butzen
Associate Superintendent Business, David S. Torres
Assistant Superintendent for Administrative Services and Special Programs, Daniel E. Cates
Assistant Superintendent for Personnel, Robert D. Grimm
Community Relations Coordinator, Thomas D. Petersen
Director Technology Services, Charles A. Peterson
Director Business Services, Christopher J. Kontney
Director Athletic Activities and Career Development, Otis G. Price
Director Food Service, Lauren C. Hummel
Director of Human Resources, Eric Wenckowski

LOCATIONS

HQ: TOWNSHIP HIGH SCHOOL DISTRICT 211 FOUNDATION
1750 S ROSELLE RD STE 100, PALATINE, IL 60067-7302
Phone: 847-755-6600
Web: WWW.D211.ORG

PRODUCTS/OPERATIONS

Schools
High Schools
James B. Conant High School
William Fremd High School
Hoffman Estates High School
Palatine High School
Schaumburg High School
Special Education Schools
District 211 Academy North
District 211 Academy South

HISTORICAL FINANCIALS

Company Type: Private

Income Statement FYE: June 30

	REVENUE ($ mil.)	NET INCOME ($ mil.)	NET PROFIT MARGIN	EMPLOYEES
06/12	257	8	3.1%	1,909
06/11	250	4	1.7%	—
06/10	0	0	41.7%	—
06/09	0	0	15.5%	—
Annual Growth	1218.6%	672.9%	—	—

TRAMMO INC.

Fertilizers liquefied petroleum gas (LPG) and petrochemicals form the lifeblood of international trader Transammonia. The company trades distributes and transports these commodities around the world. Transammonia's fertilizer business includes ammonia phosphates and urea. Its Sea-3 subsidiary imports and distributes propane to residential commercial and industrial customers in the northeastern US and Florida. The Trammochem unit trades in petrochemicals specializing in aromatics methanol methyltertiary butyl ether (MTBE) benzene and olefins. Its Trammo Gas trades LPG and propane as well as ethane butane and natural gas in the US.

Geographic Reach

Transammonia has expanded its reach into the global market establishing merchandising and trading offices in Singapore China and the United Arab Emirates. Those offices complement its other global operations in Africa Asia Europe the Middle East and South America. It has major representative offices in Amman Beijing Cairo Dubai Hong Kong and Shanghai. Its ammonia merchandising trading and logistics are conducted through representative offices in Dubai Paris and Tampa.

Operations

The company trades distributes and transports fertilizers LPG and petrochemicals through its subsidiaries.

Sea-3 is the largest importer and distributor of liquefied propane in the Northeastern US. It also supplies propane to the western and central portions of Florida. Trammochem merchandises and trades in petrochemicals around the world. Trammo Gas markets and trades LPG (primarily propane) in the US. Trammo Gas International Inc. operates two gas carriers which transport LPG worldwide for third parties.

Ownership

Transammonia is owned by founder Ronald Stanton.

Company Background

Transammonia was founded in 1965 as an international ammonia trader. It branched into fertilizer merchandising and trading in 1967 LPG trading in 1978 and petrochemicals trading in 1987.

In 2010 the company's bulk carriers division entered the commodity shipping business. TA Bulk Carriers operates a fleet of 15 to 20 vessels which trade worldwide but focus on the handysize market (25000-35000 metric tons deadweight) in the Atlantic basin. In 2010 it transported about 2.9

million metric tons of cargo primarily fertilizers and grains.

EXECUTIVES

Director Human Resources, Marguerite Harrington
SVP and CFO, Edward G. Weiner
Chairman and CEO, Ronald P. Stanton
CIO, Benjamin Tan

LOCATIONS

HQ: TRAMMO INC.
320 PARK AVE RM 1001, NEW YORK, NY 10022-6987
Phone: 212-223-3200
Web: WWW.GUIDE8480.GUIDECHEM.COM

PRODUCTS/OPERATIONS

Major Subsidiari
Sea-3 (liquefied propane)
Trammo Gas (LPG)
Trammo Gas International Inc. (LPG transportation for third parties.
Trammo Petroleum (crude oil and oil products)
Trammochem (petrochem
Transammonia (fertilize
Fertilizers and Commoditie
Nitrogen Based
Anhydrous Ammonia
Ammonium Nitrate
Ammonium Sulfate
Calcium Ammonium Nitrate
Nitrogen Phosphorus Potassium (NPK) Compounds
Urea
Urea Ammonium Nitrate Solutions
Phosphate Based
Diammonium Phosphate
Monoammonium Phosphate
NPK Compounds
Single Super Phosphate
Triple Super Phosphate
Sulphur Based
Lump/Formed/Molten Sulphur
Sulphuric Acid
Potash Based
Muriate of Potash
NPK Compounds
Sulphate of Potash
Carbon Based
Coal
Petroleum Coke
Petrochemicals
Benzene
Ethanol
Gasoline Blend Components
Methanol
Olefins
Styrene Monomer
Toluene
Xylenes and Isomers
LPG
Butane
Ethane
Iso Butane
Natural Gasoline
Propane

COMPETITORS

Agrium	Dynegy
BASF SE	HELM
CF Industries	Koch Industries Inc.
Cargill	Magellan Midstream
ConAgra	Yara

HISTORICAL FINANCIALS

Company Type: Private

Income Statement FYE: December 31

	REVENUE ($ mil.)	NET INCOME ($ mil.)	NET PROFIT MARGIN	EMPLOYEES
12/12	12,152	35	0.3%	440
12/11	11,303	31	0.3%	—
12/10	8,414	35	0.4%	—
12/09	5,485	21	0.4%	—
Annual Growth	30.4%	17.4%	—	—

2012 Year-End Financials

Debt ratio: —
Return on equity: 0.30%
Cash ($ mil.): 268
Current ratio: 0.90
Long-term debt ($ mil.): —
Dividends
Yield: —
Payout: —
Market value ($ mil.): —

TRANS-SYSTEM INC.

Freight hauler Trans-System operates through three main units: System Transport (flatbed); TW Transport (refrigerated and dry van); and James J. Williams (bulk commodities). The Trans-System trucking companies operate from eight terminals in the US and Canada; overall the company's fleet consists of about 850 tractors and 1200 trailers. Trans-System also offers logistics services and runs a driver training school. Chairman and CEO Jim Williams founded the company in 1972.

EXECUTIVES

CEO, James C. (Jim) Williams
President and CFO, Gary R. King
VP Driver Services and Personnel, Jeff Benesch
Auditors: MossAdamsLLP

LOCATIONS

HQ: TRANS-SYSTEM INC.
7405 S HAYFORD RD, CHENEY, WA 99004-9633
Phone: 509-623-4001
Web: WWW.TRANS-SYSTEM.COM

COMPETITORS

Arrow Trucking	Prime Inc.
C.R. England	Quality Distribution
CRST International	Ruan Transportation Management Systems
Comcar	Schneider National
Crete Carrier	Werner Enterprises
Maverick USA	

HISTORICAL FINANCIALS

Company Type: Private

Income Statement FYE: March 31

	REVENUE ($ mil.)	NET INCOME ($ mil.)	NET PROFIT MARGIN	EMPLOYEES
03/13	197	8	4.1%	650
03/12	191	8	4.6%	—
/ 0	0	—	—	—
Annual Growth	—	—	—	—

2013 Year-End Financials

Debt ratio: —
Return on equity: 4.10%
Cash ($ mil.): 0
Current ratio: 0.50
Long-term debt ($ mil.): —
Dividends
Yield: —
Payout: —
Market value ($ mil.): —

TRANSPERFECT TRANSLATIONS INTERNATIONAL INC.

You pick the language or languages and TransPerfect Translations International will aim to get your message through. In addition to translation and interpretation the company offers services such as document management multicultural marketing staffing subtitling and voiceover work. Its network of translators can handle approximately 170 languages through offices located in more than 70 cities spanning five continents. TransPerfect serves a wide array of industries including advertising financial services legal life science technology retail and travel. Clients include Sony American Airlines and Omnicom. TransPerfect was founded in 1992 by Liz Elting and Phil Shawe.

Mergers and Acquisitions TransPerfect is focused on international growth through acquisitions. In 2012 it acquired Tokyo-based Yamane Documentation which specializes in translation and website localization services. The prior year it purchased another translation and website localization firm WorldLingo which brought clients such as Eli Lilly Belkin and H. J. Heinz as well as several US and European government agencies. TransPerfect completed a few key acquisitions in 2010 as well. The company strengthened its software platform when it bought Astoria Software. Integrating Astoria's products helped the company to recognize cost efficiencies related to the writing translation and publishing of data. Also that year TransPerfect snatched up AD-COM a provider of translation services based in Canada. The deal extended the company's services in the French Canadian market and added a Montreal production hub to its existing three Canadian locations. Strategy The firm is also growing by opening new offices across the globe. In 2012 it established locations in Madrid and Rome. In 2011 and 2010 TransPerfect opened offices in Seoul Shanghai S?o Paulo and Palma de Mallorca as well as Dusseldorf Mexico City Lyon and Zurich.

EXECUTIVES

Co-CEO, Phil Shawe
Co-CEO, Elizabeth (Liz) Elting
SVP Global Sales, A. Brooke Christian
Vice President of Quality Assurance, Mark Peeler
VP European Operations, Angela O'Sullivan
Vice President of US Sales, Kevin Obarski
CTO, Mark Hagerty
VP Corporate Strategy, Michael Sank
COO, Roy B. Trujillo
VP Quality Systems; President Crimson Life Sciences Division, Marc H. Miller
CIO, Yu-Kai Ng
VP Legal Technology, Jordan Ellington
Vice President of Human Resources, Robert DeNoia
Vice President of Business Development, Jennifer Peters
VP Global Life Sciences, Jessica Eker
Marketing Director of easyJet, Peter Duffy
Vice President of Global Production, Jin Lee
Senior Vice President of Global Sales, Brooke Christian
Vice President Content Solutions, Matt Hauser

LOCATIONS

HQ: TRANSPERFECT TRANSLATIONS INTERNATIONAL INC.
3 PARK AVE FL 39, NEW YORK, NY 10016-5934
Phone: 212-689-5555
Web: WWW.TRANSPERFECT.COM.HK

PRODUCTS/OPERATIONS

Selected Services

Brand research
Court reporting
Document management
Graphic services
Interpretation
Linguistic validation
Multilingual typesetting
Multicultural marketing
Software localization

Staffing
Subtitling
Technical writing
Translation
Virtual data rooms
Voiceovers
Website globalization

COMPETITORS

ALT Services
Albors & Associates
Eclipse Translations
JLS Language Corporation
Language Line
Linguistic Systems
Lionbridge
Mission Essential Personnel
Wordbank

HISTORICAL FINANCIALS

Company Type: Private

Income Statement FYE: December 31

	REVENUE ($ mil.)	NET INCOME ($ mil.)	NET PROFIT MARGIN	EMPLOYEES
12/07	156	29	18.5%	950
12/06	79	11	14.8%	—
12/05	73	11	15.7%	—
Annual Growth	45.7%	58.5%	—	—

2007 Year-End Financials

Debt ratio: —
Return on equity: 18.50%
Cash ($ mil.): 11
Current ratio: 5.90
Long-term debt ($ mil.): —
Dividends
Yield: —
Payout: —
Market value ($ mil.): —

TRAYLOR BROS. INC.

HISTORY

Traylor Bros. operates from offices in Evansville Indiana and in Pleasanton and Irvine California.

LOCATIONS

HQ: TRAYLOR BROS. INC.
835 N CONGRESS AVE, EVANSVILLE, IN 477152484
Phone: 8124771542
Web: WWW.TRAYLOR.COM

HISTORICAL FINANCIALS

Company Type: Private

Income Statement FYE: December 31

	REVENUE ($ mil.)	NET INCOME ($ mil.)	NET PROFIT MARGIN	EMPLOYEES
12/13	250	0	—	500
12/12	250	0	—	—
12/11	0	0	—	—
12/10	250	0	—	—
Annual Growth	(0.0%)	—	—	—

2013 Year-End Financials

Debt ratio: —
Return on equity: —
Cash ($ mil.): 226
Current ratio: 1.40
Long-term debt ($ mil.): —
Dividends
Yield: —
Payout: —
Market value ($ mil.): —

TREE TOP INC.

EXECUTIVES

President and CEO, Tom Stokes, age 62
SVP Field Services, Lindsay Buckner, age 62
Chairman, Tom Auvil
SVP Ingredient and Foodservice Sales, Tom Hurson
SVP Sales and Marketing, Dan Hagerty, age 52
VP-HR, Scott Washburn
VP-Ops, Gary Price
Director, Bruce Allen
Director, Ray Colbert
Director, Dick Cowin
Director, Ray Keller
Director, Doug Stockwell
Director, Roger Strand
Director, Fred Valentine
Director, Ed Kershaw
Director, Randy Smith
Director, Michael Smith
Director, Warren Morgan
Auditors: MossAdamsLLP

LOCATIONS

HQ: TREE TOP INC.
220 E 2ND AVE, SELAH, WA 989421408
Phone: 5096977251
Web: WWW.TREETOP.ORG

PRODUCTS/OPERATIONS

Selected Brands and Products

Consumer products
- Applesauce (Seneca and Tree Top)
- Juice and drinks
  - Fiber rich
  - Fresh pressed
  - Fruit drinks
  - Juice from concentrate
  - Organic juice
  - trim Functional Beverages
- Other
  - Fruit Snacks

Food service products
- Beverages
- Cut produce
- Fruit bases
- Sauces
- Frozen fruit

Ingredient products
- Apple (dried chilled frozen and concentrate)
- Cherry (dried chilled frozen and concentrate)

COMPETITORS

Chiquita Brands
Coca-Cola
Cranberries Limited
Del Monte Foods
Dole Food
Dominion Citrus
Dr Pepper Snapple Group
Knouse Foods
Monster Beverage
Mott' s
Naked Juice
National Beverage
National Grape Cooperative
Ocean Spray
Odwalla
Old Orchard
PepsiCo
Snapple
Sun-Rype
Tropicana
Welch' s

HISTORICAL FINANCIALS

Company Type: Private

Income Statement FYE: July 31

	REVENUE ($ mil.)	NET INCOME ($ mil.)	NET PROFIT MARGIN	EMPLOYEES
07/13	399	57	14.4%	1,100
07/10	364	26	7.4%	—
07/09	359	37	10.4%	—
07/08	350	0	—	—
Annual Growth	2.7%	—	—	—

2013 Year-End Financials

Debt ratio: —
Return on equity: 14.40%
Cash ($ mil.): 0
Current ratio: 0.30
Long-term debt ($ mil.): —
Dividends
Yield: —
Payout: —
Market value ($ mil.): —

TRI-WEST LTD

Tri-West tends to floor both residential and commercial customers with its broad selection of floor coverings. Founded in 1981 the company distributes floor coverings through about half a dozen warehouse facilities located in the western US and the Hawaiian Islands. In addition Tri-West also serves customers in Texas and Guam. Tri-West offers major manufacturers' products including carpets ceramic and specialty tile hardwood flooring laminate and vinyl flooring and eco-friendly items such as recycled rubber tiles and bamboo flooring. As part of its business the company sells and distributes adhesives and tools from manufacturers such as Armstrong and California-based Taylor Adhesives.

Geographic Reach

Tri-West operates out of Santa Fe Springs California and has warehouses in San Diego California; Las Vegas Nevada; Phoenix Arizona; Albuquerque New Mexico; Salt Lake City Utah; and Waipahu Hawaii. It also serves Texas and Guam.

Sales and Marketing

The company serves several sectors such as commercial residential and environmentally friendly.

Operations

Tri-West sells commercial and residential flooring through manufactures the likes of Armstrong U.S. Rubber Recycling and VPI. The company sells eco-friendly flooring from Armstrong Kahrs USA LM Flooring Provenza Floors and Sound Seal among others.

EXECUTIVES

Senior Vice President, Mark Babbitt
Vice President, Naser Goyal
Vice President Operations, Jay Lubinski
Vice President Of Sales And Marketing, Allen Gage

LOCATIONS

HQ: TRI-WEST LTD
12005 PIKE ST, SANTA FE SPRINGS, CA 906706100
Phone: 5625661214

PRODUCTS/OPERATIONS

Selected Products

Adhesives & tools
Ceramic tile
Green products
Hardwood flooring
Laminate flooring
Luxury vinyl tile
Resilient flooring
Specialty products

COMPETITORS

Abbey Carpet
Adleta
B.R. Funsten
CCA Global
Florstar Sales
HD Supply
Lowe' s

HISTORICAL FINANCIALS

Company Type: Private

Income Statement FYE: December 31

	REVENUE ($ mil.)	NET INCOME ($ mil.)	NET PROFIT MARGIN	EMPLOYEES
12/13	162	14	8.7%	325
12/12	141	10	7.2%	—
12/11	117	7	6.1%	—
12/09	111	0	—	—
Annual Growth	9.8%	—	—	—

2013 Year-End Financials

Debt ratio: —
Return on equity: 8.70%
Cash ($ mil.): 8
Current ratio: 1.60
Long-term debt ($ mil.): —
Dividends
Yield: —
Payout: —
Market value ($ mil.): —

TRIMEGA PURCHASING ASSOCIATION

Smart office products dealers pledge to buya lotta TriMega. The TriMega Purchasing Association is a product and services buying group that comprises nearly 600 independently owned office-supply dealers. TriMega in turn is a member of the larger Business Products Group International (BPGI) which gives TriMega's member dealers even more buying power and helps them compete with nationwide chains such as OfficeMax and Staples. TriMega also supplies its own Value Plus brand of office products. The not-for-profit cooperative was founded in 1987 and serves company's large and small from across the US.

EXECUTIVES

EVP Member Development, Grady Taylor
EVP Purchasing, Greg Fish
Vice Chairman, Lyle D. Dabbert
President, Charlie Cleary
Rebate Manager, Rachel Dorman
Accounting Manager, Gene Rigitano
Customer Service Supervisor, Diane Pakonen
Treasurer, Mark Porter
VP Marketing, Michael Morris
Marketing Manager, Kara Noble
Marketing Coordinator, LeeAna Theberg
Vice President Enterprise Technology, Lori Stevens
Executive Vice President Strategic Planning, Mark Hampton
Business Development Manager, Dan Fenton
Chairman, Bruce Eaton
Secretary, Tricia Burke

LOCATIONS

HQ: TRIMEGA PURCHASING ASSOCIATION
5600 N RIVER RD STE 700, ROSEMONT, IL 60018-5165
Phone: 847-699-3330
Web: WWW.TRIMEGA.ORG

COMPETITORS

BJ' s Wholesale Club
Costco Wholesale
Office Depot
OfficeMax
Staples
Wal-Mart

HISTORICAL FINANCIALS

Company Type: Private

Income Statement FYE: June 30

	REVENUE ($ mil.)	NET INCOME ($ mil.)	NET PROFIT MARGIN	EMPLOYEES
06/13*	189	24	12.7%	19
12/11	387	36	9.4%	—
06/11	280	26	9.3%	—
03/09	90	10	11.5%	—
Annual Growth	20.4%	23.4%	—	—

*Fiscal year change

TRINITY HEALTH CORPORATION

Hospitals health centers and nursing homes make up Trinity Health. One of the largest Catholic health care systems in the US Trinity Health runs about 50 hospitals (with a total of 6900 beds) 30 long-term care centers (1700 beds) 400 outpatient facilities and numerous home health and hospice agencies. Of the hospitals it owns about 35 and manages another dozen for third parties. Its Trinity Senior Living Communities division operates its nursing homes and senior living facilities. Sponsored by the Catholic Health Ministries Trinity Health has facilities in 10 mostly Midwestern states and its Trinity Health International (THI) unit provides consulting and training to hospitals worldwide.

Geographic Reach

Trinity Health has locations in California Idaho Illinois Indiana Iowa Maryland Michigan and Ohio; the facilities also serve customers in Oregon and Nebraska. THI the company's international arm has conducted projects in more than 40 countries.

Operations

On both domestic and international soil Trinity Health conducts and supports a number of ministry projects to improve community health in poor or disaster-struck areas. THI's projects have included the management of infection control programs biomedical engineering training mental health training and feasibility and demand studies for other health care organizations.

Trinity Health also operates the Mount Carmel Health Plan which offers MediGold a Medicare Advantage program to seniors and others eligible for Medicare in Ohio. The program includes comprehensive health benefits and prescription drug coverage.

Altogether Trinity Health's facilities employ more than 9000 physicians discharge more than 350000 inpatients and handle more than 10 million emergency room and outpatient visits per year.

Financial Performance

Trinity Health reported a 21% increase in revenues to $8.9 billion in 2012 primarily due to growth from acquisitions and increased payment rates continuing a five-year trend of revenue growth. Net income fell 46% to some $367 million in 2012.

Strategy

To meet federal health reform guidelines Trinity Health is working to shape its organization into an accountable health network (AHN) by coordinating patient care across all regional facilities and providers both within and outside of the Trinity Health system. The company had already installed new information technology systems including the Genesis EHR (electronic health record) system and a new procurement platform at more than half of its facilities. In addition to improving the quality of care such measures aim to improve quality and lower costs for medical services.

As part of its AHN goals Trinity Health is forming collaborations with other area providers. Trinity Health announced in 2012 that it is exploring a merger with Pennsylvania-based Catholic Health East (CHE). The combination of CHE and Trinity would create a health system that serves people in 21 states from coast to coast with about 80 hospitals90 continuing care facilities and home health and hospice programs that provide nearly 2.8 million visits annually. The new system would have annual operating revenues of about $13.3 billion and assets of about $19.3 billion.

Trinity Health also expands its own network through construction efforts and by acquiring facilities. In 2010 the organization completed a new $355 million replacement hospital facility for the Saint Joseph Regional Medical Center in Indiana. It also constructed new senior living facilities and entered new home health contracts. In 2012 the company added eight new senior emergency rooms doubling the number of such facilities in the system.

Mergers and Acquisitions

In 2012 Trinity Health purchased the Mercy Hospital & Medical Center of Chicago. Mercy already participated in Trinity Health's group purchasing organization; the purchase expanded Trinity's presence in the Chicago area.

Trinity Health grew in 2011 through the acquisition of the Loyola University Health System which was previously owned by Loyola University Chicago. The purchase added the 570-bed Loyola University Medical Center (which continue to provide teaching programs with the university's medical school) the 250-bed Gottlieb Memorial Hospital and a number of specialty centers in Illinois.

In 2010 Trinity Health acquired three hospitals –Mercy Medical Center Holy Rosary Medical Center Saint Elizabeth Health Services –in Oregon and Idaho from Catholic Health Initiatives (CHI). The facilities were combined with Trinity Health's Saint Alphonsus Regional Medical Center to form a single local system called Saint Alphonsus Health System.

Company Background

The not-for-profit Trinity Health organization was formed through the 2000 merger of Mercy Health Services and Holy Cross Health System.

EXECUTIVES

SVP Organizational Integrity and Audit Services, Michael R. (Mike) Holper
President and CEO Mercy Medical Center - Sioux City, Paul Doherty
SVP Treasurer and Chief Investment Officer, James W. Bosscher
EVP Institute of Health and Community Benefits, Daniel G. (Dan) Hale
SVP Supply Chain and Capital Projects Management, Louis J. (Lou) Fierens II
SVP and CFO, Benjamin R. (Ben) Carter
Interim President and CEO, Larry Warren, age 65
SVP Strategic Planning and Marketing, Preston Gee
President CEO of St, Garry C. Faja
President Chief Executive Officer, David Spivey
President CEO, Roger W. Spoelman, age 61
SVP Clinical Quality and Patient Safety, Paul F. Conlon
EVP and Chief Clinical Officer, P. Terrence (Terry) O'Rourke
EVP and Chief Culture and Talent Effectiveness Officer, Debra A. (Deb) Canales
EVP and General Counsel, Paul G. Neumann
SVP Mission Integration, Daniel P. Dwyer

Interim President and CEO Saint Agnes Medical Center, Thomas Anderson
EVP Health Networks, Michael (Mike) Murphy
SVP Insurance and Risk Management Services, Rebecca Havlisch
Chairperson, Sister Mary Mollison
SVP and Chief Medical Officer, Donald Bignotti
SVP and CIO, Marcus B. Shipley
EVP Growth Strategy and Innovation, Scott Nordlund
Director, Sarah Ladd Eames, age 55
Director, Suzanne R. Brennan, age 62
Director, Henry R. Autry, age 63
President CEO and Director, Joseph R. Swedish, age 61
Director, Angel R. (A. R.) Sales, age 63
Director, Melanie C. Dreher
Director, Sister Mary Kelly
Director, Sister Kathleen Moroney
Director, Norma Smith
Director, Mary Mollison
Director, Robert W. (Bob) Ladenburger
Director, Linda Werthman
Auditors: Deloitte&ToucheLLP

LOCATIONS

HQ: TRINITY HEALTH CORPORATION
20555 VICTOR PKWY, LIVONIA, MI 48152-7031
Phone: 734-343-1000
Web: WWW.TRINITY-HEALTH.ORG

Selected Facilities

California
Saint Agnes Medical Center (Fresno)
Idaho and Oregon
Saint Alphonsus Medical Center - Baker City
Saint Alphonsus Medical Center - Nampa
Saint Alphonsus Medical Center - Ontario
Saint Alphonsus Regional Medical Center (Boise)
Indiana
Saint Joseph Regional Medical Center (South Bend)
Saint Joseph Regional Medical Center (Plymouth)
Illinois
Loyola University Health System (Chicago)
Loyola University Medical Center
Loyola Gottlieb Memorial Hospital
Mercy Hospital & Medical Center (Chicago)
Iowa and Nebraska
Mercy Health Network (Clinton Des Moines Dubuque Dyersville Mason City New Hampton and Sioux City Iowa; Oakland Nebraska)
Maryland
Holy Cross Hospital (Silver Spring)
Michigan
Mercy Health Partners (Muskegon)
Mercy Hospital (Cadillac)
Mercy Hospital (Grayling)
Saint Joseph Mercy Health System (Ann Arbor)
Saint Mary's Health Care (Grand Rapids)
Ohio
Mount Carmel Health System (Columbus)

COMPETITORS

Advocate Health Care
Amedisys
Ascension Health
Beaumont Health System
Community Health Systems
HCA
Health Management Associates
HealthSouth
Henry Ford Health System
Hospice of Michigan
Johns Hopkins Medicine
Kindred Healthcare
Mayo Clinic
MedStar Health
Memorial Hospital & Health System
Odyssey HealthCare
OhioHealth
Resurrection Health Care
St. Luke' s Health System
Tenet Healthcare
Universal Health Services
University of Chicago Medical Center
VITAS Healthcare
Vanguard Health Systems
Wheaton Franciscan Services

HISTORICAL FINANCIALS

Company Type: Private

Income Statement FYE: June 30

	REVENUE ($ mil.)	NET INCOME ($ mil.)	NET PROFIT MARGIN	EMPLOYEES
06/11	814	36	4.5%	51,100
06/10	738	50	6.8%	—
06/09	593	(59)	—	—
06/08	1	(0)	—	—
Annual Growth	700.0%	—	—	—

2011 Year-End Financials

Debt ratio: —
Return on equity: 4.50%
Cash ($ mil.): 2
Current ratio: —
Long-term debt ($ mil.): —
Dividends
Yield: —
Payout: —
Market value ($ mil.): —

TRINITY HEALTH SYSTEM

Despite its name Trinity Health System serves eastern Ohio through only two facilities: Trinity Medical Center East and Trinity Medical Center West. Combined they have some 470 beds and offer patients emergency and general medical diagnostic and surgical services as well as specialty care in fields including rehabilitation skilled nursing and women's health services. Hospital specialty units also include the Tony Teramana Cancer Center a sleep center and a heart center. Trinity Health's outpatient facilities include an imaging center a school of nursing and community health clinics. The not-for-profit health system is sponsored by Tri-State Health Services and Franciscan Services organizations.

Strategy

Trinity Health System works to better serve its customers by enhancing its facilities and technologies. For instance it added a new breast MRI scanning systems in 2011 as well as a new PICC (peripherally inserted central catheter) system. In addition Trinity Health is forming affiliations with area medical practitioner groups to foster collaboration and information sharing in the region. As part of this move it took control of Mercy Hospital and Medical Center in 2012.

EXECUTIVES

Director Marketing and Public Relations, Keith Murdock
President and CEO, Fred B. Brower
Auditors: Ernst&YoungLLP

LOCATIONS

HQ: TRINITY HEALTH SYSTEM
380 SUMMIT AVE, STEUBENVILLE, OH 43952-2667
Phone: 740-264-8000
Web: WWW.TRINITYHEALTH.COM

PRODUCTS/OPERATIONS

Selected Ohio Facilities

Physician Offices (Steubenville)
Ross Park Pharmacies - adjacent to Trinity West (Steubenville OH)
Tony Teramana Cancer Center (Steubenville)
Trinity Endoscopy Center (Steubenville)
Trinity ExpressCare (Steubenville)
Trinity Food Service (Steubenville)
Trinity Medical Center West (Steubenville)
Trinity Medical Center East (Steubenville)
Trinity Outpatient Center at Toronto (Toronto)
Trinity Professional Group (family physicians in Steubenville Toronto and Follansbee)
Trinity School of Nursing (Steubenville)
Trinity Women's Health Services (Steubenville)
Trinity Work Care (Occupational Health Services Steubenville)

COMPETITORS

Akron Children' s Hospital
Akron General Health System
Aultman Health Foundation
Heritage Valley Health
Jefferson Regional Medical Center of Pennsylvania
Mercy Medical Center (OH)
OhioHealth
St. Clair Health
Summa Health System
UPMC
University Hospitals Health System

HISTORICAL FINANCIALS

Company Type: Private

Income Statement FYE: December 31

	REVENUE ($ mil.)	NET INCOME ($ mil.)	NET PROFIT MARGIN	EMPLOYEES
12/09	178	21	12.2%	1,646
12/07	152	(0)	—	—
12/06	153	8	5.8%	—
12/05	0	0	—	—
Annual Growth	—	—	—	—

2009 Year-End Financials

Debt ratio: —
Return on equity: 12.20%
Cash ($ mil.): 8
Current ratio: 1.60
Long-term debt ($ mil.): —
Dividends
Yield: —
Payout: —
Market value ($ mil.): —

TRINITY HOSPITAL HOLDING COMPANY

LOCATIONS

HQ: TRINITY HOSPITAL HOLDING COMPANY
380 SUMMIT AVE, STEUBENVILLE, OH 439522667
Phone: 7402648000
Web: WWW.TRINITYHEALTH.COM

HISTORICAL FINANCIALS

Company Type: Private

Income Statement FYE: December 31

	REVENUE ($ mil.)	NET INCOME ($ mil.)	NET PROFIT MARGIN	EMPLOYEES
12/13	206	14	7.1%	1,640
12/12	200	10	5.4%	—
12/11	183	2	1.3%	—
12/10	186	0	—	—
Annual Growth	3.5%	—	—	—

2013 Year-End Financials

Debt ratio: —
Return on equity: 7.10%
Cash ($ mil.): 6
Current ratio: 1.40
Long-term debt ($ mil.): —
Dividends
Yield: —
Payout: —
Market value ($ mil.): —

TRINITY MOTHER FRANCES HEALTH SYSTEM FOUNDATION

Trinity Mother Frances Health System Foundation (dba Trinity Mother Frances Hospitals and Clinics) has a complicated name but a simple mission: to improve patient health. Consisting of three general hospitals several specialist facilities and a large physicians' group Trinity Mother Frances serves northeastern Texas. Its largest acute-care facility is Mother Frances Hospital-Tyler with more than 400 beds offering comprehensive medical surgical trauma and cardiovascular care. Two smaller hospitals in Jacksonville and Winnsboro provide emergency diagnostic surgery and select specialty services. The Trinity Clinic is a multi-specialty physician group that includes 300 doctors in 36 community clinics.

Operations

Trinity Mother Frances Hospitals and Clinics' specialty facilities include the freestanding Trinity Mother Frances Rehabilitation Hospital in Tyler which has 75 beds and is operated through a joint venture with HealthSouth. It also operates the Tyler ContinueCARE Hospital a long-term acute care hospital located within the Mother Frances Hospital-Tyler as well as several urgent care centers.

Strategy

In 2010 the network added the 35-bed Mother Frances Hospital-Winnsboro facility when it took over control of the Texas Health Presbyterian Hospital Winnsboro from Texas Health Resources. The transfer was made to align the Winnsboro hospital with the main Tyler facility where the majority of specialized cases from Winnsboro were already being transferred.

The network also added a freestanding 72-bed cardiac facility the Louis and Peaches Owen Heart Hospital in Tyler. The first phase of the center was added to the existing Mother Frances Hospital-Tyler facilities in 2010; the second stage is a six-story freestanding tower adjacent to the Tyler hospital. Construction on the tower started in early 2011 and was completed by the end of 2012.

Additionally Trinity Mother Frances Hospitals and Clinics is investing in information technology initiatives. It began installing electronic health record (EHR) systems at its facilities during 2012 as part of the US government's health care improvement initiatives.

Company Background

Trinity Mother Frances Hospitals and Clinics was established by the 1995 merger of Mother Frances Hospital and the Trinity Clinic both founded in the 1930s.

EXECUTIVES

President, J. Lindsey Bradley Jr.
President and Chief Medical Officer, David K. Teegarden
Director Trauma/Surgical Critical Care, Luis G. Fernandez, age 55
Vice President Operations, Chris Glenney
Medical Director Information, Tom Hargrove
EVP and COO, Ray Thompson
CEO Mother Franes Hospital - Tyler, Laura Owen
VP Regional Business Development, John Webb
VP Marketing, Mary Peterson
Public Information Officer, John Moore
President and Chief Medical Officer TMF; President Trinity Clinic, Steven P. Keuer
VP and CIO, Lee Portwood
Interim Chief Nursing Officer, Bobbie Ogg
Director of Operations, Marianna Svesko
EVP; Chief of Anesthesia Trinity Clinic, Gifford Eckhout
CEO Mother Frances Hospital - Jacksonville, Tom Cammack
CEO Mother Frances Hospital - Winnsboro, Janet Coates
CEO Louis and Peaches Owen Heart Hospital, John McGreevy
CEO ContinueCARE Hospital, Stephanie Hyde
CEO Trinity Mother Frances Rehabilitation Hospital, Sharla Anderson
VP and CIO, Jeff Pearson
Auditors: BKDLLP

LOCATIONS

HQ: TRINITY MOTHER FRANCES HEALTH SYSTEM FOUNDATION
800 E DAWSON ST, TYLER, TX 75701-2036
Phone: 903-531-5057
Web: WWW.TMFHS.ORG

PRODUCTS/OPERATIONS

Selected Locations

DirectCARE (urgent care multiple sites)
Louis and Peaches Owen Heart Hospital Tyler
Mother Frances Hospital-Jacksonville
Mother Frances Hospital-Tyler
Mother Frances Hospital-Winnsboro
Trinity Clinics (physician practices multiple sites)
Trinity Mother Frances Rehabilitation Hospital-Tyler
Tyler ContinueCARE Hospital

Selected Services

Anesthesiology
Audiology
Bariatric Surgery Center
Cancer
Cardiac Services
Cardiothoracic Surgery
Critical Care Intensivists
Ear Nose & Throat
Emergency Medicine
Endocrinology
Gastroenterology Hepatology and Endoscopy
Family Medicine
General Surgeons
Genetics
Hospitalists
Imaging Radiology Mammography
Internal Medicine
Neonatology
Neuroscience Institute
Obstetrics & Gynecology
Occupational Medicine - Health At Work
Ophthalmology Optometry & Optical Services
Orthopedics
Pain Medicine
Pediatrics
Physical Medicine and Rehabilitation
Plastic Surgery
Podiatry
Psychiatry
Rehabilitation Hospital
Rheumatology
Sleep Medicine
Sports Medicine
Surgery Services
Trauma Services
Urgent Care
Urology Institute & Continence Center
Vascular Institute
Women & Children
WoundCARE

COMPETITORS

Baylor Health
Community Health Systems
East Texas Medical Center Regional Healthcare
Essent Healthcare
Good Shepherd Health System
HCA
Hunt Memorial
Memorial Health System of East Texas
Parkland Health & Hospital System
Southwestern Medical Center
Tenet Healthcare
The Methodist Health System
United Surgical Partners
Wadley Regional Medical Center
Woodland Heights Medical Center

HISTORICAL FINANCIALS

Company Type: Private

Income Statement

FYE: June 30

	REVENUE ($ mil.)	NET INCOME ($ mil.)	NET PROFIT MARGIN	EMPLOYEES
06/10	603	19	3.3%	3,551
06/09	562	(27)	—	—
06/09	1,233	0	—	—
Annual Growth	—4465455.4%		—	—

2010 Year-End Financials

Debt ratio: ——
Return on equity: 3.30%
Cash ($ mil.): 48
Current ratio: 1.30
Long-term debt ($ mil.): —

Dividends
Yield: —
Payout: —
Market value ($ mil.): —

TRINITY UNIVERSITY

EXECUTIVES

VP Academic Affairs, Michael Fischer
VP Information Resources and Administrative Affairs, Charles White
VP Fiscal Affairs, Craig McCoy
VP Student Affairs, Gage E. Paine
Assistant VP University Communications, Sharon Jones Schweitzer
VP Advancement, Marc Raney
Chair Department of Business Administration, Dan Walz
Director Athletics, Bob King
Assistant VP Fiscal Affairs and Director Human Resources, Pamela (Pam) Johnston
Employment/Benefits Administrator, Jennifer Gilmore Adamo
Electronic Access and Serials Acquisition Librarian, Clinton Chamberlain
University Librarian, Diane Graves
Director Purchasing, Cynthia Lara
VP Student Affairs, Felicia J. Lee
University Registrar, Alfred Rodriguez
Director Alumni Relations, Mary Kay Cooper
Electronic Access and Serials Acquisition Librarian, Katy Ginanni
President, Dennis A. Ahlburg

LOCATIONS

HQ: TRINITY UNIVERSITY
1 TRINITY PL, SAN ANTONIO, TX 782127200
Phone: 2109997011
Web: WWW.WEB.TRINITY.EDU

COMPETITORS

Baylor University
Our Lady of the Lake University
SMU
Southwestern University
St. Edward' s
Stephen F. Austin University
Texas A&M
Texas Tech
University of Texas System

HISTORICAL FINANCIALS

Company Type: Private

Income Statement FYE: May 31

	REVENUE ($ mil.)	NET INCOME ($ mil.)	NET PROFIT MARGIN	EMPLOYEES
05/13	114	107	93.7%	700
05/12	116	(40)	—	—
05/11	179	44	25.0%	—
05/10	155	0	—	—
Annual Growth	(9.6%)	—	—	—

2013 Year-End Financials

Debt ratio: —
Return on equity: 93.70%
Cash ($ mil.): 119
Current ratio: —
Long-term debt ($ mil.): —

Dividends
Yield: —
Payout: —
Market value ($ mil.): —

TRIPPE MANUFACTURING COMPANY

Trippe sells protection from power trips. Doing business as Tripp Lite the company makes over 2500 products used to protect power and connect electronic equipment. Its surge suppressors guard against surges spikes and over-voltages that can damage personal computers and other electronic equipment. Its uninterruptible power supply (UPS) systems provide battery backup power while its inverters are used to power laptops and other products when other power sources are not available. Tripp Lite products also include power strips cables and connectors laptop accessories and power-management software.

Geographic Reach

The privately held company sells its wares in more than 60 countries worldwide.

Sales and Marketing

In addition to consumer and home office products Tripp Lite supplies equipment for use in environments where access to reliable power can be critical such as health care and industrial facilities. Other markets the company targets include telecommunications networking construction maintenance government education and global enterprises.

Tripp Light's products are sold through authorized distributors including Tech Data Ingram Micro D&H and SYNNEX. They are also sold through reseller partners and exporters such as Avnet Super Technologies and Intcomex Miami.

Strategy

Tripp Light aims to increase its market share in the Middle East India Russia and other emerging markets by partnering with local distributors and through installations at major organizations including HP Cisco and McDonald's.

It also maintains its growth by introducing new products within its vast portfolio. In 2013 it launched three new power strips under the Power It! brand and five new surge suppressors under the Protect It! brand.

Company Background

Founded in 1922 Trippe Manufacturing initially made automotive headlights. The company introduced the first UPS system designed for personal computers in the 1980s.

EXECUTIVES

VP Sales and Marketing, Priscilla Galgan
Marketing Manager de, Christy Prosapio
Director Business Development Europe the Middle East and Africa, Vipin Sharma
VP Electrical and Industrial Sales, Jim Folk
Director Product Management, David Slotten
Director Connectivity Marketing, David Posner

LOCATIONS

HQ: TRIPPE MANUFACTURING COMPANY
1111 W 35TH ST, CHICAGO, IL 60609-1404
Phone: 773-869-1111
Web: WWW.TRIPPLITE.COM

PRODUCTS/OPERATIONS

Selected Products

Cables and Connectivity
- Audio/video
- FireWire
- Network
- SCSI cabling
- Splitters
- Switches
- USB connectors

Inverters
- Battery chargers
- DC/AC

Keyspan
- Remotes
- VoIP phones
- USB adapters and device servers

Laptop accessories
- Cases and backpacks
- Coolers and stands
- Input devices
- Power plugs

Line Conditioners
Surge Suppressors
UPS Systems
- Extended run
- Hardwired
- Industrial grade
- Medical grade
- Mini desktop
- Rackmount
- Tower
- Under-monitor

Other Products
- Cooling products
- Isolation transformers
- Power management tools (software)
- Rack enclosures and cabinets

COMPETITORS

Acme Electric
Active Power
Beacon Power
Belkin
C&D Technologies
Cooper B-Line
EIS
Emerson Electric
General Devices
Liebert Corporation
Monster Cable
Power-One
SL Industries
SPX
Schneider Electric
Transistor Devices

HISTORICAL FINANCIALS

Company Type: Private

Income Statement FYE: December 31

	REVENUE ($ mil.)	NET INCOME ($ mil.)	NET PROFIT MARGIN	EMPLOYEES
12/12	350	0	—	450
12/11	300	0	—	—
12/08	0	0	—	—
12/07	0	0	—	—
Annual Growth	—	—	—	—

TROUT-BLUE CHELAN-MAGI INC.

EXECUTIVES

Assistant General Manager, Jim Divis
CEO and General Manager, Reggie Collins
CFO, Todd Kamers
CEO Chelan Fresh Marketing, Steve Terry
Human Resources Director, Alissa Senyitko

LOCATIONS

HQ: TROUT-BLUE CHELAN-MAGI INC.
8 HOWSER RD, CHELAN, WA 988169590
Phone: 5096822591

PRODUCTS/OPERATIONS

Selected Member/Growers

Blue Chelan Inc.
Gebbers Farms
Mutual Apple Growers Inc. (MAGI)
Trout Incorporated
Trout-Blue Chelan Inc.
Trout-Blue Chelan-Magi Inc. Chelan Fruit

COMPETITORS

Auvil Fruit
Cherry Central Cooperative Inc.
Chiquita Brands
Dole Food
Fresh Del Monte Produce
Gold Digger Apples
Graceland Fruit
Greenridge Fruit
Hudson River Fruit
Jack Brown Produce
Knouse Foods
Shoreline Fruit
Tree Top

HISTORICAL FINANCIALS

Company Type: Private

Income Statement FYE: August 31

	REVENUE ($ mil.)	NET INCOME ($ mil.)	NET PROFIT MARGIN	EMPLOYEES
08/14	156	4	2.6%	675
08/13	180	5	2.8%	—
08/12	149	5	3.4%	—
08/11	138	0	—	—
Annual Growth	4.2%	—	—	—

2014 Year-End Financials

Debt ratio: —
Return on equity: 2.60%
Cash ($ mil.): 12
Current ratio: 0.30
Long-term debt ($ mil.): —

Dividends
Yield: —
Payout: —
Market value ($ mil.): —

TROY UNIVERSITY

Troy University is not the topic of a Homeric poem but you'd probably find a Helen enrolled there. The school is a public institution comprised of a network of campuses throughout Alabama and worldwide. The network includes 60 campuses in some 7 US states and four other countries. Troy University has a total student enrollment of about 22000 and offers degrees in arts and sciences business communications and fine arts education and health and human services. The school also operates the Confucius Institute to promote understanding of Chinese language and culture.

Geographic Reach

Troy University has four campuses in Alabama and satellite locations in Florida Georgia North California South Carolina Tennessee Texas and Virginia as well as in Japan Korea Malaysia and Vietnam.

Operations

The university offers 110 undergraduate majors and minors 22 master's degree programs and one doctoral program as well as ROTC programs and research opportunities.

Company Background

Troy University was founded in 1887 by the Alabama Legislature as the State Normal School an institution to train teachers for Alabama's schools. The Troy University System was formed in 1982.

EXECUTIVES

Chancellor, Jack Hawkins Jr.
Executive Vice Chancellor and Provost, Ed D. Roach
Director Athletics, Stephen M. (Steve) Dennis
Senior Vice Chancellor Finance and Business Affairs, James M. Bookout
Controller, Bryan Helms
Senior Director Human Resources, Lee Vardaman
Director Information Technology, Greg Price
Dean University Libraries, Henry R. Stewart
Dean Student Services Dothan Campus, Robert G. (Bob) Willis
Vice Chancellor Phenix City Campus, Curtis H. Pitts
Director Tax Services, Kenny Marcum
Regional Development Director, Kathy Ninas
Director Alumni Affairs, Faith West Ward
Senior Vice Chancellor Advancement and External Relations, John W. Schmidt
Vice Chancellor Global Campus, Earl Ingram
Director Purchasing and Inventory Control, Ursula Bryant
Associate Vice Chancellor Marketing and Communications, Sandra Gouge
Dean First Year Studies, Eleanor Lee
Vice Chancellor Dothan Campus, Don Jeffrey
Secretary, Meredith Welch
Administrative Assistant, Donna Gilliand

LOCATIONS

HQ: TROY UNIVERSITY
ADAMS ADM RM 241, TROY, AL 36082-0001
Phone: 334-670-3108
Web: WWW.TROY.EDU

COMPETITORS

Auburn University
Birmingham-Southern College
Miles College
Spring Hill College
University of Alabama
University of Alabama at Birmingham
University of Mobile
University of South Alabama

HISTORICAL FINANCIALS

Company Type: Private

Income Statement FYE: September 30

	REVENUE ($ mil.)	NET INCOME ($ mil.)	NET PROFIT MARGIN	EMPLOYEES
09/08	156	29	18.6%	3,000
09/07*	164	21	12.8%	—
12/06	2,023	0	—	—
Annual Growth		—35074.6%	—	—

*Fiscal year change

2008 Year-End Financials

Debt ratio: —
Return on equity: 18.60%
Cash ($ mil.): 47
Current ratio: 1.70
Long-term debt ($ mil.): —
Dividends
Yield: —
Payout: —
Market value ($ mil.): —

TRUE VALUE COMPANY

To survive against home improvement giants such as The Home Depot and Lowe's True Value (formerly TruServ) is relying on the true value of service. Formed by the 1997 merger of Cotter & Company (which supplied the True Value chain) and ServiStar Coast to Coast the retailer-owned hardware cooperative serves some 4600 retail outlets in 50-plus countries. Stores offer home improvement and garden supplies as well as appliances housewares sporting goods and pet food. In addition to the flagship True Value banner members operate under the names of Taylor Rental Grand Rental Station Home & Garden Showplace and Induserve Supply among others. True Value also manufactures its own brand of paints.

HISTORY

Noting that hardware retailers had begun to form wholesale cooperatives to lower costs John Cotter a traveling hardware salesman and associate Ed Lanctot started pitching the wholesale co-op idea in 1947 to small-town and suburban hardware retailers and by early 1948 they had enrolled 25 merchants for $1500 each. Cotter became chairman of the new firm Cotter & Company.

The co-op created the Value & Service (V&S) store trademark in 1951 to emphasize the advantages of an independent hardware store. Acquisitions included the 1963 purchase of Chicago-based wholesaler Hibbard Spencer Bartlett giving Cotter 400 new members and the well-known True Value trademark which soon replaced V&S signs. Four years later Cotter broadened its focus by buying the General Paint & Chemical Company (Tru-Test paint). The V&S name was revived in 1972 for a five-and-dime store co-op V&S Variety Stores.

In 1989 Cotter died and Lanctot retired. (Lanctot died in October 2003.) By 1989 there were almost 7000 True Value Stores. Cotter moved into Canada in 1992 by acquiring hardware distributor and store operator Macleod-Stedman (275 outlets).

Juggling variety-store and hardware merchandise and delivering very small amounts of merchandise to a lukewarm co-op membership did not allow for economies of scale so in 1995 the company quit its manufacturing operations and its US variety stores (though it still serves variety stores in Canada operating as C&S Choices) tightened membership requirements and introduced new services.

Two years later Cotter formed TruServ by merging with hardware wholesaler ServiStar Coast to Coast. ServiStar had its origins in the nation's first hardware co-op American Hardware Supply which was founded in Pittsburgh in 1910 by M. R. Porter John Howe and E. S. Corlett. By 1988 the year it changed its name to ServiStar the co-op topped $1 billion in sales.

ServiStar expanded in the upper Midwest and on the West Coast in 1990 when it acquired the assets of the Coast to Coast chain (founded in 1928 as a franchise hardware store in Minneapolis); ServiStar brought Coast to Coast out of bankruptcy two years later making it a co-op. Merging its 1992 acquisition of Taylor Rental Center with its Grand Rental Station stores in 1993 made ServiStar the #1 general rental chain. In 1996 it consolidated Coast to Coast's operations into its own and changed its name to ServiStar Coast to Coast.

President Don Hoye became CEO of the company in 1999. That year TruServ slashed 1000 jobs and declared it would convert all its hardware store chains to the True Value banner. But TruServ lost $131 million in 1999 over bookkeeping gaffes and co-op members received no dividends. Of 2800 ServiStar dealers only 1900 raised the True Value flag. Others either declined to switch or were never offered the change because other True Value stores already shared their market area. In addition stores began deserting the co-op because of inventory and other problems. In late 2000 the company sold its lumber and building materials business.

As competition continued to increase in 2001 the company was facing falling sales lawsuits from shareholders and accusations by retailers of unfair practices intended to pressure them into adopting the cooperative's flagship True Value banner. TruServ also had to confront a $200 million loan default. It made cuts in its corporate staff and divested its Canadian interests. In July 2001 Hoye resigned. The company's CFO and COO Pamela Forbes Lieberman was named the new CEO that November.

In April 2002 the company reported a net loss of $50.7 million during 2001 which it attributed to restructuring charges inventory write-downs and finance fees. Also that month the company announced that it had received $200 million in long-term financing. TruServ under SEC investigation for alleged inventory accounting and other internal-control problems was one of several companies that failed in August 2002 to meet a government requirement to swear by their past financial results.

In January 2003 TruServ received about $125 million in financing from investment firm W. P. Carey & Co. in a sale-leaseback deal on seven of TruServ's distribution centers. In March TruServ settled the SEC's allegations without admitting or denying them and agreed to follow measures intended to ensure compliance with securities laws.

Lieberman resigned in November 2004. Director Thomas Hanemann was named interim CEO. TruServ changed its name to True Value in January 2005. That June Hanemann turned over the reins to Sears veteran Lyle Heidemann who joined True Value as its new president and CEO. In December the company sold its oil-based paint manufacturing operation in Chicago to Blackhawk/Halsted for about $10 million.

In 2007 True Value added more than 100 new stores in the US and experienced modest growth overseas. Also that year the company launched its new store format called Destination TrueValue.

The year 2008 marked the first time in over a decade that revenue from new stores exceeded lost revenue from terminated stores.

EXECUTIVES

President CEO and Director, Lyle G. Heidemann, age 69, $415,016 total compensation
Senior Vice President Marketing and Chief Customer Officer, Blake A. Fohl, age 54
Senior Vice President Chief Financial Officer, David A. (Dave) Shadduck, $317,750 total compensation
VP and Corporate Treasurer, Barbara L. Wagner
Senior Vice President General Counsel Secretary, Cathy C. Anderson, $312,250 total compensation
SVP and Chief Merchandising Officer, Michael Clark
Director; CEO True Value Hardware House Annapolis MD, Kenneth A. Niefeld, age 70
Director; CEO Krueger's True Value Neenah Wis., Brian A. Webb
VP Specialty Businesses, Eric Lane
Vice President Retail Growth, Mark Flowers
VP Logistics, Donald J. (Don) Deegan
SVP Retail Operations, Stephen Poplawski
VP and CIO, Rosalee Hermens
Chairman; CEO Campbell's True Value Madison Maine, Brent A. Burger

Market Exhibitor Information Contact, Maureen Feck
Vice President Logistics, Don Deegan
Senior Vice President Retail Operations, Steve Poplawski
President CEO and Director, Lyle G. Heidemann, age 69
Director, Gregory P. Josefowicz, age 60
Director, Cheryl A. Bachelder, age 57
Director; CEO True Value Hardware House Annapolis MD, Kenneth A. Niefeld, age 70
Director; CEO Krueger's True Value Neenah Wis., Brian A. Webb
Director, Richard E. George Jr., age 73
Director, M. Shan Atkins, age 57
Director; CEO Campbell's True Value Madison Maine, Brent A. Burger
Auditors: PricewaterhouseCoopersLLP

LOCATIONS

HQ: TRUE VALUE COMPANY
8600 W BRYN MAWR AVE 100S, CHICAGO, IL 606313505
Phone: 7736955000
Web: WWW.TRUEVALUE.COM

PRODUCTS/OPERATIONS

2012 Sales

	$ mil.	% of total
Hardware	1,320	94
Manufacturing &distribution	78	6
Total	**1,399**	**100**

Selected Operations

Grand Rental Station (general rental)
Home & Garden Showplace (nursery and giftware)
Induserve Supply (commercial and industrial)
Party Central (parties and corporate events)
Taylor Rental (general rental)
True Value (hardware)

COMPETITORS

84 Lumber	Menard
Ace Hardware	Northern Tool
Akzo Nobel	Orgill
Benjamin Moore	Sears
Do it Best	Sherwin-Williams
Fastenal	Stock Building Supply
Hertz	Sutherland Lumber
Home Depot	United Rentals
Kmart	Valspar
Lowe' s	Wal-Mart
McCoy Corp.	

HISTORICAL FINANCIALS

Company Type: Private

Income Statement FYE: December 28

	REVENUE ($ mil.)	NET INCOME ($ mil.)	NET PROFIT MARGIN	EMPLOYEES
12/13	1,411	55	3.9%	3,000
12/12	1,399	74	5.4%	—
12/11*	1,864	60	3.2%	—
01/11	1,804	0	—	—
Annual Growth	(7.9%)	—	—	—

*Fiscal year change

2013 Year-End Financials

Debt ratio: —
Return on equity: 3.90%
Cash ($ mil.): 4
Current ratio: 0.50
Long-term debt ($ mil.): —
Dividends
Yield: —
Payout: —
Market value ($ mil.): —

TRUMAN ARNOLD COMPANIES

EXECUTIVES

Chairman, Truman Arnold
President and CEO, Gregory A. (Greg) Arnold
SVP and CFO, Steve McMillen
VP and CIO, Michael Davis
VP Terminal Services (TAC Energy), Benny Webb
Director Marketing, David Edwards

LOCATIONS

HQ: TRUMAN ARNOLD COMPANIES
701 S ROBISON RD, TEXARKANA, TX 755016747
Phone: 9037943835
Web: WWW.TACENERGY.COM

COMPETITORS

Atlantic Aviation	SMF Energy
Getty Petroleum Marketing	Signature Flight
Gulf Oil	Sun Coast Resources
Million Air	Warren Equities

HISTORICAL FINANCIALS

Company Type: Private

Income Statement FYE: September 30

	REVENUE ($ mil.)	NET INCOME ($ mil.)	NET PROFIT MARGIN	EMPLOYEES
09/14	2,259	11	0.5%	550
09/13	2,172	54	2.5%	—
09/12	2,471	11	0.4%	—
Annual Growth	(4.4%)	3.4%	—	—

2014 Year-End Financials

Debt ratio: —
Return on equity: 0.50%
Cash ($ mil.): 5
Current ratio: 0.80
Long-term debt ($ mil.): —
Dividends
Yield: —
Payout: —
Market value ($ mil.): —

TRUMAN MEDICAL CENTER INCORPORATED

If you're miserable in Missouri Truman Medical Center (TMC) can offer TLC and health care. TMC provides primary and mental health care at two not-for-profit hospitals in the Kansas City (Missouri) area with a combined total of about 600 beds. Its Hospital Hill runs one of the busiest emergency rooms in Kansas City and is known for treatments related to asthma diabetes obstetrics ophthalmology weight management and women's health. TMC Lakewood is a leading academic medical center providing a range of health care services to the greater Kansas City metropolitan area including uninsured patients.

Operations

The hospital system has a combined capacity of more than 600 beds including 102 inpatient mental health beds and an additional 188 long-term care beds. TMC admits more than 22000 patients and handles more than 329000 medical outpatient visits and more than 226000 mental health visits annually. It also treats more than 104000 emergency room patients every year.

Truman Medical Center Hospital Hill provides an array of acute care and outpatient services. In addition to Emergency Medicine and Trauma TMC Hospital Hill is also noted for treatments of asthma and diabetes and for providing obstetrics ophthalmology weight management and women's health programs.

TMC Lakewood is home to the University of Missouri Kansas City School of Medicine Community and Family Medicine Residency program.

Truman Medical Centers Behavioral Health is a leader in the treatment of mental health and substance abuse treatment. It serves more than 17000 patients a year and provides a comprehensive array of mental health and substance abuse treatment to persons living in the Kansas City Missouri metropolitan area.

EXECUTIVES

Executive Director TMC Charitable Foundation and VP Strategic Business Development, James D. Dawson
President Chief Executive Officer, John W. Bluford III
Chief Financial Officer, Allen (Al) Johnson
VP Human Resources, Valerie Fulbright
Chief Medical Officer Truman Medical Centers Executive Medical Director University Physician Associates and Associate Dean for TMC Programs UMKC School of Medicine, Mark T. Steele
Chief Operating Officer, Marsha Lee Morgan
VP Health Policy and Government Relations, Gerard J. Grimaldi
COO TMC Lakewood, Harold Siglar
VP Public Relations and Marketing, Vicki Smith
VP Corporate Support Services and Safety Compliance, Marla Bernard
Sr. Vice President ? Strategy Business Development and Performance Integration Chief Information Officer, Mitzi Cardenas
Service Integration Leader, Suzanne Haug
Corporate Quality Medical Director, Shauna R. Roberts
Director Audit and Compliance, Barbara Zubeck
General Counsel, William H. Colby
Vice President Strategy and Human Resources in the Kansas City market, Kaiser Permanente
Associate Chairman, Peter B. Greenspan
Chief Nursing Officer, Lynette Wheeler
Chief Operating Officer Truman Medical Center Lakewood, Charlie Shields
Vice President, Jerre Wiggans
Vice President Professional, Lynda Donegan
Vice President Employee Enrichment, Marcos DeLeon

LOCATIONS

HQ: TRUMAN MEDICAL CENTER INCORPORATED
2301 HOLMES ST, KANSAS CITY, MO 64108-2677
Phone: 816-404-1000
Web: WWW.TRUMED.ORG

PRODUCTS/OPERATIONS

Truman Medical Center Hospital Hill
Asthma Center
The Birthplace
Cardiovascular Center
Chiropractic Services KC CORE
Dental Maxillofacial Surgery
Diabetes Center
Emergency Care
Eye Clinic
Eye Foundation
GI Gastrointe
Hospital Hill Medical Pavilion
Infectious Disease Clinic
Oncology
Orthopaedics
Pulmonary Fibrosis
Radiology Services
Rehabilitation Services
Sickle Cell Disease Center

Sleep Center
Trauma Services
TruMed Clinic
Weight Management
Women's Care Breast Center
Women's Health Services
TMC Lakewood
Family Medicine Center
Lakewood Family Birthplace
Chiropractic Services
Counseling Services Lakewood
Dental Services
Dental Services Elks Mobile
GI Gastrointe
Emergency Medicine
Eye Care Center
Lakewood Medical Pavilion
Longterm Care Center
Medical Detox
Orthopaedic Services
Outpatient Surgery Center
Podiatry
Rehabilitation Services
Sports Medicine
Women's Health Services

COMPETITORS

Ascension Health
Children' s Mercy Hospital
CoxHealth
Saint Luke' s Health System
Shawnee Mission Medical Center
University of Kansas Medical Center
Via Christi Health System

HISTORICAL FINANCIALS

Company Type: Private

Income Statement FYE: June 30

	REVENUE ($ mil.)	NET INCOME ($ mil.)	NET PROFIT MARGIN	EMPLOYEES
06/10	439	5	1.2%	3,000
06/09	424	16	3.8%	—
06/08	4	1	36.2%	—
06/07	357	(11)	—	—
Annual Growth	7.1%	—	—	—

2010 Year-End Financials

Debt ratio: —
Return on equity: 1.20%
Cash ($ mil.): 0
Current ratio: 0.40
Long-term debt ($ mil.): —
Dividends
Yield: —
Payout: —
Market value ($ mil.): —

TRUSTEES OF BOSTON COLLEGE

Students at Boston College (BC) get both academic excellence and the Red Sox. Located six miles from downtown Boston the university enrolls more than 14600 full- and part-time students (about a third of whom are graduate students) from every state in the US and 80 countries. It has a student-teacher ratio of 14:1. Founded in 1863 BC offers degrees in more than 55 fields of study through its schools and colleges on four campuses. The university also has more than 20 research centers including the Institute for Scientific Research and the Center for International Higher Education. BC is one of the oldest Jesuit Catholic universities in the nation and has the largest Jesuit community in the world.

About 70% of its undergraduate student body are self-identified as Catholic.

The university with campuses in Brighton Chestnut Hill Dover and Newton Massachusetts is also home to more than 20 centers and institutes designated for research and teaching. Research opportunities including participation in faculty research projects exist for both undergraduate and graduate students.

BC has enjoyed steady growth from voluntary giving by its alumni. Its endowment has grown to almost $2 billion placing it among the top 40 in the US.

Boston College's strategic plan includes adding 100 new faculty positions expanding research by faculty and graduate students increasing student financial aid to more than $128 million annually and extending undergraduate opportunities in international study internships and student formation.

During its first seven decades BC was an exclusively undergraduate institution that served sons of the Irish working class. Its liberal arts emphasis was on the Greek and Latin classics English and modern languages and philosophy and religion. Development into the college it is today did not begin until the 1920s when the Graduate School of Arts and Sciences the Law School and the Evening College (known today as the James A. Woods S.J. College of Advancing Studies) were inaugurated. All classes became co-educational in the 1970s and today BC has a fairly equal split among male and female students.

EXECUTIVES

Vp For Human Resources, Leo V Sullivan
Senior Vice President For University, Jim Husson
Vp University Mission And Ministry, Joseph A Appleyard
Vice President Human Resource, John R Burke
Chancellor, J. Donald Monan
Provost and Dean of Faculties, Cutberto (Bert) Garza
Vice Provost Faculties, Patricia DeLeeuw
Dean Carroll School of Management, Andrew C. Boynton
Dean Lynch School of Education, Joseph M. O'Keefe
Dean School of Nursing, Barbara Hazard
Co-Director Center on Aging and Work, Michael A. Smyer
Dean Graduate School of Social Work, Alberto Godenzi
University Librarian, Jerome Yavarkovsky
Director Bookstore, Thomas McKenna
Executive Vice President Boston College, Patrick J. Keating
Chairman Finance Carroll School of Management, Hassan Tehranian
VP Finance and Treasurer, Peter C. McKenzie
Director Weston Observatory, John E. Ebel
Associate VP Applications and Systems Services, Michael Bourque
Chairman Marketing Carroll School of Management, Gerald Smith
Vice Provost Research, Kevin Bedell
Executive Vice President John Hancock Financial Services, Wayne A. Budd
Executive Vice President Desai Capital Management, Frank J. Pados
Chairman and CEO, John Murphy
Executive Vice President Boston Red So, John S. Buckley
Senior Vice President, James McIntyre
Vp Information Technology, Marian Moore
Vice President, Kevin Duffy
Vice President And University Secretary, Terrence P Devino
Asst To Vice President Facilities Mgmt, Joseph Comerford
Vice President Training, Gail Wiegner
Vice President Information Technology, Mark Ben
Vp Facilities Mgmt, Daniel Bourque
Vice President Cptl Projects Managem, Mary Nardone
Vice President, Judith Speed
Department Chair, Richard W Tresch
Vice President, John Westman
Vp Governmental/cmty Affs, Thomas J Keady
Jebbit Vice President Of Business, Jonathan Lacoste
Assoc Vp Info Tech, Mary Corcoran
Assoc Vp Alumni Assoc, John Feudo
Vice President, Daniel Arroyo
Vice President Digital, Victor Lee
Vp Information Technology, Mike Bourque
Associate Vice President For Alumni Relations, Joy Moore
Student Office Assistant For Senior Vice President Of University Advancement, Elizabeth Zappala
Assistant Vice President Planning And Budget, Steven Sass
Vice President For Student Affairs, Barbara Jones
Associate Vice President For Advancement Operations And Planning, Avner Ash
VP Finance and Treasurer, Peter C. McKenzie
Chairman and CEO, John Murphy
Board Member, Maria E Luddy
Executive Secretary Treasurer, Alan J Reinerman
Secretary, Alan Lawson
Executive Board Member, Lawrence Fuerst
Associate Treasurer, Paul P Haran
Board Member, James Peiser
Auditors: PricewaterhouseCoopersLLP

LOCATIONS

HQ: TRUSTEES OF BOSTON COLLEGE
140 COMMONWEALTH AVE, CHESTNUT HILL, MA 02467-3800
Phone: 617-552-8000
Web: WWW.BC.EDU

PRODUCTS/OPERATIONS

Selected Colleges and Schools

Carolyn A. and Peter S. Lynch School of Education
College of Arts and Sciences
Graduate School of Arts and Sciences
Graduate School of Social Work
James A. Woods S.J. College of Advancing Studies
School of Law
School of Theology and Ministry
Wallace E. Carroll School of Management
William F. Connell School of Nursing

HISTORICAL FINANCIALS

Company Type: Private

Income Statement FYE: May 31

	REVENUE ($ mil.)	NET INCOME ($ mil.)	NET PROFIT MARGIN	EMPLOYEES
05/12	653	(76)	—	3,000
05/11	643	287	44.7%	—
05/10	628	177	28.2%	—
05/09	621	(318)	—	—
Annual Growth	1.7%	—	—	—

TRUSTEES OF THE ESTATE OF BERNICE PAUAHI BISHOP

Kamehameha Schools provides an education fit for a king ... or queen. The private charitable trust was founded and endowed by Princess Bernice Pauahi Bishop great granddaughter and last royal descendant of Kamehameha the Great. One of the largest independent schools in the US Kamehameha educates more than 5000 elementary middle school and high school students many of whom board at one of its three Hawaii campuses. In addition it operates some 30 preschools with a total enrollment of about 1500. Kamehameha Schools is also the largest private property owner in the state of Hawaii and uses the proceeds from its real estate operations to support its schools.

The Kamehameha School for Boys was established in 1887 followed by the Kamehameha School for Girls which opened in 1894. By 1955 the schools consolidated onto a 600-acre campus with views of Honolulu that span from Pearl Harbor to Diamond Head.

To this day Kamehameha Schools gives preferential admissions treatment to students of Hawaiian decent a long-standing policy it is fighting to preserve despite the controversy it creates. The schools have successfully fought off several lawsuits aimed at opening its doors to other ethnicities including a close decision by an appeals court in 2009.

EXECUTIVES

VP Campus Strategies, D. Rodney Chamberlain
Interim Head Community Outreach Education, Charlene Hoe
Head of Educational Support Services, Sylvia M. Hussey
Dean Extension Education Division, Juvenna Chang
Interim Vice President Chief Financial Officer, Ben Salazar
Auditors: KPMGLLP

LOCATIONS

HQ: TRUSTEES OF THE ESTATE OF BERNICE PAUAHI BISHOP
567 S KING ST STE 150, HONOLULU, HI 96813-3036
Phone: 808-523-6200
Web: WWW.KSBE.EDU

COMPETITORS

Edison Learning
Learning Care Group

HISTORICAL FINANCIALS

Company Type: Private

Income Statement FYE: June 30

	REVENUE ($ mil.)	NET INCOME ($ mil.)	NET PROFIT MARGIN	EMPLOYEES
06/11	524	159	30.5%	1,500
06/10	333	(21)	—	—
06/09	1	1	69.0%	—
06/08	1	1	69.0%	—
Annual Growth	554.0%	398.1%	—	—

2011 Year-End Financials

Debt ratio: —
Return on equity: 30.50%
Cash ($ mil.): 31
Current ratio: —
Long-term debt ($ mil.): —
Dividends
Yield: —
Payout: —
Market value ($ mil.): —

TRUSTEES OF TUFTS COLLEGE INC.

Tufts University wants to light up the minds of New England scholars. The school offers undergraduate and graduate degrees in areas such as education engineering psychology art English music and medicine. The university enrolls some 11000 students and has 1300 faculty members and it offers classes in 70 fields at three campuses in Massachusetts (Boston Medford/Somerville and Grafton). It also has an international campus in Talloires France. Tufts University's Fletcher School of Law and Diplomacy is the oldest continuous international relations graduate program in the country. The school is also home to New England's only Veterinary School.

Operations

Tufts University has a number of research programs at all three campuses including clinical studies in medical dental veterinary and nutritional fields. It also has research programs in areas such as biology engineering and technology many of which are funded through grants and fellowship funds.

Financial Performance

Tufts University has an endowment of about $1.1 billion.

Strategy

Tufts University is working to expand the resources its School of Medicine. In 2012 it moved to add a new medical research lab to study serious infectious diseases (such as tuberculosis) within the Biomedical Research and Public Health Building. It also expanded the Cummings School of Veterinary Medicine by adding a new clinic for the care and study of pets with obesity problems. The university also expands by adding new degree programs such as a doctorate in mamalian genetics in 2011.

Company Background

Tufts was founded in 1852 through a land donation by Boston-area businessman Charles Tufts to the Universalist Church. The school adopted its motto Pax et Lux (Peace and Light) in 1857.

EXECUTIVES

Vice Chair and Chair Designate, Peter R. Dolan, age 58
Chair, James A. (Jim) Stern, age 63
Dean The Fletcher School, Stephen W. Bosworth, age 74
Senior Vice President University Relations, Mary R. Jeka
VP Human Resources, Kathleen Cronin
VP Finance and Treasurer, Thomas S. McGurty
Chief of Staff and Assistant Secretary, Michael A. Baenen
Executive Director Alumni Relations, Timothy D. Brooks
VP Operations, Richard W. (Dick) Reynolds, age 71
Vice Chair, William R. (Bill) O'Reilly Jr.
Vice Chair, Jonathan M. (Jon) Tisch
Executive Vice President, Patricia L. Campbell
VP Information Technology and CIO, David J. Kahle
Associate Treasurer, Darleen Feinstein Karp
Secretary, Paul J. Tringale
President, Anthony P. Monaco
Provost and SVP ad interim, Margaret E. (Peggy) Newell
Vice President University Advancement, Eric C. Johnson
Vice President Operations, Linda Snyder
Provost and SVP, David R. Harris
Dean School of Arts and Sciences, Joanne Berger-Sweeney
Dean School of Engineering, Linda M. Abriola
Dean School of Dental Medicine, Huw F. Thomas
Dean School of Medicine, Harris Berman
Interim Dean Friedman School of Nutrition Science and Policy, Robin Kanarek
Interim Dean Tisch College of Citizenship and Public Service, Nancy Wilson
Dean Cummings School of Veterinary Medicine, Deborah T. Kochevar
Vice Chair and Chair Designate, Peter R. Dolan, age 58
Trustee, Jeffrey B. (Jeff) Kindler, age 58
Trustee, Pierre M. Omidyar, age 46
Trustee, Ellen J. Kullman, age 58
Trustee, Andrew N. Liveris, age 59
Trustee, Neal B. Shapiro, age 55
Trustee, A. Dana Callow Jr., age 61
Trustee, Fares I. Fares
Trustee, Laurie A. Gabriel
Trustee, Andrew Safran
Trustee, Steven A. Goldstein
Trustee, Steven M. (Steve) Galbraith, age 51
Trustee, Rev Gloria E. White-Hammond
Trustee, Daniel A. (Dan) Kraft
Trustee, Kathleen T. (Kathy) O'Loughlin
Trustee, Kathleen A. McCartney
Vice Chair, William R. (Bill) O'Reilly Jr.
Trustee, Thomas M. (Tom) Alperin
Trustee, Robert R. (Bobby) Bendetson
Trustee, Claire M. Davis
Trustee, Jeannie H. Diefenderfer
Trustee, Daniel J. (Dan) Doherty
Trustee, Joanne S. Gowa
Trustee, Varney J. Hintlian
Trustee, Deborah R. (Deb) Jospin
Trustee, Brian H. Kavoogian
Trustee, Debra S. Knez
Trustee, Seth I. Merrin
Trustee, Ioannis N. (Yannis) Miaoulis
Trustee, Karen M. Pritzker
Trustee, Hugh R. Roome III
Trustee, Edward M. (Ed) Swan Jr.
Trustee, Alfred I. (Fred) Tauber
Vice Chair, Jonathan M. (Jon) Tisch
Trustee, Teri Coleman Volpert
Trustee, Thomas F. (Tom) Winkler III
Trustee, James J. Wong

LOCATIONS

HQ: TRUSTEES OF TUFTS COLLEGE INC.
169 HOLLAND ST FL 3, SOMERVILLE, MA 02144-2401
Phone: 617-628-5000
Web: WWW.DENTAL.TUFTS.EDU

PRODUCTS/OPERATIONS

Schools & Colleges
Cummings School of Veterinary Science
Graduate School of Arts & Sciences
The Fletcher School
Friedman School of Nutrition Science and Policy
Sackler School of Graduate Biomedical Sciences
School of Arts & Sciences
School of Dental Medicine
School of Engineerin
School of Medicine
Tisch College of Citizenship and Public Service

HISTORICAL FINANCIALS

Company Type: Private

Income Statement FYE: June 30

	REVENUE ($ mil.)	NET INCOME ($ mil.)	NET PROFIT MARGIN	EMPLOYEES
06/12	739	(100)	—	3,500
06/11	851	83	9.8%	—
06/10	767	18	2.5%	—
06/09	671	(401)	—	—
Annual Growth	3.3%	—	—	—

2012 Year-End Financials

Debt ratio: —
Return on equity: (-13.60%)
Cash ($ mil.): 72
Current ratio: —
Long-term debt ($ mil.): —
Dividends
Yield: —
Payout: —
Market value ($ mil.): —

TRUSTEES OF UNION COLLEGE IN THE TOWN OF SCHENECTADY IN THE STAT

Union College brings liberal arts and engineering together. Union College is a private liberal arts school that offers courses in the humanities the social sciences the sciences and engineering. Notable alumni include the father of Franklin D. Roosevelt the grandfather of Winston Churchill and former US president Chester A. Arthur (class of 1848). Founded in 1795 with a class of 16 the college is supported by an endowment of more than $270 million.

EXECUTIVES

President, Stephen C. Ainlay
VP Student Affairs and Dean Students, Stephen C. (Steve) Leavitt
VP Finance and Administration, Diane T. Blake
Director Human Resources, Eric C. Noll
CIO, David V. Cossey
VP Academic Affairs and Dean Faculty, Therese A. McCarty
Director Schaffer Library, Thomas McFadden
Registrar, Penelope Adey
Associate Dean, Nic Zarrelli
VP Admissions Financial Aid and Enrollment, Matthew J. Malatesta
Director Media and Public Relations, Phillip J. Wajda
Administrative Assistant for Academic Affairs, Karen Crosby
CFO Vice President GS Group, David A. Viniar
Chief Information Officer, Ellen Borkowski
Senior Vice President for Finance and Administration, Joseph M. Hinchey
President CEO CIO, Robert DeMichele

LOCATIONS

HQ: TRUSTEES OF UNION COLLEGE IN THE TOWN OF SCHENECTADY IN THE STAT
807 UNION ST, SCHENECTADY, NY 12308-3103
Phone: 518-388-6630
Web: WWW.UNION.EDU

COMPETITORS

Bard College
Cazenovia College
Hamilton College
SUNY
Skidmore College

HISTORICAL FINANCIALS

Company Type: Private

Income Statement FYE: June 30

	REVENUE ($ mil.)	NET INCOME ($ mil.)	NET PROFIT MARGIN	EMPLOYEES
06/12	159	10	6.5%	870
06/11	145	1	0.8%	—
06/08	136	(2)	—	—
06/08	156	32	20.6%	—
Annual Growth	0.5%	(24.5%)	—	—

2012 Year-End Financials

Debt ratio: —
Return on equity: 6.50%
Cash ($ mil.): 26
Current ratio: —
Long-term debt ($ mil.): —
Dividends
Yield: —
Payout: —
Market value ($ mil.): —

TURTLE & HUGHES INC

Turtle & Hughes' longevity has ‚Âdemonstrated that slow and steady really does win the race ‚Âwhen it comes to ‚Âdistributing electrical and industrial equipment. The company's exhaustive lineup is ‚Â sold through ‚Â three subsidiaries: ‚ÂTurtle & Hughes Integrated Supply Turtle Data (wire cable and ‚Âpower protection devices) and ‚ÂTurtle Ebay Store. ‚ÂIts customers include industrial and construction companies electrical contractors telecommunications servers utilities and various government agencies. Family-owned the company is led by its fourth generation ‚ÂJayne Millard ‚Âits third female CEO. One-third ‚Âof ‚ÂTurtle & Hughes ‚Âis employee-owned.

Geographic Reach

Turtle & Hughes' branches dot the northeastern US (Connecticut New Jersey and New York). It also has a location ‚Âin Texas. The company's newest branch in Long Island City —its ninth — neighbors several main arteries to Manhattan where a number of its major accounts are established. ‚ÂThe location aims to boost ‚ÂTurtle & Hughes' marketplace presence ‚Âas well as ‚Âexpand its geographic reach. Its projects in and around the city include the electrical power distribution contract for the new World Trade Center Transportation Hub and the power distribution equipment contract (to be installed by its customers) ‚Â supplying the Freedom Tower and Tower Four.

Operations

The company operates through the following divisions:

Industrial Control & Automation Group (technical expertise and support ‚Âof high-tech automation products);

Switchgear Department ‚Â(power distribution equipment);

Commercial/Industrial Lighting Department (specialized lighting equipment);

Data Communications ‚Â(data communications and networking equipment);

Wire & Cable (inventory of wire and cable and capabilities and services including in-house cutting up to 750 mcm within 24 hours parallelling and phase identification);

Sustainable Energy Development ‚Â(distributed generation system integration company TurtlEnergy supports its customers with energy-efficient technologies and energy conservation services); and

Integrated Supply ‚Â(customized solutions to achieve cost savings and streamlining the supply chain with regard to indirect material and MRO supplies).

Sales and Marketing

Turtle & Hughes' customers include industrial firms construction companies electrical contractors telecommunications servers utilities and various government agencies and municipalities.

Ownership

Turtle & Hughes ‚Âis a family-owned employee-owned business and is certified as a Woman Business Enterprise.

Company Background

Turtle & Hughes was ‚Âfounded in 1923 as an electrical supply house.

EXECUTIVES

Vice President, Frank Millard, age 84
Vice President Of Finance, Trevor Barnett
President, Jack Sinagra
Manager Marketing, Jayne Millard
Manager Corporate Operations, Chuck Noll
EVP; Branch Manager Bridgewater Distribution Center and Plainfield Branch, Rick Reffler
President, Michael DeVoney
Vice President Sales, Mark Finke
Chief Information Officer Chief Technology Officer Vice President Information Technology, Julius Szelagiewicz
Vice President, Pete Landers
Vice President Export Sales, Abdul Hooda
Vice President, Norman Blu
Vice President, Cory Szatkiewicz
National Accounts Manager, Blake Varbero
Vice President Sales Manager, Kevin Colpoys
Vice President Sales, George Willoughby
Vice President Sales, Gary Rice
Vice President Sales, John Bernhardt
Vice President, Norman Blumenthal
Vice President, Marycarol Hoesel
Vice President And General Manager Of The Integrated Supply Division, Joseph Drummond
Vice President, Luis Valls
V P Sales, Tony Ventola
Vice President Corporate Purchasing, Prisinnia Longo
Senior Vice President, Al Fernandes
Chairman, Suzanne Turtle Millard
Auditors: AmperPolitziner&MattiaP.C.

LOCATIONS

HQ: TURTLE & HUGHES INC
1900 LOWER RD, LINDEN, NJ 070366586
Phone: 7325743600
Web: WWW.TURTLE.COM

PRODUCTS/OPERATIONS

Selected Products

Datacom categories
- Anchors and fasteners
- Burial products/innerduct
- Cabinets and enclosures
- Cable management
- Cable tray/ladder rack
- Category rated and coax cable
- Connectivity
- Fiber-optic cable
- Hand tools
- Outside plant
- Power protection
- Raceway and duct systems
- Safety
- Security fencing
- Splices connectors and lugs
- Tools testers and safety

Electrical categories
- Alarms annunciators and signals
- Anchors and plugs
- Automation products
- Ballasts and transformers
- Batteries and flashlights
- Box enclosures
- Breakers panels and switchgears
- Cable trays and struts
- Conduit fittings
- Cord connectors
- Dimming controls
- Electrical tools
- Emergency lighting
- Enclosures
- Fans
- Fluorescent lighting
- Fuse holders and terminal blocks
- Generators
- Groundings
- Heat shrink
- Heating
- High-bay lighting
- Incandescent lighting
- Lamps
- Limit temp. and proximity switch
- Lugs and terminals
- Metering equipment
- Motor control
- Motors AC and DC drivers
- Outdoor lighting
- Pole line products

Programmable controls
Relays
Strut/channel
Test equipment
Time clocks
Transformers
Wire cable and cord
Wiring accessories
Wiring devices

Industrial categories

Adhesives and tapes
Brushes and brooms
Carbide tools
Cutting fluid/lubricant
Cutting tools
Fasteners
Hand tools
Hoist chain and accessories
Industrial abrasives
Janitorial paper supplies
Ladders
Locks
Lubricating devices
Material handling
MRO supplies
Paint/markets
Pipe hangers
Pipe valves and fittings
Pneumatics
Pneumatic tools
Power tools
Safety equipment
Saw blades
Shim/shim stock
Solenoid valves
Strut/channel
Tooling accessories

COMPETITORS

C. R. Laurence	Kennametal
CPAC	MSC Industrial Direct
Consolidated Electrical	Prime Advantage
Dillon Supply	Rexel Inc.
Graybar Electric	Sonepar USA
Indoff	Steiner Electric
Interline Brands	W.W. Grainger
	WESCO International

HISTORICAL FINANCIALS

Company Type: Private

Income Statement FYE: September 30

	REVENUE ($ mil.)	NET INCOME ($ mil.)	NET PROFIT MARGIN	EMPLOYEES
09/13	555	21	3.8%	450
09/12	518	23	4.5%	—
09/11	452	17	4.0%	—
09/10	397	0	—	—
Annual Growth	11.8%	—	—	—

2013 Year-End Financials

Debt ratio: ——
Return on equity: 3.80%
Cash ($ mil.): 10
Current ratio: 1.70
Long-term debt ($ mil.): —

Dividends
Yield: —
Payout: —
Market value ($ mil.): —

U G N INC

Buying a Japanese car? Sounds good. Especially if the vehicle has acoustic molding and other sound-dampening acoustic automotive trim products made by UGN. The company produces molding from a variety of materials including cotton fiber and foam for vehicles assembled in North America by US and Japanese auto makers. UGN also makes automotive interior trim and thermal management parts. Its products are used to reduce interior noise and fine tune acoustical signals. The company's clientele has included such heavy hitters as Honda Nissan and Toyota. UGN was established in 1986 and is a joint venture between Autoneum and Nihon Tokushu Toryo (Nittoku).

Geographic Reach

Stationed in Tinley Park Illinois UGH operates through six plants in the US and one in Guanajuato Mexico.

Sales and Marketing

UGN sells its products through its stores and distributors. The company's products are sold to large OEMs such as Honda Toyota and Nissan.

Financial Performance

UGN reports more than $325 million in annual revenue. It claims revenues have increased more than 50% in the past two years.

Strategy

UGN is focused on increasing its manufacturing capacity though the opening and expanding of new facilities. In 2013 it announced plans to open a new facility to serve Southern Indiana and parts of Ohio by investing $25 million and it expects the new location to be operational by 2014.

In 2013 it also opened a 60000 sq. ft. facility in Silao Guanajuato Mexico for the manufacturing products used in Mexican-produced vehicles. The expansion marked the company's entry into the South American market.

EXECUTIVES

President and CEO, Peter C. Anthony
Vice President of Sales, Kenta Shinohara
VP Sales and Marketing, Paul Papke
CFO, Randy Khalaf

LOCATIONS

HQ: U G N INC
18410 CROSSING DR STE C, TINLEY PARK, IL 60487-6209
Phone: 773-437-2400
Web: WWW.UGNAUTO.COM

COMPETITORS

American Trim	Johnson Controls
DURA Automotive	Magna International
Delphi Automotive Systems	Trim Masters
Faurecia	Visteon

HISTORICAL FINANCIALS

Company Type: Private

Income Statement FYE: December 31

	REVENUE ($ mil.)	NET INCOME ($ mil.)	NET PROFIT MARGIN	EMPLOYEES
12/08	225	11	5.1%	1,250
12/07	239	0	—	—
12/06	223	13	5.9%	—
12/05	213	8	4.0%	—
Annual Growth	1.7%	10.3%	—	—

2008 Year-End Financials

Debt ratio: ——
Return on equity: 5.10%
Cash ($ mil.): 14
Current ratio: 1.00
Long-term debt ($ mil.): —

Dividends
Yield: —
Payout: —
Market value ($ mil.): —

U. S. TOOL GRINDING INC.

LOCATIONS

HQ: U. S. TOOL GRINDING INC.
2000 PROGRESS DR, FARMINGTON, MO 636409158
Phone: 5734313856
Web: WWW.USTG.NET

HISTORICAL FINANCIALS

Company Type: Private

Income Statement FYE: December 31

	REVENUE ($ mil.)	NET INCOME ($ mil.)	NET PROFIT MARGIN	EMPLOYEES
12/13	282	5	2.0%	450
12/12	230	7	3.4%	—
12/09	143	6	4.2%	—
12/08	149	0	—	—
Annual Growth	13.6%	—	—	—

2013 Year-End Financials

Debt ratio: ——
Return on equity: 2.00%
Cash ($ mil.): 2
Current ratio: 0.60
Long-term debt ($ mil.): —

Dividends
Yield: —
Payout: —
Market value ($ mil.): —

U.R.M. STORES INC.

EXECUTIVES

President and CEO, Dean E. Sonnenberg

LOCATIONS

HQ: U.R.M. STORES INC.
7511 N FREYA ST, SPOKANE, WA 992178043
Phone: 5094673619
Web: WWW.URMSTORES.COM

PRODUCTS/OPERATIONS

Selected Banners

CenterPlace Market
Family Foods
Harvest Foods
Trading Co. Stores
Rosauers Supermarkets
Super 1 Foods
Yoke's Fresh Market

COMPETITORS

AMCON Distributing	Nash-Finch
Albertsons	SUPERVALU
Associated Food	Safeway
C&S Wholesale	Sysco
Core-Mark	US Foods
Farner-Bocken	Unified Grocers
Fred Meyer Stores	Wal-Mart
McLane	

HISTORICAL FINANCIALS

Company Type: Private

Income Statement FYE: August 2

	REVENUE ($ mil.)	NET INCOME ($ mil.)	NET PROFIT MARGIN	EMPLOYEES
08/08*	932	8	0.9%	2,100
07/07	859	7	0.8%	—
07/06	1,562	0	0.0%	—
Annual Growth	(22.7%)	15808.9%	—	—

*Fiscal year change

2008 Year-End Financials

Debt ratio: ——
Return on equity: 0.90%
Cash ($ mil.): 2
Current ratio: —
Long-term debt ($ mil.): —

Dividends
Yield: —
Payout: —
Market value ($ mil.): —

U.S. VENTURE INC.

EXECUTIVES

Chairman, Thomas A. (Tom) Schmidt
CFO, Paul Bachman
President and CEO, John Schmidt
Director Human Resources, Lori Hoersch

LOCATIONS

HQ: U.S. VENTURE INC.
425 BETTER WAY, APPLETON, WI 549156192
Phone: 9207396101
Web: WWW.USVENTURE.COM

PRODUCTS/OPERATIONS

Selected Operations

Design Air (heating and air conditioning equipment)
Express Convenience Centers (gas stations and car washes)
U.S. AutoForce (exhaust pipe manufacturing and autoparts distribution)
U.S. Custom Manufacturing (tube bending and fabrication)
U.S. Lubricants (motor oil and related products)
U.S. Oil (gasoline fuel oil and natural gas)
U.S. Petroleum Equipment (petroleum-related equipment installation)

COMPETITORS

7-Eleven
Apex Oil
Marathon Oil
Motiva Enterprises
Quality State Oil Company
QuikTrip
Sunoco

HISTORICAL FINANCIALS

Company Type: Private

Income Statement FYE: July 31

	REVENUE ($ mil.)	NET INCOME ($ mil.)	NET PROFIT MARGIN	EMPLOYEES
07/14	9,088	49	0.5%	1,000
07/13	7,346	47	0.6%	—
07/12	5,906	60	1.0%	—
07/11	4,847	0	—	—
Annual Growth	23.3%	—	—	—

2014 Year-End Financials

Debt ratio: ——
Return on equity: 0.50%
Cash ($ mil.): 5
Current ratio: 0.90
Long-term debt ($ mil.): —

Dividends
Yield: —
Payout: —
Market value ($ mil.): —

UNDERWRITERS LABORATORIES INC.

Products that pass the muster of this company get the UL symbol of approval. Underwriters Laboratories (UL) is one of the world's leading providers of product safety and certification testing services performing more than 90000 evaluations each year. Products that successfully navigate through its stringent tests are registered with the lab and can bear the UL Mark —a widely trusted symbol for product safety and assurance. Nearly 20 billion products from 72000 manufacturers bear the UL Mark each year. UL also offers commercial inspection and regulatory training services as well as consumer safety advice. It serves mainly Asia North America and Europe. William Merrill founded the not-for-profit lab in 1894.

Geographic Reach

The company has been actively expanding its international operations and now has offices and affiliates in about 40 countries serving customers in nearly 100 different nations. It also represents US companies in gaining acceptance in foreign markets.

Operations

In addition to product testing UL serves as a leader in helping set regulatory and industry standards promoting conformity among companies and government agencies in establishing safety and performance requirements. UL is governed by a board of trustees elected by its corporate members (who are not manufacturers of products subject to UL coverage).

Strategy

UL restructured a couple of years ago to accommodate increased global demand as well as ramp up its "green" or environmentally friendly product services. Among the changes are the company's new sustainable products certification service and its environmental claims validation service which are the backbone of UL's Switzerland-based subsidiary UL Environment. Another new operating segment is Verification Services that expands the company's performance testing inspection and auditing offerings to a wider global audience.

Mergers and Acquisitions

UL made several acquisitions in 2013 including Testtech Laboratorios a Brazil-based electrical safety and energy efficiency testing laboratory that is relied upon by many of the world's leading appliance manufacturers. The acquisition positions UL as a single trusted source of the appliance certification testing and follow-up services needed to access the Brazilian market. UL will also be able to serve global appliance manufacturers seeking access to Brazil and Brazilian manufacturers seeking access to the rest of the world.

UL acquired Overland Park Kansas-based Innovadex the leading search and information exchange platform for supplier chemicals ingredients and raw materials in 2013 as well. The strategic addition expands UL's search offering to fully serve several new product categories including paints coatings adhesives inks lubricants cosmetics cleaners food and beverages. UL expanded its capabilities in the food industry in 2013 with the acquisition of Everclean Services one of North America's leading food safety audit providers.

HISTORY

In 1893 the Chicago Board of Fire Underwriters asked William Merrill an expert electrical investigator to inspect a dazzling display called the Palace of Electricity at the World's Fair. This jolted him into the realization of the need for electrical industry standardization. He founded the Underwriters' Electrical Bureau in 1894 to furnish fire risk data to insurers. Incorporated in 1901 as Underwriters Laboratories (UL) it expanded into auto parts fire extinguishers telephone wiring and even airline pilot certification which the government later took over.

Since the end of WWII UL has worked to establish international standards to facilitate global trade. In 1993 the organization introduced the first UL designation outside the US —in Canada. UL Canada became a UL affiliate in 1995. That year UL agreed with the Japan Quality Assurance Organization to exchange certification information. In 1996 UL opened offices in India and South Korea and acquired the Danish testing organization DEMKO. The company used its DEMKO subsidiary as a base to move into Sweden and Italy in 1998. It also opened a service center in China.

Alliances with organizations in Germany and Saudi Arabia followed in 1999 and Mexico in 2000. Also that year UL was recognized by the American National Standards Institute (ANSI) as one of only five organizations that can set standards without the need for ANSI review.

The company acquired Environmental Health Laboratories a leading public drinking water testing and analysis firm in 2001. Also that year UL agreed to exchange test data with the Water Quality Association (WQA) an independent water industry trade association.

In 2002 the organization acquired Eaton's Electromagnetic Compatibility (EMC) test laboratory. It also established offices in Chile and Switzerland and opened a new testing facility in Detroit. Knoblauch retired from UL in 2004.

EXECUTIVES

President and CEO, Keith E. Williams
Vp North American Operations, Al Cotrone
Svp And Chief Public Safety Officer, August (Gus) Schaefer
Vp; General Manager Global Chemical Sector, William (Bill) Colavecchio
Vp; General Manager Environment, Marcello Manca
Vp Anti-counterfeiting Operations, Brian Monks
Chief Engineer And Senior Vice President, Donald (Don) Talka
SVP and CFO, Michael Saltzman
President Verification Services, Sajeev Jesudas
President Environmental Services, Sara A. Greenstein
President Europe and Latin America, Gitte Schjotz
SVP and Chief Commercial Officer, Weifang Zhou
SVP and CIO, Christian Anschuetz
President Knowledge Services, Patrick Boyle
SVP and President Enterprise Services, Clyde Kofman
SVP and President Product Safety, Ben Miller
SVP and President Life and Health Sciences, Hiroshi Yamaki
VP and Managing Director Asia Pacific, Jason Fischer
Vice President Corporate Marketing, Susanne Lavin
Executive Vice President, Donald A Mader
Vp Global Government Affairs, Ann Weeks
Vp Oper Ul Innovadex, Wanda Comer
Sen V Pres Field Services, Stephen (Steve) Hewson
Vp; General Manager Global Power And Controls Business Unit, Gary Savin
Vp Operations And North American Leader Industrial Sector, Ralph Parker
Vp Gm, Castor Meier
Vp Infrastructure And Internal, Mark Syers
Executive Vice President, Columbus Gangemi
Vice President Customer Relations, Linda Zastrow

Senior Vice President Engineering And Information Technology, Dana Laferriere
Vice President Of Marketing, Lawrence Bruno
Vice President Customer Service, Peter Yeung
Vice President Operations, Jerry Stricker
Executive Assistant To Senior Vice President Chief Commercial Officer, Wright Janice
Legal Secretary, Sandra Brown
Legal Secretary, Gian Harris
Senior Vice President Chief Legal, Terrence Brady
Senior Vice President Global Operations, Scot Webster
Vice President Marketing At Ul Workplace Health And Safety, Kelley Maier
Vice President General Manager, Lisa Meier

LOCATIONS

HQ: UNDERWRITERS LABORATORIES INC.
333 PFINGSTEN RD, NORTHBROOK, IL 600622096
Phone: 8472728800
Web: WWW.UL.COM

PRODUCTS/OPERATIONS

Selected Services and Operations

Architectural services
Components
Consulting
EMC services
Global field services
Hazardous locations services
Market access solutions
Product safety
UL Environment
UL University
Verification services

Selected Product Certifications and Industries Served

Appliances and HVAC/R
  Appliance switches
  Appliances
  Gas oil and solid fuel appliances and equipment
HVAC/R
  Infrared thermometers
  Motors
  Pool and spa safety
Building materials
  Fire safety engineering
    Sprinklers
  Chemicals
  Electrical insulation systems
  Flammable and combustible fluids
  Plastics
Energy
  Renewable energy
  Semiconductor equipment
Food and water
  Drinking water
  Food safety
Health sciences
  Medical devices
High Tech
  Communication circuits protectors
  Consumer electronics
  Information technology equipment
  Lasers
  Power supplies
  Printed wiring boards
  Telecommunications equipment
Life safety and security
  Alarm systems
  Fire equipment
  Personal flotation devices
  Personal protective equipment
  Security and signaling
Lighting
  Decorative lighting strings
  General lighting
  Sign listing
Power and controls
  Electric vehicle components
  Electrical/electronic control equipment
  Energy meters
  Industrial control equipment
  Programmable electronics and software
  Robots and robotic equipment
Wire and cable
  Appliance wiring material
  Marine shipboard cable
  Optical fiber
  Proprietary structured cabling

COMPETITORS

BSI Group
Bureau Veritas
Canadian Standards Association
Consumers Union
Exponent
Intertek
J.D. Power
Methode Electronics
National Technical Systems
Norske Veritas
Quality Inspection Services
SGS
Silliker

HISTORICAL FINANCIALS

Company Type: Private

Income Statement FYE: December 31

	REVENUE ($ mil.)	NET INCOME ($ mil.)	NET PROFIT MARGIN	EMPLOYEES
12/08	994	(23)	—	10,846
12/07	895	160	17.9%	—
12/06	792,081	0	0.0%	—
Annual Growth	(96.5%)	—	—	—

2008 Year-End Financials

Debt ratio: ——
Return on equity: (-2.30%)
Cash ($ mil.): 46
Current ratio: 0.90
Long-term debt ($ mil.): —
Dividends
Yield: —
Payout: —
Market value ($ mil.): —

UNION HOSPITAL INC.

Union Hospital is the flagship facility of the Union Hospital Health Group a health care system that serves communities in western Indiana and eastern Illinois. The not-for-profit hospital has about 350 beds boasts an equal number of physicians and provides general medical and surgical care as well as specialty services in areas such as women's health cancer cardiovascular disease and sports medicine. It also offers occupational health and physical rehabilitation as well as medical training programs. Other facilities that comprise the Union system include Union Hospital Clinton physician practices specialty clinics and a home health agency. Union Hospital's roots go back to 1892.

Geographic Reach

The teaching hospital serves those who reside in west-central Indiana and eastern Illinois.

Operations

Besides the main Union Hospital which averages some 17000 patient admissions each year the hospital operates Union Hospital Clinton specialty clinics a home health agency and physician practices.

Strategy

Union Hospital's main campus underwent a nearly $180 million expansion project in recent years. The patient tower provides for private rooms instead of six- to eight-bed wards.

As part of a strategic focus to extend the reach of its operations Union Hospital partners with AP&S Clinic a multi -specialty physician group practice to expand the two entities' services. Operating as Union Health System the collaboration looks to increase coordination of care between physician specialists.

EXECUTIVES

EVP and CFO, Wayne R. Hutson
SVP and CIO, Kym A. Pfrank
VP and Administrator Union Hospital Clinton, Terri Hill
President and CEO, Scott L. Teffeteller
Assistant VP Human Resources, Sally Zuel
VP Medical Affairs and Chief Medical Officer, John Bolinger
VP Patient Care and Chief Nursing Officer, Rhonda Smith

LOCATIONS

HQ: UNION HOSPITAL INC.
1606 N 7TH ST, TERRE HAUTE, IN 47804-2780
Phone: 812-238-7000
Web: WWW.MYUNIONHOSPITAL.ORG

PRODUCTS/OPERATIONS

Selected Services

Acupuncture
Advanced Medical Technology
Asthma
Behavioral Healthcare
Breast Care
Cancer Care Services
Cardiovascular Testing
Clara Fairbanks Center for Women
Clay City Center for Family Medicine
Cork Medical Center
Family Medicine Center
Infections - MRSA
Joint Replacement Center
Landsbaum Center
Lugar Center for Rural Health
Medical Rehabilitation Center
Neonatal Intensive Care Unit (NICU)
Pediatrics
Pulmonary and Lung Health
Wound Healing Center
Union Hospital Terre Haute
Union Hospital Clinton
Union Hospital Foundation

COMPETITORS

Ascension Health
Carle Hospital
Franciscan Alliance
HCA
IU Health
IU Health Bloomington Hospital
Kosciusko Community Hospital
Provena Health

HISTORICAL FINANCIALS

Company Type: Private

Income Statement FYE: August 31

	REVENUE ($ mil.)	NET INCOME ($ mil.)	NET PROFIT MARGIN	EMPLOYEES
08/11	420	(0)	—	1,960
08/10	400	(3)	—	—
08/09	408	18	4.5%	—
08/08	373	14	4.0%	—
Annual Growth	4.0%	—	—	—

2011 Year-End Financials

Debt ratio: ——
Return on equity: —
Cash ($ mil.): 28
Current ratio: 1.70
Long-term debt ($ mil.): —
Dividends
Yield: —
Payout: —
Market value ($ mil.): —

UNIPRO FOODSERVICE INC

UniPro Foodservice knows there's strength in numbers. As the largest US foodservice cooperative its members include more than 650 independent member companies that provide food and food-related products to more than 800000 food-service customers including health care and educational institutions military installations and restaurants. UniPro provides training collective purchasing and marketing materials to all distributors. Its products —which include dry groceries and frozen and refrigerated foods –are sold under the brand names CODE ComSource Nifda and Nugget. Suppliers include Kraft Foods Reynolds Food Packaging Solo Cup Tyson Foods and Unilever Foodsolutions.

Geographic Reach

The cooperative operates through more than 900 distribution centers across the US.

Operations

The cooperative's Multi-Unit Group (MUG) formed in 1985 to service multi-unit foodservice operators include some of the largest member distributors in the UniPro network. MUG members are like a one-stop shop for multi-unit operators offering fresh produce paper products and small wares from a single source in an effort to improve efficiency.

Sales and Marketing

Progressive Group Alliance a business unit distributes and supplies partners with sales marketing and advice to customers. Brands include Alliance Pro (non-food) Coral Princess (seafood) GourMates (condiments) Harvest Gold (cheese butter and dairy-related products) and Premium Recipe (prepared entrees salsas and sauces).

Financial Performance

While privately-owned Unipro Foodservice doesn't report its financial results collectively the cooperatives ring up an estimated $60 billion in sales annually.

EXECUTIVES

President CEO, Roger Toomey
CIO, R. C. Alexander III
SVP Logistics/Redistribution, John L. Burke
SVP Procurement, Ray Goldman
Chief Financial Officer, David Joss
Director Human Resources, Charlotte N. Phillips
Executive Vice President Marketing, Don Gilligan
Executive Vice President of Sales West, Scott Strull
Executive Vice President of Sales East, Keith Durnell
Vice President of Sales, Spencer Peterson
Executive Vice President Procurement, David Huch

LOCATIONS

HQ: UNIPRO FOODSERVICE INC
2500 CUMBRLD PKWY SE 60 STE 600, ATLANTA, GA 30339
Phone: 770-952-0871
Web: WWW.UNIPROFOODSERVICE.COM

PRODUCTS/OPERATIONS

Selected Suppliers

Cargill Foodservice
Durable Packaging International
Handgards Inc.
Kraft Foods
Reynolds Foodservice Packaging
Solo Cup Company
Unilever Foodsolutions

COMPETITORS

Ben E. Keith
Foodbuy
Golden State Foods
Keystone Foods
MAINES
Martin-Brower
McLane Foodservice
Meadowbrook Meat Company
Nash-Finch
Performance Food Services Group of America
Sysco
US Foods

HISTORICAL FINANCIALS

Company Type: Private

Income Statement FYE: December 31

	REVENUE ($ mil.)	NET INCOME ($ mil.)	NET PROFIT MARGIN	EMPLOYEES
12/12	987	(0)	—	140
12/11	881	0	—	—
12/10	657	0	—	—
12/09	631	(0)	—	—
Annual Growth	16.0%	—	—	—

2012 Year-End Financials

Debt ratio: —
Return on equity: —
Cash ($ mil.): 6
Current ratio: 1.00
Long-term debt ($ mil.): —
Dividends
Yield: —
Payout: —
Market value ($ mil.): —

UNITED COOPERATIVE

LOCATIONS

HQ: UNITED COOPERATIVE
N7160 RACEWAY RD, BEAVER DAM, WI 539169315
Phone: 9208871756
Web: WWW.UNITEDCOOPERATIVE.COM

HISTORICAL FINANCIALS

Company Type: Private

Income Statement FYE: December 31

	REVENUE ($ mil.)	NET INCOME ($ mil.)	NET PROFIT MARGIN	EMPLOYEES
12/13	627	45	7.2%	358
12/12	641	34	5.4%	—
12/11	523	35	6.7%	—
12/10	324	0	—	—
Annual Growth	24.6%	—	—	—

2013 Year-End Financials

Debt ratio: —
Return on equity: 7.20%
Cash ($ mil.): 20
Current ratio: 0.20
Long-term debt ($ mil.): —
Dividends
Yield: —
Payout: —
Market value ($ mil.): —

UNITED DAIRYMEN OF ARIZONA

EXECUTIVES

CEO, Keith Murfield
VP-HR, Anson White

LOCATIONS

HQ: UNITED DAIRYMEN OF ARIZONA
2008 S HARDY DR, TEMPE, AZ 852821211
Phone: 4809667211
Web: WWW.UDA.COOP

PRODUCTS/OPERATIONS

Selected Products and Services

Products
- Dried
  - Dry milk blends
  - Kosher powder
  - Lactose powder
  - Milk protein concentrate
  - Nonfat dry milk
- Fluid
  - Butter
  - Cream
  - Condensed skim milk
  - Skim milk

Services
- Emergency repair
- Installation
- Preventative maintenance
- Transportation

Supplies
- Chemical
- Equipment
- Pharmaceutical

COMPETITORS

Associated Milk Producers
Dairy Farmers of America
Dairy Manufacturers
Dean Foods
Goya
Land O' Lakes
Main Street Ingredients
Nestle
Shamrock Foods
Smucker
Tate & Lyle Ingredients

HISTORICAL FINANCIALS

Company Type: Private

Income Statement FYE: September 30

	REVENUE ($ mil.)	NET INCOME ($ mil.)	NET PROFIT MARGIN	EMPLOYEES
09/11	825	21	2.6%	190
09/10	612	12	2.0%	—
09/09	51	0	0.0%	—
Annual Growth	300.9%	52165.3%	—	—

2011 Year-End Financials

Debt ratio: —
Return on equity: 2.60%
Cash ($ mil.): 30
Current ratio: 1.00
Long-term debt ($ mil.): —
Dividends
Yield: —
Payout: —
Market value ($ mil.): —

UNITED ELECTRIC SUPPLY COMPANY INC.

True to its name United Electric Supply distributes electrical parts such as lighting fasteners sensors wire connectors and voice data and fiber-optic products. The employee-owned company carries more than 23000 items from more than 250 manufacturers including Kyocera Panasonic Security and Schneider Electric. It sells to the building and industrial trades government and other markets. United Electric's wide range of services include design value engineering energy audits procurement training inventory management and E-commerce. It also offers value-added services such as next day delivery and Saturday-morning counter hours.

Geographic Reach

It has 17 branch locations in Delaware Maryland New Jersey Pennsylvania and Virginia.

Operations

United Electric divides its business into eight product groups: Data Comm; Electro-Mechanical; Energy Solutions; Gear and Control; Integrated Products; Lighting; Wire Cable and Conduit; and Solar Energy. Data Comm offers on-site consultation and assistance to deploy voice data and fiber optic technology. Electro-Mechanical provides project-specific quotations for such products as fittings boxes fasteners and tools.

Energy Solutions focuses on energy audits rebate studies lighting design and other services to increase the energy efficiency of lighting. Gear and Control offers project budgeting design and other services along with distributing products. Integrated Products markets programmable controllers operator interface products supervisory software drives and power conditioning equipment among other products. Lighting serves the construction and renovation markets with various lighting products and conducts audits of lighting systems to determine better energy efficiency. Wire Cable and Conduit offers items that range from basic building wire to multi-conductor instrumentation cables. Solar Energy provides renewable power for a variety of structures from large commercial buildings to small houses.

United Electric additionally offers a program called Supplier Inventory Management System (SIMS) that includes such services as inventory reduction through analysis of each storeroom unit and bar-coding. United Electric is also an authorized supplier through Pennsylvania's COSTARS cooperative purchasing program which unifies local organizations to achieve more competitive pricing than individual businesses could obtain on their own.

Sales and Marketing

The company sells its products through its stores and via online marketing efforts.

Strategy

United Electric grows organically and through complementary acquisitions.

The company opened its 16th location in Easton Pennsylvania in 2013 and another branch location in Timonium Maryland to serve customers in Baltimore and the surrounding counties.

It uses an extensive in-house database to provide performance measures and analysis illustrate results and highlight best practices.

Mergers and Acquisitions

In 2012 United Electric acquired Easton-based Ealer Electric to serve the Lehigh Valley customers of Pennsylvania.

Company Background

The company which was founded in 1965 by Nick Gianoulis has been an employee-owned venture since 1996.

EXECUTIVES

SVP Finance and CFO, Rich Stagliano
VP Operations and COO, Bob Crawford
Director Information Technology, Luis Varela
President and CEO, George Vorwick
Vp Distribution And Control Products, Sal Muzzi

LOCATIONS

HQ: UNITED ELECTRIC SUPPLY COMPANY INC.
10 BELLECOR DR, NEW CASTLE, DE 197201763
Phone: 8003223374
Web: WWW.UNITEDELECTRIC.COM

PRODUCTS/OPERATIONS

Selected Services

Consigned inventory
Design and build assistance
Electronic invoicing
Energy audits
Order staging
Post Order Focus
Procurement
Supplier Inventory Management Systems
Training
Value Engineering

COMPETITORS

Billows Electric
Consolidated Electrical
Gexpro
Graybar Electric
McCoy Group
Rumsey Electric
Supply

HISTORICAL FINANCIALS

Company Type: Private

Income Statement FYE: December 31

	REVENUE ($ mil.)	NET INCOME ($ mil.)	NET PROFIT MARGIN	EMPLOYEES
12/13	168	2	1.7%	292
12/12	171	3	1.8%	—
12/11	185	4	2.6%	—
12/10	164	0	—	—
Annual Growth	0.9%	—	—	—

2013 Year-End Financials

Debt ratio: —
Return on equity: 1.70%
Cash ($ mil.): 5
Current ratio: 1.00
Long-term debt ($ mil.): —
Dividends
Yield: —
Payout: —
Market value ($ mil.): —

UNITED FARMERS COOPERATIVE

EXECUTIVES

CEO and General Manager, Jeff Nielsen
CFO, Lorie Reinarts
Manager Agronomy Department, Butch Altmann
Manager Grain Department, Jim Johnson
Manager Feed Department, Steve LeBrun
Manager Farm and Consumer Supply Department, Leon Portner
Manager Energy Department, Darv Turbes
Board President, Kevin Lauwagie
Board VP, Todd Nelson
Board Secretary, David Braun
Director Marketing and Communications, Teresa Wenninger
Manager Human Resources, Cheri LeBrun
Assistant General Manager and COO, Clif Gipp
Controller, Carol Steffl
Risk Management, Marc (Pete) Peterson
Information Systems Coordinator, Ryan Altmann
Credit Manager, Shelley Quast
Board VP, Todd Nelson
Board Secretary, David Braun

LOCATIONS

HQ: UNITED FARMERS COOPERATIVE
705 E 4TH ST, WINTHROP, MN 553962362
Phone: 5072372281
Web: WWW.UFCMN.COM

COMPETITORS

ADM
CHS
Frontier Agriculture
Land O' Lakes Purina Feed
Minn-Dak Co-op
SMBSC
Watonwan Farm Service Co

HISTORICAL FINANCIALS

Company Type: Private

Income Statement FYE: August 31

	REVENUE ($ mil.)	NET INCOME ($ mil.)	NET PROFIT MARGIN	EMPLOYEES
08/07	127	2	1.9%	269
08/06	93	1	1.5%	—
08/05	782	0	0.0%	—
Annual Growth	(59.6%)	13364.0%	—	—

2007 Year-End Financials

Debt ratio: —
Return on equity: 1.90%
Cash ($ mil.): 1
Current ratio: 0.40
Long-term debt ($ mil.): —
Dividends
Yield: —
Payout: —
Market value ($ mil.): —

UNITED HARDWARE DISTRIBUTING CO

United Hardware Distributing is in the business of building relationships. The member-owned distributor delivers hammers nails and all the other hardware necessities to dealers in 18 states across the central US. The company is not a franchiser but it does provide retail support education buying markets and consulting services to its members. In addition to providing hardware United Hardware offers expertise in accounting store design pricing marketing purchasing and merchandising. Its client list of about 1200 member stores include Hardware Hank Trustworthy Hardware Golden Rule Lumber Ranch & Pet Supply and other independent retailers.

Geographic Reach

Based in Minnesota United Hardware distributes its products in 18 states. It serves Colorado Idaho Illinois Indiana Iowa Kansas Kentucky Michigan Minnesota Missouri Montana Nebraska North Dakota Ohio South Dakota Utah Wisconsin and Wyoming.

Operations

As part of its business the company serves its dealer network from a 400000-sq.-ft. distribution center located in Milbank South Dakota.

Sales and Marketing

The company serves the do-it-yourself market and supplies some 1200 hardware retailers with a variety of products.

United Hardware's membership in Distribution America a buying group with more than $2 billion in buying power lets it offer members the lowest price on merchandise. The company's South Dakota distribution center stocks more than 55000 items.

Financial Performance

United Hardware claims that it logs more than $170 million in sales each year.

EXECUTIVES

Vice President Of Operations, Lori Long
Vice President Systems And Operations, Anthony Long
Vice President Systems And Operations, Lori Baxter
Vice President, Tom Undis

LOCATIONS

HQ: UNITED HARDWARE DISTRIBUTING CO
5005 NATHAN LN N, PLYMOUTH, MN 55442-3210
Phone: 763-559-1800
Web: WWW.UNITEDHARDWARE.COM

PRODUCTS/OPERATIONS

Selected Member Stores
Golden Rule Lumber Centers
Hardware Hank
Ranch & Pet Supply
Trustworthy Hardware Stores

COMPETITORS

84 Lumber
Ace Hardware
Do it Best
Home Depot
Lowe' s
Northern Tool
Sears
Sherwin-Williams
True Value
Wal-Mart

HISTORICAL FINANCIALS

Company Type: Private

Income Statement FYE: November 30

	REVENUE ($ mil.)	NET INCOME ($ mil.)	NET PROFIT MARGIN	EMPLOYEES
11/12	195	3	2.0%	330
11/11	189	5	3.1%	—
11/10	178	3	2.2%	—
11/09	180	3	2.2%	—
Annual Growth	2.7%	(0.9%)	—	—

2012 Year-End Financials

Debt ratio: ——
Return on equity: 2.00%
Cash ($ mil.): 2
Current ratio: 0.70
Long-term debt ($ mil.): —
Dividends
Yield: —
Payout: —
Market value ($ mil.): —

UNITED HEALTH SERVICES HOSPITAL INC.

United Health Services Hospitals (UHS Hospitals) can service injuries from a slip in the snow or a slipped disc to health that's just plain slipping. The organization operates Binghamton General Hospital (about 200 beds) Wilson Medical Center (some 280 beds) and a group of primary and specialty care clinics in upstate New York. Specialty services include cardiology dialysis neurology rehabilitation pediatrics and psychiatry. The Wilson Medical Center serves as a teaching hospital offering residency and fellowship programs. UHS Hospitals is a subsidiary of United Health Services which operates a network of affiliated hospitals clinics long-term care centers and home health agencies in the region.

Geographic Reach

Binghamton General is located in Binghamton New York while Wilson Medical Center is located in Johnson City New York both within the boundaries of Broome County. UHS Hospitals also operates primary and specialty care clinics in Broome Chenango Delaware and Tioga counties in upstate New York.

Strategy

United Health Services Hospitals is investing in equipment upgrades and facility improvements at Binghamton General to help the facility remain at the forefront of medical technology and services. Wilson Medical Center which acts as a regional referral center in areas including emergency medicine newborn care neurology and heart surgery has also been the subject of enhancement measures. The hospital recently completed construction of the new Decker Center for Advanced Medical Treatment which offers high-tech diagnostic and acute care services.

EXECUTIVES

Senior Vice President Chief Financial Officer, Robert Gomulka
President and CEO; 2nd Vice Chair, Matthew J. Salanger
President and CEO Delaware Valley Hospital, David Polge
Chairman, Diana Bendz
Secretary, Susan Mistretta
VP Strategy and Business Development, Robin Kinslow-Evans
President CEO, Drake M. Lamen
EVP and COO, John Carrigg
President and CEO; 2nd Vice Chair, Matthew J. Salanger
1st Vice Chair, Bruce Bowling
Director, Barbara Chaffee
Director, William Craine
Director, Garabed Fattal
Director, Sara Gueldner
Director, Carol Miller
Director, Judith C. Peckham
Auditors: PricewaterhouseCoopersLLP

LOCATIONS

HQ: UNITED HEALTH SERVICES HOSPITAL INC.
10-42 MITCHELL AVE, BINGHAMTON, NY 13903-1617
Phone: 607-762-2200
Web: WWW.UHS.NET

COMPETITORS

Albany Medical Center
Guthrie Healthcare
Kaleida Health
Lifetime Health
Oneida Healthcare Center
SUNY Upstate Medical University
St. Joseph' s Hospital Health Center
Unity Health System
Upstate University Hospital at Community General

HISTORICAL FINANCIALS

Company Type: Private

Income Statement FYE: December 31

	REVENUE ($ mil.)	NET INCOME ($ mil.)	NET PROFIT MARGIN	EMPLOYEES
12/12	496	18	3.8%	5,000
12/11	455	18	4.0%	—
12/09	442	22	5.1%	—
12/09	412	14	3.5%	—
Annual Growth	6.3%	8.9%	—	—

2012 Year-End Financials

Debt ratio: ——
Return on equity: 3.80%
Cash ($ mil.): 18
Current ratio: 1.10
Long-term debt ($ mil.): —
Dividends
Yield: —
Payout: —
Market value ($ mil.): —

UNITED HOSPITAL SYSTEM INC.

LOCATIONS

HQ: UNITED HOSPITAL SYSTEM INC.
6308 8TH AVE, KENOSHA, WI 531435031
Phone: 2626562011
Web: WWW.UNITEDHOSPITALSYSTEM.ORG

HISTORICAL FINANCIALS

Company Type: Private

Income Statement FYE: June 30

	REVENUE ($ mil.)	NET INCOME ($ mil.)	NET PROFIT MARGIN	EMPLOYEES
06/10	277	26	9.6%	1,500
06/09	266	20	7.9%	—
06/08	924	0	—	—
Annual Growth	—	3934.3%	—	—

2010 Year-End Financials

Debt ratio: —
Return on equity: 9.60%
Cash ($ mil.): 41
Current ratio: 0.70
Long-term debt ($ mil.): —
Dividends
Yield: —
Payout: —
Market value ($ mil.): —

UNITED NEGRO COLLEGE FUND INC.

A mind is a terrible thing to waste. In this spirit the United Negro College Fund (UNCF) offers financial assistance to students of color from low-to moderate-income families pursuing a higher education. UNCF the oldest and largest higher education assistance program for African-Americans enables some 60000 students to attend college each year. About 60% of the students are the first in their families to attend college. UNCF also provides operating funds and IT services to about 40 historically black colleges and universities such as Bethune-Cookman Morehouse Xavier and Voorhees College. The not-for-profit organization was founded in 1944 by Dr. Frederick D. Patterson with 27 charter member colleges.

More than 90% of UNCF students seeking higher education require financial aid. UNCF also provides scholarships internships and fellowships to support graduate and doctoral studies. To help prepare students for college UNCF has partnered with Teach For America and the KIPP Foundation to improve high school graduation rates.

UNCF's services include funding its 39 member colleges all of them small private historically black colleges and universities. In addition the fund has worked to upgrade and modernize technology provide computers to students and faculty as well as create an e-commerce site selling current hardware and software. UNCF drives an annual television public service announcement UNCF An Evening of Stars a national campaign that serves as an advocate and fundraiser for education.

About 70% of UNCF's support is raised through contributions for grants and scholarships; some 20% is raised through contributions and gifts. In 2010 support slumped 5% from the prior year driven by a decline in contributions and gifts and gifts-in-kind. Weakening contributions echo a study suggesting that college aid recipients donate less than their alumni peers who paid full tuition. As a result program services in 2010 slipped with distributions to member institutions taking more than a 35% hit. Nonetheless funding for the Gates Millennium Scholars Program (GMSP) and scholarships which account for roughly 50% and 20% of program services respectively increased about 5% each. Fund raising efforts which accounted for 6% of 2010 expenses rose slightly from 2009 offset by a small decline in management and general supporting services.

UNCF's mission has continued to expand. Its largest scholarship program the Gates Millennium Scholars Program provides financial assistance to Hispanic American Asian/Pacific American and Native American students as well as African Americans. Students attend about 900 colleges across the US including non-UNCF member colleges.

EXECUTIVES

EVP General Counsel and Secretary of the Corporation, Sydney M. Avent
Senior Vice President Chief Administrative Officer, LaJuan H. Lyles
SVP Northeast, James N. Alston
Executive Vice President National Development, Maurice E. Jenkins
VP West, James H. Mayo III
Executive Vice President at UNCF, John Donohue
Executive Director, Fred Mitchell
Regional Development Director, Edith Pearson
Development Director, Andrea Neely
Interim General Counsel Secretary, Desiree Boykin
Regional Development Director, Jann W. Honore
Senior Vice President Research Innovation and Member Engagement, Karl W. Reid
Vice President Marketing and Communications, Richard Shropshire
Vice President Development, Therese Badon
Vice President Development, Paulette Jackson
Vice President Operations and Technology, Robert Rucker
Senior Vice President Public Policy and Government Affairs, Cheryl L. Smith

LOCATIONS

HQ: UNITED NEGRO COLLEGE FUND INC.
1805 7TH ST NW STE 100, WASHINGTON, DC 20001-3187
Phone: 800-331-2244
Web: WWW.UNCFSP.ORG

UNCF Member Institutio
Allen University Columbia SC
Benedict College Columbia SC
Bennett College for Women Greensboro NC
Bethune-Cookman University Daytona Beach FL
Claflin University Orangeburg SC
Clark Atlanta University Atlanta GA
Dillard University New Orleans LA
Edward Waters College Jacksonville FL
Fisk University Nashville TN
Florida Memorial University Miami FL
Huston-Tillotson University Austin TX
Interdenominational Theological Center Atlanta GA
Jarvis Christian College Hawkins TX
Johnson C. Smith University Charlotte NC
Lane College Jackson TX
LeMoyne-Owen College Memphis TN
Livingston College Salisbury NC
Miles College Birmingham AL
Morehouse College Atlanta GA
Morris College Sumter SC
Oakwood University Huntsville AL
Paine College Augusta GA
Paul Quinn College Dallas TX
Philander Smith College Little rock AR
Rust College Holly Springs MS
Saint Augustine's College Raleigh NC
Saint Paul's College Lawrenceville VA
Shaw University Raleigh NC
Spelman College Atlanta GA
Stillman College Tuscaloosa AL
Talladega College Talladega AL
Texas College Tyler TX
Tougaloo College Tougaloo MC
Tuskegee University Tuskegee AL
Virginia Union University Richmond VA
Voorhees College Denmark SC
Wilberforce University Wilberforce OH
Wiley College Marshall TX
Xavier University New Orleans LA

PRODUCTS/OPERATIONS

2010 Support

	$ mil.	% of total
Contributions for grants & scholarships	102	70
Contributions & gifts	30	21
Bequests & legacies	8	6
Gifts-in-kind & donated services	4	3
Total	**146**	**100**

2010 Expenses

	$ mil.	% of total
Program services		
Gates Millennium Scholars Program (GMSP)	76	51
Scholarships & special projects	30	21
Distributions to member institutions	12	8
Other program services	5	4
Institutional services	1	1
Supporting services		
Management & general	12	9
Fund raising	9	6
Total	**148**	**100**

Selected Scholarship Programs

Corporate Scholars Program
Gates Millennium Scholars Program
UNCF/Merck Science Initiative

HISTORICAL FINANCIALS

Company Type: Private

Income Statement FYE: March 31

	REVENUE ($ mil.)	NET INCOME ($ mil.)	NET PROFIT MARGIN	EMPLOYEES
03/12	208	41	19.8%	257
03/10	197	51	25.9%	—
03/09	240	89	37.3%	—
03/06	195	44	22.5%	—
Annual Growth	1.0%	(1.1%)	—	—

2012 Year-End Financials

Debt ratio: —
Return on equity: 19.80%
Cash ($ mil.): 87
Current ratio: 2.20
Long-term debt ($ mil.): —
Dividends
Yield: —
Payout: —
Market value ($ mil.): —

UNITED OIL OF THE CAROLINAS INC.

LOCATIONS

HQ: UNITED OIL OF THE CAROLINAS INC.
1627 SPENCER MOUNTAIN RD, GASTONIA, NC 280549002
Phone: 7048243561
Web: WWW.UNITEDOILONLINE.COM

HISTORICAL FINANCIALS

Company Type: Private

Income Statement FYE: March 31

	REVENUE ($ mil.)	NET INCOME ($ mil.)	NET PROFIT MARGIN	EMPLOYEES
03/14	251	0	0.2%	26
03/13	282	1	0.4%	—
03/12	292	1	0.4%	—
03/11	208	0	—	—
Annual Growth	6.5%	—	—	—

2014 Year-End Financials

Debt ratio: —
Return on equity: 0.20%
Cash ($ mil.): 6
Current ratio: 1.80
Long-term debt ($ mil.): —
Dividends
Yield: —
Payout: —
Market value ($ mil.): —

UNITED REGIONAL HEALTH CARE SYSTEM INC.

If you take a fall in Wichita Falls United Regional Health Care System (URHCS) will be there. The health care provider serves the residents of northern Texas through two hospitals that combined have some 500 beds. Specialized services include emergency medicine cardiac care diagnostic imaging surgery obstetrics and pediatrics. The health care system also offers cancer treatment childbirth wound care and sleep diagnostic centers. It is the only comprehensive cardiac care facility and only Level III trauma center in the region. URHCS operates a Care Flight Helicopter to get those traumas to care quicker.

Strategy

In 2011 URCHS initiated renovation of its Bethania Building and Administration Building and it relocated its Cardio-Pulmonary Rehab Facility. It also remodeled its United Regional Diagnostic building and extended the hospital's outpatient therapy space to accommodate more patients.

Along with building and technological expansions URHCS has been focused on increasing the number of specialists in its employ. To that end the system created a recruitment program that targets medical students residents and fellows who have ties to Wichita Falls and the surrounding areas. Hospital administration and members of the physician staff offer support and guidance to potential recruits as they progress in their medical education or as they consider making a move from another hospital.

In recent years URHCS has recruited physicians in the areas of cardiovascular surgery neurosurgery orthopedic surgery and minimally invasive general and bariatric surgery to meet the community's increased need for those medical specialties.

EXECUTIVES

VP United Regional Physician Group, Mike Jones
SVP Operations, Nancy Townley
VP Quality and Chief Medical Officer, Scott Hoyer
VP of Finance, Robert Pert
VP Facilities Management, Rick Carpenter
President and CEO, Phyllis A. Cowling
VP Marketing and Communications, Stevie J. Brown

VP of Physician Practice Services, Johnny Roberts
Vice President of Organizational Development, Kristi Faulkner
Auditors: Ernst&YoungLLP

LOCATIONS

HQ: UNITED REGIONAL HEALTH CARE SYSTEM INC.
1600 11TH ST, WICHITA FALLS, TX 76301-4300
Phone: 940-764-7000
Web: WWW.UNITEDREGIONAL.ORG/LEADERSHIP

PRODUCTS/OPERATIONS

Selected Medical Services

Advanced Technology
Bariatric Services
Cancer Care
Cardiac Services
Diabetes Education
Emergency and Trauma Services
ENT
Infusion Therapy
Neurology
Neurosurgery
Obstetrics
Orthopedics
Pediatrics
Pulmonary Rehabilitation
Radiology
Reference Laboratory
Respiratory
Stroke Program & Center of Distinction
Supportive Care
Surgical Services
Women's Services
Wound Care

COMPETITORS

HCA
Health Management Associates
Jackson County Memorial Hospital
Mercy Health
Tenet Healthcare
Texas Health Denton
Texas Health Resources

HISTORICAL FINANCIALS

Company Type: Private

Income Statement FYE: December 31

	REVENUE ($ mil.)	NET INCOME ($ mil.)	NET PROFIT MARGIN	EMPLOYEES
12/12	279	41	15.0%	1,950
12/11	289	41	14.4%	—
12/10	287	36	12.8%	—
12/09	271	49	18.1%	—
Annual Growth	0.9%	(5.2%)	—	—

2012 Year-End Financials

Debt ratio: —
Return on equity: 15.00%
Cash ($ mil.): 49
Current ratio: 2.00
Long-term debt ($ mil.): —
Dividends
Yield: —
Payout: —
Market value ($ mil.): —

UNITED SPACE ALLIANCE LLC

United Space Alliance (USA) is a space-race heavyweight; the Houston-based prime contractor has run NASA's 173000 pound Shuttles –Discovery Atlantis and Endeavour which lifted off for the final time in 2011. USA a JV between Lockheed Martin and Boeing was formed in 1996 in response to NASA's move to consolidate multiple Space Shuttle contracts under a single entity. USA has supported mission operations astronaut and flight controller training flight software development Shuttle payload integration and vehicle processing launch and recovery. It also leads training and planning for the International Space Station. USA serves the Johnson and Kennedy Space Centers and Marshall Space Flight Center.

Geographic Reach

Based in Houston the company has another location in Titusville Florida.

Strategy

In 2012 NASA awarded a one-year extension of the Integrated Mission Operations Contract to USA to continue providing mission and flight crew operations support for the International Space Station and Exploration Programs. The deal includes a further option for 2014. Throughout 2012 and 2013 however USA laid off waves of workers that resided in its former Space Shuttle program.

Company Background

The launch of space shuttle Atlantis in July 2011 marked the end of NASA's 30-year Space Shuttle program. The shuttles have transported astronauts launched recovered and repaired satellites as well as driven new research and built and stocked the International Space Station with parts and provisions.

EXECUTIVES

Vice President Chief Financial Officer Comptroller, William R. (Bill) Capel
EVP and COO, Daniel C. (Dan) Brandenstein
President Chief Executive Officer, Virginia A. (Ginger) Barnes, age 56
VP Huntsville Operations, Kimberly B. (Kim) Doering
VP Launch and Recovery; Site Executive Florida, Mark Nappi
VP Logistics and Materials, Michael (Mike) Jones
VP and General Counsel, Rochelle L. (Shelly) Cooper
Vice President Aerospace Services and Mission Operations, Scott Q. Hartwig
Vice President of Human Resources, Sherri K. Lee
CIO, Toni Russell
Vice President General Counsel, Dionne Cooper

LOCATIONS

HQ: UNITED SPACE ALLIANCE LLC
600 GEMINI ST, HOUSTON, TX 77058-2783
Phone: 281-212-6200
Web: WWW.UNITEDSPACEALLIANCE.COM

PRODUCTS/OPERATIONS

Selected Capabilities

Flight software
Ground operations and processing
GSA (General Services Administration) services
Integrated logistics
Integration and program management
Mission operations
Safety

COMPETITORS

Air Traffic Alliance
Arianespace
Astrotech
BAE SYSTEMS
EADS
Honeywell Aerospace
Meggitt-USA
Northrop Grumman
Raytheon
SGT
Thales Aerospace

HISTORICAL FINANCIALS

Company Type: Private

Income Statement FYE: December 31

	REVENUE ($ mil.)	NET INCOME ($ mil.)	NET PROFIT MARGIN	EMPLOYEES
12/07	1,859	168	9.0%	2,500
12/06	1,920	146	7.6%	—
Annual Growth	(3.2%)	14.8%	—	—

2007 Year-End Financials

Debt ratio: —
Return on equity: 9.00%
Cash ($ mil.): 57
Current ratio: 0.30
Long-term debt ($ mil.): —
Dividends
Yield: —
Payout: —
Market value ($ mil.): —

UNITED STATES BEEF CORPORATION

This company has carved out a sandwich empire in the middle of the country. United States Beef Corporation is the largest franchisee of Arby's fast-food restaurants in the US with more than 280 locations in half a dozen states mostly in Kansas Missouri and Oklahoma. The restaurants franchised from Arby's Restaurant Group (part of Wendy's/Arby's Group) serve the chain's signature roast beef sandwiches and curly fries as well as ham chicken and turkey subs. Bob Davis and his wife Connie opened their first Arby's in 1969 and founded United States Beef in 1974. The Davis family continues to own the company.

Unlike many other fast food chains Arby's has not had much success expanding its product offerings beyond roast beef sandwiches and curly fries. Regardless United States Beef Corporation plans to develop new Arby's restaurants in some of its existing markets while the company remodels older locations with modern and clean looking interiors and exteriors.

United States Beef Corporation has the exclusive franchise development rights for Arby's restaurants in Arkansas Colorado Illinois Kansas Missouri and Oklahoma.

EXECUTIVES

Vice President Operations, Al Schiltz
Senior Vice President Operations, Rick Morris
Vice President Operations, Bill Yerk
President, John R. Davis, age 52
President, Brett Pratt
CFO, Lori D. Pumphrey
COO, Bo Davis
Vice President Director Purchasing, Brenda Parrish
Vice President, Fred Fleischner
Vice President, Susan Hollingsworth
Chairman, Jeff Davis

LOCATIONS

HQ: UNITED STATES BEEF CORPORATION
4923 E 49TH ST, TULSA, OK 74135-7002
Phone: 918-665-0740
Web: WWW.USBEEFCORP.COM

COMPETITORS

American Dairy Queen
Biglari Holdings
Boddie-Noell
Burger King
Captain D' s
Checkers Drive-In
Chick-fil-A
Chipotle
Church' s Chicken
Hardee' s
Jack in the Box
K-MAC
Mazzio' s
McDonald' s
NPC Restaurant Holdings
Panera Bread
Popeyes
Quiznos
Sonic Corp.
Subway
Whataburger
YUM!

HISTORICAL FINANCIALS

Company Type: Private

Income Statement FYE: December 31

	REVENUE ($ mil.)	NET INCOME ($ mil.)	NET PROFIT MARGIN	EMPLOYEES
12/12	246	7	3.0%	2,000
12/08	246	6	2.5%	—
12/06	246	8	3.3%	—
12/06	675	0	0.0%	—
Annual Growth	(15.4%)	372.1%	—	—

2012 Year-End Financials

Debt ratio: ——
Return on equity: 3.00%
Cash ($ mil.): 2
Current ratio: 0.10
Long-term debt ($ mil.): —

Dividends
Yield: —
Payout: —
Market value ($ mil.): —

UNITED STATES FUND FOR UNICEF

The US Fund for UNICEF is one of about 40 committees in America that raises money for The United Nations Children's Fund (better known as UNICEF a not-for-profit organization that works for the human rights protection and development of children worldwide through education advocacy and fundraising. Among its dedicated programs are the five-year $100 million fundraising campaign for HIV/AIDS prevention and a campaign to protect mothers and newborns from tetanus. The US Fund for UNICEF derives revenue from public support –through its signature Trick-or-Treat for UNICEF program gifts corporate grants and the sale of greeting cards and educational materials. The organization was founded in 1947.

Geographic Reach

The US Fund for UNICEF operates a handful of regional offices in Atlanta Boston Chicago Houston Los Angeles and San Francisco.

Financial Performance

The organization's revenue increased by 1% in 2012 versus 2011 to more than $500 million. The US Fund attributed the gain to an increase in public support including major gifts Internet donations and gifts in kind. The increase in giving was partially offset by a decline in investment returns. Net income rose 7% over the same period despite an increase in expenses tied to program and support services.

Strategy

The US Fund for UNICEF is rallying around its "Believe in Zero" campaign which aims to reduce the number of preventable deaths of children under five years of age to zero. The number of under-five child deaths has dropped more than 40 percent since 1990 to 19000.

EXECUTIVES

SVP Development, Robert Thompson, age 55
Chief Operating Officer Chief Financial Officer, Edward G. Lloyd
Vice President Finance & Budget, Richard Esserman
Chairman, Anthony (Tony) Pantaleoni
President Chief Executive Officer, Caryl M. Stern
VP Public Relations, Lisa Szarkowski
VP Human Resources, William B. Sherwood
Deputy Chief of Staff to the President and CEO, Brian Meyers
Vice President Corporate Partnerships, Deanna Helmig
Senior Vice President Development, Barron Segar
President The UPS Foundation, Ed Martinez
Vice President Direct Response & Integrated Monthly Giving, Helene Vallone-Raffaele
Vice President Office of Public Policy & Advocacy, Martin Rendon
Vice President Marketing and Communications, Alisa Aydin
Director, Nelson J. Chai, age 49
Director, Vincent J. (Vince) Hemmer, age 45
Director, Daniel J. (Dan) Brutto, age 57
Director, Gary M. Cohen
Director, Tea Leoni

LOCATIONS

HQ: UNITED STATES FUND FOR UNICEF
125 MAIDEN LN FL 11, NEW YORK, NY 10038-4999
Phone: 212-686-5522
Web: WWW.UNICEF.ORG

PRODUCTS/OPERATIONS

2012 Revenue

	% of total
Gifts-in-kind	71
Direct	6
Major	6
Internet	5
Corporate	4
Foundations	3
Bequests and	2
Non-governmental	1
Special	1
Trick-or-treat	1
Total	**100**

HISTORICAL FINANCIALS

Company Type: Private

Income Statement FYE: June 30

	REVENUE ($ mil.)	NET INCOME ($ mil.)	NET PROFIT MARGIN	EMPLOYEES
06/12	211	6	3.3%	200
06/10	243	0	0.4%	—
06/09	225	2	1.0%	—
06/08	229	10	4.4%	—
Annual Growth	(2.0%)	(9.2%)	—	—

2012 Year-End Financials

Debt ratio: ——
Return on equity: 3.30%
Cash ($ mil.): 33
Current ratio: 0.40
Long-term debt ($ mil.): —

Dividends
Yield: —
Payout: —
Market value ($ mil.): —

UNITYPOINT HEALTH

The land where the tall corn grows is also the land of Iowa Health System (IHS). The integrated health care system operates some 15 acute care hospitals that serve large communities throughout Iowa as well as parts of western Illinois and eastern Nebraska. IHS also supports about a dozen rural hospitals and it manages more than 200 physician clinics located in rural and suburban areas. The system's hospitals provide general medical-surgical care as well as care in a number of medical specialties such as cardiovascular disease and home health services. Founded in 1993 HIS has about 3100 licensed beds some 630 physicians and 235 mid-level medical professionals.

Strategy IHS expands its network through affiliations. In late 2012 it brought Stewart Memorial Community Hospital in Lake City into its network just as it had done the previous year with Methodist Health Services operator of the 330-bed Methodist Medical Center of Illinois located in Peoria. IHS also committed $175 million to help Methodist-Illinois enhance its technologies and its service offerings. The health system operates many of its member hospitals through similar affiliation agreements; IHS provides administration contracting billing legal recruitment information technology and other central services.

EXECUTIVES

President Chief Executive Officer, Bill Leaver
Vice President General Counsel, Denny Drake
Chair, Jim Hoffman
Treasurer and Director, Bruce Sherman
VP and CIO, Joy M. Grosser
Senior Vice President CMO, Alan S. Kaplan
EVP and CFO, Kevin Vermeer
Vice President Finance, Kara Dunham
VP-Sys Dev, Tom Tibbitts
Vice President Government Relations, Sabra Rosener
Vice President People Excellence, Emily Porter
Senior Vice President Population, Michael Murphy
Interim Vice President Supply Chain Management, Katie Marchik
Interim Senior Vice President and Chief Fnancial Officer, Mark Johnson
Vice President Accountable Care Organization, Aric Sharp
Director, Gene Blanc
Director, Bill Prowell
Director, Kathy Eno
Director, Terri Christoffersen
Director, Ronald Klosterman
Treasurer and Director, Bruce Sherman
Director, Kurt Pittner
Auditors: Deloitte&ToucheLLP

LOCATIONS

HQ: UNITYPOINT HEALTH
1776 WEST LAKES PKWY # 400, WEST DES MOINES, IA 50266-8239
Phone: 515-241-6161
Web: WWW.IOWAHEALTH.ORG

PRODUCTS/OPERATIONS

Selected Facilities

Metropolitan Hospitals
- Allen Memorial Hospital Corporation (Waterloo Iowa)
- Iowa Lutheran Hospital (Des Moines Iowa)
- Iowa Methodist Medical Center (Des Moines Iowa)
  - Blank Children's Hospital (Des Moines Iowa)
- Methodist Medical Center of Illinois (Peoria Illinois)
- Methodist West Hospital (West Des Moines Iowa)
- St. Luke's Hospital (Cedar Rapids Iowa)
- St. Luke's Regional Medical Center (Sioux City Iowa)
- Jones Regional Medical Center (Anamosa Iowa)
- The Finley Hospital (Dubuque Iowa)
- Trinity Bettendorf (Bettendorf Iowa)
- Trinity Moline (Moline Illinois)
- Trinity Muscatine (Muscatine Iowa)
- Trinity Regional Medical Center (Fort Dodge Iowa)
- Trinity Rock Island (Rock Island Illinois)

Rural Hospitals
- Buena Vista Regional Medical Center (Storm Lake Iowa)
- Clarke County Hospital (Osceola Iowa)
- Community Memorial Hospital (Sumner Iowa)
- Greater Regional Medical Center (Creston Iowa)
- Greene County Medical Center (Jefferson Iowa)
- Grundy County Memorial Hospital (Grundy Center Iowa)
- Guthrie County Hospital (Guthrie Center Iowa)
- Guttenberg Municipal Hospital (Guttenberg Iowa)
- Humboldt County Memorial Hospital (Humboldt Iowa)
- Loring Hospital (Sac City Iowa)
- Pocahontas Community Hospital (Pocahantas Iowa)

COMPETITORS

Alegent Creighton Health
Avera Health
Blessing Hospital
Genesis Health System
McDonough District Hospital
Mercy Health Network
Methodist Health System
ORHC
OSF Healthcare System
University of Iowa Hospitals and Clinics

HISTORICAL FINANCIALS

Company Type: Private

Income Statement FYE: December 31

	REVENUE ($ mil.)	NET INCOME ($ mil.)	NET PROFIT MARGIN	EMPLOYEES
12/11	2,380	159	6.7%	18,923
12/09*	109	(51)	—	—
09/09	0	0	—	—
12/07	1,874	108	5.8%	—
Annual Growth	6.1%	10.1%	—	—

*Fiscal year change

2011 Year-End Financials

Debt ratio: —
Return on equity: 6.70%
Cash ($ mil.): 96
Current ratio: 1.00
Long-term debt ($ mil.): —
Dividends
Yield: —
Payout: —
Market value ($ mil.): —

UNIVERSITY CORPORATION FOR ATMOSPHERIC RESEARCH

The University Corporation for Atmospheric Research (UCAR) is a not-for-profit corporation founded in 1960 to promote research in atmospheric and related environmental sciences. A consortium of more than 100 universities UCAR provides real-time weather data to universities educates weather forecasters and organizes international experiments through its Office of Programs. The organization also maintains radars aircraft and computer models for weather and climate through the National Center for Atmospheric Research (NCAR). UCAR is funded by sponsors such as the National Science Foundation the National Oceanic and Atmospheric Administration and NASA.

Geographic Reach

The University Corporation for Atmospheric Research (UCAR) and the National Center for Atmospheric Research (NCAR) are both based in Boulder Colorado. They have additional operations in Cheyenne Wyoming and Washington DC. Its affiliated Mauna Loa Solar Observatory is based in Hilo Hawaii.

Operations

The UCAR consortium consists of around 75 North American universities granting doctoral degrees related to atmospheric science 25 offering bachelor's and master's programs in this dame filed and roughly 50 international affiliates.

In addition to promoting research and professional development among academia UCAR provides educational resources to the public and advocates for strong federal science budgets on behalf of the geosciences community.

Strategy

To extend its reach in 2012 the UCAR opened NCAR-Wyoming Supercomputing Center which provides advanced computing services to scientists with expertise in air pollution climate oceanography space weather energy production seismology carbon sequestration computational science and other topics.

EXECUTIVES

VP Finance and Administration, Kathryn S. (Katy) Schmoll
Director Business Development & Partnerships, Scott Rayder
Director Budget and Finance, Melissa Miller
Director Information Technology, Shawn Winkelman
President, Thomas J. Bogdan
Director Government Relations, Mike Henry

LOCATIONS

HQ: UNIVERSITY CORPORATION FOR ATMOSPHERIC RESEARCH
3090 CENTER GREEN DR, BOULDER, CO 80301-2252
Phone: 303-497-1000
Web: WWW.UCAR.EDU

PRODUCTS/OPERATIONS

Selected Research Topics

Climate
Meterology/Weather
Societal impacts of weather and climate
Pollution and air chemistry
The whole Earth system
Sun & space weather

HISTORICAL FINANCIALS

Company Type: Private

Income Statement FYE: September 30

	REVENUE ($ mil.)	NET INCOME ($ mil.)	NET PROFIT MARGIN	EMPLOYEES
09/12	260	13	5.1%	1,565
09/11	269	48	17.8%	—
09/10	241	21	9.0%	—
09/09	215	(0)	—	—
Annual Growth	6.6%	—	—	—

2012 Year-End Financials

Debt ratio: —
Return on equity: 5.10%
Cash ($ mil.): 9
Current ratio: 0.70
Long-term debt ($ mil.): —
Dividends
Yield: —
Payout: —
Market value ($ mil.): —

UNIVERSITY HEALTH CARE INC

University Health Care which does business as Passport Health Plan provides managed Medicaid insurance services to 130000 members throughout 16 counties in Kentucky. University Health Care was founded in 1997 by a group of providers that includes University of Louisville Hospital Jewish Hospital and the Louisville/Jefferson County Primary Care Association.

EXECUTIVES

Vp Public Affairs, Jill Joseph Bell
Vice President Operations, Christie Spencer

LOCATIONS

HQ: UNIVERSITY HEALTH CARE INC
305 W BROADWAY STE 300, LOUISVILLE, KY 40202-2122
Phone: 502-585-7900
Web: WWW.PASSPORTHEALTHPLAN.COM

COMPETITORS

AMERIGROUP
Aetna
Anthem Health Plans of Kentucky
Bluegrass Family Health
CIGNA
Health Net
HealthSpring
Humana
Kaiser Foundation Health Plan
UnitedHealth Group

HISTORICAL FINANCIALS

Company Type: Private

Income Statement FYE: December 31

	REVENUE ($ mil.)	NET INCOME ($ mil.)	NET PROFIT MARGIN	EMPLOYEES
12/09	913	6	0.7%	165
12/00	330	3	1.2%	—
12/99	284	5	2.0%	—
12/98	240	(1)	—	—
Annual Growth	12.9%	—	—	—

2009 Year-End Financials

Debt ratio: —
Return on equity: 0.70%
Cash ($ mil.): 60
Current ratio: 0.80
Long-term debt ($ mil.): —
Dividends
Yield: —
Payout: —
Market value ($ mil.): —

UNIVERSITY HEALTH SYSTEMS OF EASTERN CAROLINA INC.

University Health Systems of Eastern Carolina is an integrated not-for-profit health system that serves residents of eastern North Carolina. Doing business as Vidant Health it operates nine hospitals including eight community hospitals and its tertiary care center Vidant Medical Center with 900 beds and academic affiliation with the Brody School of Medicine at East Carolina University. Vidant Health also operates centers for surgery home health hospice and wellness and engages in community health programs. Its physician group has more than 300 primary and specialty care providers who operate from more than 50 locations.

Geographic Reach

The organization serves more than 1.4 million residents in 29 counties in eastern North Carolina.

Operations

In addition to its nine hospitals the organization includes the Vidant Home Health and Hospice organization the Vidant Wellness Centers and the growing line of Vidant Medical Group physician practice locations. Vidant Health's facilities handle some 68000 inpatient and 760000 emergency care and outpatient visits each year. The organization also provides some $143 million in annual community benefits including outreach programs and charity care.

Financial Performance

The company has reported increased earnings and profits in recent years due to a rise in demand for inpatient services as well as due to increased operational efficiencies and successful cost-reduction programs. In 2012 Vidant Health reported a 19% increase in revenues to $1.55 billion and a 152% increase in net income to some $125 million.

Strategy

University Health Systems rebranded itself as Vidant Health in 2012 in its effort to reflect its "vibrant and vital" position within the region as it advances its transformation to patient- and family-centered care.

Because the system operates as a not-for-profit enterprise it reinvests its earnings in capital improvements equipment and new services. In 2012 the hospital invested in upgrades to several outpatient care centers adding a new medical office building in the community of Wallace and adding specialist rehabilitation and behavioral health care units to its Vidant Chowan Hospital facility. It also discontinued skilled nursing services at the Chowan location to focus more on outpatient care. In addition a new children's hospital and pediatric emergency room was opened at the Vidant Medical Center location.

Vidant Health is also working to upgrade its health information technology systems. During 2012 it successfully connected three of its community hospitals through its electronic health record (EHR) system.

EXECUTIVES

President and COO, David C. Herman
CIO, Stuart M. James
CEO, David C. (Dave) McRae
CFO, Jack W. Holsten
General Counsel, Nancy B. Aycock
President East Carolina Health and HealthAccess, Roger Robertson
President Pitt County Memorial Hospital, Stephen J. Lawler
Public Relations Coordinator, Barbara D. Dunn
VP Human Resources, Tyree Walker
Assistant VP Financial Services, Valerie J. Dixon
VP Supply Chain Management and Finance Support Services, Preston N. Comeaux III
Senior Projects Officer, Linda Roberson
President Heritage Hospital, Wendell (Wick) Baker
Chief External Affairs Officer and President UHS/PMH Foundations, Joel K. Butler
VP Information Technology and Chief Medical Information Officer, David Michael
Chief Audit and Compliance Officer, John C. Falcetano
President Roanoke-Chowan Hospital, Susan S. Lassiter
President Bertie Memorial Hospital and Chowan Hospital, Jeffrey N. Sackrison
VP Corporate Accreditation and Regulatory Compliance, Carmen R. Vincent
Chief Design and Construction Officer, Timothy J. McDonnell
Media Specialist, Beth Anne Atkins
VP Service and Patient Family Experience, Sue Collier
Chief Strategic Development and Marketing Officer, Anissa B. Davenport
VP Financial Services East Carolina Health, Lynn Lanier
Chief Administrative Officer, Janet Mullaney
Executive Director University Health Systems of Eastern Carolina Foundation and Pitt Memorial Hospital Foundation, Kenneth M. Turpen
Chief Quality and Patient Safety Officer, Joan D. Wynn
President Duplin General Hospital, William H. Case
President The Outer Banks Hospital, Van Smith
Chief Growth and Development Officer, Kathy G. Barger
VP Community Benefit and Government Relations, Michelle Brooks
VP UHS Physician Services, Travis Douglass
Executive Director UHS Foundation, N. Kinney Hart
President Albemarle Hospital, Sharon Tanner
SVP Financial Services Vidant Health, David Hughes

LOCATIONS

HQ: UNIVERSITY HEALTH SYSTEMS OF EASTERN CAROLINA INC.
2100 STANTONSBURG RD, GREENVILLE, NC 27834-2818
Phone: 252-847-4451
Web: WWW.PCMH.COM

PRODUCTS/OPERATIONS

Selected Hospitals

Vidant Beaufort Hospital (Washington)
Vidant Bertie Hospital (Windsor)
Vidant Chowan Hospital (Edenton)
Vidant Duplin Hospital (Kenansville)
Vidant Edgecombe Hospital (Tarboro)
Vidant Medical Center (affiliated with the Brody School of Medicine at East Carolina University Greenville)
Vidant Pungo Hospital (Belhaven)
Vidant Roanoke-Chowan Hospital (Ahoskie)
The Outer Banks Hospital (jointly owned with Chesapeake Regional Medical Center Nags Head)

Selected Services

Asthma Program (Pediatric)
Audiology
Behavioral & Mental Health
Cancer Care
Child Life
Children' s Care
Children' s Emergency Department
Children' s Hospital
Community Health Programs
Diagnostic Imaging
Diabetes
Emergency Services
Endoscopy Services
Gamma Knife
Heart and Vascular Care
Heartburn Treatment Clinic
Home Health
Hospice Care
Hyperbaric Oxygen Therapy
Injury Prevention
Mammography
Medical Weight Loss (OPTIFAST)
Mental Health
MRI (Magnetic Resonance Imaging)
Neurosciences
Neurosurgery
Open MRI
Orthopedics
Pain Management
Pediatric Cardiology
Pediatric Rehabilitation
Pediatric Services
Pink Power Speaking Tour
Psychiatry
Radiology
Rehabilitation Center
Rehabilitation
Senior Services
Sleep Services
Specialty Services
Speech Pathology
Spine Surgery
Sports Medicine
Stroke Care
Surgical Services
Transplant Services
Trauma Services
Vascular Surgery
Weight Loss
Wellness & Prevention
Women' s Care
Wound Healing

COMPETITORS

Alamance Regional Medical Center
Carolinas HealthCare System
Cumberland County Hospital System
Duke University Health System
Grace Hospital
Novant Health
Rex Healthcare
Rowan Regional Medical Center
UNC Hospitals
WakeMed

HISTORICAL FINANCIALS

Company Type: Private

Income Statement FYE: September 30

	REVENUE ($ mil.)	NET INCOME ($ mil.)	NET PROFIT MARGIN	EMPLOYEES
09/13	1,601	109	6.8%	8,373
09/11*	1,304	68	5.2%	—
12/10	318	30	9.5%	—
09/09	0	0	—	—
Annual Growth	—	—	—	—

*Fiscal year change

2013 Year-End Financials

Debt ratio: —
Return on equity: 6.80%
Cash ($ mil.): 102
Current ratio: 1.60
Long-term debt ($ mil.): —
Dividends
Yield: —
Payout: —
Market value ($ mil.): —

UNIVERSITY HOSPITALS HEALTH SYSTEM INC.

University Hospitals Health System (UHHS) is on a mission to teach research and administer good health throughout northeastern Ohio. Its flagship facility University Hospitals of Cleveland (UHC) which operates as University Hospitals Case Medical Center (UHCMC) is a 1000-bed tertiary care center serving Cleveland and other parts of northeastern Ohio. The teaching hospital which is affiliated with Case Western Reserve University is also home to Rainbow Babies & Children's Hospital Seidman Cancer Center and MacDonald Women's Hospital. Founded in 1866 the not-for-profit UHHS is also home to community hospitals outpatient health and surgery centers mental health facilities and senior care centers.

Geographic Reach

UHHS operates more than 30 health centers and outpatient office buildings as well as more than 100 physician practice locations across the northeastern Ohio region.

Operations

UHHS' six community hospitals some of which are operated through affiliation agreements provide a full range of specialty and general acute care from anesthesia to vascular surgery. Along with those the system operates urgent care and neighborhood medical centers throughout the region. The UH Extended Care Campus includes a specialty hospital outpatient rehabilitation and extended care facility. UHHS also operates home health occupational health wellness and managed care (health plan) divisions.

Altogether the network's facilities handle some 65000 inpatient visits per year as well as 5.5 million outpatient procedures and 180000 emergency room visits. The UHHS facilities have a total of some 1800 beds.

In addition to conducting education and training programs for Case Western Reserve University School of Medicine students UHHS partners with the university to operate the Center for Clinical Research and Technology. The center is the largest biomedical research facility in Ohio and focuses on translational research which connects laboratory research to clinical bedside care.

Financial Performance

UHHS' revenues increased 10% to $2.2 billion in 2011 over 2010 results due to higher patient service revenues.

Strategy

The medical system is expanding by installing smaller regional and community hospitals and additional specialty care units within its larger facilities including a neonatal intensive care unit emergency care center and a cancer care center within UH Case Medical.

UHHS completed construction of the UH Ahuja Medical Center a new community hospital in 2011. It also opened a new outpatient center the UH Aurora Health Center the following year. To expand in another neighboring community the system launched renovation of an office building that will become the UH Solon Health Center in 2013.

UHHS is also in the process of implementing an electronic health records (EHR) system across its facilities. The EHR system could make the network eligible for certain government incentives if they meet government guidelines for "meaningful use."

EXECUTIVES

Chairman, Alfred M. Rankin Jr., age 72
President University Hospitals Case Medical Center, Fred C. Rothstein
CEO, Thomas F. (Tom) Zenty III, age 59
COO; COO Clinical Operations, Achilles A. Demetriou
President Community Hospitals and Ambulatory Network, Richard A. (Dick) Hanson
CFO, Michael A. (Mike) Szubski
President University Hospitals Seidman Cancer Center, Nathan Levitan
Chief Medical Officer and President University Hospitals Accountable Care Organization, Eric J. Bieber
President University Hospitals Physician Services, Michael L. Nochomovitz, age 62
Chief Nursing Officer, Catherine S. (Cathy) Koppelman
Director Media Relations, Janice Guhl
Chief Legal Officer, Janet L. Miller
Chief Administrative Officer, Steven D. (Steve) Standley
President University Hospitals Bedford and Richmond Medical Centers Campuses of UH Regional Hospitals, Laurie S. Delgado
President University Hospitals Conneaut Medical Center; President University Hospitals Geneva Medical Center, Robert G. David
President University Hospitals Geauga Medical Center, M. Steven Jones
Chief Quality Officer and Director University Hospitals Quality Institute, William L. Annable
VP and Chief Compliance Officer, Cheryl Forino Wahl
President University Hospitals Rainbow Babies and Children?s Hospital and University Hospitals MacDonald Women?s Hospital, Patricia DePompei
President University Hospitals Ahuja Medical Center, Susan V. Juris
President St. John Medical Center, William A. Young Jr.
Chief Medical Officer, Amitabh Goel
Vice President, Joseph Shawi
Director, Henry L. Meyer III, age 64
Director, Paul G. Clark, age 60
Director, Richard W. Pogue
Director, Joseph (Joe) Lopez
Director, April M. Boise
Director, Brian E. Hall
Director, Ronald G. Harrington
Director, William E. Kamatz Sr.
Director, Robert A. Salata
Auditors: Ernst&YoungLLP

LOCATIONS

HQ: UNIVERSITY HOSPITALS HEALTH SYSTEM INC.
3605 WARRENSVILLE CTR RD, SHAKER HEIGHTS, OH 44122-5203
Phone: 216-844-1000
Web: WWW.UHHOSPITALS.ORG

PRODUCTS/OPERATIONS

Selected Facilities

Main Campuses
- Case Medical Center
- MacDonald Women' s Hospital
- Rainbow Babies & Children' s Hospital
- Seidman Cancer Center

Community Hospitals
- Ahuja Medical Center
- Bedford Medical Center (UH Regional Hospitals)
- Conneaut Medical Center
- Geauga Medical Center
- Geneva Medical Center
- Richmond Medical Center (UH Regional Hospitals)

COMPETITORS

Akron Children' s Hospital
Akron General Health System
Lake Health
Mercy Medical Center (OH)
MetroHealth System
Parma Community General Hospital
Robinson Memorial Hospital
Summa Health System
The Cleveland Clinic
Trinity Health System

HISTORICAL FINANCIALS

Company Type: Private

Income Statement FYE: December 31

	REVENUE ($ mil.)	NET INCOME ($ mil.)	NET PROFIT MARGIN	EMPLOYEES
12/12	2,266	54	2.4%	30,000
12/09	1,938	110	5.7%	—
12/08	1,800	(153)	—	—
Annual Growth	5.9%	—	—	—

2012 Year-End Financials

Debt ratio: —
Return on equity: 2.40%
Cash ($ mil.): 179
Current ratio: 1.30
Long-term debt ($ mil.): —
Dividends
Yield: —
Payout: —
Market value ($ mil.): —

UNIVERSITY OF GEORGIA

Located in the quintessential college town of Athens The University of Georgia (UGA) offers a wide range of degree programs to nearly 35000 students. Forest resources veterinary medicine and law are a few of the school's academic programs. UGA which also runs 170-plus study-abroad and exchange programs administers the prestigious Peabody Awards which honors media achievements and boasts one of the nation's largest map collections. Famous alumni include former US Senator Phil Gramm TV journalist Deborah Norville and former PBS president Pat Mitchell. The University of Georgia was chartered by the State of Georgia in 1785 and graduated its first class in 1804.

Operations

As part of its business UGA offers nearly two dozen bachelor's degrees in about 140 fields and roughly 35 master's degrees in nearly 140 fields. Its doctorate or professional degrees cover a broad spectrum of disciplines such as law pharmacy veterinary medicine and 90 other areas. The university has a student-teacher ratio of about 12:1.

Strategy

Despite its annual endowment of more than $50 million UGA has logged decreases in state appropriations in recent years due to overall declines in Georgia's budget. The result spurred UGA to cut its budget increase undergraduate tuition fees institute a "Special Institutional" mandatory fee of $200 per semester reduce employer health insurance contributions and increase energy conservation measures. Going forward UGA has also not ruled out the possibility of hiking tuition further citing that an increase of up to 30% would help to replace all of the state funding the university has lost due to the recession.

Sales and Marketing

The university sources 80% of its students from the Peach State. Since 1851 25 Georgia governors have graduated from UGA. The institution also boasts nine Pulitzer Prize recipients 17 presidents or provosts of US colleges and universities and four members of the National Academy of Sciences.

EXECUTIVES

Vice Chairman, Philip A. Wilheit, age 69
President, Michael F. Adams
VP Student Affairs and Dean Students, Rodney D. Bennett
Dean Graduate School, Maureen Grasso
Dean School of Law, Rebecca H. White
Dean College of Public Health, Phillip L. Williams
Dean School of Public and International Affairs, Thomas P. Lauth
Dean School of Social Work, Maurice C. Daniels
Dean College of Veterinary Medicine, Sheila Allen
VP Public Affairs, Tom Jackson
Dean Grady College of Journalism and Mass Communication, E. Culpepper (Cully) Clark
SVP External Affairs, Tom S. Landrum
SVP Academic Affairs and Provost, Jere W. Morehead
Dean Terry College of Business, Robert T. Sumichrast
Dean Odum School of Ecology, John Gittleman
Dean College of Environment and Design, Daniel J. Nadenicek
Chairman, William Nesmith Jr.
Chancellor, Hank Huckaby
SVP Finance and Administration, Timothy P. Burgess
Dean College of Pharmacy, Svein Oie

LOCATIONS

HQ: UNIVERSITY OF GEORGIA
456 E BROAD ST, ATHENS, GA 30602-1536
Phone: 706-542-6860
Web: WWW.CCRC.UGA.EDU

PRODUCTS/OPERATIONS

Selected Schools and Colleges

Agricultural and Environmental Sciences
Arts and Sciences Business
Ecology
Education
Environment and Design
Family and Consumer Sciences
Forest Resources
Graduate School
Journalism and Mass Communication
Law
Pharmacy
Public Health
Public and International Affairs
Social Work

Veterinary Medicine
The GHSU/UGA Medical Partnership
Engineering

HISTORICAL FINANCIALS

Company Type: Private

Income Statement FYE: June 30

	REVENUE ($ mil.)	NET INCOME ($ mil.)	NET PROFIT MARGIN	EMPLOYEES
06/12	776	72	9.3%	17,800
06/11	691	(12)	—	—
06/10	636	134	21.2%	—
06/09	627	63	10.0%	—
Annual Growth	7.4%	4.5%	—	—

2012 Year-End Financials

Debt ratio: —
Return on equity: 9.30%
Cash ($ mil.): 269
Current ratio: 2.50
Long-term debt ($ mil.): —
Dividends
Yield: —
Payout: —
Market value ($ mil.): —

UNIVERSITY OF GEORGIA RESEARCH FOUNDATION INC.

LOCATIONS

HQ: UNIVERSITY OF GEORGIA RESEARCH FOUNDATION INC.
200 D W BROOKS DR, ATHENS, GA 306025016
Phone: 7065425939

HISTORICAL FINANCIALS

Company Type: Private

Income Statement FYE: June 30

	ASSETS ($ mil.)	NET INCOME ($ mil.)	INCOME AS % OF ASSETS	EMPLOYEES
06/11	434	4	1.0%	1
06/10	93	(5)	—	—
06/09	2	0	0.8%	—
Annual Growth	1368.0%	1563.2%	—	—

2011 Year-End Financials

Debt ratio: —
Return on equity: 2.50%
Cash ($ mil.): 27
Current ratio: 0.50
Long-term debt ($ mil.): —
Dividends
Yield: —
Payout: —
Market value ($ mil.): —

UNIVERSITY OF KENTUCKY HOSPITAL AUXILIARY INC.

For the times when there's a physical reason to be carried "back to my old Kentucky home" being lugged to University of Kentucky Chandler Hospital (UK Chandler Hospital) might be a better option. The 500-bed academic hospital is operated by the University of Kentucky Auxiliary. It is located within the University of Kentucky Medical Center complex which includes the specialized medical colleges of the University of Kentucky and their affiliated clinical treatment facilities (organized under the UK HealthCare umbrella). UK Chandler Hospital's services include oncology pediatrics cardiology orthopedics and women's health and it operates eastern Kentucky's only Level I trauma and Level III neonatal ICU units.

In addition to overseeing the UK Chandler Hospital UK HealthCare operates the Kentucky Children's Hospital (located within the Chandler Hospital building) the Markey Cancer Center and other outpatient clinics located within the UK Medical Center complex. UK HealthCare also manages the 300-bed UK Good Samaritan Hospital which is located nearby and numerous regional primary and specialty care clinics.

The Lexington campus also houses six UK health-related colleges: medicine nursing dentistry pharmacy health science and public health. UK Chandler Hospital conducts a variety of training and residency programs in partnership with the schools.

UK HealthCare completed the first phase of the new UK Chandler Hospital pavilion in 2011 adding new emergency trauma and inpatient bed facilities. The new pavilion is gradually being expanded and will eventually (in six to 10 years) take over as the primary building for the UK Chandler Hospital replacing the current facilities (which date back to 1962).

The UK Chandler Hospital was organized in 1957 on the university's Lexington campus and was named after former Kentucky governor Albert B. "Happy" Chandler.

EXECUTIVES

VP Medical Center Operations, Frank A. Butler
Associate VP Medical Center Operations, Murray B. Clark Jr.
EVP Health Affairs, Michael Karpf
VP Clinical Affairs; Dean College of Medicine The University of Kentucky, Jay Perman
CFO, Sergio Melgar
Chief Medical Officer, Richard (Rick) Lofgrenn
Chief of Staff, Courtney Higdon
Auditors: Deloitte&ToucheLLP

LOCATIONS

HQ: UNIVERSITY OF KENTUCKY HOSPITAL AUXILIARY INC.
800 ROSE ST, LEXINGTON, KY 40536-0001
Phone: 859-323-5000
Web: WWW.UNIVERSITYOFKENTUCKYHOSPITAL.COM

COMPETITORS

Appalachian Regional Healthcare
Baptist Health
Bon Secours Health
Catholic Health Initiatives
Community Health Systems
Highlands Health
Jewish Hospital & St. Mary's HealthCare
Norton Healthcare
Pikeville Medical Center
SunBridge Healthcare Corporation

HISTORICAL FINANCIALS

Company Type: Private

Income Statement FYE: June 30

	REVENUE ($ mil.)	NET INCOME ($ mil.)	NET PROFIT MARGIN	EMPLOYEES
06/12	912	13	1.4%	2,879
06/11	797	41	5.2%	—
06/10	785	39	5.0%	—
06/09	704	(47)	—	—
Annual Growth	9.0%	—	—	—

2012 Year-End Financials

Debt ratio: —
Return on equity: 1.40%
Cash ($ mil.): 12
Current ratio: 0.70
Long-term debt ($ mil.): —
Dividends
Yield: —
Payout: —
Market value ($ mil.): —

UNIVERSITY OF MAINE SYSTEM

University of Maine System is composed of seven public universities throughout Maine serving some 40000 students. It also operates eight regional outreach centers as well as distance education programs. The University of Maine System offers nearly 600 majors minors and concentrations; its flagship campus in Orono (UMaine) offers nearly 90 bachelor's degree programs more than 60 master's degree programs and about two dozen doctoral programs. UMaine was established in 1862 as the Maine College of Agriculture and Mechanic Arts; it adopted its current name in 1897. The University of Maine System was created in 1968 by the state legislature.

Financial Performance

In 2012 the University of Maine System saw a 2% decrease in revenue vs. 2011 resulting from a decline in residence and dining fees as fewer students made use of those services and increased scholarship allowances. The revenue decline was partially offset by rising tuition and fees. Net income fell 53% over the same period due to a decline in non-operating revenue related to a decrease in State Fiscal Stabilization Funds and declining support from state appropriatoions since 2009.

EXECUTIVES

President University of Southern Maine, Selma Botman
President University of Maine, Paul W. Ferguson
President University of Maine Farmington, Theodora J. (Theo) Kalikow
President University of Maine Machias, Cynthia E. Huggins
President University of Maine Presque Isle, Don Zillman
Chancellor, James Page
CIO, Richard Thompson
President University of Maine at Augusta, Allyson Hughes Handley
President University of Maine at Fort Kent, Wilson G. Hess
Executive Director of Public Affairs, Bob Caswell
President Phi Kappa Phi, Kreg Ettenger
CFO, Richard Campbell
CEO of US Ivy League Cooperation China, Frank Xu
Vice President, Abby Snow
Executive Vice President, Damian Labree

Assistant Vice President For Research, James Ward
Vc Fin/admin/treasurer, Rebecca Wyke
Board Member, Richard Judd
Secretary, Margaret Weigang
Board Member, Chris Boucher
Board Member, Annette Nelligan
Board Member, Samantha H Lott
Auditors: KPMGLLP

LOCATIONS

HQ: UNIVERSITY OF MAINE SYSTEM
16 CENTRAL ST, BANGOR, ME 04401-5106
Phone: 207-973-3300
Web: WWW.MAINE.EDU

PRODUCTS/OPERATIONS

System Universiti
University of Maine
University of Maine at Augusta
University of Maine at Farmington
University of Maine at Fort Kent
University of Maine at Machias
University of Maine at Presque Isle
University of Southern Maine Maine Law School

HISTORICAL FINANCIALS

Company Type: Private

Income Statement FYE: June 30

	REVENUE ($ mil.)	NET INCOME ($ mil.)	NET PROFIT MARGIN	EMPLOYEES
06/12	476	37	8.0%	5,379
06/06	390	33	8.7%	—
06/05	381	53	14.1%	—
06/04	272	0	—	—
Annual Growth	—	—	—	—

2012 Year-End Financials

Debt ratio: —
Return on equity: 8.00%
Cash ($ mil.): 1
Current ratio: —
Long-term debt ($ mil.): —
Dividends
Yield: —
Payout: —
Market value ($ mil.): —

UNIVERSITY OF MISSISSIPPI

They call her "Ole Miss" and she really is old: The University of Mississippi was chartered in 1844 as the first public university in the state and opened in 1848. Starting with 80 students the school's enrollment has grown to more than 21000 with most students attending the main Oxford campus. Ole Miss has additional campuses in Southaven (Desoto County) and Tupelo and it operates the University of Mississippi Medical Center in Jackson. The school is home to more than 30 research centers that specialize in business engineering law and other disciplines. Its academic institutes include the Croft Institute for International Studies and the William Winter Institute for Racial Reconciliation.

Geographic Reach

Minorities make up almost a fourth of Ole Miss students and more than two-thirds of all students at the university come from within the state. The student-faculty ratio is 19:1.

Operations

The Medical Center campus includes Mississippi's only children's hospital a women and infants' hospital and a critical care hospital. It is also home to the state's only level one trauma center level three neonatal intensive care nursery and organ transplant programs.

EXECUTIVES

Chancellor, Daniel W. Jones
Director Human Resources, Clayton H. (Clay) Jones
Dean of Libraries, Julia M. Rholes
Associate Provost; Dean Graduate School, Maurice Eftink
Assistant Provost Assistant to the Chancellor for Multicultural Affairs and Professor of Mathematics, Donald Cole
Vice Chancellor Research and Sponsored Programs, Alice M. Clark
Vice Chancellor Administration and Finance, Larry D. Sparks
Senior Administrative Secretary, Kim Barnes
Executive Assistant, Peggy Hunter
Senior Administrative Secretary, Janet Key
Executive Assistant to the Chancellor and Associate Professor of Education, Andrew Mullins Jr.
Assistant to the Chancellor, Sue Keiser
Provost and Vice Chancellor Academic Affairs, Morris H. Stocks
Vice Chancellor for Student Affairs, Larry D. Ridgeway
President t.co Wpdlvbounk, Scott Schulman

LOCATIONS

HQ: UNIVERSITY OF MISSISSIPPI
113 FALKNER, UNIVERSITY, MS 38677-9704
Phone: 662-915-7361
Web: WWW.LAW.OLEMISS.EDU

PRODUCTS/OPERATIONS

Selected Colleges and Schools

Colleges
- The College of Liberal Arts
- The Residential College
- The Sally McDonnell Barksdale Honors College
- The University of Mississippi
  - Booneville (branch)
  - Grenada (branch)
  - Southaven Campus
  - Tupelo Campus
- The University of Mississippi Graduate School
- The University of Mississippi Medical Center

Schools
- Meek School of Journalism and News Media
- Patterson School of Accountancy
- School of Applied Science
- School of Business Administration
- School of Education
- School of Engineering
- School of Law
- School of Nursing (at The University of Mississippi Medical Center)
- School of Pharmacy

Selected Research Centers

Center for Advanced Infrastructure Technology
Center for Applied Electromagnetic Systems Research
Center for Archaeological Research
Center for Community Earthquake Preparedness
Center for Educational Research and Evaluation
Center for Excellence in Literacy Instruction
Center for Excellence in Teaching and Learning
Center for Health Behavior Research
Center for Intelligence and Security Studies
Center for Manufacturing Excellence
Center for Marine Resources and Environmental Technology
Center for Mathematics and Science Education
Center for Pharmaceutical Marketing and Management
Center for Population Studies
Center for Speech and Hearing Research
Center for the Study of Southern Culture
Center for Water and Wetland Resources
Center for Wireless Communications
INDO-US Joint Center for Research in Indian Systems of Medicine
Jamie Whitten National Center for Physical Acoustics
Magazine Innovation Center
National Center for Computational Hydroscience and Engineering
National Center for Justice and the Rule of Law
National Center for Natural Products Research
National Center for Remote Sensing Air and Space Law
National Sea Grant Law Center
Overby Center for Southern Journalism and Politics
Public Policy Research Center
Sarah Isom Center for Women' s Studies
Sino-U.S. Traditional Chinese Medicines Research Center
University of Mississippi Geoinformatics Center

HISTORICAL FINANCIALS

Company Type: Private

Income Statement FYE: June 30

	REVENUE ($ mil.)	NET INCOME ($ mil.)	NET PROFIT MARGIN	EMPLOYEES
06/12	325	38	11.7%	8,700
06/11	302	74	24.6%	—
06/10	278	63	22.8%	—
06/09	261	43	16.5%	—
Annual Growth	7.6%	(4.0%)	—	—

2012 Year-End Financials

Debt ratio: —
Return on equity: 11.70%
Cash ($ mil.): 46
Current ratio: 1.40
Long-term debt ($ mil.): —
Dividends
Yield: —
Payout: —
Market value ($ mil.): —

UNIVERSITY OF MONTANA SYSTEM

EXECUTIVES

VP Administration and Finance, Robert A. (Bob) Duringer
VP Student Affairs, Teresa S. Branch
President and CEO University of Montana Foundation, Laura Brehm
Dean College of Health Professions and Biomedical Sciences, David Forbes
Dean School of Business Administration, Larry Gianchetta
VP Academic Affairs and Provost, Perry J. Brown
President, Royce C. Engstrom
VP External Relations, James P. Foley
Interim CIO, Loey Knapp
President, Darlene Samson
Chair, Angela McLean
VP Administration and Finance, Michael Reid
CIO, Matt Riley
Dean School of Law, Irma Russell
Dean College of Visual and Performing Arts, Stephen Kalm
Dean School of Journalism, Denise Dowling
Dean College of Arts and Sciences, Chris Comer
Dean School of Extended and Lifelong Learning, Roger Maclean
Dean Davidson Honors College, James McKusick
Dean Phyllis J. Washington College of Education and Human Sciences, Roberta D. Evans
Dean College of Forestry and Conservation, Jim Burchfield
Dean of Libraries, Shali Zhang

LOCATIONS

HQ: UNIVERSITY OF MONTANA SYSTEM
32 CAMPUS DR MAIN HALL, MISSOULA, MT 598120001
Phone: 4062430211
Web: WWW.UMT.EDU

PRODUCTS/OPERATIONS

2012 Revenue

	% of total
Student tuition &	47
Health care	20
Auxiliary	6
Grants &	4
Appropriated investment	3
Contributions	3
Released net	2
Other	15
Total	**100**

Selected Colleges and Schools

College of Arts and Sciences
College of Education and Human Sciences
College of Forestry and Conservation
College of Health Professions and Biomedical Sciences
College of Technology
College of Visual and Performing Arts
Davidson Honors College
Graduate School
School for Extended and Lifelong Learning
School of Business Administration
School of Journalism
School of Law

HISTORICAL FINANCIALS

Company Type: Private

Income Statement FYE: June 30

	REVENUE ($ mil.)	NET INCOME ($ mil.)	NET PROFIT MARGIN	EMPLOYEES
06/13	259	(8)	—	2,450
06/12	264	7	2.8%	—
06/09	246	27	11.2%	—
06/08	251	0	—	—
Annual Growth	0.7%	—	—	—

2013 Year-End Financials

Debt ratio: —
Return on equity: (-3.30%)
Cash ($ mil.): 55
Current ratio: 0.80
Long-term debt ($ mil.): —

Dividends
Yield: —
Payout: —
Market value ($ mil.): —

UNIVERSITY OF NORTH CAROLINA HOSPITALS

University of North Carolina Hospitals (UNCH) is at the heart of the UNC Health Care System (UNC HCS). The medical center provides acute care to the Tar Heel State through North Carolina Memorial Hospital North Carolina Children's Hospital North Carolina Neurosciences Hospital and North Carolina Women's Hospital. Combined the facilities have more than 800 beds. Specialties include cancer treatment (at the Lineberger Comprehensive Cancer Center a National Cancer Institute-designated facility) organ transplantation cardiac care orthopedics wound management and rehabilitation. Not-for-profit UNC HCS is owned by the state of North Carolina and is affiliated with the UNC-Chapel Hill School of Medicine.

Geographic Reach

UNCH not only serves patients from all North Carolina counties with about a third coming from the Research Triangle area it also serves patients from neighboring states.

Operations

UNCH operates under the umbrella of UNC HCS.

UNC HCS already extends beyond Chapel Hill and into the greater Triangle area through its network of primary care and specialty physician practices located in Orange Wake Durham Chatham and Lee counties. The system treats some 800000 people at UNC HCS practices and clinics annually.

UNCH handles more than 37000 patients each year and delivers 3500 babies annually.

Strategy

Being one of the primary health care providers in the area UNC HCS is nearly always expanding its services and service areas either through acquisitions or new construction.

Dedicated cancer care and cancer research is an area in which UNC HCS is expanding. It plans to open a North Carolina Cancer Hospital at Rex Hospital in 2014.

The system is also building an Imaging Research Building expected to open in 2013 to house the Biomedical Research Imaging Center and serve as a state resource for handling the acquisition processing analysis storage and retrieval of scientific images.

Other future plans call for UNC HCS to build a hospital campus in Hillsborough to meet growing patient needs. If the state approves the plan the new hospital with about 70 beds is scheduled to open in 2015.

In 2011 UNCH broke ground on 60000-square-foot 68-bed hospital north of Chapel Hill in the town of Hillsborough. Phase 1 of the Hillsborough Hospital is expected to open in 2013 with Phase 2 opening in 2015.

In 2011 the hospital also opened a new wing of the Newborn Critical Care Unit in the North Carolina Children's Hospital that houses 10 new patient beds bringing the number of beds in the unit to 58.

Company Background

UNCH was founded in 1952 under the name North Carolina Memorial Hospital. In 1989 the North Carolina General Assembly created UNCH.

EXECUTIVES

VP Business Development and Operational Efficiency, Glen Spivak
CEO UNC Health Care, William L. Roper, age 65
SVP and CFO, Chris Ellington
EVP and COO, Todd Peterson
Chief of Medical Staff, Brian P. Goldstein
President UNC Hospitals, Gary L. Park, age 58
SVP System Affiliations, Mary Beck
SVP Professional and Support Services, Sharon Coulter-James
SVP and Chief Nursing Officer, Mary Tonges
SVP Legal Services and Co-Director Compliance, Ben Gilbert
SVP Professional and Support Services, Melvin Hurston
VP Information Services, J.P. Kichak
VP Public Affairs and Marketing, Karen McCall
VP Surgical Services, Susan Phillips
SVP Professional and Support Services, Marlene Rifkin
VP Audit Security and Reimbursement Services, Patricia Moore-Boyette
President UNC Health Care, Allan Daugird
VP Human Resources, William (Bill) Rotella
Director UNC Comprehensive Cancer Support Program, Donald L. Rosenstein
VP Planning and Network Development, Amy Bragg
VP Facility Planning and Development, Ray Lafrenaye
Media Relations Manager, Stephanie Crayton
Managing Editor, Tom Hughes
Director Research Communications and Assistant Director of Public Affairs and Marketing, Les Lang
Associate Director, Clinton Colmenares
Purchasing Manager, Jeff Yardley
CIO UNC Health Care, Tracy Parham
CTO UNC Health Care, John Baba
CFO UNC Health Care, John Lewis

LOCATIONS

HQ: UNIVERSITY OF NORTH CAROLINA HOSPITALS
101 MANNING DR BLDG 2, CHAPEL HILL, NC 27514-4423
Phone: 919-966-5111
Web: WWW.DENTISTRY.UNC.EDU

PRODUCTS/OPERATIONS

Selected Facilities

North Carolina Cancer Hospital (Chapel Hill)
UNC Lineberger Comprehensive Cancer Center
North Carolina Children's Hospital (Chapel Hill)
North Carolina Memorial Hospital (Chapel Hill)
North Carolina Neurosciences Hospital (Chapel Hill)
North Carolina Women's Hospital (Chapel Hill)

COMPETITORS

Alamance Regional Medical Center
Annie Penn Hospital
Carolinas HealthCare System
Cone Health
Cumberland County Hospital System
Danville Regional Medical Center
Duke University Health System
Emory Healthcare
Grady Health System
High Point Regional Health System
Morehead Memorial Hospital
New Hanover Regional Medical Center
Rowan Regional Medical Center
Vidant Health
WakeMed

HISTORICAL FINANCIALS

Company Type: Private

Income Statement FYE: June 30

	REVENUE ($ mil.)	NET INCOME ($ mil.)	NET PROFIT MARGIN	EMPLOYEES
06/07	787	182	23.2%	6,000
06/06	652	36	5.6%	—
06/05	614	25	4.1%	—
06/04	550	5	0.9%	—
Annual Growth	12.7%	229.6%	—	—

2007 Year-End Financials

Debt ratio: —
Return on equity: 23.20%
Cash ($ mil.): 213
Current ratio: 2.50
Long-term debt ($ mil.): —

Dividends
Yield: —
Payout: —
Market value ($ mil.): —

UNIVERSITY OF NORTH DAKOTA

Way up in the Upper Midwest is the University of North Dakota (UND) the largest and oldest institution of higher learning in the state with an enrollment of approximately 15000 students. It offers undergraduate and graduate programs in close to 225 fields through nine colleges and schools (aerospace sciences arts and sciences business and public administration education and human development engineering and mines law medical and health sciences nursing and a graduate school). The university also has nearly 20 doctoral programs as well as certificate degree programs distance degree programs and a continuing education division. UND was founded in 1883 six years before North Dakota achieved statehood.

Operations

UND has an international reputation for research most notably in the health sciences nutrition energy and environmental protection aerospace and engineering. The university receives funding from various sources to perform research projects in areas that include neuroscience unmanned aerial systems vaccines advanced electronics nanotechnology high-tech coatings and alternative fuels.

EXECUTIVES

Director Human Resources, Diane Nelson
VP Student and Outreach Services, Robert Boyd
President, Robert O. Kelley
VP Finance and Operations, Alice Brekke
VP Academic Affairs and Provost, Paul LeBel
VP Health Affairs and Dean School of Medicine and Health Sciences, H. David Wilson
SEVP Health Affairs and Executive Dean School of Medicine and Health Science, Joshua Wynne
Associate Vice President for Research & Economic Development Research Development & Compliance, Barry Milavetz
CIO, Joshua Riedy
University Registrar, Suzanne Anderson
Executive Associate Vice President for University Relations, Peter Johnson
General Counsel, Julie Evans
executive Vice President CEO of the UND Alumni Association & Foundation, Tim O'Keefe
Director Campus Safety and Security and Risk Manager, Jason Uhlir
Director Student Financial Aid, Robin Holden
Associate VP Enrollment Management, Alice Hoffert
Director Career Services, Mark Thompson
Vice President for Student Affairs, Lori Reesor
Vice President for Research & Economic Development, Phyllis E. Johnson
Vice President and Dean Wynne, Gwen Halaas
Associate Vice President Myers, Mary Metcalf
Associate Vice President Lucke, Dawn Pladson
Associate Vice President Halgren, Elaine Metcalfe
Vice President Brekke, Margaret Myers
Vice President for Academic Affairs and Provost, Thomas DiLorenzo
Associate Vice President for Research Capacity Building North Dakota Experimental Program to Stimulate Competitive Research ND EPSCoR Co-Project Director, Mark Hoffmann
Associate Vice President for Intellectual Property Commercialization & Economic Development, Michael Moore
Associate Vice President Betting, Kay Mendick
Vice President for University & Public Affairs, Susan Walton

LOCATIONS

HQ: UNIVERSITY OF NORTH DAKOTA
264 CENTENNIAL DR, GRAND FORKS, ND 58202-6059
Phone: 701-777-2015
Web: WWW.AERO.UND.EDU

PRODUCTS/OPERATIONS

Selected Schools and Colleges

John D. Odegard School of Aerospace Sciences
College of Arts and Sciences
College of Business and Public Administration
College of Education and Human Development
School of Engineering and Mines
The Graduate School
School of Law
School of Medicine and Health Sciences
College of Nursing

HISTORICAL FINANCIALS

Company Type: Private

Income Statement FYE: June 30

	REVENUE ($ mil.)	NET INCOME ($ mil.)	NET PROFIT MARGIN	EMPLOYEES
06/11	278	27	9.8%	2,756
06/09	637	(40)	—	—
06/08	616	31	5.1%	—
Annual Growth	(23.3%)	(4.6%)	—	—

2011 Year-End Financials

Debt ratio: —
Return on equity: 9.80%
Cash ($ mil.): 16
Current ratio: 0.70
Long-term debt ($ mil.): —
Dividends
Yield: —
Payout: —
Market value ($ mil.): —

UNIVERSITY OF PUGET SOUND

The University of Puget Sound is a private liberal arts college located in the Pacific Northwest with an enrollment of some 2600 students and a student-faculty ratio of 12:1. It boasts more than 50 traditional and interdisciplinary programs and about 1200 courses. Based south of Seattle in Tacoma Washington the school offers a wide range of undergraduate degrees as well as graduate degrees in education occupational therapy and physical therapy. Students come from nearly 50 states and 15 countries. Founded in 1888 by the Methodist Church The University of Puget Sound divested its affiliation with the church in 1980. Notable alumni include Verio founder Justin Jaschke and Alaska governor Sean Parnell.

Geographic Reach

The University of Puget Sound operates its school on nearly 100 acres south of Seattle in the city of Tacoma Washington.

Sales and Marketing

The school sources its students from 49 states and 14 countries. Some 76% of its students arrive at The University of Puget Sound from outside Washington State. Its student population of 2600 students comprises 57% women and 43% men.

Financial Performance

Increases in net tuition and fees and a boost in student enrollment and student room and board revenues all contributed toward a 3% rise in 2012 revenue as compared to 2011. Net income decreased by 116% in 2012 vs. 2011 however due to rising operating expenses attributed to increases in educational and general expenses auxiliary enterprises expenses and net losses on endowment investments net of distributions during the same reporting period. During the same time frame cash flow dipped $7.9 million. Attributing to the loss are increases in investment purchases decreases in net sales of short-term investments and the net receipt of assets restricted for investment in campus facilities in 2012 vs. 2011.

EXECUTIVES

Vice Chairman, Robert C. Pohlad, age 59
President and Trustee, Ronald R. Thomas
VP Finance and Administration, Sherry Mondou
Chairman, Richard M. Brooks
Academic VP and Dean of University, Kristine (Kris) Bartanen
Dean of Graduate Studies, Sunil Kukreja
Dean of Students, Mike Segawa
CIO, William Morse
Vice Chairman, Robert C. Pohlad, age 59
President and Trustee, Ronald R. Thomas

LOCATIONS

HQ: UNIVERSITY OF PUGET SOUND
1500 N WARNER ST 1075, TACOMA, WA 98416-0005
Phone: 253-879-3100
Web: WWW.PUGETSOUND.EDU

PRODUCTS/OPERATIONS

Selected Undergraduate Degrees

African American Studies
Art
Asian Languages & Cultures
Asian Studies
Biochemistry & Molecular Biology
Biology
Business & Leadership
Chemistry
Classics
Communication Studies
Comparative Sociology
Computer Science
Economics
Engineering Dual Degree
English
Environmental Policy & Decision Making
Exercise Science
Foreign Languages & Literature
Gender Studies
Geology
Global Development Studies
History
Honors
Humanities
International Political Economy
Latin American Studies
Mathematics & Computer Science
Music
Natural Science
Neuroscience
Philosophy
Physical Education
Physics
Politics & Government
Psychology
Religion
Science Technology & Society
Special Interdisciplinary Major
Theatre Arts

HISTORICAL FINANCIALS

Company Type: Private

Income Statement FYE: June 30

	REVENUE ($ mil.)	NET INCOME ($ mil.)	NET PROFIT MARGIN	EMPLOYEES
06/12	162	10	6.3%	850
06/11	147	1	1.2%	—
06/09	139	1	0.7%	—
06/09	126	0	—	—
Annual Growth	8.7%	—	—	—

2012 Year-End Financials

Debt ratio: —
Return on equity: 6.30%
Cash ($ mil.): 41
Current ratio: —
Long-term debt ($ mil.): —
Dividends
Yield: —
Payout: —
Market value ($ mil.): —

UNIVERSITY OF RHODE ISLAND

The University of Rhode Island (URI) offers more than 80 undergraduate majors specializing in nursing psychology communication studies kinesiology and human development. It also offers master's doctoral and professional degrees from its nine colleges at four campuses across the state. URI's main campus is located in Kingston the W. Alton Jones Campus is in West Greenwich its Graduate School of Oceanography is located on Narragansett Bay and Providence is home to the university's Alan Shawn Feinstein College of Continuing Education. URI which has an enrollment of more than 16500 students was chartered as the state's agricultural school in 1888.

Geographic Reach

The University of Rhode Island spans four campus locations in Kingston Providence Narragansett Bay and West Greenwich. Its student population comes from 53 US territories and the District of Columbia.

Financial Performance

Revenue has increased for URI during the past three years due to increasing tuition and fees rising enrollment of out-of-state students and increasing grants and contracts. Tuition and fees contributed some 60% of revenue in fiscal 2012. Net income was flat in 2012 as compared to 2011 thanks to increased capital appropriations state contributed capital and capital gifts. These were partially offset however by rising expenses and declining non-operating revenues.

EXECUTIVES

President, Robert L. Carothers
Assistant VP Human Resources Administration, Anne Marie Coleman
Assistant VP Public Affairs, Andrea M. Hopkins
VP University Advancement, Robert M. Beagle
VP Student Affairs, Thomas R. Dougan
VP Administration, Robert A. Weygand
Associate VP Development, Paul H. Witham
Assistant VP Business Services, J. Vernon Wyman
Assistant VP Student Affairs, Lester K. Yensan
VP Academic Affairs and Provost, Donald H. Dehayes
Director Budget and Financial Planning, Linda Barrett
Vice Provost Information Technology Services, Garry Bozylinsky
Director Security, Robert F. Drapeau
Director Enrollment Services, Horace J. Amaral Jr.
VP Research and Economic Development, Peter Alfonso
Director Purchasing and University Stores, Elizabeth A. Gil

LOCATIONS

HQ: UNIVERSITY OF RHODE ISLAND
75 LOWER COLLEGE RD, KINGSTON, RI 02881-1966
Phone: 401-874-1000
Web: WWW.URI.EDU

PRODUCTS/OPERATIONS

Selected Schools and Colleges

College of Arts and Sciences
College of Business Administration
College of Continuing Education
College of Engineering
College of Environment and Life Sciences
College of Human Science and Services
College of Nursing
College of Pharmacy
Graduate School of Oceanography
University College

HISTORICAL FINANCIALS

Company Type: Private

Income Statement

FYE: June 30

	REVENUE ($ mil.)	NET INCOME ($ mil.)	NET PROFIT MARGIN	EMPLOYEES
06/11	392	58	14.9%	2,500
06/08	319	49	15.5%	—
06/07	290	43	15.1%	—
06/06	258	0	—	—
Annual Growth	8.7%	—	—	—

2011 Year-End Financials

Debt ratio: —
Return on equity: 14.90%
Cash ($ mil.): 96
Current ratio: 2.40
Long-term debt ($ mil.): —
Dividends
Yield: —
Payout: —
Market value ($ mil.): —

UNIVERSITY OF RICHMOND

Suffering from arachnophobia? You may want to steer clear of the more than 4300 Spiders who are enrolled at the University of Richmond (UR). UR consists of five schools: Jepson School of Leadership Studies Richmond School of Law Robins School of Business School of Arts and Sciences and School of Continuing Studies. The university offers some 60 undergraduate majors as well as graduate and master's programs in business accounting and law. UR also offers some 75 study-abroad programs in which more than half of its students participate. Founded in 1830 by Virginia Baptists as a seminary for men the school became Richmond College in 1840.

Geographic Reach

From its campus in Richmond Virginia UR serves students from nearly all 50 US states including Puerto Rico and Washington D.C. Its student population consists of more than 3000 undergraduates that come more than 70 countries.

Operations

UR with about 320 full-time undergraduate faculty members boasts a student-faculty ratio of 9:1. Through its Richmond Quadrangle LLC (a wholly controlled affiliate of UR) the university owns and operates a building and land located in Richmond. UR's Spider Management Company LLC is another wholly controlled affiliate that provides investment research advice counsel and management related to the university's endowment assets.

Financial Performance

Revenue for UR rose 8% in fiscal 2012 as compared to 2011 due to an increase in tuition and fees grants and contracts contributions endowment spending distribution and auxiliary enterprises. Net income for the same reporting period decreased by 112% thanks to rising operating expenses and declining contribution and net unrealized losses.

EXECUTIVES

VP Information Services, Kathryn J. (Kathy) Monday
Associate VP Human Resources, Carl Sorensen
VP Student Development, Steve Bisese
Registrar, Susan D. Breeden
Director Media and Public Relations, Brian Eckert
Assistant VP Alumni Relations, Kristin Woods
Director Career Development Center, Leslie Williams Stevenson
University Librarian, Jim Rettig
President, Edward L. Ayers
VP Business and Finance, Hossein Sadid
Assistant VP Communications, Lisa Van Riper
Administrative Coordinator Communications, Debbie Hardy
Associate Director Marketing Communications, Jan Hatchette
Assistant Director Media and Public Relations, Linda Evans
Media and Public Relations Officer, Holly Rodriguez
Head Library Systems, Nancy Woodall
Provost and VP Academic Affairs, Steve Allred
Chief Executive Officer, Steve Kneeley
President Chief Investment Officer, Rob Blandford
Chief Operating Officer, Paul Costello
Auditors: KPMGLLP

LOCATIONS

HQ: UNIVERSITY OF RICHMOND
28 WESTHAMPTON WAY, RICHMOND, VA 23173-0002
Phone: 804-289-8133
Web: WWW.SPCS.RICHMOND.EDU

PRODUCTS/OPERATIONS

Selected Schools

Arts and Sciences
Business
Leadership Studies
Law
Professional and Continuing Studies

HISTORICAL FINANCIALS

Company Type: Private

Income Statement

FYE: June 30

	REVENUE ($ mil.)	NET INCOME ($ mil.)	NET PROFIT MARGIN	EMPLOYEES
06/10	210	83	39.7%	1,400
06/09	197	(314)	—	—
06/09	0	0	—	—
Annual Growth	—	—	—	—

2010 Year-End Financials

Debt ratio: —
Return on equity: 39.70%
Cash ($ mil.): 224
Current ratio: —
Long-term debt ($ mil.): —
Dividends
Yield: —
Payout: —
Market value ($ mil.): —

UNIVERSITY OF SAN FRANCISCO INC

Known for their devotion to education as well as their investment portfolio the Jesuits are evident to all who visit the University of San Francisco (USF). One of 28 Jesuit Catholic colleges and universities in the US the main USF campus sits on 55 acres near Golden Gate Park in San Francisco. The school which was formed in 1855 as St. Ignatius Academy enrolls more than 10000 students. It operates five schools and colleges including the schools of business and management education law and nursing and the colleges of arts and sciences. In addition to its main campus the university operates five satellite sites in Northern and Southern California.

Operations

USF operates a handful of schools and colleges including schools of management education law nursing and the colleges of arts and sciences. More than 400 full-time faculty members offer 100-plus undergraduate and degree programs. With a student-faculty ratio of 16:1 USF's 10000-plus student enrollment includes 6250 undergraduates 2950 graduates 670 law students and 150 non-degree students.

The independent private not-for-profit university is one of the nation's most ethnically diverse schools. Some 43% of its students are Asian African-American Latino Native Hawaiian/Pacific Islander or multi-ethnic.

Strategy

To keep up with growth USF in 2011 acquired the Folger Building located at 101 Howard Street in downtown San Francisco. The university also changed the name of its school of nursing to the School of Nursing and Health Professions to reflect the institution's commitment and expansion of its master of public health degree.

Financial Performance

USF logged a 10% decrease in revenue in 2012 as compared to 2011 due to contribution declines and a net realized and unrealized loss on investments in 2012 over a gain in 2011. Meanwhile net income dropped 85% during the same reporting period. Dips in revenue and rises in total expenses both attributed to increases in auxiliary enterprises scholarships and fellowships and institutional support expenses.

EXECUTIVES

President and Trustee, Rev Stephen A. Privett, age 72
VP Business and Finance, Charles E. (Charlie) Cross
Chancellor, Rev John Lo Schiavo
Executive Assistant to the President and Secretary of the Board, Jaci Neesam
VP Communications and Marketing, David F. MacMillan
VP International Relations, Stanley D. Nel
General Counsel, Donna J. Davis
Provost and Academic VP, Jennifer E. Turpin
Dean School of Education, Walter H. Gmelch
Dean School of Law, Jeffrey S. Brand
Dean University Library, Tyrone H. Cannon
Vice Provost and Dean Academic and Enrollment Services, Elizabeth J. Johnson
Director Budget, Michael Harrington
Director Institutional Research, Alan Ziajka
Director Recreation Sports, Charlies B. White Jr.
Associate VP Accounting and Business Services, Kim Kvaal
Manager University Bookstore, Robert Gibson
Associate VP University Advancement and Director Corporate/Foundation Relations, Sally Dalton
Assistant VP University Advancement and Director Planned Giving, David Cunningham
Director Alumni Relations, Annette Anton
Assistant VP Public Affairs and University Communications, Gary McDonald
Assistant Dean Academic Programs, Sue Stavn
University Librarian, Joseph Garity
Head Special Collections University Library, John Hawk
Head of Collection Reference and Research Services Library, Locke J. Morrisey
Reference Librarian Law Library, Lee Ryan
Head Acquisitions University Library, Kathy Woo
Director Priscilla A. Scotlan Career Services Center, James Catiggay
Vice Provost Planning Budget and Review and Professor of Accounting, Salvador Aceves
Senior Associate VP Advancement, Nancy Sackson
Vice Provost Academic Affairs and Professor of Psychology, Gerardo Marin
Dean School of Nursing and Health Professions, Judith F. Karshmer
Director Center for Global Education, Sharon Li
Director Sponsored Projects, Pamela Miller
Director Institutional Assessment, William Murry
Associate Dean Student Development, Linda L. Thomas
Assistant Dean Multicultural Student Services, Mary Grace Almandrez
Assistant Dean Students, Julie E. Orio
Vice Chair, Charles H. Smith
VP Information Technology, Stephen J. Gallagher
Chairman, Thomas E. Malloy
Dean College of Arts and Sciences, Marcelo F. Camperi
Dean School of Management, Michael J. Webber
Senior Vice President CBRE Hotels, Henry Bose
Sr. Vice President Growth and Development, Randall Kies
Sr. Vice President Strategic Marketing and Business, Lisa McEuen
Vice President and General Manager, Stephen Revetria
Vice President Global Conferences and Events, Jana Atlas
Vice President Controller, Matthias Kowalsky
President and Trustee, Rev Stephen A. Privett, age 72
Vice Chair, Charles H. Smith
Trustee, Alfonso T. Yuchengco
Trustee, David Agger
Trustee, Richard L. Bechelli
Trustees, Joseph J. Bonocore
Trustee, Teresa J. Win
Trustee, Patrick McNicholas
Trustee, Susan G. Marineau
Trustee, Rev Philip L. Boroughs
Trustee, Rev J. Dean Brackley
Trustee, Francis J. Butler
Trustee, Rev Gregory Chisholm
Trustee, Rt. Hon. Martin J. Jenkins
Trustee, Rev Thomas J. Scirghi
Trustee, Alfred S. Chuang
Trustee, Rev Jon D. Fuller
Trustee, Suzanne Troxel
Trustee, J. Malcolm Visbal
Trustee, Arthur A. Ciocca
Trustee, Rt. Hon. Maria P. Rivera
Trustee, Jeanne M. Cunicelli, age 46
Trustee, Ricky J. Curotto
Trustee, Steven M. Read
Trustee, Charles M. Geschke
Trustee, Suzanne M. Giraudo
Trustee, Rose Guilbault
Trustee, Wayne E. Jerves
Trustee, Lawrence R. O'Connor
Trustee, Oliver T. Johnson
Trustee, Rev William R. Stoeger
Trustee, Peter K. Maier
Trustee, Antoinette M. Malveaux
Trustee, Rev Michael J. Sheeran
Trustee, Putra Masagung
Trustee, Rev Mark Ravizza
Trustee, Rev Mario J. Prietto
Trustee, Rev John J. O'Callaghan
Trustee, Joan M. McGrath
Trustee, John F. Nicolai
Trustee, Rev Patrick B. O'Leary
Auditors: Deloitte&ToucheLLP

LOCATIONS

HQ: UNIVERSITY OF SAN FRANCISCO INC
2130 FULTON ST, SAN FRANCISCO, CA 94117-1050
Phone: 415-422-5555
Web: WWW.USFCA.EDU

PRODUCTS/OPERATIONS

Selected Schools and Colleges

College of Arts
College of Sciences
School of Education
School of Law
School of Management
School of Nursing

HISTORICAL FINANCIALS

Company Type: Private

Income Statement

FYE: May 31

	REVENUE ($ mil.)	NET INCOME ($ mil.)	NET PROFIT MARGIN	EMPLOYEES
05/12	390	36	9.3%	1,200
05/11	380	55	14.5%	—
05/09	334	25	7.7%	—
05/09	299	0	—	—
Annual Growth	9.2%	—	—	—

2012 Year-End Financials

Debt ratio: —
Return on equity: 9.30%
Cash ($ mil.): 104
Current ratio: —
Long-term debt ($ mil.): —
Dividends
Yield: —
Payout: —
Market value ($ mil.): —

UNIVERSITY OF SCRANTON

The University of Scranton is a Catholic and Jesuit liberal arts university with a student population of 5900 including more than 600 graduate students. Its schools and colleges include the College of Arts & Sciences Panuska College of Professional Studies and Kania School of Management. It offers programs in areas such as theology music technology athletics nursing and continuing education and has some 300 faculty members. The University of Scranton offers 61 undergraduate and 25 graduate programs. It is overseen by the Society of Jesus (the Jesuits).

Operations

Some 85% of the University of Scranton's instructional faculty hold doctoral or other terminal degrees and the school has a student-to-faculty ratio of 11:1. It sponsors 18 NCAA Division III (non-scholarship) athletic programs (nine for men and nine for women).

The Harry and Jeanette Weinberg Memorial Library holds more than 512890 volumes and 21285 non-print items. The library has an integrated online catalog with a discovery layer that enables users to find books and journal in a single search.

Financial Performance

The university charged $37106 undergraduate tuition for 2012-13.

The school is supported by a $125 million endowment.

Strategy

The university focuses on integrating international study service and research opportunities for students faculty and staff and on upgrading campus facilities. Since 2003 it has invested more than $285 million in campus improvements.

In 2013 the school announced a $47.5 million project to build an eight-story rehabilitation center to provide a state-of-the-art facility for undergraduate and graduate programs in the Departments of Exercise Science Occupational Therapy and Physical Therapy.

The Loyola Science Center was completed in two phases in 2011 and 2012.

In 2011 the University of Scranton opened the Pilarz and Montrone Halls to house 400 upperclass students and a fitness center.

Company Background

The University of Scranton was founded in 1888 as Saint Thomas College.

The school's more than 45000 graduates are all members of the Alumni Society which has 20 clubs worldwide.

EXECUTIVES

Asst Vp Physical Plant, James Devers
Vice President For University Mission & Ministry, Richard Malloy
Vp University Ministries, Terrence P Devino
Provost/academic Vp, Harold W Baillie
Asst Vp Of Human Resources, Patricia Tetreault
Vp Of Finance/treasurer, Edward J Steinmetz

LOCATIONS

HQ: UNIVERSITY OF SCRANTON
800 LINDEN ST, SCRANTON, PA 18510-4501
Phone: 570-344-6685
Web: WWW.MATRIX.SCRANTON.EDU

PRODUCTS/OPERATIONS

Schools and Colleges
College of Arts and Sciences
College of Graduate and Continuing Education
Kania School of Management
Panuska College of Professional Studies

HISTORICAL FINANCIALS

Company Type: Private

Income Statement

FYE: May 31

	REVENUE ($ mil.)	NET INCOME ($ mil.)	NET PROFIT MARGIN	EMPLOYEES
05/13	158	33	21.0%	1,050
05/12	212	16	7.6%	—
05/08	138	(1)	—	—
05/08	135	14	10.6%	—
Annual Growth	3.3%	18.4%	—	—

2013 Year-End Financials

Debt ratio: ——
Return on equity: 21.00%
Cash ($ mil.): 14
Current ratio: —
Long-term debt ($ mil.): —
Dividends
Yield: —
Payout: —
Market value ($ mil.): —

UNIVERSITY OF SOUTH FLORIDA

The University of South Florida (USF) is bullishly educational. The school has some 48000 students at three campuses in Tampa St. Petersburg and Sarasota/Manatee. It offers some 230 undergraduate graduate specialty and doctoral degree programs through more than a dozen colleges including Arts and Sciences Business Education Engineering Marine Science Pharmacy and Public Health. USF also offers graduate certificates continuing education courses and teacher certifications and it is a major research institution among US universities. USF was founded in 1960; its mascot is the bull.

Geographic Reach

USF has increased enrollment of international students by about 90% between 2007 and 2012. It has a total of more than 2100 international students or about 4% of the total student population. USF also supports study abroad programs. The university's campuses in Florida encompass some 1600 acres. The main Tampa campus includes the USF Health facilities and health-related schools

Operations

The university has some 2000 teaching faculty members and maintains a 24:1 student-to-faculty ratio. USF's core offerings include extensive health sciences program including medical nursing pharmacy and public health colleges grouped under the USF Health banner. The health organization also includes patient care facilities such as family care practices emergency clinics and Alzheimer's centers.

USF Health also hosts medical research programs in areas such as neurological conditions cardiovascular care pediatrics infectious disease and biotechnology. The university also has research programs in a range of science engineering and arts fields such as veteran reintegration and photovoltaic energy technologies. Altogether USF's research programs were granted more than $400 million in awards and contracts during the fiscal 2012 year.

Extracurricular activities include 17 men's and women's varsity teams that participate in the American Athletics Conference at the NCAA level.

Financial Performance

Operating revenue increased by 3% to $629.6 million in fiscal 2012 as the university reported higher tuition and fee income as well as auxiliary enterprise sales and services (including revenues from intercollegiate sports). The increased revenue streams were offset by lower federal state and local grant and contract income and income from other revenue sources. Undergraduate tuition runs around $6000 for state residents and 17000 for nonresidents. Scholarship grants total more than $60 million each year.

USF has a budget of some $1.5 billion annually as well as an annual economic impact of some $3.7 billion. The university has an endowment of some $364 million.

Strategy

In the face of rising competition in Florida's health care market USF is looking to further its medical training capabilities by forming partnerships with hospital systems in the eastern US. It completed construction of a $30 million high-tech surgical training facility in Tampa in 2012. In addition USF Health formed a partnership with Florida Hospital (part of Adventist Health System) to conduct research programs and provide collaborative care in the region.

Also in 2012 USF moved to increase international relations and improve geopolitical study programs by establishing a Center for Strategic and Diplomatic Studies. In 2013 the university moved to expand by opening new marine science laboratories.

Another area of growth for USF has been music: The university completed construction of a new School of Music facility in 2011. The $38 million project includes new concert halls classroom and studios and practice rooms. The building is part of a larger university capital improvement plan that started in 1982.

In 2012 the USF Polytechnic satellite campus in Lakeland became a separate entity known as Florida Polytechnic University; other USF programs located in Lakeland were moved to the Florida campus.

EXECUTIVES

President and Corporate Secretary, Judy L. Genshaft
President Obamas address by First Lady, Stephen K. Klasko
Vice Provost Human Resources Management and Space Planning, Kofi Glover
VP Administrative Services, Sandy Lovins
Associate VP Information Technologies, George W. Ellis
Regional Chancellor USF Sarasota-Manatee Campus, Arthur M. Guilford
VP Information Technology, Michael A. Pearce
EVP and Provost, Ralph Wilcox
Senior Vice President for Research, Karen A. Holbrook
General Counsel, Steven D. Prevaux
Director Financial Aid, Billie Jo Hamilton
Director Registrar Office, Angela DeBose
Associate VP Decision Support, Michael Moore
Director Career Center, Drema Howard
COO, John W. Long
Senior Vice Provost, Dwayne Smith
Vice Provost Strategic and Budget Planning, Graham Tobin
Vice Provost Student Success, Paul Dosal
Treasurer, Fe;; Stubbs
Regional Chancellor USF St. Petersburg Campus, Margaret Sullivan
Interim Regional Chancellor and Campus Executive Officer USF Polytechnic, David M. Touchton
Communications Director, Tom Scherberger
Assistant Director of Communications, Ashley Walker
Director for Communications, Jeremy Sharpe

LOCATIONS

HQ: UNIVERSITY OF SOUTH FLORIDA
4202 E FOWLER AVE, TAMPA, FL 33620-8000
Phone: 813-974-1587
Web: WWW.HOUSING.USF.EDU

PRODUCTS/OPERATIONS

2012 Operating Revenue

% of total	
Federal grants &	47
Student tuition &	35
Nongovernmental grants &	18
Auxiliary enterprises sales &	-
State & local grants &	-
Total	**100**

Selected Colleges

The Arts
Arts & Sciences
Behavioral & Community Sciences
Business
Education
Engineering
Global Sustainability
Honors College
Marine Science
Medicine
Nursing
Pharmacy
Public Health
University College (graduate school)

COMPETITORS

Florida Atlantic University
Florida International University
Florida State University
University of Central Florida
University of Florida
University of Miami
University of North Florida

HISTORICAL FINANCIALS

Company Type: Private

Income Statement

FYE: June 30

	REVENUE ($ mil.)	NET INCOME ($ mil.)	NET PROFIT MARGIN	EMPLOYEES
06/11	1,013	94	9.3%	16,165
06/09	892	42	4.7%	—
06/07	533	148	27.8%	—
06/06	480	35	7.4%	—
Annual Growth	16.1%	21.8%	—	—

2011 Year-End Financials

Debt ratio: ——
Return on equity: 9.30%
Cash ($ mil.): 116
Current ratio: 0.90
Long-term debt ($ mil.): —
Dividends
Yield: —
Payout: —
Market value ($ mil.): —

UNIVERSITY OF SOUTHERN MISSISSIPPI

You don't have to be a belle to attend Southern Miss but it never hurts. The University of Southern Mississippi (USM or Southern Miss for short) was established by the state legislature in 1910 to educate Mississippi's teachers. The school has grown to boast an enrollment of more than 15000 students with a student-teacher ratio of 17:1. USM offers bachelor's master's doctoral and post-master's degrees through five colleges: College of Arts and Letters College of Business College of Education and Psychology College of Health and College of Science and Technology. Southern Miss also runs an Honors College and engages in extensive research in a range of disciplines including health and technology.

EXECUTIVES

Director Human Resources, Russell H. Willis
VP Research and Economic Development, Cecil D. Burge
VP Student Affairs, Joseph S. (Joe) Paul
CIO, Homer Coffman
Director Intercollegiate Athletics, Richard Giannini
Associate Provost, Cynthia R. Easterling
Benefits Coordinator, Kameron E. Dale
CFO, Joe Morgan
Bursar, Barbara E. Madison
Controller, Allyson G. Easterwood
Director Physical Plant, Carl R. Postlewate
Director Physical Plant Accounting, William L. Wheat
Director Safety and Environmental Services, Rodger H. Jackson
Instructional Services Coordinator Cook Library, Mary Beth E. Applin
Associate University Librarian Library Service Cook Library, Cheryl H. Laughlin
President, Martha D. Saunders, age 66
University Registrar, Gregory W. (Greg) Pierce
Associate Controller, Linda Smith
Director Gulf Coast Research Laboratory, William E. (Bill) Hawkins
Provost, Robert D. Lyman
VP Advancement, David Wolf
Interim Associate Provost, William Powell
Vice President for finance and administration, Douglas H. Vinzant
President Dawn Smith, Erick Brown
President of The University of Southern Mississippi on, Rodney D. Bennett

LOCATIONS

HQ: UNIVERSITY OF SOUTHERN MISSISSIPPI
118 COLLEGE DR BOX 5005, HATTIESBURG, MS 39406-0001
Phone: 601-266-4111
Web: WWW.USM.EDU

HISTORICAL FINANCIALS

Company Type: Private

Income Statement FYE: June 30

	REVENUE ($ mil.)	NET INCOME ($ mil.)	NET PROFIT MARGIN	EMPLOYEES
06/11	193	13	7.2%	4,500
06/09	179	30	17.2%	—
06/08	172	17	10.3%	—
06/07	1,432	0	0.0%	—
Annual Growth	(39.4%)	1439.3%	—	—

2011 Year-End Financials

Debt ratio: —
Return on equity: 7.20%
Cash ($ mil.): 30
Current ratio: 2.30
Long-term debt ($ mil.): —
Dividends
Yield: —
Payout: —
Market value ($ mil.): —

UNIVERSITY OF ST. THOMAS

EXECUTIVES

Non-Executive Chairman, Stephen P. Nachtsheim
President Emerita University of Detroit Mercy, Maureen A. Fay, age 79
President, Father Dennis Dease
VP Information Resources and Technologies, Samuel (Sam) Levy
VP Business Affairs and CFO, Mark D. Vangsgard
EVP and Chief Administrative Officer, Mark Dienhart
Associate VP Enrollment Services, Marla Friederichs
VP Mission, Gene Scapanski
VP University and Government Relations, Doug Hennes
Executive Director Development, Steve Hoeppner
Executive Director Alumni and Constituent Relations, Rachel Wobschall
Executive Director Institutional Advancement, Kristine M. Aasheim
VP Student Affairs, Jane Canney
Director Alumni Association, Greg Hendricks
Associate VP Human Resources, Edna R. Comedy
Director News Service, Jim Winterer
Executive Director Marketing Communications, William V. Kirchgessner
Director Neighborhood Relations, John Hershey
Associate VP Academic Affairs, Angeline Barretta-Herman
University Regsitrar, Paul M. Simmons
Director International Education, Sarah A. Stevenson
Associate VP Academic Affairs, Joseph L. Kreitzer
Director International Studies Program, Robert J. Riley
Director Faculty Grants, David F. Steele
Associate VP Administration, Linda Halverson
Director University Libraries and Information Technology, Dan R. Gjelten
Director Web and Media Services, Elizabeth J. Houle
Director Telecommunication and Network, Dave L. Naugle
Director Athletics and Recreation, Steven J. Fritz
Associate VP and Controller, Gary L. Thyen
Associate VP Auxiliary Services, Bruce Van den Berghe
President University of Detroit Mercy, Antoine M. Garibaldi
Jr. Chairman, Harry G. McNeely Jr.
Jr. President, Frank B. Wilderson
President Owner, Geoffrey C. Gage
VP Mission and Trustee, Rev John M. Malone
VP St. Paul Seminary School of Divinity and Rector, Aloysius Callaghan
Director Purchasing Services, Karen M. Harthorn
Director Information Security, Christopher S. Gregg
Head, Chris Olean
Head Athletic Trainer, Roger Casey
Dean College of Arts and Sciences, Terence Langan
Dean Opus College of Business, Christopher Puto
Interim Dean College of Education Leadership and Counseling, David Rigoni
Dean School of Social Work, Barbara Shank
Academic Dean School of Divinity, Christopher Thompson
Dean School of Law, Robert Vischer
Dean School of Engineering, Donald Weinkauf
Associate Vice President Academic Services and Special Programs, Eleni Roulis
President Zeller Realty Group, James P. Gearen
Managing Partner President The Penrose Group, Mark W. Gregg
Vice President and Chief Counsel, Michelle Miller
Vice President of Claims at Minnesota Lawyers Mutual Insurance Company, Timothy Gephart
Executive Chairman of the Board, George W. Buckley, age 67
Trustee, Gail J. Dorn
Trustee, Richard M. (Dick) Schulze, age 73
Trustee, Robert J. (Bob) Ulrich, age 70
Trustee, Stephen J. (Steve) Hemsley, age 61
Trustee, John M. Morrison, age 77
Trustee, Mark A. Zesbaugh, age 49
Trustee, Ann L. Winblad
Trustee, Lee R. Anderson Sr.
Trustee, Gerald A. (Gerry) Rauenhorst
Trustee, Michael V. Ciresi, age 68
Trustee, Stanley S. Hubbard
Trustee, Timothy P. Flynn, age 63
Trustee, Rodney P. Burwell, age 75
Trustee, Michael E. Dougherty, age 73
Trustee, Kathleen J. (Kathy) Higgins Victor, age 57
President and Trustee, Father Dennis Dease
Trustee, Rev Edward A. Malloy, age 73
Trustee, Burton Cohen
Trustee, John J. (Hap) Fauth
Trustee, Father Harry J. Flynn
Trustee, Eugene U. Frey
Trustee, Rev Kevin McDonough
Trustee, Diana E. Murphy
Trustee, John F. O'Shaughnessy Jr.
President Owner, Geoffrey C. Gage
Chairman Director GHR Foundation, Amy R. Goldman
Trustee, Daniel J. Haggerty
Trustee, Sister Carol Keehan
VP Mission and Trustee, Rev John M. Malone
Trustee, Mary G. Marso
Trustee, Alvin E. McQuinn

LOCATIONS

HQ: UNIVERSITY OF ST. THOMAS
2115 SUMMIT AVE, SAINT PAUL, MN 551051096
Phone: 6519625000
Web: WWW.STTHOMAS.EDU

PRODUCTS/OPERATIONS

Academic Divisions
College of Arts and Sciences (Bachelor's and Master&apo
College of Education Leadership and Counseling Education (Bachelor's Master's Specialist Doctorate) and Professional Psychology (Master's and Doctorate)
Opus College of Business (Bachelor's and Master&apo
Saint Paul Seminary School of Divinity (Master&ap
School of Engineering (Bachelor's and Master&apo
School of Law (Juris Doctor)
School of Social Work (Bachelor's and Master&apo

HISTORICAL FINANCIALS

Company Type: Private

Income Statement FYE: June 30

	REVENUE ($ mil.)	NET INCOME ($ mil.)	NET PROFIT MARGIN	EMPLOYEES
06/14	253	62	24.8%	1,900
06/13	260	69	26.7%	—
06/12	239	2	1.2%	—
06/11	56	0	—	—
Annual Growth	65.0%	—	—	—

2014 Year-End Financials

Debt ratio: —
Return on equity: 24.80%
Cash ($ mil.): 0
Current ratio: —
Long-term debt ($ mil.): —

Dividends
Yield: —
Payout: —
Market value ($ mil.): —

UNIVERSITY OF TENNESSEE

Whether you want to learn the art of aviation or get ready for a career in public service the University of Tennessee System (UT) is here to help. The 200-year-old school provides undergraduate graduate and professional academic programs to about 50000 students; programs include business engineering law pharmacy medicine and veterinary medicine. It has a student-teacher ratio of about 16:1. Campuses include the flagship Knoxville location as well as the Health Science Center at Memphis the Space Institute at Tullahoma the statewide Institute for Public Service and the Institute of Agriculture. Other UT System campuses are located in Chattanooga and Martin. UT was founded in 1794 as Blount College.

Financial Performance

UT's funding comes from gifts grants and contracts (about 30%) state appropriations (roughly 28%) tuition and fees (20%) and a handful of auxiliary enterprises and independent operations (the remainder).

Company Background

Notable alumni include former Senate Majority Leader Howard Baker Nobel Prize-winning economist James Buchanan and author Cormac McCarthy.

EXECUTIVES

Treasurer Chief Investment Officer and CFO, Charles M. (Butch) Peccolo
EVP and VP Research President UT Research Foundation, David Milhorn
Chancellor The University of Tennessee Martin, Thomas A. Rakes
Chancellor The University of Tennessee Knoxville, Jimmy G. Cheek
President, Joe DiPietro
Chancellor University of Tennessee Health Science Center, Steve J. Schwab
Chancellor University of Tennessee Chattanooga, Steve R. Angle
Chancellor University of Tennessee Institute of Agriculture, Larry R. Arrington
V Pres, Anthony Haynes
Vice President For Human Resources, Robert Moore
Asst Vp Annual Giving, Kerry W Witcher
Vp Public/govt Relations, Hank Dye
Vp For Development/alumni Affs, Johnnie Ray
Asst Vp Planned Giving, Woody Henderson
Chair, Bill Haslam
Vice Chair, J. Brian Ferguson
Auditors: StateofTennesseeDepartmentofAudit

LOCATIONS

HQ: UNIVERSITY OF TENNESSEE
1331 CIRCLE PARK DR, KNOXVILLE, TN 379163801
Phone: 8659742303
Web: WWW.TREASURER.TENNESSEE.EDU

PRODUCTS/OPERATIONS

Selected Colleges Schools and Institutes

College of Agricultural Sciences and Natural Resources
College of Allied Health Sciences
College of Architecture and Design
College of Arts and Sciences
College of Business Administration
College of Communication and Information
College of Dentistry
College of Education Health and Human Sciences
College of Engineering
College of Graduate Health Sciences
College of Health Science Engineering
College of Law
College of Medicine
College of Nursing
College of Pharmacy
College of Social Work
College of Veterinary Medicine
Graduate School of Medicine
School of Art
School of Music
Space Institute

HISTORICAL FINANCIALS

Company Type: Private

Income Statement FYE: June 30

	REVENUE ($ mil.)	NET INCOME ($ mil.)	NET PROFIT MARGIN	EMPLOYEES
06/13	1,122	92	8.2%	12,000
06/12	1,092	60	5.5%	—
06/11*	1,034	296	28.7%	—
12/08	1	0	—	—
Annual Growth	443.8%	—	—	—

*Fiscal year change

2013 Year-End Financials

Debt ratio: —
Return on equity: 8.20%
Cash ($ mil.): 292
Current ratio: 0.90
Long-term debt ($ mil.): —

Dividends
Yield: —
Payout: —
Market value ($ mil.): —

UNIVERSITY OF THE PACIFIC

Situated next to the largest body of water on earth the University of the Pacific holds a sizable body of knowledge. The school offers more than 80 undergraduate majors and about 20 graduate programs in such fields as art language biology business computer science engineering history and pharmacy. It offers undergraduate graduate and professional degree programs in nine colleges and enrolls about 7000 students at its main campus in Stockton California the McGeorge School of Law in Sacramento and the Arthur A. Dugoni School of Dentistry in San Francisco. California's first chartered institution of higher education University of the Pacific was founded in 1851.

Geographic Reach

More than 85% of University of the Pacific's students are California residents. The remainder of the university's student base comes from 35 other US states as well as 25 international countries.

Operations

University of the Pacific has about 500 full-time faculty members and a student-to-teacher ratio of 13:1. Tuition at the university runs at about $38000 per year.

Financial Performance

University of the Pacific reported a 5% revenue rise to $331 million in 2012 due to increased tuition as well as from private grants gifts and bequests. Net income decreased by 53% to $21 million however due to increased expenses and lower investment returns.

Endowment funds contributed about $8 million of University of the Pacific's operating budget in fiscal 2012. The school has a total endowment of some $200 million.

Strategy

University of the Pacific is expanding its academic programs in targeted fields such as health-related education and training programs. It also is working to increase technology resources and implement related learning models as new high-tech generations join its ranks.

Other initiatives include recruiting teachers with scholarly experience attracting diverse and ambitious students and increasing job preparedness programs for students. University of the Pacific is also working to increase enrollment and fundraising efforts to generate new resources that will support its growth plans.

EXECUTIVES

VP Business and Finance, Patrick D. Cavanaugh
Dean Arthur A. Dugoni School of Dentistry, Patrick J. Ferrillo Jr., age 62
Provost, Philip N. Gilbertson
Associate Provost and CIO, Larry Frederick
Univeristy Registrar, Cecilia M. Rodriguez
Associate VP and Chief Investment Officer, Larry G. Brehm
Executive Director Pacific Alumni Association, Bill Coen
Assistant VP Diversity and Community Engagement, John Carvana
Dean McGeorge School of Law, Elizabeth Rindskopf Parker
VP Student Life, Elizabeth Griego
President of University of the Pacific on, Pamela A. (Pam) Eibeck
Chair, Tom Zuckerman
VP University Advancement, Ted Leland
Executive Director Marketing and University Communications, Richard Rojo
Director International Programs and Services, David Schmidt
Dean Library, C. Brigid Welch
Director Institutional Research, Mike Rogers
Director Admission, Richard Toledo
Director Financial Aid, S. Lynn Fox
Director Human Resources, Kara Bell
Dean Eberhardt School of Business, Richard Flaherty
Dean Students, Joanna Royce-Davis
Dean College of the Pacific, Thomas Krise
Dean Conservatory of Music, Giulio Maria Ongaro
Dean Gladys L. Benerd School of Education, Lynn G. Beck
Dean School of Engineering and Computer Science, Ravi K. Jain
Dean School of International Studies and Associate Provost International Initiatives, Margee Ensign
Dean Thomas J. Long School of Pharmacy and Health Sciences, Phillip Oppenheimer
Dean Graduate Studies and Associate Provost Research and Collaborative Programs, Jin Gong
Manager Purchasing, Ronda Marr
Director Public Safety, Mike Belcher
Executive Assistant Vice President, Laura Merry
Vice President Secretary, Mary Lackey
Executive Assistant President & Office Coordinator, Gloria Yip
Administrative Assistant, Dinelle Davis
Regent, Steven F. Leer
Regent, Walter E. Robb IV, age 61
Regent, Diane D. Miller, age 61
President and Regent, Pamela A. (Pam) Eibeck
Regent, Janice R. Brown
Regent, Sigmund H. Abelson
Regent, Connie M. Callahan

Regent, Tony Chan
Regent, Ronald D. (Ron) Cordes
Regent, Robert J. Corkern
Regent, Morrison C. England Jr.
Regent, Steven J. Goulart, age 55
Regent, Jose M. Hernandez
Regent, Kathleen Lagorio Janssen
Regent, Howard M. Koff
Regent, Larry Leasure
Regent, Russell E. Leatherby
Regent, Jim Mair
Regent, Hayne R. Moyer
Regent, Fredric C. Nelson
Regent, Dianne Philibosian
Regent, Jeannette Powell
Regent, Ronald Redmond
Regent, Barry L. Ruhl
Regent, Elizabeth A. (Betsy) Sanders
Regent, Lori Best Sawdon
Regent, Naka (Nick) Ushijima
Auditors: KPMGLLP

LOCATIONS

HQ: UNIVERSITY OF THE PACIFIC
3601 PACIFIC AVE, STOCKTON, CA 95211-0197
Phone: 209-946-2401
Web: WWW.PACIFIC.EDU

PRODUCTS/OPERATIONS

Selected Schools and Colleges

Arthur A. Dugoni School of Dentistry
College of the Pacific (Arts and Sciences)
Conservatory of Music
Eberhardt School of Business
Gladys L. Benerd School of Education
McGeorge School of Law
School of Engineering and Computer Science
School of International Studies
Thomas J. Long School of Pharmacy and Health Sciences

HISTORICAL FINANCIALS

Company Type: Private

Income Statement FYE: June 30

	REVENUE ($ mil.)	NET INCOME ($ mil.)	NET PROFIT MARGIN	EMPLOYEES
06/12	330	20	6.3%	1,500
06/11	317	43	13.8%	—
06/10	354	11	3.2%	—
06/09	309	0	—	—
Annual Growth	2.2%	—	—	—

2012 Year-End Financials

Debt ratio: —
Return on equity: 6.30%
Cash ($ mil.): 5
Current ratio: —
Long-term debt ($ mil.): —
Dividends
Yield: —
Payout: —
Market value ($ mil.): —

UNIVERSITY OF WASHINGTON INC

The University of Washington (UW) is Husky indeed with an annual enrollment of more than 92000 students. Founded in 1861 as the Territorial University of Washington UW (pronounced "U-dub" by those on campus) has smaller branches in Tacoma and Bothell in addition to its main campus in downtown Seattle. The university whose mascot is a Husky offers undergraduate graduate and professional degree programs through 16 colleges and schools. It also operates a health sciences center and an academic medical center which includes the University of Washington Medical Center and Harborview Medical Center.

With more than 250 degree options the UW confers some 12000 bachelor's master's doctoral and professional degrees each year. Its graduates include about 135 Fulbright and 35 Rhodes scholars. The school's top five bachelor degree fields include biology psychology political science economics and communications.

Research is a cornerstone of the university which has more than 270 specialized research centers. The school's annual sponsored grant and contract research funding exceeds $1 billion and it has received more federal research funding than any other public university in the US since 1974. More than 250 new companies have emerged based on UW research advances.

Along with many institutions of higher learning UW is facing significant state budget cuts (by as much as 17%) through fiscal 2013. Untouched in recent proposals however are the state's current funding levels for need-based grants.

EXECUTIVES

VP Medical Affairs; Dean School of Medicine, Paul G. Ramsey
Senior Vice President Treasurer, V'Ella Warren
President, Michael K. Young, age 64
VP Human Resources, Mindy R. Kornberg
Provost, Ana Mari Cauce
VP Minority Affairs and Vice Provost Diversity, Sheila E. Lange
Vice Provost Information Management, Sara Gomez
Vice Provost Academic Personnel, Cheryl A. Cameron
Vice Provost Student Life, Eric Godfrey
Executive Vice Provost, Doug Wadden
Interim VP External Affairs, Randy Hodgins
Vice Provost Educational Outreach, David Szatmary
Vice Provost Global Affairs, Stephen E. Hanson
Dean and Vice Provost Graduate School, Gerald (Jerry) Baldasty
Vice Provost Research, Mary Lidstrom
Vice Provost Special Programs, Gus K. J. Kravas
Vice Provost Undergraduate Academic Affairs, Ed Taylor
Director Finance and Administration, Kathryn Daughhetee
Vice President for UW Information Technology and Chief Information Officer, Kelli Trosvig
Interim Dean College of Arts & Sciences, Robert Stacey
Interim Dean College of Built Environments, John Schaufelberger
Dean School of Dentistry, Joel H. Berg
Dean College of Education, Tom Stritikus
Associate Vice President Access Policy and Planning, Enrique Morales
Associate Vice President of Student Services and Academic Support Programs, Gabriel E. Gallardo
Auditors: KPMGLLP

LOCATIONS

HQ: UNIVERSITY OF WASHINGTON INC
4311 11TH AVE NE STE 600, SEATTLE, WA 98105-6369
Phone: 206-543-2100
Web: WWW.AA.WASHINGTON.EDU

PRODUCTS/OPERATIONS

Selected Colleges and Schools

College of Arts and Sciences
College of Built Environments
College of Education
College of Engineering
College of the Environment
Evans School of Public Affairs
The Graduate School
Information School
Michael G. Foster School of Business
School of Dentistry
School of Law
School of Medicine
School of Nursing
School of Pharmacy
School of Public Health
School of Social Work

HISTORICAL FINANCIALS

Company Type: Private

Income Statement FYE: June 30

	REVENUE ($ mil.)	NET INCOME ($ mil.)	NET PROFIT MARGIN	EMPLOYEES
06/12	4,258	5	0.1%	27,228
06/11	3	0	14.4%	—
06/09	2,902	(374)	—	—
06/07	2,590	595	23.0%	—
Annual Growth	10.5%	(60.3%)	—	—

2012 Year-End Financials

Debt ratio: —
Return on equity: 0.10%
Cash ($ mil.): 95
Current ratio: 0.80
Long-term debt ($ mil.): —
Dividends
Yield: —
Payout: —
Market value ($ mil.): —

UNIVERSITY OF WISCONSIN FOUNDATION

Because even Badgers need help the University of Wisconsin Foundation raises funds receives gifts and manages assets for The University of Wisconsin-Madison and other donor-designated units of The University of Wisconsin System. (Bucky Badger is the school's mascot.) The foundation supports special programs and projects including professorships fellowships scholarships research efforts and building projects. The not-for-profit organization has received more than $2.4 billion in donations since it was founded in 1945.

EXECUTIVES

President, Andrew A. (Sandy) Wilcox
VP Planned Giving and Legal Affairs, Russ Howes
Secretary, Catherine M. (Cathy) Ahrens
Senior Director Development Corporate and Foundation Relations, Rudie Flietner
VP Health and Life Sciences, Mark Lefebvre
Director Development School of Medicine and Public Health, David Simon
Treasurer, Bridget A. Bush
Director Development Corporate and Foundation Relations, Aaron M. Zitzelsberger

LOCATIONS

HQ: UNIVERSITY OF WISCONSIN FOUNDATION
1848 UNIVERSITY AVE, MADISON, WI 53726-4090
Phone: 608-263-4545
Web: WWW.UWHEALTH.ORG

HISTORICAL FINANCIALS

Company Type: Private

Income Statement FYE: December 31

	REVENUE ($ mil.)	NET INCOME ($ mil.)	NET PROFIT MARGIN	EMPLOYEES
12/12	434	183	42.3%	150
12/10	444	206	46.6%	—
12/09	423	143	33.8%	—
Annual Growth	0.8%	8.7%	—	—

2012 Year-End Financials

Debt ratio: —
Return on equity: 42.30%
Cash ($ mil.): 94
Current ratio: —
Long-term debt ($ mil.): —

Dividends
Yield: —
Payout: —
Market value ($ mil.): —

UNIVERSITY OF WISCONSIN MEDICAL FOUNDATION INC.

UW Medical Foundation provides administrative services to faculty physicians at the University of Wisconsin School of Medicine and Public Health. The foundation a not-for-profit entity is a physician practice organization that works in cooperation with the UW Hospital and Clinics and other medical offices and clinics throughout the Badger State. The foundation coordinates clinical sites and provides technical and professional staffing services as well as administrative support for legal marketing information technology and logistics functions.

Operations

UW Medical Foundation provides support services for more than 1200 member doctors located at about 45 physician practices and 60 clinical outreach locations. It also helps clinical practices with quality initiatives. The foundation provides some $200 million in charity care each year. Its community activities include sponsoring health outreach events and donating safety products to low-income families.

Physicians in the organization provide services across a number of medical specialties including oncology gastroenterology women's health kidney care orthopedics respiratory therapy and urology.

Company Background

The organization has expanded over time: UW Medical Foundation merged with Physicians Plus Medical Group in 1998 and with the University Community Clinics in 2003.

EXECUTIVES

President CEO and Director, Jeffrey Grossman
EVP and COO, Peter Christman
Vice President Marketing and Public Affairs, Elizabeth Zaher
VP Patient Business Services, Connie Kinsella
Medical Director Ambulatory Clinic Operations, Richard Welnick
Medical Director Care Management, Lawrence Fleming
VP Legal Services and Compliance, Claudia Sanders
VP Human Resources, William Schrum
VP Operations, Steven Sibley
VP Public Affairs, Ronald Gilmore
VP Care and Quality Innovations, Sue Ertl
VP Leadership and Strategy Development, Roger A. Formisano
Medical Director Care and Quality Innovations, Sally Kraft
VP Information Services, Sandy Clark
Senior Vice President Human Resources, Janice Bultema
Vice President Ambulatory Operations, Mark Hamilton
Senior Vice President Chief Financial Officer, Michael Buhl
Director, Patricia Lipton
President CEO and Director, Jeffrey Grossman
Director, Robert Golden
Director, James E. Burgess
Director, Caroline Fribance
Director, Roger Hauck
Director, Byron J. Marquez
Director, Dennis P. Lund
Director, Frederick Wenzel
Director, Eliot Williams
Director, Christopher Green
Director, Thomas M. Grist
Director, Nizar Jarjour
Director, K. Craig Kent
Director, Stephen Y. Nakada
Director, Richard Page
Director, Rodney A. Welch
Auditors: Ernst&YoungLLP

LOCATIONS

HQ: UNIVERSITY OF WISCONSIN MEDICAL FOUNDATION INC.
7974 UW HEALTH CT, MIDDLETON, WI 53562-5531
Phone: 608-821-4223
Web: WWW.FAMMED.WISC.EDU

COMPETITORS

Ascension Health
Beaver Dam Community Hospitals
Beloit Health System
Catholic Health Initiatives
Dean Health Systems Inc.
Hospital Sisters Health System
Marian Health System
Meriter Health Services
ProHealth Care
SSM Health Care
Stoughton Hospital
ThedaCare Inc.
Tomah Memorial Hospital

HISTORICAL FINANCIALS

Company Type: Private

Income Statement FYE: June 30

	REVENUE ($ mil.)	NET INCOME ($ mil.)	NET PROFIT MARGIN	EMPLOYEES
06/12	655	15	2.3%	3,200
06/11	604	10	1.8%	—
06/09	571	22	4.0%	—
06/09	518	(8)	—	—
Annual Growth	8.1%	—	—	—

2012 Year-End Financials

Debt ratio: —
Return on equity: 2.30%
Cash ($ mil.): 106
Current ratio: —
Long-term debt ($ mil.): —

Dividends
Yield: —
Payout: —
Market value ($ mil.): —

UNIVERSITY OF WISCONSIN SYSTEM

Unfortunately there is no School of Cheese in the University of Wisconsin System (UW System) but across its vast operations there are 11 four-year universities two doctoral campuses 13 two-year UW Colleges campuses and a statewide extension program that has offices in every Wisconsin county. The UW System is one of the largest public university systems in the US with more than 180000 students. Its top school is UW at Madison which offers more than 400 undergraduate majors master's degree programs and doctoral programs to some 42000 students. The system's other major campus is UW at Milwaukee with about 30000 students. The UW System has a student-teacher ratio of 17:1.

Geographic Reach

One of the nation's largest public universities the UW system boasts offices or campuses in every county in Wisconsin.

Operations

Nearly one-quarter of the UW System's annual budget comes from state funds. Student fees federal grants fund raising and other sources account for the balance. To this end the university system's 2012-2013 annual budget includes the distribution of more than $34 million in new tuition dollars for the colleges universities and UW extension to maintain student access and educational quality. The distribution is also intended to be used to address critical campus needs that otherwise would not be met by state funds.

Combined the UW System's students have access to more than 250 undergraduate degree programs approximately 225 master's programs and 125 doctoral programs.

Strategy

As an increasing number of its students are working adults or students with nontraditional schedules the university has developed online accelerated and collaborative degree programs tailored to specific industries and emerging workforce needs.

Financial Performance

UW System has seen revenue rise in recent years thanks to increasing tuition and fees. Revenue increased some 2% in 2012 as compared to 2011 due to increases in student tuition and fees primarily attributable to sales and services of educational activities and tuition rate increases approved by the Board of Regents. During the same reporting period UW System logged a marginal net income decrease of 1% resulting from increases in operating expenses and decreases in capital appropriation expenses.

Sales and Marketing

About 80% of the system's students come from Wisconsin.

HISTORY

When Wisconsin became a state in 1848 its constitution called for the establishment of a state university. A board of regents was named and it first established a preparatory school because regents felt Wisconsin's secondary schools were not advanced enough to prepare students for university studies. The school began classes in 1849 with 20 students in the Madison Female Academy Building. The University of Wisconsin's first official freshman class began studies in the fall of 1850. A campus was established a mile west of the state capitol in Madison. By 1854 when it held its first commencement (with two graduates) the school had 41 students.

Enrollment dipped during the Civil War (all but one of the school's senior class joined the army) but soon rebounded and by 1870 the university had almost 500 students. Meanwhile it established a school of agriculture (1866) and a school of law (1868). The state established normal schools (teachers' colleges) in Platteville (1866) Whitewater (1868) Oshkosh (1871) and River Falls (1874).

There was also a teachers' course for women at the university in Madison. However when John Bascom became president in 1874 he transformed the university into a truly coeducational institution putting women "in all respects on precisely the same footing" with the men.

While the university at Madison remained Wisconsin's primary seat of learning the state continued to establish normal schools. It opened institutions in Milwaukee (1885) Superior (1893) Stevens Point (1894) La Crosse (1909) and Eau Claire (1916). The nine normal schools eventually became a system of state colleges called Wisconsin State Universities.

The university at Madison also continued to grow and by the late 1920s it had almost 9000 students. WWII brought a drop in enrollment but afterward it took off jumping from about 7000 in 1945 to over 22000 by the late 1950s. The University of Wisconsin-Milwaukee branch was founded in 1956. Other branch campuses were established in Green Bay (1965) and Kenosha (1968).

The Madison campus became a focal point for student protests during the Vietnam War. Events came to a head in 1970 when President Fred Harrington resigned during a four-day standoff between students and the National Guard. War protesters also placed a bomb outside Sterling Hall which housed the Army Math Research Center; the explosion killed one student and injured three others.

The state legislature merged the University of Wisconsin and the Wisconsin State Universities in 1971 to create The University of Wisconsin System.

EXECUTIVES

VP Finance, Deborah A. (Debbie) Durcan
Assistant Vp Capital Planning And Budget, David Miller
Chancellor Madison Campus, Rebecca M. Blank
President, Kevin P. Reilly
Interim Director Information Services, Lori Docken
Chancellor Eau Claire Campus, Gilles Bousquet
Chancellor Green Bay Campus, Thomas Harden
Chancellor La Crosse Campus, Joe Gow
Chancellor Milwaukee Campus, Michael Lovell
Chancellor Oshkosh Campus, Richard Wells
Chancellor Parkside Campus, Deborah (Debbie) Ford
Chancellor Platteville Campus, Dennis Shields
Chancellor River Falls Campus, Dean Van Galen
Chancellor Stevens Point Campus, Bernie Patterson
Chancellor Stout Campus, Charles W. Sorensen
Chancellor Superior Campus, Ren Æ Wachter
Chancellor Whitewater Campus, Richard J. Telfer
Senior Vp Of Ad, Michael Morgan
Regent President, Brent Smith
Regent VP, Michael Falbo
Auditors: StateofWisconsinLegislativeAuditBureau

LOCATIONS

HQ: UNIVERSITY OF WISCONSIN SYSTEM
1220 LINDEN DR, MADISON, WI 53706-1525
Phone: 608-262-2291
Web: WWW.WISCONSIN.EDU

PRODUCTS/OPERATIONS

Selected Four-Year Campuses

UW-Eau Claire
UW-Green Bay
UW-La Crosse
UW-Madison
UW-Milwaukee
UW-Oshkosh
UW-Parkside
UW-Platteville
UW-River Falls
UW-Stevens Point
UW-Stout
UW-Superior
UW-Whitewater

Selected Two-Year Colleges

UW-Baraboo/Sauk County
UW-Barron County
UW-Fond du Lac
UW-Fox Valley
UW-Manitowoc
UW-Marathon County
UW-Marinette
UW-Marshfield/Wood County
UW-Richland
UW-Rock County
UW-Sheboygan
UW-Washington County
UW-Waukesha

HISTORICAL FINANCIALS

Company Type: Private

Income Statement FYE: June 30

	REVENUE ($ mil.)	NET INCOME ($ mil.)	NET PROFIT MARGIN	EMPLOYEES
06/11	3,331	411	12.4%	31,992
06/10	3,116	329	10.6%	—
06/07	2,541	0	—	—
06/06	2,427	165	6.8%	—
Annual Growth	6.5%	20.1%	—	—

2011 Year-End Financials

Debt ratio: —
Return on equity: 12.40%
Cash ($ mil.): 1,077
Current ratio: 2.40
Long-term debt ($ mil.): —
Dividends
Yield: —
Payout: —
Market value ($ mil.): —

UNIVERSITY OF WYOMING

For folks who live in Wyoming the University of Wyoming (UW) is it –the only place offering baccalaureate and graduate degrees as well as research and outreach services that stretch across the state. The main campus is in Laramie but the school also has a campus in Casper (offering coordinated education programs with the Casper College) plus regional outreach education centers stationed throughout the state. Founded in 1887 UW has grown to serve more than 13000 students with about 200 programs of study through seven academic colleges as well as numerous schools and institutes. The university has a student-to-faculty ratio of 14:1.

Geographic Reach

Though most of its students come from Wyoming UW also attracts students from all 50 US states and about 90 countries. The university also offers a number of study abroad opportunities.

Strategy

In 2012 UW launched three construction projects to expand or upgrade a number of instructional research athletic and outreach facilities. One program will put about $10 million towards upgrading HVAC (heating ventilation and air conditioning) and lighting systems in the Biological Sciences building on the main Laramie campus. UW also completed construction of its new Visual Arts building in early 2012.

EXECUTIVES

VP Governmental Community and Legal Affairs, Rick Miller
VP Information Technology, Robert Aylward
President, Thomas (Tom) Buchanan
VP Institutional Advancement, Ben Blalock
Athletic Director Intercollegiate Athletics, Tom Burman
Dean University Library, Maggie Farrell
VP Academic Affairs, Myron Allen
VP Student Affairs, Sara Axelson
VP Research, William Gern
VP Administration, Douglas Vinzant
Dean College of Business, Brent A. Hathaway, age 52
Dean College of Law, Jerry Parkinson
Dean of Students, David S. Cozzens
Dean College of Agriculture, Frank Galey
Dean College of Arts and Science, B. Oliver Walter
Dean College of Engineering and Applied Science, Rob Ettema
Director Office of Student Financial Aid, David Gruen
Registrar, Tammy Aagard
Interim Vice President for Administrative Operations, Mark Collins
President Buchanan Announces Retirement, Barbara John

LOCATIONS

HQ: UNIVERSITY OF WYOMING
1000 E UNIVERSITY AVE # 3434, LARAMIE, WY 82071-2001
Phone: 307-766-2250
Web: WWW.WWWENG.UWYO.EDU

PRODUCTS/OPERATIONS

Selected Colleges and Schools

College of Agriculture and Natural Resources
College of Arts and Sciences
College of Business
College of Education
College of Engineering and Applied Science
College of Health Sciences
College of Law
Graduate Education
Outreach School
School of Energy Resources
School of Environment and Natural Resources

HISTORICAL FINANCIALS

Company Type: Private

Income Statement FYE: June 30

	REVENUE ($ mil.)	NET INCOME ($ mil.)	NET PROFIT MARGIN	EMPLOYEES
06/10	195	31	16.2%	7,000
06/09	195	52	27.0%	—
06/08	185	36	19.5%	—
Annual Growth	2.6%	(6.5%)	—	—

2010 Year-End Financials

Debt ratio: —
Return on equity: 16.20%
Cash ($ mil.): 87
Current ratio: 1.50
Long-term debt ($ mil.): —
Dividends
Yield: —
Payout: —
Market value ($ mil.): —

UNIVERSITY SYSTEM OF NEW HAMPSHIRE

The University of New Hampshire (UNH) is a liberal arts college that serves about 12600 undergraduate and more than 2200 graduate students. The institution offers more than 100 majors and academic programs of study at nine colleges and schools. The student-faculty ratio is 20:1. UNH is the flagship institution of the University System of New Hampshire. In 2007 the university graduated its first international class in Seoul under a program run by its Whittemore School of Business and Economics. Founded in 1866 as the New Hampshire College of Agriculture and the Mechanic Arts UNH is a designated land-grant sea-grant and space-grant chartered school.

Geographic Reach

In addition to its main campus in Durham UNH has a campus in Manchester and its School of Law is in Concord. Almost 60% of the school's student body comes from within state with a concentration of others coming from the northeastern region of the US. UNH is developing new academic programs expanding its online courses and opportunities and creating new international initiatives for faculty and students in Costa Rica Chile Ghana India South Korea and China.

Operations

UNH's most popular bachelor's programs include business administration undeclared liberal arts psychology English and communication followed by mechanical engineering biology biomedical science civil engineering and political science.

The University System of New Hampshire includes Keene State College Plymouth State University and Granite State College in addition to UNH.

Strategy

UNH is engaged in a strategic plan to support its growth through 2020. Its plan for creating a learning-centered environment includes such initiatives as establishing a New Venture Fund to promote collaborative research and teaching opportunities; developing new programs to support independent research and scholarship; commercializing UNH's intellectual capital; and promoting diversity and inclusiveness as well as international opportunities. It also includes making major capital investments in technology to build a high-capacity cyber-infrastructure and a learning portal to promote interdisciplinary collaboration; renovating restoring and adding on to facilities; and constructing a new center for the arts.

EXECUTIVES

Provost, Lisa MacFarlane
President, Mark W. Huddleston
VP Finance and Administration, Chris Clement

LOCATIONS

HQ: UNIVERSITY SYSTEM OF NEW HAMPSHIRE
25 CONCORD RD, LEE, NH 038616659
Phone: 6038621800
Web: WWW.USNH.EDU

PRODUCTS/OPERATIONS

Selected Colleges and Schools

College of Engineering and Physical Sciences
College of Health and Human Services
College of Liberal Arts
College of Life Sciences and Agriculture
The Graduate School
Thompson School of Applied Science
University of New Hampshire at Manchester
University of New Hampshire School of Law
Whittemore School of Business and Economics

Special Academic Opportunities
Graduate Research Conference
Hamel Center for Undergraduate Reasearch
Honors program
International research opportunities program
Student internships
Study abroad
Undergraduate research opportunities program

HISTORICAL FINANCIALS

Company Type: Private

Income Statement

FYE: June 30

	REVENUE ($ mil.)	NET INCOME ($ mil.)	NET PROFIT MARGIN	EMPLOYEES
06/14	676	128	19.1%	3,800
06/13	800	111	14.0%	—
06/12	0	40	—	—
06/08	558	0	—	—
Annual Growth	3.3%	—	—	—

2014 Year-End Financials

Debt ratio: —
Return on equity: 19.10%
Cash ($ mil.): 80
Current ratio: 0.70
Long-term debt ($ mil.): —
Dividends
Yield: —
Payout: —
Market value ($ mil.): —

UNMC PHYSICIANS

If you find your prairie schooner parked at the office of a physician in Nebraska you may be seeing a doc affiliated with UNMC Physicians (formerly University Medical Associates). The more than 500 physicians in the UMA group practice are faculty members at The Nebraska Medical Center an affiliate of the University of Nebraska. The physicians who also employ 10 family health clinics in the area provide services in about 50 specialties such as obstetrics cancer care family medicine cardiology and pediatrics.

EXECUTIVES

Chairman President and CEO, Rodney S. (Rod) Markin, age 53
Chairman Surgery, Byers W. Shaw Jr.
EVP and Chief Administrative Officer, Cory D. Shaw
Human Resources Director, Keli Royal
Media Relations, Cherie Lytle
Marketing and Media Relations, Genna Campbell
CFO, Troy Wilhelm
Chairperson Neuorsciences, Terri Mashek
Secretary Treasurer and Chairperson Radiation and Oncology, Charles Enke
Vice Chairman, Kevin Garvin
Secretary Treasurer and Chairperson Radiation and Oncology, Charles Enke
Vice Chairman, Kevin Garvin

LOCATIONS

HQ: UNMC PHYSICIANS
988101 NEBRASKA MED CTR, OMAHA, NE 68198-0001
Phone: 402-559-9700
Web: WWW.UNMC.EDU

COMPETITORS

Alegent Creighton Health
Children' s Hospital & Medical Center
Methodist Health System

HISTORICAL FINANCIALS

Company Type: Private

Income Statement

FYE: June 30

	REVENUE ($ mil.)	NET INCOME ($ mil.)	NET PROFIT MARGIN	EMPLOYEES
06/12	218	(1)	—	1,200
06/11	219	5	2.7%	—
06/10	203	1	0.8%	—
06/09	176	(0)	—	—
Annual Growth	7.3%	—	—	—

2012 Year-End Financials

Debt ratio: —
Return on equity: (-0.70%)
Cash ($ mil.): 26
Current ratio: —
Long-term debt ($ mil.): —
Dividends
Yield: —
Payout: —
Market value ($ mil.): —

UPMC ALTOONA

Altoona Regional Health System moves patients upstream towards better health. Operating in Altoona and surrounding areas in central Pennsylvania the health system's facilities include Altoona Hospital an acute care center with 380 licensed beds that provides specialized care in areas including cardiovascular ailments cancer behavioral health and neurology as well as general emergency trauma birthing and surgery services. Altoona Regional Health System also offers a variety of outpatient care facilities and programs including home health care a primary care physicians' group and laboratory services. The not-for-profit system is governed by a board of community representatives.

Geographic Reach

Altoona Regional Health System provides services to residents of about 20 counties in central Pennsylvania.

Operations

Altoona Regional Health System was a two-hospital system until March 2012 when it closed the Bon Secours-Holy Family Hospital. At that time one of Altoona Regional Health System's sponsors Catholic hospital operator Bon Secours Health System withdrew from the partnership.

While it worked towards closing one campus the company conducted numerous expansion and upgrade projects at its Altoona Hospital campus to prepare for the resulting increase in patients and to provide a consolidated efficient and modern regional care center. It also moved a number of ambulatory care services to the outpatient facility Station Medical Center.

Strategy

In 2013 Altoona Regional Health System entered into talks over a potential affiliation with Pennsylvania hospital operator UPMC. The relationship would strengthen Altoona's resources and presence in the region.

Company Background

In 2004 Altoona Hospital's parent Central Pennsylvania Health Services Corporation and Bon Secours-Holy Family Hospital's parent Bon Secours Health System merged the two campuses and affiliated companies to form Altoona Regional Health System.

EXECUTIVES

COO, Ronald J. (Ron) McConnell
SVP and Chief Nursing Officer, Chris Rickens
VP Supply Chain and Facilities Operations, Gary W. Zuckerman

President and CEO, Jerry Murray
VP and CIO, Dale Fuller
SVP Quality Medical Affairs and Chief Medical Officer, Linnane R. Batzel
Vice President, R S Magley
Vice President, Kevin Hockenberry
Infection Control Director, Tom Zeek
Director Of Home Healthcare, Joseph Fromknecht
Vp Mission Services, Jean Dobson Johnstone
Senior Vice President Finance, Betsy Kreuz
Senior Vice President, Warren Rhyner
Ambulatory Services Director, Lori Snyder
Director Of Pharmacy, Chris Barackman
Vice President Group Information, Heidi Handy
Board Member, Carlos Wiegering
Treasurer, Dorothy Vineglas
Board Member, Bruce Erb
Secretary, Nancy Robison
Secretary, Schmitt Rose

LOCATIONS

HQ: UPMC ALTOONA
620 HOWARD AVE, ALTOONA, PA 16601-4804
Phone: 814-889-2011
Web: WWW.ALTOONAREGIONAL.ORG

PRODUCTS/OPERATIONS

Selected Services

Behavioral Health
Birth & Growth
Cancer Care
Cardiac Care
Center for Weight Loss and Bariatric Surgery
Central Pennsylvania Cardiovascular Associates
Emergency Medicine and Trauma
HealthForce (Occupational Medicine)
Imaging Services
Institute for Sleep Medicine
Neurosurgery
Orthopedics
Physical Medicine and Rehabilitation
Primary Stroke Center
Surgical Services
Wound Care and Ostomy Program

COMPETITORS

Clearfield Area Health Services
Conemaugh Health System
Hanover Healthcare
Hershey Medical Center
J. C. Blair Memorial Hospital
Lancaster General
PinnacleHealth System
WellSpan Health

HISTORICAL FINANCIALS

Company Type: Private

Income Statement

FYE: June 30

	REVENUE ($ mil.)	NET INCOME ($ mil.)	NET PROFIT MARGIN	EMPLOYEES
06/12	485	36	7.5%	2,494
06/10*	321	5	1.6%	—
12/09	0	0	3.2%	—
06/09	436	(33)	—	—
Annual Growth	3.6%	—	—	—

*Fiscal year change

2012 Year-End Financials

Debt ratio: —
Return on equity: 7.50%
Cash ($ mil.): 30
Current ratio: 1.50
Long-term debt ($ mil.): —
Dividends
Yield: —
Payout: —
Market value ($ mil.): —

USS POSCO INDUSTRIES

US and Korean steel manufacturing interests come together in the form of USS-POSCO Industries (UPI) a joint venture between United States Steel (US Steel) and POSCO. The company operates a steel plant (formerly owned by US Steel) in Pittsburg Northern California. It manufactures flat-rolled steel sheets in various forms: cold-rolled steel galvanized steel and tinplate. In addition USS-POSCO churns out iron oxide which is used to make hard and soft ferrites. UPI sells its products to more than 150 customers in more than dozen states throughout the western US. End products include office furniture computer cabinets metal studs culverts and metal building materials.

Operations

UPI's main product lines include cold rolled sheet galvanized sheet hot rolled pickled and oiled sheet and tin plate.

Sales and Marketing

The company sells its products to a wide range of manufacturers whose end products include automotive parts computer cabinets culverts food packaging metal buildings metal studs and office furniture.

Strategy

Its Korean co-owner supplied high quality raw materials for use at the plant. In order to stay competitive in the face of cheaper steel imports UPI jettisoned non-core product lines to focus on steel sheet and tin. However strong competition and poor market prices forced the company in 2011 to introduce furloughs at the plant and enforce temporary shutdowns of the facility.

Ownership

UPI is a joint venture of US Steel and POSCO.

Company Background

US Steel teamed up with POSCO (then Pohang Iron & Steel Company) in1986 as part of a major reorganization of the aging Pittsburg plant which first opened in 1910.

The company rebounded from a major fire in 2001. In 2010 invested heavily in remediation measures to clean up soil and groundwater impacted by its plant activities.

EXECUTIVES

Director Business Planning and Customer Service, P. Michael Obermire
President, Robert R. (Bob) Smith
VP Operations, Salvatore S. (Sal) Sbranti
Secretary and General Counsel, Christopher A. (Chris) Conkling
General Manager Employee Relations, George Kunst
Marketing Manager USA, Kellie Williams
General Manager Sales, Julie Renner
Customer Service Manager, Beth Lindberg
Marketing Manager - International, Kory Yi
President, Kevin Kim
Vice President Commercial, Charles Kearney
Vice President - Administration & Finance, Alan Gardner
Vice President - Operations, Greg Isola

LOCATIONS

HQ: USS POSCO INDUSTRIES
900 LOVERIDGE RD, PITTSBURG, CA 94565-2808
Phone: 800-877-7672
Web: WWW.USSPOSCO.COM

COMPETITORS

AK Steel Holding Corporation
ArcelorMittal USA
BlueScope Steel
Gerdau Ameristeel
Nucor
Steel Dynamics

HISTORICAL FINANCIALS

Company Type: Private

Income Statement

FYE: December 31

	REVENUE ($ mil.)	NET INCOME ($ mil.)	NET PROFIT MARGIN	EMPLOYEES
12/08	1,198	11	1.0%	759
12/07	998	(40)	—	—
12/06	1,034	14	1.4%	—
12/05	854	(24)	—	—
Annual Growth	11.9%	—	—	—

2008 Year-End Financials

Debt ratio: —
Return on equity: 1.00%
Cash ($ mil.): 1
Current ratio: 0.40
Long-term debt ($ mil.): —
Dividends
Yield: —
Payout: —
Market value ($ mil.): —

UTAH STATE UNIVERSITY

Utah State University (USU) has more than 40 academic departments at colleges of agriculture arts business education and human services engineering science natural resources and humanities and social sciences. It offers more than 170 bachelor's degree programs and about 140 graduate degree programs. Biology elementary education mechanical and aerospace engineering and business administration are among the university's most popular majors. About 29000 students attend its main campus in northern Utah its three branch campuses or extension facilities located across the state. USU was established in 1888 as an agricultural college.

Geographic Reach

USU students hail from all 50 US states and some 80 international countries. The university's students have the opportunity to study abroad through partnerships with 140 other institutions located around the world. USU's main campuses or branch offices in Utah are located in Brigham City Logan San Juan Tooele and Uintah Basin.

Operations

USU has a student-to-faculty ratio of 18:1. Alumni of the university include Greg Carr founder of the Greg C. Carr Foundation and Charlie Denson former president of NIKE.

Financial Performance

Revenues increased at USU by 4% to some $340 million due to increased income from tuition and fees higher enrollment and increased state appropriations. The gain was offset by decreases in gifts grants and contracts. Net income fell 41% to $68 million due to higher operating expenses from salary benefit and other costs.

Strategy

To expand its facilities and meet growing student needs USU is adding a new school of business building and a new athletics center to its main campus. The university recently completed construction of a new $47 million agricultural building on the main campus as well as a new administration building on the USU Eastern campus. In addition USU is building a new distance education building on its Logan campus.

To further expand resources for students USU began offering a Master of Business Administration (MBA) program at the Brigham Young University's Idaho campus in 2013.

EXECUTIVES

Vp Operations Production Mfg, Brent Miller

LOCATIONS

HQ: UTAH STATE UNIVERSITY
2400 OLD MAIN HL, LOGAN, UT 84322-2400
Phone: 435-797-1064
Web: WWW.USU.EDU

PRODUCTS/OPERATIONS

Selected Colleges

Caine College of the Arts
College of Agriculture
College of Engineering
College of Humanities and Social Sciences
College of Science
Emma Eccles Jones College of Education and Human Services
Jon M. Huntsman School of Business
S.J. & Jessie E. Quinney College of Natural Resources

HISTORICAL FINANCIALS

Company Type: Private

Income Statement FYE: June 30

	REVENUE ($ mil.)	NET INCOME ($ mil.)	NET PROFIT MARGIN	EMPLOYEES
06/12	340	68	20.1%	6,000
06/11	328	53	16.4%	—
06/10	286	60	21.3%	—
06/09	268	(14)	—	—
Annual Growth	8.3%	—	—	—

2012 Year-End Financials

Debt ratio: —
Return on equity: 20.10%
Cash ($ mil.): 32
Current ratio: 1.00
Long-term debt ($ mil.): —
Dividends
Yield: —
Payout: —
Market value ($ mil.): —

VALLEY HEALTH SYSTEM

Valley Health's medical centers can be found in the in the Shenandoah Valley region. The not-for-profit organization operates six hospitals in Virginia and West Virginia that house a combined total of roughly 610 beds. The facilities include the flagship Winchester Medical Center as well as Warren Memorial Hospital Shenandoah Memorial Hospital and a handful of smaller community hospitals. Valley Health also operates outpatient surgery nursing home rehabilitation urgent care and family practice centers and it offers ambulance and home health care services. The system can trace its beginnings back to the opening of Winchester Memorial Hospital in 1903.

Geographic Reach

Valley Health operates in the northern Shenandoah Valley region including areas of Maryland Virginia and West Virginia. For years the company has been intent on increasing its geographic reach especially in rural markets. Its most recent additions were in Berkeley Springs West Virginia (the 40-bed War Memorial Hospital 2010); Luray Virginia (the 25-bed Page Memorial Hospital 2009) and Romney West Virginia (the 44-bed Hampshire Memorial Hospital 2008).

Operations

Valley Health sees some 30000 inpatients per year as well as 110000 ER visits and 875000 outpatient encounters. It also handles about 3000 births. In addition to its 610 inpatient beds Valley Health's senior care facilities house some 170 long-term care beds.

Along with its hospital services Valley Health provides patient transport services to more than a dozen counties in three states (Maryland Virginia and West Virginia) through its Valley Medical Transport division and urgent care through its Quick and Urgent Care segments. It also supplies pharmaceuticals and home health care equipment through Valley Pharmacy and Valley Home Care.

Strategy

In addition to adding facilities in new geographic territories Valley Health is widening its service capabilities by conducting expansion and renovation projects at its various existing facilities. The company completed construction of the new Hampshire Memorial Hospital in 2011 (replacing the smaller aging original hospital building) and in 2012 it opened a new patient tower at the Winchester Medical Center.

In addition Valley Health is investing $38 million to build a replacement hospital facility for Page Memorial which is scheduled for completion by 2014. Valley Health is also expanding and upgrading its War Memorial facilities and it is opening a number of new outpatient care centers in the region.

Company Background

Valley Health was formed through the merger of Winchester Medical Center and Warren Memorial Hospital in 1993.

EXECUTIVES

Chairman, F. Dixon Whitworth Jr., age 70
President CEO and Director, Michael J. Halseth
SVP and CFO, J. Craig Lewis
Corporate Director Marketing and Public Relations, Tom Urtz
VP Human Resources, Adrienne McKenna
President Warren Memorial Hospital, Patrick Nolan
VP and CIO, Joan Roscoe
President Shenandoah Memorial Hospital, Floyd Heater
SVP Valley Physician Enterprise, Timothy Willox
SVP Regional Operations, Todd Way
Privacy Officer, Walt Sowers
VP; President Winchester Medical Center, Al Pilong Sr.
President CEO and Director, Michael J. Halseth
Director, Harry F. Byrd III
Director, James T. Holland
Director, Douglas B. Keim
Director, William F. Brandt Jr.
Director, Jim Long
Director, William B. Major
Director, John S. Scully IV
Director, Joseph F. Silek Jr.
Director, Katherine P. Napier
Director, Patrick D. Ireland

LOCATIONS

HQ: VALLEY HEALTH SYSTEM
1840 AMHERST ST, WINCHESTER, VA 22601-2808
Phone: 540-536-8000
Web: WWW.VALLEYHEALTHLINK.COM

PRODUCTS/OPERATIONS

Selected Facilities and Divisions

Hampshire Memorial Hospital (Romney WV)
Page Memorial Hospital (Luray VA)
Quick Care (Strasburg VA)
Shenandoah Memorial Hospital (Woodstock VA)
Shenandoah Surgery Center (Woodstock VA)
Surgi-Center of Winchester (Winchester VA)
Urgent Care (Winchester Front Royal VA)
Valley Home Care (Front Royal Winchester Woodstock VA)
Valley Medical Transport
Valley Pharmacy (Winchester VA)
War Memorial Hopsital (Berkeley Springs WV)
Warren Memorial Hospital (Front Royal VA)
Winchester Medical Center (Winchester VA)
Winchester Rehabilitation Center (Winchester VA)

COMPETITORS

Fauquier Hospital
Frederick Memorial
Georgetown University Hospital
HCA
Inova
Loudoun Healthcare
MedStar Health
Meritus Health
Novant Health
Prince William Health System
Providence Hospital (Washington DC)
Rockingham Memorial Hospital

HISTORICAL FINANCIALS

Company Type: Private

Income Statement FYE: December 31

	REVENUE ($ mil.)	NET INCOME ($ mil.)	NET PROFIT MARGIN	EMPLOYEES
12/07	612	52	8.5%	4,300
12/06	564	75	13.5%	—
12/05	1,286	0	—	—
Annual Growth	—	43836.8%	—	—

2007 Year-End Financials

Debt ratio: —
Return on equity: 8.50%
Cash ($ mil.): 36
Current ratio: 1.40
Long-term debt ($ mil.): —
Dividends
Yield: —
Payout: —
Market value ($ mil.): —

VALLEY MEDICAL FACILITIES INC.

Heritage Valley Health System has a legacy of serving the health care needs of residents of southwestern Pennsylvania eastern Ohio and the West Virginia Panhandle. The two hospital system includes the flagship Heritage Valley Beaver hospital in Beaver Pennsylvania with about 360 beds and a smaller facility in nearby Sewickley with roughly 185 beds. In addition to its acute-care facilities the system operates several satellite facilities and provides primary care through a network of three affiliated physician groups. Heritage Valley Health System was formed in 1996 when the two hospitals merged but it has roots going back to 1894.

Strategy

The health system expands its service offerings and increases its geographic reach in part by forming collaborative relationships with health care providers and other organizations. For example it operates immediate care clinics at local Wal-Mart stores to offer patients routine care such as immunizations screenings and treatment of minor injuries and illnesses. Heritage Valley also partners with UPMC to offer radiation therapy and medical oncology services at Heritage Valley Beaver. Additionally Heritage Valley and UPMC Health Plan operate LifeSmart which identifies patients at risk for diabetes connects them with a primary care physician and provides them with lifestyle intervention programs.

Heritage Valley Health System entered an alliance in 2011 with Good Samaritan Hospice (GSH) that allowed it to serve more individuals in need of hospice care in the southwestern Pennsylvania region. Under the agreement Heritage Valley Health System gained partial share in GSH which includes the Good Samaritan House in Wexford and the Good Samaritan Cabot Unit in Cabot Pennsylvania.

Along with increasing its medical offerings through partnerships Heritage Valley hires specialists and adds new services to meet community demand. Some areas of focus include infectious disease endocrinology inpatient rehabilitation and wound care.

EXECUTIVES

President and CEO, Norman F. Mitry
Vice President Community, Daniel Brooks
CIO, David Carleton
VP and CFO, Bryan J. Randall
Chairman, G. R. Orr III
Vice Chairman, Dennis Pegden
Vice President Institutional Advancement, Daniel Murphy
Vice President Physician Practices, Laura Wagner
VP and Chief Medical Officer, John T. Cinicola
VP and Chief Nursing Officer Surgical Services and Cardiology, Kathleen Harley
Vice President General Counsel, Sharon Loftus
VP and Chief Nursing Officer Patient Care Services Heritage Valley Beaver, Marcia Ferrero
VP and Chief Nursing Officer Patient Care Services Heritage Valley Sewickley, Linda F. Homyk
Vice President and chief quality officer for the, John Luellen
Vice President AWARDED THE, Richard E. Humanity

LOCATIONS

HQ: VALLEY MEDICAL FACILITIES INC.
1000 DUTCH RIDGE RD, BEAVER, PA 15009-9727
Phone: 724-728-7000
Web: WWW.HERITAGEVALLEY.ORG

PRODUCTS/OPERATIONS

Selected Medical Services

Advanced Cardiology
Bariatric Surgery
Behavioral Health
Breast Imaging
Cancer Treatment
Cardiac Computed Tomography (Cardiac CT)
Cardiology
Community Advanced Ilness Program (CAIP)
Community Health Services
Diabetes Radiology
Diagnostic Centers
Emergency
Endoscopy Center
Family Planning
Heart and Vascular Center
Inpatient Rehabilitation
Laboratory
LIFE Beaver and Lawrence County
Maternity
MRI Services
Neurology
Nutrition Counseling
Occupational Medicine
Orthopedics Services
Osteoporosis
Pediatric Asthma
Pharmacy retail
Pulmonary Services
Signature BusinessCare
Signature Rehab
Signature SportsCare
Sleep Lab
Surgery Centers
VeinCare
Weight Loss
WoundCare

COMPETITORS

Butler Health System
Children' s Hospital of Pittsburgh
Conemaugh Health System
Excela Health
Jefferson Regional Medical Center of Pennsylvania
Kindred Healthcare
Ohio Valley General
Sharon Regional Health System
St. Clair Health
Trinity Health System
UPMC
Weirton Medical Center
West Penn Allegheny Health System

HISTORICAL FINANCIALS

Company Type: Private

Income Statement FYE: June 30

	REVENUE ($ mil.)	NET INCOME ($ mil.)	NET PROFIT MARGIN	EMPLOYEES
06/12	453	(53)	—	4,291
06/11	449	40	9.0%	—
06/10	445	13	2.9%	—
06/09	432	(65)	—	—
Annual Growth	1.6%	—	—	—

2012 Year-End Financials

Debt ratio: —
Return on equity: (-11.90%)
Cash ($ mil.): 22
Current ratio: 1.10
Long-term debt ($ mil.): —
Dividends
Yield: —
Payout: —
Market value ($ mil.): —

VALUE DRUG COMPANY

EXECUTIVES

President, John Letizia
VP Production, Richard T. (Dick) Moran
VP Finance, Robert (Gene) Tyler
Secretary, Robert Maher
Manager Sales and Marketing, Karla Moschella
Human Resources, Regis Myers

LOCATIONS

HQ: VALUE DRUG COMPANY
1 GOLFVIEW DR, ALTOONA, PA 166019398
Phone: 8149449316
Web: WWW.VALUEDRUGCO.COM

COMPETITORS

AmerisourceBergen
Cardinal Health
H. D. Smith Wholesale Drug
Kinray
McKesson
Quality King

HISTORICAL FINANCIALS

Company Type: Private

Income Statement FYE: December 31

	REVENUE ($ mil.)	NET INCOME ($ mil.)	NET PROFIT MARGIN	EMPLOYEES
12/13	715	0	0.1%	107
12/09	751	0	0.0%	—
12/08	732	0	0.0%	—
12/07	1,599	0	—	—
Annual Growth	(12.6%)	—	—	—

2013 Year-End Financials

Debt ratio: —
Return on equity: 0.10%
Cash ($ mil.): 1
Current ratio: 0.80
Long-term debt ($ mil.): —
Dividends
Yield: —
Payout: —
Market value ($ mil.): —

VARIETY CHILDREN'S HOSPITAL

Miami Children's Hospital a not-for-profit medical center boasts some 290 beds and offers more than 40 different health care specialties and subspecialties represented by more than 650 physicians. Some specialties include pediatric emergency care cancer treatment orthopedics and rehabilitation services. The hospital's neonatal unit treats newborns referred from other hospitals. Miami Children's Hospital operates the region's only free-standing pediatric trauma center. The hospital first opened its doors in the 1940s as Miami Tent #33 of Variety Clubs International. Variety Children's Hospital opened in 1950 and became Miami Children's Hospital in 1986.

Geographic Reach

MCH caters to young Florida residents and their families as well as those in South America and Europe through its Dan Marino Outpatient Center which assists children with special needs and provides neurological and development services for special needs children.

Operations

As part of its health network MCH also operates a handful of ambulatory care centers that administer pediatric outpatient services in Doral Miami Lakes Palmetto Bay Weston and West Kendall Florida. The health system also operates mobile health units that provide preventive care to uninsured children throughout its service area. The units provide immunizations tuberculosis tests and hearing and vision screenings among other services.

The hospital's neonatology division admits more than 900 newborns each year virtually all of them referred from general acute-care hospitals because they are in need of an advanced level of tertiary care.

Sales and Marketing

The hospital is at the tail end of a multiyear nearly $70 million project to install an electronic medical record system at the medical center. The first phase of the project which wrapped up in 2012 included new prescribing methods and lab test protocols. It will also engender better communication between hospital staff. The entire system should be installed by 2015.

EXECUTIVES

Secretary and Director, Christian C. Patrick
SVP and Chief Nursing Officer, Jacqueline L. (Jackie) Gonzalez
SVP and CFO, Pedro Alfaro
President CEO and Director, M. Narendra Kini
Chairman, Gary Gregory
SVP Medical and Academic Affairs Chief Medical Officer and Director, Deise Granado-Villar
Secretary, Ghislain Gouraige Jr.
COO, Martha McGill
President Medical Staff, Luis Gonzalez-Mendoza
Vice Chairman, Mario Murgado
Chairman Brain Institute, Prasanna Jayakar
Director Division Allergy and Immunology, Vivian Hernandez-Trujillo
SVP and Chief Talent Officer, Michael Kushner
Nursing Administrative Director Emergency Department, Maryann Henry
Director Division Adolescent Medicine, Lorena M. Siqueira
VP Transformation, Nikole Sanchez-Rubiera
CIO, Edward Martinez
Vice President Brain Institute, Jose Perdomo

Vice President Medical Staff, Ruben Gonzalez-Vallina
Director, Juan Carlos Mas, age 47
Secretary and Director, Christian C. Patrick
President CEO and Director, M. Narendra Kini
SVP Medical and Academic Affairs Chief Medical Officer and Director, Deise Granado-Villar
Director, Jose Carro
Director, Ghislain Gouraige Jr.
Director, Joanne M. Youngblut
Director, Andrew Labbie
Vice Chairman, Mario Murgado
Directors, Jose Perez-Rodriguez
Director, Keith Ward
Director, Roberto Warman

LOCATIONS

HQ: VARIETY CHILDREN' S HOSPITAL
3100 SW 62ND AVE, MIAMI, FL 33155-3009
Phone: 305-666-6511
Web: WWW.MCH.COM

PRODUCTS/OPERATIONS

Selected Services

Cardiology and Cardiovascular Surgery
Children's Medical Services Primary Care Program
Clinical Research
Dermatology Early Steps Southernmost Coast
Endocrinology & Diabetes
Gastroenterology
Hematology & Oncology
MCH Pediatric Care Center
Neuroscience Center
Neurosurgery
Ophthalmology
Orthopaedics
Otolaryngology Outpatient Centers
Pediatric Advanced Comprehensive Care Team
Pediatric Critical Care Medicine
Pediatric Hospital Medicine Team Pediatric Medicine
Pediatric Surgery & Anesthesiology
Psychiatry & Psychology
Pulmonology
Radiology
Rehabilitation Services
Rheumatology
Urology

Selected Locations

Miami Children's Hospital Dan Marino Center
Miami Children's Hospital Doral Center
Miami Children's Hospital Miami Lakes Rehabilitation Center
Miami Children's Hospital Nicklaus Care Center
Miami Children's Hospital Palmetto Bay Center
Miami Children's Hospital West Kendall Center

COMPETITORS

Adventist Health System Sunbelt Healthcare
All Children' s Hospital
Baptist Health South Florida
Children' s Hospital of Philadelphia
HCA
Jackson Health System
Mount Sinai Medical Center of Florida
NCH Healthcare
Shriners Hospitals For Children
South Broward Hospital District
South Miami Hospital
UF&Shands
University of Miami
University of Miami Hospital

HISTORICAL FINANCIALS

Company Type: Private

Income Statement FYE: December 31

	REVENUE ($ mil.)	NET INCOME ($ mil.)	NET PROFIT MARGIN	EMPLOYEES
12/08	381	269	70.5%	3,700
12/07	385	37	9.7%	—
12/06	819	0	—	—
Annual Growth	—76479.7%		—	—

2008 Year-End Financials

Debt ratio: —
Return on equity: 70.50%
Cash ($ mil.): 11
Current ratio: 0.70
Long-term debt ($ mil.): —
Dividends
Yield: —
Payout: —
Market value ($ mil.): —

VASSAR COLLEGE

A cool nickname and certain heritage aren't enough to assure some students entrance into Vassar College. The highly selective school enrolls some 2400 students annually most of whom graduated in the top 20% of their high school class. It has a student-faculty ratio of 8:1 and a list of alumni that includes standouts in areas from business to philanthropy. Because Vassar has no core curriculum students may concentrate in a single discipline a multidisciplinary program or design an independent major. The only universal requirements for graduation are proficiency in a foreign language a freshman composition class and a quantitative class. Vassar was founded in 1861 as a women's school; it went coed in 1969.

Geographic Reach

From its campus in Poughkeepsie New York Vassar serves students globally. Interantional students which comprise about 10% of its student body come from more than 50 countries. Typically juniors study for a year or semester in Vassar-sponsored programs in France Germany Ireland Italy Russia and Spain.

Operations

Vassar is considered one of the Seven Sisters seven women's liberal arts colleges founded in the northern US between 1837 and 1889. Besides Vassar they include Barnard Bryn Mawr Mount Holyoke Radcliffe Smith and Wellesley. Radcliffe is defunct and Vassar went co-ed; the rest remain women's schools.

With an annual cost of more than $49000 for tuition room and board and fees Vassar consistently ranks as one of the most expensive schools in the nation.

Strategy

As a way to further market itself and offer a place where military veterans can pick up an education Vassar in 2012 partnered with the Posse Foundation's Veterans Posse Program which is focused on boosting college attendance and graduation rates for military veterans at selective colleges and universities nationwide.

Sales and Marketing

Vassar sources its students from both public high schools (60%) and private schools (40%). For its tuition costs the college offers an impressive student-faculty ratio given its 290 faculty members.

Financial Performance

The New York college logged a 3% drop in revenue in fiscal 2012 as compared to 2011 due to decreases in net tuition fees room and board government grants and private gifts and grants. Net income for the same reporting period declined some 123%. Vassar points to non-operating activities for the drop attributable to decreases in investment returns and realized and unrealized gains spending on realized gains used to meet spending policy and increases in loss from adjustment for pension liability and post-retirement benefits changes other than net periodic benefits costs.

EXECUTIVES

Dean Students, David H. Brown
Associate VP Human Resources, Ruth E. Spencer
President, Catharine B. (Cappy) Hill
VP College Relations, Susan DeKrey
Executive Director Alumnae Administrative, Patricia D. Lichtenberg
Director Alumnae Relations for Programs, Catherine A. Lunn
Director Alumnae Relations for Operations, Willa C. McCarthy
Dean Admissions and Financial Aid, David M. Borus
Director International Services, Andrew F. Meade
Director Athletics and Physical Education, Sharon R. Beverly
Executive Director Buildings and Grounds Services, Thomas Allen
Executive Director Campus Activities, Teresa Quinn
Director Career Development, Mary P. Raymond
Director Web Development, Carolyn Guyer
Director Media Relations, Jeffrey B. Kosmacher
Director Administrative Information Services, Suzanne (Sue) Aber
Director User Services, John M. Collier
VP Computer Information Systems, Bret L. Ingerman
Director Health Education, Michelle C. Soucy
Director Academic Services, Kathleen A. Brown
VP Development, Catherine E. Baer
VP Finance and Administration, Elizabeth Eismeier
Assistant Dean Students and Director Residential Life, Luis Inoa
Registrar, Daniel J. Giannini
Associate VP and Director Investments Office, Stephen R. Dahnert
Director Health Services, Irena T. Balawajder
Director Grants Administration, Amanda L. Thornton
Director Financial Aid, Michael P. Fraher
Director Field Work, Peter Leonard
Director Libraries, Sabrina Pape
Assistant VP Budget and Planning, David A. English
Director Information Management, Maria T. Sutcliffe
Director Development Campaign Operations, Mary C. Starke
Director Corporate Foundation and Government Relations, James M. (Jim) Olson
Director Development Regional Programs, John S. Mihaly
Director Purchasing, Rosaleen Cardillo
Controller, Don Barton
Dean Freshmen, Benjamin Lotto
Dean of the College, Prof Christopher F. Roellke
Dean Studies, Joanne Long
Director Security, Donald Marsala
Assistant Dean Studies and Director International Programs, Susan Correll
Associate Dean Students and Director Psychological Counseling Services, Sylvia R. Balderrama
Associate Dean of the College and Director Disability and Support Services, Belinda Guthrie
Dean Planning and Academic Affairs, Prof Rachel Kitzinger
Dean Faculty, Prof Jonathan L. Chenette
Director Research Development, Maria Hohn
Director Individual Giving, Ryan Hart
Director Leadership Gifts, Peter Wilkie

Director Parent Giving and Assistant Director Principal Gifts, Mariana B. Mensch
Director Research and Associate Director Development for Operations, Kara M. Wern
Director Donor Relations, Diane Sauter
Director Networks and Systems, Emily Harris

LOCATIONS

HQ: VASSAR COLLEGE
124 RAYMOND AVE BOX 12, POUGHKEEPSIE, NY 12604-0001
Phone: 845-437-7000
Web: WWW.VASSAR.EDU

PRODUCTS/OPERATIONS

Selected Departments and Programs

Africana Studies Program
American Culture Program
Anthropology Department
Art Department
Asian Studies Program
Astronomy Department
Biology Department
Chemistry Department
Chinese and Japanese Department
Classics Department
Cognitive Science Program
College Courses
Computer Science Department
Dance Department
Drama (and Film) Department
Earth Science and Geography Department
Earth Science and Society Program
Economics Department
Education Department
English Department
Environmental Studies Program
Field Work Office
Film Department Drama and
French and Francophone Studies Department
Geography-Anthropology Program
Geography Department Earth Science and
German Studies Department
Hispanic Studies Department
History Department
Independent Program
Interdepartmental Courses
International Studies Program
Italian Department
Japanese Department Chinese and Jewish Studies Program
Latin American and Latino/a Studies Program
Mathematics Department
Media Studies Program
Medieval and Renaissance Studies Program
Music Department
Neuroscience and Behavior Program
Philosophy Department
Physical Education Department
Physics and Astronomy Department
Physics and Biochemistry Program
Political Science Department
Psychology Department
Religion Department
Russian Studies Department
Science Technology and Society Program
Self-Instructional Language Program
Sociology Department
Urban Studies Program
Victorian Studies Program
Women's Studies Program

HISTORICAL FINANCIALS

Company Type: Private

Income Statement FYE: June 30

	REVENUE ($ mil.)	NET INCOME ($ mil.)	NET PROFIT MARGIN	EMPLOYEES
06/12	153	(33)	—	974
06/11	229	12	5.4%	—
06/10	205	(7)	—	—
06/09	158	(55)	—	—
Annual Growth	(0.9%)	—	—	—

2012 Year-End Financials

Debt ratio: —
Return on equity: (-21.50%)
Cash ($ mil.): 11
Current ratio: —
Long-term debt ($ mil.): —
Dividends
Yield: —
Payout: —
Market value ($ mil.): —

VESCO OIL CORPORATION

EXECUTIVES

President and CEO, Donald R. Epstein
Corporate VP, Marjory Epstein

LOCATIONS

HQ: VESCO OIL CORPORATION
16055 W 12 MILE RD, SOUTHFIELD, MI 480762979
Phone: 2485570260
Web: WWW.VESCO-OIL.COM

COMPETITORS

Apex Oil
Blarney Castle Oil and Propane
Crystal Flash Energy
Dixie Gas & Oil
Lykins
PetroLiance
Petroleum Traders Corporation
RKA Petroleum
SPF Energy
U.S. Venture

HISTORICAL FINANCIALS

Company Type: Private

Income Statement FYE: December 31

	REVENUE ($ mil.)	NET INCOME ($ mil.)	NET PROFIT MARGIN	EMPLOYEES
12/10	108	3	3.0%	210
12/09	100	(0)	—	—
12/08	1,486	0	0.0%	—
Annual Growth	(73.0%)	19257.2%	—	—

VETERANS OF FOREIGN WARS OF THE UNITED STATES

EXECUTIVES

Commander-in-Chief, Glen Gardner
Senior Vice Commander-in-Chief, Thomas Tradewell
Surgeon General, C.O. (Doc) Bohlman
Junior Vice Commander-in-Chief, Richard L. Eubank
Associate Director Field Operations, Robert Krause

LOCATIONS

HQ: VETERANS OF FOREIGN WARS OF THE UNITED STATES
406 W 34TH ST FL 11, KANSAS CITY, MO 641112736
Phone: 8167563390
Web: WWW.VFWCA.ORG

HISTORICAL FINANCIALS

Company Type: Private

Income Statement FYE: August 31

	REVENUE ($ mil.)	NET INCOME ($ mil.)	NET PROFIT MARGIN	EMPLOYEES
08/13	100	23	23.3%	185
08/12	103	4	4.7%	—
08/11	101	11	10.9%	—
08/10	94	0	—	—
Annual Growth	1.9%	—	—	—

2013 Year-End Financials

Debt ratio: —
Return on equity: 23.30%
Cash ($ mil.): 16
Current ratio: 0.30
Long-term debt ($ mil.): —
Dividends
Yield: —
Payout: —
Market value ($ mil.): —

VIDEO GAMING TECHNOLOGIES INC

It takes more than pencil and paper to make a good video game. Video Gaming Technologies (VGT) is a leading manufacturer of Class II-based gaming machines which mostly include bingo-style platforms found outside the Las Vegas market. The company additionally makes video terminals for skill-based games. It serves primarily the Native American gaming industry and its Live-Call Bingo game is the top-earning bingo based Class II platform for Native American casinos. VGT also serves emerging gaming markets. The company has manufacturing research and development marketing and support services. It does business in Oklahoma Washington Kansas California and Texas. CEO Jon Yarbrough founded VGT in 1991.

EXECUTIVES

Senior Management Senior Vice President, John Plunkett

LOCATIONS

HQ: VIDEO GAMING TECHNOLOGIES INC
308 MALLORY STATION RD, FRANKLIN, TN 37067-8210
Phone: 615-372-1000
Web: WWW.VGT.NET

PRODUCTS/OPERATIONS

Selected Games

Crazy Billions
Jewels and Gems
Live Call Bingo
Lucky Ducky
Mount Cashmore
Mr. Millionare
Pick a Duck
Super Hits!
Victory Lap

COMPETITORS

Aristocrat Technologies
GameTech
International Game Technology
Multimedia Games
WMS Industries

HISTORICAL FINANCIALS

Company Type: Private

Income Statement FYE: December 31

	REVENUE ($ mil.)	NET INCOME ($ mil.)	NET PROFIT MARGIN	EMPLOYEES
12/08	199	24	12.2%	600
12/06	180	5	3.3%	—
12/05	1,063	0	—	—
Annual Growth	(42.8%)	28904.0%	—	—

2008 Year-End Financials

Debt ratio: —
Return on equity: 12.20%
Cash ($ mil.): 36
Current ratio: 1.20
Long-term debt ($ mil.): —
Dividends
Yield: —
Payout: —
Market value ($ mil.): —

VIKING YACHT COMPANY

Leif Eriksson's oceangoing Viking explorers could only dream of vessels like those made by the Viking Yacht Company. Viking Yacht can build more than 100 semi-custom fiberglass pleasure boats primarily used for sport fishing. About 90% of each yacht is made in-house. Its line of yachts vary in length from approximately 42 to 92 feet and include convertible and enclosed-bridge convertible vessels open sportfish models and a 52-foot sport yacht. The luxury boats are sold through a network of more than 40 dealers six of which are based outside the US. Founders and brothers Bob and Bill Healey own Viking Yacht Company.

Operations

Viking operates through several businesses and divisions. Atlantic Marine Electronics provides sales installation and service support for yacht electronics including navigation communication and entertainment systems equipment. Its Viking Yachting Center acts as a weather-protected storage area for boats up to 50 feet and provides full services to all brands of yachts including 250 deepwater slips a pool and pool house barbeque and picnic areas bathhouse fuel dock and nighttime security.

Palm Beach Towers designs and engineers aluminum tuna towers used aboard Viking yachts and other boats. In addition Palm Beach Towers produces fiberglass hardtops rod lockers and electronic boxes and other custom aluminum and fiberglass accessories. Palm Beach Towers has locations in New Jersey and Florida.

Sales and Marketing

The company has a sales network of waterfront locations across the US as well as in the Caribbean Central and South America Africa Asia Middle East and Australia.

Strategy

To attract additional customers Viking is focused on launching new models of yachts. It launched seven new models during 2011 and 2012 and in 2013 it launched sleek and sporty new generation 55 and 62 Convertibles ass had a 92 Convertible on the docket.

Normal 0 false false false EN-US X-NONE X-NONE /* Style Definitions */ table.MsoNormalTable {mso-style-name:"Table Normal"; mso-tstyle-rowband-size:0; mso-tstyle-colband-size:0; mso-style-noshow:yes; mso-style-priority:99; mso-style-parent:""; mso-padding-alt:0in 5.4pt 0in 5.4pt; mso-para-margin-top:0in; mso-para-margin-right:0in; mso-para-margin-bottom:10.0pt; mso-para-margin-left:0in; line-height:115%; mso-pagination:widow-orphan; font-size:11.0pt; font-family:"Calibri""sans-serif"; mso-ascii-font-family:Calibri; mso-ascii-theme-font:minor-latin; mso-hansi-font-family:Calibri; mso-hansi-theme-font:minor-latin;}To help cut greenhouse gas emissions and control costs in 2012 Viking built a tri-generation power plant with six natural gas-fueled turbines at its New Jersey manufacturing facility enabling the company to produce its own electricity.

Company Background

Viking was founded in 1964 and has produced more than 4000 vessels.

EXECUTIVES

Chairman and CEO, Robert T. (Bob) Healey
President and COO, Bill Healey
EVP and CFO, Gerard D. Straub Sr.
EVP, Patrick J. (Pat) Healey
President Sports Cruisers, Thomas Carroll
CIO, John Kasinski

LOCATIONS

HQ: VIKING YACHT COMPANY
ON THE BASS RIV RR 9, NEW GRETNA, NJ 08224
Phone: 6092966000
Web: WWW.VIKINGYACHTS.COM

PRODUCTS/OPERATIONS

Selected Models of Yachts

Enclosed Bridge Convertible
Motor Yachts
Open
Open Bridge Convertible
Sport Yacht

COMPETITORS

Brunswick Boat
Fountain Powerboat
Hatteras Yachts
Marine Products Corp.
Sea Fox Boats
Sea Ray Boats
Sunseeker

HISTORICAL FINANCIALS

Company Type: Private

Income Statement FYE: July 31

	REVENUE ($ mil.)	NET INCOME ($ mil.)	NET PROFIT MARGIN	EMPLOYEES
07/14	194	16	8.4%	775
07/13	154	10	6.7%	—
07/12	143	6	4.2%	—
07/11	142	0	—	—
Annual Growth	10.9%	—	—	—

2014 Year-End Financials

Debt ratio: —
Return on equity: 8.40%
Cash ($ mil.): 20
Current ratio: 0.80
Long-term debt ($ mil.): —
Dividends
Yield: —
Payout: —
Market value ($ mil.): —

VILLANOVA UNIVERSITY IN THE STATE OF PENNSYLVANIA

Founded in 1842 by the friars of the Order of St. Augustine and named for St. Thomas of Villanova Villanova University retains its Catholic identity to this day. The oldest and largest Catholic institution of higher learning in Pennsylvania the university offers more than 50 academic undergraduate programs at its four main colleges: Business Engineering Liberal Arts and Science and Nursing. It also has a School of Law and it offers graduate programs in most of its disciplines. Villanova University has an enrollment of more than 10000 undergraduate and graduate students and has a student-to-faculty ratio of 12:1.

Geographic Reach

Villanova is located on a 270-acre campus with 76 buildings located in Radnor Township in Delaware County Pennsylvania. It also operates a 30-acre conference center location in close proximity to the main campus. The university's enrollment includes students from most US states and 50 international countries.

Operations

While it is focused on providing a well-rounded Catholic-based liberal arts education to its students Villanova University also strives to participate in the community of Philadelphia through outreach and service efforts. The school has 44 clubs and about 270 extracurricular activities and groups. In addition Villanova has some two dozen varsity sports offerings and prides itself on having produced about 60 Olympic athletes.

Student tuition and fees account for about two-thirds of sales. Other sources of income include auxiliary enterprises private gifts and grants endowment resources and government grants.

Financial Performance

Operating revenue in fiscal 2012 increased 2% to $386 million on higher income from student tuition and fees auxiliary enterprise sales and private gifts and grants. Average tuition runs at about $44000 plus room and board of some $12000.

Strategy

The university has launched a long-term plan to upgrade the university's campus facilities. As part of the campus master plan in 2011 Villanova launched a $22.5 million project to enhance its landscape including adding aesthetic mobility and pedestrian solutions with the ultimate goal of making the campus vehicle-free. By 2013 the first two phases were completed with phase three efforts in progress including the redesign of the Alumni Quad. The university also plans to add more residence halls a performing arts center and retail and parking facilities.

In 2013 Villanova expanded its academic programs by adding new graduate programs in biochemical engineering and cybersecurity at the College of Engineering. In addition the School of Law opened a new center for law entrepreneurship and innovation as well as a clinic for interdisciplinary mental and physical health law.

Other strategic efforts include increasing the university endowment better defining its values and identity establishing national stature for scholarship and graduate offerings attracting high-quality students and revamping the undergraduate curriculum to enhance critical thinking and leadership skills among students.

EXECUTIVES

VP Administration and Finance, Kenneth G. (Ken) Valosky
VP and General Counsel, Dorothy A. Malloy
VP Student Life, Rev John P. Stack
VP Technology and CIO, Stephen W. Fugale
Dean Students, Paul F. Pugh
President and Trustee, Rev Peter M. Donohue, age 62
VP Mission and Ministry, Barbara E. Wall
VP University Advancement, Michael J. (Mike) O'Neill
VP University Communication, Ann E. Diebold

Chairman, Terence M. O'Toole
Vice Chair, Catherine M. Keating
VP Academic Affairs, Rev Kail C. Ellis
Associate VP and Affirmative Action Officer, Ellen Ryan Krutz
Interim Dean Villanova School of Business, Kevin D. Clark
Dean Liberal Arts & Sciences, Jean Ann Linney
Dean College of Nursing, M. Louise Fitzpatrick
Dean Engineering, Gary A. Gabriele
President General Counsel, Susan Warner
President and Trustee, Rev Peter M. Donohue, age 62
Trustee, Richard P. Brennan
Trustee, Kimble A. Byrd
Trustee, Tara S. Cortes
Trustee, James C. Curvey
Trustee, James D. Danella
Trustee, James C. Davis
Trustee, Denise L. Devine
Trustee, Nance K. Dicciani
Trustee, Rev Raymond F. Dlugos
Trustee, Darryl J. Ford
Trustee, Rev Paul W. Galetto
Trustee, William M. Gibson
Trustee, Patricia H. Imbesi
Trustee, John P. Jones III
Vice Chair, Catherine M. Keating
Trustee, Leonard J. LoBiondo
Trustee, Rev Gary N. McCloskey
Trustee, Anne Welsh McNulty
Trustee, Thomas M. Mulroy
Trustee, Mary D. Naylor
Trustee, James V. O?Donnell
Trustee, James F. Orr III
Trustee, Rev Donald F. Reilly
Trustee, Rev Bernard C. Scianna
Trustee, Robert Thornton
Trustee, Joseph V. Topper Jr., age 58
Trustee, Paul A. Tufano
Auditors: PricewaterhouseCoopersLLP

LOCATIONS

HQ: VILLANOVA UNIVERSITY IN THE STATE OF PENNSYLVANIA
800 E LANCASTER AVE, VILLANOVA, PA 19085-1603
Phone: 610-519-4500
Web: WWW.VILLANOVA.EDU

PRODUCTS/OPERATIONS

2012 Sales

	$ mil.	% of total
Student tuition & fees	260	68
Auxiliary enterprises	65	17
Private gifts & grants	20	5
Endowment resources	15	4
Government grants	7	2
Investment income	0	
Other	15	4
Total	**385**	**100**

Selected Schools and Programs

Undergraduate
- College of Arts & Sciences
- College of Engineering
- College of Nursing
- Villanova School of Business

Graduate Studies
- Engineering
- Liberal Arts and Sciences
- Nursing
- School of Law
- Villanova School of Business

Other Offerings
- Continuing Studies
- Part-Time Studies

HISTORICAL FINANCIALS

Company Type: Private

Income Statement FYE: May 31

	REVENUE ($ mil.)	NET INCOME ($ mil.)	NET PROFIT MARGIN	EMPLOYEES
05/13	401	101	25.4%	2,022
05/12	385	(4)	—	—
05/10	378	89	23.7%	—
05/10	368	56	15.4%	—
Annual Growth	2.9%	21.7%	—	—

2013 Year-End Financials

Debt ratio: —
Return on equity: 25.40%
Cash ($ mil.): 145
Current ratio: —
Long-term debt ($ mil.): —
Dividends
Yield: —
Payout: —
Market value ($ mil.): —

VISALIA UNIFIED SCHOOL DISTRICT

LOCATIONS

HQ: VISALIA UNIFIED SCHOOL DISTRICT
5000 W CYPRESS AVE, VISALIA, CA 932778300
Phone: 5597307300
Web: WWW.VUSD.ORG

HISTORICAL FINANCIALS

Company Type: Private

Income Statement FYE: June 30

	REVENUE ($ mil.)	NET INCOME ($ mil.)	NET PROFIT MARGIN	EMPLOYEES
06/12	241	8	3.7%	4,000
06/11	228	8	3.6%	—
06/08	267	5	2.1%	—
06/07	245	0	—	—
Annual Growth	(0.3%)	—	—	—

2012 Year-End Financials

Debt ratio: —
Return on equity: 3.70%
Cash ($ mil.): 65
Current ratio: 4.40
Long-term debt ($ mil.): —
Dividends
Yield: —
Payout: —
Market value ($ mil.): —

VIZIO INC.

VIZIO has done for HDTVs what Dell did for PCs and Southwest Airlines did for air travel: sell them for less. The company sells low-cost flat panel and plasma LCD HDTVs. It competes head-to-head with Japan's Sonyand Samsung; its products however are made in China and Taiwan. VIZIO has logged large annual revenue gains by selling quality televisions for hundreds if not thousands of dollars less than its competitors. The company was founded by CEO William Wang in 2002 and initially its TVs were only sold at membership retailers such as Costco Wholesale BJ's Wholesale Club and Sam's Club. Since then it has extended its reach to discount retailers Wal-Mart and Sears. VIZIO entered the PC arena in 2012.

Operations

Best known for its TVs VIZIO also makes Blue-Ray disc players speakers headphones Internet routers and other consumer electronics products including PCs.

Strategy

With home computers becoming an integral part of home entertainment systems VIZIO entered the PC market in mid-2012 with a new line of laptops and desktops starting at about $890. By combining its entertainment know-how with the power of the latest Intel Core processors VIZIO hopes to set a new standard for the Windows experience. The line consists of the VIZIO Thin + Light Notebook and All-in-One PC.

VIZIO also controls the design and marketing of its products and partners with contract manufacturers to make TVs less expensively than its competitors. Its collaboration with AmTran Technology Co. based in Taipei has proven to be an integral part of the success of both VIZIO and AmTran. AmTran which has an ownership stake in VIZIO generates some 80% of its revenue from sales to VIZIO while VIZIO relies on AmTran as a supplier for most of its TVs.

VIZIO's low-cost business model and partnerships with high-volume retailers such as Wal-Mart has paid off for the company which was named the #1 shipper of LCD TVs in the US in 2009. Since 2002 VIZIO has sold more than 30 million TVs. To VIZIO having the top LCD TV in the US is a first step. The TV maker also entered after the market for smart TVs which are integrated with Internet functionality shipping its first model during the second half of 2011.

EXECUTIVES

Director Marketing, Jason Maciel
CEO, William Wang
CFO, Kurt Binder

LOCATIONS

HQ: VIZIO INC.
39 TESLA, IRVINE, CA 92618-4603
Phone: 949-428-2525
Web: WWW.VIZIO.COM

PRODUCTS/OPERATIONS

Selected Products

Cables and other accessories
Blue-ray disc players
HDTVs
HD home theater systems
Headphones
Internet routers
Personal computers
Tablet computers
Speakers

COMPETITORS

Acer	LG Electronics
Bose	Lenovo
Dell	Panasonic Corp
Funai Electric	Philips Electronics
Harman International	Pioneer Corporation
Hewlett-Packard Limited	Samsung Electronics
	Sony
Koss	Westinghouse

HISTORICAL FINANCIALS

Company Type: Private

Income Statement FYE: December 31

	REVENUE ($ mil.)	NET INCOME ($ mil.)	NET PROFIT MARGIN	EMPLOYEES
12/08	2,006	10	0.5%	225
12/07	1,929	7	0.4%	—
12/06	671	1	0.2%	—
12/04	46	0	1.0%	—
Annual Growth	155.8%	115.7%	—	—

2008 Year-End Financials

Debt ratio: —
Return on equity: 0.50%
Cash ($ mil.): 42
Current ratio: 0.90
Long-term debt ($ mil.): —

Dividends
Yield: —
Payout: —
Market value ($ mil.): —

VOLTA OIL COMPANY INC.

LOCATIONS

HQ: VOLTA OIL COMPANY INC.
1 ROBERTS RD STE 2, PLYMOUTH, MA 023605087
Phone: 5087473778
Web: WWW.VOLTAOIL.COM

HISTORICAL FINANCIALS

Company Type: Private

Income Statement

FYE: September 30

	REVENUE ($ mil.)	NET INCOME ($ mil.)	NET PROFIT MARGIN	EMPLOYEES
09/13	220	0	0.2%	107
09/12	230	0	0.2%	—
09/11	206	0	0.1%	—
09/07	90	0	—	—
Annual Growth	16.0%	—	—	—

2013 Year-End Financials

Debt ratio: —
Return on equity: 0.20%
Cash ($ mil.): 1
Current ratio: 0.90
Long-term debt ($ mil.): —

Dividends
Yield: —
Payout: —
Market value ($ mil.): —

VOLUNTEER ENERGY COOPERATIVE

In the strong tradition of volunteering in Tennessee Volunteer Energy Cooperative is voluntarily cooperating with its members to serve their energy needs. The distribution utility serves more than 109000 customers (who also own the cooperative) in 17 central and eastern Tennessee counties. It operates more than 9000 miles of power lines. ‚ÄVolunteer Energy purchases its power supply from the Tennessee Valley Authority. The company also ‚Â provides metered natural gas and ‚Âpropane service and ‚Âoffers telecommunications (Internet access and long-distance phone) services. In addition Volunteer Energy offers its customer surge protection and security equipment.

The cooperative grows its customer base by about 2000 new accounts per year. ‚ÂIt plans to add a number of electrical substations to keep pace with growing demand.

Volunteer Energy is governed by a board of 12 members who represent the 17 counties in its service area.

Higher rates and increased demand lifted the company's revenue and net income in 2011 despite the extra costs incurred by infrastructure damage caused by six tornados that ripped through the cooperative's service area in April 2011.

Volunteer Energy was formed as Meigs County Electric Membership Cooperative in 1935 largely at the prompting of Tennessee Agricultural Extension Agent for Meigs County Willis Shadow.

EXECUTIVES

Vice President Of Finance, Charles Fitch
Vice President Marketing, Patty Hurley
Vice President Information Technology, Karen Davis
Vice President Information Technology, Karen Zitek
Senior Vice President And Chief, Dale Macdiarmid
Vice Chairman, James Brook

LOCATIONS

HQ: VOLUNTEER ENERGY COOPERATIVE
18359 STATE HIGHWAY 58 N, DECATUR, TN 373227825
Phone: 4233341020
Web: WWW.VEC.ORG

PRODUCTS/OPERATIONS

2011 Sales

	$ mil.	% of total
% of total		
Electric energy		
Residential		65
Industrial		22
Commercial		9
Street lighting &		2
Other		2
Total		**100**

COMPETITORS

AGL Resources
CenturyLink
Crestwood Equity

HISTORICAL FINANCIALS

Company Type: Private

Income Statement

FYE: June 30

	REVENUE ($ mil.)	NET INCOME ($ mil.)	NET PROFIT MARGIN	EMPLOYEES
06/14	244	12	5.1%	175
06/12	228	15	6.8%	—
06/11	235	13	5.5%	—
06/10	206	0	—	—
Annual Growth	4.3%	—	—	—

2014 Year-End Financials

Debt ratio: —
Return on equity: 5.10%
Cash ($ mil.): 33
Current ratio: 2.80
Long-term debt ($ mil.): —

Dividends
Yield: —
Payout: —
Market value ($ mil.): —

VOLUNTEER ENERGY SERVICES INC.

LOCATIONS

HQ: VOLUNTEER ENERGY SERVICES INC.
790 WINDMILLER DR STE A, PICKERINGTON, OH 431476879
Phone: 6148563128
Web: WWW.VOLUNTEERENERGY.COM

HISTORICAL FINANCIALS

Company Type: Private

Income Statement

FYE: December 31

	REVENUE ($ mil.)	NET INCOME ($ mil.)	NET PROFIT MARGIN	EMPLOYEES
12/11	204	12	6.3%	65
12/08	152	3	2.0%	—
12/07	92	3	4.3%	—
12/06	71	0	—	—
Annual Growth	23.6%	—	—	—

2011 Year-End Financials

Debt ratio: —
Return on equity: 6.30%
Cash ($ mil.): 4
Current ratio: 1.90
Long-term debt ($ mil.): —

Dividends
Yield: —
Payout: —
Market value ($ mil.): —

VOLUNTEERS OF AMERICA INC.

There's a volunteer everywhere you look at Volunteers of America a national faith-based organization that provides community-level human services to more than 2.5 million people a year. It works to help abused and neglected children at-risk youth disabled people the homeless people with substance abuse problems the elderly and prisoners and former prisoners. The group operates from about 45 offices across the US and counts some 65000 volunteers in its ranks. It receives government grants as well as support from the public. Volunteers of America was organized in 1896 by Ballington and Maud Booth. Ballington's father William Booth founded the Salvation Army.

Geographic Reach

As its name suggests Volunteers of America helps more than 2.5 million people in more than 400 communities in 46 US states the District of Columbia and Puerto Rico.

Operations

Volunteers of America (VoA) expanded its charitable reach in 2013 with the opening of the Anoka Rehabilitation and Living Center a 120-bed skilled care center in Anoka Minnesota. In 2012 VoA opened a 52-bed assisted living facility in Arlington Virginia for low-income seniors with intellectual disabilities and mental illness.

Financial Performance

Volunteers of America reported revenue of $1 billion in 2012 (down 3% versus 2011) of which nearly 45% came from the federal government. About 25% came from state and local governments while program fees accounted for about 15% and public support more than 10%. Expenses amounted to about 96% of total revenue in 2012.

The charity has community corporate and private philanthropy partners such as The Players Trust Hasbro and The Home Depot Foundation. The Home Depot Foundation pledged in 2012 some $1.4 million in new grants to Volunteers of America for 16 programs that will aid homeless US military veterans find transitional or permanent housing.

EXECUTIVES

Vice President Business Development, Rosemarie Rae
Executive Vice President General Counsel, David T. Bowman

Executive Vice President of External Affairs, Jatrice Martel Gaiter
President and CEO, Michael (Mike) King
Executive Vice President of Affiliate Relations, Margaret Ratcliff
Executive Vice President for Military Communities and Chief Medical Officer, Jonathan Sherin
COO, Thomas Turnbull
Executive Vice President Chief Financial Officer, Joseph A. Budzynski
Co Vice President Of Human Resources, Maureen Dobosz
Executive Vice President, Julie Bettcher, age 53
Executive Vice President, Heath Steel
Executive Assistant To The Assistant Vice President Of Nyc Housing Services, Jameece Pope
Vice President Intellectual Disabilities Services, Belinda Tiller
Vice President Finance Managing, Bay Obrien
Vice President Strategic Development Volunteers Of America, Nicole Driebe
Vice President Of Pace Operations, Michael Snow
Regional Vice President, Wanda Ozier
Executive Vice President Retail, Don Markelonis
Vice President Low Income Tax Credit, Mike Seltz
Svp Integrated Care Strategies, Peter Fitzgerald
Regional Vice President, Judith Mower
Director Of Clinical Services, Patsy Jones
Executive Vice President Veterans Affairs And Chie, Jonathan Baum
Secretary And Director, Nancy Gofus
Board Member, Matthew French
Board Member, Sidney Davis
Vice Chairman, Don Conley
Board Member, Kurt Maloney
Board Member, William Utley
Board Member, Ruthie Norton
Board Member, Michael Latino
Board Member, Curt Zaske
Member Board Of Directors, Gina Adams
Secretary, Adebimpe Ogundare

LOCATIONS

HQ: VOLUNTEERS OF AMERICA INC.
1660 DUKE ST STE 100, ALEXANDRIA, VA 22314-3427
Phone: 703-341-5000
Web: WWW.VOA.ORG

PRODUCTS/OPERATIONS

2012 Revenue

	$ mil.	% of total
Government awards	704	70
Public support	130	13
Other	175	17
Total	**1,009**	**100**

HISTORICAL FINANCIALS

Company Type: Private

Income Statement FYE: June 30

	REVENUE ($ mil.)	NET INCOME ($ mil.)	NET PROFIT MARGIN	EMPLOYEES
06/13	238	13	5.6%	3,000
06/08	6	5	88.7%	—
06/06	29	0	3.0%	—
06/05	1,474	0	—	—
Annual Growth	—	311.7%	—	—

2013 Year-End Financials

Debt ratio: —
Return on equity: 5.60%
Cash ($ mil.): 22
Current ratio: 1.30
Long-term debt ($ mil.): —

Dividends
Yield: —
Payout: —
Market value ($ mil.): —

VP HOLDINGS CORPORATION

LOCATIONS

HQ: VP HOLDINGS CORPORATION
1508 W BADGER RD, MADISON, WI 537132308
Phone: 6082561988

HISTORICAL FINANCIALS

Company Type: Private

Income Statement FYE: September 30

	REVENUE ($ mil.)	NET INCOME ($ mil.)	NET PROFIT MARGIN	EMPLOYEES
09/10	203	2	1.4%	269
09/09	192	2	1.3%	—
09/08	1,868	0	—	—
Annual Growth	—	8762.6%	—	—

2010 Year-End Financials

Debt ratio: —
Return on equity: 1.40%
Cash ($ mil.): 1
Current ratio: 0.70
Long-term debt ($ mil.): —

Dividends
Yield: —
Payout: —
Market value ($ mil.): —

W. DOUGLASS DISTRIBUTING LTD.

LOCATIONS

HQ: W. DOUGLASS DISTRIBUTING LTD.
325 E FOREST AVE, SHERMAN, TX 750908832
Phone: 9038931181
Web: WWW.DOUGLASSDIST.COM

HISTORICAL FINANCIALS

Company Type: Private

Income Statement FYE: December 31

	REVENUE ($ mil.)	NET INCOME ($ mil.)	NET PROFIT MARGIN	EMPLOYEES
12/13	428	1	0.3%	130
12/12	422	0	0.1%	—
12/11	368	1	0.4%	—
12/10	275	0	—	—
Annual Growth	15.9%	—	—	—

2013 Year-End Financials

Debt ratio: —
Return on equity: 0.30%
Cash ($ mil.): 0
Current ratio: 0.80
Long-term debt ($ mil.): —

Dividends
Yield: —
Payout: —
Market value ($ mil.): —

W. E. AUBUCHON CO. INC.

EXECUTIVES

Founder, William E. Aubuchon III
President, M. Marcus Moran Jr.

LOCATIONS

HQ: W. E. AUBUCHON CO. INC.
95 AUBUCHON DR, WESTMINSTER, MA 014731470
Phone: 9788740521

PRODUCTS/OPERATIONS

Selected Services

Cut Glass & Plexiglasss
Knife & Sharpening Services
Lamp Repair
Lock Servives & Key Duplication
Pipe Cutting
Propane Filling and/or Exchange Tanks
Window Screen Repair
Window Shade Cutting

Selected Products

Electrical
Farm & Pet
Fasteners
Hand Tools
Hardware
Heating & Cooling
Housewares
Lawn & Garden
Outdoor Living
Paint & Supplies
Plumbing
Power Tools

COMPETITORS

84 Lumber
Ace Hardware
Do it Best
Home Depot
Kmart
Lowe' s
McCoy Corp.
Menard
Northern Tool
Office Depot
OfficeMax
Sears
Staples
Stock Building Supply
Target Corporation
True Value
Wal-Mart

HISTORICAL FINANCIALS

Company Type: Private

Income Statement FYE: December 31

	REVENUE ($ mil.)	NET INCOME ($ mil.)	NET PROFIT MARGIN	EMPLOYEES
12/13	146	(3)	—	1,252
12/12	142	1	1.4%	—
12/11	140	1	1.0%	—
12/10	133	0	—	—
Annual Growth	3.1%	—	—	—

2013 Year-End Financials

Debt ratio: —
Return on equity: (-2.20%)
Cash ($ mil.): 0
Current ratio: 0.10
Long-term debt ($ mil.): —

Dividends
Yield: —
Payout: —
Market value ($ mil.): —

W. K. KELLOGG FOUNDATION

Charitable grants from W.K. Kellogg Foundation are grrrrrrrrreat! Founded in 1930 by cereal industry pioneer Will Keith Kellogg the foundation provides more than $300 million in grants annually to programs focused on youth and education health food systems and rural development and philanthropy and volunteerism. ‚Â About two-thirds ‚Âof its grants go to initiatives in the US (mostly in Michigan Mississippi and New Mexico) although it ‚Âalso serves others ‚Âthrough grants in Latin America Mexico the Caribbean Brazil and South Africa. The work of the W.K. Kellogg Foundation is supported by a related trust; together they have ‚Âassets of ‚Âmore than ‚Â$9 billion – mainly in ‚ÂKellogg Company ‚Âstock.

With a rise in Kellogg Company stock prices throughout 2009 the foundation stands to benefit. Although they share a founder and a home city the Kellogg Foundation and the Kellogg Company are governed independently.

Charity really does begin at home for the W.K. Kellogg Foundation which allocated ‚Âabout 18% of its US grant money to activities in Michigan in 2008.

W.K. Kellogg Foundation is guided by its founder's desire "to help people help themselves" and prefers to support programs that offer long-term solutions rather than quick handouts.

HISTORY

Born in 1860 Will Keith Kellogg began his career with ‚Âjobs as a stock boy and traveling broom salesman. He also worked as a clerk (and later bookkeeper and manager) at the Battle Creek Sanitarium a renowned homeopathic hospital where his older brother John Harvey Kellogg was physician-in-chief. The brothers' experiments to improve vegetarian diets led to a happy accident in 1894 that resulted in the first wheat flakes. In 1906 W.K. Kellogg started the Battle Creek Toasted Corn Flake Company. Through marketing genius and innovative products Kellogg's company became a leader in the industry.

A philanthropist by inclination Kellogg established the Fellowship Corporation in 1925 to build an agricultural school and a bird sanctuary as well as to set up an experimental farm and a reforestation project. He also gave $3 million to hometown causes such as the Ann J. Kellogg School for disabled children and for the construction of an auditorium a junior high school and a youth recreation center.

After attending a White House Conference on Child Health and Protection Kellogg established the W.K. Kellogg Child Welfare Foundation in 1930. A few months later he broadened the focus of the charter and renamed the institution the W.K. Kellogg Foundation. That year the foundation began its landmark Michigan Community Health Project (MCHP) which opened public health departments in counties once thought too small and poor to sustain them. In 1934 Kellogg placed more than $66 million in Kellogg Company stock and other investments in a trust to fund his foundation.

During WWII the foundation expanded its programming to Latin America funding advanced schooling for dentists physicians and other health professionals. After the war it broadened its programming to include agriculture to help war-torn Europe. It funded projects in Germany Iceland Ireland Norway and the UK. Following Kellogg's death in 1951 the organization began providing support for graduate programs in health and hospital administration as well as for rural leadership and community colleges.

During the 1970s the foundation lent its support to the growing volunteerism movement and to aiding the disadvantaged with a special emphasis on programs for minorities. A review of operations in the late 1970s led the Kellogg Foundation to reassert its emphasis on health education agriculture and leadership. The foundation also expanded its programs to southern Africa.

In 1986 the Kellogg Foundation began funding the Rural America Initiative –a series of 28 projects meant to develop leadership train local government officials and revitalize rural areas. William Richardson became president and CEO of the foundation in 1995 leaving his post as president of The Johns Hopkins University. Also during the 1990s the foundation supported the Community-Based Public Health Initiative which assisted universities in educating public health professionals by presenting community-based approaches to students and faculty.

In 1998 the organization announced a five-year $55 million plan to bring health care to the nation's poor and homeless. Also that year it gave Portland State University a $600000 grant to develop its Institute for Nonprofit Management. In 1999 the Kellogg Foundation started its first geographically based program pledging $15 million in grants for development of Mississippi River Delta communities in Arkansas Louisiana and Mississippi. In 2001 the foundation pledged an additional $20 million to support economic growth in the region through the Emerging Markets Partnership. In 2002 the Kellogg Foundation awarded about $2 million in grants to SPARK (Supporting Partnerships to Assure Ready Kids) to help prepare low-income children for ‚Âschool. The organization funded a national campaign to improve men's health in 2003.

After a decade as president and CEO Richardson stepped down in 2005. ‚ÂSterling Speirn who had led the San Mateo California-based Peninsula Community Foundation since 1990 took over as president and CEO of the Kellogg Foundation in January 2006.

EXECUTIVES

Senior Vice President Programs, Jim M Hale
VP and Chief Investment Officer, Joel R. Wittenberg, age 51
VP Information Systems and Technology, Ross Comstock
SVP CFO and Treasurer, La June Montgomery Tabron
COO, Linh C. Nguyen
VP Finance and Treasurer, Donald G. Williamson
A Partner With Communities Where Children Came First Vice President, Carla Thompson
Assistant To Senior Vice President For Programs, Denice Bates
VP Finance and Treasurer, Donald G. Williamson
Board Of Directors, Celeste Clark

LOCATIONS

HQ: W. K. KELLOGG FOUNDATION
1 MICHIGAN AVE E, BATTLE CREEK, MI 490174012
Phone: 2699681611
Web: WWW.WKKF.ORG

PRODUCTS/OPERATIONS

2009 Grants

	$ mil.	% of total
National	175	65
Michigan	49	18
Mississippi	19	7
New Mexico	6	2
International	18	7
Total	**270**	**100**

HISTORICAL FINANCIALS

Company Type: Private

Income Statement

FYE: August 31

	ASSETS ($ mil.)	NET INCOME ($ mil.)	INCOME AS % OF ASSETS	EMPLOYEES
08/13	428	92	21.5%	210
08/12	442	(106)	—	—
08/11	465	(13)	—	—
08/09	442	0	—	—
Annual Growth	(0.8%)	—	—	—

2013 Year-End Financials

Debt ratio: —	
Return on equity: 28.00%	Dividends
Cash ($ mil.): 37	Yield: —
Current ratio: —	Payout: —
Long-term debt ($ mil.): —	Market value ($ mil.): —

W. L. BUTLER CONSTRUCTION INC.

W. L. Butler Construction is building up its reputation in the Golden State. The company caters to customers needing commercial and light industrial construction services in California. W. L. Butler Construction also has the capability to complete electrical and HVAC services. Projects include car dealerships retail centers medical offices industrial warehouses and not-for-profit organizations. Commercial clients include Aetna Life Insurance Cisco Systems Home Depot Target and Walgreen's. W. L. Butler Construction was founded in 1975 by CEO William Butler as a residential remodeling contracting operation.

EXECUTIVES

CEO, William L. (Bill) Butler
President, Frank York
VP Construction Northern California, David Nevens Jr.
VP Construction Southern California, David J. Fister
VP Finance, Gina Henson
Owner, Franklin Covey
Auditors: S.J.GallinaLLP

LOCATIONS

HQ: W. L. BUTLER CONSTRUCTION INC.
204 FRANKLIN ST, REDWOOD CITY, CA 94063-1929
Phone: 650-361-1270
Web: WWW.WLBUTLER.COM

PRODUCTS/OPERATIONS

Selected Projects

Costco (La Quinta CA)
Hawthorn Suites (Newark CA)
Pier 1 Imports (Concord CA)
Target Corporation (Richmond CA)
Village at University Park (Palm Desert CA)
Westridge Shopping Center (Valencia CA)

COMPETITORS

Bernards Brothers
C.W. Driver
Charles Pankow Builders
Howard Building Corporation
Irvine Company
KPRS Construction
Moorefield Construction
Panattoni Construction
Parsons Corporation
Sierra Pacific Industries
Swinerton Builders
Webcor Builders

HISTORICAL FINANCIALS

Company Type: Private

Income Statement FYE: December 31

	REVENUE ($ mil.)	NET INCOME ($ mil.)	NET PROFIT MARGIN	EMPLOYEES
12/11	172	2	1.4%	150
12/10	129	1	1.2%	—
12/09	160	2	1.6%	—
12/08	220	3	1.6%	—
Annual Growth	(7.9%)	(11.4%)	—	—

2011 Year-End Financials

Debt ratio: —
Return on equity: 1.40%
Cash ($ mil.): 4
Current ratio: 0.90
Long-term debt ($ mil.): —
Dividends
Yield: —
Payout: —
Market value ($ mil.): —

W.S. BADCOCK CORPORATION

EXECUTIVES

VP Merchandising Buyer, Mike Estridge

LOCATIONS

HQ: W.S. BADCOCK CORPORATION
205 NW 2ND ST, MULBERRY, FL 338602405
Phone: 8634254921
Web: WWW.BADCOCK.COM

PRODUCTS/OPERATIONS

Selected Products

Accessories
Appliances
Electronics
Furniture
Mattresses

COMPETITORS

Aaron' s Inc.
Ashley Furniture
Baer' s Furniture
Bassett Furniture
City Furniture
El Dorado Furniture
Ethan Allen
Havertys
Klaussner Furniture
La-Z-Boy
Rooms To Go
Sealy

HISTORICAL FINANCIALS

Company Type: Private

Income Statement FYE: June 30

	REVENUE ($ mil.)	NET INCOME ($ mil.)	NET PROFIT MARGIN	EMPLOYEES
06/14	518	11	2.3%	1,000
06/13	463	6	1.5%	—
06/12	455	12	2.6%	—
06/11	431	0	—	—
Annual Growth	6.3%	—	—	—

2014 Year-End Financials

Debt ratio: —
Return on equity: 2.30%
Cash ($ mil.): 1
Current ratio: 3.10
Long-term debt ($ mil.): —
Dividends
Yield: —
Payout: —
Market value ($ mil.): —

WADA FARMS MARKETING GROUP LLC

The Wada folks have heard absolutely all the ,Â Mr. Potato ,Â Head ,Â jokes known to mankind; still they press resolutely on growing packing and supplying ,ÂIdaho potatoes all of us meat-and-potatoes folks. ,ÂAnd in ,Âaddition to everyone's favorite starchy tuber Wada Farms ,ÂPotatoes does the same with sweet potatoes and onions. ,ÂIt also offers value-added items such as Easy-Bakers and Easy-Steamers –potatoes packaged in special plastic that can be cooked ,Âright in their packaging. The Idaho company ,Âcultivates more than 30000 acres of farmland and operates a 140000-sq.-ft. processing facility. ,ÂWada's customers include retail food food wholesaler and foodservice companies throughout the US. ,Â,Â

Through its Wada Farms Marketing Group the company has ,Âan exclusive marketing agreement for all potatoes (white and sweet) ,Â and onions ,Âsold under the ,ÂDole label in the US. ,ÂIt has been a ,ÂWal-Mart ,Âsupplier for more than 15 years.

Wada ,Â formed a ,Â relationship with the Shoshone Bannock Tribe and in 2009 the company ,Âbegan growing ,Âmore than 13000 acres of grain and potatoes on the Shoshone Bannock Tribe Reservation near Blackfoot Idaho. ,Â

EXECUTIVES

Vice President Of Sourcing And Grower Relations, Shane Watt

LOCATIONS

HQ: WADA FARMS MARKETING GROUP LLC
2155 PROVIDENCE WAY, IDAHO FALLS, ID 834044951
Phone: 2085422898
Web: WWW.WADAFARMS.COM

COMPETITORS

Agrow Fresh Produce
Appleton Produce
Chiquita Brands
Fresh Del Monte Produce
Idaho Fresh-Pak
Idaho Supreme Potatoes
JR Simplot
Jones Produce
Larsen Farms
MountainKing Potatoes
Nonpareil Corporation
O' Leary Potato

HISTORICAL FINANCIALS

Company Type: Private

Income Statement FYE: December 31

	REVENUE ($ mil.)	NET INCOME ($ mil.)	NET PROFIT MARGIN	EMPLOYEES
12/13	181	3	1.7%	30
12/12	165	1	1.2%	—
12/11	201	2	1.0%	—
12/10	150	0	—	—
Annual Growth	6.3%	—	—	—

2013 Year-End Financials

Debt ratio: —
Return on equity: 1.70%
Cash ($ mil.): 2
Current ratio: 1.40
Long-term debt ($ mil.): —
Dividends
Yield: —
Payout: —
Market value ($ mil.): —

WAKE FOREST BAPTIST MEDICAL CENTER

LOCATIONS

HQ: WAKE FOREST BAPTIST MEDICAL CENTER
MEDICAL CENTER BLVD, WINSTON SALEM, NC 271570001
Phone: 3367138000
Web: WWW.WAKEHEALTH.EDU

HISTORICAL FINANCIALS

Company Type: Private

Income Statement FYE: June 30

	REVENUE ($ mil.)	NET INCOME ($ mil.)	NET PROFIT MARGIN	EMPLOYEES
06/10	967	55	5.8%	7,612
06/09	992	(126)	—	—
Annual Growth	(2.5%)	—	—	—

2010 Year-End Financials

Debt ratio: —
Return on equity: 5.80%
Cash ($ mil.): 85
Current ratio: 0.40
Long-term debt ($ mil.): —
Dividends
Yield: —
Payout: —
Market value ($ mil.): —

WAKEFERN FOOD CORP.

HISTORY

Wakefern Food was founded in 1946 by seven New York- and New Jersey-based grocers: Louis Weiss Sam and Al Aidekman Abe Kesselman Dave Fern Sam Garb and Albert Goldberg. The company got its name by taking the first letters of the last names of five of the original founders (Weiss Sam and Al Aidekman Kesselman and Fern). Like many cooperatives the association sought to lower costs by increasing its buying power as a group.

They each put in $1000 and began operating a 5000-sq.-ft. warehouse often putting in double time to keep both their stores and the warehouse running. The shopkeepers' collective buying power proved valuable enabling the grocers to stock many items at the same prices as their larger competitors.

In 1951 Wakefern members began pooling their resources to buy advertising space. A common store name –ShopRite –was chosen and each week co-op members met to decide which items would be sale priced. Within a year membership had grown to over 50. Expansion became a priority and in the mid-1950s co-op members united in small groups to take over failed supermarkets. One such group called the Supermarkets Operating Co. (SOC) was formed in 1956. Within 10 years it had acquired a number of failed stores remodeled them and given them the ShopRite name.

During the late 1950s sales at ShopRite stores slumped after Wakefern decided to buck the supermarket trend of offering trading stamps (which could then be exchanged for gifts) figuring that offering the stamps would ultimately lead to higher food prices. The move initially drove away customers but Wakefern cut grocery prices across the board and sales returned. The company did embrace another supermarket trend: stocking stores with nonfood items.

The co-op was severely shaken in 1966 when SOC merged with General Supermarkets a similar small group within Wakefern becoming Supermarkets General Corp. (SGC). SGC was a powerful entity with 71 supermarkets 10 drugstores six gas stations a wholesale bakery and a discount department store. Many Wakefern members opposed the merger and attempted to block the action with a court order. By 1968 SGC had beefed up its operations to include department store chains as well as its grocery stores. In a move that threatened to break Wakefern SGC broke away from the co-op and its stores were renamed Pathmark.

Wakefern not only weathered the storm it grew under the direction of chairman and CEO Thomas Infusino elected shortly after the split. The co-op focused on asserting its position as a seller of low-priced products. Wakefern developed private-label brands including the ShopRite brand. In the 1980s members began operating larger stores and adding more nonfood items to the ShopRite product mix. With its number of superstores on the rise and facing increased competition from club stores in 1992 Wakefern opened a centralized nonfood distribution center in New Jersey.

In 1995 30-year Wakefern veteran Dean Janeway was elected president of the co-op. The company debuted its ShopRite MasterCard co-branded with New Jersey's Valley National Bank in 1996. The following year the co-op purchased two of its customers' stores in Pennsylvania then threatened to close them when contract talks with the local union deteriorated. In 1998 Wakefern settled the dispute then sold the stores.

The company partnered with Internet bidding site priceline.com in 1999 offering customers an opportunity to bid on groceries and then pick them up at ShopRite stores. Big V Wakefern's biggest customer filed for Chapter 11 bankruptcy protection in 2000 and said it was ending its distribution agreement with the co-op. In July 2002 however Wakefern's ShopRite Supermarkets subsidiary acquired all of Big V's assets for approximately $185 million in cash and assumed liabilities.

Infusino retired in May 2005 after 35 years with Wakefern Food. He was succeeded by former vice chairman Joseph Colalillo. The cooperative added to its footprint in 2007 when it acquired about 10 underperforming retail locations from Stop & Shop. The stores located mostly in South Jersey were rebranded under the ShopRite banner.

LOCATIONS

HQ: WAKEFERN FOOD CORP.
5000 RIVERSIDE DR, KEASBEY, NJ 088321209
Phone: 9085273300
Web: WWW.WAKEFERN.COM

PRODUCTS/OPERATIONS

2012 Corporate Stores

	No.
PriceRite	48
ShopRite	40
Total	**88**

COMPETITORS

A&P
Acme Markets
Associated Wholesalers
Bozzuto' s
C&S Wholesale
CVS Caremark
Hannaford Bros.
IGA
Krasdale Foods
Nash-Finch
Pathmark Stores
SUPERVALU
Stop & Shop
Wal-Mart
Wawa Inc.
White Rose

HISTORICAL FINANCIALS

Company Type: Private

Income Statement

FYE: September 28

	REVENUE ($ mil.)	NET INCOME ($ mil.)	NET PROFIT MARGIN	EMPLOYEES
09/13	11,455	0	0.0%	3,500
09/12*	11,010	5	0.0%	—
10/11	10,325	5	0.0%	—
09/08	8,396	0	—	—
Annual Growth	6.4%	—	—	—

*Fiscal year change

2013 Year-End Financials

Debt ratio: —
Return on equity: —
Cash ($ mil.): 129
Current ratio: 0.10
Long-term debt ($ mil.): —
Dividends
Yield: —
Payout: —
Market value ($ mil.): —

WAKEMED

If you wake up in a hospital in Wake County North Carolina you may be at one of WakeMed health system's facilities. WakeMed is a network of medical centers including two hospitals outpatient and emergency clinics rehabilitation facilities skilled nursing centers laboratories physicians' offices and home care service agencies. Its hospitals the WakeMed Raleigh Campus and the WakeMed Cary Hospital include specialty divisions such as heart care stroke trauma critical care diabetes asthma and children's and women's centers. Combined its facilities offer about 870 beds. Founded in 1961 WakeMed also conducts research and medical training programs.

Operations

WakeMed's facilities handle about 46000 inpatient visits 7500 births and 225000 emergency room visits each year. The system's pediatric emergency room (located in the Raleigh Campus' children's hospital wing) sees about 40000 children per year. Other units provide mobile critical care and emergency transportation by ground and air. The organization also provides some $180 million in community benefits each year as well including charity care unpaid Medicare bills health profession education and improvement and outreach programs.

WakeMed's medical staff includes more than 1000 affiliated physicians and 1000 volunteers. The WakeMed Physician Practices organization includes about 150 doctors who operate primary care and specialist offices in the region.

Strategy

The company has expanded its Raleigh Campus to include a new patient tower with intensive care cardiac care and pediatric facilities. Construction of the patient tower –featuring two new heart and vascular inpatient floors a mother's milk bank and Wake County's only dedicated Children's Hospital –was completed in 2010. The organization expanded its pediatric services further in 2012 when it formed a partnership with Duke Medicine to provide collaborative specialist care to children in the region. In addition WakeMed expanded the Raleigh Campus' rehabilitation unit in 2012 and 2013 by adding additional patient beds.

To expand its outpatient facilities WakeMed opened a sixth emergency department in 2011 at the Brier Creek Healthplex adding a dozen private rooms diagnostic imaging units lab services and doctors' offices. In 2012 the system added a new diagnostic clinic and an outpatient surgery center near the Raleigh Campus.

EXECUTIVES

President and CEO, William K. (Bill) Atkinson II
President and CEO, Donald R. Gintzig
SVP and Administrator Cary Hospital, David C. Coulter
EVP Finance and CFO, Michael D. DeVaughn
VP Corporate Planning, W. Stan Taylor
SVP Human Resources, Jeanene R. Martin
Senior VP Physician Services, John S. Piatkowski
VP Operations, Georgia Sumiel
EVP Operations and Ambulatory Development, Kathleen K. Gormley
VP Legal Services and General Counsel, Claire L. Moritz
VP Facilities and Construction, Thomas G. Cavender
VP Health Information and Utilization Management, Rebecca E. Andrews
VP and CIO, Denton Arledge
Chief Medical Officer, H. West Lawson
VP; SVP President and CEO Harnett Health System, Kenneth Bryan
VP Heart and Vascular Services, Betsy Gaskins-McClaine
VP Quality and Patient Safety, Meera Kelley
VP Ambulatory Services, Carolyn Knaup
VP Public Relations, Debra Z. Laughery
VP Revenue Cycle, Dudley B. Harrington
VP Regional Operations, Dale Armstrong
EVP Medical Affairs, Susan Weaver
EVP and COO, Tom Gettinger
SVP and Raleigh Campus Administrator, Vicki Block
SVP and Chief Nursing Officer, Cindy A. Boily
Vice President Government Affairs, Christine Craig
Chief Compliance Officer, Pandora Holloway

LOCATIONS

HQ: WAKEMED
3000 NEW BERN AVE G100, RALEIGH, NC 27610-1231
Phone: 919-350-8000
Web: WWW.WAKEMED.ORG

PRODUCTS/OPERATIONS

Selected North Carolina Facilities

Blue Ridge Surgery Center (Raleigh)
Brier Creek Healthplex (Raleigh)
Knightdale Medical Building (Knightdale)
WakeMed Apex Healthplex (Apex)
WakeMed Brier Creek Medical Park (Raleigh)
WakeMed Cary Hospital (Cary)
WakeMed Clayton Medical Park (Clayton)
WakeMed Fuquay-Varina Outpatient and Skilled Nursing Facility (Fuquay-Varina)
WakeMed Garner HealthPlex (Garner)
WakeMed Home Health (Raleigh)
WakeMed North Healthplex (Raleigh)
WakeMed Raleigh Campus (Raleigh)
WakeMed Rehab Hospital (Raleigh)
WakeMed Wake Forest Road Outpatient Rehab Center (Raleigh)
WakeMed Zebulon/Wendell Outpatient and Skilled Nursing Facility (Zebulon)

COMPETITORS

Carolinas HealthCare System
Cone Health
Cumberland County Hospital System
Duke University Health System
FirstHealth of the Carolinas
Morehead Memorial Hospital
Novant Health
Rex Healthcare
Rowan Regional Medical Center
Vidant Health
Wake Forest University Baptist Medical Center

HISTORICAL FINANCIALS

Company Type: Private

Income Statement FYE: September 30

	REVENUE ($ mil.)	NET INCOME ($ mil.)	NET PROFIT MARGIN	EMPLOYEES
09/09	883	0	—	7,933
09/08	837	12	1.5%	—
09/07	780	49	6.3%	—
09/06	771	77	10.1%	—
Annual Growth	4.6%	—	—	—

2009 Year-End Financials

Debt ratio: —
Return on equity: —
Cash ($ mil.): 434
Current ratio: 0.80
Long-term debt ($ mil.): —
Dividends
Yield: —
Payout: —
Market value ($ mil.): —

WALSH BROTHERS INCORPORATED

LOCATIONS

HQ: WALSH BROTHERS INCORPORATED
210 COMMERCIAL ST, BOSTON, MA 021091463
Phone: 6178784800
Web: WWW.WALSHBROTHERS.COM

COMPETITORS

Clark Construction Group
Commodore Builders
Cutler Associates
Dimeo Construction
E.A. Colangeli Construction
Engelberth Construction
Gilbane
Morganti
Shawmut Design and Construction
Suffolk Construction

HISTORICAL FINANCIALS

Company Type: Private

Income Statement FYE: December 31

	REVENUE ($ mil.)	NET INCOME ($ mil.)	NET PROFIT MARGIN	EMPLOYEES
12/09	408	6	1.5%	—
12/08	545	9	1.7%	—
12/07	383	0	0.0%	—
Annual Growth	3.3%	43001.7%	—	—

2009 Year-End Financials

Debt ratio: —
Return on equity: 1.50%
Cash ($ mil.): 22
Current ratio: 1.10
Long-term debt ($ mil.): —
Dividends
Yield: —
Payout: —
Market value ($ mil.): —

WALSH CONSTRUCTION COMPANY

LOCATIONS

HQ: WALSH CONSTRUCTION COMPANY
929 W ADAMS ST, CHICAGO, IL 606073021
Phone: 3125635400
Web: WWW.WALSHCONSTRUCTIONCO.COM

HISTORICAL FINANCIALS

Company Type: Private

Income Statement FYE: December 31

	REVENUE ($ mil.)	NET INCOME ($ mil.)	NET PROFIT MARGIN	EMPLOYEES
12/10	1,627	35	2.2%	3,000
12/09	1,711	56	3.3%	—
Annual Growth	(4.9%)	(35.8%)	—	—

2010 Year-End Financials

Debt ratio: —
Return on equity: 2.20%
Cash ($ mil.): 281
Current ratio: 1.30
Long-term debt ($ mil.): —
Dividends
Yield: —
Payout: —
Market value ($ mil.): —

WALTON ELECTRIC MEMBERSHIP CORPORATION

EXECUTIVES

President CEO, Ronnie Lee
SVP Corporate Services, Russell DeLong
SVP Engineering and Operations, Ron Marshall
Executive Assistant, Kathy Joiner
Director Safety and Training, Larry Thompson
Communications Coordinator, Greg Brooks
EMC Security, Michael Morton
Director Natural Gas Operations, Allen Powers
VP Power Supply, Robert Rentfrow
Director Marketing and Member Services, Howard Turner
VP Finance, Marsha Shumate
Administrative Assistant, Debra Jackson
Account Executive, Keith Taylor
Account Executive, Scott Walker
Director, Warren Few
Director, Bud Wiley
Director, Jim Whitley
Director, Tommy Adcock
Director, Bobby Williams
Director, Sam Simonton
Director, Dan Chelko
Director, Johnny Allgood

LOCATIONS

HQ: WALTON ELECTRIC MEMBERSHIP CORPORATION
842 HIGHWAY 78 NW, MONROE, GA 306554475
Phone: 7702672505
Web: WWW.WALTONEMC.COM

PRODUCTS/OPERATIONS

2010 Sales

	$ mil.	% of total
% of total		
Residential &		71
Commercial &		26
Public buildings &		3
Total		100

COMPETITORS

AGL Resources
Georgia Power
Piedmont Natural Gas
SCANA

HISTORICAL FINANCIALS

Company Type: Private

Income Statement FYE: December 31

	REVENUE ($ mil.)	NET INCOME ($ mil.)	NET PROFIT MARGIN	EMPLOYEES
12/13	243	0	—	273
12/09	227	6	2.7%	—
12/08	215	17	8.0%	—
12/07	212	0	—	—
Annual Growth	2.3%	—	—	—

2013 Year-End Financials

Debt ratio: —
Return on equity: —
Cash ($ mil.): 1
Current ratio: 1.60
Long-term debt ($ mil.): —
Dividends
Yield: —
Payout: —
Market value ($ mil.): —

WARD TRUCKING LLC

Less-than-truckload (LTL) carrier Ward Trucking operates primarily in the northeastern and mid-Atlantic US. (LTL carriers consolidate freight from multiple shippers into a single truckload.) In addition to its LTL business the company offers full truckload and logistics services through the Ward Transport & Logistics ,Âbrand name. Ward Trucking operates a fleet of about ,Â450 tractors ,Â60 trucks ,Âand ,Â1180 trailers from a network of terminals stretching from New York to Illinois. William W. Ward founded the company in 1931 to haul freight from central Pennsylvania to New York City. Ward Trucking is run by members of the Ward family.

EXECUTIVES

Vp Ltl, Rick Fleischer
Asst Treas, Tim Mikesic

LOCATIONS

HQ: WARD TRUCKING LLC
1436 WARD TRUCKING DR, ALTOONA, PA 166027110
Phone: 8149440803
Web: WWW.WARDTRUCKING.COM

COMPETITORS

Con-way Freight
Estes Express
J.B. Hunt
NEMF
Old Dominion Freight
Pitt Ohio Express
Schneider National
UPS Freight
YRC Worldwide

HISTORICAL FINANCIALS

Company Type: Private

Income Statement FYE: December 31

	REVENUE ($ mil.)	NET INCOME ($ mil.)	NET PROFIT MARGIN	EMPLOYEES
12/13	139	1	1.4%	1,057
12/12	149	1	0.8%	—
12/11	150	10	7.2%	—
12/10	137	0	—	—
Annual Growth	0.6%	—	—	—

2013 Year-End Financials

Debt ratio: —
Return on equity: 1.40%
Cash ($ mil.): 0
Current ratio: 1.10
Long-term debt ($ mil.): —
Dividends
Yield: —
Payout: —
Market value ($ mil.): —

WARREN DISTRIBUTION INC.

LOCATIONS

HQ: WARREN DISTRIBUTION INC.
727 S 13TH ST, OMAHA, NE 681023204
Phone: 4023419397
Web: WWW.WD-WPP.COM

HISTORICAL FINANCIALS

Company Type: Private

Income Statement FYE: February 23

	REVENUE ($ mil.)	NET INCOME ($ mil.)	NET PROFIT MARGIN	EMPLOYEES
02/13	485	10	2.1%	600
02/12	470	5	1.1%	—
02/11	378	11	3.1%	—
02/10	315	0	—	—
Annual Growth	15.4%	—	—	—

2013 Year-End Financials

Debt ratio: —
Return on equity: 2.10%
Cash ($ mil.): 0
Current ratio: 1.00
Long-term debt ($ mil.): —
Dividends
Yield: —
Payout: —
Market value ($ mil.): —

WARREN RURAL ELECTRIC COOPERATIVE CORPORATION

This Warren needs no commission just a cooperative in order to deliver electric results to the people. Warren Rural Electric Cooperative Corporation (Warren RECC) provides its member customers with electricity security systems and surge suppression equipment as well as with floodlighting and street lighting. It offers propane through non-affiliated Propane Energy Partners. The ,Äco-op serves more than 55300 customers in an eight-county service area (Barren Butler Edmonson Grayson Logan Ohio Simpson and Warren counties) in rural ,Äsouth-central Kentucky. Warren RECC is affiliated with the ,ÄTennessee Valley Authority ,Äand a member of ,ÄTouchstone Energy a ,Ä600-member alliance of electricity co-ops.

After ice storms in early 2009 knocked out power to the area (Warren county was declared a disaster area) Warren RECC received a $6.5 million FEMA grant to help with associated repair costs. The coop spent about $15 replacing snapped poles and repair hundreds of miles of lines; it typically budgets about $200000 annually for repair work.

EXECUTIVES

Attorney, Keith Carwell
Chairman, Michael W. McGuirk
Secretary/Treasurer and Director, Dennis P. Ingram
President and CEO, Gary K. Dillard
Attorney, Keith Carwell
Director, Terry Garmon
Director, Joe B. Neely
Director, Kenneth H. Robbins
Director, Orville W. (Pete) Dotson
Director, Rebecca L. Goad
Secretary/Treasurer and Director, Dennis P. Ingram
Director, B.W. Lyons

LOCATIONS

HQ: WARREN RURAL ELECTRIC COOPERATIVE CORPORATION
951 FAIRVIEW AVE, BOWLING GREEN, KY 421014937
Phone: 2707939857
Web: WWW.WRECC.COM

COMPETITORS

AmeriGas Partners
Duke Energy Kentucky
Kenergy

HISTORICAL FINANCIALS

Company Type: Private

Income Statement FYE: June 30

	REVENUE ($ mil.)	NET INCOME ($ mil.)	NET PROFIT MARGIN	EMPLOYEES
06/13	177	4	2.7%	165
06/12	171	4	2.8%	—
06/09	170	2	1.3%	—
06/08	152	0	—	—
Annual Growth	3.1%	—	—	—

2013 Year-End Financials

Debt ratio: —
Return on equity: 2.70%
Cash ($ mil.): 16
Current ratio: 0.30
Long-term debt ($ mil.): —
Dividends
Yield: —
Payout: —
Market value ($ mil.): —

WASHINGTON HEALTHCARE MARY

Health care is Mary Washington Healthcare's realm in the Old Dominion State. The medical provider offers a comprehensive range of health services to residents of Fredericksburg and surrounding communities in central Virginia through its not-for-profit regional system of two hospitals and 28 healthcare facilities. The hub of this system is Mary Washington Hospital a 400-bed acute care medical center that provides services including emergency/trauma care and surgical procedures. The health system also includes outpatient care programs and facilities providing primary care and specialty care services for women seniors and children.

Operations

Other facilities provide hospice care and behavioral health services that include inpatient psychiatric care. Its Homecare America segment is a full-service unit providing home health care products and training. Mary Washington Healthcare also owns 14 specialty practices.

Geographic Reach

The company serves patients in Fredericksburg and surrounding communities in central Virginia.

Strategy

Expanding its network to meet growing demand in 2013 Mary Washington Healthcare purchased Reese Medical Associates (its third primary care practice). The company also owns Ladysmith Medical Center and the Medical Center of Stafford on Garrisonville Road.

Company Background

In an attempt to reduce overcrowding at its Mary Washington Hospital the health system opened a 100-bed full service hospital in 2009 called Stafford Hospital Center. The hospital features all private inpatient rooms a full service emergency department a dedicated birthing unit inpatient and outpatient surgery and a comprehensive range of advanced diagnostic capabilities including MRI and CT scan.

EXECUTIVES

Presidentand CEO, Fred M. Rankin III
EVP and COO, Walter J. Kiwall
EVP and Chief Medical Officer, J. Thomas (Tom) Ryan
EVP and CFO, Sean T. Barden
Senior Vice President Regulatory & Risk Management, Jina Haikey
Senior Vice President and Chief Nursing Officer, Marianna Bedway
EVP Community Affairs; President MWH Foundation, Xavier R. Richardson
Senior Vice President and Administrator, Cathy Yablonski
Senior Vice President Marketing and Communications, Eric K. Fletcher
Senior Vice President Chief Information Officer, Joyce Hanscome
senior Vice President and administrator of operations for Mary Washington Hospital, Van Renan
Executive Vice President Human Resources and Organizational Development, Kathryn Wall
Senior Vice President Properties and Ambulatory Services, Marie Fredrick

LOCATIONS

HQ: WASHINGTON HEALTHCARE MARY
2300 FALL HILL AVE # 313, FREDERICKSBURG, VA 22401-3342
Phone: 540-741-2507
Web: WWW.MWHCCAREERS.COM

PRODUCTS/OPERATIONS

Selected Operations

Cancer Center of Virginia
Carriage Hill Rehabilitation and Nursing Center
Diabetes Management - MWH
The Family Health Center at North Stafford
Fredericksburg Ambulatory Surgery Center Inc. (FASC)
Homecare America
Imaging Center for Women
Kids' Station
Ladysmith Medical Center
Mary Washington Hospice
Mary Washington Hospital
Mary Washington Hospital Foundation
Mary Washington Hospital Home Health
Mary Washington Thrift Shoppe to benefit Mary Washington Hospital
MediCorp Medical Center
MWH Auxiliary Regional Mobile Health Clinic
MWH Community Services Fund
MWH Outreach Laboratories
Medical Arts Pharmacy
Medical Center of Stafford
Medical Imaging of Fredericksburg
Medical Imaging at Lee's Hill
MediCorp Health Link
Mobile Mammography
Psychiatric Associates
Rappahannock Wound Healing Center
Rehabilitation Services of Fredericksburg
Rehabilitation Services of Lee's Hill
Rehabilitation Services of North Stafford
School of Radiologic Technology
Senior Care Services
Sleep Disorders Center
Snowden Academy (mental health)
Snowden at Fredericksburg (mental health)
Stafford Hospital

COMPETITORS

Bon Secours Health
Centra Health Inc.
Civista Health
Dimensions Healthcare
Fauquier Hospital
Georgetown University Hospital
HCA Capital Division
Inova
Martha Jefferson Hospital
MedStar Health
Prince William Health System
University of Virginia Health System

HISTORICAL FINANCIALS

Company Type: Private

Income Statement FYE: December 31

	REVENUE ($ mil.)	NET INCOME ($ mil.)	NET PROFIT MARGIN	EMPLOYEES
12/12*	573	(25)	—	4,000
03/12	154	6	4.5%	—
03/11	174	6	3.8%	—
12/10	712	16	2.3%	—
Annual Growth	(10.3%)	—	—	—

*Fiscal year change

2012 Year-End Financials

Debt ratio: —
Return on equity: (-4.50%)
Cash ($ mil.): 61
Current ratio: 1.90
Long-term debt ($ mil.): —
Dividends
Yield: —
Payout: —
Market value ($ mil.): —

WASHINGTON HOSPITAL CENTER CORPORATION

Washington Hospital Center may be the official hospital of the Washington Redskins but you don't have to be a professional football player to make use of the facility's services. The hospital at the heart of the MedStar Health system serves about 455000 patients living in and around the nation's capital each year. Washington Hospital Center has approximately 925 beds and includes specialized care centers for cancer cardiovascular conditions and neurosciences. Other services include organ transplantation and a regional burn treatment center as well as emergency air transportation. The hospital also conducts clinical research and offers educational residency and fellowship programs.

It has about 1400 doctors and dentists on staff; many of whom are involved in Washington Hospital Center's 350 clinical research trials. The hospital is affiliated with the medical schools of The George Washington University Georgetown University Johns Hopkins and several other regional educational institutions. Its more than two dozen clinical residency and fellowship programs enroll more than 300 medical students each year.

Washington Hospital Center has a global presence through its International Services Department which administers care to international patients and those who travel to the US specifically to receive medical treatments at Washington Hospital Center. The hospital has also earned a reputation in the US for treating some of the most complex patient cases. Partially because its doctors are able to see trauma patients quickly through the hospital's affiliation with MedSTAR Transport air and ground ambulance service. The MedSTAR Trauma program at Washington Hospital Center has flown nearly 50000 patients since its inception in 1983.

The hospital is also known for its charity care. In 2010 Washington Hospital Center provided nearly $110 million in unsponsored care to patients who were unable to pay their bills for one reason or another. The money was a combination of more than $17 million in charity care and about $90 million in bad debt (billed but unpaid bills).

Washington Hospital Center was created through the merger of three regional hospitals: Emergency Garfield and Episcopal Eye Ear and Throat. The actual idea of the Hospital Center was conceived in 1943 but it took nearly 15 years for funding planning and construction to be completed.

EXECUTIVES

President, James F. (Jim) Caldas
SVP and COO, Dennis Pullin
SVP Medical Affairs and Chief Medical Director, Janis M. Orlowski, age 56
SVP Human Resources, Christina Younger
SVP Development, Arlene A. Snyder
VP Professional Services, Cathie Monge
Director Media Relations, Paula Faria
SVP and CFO, Dan A. Macksood
VP Heart and Vascular Services, Maureen Clancy
SVP and Chief Nursing Officer, Elizabeth Wykpisz
VP Academic Affairs, Wm. James Howard
VP Cancer and Neurosciences, Jill Donaldson
VP Medical Staff Development, Anthony Watkins
VP Strategic Planning and Business Development, Anne Large
Assistant VP Information Systems Customer Service, Joseph Brothman

LOCATIONS

HQ: WASHINGTON HOSPITAL CENTER CORPORATION
110 IRVING ST NW, WASHINGTON, DC 20010-3017
Phone: 202-877-7000
Web: WWW.WHCENTER.ORG

COMPETITORS

Adventist HealthCare
Bon Secours Health
Children' s National Medical Center
Dimensions Healthcare
Doctors Community Hospital
Georgetown University Hospital
HSC Pediatric Center
Health Net Federal Services
Inova
Johns Hopkins Medicine
Mary Washington Healthcare
Providence Hospital (Washington DC)
Sibley Memorial Hospital
Suburban Hospital

HISTORICAL FINANCIALS

Company Type: Private

Income Statement FYE: June 30

	REVENUE ($ mil.)	NET INCOME ($ mil.)	NET PROFIT MARGIN	EMPLOYEES
06/08	1,028	14	1.4%	5,637
06/05	880	22	2.5%	—
Annual Growth	5.3%	(13.5%)	—	—

2008 Year-End Financials

Debt ratio: —
Return on equity: 1.40%
Cash ($ mil.): 25
Current ratio: 0.60
Long-term debt ($ mil.): —
Dividends
Yield: —
Payout: —
Market value ($ mil.): —

WASHINGTON REGIONAL MEDICAL CENTER

Washington Regional Medical System (formerly Washington Regional Medical Center) provides acute care services to the people of northwestern Arkansas. The system's main hospital has about 370 beds and also includes assisted living facilities home health and hospice services and general practice and specialty clinics. Specialty services at the medical center include cardiac and vascular care (Walker Family Heart and Vascular Institute) emergency medicine kidney dialysis women's health services (Johnelle Hunt Women's Center) cancer treatment and rehabilitation.

Strategy

Striving to expand its reach and attract additional patients Washington Regional Medical System in 2011 added Washington Regional Rheumatology Clinic Washington Regional Sleep Medicine and Harrison Family Practice Clinic to its network of clinics.

Company Background

Washington Regional Medical System started out in 1950 as Washington County Hospital and moved into its modern facility in 2002. The system completed a $64 million expansion effort in 2008 that added over 100 beds and enhanced emergency senior support and pharmacy units.

EXECUTIVES

CFO, Dan Eckels
VP and CIO, Becky Magee
President and CEO, W. L. (Bill) Bradley
Chairman Medicine, Susan Portis Ferguson, age 48
Chairman Surgery, Randall D. Hightower, age 59
Chairman, Dorothy J. Hanby
Chief of Staff, Ted Fish
Chief Medical Officer, David Ratcliff
Auditors: KPMGLLP

LOCATIONS

HQ: WASHINGTON REGIONAL MEDICAL CENTER
3215 N NORTHHILLS BLVD, FAYETTEVILLE, AR 72703-4424
Phone: 479-713-1000
Web: WWW.WREGIONAL.COM

PRODUCTS/OPERATIONS

Selected Medical Services

Assisted Living
Asthma
Bariatric
Bone Density
Cancer Services
Center for Exercise
Clinical Research
Diabetes Education
Dialysis
Emergency Services
Faith In Action
Gynecologic Oncology
Gynecology
Heart Health
Home Health
Hospice
Hyperbaric Oxygen Therapy
Imaging
IV Infusion
LIFELINE Personal Emergency Response System
Mammography
Neurology
Neurosurgery
Obstetrics
Pain Management
Pelvic Therapy
Senior Health
Senior Specialty Unit

Sleep Disorders
Urology
Women's Health
Wound Care

COMPETITORS

Baptist Health (Arkansas)
Baxter Regional Medical Center
Community Health Systems
Health Management Associates
Mercy Health
Sparks Health System

HISTORICAL FINANCIALS

Company Type: Private

Income Statement FYE: December 31

	REVENUE ($ mil.)	NET INCOME ($ mil.)	NET PROFIT MARGIN	EMPLOYEES
12/12	205	33	16.4%	1,600
12/09	229	14	6.2%	—
12/02	203	0	0.0%	—
12/02	139	7	5.1%	—
Annual Growth	3.9%	16.9%	—	—

2012 Year-End Financials

Debt ratio: —
Return on equity: 16.40%
Cash ($ mil.): 12
Current ratio: 1.30
Long-term debt ($ mil.): —
Dividends
Yield: —
Payout: —
Market value ($ mil.): —

WATONWAN FARM SERVICE INC

EXECUTIVES

CFO, Bill Day
Manager Energy Division, Randy Cole
Agronomy and Grain Operations Manager, Mike Minnehan
Director Human Resources, Dawn Abel
Marketing Communications Director p, Jo Ann Gumto
CEO, Todd Ludwig
Director Marketing and Communications, Jo Anne Gumto
Manager Grain Division, Craig Kilian
Chairman, Ken Klug
Vice President of Feed, Merlyn Kruger
Sales Manager p, Andy Lindsay
Sales Manager c, Thomas Chandler
Director, Charlie Johnson
Director, Neil Schlaak
Director, Danny Rynearson

LOCATIONS

HQ: WATONWAN FARM SERVICE INC
233 W CIRO ST, TRUMAN, MN 560882018
Phone: 5077761244
Web: WWW.WFSAG.COM

COMPETITORS

ADM
Ag Processing Inc.
CHS
Cargill
Farm Service Cooperative
Farmers Cooperative Society
Gold-Eagle Cooperative
Heartland Co-op
Minn-Dak Co-op
NEW Cooperative
United Farmers Cooperative

HISTORICAL FINANCIALS

Company Type: Private

Income Statement FYE: July 31

	REVENUE ($ mil.)	NET INCOME ($ mil.)	NET PROFIT MARGIN	EMPLOYEES
07/14	468	7	1.7%	255
07/13	701	7	1.1%	—
07/12	592	6	1.1%	—
07/11	534	0	—	—
Annual Growth	(4.3%)	—	—	—

2014 Year-End Financials

Debt ratio: —
Return on equity: 1.70%
Cash ($ mil.): 19
Current ratio: 0.60
Long-term debt ($ mil.): —
Dividends
Yield: —
Payout: —
Market value ($ mil.): —

WAUKESHA MEMORIAL HOSPITAL INC.

Waukesha Memorial Hospital is a 300-bed teaching hospital that provides health care services for Wisconsin's Milwaukee Waukesha and Dane counties. With about 670 physicians representing several specialties and 2700 employees the hospital operates centers for excellence focused on cardiology oncology neurology women's health and orthopedics as well as emergency neonatal and family practice services. Additionally Waukesha Memorial Hospital conducts a physician residency program. Established in 1914 the medical facility is a subsidiary of not-for-profit ProHealth Care a medical network that serves southeastern Wisconsin with acute care and specialty health services.

Operations

ProHealth Care runs Waukesha Memorial Hospital alongside its other critical-care hospital Oconomowoc Memorial Hospital. As part of its operations the hospital boasts a neuroscience center orthopedic center regional cancer center regional heart and vascular center and a women's center. Its newborn intensive care unit and its emergency department which averages more than 39000 visits are both Level III.

Geographic Reach

Despite its name Waukesha Memorial Hospital serves the residents of Milwaukee and Dane counties along with Waukesha County.

EXECUTIVES

CFO, Nancy (Nan) Nelson
Medical Director, James Gardner
Development Officer Waukesha Memorial Hospital Foundation, Kristin M. Freiberg

LOCATIONS

HQ: WAUKESHA MEMORIAL HOSPITAL INC.
725 AMERICAN AVE, WAUKESHA, WI 53188-5099
Phone: 262-928-1000
Web: WWW.WAUKESHARIVERWALK.ORG

PRODUCTS/OPERATIONS

Selected Services

Birthing
Blood / Lymphatic
Bones Joints & Muscles
Brain & Nerves
Cancer
Cancer Second Opinion
Children's Health
CyberKnife
Diabetes
Diagnostic Services
Digestive
Ear Nose & Throat
Emergency Services/Urgent Care
Eyes & Vision
General Surgery
Genetics
Heart & Vascular
Infections
Integrative Medicine
Kidneys & Urinary System
Lungs / Breathing
Men's Health
Mental Health
Nutrition
Orthopedic
Pain
Rehabilitation Services
Senior's Health
Sleep
Stroke
Wellness & Lifestyle
Women's Health

COMPETITORS

Children' s Hospital and Health System
Columbia St. Mary' s
Froedtert Hospital
Hospital Sisters Health System
Ministry Health Care
SwedishAmerican Health System
University of Wisconsin Hospital and Clinics

HISTORICAL FINANCIALS

Company Type: Private

Income Statement FYE: September 30

	REVENUE ($ mil.)	NET INCOME ($ mil.)	NET PROFIT MARGIN	EMPLOYEES
09/12*	456	53	11.7%	2,071
06/07	277	48	17.6%	—
/ 0	0			
Annual Growth	—	—	—	—

*Fiscal year change

2012 Year-End Financials

Debt ratio: —
Return on equity: 11.70%
Cash ($ mil.): 16
Current ratio: 1.40
Long-term debt ($ mil.): —
Dividends
Yield: —
Payout: —
Market value ($ mil.): —

WAUKESHA-PEARCE INDUSTRIES INC.

Waukesha-Pearce Industries (WPI) wants its customers to start their engines. Through its Engine Division the company designs and packages engine-driven equipment such as power generators pumps blowers control panels and switchgear. WPI also offers a slate of heavy construction and mining products including earth movers and demolition equipment made by such OEMs as Komatsu and Gradall Industries through its Construction Machinery Division. As part of its business the company sells used equipment and leases heavy earth-moving equipment. Founded as Portable Rotary Rig Co. in 1924 by Louis M. Pearce Sr. the company is owned and run by the Pearce family.

Geographic Reach

From its headquarters in Houston WPI serves customers through more than a dozen locations in Texas and another 15 across Louisiana Oklahoma

New Mexico Arkansas Alabama Kansas California Rhode Island Pennsylvania and West Virginia. The company's training facility is located in Sugar Land Texas outside Houston.

Operations

WPI's Engine Equipment lineup includes its own Enginator used in field gas compression and power generation. Its Engine Division further supports WPI's performance by offering less economy-driven services such as certified remanufactured engines and revamping.

WPI's Construction Machinery arm benefits from a broad products portfolio paired with distributor affiliations. Such alliances include Bomag (compaction equipment) Allied/Rammer (demolition equipment) Esco Crushing (wearparts) Sennebogen (material handling) and Valmet (cranes). Like the Engine Equipment Division this segment is able to mitigate a recession's impact on capital equipment sales by providing repair and onsite maintenance services along with a multi-million-dollar inventory of used and rental equipment and parts.

The company also offers construction and mining products from equipment brands such as Komatsu Gradall Takeuchi Doppstadt NPK LaBounty and Vacall.

Sales and Marketing

Core markets for WPI include land clearing highway and heavy construction site development mining scrap petrochemical energy exploration and utility construction as well as a number of government agencies.

Strategy

In 2013 Takeuchi-U.S. named Waukesha-Pearce Industries as the latest addition to its expanding dealer network in North America. WPI will carry the full Takeuchi line of compact earthmoving equipment at its locations across Texas.Expanding its network in 2012 Waukesha-Pearce opened a full service facility in Buffalo Texas.

Company Background

WPI in 2011 extended the reach of its territory from seven to 30 states through its affiliation with behemoth GE. When GE acquired Dresser that year GE reviewed the North American distributors for the Waukesha line of gas compression engines and subsequently named WPI one of two distributors in North America and significantly boosting its sales territory.

EXECUTIVES

Vice President Operations Construction, Michael Green
Vice President, Jim Adian
Vice President Adp, Jim Johnson

LOCATIONS

HQ: WAUKESHA-PEARCE INDUSTRIES INC.
12320 MAIN ST, HOUSTON, TX 770356206
Phone: 7137231050
Web: WWW.WPI.COM

PRODUCTS/OPERATIONS

Selected Services

Earth moving
Gas compression
Mining
Power generation
Recycling
Service and replacement parts
Small engine and lawn

Selected Products

Engines
- Arrow VR engines
- BOB-CAT mowers
- Dresser Waukesha
- Generac Industrial
- Generac Residential
- HIPOWER generating sets
- Kohler engines
- Little Wonder products
- Mantis yard & garden products
- Powerhouse catalytic converters
- Remanufactured engines
- Revamp services
- Ryan turf renovation products
- WPI brand

Construction Machinery
- Allied/Rammer
- Bomag
- Bucyrus Blades
- Cummins Engines
- Dressta
- Esco
- Fleetguard Filters
- Gradall
- Hensley
- JRB
- Komatsu
- LaBounty
- Sennebogen
- Valmet

COMPETITORS

AGCO
Berry Companies
Caterpillar
Connell Company
Cummins Power Generation
Deere
Dewey Electronics
Emerson Electric
Kubota

HISTORICAL FINANCIALS

Company Type: Private

Income Statement — FYE: March 31

	REVENUE ($ mil.)	NET INCOME ($ mil.)	NET PROFIT MARGIN	EMPLOYEES
03/13	369	10	2.9%	600
03/11	248	4	1.9%	—
03/10	197	1	0.8%	—
03/03	183	0	—	—
Annual Growth	7.3%	—	—	—

2013 Year-End Financials

Debt ratio: —
Return on equity: 2.90%
Cash ($ mil.): 0
Current ratio: —
Long-term debt ($ mil.): —
Dividends
Yield: —
Payout: —
Market value ($ mil.): —

WAYNE J. GRIFFIN ELECTRIC INC.

Wayne J. Griffin Electric brings a certain spark to New England and the Southeast. With offices in Massachusetts Georgia North Carolina and Alabama the electrical contractor offers construction and installation services on hospitals hotels industrial and high-tech buildings offices prisons research laboratories retirement communities and schools. The company's service division provides small project management and facility maintenance while its telecom division designs and installs fiber optics fire alarm and security systems as well as systems that control energy use from lighting to heating ventilation and air conditioning (HVAC). Founded in 1978 Wayne J. Griffin Electric is privately held.

Since serving its first major customer the Coca-Cola Bottling Company at its Massachusetts plant Wayne J. Griffin Electric has been expanding into different commercial industrial and institutional sectors. It has worked for such clients as Boeing and EMC Corporation. It has also worked on electrical expansion projects for the Valley Creek Wastewater Treatment Facility in Alabama and the Raleigh-Durham International Airport in North Carolina.

More current work involves building the primary and emergency standby electrical systems for the Women & Infant's Center at the University of Alabama at Birmingham. The project also involves providing the conduit systems for nurse call fire alarm intercom and paging.

EXECUTIVES

President and CEO, Wayne J. Griffin

LOCATIONS

HQ: WAYNE J. GRIFFIN ELECTRIC INC.
116 HOPPING BROOK RD, HOLLISTON, MA 01746-1455
Phone: 508-429-8830
Web: WWW.WAYNEJGRIFFIN.COM

COMPETITORS

ADCO Electrical
Bergelectric
E-J Electric Installation Co.
EMCOR
Integrated Electrical Services
J.F. White Contracting
Mass Electric
Quanta Services

HISTORICAL FINANCIALS

Company Type: Private

Income Statement — FYE: December 31

	REVENUE ($ mil.)	NET INCOME ($ mil.)	NET PROFIT MARGIN	EMPLOYEES
12/12	286	15	5.5%	1,100
12/11	286	15	5.5%	—
12/10	285	25	9.0%	—
12/09	238	35	15.0%	—
Annual Growth	6.2%	(24.1%)	—	—

2012 Year-End Financials

Debt ratio: —
Return on equity: 5.50%
Cash ($ mil.): 21
Current ratio: 1.10
Long-term debt ($ mil.): —
Dividends
Yield: —
Payout: —
Market value ($ mil.): —

WEBSTER UNIVERSITY

They have more than dictionaries at this Webster. Webster University is a private school that serves about 22000 undergraduate and graduate students through an international network of more than 100 campuses. Its main campus in St. Louis Missouri has an enrollment of more than 8000 students and 700 faculty and staff members. Other locations span the US and are also present in Europe Asia and other regions; many campuses are on military bases. Alumni include former shuttle commander Eileen Collins actress Marsha Mason and Indonesia's first democratically elected president Susilo Bambang Yudhoyono. Webster University was founded as a small Catholic women's college in 1915.

Geographic Reach

Students attending Webster hail from all 50 US states and about 150 countries. The university's main campus is located in St. Louis Missouri. It also has satellite campuses –including traditional military corporate and metropolitan-style locations –in more than 20 US states and in Africa (Ghana) Asia (China and Thailand) and Europe (Austria the Netherlands Switzerland and the UK) as well as an online presence.

Operations

The university has a faculty-to-student ratio of 1:9 and offers more than 100 program selections for majors and minors. Webster University's main campus serves students through five colleges and schools focusing on arts and sciences fine arts communications education and business and technology.

Financial Performance

Revenue fell 2% to some $210 million in fiscal 2013 due to lower student income (tuition and fees) and private contributions (gifts and grants). Net income rose by more than 200% to $23 million due to higher investment returns and changes in split-interest agreement values.

Webster University has an endowment of some $111 million. Full-time tuition runs at about $24000 per year.

Strategy

The strategic plan at Webster includes investments in infrastructure human resources and academic program improvements. In addition the university is working to enhance financial resources (including through fundraising efforts) increasing local and global partnerships building a stronger reputation and improving communication programs.

The organization expanded its geographic reach by establishing a campus in Ghana in 2013. Webster enhanced its network of global affiliates (called the Webster International Network of Schools or WINS) by adding Carroll University in 2012 and Mexico-based CETYS University in 2013.

Also in 2012 the university improved technology resources by launching a new online learning management system. In 2013 it introduced a new brand marketing campaign (including television and print advertisements) and added a new degree program in business management.

EXECUTIVES

Chairman, George H. Walker III
VP Finance and Administration and Treasurer, David Garafola
Associate VP Human Resources, Betsy Schmutz
President, Neil George
Dean Student Affairs Office, Ted F. Hoef
Director Professional Development, Larry Mabrey
Benefits Representative, Gloria Barbre
Head of Reference Services Library, Ellen Eliceiri
Acquisitions Library, Maya Grach
Secretary, Laura Rein
Director Advancement Services, Ryan Elliott
Director Alumni Programs, Jennifer Jezek-Taussig
Director Global MBA Program, Trevor Barker
Director Career Services, Tamara Gegg-LaPlume
Director Operations, Caprice Moore
Associate Chair, Alyce Herndon
Secretary, Kristi Evans
Compensation Chair, Terri Jones
Membership Chair, Bethany Keller
Special Events Chair, DeLyle Bowen
VP Academic Affairs, James Staley
VP Development and Alumni Programs, Faith D. Maddy
VP Executive Assistant to President and Secretary, Karen M. Luebbert
Vice Chairman, Laurance L. Browning Jr.
Trustee, James D. Weddle
senior Director of one of Webster Universitys oldest campuses, Richard Crosby
Senior Vice President, Julian Schuster
President, Oren Yagil
President, Ralph Olliges
Vice President Chief Financial Officer, Greg Gunderson
Sr. Vice President in Administration, Robert M. Cox
Trustee, A. Bayard Clark III, age 68
Trustee, George F. Scherer
Trustee, Michael A. (Mike) DeHaven
Trustee, Richard A. (Dick) Liddy, age 78
Trustee, Michael F. Neidorff, age 71
Trustee, Brenda D. Newberry, age 60
Trustee, Thomas G. Cornwell
Trustee, P. Joseph (Joe) McKee III
Trustee, Susan M. (Sue) Neumann, age 61
Trustee, Donna M. Vandiver
Trustee, Michael Staenberg, age 60
Trustee, Mark E. Burkhart
Trustee, George C. Roman
Trustee, Randy Adams
Trustee, Sheila Baxter
Trustee, Amelia Bond
Trustee, Dale Cammon
Trustee, Donna K. Martin
Trustee, Jerry E. Ritter
Vice Chairman, Laurance L. Browning Jr.
Trustee, Steven O. Swyers
Trustee, Elizabeth T. Robb
Trustee, Paul Lee
Trustee, John R. Capps
Trustee, David Steward
Trustee, John R. Roberts
Trustee, Donald M. Suggs
Trustee, Robert Q. Costas
Trustee, Julie Reese
Trustee, James D. Weddle
Trustee, Joseph J. Mokwa
Trustee, Margaret Bush Wilson
Trustee, Jane B. Hart
Trustee, Mary Alice Dwyer-Dobbin
Trustee, Ronald J. Kruszewski
Trustee, Tom Irwin
Trustee, Douglas E. Hill
Trustee, Edward L. Glotzbach
Trustee, Steven L. Finerty

LOCATIONS

HQ: WEBSTER UNIVERSITY
470 E LOCKWOOD AVE, SAINT LOUIS, MO 63119-3194
Phone: 314-968-6900
Web: WWW.WEBSTER.EDU

PRODUCTS/OPERATIONS

Selected Schools and Colleges

College of Arts and Sciences
George Herbert Walker School of Business and Technology
Leigh Gerdine College of Fine Arts
School of Communications
School of Education

HISTORICAL FINANCIALS

Company Type: Private

Income Statement FYE: May 31

	REVENUE ($ mil.)	NET INCOME ($ mil.)	NET PROFIT MARGIN	EMPLOYEES
05/12	213	7	3.4%	4,500
05/11	202	21	10.4%	—
05/10	199	21	10.8%	—
05/09	193	4	2.2%	—
Annual Growth	3.4%	20.3%	—	—

2012 Year-End Financials

Debt ratio: —
Return on equity: 3.40%
Cash ($ mil.): 21
Current ratio: 1.40
Long-term debt ($ mil.): —
Dividends
Yield: —
Payout: —
Market value ($ mil.): —

WELCH FOODS INC. A COOPERATIVE

Welch Foods has a taste for the grape. An operating subsidiary of the 1000-plus-farmer owner National Grape Cooperative Welch produces the Welch's brand grape and white grape juices and jellies. Its beverage line includes refrigerated and sparkling juices and cocktails frozen and shelf-stable concentrates and single-serve drinks. Welch supplies fresh grapes as well as preserved offerings (jams and spreads) which are also sold under the BAMA label. The co-op licenses the Welch's name to other manufactures of frozen fruit confections dried fruit and carbonated beverages among many. Its 400-plus products are purchased by grocery retailers and food service operators in the US and nearly 50 other countries.

Geographic Reach

Massachusetts-based Welch Foods has vineyards in Pennsylvania Michigan New York Ohio Washington and Ontario Canada.

Financial Performance

Welch Foods reported net sales of $649.5 million in 2012. Volume and net sales increased by 2% and 1% respectively in 2012 compared with 2011 with all core product categories showing market share and volume growth. Net income declined by $4 million to $20 million driven primarily by commodity cost increases among other factors.

Strategy

Despite a difficult year the cooperative added new products to its portfolio and made improvements to its manufacturing operations. The improved financial and operational performance of Welch Foods in 2012 followed consolidation of its manufacturing and distribution activities in 2011 and a headcount reduction at its corporate headquarters of more than 15% in 2010. The aggressive cost cutting efforts were necessary because cash-strapped consumers traded down to lower-priced products during the Great Recession cutting into Welch Foods' sales and profits.

The coop launched four new flavors (lemonade strawberry lemonade raspberry limeade and mango) of its sparkling juice cocktails in summer 2012 resulting in a an increase in volume of 29% during the summer months and market share gain during the holiday season. Welch Foods low-growth spreads business got a boost in 2012 with the launch of Welch's Nautrals an all natural no high fructose corn syrup formation that resonated with consumers.

EXECUTIVES

Vp Human Resources, Lisa Delisle Flynn
V Pres Ops & Tech, David F Engelkemeyer, age 61
President and CEO, Bradley C. Irwin, age 55
V Pres International, Wayne D Lutomski
Vice President Corporate Planning, Judy Carr
Vice President Operations, David Titus
Vice President Research And Development, Judy Bolander
Vice President, Jay Schaudies
Vice President Sales And Marketing, Michael Dana
Asst Treas, Steve Roberts
Chairman of the Board, Joseph C. Falcone
Auditors: KPMGLLP

LOCATIONS

HQ: WELCH FOODS INC. A COOPERATIVE
300 BAKER AVE STE 101, CONCORD, MA 017422131
Phone: 9783711000
Web: WWW.WELCHS.COM

PRODUCTS/OPERATIONS

Selected Brands and Products

BAMA
- Jams jellies and preserves
- Peanut butter

Welch
- Bottled and canned juices
- Dried fruit
- Fresh table grapes
- Frozen juices
- Fruit juice bars
- Jams jellies and preserves
- Pourable concentrated juices
- Refrigerated juices
- Single-serve juices

COMPETITORS

Chiquita Brands
Citrus World
Coca-Cola
Coloma Frozen Foods
Dole Food
Fresh Del Monte Produce
Great Western Juice
Lion Raisins
Monster Beverage
Mott' s
Naked Juice
National Raisin
Ocean Spray
Odwalla
Old Orchard
Silver Springs
Smucker
Snapple
South Beach Beverage
Stapleton-Spence Packing
Sun-Maid
Sunny Delight
Sunview Vineyards
Tree Top
Tropicana
Unilever NV
Wet Planet Beverages

HISTORICAL FINANCIALS

Company Type: Private

Income Statement

FYE: August 31

	REVENUE ($ mil.)	NET INCOME ($ mil.)	NET PROFIT MARGIN	EMPLOYEES
08/14	609	76	12.6%	1,000
08/13	608	65	10.7%	—
08/12	649	74	11.5%	—
08/11	640	0	—	—
Annual Growth	(1.6%)	—	—	—

2014 Year-End Financials

Debt ratio: ——
Return on equity: 12.60%
Cash ($ mil.): 4
Current ratio: 0.60
Long-term debt ($ mil.): —
Dividends
Yield: —
Payout: —
Market value ($ mil.): —

WELLMONT HEALTH SYSTEM

At Wellmont Health System wellness is paramount. Wellmont Health System provides general and advanced medical-surgical care to residents of northeastern Tennessee and southwestern Virginia. The health system consists of about a dozen owned and affiliated hospitals that collectively have more than 1000 licensed beds. One of its facilities is a rehabilitation hospital operated in partnership with HealthSouth. Wellmont also operates numerous ancillary facilities including an assisted living center a mental health clinic home health care and hospice agencies and outpatient centers.

Operations

Today Wellmont is one of the region's largest employers with a staff of more than 6500 medical professionals. Nearly 600 physicians deliver care at Wellmont's facilities that include eight hospitals in Tennessee and Virginia. Other facilities include an outpatient surgery center a child development center hospice a cancer center urgent care centers and a health network of physicians that include occupational health providers. The hospital also offers urgent care transportation with its Wellmont One Air Transport.

Financial Performance

Revenues increased 4% in 2012 due to increase outpatient visits and birthing and surgical facilities as well as from incentives on the system's electronic health record (EHR) system implementation. Net income also rose 41% in 2012 on higher investment income.

Strategy

Wellmont has expanded by opening new outpatient facilities including a new physical therapy clinic in 2013. During 2012 it added new personnel and digital imaging equipment at its Johnson City facilities as well as a new sleep diagnostic center at the Lonesome Pine campus. It also expands its service territory by partnering with other area care providers.

Company Background

Founded in 1996 Wellmont has grown over the years primarily through acquisitions including Lee Regional Medical Center Mountain View Regional Medical Center and the Takoma Regional Hospital in Tennessee (through a partnership with Adventist Health).

EXECUTIVES

President and CEO, Margaret (Denny) DeNarvaez, age 58
Senior Vice President of Business Development and Rural Strategy, David L. Brash
SVP Human Resources, Hamlin Wilson
President Bristol Regional Medical Center, Bart Hove
Interim President Bristol Regional Medical Center, Greg Neal
Interim President and CEO Community Hospital Division, Fred Pelle
Senior Vice President of Legal Affairs and General Counsel, Gary Miller
Vice President of finance and operations, Troy Clark
Executive Director Wellmont Foundation, Todd Norris
President Holston Valley Medical Center, Virginia Frank
COO, Tracey Moffatt
President Takoma Regional Hospital, Daniel Wolcott
EVP Legal and Corporate Affairs; President and CEO Wellmont Medical Associates, John Howard
CFO, Alice Pope
Vice President of finance, Dale Poe
Chief Financial Officer, Tom VandenHoven
Vice President of medical affairs, Maurice Nida
Vice President, Jo Hawthorne
Vice President of the Wellmont CVA, Tim Attebery
Director, David Crockett Sr.
Director, John Williams
Director, Ravan Krickbaum
Auditors: KPMGLLP

LOCATIONS

HQ: WELLMONT HEALTH SYSTEM
1905 AMERICAN WAY, KINGSPORT, TN 37660-5882
Phone: 423-230-8200
Web:
WWW.WELLMONT.NEWSROOM.MELTWATERPRESS.COM

PRODUCTS/OPERATIONS

Selected Facilities

Bristol Regional Medical Center (Bristol Tennessee)
Hancock County Hospital (Sneedville Tennessee)
Hawkins County Memorial Hospital (Rogersville Tennessee)
HealthSouth Rehabilitation Hospital of Kingsport (HealthSouth partnership; Kingsport Tennessee)
Holston Valley Medical Center (Kingsport Tennessee)
Lee Regional Medical Center (Pennington Gap Virginia)
Lonesome Pine Hospital (Big Stone Gap Virginia)
Mountain View Regional Medical Center (Norton Virginia)
Takoma Regional Hospital (Adventist Health partnership; Greeneville Tennessee)

Selected Services

Cancer Care
Children
Diabetes
Emergency and Trauma
Family Medicine
Hearing Services
Heart Care
Home Care
Hospice
Hospitalists
Marsh Regional Blood Center
Neurology
Occupational Medicine
Orthopedics
Palliative Care
Psychiatry
Radiology
Rehabilitation and Therapy
Sleep Medicine
Stroke Care
Surgical Services
Weight Loss
Women' s Health

COMPETITORS

Ascension Health
Baptist Memorial Health Care
Community Health Systems
Cookeville Regional Medical Center
Kindred Healthcare
LifePoint Hospitals
Mountain States Health
Tenet Healthcare

HISTORICAL FINANCIALS

Company Type: Private

Income Statement

FYE: June 30

	REVENUE ($ mil.)	NET INCOME ($ mil.)	NET PROFIT MARGIN	EMPLOYEES
06/10	622	33	5.5%	6,114
06/09	2	0	—	—
06/09	1,771	0	0.0%	—
Annual Growth	(64.9%)	207053.7%	—	—

2010 Year-End Financials

Debt ratio: ——
Return on equity: 5.50%
Cash ($ mil.): 29
Current ratio: —
Long-term debt ($ mil.): —
Dividends
Yield: —
Payout: —
Market value ($ mil.): —

WELLSTAR HEALTH SYSTEM INC.

With WellStar in your corner you won't need to wish upon a star for good health and wellness. The not-for-profit WellStar Health System serves four counties in northwest Georgia through five acute care hospitals a physician group and an array of outpatient services. The network's hospitals specialize in cardiac and cancer care diabetes treatments and women's health; together the five hospitals house about 1700 beds. WellStar's physician group operates through some 80 locations with more than 400 providers. The network is also home to hospice and home care programs; Atherton Place an independent living center for senior citizens; and several urgent care facilities.

Other network facilities offer outpatient medical imaging wound care and women's health and prenatal care. WellStar operates an outpatient cardiac group called Cardiovascular Medicine (CVM) one of Atlanta's largest cardiology groups joined the health system. WellStar CVM has 30 doctors practicing out of eight locations scattered throughout the region.

The health system also manages the WellStar Physicians Group which is installing electronic medical records (EMR) at certain practices to connect patients with their records no matter which care site they visit. The project calls for EMRs to be put in place throughout the entire medical group as a way to improve quality of care and increase provider access to patient information. WellStar has more than 100 locations and 500 medical providers in 30 specialties.

The organization's WellStar Institute for Better Health provides patients and their families with programs resources and educational materials designed to promote healthy lifestyles. The institute also contributes to medical and scientific learning by supporting community-wide programs and keeping health care providers in the know about the latest treatments and procedures.

WellStar Health System has received a Certificate of Need (CON) approval from the Department of Community Health to build a replacement hospital to replace the replace the WellStar Paulding Hospital Paulding County. The state approved WellStar's CON on in late 2011 allowing construction on the $125 million hospital to begin immediately. The replacement hospital will built in Hiram and plans call for the new larger facility include 30 adult emergency exam rooms 10 pediatric emergency exam rooms and six surgery suites. The new hospital will initially open with about 55 inpatient beds and will grow to 112 beds by 2016.

The first element of construction has already begun with the new entrance to the hospital campus. WellStar has developed a plan that will start construction on the hospital as well as a new medical office building in April or May 2012 which is two months earlier than projected in the original Hospital plans. The replacement hospital is expected to open in April 2014.

The hospital and adjacent medical office building will be built next to WellStar's existing medical office building in Hiram. When complete the campus will include an emergency department comprehensive surgical services a cancer center women's imaging and a multitude of other healthcare services. It will also be a completely digital hospital.

The health system grew even more in 2012 when it agreed to buy OrthoSport Physical Therapy for $3.4 million. WellStar's latest gift to itself will be run by OrthoSport's former owner Kim Chastain. Chastain is now be the executive director of outpatient rehabilitation services at WellStar.

EXECUTIVES

Asst Vp Of Finance, Nicole Ashe
Vice President Chief Nursing Officer, Elizabeth K Person
President and CEO, Reynold J. Jennings
EVP Human Resources Organizational Learning and Chief Compliance Officer, David Anderson
SVP; President WellStar Cobb Hospital, Kem M. Mullins
SVP Real Estate and Construction and President WellStar Paulding Hospital, Mark Haney
COO, Candice Saunders
Chief Medicine Division Officer, Jeffrey Tharp
SVP and Chief Nursing Executive, Mary Lou Wesley
Chief Cancer Network Officer, Michael Andrews
Chief Pediatrics Officer, Avril Beckford
EVP and CFO, Jim Budzinski
Chief Obstetrics and Gynecology Officer, Perry (Chip) Busbee
EVP; President and Chief Administrative Medical Officer WellStar Medical Group, Robert Jansen
SVP Post Acute Services; President WellStar Windy Hill Hospital, Lou Little
Chief Cardiology Officer, Barry Mangel
Chief Surgical Officer, Bill Mayfield
SVP and CIO, Jon Morris
Chief Pulmonary Officer, Alan Muster
SVP; President WellStar Douglas Hospital, Craig Owens
EVP and General Counsel, Leo Reichert
SVP; President WellStar Kennestone Hospital, Dan Woods
VP; COO WellStar Kennestone Hospital, Monte Wilson
Vice President Managed Care, Barbara Corey
Svp Strategic Business Development, Chris Kane
Pharmacy Manager, Margaret Chastine
Medical Director, Richard Hart
Senior Vice President Chief Medical, Kenneth C (Kc) Kunze
Vice President And Chief Of Hospitalist Services, Val Akopov
Operating Room Director, Karen Beard
Director Of Radiology Services, Jeffrey Walker
Director Of Health Information, Lynn Rosario
Vice President Human Resources, Joe Herzberg
Svp And Health Parks Administrator, Joe Brywczynski
Senior Vice President, Andrew Tatnall
Vice President Information Systems, Elizabeth Theobald
Director Physician Recruitment, Jennifer Pizzolatto
Vp Financial Planning And Analysis, Elizabeth Hoffman
Assistant Vice President Compliance, Sheryl Spohn
Director Of Him, Beth Kost
Vice President Chief Finc Ofc, Barry Chance
Vice President Operations, Ellena Evans
Vice President Operations, Frederic Rnsom
Nursing Director, Joyce Hulsey
Vice President Medical Management, Robin Wilson
Senior Vice President Group Account, Ellen Cross
Assistant Vice President Cno Patient Care Srvs, Vicky Hogue
Vice President Executive Director Business Technology, Michael Streetman
Infection Control Director, Cecilia Vincent
Ambulatory Services Director, Gary Duke
Medical Director, Ann Vincent
Executive Vice President Operations, John Fitzgerald
Vice President Nursing Pt Care, Shella Black
Director Of Respiratory Therapy, Martha Egger
Vice President Finance Corporate Busin, Sheryl Allen
Vice President And Controller Filmed Entertainment Accounting Group, Terry Abinson
Vice President Prof Services, Christopher York
Director Of Medical Records, Kathy Richardson
Ma Ms Mba Pmp Vice President, Jim Francis
Vice President Nursing Pt Care, Pam Lord
Director Of Him, Robert Kost
Vice President Of Medical Affairs, Bob Lubitz
Vice President Finance, Karen Sandlin
Vice President, Amanda Fache
Vice President Information Systems, Chinwe Gaines
Senior Vice President And Medical Director, Donald Hrolcco
Vice President Information Technology, Bradford Newton
Assistant Vice President Nursing, Patsy Norton
Vice President Post Acute Srvs And Cno, Jerry Hooks
Nursing Director, Tarey Ray
Vice President Cardiac Services, Patrick Jansen
Director Physician Recruitment, Richard Hammonds
Director Of Him, Ed Franks
Vice President Engineering, Kelly Rahming
Vice President Emea Sales, Vanessa Grigsby
Vice President Information Technology, Bradford Parrish
Senior Vice President And Chief, Ivan Banks
Senior Vice President Chief Financial, Dinesh Gonsalkorale
Vice President Finance, Barbara Rogness
Vice President Cardiac Network, Carol Liu
Director Of Physical Therapy, Kathleen Ruffino Dearde
Senior Vice President Finance Secy, Joseph Desantis
Vice President Finance, Jayne Grubard
Assistant Vice President Risk Management Wellstar Health System, Steve Johnson
Operations Vice President, Ilona L Wpozniak
Senior Vice President Public, Kim Menesee
Hr Director & Vp, Mary Tavernero
Infection Control Director, Nickie Graves
Assistant Vice President And Cno Patient Services, Martha Seahorn
Senior Vice President And Admin, Craig Wens
Senior Vice President Supply Chain, Tony Trupiano
Assistant Vice President Accounting, Jimmy Swartz
Treas, James Nalley
Secretary, Shemieka King
Board Trustees Member, Christopher Poston
Chair Treasurer, Mark Sanders
Vice Chairman, Bonnie Standridge
Auditors: KPMGLLP

LOCATIONS

HQ: WELLSTAR HEALTH SYSTEM INC.
805 SANDY PLAINS RD, MARIETTA, GA 30066-6340
Phone: 770-792-7600
Web: WWW.WELLSTAR.ORG

PRODUCTS/OPERATIONS

Selected Facilities

Atherton Place (Marietta Georgia)
The Jean and Mack Henderson Women's Center at Kennestone (Marietta Georgia)
WellStar Cobb Hospital (Austell Georgia)
WellStar Community Hospice (Austell Georgia)
WellStar Douglas Hospital (Douglasville Georgia)
WellStar Kennestone Hospital (Marietta Georgia)
WellStar Paulding Hospital (Dallas Georgia)
WellStar Paulding Nursing Center (Dallas Georgia)
WellStar Windy Hill Hospital (Marietta Georgia)
Urgent Care Centers
Cooper Lake Urgent Care Center
Delk Road Urgent Care Center
Kennesaw Urgent Care Center
Shallowford Urgent Care Center
Towne Lake Urgent Care Center

COMPETITORS

Athens Regional Medical Center
Central Georgia Health Systems
Children' s Healthcare of Atlanta
DeKalb Medical
Doctors Hospital of Augusta
Emory Healthcare
Floyd Medical Center
Grady Health System
HCA
Northeast Georgia Health System
Phoebe Putney Memorial Hospital
St. Mary' s Health Care
Tenet Healthcare
West Georgia Health System

HISTORICAL FINANCIALS

Company Type: Private

Income Statement FYE: June 30

	REVENUE ($ mil.)	NET INCOME ($ mil.)	NET PROFIT MARGIN	EMPLOYEES
06/11	595	136	22.9%	11,000
06/09	397	0	—	—
06/08	5	1	33.1%	—
Annual Growth	380.1%	324.7%	—	—

2011 Year-End Financials

Debt ratio: —
Return on equity: 22.90%
Cash ($ mil.): 21
Current ratio: 0.10
Long-term debt ($ mil.): —
Dividends
Yield: —
Payout: —
Market value ($ mil.): —

WESLEYAN UNIVERSITY

Wesleyan University is a private institution offering liberal arts and sciences education from its 360-acre campus in Middleton Connecticut. Some 3500 undergraduate and graduate students attend the university which has programs in academic areas including American studies film studies and psychology. Notable alumni include television producer Joss Whedon and educational writer Ted Fiske. Founded in 1831 Wesleyan was the first of several US colleges and universities to be named after John Wesley founder of the Methodist church; it ended its formal affiliation with the church in 1937.

EXECUTIVES

VP Finance and Administration, John Meerts
VP University Relations, Barbara-Jan Wilson
Director Human Resources, Julia Hicks
Associate VP Information Technology Services, Ganesan Ravishanker
VP Academic Affairs and Provost, Joseph Bruno
Registrar, Anna van der Burg
President, Michael S. Roth
Senior executive Vice President Chief Marketing Officer, Amy Radin
Head of Reference, Diane Klare
Head of Cataloging, Sally Grucan

LOCATIONS

HQ: WESLEYAN UNIVERSITY
45 WYLLYS AVE, MIDDLETOWN, CT 06459-3211
Phone: 860-685-2000
Web: WWW.WESLEYAN.EDU

HISTORICAL FINANCIALS

Company Type: Private

Income Statement FYE: June 30

	REVENUE ($ mil.)	NET INCOME ($ mil.)	NET PROFIT MARGIN	EMPLOYEES
06/11	194	67	34.6%	900
06/07	179	90	50.3%	—
06/06	172	95	55.2%	—
06/05	163	23	14.2%	—
Annual Growth	2.9%	19.4%	—	—

2011 Year-End Financials

Debt ratio: —
Return on equity: 34.60%
Cash ($ mil.): 15
Current ratio: —
Long-term debt ($ mil.): —
Dividends
Yield: —
Payout: —
Market value ($ mil.): —

WEST TEXAS GAS INC.

With a deep understanding the utility of natural gas natural gas utility West Texas Gas distributes more than 25 billion cu. ft. of natural gas propane and other petroleum products to more than 25000 residential commercial agricultural and governmental customers in Texas and Oklahoma Panhandle region. The company the fourth-largest investor-owned public utility in Texas also operates retail gasoline stations and convenience stores and has gas gathering production transmission and marketing operations. West Texas Gas is 100%-owned by CEO J. L. Davis.

Like other energy companies West Texas Gas saw its revenues drop on 2009 as the global recession hammered commodity prices and weakened demand. A rebounding economy and a rise in oil and gas prices helped the company's sales and income in 2010.

West Texas Gas was founded in 1976 by J. L. Davis a midstream oil and gas industry veteran with more than 50 years of experience in the business. He began his professional career in 1949 with Magnolia Oil Company.

Seeking to expand its gas distribution into Mexico in 2008 the company acquired Reef International a marketer of gas to Mexico and which controlled a natural gas pipeline that ties the US-Mexico border to intrastate gas facilities on the US side of the Rio Grande. West Texas Gas subsequently acquired the pipeline from Reef International.

EXECUTIVES

President and CEO, J. L. Davis
VP, Richard D. Hatchett
Manager Gas Supply, Dave Freeman
Manager Gas Marketing, J. J. King
Customer Service Manager, Jan Thompson
Representative Gas Supply, Carson Watt
Representative Gas Marketing, Hershel Sorrels
EVP, David L. Davis
VP, Michael Davis
Representative Gas Marketing, Donald Bland
Auditors: JohnsonMiller&Co.

LOCATIONS

HQ: WEST TEXAS GAS INC.
211 N COLORADO ST, MIDLAND, TX 79701-4607
Phone: 432-682-4349
Web: WWW.WESTTEXASGAS.COM

COMPETITORS

Atmos Energy
Gateway Energy
Martin Midstream Partners
Oncor Electric Delivery
Southwestern Energy
Texas New Mexico Power

HISTORICAL FINANCIALS

Company Type: Private

Income Statement FYE: December 31

	REVENUE ($ mil.)	NET INCOME ($ mil.)	NET PROFIT MARGIN	EMPLOYEES
12/07	889	40	4.5%	600
12/06	745	65	8.8%	—
12/05	795	36	4.6%	—
12/04	625	23	3.8%	—
Annual Growth	12.4%	19.2%	—	—

2007 Year-End Financials

Debt ratio: —
Return on equity: 4.50%
Cash ($ mil.): 73
Current ratio: 1.50
Long-term debt ($ mil.): —
Dividends
Yield: —
Payout: —
Market value ($ mil.): —

WESTAT INC.

Survey the market research business and you'll find Westat among the leaders of the pack. A statistical survey organization the company provides research and consulting services including study design and analysis data collection program evaluation and communications campaign development. It has technical expertise in survey and analytical methods computer systems technology biomedical science and clinical trials. Westat serves US state and local government clients in addition to businesses and foundations. It has offices in six US states as well as international locations around the world. The company was founded in 1963 and is employee-owned.

Geographic Reach

Westat has offices in Bethesda Maryland; Atlanta; Cambridge Massachusetts; Raleigh/Durham North Carolina; Philadelphia; and Houston. International offices are located in Beijing Costa Rica Ethiopia India South Africa and Thailand.

Strategy

In late 2012 Westat expanded through the acquisition of Atlanta-based GeoStats a research and technology firm. Because of the advanced technology Geostats uses the deal enhanced Westat's expertise in collecting and analyzing geospatial mobility and physical activity data.

EXECUTIVES

VP Accounting Contracts, Peter R. Gill
VP Telecom and Data Processing, Tom Jones
President, James E. Smith
VP Administration, Bruce F. Romer
VP Planning and Finance, Patricia Espey-English

LOCATIONS

HQ: WESTAT INC.
1600 RESEARCH BLVD, ROCKVILLE, MD 20850-3129
Phone: 301-251-1500
Web: WWW.WESTAT.COM

PRODUCTS/OPERATIONS

Selected Operations and Services

Program areas
- Alcohol tobacco and other drug studies
- Consulting services and marketing research
- Customer satisfaction
- Education
- Employment and training
- Energy
- Environmental protection
- Health and medical studies
- Housing
- Military human resources
- Organizational and personnel studies
- Science and technology
- Social services and community development
- Transportation

Research services
- Clinical trials management
- Conference planning and support
- Data analysis and reporting
- Data preparation and processing
- Focus groups
- Program evaluation
- Qualitative studies
- Statistical sample design
- Study design

Survey Services
- Data collection from institutions and businesses
- Data preparation and processing
- Design
- In-field measurement and biospecimen collection
- Interviewing
- Mail surveys
- On-site data collection coordination
- Telephone surveys
- Web-based surveys

COMPETITORS

Gallup
GfK
Harris Interactive
IMS Health
Ipsos
J.D. Power
Kantar Group
Maritz Research
Nielsen Holdings
ORC International
QinetiQ
SDI Health
Social & Scientific Systems
Walker Information

HISTORICAL FINANCIALS

Company Type: Private

Income Statement FYE: December 31

	REVENUE ($ mil.)	NET INCOME ($ mil.)	NET PROFIT MARGIN	EMPLOYEES
12/12	495	28	5.8%	2,000
12/11	506	27	5.4%	—
12/10	455	21	4.6%	—
12/09	501	24	5.0%	—
Annual Growth	(0.4%)	4.6%	—	—

2012 Year-End Financials

Debt ratio: —
Return on equity: 5.80%
Cash ($ mil.): 13
Current ratio: 1.50
Long-term debt ($ mil.): —
Dividends
Yield: —
Payout: —
Market value ($ mil.): —

WESTERN AGCREDIT

LOCATIONS

HQ: WESTERN AGCREDIT
10980 S JORDAN GTWY, SOUTH JORDAN, UT 840954125
Phone: 8015719200
Web: WWW.WESTERNAGCREDIT.COM

HISTORICAL FINANCIALS

Company Type: Private

Income Statement FYE: December 31

	ASSETS ($ mil.)	NET INCOME ($ mil.)	INCOME AS % OF ASSETS	EMPLOYEES
12/12	676	16	2.4%	57
12/11	619	21	3.5%	—
12/10	594	9	1.7%	—
12/08	548	0	—	—
Annual Growth	5.4%	—	—	—

2012 Year-End Financials

Debt ratio: —
Return on equity: 48.50%
Cash ($ mil.): 4
Current ratio: —
Long-term debt ($ mil.): —
Dividends
Yield: —
Payout: —
Market value ($ mil.): —

WESTERN FARMERS ELECTRIC COOPERATIVE

EXECUTIVES

Vice President Power Delivery, Ron Cunningham
Vice President of legal and corporate services, Brian Hobbs
Vice President Chief Financial Officer, Jane Lafferty
General Manager Power Resources, Bob Orme
General Manager Power Production, Gary Gilleland
Director Marketing, Mark Faulkenberry
Commercial and Industrial Marketing Manager and Legislative Coordinator, Scott Williams
VP, Bob Thomasson
President, Bob Allen
Secretary and Treasurer, Ray Smith
Assistant Secretary-Treasurer, Rusty Grissom
Executive VP CEO, Randy Ethridge
Vice President, Charles Hickey
Senior Manager of Planning, Dan Fleming
Executive V.P. CEO, Jim Jackson
Senior Manager of Market Planning, Roy Klusmeyer
Executive V.P. CEO, Gary Hurse
Auditors: KPMGLLP

LOCATIONS

HQ: WESTERN FARMERS ELECTRIC COOPERATIVE
701 NE 7TH ST, ANADARKO, OK 730052297
Phone: 4052473351
Web: WWW.WFEC.COM

PRODUCTS/OPERATIONS

2012 Fuel Mix

Coal		30
Natural gas		16
Hydropower		6
Total	0	100

2012 Sales

	$ mil.	% of total
Members & cities	418	92
Other	38	8
Total	457	100

COMPETITORS

Empire District Electric
Entergy
Grand River Dam Authority
OGE Energy
ONEOK
PG&E Corporation

HISTORICAL FINANCIALS

Company Type: Private

Income Statement FYE: December 31

	REVENUE ($ mil.)	NET INCOME ($ mil.)	NET PROFIT MARGIN	EMPLOYEES
12/13	525	21	4.1%	378
12/12	457	13	2.9%	—
12/11	462	10	2.3%	—
12/10	455	0	—	—
Annual Growth	4.9%	—	—	—

2013 Year-End Financials

Debt ratio: —
Return on equity: 4.10%
Cash ($ mil.): 10
Current ratio: 0.60
Long-term debt ($ mil.): —
Dividends
Yield: —
Payout: —
Market value ($ mil.): —

WESTERN ILLINOIS UNIVERSITY FOUNDATION

LOCATIONS

HQ: WESTERN ILLINOIS UNIVERSITY FOUNDATION
1 UNIVERSITY CIR, MACOMB, IL 614551390
Phone: 3092981861
Web: WWW.GOLEATHERNECKS.COM

HISTORICAL FINANCIALS

Company Type: Private

Income Statement FYE: June 30

	ASSETS ($ mil.)	NET INCOME ($ mil.)	INCOME AS % OF ASSETS	EMPLOYEES
06/13	50	2	4.1%	1
06/12	46	2	5.2%	—
06/11	45	4	10.1%	—
Annual Growth	5.5%	(33.0%)	—	—

2013 Year-End Financials

Debt ratio: —
Return on equity: 25.50%
Cash ($ mil.): 3
Current ratio: 17.70
Long-term debt ($ mil.): —
Dividends
Yield: —
Payout: —
Market value ($ mil.): —

WESTERN STATES FIRE PROTECTION COMPANY INC

Western States Fire Protection (WSFP) is sprinkling its own brand of safety west of the Mississippi. The company a division of APi Group installs water-based fire sprinklers and other fire suppression systems for the commercial residential and industrial markets primarily in the western US. It designs installs and maintains fire protection systems at defense gaming high-tech institutional medical processing and sports facilities. Specific projects include installing systems at the Colorado Convention Center and Microsoft's data storage facility in Washington. WSFP also manufactures fire sprinklers at its own fabrication workshops. The company was founded in 1985.

In addition to its water-based fire sprinklers WSFP serves hazardous facilities with FM-200 and carbon dioxide systems. FM-200 is a dry chemical that extinguishes fire through a combination of chemically-based inhibition and cooling. These systems are used in facilities where water damage must be avoided such as art galleries historical libraries and record and storage facilities.

EXECUTIVES

Chairman, Lee R. Anderson Sr.
Treasurer, Sandra Barker
President, Gene Postma
VP, Rick Charles
Business Development Manager, Glenn Viloria
Operations Manager Sales, Jason Haffner
Executive Vice President, Jeff Daane

Vice President, Joe Depriest
Sales Manager, Kyle Kalina
Operations Manager, Leonard VanAusdle
Operations Manager, Mark Harris
Operations Manager, Travis Sticka

LOCATIONS

HQ: WESTERN STATES FIRE PROTECTION COMPANY INC
7026 S TUCSON WAY, CENTENNIAL, CO 80112-3921
Phone: 303-792-0022
Web: WWW.DATACENTERFIREPROTECTION.COM

COMPETITORS

ADT Worldwide
COSCO Fire Protection
China Fire
Sharpfibre
Siemens Building Technologies
SimplexGrinnell
UTC Fire & Security

HISTORICAL FINANCIALS

Company Type: Private

Income Statement FYE: December 31

	REVENUE ($ mil.)	NET INCOME ($ mil.)	NET PROFIT MARGIN	EMPLOYEES
12/12	202	17	8.5%	1,429
12/11	165	12	7.3%	—
12/10	150	11	7.5%	—
12/09	185	13	7.4%	—
Annual Growth	3.0%	8.2%	—	—

2012 Year-End Financials

Debt ratio: —
Return on equity: 8.50%
Cash ($ mil.): 0
Current ratio: 0.80
Long-term debt ($ mil.): —
Dividends
Yield: —
Payout: —
Market value ($ mil.): —

WESTERN WASHINGTON UNIVERSITY

If you're in the West and you're looking for a liberal arts education look no further than Western Washington University. The university is located in northwest Washington state and is one of a handful of state-funded four-year institutions of higher education in Washington. The school has an enrollment of about 15000 students; roughly 95% of those are undergraduate students. Western Washington University has a student-teacher ratio of roughly 21:1.The university has students from almost every other state and from three dozen other countries. Western which began as a teachers college accepting its first students in 1899 became a full university in 1977.

Geographic Reach

The university serves mostly undergraduate students in northwest Washington state.

Operations

Western Washington University offers its students five colleges with more than 160 academic programs. Students can also design their own degrees such as some recent choices: Medicine and Social Justice Eco-Cultural Studies in Education and Law Diversity & Public Policy.

Financial Performance

The university has been growing in recent years. New enrollment and improved retention have helped Western Washington University post an 8% increase in revenue in 2012 as compared to 2011. Attracting students through scholarship allowances eroded some of its 13% increases in tuition revenue. The educational institution also generated revenue from state and local grants and contracts as well as sales services of educational activities. Net income meanwhile dropped some 46% during the same reporting period. Non-operating revenue such as declines in income from state appropriation loss on endowments and rental property expenses all contributed toward the net income slip.

Strategy

Western Washington University works to regularly provide additional programs. In 2013 the school's College of Sciences and Technology and Whatcom Community College partnered to offer a bachelor's degree in Computer and Information Systems Security. It also introduced a Bachelor's Degree Program in Nursing.

To provide a more flexible education option for students Western Washington University's Woodring College of Education offers a Master of Education in Continuing and College Education degree program through an online-only basis. It has also rolled out an online-only TESOL Certificate Program.

The university provides for studying abroad through its Center for International Studies. Students enrolled in this program generally learn a foreign language and have the opportunity to immerse themselves in their chosen culture. Conversely the school offers international students the opportunity to learn English through the International Students at Western program.

Western Washington University also runs a program called Query a faculty research database that allows other faculty members and students to keep tabs on what the university's teachers are interested in and possibly looking to teach. Members can look up who researched specific subjects. Query which can be used to search by subject area last name or by department gives members the ability to find out what Western Washington University's faculty are working on.

EXECUTIVES

Vp Business/fin Affairs, Richard Van Den Hul

LOCATIONS

HQ: WESTERN WASHINGTON UNIVERSITY
516 HIGH ST, BELLINGHAM, WA 98225-5996
Phone: 360-650-3000
Web: WWW.WWU.EDU

PRODUCTS/OPERATIONS

Selected Colleges

College of Business and Economics
College Of Fine and Performing Arts
College of Humanities and Social Sciences
College of Sciences and Technology
Fairhaven College of Interdisciplinary Studies
Graduate School
Huxley College of the Environment
Woodring College of Education

HISTORICAL FINANCIALS

Company Type: Private

Income Statement FYE: June 30

	REVENUE ($ mil.)	NET INCOME ($ mil.)	NET PROFIT MARGIN	EMPLOYEES
06/12	181	14	8.0%	466
06/11	167	27	16.2%	—
06/09	151	20	13.8%	—
06/08	145	47	32.7%	—
Annual Growth	5.6%	(25.7%)	—	—

2012 Year-End Financials

Debt ratio: —
Return on equity: 8.00%
Cash ($ mil.): 41
Current ratio: 1.50
Long-term debt ($ mil.): —
Dividends
Yield: —
Payout: —
Market value ($ mil.): —

WESTMINSTER VILLAGE WEST LAFAYETTE INC

LOCATIONS

HQ: WESTMINSTER VILLAGE WEST LAFAYETTE INC
2741 N SALISBURY ST, WEST LAFAYETTE, IN 479061499
Phone: 7654636768
Web: WWW.WVWL.ORG

HISTORICAL FINANCIALS

Company Type: Private

Income Statement FYE: June 30

	ASSETS ($ mil.)	NET INCOME ($ mil.)	INCOME AS % OF ASSETS	EMPLOYEES
06/13	56	(0)	—	150
06/12	54	0	0.2%	—
06/11	42	1	3.1%	—
06/10	33	0	—	—
Annual Growth	19.0%	—	—	—

2013 Year-End Financials

Debt ratio: —
Return on equity: (-4.30%)
Cash ($ mil.): 10
Current ratio: 0.40
Long-term debt ($ mil.): —
Dividends
Yield: —
Payout: —
Market value ($ mil.): —

WEXFORD HEALTH SOURCES INC.

Wexford Health Sources provides health care services to inmates doing time in the big house. The company has contracts at more than 100 government-run facilities including county jails state and federal prisons juvenile detention centers substance abuse treatment centers psychiatric hospitals and correctional centers for sex offenders. Wexford Health staffs professionals that perform medical and mental health care dentistry pharmacy services and administration services and serves about 90000 inmates and patients through contracts in five states —Illinois Mississippi Ohio Pennsylvania and West Virginia. Wexford Health was founded in 1992.

EXECUTIVES

CEO and President, Mark W. Hale
EVP and COO, Daniel L. Conn
SVP Human Resources and Risk Management, Elaine J. Gedman
SVP Operations and Strategic Development, Darius Holmes
Corporate Medical Director Utilization Management and Clinical Services, Thomas M. Lehman
Vice President of Finance, John M. Froehlich

LOCATIONS

HQ: WEXFORD HEALTH SOURCES INC.
425 HOLI DR FOST PLZ TWO FOSTER,
PITTSBURGH, PA 15220
Phone: 888-633-6468
Web: WWW.WEXFORDHEALTH.COM

COMPETITORS

Conmed Healthcare
Corizon
Correctional Medical Services
Corrections Corporation of America
GEO Group
MHM Services
PHS Correctional Healthcare

HISTORICAL FINANCIALS

Company Type: Private

Income Statement FYE: December 31

	REVENUE ($ mil.)	NET INCOME ($ mil.)	NET PROFIT MARGIN	EMPLOYEES
12/08	159	16	10.4%	1,525
12/05	160	6	4.0%	—
12/01	1,793	0	—	—
Annual Growth	—	168.8%	—	—

2008 Year-End Financials

Debt ratio: —
Return on equity: 10.40%
Cash ($ mil.): 5
Current ratio: 1.60
Long-term debt ($ mil.): —
Dividends
Yield: —
Payout: —
Market value ($ mil.): —

WHALLEY COMPUTER ASSOCIATES INC.

EXECUTIVES

President, John Whalley
VP, Paul H. Whalley
VP Operations, Thomas E. (Tom) Hanson
Sales Associate, Cynthia A. (Cindy) Wells
Senior Corporate Account Executive, Adam D. Scolnick
Senior Account Executive, Michael J. Noftall
Senior Account Executive, Michael T. Sheil
Business Development Specialist, Stan Bates
Senior Account Executive, William J. Oleksak
Inside Account Manager, Ania K. Sadowski
Director of Sales Operations, Steve M. Cross
Emerging Technologies Director, Dean M. LeClerc
Regional Service Department Manager, Daniel J. (Dan) Jury
Services Director, Kevin Learned
Administrative Assistant and Service Contract Coordinator, Linda Muldrew
Assistant Regional Service Department Manager, Derek M. Catelotti
Senior Service Department Administrator, Lisa F. Renkowicz
Parts Acquisition Administration, Lee Ann Martin
Parts Acquisition Administration, Julie M. LaBrecque
Account Exectutive, Tim Weaver
Service Dispatch, George Zina
Corporate Account Executive, Matthew Annunziata
Business Development Specialist, Mike Duarte
Business Development Specialist, Justin Newman
Sales Associate, Lauren Henderson
Sales Associate, Tina Miles
Director of Operations, Peggie Acerra

LOCATIONS

HQ: WHALLEY COMPUTER ASSOCIATES INC.
1 WHALLEY WAY, SOUTHWICK, MA 010779222
Phone: 4135694200
Web: WWW.WCA.COM

COMPETITORS

Dell
Hewlett-Packard
IBM Global Services

HISTORICAL FINANCIALS

Company Type: Private

Income Statement FYE: December 31

	REVENUE ($ mil.)	NET INCOME ($ mil.)	NET PROFIT MARGIN	EMPLOYEES
12/07	101	4	4.4%	104
12/06	87	3	4.4%	—
12/05	73	3	4.1%	—
12/04	67	0	—	—
Annual Growth	14.9%	—	—	—

2007 Year-End Financials

Debt ratio: —
Return on equity: 4.40%
Cash ($ mil.): 0
Current ratio: 1.10
Long-term debt ($ mil.): —
Dividends
Yield: —
Payout: —
Market value ($ mil.): —

WHEATBELT INC.

LOCATIONS

HQ: WHEATBELT INC.
11721 NW PLAZA CIR, KANSAS CITY, MO 641532023
Phone: 8162438222
Web: WWW.WHEATBELTINC.COM

HISTORICAL FINANCIALS

Company Type: Private

Income Statement FYE: December 31

	REVENUE ($ mil.)	NET INCOME ($ mil.)	NET PROFIT MARGIN	EMPLOYEES
12/07	210	0	0.0%	25
12/02	165	0	0.2%	—
12/01	150	0	0.3%	—
12/00	145	0	—	—
Annual Growth	5.4%	—	—	—

2007 Year-End Financials

Debt ratio: —
Return on equity: —
Cash ($ mil.): 0
Current ratio: 0.70
Long-term debt ($ mil.): —
Dividends
Yield: —
Payout: —
Market value ($ mil.): —

WHEATON FRANCISCAN SERVICES INC.

Wheaton Franciscan Services (WFSI) is the parent company for more than 100 health care housing and social service organizations in Colorado Illinois Iowa and Wisconsin. Also known as Wheaton Franciscan Healthcare WFSI operates more than 15 hospitals including Affinity Health System Rush Oak Park Hospital and United Hospital System. WFSI also includes long-term care centers home health agencies and physician offices. Its Franciscan Ministries division provides affordable housing units including assisted-living facilities and low-income dwellings. The not-for-profit health system is sponsored by The Franciscan Sisters Daughters of the Sacred Hearts of Jesus and Mary.

Many of WFSI's hospitals are operated in partnership with other area providers. For instance the Affinity Health System in Wisconsin is jointly sponsored by Wheaton Franciscan Sisters and Ministry Health Care while the Rush Oak Park Hospital in Illinois is operated through a partnership between WFSI and the Rush System for Health.

The health care system occasionally expands its network both by forming new partnerships and through acquisitions. In 2009 WFSI opened the Midwest Orthopedic Specialty Hospital in partnership with a group of independent orthopedic doctors. The new orthopedic center is part of the Franklin Hospital; WFSI completed construction on the new $90 million acute care facility in Franklin Wisconsin in 2008. The Franklin Hospital provides emergency surgery imaging and primary and specialty care.

The health system also partnered with the YMCA of Milwaukee to try to address chronic health concerns of area residents. The two organizations converted a local YMCA campus into the YMCA Healthy Lifestyle Village which opened in 2009. The center offers health screenings health education outpatient therapy and fitness services. WFSI and the YMCA have more Healthy Lifestyle Village campuses planned for other locations within their service areas.

In addition to increase the scope of specialty health care services it can provide to the community WFSI continues to recruit new physicians and specialists to the Wheaton Franciscan Medical Group. The system is also working to improve communication among its physicians and facilities by adding electronic health record (EHR) systems.

The Franciscan Sisters Daughters of the Sacred Hearts of Jesus and Mary (also known as the Wheaton Franciscan Sisters) founded WSFI in 1983 as a holding company for their ministry operations. The health system traces its roots back to the founding of the St. Mary's Hospital in Racine Wisconsin in 1882.

EXECUTIVES

President South Market Southeast Wisconsin, Kenneth R. (Ken) Buser
President CEO and Director, John D. Oliverio
SVP and CIO, Gregory A. (Greg) Smith
SVP and Chief Administrative Officer, Michael Lepore
SVP Strategy and Corporate Affairs, Richard J. Canter
SVP and COO Wheaton Franciscan and All Saints, Susan E. Boland
SVP Mission Services, Therese M. (Terri) Rocole
VP Payer Contracting and Relations, Coreen Dicus-Johnson
President and CEO Wheaton Franciscan Healthcare Iowa, Jack Dusenbery
President and CEO United Hospital System, Richard O. Schmidt Jr.
President and CEO Marianjoy, Kathleen C. Yosko
SVP Organizational Change and Leadership Development, Brenda J. Bowers
SVP Human Resources, Wayne Frangesch
President Wheaton Franciscan Continuing Care and Allied Services, James (Jim) Gresham
SVP and General Counsel, Sarah Herzog
President Central Market Southeast Wisconsin, Dan Mattes
President North Market Southeast Wisconsin, Debra K. Standridge

Chief Nursing Officer Iowa, Nancy Weber
CFO, Jon W. Sohn
Interim Chief Medical Officer and Chief Medical Information Officer, Rita Hanson
Senior Vice President Chief Administrative Officer, Mike Lepore
Senior Vice President Mission Services, Terri Rocole
Director, Michael J. Murry, age 64
President CEO and Director, John D. Oliverio
Director, Sister Mary Beth Glueckstein
Director, James Concannon
Director, Carolyn Hodge-West
Director, Robert O. Walker
Director, Parke Behn

LOCATIONS

HQ: WHEATON FRANCISCAN SERVICES INC.
26W 171 ROOSEVELT RD, WHEATON, IL 60187
Phone: 414-465-3000
Web: WWW.WFHEALTHCARE.ORG

PRODUCTS/OPERATIONS

Selected Operations

Franciscan Ministries Inc. (housing in Colorado Illinois Iowa and Wisconsin)
Illinois
- Marianjoy Rehabilitation Hospital (Wheaton)
- Rush Oak Park Hospital (affiliate Oak Park)

Iowa (Wheaton Franciscan Healthcare of Iowa)
- Covenant Medical Center (Waterloo)
- Mercy Hospital (Oelwein)
- Sartori Memorial Hospital (Cedar Falls)

Wisconsin
- Affinity Health System (partnership with Minstry Health Care)
  - Calumet Medical Center (Chilton)
  - Mercy Medical Center (Oshkosh)
  - St. Elizabeth Hospital (Appleton)
- Wheaton Franciscan Healthcare of Southeast Wisconsin
  - All Saints Hospital (two campuses in Racine)
  - Elmbrook Memorial Hospital (Brookfield)
  - Franklin Hospital (Franklin)
  - St. Francis Hospital (Milwaukee)
  - St. Joseph Hospital (Milwaukee)
  - Wisconsin Heart Hospital (Wauwatosa)
- United Hospital System Inc. (affiliated system)
  - Kenosha Medical Center (Kenosha)
  - St. Catherine's Medical Center (Pleasant Prairie)

COMPETITORS

Advocate Health Care
Alden Management Services
Children' s Hospital and Health System
Columbia St. Mary' s
Elmhurst Memorial Healthcare
FHN
Froedtert Hospital
Hospital Sisters Health System
KishHealth
Loyola University Health System
Ministry Health Care
Morris Hospital
NorthShore University HealthSystem
OSF Healthcare System
ProHealth Care
Resurrection Health Care
Rockford Health System
SwedishAmerican Health System

HISTORICAL FINANCIALS

Company Type: Private

Income Statement FYE: June 30

	REVENUE ($ mil.)	NET INCOME ($ mil.)	NET PROFIT MARGIN	EMPLOYEES
06/13	1,763	177	10.1%	18,000
06/12	1,723	(112)	—	—
06/10	1,710	173	10.2%	—
06/10	1,850	56	3.1%	—
Annual Growth	(1.6%)	46.4%	—	—

2013 Year-End Financials

Debt ratio: —
Return on equity: 10.10%
Cash ($ mil.): 25
Current ratio: 0.70
Long-term debt ($ mil.): —
Dividends
Yield: —
Payout: —
Market value ($ mil.): —

WHEELING-NISSHIN INC.

Wheeling-Nisshin a subsidiary of Nisshin Steel produces a variety of hot-dip coated steels such as stainless steel. The company's output includes 400000 tons produced at its aluminizing and galvanizing line facility and 300000 tons produced at its continuous galvanizing line facility. Both of the facilities are located at the company's headquarters site in West Virginia. Its primary customers are in the automotive appliance and construction industries. Wheeling-Nisshin was founded in 1986. It had been a joint venture between Nisshin and US steel producer Wheeling Pitt (now operating as Severstal Wheeling) until the Japanese steel company bought out its partner in early 2008.

EXECUTIVES

EVP and General Manager Commercial, Ricky Onishi
Manager Information Systems, Greg Lauri
Manager Quality Assurance and Customer Service, Art Bertol
General Manager Operations, Pat Pendleton
Manager Operations, Frank Mollica
CEO, Noboru Onishi
Purchasing Manager, Brian Petrella
General Manager Commercial, Walter Kaneko
Assistant Manager Operations, Larry Persina

LOCATIONS

HQ: WHEELING-NISSHIN INC.
400 PENN ST, FOLLANSBEE, WV 26037-1412
Phone: 304-527-2800
Web: WWW.WHEELING-NISSHIN.COM

COMPETITORS

Dofasco
ThyssenKrupp Stainless
United States Steel

HISTORICAL FINANCIALS

Company Type: Private

Income Statement FYE: December 31

	REVENUE ($ mil.)	NET INCOME ($ mil.)	NET PROFIT MARGIN	EMPLOYEES
12/12	426	6	1.6%	175
12/11	489	9	2.0%	—
12/10	434	10	2.4%	—
12/09	271	2	1.1%	—
Annual Growth	16.2%	32.1%	—	—

2012 Year-End Financials

Debt ratio: —
Return on equity: 1.60%
Cash ($ mil.): 46
Current ratio: 2.90
Long-term debt ($ mil.): —
Dividends
Yield: —
Payout: —
Market value ($ mil.): —

WHITE COUNTY MEDICAL CENTER

If you're sick in Searcy you may want to visit White County Medical Center (WCMC). The organization provides health care to Central Arkansas' residents. It has about 440 licensed inpatient beds on two hospital campuses (WCMC North and WCMC South) as well as a number of outpatient surgery centers primary care clinics and a retirement community called River Oaks Village. The WCMC South campus features an inpatient rehabilitation center that helps patients recover from injury and illness as well as a long-term acute care hospital for patients needing extended general care. In addition WCMC provides home health care services and runs a training program for certified nurse assistants.

Geographic Reach

The hospital serves patients in Independence Jackson Lonoke Prairie White and Woodruff Counties.

Operations

The Center's operations include Family Practice Associates Orthopaedic and Spine Center of Central Arkansas Searcy Medical Center and Searcy Medical Center - West Clinic Westside Family Medical Clinic WCMC Cardiology Clinic and White County Oncology.

WCMC employs some 1700 health care professionals including 150 physicians. Most of its general and specialty acute care services are provided at the main WCMC North Campus location including critical care cardiac rehabilitation and radiology. Its specialty services include cancer care diabetes education diagnostic imaging and labor and delivery services. It also operates a 31-bed inpatient rehabilitation center.

Strategy

In 2013 the Center created a comprehensive center to better care for patients with orthopaedic and spine needs –the Orthopaedic and Spine Center of Central Arkansas in Searcy.

In 2012 the Arkansas Department of Health made WCMC a Level III Trauma Center an integral part of the statewide trauma system.

Company Background

Founded in 1967 WCMC later acquired fellow health care provider Central Arkansas Hospital also located in Searcy and subsequently renamed it WCMC South. The South campus was expanded in 2008 with the opening of Compass an inpatient psychiatric facility for adults.

EXECUTIVES

Chairman, Wayne Hartsfield
President and CEO, Raymond W. (Ray) Montgomery II
Director Marketing Community Relations and Foundation, Cassandra Feltrop
VP and Treasurer, Stuart Hill
Director Human Resources, Pam Williams
Administrator Advanced Care Hospital, Eugene Zuber
VP Patient Services, LaDonna Johnston
President White County Medical Center Auxiliary, Buddy Muirhead
Auditors: BKDLLP

LOCATIONS

HQ: WHITE COUNTY MEDICAL CENTER
3214 E RACE AVE, SEARCY, AR 72143-4810
Phone: 501-268-6121
Web: WWW.WCMC.ORG

PRODUCTS/OPERATIONS

Selected Centers and Services

Advanced Care Hospital of White County (long term acute care hospital)
Cancer care
Cardiac care
Clearview Geriatrics (senior psychiatric care)
Compass (adult psychiatric care)
Critical care
Diabetes education
Durable medical equipment
Emergency services
Healthworks (industrial and occupational medicine)
Home health
Imaging Center (X-ray ultrasound cath lab)
Inpatient rehabilitation unit
Inpatient hospice
New Life Center (labor delivery)
Outpatient rehabilitation
Pharmacy program
PrimeTimes (seniors' program)
River Oaks Village (retirement center offering independent and assisted living)
Searcy Medical Center (physician practice locations)
Sleep study
Sports medicine
Weight loss surgery
White County Outpatient Surgery Center
Wound care

COMPETITORS

Arkansas Children's Hospital
Arkansas Heart Hospital
Baptist Health (Arkansas)
Community Health Systems
Conway Regional Health System
Jefferson Regional Medical Center of Arkansas
St. Vincent Health System
WRMC

HISTORICAL FINANCIALS

Company Type: Private

Income Statement FYE: September 30

	REVENUE ($ mil.)	NET INCOME ($ mil.)	NET PROFIT MARGIN	EMPLOYEES
09/09	482	11	2.5%	1,010
09/08	415	8	2.1%	—
09/06*	365	7	2.0%	—
12/05	125	8	6.4%	—
Annual Growth	40.0%	10.2%	—	—

*Fiscal year change

2009 Year-End Financials

Debt ratio: —
Return on equity: 2.50%
Cash ($ mil.): 48
Current ratio: 1.80
Long-term debt ($ mil.): —
Dividends
Yield: —
Payout: —
Market value ($ mil.): —

WIDENER UNIVERSITY

You probably won't find any narrow-minded students at Widener. A private co-educational liberal arts college Widener University offers a curriculum that emphasizes social awareness and civic engagement. It has an enrollment of some 6500 students and a student-to-faculty ratio of 12:1. The university grants undergraduate and graduate degrees in about 60 different fields; its programs are divided into eight schools and colleges that cover areas including arts and sciences business engineering law hospitality human services and nursing. Widener University has had its current name since 1979 but its roots reach back to a group of 19th century boys' military academies.

Geographic Reach

In addition to its main 110-acre campus located about 20 miles outside of Philadelphia in Chester Pennsylvania Widener operates three auxiliary campuses in Pennsylvania (Harrisburg and Exton) and Delaware (Wilmington) including the University College campus geared towards part-time adult undergraduates. The university's students come from more than 20 states and 25 countries. About 35% of its student base participates in study abroad programs.

Financial Performance

Widener reported a 2% increase in revenues in fiscal 2011 to some $155 million. Operating income was also up $5 to nearly $7 million.

Strategy

Widener has enhanced its attractiveness to students and faculty alike in recent years by expanding and upgrading facilities including the completion of a new nursing school building. In 2012 it opened a new international study center to help non-US students acclimate.

As part of its civic engagement curriculum Widener encourages students to participate in community service activities volunteer programs and internships. To help facilitate such activities as well as to enhance community relations in 2012 Widener opened a new science learning center wing on its Widener Partnership Charter School (a partnership with Chester Pennsylvania) and it established an early career and college partnership with the Sussex Technical School District.

EXECUTIVES

President, James T. Harris III
Senior Vice President for Administration and Finance, Joseph J. Baker
SVP and Provost, Jo Allen
VP University Advancement, Linda S. Durant
Associate VP Administration, George E. Hassel
Assistant VP University Relations, LouAnne Bulik
President Mardel Investments, Peter B. Zacharkiw
Associate VP and Controller, Catherine McGeehan
Director Operations, Carl G. Pierce
CIO, Peter Shoudy
Associate Provost and Dean Students, Deborrah Hebert
Director Campus Safety, Patrick Sullivan
Director Student Financial Services, Thomas K. Malloy
Founder President Pacific Millennium Group, Richard L. Tan
Senior Vice President General Counsel, John F. Schmutz
Vice President General Manager Vertical Lift, Leanne Caret
President Charter Associates, Thomas H. Bown
Executive Vice President CFO, James J. Hargadon
Senior Vice President Global Compliance and Quality Systems, Cynthia H. Sarnoski
Auditors: KPMGLLP

LOCATIONS

HQ: WIDENER UNIVERSITY
1 UNIVERSITY PL, CHESTER, PA 19013-5792
Phone: 610-499-4000
Web: WWW.ALUMNI.WIDENER.EDU

PRODUCTS/OPERATIONS

Selected Colleges and Schools

College of Arts and Sciences
School of Business Administration
School of Engineering
School of Hospitality Management
School of Human Service Professions
School of Law
School of Nursing
University College

HISTORICAL FINANCIALS

Company Type: Private

Income Statement FYE: June 30

	REVENUE ($ mil.)	NET INCOME ($ mil.)	NET PROFIT MARGIN	EMPLOYEES
06/11	200	9	4.9%	1,021
06/10	188	5	2.7%	—
06/09	184	9	5.2%	—
06/08	172	4	2.4%	—
Annual Growth	5.1%	33.8%	—	—

2011 Year-End Financials

Debt ratio: —
Return on equity: 4.90%
Cash ($ mil.): 40
Current ratio: —
Long-term debt ($ mil.): —
Dividends
Yield: —
Payout: —
Market value ($ mil.): —

WILBUR SMITH ASSOCIATES INC.

For many cities around the world where there's a Wilbur there's a roadway. Wilbur Smith Associates provides engineering design planning construction and economic consulting services for municipal works and infrastructure jobs including highways bridges railroads waterways airports and public buildings. Wilbur Smith is active throughout the US Europe Central America the UK the Middle East and Asia. Pioneer transportation engineer Wilbur Smith founded the firm in 1952. The company was acquired by Camp Dresser & McKee (CDM) in 2011. The deal helped broaden both firms' service capabilities and geographic reach.

Auditors: Davis&Co.CPAsP.C.

LOCATIONS

HQ: WILBUR SMITH ASSOCIATES INC.
1301 GERVAIS ST STE 1500, COLUMBIA, SC 29201-3356
Phone: 803-758-4500
Web: WWW.WILBURSMITH.COM

COMPETITORS

AECOM
David Evans
Jacobs Engineering
Michael Baker
Parsons Brinckerhoff
URS

HISTORICAL FINANCIALS

Company Type: Private

Income Statement FYE: December 25

	REVENUE ($ mil.)	NET INCOME ($ mil.)	NET PROFIT MARGIN	EMPLOYEES
12/09	182	1	0.7%	1,217
12/08	183	3	1.8%	—
12/07	436	0	—	—
Annual Growth	—	789.0%	—	—

2009 Year-End Financials

Debt ratio: —
Return on equity: 0.70%
Cash ($ mil.): 1
Current ratio: 1.10
Long-term debt ($ mil.): —
Dividends
Yield: —
Payout: —
Market value ($ mil.): —

WILBUR-ELLIS COMPANY

Seed 'em weed 'em and feed 'em could be the motto of San Francisco's Wilbur-Ellis Co. (aka WECO). Through its agribusiness division WECO sells fertilizer herbicides insecticides seed and farm machinery in North America. The Connell Bros. unit exports and distributes food ingredients and specialty chemicals throughout the Pacific Rim. Its feed division serves international customers in the livestock pet food and aquaculture industries. Additionally WECO provides consulting pesticide application and other agriculture-related services. Beyond North America WECO has operations in about 15 countries in the Asia-Pacific Region. WECO was founded in 1921 by Brayton Wilbur Sr. and Floyd Ellis.

Geographic Reach

The San Francisco-based company has agribusiness operations in the West Southwest and Midwest regions on the US. Connell Bros. has offices in 16 countries across the Asia-Pacific Region including Australia China and Vietnam. The Feed unit has operations in North America and in Australia and New Zealand.

Operations

WECO's Agribusiness division is one of the top marketers and distributors of agricultural products in the US with sales of $2 billion. Connell Bros. is the largest marketer and distributor of specialty chemicals and ingredients with about three dozen offices across the Asia Pacific region and annual sales of about $815 million. The $500-million-in-sales Feed division supplies value-added feed ingredients and markets for customers' by-products.

Financial Performance

WECO's sales exceeded $3 billion in 2012.

Strategy

WECO employs a strategy of acquiring successful businesses and integrating them into its existing operations. Geography is no barrier when it comes to buying companies. Indeed WECO has acquired operations in such faraway places as Malaysia Taiwan the Philippines China Australia and New Zealand. WECO continues to expand both through acquisitions and organically across its three divisions. Its Connell Bros. division expanded its food formulation services in Australia and New Zealand with the opening in 2012 of a food formulation facility in Sydney. Other infrastructure and facility investments made by Connell Bros. in 2012 include the construction of a 20000 square-foot warehouse in Mumbai India and a coatings lab in Bangkok.

Mergers and Acquisitions

After an acquisitive 2013 WECO maintained its active acquisition schedule in 2014. In February the company acquired one of its alliance partners New Horizons Ag Service an agricultural retail business in Elgin North Dakota. New Horizons will become part of Wilbur-Ellis Midwest. In January it acquired Accu-Rate Services a full-service agricultural retailer in Sedgwick Kansas and Advanced Ag LLC located in Creston Iowa. Also in January WECO's Connell Brothers unit purchased Enzyme Solutions Pty Ltd. of Melbourne Australia extending its capabilities in enzymes.

In 2013 WECO made about a half a dozen purchases including Nueces Ag an aerial spraying business in Texas' Coastal Bend area. It also bought Orange Belt Supply (OBS) a full-service agricultural retail operation located in Exeter California that serves the citrus belt in the San Joaquin Valley. Eying growth opportunities in seed aerial application nutrition and crop protection in Nebraska the company acquired Orchard Fertilizer Service there. It also bought S&S Agricultural Supply an agronomy business in Watervliet Michigan expanding its ability to service growers in southwest Michigan. Other purchases include Chester Farm Service Corp. in South Dakota.

WECO's Feed division was also active overseas through the purchase in 2011 of the assets of New Zealand and Australian Pet Food Ingredients (NZAPFI) including deboning facilities in New Zealand. Closer to home the Agribusiness division acquired the assets of Smith Air LLC an aerial application business that applies crop protection and fertility products to alfalfa dry beans potatoes and other crops in Eastern Washington. The purchase added to WECO's Agribusiness unit's aerial operations in California Texas and several other agricultural states.

Ownership

Family-owned WECO is transitioning to the fourth generation of family ownership. CEO and president John Thacher is the grandson of founder Brayton Wilbur Sr.

EXECUTIVES

V Pres, Kenneth J Manning, age 60
VP Treasurer and CFO, James D. Crawford
President Agribusiness Division, Daniel R. (Dan) Vradenburg
VP Strategic Planning and Business Development, John P. Thacher
VP South Central Operations, Steven J. Dietze
VP Western Operations, Scott Hushbeck
President Feed Division, Rob Fullerton
President Connell Brothers, Ted L. Eliot
President Wilbur-Ellis Japan, Iguchi Shinichi
Vice President Finance, Steve Flowers
Chairman, Herbert B. Tully
Treasurer, Alison Amonette
VP Treasurer and CFO, James D. Crawford
Auditors: Hood&Strong

LOCATIONS

HQ: WILBUR-ELLIS COMPANY
345 CALIFORNIA ST FL 27, SAN FRANCISCO, CA 941042644
Phone: 4157724000
Web: WWW.WILBUR-ELLIS.COM

PRODUCTS/OPERATIONS

Selected Products and Services

Agribusiness Division
- Agricultural chemicals
- Fertilizers
- Fungicides
- Herbicides
- Insecticides
- Machinery
- Pesticides
- Seed protectants
- Seed treatments
- Sprayers
- Supply-chain management

Connell Bros. Division
- Industrial chemicals

Feed Division
- Aquaculture products
- Feed ingredients
- Food oils
- Forage products
- Pet food

Professional Products
- Forestry
  - Fungicides
  - Herbicides
- Golf
  - Fungicides
- Landscape
  - Fungicides
- Nursery/Greenhouse
  - Fungicides
- Vegetation Management
  - Selective and nonselective growth regulators

COMPETITORS

ADM
AGRI Industries
Ag Processing Inc.
Agrium
Andersons
BASF SE
Bayer CropScience
CF Industries
CHS
Cargill
Dow AgroSciences
DuPont Agriculture
Frontier Agriculture
GROWMARK
Goulding Chemicals
Ingredion
JR Simplot
Land O' Lakes Purina Feed
Monsanto Company
Southern States

HISTORICAL FINANCIALS

Company Type: Private

Income Statement FYE: December 31

	REVENUE ($ mil.)	NET INCOME ($ mil.)	NET PROFIT MARGIN	EMPLOYEES
12/11	2,812	0	—	3,200
12/10	2,342	0	—	—
12/09	0	0	—	—
12/00	1,100	0	—	—
Annual Growth	8.9%	—	—	—

WILDLIFE CONSERVATION SOCIETY

From Congo gorillas to humpback whales off the coast of Gabon all life is worth conserving to the Wildlife Conservation Society (WCS). The group founded in 1895 works to protect wildlife and lands throughout the world and to instill in humans a concern about nature. The not-for-profit organization operates New York City's Bronx Zoo New York Aquarium Central Park Zoo Prospect Park Zoo and the Queens Zoo. WCS's environmental education programs are used in US schools as well as those in other nations. The society has ongoing efforts in more than 60 countries to protect endangered species and ecosystems. About a quarter of the funding for its work comes from visitors at its handful of parks.

Geographic Reach

The society operates country programs across four continents including Africa Asia Latin America and North America. It boasts ongoing efforts in 60-plus countries.

Operations

WCS manages about 500 conservation projects nationwide and works to educate millions of visitors at its handful of living institutions: the Bronx Zoo New York Aquarium Central Park Zoo Prospect Park Zoo and Queens Zoo. As part of its operations WCS manages more than 200 million acres of protected lands globally and retains a staff of 200-plus scientists.

Financial Performance

Despite the anemic economy in recent years WCS has logged healthy attendance of about 4 million visitors across its five New York City parks. As Americans chose to vacation at home WCS has benefitted. With those visitors came a noteworthy boost in income from gate admissions exhibits and contributions from visitor services such as food merchandising and parking. Attendance-driven revenues reach more than $50 million.

The conservation group points to its operational diversity for being able to keep its head above water when funding from the state and other entities it had relied on had slimmed.

Sales and Marketing

WCS is working to ramp up its construction. The group's revised Master Plan includes enhancements at the Bronx Zoo's C.V. Starr Science Campus with the Special Care Unit and LaMattina Wildlife Ambassador Center the Queens Zoo's jaguar exhibit and the Ocean Wonders exhibit.

During the past decade WCS has spent $243 million to fund physical plant improvements on its five campuses. They were financed through grants from New York City and the federal government private gifts and the proceeds from WCS's Series 2004 tax-exempt bond issue.

Company Background

To stay true to its mission and remain a viable wildlife supporter WCS was forced to make some cuts in 2010. It opted cease publication of its namesake magazine Wildlife Conservation which had cost WCS $1.4 million to produce in 2009. Besides also eliminating personnel WCS cut its capital expenditures from $33.8 million in 2009 to a noteworthy $13.9 million in 2010 by putting off many planned improvements at its parks.

EXECUTIVES

Executive Vice President Public Affairs, John Calvelli
Executive Vice President Conservation & Science, John G. Robinson
Executive Vice President for Administration & Chief Financial Officer, Patricia Calabrese
Executive Vice President Director Zoos and Aquarium, James J. Breheny
EVP Global Resources, Bertina Ceccarelli
President Chief Executive Officer, Cristi Ã .Ặn Samper
Exec V Pres-gen Dir, Robert A Cook Mpa
Vice President & General Curator, Patrick R Thomas
Vice President Global Program Development, Susan Tressler
Vice President Species Conservation, Elizabeth L Bennett
Senior Vice President Global Conservation Program, Joshua R Ginsberg
V Pres, Linda I Krueger
Senior Vice President And General, Christopher McKenzie
Vp Budget And Financial Planning, Sarah Gillman
Vice President And Comptroller, Patty Callabri
Svp Business Development And Treasurer, Mitchel Greene
Vice President Planning Design, John Quinn
Co Director, Rosario Painter
Vice President Finance And Controller, Ken Getty
Senior Vice President Business Services, Robert Moskovitz
Secretary, Andrew H Tisch
Treasurer, John N Irwin, age 57
Assistant Treasu, Sean Cover

LOCATIONS

HQ: WILDLIFE CONSERVATION SOCIETY
2300 SOUTHERN BLVD, BRONX, NY 10460-1090
Phone: 718-220-5100
Web: WWW.BRONXZOO.COM

PRODUCTS/OPERATIONS

Selected Areas of Focus

Climate change
Natural resource exploitation
Sustainable development of human livelihoods

HISTORICAL FINANCIALS

Company Type: Private

Income Statement

FYE: June 30

	REVENUE ($ mil.)	NET INCOME ($ mil.)	NET PROFIT MARGIN	EMPLOYEES
06/11	206	0	0.0%	4,000
06/10	228	9	4.1%	—
06/09	197	0	—	—
06/06	227	52	22.9%	—
Annual Growth	(2.0%)	(74.4%)	—	—

2011 Year-End Financials

Debt ratio: —
Return on equity: —
Cash ($ mil.): 65
Current ratio: 0.60
Long-term debt ($ mil.): —
Dividends
Yield: —
Payout: —
Market value ($ mil.): —

WILLIAM MARSH RICE UNIVERSITY INC

You have to be as wise as an owl to attend Rice University and have really good SAT scores. Often referred to as the "Ivy League of the South" Rice – with mascot "Sammy the Owl" –consistently appears at the top of college academic rankings including those published by U.S. News & World Report. The private university has an enrollment of more than 6000 and about 1100 full-time part-time and adjunct faculty members (giving it a student-teacher ratio of about 6:1). Rice offers programs through eight schools in areas such as engineering computer science economics music and architecture. The university opened in 1912 with funds from the estate of William Marsh Rice.

Operations Rice's research programs span a dizzying array of disciplines that include energy health and tax policy science and technology conflict resolution and border policy. About 80% of Rice students are from the US including about 45% from Texas. Strategy The school is in the process of increasing the number of its undergraduates to 3800 students while still maintaining its very low student-faculty ratio. The change which began in 2008 and will take place over 10 years could involve building two new residential colleges the expansion of existing colleges and a possible Rice-affiliated off-campus facility to house both undergraduate and graduate students.

EXECUTIVES

Chair, James W. Crownover
President, David W. (Dave) Leebron, age 59
VP Finance, Kathy Collins
Provost, George L. McLendon
Vice Provost Information Technology, Kamran Khan
Vice Provost and University Librarian, Sara Lowman
VP Administration, Kevin E. Kirby
VP Enrollment, Chris Mu?oz
VP Public Affairs, Linda L. Thrane
VP Resource Development, Darrow Zeidenstein
General Counsel, Richard A. Zansitis
Dean Wiess School of Natural Sciences, Daniel Carson
Dean Jesse H. Jones Graduate School of Business, William Glick
Dean Undergraduates, John Hutchinson
Dean Susanne M. Glasscock School of Continuing Studies, Mary B. McIntire
Dean School of Social Sciences, Lyn Ragsdale
Dean Graduate and Postdoctoral Studies, Paula Sanders
Dean School of Humanities, Nicolas Shumway
Dean George R. Brown School of Engineering, Edwin Thomas
Dean School of Architecture, Sarah M. Whiting
Dean Shepherd School of Music, Robert Yekovich
Auditors: PricewaterhouseCoopersLLP

LOCATIONS

HQ: WILLIAM MARSH RICE UNIVERSITY INC
6100 MAIN ST, HOUSTON, TX 77005-1827
Phone: 713-348-4055
Web: WWW.EXPLORE.RICE.EDU

PRODUCTS/OPERATIONS

Selected Departments and Interdisciplinary Programs

Air Force Science
Ancient Mediterranean Civilizations
Anthropology
Applied Physics Graduate Program
Architecture
Art History
Asian Studies
Bioengineering
Biosciences
Center for Digital Learning and Scholarship
Center for the Study of Languages
Chemical Engineering
Chemistry
Civil and Environmental Engineering
Classical Studies
Cognitive Sciences
Computational and Applied Mathematics
Computer Science
Earth Science
Economics
Education
Education Certification
Electrical and Computer Engineering
English
Environmental Analysis and Decision Making
Environmental Studies
French Studies
German and Slavic Studies
Hispanic Studies
History
Kinesiology
Leadership Rice
Lifetime Physical Activity Program
Linguistics
Management and Accounting
Managerial Studies
Master of Liberal Studies
Mathematics
Mechanical Engineering and Materials Science
Medieval Studies
Military Science
Music
Nanoscale Physics
Naval Science
Neurosciences
Philosophy
Physics and Astronomy
Policy Studies
Political Science
Psychology
Religious Studies
Sociology
Statistics
Subsurface Geoscience
The Program for the Study of Women and Gender

HISTORICAL FINANCIALS

Company Type: Private

Income Statement FYE: June 30

	REVENUE ($ mil.)	NET INCOME ($ mil.)	NET PROFIT MARGIN	EMPLOYEES
06/13	568	459	80.9%	2,600
06/12	551	(33)	—	—
06/10	550	695	126.2%	—
06/10	519	189	36.5%	—
Annual Growth	3.0%	34.4%	—	—

2013 Year-End Financials

Debt ratio: —
Return on equity: 80.90%
Cash ($ mil.): 7
Current ratio: —
Long-term debt ($ mil.): —
Dividends
Yield: —
Payout: —
Market value ($ mil.): —

WILSON TRUCKING CORPORATION

EXECUTIVES

President, C. L. (Chuck) Wilson
EVP, T. Guy Wilson
EVP and CFO, J. M. Herndon
Director Information Systems, L. A. Combs
VP Sales and Marketing, D. B. Collier
VP Customer Service, A. L. Branch
VP Safety and Human Resources, F. J. Bailey Jr.
Senior Director Corporate Contracts, E. L. Guffey
VP Operations Region 1, J. R. Clark Jr.
VP Operations Region 2, J. W. Saunders
Secretary, R. E. East
Treasurer, C. E. Baldwin
Director Fleet Services, J. Lane
VP Operations, M. P. Monroe
VP Pricing and Revenue Management, W. L. McGinley
Regional Sales Director, Donald C. Maguire

LOCATIONS

HQ: WILSON TRUCKING CORPORATION
137 WILSON BLVD, FISHERSVILLE, VA 22939
Phone: 5409493200
Web: WWW.WILSONTRUCKING.COM

COMPETITORS

AAA Cooper Transportation
Arkansas Best
Averitt Express
Benton Express
Con-way Freight
Estes Express
FedEx Freight
Old Dominion Freight
Saia Inc.
Southeastern Freight Lines
UPS Freight
YRC Worldwide

HISTORICAL FINANCIALS

Company Type: Private

Income Statement FYE: December 31

	REVENUE ($ mil.)	NET INCOME ($ mil.)	NET PROFIT MARGIN	EMPLOYEES
12/12	150	(6)	—	1,400
12/11	136	(1)	—	—
12/10	125	(2)	—	—
12/09	122	0	—	—
Annual Growth	7.1%	—	—	—

2012 Year-End Financials

Debt ratio: —
Return on equity: (-4.40%)
Cash ($ mil.): 0
Current ratio: 1.90
Long-term debt ($ mil.): —
Dividends
Yield: —
Payout: —
Market value ($ mil.): —

WINCHESTER MEDICAL CENTER AUXILIARY INC.

Winchester Medical Center is the flagship facility of Valley Health System a not-for-profit health care organization serving the residents of Virginia's Shenandoah Valley. The full-service general hospital which has more than 400 inpatient beds serves as a regional referral center for the system's smaller community hospitals. It provides medical services across a number of specialties (including neuroscience heart disease and cancer) and offers surgical diagnostic and rehabilitative care. The hospital's campus also features outpatient diagnostic and surgical facilities an adult psychiatric facility and doctors' offices. Winchester Medical Center opened its doors in 1903.

The hospital opened a new $160 million tower in 2012 that replaces many of the aging equipment and parts of the building that were nearly two decades old. The tower opened in stages starting in 2009. The site includes a Heart & Vascular Center and a clinical lab expansion an expanded Emergency Department and a nearly 50-bed critical care unit. It also includes a larger labor and delivery unit and an all-private room Neonatal ICU increasing Winchester Medical Center's licensed beds from 411 to 445.

The new tower was designed to give medical providers and their patients more room and work spaces for better patient care. The three year construction project produced more than 350000 square feet of new space and 78000 square feet of renovated space. The two top floors of the North Tower are shelled for future growth.

Winchester Medical Center began with with just 36-beds; today it is a full-service referral center offering a range of medical surgical diagnostic and rehabilitative services to roughly 400000 residents in the tri-state area.

EXECUTIVES

SVP and CFO, J. Craig Lewis
Chairman, Harry F. Byrd III
President and CEO, Reese Jackson
President Medical Staff, Sherif Kaiser
Vice President of Operations, Tonya Smith
Vice President of Information Systems & Chief Information Officer, Joan Roscoe
Vice President of Clinical Operations, George Goldman
Vice President of Human Resources, Elizabeth Savage-Tracy

LOCATIONS

HQ: WINCHESTER MEDICAL CENTER AUXILIARY INC.
190 CAMPUS BLVD STE 220, WINCHESTER, VA 22601-2872
Phone: 540-536-8000
Web: WWW.VALLEYHEALTHLINK.COM

COMPETITORS

Ascension Health
Carilion Clinic
Fauquier Hospital
Georgetown University Hospital
HCA
Inova
Johns Hopkins Health System
Loudoun Healthcare
Martha Jefferson Hospital
MedStar Health
Novant Health
Prince William Health System
Providence Hospital (Washington DC)
Rockingham Memorial Hospital
Sentara Northern Virginia Medical Center

HISTORICAL FINANCIALS

Company Type: Private

Income Statement FYE: December 31

	REVENUE ($ mil.)	NET INCOME ($ mil.)	NET PROFIT MARGIN	EMPLOYEES
12/07	453	48	10.8%	2,046
12/06	413	61	14.9%	—
12/05	134	0	0.0%	—
Annual Growth	83.9%	40861.4%	—	—

2007 Year-End Financials

Debt ratio: —
Return on equity: 10.80%
Cash ($ mil.): 18
Current ratio: 1.70
Long-term debt ($ mil.): —
Dividends
Yield: —
Payout: —
Market value ($ mil.): —

WINDRIVER GRAIN L.L.C.

LOCATIONS

HQ: WINDRIVER GRAIN L.L.C.
2810 E US HIGHWAY 50, GARDEN CITY, KS 678468528
Phone: 6202752101
Web: WWW.WINDRIVERGRAIN.COM

HISTORICAL FINANCIALS

Company Type: Private

Income Statement FYE: April 30

	REVENUE ($ mil.)	NET INCOME ($ mil.)	NET PROFIT MARGIN	EMPLOYEES
04/14	286	5	1.9%	16
04/13	370	3	0.8%	—
04/12	313	4	1.3%	—
04/11	264	0	—	—
Annual Growth	2.7%	—	—	—

2014 Year-End Financials

Debt ratio: —
Return on equity: 1.90%
Cash ($ mil.): 1
Current ratio: 0.30
Long-term debt ($ mil.): —
Dividends
Yield: —
Payout: —
Market value ($ mil.): —

WINSTON & STRAWN LLP

Over the years Winston & Strawn has developed a reputation for its work in litigation and labor and employment law but the firm's practices encompass a wide range of specialties from antitrust to intellectual property to tax. The firm has around 1000 lawyers in about 15 offices in the US Europe and Asia. Clients have included Abbott Laboratories McDonald's Yahoo Wells Fargo and Philip Morris USA. Winston & Strawn was founded in 1853; since 2000 it has expanded by taking in firms such as New York-based Whitman Breed Abbott & Morgan and San Francisco-based Murphy Sheneman Julian & Rogers.

Geographic Reach

Winston & Strawn has offices in Beijing Charlotte Chicago Geneva Hong Kong Houston London Los Angeles Moscow New York Newark Paris San Francisco Shanghai and Washington D.C.

EXECUTIVES

Managing Partner New York, Michael S. Elkin
Managing Partner Washington D.C., Thomas L. Mills
COO, Scot J. Farrell
Managing Partner San Francisco, Charles S. (Chuck) Birenbaum
Managing Partner Paris, Vincent Sol
Partner Chicago, Thomas P. Fitzgerald, age 57
Managing Partner London, Thomas J. Benz
CFO, David S. (Dave) McDonald
Managing Partner Chicago, Lawrence R. (Larry) Desideri
Managing Partner Los Angeles, Laura R. Petroff
Managing Partner Moscow, Nikolai B. Krylov
Managing Partner Houston, Stephen H. (Steve) Cagle
Managing Partner Beijing, Jem Z. Li
Managing Partner Charlotte, T. Thomas Cottingham
Managing Partner Geneva, Ricardo E. Ugarte
Managing Partner Asia, David G. Hall-Jones
Chief Information Officer, David Cunningham
Legal Secretary, Mary Lever
Legal Secretary, Cynthia A Linn
Legal Secretary, Gladys Pacheco
Legal Secretary, Nina Alexander
Legal Secretary, Dolores Kaponyas
Legal Secretary, Gwendolyn McRae
Legal Secretary, Lorrie Nicpon
Legal Secretary, Marian Lotito
Legal Secretary, Patricia Finnegan
Legal Secretary, Rebecca Garib
Legal Secretary, Carol Ortiz
Legal Secretary, Lucy Fera
Legal Secretary, Patricia Waters
Vice President, Desiree Ripo
Legal Secretary, Barbara Sommars
Legal Secretary, Valerie Walker
Legal Secretary, Julie Brittis
Legal Secretary, Maria Villano
Legal Secretary, Diana Vidutis
Legal Secretary, Robin Salyer
Legal Secretary, Hilbania Dejesus
Legal Secretary, Grace Barit
Legal Secretary, Kim Pietrucha
Legal Secretary, Peggy Hufford
Legal Secretary, Jane Sergi
Legal Secretary, Deborah Minucci
Legal Secretary, Debra Elliott
Legal Secretary, Diane Sorensen
Legal Secretary, Laura Marmo
Legal Secretary, Mary Davies
Legal Secretary, Nancy Wagner-tawil
Legal Secretary, John Markasevic
Legal Secretary, Rosetta Triolo
Legal Secretary, Bridget Giuca
Legal Secretary, Glenda Thomas
Legal Secretary, Gerda Goettel
Division Vice President Field Operations, Melissa Nocera
Legal Secretary, Heidi Hammon
Legal Secretary, Jacqueline Hammer
Legal Secretary, Karen Overman
Legal Secretary, Linda Bernardi
Legal Secretary, Joanne Michalski
Legal Secretary, Fanny Tsui
Legal Secretary, Paula Trimble
Legal Secretary, Joyce Kuhns
Legal Secretary, Nancy Posadas
Legal Secretary, Damarys Ocasio
Legal Secretary, Carol McBride
Legal Secretary, Lisa Schuh
Legal Secretary, Gwen Chavez
Legal Secretary, Joy Aberdeen
Legal Secretary, Jennifer Jaksinick
Legal Secretary, Maria Follenius
Legal Secretary, Sandra Bauske
Legal Secretary, Lori Whitley
Legal Secretary, Keith Schumacher
Executive Legal Secretary, Elizabeth Mitchell
Vice President Media Planning And Research, Laurie Deprete
Vice President Legal, Sabrina Schmitt
Legal Secretary, Nancy Hanzalik
Legal Secretary, Patty Brown
Legal Secretary, Mary Anne Hagedorn
Legal Secretary, Pamela Al Amin
Legal Secretary, Eleanor Morrell
Legal Secretary, Ruth Vega
Legal Secretary, Kathleen Boyd
Legal Secretary, Kimberly Pietrucha
Legal Secretary, Lorene Wilson
Legal Secretary, Peter Struble
Legal Secretary, Ann Newman
Legal Secretary, Carrie Lullo
Legal Secretary, Dyhan Slaughter
Senior Chairman, James R. Thompson, age 77
Chairman Litigation Department, Dan K. Webb, age 67

LOCATIONS

HQ: WINSTON & STRAWN LLP
35 W WACKER DR STE 4200, CHICAGO, IL 60601-1695
Phone: 312-558-5600
Web: WWW.WINSTONANDSTRAWN.COM

Selected Office Locations

Chicago
Beijing
Geneva
Hong Kong
Houston
London
Los Angeles
Moscow
New York
Newark
Paris
San Francisco
Shanghai
Washington DC

PRODUCTS/OPERATIONS

Selected Practice Areas

Advertising marketing promotions
Antitrust and trade regulation
Appellate and critical motions
Construction law
E-discovery and electronic information
Employee benefits and executive compensation
Energy
English law
Environmental law
Finance
Financial services
French and European Union law
Government contracts
Government relations
Health care law
Higher education law
Intellectual property
International arbitration
International trade
Labor and employment
Litigation
Maritime and admiralty
Private equity
Real estate
Restructuring and insolvency
Securities/M&A
Tax
Trusts and estates

COMPETITORS

Baker & McKenzie	Mayer Brown
Cravath Swaine	McDermott Will & Emery
Jenner & Block	Ogletree Deakins
Jones Day	Sidley Austin
Kirkland & Ellis	Skadden Arps

HISTORICAL FINANCIALS

Company Type: Private

Income Statement FYE: January 31

	REVENUE ($ mil.)	NET INCOME ($ mil.)	NET PROFIT MARGIN	EMPLOYEES
01/12	754	258	34.3%	1,928
01/11	717	238	33.3%	—
01/09	0	0		
01/08	697	228	32.7%	—
Annual Growth	2.0%	3.2%	—	—

2012 Year-End Financials

Debt ratio: —
Return on equity: 34.30%
Cash ($ mil.): 115
Current ratio: —
Long-term debt ($ mil.): —

Dividends
Yield: —
Payout: —
Market value ($ mil.): —

WINTER HAVEN HOSPITAL INC.

Winter Haven Hospital serves eastern Polk County in central Florida with general medical surgical and emergency care. The health care facility also offers specialty care in areas such as cancer heart disease stroke and a memory clinic for patients suffering from dementia and other memory disorders. The hospital's Regency Medical Center provides maternity and other health care services for women and newborns. Outpatient care is provided through an ambulatory surgery and diagnostic center and several community clinics. Winter Haven Hospital is owned by the local not-for-profit Mid-Florida Medical Services; it was founded in 1926 as a charter hospital.

Change in Company Type

After determining that it needs to be part of a larger health care organization to compete in the changing marketplace in 2012 Winter Haven Hospital agreed to be acquired by Tampa-based BayCare Health System. If the deal goes through Winter Haven could become part of BayCare Health by mid-2013.

Geographic Reach

Winter Haven Hospital serves the roughly 660000 people in Polk County and Highlands County.

Operations

With nearly 530 licensed beds Winter Haven Hospital's main campus is the largest of the two inpatient facilities in its health care system; the other is its Regency Center for Women and Infants. Other facilities include a community blood center the ambulatory surgery center and half a dozen family health centers. Together the medical provider's facilities handle some 17000 inpatient visits per year as well as 60000 outpatients and 1600 births.

Winter Haven Hospital has more than 300 physicians on its staff providing a range of specialty services. It is affiliated with the University of Florida College of Medicine and Shands Healthcare in areas including oncology and urology. It also partnered with USF Polytechnic to expand its mental health services in 2012.

Ownership

The hospital though a division of Mid-Florida Medical Services is a locally owned and operated not-for-profit organization. It is governed by an independent Board of Trustees made up of local business and civic leaders who serve without pay.

EXECUTIVES

Chairman, Robert C. (Bob) Carter
President Chief Executive Officer, Lance W. Anastasio
VP and Corporate Counsel, John Parman
VP and Chief Nursing Officer, Mary Jo Schreiber
Treasurer and Trustee, Don Ingram
First Vice Chairman, Charles W. McPherson
Second Vice Chairman, Brian K. Swain
Chairman, Eric Adamson
Vice President of Medical Affairs, Donald Gale
Vice President, Debra Nieto-Wolf
Director of Research, Sally Raiden
VP CFO, Dave MacDougall
Trustee, Richard Honer
Trustee, Mark Bostick
Treasurer and Trustee, Don Ingram
First Vice Chairman, Charles W. McPherson
Trustee, Kelly Gray-Eurom
Second Vice Chairman, Brian K. Swain
Chairman, Eric Adamson
Auditors: PricewaterhouseCoopersLLP

LOCATIONS

HQ: WINTER HAVEN HOSPITAL INC.
200 AVENUE F NE, WINTER HAVEN, FL 33881-4193
Phone: 863-293-1121
Web: WWW.WINTERHAVENHOSPITAL.ORG

PRODUCTS/OPERATIONS

Selected Services and Centers

Ambulatory Surgery & Diagnostic Center
Bostick Heart Center
Cassidy Cancer Center
Clinical Laboratory
Community Blood Center
Community Calendar
Community Education
Diabetes Center
Emergency Department
Family Health Centers
Health Connection
Mental Health Services
Patient Services/Nursing
Professional Education
Radiation Oncology
Regency Center for Women and Infants
Rehabilitation Services
Respiratory Care Services
Stroke Center
Urology Care
Winter Haven Hospital Foundation

COMPETITORS

Adventist Health System Sunbelt Healthcare
Bayfront Health
Catholic Health East
DeSoto Memorial
Florida Hospital Tampa Bay Division
HCA
Health Management Associates
Heart & Family Health Institute
Iasis Healthcare
Lakeland Regional Medical Center
Lee Memorial
Manatee Memorial Hospital
Northside Hospital and Heart Institute
Oak Hill Hospital
Orlando Health
Sarasota Memorial Hospital
St. Joseph' s-Baptist Health Care
Tampa General Hospital
Tenet Healthcare

HISTORICAL FINANCIALS

Company Type: Private

Income Statement FYE: September 30

	REVENUE ($ mil.)	NET INCOME ($ mil.)	NET PROFIT MARGIN	EMPLOYEES
09/12	253	11	4.6%	1,480
09/11	262	(0)	—	—
09/10	278	0	0.0%	—
09/09	283	(0)	—	—
Annual Growth	(3.7%)	—	—	—

2012 Year-End Financials

Debt ratio: —
Return on equity: 4.60%
Cash ($ mil.): 14
Current ratio: 1.40
Long-term debt ($ mil.): —

Dividends
Yield: —
Payout: —
Market value ($ mil.): —

WINTHROP-UNIVERSITY HOSPITAL INC

From providing it to teaching it Winthrop-University Hospital is focused on health care. The medical center boasts some 590 beds and offers a full range of acute and tertiary health care services. Services include pediatric women's health and cancer care as well as home health services. Winthrop-University Hospital is also a leading provider of cardiovascular surgeries in the region. The hospital is a member of Winthrop-South Nassau University Health System along with sister facility South Nassau Communities Hospital. Founded in 1896 Winthrop-University Hospital serves as a teaching hospital for the SUNY at Stony Brook School of Medicine.

Geographic Reach

Based in Mineola New York Winthrop-University Hospital serves patients in New York's Nassau Suffolk and Queens counties.

Operations

Specialty divisions within the Winthrop-University Hospital include the Minstretta Emergency Diagnostic Imaging Center and a pediatric emergency unit both located within the emergency department as well as centers for dialysis digestive disorders neuroscience and diabetes education. Other specialty programs include orthopedics sports medicine wound healing radiosurgery (CyberKnife) and bariatric surgery. Overall the Winthrop-University Hospital logs more than 66000 emergency visits and 33000-plus inpatient visits each year.

Winthrop-University Hospital is also a member of the Long Island Health Network which comprises 10 hospitals in Nassau and Suffolk counties. Member hospitals include Brookhaven Memorial Hospital Medical Center John T. Mather Memorial Hospital and South Nassau Communities Hospital among others.

Strategy

The hospital has earned the title as a New York State-designated regional trauma center employing some 1500 nurses and another 1500 medical staff members. The first hospital on Long Island to acquire the daVinci Si HD Surgical System Winthrop-University Hospital is one of the top hospitals for minimally invasive surgeries. It is also the first hospital in the New York City metropolitan area to perform CyberKnife radiosurgery procedures. In 2012 it expanded specialist services in fields including orthopedics neurology and cardiac care procedures.

To expand its outpatient care services to community residents the hospital opened a family dental practice location in 2013. The previous year Winthrop-University Hospital launched an $80 million construction project to add a research and academic center on the main hospital campus.

EXECUTIVES

VP External Affairs and Development, John P. Broder
VP Administration, Dennis Sheridan
Senior Vice President Human Resources and Organizational Development, Stacey Pfeffer
Vice Chairman, Joan Cox
Chairman, Charles M. Strain
President and CEO, John F. Collins
Secretary, James J. Daly
Vice Chairman, John H. Treiber
Assistant VP Case Management and Quality Metrics, Ann Hanford
VP Administration, James S. Flaherty
Senior Vice President Administration, Barbara L. Kohart-Kleine
Senior Vice President Chief Nursing Officer, Valerie Terzano
Assistant VP Patient Financial Services, Amy Wolin
Assistant VP Materials Management, John H. Pfeifer
Assistant VP Risk Management and Insurance Services, Bruce M. Cohn
Vice Chairman, Kevin T. Curran
Treasurer, Palmira M. Cataliotti
VP Engineering and Facilities, Joseph Burke
VP Marketing and Advertising, J. Edmund (Ed) Keating
Program Director Message, Lucy O. Macina
Director, John T. Lane, age 71
Director, Patrick K. Long
Vice Chairman, Joan Cox
Director, Edward Travaglianti
Director, John F. Aloia
Director, James F. Campbell
Director, Maureen E. Clancy
Director, Theodora Hooton
Director, Joseph Mancino
Director, Ronald H. McGlynn
Director, Nancy Nammack
Director, Richard A. Newhouse Jr.
Director, Veronica Renken
Director, Charles Ruoff
Director, Harriette P. Thayer
Vice Chairman, John H. Treiber
Director, Shepard T. Poole
Vice Chairman, Kevin T. Curran
Director, Eric Krasnoff
Director, John D. Miller
Director, Yvonne M. Mowatt

LOCATIONS

HQ: WINTHROP-UNIVERSITY HOSPITAL INC
259 1ST ST, MINEOLA, NY 11501-3987
Phone: 516-663-0333
Web: WWW.WINTHROP.ORG

PRODUCTS/OPERATIONS

Selected Services

Angioplasty
Arthritis
Asthma
Bariatric Surgery
Breast Cancer
Cancer Care
Cardiology
Childhood Cancer
Children's Health
Clinical Trials
CyberKnife
Diabetes

Dialysis
Digestive Care
Education
Emergency Dept.
Family Care
Gastroenterology
Heart Care
Home Health Care
Hyperbarics
Joint Replacement
Kidney Disease
Lung Cancer
Lung Care
Maternity
Neurology
Neurosciences
Neurosurgery
OB/GYN
Open Heart Surgery
Orthopedics
Pediatric Cancer
Pediatrics
Physicians
Prostate Cancer
Pulmonary Care
Research
Sleep Disorders
Stroke
Trauma Center
Urology
Weight Loss

COMPETITORS

Barnabas Health
Bronx-Lebanon Hospital
Catholic Health East
Catholic Health Services of Long Island
Continuum Health Partners
Franklin Hospital
HealthSouth
Long Beach Medical Center
Long Island Jewish Medical Center
Lutheran HealthCare
MediSys Health Network
New York City Health and Hospitals
NewYork-Presbyterian Healthcare
Newark Beth Israel Medical Center
North Shore-Long Island Jewish Health System
Queens-Long Island Medical Group
SUNY Downstate

HISTORICAL FINANCIALS

Company Type: Private

Income Statement FYE: December 31

	REVENUE ($ mil.)	NET INCOME ($ mil.)	NET PROFIT MARGIN	EMPLOYEES
12/08	725	(134)	—	6,000
12/07	669	0	0.0%	—
12/06	610	15	2.5%	—
12/05	0	0	—	—
Annual Growth	—	—	—	—

2008 Year-End Financials

Debt ratio: —
Return on equity: (-18.50%)
Cash ($ mil.): 74
Current ratio: 0.80
Long-term debt ($ mil.): —
Dividends
Yield: —
Payout: —
Market value ($ mil.): —

WITHLACOOCHEE RIVER ELECTRIC COOPERATIVE INC

Withlacoochee River Electric Cooperative keeps the power flowing to the residences and businesses of more than 200360 member-owners in five counties along the central Florida Gulf Coast. The power distribution utility which was originally set up in 1941 receives wholesale generation and transmission services from the Seminole Electric Cooperative. Withlacoochee River Electric a non-profit organization returns any funds remaining at the end of each year to its membership. The cooperative has returned more than $190 million to its member-owners.

Pushing green energy and recycling in 2008 the company reported that in addition to supplying reliable electricity it was seeking to reduce carbon emissions through providing its members with compact fluorescent bulbs. That year Withlacoochee River Electric also recycled more than 442000 pounds of materials installed a 3.15 kV solar panel display at its corporate headquarters in Dade City and added more than 3220 new customers.

"Withlacoochee River" was chosen as the name for the organization because the river was the common link for the cooperative's original service region (Citrus Hernando and Pasco counties).

EXECUTIVES

General Manager and EVP, Billy E. Brown

LOCATIONS

HQ: WITHLACOOCHEE RIVER ELECTRIC COOPERATIVE INC
14651 21ST ST, DADE CITY, FL 33523-2920
Phone: 352-567-5133
Web: WWW.WREC.NET

PRODUCTS/OPERATIONS

2008 Sales

	$ mil.	% of total
% of total		
Residential		71
Commercial		25
Other		4
Total		**100**

HISTORICAL FINANCIALS

Company Type: Private

Income Statement FYE: December 31

	REVENUE ($ mil.)	NET INCOME ($ mil.)	NET PROFIT MARGIN	EMPLOYEES
12/12	421	25	6.1%	458
12/11	423	28	6.7%	—
12/08	0	0	45.8%	—
12/08	408	0	—	—
Annual Growth	0.7%	—	—	—

2012 Year-End Financials

Debt ratio: —
Return on equity: 6.10%
Cash ($ mil.): 192
Current ratio: 0.50
Long-term debt ($ mil.): —
Dividends
Yield: —
Payout: —
Market value ($ mil.): —

WOLVERINE POWER SUPPLY COOPERATIVE INC.

EXECUTIVES

VP Engineering and Operations, Danny R. Janway
President and CEO, Eric D. Baker
EVP, Craig A. Borr
VP Human Resources, Craig S. Borton
Staff Attorney, Brian E. Valice
VP Finance Accounting and Risk Management, Richard R. Kehl
VP Generation, Daniel H. (Dan) DeCoeur
VP Rates and Administrative Services, Kimberly B. Molitor
VP Power Supply and Energy Control, Michael P. (Peter) Chase
Executive Assistant, Dawn Coon
Chairman, Frederick F. Vermeersch
Vice Chairman, Jerry Akers
CFO, Janet L. Kass
Chief Compliance Officer, Michelle Denike
Director, John Olson
Director, Glen Alsobrooks
Director, Dave Williamson
Director, Laverne Hansen
Director, Allen Bruder
Director, Wayne Swiler
Vice Chairman, Jerry Akers
Director, Jack Pope
Director, Dale Farrier
Director, Mike McDonald

LOCATIONS

HQ: WOLVERINE POWER SUPPLY COOPERATIVE INC.
10125 W WATERGATE RD, CADILLAC, MI 496018458
Phone: 2317755700
Web: WWW.WPSCI.COM

COMPETITORS

ITC Holdings Corp.
Lansing Board of Water and Light
Midland Cogeneration Venture

HISTORICAL FINANCIALS

Company Type: Private

Income Statement FYE: December 31

	REVENUE ($ mil.)	NET INCOME ($ mil.)	NET PROFIT MARGIN	EMPLOYEES
12/10	294	(16)	—	110
12/09	256	13	5.2%	—
12/07	164	0	0.0%	—
Annual Growth	21.3%	—	—	—

2010 Year-End Financials

Debt ratio: —
Return on equity: (-5.80%)
Cash ($ mil.): 2
Current ratio: 0.30
Long-term debt ($ mil.): —
Dividends
Yield: —
Payout: —
Market value ($ mil.): —

WOMAN"S HOSPITAL FOUNDATION INC

LOCATIONS

HQ: WOMAN' ' S HOSPITAL FOUNDATION INC
100 WOMANS WAY, BATON ROUGE, LA 708175100
Phone: 2259271300
Web: WWW.WOMANS.ORG

PRODUCTS/OPERATIONS

Selected Services

Audiology
Breast Care
Breastfeeding
Cancer Care
Childbirth
Day Spa
Diabetes Care
Fertility
Fitness Club
Genetics
Health Screenings
Heart Health
Mammography
Metabolic Health
Nutrition
Philanthropy
Pregnancy
Social Services
Weight Loss

HISTORICAL FINANCIALS

Company Type: Private

Income Statement FYE: September 30

	REVENUE ($ mil.)	NET INCOME ($ mil.)	NET PROFIT MARGIN	EMPLOYEES
09/13	217	(12)	—	1,850
09/12	217	22	10.3%	—
09/11	219	46	21.0%	—
Annual Growth	(0.4%)	—	—	—

WOODFORD OIL COMPANY

LOCATIONS

HQ: WOODFORD OIL COMPANY
13TH & LIVINGSTON ST, ELKINS, WV 26241
Phone: 3046362688
Web: WWW.WOODFORDCOMPANIES.COM

HISTORICAL FINANCIALS

Company Type: Private

Income Statement FYE: December 31

	REVENUE ($ mil.)	NET INCOME ($ mil.)	NET PROFIT MARGIN	EMPLOYEES
12/07	227	1	0.6%	50
12/06	202	1	0.6%	—
12/05	167	0	0.4%	—
12/04	86	0	—	—
Annual Growth	38.0%	—	—	—

2007 Year-End Financials

Debt ratio: —
Return on equity: 0.60%
Cash ($ mil.): 2
Current ratio: 1.20
Long-term debt ($ mil.): —
Dividends
Yield: —
Payout: —
Market value ($ mil.): —

WORLD FINER FOODS INC

Fine food is quite a find for this company and its customers. World Finer Foods distributes more than 900 specialty food items to US supermarkets and gourmet food stores. Its inventory boasts some 40 brands including Blanchard & Blanchard La Vie Mrs. Leeper's Pasta and Panni. The company also markets its own food products under such names as DaVinci London Pub Pritikin and Reese. Its InterNatural Foods unit represents its natural foods division while its Liberty Richter division distributes domestic and imported gourmet food items. Founded as VIP Foods in 1971 World Finer Foods is a cooperative owned by food distributors Millbrook Distribution (a unit of United Natural Foods) and Kehe Food.

Geographic Reach

Based in New Jersey World Finer Foods serves supermarkets and gourmet food stores nationwide and internationally with its vast menu of specialty food items.

Operations

Through past acquisitions the company provides specialized natural foods thanks to its Inter-Natural Foods division and premium gourmet specialty items via its Liberty Richter division which has expertise in distributing both domestic and imported gourmet food items.

It sells markets and distributes specialty food products including cookies candies crisp bread crackers mustards spices herbs and oils sauces soups pasta cereals pickles vinegar products oatmeal jellies berries instant meals chutney and curry powders among others.

Sales and Marketing

World Finer Foods sells its products through a network of specialty food distributors that supply supermarket retailers as well as through its online store.

Strategy

As part of its business World Finer Foods has become an experienced global sourcing expert. To this end the company is well-versed in several functions such as purchasing inventory management freight forwarding and consolidation issues related to the US Food and Drug Administration US Customs clearance warehousing and food labeling.

Some of its new products include the Reese line of fine foods Panda Candy Coated Licorice Pieces Bonne Maman French preserves and organic-certified and natural Spice Grinders from Drogheria & Alimentari.

Company Ownership

A cooperative World Finer Foods is owned by Millbrook Distribution (a unit of United Natural Foods) and Kehe Food both food distributors.

EXECUTIVES

Chairman Emeritus, John Beers
President CEO and Chairman, Frank Muchel
VP Marketing, Todd Newstadt
General Manager Liberty Richter, David Billings
Director Sales Liberty Richter, Mark Klarich
Senior Marketing Manager Liberty Richter, Kathy Bonynge
Director Marketing Liberty Richter, John H. Affel
CFO, Barry O'Brien
VP and Controller, Neal Kaskel
VP Sales, Kevin Hubbard
VP Purchasing, Barbara Harloe
Director Marketing Liberty Richter, Marybeth DePersio

LOCATIONS

HQ: WORLD FINER FOODS INC
1455 BROAD ST STE 4, BLOOMFIELD, NJ 07003-3039
Phone: 973-338-0300
Web: WWW.WORLDFINER.COM

PRODUCTS/OPERATIONS

Selected Brands

Allegro
Bahlsen
Bonne Maman
Candoni
Colman' s
DaVinci
Dr. Woods
Drogheria & Alimentari
Eddie' s
El Rio
Familia
Felix
Fifty50
Honeycup Gourmet Mustards
Jules Destrooper
LaVie
McCann' s
Monari Federzoni
Mrs. Leeper' s
Panda
Panni
Pritkin
Reese
Ryvita
Storehouse Foods
Sun Brand
Sylvia' s
Ty Ling
Wellington

COMPETITORS

Associated Wholesale Grocers
C&S Wholesale
DPI Specialty Foods
European Imports
Haddon House
Kroger
Nash-Finch
Performance Food Group
SUPERVALU
Wal-Mart
atalanta

HISTORICAL FINANCIALS

Company Type: Private

Income Statement FYE: December 31

	REVENUE ($ mil.)	NET INCOME ($ mil.)	NET PROFIT MARGIN	EMPLOYEES
12/10	161	0	0.0%	78
12/08	125	0	0.6%	—
Annual Growth	13.2%	(68.7%)	—	—

2010 Year-End Financials

Debt ratio: —
Return on equity: —
Cash ($ mil.): 0
Current ratio: 0.10
Long-term debt ($ mil.): —
Dividends
Yield: —
Payout: —
Market value ($ mil.): —

WORLD OF JEANS & TOPS

EXECUTIVES

VP Marketing, Cheryl A. Rudich, age 52
President CEO and Director, Daniel (Dan) Griesemer, age 53
VP Real Estate, John Burgess, age 60
Chairman and Chief Strategy Officer, Hezy Shaked, age 58
SVP and CFO, William (Bill) Langsdorf, age 56
VP COO and Chief Information Officer, Craig DeMerit, age 43
VP and General Merchandising Manager, Debbie Anker-Boetes, age 54
VP General Counsel and Secretary, Patrick Grosso, age 40
VP Stores, Shelly Johnson, age 43
VP Vendor Relations, Tilly Levine, age 57
VP Merchandise Planning and Allocation, Carolyn S. McNamara, age 48
VP Finance and Controller, Rochelle Myers, age 46
Founder, Chet Thomas
Director, Seth R. Johnson, age 59
Director, Bernard Zeichner, age 69
President CEO and Director, Daniel (Dan) Griesemer, age 53
Director, Jerold H. Rubinstein, age 74
Director, Janet E. Kerr, age 58
Auditors: Deloitte&ToucheLLP

LOCATIONS

HQ: WORLD OF JEANS & TOPS
10 WHATNEY, IRVINE, CA 926182807
Phone: 9496095599
Web: WWW.TILLYS.COM

2012 Stores

	No.
Arizona	18
California	78
Colorado	3
Delaware	1
Florida	16
Maryland	2
Nevada	6
New	7
New	2
Pennsylvania	1
Utah	1
Virginia	3
Washington	1
Wisconsin	1
Total	**140**

COMPETITORS

Abercrombie & Fitch
Aeropostale
American Eagle Outfitters
Forever 21
Hot Topic
Pacific Sunwear
The Buckle
Urban Outfitters
Wet Seal
Zumiez

HISTORICAL FINANCIALS

Company Type: Private

Income Statement

FYE: January 29

	REVENUE ($ mil.)	NET INCOME ($ mil.)	NET PROFIT MARGIN	EMPLOYEES
01/11	332	24	7.3%	4,000
01/10	282	20	7.3%	—
01/09	1,486	0	—	—
Annual Growth	—67773.4%	—	—	—

2011 Year-End Financials

Debt ratio: —
Return on equity: 7.30%
Cash ($ mil.): 29
Current ratio: 0.80
Long-term debt ($ mil.): —
Dividends
Yield: —
Payout: —
Market value ($ mil.): —

WORLD WILDLIFE FUND INC.

A fuzzy-wuzzy with kung fu strength the panda embodies mission of the World Wildlife Fund (WWF). The conservation organization has worked on more than 13000 projects in about 100 countries to save endangered species and natural areas as well as to address threats such as global warming and the exploitation of forests. By 2020 WWF aims to conserve 15 of the world's more ecologically important regions. Its work crosses Africa Asia Latin America North America and Eurasia through national affiliates in about 100 countries. The group publishes data on wildlife wild places and global environmental challenges. Founded in 1961 WWF is joined by 1.2 million members in the US and some 5 million overseas.

Geographic Reach

While the Anchorage Alaska-based WWF is active in some 100 countries the organization targets the world's most ecologically important regions for conservation including the Arctic Amazon Congo Basin the Galapagos eastern Himalayas and the Northern Great Plains in the US.

Operations

As part of WWF's operations the fund created the debt-for-nature swap. Partnering with governments and lending institutions worldwide a country's debt (say $14 million) is canceled if the government gives local money (say $10 million) to that country's conservation groups. The fund has also helped ban ivory trading in 1990.

Financial Performance

The conservation organization's total revenue including pledges for future years grew by 9% in 2012 versus 2011 due to support from foundations whose giving increased 200% over 2011 totals and success of the Arctic Home campaign with The Coca-Cola Company. Support from individual donors remained the single largest source of WWF's unrestricted revenue.

For the first time since WWF's founding funding for conservation programs topped $200 million in 2011. The record level represents about 85% of all WWF's expenses.

EXECUTIVES

President CEO, Carter S. Roberts
Senior Vice President Conservation Strategy and Science, Ginette Hemley
Chief Scientist and VP Conservation Science, Eric Dinerstein
Director Conservation Science Program, Taylor Ricketts
VP Marine and Arctic Policy and Acting VP US Government Relations, William M. (Bill) Eichbaum
Vice President Africa Program, Richard W. Carroll
Managing Director Coral Triangle Program, Katherine E. (Kate) Newman
Managing Director People and Conservation, Judy Oglethorpe
Managing Director Global Forest Program, Bruce J. Cabarle
SVP Field Programs, Thomas C. (Tom) Dillon
Senior Vice President Markets, Jason Clay
Senior Vice President Policy, David W. Reed
Director Indigenous Peoples Governance and Livelihoods, Jenny Springer
Managing Director Amazon, Margaret (Meg) Symington
SVP and General Counsel, Margaret L. Ackerley
Chief Financial Officer, Michael Bauer
Chairman, Bruce E. Babbitt
Vice Chairman, Jared M. Diamond
Secretary, Marshall Field
Vice Chairman, Lawrence H. Linden
Chief Operating Officer, Marcia Marsh
VP and Director Marine Program Mexico, Stephen (Steve) Cox
VP and Managing Director Business and Industry, Suzanne Apple
Treasurer, Roger W. Sant
Director TRAFFIC North America, Crawford Allan
Managing Director Amur-Heilong, Darron Collins
Director US Bycatch Initiative Marine Fisheries Program, Kimberly (Kim) Davis
VP and Managing Director Fisheries, Bill Fox
Managing Director Northern Great Plains, Martha Kauffman
Managing Director Species Conservation Program, Sybille Klenzendorf
Director US Policy on International Climate Affairs, Lou Leonard
VP and Managing Director Agriculture, Dave McLaughlin
Managing Director Eastern Himalayas, Jon Miceler
VP and Managing Director Climate Change, Richard Moss
Director Coral Triangle Program, Cathy Plume
Director Agriculture and Market Transformation, Kai Robertson
Managing Director Galapagos, Lauren Spurrier
Managing Director Borneo and Sumatra and Head Borneo Network Initiative, Adam Tomasek
Director Humanitarian Partnerships, Anita van Breda
Director Aquaculture Program, Jose Villalon
Director Freshwater Conservation, Christopher Williams
Managing Director Bering Sea and Kamchatka Program, Margaret Williams
Senior Vice President Communications and Marketing, Terry Macko
Vice President Chief Scientist, Jon Hoekstra
Senior Vice President Development, Julie Miller
Senior Vice President Technical Infrastructure Google Mountain, Urs Holzle
Senior Vice President Field Programs, Tom Dillon
Board Member, S. Curtis (Curt) Johnson III, age 58
Board Member, John P. Sall
Board Member, Pamela Daley, age 62
Board Member, Thomas W. Tusher, age 72
Board Member, Brenda S. Davis
Board Member, Fabiola Arredondo, age 47
Board Member, Cristian Samper, age 48
President CEO and Board Member, Carter S. Roberts
Board Member, Pamela Ebsworth
Vice Chairman, Jared M. Diamond
Vice Chairman, Lawrence H. Linden
Board Member, Pamela Matson
Board Member, Virginia (Ginger) Sall
Board Member, Leigh H. Perkins
Board Member, Robert Litterman
Board Member, Thomas Lovejoy

LOCATIONS

HQ: WORLD WILDLIFE FUND INC.
1250 24TH ST NW FL 2, WASHINGTON, DC 20037-1193
Phone: 202-293-4800
Web: WWW.PANDA.ORG

PRODUCTS/OPERATIONS

2012 Expenses

% of total	
Program	84
Fundraising	11
Finance &	5
Total	**100**

2012 Revenue

% of total	
Individual	37
In-Kind & other	24
Government grants &	17
Foundation	6
Corporate	6
WWF Network	5
Other/non-operating	5
Total	**100**

Selected Goals

Ensure that the value of nature is reflected in the decisions made by individuals communities governments and businesses
Mobilize hundreds of millions of people to support conservation
Protect and restore species and their habitats
Strengthen local communities' ability to conserve the natural resources they depend upon
Transform markets and policies to reduce the impact of the production and consumption of commodities

HISTORICAL FINANCIALS

Company Type: Private

Income Statement FYE: June 30

	REVENUE ($ mil.)	NET INCOME ($ mil.)	NET PROFIT MARGIN	EMPLOYEES
06/12	208	16	8.1%	2,500
06/11	182	(1)	—	—
06/09	151	(31)	—	—
06/08	194	(21)	—	—
Annual Growth	1.8%	—	—	—

2012 Year-End Financials

Debt ratio: —
Return on equity: 8.10%
Cash ($ mil.): 65
Current ratio: 1.50
Long-term debt ($ mil.): —
Dividends
Yield: —
Payout: —
Market value ($ mil.): —

WORLEY & OBETZ INC.

LOCATIONS

HQ: WORLEY & OBETZ INC.
85 WHITE OAK RD, MANHEIM, PA 175458550
Phone: 7176656891
Web: WWW.WORLEYOBETZ.COM

HISTORICAL FINANCIALS

Company Type: Private

Income Statement FYE: August 31

	REVENUE ($ mil.)	NET INCOME ($ mil.)	NET PROFIT MARGIN	EMPLOYEES
08/14	466	1	0.4%	68
08/13	383	1	0.3%	—
08/12	417	1	0.3%	—
08/11	478	0	—	—
Annual Growth	(0.8%)	—	—	—

2014 Year-End Financials

Debt ratio: —
Return on equity: 0.40%
Cash ($ mil.): 0
Current ratio: 1.20
Long-term debt ($ mil.): —
Dividends
Yield: —
Payout: —
Market value ($ mil.): —

WRIGHT STATE UNIVERSITY

Wright State University named after aviation pioneers the Wright Brothers has an enrollment of some 20000 students and offers more than 100 undergraduate degrees and about 90 graduate and professional degrees. It consists of eight colleges (including education and human services business engineering and computer science liberal arts nursing and health and science and mathematics) and three schools (graduate studies medicine professional psychology). Wright State has about 900 faculty members. Originally a branch campus of Ohio State University and Miami University Wright State became an independent university in 1967.

Geographic Reach

Along with its main campus in Dayton Ohio Wright State also offers classes at its smaller Lake Campus in Celina Ohio.

Financial Performance

Wright State University reported a 2% increase in revenues to $263 million in fiscal 2012 due to increased student tuition and fees for the third year running. Increased earnings in 2012 were partly offset by lower government appropriations (state and federal) grants and contracts and auxiliary revenues. Net income dropped to a loss of $9 million (down from profits of $40 million in 2011) due to lower appropriations and higher expenses in areas including salaries benefits instruction research and academic support.

Tuition runs at over $8000 per year for Ohio residents and $16000 for out-of-state students. The university has increased tuition in recent years to replace lower state appropriation levels (resulting from harsh economic conditions).

Strategy

In 2012 Wright State issued $55 million in bonds to pay for construction and renovation efforts on academic and administrative buildings both on new and existing facilities. It is also upgrading campus infrastructures and student recreation and athletic facilities.

In addition the university is adopting a new budgeting model that it hopes will provide more transparency while allowing academic units to strategically identify new revenue sources. The system also aims to help divisions identify programs that are not adding academic or financial value.

EXECUTIVES

VP Business and Fiscal Affairs, Mark Polatajko
President, David R. Hopkins
VP Student Affairs, Dan Abrahamowicz
General Counsel, Gwen M. Mattison
EVP Planning, Robert J. Sweeney
VP Research and Grad Studies, Robert E. Fyffe
Vice Chairman, Nina Joshi
Chairman, Larry R. Klaben
Secretary, John C. Kunesh
Dean University Libraries, Stephen P. Foster
Interim Provost, Thomas Sudkamp
Vice President Human Resources, Michael Edicola
Provost, Sundaram Narayanan
VP Communications and Marketing, George Heddleston
Interim Dean Graduate School, R. William Ayres
Dean College of Education and Human Services, Charlotte Harris
Dean School of Professional Psychology, Larry C. James
Dean College of Engineering and Computer Science, Nathan Klingbeil
Dean Raj Soin College of Business, Joanne Li
Dean College of Science and Mathematics, Yi Li
Dean College of Nursing and Health, Rosalie O'Dell Mainous
Dean Lake Campus, Bonnie K. Mathies
Dean College of Liberal Arts, Kristin D. Sobolik
Dean Boonshoft School of Medicine, Marjorie Bowman
Vice-President for Enrollment Management, Jacqueline McMillan
Assistant Vice-President for Enrollment Marketing and Services, Nadine Brown
Assistant Vice-President of Undergraduate Admissions, Cathy Davis
Auditors: CroweHorwathLLP

LOCATIONS

HQ: WRIGHT STATE UNIVERSITY
3640 COLONEL GLENN HWY, DAYTON, OH 45435-0002
Phone: 937-775-3333
Web: WWW.WRIGHT.STATEUNIVERSITY.COM

PRODUCTS/OPERATIONS

Selected Schools and Colleges

Colleges
- Education and Human Services
- Engineering and Computer Science
- Liberal Arts
- Nursing and Health
- Raj Soin College of Business
- Professional Psychology
- Science and Mathematics
- University College
- WSU-Lake Campus

Schools
- Boonshoft School of Medicine
- Graduate Studies
- Professional Psychology

HISTORICAL FINANCIALS

Company Type: Private

Income Statement FYE: June 30

	REVENUE ($ mil.)	NET INCOME ($ mil.)	NET PROFIT MARGIN	EMPLOYEES
06/12	267	(10)	—	2,748
06/11	263	53	20.4%	—
06/10	253	24	9.7%	—
06/09	237	(25)	—	—
Annual Growth	4.1%	—	—	—

2012 Year-End Financials

Debt ratio: —
Return on equity: (-4.00%)
Cash ($ mil.): 20
Current ratio: 0.50
Long-term debt ($ mil.): —
Dividends
Yield: —
Payout: —
Market value ($ mil.): —

WYCKOFF HEIGHTS MEDICAL CENTER

Wyckoff Heights is taking health care to new levels. Serving the New York boroughs of Brooklyn and Queens Wyckoff Heights Medical Center maintains some 350 beds and provides a comprehensive range of specialized services including diagnostics radiology cardiology obstetrics pediatrics surgery and rehabilitative care. The hospital also provides educational services through a partnership with the Weill Medical College of Cornell University and it offers outpatient services through several family health clinics in the area. The not-for-profit medical center is an affiliated member of the New York-Presbyterian Healthcare System but is governed by an independent board of trustees.

Operations

The hospital has 75000 visits a year at its Pediatric/Adult Emergency Departments. Every year it also delivers 2000 babies offers outpatient services to thousands through a network of community ambulatory care centers and conducts extensive community health education and screening programs.

Strategy

Wyckoff Heights is responding to the growing healthcare needs of the communities they serve by acquiring new equipment and expanding clinical programs. The center has added an on-site MRI to ensure that community residents do not have to travel outside the neighborhood to access advanced radiologic procedures the center established a cardiac catheterization lab for definitive diagnostic tests that assess coronary circulation and overall heart function implemented a a bloodless medicine and surgery program to accommodate those individuals who for religious or other reasons choose treatment options that do not include blood installed hyperbaric chambers to aid in the healing of wounds encountered by diabetic patients and burn victims and access to a discrete Women's Health Center that offers a comprehensive range of obstetrical and gynecological services in maximum privacy and comfort for female patients of all ages.

Company Background

Wyckoff Heights was founded in 1889.

EXECUTIVES

SVP Medical Director and Board Trustee, Nirmal Mattoo
VP Legal Council, David N. Hoffman
Vice President Regulatory Services Compliance Officer, Karen Carey
VP Graduate Medical Eduaction; Chairman Graduate Medical Education, E. Kenneth Freiberg
Vice President Nursing, Margaret Pelkowski
Vice President Patient Safety and Satisfaction, Ruth Krauthamer
EVP and COO, Frances (Fran) Heaney
VP Strategic Development and Physician Recruitment, Yashpal Arya
Director Vascular Surgery Division, Mohan Badhey
Director Infectious Diseases Division, John Vernaleo
Director Nephrology Division, Tsega Denneke
Director Pediatric Emergency Medicine Division, Sol Gourji
Director Otolaryngology (ENT) Division, Sam Huh
Director Pulmonary Disease & Critical Care Division, Harish Patel
Director Urology Division, Sheldon Rosenthal
Director Cardiology Division, Kul Chadda
Director Podiatry Division, Stephen D'Orazi
Director Neonatology Division, Sanjay Patel
Director Ophthalmology Division, Harry Koster
Director Hematology Oncology Division, Vijay Mattoo
Director Physical Medicine & Rehabilitation Division, Don Pirraglia
Director Molecular Medicine & Genetics Division, Arvind Babu
Director Obstetrics Division, Prasanta Chandra
Director Surgery Division, Percy Erachshaw
Director Bone Marrow Transplantation Division, Subhash Gulati
Director Endocrinology Division, Narinder Kukar
Director Neurology Division, Sham Mendiratta
Director Gynecology Division, John Riggs
Director Orthopedic Surgery Division, Edward Toriello
Vice Chairperson, John H. Cook Jr.
Chairman Department Surgery and Board Trustee, Addagada C. Rao
Secretary and Board Trustee, Fred T. Haller III
Chief Medical Officer and SVP Medical Affairs; Chairman Department Internal Medicine, Pradeep Chandra

Chairman Department Family Practice, Farideh Zonouzi
Chairman Department Radiology Oncology, Mounzer Tchelebi
Chairman Department Anesthesiology, Robert Raggi
Chairman Department Pathology and Laboratories, William Thelmo
Chairman Department Dentistry, Burton Wasserman
President WHMC Alumni Association, Parvez A. Mir
Vice President Emergency Services, Clifford Miller
Vice President Human Resources, Margaret Cornelius
Vice President Chief Information Officer, Jebashini Jesurasa
SVP and Chief Medical Officer, Gustavo DelToro
Vice President of Finance and Chief Financial Officer, Frank Vutrano
President and CEO, Ramon J. Rodriguez
Vice President General Counsel, Kevin Smyley
Vice President Medical Education, Kenneth Freiberg
Senior Vice President Chief Medical Officer, Gustavo Toro
Executive Vice President Chief Operating Officer, David Rock
Vice President Nursing, Rosetta Melvin
SVP Medical Director and Board Trustee, Nirmal Mattoo
Board Trustee, Vito J. D'alessandro
Board Trustee, Adam Figueroa
Board Trustee, Edmondo Modica
Chairman Department Surgery and Board Trustee, Addagada C. Rao
Secretary and Board Trustee, Fred T. Haller III
Board Trustee, Herman Hochberg
Board Trustee, Andrew Boisselle
Auditors: Ernst&YoungLLP

LOCATIONS

HQ: WYCKOFF HEIGHTS MEDICAL CENTER
374 STOCKHOLM ST, BROOKLYN, NY 11237-4006
Phone: 718-963-7272
Web: WWW.WYCKOFFHOSPITAL.ORG

PRODUCTS/OPERATIONS

Selected Services

Anesthesiology
Asthma
Breast Surgery
Cardiology/Heart
Colorectal Surgery
Dermatology
Ear Nose & Throat (ENT)
Emergency Medicine
Endocrinology (Diabetes)
Family Medicine
Gastroenterology
General Surgery
Genetics
Geriatrics
Head & Neck Surgery
Hyperbaric Medicine/Wound Care
Infectious Diseases
Internal Medicine
Medical Oncology
Nephrology
Neurology/Designated Stroke Center
Neurosurgery
Nursing
Obstetrics & Gynecology
Ophthalmology/Eye
Orthopedics
Otolaryngology
Pain Management
Pathology
Pediatrics
Physical Medicine & Rehabilitation
Plastic Surgery
Podiatry
Psychiatry
Pulmonary Medicine
Radiation Oncology
Radiology
Respiratory Therapy
Rheumatology
Thoracic Surgery
Urology

COMPETITORS

Catholic Healthcare System
Continuum Health Partners
Kingsbrook Jewish Medical Center
Maimonides Medical Center
MediSys Health Network
Memorial Sloan-Kettering
Montefiore Medical
New York City Health and Hospitals
North Shore-Long Island Jewish Health System

HISTORICAL FINANCIALS

Company Type: Private

Income Statement FYE: December 31

	REVENUE ($ mil.)	NET INCOME ($ mil.)	NET PROFIT MARGIN	EMPLOYEES
12/12	246	4	1.9%	1,900
12/09	286	8	3.0%	—
12/08*	233	(32)	—	—
11/08	2	0	0.7%	—
Annual Growth	207.5%	290.9%	—	—

*Fiscal year change

2012 Year-End Financials

Debt ratio: ——
Return on equity: 1.90%
Cash ($ mil.): 5
Current ratio: 0.30
Long-term debt ($ mil.): —

Dividends
Yield: —
Payout: —
Market value ($ mil.): —

WYOMING MEDICAL CENTER INC.

Wyoming Medical Center is The Cowboy State's largest medical facility. The hospital founded in 1911 offers those who live in and around Wyoming's Natrona County more than 50 medical specialties thanks to its 150 physicians. The health care services provider boasts nearly 1300 skilled staff members and more than 190 beds. It offers services such as an emergency air transport system trauma care diagnostic services diabetes care center nephrology and surgical care. The facility is a community-owned not-for-profit hospital.that also operates the Heart Center of Wyoming the Wyoming Neuroscience and Spine Institute and a network of about a dozen community clinics throughout Wyoming.

Geographic Reach

The health care provider serves the Wyoming communities of Natrona County and its surrounding counties.

EXECUTIVES

SVP and CFO, Don Claunch
President and CEO, Vickie Diamond
Chairman, Chris Muirhead
Marketing and Public Relations Representative, Shauna VanderLinden
Chief Planning Officer, Mary Lynne Shickich
SVP Patient Care Services and COO, Julie Cann-Taylor
Chief of Staff and Director, David Wheeler
Vice Chairman, John Masterson
Chief of Staff, Mary MacGuire
Secretary, Eugene Duquette
Chief Medical Officer, Carol Solie
Director, John Baily
Director, James Anderson
Director, Linda Young
Director, Mark Dowell
Chief of Staff and Director, David Wheeler
Vice Chairman, John Masterson
Director, Ruth Moran

LOCATIONS

HQ: WYOMING MEDICAL CENTER INC.
1233 E 2ND ST, CASPER, WY 82601-2988
Phone: 307-577-7201
Web: WWW.WMCNET.ORG

PRODUCTS/OPERATIONS

Selected Services

AHA Training
Casper Pulmonary
da Vinci System
Diabetes Care Center
Heart Center of Wyoming
Hometown Specialty Clinics
Professional Lab Services
Sage Primary Care
Weight Management Program
Wyoming Brain & Spine Associates
Wyoming Life Flight
Wyoming Nephrology
Wyoming Relay Health

COMPETITORS

Banner Health
Billings Clinic
Evanston
LifePoint Hospitals
North Colorado Medical Center
Poudre Valley Health System
Universal Health Services

HISTORICAL FINANCIALS

Company Type: Private

Income Statement FYE: June 30

	REVENUE ($ mil.)	NET INCOME ($ mil.)	NET PROFIT MARGIN	EMPLOYEES
06/11	227	14	6.3%	1,033
06/10	236	8	3.7%	—
06/09	204	(24)		
06/08	206	11	5.5%	—
Annual Growth	3.3%	8.1%	—	—

2011 Year-End Financials

Debt ratio: —
Return on equity: 6.30%
Cash ($ mil.): 41
Current ratio: 1.70
Long-term debt ($ mil.): —
Dividends
Yield: —
Payout: —
Market value ($ mil.): —

XANTERRA INC.

LOCATIONS

HQ: XANTERRA INC.
6312 S FIDDLERS GREEN CIR 600N, GREENWOOD VILLAGE, CO 801114943
Phone: 3036003400
Web: WWW.XANTERRA.COM

HISTORICAL FINANCIALS

Company Type: Private

Income Statement FYE: December 25

	REVENUE ($ mil.)	NET INCOME ($ mil.)	NET PROFIT MARGIN	EMPLOYEES
12/13	304	11	3.7%	3,500
12/12	305	13	4.3%	—
12/11	301	7	2.4%	—
12/10	305	0	—	—
Annual Growth	(0.1%)	—	—	—

2013 Year-End Financials

Debt ratio: —
Return on equity: 3.70%
Cash ($ mil.): 18
Current ratio: 0.30
Long-term debt ($ mil.): —
Dividends
Yield: —
Payout: —
Market value ($ mil.): —

XAVIER UNIVERSITY

Xavier University is a not-for-profit Jesuit Catholic institution that operates from a single campus located in Cincinnati Ohio. The private school which has recently grown its enrollment numbers to about 7000 students offers nearly 90 undergraduate programs and about 20 graduate programs. Xavier University's programs range from arts and sciences to social sciences and business. Boasting small class sizes the university's student-to-faculty ratio is a noteworthy 12:1. Known among sports circles as having a highly respected men's basketball program Xavier University also manages to graduate every member of its men's Musketeers group. Xavier University was founded in 1831.

Geographic Reach

The university serves about 7000 students from its 190-acre campus located in Cincinnati Ohio.

Operations

The university is the nation's sixth-oldest Catholic university as compared to 27 other Jesuit colleges in the US. Xavier University's enrollment of about 7000 students includes 4540 undergraduates. Across its three colleges the university offers 87 undergraduate majors 55 minors and 19 graduate programs.

Sales and Marketing

Xavier University is the top school in the Midwest for graduation and approximately 77% of its student population is accepted to medical school. Across the university's sports disciplines it has 16 Division I teams.

Financial Performance

For the reporting period of 2012 vs. 2011 Xavier University posted flat revenue due to an increase in tuition and fees and auxiliary enterprise revenue. This was offset however by a decrease in government grants as well as a decline in contracts private gifts grants and endowment income. Net income for 2012 as compared to 2011 declined by 199% thanks to contributions and change in contributions receivable for non-operating purpose and investment return net of amounts in operations.

EXECUTIVES

Chairman Board of Trustees, Robert J. (Bob) Kohlhepp, age 70
President, Rev Michael J. Graham
Assistant VP Human Resources, Kathleen Riga
Academic VP and Provost, Roger A. Fortin
Administrative VP, John F. Kucia
VP University Relations, Gary R. Massa
Associate Provost Student Life and Leadership, Kathleen E. Simons
VP Student Enrollment, Terry Richards
VP Information and CIO, David Dodd
Interim VP Mission and Identity, Rev Eugene (Gene) Charmichael
Vice Provost Diversity, Cheryl L. Nu?ez
University Registrar, Allen Cole
SVP and CFO, Maribeth Amyot
Associate Provost Academic Affairs, Kandi Stinson
Director Public Relations, Debora Del Valle
Provost and Chief Academic Officer, Scott A. Chadwick
Associate Provost and CIO, Annette Marksberry
Dean College of Social Science Health and Education, D. Mark Meyers
Dean Williams College of Business, Brian Till
Dean College of Arts and Science, Janice Walker
Vice President Financial Advisor, Michael J. Cason
Vice President - Investments Investment Officer, Robert E. Prangley
Auditors: Ernst&YoungLLP

LOCATIONS

HQ: XAVIER UNIVERSITY
3800 VICTORY PKWY UNIT 1, CINCINNATI, OH 45207-1092
Phone: 513-745-3000
Web: WWW.XAVIER.EDU

PRODUCTS/OPERATIONS

Selected Colleges

College of Arts& Sciences
College of Social Sciences Health & Education
Williams College of Business

HISTORICAL FINANCIALS

Company Type: Private

Income Statement FYE: June 30

	REVENUE ($ mil.)	NET INCOME ($ mil.)	NET PROFIT MARGIN	EMPLOYEES
06/13	163	14	8.7%	940
06/12*	166	(22)		—
05/10	167	22	13.5%	—
05/10	154	24	15.7%	—
Annual Growth	2.0%	(16.1%)	—	—

*Fiscal year change

2013 Year-End Financials

Debt ratio: —
Return on equity: 8.70%
Cash ($ mil.): 20
Current ratio: —
Long-term debt ($ mil.): —
Dividends
Yield: —
Payout: —
Market value ($ mil.): —

YAKIMA VALLEY MEMORIAL HOSPITAL ASSOCIATION INC

EXECUTIVES

Director Human Resources, Kathy Franz
VP Communications and Development, Anne Caffery
Vice President Services, Jim Aberle
President CEO, Verlynn Best
Account Executive, Carolyn Gray
Marketing Director, Thane Phelan
Development Director, Elizabeth Fitzgerald
Account Executive, Scott Filkins

LOCATIONS

HQ: YAKIMA VALLEY MEMORIAL HOSPITAL ASSOCIATION INC
2811 TIETON DR, YAKIMA, WA 989023761
Phone: 5092495129
Web: WWW.YAKIMAMEMORIAL.ORG

PRODUCTS/OPERATIONS

Selected Services and Locations

16th Avenue Pavilion
Apple Valley Family Medicine
Cardiac Rehabilitation and Wellness Center
Cascade Surgical Partners
Children's Village
Family Medicine of Yakima
Garden Village
Home Health and Hospice
Memorial Cornerstone Medicine
Memorial Hospitalist Program
Memorial's Valley Imaging
North Star Lodge Cancer Center
'Ohana Mammography Center
Pacific Crest Family Medicine
Selah Family Medicine
Sleep Center at Memorial
Surgi-Center at Memorial
The Springs Rehabilitation and Occupational Medicine
Water's Edge Pain Relief Institute
Yakima Gastroenterology Associates
Yakima Internal Medicine
Yakima Neurosurgery Associates
Yakima Plastic Surgery Associates
Yakima Vascular Associates

COMPETITORS

Adventist Health
Catholic Health Initiatives
Franciscan Health System
HCA
Harrison Medical Center
MultiCare Health System
Overlake Hospital
PeaceHealth
Providence Health & Services
Sacred Heart Medical Center
Swedish Health Services
Watson Institute

HISTORICAL FINANCIALS

Company Type: Private

Income Statement FYE: October 31

	REVENUE ($ mil.)	NET INCOME ($ mil.)	NET PROFIT MARGIN	EMPLOYEES
10/13	361	39	10.9%	1,150
10/12	309	(6)	—	—
10/09	276	(18)	—	—
10/08	245	0	—	—
Annual Growth	8.1%	—	—	—

2013 Year-End Financials

Debt ratio: —
Return on equity: 10.90%
Cash ($ mil.): 11
Current ratio: 1.30
Long-term debt ($ mil.): —
Dividends
Yield: —
Payout: —
Market value ($ mil.): —

YESHIVA UNIVERSITY

Yeshivas are traditional Jewish schools and Yeshiva University believes strongly in following tradition. The Jewish higher education institution serves more than 7000 undergraduate and graduate students at four campuses in New York City. Subjects taught include liberal arts sciences medicine law business social work and psychology. It also has extensive Jewish studies and education programs including study abroad opportunities. Yeshiva University also known as YU has an undergraduate student-to-teacher ratio of 6:1. Its graduate programs include medicine law psychology and Jewish education.

Geographic Reach

Yeshiva University's four New York City campuses consist of the Brookdale Center the Israel Henry Beren Campus and the Wilf Campus in Manhattan and the Jack and Pearl Resnick Campus in the Bronx. It also has a campus in Jerusalem that coordinates its study abroad programs.

Operations

Yeshiva University operates three undergraduate schools: Yeshiva College Stern College for Women and Sy Syms School of Business. Undergraduates may also enroll in the Joint Israel Program a formal arrangement between Yeshiva University and more than 45 yeshivot and seminaries in Israel. Enrolled students get to spend a year studying at Israeli institutions in fields including Talmud Bible Jewish Law and Jewish thought Philosophy Zionism Jewish History and oral and written Hebrew.

Beyond undergraduate education the university operates the Albert Einstein School of Medicine which provides medical training and research opportunities. With roughly 1000 students Albert Einstein School of Medicine is a major biomedical and clinical research facility and receives some $200 million in annual funding from the National Institutes of Health. Areas of research include diabetes cancer liver disease and HIV/AIDS.

Other graduate programs include schools and affiliate institutions in areas including law social work psychology Jewish studies and theology.

Company Background

The university traces its roots to the 1915 merging of two schools from New York's Lower East Side: Yeshiva Eitz Chaim founded in 1886 and the Rabbi Isaac Elchanan Theological Seminary (RIETS) founded in 1896.

EXECUTIVES

Chancellor, Norman Lamm, age 86
President, Richard M. Joel
VP Communication and Public Affairs, Georgia Pollak
VP Business Affairs and CFO, J. Michael Gower
VP University Life, Hillel Davis
VP University Affairs, Herbert Dobrinsky
Vice President for Institutional Advancement, Daniel T. Forman
Senior Vice President for Academic Affairs, Morton Lowengrub
Dean Sy Syms School of Business, Michael J. Ginzberg
Senior Vice President, Josh Joseph
Vice President for Administrative Services, Jeffrey Rosengarten
Chief Procurement Officer, Jack D. Zencheck
Vice President for Legal Affairs, Andrew J. Lauer
VP Information Technology and CIO, Marc Milstein
VP Medical Affairs, Allen M. Spiegel
Director Admissions, Michael Kranzler
Dean University Libraries, Pearl Berger
Senior Director Alumni Affairs and Annual Giving, Lisa Horowitz
Executive Director Career Development Center, Marc Goldman
Digital Collections Librarian University Library, Heather Rolen
Dean of Students, Victor Schwartz
Director Student Aid Operations, Marianela Cabral
Director Student Finance, Robert Friedman
Administrative Assistant, Millie Gore
Executive Secretary, Kerry Fonville
Senior Director Alumni Affairs and Annual Giving, Barbara Birch
President of the American Committee for the United Charities in Israel, Rabbi Charlop
senior Vice President at Yeshiva University, Rabbi Joseph
Auditors: KPMGLLP

LOCATIONS

HQ: YESHIVA UNIVERSITY
500 W 185TH ST, NEW YORK, NY 10033-3299
Phone: 212-960-5400
Web: WWW.YUHSB.ORG

PRODUCTS/OPERATIONS

Schools and Colleges
Albert Einstein College of MedicineMS MD
Azrieli Graduate School of Jewish Education and AdministrationMS EdD
Benjamin N. Cardozo School of LawJD LLM
Bernard Revel Graduate School of Jewish Studies MA PhD
Ferkauf Graduate School of PsychologyMA MS PhD PsyD
Stern College for WomenBA
Sue Golding Graduate Division of Medical SciencesMS PhD
Sy Syms School of BusinessBS
Wurzweiler School of Social WorkMSW CJCS PhD
Yeshiva CollegeBA
Special Institutio
Marsha Stern Talmudical Academy for Boys
Rabbi Isaac Elchanan Theological Seminary
Samuel H. Wang Yeshiva University High School for Girls
Yeshiva University High Schools
Yeshiva University Museum
Centers/Institutions
Center for Israel Studies at Yeshiva University
Center for Jewish Law and Contemporary Civilizati
Center for the Jewish Future
Graduate Program in Advanced Talmudic Studies at Stern College for Women
Institute for Public Health Sciences
Rabbi Arthur Schneier Center for International Affairs
The Center for Ethics at Yeshiva University

HISTORICAL FINANCIALS

Company Type: Private

Income Statement FYE: June 30

	REVENUE ($ mil.)	NET INCOME ($ mil.)	NET PROFIT MARGIN	EMPLOYEES
06/11	674	(85)	—	4,500
06/10	657	(94)	—	—
06/09	541	(181)	—	—
06/08	626	(61)	—	—
Annual Growth	2.5%	—	—	—

2011 Year-End Financials

Debt ratio: —
Return on equity: (-12.70%)
Cash ($ mil.): 4
Current ratio: —
Long-term debt ($ mil.): —
Dividends
Yield: —
Payout: —
Market value ($ mil.): —

YORK HOSPITAL

York Hospital operating as WellSpan York Hospital takes its name from the community whose health it seeks to preserve. Part of WellSpan Health the medical center has about 570 beds and serves residents of York and surrounding area of south-central Pennsylvania. It is a regional leader in cardiovascular and orthopedic care and has programs in other specialty areas including oncology behavioral health and geriatrics. Additionally WellSpan York Hospital operates a Level 1 trauma center offers outpatient surgery emergency home health and diagnostic imaging services. It is also has teaching and research programs. The hospital was founded in 1880.

Operations

WellSpan York Hospital has been recognized as a top 100 US hospital by US News for more than five years in a row. It is also recognized for its cardiovascular and orthopedic programs. The center employs about 700 doctors.

The hospital's education programs include five allied health schools and seven residency programs. Affiliated organizations include the medical schools of Drexel University Pennsylvania State University and University of Maryland.

Strategy

WellSpan York Hospital is working to improve its specialist programs to meet the growing medical needs of area residents. In 2011 for instance it collaborated with technology firm Cerner and pharmaceuticals firm Hospira to form an infusion management program for its intensive care unit; the program aims to reduce infusion-related errors. In addition it launched a urinary catheter removal protocol to reduce infection rates and it implemented an aortic valve replacement program (making it one of three facilities in Pennsylvania to offer the open-heart surgery alternative).

EXECUTIVES

VP Marketing and Public Relations, Maria Royce
VP Operations, Raymond Rosen

LOCATIONS

HQ: YORK HOSPITAL
1001 S GEORGE ST, YORK, PA 17403-3645
Phone: 717-337-4123
Web: WWW.WELLSPAN.ORG

COMPETITORS

Ascension Health	Hanover Healthcare
Catholic Health Initiatives	Hershey Medical Center
Geisinger Health System	Holy Spirit
Guthrie Healthcare	Lancaster General
	Memorial Hospital (PA)
	PinnacleHealth System

HISTORICAL FINANCIALS

Company Type: Private

Income Statement — FYE: June 30

	REVENUE ($ mil.)	NET INCOME ($ mil.)	NET PROFIT MARGIN	EMPLOYEES
06/12	806	27	3.4%	6,200
06/11	807	90	11.2%	—
06/10	755	73	9.8%	—
06/09	708	(65)	—	—
Annual Growth	4.4%	—	—	—

2012 Year-End Financials

Debt ratio: ——
Return on equity: 3.40%
Cash ($ mil.): 61
Current ratio: 2.80
Long-term debt ($ mil.): —
Dividends
Yield: —
Payout: —
Market value ($ mil.): —

YOUNG LIFE

Young Life is focused on promoting Christianity among teenagers in the US and in more than 50 other countries. Founded in 1941 the not-for-profit organization provides activities and support for junior high middle school and high school students located in rural and urban communities. Young Life also operates week-long summer camp programs at about 20 locations throughout North America as well as retreats held throughout the year. The group has grown throughout the years from a single club in Texas to about 600 international Young Life ministries dotting the globe. The organization boasts about 3000 staffers and more than 27000 volunteers.

EXECUTIVES

Svp Western Division, Ty Saltzgiver
Svp International North Division, Lee Corder
Svp Southern Division, John Vicary
Vp Of It, Jeff Mawhirter
Vice President Interim And Chief, Kerry Alberti
Svp International South Division, Marty Caldwell
Svp Northern Division, Gail Ebersole
Vice President Field Ministries, Jan Marable
Auditors: BKDLLP

LOCATIONS

HQ: YOUNG LIFE
420 N CASCADE AVE, COLORADO SPRINGS, CO 80903-3352
Phone: 719-381-1800
Web: WWW.SC.YOUNGLIFE.ORG

HISTORICAL FINANCIALS

Company Type: Private

Income Statement — FYE: September 30

	REVENUE ($ mil.)	NET INCOME ($ mil.)	NET PROFIT MARGIN	EMPLOYEES
09/12	237	0	0.1%	3,100
09/11*	245	19	7.8%	—
12/09	222	6	2.9%	—
12/09	236	14	6.3%	—
Annual Growth	0.2%	(77.2%)	—	—

*Fiscal year change

2012 Year-End Financials

Debt ratio: ——
Return on equity: 0.10%
Cash ($ mil.): 52
Current ratio: 2.80
Long-term debt ($ mil.): —
Dividends
Yield: —
Payout: —
Market value ($ mil.): —

YUMA REGIONAL MEDICAL CENTER INC

Yuma Regional Medical Center (YRMC) is an acute care hospital that provides medical services for Yuma Arizona and its surrounding communities. The hospital which has about 400 beds and 300 doctors provides general medical surgical and emergency services as well as 40 specialties through units including a cardiac catheterization lab children's and women's health centers a weight loss department and a cancer treatment center as well as outpatient care divisions. YRMC also offers home health care school health care medical equipment rentals (through First Health Medical Supply) and cardiac and pulmonary rehabilitation services off-site.

Ownership

The not-for-profit YRMC organization is governed by a 12-member board composed of community volunteers. The hospital is funded by the Foundation of Yuma Regional Medical Center which raises money through various means including donations bequests and special events. Since it is located on property leased from the area hospital district it is also eligible to receive financial support from tax-exempt revenue bonds for construction projects.

Strategy

Being a regional hospital YRMC works hard to recruit physicians who might otherwise be drawn to larger teaching hospitals with more advanced technological equipment and complex patient cases. In order to lure in such specialists the hospital offers extended medical education career weekends and a number of specialized centers in which physicians can perform procedures solely in their specialty such as a neonatal ICU and a pediatric sub-specialty unit. It opened a new cardiovascular operating room in 2013 and it broke ground on a new cancer care center.

YRMC also offers a free program called Silver Care in which patients who are 55 and older are encouraged to live active and healthy lives by being offered a number of benefits such as discounts at local stores specially reduced rates on selected lab tests including cholesterol and blood glucose screenings. Additionally Silver Care members are eligible for free membership in the Fit for Life cardiac wellness program.

EXECUTIVES

Vp Of Marketing, Machele Headington
Vp Professional And Support Services, Jim Hall
Interim CFO, Tony Struck
President and CEO, Pat Walz
Director MedWest, Claudette Rodstrom
Medical Librarian, Leone Neegan
Vice President Clinical Service Lines, Camie Overton
Chief Medical Officer And Vice President Of Medical Affairs, Carl F Myers
Director Of Physical Therapy, Jennifer Breen
Director Of Infection Control, Deborah Aders
Medical Director, Ismael I Guerrero
Vice Chairperson, Tom Tyree
Member Board Of Directors, Sridhar Rajamani

LOCATIONS

HQ: YUMA REGIONAL MEDICAL CENTER INC
2400 S AVENUE A, YUMA, AZ 85364-7170
Phone: 928-344-2000
Web: WWW.YUMAREGIONAL.ORG

PRODUCTS/OPERATIONS

Selected Services

Children
Cancer Care
Children' s Rehabilitative Services
Critical Care
Diabetes Education
Diagnostic Imaging
Emergency Department
First Health Medical Supply
Gastroenterology
Heart
Hospitalist Program
Lab
Medical Staff Services
Nursing Units
Outpatient Surgical Center
Pharmacy
Spiritual Care and Patient Advocacy
Surgical Services
Weight Loss
Women' s Services
Wound Care Center

COMPETITORS

- Banner Health
- Community Health Systems
- Dignity Health
- HCA
- Iasis Healthcare
- Inova
- John C. Lincoln Health Network
- Northern Arizona Healthcare
- Phoenix Children' s Hospital
- Poudre Valley Health System
- Providence Health & Services
- Scottsdale Healthcare
- St. Joseph Health System
- University of Arizona Health Network

HISTORICAL FINANCIALS

Company Type: Private

Income Statement FYE: September 30

	REVENUE ($ mil.)	NET INCOME ($ mil.)	NET PROFIT MARGIN	EMPLOYEES
09/12	346	22	6.6%	1,600
09/11	330	4	1.2%	—
09/10	317	21	6.7%	—
09/09	328	10	3.1%	—
Annual Growth	1.7%	31.5%	—	—

2012 Year-End Financials

Debt ratio: —
Return on equity: 6.60%
Cash ($ mil.): 34
Current ratio: 3.10
Long-term debt ($ mil.): —
Dividends
Yield: —
Payout: —
Market value ($ mil.): —

Z GALLERIE

Cain and Abel they're not! Brothers and executives Joe and Mike Zeiden founded Z Gallerie in 1979 using their parents' garage for a warehouse and production facility. Initially Z Gallerie (later joined by sister Carole Malfatti) sold poster art but in the 1980s the trio added home furnishings and accessories to the merchandising mix. Today Z Gallerie stores which span some 10000 sq. ft. on average feature bedding and pillows dinnerware glassware rugs lamps candleholders clocks frames and albums games and gifts. The firm's eclectic pieces are sold through its website and some 55 US retail locations in nearly 20 states. Z Gallerie is privately owned.

Geographic Reach

Los Angeles-based Z Gallerie has stores in 19 states. Its biggest markets are California Florida and Texas home to more than half of its stores. The furniture retailer has buying offices in Berkeley.

Strategy

After a six-month stint in bankruptcy ending in 2009 Z Gallerie is spending its time prudently shopping for new locations for its stores while the company keeps a close eye on performance. The housing crisis in California was particularly painful for the home furnishings retailer due to its heavy presence there.

EXECUTIVES

President and CEO, Joseph (Joe) Zeiden
CFO, Michael (Mike) Zeiden
SEVP Merchandising and Marketing, Carole Malfatti

LOCATIONS

HQ: Z GALLERIE
1855 W 139TH ST, GARDENA, CA 90249-3013
Phone: 310-630-1200
Web: WWW.Z-GALLERIE.PISSEDCONSUMER.COM

2012 Stores

	No
Alabama	1
Arizona	4
California	16
Colorado	1
Florida	8
Georgia	2
Illinois	2
Indiana	1
Kansas	1
Kentucky	1
Louisiana	1
Nevada	1
North Carolina	1
Oregon	1
Tennessee	1
Texas	8
Utah	2
Virginia	1
Washington	1
Total	**54**

PRODUCTS/OPERATIONS

Selected Products

- Accessories
- Area Rugs
- Art
  - Abstract
  - Canvas
  - Lanscapes
  - Vintage
- Bedding
- Drapery Panels
- Furniture
  - Bedroom
  - Dining Room
  - Office
  - Outdoor
- Lamps
  - Floor Lamps
  - Hanging Lamps
  - Table Lamps
- Mirrors
- Tabletop items

COMPETITORS

- Amazon.com
- Bed Bath & Beyond
- Cost Plus
- Euromarket Designs
- Four Hands
- Hanover Direct
- IKEA
- Macy' s
- Pier 1 Imports
- Provide Gifts
- Restoration Hardware
- Room & Board
- Williams-Sonoma

HISTORICAL FINANCIALS

Company Type: Private

Income Statement FYE: December 31

	REVENUE ($ mil.)	NET INCOME ($ mil.)	NET PROFIT MARGIN	EMPLOYEES
12/12	176	25	14.5%	700
12/11	154	20	13.4%	—
Annual Growth	14.2%	23.7%	—	—

2012 Year-End Financials

Debt ratio: —
Return on equity: 14.50%
Cash ($ mil.): 20
Current ratio: 0.90
Long-term debt ($ mil.): —
Dividends
Yield: —
Payout: —
Market value ($ mil.): —

ZOOLOGICAL SOCIETY OF SAN DIEGO

Talk about animal magnetism! The Zoological Society of San Diego is a not-for-profit organization that operates the 100-acre San Diego Zoo which cares for more than 4000 individual animals as well as a collection of some 3500 species of plants. The Zoological Society also manages the 1800-acre San Diego Zoo Safari Park and the center for Conservation and Research. The zoo entertains all with its daily shows in-park restaurants guided tours and special events. The society also supports conservation education and efforts such as planned travel adventure-tours to exotic destinations in Mexico and Africa. It was founded by Dr. Harry Wegeforth in 1916 and is managed by a 12-member board.

Operations

The society is the largest zoological membership group in the world with more than half a million members (including 130000 children). Members receive free zoo and safari park admission a subscription to the society's magazine and other benefits.

EXECUTIVES

President and Trustee, Berit N. Durler
Treasurer and Trustee, Frank C. Alexander
VP and Trustee, Frederick A. Frye
President, Rick Gulley
Executive Director, Douglas G. Myers
Treasurer and Trustee, Frank C. Alexander
VP and Trustee, Frederick A. Frye
Secretary and Trustee, Rick Gulley
Trustee, David S. Woodruff
Trustee, Thompson Fetter
Trustee, Weldon Donaldson
Trustee, George L. Gildred
Trustee, Judith A. Wheatley
Trustee, Nan Katona
Trustee, Sandra Brue
Trustee, William H. May

LOCATIONS

HQ: ZOOLOGICAL SOCIETY OF SAN DIEGO
2920 ZOO DR, SAN DIEGO, CA 92101-1646
Phone: 619-231-1515
Web: WWW.SANDIEGOZOO.ORG

HISTORICAL FINANCIALS

Company Type: Private

Income Statement FYE: January 1

	REVENUE ($ mil.)	NET INCOME ($ mil.)	NET PROFIT MARGIN	EMPLOYEES
01/12*	227	6	2.9%	2,300
12/10	193	(6)	—	—
12/09	173	(15)	—	—
01/06	173	17	10.0%	—
Annual Growth	4.6%	(15.0%)	—	—

*Fiscal year change

2012 Year-End Financials

Debt ratio: —
Return on equity: 2.90%
Cash ($ mil.): 40
Current ratio: 0.30
Long-term debt ($ mil.): —
Dividends
Yield: —
Payout: —
Market value ($ mil.): —

Hoover's Handbook of

Private Companies

Index of Executives

Index of Executives

A

B

C

D

G

H

I

J

K

M

N

O

P

Q

R

T

X

Y

Z